Devised and Compiled by Chris Philip

Edited by Tony Lord

British Library Cataloguing in Publication Data.

Philip, Chris *1928-*
The Plant Finder. - 8th. ed.
1. Great Britain. Gardens. Hardy plants
I. Title II. Lord, Tony *1949-*
635.9

ISBN 0-9512161-6-3
ISSN 0961-2599

First edition April 1987
Second edition April 1988
Reprinted August 1988
Third edition April 1989
Reprinted September 1989
Fourth edition April 1990
Fifth edition April 1991
Reprinted September 1991
Sixth edition April 1992
Reprinted September 1992
Seventh edition April 1993
Eighth edition April 1994

Compiled, Produced and Computer typeset by:
Headmain
Lakeside
Whitbourne
Worcs. WR6 5RD

Maps by:
à la carte
13 Lloyd Street
Llandudno
Gwynedd LL30 2UU

Printed by:
Richard Clay Ltd.
Bungay
Suffolk NR35 1ED

Cover:
Anemone *blanda*
Photos Horticultural Picture Library

Contents

Symbols and Abbreviations

*	Name not validated. Not listed in the appropriate International Registration Authority checklist nor in works cited in the Bibliography. For fuller discussion see **Nomenclature** on page 9
¶	New plant entry in this year's Edition, (or reinstated from list of previously deleted plants)
®	Registered Trade Mark or Selling name
♦	New or amended synonym or cross-reference included for the first time this year
§	Plant listed elsewhere in the **PLANT DIRECTORY** under a synonym
†	National Council for the Conservation of Plants and Gardens (NCCPG) Collection exists for all or part of this genus.
AGM	The Royal Horticultural Society's Award of Garden Merit.
C	Culinary (for Fruit)
cv(s)	Cultivar(s)
D	Dessert (for Fruit)
d	Double flowered
F	Fruit
f.	forma (botanical form)
g	grex
(g.&cl.)	grex and clone (Rhododendron)
I	Invalid name. See International Code of Nomenclature for Cultivated Plants 1980. For fuller discussion see **Nomenclature** on page 9
N	Refer to **Nomenclature Notes** on page 13
nm.	nothomorph (hybrid form)
nssp.	nothosubspecies (hybrid ssp.)
nvar.	nothovarietas (hybrid var.)
S	Shrubby
(s-p)	Self-pollinating
sp.	species
ssp.	subspecies
svar.	subvarietas (botanical subvariety)
(v)	Variegated plant
var.	varietas (botanical variety)

For **Collector's References** see page 24

For abbreviations relating to individual genera see **Classification of Genera** page 19

IMPORTANT NOTE TO USERS

This, the Eighth Edition of **THE PLANT FINDER,** contains over 65,000 plants and details of the nurseries which have advised us that they can supply them. No nursery, by the very nature of its business, will be able to provide everything in its list at all times. This is, of course, particularly true of plants which are rare, seldom asked for, or difficult to propagate.

To avoid disappointment, we suggest that you always:

CHECK WITH THE NURSERY BEFORE VISITING OR ORDERING

THE PLANT FINDER exists to put gardeners in touch with nurserymen. It does *not* offer value judgements on the nurseries or the plants it lists nor intend any reflection on any other nursery or plant *not* listed.

In addition, **THE PLANT FINDER** tries to cross-reference plant names to their correct *valid* name, although in some cases it is all too easy to understand why British nurserymen have preferred a more immediately comprehensible English name! *Every* name, apart from 'Common' names, that has been shown in a Catalogue has been listed, which is why there are so may cross-references. It is, clearly, the nursery's responsibility to ensure that its stock is accurately named both in its catalogue and on the plant when it is sold.

Caveat Emptor.

The Compiler and Editor of **THE PLANT FINDER** have taken every care, in the time available, to check all the information supplied to them by the nurseries concerned. Nevertheless, in a work of this kind, containing as it does, almost half-a-million separate computer encodings, errors and omissions will, inevitably, occur. Neither The Royal Horticultural Society nor the Compiler or Editor can accept responsibility for any consequences that may arise from such errors.

If you find mistakes we hope that you will let us know so that the matter can be corrected in the next edition.

Preface - 1994/95 Edition

The Royal Horticultural Society

The most important change to have taken place to ***The Plant Finder*** during the past year is the acquisition by The Royal Horticultural Society of the copyright to the publication. The present compiler and editor, Chris Philip and Tony Lord will continue as before, but we now have all the expertise and resources of the Society to call upon to ensure accuracy, consistency and, hopefully, a greater degree of nomenclatural stability.

It was the Nottingham Branch of The Hardy Plant Society who first published a Plant Directory in 1975 as a guide to assist members of the Society to find the rarer and more unusual herbaceous plants. In 1986 Chris Philip approached the Society with the idea of computerising and enlarging the Directory in order to include a greater range of plants and also to publish regularly so that it would reach more gardeners many of whom were not members. The Hardy Plant Society has therefore been associated with ***The Plant Finder*** for the last seven editions. During that period the number of nurseries included has risen from just under 200 to nearly 700 and the number of plant names listed has increased from 22,000 to over 65,000.

The Compiler and Editor have long felt, as was mentioned in the preface last year, that there should be a greater effort made to standardise plant nomenclature, at least for horticultural purposes, in order to avoid the cost and confusion that is inevitably caused by botanical uncertainty and vacillation. Gardeners perhaps take a more pragmatic view of a plant's appearance and cultivation requirements than that of a botanist. If, as a result of new research or new methods of measuring a plant's features, a botanist feels it necessary to change the name of a particular plant the gardener need not necessarily be affected since the plant, to him, will still look the same and will still require the same conditions as before.

As a result therefore of the new association with the RHS a committee has been set up under the chairmanship of Chris Brickell, the recently retired Director General of the RHS, to consider and recommend the standardisation of generic and specific names in those cases where botanical opinion differs.

Award of Garden Merit

In 1992 The Royal Horticultural Society re-introduced and completely revised its Award of Garden Merit (AGM), which is given to plants of outstanding garden excellence. This listing will be constantly reviewed and updated by the RHS. At present over 3,000 plants in ***The Plant Finder*** have been marked **AGM.**

Name Changes

There are substantially fewer changes this year than in the past and such changes as there are are discussed in the chapter on Nomenclature.

European Community

Although, strictly speaking, since Maastricht we should talk of the EU rather than the EC, the latter will probably remain the more familiar acronym. Nevertheless the result of the removal of most of the trade barriers so far as plants are concerned is already beginning to have a beneficial effect. Several European nurseries have taken Display Advertisements in this edition and, as can be seen from the Nursery Indexes at the end, many UK nurseries offer a Mail Order service to Europe as well as the UK. The addresses of these British nurseries are printed in **bold** type.

How to use the Directory

Nursery Codes

Look up the plant you require in the alphabetical **Plant Directory.** Against each plant you will find a four-letter Code, or Codes, for example 'ECha SDix', each code representing one nursery offering that plant. The first letter of each Code indicates the main area of the country in which the nursery is situated, based on their county:

C = South West England

Avon, Devon, Dorset, Channel Isles, Cornwall, Isles of Scilly, Somersetshire & Wiltshire.

E = Eastern England

Cambridgeshire, Essex, Lincolnshire, Norfolk & Suffolk.

G = Scotland

Borders, Central, Dumfries & Galloway, Fife, Grampian, Highlands, Inverness, Strathclyde.

I = Northern Ireland & Republic of Ireland.

L = London area

Bedfordshire, Berkshire, Buckinghamshire, Hertfordshire, London, Middlesex, Surrey.

M = Midlands

Cheshire, Derbyshire, Isle of Man, Leicestershire, Northamptonshire, Nottinghamshire, Oxfordshire, Staffordshire, Warwickshire, West Midlands.

N = Northern England

Cleveland, Cumbria, Durham, East Yorkshire, Greater Manchester, Humberside, Lancashire, Merseyside, Northumberland, North Yorkshire, South Yorkshire, Tyne & Wear, West Yorkshire.

S = Southern England

East Sussex, Hampshire, Isle of Wight, Kent, West Sussex.

W = Wales & Western England

Dyfed, Clywd, Glamorganshire, Gloucestershire, Gwent, Gwynedd, Herefordshire & Worcestershire, Powys, Shropshire.

Turn to the **Code-Nursery Index** on page 661 where, in alphabetical order of Codes, you will find details of each nursery which offers the plant in question. If you wish to visit any of these nurseries you can find its *approximate* location on one of the maps at the back. Those few nurseries which sell *only* by Mail Order are not shown on the maps. Always check that the nursery you select has the plant in stock before you set out.

Widely available plants

Clearly, if we were to include *every* plant listed by all nurseries, ***The Plant Finder*** would become unmanageably bulky. We have therefore had to ask nurseries to restrict their entries to only those plants that are not already well represented. As a result, if more than 30 nurseries offer any plant the Directory gives no Code and the plant is listed as 'Widely available'. In this Edition there are just under 1000 plants listed as 'Widely available' and you should have little difficulty in finding these in local nurseries or Garden Centres. However, if any readers do have difficulty in finding such plants, we will be pleased to send them a full list of all the nurseries that we have listed and this could include anything from 31 to a maximum of 50. Please write to:

THE PLANT FINDER,
Lakeside, Whitbourne, Worcester WR6 5RD

All such enquiries *must* include the full name of the plant being sought, as shown in **THE PLANT FINDER**, together with a *stamped addressed envelope.*

Nursery-Code Index

For convenience, a reverse **Nursery-Code Index** is included on page 654 . This gives the names of the nurseries listed in the **Plant Directory** in alphabetical order of nursery names together with their relevant Codes.

Additional Nursery Index

There is also an **Additional Nursery Index**, on page 734, containing brief details of other nurseries that have not been included in the **Plant Directory**. They may be listed in this Index for a number of reasons, for example, their stock is small and changes too quickly for them to be able to issue a viable catalogue, or the major part of their stock would have to be listed as 'Widely available', or simply because their latest Catalogue was not received in time for inclusion. Again, their catalogues may either give mainly English names, (and this particularly applies to Herb nurseries) or Latin names which do not provide sufficient information to establish easily the genus or species of the plant concerned. The location of these nurseries on the maps are marked by their listed numbers.

How to find your plant

If you cannot immediately find the plant you seek in the **Plant Directory**, look through the various species of the genus. You may be using an incomplete name. The problem is most likely to arise in very large genera such as *Phlox* where there are a number of possible species, each with a large number of cultivars. A search through the whole genus may well bring success.

New Cross-references

Major new cross-references and synonyms have been marked with a ♦. This sign has only been used when the genus, species or cultivar name has been altered, but not where there have been merely minor typographic or orthographic changes.

If the plant you seek is not listed in the **Plant Directory,** it is possible that a nursery in the **Additional Nursery Index** which specialises in similar plants may be able to offer it. In addition to the plants listed in their catalogues, many nurseries are often able to supply other plants of the same general type that they specialise in. They may not list them if they only have a few available. In some cases they can arrange to propagate special items from their stock plants.

Nurseries

The details given for each nursery (listed in the Indices at the back) have been compiled from information supplied to us in answer to a questionnaire. In some cases, because of constraints of space, the entries have been slightly abbreviated and blanks have been left where no information has been provided.

Telephone Numbers

With effect from APRIL 16TH 1995 ALL telephone numbers in the UK (including Northern Ireland) will change. In practice this change can be used as from August 1st 1994. The figure '1' must be added following the initial '0'. Thus London codes will become either 0171 or 0181. International Codes will also be changed at the same time and must be prefixed by '00' instead of '010'.

Opening Times

The word 'daily' implies every day including Sunday and Bank Holidays. Although opening times have been given as provided and where applicable, it is *always* advisable, especially if travelling a long distance, to check with the nursery first.

Mail Order - UK & EC

Many nurseries provide a Mail Order service which, in many cases, now extends to all members of the European Community. Where it is shown that there is "No minimum charge" ("Nmc") it should be realised that to send even one plant may involve the nursery in substantial postage and packing costs. Even so, some nurseries may not be prepared to send tender or bulky plants. Nurseries that are prepared to undertake Mail Order to both UK and EC destinations are shown in **bold** type in the **Code-Nursery Index.**

Catalogue Cost

Some nurseries offer their catalogue free, or for a few stamps (the odd value quoted can usually be made up from a combination of first or second class stamps), but a *large*, at least (A5) stamped addressed envelope is always appreciated as well. Overseas customers should use an equivalent number of International Reply Coupons (IRCs) in place of stamps.

Wholesale or Retail

The main trading method is indicated, but it should be stressed that some wholesalers do have retail outlets and many retailers also have a wholesale trade and would frequently be prepared to offer discounts for large single orders.

Export - (Outside the EC)

Nurseries that are prepared to consider exporting are indicated. However, there is usually a substantial minimum charge and, in addition, all the additional costs of Phytosanitary Certificates and Customs would have to be met by the purchaser.

Variegated Plants

Following a suggestion from the Variegated Plant Group of the Hardy Plant Society, we have added a (v) to those plants which are 'variegated' although this may not be apparent from their name. Plants named 'Variegata' or 'Marginata' (in combination) are not coded as all except *Iris variegata, Rosa* 'Variegata di Bologna' and *R.* 'Centifolia Variegata' have variegated leaves rather than flowers. The dividing line between variegation and less distinct colour marking is necessarily arbitrary and plants with light veins, pale, silver or dark zones or leaves flushed in paler colours are not shown as being variegated unless there is an absolutely sharp distinction between paler and darker zones.

For further details of the Variegated Plant Group, please write to:

Stephen Tafler, 18 Hayes End Manor, South Petherton, Somerset TA13 5BE.

Hardy Plant Society Search List

During the last few years the Hardy Plant Society has instigated several searches in Europe for scarce and desirable plants that may not be available in this country. As a result, several new plants have been introduced into cultivation in the UK, and the HPS has built up a list of about 1000 plants about which it is keen to obtain further information. This list appears on page 800.

Deleted Plants

The **Plant Deletions Index** contains some 10,000 plant names that were listed in one or other of the seven previous editions of ***The Plant Finder***, but are now no longer represented. As a result there are a few instances where a Genus exists in the main **Plant Directory** but with no apparent entries for either species or cultivars. These will be found in the **Plant Deletions Index** on page 756. It is also possible that some cross-references may not apparently refer to an entry in the main Directory. Again this is because the plant in question had a supplier or suppliers but is now in the **Plant Deletions Index.** These references are deliberately kept so as to provide an historic record of synonyms and plant availability and to aid those who wish to try and find any of these 'deleted' plants.

These deletions arise, not only because the nursery that supplied the plants may have gone out of business, but also because some nurseries who were included previously have not responded to our latest questionnaire and have thus had to be deleted. Such plants may well be still available but we have no current knowledge of their whereabouts. Furthermore, some items may have been misnamed by nurseries in previous editions, but are now appearing under their correct name.

For those who wish to try and find previously listed plants, back editionsof ***The Plant Finder*** are still available at £6.00 (incl. p&p) from the address given below.

Deleted Nurseries

Every year a few nurseries ask to be deleted. This may be because they are about to move or close, or they are changing the way in which they trade.

Please, never use an old edition.

New Nursery Entries

Nurseries that are appearing in ***The Plant Finder*** for the first time this year are printed in **bold type** in the **Nursery-Code Index** starting on page 654.

If any other nursery wishes to be considered for inclusion in the next edition of ***The Plant Finder*** (1995/96) it should write for details to:

The Plant Finder
Lakeside
Gaines Road
Whitbourne
Worcs WR6 5RD

The closing date for new entries will be January 31st 1995.

Nomenclature

"The question of nomenclature is always a vexed one. The only thing certain is, that it is impossible to please everyone."
W J Bean - Preface to First Edition of
Trees & Shrubs Hardy in the British Isles.

Following the acquisition of ***The Plant Finder*** by the Royal Horticultural Society, a small informal committee has been set up to try to establish an agreed list of plant names used in this and other RHS publications. The committee, chaired by Chris Brickell and including also Tony Lord, Alan Leslie and Piers Trehane will look at all recent and current proposals to change names and will try to establish a balance between the stability of well-known names and botanical and taxonomic correctness according to the codes of nomenclature.

Clearly it would be unreasonable to expect the RHS to wish to adopt every name used in previous editions of ***The Plant Finder***, particularly in the many cases in which there are strong and conflicting opinions. The new committee has already begun the work of examining some of the more difficult cases and for some plants has decided that it is in the interest of gardeners and taxonomically acceptable to return to better known names for this editions. Thus Zauschneria, Cyrtomium and Pratia are used here and a number of other important generic names will be studied during the coming year. Many proposals to make further changes have been resisted until the committee has had time to study them more fully. However if nomenclatural arguments are finely balanced, old names will be retained in the interests of stability.

This does not alter the fact that all involved in the publication of ***The Plant Finder*** remain committed to the use of plant names which are as correct as possible. As before, gardeners and nurserymen may still choose to differ and use what names they want, many preferring a more conservative and a few a more radical, approach to naming. Except for those names in which we have made corrections of a couple of letters to bring them in line with the codes of nomenclature, we are responsible for ***none*** of the name changes in this or any other edition of ***The Plant Finder***.

Rules of Nomenclature

Throughout ***The Plant Finder*** we try to follow the rules of nomenclature set out in the *International Code of Botanical Nomenclature* 1988 (ICBN) and the *International Code of Nomenclature for Cultivated Plants* 1980 (ICNCP). Cultivar names which are clearly not permissible under this code and for which there seems to be no valid alternative are marked "I" (for invalid). The commonest sorts of invalid names seem to be those that are wholly or partly in Latin (not permissible since 1959, eg 'Pixie Alba', 'Superba', 'Variegata') and those which use a latin generic name as a cultivar name (eg *Rosa* 'Corylus', *Viola* 'Gazania'). If no prior valid name exists, an enterprising nurseryman may publish a new valid name for any such plant. This would be considered validly published if it appeared in a dated catalogue with a clear description of the plant; the originator, if still alive, must be willing to accept the new name.

Apart from being discourteous to the plants' originators and their countries, the translating of foreign plant names into English is a bad and insular practice that is likely to cause confusion; it may be years yet before we make sense of the host of German names and apparent English translations for a genus such as *Coreopsis*, many of which must be synonyms. Throughout ***The Plant Finder***, we have tried to give preference to the original name in every case, although English names are also given.

The substitution of slick selling names by nurseries which do not like, or have not bothered to find out, the correct names of the plants they sell is sharp practice not expected of any reputable nursery; it is also a probable breach of the Trades Description Act.

XVth International Botanical Congress Tokyo 1993

The importance of stability in plant names was recognised at the Tokyo Congress which passed a resolution urging plant taxonomists "*to avoid displacing well established names for purely nomenclatural reasons, whether by changing their application or by resurrection of long forgotten names*". Had this ruling been in place some years ago, we need not have suffered the changes of Nepeta *mussinii* to N. *racemosa* nor Rhus *typhina* to R. *hirta*. However, it is unlikely that such little-known older names could be rejected now that they are being used once more. In such cases in future if a well-known name needs to be conserved, a proposal must be published to be considered at the next Botanical Congress.

This resolution is already being widely quoted as an excuse for ignoring, in the interests of stability, any article of the Codes of Nomenclature which requires some correction to a plant name such as a faulty termination, compounding form, or orthographic error in a commemorative epithet. This is not the case - indeed if it were it would render large parts of the code redundant - the resolution applies mainly to widely-known generic and specific names.

Orthography

The Congress chose not to revoke the recent ruling on orthography, that is, retention, in commemorative names, of their original form. This subject is discussed in the supplement to Bean's *Trees and Shrubs Hardy in the British Isles* (1988) and is given in ICBN Article 73.10, further clarified by Article 73.7 Example 10, 1988. The gist of this is, that except for full-scale latinisations of names (eg *brunonius* for Brown, thus *Rosa brunonii*), the name of the person commemorated should remain in its original form. Some names falling into this category were corrected in our previous editions and further corrections will be found this year. Names ending in -er (eg Solander, Faber) may be become *solandri* (as in pure Latin, because -er is a usual Latin termination) or *solanderi*, if the specific name was originally spelt in this way. According to ICBN, names such as *backhousiana, catesbaei, mackaiana, glazoviana, manescavii and bureavii* are **not** allowed and must be corrected to *backhouseana, catesbyi, mackayana, glaziouana, manescaui and bureaui* respectively.

Botanical epithets

Botanical epithets commemorating someone whose name has been transliterated from script other than Roman (e.g. Cyrillic or Japanese) present great problems and the ruling on orthography is difficult to apply to these: although there is widespread acceptance of Hepburn's system of transliteration from Japanese, there is no apparent universal approval for a system for transliteration from Cyrillic; without this it seems difficult to reach any concensus on the orthography of, for instance, Russian commemorative names. However, implementation of this rule has been assisted by another new publication from Kew, *Authors of Plant Names*, which is particularly helpful in giving acceptable transliterations of names which were originally in Cyrillic.

Dr McAllister's researches with Alison Rutherford on ivies are incorporated in the *New RHS Dictionary of Gardening* and will also appear in *European Garden Flora*. Their treatment of the Algerian and Canary Island ivies and recognition of *Hedera hibernica* as a separate species are retained again in this edition, though strongly criticised by some members of The British Ivy Society.

We do not expect to make further changes in the treatment here until research is complete and full concensus has been achieved.

Verification of names

Although we find that many nurseries have greatly improved the accuracy of their plant names, plants which are new entries often appear in their catalogues under a bewildering variety of wrong names and misspellings. This is partly a reflection on the rarity of the plants and nurserymen are not to be blamed for not finding correct names for plants which do not appear in recent authoritative garden literature. Some plants are simply too new for valid names and descriptions yet to have appeared in print.

Although we try to verify every name which appears in these pages, the amount of time which can be allotted to checking each of over 60,000 entries must be limited. There is always a proportion which do not appear in any of the reference sources used (i.e. those listed in the Bibliography) and those unverified names for which there may be scope for error are marked with an asterisk. Such errors may occur with species we cannot find listed (possibly synonyms for more recent and better known names) or may include misspellings (particularly of names transliterated from Japanese or Chinese, or commemorating a person). We are especially circumspect about names not known to the International Registrar for a particular genus. We are always grateful to receive information about the naming and origin of any asterisked plant and once we feel reassured about the plant's pedigree, the asterisk will be removed. Of course, many such names will prove to be absolutely correct and buyers can be reassured if they know that the selling nursery takes great care with the naming of its plants.

We have great sympathy for gardeners who want to find a particular cultivar but are not sure to which species it belongs. The problem is acute for genera such as Juniperus and readers must search through all the entries to find their plants; even nurseries seem uncertain of the species of 'Skyrocket'. We have felt that saxifrages, astilbes (and a few others), were so impossible that they must be listed by cultivar first, giving the species in parentheses.

Adjectival names

Latin adjectival names, whether for species, subspecies, cultivar etc., must agree in gender with the genus, *not* with the specific name if the latter is a noun (as for *Phyllitis scolopendrium, Lonicera caprifolium* etc.). Thus azaleas have to agree with *Rhododendron*, their true genus (neuter), rather than *Azalea* (feminine). For French cultivar names, adjectives should agree with whatever is being described; for roses, this is almost always *la rose* (feminine) but on rare occasions *le rosier* (when describing vegetative characteristics such as climbing forms), *l'oeillet* or *le pompon* (all masculine).

It is often the case that gardeners consider two plants to be distinct but botanists, who know of a whole range of intermediates linking the two, consider them to be the same species. The most notable example is for the rhododendrons, many species of which were "sunk" in Cullen and Chamberlain's recent revision. In such cases we have always tried to provide names that retain important horticultural entities, even if not botanically distinct, often by giving the sunk species a Group name, such as *Rhododendron rubiginosum* Desquamatum Group. Rhododendrons and orchids are also blessed with grex names for swarms of hybrids with the same parentage such as *R.* Polar Bear or *Pleione* Shantung. Such names are not enclosed in quotes but, particularly for rhododendrons, a single clone from the grex may be given the same cultivar name, ie 'Polar Bear'. In many cases nursery catalogues do not specify whether the named clone is being offered or other selections from the hybrid swarm and entries are therefore given as eg *Rhododendron* Polar Bear (g.&cl.) (i.e. grex and clone).

There are a few cases in which it is difficult to tell whether a "sunk" species remains horticulturally distinct enough to merit a group name, as for many of the rhododendrons; we would be grateful if users would let us know of any plants that we have "sunk" in synonymy but which still need to be distinguished by a separate name. In many cases, the plants gardeners grow will be the most extreme variants of a species; although one "end" of the species will seem to be quite a different plant from the other "end" to the gardener, the botanist will see them as the outer limits of a continuous range of variation and will give them the same species name. We often hear gardeners complain "How can these two plants have the same name? They are different!"; in such cases, although the botanist may have to "lump" them under the same name, we will always try to provide an acceptable name to distinguish an important horticultural entity, even if it is not botanically distinct.

Taxonomic rank

This edition is the third in which we have included taxonomic rank for infraspecific taxa. Thus subspecies, varietas and forma are shown as ssp., var. and f. respectively. For hybrid species, the corresponding ranks are nothosubspecies, nothovarietas and nothomorph (nssp., nvar. and nm.), e.g. *Mentha x villosa* nm. *alopecuroïdes.* Each of these ranks indicates a successively less significant change in the characteristics of the plant from the original type on which the species was based; in general terms, a subspecies may be expected to be more markedly different from the typical species than a forma which may differ in only one characteristic such as flower colour, hairiness of leaf or habit. In rare cases, taxonomists have felt the need to impose another "layer" in this heirarchy, the subvarietas, shown here as svar.

Though we have shown the rank of a considerably greater proportion of infraspecific epithets, some remain to be added in future editions. In many cases, it is not at all clear whether a colour form shown as, say, *alba* is a true botanical forma or a cultivar of garden origin. Our inclination here is not to treat such plants as cultivars if they are recorded as being naturally occurring, nor if they embrace considerable variation: forma *alba* would be preferred if a valid publication is recorded, otherwise a suitable Group name. In the absence of conclusive evidence we will leave such names styled as they are at present.

In many cases the same species name has been used by two or more authors for quite different plants. Thus *Bloomingthingia grandiflora* of Linnaeus might be an altogether different species from *B. grandiflora* of gardeners (*B. grandiflora* hort.). In such circumstances it becomes necessary to define whose *Bloomingthingia* we are considering by quoting the author of the name directly after the species name. Generally the more recent name will be invalid and may be cross referenced to the plant's first validly published name. Author's names appear directly after the species name and are usually spelled in full here, except for longer citations for which abbreviations are listed in e.g. Mabberley's *The Plant-Book* or given in full in *Index Hortensis.* Such names do not appear in quotes so should not be confused with cultivar names.

Hyphenation

Some items of the International Code of Botanical Nomenclature have been "more honour'd in the breach than in the observance". One such is the ruling on hyphenation (Article 73.9) which forbids the use of hyphens after a "compounding form" (i.e. albo, pseudo, aureo, neo). Hyphens are still permitted to divide separate words such as novae-angliae or bella-donna and following the

Tokyo Congress, after a vowel terminating a compounding form when followed by the same vowel (eg. Gaultheria *semi-infera*, Gentiana *sino-ornata*).

Commemorative names

Another item of the code which is often ignored is that covering terminations of commemorative names (Article 73.10, referring to Recommendation 73C). A botanical epithet commemorating Helena must be styled *helenae* whereas one commemorating Helen may be styled either *heleniae* or, following Helena as an established Latin form of the same name or, quite frequently, of Ellen, *helenae*; in such cases when either spelling could be legitimate, the original is followed. When there is no accepted Latin alternative, the *-iae* ending is used and this seems to be more correct for *murieliae* and *edithiae*. The genitive form of names ending in *-a* is always *-ae*, even if a man is being commemorated (as for *Picea koyamae*). It is this same article which requires that the well known *Crocosmia* be spelt *masoniorum* and not *masonorum*.

The Plant Finder is useful not only as a directory of plant sources but as a "menu" of plants grown by British gardeners. Such a list is of great value not only to private gardeners; landscapers can use it to check the range of plants they can incorporate in designs; gardeners in countries of the European Union can check which plants they can import by Mail Order; botanists can discover the species grown in Britain, some of them from recorded natural sources; nurserymen can use it to select for propagation first-rate plants that are still not readily available; horticultural authors, who often only want to write about plants the public are able to buy, will find it invaluable. For all such users, ***The Plant Finder*** can be recommended as a source of standard, up-to-date and reliable nomenclature.

Chris Philip and Tony Lord
April 1994

Nomenclature Notes

These notes refer to plants in the main **PLANT DIRECTORY** that are marked with a 'N'.

'Bean Supplement' refers to W J Bean *Trees & Shrubs Hardy in the British Isles* (Supplement to the 8th edition) edited by D L Clarke 1988.

Acer *palmatum coreanum*
This has nothing to do with A. *p.* 'Koreanum'

Acer *palmatum* 'Sango-kaku'/'Senkaki'
Two or more clones are offered under these names A. p. 'Eddisbury' is similar with brighter coral stems

Acer *pseudoplatanus* 'Leopoldii;
True 'Leopoldii' has leaves stained with yellowish pink and purple. Plants are often A. *p.* f. *variegatum.*

Acer *p.* 'Spaethii'
Has large leaves with light yellow specks.

Aconitum *autumnale*
A synonym of A. *napellus* and A. *carmichaelii wilsonii.*

Achillea *ptarmica* The Pearl Group
Refers to variable seed raised double-flowered plants. The cultivar names 'The Pearl' and 'Boule de Neige' apply only to plants propagated vegetatively from the originals.

Acorus *gramineus* 'Oborozuki' & 'Ogon'
Although these seem to be the same clone in British gardens, 'Oborozuki' is a distinct brighter yellow cultivar in the USA.

Alchemilla *alpina*
The true species is very rare in cultivation. Plants under this name are usually A. *plicatula* or A. *conjuncta.*

Alchemilla *splendens*
The true species is probably not in cultivation in the British Isles.

Alopecurus *pratensis* 'Aureus'
Name applies only to plants with all gold leaves, not with green & gold striped forms.

Anemone *magellanica*
According to *European Garden Flora* this is a form of the very variable A. *multifida.*

Anemone *nemorosa* 'Alba Plena'
This name is used for several double white forms including A. *n.* 'Flore Pleno' and A. *n.* 'Vestal'.

Anthemis *tinctoria* 'Grallach Gold'
The true cultivar of this name has golden yellow flowers. Plants with orange yellow flowers are **A.** *t.* 'Beauty of Grallach'.

Artemisia 'Faith Raven' & 'Powis Castle'
Most plants labelled 'Faith Raven' are identical with 'Powis Castle'.

Artemisia *ludoviciana* 'Silver Queen'
Two cultivars are grown under this name, one with cut leaves, the other with entire leaves.

Artemisia *ludoviciana* var. *latiloba*/ A. *l.*'Valerie Finnis'
Leaves of the former are glabrous at maturity, those of the latter are not.

Aster *amellus* 'Violet Queen'
It is probable that more than one cultivar is sold under this name.

Aster *dumosus*
Many of the Asters listed under *A. novi-belgii* contain varying amounts of A. *dumosus* blood in their parentage. It is not possible to allocate these to one species or the other and they are therefore listed under A. *novi-belgii.*

Aster x *frikartii* 'Mönch'
The true plant is very rare in British gardens. Most plants are another form of A. x *frikartii* usually 'Wunder von Stfa'.

Aster *novi-belgii*
See note under A. *dumosus.*

Berberis *aristata*
Plants so named may be either B. *chitria* or B. *floribunda.*

Berberis x *ottawensis* nm. *purpurea*/ 'Superba'
'Superba' is a clonal selection from nm. *purpurea*

Berberis x *ottawensis* 'Superba'
See note in Bean Supplement, p 109.

Berberis *stenophylla* 'Lemon Queen'
This sport from 'Pink Pearl' was first named in 1982. The same mutation occured again and was named 'Cream Showers'. The older name has priority.

Bergenia Ballawley Hybrids
The name 'Ballawley' refers only to plants vegetatively propagated from ther original clone. Seed raised plants, which may differ considerably, should be called Ballawley Hybrids.

Betula *pendula* 'Dalecarlica'
The true plant of this name is rare in cultivation in the British Isles and is probably not available from nurseries.

Betula *utilis* var. *jacquemontii*
Plants are often the clone 'Inverleith' which may or may not be a form of B. *utilis.*

Brachyscome
Originally published as BRACHYSCOME by Cassini who later revised his spelling to BRACHYCOME. The original spelling has been internationally adopted.

Brachyglottis *greyi* and *laxifolia*
Both these species are extremely rare in cultivation. Plants under these names usually being B. 'Sunshine'.

Buddleja *davidii* Petite Indigo ®, Petite Plum ® 'Nanho Blue', 'Nanho Purple'
These cultivars or hybrids of B. *d. nanhoensis* are claimed by some to be synonyms while others claim the 'Nanho' plants were raised in Holland and the 'Petite' plants in the USA. We are not yet certain whether these names are synonyms and if so which have priority.

Buddleja *fallowiana*
Many plants in cultivation are not the true species but the hybrid 'West Hill'.

Camassia *leichtlinii* 'Plena'
This has starry, transparent creamy-white flowers, creamy-white 'Semiplena' is sometimes offered under this name.

Camellia 'Campbellii'
This name is used for five cvs. including 'Margherita Coleoni' but applies correctly to Guichard's 1894 cultivar, single to semi-double full rose pink.

Camellia 'Cleopatra'
There are three cultivars with this name.

Camellia 'Perfecta'
There are three cultivars under this name. This is 'Perfecta' of Jury.

Campanula *persicifolia*
Plants under 'cup and saucer white' are not definitely ascribed to a particular cultivar. 'White Cup and Saucer' is a cultivar named by Margery Fish.

Carex *conica* 'Hime-kansuge'/ 'Hino-kansuge'/ 'Variegata'
This variegated sedge is listed under over a dozen variants of the above names, none of which is legitimate. Dr Alan Leslie has proposed the cultivar name 'Snowline' for this plant.

Carex *morrowii* 'Variegata'
C. *oshimensis* 'Evergold' is sometimes sold under this name.

Carya *illinoinensis*
The correct spelling of this name is discussed in Baileya Vol 10. No. 1 1962.

Cassia *corymbosa*
See note in Bean Supplement, p 148.

Cassinia *retorta*
Now included within C. *leptophylla*. A valid infra-specific epithet has yet to be published.

Cedrus *deodara* 'Prostrata'
The true plant is extremely rare if not lost to cultivation. Most plants under this name are in fact C. *d.* 'Pendula'.

Ceanothus 'Italian Skies'
Many plants under this name are not true to name.

Chamaecyparis *lawsoniana* 'Columnaris Glauca'
Plants under this name may be C. *l.* 'Columnaris' or a new illegitimately named cultivar.

Chamaecyparis *lawsoniana* 'Elegantissima'
This name has ben applied to two cultivars, 'E.' of Schelle and subsequently (illegitimately) 'E.' of Hillier.

Chamaecyparis *lawsoniana* 'Smithii'
May include some which are C. *l.* 'Darleyensis'.

Chamaecyparis *pisifera* 'Squarrosa Argentea'
There are two plants of this name, one (valid) with variegated foliage, the other (illegitimate) with silvery foliage.

Cistus *hirsutus* and C. *h. psilosepalus*
These do not appear to be distinct in cultivation.

Cistus x *loretii*
Plants in cultivation under this name are usually forms of C. *dansereaui.*

Cistus x *purpureus*
Most plants in cultivation may be the cultivar 'Betty Taudevin'

Clematis *chrysocoma*
The true C. *chrysocoma* is a non-climbing erect plant with dense yellow down on the young growth, still uncommon in cultivation.

Clematis *heracleifolia* 'Campanile'
May be *C.*x *bonstedtii* 'C'.

Clematis *heracleifolia* 'Cote d'Azur'
May be C. x *bonstedtii* 'C. d'A.'

Clematis 'Jackmanii Superba'
Plants under this name are usually C. 'Gipsy Queen'

Clematis *montana*
This name should refer to the white-flowered form only. Pink-flowered forms are referrable to C. *m.*var. *rubens.*

Colchicum 'Autumn Queen'
Entries here may refer to the slightly different *C.* 'Prinses Astrid'.

Cornus 'Norman Hadden'
See note in Bean Supplement. p 184.

Cotoneaster *buxifolius*
Plants in gardens under this name may be C. *astrophoros* or C. *lidjiangensis*

Cotoneaster *dammeri*
Plants sold under this name are usually C. *d.*'Major'.

Crataegus *coccinea*
Plants may be CC. *intricata, pedicellata* or *bilmoreana.*

Crocosmia x *crocosmiiflora* 'Citronella'
The true plant of this name has a dark eye and grows at Wisley. The plant usually offered may be more correctly *C.* 'Golden Fleece'.

Crocosmia x *crocosmiiflora* 'Honey Angels'
Also wrongly referred to as 'Citronella'.

Crocosmia x *crocosmiiflora* 'James Coey'
Has large tomato-red flowers. A smaller flowered plant similar to C. x *c.* 'Carmin Brillant' is sometimes sold under this name.

Crocosmia x *crocosmiiflora* 'Solfaterre'
This the original spelling.

Crocus *cartwrightianus albus*
The plant offered is the true form and not C. *hadriaticus.*

Cupressus *arizonica* var. *bonito*
See discussion in *International Conifer Register* Part 3.

Dendranthema 'Anastasia Variegata'
Despite its name, this seems to be derived from 'Mei-kyo' not 'Anastasia'

Dianthus 'Musgrave's Pink' (p)
This is the registered name of this white-flowered cultivar.

Diascia 'Apricot'
Plants under this name are either 'Hopley's Apricot' or 'Blackthorn Apricot'.

Dryopteris *affinis polydactyla*
This name covers at least three different clones.

Elymus *magellanicus*
Although this is a valid name Mr Roger Grounds has suggested that many plants might belong to a different, perhaps unnamed species.

Erigeron *salsuginosus*
Is a synonym of ASTER *sibiricus* but plants in cultivation under this name may be E. *peregrinus callianthemus*

Erodium *cheilanthifolium*
Most plants under this name are hybrids.

Erodium *glandulosum*
Plants under this name are often hybrids.

Erodium *guttatum*
Doubtfully in commerce, plants under this name are usually E. *heteradenum*, E. *cheilanthifolium* or hybrids.

Erodium *petraeum*
Many are hybrids, often E. 'Merstham Pink'.

Erysimum *cheiri* 'Baden-Powell'
Plant of uncertain origin differing from E. *c*. 'Harpur Crewe' only in its shorter stature.

Erysimum 'Variegatum'
This name may refer to any of the variegated cultivars of *Erysimum*.

Eucryphia 'Penwith'
The cultivar name 'Penwith' was originally given to a hybrid of E. *cordifolia* x *E. lucida*, not E. x *hillieri*.

Euphorbia *wallichii*
Many plants are E. *donii* or E. *cornigera*.

Fagus *sylvatica* Copper Group / Purple Group
It is desirable to provide a name, Copper Group, for less richly coloured forms, used in historic landscapes before the purple clones appeared.

Fagus *sylvatica* 'Pendula'
This name refers to the Knap Hill clone, the most common weeping form in English gardens. Other clones occur, particularly in Ireland.

Forsythia 'Beatrix Farrand'
The true plant may not be in cultivation.

Fragaria *chiloensis* 'Variegata'
Most, possibly all, plants under this name are F. x *ananassa* 'Variegata'.

Freesia *refracta alba*
Plants may be F. *lactea* or F. *sparrmannii*.

Fuchsia
All names, except the following, marked N refer to more than one cultivar or species.

Fuchsia *decussata*
A hybrid form of F. *magellanica* is also offered under this name.

Fuchsia *loxensis*
For a comparison of the true species with the hybrids 'Speciosa' and 'Loxensis' commonly grown under this name, see Boulemier's *Check List* (2nd ed.) p.268.

Fuchsia *minimiflora*
Some plants may be F. x *bacillaris*.

Fuchia 'Pumila'
Plants under this name may be F. *magellanica* var. *pumila*.

Gentiana *cachemirica*
Most plants sold are not true to type.

Geum 'Borisii'
This name refers to cultivars of G. *coccineum* Sibthorp & Smith, especially G. *c*. 'Werner Arends' and not to G. x *borisii* Kelleper.

Halimium *alyssodes* and H. *halimifolium*
Plants under these names are sometimes H. x *pauanum or H*. x *santae*.

Hebe 'Amy'
May include entries which refer to H. 'Purple Queen'.

Hebe 'C P Raffill'
See note in Bean Supplement, p 265.

Hebe 'Carl Teschner'
See note in Bean Supplement, p 264.

Hebe 'Glaucophylla'
This plant is a green reversion of the hybrid H. 'Glaucophylla Variegata'.

Hedera *helix helix* 'Caenwoodiana'/ 'Pedata'
Some authorities consider these to be distinct cultivars whilst others think them different morphological forms of the same unstable clone.

Hedera *helix helix* 'Oro di Bogliasco'
Priority between this name and 'Jubilum Goldherz' and 'Goldheart' has yet to be finally resolved.

Helleborus *orientalis*
Plants under this name are almost invariably hybrids and have been named H. x *hybridus*.

Hemerocallis *fulva* 'Kwanso', 'Kwanso Variegata', 'Flore Pleno' and 'Green Kwanso'
For a discussion of these plants see *The Plantsman* (Vol. 7 Pt. II).

Heuchera *micrantha* 'Palace Purple'
This cultivar name refers only to plants with deep purple-red foliage. Seed-raised plants of inferior colouring should not be offered under this name.

Hosta 'Marginata Alba'
This name is wrongly used both for H. *crispula* and, more commonly, for H. *fortunei* 'Albomarginata'.

Hosta *montana*
This name refers only to plants long grown in Europe, which differ from H. *elata*.

Hosta 'Venusta Variegated'
In spite of its name this plant is not a form of H. *venusta*.

Hypericum *fragile*
The true H. *fragile* is probably not available from British nurseries.

Hypericum *leschenaultii*
Plants are usually HH. *addingtonii, choisyanum, augustinii* or 'Rowallane'.

Ilex x *altaclerensis*
The argument for this correct spelling is given by Susyn Andrews (*The Plantsman* Vol.5, Pt.II) and is not superceded by the more recent but erroneous comments in the Supplement to Bean's *Trees and Shrubs*.

Iris *pallida* 'Variegata'
The white-variegated I. *p.* 'Argentea Variegata' is sometimes wrongly supplied under this name, which refers only to the gold-variegated form.

Lamium *maculatum* 'Chequers'
This name refers to two plants; the first, validly named, is a large and vigorous form of L. *maculatum* with a stripe down the centre of the leaf; the second is silver-leaved and very similar to L. *m.* 'Beacon Silver'.

Lavandula 'Alba'
May be either L. *angustifolia* 'Alba' or L. x *intermedia* 'Alba'

Lavandula *spica*
This name is classed as a name to be rejected (nomen rejiciendum) by the International Code of Botanical Nomenclature.

Lavandula 'Twickel Purple'
Two cultivars are sold under this name, one a form of L. x *intermedia*, the other of L. *angustifolia*.

Lavatera *olbia & thuringiaca*
Although L. *olbia* is usually shrubby and L. *thuringiaca* usually herbaceous, both species are very variable. Cultivars formally ascribed to one species or the other are quite possibly hybrids and are listed by cultivar name alone pending the results of further research.

Leptospermum *flavescens*
This name is usually applied to plants correctly named L. *glaucescens*.

Lobelia 'Russian Princess'
This has green, not purple leaves and rich pink, not purple flowers.

Lonicera x *americana*
Most plants offered by nurseries under this name are correctly L. x *italica*. The true *americana* is still widely grown but is hard to propagate. See *The Plantsman* (Vol. 12 Pt. II).

Lonicera x *brownii* 'Fuchsioides'
Plants under this name are usually L. x *brownii* 'Dropmore Scarlet'.

Lonicera *periclymenum* 'Belgica'
L. x *italica* is sometimes offered under this name.

Lonicera *periclymenum* 'Serotina'
See note in Bean Supplement, p 315.

Lonicera *sempervirens* f. *sulphurea*
Plants in the British Isles usually a yellow-flowered form of L. *periclymenum*.

Macleaya *cordata*
Most, if not all plants offered are M. x *kewensis*.

Magnolia x *highdownensis*.
Believed to fall within the range of variation of M. *wilsonii*.

Magnolia *obovata*
This name refers to either M. *hypoleuca* or M. *officinalis*. The former is more common in cultivation.

Magnolia x *soulangeana* 'Burgundy'
Most plants under this name are M. x *s.* 'Purpliana'

Mahonia *pinnata*
Plants in cultivation are believed to belong to M. x *wagneri* 'Pinnacle'.

Malus *domestica* 'Dumeller's Seedling'
The phonetic spelling 'Dumelow's Seedling' contravenes the ICBN ruling on orthography, i.e. that commemorative names should retain the original spelling of the person's name.

Melissa *officinalis* 'Variegata'
The true cultivar of this name was striped with white.

Nemesia *fruticans*
The lavender blue clone 'Joan Wilder', described and illustrated in *The Hardy Plant*, Vol.14 No.1 pp 11-14, does not come true from seed; it may only be propagated from cuttings. Blue & lilac flowered plants including those grown as N. *foetens* and N. *umbonata* might be N. *caerulea*.

Osmanthus *heterophyllus* 'Gulftide'
Probably correctly x fortunei 'Gulftide'.

Papaver *orientale* 'Trkenlouis'/ 'Turkish Delight'
These names are definitely synonymous. However, other cultivars have subsequently been named 'Turkish Delight' and so lack a legitimate name.

Pelargonium 'Beauty of Eastbourne'
This should not be confused with P. 'Eastbourne Beauty', a different cultivar.

Pelargonium 'Lass o'Gowrie'
The American plant of this name has pointed, not rounded leaf lobes.

Pelargonium *quercifolium*
Plants under this name are mainly hybrid. The true species has pointed, not rounded leaf lobes.

Pernettya
Botanists now consider that PERNETTYA (fruit a berry) is not separable from GAULTHERIA (fruit a capsule) because in some species the fruit is intermediate bewteen a berry and a capsule. For a fuller explanation see D. Middleton *The Plantsman.* 1991 (Vol 12 Pt. III).

Picea *pungens* 'Glauca Pendula'
This name may be one of several blue cultivars.

Pinus *aristata*
May include plants referrable to P. *longaeva.*

Pinus *ayacahuite*
P. *a.* var. *veitchii* (syn P. *veitchii*) is occasionally sold under this name.

Pinus *montezumae*
Plants propagated from mature trees in Britich gardens are mostley an un-named long-needled variety of P. *rudis*

Pinus *nigra* 'Cebennensis Nana'
A doubtful and illegitimate name, probably a synonym for P. *n.* 'Nana'.

Polygonatum *odoratum* 'Variegatum'
Plants under this name be P. x *falcatum* 'Variegatum.

Polemonium *archibaldiae*
Usually sterile with lavender-blue flowers. A self-fertile white-flowered plant is sometimes sold under this name.

Polystichum *setiferum* 'Wollaston'
Incomplete name which may refer to either of two cultivars.

Populus *nigra italica*
See note in Bean Supplement, p 393.

Prunus *cerasifera* 'Nigra'
Plants under this name may be referrable to P. *c.* 'Woodii'.

Prunus *laurocerasus* 'Castlewellan'
We are grateful to Dr Charles Nelson for informing us that the name 'Marbled White' is not valid because although it has priority of publication it does not have the approval of the originator who asked for it to be called 'Castlewellan'

Prunus *laurocerasus* 'Variegata'
The true 'Variegata', (marginal variegation), dates from 1811 but this name is also used for the relatively recent cultivar P. *l.* 'Castewellan'.

Prunus *serrulata* var. *pubescens*
See note in Bean Supplement, p 398.

Prunus x *subhirtella* 'Rosea'
Might be P. *pendula* var. *ascendens* 'Rosea', P. *p.* 'Pendula Rosea', or P. x *subhirtella* 'Autumnalis Rosea'.

Pyracantha 'Orange Charmer'
Possibly a synonym of 'Golden Charmer'

Rheum x *cultorum*
The name R. x *cultorum* was published without adequate description and must be abandoned in favour of the validly published R. x *hybridum.*

Rhododendron Azalea
All names marked N refer to more than one cultivar.

Rhododenron Hybrid 'Arctic Tern'
Registered as this name, but considered by some authorities to be X Ledodendron 'Arctic Tern'.

Rhododenron Hybrid Loderi/Kewense
The grex name Kewense has priority of 13 years over the name Loderi for hybrids of R. *griffithianum* x *fortunei* ssp. *fortunei* and would, under normal circumstances be considered correct. However, the RHS as IRA for Rhododendron has declared Loderi as a name to be conserved.

Rhus *typhina*
Linnaeus published both R. *typhina* and R. *hirta* as names for the same species but R. *hirta* has priority and should be used in preference to the newer name.

Robinia *hispida* 'Rosea'
This name is applied to R. *hispida,* (young shoots with bristles), R. *elliottii,* (young shoots with grey down) and R. *boyntonii,* (young shoot with neither bristles nor down).

Rosa
New cultivar names, the first three letters of which normally derive from the name of the breeder, are not given for ROSA. These are usually sold under Registered Trade Marks '®'. Roses often known by common names, eg. Rosa Mundi, Hume's Blush are referred to botanical names as given in Bean.

Rosa *gentiliana*
Plants may be RR. *multiflora* 'Wilsonii', *multiflora* var. *cathayensis, henryi* or a hybrid.

Rosa 'Gros Choux de Hollande' (Bb)
It is doubtful if this name is correctly applied.

Rosa 'Maiden's Blush'
R. 'Great Maiden's Blush' may be supplied under this name.

Rosa 'Marchesa Boccella'
For a discussion on the correct identity of this rose see *Heritage Rose Foundation News* Oct 1989 & Jan 1990.

Rosa 'Professeur Emile Perrot'
For a discussion on the correct identity of this rose see *Heritage Roses* Nov 1991.

Rosa Sweetheart ®
This is not the same as the Sweetheart Rose, a common name for R. 'Cécile Brunner'.

Salix *alba* 'Tristis'
This cultivar should not be confused with S. *tristis*, which is now correctly S. *humilis*. Although this cultivar is distinct in European gardens, most plants under this name in the British Isles are S. x *sepulcralis* var. *chrysocoma*.

Salvia *officinalis* 'Aurea'
S. *o. aurea* is a rare form of the common sage with leaves entirely of gold. It is represented in cultivation by the cultivar 'Kew Gold'. The plant usually offered as S. *o.* 'Aurea' is the gold variegated sage S. *o.* 'Icterina'.

Salvia *sclarea* var. *turkestanica*
Plants in gardens under this name are not S. *s. turkistaniana* of Mottet.

Sambucus *nigra* 'Aurea'
Plants under this name are usually not S. *nigra*.

Sedum *nevii*
The true species is not in cultivation. Plants under this name are usually either S. *glaucophyllum*, occasionally S. *beyrichianum*.

Sedum *spathulifolium* 'Cape Blanco'
This is the correct spelling.

Sempervivum *arachnoideum tomentosum*
Entries here may include plants classified as *S.* 'Hookeri'.

Skimmia *japonica* 'Foremanii'
The true cultivar, which belongs to S. *japonica* Rogersii Group, is believed to be lost to cultivation. Plants offered under this name are usually S. *japonica* 'Veitchii'.

Sophora *prostrata*
Plants may be the hybrid S. 'Little Baby'.

Spiraea *japonica* 'Shirobana'
Shirobana-shimotsuke is the common name for S. *j. albiflora*. Shirobana means white-flowered and does not apply to the two-coloured form.

Staphylea *holocarpa* var. *rosea*
This botanical variety has woolly leaves. The cultivar 'Rosea', with which it is often confused, does not.

Stewartia *ovata* var. *grandiflora*.
Most, possibly all, plants available from British nurseries under this name are not true to name but are derived from the improved Nymans form.

Thymus 'Silver Posie'
The cultivar name 'Silver Posie' is applied to several different plants, not all of them T. *vulgaris*.

Tricyrtis Hototogisu
This is the common name applied generally to all Japanese Tricyrtis and specifically to T. *hirta*.

Tricyrtis *macropoda*
This name has been used for at least five different species.

Uncinia *rubra*
This name is loosely applied to UU. *egmontiana* and *unciniata*.

Verbena 'Kemerton'
Origin unknown, not from Kemerton.

Viburnum *opulus* 'Fructu Luteo'
See note below.

Viburnum *opulus* 'Xanthocarpum'
Entries here include the closely similar V. *o.* 'Fructu Luteo'.

Viburnum *plicatum*
Entries may include the "Snowball" form, V. *plicatum* 'Sterile'.

Viola *labradorica*
See Note in *The Garden*, Vol. 110 Pt. 2 pg 96.

Classification of Genera

CHRYSANTHEMUM

(Now correctly DENDRANTHEMA)

(By the Floral Committee of the National Chrysanthemum Society)

Indoor Cultivars

Section 1 LARGE EXHIBITION

Section 2 MEDIUM EXHIBITION

Section 3 INCURVED

(a) Large-flowered
(b) Medium-flowered
(c) Small-flowered

Section 4 REFLEXED

(a) Large-flowered
(b) Medium-flowered
(c) Small-flowered

Section 5 INTERMEDIATE

(a) Large-flowered
(b) Medium-flowered
(c) Small-flowered

Section 6 ANEMONES

(a) Large-flowered
(b) Medium-flowered
(c) Small-flowered

Section 7 SINGLES

(a) Large-flowered
(b) Medium-flowered
(c) Small-flowered

Section 8 POMPONS

(a) True Poms
(b) Semi-Poms

Section 9 SPRAYS

(a) Anemones
(b) Pompons
(c) Reflexed
(d) Singles
(e) Intermediate
(f) Spider, Quills, Spoons and any other type

Section 10

(a) Spiders
(b) Quills
(c) Spoons

Section 11 ANY OTHER TYPES

Section 12

(a) Charms
(b) Cascades

October-flowered Chrysanthemums

Section 13 INCURVED

(a) Large-flowered
(b) Medium-flowered
(c) Small-flowered

Section 14 REFLEXED

(a) Large-flowered
(b) Medium-flowered
(c) Small-flowered

Section 15 INTERMEDIATE

(a) Large-flowered
(b) Medium-flowered
(c) Small-flowered

Section 16 LARGE OCTOBER FLOWERING

Section 17 SINGLES

(a) Large-flowered
(b) Medium-flowered
(c) Small-flowered

Section 18 POMPONS

(a) True Poms
(b) Semi-poms

Section 19 SPRAYS

(a) Anemones
(b) Pompons
(c) Reflexed
(d) Singles
(e) Intermediate
(f) Spider, Quills, Spoons and any other type

Section 20 ANY OTHER TYPES

Early-flowering Chrysanthemums

Outdoor Cultivars

Section 23 INCURVED

(a) Large-flowered
(b) Medium-flowered
(c) Small-flowered

Section 24 REFLEXED

(a) Large-flowered
(b) Medium-flowered
(c) Small-flowered

Section 25 INTERMEDIATE

(a)	Large-flowered
(b)	Medium-flowered
(c)	Small-flowered

Section 26 ANEMONE

(a)	Large-flowered
(b)	Medium-flowered

Section 27 SINGLES

(a)	Large-flowered
(b)	Medium-flowered

Section 28 POMPONS

(a)	True Poms
(b)	Semi-poms

Section 29 SPRAYS

(a)	Anemones
(b)	Pompons
(c)	Reflexed
(d)	Singles
(e)	Intermediate
(f)	Spider, Quills, Spoons and any other type
K	Korean
Rub	Rubellum

Section 30 ANY OTHER TYPE

BEGONIA

C	Cane
R	Rex
S	Semperflorens
T	x tuberhybrida (Tuberous)

CLEMATIS

(A)	Alpina Group (Section Atragene)
(D)	Diversifolia Group
(F)	Florida Group
(Fo)	Fosteri Group
(J)	Jackmanii Group
(L)	Languinosa Group
(P)	Patens Group
(T)	Texensis Group
(Ta)	Tangutica Group
(Vt)	Viticella Group

DAHLIAS

(By The National Dahlia Society)

1	Single	Sin
2	Anemone-flowered	Anem
3	Collerette	Col
4B	Waterlily, Large	LWL
4C	Waterlily, Medium	MWL
4D	Waterlily, Small	SWL
4E	Waterlily, Miniature	MinWL
5A	Decorative, Giant	GD
5B	Decorative, Large	LD
5C	Decorative, Medium	MD
5D	Decorative, Small	SD
5E	Decorative, Miniature	MinD
6A	Small ball	SBa
6B	Miniature Ball	MinBa
7	Pompon	Pom
8A	Cactus, Giant	GC
8B	Cactus, Large	LC
8C	Cactus, Medium	MC
8D	Cactus, Small	SC
8E	Cactus, Miniature	MinC
9A	Semi-cactus, Giant	GSC
9B	Semi-cactus, Large	LSC
9C	Semi-cactus, Medium	MSC
9D	Semi-cactus, Small	SSC
9E	Semi-cactus, Miniature	MinSC
10	Miscellaneous	Misc
-	Orchid flowering	O
-	Botanical	B
-	Dwarf Bedding	DwB
-	Fimbriated	Fim
	Lilliput	Lil

DIANTHUS

(p)	Pinks
(p,a)	Annual pinks
(pf)	Perpetual flowering
(b)	Border
(m)	Malmaison

GLADIOLUS

(B)	Butterfly
(Colv)	Colvillei
(G)	Giant
(L)	Large
(M)	Medium
(Min)	Miniature
(N)	Nanus
(P)	Primulinus
(S)	Small
(Tub)	Tubergenii

HYDRANGEA macrophylla

H	Hortensia
L	Lacecap

IRIS

(AB)	Arilbred
(BB)	Border Bearded
(Cal-Sib)	Series Californicae x Series Sibiricae
(CH)	Californian Hybrid
(DB)	Dwarf Bearded
(Dut)	Dutch
(IB)	Intermediate Bearded

(MDB)	Miniature Dwarf Bearded
(MTB)	Miniature Tall Bearded
(SDB)	Standard Dwarf Bearded
(Sp)	Spuria
(TB)	Tall Bearded

LILIUM

'International Lily Register' (Third Edition)
The Royal Horticultural Society 1982

I	Hybrids derived from LL.*lancifolium cernuum, davidii, leichtlinii,* x *maculatum,* x *hollandicum, amabile, pumilum, concolor,* & *bulbiferum*
I(a)	Early flowering with upright flowers, single or in an umbel
I(b)	Outward facing flowers
I(c)	Pendant flowers
II	Hybrids of Martagon type, one parent having been a form of LL. *martagon* or *hansonii*
III	Hybrids from LL. *candidum, chalcedonicum* and other related European species (ex. L. *martagon*)
IV	Hybrids of American species
V	Hybrids derived from LL. *longiflorum* & *formosanum*
VI	Hybrid Trumpet Lilies & Aurelian Hybrids from Asiatic species, incl. L. *henryi* but excluding those from LL. *auratum, speciosum, japonicum* & *rubellum*
VI(a)	with trumpet-shaped flowers
VI(b)	with bowl-shaped & outward-facing
VI(c)	with pendant flowers
VI(d)	with flat, star-shaped flowers
VII	Hybrids of Far Eastern species as, LL *auratum, speciosum, rubellum,* & *japonicum*
VII(a)	with trumper-shape flowers
VII(b)	with bowl-shaped flowers
VII(c)	with flat flowers
VII(d)	with recurved flowers
VIII	All Hybrids not in another division
IX	All species & their varieties & forms

NARCISSUS

Classification by The Royal Horticultural Society (Revised 1977)

Division 1	Trumpet
Division 2	Large-cupped
Division 3	Small-cupped
Division 4	Double
Division 5	Triandrus
Division 6	Cyclamineus
Division 7	Jonquilla
Division 8	Tazetta
Division 9	Poeticus
Division 10	Species and wild forms & hybrids
Division 11	Split-corona
Division 12	Miscellaneous

NYMPHAEA (Waterlilies)

H	Hardy
D	Day-blooming
N	Night1-blooming
T	Tropical

PELARGONIUM

A	Angel
C	Coloured foliage (in combination)
Ca	Cactus (in combination)
d	Double (in combination)
Dec	Decorative
Dw	Dwarf
DwI	Dwarf Ivy-leaved
Fr	Frutetorum
I	Ivy-leaved
Min	Miniature or Dwarf
MinI	Miniature Ivy-leaved
R	Regal
Sc	Scented-leaved
St	Stellar (in combination)
T	Tulip (in combination)
U	Unique
Z	Zonal

PRIMULA

(1)	Amethystina
(2)	Auricula
(3)	Bullatae
(4)	Candelabra
(5)	Capitatae
(6)	Carolinella
(7)	Cortusoides
(8)	Cuneifolia
(9)	Denticulata
(10)	Dryadifolia
(11)	Farinosae
(12)	Floribundae
(13)	Grandis
(14)	Malacoides
(15)	Malvacea
(16)	Minutissimae
(17)	Muscarioides
(18)	Nivales
(19)	Obconica
(20)	Parryi
(21)	Petiolares
(22)	Pinnatae
(23)	Pycnoloba
(24)	Reinii
(25)	Rotundifolia

(26)	Sikkimensis
(27)	Sinenses
(28)	Soldenelloideae
(29)	Souliei
(30)	Vernales
(A)	Alpine Auricula
(B)	Border Auricula
(D)	Double
(Poly)	Polyanthus
(Prim)	Primrose
(S)	Show Auricula

RHODODENDRON (Azalea)

(E)	Evergreen
(G)	Ghent
(K)	Knaphill or Exbury
(M)	Mollis
(O)	Occidentalis
(R)	Rustica
(Vs)	Viscosa

RHODODENDRON

(A)	Azalea species
(EA)	Evergreen azalea species

ROSA

(A)	Alba
(Bb)	Bourbon
(Bs)	Boursault
(Ce)	Centifolia
(Ch)	China
(Cl)	Climbing
(Co)	Compacta
(D)	Damask
(DPo)	Damask Portland
(F)	Floribunda or Cluster-flowered
(G)	Gallica
(Ga)	Garnette
(GC)	Ground Cover
(HScB)	Hybrid Scots Briar
(HSwB)	Hybrid Sweet Briar
(HM)	Hybrid Musk
(HP)	Hybrid Perpetual
(HT)	Hybrid Tea or Large-flowered
(Min)	Miniature
(Mo)	Moss
(N)	Noisette
(Patio)	Patio or Miniature Floribunda
(Poly)	Polyantha
(Ra)	Rambler
(Ru)	Rugosa
(S)	Shrub
(T)	Tea

SAXIFRAGA

1	Micranthes
2	Hirculus
3	Gymnopera
4	Diptera
5	Trachyphyllum
6	Xanthizoon
7	Aizoonia
8	Porophyllum
9	Porophyrion
10	Miscopetalum
11	Saxifraga
12	Trachyphylloïdes
13	Cymbalaria
14	Discogyne

TULIPA

'Revised Classification of Tulips' by Koninklijke Algemeene Vereening voor Bloembollenculture 1981

Early Flowering

1	Single Early
2	Double Early

Mid-Season

3	Triumph
4	Darwin Hybrid

Late Flowering

5	Single Late (incl. Darwin)
6	Lily-Flowered
7	Fringed
8	Viridiflora
9	Rembrandt
10	Parrot
11	Double Late

Species and their Hybrids

12	Kaufmanniana
13	Fosteriana
14	Greigii

VIOLA

(C)	Cornuta hybrid
(dVt)	Double Violet
(ExVa)	Exhibition Viola
(FP)	Fancy Pansy
(SP)	Show Pansy
(T)	Tricolor
(Va)	Viola
(Vt)	Violet
(Vtta)	Violetta

VITIS

B	Black
G	Glasshouse
O	Outdoor
R	Red
W	White

Acknowledgements

For the compilation of this edition, we are especially indebted to Messrs D J Bradshaw, R Cooper, P J Foley, M Frankis, R Gardner, J G S Harris, H Harrison, G Hutchins, J H Irons, H Noblett, M Parr, J Porter, R Poulett, R Whitehouse, Dr P S Green, Mrs C Boulby and Mrs E Strangman for many helpful comments on plant nomenclature. Particular thanks go to Chris Brickell, Alan Leslie and Piers Trehane, my colleagues on the committee set up to help standardise, stabilise and correct the names of garden plants following the recent acquisition of ***The Plant Finder*** by the Royal Horticultural Society.

Artemisia	Dr J D Twibell. ('94)
Bamboos	D McClintock. ('90-'94)
Bougainvillea	S Read. ('94)
Camellia	T J Savige, International Registrar, NSW. ('93)
Cimicifuga	J Compton. ('94)
Conifers	J Lewis, International Registrar, RHS Wisley. ('93)
	H J Welch, World Conifer Data Pool. ('90-'93)
	P Trehane, International Registrar, RHS Wisley. ('94)
Cotoneaster	Jeanette Fryer, NCCPG Collection Holder. ('91-'92)
Cyclamen	Dr C Grey-Wilson. ('94)
Dahlia	D Pycraft, International Registrar, RHS Wisley. ('91)
Delphinium	Dr A C Leslie, International Registrar, RHS Wisley. ('91 & '93)
Dianthus	Dr A C Leslie, International Registrar, RHS Wisley. ('91-'94)
Euphorbia	R Turner. ('91)
Fuchsia	Mrs D Logan, International Registrar, American Fuchsia Society. ('91)
Gesneriaceae	J D Dates. Internatioanl Registrar. ('94)
Gladiolus	F N Franks. ('92)
Heathers	D McClintock. ('92)
Hebe	Mrs J Hewitt. ('94)
Hedera	P Q Rose & Mrs H Key. ('91 & '93)
	Alison Rutherford. ('92-'94)
Helianthemum	H Gardner. ('91)
Hoya	D Kent. ('91)
Hypericum	Dr N K B Robson. ('94)
Ilex	Ms S Andrews. ('92-'94)
Jovibarba & Sempervivum	P J Mitchell, International Registrar, Sempervivum Society. ('91-'93)
Juniperus	J Lewis. International Registrar. ('94)
Lavandula	Ms S Andrews. ('92 &'94)
Narcissus	Mrs S Kington. International Registrar. ('91-'94)
Passiflora	D Kent. ('91)
Pelargonium	Mrs H Key. ('91-'94)
Pelargonium spp.	Mrs D Miller. ('93)
Phormium	L J Metcalf, International Registrar. ('91)
Polemonium	Mrs D Allison. ('94)
Rhododendron	Dr A C Leslie, International Registrar, RHS Wisley. ('91-'94)
Salix	Dr R D Meikle. ('93)
Salvia	J Compton. ('92 & '94)
Zauschneria	P Trehane. ('94)

To all these, as well as the many readers and nurseries who have also made comments and suggestions, we are, once again, sincerely grateful.

Collectors' References

AB&S	Archibald, Blanchard & Salmon. Morocco 1980's
AC&H	Apold, Cox & Hutchinson. 1962 expedition to NE Turkey
ACL	A C Leslie
AC&W	Albury, Cheese & Watson
AGS/ES	Alpine Garden Society expedition to Sikkim
AGSJ	Alpine Garden Society expedition to Japan
Akagi	Akagi Botanical Garden
A&JW	Anita & John Watson to S. America
AL&JS	Sharman & Leslie. Yugoslavia 1990
A&L	Ala & Lancaster expedition to N Iran 1972
B	Len Beer
BB	B Bartholemew
BC&W	Beckett, Cheese & Watson
BL&M	Beer, Lancaster & Morris NE Nepal 1971
B&L	Brickell & Leslie, China
BM	Brian Mathew
B&M	Chris Brickell & Brian Mathew
BM&W	Binns, Mason & Wright
B&S	Peter Bird & Mike Salmon
BSBE	Bowles Scholarship Botanical Expedition
B&SWJ	Bleddyn & Sue Wynn-Jones. Far East 1993
CC	Chris Chadwell
CC&McK	Chadwell & McKelvie 1990 to Central Nepal
CC&MR	Chris Chadwell & Magnus Ramsey 1985 to Kashmir, 1989 to Himachal Pradesh & W Himalaya
CDB	C D Brickell
CD&R	Compton, D'Arcy & Rix. China & Drakensburg
CE&H	Christian, Elliott & Hoog. Yugoslavia & Greece 1982
CH&M	Cox, Hutchinson & MacDonald
CHP&W	Chadwell, Hudson, POwell & Wright. Kashmir 1983
CL	Dr C Lovell
CLD	Kew, Edinburgh & RHS. China 1990
CM&W	M Cheese, J Mitchel & J Watson
Cooper	Roland Edgar Cooper (1890-1962)
C&Mc	Chadwell & McKelvie 1990/1/2. To Nepal & W. Himalaya
C&H	Cox & Hutchinson. 1965 expediton to Assam, NE Frontier & N Bengal
C&R	Christian & Roderick. (California, Oregon, Washington).
C&W	Cheese & Watson
CT	Carla Teune
DF	Derek Fox
DS&T	Drake, Sharman & Thompson. Turkey 1989
EGM	E G Millais
EKB	E K Balls
EM	East Malling Research Station. Clonal selection scheme
EMR	E Martyn Rix
F	George Forrest (1873-1932)
Farrer	Reginald Farrer (1880-1920)
FK	Fergus Kinimount. China & Nepal
FMB	F M Bailey
F&W	Anita Flores & John Watson. Chile 1992
G	M Gardner
GS	George Sherriff (1898-1967)
G&K	M Gardner & S Knees
G-W&P	Grey-Wilson & Phillips
G&P	Gardner & Page, Chile '92
Guitt	Prof. G G Guittonneau
Guiz	Guizhou Expedition 1985
H	Paul Huggins. Oxford University Expedition to the Tehri-Garwal, Central Himalaya
Harry Smith	Karl August Harald Smith (1889-1971)
H&B	Hilliard & Burtt
HM&S	Halliwell, Mathew & Smallcombe
H&W	Hedge & Wendelbo. 1969 to Afghanistan
JCA	J C Archibald
JJH	Josef Halda Collection
JLS	J L Sharman. USA 1988
JR	J Russell
JRM	Dr John Marr. Expedition to Greece & Turkey 1975
JW	J Watson
K	G Kirkpatrick
KBE	Kashmir Botanical Expedition, Chadwell, Howard, Powell & Wright 1983
K&E	Kew & Edinburgh. Chine 1989
KGB	Kunming-Gothenburg Expedition. NW Yunnan 1993
K&Mc	George Kirkpatrick and Ron McBeath.
KR	Keith Rushforth
KW	Frank Kingdon-Ward (1885-1958)
L	Roy Lancaster
LA	Long Ashton Research Station. Clonal Selection scheme.
L&S	Ludlow (1885-1972) & G Sherriff
LS&E	Ludlow, Sherriff & Elliott
LS&H	Ludlow, Sherriff & Hicks, 1949 to Bhutan

LS&T	Ludlow Sherriff & Taylor. 1938 to SE Tibet
Mac&W	MacPhail & Watson
McB	Ron McBeath
McLaren	Henry McLaren, 2nd Baron Aberconway (1879-1953)
MS	Mike Salmon
MSF	M S Fillan. Tenerife 1988, South Korea 1989
NS	Nick Turland (Northside Seeds)
M&T	B Mathew & J Tomlinson
PB	Peter Bird
PD	Peter Davis
PF	Paul Furse
PJC	P J Christian
PJC&AH	P J Christian & A Hoog. Greece & Yugoslavia 1985
Pras	Milan Prasil
PS&W	Polunin, Sykes & Williams. 1952 W. Nepal
P&W	Polastri & Watson
R	J F C Rock (1884-1962)
RV	Richard Valder
SBEC	Sino-British expedition to Cangshan, SW China (1981)
SB&L	Salmon, Bird & Lovell. Jordan & Morocco
Sch	A D Schilling
SEP	Swedish expedition to Pakistan
S&B	Mike Salmon & John Blanchard
SF	S Forde, Bhutan Oct '90
S&F	Salmon & Fillan. Spain & Morocco
S&L	Mike Salmon & Dr Chris Lovell
S&SH	Sheilah & Spencer Hannay. Lesotho, NE Cape Province 1989&91 & C Nepal 1993.
SS&W	Stainton, Sykes & Williams 1954 to Central Nepal
T	Nigel Taylor
TSS	T Spring-Smyth
T&K	Taylor & Knees
TW	Tony Weston
USNA	United States National Arboretum
VH	Professor Vernon Heywood
W	E H Wilson, (1876-1930)
W A	E H Wilson, for Arnold Arboretum - (1906-1919)
WM	Will McLewin.
Wr	David & Anke Wraight
W V	E H Wilson, for Veitch - (1899-1905)
Yu	Tse Tsun Yu (1908-1986)

NOTE: Collectors' numbers which do not appear to relate to the species listed are given an asterisk after the number. For the Collections of Joseph Rock, a number of nurseries quote United States Department of Agriculture numbers rather than Rock's own collection number. We have tried to make clear which of the two numbers is quoted and to give Rock's own numbers wherever possible.

PLANT DIRECTORY

ABELIA † (Caprifoliaceae)

§ ***chinensis***	CB&S CBow CChu CCla CGre CHan CPle SGil SHil SLon SPer SReu WHCG WWat
'Edward Goucher' AGM	CB&S CBot CBow CCla CDoC CPle CSco CWit EBre ELan ESma LBre MAll MGos SFis SHil SPla WOld WPat WSHC WWeb
engleriana	CPle CSam ECtt EHic EPla MHlr NWyt SGil SHer WWat
floribunda AGM	CAbb CB&S CBot CBow CChu CDoC CLan CMHG CPle CSam CSco CTbh CTrw EBre ELan IMal IOrc LBre LHop MRav SHer SHil SPer WAbe WWat
graebneriana	CHan CPle
§ x ***grandiflora*** AGM	Widely available
– 'Aurea'	See A. x ***g.*** 'Goldsport'
– 'Francis Mason' AGM	Widely available
– 'Gold Strike'	See A. x ***g.*** 'Goldsport'
§ – 'Goldsport'	CAbb CB&S CCla CDoC CPMA EBre IOrc LBre LHop MPla MWat SBod SCro WPat WWat
– 'Prostrata'	CBot
– 'Variegata'	CLan EWri WWat WWin
rupestris	See A. x ***grandiflora***
rupestris Lindley	See A. ***chinensis***
schumannii	CB&S CBot CBra CChu CCla CLan CMHG CPle CSam CSco EBre ELan ENot LBre LHop SDry SHBN SLon SPer SPla SReu SSta WAbe WHCG WOld WPat WSHC
triflora	CBot CHan CPle ECtt EHic LHop SPla WSHC WWat
¶ ***zanderi***	CPle

ABELIOPHYLLUM (Oleaceae)

distichum	CB&S CBot CBow CHan CMHG CPMA CPle CSco ELan ENot GWht MBri MUlv NSti NWyt SGil SHBN SHil SPer SPla SReu SSta WBod WHCG WSHC WWat WWin
– Roseum Group	CB&S CPMA CSam EHic ELan EWri MPla MUlv

ABELMOSCHUS (Malvaceae)

See Plant Deletions

ABIES † (Pinaceae)

alba	CDoC LCon MBar WDin
– 'Compacta'	CKen
– 'Green Spiral'	CKen
¶ – 'King's Dwarf'	CKen
– 'Pendula'	LPan
– 'Tortuosa'	CKen
amabilis	WFro
balsamea f. ***balsamea***	WCoo WFro
– f. ***hudsonia*** AGM	CDoC CKen CMac EHul ENHC GDra IOrc LCon LLin MBal MBar MGos NHar NHed NHol SLim SPla WDin WThu
– 'Nana'	CKen EBre EHul ELan IDai IJoh LBee LBre LCon MAsh MBri MPla MRPP NHar NRoo SPer WAbe WDin WStI
¶ – 'Piccolo'	CKen
– 'Prostrata'	LCon
bornmuelleriana	See A. ***nordmanniana equi-trojani***
– 'Archer'	CKen
brachyphylla dwarf	See A. ***homolepis*** 'Prostrata'
bracteata	ISea LCon SMad WCoo
cephalonica	EHar LCon
§ – 'Meyer's Dwarf'	EBre LBre LCon LLin MBar
I – 'Nana'	See A. ***c.*** 'Meyer's Dwarf'
'Compacta' (***grandis***)	CKen
concolor AGM	CB&S CDoC CGre EArb EHar GRei IJoh IOrc ISea LBee LCon MBal MBar NWea SPer WCoo WDin WFro
– 'Archer's Dwarf'	CKen MGos
§ – 'Argentea'	LCon LPan
– 'Candicans'	See A. ***c.*** 'Argentea'
§ – 'Compacta' AGM	CBra CDoC CKen EBre LBre LCon LLin MAsh MBal MBar MGos SHil SLim SSta
– 'Fagerhult'	CKen
– 'Gable's Weeping'	CKen
– 'Glauca'	See A. ***c.*** 'Violacea'
– 'Glauca Compacta'	See A. ***c.*** 'Compacta'
– 'Hillier Broom '	See A. ***c.*** 'Hillier's Dwarf'
§ – 'Hillier's Dwarf'	CKen
– var. ***lowiana*** 'Creamy'	CKen
– 'Masonic Broom'	CKen
– 'Piggelmee'	CKen
§ – 'Violacea'	EBre LBre LCon MAsh MBar MBri MGos SSta
– 'Wattezii'	CKen LCon LLin MAsh
delavayi var. ***delavayi***	IBar IOrc
– – Fabri Group	See A. ***fabri***
– 'Major Neishe'	CKen
¶ ***densa*** S&L 5538	WHCr
ernestii	See A. ***recurvata e.***
§ ***fabri***	WCoo
fargesii 'Headfort'	MBar
firma	WCoo
fraseri	LCon MBal
– 'Kline's Nest'	CKen
grandis AGM	EHar ENot GRei IOrc LCon MBar NWea SHBN SMad WDin WMou
holophylla	CMCN LCon WCoo
homolepis	ISea LCon MBlu WCoo
§ – 'Prostrata'	CKen
koreana	Widely available
– 'Aurea'	See A. ***k.*** 'Flava'
– 'Blaue Zwo'	CKen
– 'Compact Dwarf'	LLin MGos SSta WAbe
§ – 'Flava'	CDoC CKen EBre GAri LBre LCon MBar MBri NHol
– 'Golden Wonder'	COtt
– 'Inverleith'	CKen
– 'Nisbet'	CKen LCon
– 'Piccolo'	CKen
¶ – 'Pinocchio'	CKen
– 'Silberlocke' AGM	CBra CDoC CKen CSco EBre GAri IOrc LBee LBre LCon LLin MAsh MBar MBri MGos MPla NHol SEng SHil SLim SPer SSta
– 'Silberperl'	CKen
– 'Silver Show'	CKen
– 'Starker's Dwarf'	CKen
lasiocarpa	LCon WDin
– var. ***arizonica***	LCon SSta

– 'Arizonica Compacta' AGM	CDoC CKen CMac COtt CSco EBre EHar EHul IOrc LBee LBre LCon LLin LPan MAsh MBar MBri MGos NHar NHol SLim SMad SSta WDin WStI
– – 'Kenwith Blue'	CKen
– 'Glauca'	See A. ***concolor*** 'Violacea'
– 'Green Globe'	CKen LCon
magnifica	EHar EHul LCon LPan WCoo
I – 'Nana'	CKen
marocana	See A. ***pinsapo marocana***
nephrolepis	CMCN
nobilis	See A. ***procera***
nordmanniana AGM	CDoC EHar EHul EMil LBuc LCon LPan MBal MBar MGos NWea SLim WDin WFro
– 'Barabits' Compact'	MBar
§ – ssp. ***equi-trojani***	LCon
– 'Golden Spreader' AGM	CDoC CKen EBre LBee LBre LCon LLin MAsh MBar MGos NHol SLim SPer SSta
I – 'Pendula'	LPan
I – 'Reflexa'	LPan
numidica	LPan
– 'Lawrenceville'	LCon
– 'Pendula'	CKen
pindrow	CGre EHal
pinsapo	EHar LCon MBar
– 'Aurea'	CKen EBre LBre LBuc WThu
– 'Glauca' AGM	CDoC CKen EHar ELan IOrc LCon LPan MBar MBlu MBri NHol SHil WDin
– 'Hamondii'	CKen
I – 'Horstmann'	CKen MBar
– 'Kelleriis'	LCon
– var. ***marocana***	CGre
§ ***procera*** AGM	CDoC CGre EHul EMil GAri GRei IDai LCon MBal MBar NRoo NWea STre WDin WMou
– 'Blaue Hexe'	CKen
– 'Compacta'	See A. ***p.*** 'Prostrata'
– Glauca Group	CDoC CMac EBre EHar IOrc LBre LCon LLin LPan MBar MBri MGos NHar SLim
– 'Glauca Prostrata'	EBre EHul ENHC GAri IOrc LBee LBre LPan MAsh MBal MBar MGos NHol SSta WDin
– 'Mount Hood'	CKen
§ – 'Prostrata'	LCon
recurvata var. ***ernestii***	CMCN LCon
religiosa	GAri
spectabilis	GWht WCoo
squamata	CMCN LCon
sutchuenensis	See A. ***fargesii***
veitchii AGM	GRei IOrc LCon MBar
– 'Hedergott'	CKen
– 'Heine'	CKen
¶ ***vejarii***	WCoo

ABROMEITIELLA (Bromeliaceae)

brevifolia AGM	CFil

ABRONIA (Nyctaginaceae)

See Plant Deletions

ABROTANELLA (Compositae/Asteraceae)

See Plant Deletions

ABUTILON † (Malvaceae)

¶ 'Alpha Glory'	ERom
'Amsterdam'	ERea
'Ashford Red' AGM	CBot CCan CTre EBre IBlr IJoh IOrc LAbb LBre SLMG SMrm WOMN WOld
'Boule de Neige'	CBot CBrk CGre ERea LHil LRHS MBri SLMG
'Canary Bird' AGM	CAbb CB&S CBar CBot CBow CBrk CGre CPle CTre CTro ERea ERom LBlm LGre LHil LHop MBri NWyt SHBN SHer SLMG SMrm WOMN WOld
'Cannington Carol' AGM	CAbb CBrk CCan ERea LBlm LHil WOld
'Cannington Peter' AGM	CBrk CCan ERea ERom
'Cannington Sonia' (v)	ERea
'Cerise Queen'	CCan
'Cloth of Gold'	EPla IJoh
'Fireball'	CBrk EPla LGre LHop SMrm
'Glenroy Snowdrift'	MAll MBal
globosum	See A. x ***hybridum***
'Golden Fleece'	CKni ERea GCal IBlr
'Hinton Seedling'	CBow CBrk CDoC EMil LHop MUlv SLMG WEas
§ x ***hybridum***	CNew CTro MBri
¶ 'Imp'	EPla
'Kentish Belle' AGM	CAbb CB&S CBot CBra CCan CMHG CPle CSco CTre EBre ECot ENot IOrc ISea LBre SBra SHBN SHer SLMG SPer WWye
'Louise Marignac'	CBrk CCan ERea ERom LBlm
'Master Michael'	CCla CKni EMil ERea LHil
megapotamicum AGM	CB&S CBot CBra CCan CCla CLan CMHG CPle CSco CTro ELan ENot ERea GWht IBar ISea MBal MGos NKay SBra SDix SHBN SLMG SLon SPer WBod WEas WSHC WWat
– 'Variegatum'	CAbb CB&S CBot CBow CBrk CCla CLan CSco CWit ECtt ELan EWri GCal GCra IBar IBlr IOrc LBlm LHil MBri NWyt SBod SBra SHBN SLMG SLon SPer
– 'Wisley Red'	CCla CDoC
x ***milleri*** AGM	CB&S CBot CCla CGre ELan ERea IOrc LBlm SBra SHBN WSHC
– 'Variegatum'	CB&S CBrk CCan CDoC CKni CMHG CPle SHBN SLMG
'Nabob' AGM	CBrk CCan CGre CTre CTro CWit ERea LHil LHop LRHS MBri SLMG WEas WOld
'Orange Glow' AGM	CTre
'Orange King'	CB&S
'Patrick Synge'	CBrk CGre CMHG CSco CTro ERav ERea LBlm LGre SLMG SMrm
§ ***pictum***	ERea LBlm MBri
– 'Thompsonii' (v)	CBot CBrk CTro EFol ERea IBlr ISea LBlm LHil SLMG
* – ***variegatum***	EFol
'Pink Lady'	CB&S EMil ERea
¶ 'Red Bells'	CPBP

¶ 'Rotterdam'	LHil
'Savitzii' (v)	CB&S CBar CBot CBrk ERea ERom IReg LHil SRms
sellowianum	
var. ***marmoratum***	ERea SLMG
'Souvenir de Bonn' **AGM**	CBrk CGre ERea IBlr LBlm LHil
striatum	See A. ***pictum***
x ***suntense***	CB&S CCan CCla CGle CHEx CMHG CPle CSco CWSG EBre ELan ERav LAbb LBre LHop MBal NPer NRar SHBN SHer SLMG SSta WBod WEas WPat
– 'Jermyns' **AGM**	CAbb CCla CDoC CWSG CWit EBre ECtt EHal EOrc ISea LBre LGre MGos MUlv NWyt SFis SGil SHer SHil SMrm SSta WPat WWat
¶ – 'Ralph Gould'	LHop
– 'Violetta'	CAbb CBot CTre ECtt NSti NWyt SReu SSta
theophrasti	MSal WHaw WHer
vitifolium	CB&S CBot CCan CCla CMil CNew CTre ECot ERea EWri GWht IOrc LHop MHlr SChu SHer SPer WCru WWat WWin WWye
– var. ***album***	CAbb CB&S CBot CGle CMHG CSco CWit ECha ELan ERav IMal LHop MBal NRar NTow SChu SPer SSta WBod WSHC WWat WWye
– 'Ice Blue'	CBot
– 'Tennant's White' **AGM**	CAbP CBot CCan CGre ERea LGre NWyt SHBN SHil SMad
– 'Veronica Tennant' **AGM**	CCan ERav ERea LGre NWyt SHil SMrm WPat
¶ – 'Wild Forest'	WHaw

ACACIA † (Leguminosae/Mimosaceae)

acinacea	CGre
alpina	WCel
♦***armata***	See A. ***paradoxa***
baileyana **AGM**	CB&S CBow CWSG ECot EMil ERea LBlm
– 'Purpurea' **AGM**	CAbb CB&S CBow CDoC CGre CPle CTro CWSG CWit EMil ERea LAbb LHil LHop MBlu MUlv SFai
beckleri	CGre
¶ ***brachybotrya***	CGre
burkittii	CGre
cultriformis	ERea IOrc
dealbata **AGM**	CAbb CB&S CBow CBra CDoC CGre CHEx CHan CPle CSco CTre CWSG ELan ERea EWri IDai IMal IOrc LAbb LBlm LHil MBal MBlu NPal SHBN SIgm SPer WBod WNor
¶ – 'Gaulois Astier'	ERea
– 'Mirandole'	ERea
¶ – 'Reve d'Or'	ERea
– ***subalpina***	SArc WCel
Exeter hybrid	CGre ERea
extensa	CGre
filicifolia	WCel
floribunda 'Lisette'	ERea
frigescens	SArc WCel
gillii	CGre
§ ***glaucocarpa***	LHil
julibrissin	See ALBIZIA ***j.***
juniperina	See A. ***ulicifolia***
karroo	CArn CTro
kybeanensis	WCel
longifolia	CB&S CHEx CPle CTro IOrc NPal
mearnsii	CTbh WCel
melanoxylon	IOrc ISea WCel
motteana	ECot ERea
mucronata	CB&S GWht
obliquinervia	WCel
§ ***paradoxa***	CB&S ERea IMal IOrc LHil LHop MBri
– ***angustifolia***	LBlm
pendula	MBri
podalyriifolia	CB&S CMHG
polybotrya hort.	See A. ***glaucocarpa***
pravissima	CB&S CChu CDoC CFee CGre CHEx CMHG CPle CTbh CWit ERea LBlm LHil LHop MBal SArc SFai WCel WNor
retinodes **AGM**	CDoC CGre CNew CPle CTro ERea SRms
riceana	CB&S WCel
¶ ***rivalis***	ERea
rubida	CTbh
saligna	IOrc
sentis	See A. ***victoriae***
sophorae	GWht
§ ***ulicifolia***	CGre CPle CWit
verticillata	CB&S CGre CPle
§ ***victoriae***	ERea

ACAENA (Rosaceae)

****acris***	LBlm
adscendens 'Glauca'	LHop MBel NBir NNor
adscendens Margery Fish	See A. ***affinis***
adscendens misapplied	See AA. ***magellanica magellanica,*** 'Blue Haze'
♦***adscendens*** Vahl	See A. ***magellanica laevigata***
affinis	CRow ECha SDix
§ ***anserinifolia*** Druce	CLew ECha GLil GTou NCat NHol NRar NRed WEas WPer WWin
anserinifolia hort.	See A. ***novae-zelandiae***
argentea	SBla
§ 'Blue Haze'	Widely available
buchananii	CNic CRiv CShe CTom ECro EPar EPot GIsl GTou MBar MBri MCas MFir NKay NNor SIng SSmi WAbe WByw WCla WHoo WMer WPbr WPer WWye
caerulea	See A. ***caesiiglauca***
§ ***caesiiglauca***	CBar CLew CMer CNic CRiv ECoo ECro EJud GAbr GGar GTou MWat NCat NNor NSti WEas WPer
fissistipula	GGar
¶ ***glabra***	GIsl
glaucophylla	See A. ***magellanica magellanica***
inermis	CLew CMer ELan EPot GIsl NNrd SIng SSmi WPer
§ ***magellanica***	
ssp. ***laevigata***	CNic CRiv ECro ECtt EHoe EMon GAri GGar GIsl GTou NNor WPbr WWin
§ – ssp. ***magellanica***	ECro GCal GTou WMer

microphylla **AGM**	EBre ECro EPar ESis GGar GIsl LBre MBar MBri MBro MFir MRav MWat NGre NMen NRed NRoo SHer SIng SSmi WByw WCla WEas WHoo WPer WTyr
– 'Glauca'	See A. ***caesiiglauca***
§ – 'Kupferteppich' ('Copper Carpet')	CRiv CRow ECro EHoe GAbr GAri GGar GLil MBri MRav NCat NVic SIng WCra WPat
– 'Pallidolivacea'	CRow
– 'Pulchella'	CTom EBre ECha GAri LBre MRav NHol
myriophylla	WPer
§ ***novae-zelandiae***	CRiv CRow ECro EJud GIsl GTou MFir NRed SDix SIgm SIng WHaw WPer
ovalifolia	CNic CRow CTom GTou MFir NCat NRed SAxl SIng WHaw WPer
'Pewter'	See A. 'Blue Haze'
¶ ***pinnatifida***	GTou MFir WPer
♦ ***profundeincisa***	See A. ***anserinifolia*** Druce
'Purple Carpet'	See A. ***microphylla*** 'Kupferteppich'
sanguisorbae Linnaeus f.	See A. ***anserinifolia*** Druce
sericea	CLew EWes WDav WPer
sp. CC 451	MRPP NWCA WDav
sp. CC 577	NWCA
♦ ***viridior***	See A. ***anserinifolia***

ACALYPHA (Euphorbiaceae)

hispida **AGM**	MBri
– 'Hispaniola'	CBrk ERea
♦ ***pendula***	See A. ***reptans***
§ ***reptans***	CBar

ACANTHOCALYX See MORINA

ACANTHOLIMON (Plumbaginaceae)

androsaceum	See A. ***ulicinum***
glumaceum	MDHE NHol NMen SHer WDav
§ ***ulicinum***	EPot NGre NWCA

ACANTHOPANAX See ELEUTHEROCOCCUS

ACANTHUS † (Acanthaceae)

australis	SLMG
balcanicus	See A. ***hungaricus***
dioscoridis var. ***perringii***	CGle CHan CMil LGre
hirsutus	EMon LGre SCro
– ssp. ***syriacus*** JCA 106.500	CGle LGre SBla
§ ***hungaricus***	CArn CCla CHan CMil ECED ECha EMon EPla GCal MFir SBla SDix SFis SPer WCru WRus
– AL&JS 90097YU	EMon
longifolius	See A. ***hungaricus***
mollis	CArn CB&S CCla CGle CHEx CRDP CRow CTom CTre EBre ECED ECha EFol ELan Effi LBre LHol MBri MFir NDea NKay NNor NRoo NSti SAxl SIde SLMG SUsu WHil WRus
¶ – 'Hollard's Gold'	WCot
– Latifolius Group	CMGP CSco EBre ECro EFou EGol EPla LBre MRav MUlv NHol NWyt SChu SHer SPer WWat
spinosus **AGM**	Widely available
– 'Lady Moore'	IFer
– Spinosissimus Group	CGle ECha EOrc EPla MUlv SBla

ACCA (Myrtaceae)

F ***sellowiana***	CArn CB&S CCla CHan CMHG CPle CSam ELan EMil EPla ERea ESim LAbb LHop MBrk MUlv SEng SHBN SLon SSta WBod WPat WSHC
F – 'Apollo'	ERea
F – 'Coolidge'	ERea
F – 'Mammoth'	ERea
F – 'Triumph'	ERea
F – 'Variegata'	CGre

ACER † (Aceraceae)

acuminatum	CMCN WAce WNor
albopurpurescens	CMCN
amplum	CMCN
argutum	CMCN WAce WCoo WNor
barbinerve	CMCN
buergerianum	CLnd CMCN EHar GAbr GAri MUlv STre WCoo WMou WNor
– 'Goshiki-kaede' (v)	CPMA LNet
¶ – var. ***ningpoense***	WHCr
¶ – 'Tanchô'	LNet
caesium	CMCN
campbellii	CMCN LNet
– SF 29	ISea
– var. ***yunnanense***	CMCN
campestre **AGM**	CBra CDoC CKin CLnd CMCN CPer CSco EBre ENot GRei IOrc LBre LBuc MBar MBri MGos NBee NRoo NWea SHBN SPer STre WAce WCoo WDin WMou WNor
– 'Autumn Red'	WMou
– 'Carnival'	CB&S LNet MBri SHBN SMad WMou
– 'Elsrijk'	CLnd WMou
– 'Nanum'	WMou
– 'Postelense'	CMCN LMer LNet SHil WAce WMou
– 'Pulverulentum' (v)	CMCN LNet
– 'Queen Elizabeth'	WMou
– 'Red Shine'	MGos WMou
– 'Rockhampton Red Stem'	WMou
– 'Royal Ruby'	CTho LNet WMou
– 'Schwerinii'	CMCN WMou
– 'Weeping'	WMou
– 'William Caldwell'	CTho MBri WMou
capillipes **AGM**	CB&S CBra CCla CMCN CSam EArb EBar EHar ELan ENot GAbr IJoh IOrc LMer MBar MBri MGos SHer SPer SSta STre WAce WDin WNor WWat
cappadocicum	CMCN WAce WCoo WDin WNor
– 'Aureum' **AGM**	CAbP CB&S CDoC CLnd CMCN CSco EHar ELan ENot ESma IOrc LNet MBri MUlv SHBN SHil SMad SPer WAce WMou
– var. ***mono***	See A. ***mono***

– 'Rubrum' AGM	CCla CDoC CGre CLnd CMCN EHar ENot IHos IOrc MBlu MUlv SPer WDin
– var. ***sinicum***	CMCN
carpinifolium	CLnd CMCN LNet SHil WAce WCoo WWes
catalpifolium	See A. ***longipes c.***
§ ***caudatifolium***	CMCN
§ ***caudatum***	CMCN
cinerascens	CMCN
§ ***cinnamomifolium***	CMCN
circinatum AGM	CMCN CSam ECtt EHar ESma GWht LNet SHil SSta WAce WCoo WNor WWat
– 'Little Gem'	CMCN LNet
– 'Monroe'	CMCN LNet WAce
cissifolium	CB&S CMCN WAce WWes
¶ ***conspicuum*** 'Elephant's Ear'	CPMA SMad
– 'Phoenix'	CPMA LNet
¶ – 'Silver Vein'	LNet
§ ***cordatum***	CMCN
coriaceifolium	See A. ***cinnamomifolium***
x ***coriaceum***	CMCN CSam WAce
crataegifolium	CMCN
– 'Veitchii' (v)	CMCN CPMA LNet
creticum	See A. ***sempervirens***
dasycarpum	See A. ***saccharinum***
davidii	CAbP CB&S CBow CCla CDoC CMCN CMHG CSco EArb EHar ENot IBar IOrc MBal MBar MGos MRav SHBN SPer SPla WAce WCoo WDin WFro WNor
– 'Ernest Wilson'	CB&S CMCN COtt ELan MBrk WNor
– 'George Forrest' AGM	CB&S CLew CMCN ELan MUlv WThu
– 'Karmen'	MBri MGos
– 'Rosalie'	MBri
– 'Serpentine' AGM	CB&S CBow CPMA EHar ELan EPla MBri NBee SMad SPer
– 'Silver Cardinal' (v)	CPMA
diabolicum	CMCN
x ***dieckii***	CMCN
distylum	CMCN WAce
divergens	CMCN
elegantulum	CMCN
erianthum	CLnd CMCN WNor
fabri	CMCN
flabellatum	CMCN
forrestii	CMCN WAce WCoo WNor
¶ – CLD 596	WHCr
* – 'Alice'	CB&S CBow CDoC CPMA LNet MBri WWes
franchetii	CMCN
fulvescens	See A. ***longipes***
ginnala	See A. ***tataricum ginnala***
giraldii	CMCN
glabrum	CMCN WAce WNor
– var. ***douglasii***	CMCN
globosum	See A. ***platanoïdes*** 'Globosum'
grandidentatum	See A. ***saccharum g.***
griseum AGM	Widely available
grosseri	CMCN WFro
– var. ***hersii*** AGM	CBra CChu CDoC CLnd ECtt EHar ELan ENot GAbr MBal MBri MRav MUlv NWea SHil SPer SSta WAce WDin WNor WWat
heldreichii	CLnd CMCN WAce
henryi	CGre CMCN ENot LNet WNor WWes
x ***hillieri***	CMCN
hookeri	CMCN
hyrcanum	CMCN
japonicum	CMCN LNet MBal MBar SSta WAbe WAce WDin WFro WNor WWat
§ – 'Aconitifolium' AGM	CAlt CMCN CPMA CSco CShe EHar ELan ENot IHos IOrc LNet MBar MBlu MBri MGos MMor NBee NHip NJap SHBN SPer SReu SSta WAce WDin WNor WWat
– f. ***aureum***	See A. ***shirasawanum aureum***
– 'Ezo-no-momiji'	CMCN
– 'Green Cascade'	CAlt CBow CMCN CPMA WAce WPat
– 'Laciniatum'	See A. ***j.*** 'Aconitifolium'
– f. ***microphyllum***	See A. ***shirasawanum m.***
– 'Ogurayama'	LNet WNor
– 'O-isami'	CMCN
– 'O-taki'	WAce
– ***viride***	WDin
– 'Vitifolium' AGM	CAlt CDoC CMCN CSco ELan IOrc LNet MBlu NPal SHil SPer SReu SSta WAce WDin
kawakamii	See A. ***caudatifolium***
laevigatum	CMCN
lanceolatum	CMCN
laxiflorum	CLnd CMCN
lobelii	CLnd CMCN EHar ENot NWea SHil WAce WNor
§ ***longipes***	CMCN
– ssp. ***catalpifolium***	CMCN
macrophyllum	CMCN EHar IOrc LHyd WAce
– 'Kimballae'	CMCN
– 'Seattle Sentinel'	CMCN
§ ***maximowiczianum***	CB&S CDoC CLnd CMCN CSam EHar ELan IOrc MBal MBri MUlv SMad SPer SReu WNor WThu WWat WWes
maximowiczii	CChu CMCN EHal MGos WNor
micranthum AGM	CMCN WAce WCoo WNor
miyabei	CMCN WAce WNor
§ ***mono***	CMCN WAce
– 'Hoshiyadori' (v)	CMCN
– 'Shufu-nishiki'	CMCN
– var. ***tricuspis***	CMCN
monspessulanum	CFil CMCN WAce
morrisonense	See A. ***caudatifolium***
negundo	CLnd CMCN ELan ENot WDin WNor
– 'Argenteovariegatum'	See A. ***n.*** 'Variegatum'
– 'Auratum'	CMCN MBar SPer WDin WPat
– 'Aureovariegatum'	CB&S ELan MBar MUlv NJap SHBN
§ – 'Elegans' (v)	CDoC CLnd CMCN COtt EBre ELan ENot LBre NHol NJap NKay SHBN SPer
– 'Elegantissimum'	See A. ***n.*** 'Elegans'

– 'Flamingo' **AGM**	CB&S CCla CMCN CSco EBre EHar ELan IBar IJoh IOrc LBre LBuc LHop LNet MBar MBri MGos MMor NHol NJap SHBN SLon SMad SPer SReu SSta WDin WPat WWat
– 'Kelly's Gold'	CB&S SEng
§ – 'Variegatum'	CB&S CBra CLnd CSco EGol EHoe ENot IDai MBri MGos NBee SHer SPer WDin
– var. ***violaceum*** **AGM**	CMCN ELan EPla SHil SPer
nikoense	See A. ***maximowiczianum***
nipponicum	CMCN
oblongum	CMCN
§ ***obtusifolium***	CMCN
okamotoanum	CMCN
oliverianum	CMCN WNor
opalus	CMCN WAce WNor
orientale	See A. ***sempervirens***
palmatum	CBow CLan CMCN CMHG ENot ESis GAbr LNet MBal MBar MMor SHBN SPer SPla SSta STre WAbe WAce WCoo WDin WFro WNor WPat WThu WWat
– 'Aka Shigitatsusawa'	CMCN LNet NHip NJap WAce
– 'Akegarasu'	CMCN WAce
– 'Aoshime-no-uchi'	See A. ***p.*** 'Shinobugaoka'
– 'Aoyagi'	CMCN CPMA LNet NJap WAce
♦– 'Arakawa'	See A. ***p.*** 'Rough Bark Maple'
– 'Asahi-zuru' (v)	CB&S CBow CMCN CPMA IBar LNet MMor SHil SSta WAce WNor WPat
– f. ***atropurpureum***	CAlt CB&S CSco CShe EBre ELan ENot GRei ISea LBre LHyd LNet MBal MBar MGos MMor NJap NKay NWea SBod SHBN SPer SReu WAce WBod WCoo WDin WPat WStI WWat
– 'Atropurpureum Superbum'	CMCN MBri MRav
– 'Aureum'	CAlt CBow CMCN CPMA CSco LNet MBri SBod SReu SSta WAce
– Autumn Glory Group	CPMA
– 'Azahi-zuru'	MGos
– 'Azuma-murasaki'	CMCN WAce
– 'Beni-kagami'	CMCN LNet NJap WAce
– 'Beni-kawa'	LNet
– 'Beni-komachi'	CB&S CMCN CPMA LNet WNor
– 'Beni-maiko'	CBow CMCN CPMA LNet SHil WNor
– 'Beni-otake'	NHip
– 'Beni-schichihenge' (v)	CAbP CMCN CPMA LNet MAsh SHil SSta WAce WNor
– 'Beni-shidare Variegated'	CMCN CPMA LNet
– 'Beni-tsukasa' (v)	CPMA LNet NJap WAce
– 'Bloodgood' **AGM**	CAlt CB&S CCla CMCN CPMA CSam EBre EHar ELan ENot IBar LBre LNet MBar MBri MGos MMor NBee NHip NJap SBod SHBN SHer SPer SReu SSta WBod WDin WPat WWat
– 'Bonfire'	See A. ***p.*** 'Akaji-nishiki'
– 'Brocade'	CMCN WPat
– 'Burgundy Lace' **AGM**	CAlt CBow CMCN COtt CPMA CSPN IOrc LNet MGos NHip NJap WAce WPat
– 'Butterfly' **AGM**	CAlt CB&S CMCN CPMA EBre ELan IBar IOrc LBre LNet MAsh MBal MBar MBri MGos NHip NHol NJap SBod SPer SPla SReu SSta WAce WNor WPat WStI
– 'Chirimen-nishiki' (v)	CMCN LNet
– 'Chishio'	See A. ***p.*** 'Shishio'
– 'Chishio Improved'	See A. ***p.*** 'Shishio Improved'
– 'Chitoseyama' **AGM**	CAlt CBow CMCN CPMA LNet MBri MMor NHip SSta WAce WNor WPat
– 'Coonara Pygmy'	CMCN CPMA LNet WAce
– 'Corallinum'	CMCN CPMA NHip WAce WPat
N– var. ***coreanum***	CSam NJap WNor WWat
– 'Crimson Queen' **AGM**	CAlt CB&S CDoC CMCN CPMA CSco ENot IOrc LAbb LNet MAsh MBal MBri MGos MMor NHip NJap SPer SReu WAce WNor WPat
– 'Crippsii'	SEng
– 'Deshôjô'	CMCN MBlu SEng WAce WPat
– var. ***dissectum*** **AGM**	CBow CBra CDoC CShe ENot IJoh IOrc LHyd MBar MBri MGos NWea SHBN SReu WDin WFro WNor WPat WStI WWat
– – Dissectum Atropurpureum Group	CAlt CB&S CBra CPMA CSco CShe EBre ELan ENot IBar IDai IJoh LBre LHyd LNet LPan MBal MBar MGos NWea SHBN SPer SPla SReu SSta WAce WBod WDin WPat WWat
– – Dissectum Viride Group	CAlt CB&S CBow CBra CMCN CPMA CSco ELan GRei IDai LNet MAsh MMor NHip NJap NKay SPer SPla SSta WBod
– – 'Dissectum Flavescens'	CMCN NHip
§ – – 'Dissectum Nigrum'	CAlt EHoe LNet MAsh MGos WPat
– – 'Dissectum Ornatum'	CDoC COtt ELan MGos
– – 'Dissectum Palmatifidum'	LNet
§ – – 'Dissectum Variegatum'	CPMA LNet SEng SPla SSta
– 'Eddisbury'	MMor SSta WAce
– 'Ever Red'	See A. ***p. dissectum*** 'Dissectum Nigrum'
– 'Filigree'	CAlt CB&S CMCN CPMA EHar LNet MGos NHip NJap
– 'Fireglow'	CBow COtt CPMA NHip WPat
– 'Frederici Guglielmi'	See A. ***p.*** 'Dissectum Variegatum'
– 'Garnet' **AGM**	CMCN CPMA CSam EBre EHar ELan IHos LBre LPan MAsh MBal MBar MBri MMor NHip NJap SMad SPer SSta WDin WPat WStI WWat
– 'Goshiki-kotohime' (v)	CMCN
– 'Goshiki-shidare' (v)	CMCN LNet
§ – 'Hagoromo'	LNet SPer WAce WNor
– 'Hanami-nishiki'	CMCN
– 'Harusame' (v)	LNet
– 'Hazeroino' (v)	CMCN
– var. ***heptalobum***	CMCN
§ – 'Heptalobum Elegans'	CBow CCla CMCN CPMA SHBN SPer SReu WAce
– 'Heptalobum Elegans Purpureum'	See A. ***p.*** 'Hessei'

§ – 'Hessei'	CMCN CSco LNet NHip SReu WAce WPat
– 'Higasayama' (v)	CB&S CBow CMCN CPMA CSco LNet NJap WAce WNor WPat
– 'Hôgyoku'	CMCN NHip NJap WAce
– 'Ichigyôji'	CMCN NJap WAce
– 'Improved Shishio'	See A. ***p.*** 'Shishio Improved'
– 'Inaba-shidare' **AGM**	CDoC CPMA CSam CSco GRei IMal LNet MBar MBri MGos MMor NHip NJap SPer SReu SSta
– 'Inazuma'	CB&S CMCN NJap WAce
– 'Kagero' (v)	CPMA
§ – 'Kagiri-nishiki' (v)	CMCN COtt CPMA CSco LNet MGos NJap SHil SSta WNor
– 'Kamagata'	CMCN NHip SSta WAce WNor WPat
– 'Karaori-nishiki' (v)	LNet NJap WAce
– 'Karasugawa' (v)	CMCN SHil WAce
– 'Kasagiyama'	CAlt CMCN LRHS NJap WPat
– 'Kashima'	CMCN NJap WNor
– 'Katsura'	CB&S CMCN CPMA CSco EBre ELan LBre MAsh MBri NHip NJap SEng SPer SSta WAce WNor WPat
– 'Kinran'	CMCN LNet WAce WPat
– 'Kinshii'	CMCN LRHS MAsh SSta
¶ – 'Kiri-nishiki'	WPat
– 'Kiyohime'	CMCN
– 'Ki-hachijô'	CMCN NJap WAce
N – 'Koreanum' **AGM**	CMCN SHil
– 'Koshibori-nishiki'	CPMA
– 'Kotohime'	CMCN
– 'Koto-no-ito'	CMCN
– 'Kurui-jishi'	LNet
– 'Linearilobum' **AGM**	CAlt CMCN LHyd LNet NJap SHil WAce WNor WPat
– 'Linearilobum Atropurpureum'	SSta WNor
– 'Little Princess'	See A. ***p.*** 'Mapi-no-machihime'
– 'Mama'	CMCN
§ – 'Mapi-no-machihime'	ELan LNet MAsh NHol SSta WWat
– 'Masukagami' (v)	CAlt NHip WAce
– 'Matsukaze'	COtt CPMA NJap WAce
– 'Mirte'	LNet
– 'Mizu-kuguri'	WAce
– 'Monzukushi'	WAce
– 'Moonfire'	CMCN LNet NHip NJap WAce
– 'Mure-hibari'	CMCN
– 'Murogawa'	CMCN WAce
– 'Nicholsonii'	CMCN WAce
– 'Nigrum'	CMCN SEng WPat
– 'Nishiki-gawa'	See A. ***p.*** 'Pine Bark Maple'
– 'Nomurishidare'	CBow LRHS WAce
– 'Nuresagi'	CMCN LNet WPat
– 'Ogon-sarasa'	WAce
– 'Okushimo'	CMCN LNet NHip SSta WAce WNor
– 'Omurayama'	LNet LRHS NJap SSta WNor
¶ – 'Orange Dream'	NHip
– 'Orido-nishiki' (v)	CAlt CMCN CPMA ELan LNet MBlu MGos NHip WAce WNor
– 'Ornatum'	CDoC IBar MBri NHip NJap SPer WAce
– 'Osakazuki' **AGM**	Widely available
– 'Oshû-beni'	CMCN WAce
– 'Oshû-shidare'	CMCN
– 'O-kagami'	COtt LNet MBri NHip
§ – 'O-nishiki'	LNet NJap
– 'Pendulum Julian'	CMCN WAce WPat
§ – 'Pine Bark Maple'	CMCN
– 'Red Dragon'	CB&S COtt SEng
– 'Red Pygmy' **AGM**	CAlt CB&S CBow CDoC CMCN COtt CPMA CSco LNet MAsh MBri MGos NHip NJap SPer SSta WAce WPat
– 'Reticulatum'	See A. ***p.*** 'Shigitatsu-sawa'
– 'Ribesifolium'	See A. ***p.*** 'Shishigashira'
– 'Roseomarginatum'	See A. ***p.*** 'Kagiri-nishiki'
§ – 'Rough Bark Maple'	CMCN GAri WAce
– 'Rubrum'	CMCN MBal NJap SHer
– 'Rufescens'	CMCN WAce
– 'Sagara-nishiki' (v)	CMCN
– 'Samidare'	CMCN NJap WAce
N – 'Sango-kaku' **AGM**	Widely available
– 'Saoshika'	CMCN WAce
– 'Sazanami'	CMCN NJap WNor
– 'Schichihenge'	WAce
– 'Seigen'	CMCN
– 'Seiryû' **AGM**	CAlt CB&S CMCN CPMA EHar ELan LNet MBri MGos MMor NBee NHip NHol NJap SEng SHer SPer SSta WDin WNor
¶ – 'Sekimori'	CPMA WPat
♦ – 'Senkaki'	See A. ***p.*** 'Sango-kaku'
– 'Septemlobum Elegans'	See A. ***p.*** 'Heptalobum Elegans'
– 'Septemlobum Purpureum'	See A. ***p.*** 'Hessei'
– 'Sessilifolium' (dwarf)	See A. ***p.*** 'Hagoromo'
– 'Sessilifolium' (tall)	See A. ***p.*** 'Koshimino'
– 'Sherwood Flame'	CBow CMCN CPMA LNet MBri MGos NHip NJap WAce WPat
§ – 'Shigitatsu-sawa' (v)	CB&S CMCN MAsh NHip SPer WAce
– 'Shime-no-uchi'	CMCN LNet WAce WPat
– 'Shindeshôjô'	CBow CDoC CMCN CPMA ELan LNet MAsh MBri NHol NJap SBod SHer SSta WNor
§ – 'Shinobugaoka'	CBow CMCN CPMA LNet
– 'Shinonome'	CMCN COtt CSco
§ – 'Shishigashira'	CMCN EHar MBri MGos MMor NHip SSta WPat
§ – 'Shishio'	CB&S CMCN COtt LHop LHyd LNet NJap SEng WAce
§ – 'Shishio Improved'	CAlt LNet MAsh MBlu MGos MMor NHip NJap WAce WNor
– 'Shôjô-nomura'	COtt
¶ – 'Shôjô-shidare'	COtt
– 'Stella Rossa'	CPMA NHip
– 'Suminagashi'	CMCN LNet
– 'Takinogawa'	SSta WAce
– 'Tamahime'	NJap WAce WNor
– 'Tamukeyama'	CMCN
– 'Tana'	CMCN NHip NJap WAce WNor WPat
– 'Tatsuta-gawa'	WAce
– 'Trompenburg'	CAbP CBow CMCN COtt CPMA LNet MAsh MBri NHip NJap SHil SPla SSta WAce WNor WPat
– 'Tsuchigumo'	CMCN
¶ – 'Tsukomo'	WPat
– 'Tsukubane'	CMCN
– 'Tsukushigata'	WAce
– 'Tsuma-beni'	CMCN SSta WAce WPat
– 'Tsuma-gaki'	CMCN

– 'Ukigumo' (v)	CAlt CB&S COtt CPMA LNet MGos NHip NJap SPer SPla SSta WAce
– 'Ukon'	CMCN NHip NJap WAce WNor
– 'Umegae'	CMCN
– 'Utsu-semi'	CMCN WAce
– 'Versicolor' (v)	LNet NJap
– 'Villa Taranto'	CMCN LNet MAsh MBlu MGos NJap WAce
– 'Volubile'	CMCN WAce
– 'Wabito'	CMCN WAce
– 'Wada's Flame'	SSta
– 'Waterfall'	CMCN CPMA LNet MGos NJap
– 'Wou-nishiki'	See A. ***p.*** 'O-nishiki'
– 'Yezo-nishiki'	NHip
– 'Yûgure'	MGos NHip WAce
papilio	See A. ***caudatum***
paxii	CMCN
pectinatum	CMCN
*– 'Sirene'	CPMA MGos
– 'Sparkling'	MBri
pensylvanicum AGM	CCla CDoC CMCN CSam GRei ISea MGos MRav NBee NWea SHBN SHil SPer SReu WAce WCoo WDin WNor WWeb
– 'Erythrocladum' AGM	CMCN CPMA LNet MAsh MBlu NHol SHil
pentaphyllum	CMCN LNet SHil WAce
§ ***pentapotamicum***	CMCN
pictum	See A. ***mono***
platanoïdes AGM	CKin CLnd CMCN CPer ELan ENot GRei IDai IJoh LBuc LPan MGos NWea SPer STre WAce WDin WMou WNor
– 'Autumn Blaze'	WMou
– 'Cleveland'	CB&S ENot
– 'Columnare'	CDoC CMCN ENot IOrc
– 'Crimson King' AGM	CB&S CBra CCla CMCN CSam CSco CTho EBre ECtt ELan GRei IDai IJoh LBre LBuc LNet MBar NBar NBee NWea SChu SHBN SPer SReu SSta WDin WJas
– 'Crimson Sentry'	COtt EBee IHos LNet MBri SHil SMad
– 'Deborah'	CDoC CLnd CTho SHBN
– 'Drummondii' AGM	Widely available
– 'Emerald Queen'	CDoC CLnd ENot SHBN
– 'Erectum'	CMCN
§ – 'Globosum'	CLnd CMCN ENot LPan
– 'Goldsworth Purple'	CLnd MGos WAbe
– 'Laciniatum'	CMCN ENot SPer
– 'Lorbergii'	See A. ***p.*** 'Palmatifidum'
– 'Olmstead'	ENot LNet
§ – 'Palmatifidum'	CSam
– 'Reitenbachii'	CTho
– 'Royal Red'	ENot MBri
– 'Schwedleri' AGM	CBra CLnd CSco ENot MGos SPer WDin
pseudoplatanus	CB&S CKin CLnd CMCN CPer ELan ENot GRei IDai LBuc LPan MBar MGos NWea SHer WDin WMou
§ – 'Atropurpureum' AGM	CDoC CLnd CTho ENot IOrc NWea
– 'Brilliantissimum' AGM	CB&S CBra CCla CLnd CMCN CSco CTho EBre EHar ELan IJoh LBre LNet MBar MBri MGos NBar NBee NHip NWea SHBN SMad SPer SReu SSta WDin WPat
– 'Corstorphinense'	CMCN
– 'Erectum'	ENot
¶ – 'Erythrocarpum'	EMon
N– 'Leopoldii' AGM	CB&S CBra CDoC CLnd CMCN COtt CSco CTho ELan ENot IOrc LPan MBar MBri NBee SChu SHBN SPer WDin
– 'Negenia'	CDoC
– 'Nizetii' (v)	EHar MBri SHil
– 'Prinz Handjery'	CAbP CB&S CBow CBra CDoC CMCN CSco CTho EHar LNet LPan MBar NJap SHBN
– 'Simon-Louis Frères' (v)	CBra CDoC CLnd CTho ELan LNet MBri MGos NJap SHer
– f. ***variegatum***	WCot
– 'Worleei' AGM	CB&S CBra CDoC CLnd CMCN COtt CSco ECtt EHar ENot IOrc MBri NWea SHBN SHil SPer WDin WMou
N***pseudoplatanus*** hort. 'Spaethii' (v)	See A. ***p.*** 'Atropurpureum'
pseudosieboldianum	CMCN WAce WNor
pycnanthum	CMCN
regelii	See A. ***pentapotamicum***
rubescens	CSam
rubrum	CB&S CBow CBra CDoC CGre CLnd CMCN GCHN NBee NWea SPer WAce WDin WNor
– 'Morgan'	MBri
– 'October Glory' AGM	CBra CDoC CMCN CMHG CSam EHar IOrc MBlu MBri MUlv SHil SSta WAce WWeb
– 'Red Sunset'	CMCN MBri MUlv SHil WAce
– 'Scanlon' AGM	CDoC CMCN SHil SMad
– 'Schlesingeri'	CMCN
– 'Tridens'	CMCN
rufinerve AGM	CB&S CDoC CLnd CMCN CMHG EHar ENot GAul IOrc LPan MBri NWea SPer WAce WNor WStI
¶ – Akaji 353	WHCr
– 'Albolimbatum'	See A. ***r.*** 'Hatsuyuki'
– 'Albomarginatum'	See A. ***r.*** 'Hatsuyuki'
§ – 'Hatsuyuki' (v)	CMCN CPMA ELan MBri MUlv SMad
§ ***saccharinum*** AGM	CB&S CGre CLnd CMCN EHar ENot MGos NWea SPer SSta WDin
– 'Elegans'	CDoC CMCN
– 'Fastigiatum'	See A. ***s.*** 'Pyramidale'
– f. ***laciniatum***	CDoC CMCN EHar ENot MBlu MGos NBee SPer WDin
– f. ***lutescens***	CMCN EHar ENot SHer SHil SPer WMou
§ – f. ***pyramidale***	CDoC CLnd CMCN CSam EHar ENot GRei IOrc
– 'Wieri'	CLnd CPMA
saccharum	CBra CDoC CLnd CMCN EHar SHil SPer STre WNor
*– 'Aureum'	IOrc
– ***barbatum***	CMCN
– ssp. ***leucoderme***	CMCN
– 'Newton Sentry'	CMCN
– ssp. ***nigrum***	CMCN
– 'Temple's Upright'	CMCN LNet
§ ***sempervirens***	CMCN
serrulatum	CMCN
shirasawanum	CMCN CSco WAce WNor

§ – f. ***aureum*** AGM	CAlt CCla CMCN CPMA EHar ELan ENot IDai IJoh LHyd LNet MAsh MBar MBri MGos MMor NBee NHip NHol NJap SMad SPer SSta WPat WStI WWat
§ – ***microphyllum*** AGM	CMCN LNet WNor
– 'Palmatifolium'	CMCN CPMA MGos WStI
sieboldianum	CLnd CMCN EHar WAce WNor
– 'Kinugasayama'	WAce
– 'Sode-no-uchi'	CMCN WAce
'Silver Vein'	CMCN CPMA EBee EBre EHar LBre MBri SHil
sinense	CMCN
sinopurpurascens	CMCN
spicatum	CMCN WAce WNor
¶ sp. CLD 404	WHCr
stachyophyllum	See A. ***tetramerum***
§ ***sterculiaceum***	CMCN
syriacum	See A. ***obtusifolium***
takesimense	CMCN
taronense	CMCN
§ ***tataricum*** ssp. ***ginnala*** AGM	CB&S CLnd CMCN CMHG EBar EHar ENot IOrc MBal MBlu MGos NHip NJap SHBN SPer SReu SSta WAce WCoo WNor WTyr WWat
*– – 'Fire'	LNet
– – 'Flame'	CMCN
– ***grandidentatum***	CMCN
– ssp. ***semenowii***	CMCN
tegmentosum	CMCN WCoo
– ssp. ***glaucorufinerve***	See A. ***rufinerve***
tenuifolium	CMCN WAce
§ ***tetramerum***	CMCN
¶ – CLD 736	WHCr
thomsonii	CMCN
trautvetteri	CMCN WNor
triflorum	CMCN MBlu WAce
truncatum	CMCN WAce WFro WNor
– 'Akikaze-nishiki' (v)	LNet
tschonoskii	CMCN EHar
turkestanicum	CMCN
ukurunduense	CMCN WNor
velutinum	CMCN
villosum	See A. ***sterculiaceum***
wilsonii	CMCN
x ***zoeschense***	CMCN
– 'Annae'	IOrc

ACERIPHYLLUM See MUKDENIA

X ACHICODONIA (Gesneriaceae)

§ 'Cornell Gem'	NMos

ACHILLEA † (Compositae/Asteraceae)

abrotanoïdes	CRDP ELan EMon NGre
ageratifolia AGM	ECha EFol GTou MBro MHig MRPP MTho NHol NMen NNor NWCA SHer SIgm SSmi WByw
¶ – ssp. ***ageratifolia***	MRPP
§ – ssp. ***aïzoön***	NKay WPer
§ ***ageratum***	CArn CSFH Effi GBar GPoy LGan LHol MChe MSal SIde WPer WWye
– 'W B Child'	CBos CChu CGle ECha ELan EMon GBuc LGre MMil WEas
'Alabaster'	EMon MBel
'Anthea'	LRHS MArl MBel MUlv NRoo SCro
'Apfelblüte' ('Appleblossom')	CMGP CSco EBre ECha ECtt EFol EFou ELan EOrc EPla LBlm LBre LHop MBri NHol SHer SPer SUsu WMer
argentea hort.	See AA. ***clavennae, umbellatum***
argentea Lamarck	See TANACETUM ***argenteum***
aurea 'Grandiflora'	See A. ***chrysocoma*** 'G.'
'Bahama'	NFai
¶ 'Bloodstone'	GMac
cartilaginea	CBre EFou LHop NCat
¶ ***chamaemelifolia***	WHil
chrysocoma	ELan ESis MCas MWat NKay NMen NTow SHer SIng SSmi
§ – 'Grandiflora'	CDec CHad EHal
§ ***clavennae***	CGle CShe CTom EHoe GCHN MCas MHig MPla MWat NMen NNor NRoo NTow SBla SHer SRms WAbe WHil WOld
– ssp. ***integrifolia***	EWes NHol WDav
coarctata	WPer
'Coronation Gold' AGM	CBre CDoC CKel CSco CShe EBre ECED EFou ELan ENot LBre MBri MWat NKay SPer WEas
'Credo'	CGle EFou EMon MHlr WCot
'Croftway'	SCro
decolorans	See A. ***ageratum***
erba-rotta ssp. ***rupestris***	CLew ESis MDHE MHig NKay WPer
§ 'Fanal'	CMGP COtt CSco CSev EBre ECha ELan EOrc EPla GMac LBlm LBre LHop MTho NHol SChu SCro SHer SPer WWin
'Feuerland'	ECha EFou EMon WCot
filipendulina	MFir MHew NSti WWin
– 'Cloth of Gold'	CBow CDoC EBar EBre ECED ECtt EJud LAbb LBre MBri MPit NFai NMir NNor NRoo SPla SSvw WByw WHoo WPer
– 'Gold Plate' AGM	CBow CChu CDec CSco CShe CTom EBre ECha ECtt EFou ELan LBre MBel NKay NOrc SCro SMad SPer WEas WHil
– 'Parker's Variety'	EJud GBuc NOak
'Forncett Beauty'	EFou
'Forncett Candy'	EFou
'Forncett Fletton'	EFou SCro
'Forncett Ivory'	EFou MSte
glaberrima	SSvw WPer
grandifolia	CChu CHan CMil CPou CRDP EGle EMon EOrc EPad LGre MUlv NCat NTow WAbb WCot
'Great Expectations'	See A. 'Hoffnung'
'Hartington White'	EMon LRHS MSte SCro
§ 'Hoffnung'	CMGP COtt CSco CSev EBre ECtt EFou EOrc EPla GAbr LBre MBro NHol SCro SPer WPer WWin
¶ ***holosericea***	SIgm
'Huteri'	CLew CMHG CNic CSam CShe ECtt ELan EMNN EPot ESis GPlt LBee MBro MCas MHig NCat NHol NMen NNor NNrd NTow SChu SGil SSmi WAbe WEas WPer WWin

x *jaborneggii*	GCHN NKay
x *kellereri*	MBro MCas MHig SSmi
x *kolbiana*	EOrc LHop MHig MWat NHol NMen NNrd NRoo SSmi WPat WWin
§ – 'Weston'	CMHG MHig NRoo NTow
§ 'Lachsschönheit' ('Salmon Beauty')	CHad CMea COtt CSco CSev EBar EBre ECha ECtt EFol EFou ELan EPla GAbr GMac LBlm LBre LHop NBir NHol NSti SChu SCro SHer SPer WHal WMer WPer WWin
x *lewisii*	NMen
– 'King Edward' **AGM**	CLew CMea CNic CSam EBre ECha EFol EFou ELan ESis LBee LBre MTho NBir NHol NKay NRoo NTow NVic SBla SHer SIgm SIng SSmi WAbe WPer
'Libella'	NFai
'Martina'	EFou EHal EMon GBuc LRHS SCro
millefolium	CArn CGle CSFH ECWi EEls EJud EWFC Effi GBar GPoy IEde LHol MHew NLan NMir SHer SIde WByw WNdy WOak WWye
– var. *borealis*	MSal
– 'Burgundy'	EOrc
– 'Cerise Queen'	CB&S CBow CGle CKel CNic CSco CShe EBre ECha ELan EPar EPla GCHN LBlm LBre LHop MPit MWat NFai NKay NNor NOrc SPer SSvw WEas WPer
¶ – 'Colorado'	WHil
– 'Lansdorferglut'	MBri NBar
– 'Lavender Beauty'	See A. *m.* 'Lilac Beauty'
§ – 'Lilac Beauty'	CB&S CBos CGle CLew CMil CTom ECha EFol EFou EOrc MBel SHer WMer
– 'Lilac Queen'	MArl MBri NFai
– 'Melanie'	WMer
– 'Paprika'	CBow CDoC EBar EBre EPar GBuc LBre MBri NBar WByw
– 'Red Beauty'	EPar GLil NCat NRar SRms
– f. *rosea*	EJud MBal NMir NRoo SRms WOMN
– 'Sammetriese'	CRDP EFou ELan EMon GBuc WHoo
– 'White Queen'	WMer WPer
'Moonbeam'	EOrc SHer
'Moonshine' **AGM**	Widely available
'Moonwalker'	CBow NFai SIde WPla
nana	LGan WPla
nobilis ssp. *neilreichii*	CRDP EMon MHlr WCot
'Obristii'	NMen
'Peter Davis'	See HIPPOLYTIA *herderi*
ptarmica	CArn CKin ECWi EWFC GBar LHol MChe MHew MSal SIde SPer SSvw WGwy WHaw WHil WWye
*– 'Ballerina'	EFou
– 'Major'	WCot
– 'Nana Compacta'	ECha ECro
– 'Perry's White'	CBre EMon EPla GCal GLil LBlm MBri MHlr MUlv NCat SPla WByw WCot WMer
– 'Unschuld' ('Innocence')	NBir
N *ptarmica* The Pearl Group (seed-raised) (d)	CElw CGle CKel CSco EBre ECha EFou ELan EPar GCHN IDai LBre LHop MBel MBri MFir MWat NFai NKay NMir NNor NSti SPer WEas WOld WWin
pumila	See A. *distans tanacetifolia*
'Salmon Beauty'	See A. 'Lachsschönheit'
'Schwefelblüte' ('Flowers of Sulphur')	CSco EFol ELan NBir WCot
'Schwellenburg'	EFou EGle SCro
sibirica	CLew
– AGS 1241	CNic
– 'Kiku-san'	EMon
'Smiling Queen'	NFai
Summer Pastels	CBot CBow ECro GAbr MFir MSte MWil NMir NNor NOak NRoo WFro WPer
¶ 'Summerwine'	ECha EMon GLil
I 'Taygetea'	CGle CSam EBre ECha ELan EPar LBlm LBre MBel MBri MUlv MWat NSti SChu SDix SPer WByw WCot WHer WKif WRus WSHC WSun
¶ 'Terracotta'	EFou EMon WCot
'The Beacon'	See A. 'Fanal'
'Theo Ploeger'	EMon
tomentosa **AGM**	CMer CTom ECha ECtt ELan IDai LHop MBal MPit NKay NNor NRoo WByw
§ – 'Aurea'	ECro ECtt EMon LHol MPit NHol NMir SIde WHen WHil WPer WWin
– 'Maynard's Gold'	See A. *t.* 'Aurea'
umbellata	NTow SIgm
– NS 390	NWCA
– 'Weston'	See A. x *kolbiana* 'Weston'
'Wesersandstein'	EMon MBri WCot WElm
'Wilczekii'	CRiv NCat SBod SGil SHer SPla SRms

X ACHIMENANTHA (Gesneriaceae)

'Cerulean Mink'	See X SMITHICODONIA 'C.M'
'Dutch Treat'	NMos
'Ginger Peachy'	NMos
'Inferno'	NMos WDib
* 'Rose Bouquet'	NMos
'Royal'	NMos

ACHIMENES (Gesneriaceae)

'Adelaide'	NMos
'Adèle Delahaute'	NMos
'Admiration'	LAma NRog
'Adonis Blue'	NMos
'Almandine'	NMos
'Ambleside'	NMos
'Ambroise Verschaffelt'	LAma NMos
'Ami Van Houtte'	NMos
'Ann Marie'	NMos
'Apricot Glow'	NMos
'Aquamarine'	NMos
'Bassenthwaite'	NMos
'Bea'	NMos
bella	See EUCODONIA *verticillata*

'Bernice'	NMos
'Blauer Planet'	NMos
'Bloodstone'	NMos
'Blue Gown'	NMos
'Brilliant'	NMos
'Butterfield Bronze'	NMos
'Buttermere'	NMos
'Camberwell Beauty'	NMos
'Cameo Rose'	NMos
'Cameo Triumph'	NMos
'Camille Brozzoni'	NMos
candida	NMos
'Carmine Queen'	NMos
'Cascade Cockade'	NMos
'Cascade Evening Glow'	NMos
'Cascade Fairy Pink'	NMos
'Cascade Fashionable Pink'	NMos
'Cascade Rosy Red'	NMos
'Cascade Violet Night'	NMos
'Cattleya'	LAma NMos
'Chalkhill Blue'	NMos
'Charm'	LAma NMos
'Clouded Yellow'	NMos
'Compact Great Rosy Red'	NMos
'Coniston Water'	NMos
'Copeland Boy'	NMos
'Copeland Girl'	NMos
'Coral Sunset'	NMos
'Cornell Favourite 'A''	NMos
'Cornell Favourite 'B''	NMos
'Crimson Beauty'	NMos
'Crimson Glory'	NMos
'Crimson Tiger'	NMos
'Crummock Water'	NMos
'Cupido'	NMos
'Dentoniana'	NMos
'Derwentwater'	NMos
'Dorothy'	NMos
'Dot'	NMos
dulcis	NMos
'Early Arnold'	NMos
ehrenbergii	See EUCODONIA ***e.***
'Elke Michelssen'	NMos
'English Waltz'	NMos
erecta	WDib
'Escheriana'	NMos
'Flamenco'	NMos
'Flamingo'	SDeJ
flava	NMos
'Fritz Michelssen'	NMos
'Gary John'	NMos
'Gary/Jennifer'	NMos
'Germanica'	LAma
'Grape Wine'	NMos
'Grasmere'	NMos
'Harry Williams'	LAma
§ 'Harveyi'	NMos
'Haweswater'	NMos
'Hilda Michelssen'	NMos
'Honey Gold'	NMos
'Ida Michelssen'	NMos
'India'	NMos
§ 'Jaureguia Maxima'	NMos
'Jennifer Goode'	NMos
'Jewell Blue'	NMos
'Johanna Michelssen'	NMos
'Jubilee Gem'	NMos
'Lake City'	LAma
'Lakeland Lady'	NMos
'Lavender Fancy'	NMos
'Little Beauty'	LAma NMos
'Little Red Tiger'	NMos
longiflora	LAma NMos
– 'Alba'	See A. 'Jaureguia Maxima'
– 'Major'	NMos
'Magnificent'	NMos
'Margaret White'	LAma
'Marie'	NMos
'Master Ingram'	LAma
'Masterpiece'	NMos
'Mauve Queen'	LAma
'Maxima'	LAma NRog
'Menuett '80'	NMos
'Milton'	NMos
'Minute'	LAma
misera	NMos
'Miss Blue'	LAma
'Moonstone'	NMos
'Nessida'	LAma
'Old Rose Pink'	LAma NMos
'Orange Queen'	NMos
'Pally'	NMos
'Panic Pink'	NMos
'Patens Major'	NMos
'Patricia'	NMos
'Paul Arnold'	LAma NMos SDeJ
'Peach Blossom'	LAma NMos SDeJ
'Peach Glow'	NMos
'Peacock'	NMos
'Pearly Queen'	NMos
'Pendant Blue'	NMos
'Pendant Purple'	NMos
'Petticoat Pink'	NMos
'Pink Beauty'	NMos
'Pinocchio'	NMos
'Prima Donna'	LAma NMos
'Pulcherrima'	LAma
'Purple King'	LAma NMos
'Queen of Sheba'	NMos
'Quickstep'	NMos
'Rachael'	NMos
'Red Admiral'	NMos
'Red Giant'	NMos
'Red Imp'	NMos
'Red Top Hybrid'	NMos
'Robin'	NMos
'Rosenelfe'	NMos
'Rosy Doll'	NMos
'Rosy Frost'	NMos
'Ruby'	LAma
'Rydal Water'	NMos
'Scafell'	NMos
'Shirley Dwarf White'	NMos
'Shirley Fireglow'	See A. 'Harveyi'
'Show-Off'	NMos
'Silver Wedding'	NMos
'Snow Princess'	SDeJ
'Sparkle'	NMos
'Stan's Delight'	NMos
'Sue'	NMos

'Tango'	NMos
'Tantivvy'	NMos
'Tarantella'	NMos
'Teresa'	NMos
'Tiny Blue'	NMos
'Topsy'	LAma NMos
'Troutbeck'	NMos
'Ullswater'	NMos
'Vanessa'	NMos
'Viola Michelssen'	NMos
'Violacea Semiplena'	NMos
'Violetta'	LAma
'Vivid'	LAma NMos NRog
'Warren'	NMos
'Wastwater'	NMos
'Wetterflow's Triumph'	NMos
'White Admiral'	NMos
'White Rajah'	NMos
'Wilma'	NMos
'Windermere'	NMos

ACHLYS (Berberidaceae)
See Plant Deletions

ACHNATHERUM See **STIPA**

ACIDANTHERA See **GLADIOLUS**

ACINOS (Labiatae/Lamiaceae)

§ ***alpinus***	CLew CShe MHig NMen NNrd SChu SUsu
– ssp. ***meridionalis***	EGle NHol NTow
arvensis	See CLINOPODIUM ***acinos***
§ ***corsicus***	ESis SFis WPat WWin

ACIPHYLLA (Umbelliferae/Apiaceae)

aurea	CAbb EHal EPot GAbr GCal MBal MBro NHar NHol SArc SIgm WAbe WCot WPla
colensoi	WAbe
dobsonii	GCLN
glaucescens	GAbr GDra LBlm MBal NHar NHol SArc
hectorii	GDra
monroi	EPot GDra WHal
pinnatifida	NHar
procumbens	NHar
scott-thomsonii	ECou EPot GAul GCal NHar NHol WPla
squarrosa	GCal
subflabellata	CLew GArf GCal

ACNISTUS (Solanaceae)

australis	See DUNALIA ***a.***

ACOELORRHAPHE (Palmae/Arecaceae)

¶ ***wrightii***	CTrh

ACOKANTHERA (Apocynaceae)

§ ***oblongifolia***	CTro
♦ ***spectabilis***	See A. ***oblongifolia***

ACONITUM (Ranunculaceae)

anglicum	See A. ***napellus napellus*** Anglicum Group
anthora	NHol
N ***autumnale***	NBir
¶ ***bartlettii*** B&SWJ 337	WCru
'Blue Sceptre'	CSco EBre LBre NOak NRoo SRms
'Bressingham Spire' AGM	CBow CChu CCla CDoC CMGP CShe EBre ECtt EFou EPla GAbr LBre MBel MBri MWat NDea NKay NOrc NRoo SChu SHer SPer
x ***cammarum***	
'Bicolor' AGM	CBow CCla CDoC CGle CMGP EBre ECro EFou EGol ELan EOrc GBri GCal GCra LBlm LBre MBri MWat NBar NFai NRoo NSti SChu SPer WByw WDav WEas WOld
¶ – 'Franz Marc'	EMon
– 'Grandiflorum Album'	ELan NRoo
§ ***carmichaelii***	CArn CBot CGle CHad CKel EBar EBre ECED ECro EFou ELan GMac LBre MBro MRav NRoo SCro SUsu WHoo WRus
– 'Arendsii'	CCla CSco EBre ECha ECro ECtt EOrc LBre MBri MNFA MSte NBar NDea NFai NRoo SChu SFis SPer SPla WCot WEas WPer
carmichaelii Wilsonii Group	CBow CChu CHan CRDP ECro EOrc GCra GGar LGan MSte MTol SChu SMad SPer WPer
§ – – 'Barker's Variety'	CPou CRow EFou GBuc MFir MUlv NDea NHol NSti WMer WRus WSHC
– – 'Kelmscott' AGM	EGle ELan MUlv SBla SPer WByw
cilicicum	See ERANTHIS ***hyemalis*** Cilicica Group
compactum	See A. ***napellus vulgare***
'Eleonara'	EFou
elwesii	GGar
¶ ***episcopale*** CLD 1426	SWas
fischeri hort.	See A. ***carmichaelii***
¶ ***gymnandrum***	EMon
§ ***hemsleyanum***	CArn CBos CBot CChu CGle CRDP CRow CVer ECro ELan GCal GCra GMac LGre LHol MFir MSto MTho NSti NTow SAxl SBla SMad WCru WEas WOld
hyemalis	See ERANTHIS ***hyemalis***
'Ivorine'	CBot CCla CGle CHan CKel CRow CSco CSpe EBre ECha EFou EGol ELan ELun EOrc LBre MArl MBri NDea NOak NRoo NSti SAxl SFis SPer WEas WRus WWin
lamarckii	See A. ***lycoctonum neapolitanum***
lycoctonum	NBrk WPla
§ – ssp. ***lycoctonum***	ECED MSal SRms
§ – ssp. ***neapolitanum***	EBee ELan MSto WHaw WPer
§ – ssp. ***vulparia***	CArn CTom ECha ECtt EFou GCal GPoy LBlm LHol LWad MSal NDea NRoo SUsu WByw WPla

napellus	CArn CChu CShe CTom ECro ECtt EFou EWFC GAbr GPoy LGan LHil LHol MBro MHew MPit MWat NFai NNor SIde WHoo WOld WPla WRus WWye
§ – *napellus* Anglicum Group	CBre CRow GBuc MHlr MSal MSte NHol NSti WCot
¶ – 'Rubellum'	GLil NPri
– 'Sphere's Variety'	NOrc
– ssp. *vulgare* 'Albidum'	CBot CMGP CSco ECha EFou LBlm LHil MBri NBrk NPri NSti WByw
§ – – 'Carneum'	CBos EBre ECha ELan GCra LBre NRoo NSti SChu WByw WDav WEas WHer WKif WPla WRus
neapolitanum	See A. ***lycoctonum neapolitanum***
'Newry Blue'	CBos EHal ELan LWad MBri MPit NHol NKay WHil WMer WPer
orientale hort.	See A. ***lycoctonum vulparia***
pyrenaicum	See A. ***lycoctonum neapolitanum***
septentrionale	See A. ***lycoctonum lycoctonum***
smithii	CBrd
'Spark's Variety' AGM	CBre CChu CDoC CHan CSco EBar EBre ECED EFou ELan EOrc GBri GCal LBre LGre LHil LWad MBel MBri MNFA MRav NKay NOrc NRoo NSti SChu SCro SDix SHig SMad
¶ sp. CLD 1426	MSto
¶ *stapfianum* B&L 12038	WThi
x *tubergenii*	See ERANTHIS ***hyemalis*** Tubergenii Group
volubile hort.	See A. ***hemsleyanum***
vulparia	See A. ***lycoctonum v.***

ACONOGONON See **PERSICARIA**

ACORUS (Acoraceae)

calamus	CArn CBen CRow CWGN EHon EWav Effi GPoy LMay MHew MSta NDea SHig SWat SWyc WChe WHol
– 'Purpureus'	WPer
– 'Variegatus'	CB&S CBen CGle CRDP CRow CWGN EBre ECha ECtt EGol EHon EMFW EPla EWav GAbr GCal LBre LMay MBal MSta NDea SHig SLon SPer SWat SWyc WChe WHol WWye
gramineus	CBen CRow EFou EMFW LMay SHer SWat WWye
N– 'Oborozuki'	CRow EGle EPla
N– 'Ogon' (v)	Widely available
– 'Pusillus'	CLew CRDP CRiv CRow EPla LHil
– 'Variegatus'	Widely available
– 'Yodo-no-yuki'	CRow

ACRADENIA (Rutaceae)

frankliniae	CAbb CChu CMHG CPle GAbr IBar IBlr SArc SBor WBod WSHC

ACRIDOCARPUS (Malpighiaceae)

natalitius	CTro

ACROCLADIUM See **CALLIERGON**

ACTAEA (Ranunculaceae)

§ *alba* AGM	CBrd CCMG CChu CCla CHan CPou CRow ECha EPar GPoy IBlr MBri MFir MSal MUlv NBro NHol SAxl SMad WMer WOMN WWat WWye
§ *erythrocarpa* Fischer	CHan CRDP ECro GDra GPoy MSte NHol SDix WEas WOMN WWin
erythrocarpa hort.	See A. ***rubra***
pachypoda	See A. ***alba***
§ *rubra* AGM	CBro CCla CHan CMHG CRow ECha ECro ELun EPar GCal IBlr MBri MUlv NHol NRar NSti SFar SHer SLga WByw WCru WHal WMer WWat
– *alba*	See A. ***r. neglecta***
– ssp. *arguta*	NHol
§ – f. *neglecta*	CBos CHan NRar
spicata	CLew CRDP ECro GPoy MHew MSal MSte NHol NSti WCru WDav
– var. *alba*	See A. ***spicata***
– var. *rubra*	See A. ***erythrocarpa*** Fischer

ACTINELLA (Compositae/Asteraceae)

scaposa	See TETRANEURIS ***scaposa***

ACTINIDIA † (Actinidiaceae)

arguta	CB&S CCla CDoC
– (m)	CB&S ESim SHBN
– 'Ananasnaya' (f)	ESim
– 'Blake' (f)	LBuc
– 'Issai' (s-p)	ERea ESim LBuc WHig WStI
– 'Stamford' (f)	ESim
chinensis hort.	See A. ***deliciosa***
§ *deliciosa*	CBow CGre CLan CMac CSco CWit ELan EMil ENot ERom ISea LHol MGos NBar WCru WSHC WStI
F– (f)	IJoh SHBN SPer WDin WHig
– (m)	IJoh SDea SPer WDin WHig
– 'Atlas'	MBri
F– 'Hayward' (f)	CB&S CBow CDoC CMac COtt EBre ELan EMil ERea IOrc ISea LBre MBri MGos MMor MWat NPal SBra SDea SHBN WStI WWeb
F– 'Jenny' (s-p)	MGos SDea
– 'Tomuri' (m)	CB&S CBow CDoC CMac COtt EBre ELan EMil ERea IOrc ISea LBre MWat NPal SBra SHBN WStI WWeb
kolomikta AGM	Widely available
pilosula	GCal

ACTINOTUS (Umbelliferae/Apiaceae)

See Plant Deletions

ADELOCARYUM See **LINDELOFIA**

ADENOPHORA † (Campanulaceae)

aurita	CB&S CChu EFou EMon EOrc GAbr NSti SApp SBla SCro SHer WCot WWat

¶ ***axilliflora*** EPad
bulleyana CHan CSev ECro EPad EPot IBlr NBro NOak WPer WTyr
* ***campanulata*** WPer
confusa LAbb
coronopifolia EPad
¶ ***divaricata*** EPad
forrestii CHan GCHN LHil
himalayana CLew ECro EGle EPad GBri LBlm LHil NRed WHil WPer
latifolia Fischer GBri
latifolia hort. See A. ***pereskiifolia***
liliifolia CBrd CDec CRDP ECro ELan EMar EPad EPot GAul GCal GMac MNFA NBro NCat NPer NSti SAxl SBla SCro SHer SMrm SSvw SUsu WHoo WPer
nikoensis EBee ECro EPad MHig WHaw
– ***stenophylla*** EPad MHig
nipponica See A. ***nikoensis stenophylla***
§ ***pereskiifolia*** CRDP EBee ECro EPad MHlr MNFA MSto MTol NNrw WCot WPer
¶ – 'Alba' WCot
– var. ***heterotricha*** EPad
¶ – ***uryuensis*** EPad
polyantha CHan ECro EPad MTol NNrw WByw WOld WPla
polymorpha See A. ***nikoensis***
potaninii CHan ECro EGle EHic EPad GBuc GCal MNFA MSto NBro SBla SFis WPer
– 'Alba' CHan WPer
– dark form EFol
¶ – lilac WPer
remotiflora ECro
¶ ***stricta*** EHal SUsu
¶ – ssp. ***sessilifolia*** EPad
sublata CHan
takedae ECro EPad LAbb
– var. ***howozana*** EPad
tashiroi CElw CHan CNic CRDP EPad GBri GBuc MTol NBro NNrw NSti NTow SCro SIgm SUsu WHal WHoo
triphylla EPad
– var. ***japonica*** EPad
¶ – var. ***puellaris*** EPad
¶ ***uehatae*** B&SWJ 126 WCru

ADIANTUM † (Adiantaceae)

♦ ***aleuticum*** See A. ***pedatum subpumilum***
capillus-veneris CHEx NMar SRms
– 'Banksianum' NMar
– 'Mairisii' See A. x ***mairisii***
– 'Pointonii' NMar
concinnum NMar
cuneatum See A. ***raddianum***
diaphanum NMar
edgeworthii NMar
formosum NMar
henslowianum NMar
§ x ***mairisii*** NMar
monochlamys NKay
* ***monocolor*** MBri
pedatum AGM CDec CFil CGle CHEx CRDP EBre EBul ECha EFou ELan LBre LWad MBal MBri NHol NKay NOrc SPer SWas SWat WAbe
– var. ***aleuticum*** See A. ***p. subpumilum***
§ – Asiatic form CFil CMil CRDP CWGN ELan LWad MBri NBir NHol NKay SMad SRms WCot
– 'Imbricatum' NHar NHol NMar SBla SRms
– ***japonicum*** See A. ***p.*** Asiatic form
– 'Laciniatum' CFil NKay SRms
– var. ***minus*** See A. ***p. subpumilum***
– 'Miss Sharples' NMar SRms
– ***roseum*** See A. ***p.*** Asiatic form
§ – var. ***subpumilum*** CFil CRDP ELan IOrc MBri NBro NHar NHol NKay SBla SLga WRic WWat
– – f. ***minimum*** NMar
peruvianum MBri
pubescens MBri NMar
§ ***raddianum*** CFil NMar
– 'Brilliantelse' MBri NMar
– 'Crested Majus' NMar
– 'Crested Micropinnulum' NMar
– 'Deflexum' NMar
– 'Elegans' NMar
– 'Feltham Beauty' NMar
– 'Fragrans' See A. ***r.*** 'Fragrantissimum'
§ – 'Fragrantissimum' MBri NMar
– 'Fritz Luthi' MBri NMar
– 'Gracilis' See A. ***r.*** 'Gracillimum'
§ – 'Gracillimum' NMar
– 'Grandiceps' NMar
– 'Gympie Gold' NMar
– 'Kensington Gem' AGM NMar
– 'Legrand Morgan' NMar
– 'Legrandii' NMar
– 'Micropinnulum' NMar
– 'Pacific Maid' NMar
– 'Pacottii' NMar
– 'Triumph' NMar
– 'Tuffy Tips' NMar
– 'Variegated Tessellate' NMar
– 'Victoria's Elegans' NMar
– 'Weigandii' NMar
venustum AGM CBos CDec CDoC CFil CGle CRDP EBul ECha ELan EPot MBal NKay NMar SBla SDix SFar SWas SWat WAbe WCot WEas WFib WOMN WRic

ADLUMIA (Papaveraceae)

fungosa CGle ECro EMar GCra WCot WCru WHer WMar

ADONIS (Ranunculaceae)

aestivalis ECWi
amurensis EBre ELan EPar EPot LAma LBre MUlv
– 'Flore Pleno' CRDP EBre EGol EPar LBre MBri MUlv SPer SRms
– 'Fukujukai' EBre ECha ECro LBre LRHS MUlv
annua EWFC MHew
vernalis EPar EPot GPoy SMrm SRms WChr

ADOXA (Adoxaceae)

moschatellina CKin CNat MTho WHer WWye

AECHMEA † (Bromeliaceae)

caerulea	See A. ***lueddemanniana***
chantinii AGM	MBri
fasciata AGM	MBri
Foster's Favorite AGM	SLMG
*'Grand Prix'	MBri
'Romero'	MBri

AEGLE (Rutaceae)

sepiaria	See PONCIRUS ***trifoliata***

AEGOPODIUM (Umbelliferae/Apiaceae)

*****podagaria*** 'Dangerous form' (v)	CNat
podagraria 'Variegatum'	Widely available

AEONIUM (Crassulaceae)

arboreum AGM	CHEx CTbh GAri SLMG
– 'Atropurpureum' AGM	CHEx CTro ERea IBlr LBlm MBri SHer SLMG WEas
*– ***magnificum***	SArc
– var. ***rubrolineatum***	NRar
balsamiferum	CHEx NRar
canariense	CHEx
cuneatum	CHEx CTbh SArc
x ***domesticum***	See AICHRYSON x ***d.***
haworthii AGM	CHEx CTro GAri
– 'Variegatum'	CHEx
holochrysum	IBlr
nobile	CHEx SLMG
percarneum	SLMG
simsii	CHEx
tabuliforme AGM	CHEx CTbh SLMG
undulatum AGM	CHEx
'Zwartkop' AGM	CBar CHEx CTrh NRar NWyt WEas

AESCHYNANTHUS (Gesneriaceae)

'Big Apple'	WDib
hildebrandii	WDib
'Hot Flash'	WDib
'Little Tiger'	WDib
lobbianus	See A. ***radicans***
§ ***longicaulis*** AGM	MBri
marmoratus	See A. ***longicaulis***
'Mira'	MBri
'Mona'	MBri
parvifolius	See A. ***radicans***
I 'Pulobbia'	MBri
'Purple Star'	MBri
§ ***radicans***	EBak MBri
– ***lobbianus***	See A. ***radicans***
'Rigel'	MBri
*****rigidus***	SLMG
speciosus AGM	CTro LAbb
*– ***rubens***	MBri
'Topaz'	MBri

AESCULUS † (Hippocastanaceae)

x ***arnoldiana***	CMCN
§ x ***bushii***	LBuc
californica	CChu CCla CTho CTrw EArb WWat
x ***carnea***	CDoC EArb ELan GRei ISea MBal MBar
– 'Aureomarginata'	EMon SMad
– 'Briotii' AGM	CBra CDoC CLnd COtt CSco EBre EHar ELan ENot IHos IJoh IOrc LBre LBuc LPan MBri MGos MWat NBee NWea SHBN SHer SPer SSta WDin WStI
– 'Plantierensis'	CTho ENot MBlu
¶ +***dallimorei***	SMad
§ ***flava*** AGM	CCla CMCN CSco CTho EHar ENot MMea SSta WCoo
– ***vestita***	CDoC MBlu
georgiana	See A. ***sylvatica***
glabra	CLnd CMCN EArb EHar MUlv
hippocastanum AGM	CB&S CBra CKin CLnd CPer CSco ELan ENot GRei IDai IJoh ISea LBuc MBal MBar MBri NBee NWea SHBN SPer WDin WMou WStI
§ – 'Baumannii' AGM	CDoC CLnd COtt CSco ENot MBri MGos SHBN SPer WDin WStI
– 'Digitata'	SMad
– 'Flore Pleno'	See A. ***h.*** 'Baumannii'
¶ – 'Laciniata'	MBlu SMad
¶ – 'Memmingeri'	SMad
– 'Pyramidalis'	EHar
indica AGM	CCla CHEx CLnd CSam CSco CTrw EBre ELan ENot IHos IOrc ISea LBre MBri SPer SSta WCoo WDin WMou
– 'Sydney Pearce'	CMCN EHar LBuc MBri MMea SHil
♦ x ***mississippiensis***	See A. ***bushii***
x ***mutabilis*** 'Induta'	MBlu MBri SHil SMad
– 'Penduliflora'	CDoC CTho SMad
x ***neglecta***	CLnd
– 'Erythroblastos' AGM	CLnd CMCN CPMA CTho EHar LNet MBlu SHil WMou WPat WWat
x ***neglecta georgiana***	See A. ***sylvatica***
octandra	See A. ***flava***
parviflora AGM	CB&S CCla CGre CMCN COtt CSco CTho EHar ELan EMil ENot ERav LNet MBal MBlu MBri MUlv SHil SMad SPer WDin WWat
§ ***pavia*** AGM	CChu CCla CMCN CTho EHar ISea MBlu
– 'Atrosanguinea'	CDoC MBri NPal SHil SMad
– 'Koehnei'	MBri
– 'Rosea Nana'	CMCN MBlu
splendens	See A. ***pavia***
turbinata	CLnd CMCN CTho EArb EHar ISea SMad

AETHIONEMA (Cruciferae/Brassicaceae)

armenum	CSam ECro EPot ESis GPlt MBro NGre NPri NRar SFis WPer
¶ ***caespitosum***	WDav
coridifolium	ESis WPer
graecum	See A. ***saxatile***
grandiflorum AGM	CMHG CShe LBee MHig NBro NNor NTow NWCA SBla WPer
– Pulchellum Group AGM	CNic EPot GTou LHop MBro MCas NHol NKay NMen WWin
iberideum	MWat NKay SRms
oppositifolium	EPot MBro MWat NHar NKay NMen NNrd NWCA SSmi WDav WHoo
schistosum	CNic NMen WDav

'Warley Rose' AGM	CLew CNic CShe EBre EFou ELan EPot LBee LBre LHop MCas MHig MPla MTho MWat NHed NHol NKay NMen NNor SBla SIng WAbe WHil WHoo WPat WWin
'Warley Ruber'	CNic MHig

AGAPANTHUS † (Liliaceae/Alliaceae)

§ ***africanus*** AGM	EBee ESma IBlr NRog SArc SLMG WPer WTyn WWat
*– ***albus*** AGM	CB&S CBow WPer
– ***minor***	CTro
¶ 'Albatross'	ECha
****alboroseus***	WThi
¶ 'Ardernei'	LGre
Ardernei Hybrid	CBot ECha GCal IBlr MUlv
'Ben Hope'	MUlv
¶ 'Bicton Hybrid'	CRDP
'Blue Baby'	CB&S MUlv
'Blue Giant'	EFou MUlv SPla WMer
'Blue Imp'	ECtt ESma
'Blue Moon'	CBro ECha MUlv WTyn
'Blue Star'	MUlv WTyn
'Blue Triumphator '	IBar LBow WMer
'Bressingham Blue'	EBre EFou GCal LBre MRav MUlv NRoo
'Bressingham Bounty'	MUlv
'Bressingham White'	CGle CSco EBre ECtt EFol GAri GCHN LBre MRav MUlv NRoo WRus
§ ***campanulatus***	CGle CKel CMon CRDP EBre ELan ERav GDra IDai ISea LBre MHlr SCro WDav WTyn
– var. ***albidus***	CBos CCla CHad CMGP CRDP CSco EBre ECha EFou ELan GPlt IBlr IDai LBre MSte NHol NRoo NSti NVic SChu SGil SHer SHig SPer
– ***albovittatus***	CRow LGre WTyn
– bright blue	GCal
– cobalt blue	ECha WTyn
– 'Isis'	CAvo CBro EBre ECha EGol GCHN GCal IBlr LBre MUlv SApp SPer WTyn
– ssp. ***patens*** AGM	EBre LBre SApp SHig SPer WTyn WWat
– 'Profusion'	ECha MUlv WTyn
– variegated	ECha WCot
'Castle of Mey'	LGre LHyd MUlv
caulescens AGM	IBlr
comptonii	CMon
– forms	SLMG
'Donau' ('Danube')	CBow MUlv
'Findlay's Blue'	SWas
Giant hybrids	ERav
§ Headbourne hybrids	Widely available
– 'Golden Rule' (v)	CRow EHoe ELan LGre SApp SHig WTyn
'Holbrook'	CSam
'Hydon Mist'	LHyd
inapertus hollandii	CChu GCal IBlr
– ssp. ***intermedius***	CHan GCal IBlr
'Kew White'	SDix
'Kingston Blue'	ECha SWas
'Lady Moore'	SApp SWas
'Lilliput'	Widely available
'Loch Hope' AGM	MUlv
'Midnight Blue'	CGle ECha ELan GCal IBlr LHil MBel MSte MUlv SWas WTyn
'Midnight Star'	ERav MUlv WTyn
'Mooreanus'	SUsu WTyn
'Norman Hadden'	EBul WTyn
nutans 'Albus'	GCal
Palmer's hybrids	See A. Heabourne hybrids
'Peter Pan'	CBow CRow CSpe EPla GBuc LBlm LGre SAxl
¶ 'Podge Mill'	SWas
¶ 'Polar Ice'	WMer
praecox	CDoC IBlr
– 'Flore Pleno'	ECha EMon LGre
– 'Maximus Albus'	IBlr SHig
– ssp. ***minimus***	IBlr
§ – ssp. ***orientalis***	CHEx CHan EBul ERea GAri LHil NPal WWat
– – var. ***albiflorus***	CAvo CDoC LBow NPal
– – 'Mount Thomas'	CHan
– ssp. ***praecox***	EBre LBre
– 'Variegatus' AGM	SLMG
– ***vittatus*** (v)	CHan WCot
¶ 'Profusion'	CBro
'Purple Cloud'	CB&S CRos
¶ 'Royal Blue'	ECtt EHic
'Sapphire'	CB&S
'Sky Star'	ERav MUlv
¶ 'Snowy Baby'	CRos
'Snowy Owl'	MUlv
¶ 'Streamline'	SFai
'Tinkerbell'	CRos SFai SPla WCot WHal WMer
'Torbay'	MUlv SBla SHig
umbellatus	See AA. ***campanulatus, praecox orientalis***
'Underway'	CMon GCal SApp SHig
'White Dwarf'	EFou EGol GCra WWat
¶ 'White Giant'	SPla
'White Star'	ERav MUlv WTyn
'White Starlet'	MUlv
¶ 'White Umbrella'	CBow CHol EOrc SApp SHer WWat
'Zella Thomas'	LHyd

AGAPETES (Ericaceae)

buxifolia	WBod
'Ludgvan Cross'	CGre CTro MBal
serpens AGM	CGre MBal
– 'Nepal Cream'	CGre CTro GCal MBal

AGARISTA (Ericaceae)

§ ***populifolia***	WWat

AGASTACHE (Labiatae/Lamiaceae)

anethiodora	See A. ***foeniculum***
anisata	See A. ***foeniculum***
barberi 'Firebird'	CBot CBrk CChu CGle CRDP GCal LGre LHop SBla SUsu WCot
§ ***cana***	CGle LGre MHlr WCot WDav
§ ***foeniculum***	CArn CBow CCla CGle CHan CSFH CSco CSev CTom ECha EFou ELan EMar GCHN GPoy LHol LHop MBri MChe MHew MSal NBro NNor SIde SUsu WDav WPer WWye

– 'Alabaster'	CChu CCla CGle ECha ECro EFou EMon GCal LGan LGre NNrw SAxl WWye
– 'Alba'	CBot CBow CTom SIde
§ *mexicana*	CHan ECro EFol ELan GCal GMac LHop MHew NTow SMrm SUsu WHer WWye
– 'Carille Carmine'	CChu SHer WCot WPer
– 'Champagne'	WElm WPer
¶ – 'Mauve Beauty'	CChu GCal NPri WCot
♦ – 'Rosea'	See A. *cana*
nepetoïdes	MHew MSal WWye
pallidiflora	LGre WDav
rugosa	CArn CSev ECro EWes GBar GPoy MHew MSal NPri SWat WPer
urticifolia	CHol EBee MHew MSal
– 'Alba'	EBee ECro EHal EJud NPri WEas WPer
¶ – 'Alba Variegata'	WPer
¶ – 'Liquorice Blue'	WPer

AGATHAEA See FELICIA

AGATHIS (Araucariaceae)

australis	CTre

AGAVE (Agavaceae)

affinis	See A. *sobria sobria*
* *africana*	ISea
americana	CAbb CB&S CGre CHEx CTro ECha GCra IBlr LHil LPal LPan MUlv SArc SLMG SMad
– 'Marginata'	CGre CTbh IBlr LHop SHer
– 'Mediopicta'	CTbh SArc SLMG
– 'Variegata'	CAbb CB&S CHEx CTbh CTro ECha MBri SArc SCro SLMG
angustifolia	SLMG
¶ – var. *rubescens*	CTrh
¶ *attenuata*	SArc
avellanidens	See A. *sebastiana*
¶ *bovicornuta*	CTrh
§ *celsii*	CHEx CTbh CTrh SArc
cerulata	See A. *sobria sobria*
¶ – ssp. *nelsonii*	CTrh
¶ – ssp. *subcerulata*	CTrh
¶ *chrysantha*	CTrh
coarctata	See A. *mitriiformis*
¶ *deserti* ssp. *deserti*	CTrh
¶ – ssp. *pringlei*	CTrh
ferdinandi-regis	CTbh
ferox	CHEx SArc SLMG
filifera	CHEx SLMG
franzosinii	CAbb
¶ *ghiesbreghtii*	CTrh
gigantea	See FURCRAEA *foetida*
¶ *kerchovei*	CTrh
¶ *lurida*	CTrh
¶ *mckelveyana*	CTrh
♦ *mitis*	See A. *celsii*
neomexicana	SIgm
¶ *pachycentra*	CTrh
¶ *palmeri*	CTrh
parryi	CGre CHEx CTro SArc SIgm
– *couesii*	See A. *p. parryi*
¶ – var. *huachucensis*	CTrh
– var. *parryi*	CTbh
potatorum var. *verschaffeltii*	CTbh
¶ *salmiana* var. *ferox*	CTrh
schottii	CTbh SIgm
§ *sebastiana*	CTbh
¶ *shawii* ssp. *goldmaniana*	CTrh
* *striata rubra*	SIgm
¶ *titanota*	CTrh
utahensis	SIgm
– var. *discreta*	CTbh
– var. *eborispina*	CTbh
– ssp. *kaibabensis*	CTbh SArc
victoriae-reginae	CTbh WMar
¶ *vilmoriniana*	CTrh
weberi	CHEx
xylonacantha	CHEx

AGERATINA See EUPATORIUM

AGERATUM (Compositae/Asteraceae)

See Plant Deletions

AGLAONEMA (Araceae)

§ *crispum*	MBri
* – 'Marie'	MBri
'Malay Beauty'	MBri
roebelinii	See A. *crispum*
'Silver Queen' AGM	MBri

AGRIMONIA (Rosaceae)

eupatoria	CArn CKin ECWi EWFC Effi GPoy LHol MChe MHew NLan SHer SIde SWat WCla WGwy WOak WWye
odorata	See A. *repens*
§ *repens*	GBar MHew MSal WGwy WNdy

AGROPYRON (Gramineae/Poaceae)

glaucum	See ELYMUS *hispidus*
magellanicum	See ELYMUS *magellanicus*
pubiflorum	See ELYMUS *magellanicus*
scabrum	See ELYMUS *scabrus*

AGROSTEMMA (Caryophyllaceae)

coronaria	See LYCHNIS *coronaria*
githago	CSFH ECWi EWFC MHew MSal NMir WCla WHaw

AGROSTIS (Gramineae/Poaceae)

canina 'Silver Needles' (v)	CNic CTom EGle EHoe EMon ETPC GCal SHer
karsensis	See A. *stolonifera*
stolonifera	ETPC

AGROSTOCRINUM (Liliaceae/Phormiaceae)

See Plant Deletions

AICHRYSON (Crassulaceae)

§ x *domesticum*	CHEx SLMG
– 'Variegatum' AGM	EBak ESis SLMG

AILANTHUS (Simaroubaceae)

§ *altissima* AGM — CB&S CBra CChu CHEx CLnd CSco CWSG EArb EBre ELan EMil ENot IOrc LBre LPan MBlu MGos NBee SArc SPer WCoo WDin WNor WStI
glandulosa — See A. *altissima*

AINSLIAEA (Compositae/Asteraceae)

¶ *latifolia* S&SH 103 — CHan
¶ *paucicapitata* B&SWJ 103 — WCru

AIPHANES (Palmae/Arecaceae)

caryotifolia — LPal

AJANIA (Compositae/Asteraceae)

♦*pacifica* — See DENDRANTHEMA *p.*
tibetica — CNic

AJUGA (Labiatae/Lamiaceae)

¶ *genevensis* 'Pink Beauty' — GMac
– 'Tottenham' — MBri WMer
metallica — See A. *pyramidalis*
¶ 'Monmotaro San' — SApp
§ *pyramidalis* — CNat ECha EGol SCro WHer
– 'Metallica Crispa' — CLew CMHG CRDP CShe ESma NMir NNrd WMer WPer WThu
reptans — CHan CKin CSFH ECWi ECtt EWFC GPoy LHol LMay MChe MHew MPla MSal NBrk NMen NMir WChe WGwy
– 'Alba' — CArn CBre CCot CGle CHan CNat CNic CRiv CRow CTom CWGN ECha EFou EGol GCal GMac LHop NBro NSti SMrm SPer WBon WByw WHal WMer WPer WWye
§ – 'Atropurpurea' AGM — Widely available
– 'Braunherz' AGM — CB&S CElw CGle CHad CRow CSam EBar EBre ECtt EFol EFou EGol EHoe ELan EPot GAbr GMac LBre LHop MBri MFir MRav MSte NEgg NOak NSti WHal WHen WHoo WMer
– 'Burgundy Glow' AGM — Widely available
*– 'Burgundy Red' — GDra
§ – 'Catlin's Giant' AGM — Widely available
– 'Delight' (v) — ECot EFol EFou ELan EMon EPot IBar MBri MFir NMir NNrd SBod SHer WCHb WCra WEas
– 'Harlequin' — WMer
¶ – 'Julia' — EMon
♦– 'Jumbo' — See A. *r.* 'Jungle Beauty'
§ – 'Jungle Beauty' — CElw CGle CHan CSco CWGN EBre EFou EGol EOrc EPar EPla GCal GMac LBre NFai NHol SApp SAxl SPer SUsu WHen WHer WTyr
– 'Macrophylla' — See A. *r.* 'Catlin's Giant'
– 'Multicolor'/ 'Rainbow'/ 'Tricolor' (v) — CArn CBre CGle CSFH CSev CWGN ECha EFol EFou EHoe ELan EMar EPar EPla EPot GAbr GDra LGro MBar MPit MWat NGre NNor NNrd SBod SPer WCra WEas WPer
– 'Pink Elf' — CNic CRow CTom EBre EBur ECha EFol ELan ESis LBre LHop NBro NNor NOak NSti SApp SHer SUsu WHoo WPer
¶ – 'Pink Splendour' — CBre
– 'Pink Surprise' — CElw CGle CRow EFol EFou EGol EHoe EMar EMon LRHS MMil NGre NHol WBon WByw WCHb WHal WTyr
– 'Purple Torch' — CGle ECha ESis MBal MBri WBon WEas WMer
– 'Purpurea' — See A. *r.* 'Atropurpurea'
¶ – 'Silver Carpet' — WCot
– 'Silver Shadow' — EMon WCHb
– 'Tortoiseshell' (v) — CGle
– 'Variegata' ('Argentea') — Widely available

AKEBIA (Lardizabalaceae)

x *pentaphylla* — CBow EMil EPla ERea SBra
quinata — Widely available
trifoliata — CB&S CChu MUlv SBra

ALANGIUM (Alangiaceae)

chinense — CB&S CFil
platanifolium — CBot CLan CMCN EPla MBlu

ALBIZIA (Leguminosae/Mimosaceae)

distachya — See PARASERIANTHES *lophantha*
§ *julibrissin* — CB&S CHan CWit ELan ISea LHil SEng WFro
– var. *rosea* AGM — CGre CHEx CPle CTro EHar EOrc ESma EWri IOrc MUlv SArc SDry SHil WBod WNor WWeb
lophantha — See PARASERIANTHES *l.*

ALBUCA (Liliaceae/Hyacinthaceae)

canadensis — NRog
caudata — CMon
humilis — CAvo EPot ESis MHig NRog SIng WAbe WHil WOMN
juncifolia — CMon
nelsonii — CAvo CMon NRog
¶ *tortuosa* S&SH 53 — CHan

ALCEA (Malvaceae)

ficifolia — CGle LCot SSvw
§ *rosea* — CGle EJud GPoy LWad MBri SSvw WEas WHaw
– Chater's Double Group — CB&S CBow CMil CSco EBre ECtt EFou ELan LBre LWad MBri NNor SHer SRms
– forms — LCot LWad SMad WRus
– Majorette Group — ECtt SHer
– 'Nigra' — CArn CCMG CGle CHad CMil CSFH EFou GCra LWad MHlr MSte MUlv NNor NPri NRoo SMad SSvw WEas WHal
– Powder Puff Group — ELan
– single white — WHaw
– 'Summer Carnival' — SRms WGor WHil
– yellow — LWad MWil
§ *rugosa* — CGle CHad CMil CSam ELan EOrc EPad LGan MSte SDix SHer WCot WEas WOMN WOld WRus
¶ – *alba* — WHil

ALCHEMILLA † (Rosaceae)

§ ***abyssinica***	CDoC CElw CGle CNic CRiv CRow GAbr GBuc MBel NCat NSti SHer SIng
* ***affinis venosa***	EPla
N ***alpina***	Widely available
arvensis	See APHANES ***a.***
conjuncta	CBot CBre CElw CGle CHan CLew CNic ECha ECro EFou EGol ELan ELun EMar GAbr LHop MBel MTho NBrk NBro NHol NOak NRya NWCA SMrm SPer WByw WEas WGwy WWye
elisabethae	EMon EPad EPla NBrk WCHb
ellenbeckii	Widely available
erythropoda AGM	Widely available
faeroensis	EGle LBee MDHE NHol WPer WWat
glaucescens	CNat
lapeyrousei	EMon
mollis AGM	Widely available
* – 'Grandiflora'	MUlv
* – 'Robusta'	ECro ESma WHal
'Mr Poland's Variety'	See A. ***venosa***
♦ ***pedata***	See A. ***abyssinica***
¶ ***pentaphylla***	EBee
plicatula	EPad
pumila	ECro
saxatilis	NHol WPla
¶ ***speciosa***	EBee
N ***splendens***	CArn CRiv EBee ECro EOrc GAri LGan NHol NRoo
§ ***venosa***	SAxl SPer SUsu WWat
¶ ***vestita*** 'Minima'	CNat
vulgaris hort.	See A. ***xanthochlora***
§ ***xanthochlora***	ECro EGol Effi GGar GPoy MHew MSal NMir WHaw

ALECTRYON (Sapindaceae)

excelsus	CHEx

ALETRIS (Liliaceae/Melanthiaceae)

farinosa	MSal

ALISMA (Alismataceae)

lanceolatum	WChe
plantago-aquatica	CBen CKin CRow CWGN ECWi EHon EMFW GBar LMay MHew MSta NDea SHig SWat WChe WHol WWye
– ***parviflorum***	CBen CWGN EMFW LMay MSta NDea SHig SRms SWat WChe

ALKANNA (Boraginaceae)

orientalis	WCru
tinctoria	MChe WHaw

ALLAMANDA (Apocynaceae)

§ ***blanchetii***	CNew
cathartica	MBri
– 'Birthe'	MBri
* – 'Chocolate Swirl'	CNew
– 'Stansill's Double'	CNew
neriifolia	See A. ***schottii***
violacea	See A. ***blanchetii***

ALLARDIA (Compositae/Asteraceae)

♦ ***glabra***	See A. ***tridactylites***
§ ***tridactylites***	GTou

ALLIARIA (Cruciferae/Brassicaceae)

petiolata	CArn CKin CSev ECWi EWFC MWil WCla WHer

ALLIUM † (Liliaceae/Alliaceae)

acuminatum	GCHN MFos NBir NGar WChr WCot
aflatunense Fedtschenko	CBro CGle CMon ECha ECtt EFou EPar ETub LAma LBow MNFA MWBu NEgg NRog NSti SIng SUsu WCra WPer
– 'Purple Sensation'	CAvo CBro CGle ECha EFou EPar EPot ETub LAma LBow MHlr MWBu NRog SApp SMad SUsu WHoo WPer
aflatunense hort.	See A. ***stipitatum***
akaka	LAma NRog
albidum	See A. ***denudatum***
albopilosum	See A. ***christophii***
altissimum	LRHS NRog
amabile	See A. ***mairei a.***
ampeloprasum	ECha SIde
– var. ***babingtonii***	CNat IEde
amplectens	GDra NRog WChr
§ ***angulosum***	GAul MMil MSto WCot
atropurpureum	ECha EPar LBow NHol NRog SPou WCot
azureum	See A. ***caeruleum***
'Beau Regard'	LAma LBow NRog
beesianum hort.	See A. ***cyaneum***
beesianum AGM	CGle EBre EBur EPot ESis GPlt LBre MBal MHig MNFA MSte MSto NBir NHol NRya NWCA SPou WCot WOMN
bucharicum	CMon
bulgaricum	See NECTAROSCORDUM ***siculum bulgaricum***
§ ***caeruleum*** AGM	CArn CAvo CBro CGle ELan EPar ETub LAma LBow MBri MNFA MSto NBir NRog SGil WHal WPer WSun
– ***azureum***	See A. ***c.***
caesium	SPou
callimischon	CBro CMon EPot MHig NRog WChr
– ssp. ***haemostictum***	EBul LBow NRog SIng SPou SWas
canadense	CLew CSam WHal
§ ***carinatum***	EBee GCHN
§ – ssp. ***pulchellum*** AGM	Widely available
– – f. ***album***	CAvo CBro CMon CVer ECha EFou EMon EPar EPot ETub LBow MBal MBro NRog NSti NTow SMrm SUsu WPer WWin
¶ ***carolinianum***	MSto
cepa AGM	CMil CSFH GBar
– Aggregatum Group	GPlt WHil
– 'Perutile'	CArn GBar GPoy ILis SHer SIde
– Proliferum Group	CArn CSev EJud GPoy IEde ILis MChe MFir SHer SIde WCHb WGwy WOak
cernuum AGM	Widely available
– 'Hidcote'	WCot
– var. ***neomexicanum***	EBul
¶ ***chamaemoly***	EBul

– ***littorale*** AB&S 4387	CMon
§ ***christophii*** AGM	CAvo CBro CGle EBre ECha EFou ELan EOrc EPar EPot ERav ETub LAma LBow LBre MBri MWBu NBrk NRog NSti SUsu WEas WHoo WKif WPer
cirrhosum	See A. ***carinatum pulchellum***
cowanii	See A. ***neapolitanum*** Cowanii Group
¶ ***crenulatum***	MSto
cupanii	CMon
¶ – ssp. ***hirtovaginatum***	EHic
§ ***cyaneum*** AGM	CBro CGle CTom EFol ELan EPot LBee LGan MCas MFos MHig NHol NNrd NRya NWCA SGil SPou WEas WRus WWin
– ***album***	SPou
cyathophorum	CArn NRog
– var. ***farreri***	CArn CAvo CBro CLew CMon CNic CRiv CVer ELan EPot ESis LLWP MBal MHig NHol NNrd SApp SHer WAbe WDav WEas WHil WOMN WPer WThu
dichlamydeum	CBro NRog SPou WChr
elatum	See A. ***macleanii***
¶ ***ericetorum***	MSto
falcifolium	WChr
farreri	See A. ***cyathophorum f.***
¶ ***fimbriatum*** var. ***abramsii***	WChr
– var. ***purdyi***	WChr
fistulosum	CArn CSFH EHer EJud ELan EPla GBar GPoy IEde ILis MChe MHew NBrk SHer SIde WGwy WOak WPer WTyr WWye
flavum AGM	CArn CAvo CBro CGle CMon CTom EBar ECha ELan EPar LBow LHop LLWP MHig MWat NHol NMen NRog SChu SIng WCla WGor WHil WPer WRus
§ – 'Blue Leaf'	EBar EPot
– forms	SPou
– ***glaucum***	See A. ***f.*** 'Blue Leaf'
– 'Golden Showers'	EBar WPla
– var. ***minus***	CNic ELan MTho NHol NWCA WHaw
– var. ***nanum***	MCas MFos
– ssp. ***tauricum***	CMon
geyeri	WChr
giganteum	CArn CB&S CBot CBow EFou ELan EOrc EPar ETub GCra LAma LBow MBri MFir MRav NNor NRog SIng WCra
'Gladiator'	LAma LBow NRog
glaucum	See A. ***senescens montanum glaucum***
¶ 'Globemaster'	LBow
'Globus'	EPot MHFP
goodingii	CNic
♦ ***griffithianum***	See A. ***rubellum***
¶ ***haematochiton***	WChr
hierochuntinum S&L 79	CMon
hyalinum	CMon NRog NSla WChr
insubricum AGM	MS&S MSto NBir WPla
kansuense	See A. ***sikkimense***
karataviense AGM	Widely available
kharputense	LAma
libani	MSto WPer
libonicum	WPer
loratum	EPar
'Lucy Ball'	LAma LBow NRog
§ ***macleanii***	EPar ETub LAma LBow NRog
macranthum	GCHN MSte MSto NHol SWas WDav
macrochaetum	LAma
mairei	CBro CNic CRiv EPot EWes GCHN MCas MDHE SGil WAbe WHal
§ – var. ***amabile***	MBal MFos MHig NHol NNrd NRya NTow SGil WDav WOMN
– – pink	NBir SPou
¶ – – red	SPou
maximowiczii	WThi
moly AGM	CAvo CBro CCla CGle CNic CRiv ELan EPar ETub LAma LBow MBri MHig MWBu NHol NMen NRog NRoo NRya SIng WCla WEas WPer WThu WWin
– 'Jeannine' AGM	CBro
multibulbosum	See A. ***nigrum***
murrayanum hort.	See A. ***unifolium***
narcissiflorum	See A. ***insubricum***
narcissiflorum Villars	EPot LHil MSto NHol NMen NSla NSti NWCA WAbe
– pink	NHar NNrd
neapolitanum	CArn CGle CLTr EBul ELan EPar LAma LBow MBri MBro MNFA MWBu NHol NRog NSti SIng WHil WPer
§ – Cowanii Group	CBro CLew NHol WPer
– 'Grandiflorum'	ETub NRog
§ ***nigrum***	EBul EFou EPar ETub LAma LBow MHlr MNFA MWBu NRog SIng WCot WHal WPer
nuttallii	See A. ***drummondii***
§ ***obliquum***	CAvo ECha MSto SWas
odorum Linnaeus	See A. ***ramosum***
olympicum	MBro SPou WThu
§ ***oreophilum*** AGM	CAvo CBro CMea CRiv ECha ECtt LAma LBow MFos MHig MNFA MWBu NBrk NHol NNrd NRog NRoo WCla WHil WHoo WPer WSun
– 'Zwanenburg' AGM	CBro EPot ETub NMen NRog
orientale	EPot LAma
ostrowskianum	See A. ***oreophilum***
pallens	CBre EFol ERav MTho NBir
§ ***paniculatum***	CAvo EHic MMil NRog SChu
¶ – ssp. ***fuscum***	EHic
paradoxum	NBir NRog
– PF 5085	CMon
pedemontanum	See A. ***narcissiflorum*** Villars
peninsulare	WChr
polyastrum	GCHN
¶ ***porrum*** 'Saint Victor'	MHlr WCot
pskemense	SPou
pulchellum	See A. ***carinatum p.***
pyrenaicum Costa & Vayreda	CAvo EBee ELan MNFA SApp
pyrenaicum hort.	See A. ***angulosum***
♦ ***ramosum*** Jacquin	See A. ***obliquum***
§ ***ramosum*** Linnaeus	LAma MSto NCat WPer
'Rien Poortvliet'	LAma NRog
rosenbachianum	CBro EPar EPot ETub LAma LBow NRog NSti
– 'Album'	EPar LAma NRog SIng
roseum	CAvo CLTr ECtt EMon ETub GPlt LAma LBow NHol NRog SIng WPer

– B&S 396	CMon
– 'Grandiflorum'	See A. ***r. bulbiferum***
sativum	CArn EEls EJud GPoy IEde MHew SHer SIde WOak
– var. ***ophioscordon***	GPoy ILis WHaw
scabriscapum	CMon WChr
schmitzii	CMon
schoenoprasum	CArn CSFH CSev CTom ECha EHer GPoy IEde LBlm LHol MBal MBri MBro MChe MFir MHew MPit NCat NFai NHol NNor SHer SIde WEas WHil WPer WThu WWye
– 'Corsican White'	EMon
– fine-leaved	MWil
– 'Forescate'	COtt CSFH EBre ECha EFou LBre LHol MBal MBri MMil MUlv NHol SHer SLga WCot
– 'Polyphant'	CBre CSFH
– ***roseum***	GBar GPoy
– 'Shepherds Crooks'	WThu
– var. ***sibiricum***	EJud GBar GPoy IEde MBri SDix SIde
– 'Wallington White'	EMon
– white	EPla LGre MSte SApp WBon WCot WHer WWye
schubertii	CAvo CBro EPar ETub LAma LBow NRog SIng SMrm
scorodoprasum ssp. ***jajlae***	LBlm MBel NHol NMen WPer
senescens	CArn EBre ECro ELan EPar GCHN LBre MNFA NMen NSti
§ – ssp. ***montanum***	CLew EBul ELan EPot ERav MBro MCas MHig SDix SIng WThu
§ – – ssp. ***glaucum***	CHan CMea CRiv CTom ECha EPla ESis GCHN MBel MHig MHlr MSto NHol WDav WEas WHal WPbr WPer
– ssp. ***senescens***	EMon
♦***sibthorpianum***	See A. ***paniculatum***
siculum	See NECTAROSCORDUM ***siculum***
§ ***sikkimense***	GDra MBro MSto NFai NHol NMen NNrd NTow NWCA SHer SPou SWas WEas WHil WOMN WPer
sphaerocephalon	CArn CAvo CHad ECha ELan EPar ETub LAma LBow LHop MNFA NLan NOak NRog SIng SMrm SUsu WEas WPer WShi
stellerianum	GCHN WCot WHal WPer WPla
– var. ***kurilense***	WThu
§ ***stipitatum***	LAma LBow NRog WCot
– ***album***	CBro ETub LAma LBow NRog
subhirsutum	CSam
subvillosum	CMon
tanguticum	GCHN WHaw
thunbergii	CAvo CMon EWes NBir WChr
tibeticum	See A. ***sikkimense***
triquetrum	CAvo CGle CLTr CTom ELan ETub GBar GGar IBlr IEde ILis LAma LBow NBir NLan NRog SIng WCru WPer WWin
tuberosum	CArn CAvo CLew CSFH CSev EBul ECha EFou EHer EJud EPar GPoy IEde ILis LHol MBri MChe MFir MHew SHer SIde WCHb WHal WPer WWye
§ ***unifolium***	CAvo CBro CGle CMon EBul EPot ESma ETub LAma LBow MBri MNFA NBir NCat NRog NSti WChr WCla WDav WPer WRus
ursinum	CArn CAvo CKin ETub GPoy IEde LAma LHol NMir NRog SIng WGwy WHen WShi WWye
validum	WDav
vineale	CArn
violaceum	See A. ***carinatum***
wallichii	EBar LAma NBir
– B 445	WDav
zebdanense	ETub LAma LBow MSto NHol NRog WCla

ALLOCASUARINA (Casuarinaceae)

distyla	ISea
§ ***verticillata***	CGre

ALMOND See PRUNUS *dulcis*

ALNUS † (Betulaceae)

cordata AGM	CB&S CDoC CKin CLnd CPer CSto EHar ELan ENot GRei IJoh IOrc LBuc NRog SHBN SPer SSta WDin WFro WMou
– wild origin	CSto
cremastogyne	CMCN
fauriei	CSto
firma	EPla MBlu
– var. ***multinervis***	See A. ***pendula***
– var. ***sieboldiana***	See A. ***sieboldiana***
formosana	EArb MNes
¶***fruticosa***	CSto
glutinosa	CB&S CDoC CKin CLnd CPer CSam CSto ENot GRei IDai IOrc LBuc MGos NBee NRog NRoo NWea SHBN SPer WDin WMou WStI
– 'Aurea'	EBee EHar WMou
– var. ***barbata***	CSto
– 'Imperialis' AGM	CBow CLnd CPMA CSco CTho EHar ELan ENot MBri SHil SPer WDin WMou WWat
– f. ***incisa***	ELan
– 'Laciniata'	CDoC CSco CTho IOrc MBlu
– 'Pyramidalis'	WMou
hirsuta	CMCN CSto
incana	CDoC CKin CLnd CPer CSto ENot GRei IOrc LBuc MBar NRog NWea SHBN WDin WMou
– 'Aurea'	CB&S CCla CLnd CMHG COtt CSco CTho EHar ELan ENot IOrc MBar MBlu MBri SEng SHBN SHer SPer WDin WMou
– 'Laciniata'	COtt CTho EHar ENot WDin WMou
– 'Pendula'	CTho EHar SHil WMou
japonica	CSto
maritima	CSto
maximowiczii	CSto
nepalensis	CSto
oblongifolia	CSto
oregona	See A. ***rubra***
§ ***pendula***	CSto
****pinnatisecta***	EHar
rhombifolia	CSto

§ *rubra*	CDoC CKin CLnd CSto ELan ENot GAri GCHN GRei IOrc LBuc WDin WMou
§ *rugosa*	CMCN CSto
serrulata	See A. *rugosa*
§ *sieboldiana*	CGre CSto
sinuata	CSto CTho
x *spaethii* AGM	CTho SHil WMou
subcordata	CLnd EArb
tenuifolia	CSto
viridis	CSto GAri NWea WMou
¶ – ssp. *crispa*	CSto

ALOCASIA (Araceae)

x *amazonica* AGM	CTro MBri
sanderiana	CTro

ALOË (Liliaceae/Aloëaceae)

arborescens	CHEx
aristata	CBow CHEx CTbh LBlm MBri SArc SCro SLMG
barbadensis	See A. *vera*
brevifolia	CHEx CTbh
camperi 'Maculata'	MBri
ciliaris	CHEx CTro ERea
descoingsii	SGil
humilis	IBlr
karasbergensis	LHil
mitriformis	LHil
saponaria	CTro SLMG
sp. yellow flowered	IBlr
striata	CHEx
¶ *variegata*	CTrh
§ *vera* AGM	CArn ERea GPoy ILis SArc SHer SIde SLMG WHer
'Walmsley's Blue'	MBri

ALONSOA (Scrophulariaceae)

acutifolia	LHil
– coral	ERav
¶ *linearis*	LCot WHaw
meridionalis	WHil
'Pink Beauty'	ELan GCal LAbb
warscewiczii AGM	CMHG CSam ELan ERea IBlr LAbb LGan SAxl SChu SHer SUsu WEas WOMN WPer WWin
– pale form	See A. *w.* 'Peachy-Keen'
§ – 'Peachy-Keen'	CElw CHad CMHG CSam CSpe ERea LHop SAxl SGil SHer SUsu WHal WPer WRus

ALOPECURUS (Gramineae/Poaceae)

alpinus	EHoe EMon EPla ETPC SFar
– ssp. *glaucus*	EHoe
arundinaceus	ETPC
lanatus	NRya SGil SIng
pratensis	MWil
– 'Aureovariegatus'	EHal EHoe EMon EPla ETPC GCal IBlr LHop MSte NBar NEgg NFai NHar NRar SAxl SCro SPer SPla WHow
N– 'Aureus'	CMGP CNic CRiv ECha EFou EPar EPot GAbr LHil MBal NBro NHol NSti SCob SFar SLga WByw WPer WWin

ALOPHIA (Iridaceae)

lahue	See HERBERTIA *l.*

ALOYSIA (Verbenaceae)

¶ *chamaedryfolia*	CGre
citriodora	See A. *triphylla*
§ *triphylla*	Widely available

ALPINIA (Zingiberaceae)

purpurata	CNew
sanderae	See A. *vittata*
speciosa	See A. *zerumbet*
§ *vittata*	CNew
§ *zerumbet*	CNew

ALSOBIA See EPISCIA

ALSTROEMERIA †
(Liliaceae/Alstroemeriaceae)

aurantiaca	See A. *aurea*
§ *aurea*	CGle CGre CTro ELan EMar MHlr MUlv NCat NNrw NSti
– 'Dover Orange'	CB&S CGle CMGP EBee EBre LBre MMil NBar NCat SHer SMrm SPla
– 'Orange King'	CDoC CKel NFai SDeJ SRms WStI
Beatrix ® / 'Stadoran'	SSmt
brasiliensis	CBro CChu CGle WCot
Diana ®	See A. Mona Lisa ®
Doctor Salter's Hybrids	EFou WOMN
¶ *exserens* F&W 7207	SIgm
Frederika ® / 'Stabrons'	SSmt
Grace ®	See A. King Cardinal ®
hookeri	MSto SWas WOMN
Ileana ®	See A. 'Rita'
Inca hybrids	CB&S
King Cardinal ® / 'Starodo'	SSmt
Ligtu hybrids AGM	CAvo CB&S CBow CDoC CGle CMea CShe ECha ELan ERav LHop MBri NPer SDeJ SDix SHer SPer SUsu WRus
Manon ® / 'Zelanon'	SSmt
Margaret ® / 'Stacova'	SSmt
Marie-Louise ®	See A. Manon ®
¶ 'Marina'	SPla
Meyer hybrids	SMrm
'Ohio'	LRHS MBri
¶ 'Orange Glory'	SPla
¶ *pallida* F&W 7241	SIgm
pelegrina	CMon MTho
¶ – 'Alba'	CBro EHic
¶ 'Pink Perfection'	SPla
§ *psittacina*	CChu CGle CGre CHad CHan CRDP CTro ECro ELan EPar ERav GCal LHil LHop MSte MUlv NCat NTow SAxl SHer SLMG WSHC
*– *variegata*	CRDP ELan
pulchella	See A. *psittacina*
pulchra BC&W 4751	CMon
– BC&W 4762	SBla
'Purple Joy'	COtt
pygmaea	MSto MTho NTow SWas
'Red Beauty'	NBir

'Rosy Wings'	COtt LRHS MBri WMer
'Saffier'	LRHS MBri
Sarah ® / 'Stalicamp'	SSmt
'Saxony'	LRHS MBri
Sophia ®	See A. Yellow King ®
'Sovereign'	COtt LRHS MBri
sp. Wr 8893	SIgm
'Sunrise'	LRHS MBri
I 'Vanitas'	LRHS MBri
Victoria ® / 'Regina'	SSmt
¶ ***violacea***	WCot
¶ 'White Apollo'	SPla
¶ 'Yellow Friendship'	SPla
Yellow King ® / 'Stajello'	SSmt

ALTHAEA (Malvaceae)

armeniaca	EMon GBuc LRHS
cannabina	GCal MUlv WHoo WRus
officinalis	CArn CHan CKin CSFH CSev ECoo ELan EMon EWFC Effi GMac GPoy ILis LHol LHop MChe MHew MMil MSal NDea NFai SHer SIde SMad WOak WPer WWye
rosea	See ALCEA ***rosea.***
rugosostellulata	See ALCEA ***rugosa***

ALYOGYNE (Malvaceae)

hakeifolia	CSpe ERea LAbb LBlm LHop SMad
huegelii	CAbb LBlm
– 'Santa Cruz'	CSpe CTro ERea ESma LAbb LHop NWyt SMad

ALYSSOÏDES (Cruciferae/Brassicaceae)

utriculata	CMHG CNic CTom EBar ELan GAul LHop WByw WPer WPla WWin
– NS 431	NWCA
– var. ***graeca***	MSte NHol

ALYSSUM (Cruciferae/Brassicaceae)

argenteum hort.	See A. ***murale***
caespitosum	NWCA
cuneifolium	WAbe
*– ***pirinicum***	MHig
gemonense	See AURINIA ***petraea***
idaeum	MWat WThi
¶ ***longistylum***	WDav
moellendorfianum	EPot NMen
montanum	CNic CShe ECha ELan EMNN GAbr MPit MPla NMen SChu SHer
– 'Berggold' ('Mountain Gold')	CB&S EBee GAul LAbb LBee MCas NPri NRoo NVic
§ ***murale***	NPri
¶ ***ovirense***	CNic
¶ ***oxycarpum***	EWes SBla SIng WAbe
petraeum	See AURINIA ***petraea***
propinquum	NWCA
pulvinare	MHig NGre WAbe
pyrenaicum	NMen NWCA SIgm
repens	NGre
saxatile	See AURINIA ***saxatilis***
serpyllifolium	MHig NHol NKay NTow NWCA SIgm
spinosum	MBro MTho NKay WAbe
– ***roseum*** AGM	CLew CMHG CShe ECha EFol ELan EPad EPot LHop MPla MWat NGre NMen NSla NTow NWCA SBla WAbe WHal WPat WPer WSHC WWin
tortuosum	MHig NMen WAbe WCla
wulfenianum	CMHG CNic MHig NPri NWCA WHil

AMANA See TULIPA

X AMARCRINUM (Liliaceae/Amaryllidaceae)

howardii	CMon NRog
¶ ***memoria-corsii***	LBow

X AMARINE (Liliaceae/Amaryllidaceae)

¶ 'Fletcheri'	CMon
tubergenii	LBow NRog
– 'Zwanenburg'	CAvo LBow NRog

X AMARYGIA (Liliaceae/Amaryllidaceae)

parkeri	LBow NRog
§ – 'Alba'	CAvo LBow NRog

AMARYLLIS (Liliaceae/Amaryllidaceae)

§ ***bella-donna***	CB&S CBro CHEx CMon EOrc EPar IHos LAma LBow LHop MBri MUlv NHol NRog SDeJ SIng WHil WThu
– 'Johannesburg'	CAvo LBow NRog
– 'Kimberley'	LBow NRog
– 'Major'	CAvo
– 'Parkeri Alba'	See X AMARYGIA ***parkeri*** 'Alba'

AMBROSIA (Compositae/Asteraceae)

¶ ***mexicana***	SHer

AMBROSINIA (Araceae)

bassii S&L 315	CMon

AMELANCHIER † (Rosaceae)

alnifolia	CBow CPle EPla ESim WWat
asiatica	ELan
'Ballerina' AGM	CB&S CBow CCla CDoC CPMA CSPN CSco EBre EHar ELan ESim LBre LNet MAsh MBri MGos MWat NBee SHBN SPer SSta WHCG WPat WWat
bartramiana	SSta
canadensis	Widely available
– 'Micropetala'	MUlv NHol
florida	See A. ***alnifolia semiintegrifolia***
x ***grandiflora*** 'Rubescens'	CPMA
laevis	CB&S CBot CChu CSco MBal NBee NNor SPer
lamarckii AGM	CB&S CBow CChu CCla CDoC CMHG CPMA CSco EBre EGol ELan ENot IDai IHos IOrc LBre LBuc MGos NBee NKay SHBN SHer SPer SReu SSta WDin WWat

pumila CB&S CLew EHic GDra LHop MBal MSte NHol NTow WAbe WNor WThu

AMICIA (Leguminosae/Papilionaceae)
zygomeris CBot CBrd CPle GBuc GCal GCra SMrm WSHC

AMMI (Umbelliferae/Apiaceae)
¶ *majus* LBlm MSal WHaw
¶ *visnaga* MSal

AMMOPHILA (Graminae)
¶ *arenaria* ECWi

AMOMUM (Zingiberaceae)
cardamomum See A. ***compactum***
§ *compactum* CNew CTro

AMOMYRTUS (Myrtaceae)
§ *luma* CLan CMHG CPle CTrw ISea SArc WBod

AMORPHA (Leguminosae/Papilionaceae)
canescens CB&S CPle ECro ESma MBel NRog NSti SSte
fruticosa CB&S CBot CBow CLew CPle ECro EOrc IOrc NRog

AMORPHOPHALLUS (Araceae)
bulbifer NRog

AMPELODESMOS (Gramineae/Poaceae)
mauritanicus EHoe ETPC GCal

AMPELOPSIS † (Vitaceae)
glandulosa
var. *brevipedunculata* CBra CHan EMil EOrc GAri SIgm SPer WCru WWat
§ – – 'Elegans' (v) CChu CCla CHan CMac EBre ECtt EHar ELan EPla EWri IJoh IMal LBre LHop LNet MBar MRav NBar NHol NRog SBra SHBN SHil SPer SPla SSta WDin WPat WSHC WStI
– – 'Tricolor' See A. ***g. b.*** 'Elegans'
henryana See PARTHENOCISSUS ***h.***
megalophylla CBot CGre ELan ISea SHil WCru
sempervirens hort. See CISSUS ***striata***
¶ *sinica* WCru
tricuspidata 'Veitchii' See PARTHENOCISSUS ***t.*** 'V.'

AMPHICOME See **INCARVILLEA**

AMSONIA (Apocynaceae)
ciliata EBee WCot WHow WMer WPer
orientalis **AGM** CGle EBee EBre ECha EMon EPar EPla ERea LBre LHop SWas WHal WOld WPer WWin
tabernaemontana CHan ECro ELan EMon EPot GBuc LGre MBel SUsu SWas WCot WPla
– var. *salicifolia* CGre CLew CShe EBre ECha ECro LBre SLga

AMYGDALUS See **PRUNUS**

ANACYCLUS (Compositae/Asteraceae)
pyrethrum GBar GPoy
– var. *depressus* CGle CLew CNic CSam EBre EFou ELan EMNN EMar ESis GAbr LBee LBre LHop MBel MFir MHig MRPP NHol NNor NNrw NWCA SBla SIng WCru WEas WHoo WOMN WPer WWin
– – 'Golden Gnome' EBar EHal NMir WHil
– – 'Silberkissen' NHol WHil

ANAGALLIS (Primulaceae)
* *alternifolia repens* CRDP GArf
arvensis ECWi EWFC GPoy MHew MSal WEas WWye
– var. *caerulea* EWFC
foemina ECWi MSal
linifolia See A. ***monelli***
§ *monelli* **AGM** CElw CRiv ELan EPot LBee SBla SMrm SUsu WCla WCru WOMN WPer WWin
– 'Sunrise' CRiv EPot MHlr MSto MTho SUsu WCot WCru WOMN
tenella ECWi NHar SFis
– 'Studland' **AGM** CRDP EPot GArf NGre NMen NTow NWCA SHer SIng WAbe WCru WOMN WPer

ANANAS (Bromeliaceae)
comosus var. *variegatus* CTbh MBri

ANAPHALIS (Compositae/Asteraceae)
alpicola EPot NCat NTow WHaw
cinnamomea See A. ***margaritacea c.***
margaritacea CBot CBow CLew CSco CTom ECtt EFou EJud GCHN GPlt LBlm MBri NBro NKay NOak NSti SPer WByw WHal
§ – var. *cinnamomea* CGle CHan CLew CSco ECED EJud ELan EMar NHol NKay SCro SHer WEas
– 'Neuschnee' ('New Snow') CHol CSam GAul NHol NPri NRoo SFis SPla WPer
– var. *yedoensis* **AGM** EBee ECha ECoo ECot EGle EPar MWat SDix WHil
§ *nepalensis*
var. *monocephala* CB&S CGle CMea ELan EMon MWat NSti SHer
– var. *monocephala* C&Mc 550 GCHN
nubigena See A. ***nepalensis monocephala***
sinica ssp. *morii* ECha EPla
§ *subrigida* ECou
§ *trinervis* CBow
triplinervis **AGM** CBos CBow CBre CGle CNic CShe EBre EFol EFou ELan ESiP GDra IDai LBre LGan NBro NHol NKay NNor SCro WByw WEas WHoo WOld WRus WTyr WWin
– var. *intermedia* See A. ***nepalensis***

– 'Sommerschnee' ('Summer Snow') AGM — CCla CKel CSco EBre ECha ECot ECtt EHal EOrc EPla LBre MBel MBri MHFP NCat NNor SHer SPer WElm WPer
yedoensis — See A. ***margaritacea y.***

ANARRHINUM (Scrophulariaceae)

bellidifolium — EBee EJud NPri WHil WPer

ANCHUSA (Boraginaceae)

angustissima — See A. ***leptophylla incana***
arvensis — MHew MSal
§ *azurea* — EHic MWil NBee NOrc WHal WPer
¶ – 'Blue Angel' — WHil
– 'Dropmore' — CBow CDoC EHal EMil SIde SRms WPer
– 'Feltham Pride' — CBot CBow CHol ECtt LAbb MBro NRoo NVic SFis WHoo WPer WTyr
– 'Little John' — CRDP CSco CSev EBre ECot EMil GCal LBre LWad NRoo SHer SPer SRms WMer WTyr
– 'Loddon Royalist' AGM — CB&S CCla CDoC CGle CKel CSco CSev CShe CSpe EBre ECED EFou ELan LBre LHop MBri MWat NBar NWyt SChu SPer WCra WMer WTyr
– 'Morning Glory' — CSco SFis
– 'Opal' — CGle CMGP CSco EBee ECot ECro EFou GCal MWat NRoo SPer
– 'Royal Blue' — CPou ECro GAbr WMer
barrelieri — WPer
caespitosa hort. — See A. ***leptophylla incana***
caespitosa AGM — EBre ELan EPad EPot LBre LHop NHar WAbe WThu
capensis — WPer
italica — See A. ***azurea***
laxiflora — See BORAGO ***pygmaea***
§ *leptophylla* ssp. *incana* — EMon SHer WCru WHaw
myosotidiflora — See BRUNNERA ***macrophylla***
officinalis — CArn CSFH EJud EWFC LHol MHew MSal SIde
sempervirens — See PENTAGLOTTIS ***sempervirens***

ANDROCYMBIUM (Liliaceae/Colchicaceae))

europaeum MS 510 — CMon
¶ *gramineum* SB&L 26 — CMon
punicum S&L 325 — CMon

ANDROMEDA (Ericaceae)

glaucophylla — IOrc MBar WDav
polifolia — CBow CMHG CRiv CSam EBre EPla IOrc LBre NBar SLon WBod
– 'Alba' — EBre ELan ESis GAbr GArf LBre MBal MBar MBlu MGos MHig MPla NHar NHol NRya SBod SGil SHer SIng SSta WAbe WDav WPat WThu
– 'Compacta' AGM — EBre ELan EMNN EPot ESis GCHN LBre MBal MBar MBlu MBri MGos MPla NHar NMen NRya SChu SGil SHer SIng SPer SReu WPat WWin
– 'Grandiflora' — ITim MAsh MBal MGos NNrd SBod SPer WThu
– 'Hayachine' — GArf NHol
– 'Kiri-Kaming' — ELan MAsh MBal MBri MGos MHig SSta WAbe WPat
– 'Macrophylla' AGM — EPot ESis GAbr GArf GDra ITim MBal MHig NHar SSta WAbe WPat WThu
– 'Major' — MBal
– 'Minima' — MBal
– 'Nana' — ELan EPot GAbr LNet MAsh MGos MHig SPer STre WDav WRus WStI WWat WWeb
– 'Nikko' — EBar IJoh MBal MBar MGos MHig NHar NHol SHer WPat
¶ – 'Red King' — MBlu
– 'Red Winter' — CNic CRos LRHS
– 'Shibutsu' — GArf MGos MPla NHol SPer SSta

ANDROPOGON (Gramineae/Poaceae)

gerardii — EMon EPla ETPC WPer
scoparius — See SCHIZACHYRIUM ***scoparium***

ANDROSACE (Primulaceae)

albana — CNic NHol NWCA
armeniaca macrantha — MHig NGre NWCA
¶ *barbulata* — CNic GCHN
carnea — CMea CNic CWes EMNN EPot GCHN LBee MCas MTho NHar NHol NMen SIng WCla WHal
– *alba* — CNic LBee MBro NGre NHar NHol NWCA WDav WHoo WThu
– 'Andorra' — GArf
– ssp. *brigantiaca* — ESma GTou MCas MHig NGre NHar NHol NKay NMen NRed NWCA SIng WAbe WDav
– var. *halleri* — See A. ***c. rosea***
– ssp. *laggeri* AGM — EMNN EPot GTou NHar NWCA
– x *pyrenaica* — EPot GCHN GDra MHig NHar NMen SIng WAbe WDav
§ *carnea* ssp. *rosea* AGM — ESma GDra GTou MCas NHol NTow NWCA WCla
– ssp. *rosea* x ssp. *carnea laggeri* — NHol
ciliata — EPot GTou MCas NMen NSla NTow WAbe
cylindrica — EPot GCHN GDra GTou LBee MCas NGre NHar NHol NMen NNrd NWCA SBla SIng WDav
– x *hirtella* — CNic EPot GDra NGre NHar NWCA SIng WAbe
delavayi — EPot ITim NWCA
elongata — EBar
geraniifolia — CRDP ECha GCHN MNFA MTho
globifera — EPot
hausmannii — GCHN GTou NGre NTow
hedraeantha — CNic EPot NGre NHar NHol WAbe WDav
¶ x *heeri* — GTou
– 'Alba' — EPot EWes GCHN GCLN ITim WDav
helvetica — GTou
hirtella — CNic EPot GCHN GTou MRPP NGre NHar NTow NWCA SIng WDav
jacquemontii — See A. ***villosa jacquemontii***
lactea — CNic GCHN GTou LHop NGre NNrd SMrm WAbe
§ *lactiflora* — GTou

laevigata — EPad EPot GCLN NSla
– var. *ciliolata* — EPad GTou NWCA
lanuginosa AGM — CGle CLew CMHG CRiv CShe ELan EPad GMac LBee LHop MBro MHig MWat NMen NRoo SBla SIng SWas WAbe WHil WOMN WWin
– 'Leichtlinii' — EHic WThu
– 'Wisley Variety' — SIgm
lehmannii EMAK 951 — NMen
limprichtii — See A. ***sarmentosa watkinsii***
mathildae — GArf GTou NHar NHol NNrd NTow SIng WDav
– x *carnea* — NMen
microphylla — See A. ***mucronifolia*** Walt
mollis — See A. ***sarmentosa yunnanensis***
montana — EPad WAbe
¶ *mucronifolia* CHP&W 296 — NWCA
mucronifolia hort. — See A. ***sempervivoïdes***
§ *mucronifolia* Watt — GArf GTou ITim NGre
muscoidea — MHig NTow NWCA
¶ *muscoïdea* C&R 188 — GTou
nivalis — NSla NTow
¶ – K 91.3269 — WDav
obtusifolia — NNrd
¶ *occidentalis* — CNic
primuloïdes 'Salmon's Variety' — See A. ***sarmentosa*** 'S.V.'
primuloïdes Duby — CWes NCat SFis WDav
primuloïdes hort. — See A. ***sarmentosa***
pubescens — CNic EPot GCHN GDra GTou LBee MFos NHar NHol SBla SIng WDav
pyrenaica — CNic EPot GCHN GTou ITim NGre NHar NHol NTow NWCA SBla SIng WAbe WThu
rotundifolia — CNic EPot ESma GCHN GTou LBee NHol WCru
salicifolia — See A. ***lactiflora***
§ *sarmentosa* AGM — CLew CNic EBro ELan EPar GTou ITim LBee MBro MFir MHig MWat NGre NMen NNrd NRya SChu SHer SSmi WAbe WCla WEas WHal WHoo
– 'Brilliant' — CNic ELan
– 'Chumbyi' — CLew CRDP CRiv ESis MBro MCas MFos NHar NHol NKay NTow NWCA SBla SHer SIng WOMN WPat WThu WTyr
– *monstrosa* — NHol
§ – 'Salmon's Variety' — CMea CWes MCas NTow SIgm
– 'Sherriff's' — CGle CMHG CShe EPot GCHN MBro MCas NHar NTow SBla SIgm SIng WDav WHal WPat
§ – var. *watkinsii* — EPot MBro NHar NMen SIng WDav WThu
§ – var. *yunnanensis* — EPot MBro MHig NHar NHol NTow SIng WDav
sempervivoïdes AGM — CLew EBro ECha ELan EPot GCHN GDra LBee MBro MCas MHig NGre NHar NHed NMen NRed NWCA SBod SHer SIgm SIng WAbe WDav WHil WHoo WOMN WPat WThu WWin
septentrionalis puberulenta — NHol WHil
strigillosa — CNic EPad
studiosorum — GCHN
* *tridentata* — WDav
vandellii — CNic EPot GCHN GTou MHig NGre NHar NHol NTow NWCA WAbe
villosa — MHig WDav
– var. *arachnoidea* 'Superba' — EPot
§ – var. *jacquemontii* — CMea CNic CWes EPot GArf MHig NHar NNrw NRya NTow SBla SHer SIgm WAbe WDav WThu
– – pink — EPot NHol
vitaliana — See VITALIANA ***primuliflora***
watkinsii — See A. ***sarmentosa watkinsii***

ANDRYALA (Compositae/Asteraceae)

agardhii — EFol ESis MCas MFos MHig NHol NTow NWCA
lanata — See HIERACIUM ***lanatum***

ANEMARRHENA (Liliaceae/Asphodelaceae)

¶ *asphodeloïdes* — MSal

ANEMIA (Schizaeaceae)

phyllitidis — NMar

ANEMONE † (Ranunculaceae)

altaica — EBar NNrd NRoo WHaw WHil WOld
¶ 'Andrea Atkinson' — EBee
apennina AGM — CBro EPar NTow SCro SIng SPou
– CE&H 538 — LRHS
– var. *albiflora* — SPou WChr
baicalensis — EHic GLil NHol SUsu
baldensis — CGle CPou CSam ECro EPot ESis LBee LHop MNFA NHol NMen NNrd NOak NWCA SHer WOMN
biarmiensis — See A. ***narcissifolia b.***
blanda AGM — CBow EFou EOrc GPlt LAma LBow LHop MBri MBro MHig NNrd NRog NRya SChu SHer WHil WPat WPer
– 'Atrocaerulea' — See A. ***b.*** 'Ingramii'
– blue — CAvo CBro CMea CRiv ELan EPot ETub LAma MBri MHlr MNFA SHer WCru WPat
– 'Blue Mist' — NNor
¶ – 'Blue Star' — MS&S
– 'Charmer' — CCla EPar EPot ETub NMen NNrd SIng WPat
§ – 'Ingramii' AGM — CCla ELan EPar LAma MBal NNrd NRog SIng WHoo WPat
– 'Pink Star' — CBro CMea CRiv EPot LAma LBow MHig NBir NNor NRog WHoo
– 'Radar' AGM — CAvo CBro ELan EPar EPot ETub LAma LBow NBir NRog SHer WChr WPat
– var. *rosea* AGM — CAvo EFou ELan ETub LAma NEgg WCru WPer
– 'Violet Star' — CBro EPot SHer
– 'White Splendour' AGM — CAvo CBro CCla CGle CMea ECha EFou ELan EOrc EPar EPot ETub LAma LBow MHig NMen NRog SChu SHer SIng WPat WPer
canadensis — CCla CNic WHaw
caroliniana — CGle EBee EPot ESis GBuc MNFA NRoo NTow SHer

caucasica	EPot
¶ ***cernua***	ESis
coronaria De Caen Group	CRDP CSut ETub LAma WHil
– – 'Die Braut' ('The Bride')	CGle MWBu NRog
– – forms	NRog
♦– – 'His Excellency'	See A. ***c.*** 'Hollandia'
§ – – 'Hollandia'	MWBu
– – 'Mister Fokker'	LAma MWBu NRog WHil
– – 'The Governor'	NRog
– Mona Lisa Group 'Sylphide'	MWBu NRog
– Saint Brigid Group	CSut ETub LAma MBri NRog SApp SDeJ SIng
– – 'Lord Lieutenant'	NRog
– – 'Mount Everest'	ETub
– – 'The Admiral'	NRog
– Saint Piran Group	SDeJ
¶ ***crinita***	WThi
cylindrica	CGle EMar EMon MNFA NHol WCru
decapetala	GCal
drummondii	MHig NWCA WCla
flaccida	CBro CRDP EPot LGre SIng
x ***fulgens***	ECha LAma NWCA SRms
– 'Annulata Grandiflora'	CBro CMon
– 'Multipetala'	CBro NRog
– Saint Bavo Group	CBro LAma
globosa	See A. ***multifida***
hepatica	See HEPATICA ***nobilis***
§ ***hortensis***	CMon ECro WWat
– MS 958	CMon
– ***alba***	CMon
hupehensis	CBos CBot CBow CCla LWad NOrc SFis WCot
§ – 'Bowles' Pink'	CRDP MBri MUlv MWat WCot
– 'Eugenie'	CGle
– 'Hadspen Abundance' **AGM**	CDec CHad CRDP EBee ECha ELun GCal GMac LGre MArl NBir NTow SAxl SBla WAbb
– var. ***japonica***	CBos CGle CHan CPou CRDP GCal LGro NMir NNor WCru WEas WRus
§ – – 'Bressingham Glow'	CMHG CSco CShe EBre EGol ELan ELun EOrc EPot LBre LHop MBri MPit MRav NBar NHol NOrc NRoo NVic SHer SPer WAbb WAbe WOld WTyr
§ – – 'Prinz Heinrich' **AGM**	CB&S CCla CHad CHol ECha EFou LGre LHop MBri MBro NJap SApp SAxl SHer SPer SPla WAbe WHoo WOld
– 'Praecox'	CMGP CMea EBee ECro EFou MBri NHol NSti SCro SMrm WAbb WAbe WHal WHow
– 'Rosenschale'	GCal MBal
– 'September Charm' **AGM**	CB&S CBow CCla CDoC ECha EFol EFou EGol ELan EOrc MBri NBar NSti SChu SDix SPer SPla
– 'Splendens'	CBow EFou WAbb WHal
§ x ***hybrida***	CAvo CBos CGle IHos MBro NBar NOak SChu SPla WAbe WCru WHil WHoo WOld
– 'Alba' (hort.(UK))	See A. x ***h.*** 'Honorine Jobert'
– 'Alba' (hort.(USA))	See A. x ***h.*** 'Lady Ardilaun'
– 'Alba Dura'	WCot
– 'Bowles' Pink'	See A. ***hupehensis*** 'B.P.'
– 'Bresssingham Glow'	See A. ***hupehensis japonica*** 'B.G.'
– 'Coupe d'Argent'	CSco GCal
– 'Elegans'	EFou
§ – 'Géante des Blanches' **AGM**	CPou ECro ECtt EFou NNor NRoo SApp SPer
§ – 'Honorine Jobert' **AGM**	Widely available
– 'Königin Charlotte' ('Queen Charlotte') **AGM**	Widely available
– 'Kriemhilde'	MHlr NJap WCot
– 'Lady Gilmour'	See A. x ***h.*** 'Margarete'
– 'Loreley'	CMea WCot
– 'Luise Uhink'	CCla CDoC CGle CPou CSco EBre LBre NBir WCot WEas
§ – 'Margarete'	CCla CDec CMGP CPou CRDP EBre ECro ECtt EFou EGol ELan EOrc LBre MWat NBir NCat NHol NJap SChu SCro SPer WHoo WTyr
– 'Max Vogel'	CDoC CSco
– 'Monterosa'	CGle CPou CRDP ECro EOrc GCal MBal MHlr NBar NBir WCot
– 'Pamina'	CGle GCal MBri WHoo WOld
– 'Prinz Heinrich' ('Prince Henry')	See A. ***hupehensis japonica*** 'P.H.'
– 'Profusion'	MHlr WCot WOld WRus
– 'Richard Ahrens'	CCla CMGP EBee ECro EGle EOrc LBuc LHop MBri MMil NCat NHol SAxl SCro SMrm SUsu SWas WAbe
§ – 'Superba'	SBla WKif
– 'Whirlwind' ('Wirbelwind')	CB&S CDoC CGle CMea CRDP EFou EGol ELan EOrc GCal LHop MBel MBri NHol NJap NRoo NSti SApp SChu SCro SHer SPer SUsu WAbe WCot WCru WHoo WOld WRus WWat
– 'White Queen'	See A. x ***h.*** 'Géante des Blanches'
japonica	See AA. x ***hybrida, hupehensis***
x ***lesseri***	Widely available
leveillei	GLil LGre NHol WDav
§ x ***lipsiensis***	CBro CMon CRDP ECha EPar EPot GCHN LGre MNFA MTho NGar NHol NNrd NTow SAxl SWas WAbe WChr WThu
– 'Pallida'	CRDP MNFA SPou
N ***magellanica*** hort.	See A. ***multifida***
mexicana	WHil
§ ***multifida***	Widely available
– 'Major'	CLew CNic LGan LGre MTol NHol NKay SBla SUsu SWas WSun
– red	NRoo SSvw WDav WHil
♦ ***narcissiflora***	See A. ***narcissifolia***
§ ***narcissifolia***	CPou LGan LGre NHar
– ssp. ***biarmiensis***	CNic
nemorosa **AGM**	CBro CGle CHol CKin CRDP ECWi EPar EPot EWFC GPlt LAma LBow LGan MBal MHew MSal NGar NHar NHol NLan SHer SIng WGwy WMer WShi

N– 'Alba Plena'	CAvo CBos CBro CLew CMil CRDP ECha EPot GMac MHig NNrd NRar SAxl SIng WAbb WChr WCru WEas WRus
– 'Allenii' AGM	CAvo CBro ECha EOrc EPot LGre MBal MCas MNFA NGar NHar NRya NTow SIng SWas WAbe WChr WCru WMar
– 'Atrocaerulea'	EPar EPot MNFA NGar NHol
– 'Blue Beauty'	EPot MBal NGar NHol NNrd SAxl SPou
– 'Blue Bonnet'	CChu CElw GBuc
– 'Blue Queen'	EPot
– 'Bowles' Purple'	EPar EPot GAbr NGar NRya NTow SWas WAbe WChr WMar
– 'Bracteata Pleniflora'	EPot LHop MBal NGar
¶ – 'Bracteata, New Zealand'	WAbe
– 'Caerulea'	EPot
– 'Cedric's Pink'	CRDP
– 'Celestial'	SPou
– 'Danica'	MBal
¶ – 'Dee Day'	CRDP SPou
– 'Flore Pleno'	EOrc EPar GArf MBal NGar WAbe
– forms	CMon
– 'Green Fingers'	EPot LGre SPou WChr
– 'Hannah Gubbay'	EPar MBal SIng
– 'Hilda'	EPar EPot MBal NNrd NRya
– 'Leeds' Variety' AGM	CRDP EPot LGre NGar NHar NHol SBla SPou WChr
– 'Lychette'	EPar EPot LGre MBal
– 'Monstrosa'	EPar EPot NNrd
– 'Pentre Pink'	SPou WAbe WChr
¶ – pink	LGre
– 'Robinsoniana' AGM	CBro CChu CGle CHad CRDP ECha EPar EPot LBow LGre MBal MBro MCas MHig MNFA MTho NGar NHol NRya NSti NTow SBla SIng WAbe
– 'Rosea'	CGle EPot LAma NHol WAbe WChr
– 'Royal Blue'	CNic CRDP EPot LAma NHol SBla SWas WAbe
– 'Vestal' AGM	CGle EPot LGre MNFA NGar NMen SBla SPou WBon
– 'Virescens'	NGar WAbe
– 'Viridiflora'	CRDP LGre MTho WChr WCru
– 'Wilks' White'	EPar EPot MBal
– 'Wyatt's Pink'	LGre WAbe
– x *ranunculoïdes*	See A. x ***lipsiensis***
obtusiloba	CRDP GDra GTou NHar SBla
– ***alba***	CRDP GDra NHar NHol SBla
¶ ***palmata***	SWas WOMN
– MS 413	CMon
– 'Alba'	CMon
parviflora	EPot ESis ESma WHaw
patens	See PULSATILLA ***p.***
pavonina	LGre NBir SIng SWas
– var. ***ocellata*** JCA 161.901	CNic
polyanthes	WThi
pseudoaltaica	EPot
pulsatilla	See PULSATILLA ***vulgaris***
ranunculoïdes AGM	CAvo CBro CMon CRDP EPar EPot GArf LAma MHig MNFA NGar NHar NHol NKay NNrd NSti NTow SIng WAbe WChr WCru WEas WOMN
– 'Pleniflora'	ECha EPar EPot NGar WChr WMar
rivularis	Widely available
rupicola	GCra NBir NHol
x ***seemannii***	See A. x ***lipsiensis***
* ***sherriffii***	WHaw
sp. CLD 573	NHol
stellata	See A. ***hortensis***
sulphurea	See PULSATILLA ***alpina apiifolia***
sylvestris	CCla CGle CHan CRDP ECha ECro ELun EPar EPot LGan MBri MNFA MSal NBir NHol NRoo NSti SFis SIng SPer WHal WHil WRus WWin
tetrasepala	GCra NHol
§ ***tomentosa***	CBow CGle CMGP ECha EHic GLil MSte NHol NRoo NSti SCro SMrm WCot WEas WHow
– 'Robustissima'	CDoC CGle CSco ECro EFou EGol EHic EPla GCal MBri MBro SAxl SPla WAbb WMer WRus
¶ – 'September Glanz'	MUlv
¶ – 'Serenade'	MUlv
trifolia	CRDP ECha EPot MBal NHol NMen SBla SPou SUsu SWas WAbe
¶ – pink	SPou
trullifolia SBEC 797	GTou NHol NTow
– ***alba***	NTow
tschernjaewii	EPot
vernalis	See PULSATILLA ***vernalis***
virginiana	ECro EWoo GLil MSte NHol WCru
vitifolia De Candolle	CBos ECro ESma GGar LGre SBla
¶ – B&SWJ 120A	WCru
– C&Mc 43	CGle MBro
vitifolia hort.	See A. ***tomentosa***

ANEMONELLA (Ranunculaceae)

thalictroïdes	CRDP EPar LAma LGre NGar NHar NRog NTow SBla SWas WAbe
¶ – 'Atlas Double'	NRog
¶ – 'Cameo'	NRog
– pink	CRDP NRog
– semi-double white	CRDP

ANEMONOPSIS (Ranunculaceae)

macrophylla	CBos CPou CRDP EBre ECha ECro GCra GTou LBre LGre MUlv NTow SBla WEas WOMN

ANEMOPAEGMA (Bignoniaceae)

¶ ***chamberlaynii***	CTro

ANETHUM (Umbelliferae/Apiaceae)

graveolens	CArn EHer GPoy IEde LHol MChe MHew MPit SHer SIde WPer
– 'Dukat'	CSFH GPoy SHer

ANGELICA (Umbelliferae/Apiaceae)

archangelica	CArn CBow CGle CSFH CSco CSev ECha EEls EFou EHer ELan EMar Effi GAbr GPoy IEde LHol MBri MChe MHew NBro NFai NRoo SChu SHer SIde WOak WPer WWye
atropurpurea	MSal WHaw

curtisii	See A. ***triquinata***
gigas	CBot CGle CRDP ECha EMon LGre MSte SIgm SPou WCot WHal WHer
montana	See A. ***sylvestris***
¶ *pachycarpa*	WCot
§ *sylvestris*	CArn CKin GBar MHew MSal MWil WHer
¶ – pink	WBon
§ *triquinata*	MSal

ANIGOZANTHOS (Haemodoraceae)

flavidus	CHan CSev MBri WThi
– red	CRDP CTro
– yellow	LHil
manglesii AGM	CTro WPer
– 'Bush Dawn'	CB&S
preissii	LBlm

ANISODONTEA (Malvaceae)

capensis	CB&S CBar CBrk CHad CSpe CTro ELan ERea ESis ESma IBlr IMal LHil LHop MPla NBrk SChu SFis SGil SHer SMrm WBod WEas WWin
* *hugeli*	SMrm
§ x *hypomandarum*	CElw CMHG CSev CTre ECtt EOrc LAbb LBlm MBel MUlv NPer NRar NTow SMad SUsu WAbe WHal WOMN WOld WPer WRus
malvastroïdes	CBrk GCal LHil WCot
scabrosa	CAbb CChe CDoC SLon

ANISOTOME (Umbelliferae/Apiaceae)

imbricata	GDra

ANNONA (Annonaceae)

cherimola	CTro

ANODA (Malvaceae)

¶ *crenatiflora*	EBee
¶ *cristata*	WHaw
– 'Opal Cup'	EMon

ANOIGANTHUS See CYRTANTHUS

ANOMATHECA (Iridaceae)

cruenta	See A. ***laxa***
§ *laxa*	CAvo CBro CFee CNic CRDP ECha ELan EPot LBee LGre LHop MFir MFos MTho NGar SChu SDix SHer WAbe WCla WCru WHal WOMN WPat WPer WWin
– var. *alba*	CAvo CRDP ELan EPot LBee LBlm LGre MPit SChu SHer WAbe WHoo WOMN WThu
– 'Joan Evans'	EPot
moisii	WCru
viridis	CAvo CMon LBow SSad

ANOPTERUS (Escalloniaceae)

glandulosus	CHEx IBlr

ANREDERA (Basellaceae)

§ *cordifolia*	LBow LHop NHex SLMG WCot

ANTENNARIA (Compositae/Asteraceae)

aprica	See A. ***parvifolia***
¶ *dimorpha*	SIng
dioica	CRiv ECro ELan EPad GCHN GPoy LHol MBro MFir MHew SHer WCla WHal WHil WHoo WWye
– 'Alba'	EHoe
¶ – 'Alex Duguid'	SBla
– 'Aprica'	See A. ***parvifolia***
§ – var. *hyperborea*	CLew LGro MNFA SSmi WAbe
– 'Minima'	CLew EPot GDra MHig MPla MWat NHar NHol NMen NNrd SIng
*– *nana*	GTou
– 'Nyewoods Variety'	CLew CNic EPot GDra MHig NHol NTow
– red	SIng WDav
– *rosea*	See A. ***rosea***
*– 'Rubra'	ECha GAri GLil NHol NKay SBla SHer SSmi WAbe WHen
– *tomentosa*	See A. ***d. hyperborea***
macrophylla	WEas
macrophylla hort.	See A. ***microphylla***
neglecta var. *gaspensis*	NHol
§ *parvifolia*	CNic EPot ESis GCHN GDra LBee MBar MHig MPla NHar NNrd NSti SBod SIng WCla WHil WPer WWin
– *rosea*	See A. ***rosea***
rosea AGM	CLew CMHG CRiv EBre EMNN GArf GPlt IDai LBee LBre LGan MBar MCas MFir MPla NEgg NHar NHol NKay NMen NNor NWCA SBod SIng SRms SSmi WHal WPat WPer WWin
– 'Plena'	NKay

ANTHEMIS (Compositae/Asteraceae)

aïzoön	See ACHILLEA ***ageratifolia a.***
¶ *arvensis*	ECWi
biebersteinii	See A. ***marschalliana***
carpatica	CGle ECha GCHN LGre NBro SMrm
cretica	EBee NTow SWas
'Eva'	NCat WEas WOld
frutescens	See ARGYRANTHEMUM ***frutescens***
§ *marschalliana*	CGle CHan CShe ECha ELan EPot ESis LBee LHil MHig NEgg NKay NNor NNrd NOak SIgm SSmi WAbe WHil WPer
montana	See A. ***cretica cretica***
nobilis	See CHAMAEMELUM ***nobile***
punctata ssp. *cupaniana* AGM	Widely available
– – 'Nana'	NPer
rudolphiana	See A. ***marschalliana***
sancti-johannis	CBow CGle CLew CSFH CSam CSco EBar EBre EMon LBre MBri MFir MHew NBro NHol NOak NPer NTow SHer SMad SPer WHal WHil WPer

'Tetworth'	ECha ELan EMon MHlr MMil NPer WCot
tinctoria	CArn CGle CSFH ECED EJud ELan EMon EWFC GPoy LHol MBel MChe MHew MPit NBee NKay NPer SIde WAbe WByw WSun WWin WWye
– 'Alba'	CGle ECha EFol EHal EMar EMon GCal LBlm LGre MBel NCat NPer NRoo SChu WCot WHen WRus
*– 'Compacta'	EOrc
– 'E C Buxton'	Widely available
N– 'Grallach Gold'	CDoC CGle ECha EMon EOrc ESma IDai MBel MUlv MWat NCat NHol NPer SCro SFis SHer WEas WMer WOld
– 'Kelwayi'	CBow CGle CHol CRiv EBar ECtt ESma GAbr GCHN LHop MFir NBro NFai NMir NPer NRoo NTow SHer SPla SSvw WHal WHen WPer WSun
– 'Powis White'	CHan
– 'Pride of Grallach'	EMon GCal GMac
– 'Sauce Hollandaise'	CBre CGle ECtt EFou EHal EMon EOrc ESma EWll GAbr GCal LBlm LRHS MBel MFir MMil MSte NBro NCat NPer NSti SAxl SChu SFis SHer SMrm WByw WHen WOld WSun
– 'Wargrave'	CBre CElw CGle CLew CSam ECha ECtt EFol EFou ELan EMon GAbr GMac MUlv MWat NBro NFai NPer SAxl SChu SDix SFis SMrm SSvw WRus WSun
tuberculata	EBre LBre MCas SBla SIng SMrm SUsu

ANTHERICUM † (Liliaceae/Anthericaceae)

algeriense	See A. ***liliago major***
baeticum	CMon EPot WDav
liliago AGM	CBro CGle CLew EBul ECED ELan ESis GCal GDra LBee LGan LHop MSte NRoo SMrm SUsu WCla WHow WOld WPer
§ – var. ***major***	CAvo ECha EPot GDra IBlr LGre WDav WOld
ramosum	CMon EBul ECha ELan EMon GDra LGre MBro NHol NWCA WCla WOMN WPer
– JCA 166.300	CAvo WDav
– ***plumosum***	CBro

ANTHOCERCIS (Solanaceae)

See Plant Deletions

ANTHOLYZA (Iridaceae)

coccinea	See CROCOSMIA ***paniculata***
paniculata	See CROCOSMIA ***paniculata***

ANTHOXANTHUM (Gramineae/Poaceae)

odoratum	CSFH GBar GPoy MWil SIde

ANTHRISCUS (Umbelliferae/Apiaceae)

cerefolium	CArn CSFH CSev EJud GPoy IEde ILis LHol MChe MHew SHer SIde WOak WPer
sylvestris	ECWi

– 'Moonlight Night'	EHoe
– 'Ravenswing'	CBot CElw CGle CHad CRDP ECoo EMar EMon EPla GBri LBlm LGre LHil LHop LRHS MBri MUlv NBir NNrw NSti SAxl SFis SIgm SMad SUsu WByw WCHb WCot WDav WRus

ANTHURIUM (Araceae)

amazonicum	MBri
andreanum	MBri
– 'Acropolis'	MBri
– 'Rose'	See A. x ***ferrierense*** 'Roseum'
cordatum	See A. ***leuconeurum***
'Flamingo'	MBri
scherzerianum	MBri
– 'Rosemarie'	MBri

ANTHYLLIS (Leguminosae/Papilionaceae)

hermanniae	CHan CMHG CSam MAll MCas SHil WAbe
– ***compacta***	See A. ***h.*** 'Minor'
– 'Minor'	EPot NMen NTow WDav
– prostrate form	LGre
montana	CLew ELan GPlt LHil WHaw
– 'Rubra' AGM	ECoo EGle EPot GTou MRPP NKay NTow SHer WOMN WWin
– 'Rubra Compacta'	WThu
vulneraria	CKin ECWi EWFC GTou MChe MHew NKay NLan NMir NPri WCla WNdy WPer
– var. ***coccinea***	CMHG CNic EBar EFol GAbr MSte MSto MTho NHol NNrd NTow NWCA SUsu WAbe WHil WHoo
¶ – var. ***iberica***	GLil

ANTIGONON (Polygonaceae)

leptopus	CNew CTro SLMG

ANTIRRHINUM (Scrophulariaceae)

asarina	See ASARINA ***procumbens***
'Black Prince'	CHad LCot
braun-blanquetii	CBow EBee ECro ELan GAbr GGar LBlm LCot LHop MDHE MSto MTol NCat SIde SMrm SOkh WHaw WHil
glutinosum	See A. ***hispanicum hispanicum***
§ ***hispanicum***	CGle GCal MDHE NRar WCla WOMN
§ – ssp. ***hispanicum roseum***	CSam CSpe CVer ELan MSto NRar NTow WCot WOld WPer
majus ssp. ***linkianum***	ECro LHop MSto WOMN WOld
– 'Taff's White' (v)	CBot CElw CRDP LGre MTho SMrm SUsu WHal WHil WRus
molle	CBot CElw CSpe ECro ELan EOrc ERom ESis GCal GTou LHop MSte MSto MTho NBir NFai NMen NPer NTow NWCA SIng SUsu WCru WHal WPer
– pink	CElw CRiv EOrc GCal WCru
pulverulentum	CCMG CSam LGre LHop MArl MDHE MSto SMrm WEas WKif WOMN
sempervirens	CRiv EPad MSto SOkh SWas WOMN

¶ *siculum* WHaw

APHANES (Rosaceae)

§ *arvensis* GPoy MHew MSal NHex WWye

APHELANDRA (Acanthaceae)

alexandri SLMG
squarrosa (v) MBri
– 'Dania' (v) MBri

APHYLLANTHES (Liliaceae/Aphyllanthaceae)

monspeliensis CLew MCas MHig

APIOS (Leguminosae/Papilionaceae)

§ *americana* EMon WCru WSHC
tuberosa See A. ***americana***

APIUM (Umbelliferae/Apiaceae)

graveolens EHer EJud GPoy MSal SIde
nodiflorum ECWi

APOCYNUM (Apocynaceae)

androsaemifolium MSal
cannabinum CArn GPoy MSal

APONOGETON (Aponogetonaceae)

distachyos CBen CHEx CRDP CRow CWGN EBre EHon ELan EMFW EWav IMal LBre LMay MBal MSta NDea SHer SHig SLon SWat SWyc WChe WHol
krausseanus See A. ***desertorum***

APPLE See MALUS *domestica*

APPLE, Crab See MALUS

APRICOT See PRUNUS *armeniaca*

APTENIA (Aizoaceae)

cordifolia CHEx CSev LHil NPer
– 'Variegata' CBrk LHil

AQUILEGIA † (Ranunculaceae)

akitensis hort. See A. ***flabellata pumila***
alpina CBot CBow CCla CHad CMea CNic CShe ECtt EDra ELan ESis GAbr GCHN GTou LHil NBee NHol NNor SGil SPer SSvw WCla WDav WHal WHen WPer WStI WTyn WWin WWye
– 'Alba' NOak
*– 'Carl Ziepke' EDra GCal
– 'Hensol Harebell' See A. 'H.H.'
'Alpine Blue' CSco SIde
amaliae See A. ***ottonis a.***
§ *atrata* CGle CHad CMea ECro EDra ESis GAbr GCHN MHig MSte NOak WEas WHal WPer WTyn
aurea EDra
baicalensis See A. ***vulgaris*** Baicalensis Group
barnebyi CPou EDra GCra LGre MSto NWCA WDav
bertolonii AGM CFee CGle CLew CNic CRiv EDra EPot GAbr GMac GTou LBee LHop MBro NHar NMen NOak NRoo SBla SSmi SWas WAbe WHoo WTyn
– *alba* NWCA
– 'Blue Berry' ESis MBro MPla WHoo
'Biedermeier' CBow EDra GMac MTol NMir NOrc SFis SHer WDav WHil WPer
'Blue Berry' NHar WDav WOMN
'Blue Spurs' EDra
buergeriana CPou EDra GCra GGar GMac NHol WDav WPer
¶ – f. *flavescens* MSto
caerulea AGM ECro EDra EPad GAri GCHN GDra LAbb NCat NWyt SIgm WDav WPla WTyn
– 'Kristall' WMer
– 'Mrs Nicholls' MBri WMer
– var. *ochroleuca* EDra GCHN
canadensis AGM CBoy CGle CMil EBar EBre EDra ELan EPad ESma GAbr GDra GMac LBre MBal MHew MSal NBir NBro NGre NOak NSti SFis SSte WEas WHer WPer WTyn
– 'Nana' CNic CSam EDra GArf GBuc MSte MSto NHol
cazorlensis See A. ***pyrenaica c.***
'Celestial Blue' ELan
¶ *chaplinei* MSto NHol
chrysantha EDra EPad ESma GCHN GCal GCra LGre MNFA NHar NPri SChu SIgm WDav WPer WRus WTyn
– var. *chaplinei* CBot ECro EDra GAul GCal GMac LGre NBir NHol WCra
– double dark red CMil WTyn
– 'Yellow Queen' CMil EDra EFou GCal NHol WHil
clematiflora See A. ***vulgaris stellata***
'Crimson Star' CBow CCla CKel CSco EBre EDra ELan LBre NBar NWyt SPer SUsu
desertorum CNic NHar WAbe WDav
dinarica EDra
discolor CLew CMea CNic CRiv EDra ESis GAbr GDra MBro MPla NGre NHed NKay NRoo NTow NWCA SIng WDav WOMN WPat WPer WThu
¶ 'Dove' NHol
'Dragonfly' CB&S CBow GAbr GAri LAbb LWad MBri MPit MRav NMir NOak NVic WPer WRus WSun WTyn
¶ 'Dwarf Fairyland' WTyn
'Eastgrove' WEas
ecalcarata See SEMIAQUILEGIA ***ecalcarata***
einseleana CBot EDra MNFA SHer WHaw
elegantula CMea ESis GDra LGre MSto NHar WHal WOMN WPer
¶ – JJA 11390 SIgm
eximia EDra
flabellata AGM CGle CHad CNic EDra GAri GCHN GPlt NMen WHal WPat WPer WPla WTyn
§ – f. *alba* CBot ELan GCHN GGar GTou NGre NHol NWCA SBla WEas
¶ – 'Blue Angel' WPer

– 'Ministar'	CNic EBar EBre EDra EFou ESis GLil LBre MRav NMen NMir NOak NRoo SHer WHil WHoo WPer WWin
– var. ***nana***	See A. ***f. pumila***
– 'Nana Alba'	See A. ***f. pumila alba***
§ – var. ***pumila*** AGM	Widely available
– – ***alba*** AGM	CBot CGle EBar EBre ECha EDra EFol ESis GCal GDra LBee LBre LHop MBal MBro MFos MHig MSte NHol NNrd NRoo NSti SBla SGil SHer SIng WRus WTyn WWin
– – f. ***kurilensis***	GDra LBlm MSte NKay NNrd WCla
– – Mount Hakkado form	EDra
*– 'White Angel'	EFou WPer
flavescens	EDra NBrk WPer
formosa	CBot EBar ECha EDra EFol GAbr GCHN GCal GGar GMac GTou LGan MSto NHol NPri NRoo NWCA SBla SHer SUsu WCru WHal WPer
– var. ***truncata***	CGle EDra GCra
– x ***longissima***	EDra
§ ***fragrans***	CArn CGle CHad CNic CPou EDra EPad ESis GAbr GCHN GMac LGan LGre MMil MTho NOak NWCA SBla WCra WDav WEas WHoo WOMN
glandulosa	CSam EDra GCra GDra ITim NHol NRoo WEas
– var. ***jucunda***	EDra
glauca	See A. ***fragrans***
grata	EDra GAul GCHN LGre SChu
'Hensol Harebell' AGM	CGle CHan CPou EBee EDra LGan MBro NHol NKay SPer WHil WHoo WSun
hinckleyana	See A. ***chrysantha h.***
hirsutissima	See A. ***viscosa h.***
japonica	See A. ***flabellata pumila***
Jewel hybrids	NRoo WHil WPer
jonesii	CNic GTou MFos NKay
– x ***saximontana***	MFos
laramiensis	CNic EDra ESis MSto NHar NTow WDav
longissima	CGle CHad CSam EDra MMil MTho SBla SMrm SUsu WCla WEas WHal WHil
¶ – 'Alba'	WEas
Lowdham strain	EDra
* 'Magpie'	CBos EWll NRar
'Maxi Star'	EDra
McKana hybrids	CBow CKel CSco CShe EBre ECED EDra ELan ENot GAbr GCHN IDai LBre LHop MFir MWat NBee NNor NOak NVic SHer SPer WPer WTyn WTyr
* ***melange pygmaea***	NHol
* 'Mellow Yellow'	CPla CRDP NPer
micrantha	GCHN
microphylla	EDra GTou NHol
* 'Modra Pisen'	EDra
Mrs Scott-Elliot Hybrids	CBow EDra GAbr MBri SHer SMrm SPer WTyn
'Mrs Shaw's Double'	WEas
Music Series Hybrids AGM	NOak NRoo SHer SMrm SPla SRms WByw WTyn
nevadensis	See A. ***vulgaris n.***
nigricans	See A. ***atrata***
nivalis	NGre SBla SWas WAbe
§ ***olympica***	EDra LGre WHaw WPer
– JCA 173.600	NHol
ottonis	EDra LRHS
§ – ssp. ***amaliae***	MRPP WAbe
¶ – ssp. ***ottonis***	NHar
oxysepala	CChu CMil EDra GCra MSto WBon WHal
'Phyll's Bonnet'	GCal
'Pink Bonnet'	GCal
pubiflora	GCHN GCra
– CC&MR 96	WDav
pyrenaica	CNic EDra NHol NTow WCla WOMN WWin
– ssp. ***cazorlensis***	CMea CWes EDra GCHN
¶ 'Red Hobbit'	NHol
rockii CLD 0437	EMon NHol
saximontana	CMil CNic EDra EPot GCHN GTou LBee MSto NHol NMen NTow NWCA WPer
¶ – x ***jonesii***	GTou MFos MRPP
§ 'Schneekönigin' ('Snow Queen')	CCla CSco ELan GCHN NOak WEas WHen WHil WPer WRus
scopulorum	CLew EDra MFir MFos MSto WDav WPer
* ***secundiflora***	MSto
shockleyi	CPou EDra GBuc MBel NHar WAbe WHil
sibirica	EBee EDra WPer
'Silver Queen'	CKel
skinneri	EDra MSto NHol NRed SIgm WCru WDav WHil WPer
'Snow Queen'	See A. 'Schneekönigin'
¶ Songbird series	WTyn
sp. ACL 7781	NHol
¶ sp. CLD 0437	WDav
sp. from Zigana Pass	EDra
stellata	See A. ***vulgaris s.***
thalictrifolia	NRed
– JCA 174.400	WDav
transsilvanica	EBar EDra WPer
triternata	CPou EDra ESis LGre NHol NTow SIgm
viridiflora	Widely available
viscosa	EDra
vulgaris	CArn CWGN ECWi EDra GPoy IEde LHol MChe MHew NBro NMir NNor SIde WBon WOak WPer WTyn WWye
– 'Adelaide Addison'	CBro CGle ECha EDra ELan EMar LGan MNFA NFai NRoo SFis SUsu SWas WEas WHal WMer WTyn
– ***alba***	CArn CLTr CMea CRDP GMac WByw
– 'Anne Calder'	EDra
– 'Aureovariegata'	See A. ***v.*** 'Vervaeneana Group'
§ – Baicalensis Group	EDra GCHN GMac
– 'Belhaven Blue'	EDra
– 'Blue Star'	ECtt EFou GAbr GCHN NMir SHer SPer SUsu WPer
– from Brno Czechoslovakia	EDra
– ***clematiflora***	See A. ***v. stellata***
– var. ***flore-pleno***	CLTr ECro ECtt EFol EHic SMrm SSvw WByw WHil WPer WSun
– – black	LHop

– – blue	LWad
– – pink	GAbr LWad NFai
– – red	EDra GCra MNFA WDav
– – white	EPot LGre SWas WDav
– 'Gisela Powell'	EDra
*– 'Gold Finch'	CBot NRoo
– golden-leaved	SHer
– 'Heidi'	CBot WPer
– var. ***hispanica***	EDra
– 'Jane Hollow'	CPou CRow
*– 'Mathew Strominger'	ECro EDra MTol NPri WPer
– 'Miss Coventry'	SUsu SWas
§ – ssp. ***nevadensis***	EPad
– 'Nivea' ('Munstead White') **AGM**	CBot CCla CGle CHad CMil CPou ECha ELan EMon GAbr LBlm MNFA NCat NRoo SBla SFis SHig SIde WCla WHer WRus WTyn
– 'Nora Barlow' **AGM**	Widely available
– Olympica Group	See A. ***olympica***
– 'Patricia Zavros'	EDra
– 'Pink Spurless'	See A. ***vulgaris stellata*** pink
– 'Red Star'	ECtt EFou GAbr GCHN NMir NOak SHer WPer WRus WTyn
– 'Reverend E Baty'	EDra
– from Rize, Turkey	EDra
– 'Robin'	CBot NRoo
– 'Ruby Port'	GCal GMac NHol
– scented	EDra
– 'Snowdust'	CRDP EHoe
§ – var. ***stellata***	CBot CGle CLew EBar ECro EDra ESma GCHN LWad MTol NBro NFai NHol NPer WDav WHal WHer WHil WHoo WPer WRus WTyn WWin
§ – – pink	EDra EFou MBel
¶ – – red	GAbr
§ – – white	CGle EDra EFou GCHN LHop NBro WDav WTyn
¶ – 'Sunlight White'	NPri SSvw WPer
– 'Tom Fairhurst'	EDra
– variegated foliage	See A. ***v.*** Vervaeneana Group
*– 'White Bonnets'	SRos
– 'White Spurless'	See A. ***v. stellata*** white
– 'White Star'	CVer ECtt EFou GAbr GCHN LWad NMir NPri NRoo SPer WPer WRus WTyn
– 'William Guiness'	CMil EBee EFou ELan ESma GBri MTol NPri SMad WHoo WPer
N ***vulgaris*** Vervaeneana Group (v)	Widely available
– – 'Graeme Iddon'	GCra LGre NFai
– – 'Woodside'	See A. ***v.*** Vervaeneana Group
¶ ***yabeana***	EMon

ARABIS † (Cruciferae/Brassicaceae)

albida	See A. ***caucasica***
alpina	CB&S CLew NMen
§ – ssp. ***caucasica***	MBar WPla
§ – – ***rosea***	LAbb NBir NMen SRms WSun
§ – – 'Flore Pleno'	CNic CShe EBre ECha ECtt ELan EOrc EPar IDai LBre LGro LHop MCas MFir MTho MWat NKay NRoo SBod SFis SHer SIng WByw WDav WEas WHil WWin
– – 'Gillian Sharman' (v)	EMon
– – 'Pink Pearl'	EBee GAul LAbb
¶ – – 'Pinkie'	NPri
– – 'Rose Frost'	EMNN SHer
§ – – 'Schneehaube' ('Snowcap') **AGM**	EBar ECtt EMNN MBar NKay NMir NRoo SRms
* – – 'Snow White'	NGre
– – 'Snowdrop'	MCas MRav NPri
– – 'Variegata'	CBot CRow CShe ECha EFol EHoe ELan EOrc EPar EPot GAbr IDai LBee LHop MBri MCas MTho NNrw NRoo SHer WByw WEas WHil WPbr WPer WWin
alpina Arendsii Group 'Compinkie '	CBow CDoC ECtt NNrw NOak NRoo SRms
– – 'La Fraicheur'	WMer
– – 'Rosabella'	ECha LHop MRav
androsacea	EPar GTou MBro MCas MHig MPla NGre NHed NMen NTow
x ***arendsii***	See A. ***alpina*** Arendsii Group
aubrietoïdes	WDav
blepharophylla	ESma GAbr MFir WCot WHil
§ – 'Frühlingszauber' ('Spring Charm') **AGM**	CB&S GDra LAbb MPit NGre NKay NRoo SHer SRms WCla WGor
bryoïdes	GTou NGre
♦ ***caucasica***	See A. ***alpina c.***
cypria	WOMN
ferdinandi-coburgi	CRow EOrc EPot LGro MPla NBro NRed NVic SBod WCla WEas WWin
– 'Aureovariegata'	CMHG CMea CRiv EHoe NGre NRar
– 'Old Gold'	Widely available
– 'Variegata' **AGM**	Widely available
¶ ***glabra***	WPer
x ***kellereri***	NHol WDav
* ***lucida*** 'Variegata'	EFol EWes
muralis	See A. ***collina***
rosea	See A. ***collina***
§ ***scabra***	CNat
soyeri	NRed NTow
§ – ssp. ***coriacea***	NRed
♦ – ***jacquinii***	See A. ***s. coriacea***
– 'Variegata'	MFir
¶ ***sparsiflora rubra***	WHil
stelleri var. ***japonica***	NWCA
♦ ***stricta***	See A. ***scabra***
x ***sturii***	MHig NGre
x ***suendermannii***	MPla

ARACHNIODES (Dryopteridaceae)

aristata 'Variegata'	NMar
simplicior C&L 236	SApp SBla

ARAIOSTEGIA (Davalliaceae)

pseudocystopteris	CFil

ARALIA † (Araliaceae)

cachemirica	CHad MUlv SDix
californica	GPoy MSal
chinensis	CB&S CSam EPla MBel NHol SPer
chinensis hort.	See A. ***elata***

continentalis	CHan
cordata	GCal
§ *elata* AGM	CBow CBra CDoC CHEx CHad CHan CLnd CWSG EBre ELan ENot IOrc ISea LBre LNet MBal MBlu NBee NNor SArc SMad SPer WDin WNor
– 'Albomarginata'	See A. *e.* 'Variegata'
– 'Aureovariegata'	CB&S CBow CDoC CPMA CSco EHar ELan ENot IJoh IOrc LNet MBri NPal SHil WDin WPat
§ – 'Variegata' AGM	CB&S CBot CBow CDoC CPMA CSco EHar ELan EMil ENot IOrc LNet MBlu MBri NPal SEng SHBN SHer SHil WDin WPat
racemosa	GCal GPoy MSal MSte SAxl
sieboldii hort.	See FATSIA *japonica*

ARAUCARIA (Araucariaceae)

angustifolia	CHEx GAri
§ *araucana*	CB&S CBra CDoC CHEx CMac CSco EHar ELan ENot GRei IJoh LCon LLin LNet MBal MBar MBri MGos NBee NHol SArc SHBN SLim SMad SPer WDin WMou WThu
§ *columnaris*	CTro
♦ *cookii*	See A. *columnaris*
excelsa	See A. *heterophylla*
§ *heterophylla* AGM	EBre LBre MBri
imbricata	See A. *araucana*

ARAUJIA (Asclepiadaceae)

grandiflora	SLMG
sericifera	CAbb CB&S CDoC CGre CMHG CRHN CTro EMil ERea LHop MGos

ARBUTUS † (Ericaceae)

andrachne	CFil WCoo
x *andrachnoïdes* AGM	Widely available
glandulosa	See ARCTOSTAPHYLOS *g.*
marina	CRos ELan LRHS MAsh SMad SSta
menziesii AGM	CBot CFil LNet MBal SHil SMad WBod WCoo WWat
unedo AGM	Widely available
– 'Compacta'	CBow CChu CDoC CSco EBre IBar LBre MGos NHol SHBN
– 'Quercifolia'	MBal WPat
– f. *rubra* AGM	CB&S CBow CBra CChu CCla CDoC CMHG CPMA CSco EBre ECtt EHar ELan IOrc LBre LHop LNet MBal MBri MUlv SPer SReu SSta WAbe WBod WPat WSHC

ARCHONTOPHOENIX (Palmae/Arecaceae)

cunninghamiana AGM	NPal

ARCTANTHEMUM (Compositae/Asteraceae)

§ *arcticum*	MSte
– 'Schwefelglanz'	ECha WCot

ARCTERICA See PIERIS

ARCTIUM (Compositae/Asteraceae)

lappa	CArn CKin EWFC Effi GPoy LHol MChe MSal NHex SIde WHer
minus	CKin ECWi EWFC MHew MSal
pubens	CKin

ARCTOSTAPHYLOS (Ericaceae)

* *californica*	MBal
§ *glandulosa*	SArc
x *media* 'Snow Camp'	CMHG ELan MAsh MBal
– 'Wood's Red'	GGGa MBal MBar MGos WAbe
myrtifolia	GAri MBar SSta WSHC
nevadensis	MBal MBar SReu SSta
nummularia	MBal
patula	LRHS SMad
stanfordiana C&H 105	GGGa
uva-ursi	CArn ELan ENot GArf GPoy IDai IOrc MBal MBar MGos MHig MPla NNor SBod SEng SHBN SPer SSta WBod WDin
– 'Massachusetts'	EBre ELan LBre
– 'Point Reyes'	SSta
¶ – 'Snowcap'	MAsh
– 'Vancouver Jade'	IJoh MAsh MBar MGos MUlv NHol SReu SSta

ARCTOTIS (Compositae/Asteraceae)

x *hybrida* 'Apricot'	CBow CBrk LHop MSte SMrm SUsu
¶ – 'Bacchus'	LHop
¶ – 'Champagne'	CBar LHop
– 'China Rose'	LBlm SAxl SMrm SUsu
– 'Flame'	CBar CBrk CHad CSpe LBlm LHop MSte SChu SMrm SUsu WPer
¶ – 'Irene'	WPer
¶ – 'Mahogany'	CBar
¶ – 'Midday Sun'	CBar
– 'Pink'	SChu
¶ – 'Pollen'	CBar
¶ – 'Raspberry'	LBlm
¶ – 'Rosita'	LHop
¶ – 'Terracotta'	CBar
– 'White'	MSte
– 'Wine'	CBar CBrk CHad LHop
– 'Yellow'	CBrk

ARDISIA (Myrsinaceae)

crenata	MBri

ARECA (Palmae/Arecaceae)

catechu	MBri

ARECASTRUM See SYAGRUS

ARENARIA (Caryophyllaceae)

§ *alfacarensis*	WOld WWin
balearica	CLew CNic CSpe ELan EPar EPot GCHN GPlt GTou LBee MFir MRPP MTho NGre NHol NMen SBod SHer SIng WEas WHoo WWin
bertolonii	LBee WPer

caespitosa	See MINUARTIA ***verna c.***
festucoïdes	GCHN WDav
– C&Mc 405	GTou
grandiflora	ESis WAbe
hookeri	MFos NHar NWCA WDav
¶ *kingii*	GLil
ledebouriana	MHig MWat NTow WAbe WThu
♦ *lithops*	See A. ***alfacarensis***
longifolia	MNFA
* *magellanica*	NWCA
montana AGM	CGle CLew ECha ECtt EFou ELan EMNN EOrc EPar GCHN IDai MTho NNor NRar NRoo SIng WAbe WEas WHil WHoo WPat WPbr WPer WWin
nevadensis	ITim WAbe
norvegica	CNat WHil
– ssp. *anglica*	WOMN
obtusiloba	See MINUARTIA ***o.***
pinifolia	See MINUARTIA ***circassica***
procera glabra	WHaw WHil
pulvinata	See A. ***alfacarensis***
purpurascens	ECtt ELan EMNN EPot ESis GArf MBro MCas MHig MRPP NKay NNrd NRoo SHer WHoo WOMN
– 'Elliott's Variety'	NGre
tetraquetra	EGle EPad GArf GDra MFos MTho MWat NTow NWCA WThu
– JJA 188.450	SBla
§ – ssp. *amabilis*	EPot LBee MHig MRPP NGre NNrd NRed NSla NTow SIng WHil
♦– *granatensis*	See A. ***t. amabilis***
tmolea	NNrd NTow WOMN
verna	See MINUARTIA ***verna***

ARENGA (Palmae/Arecaceae)

See Plant Deletions

ARGEMONE (Papaveraceae)

grandiflora	EJud ELan
mexicana	EBee ELan WHaw WOMN

ARGYRANTHEMUM † (Compositae/Asteraceae)

¶ 'Apricot Surprise'	CSpe EOrc
§ 'Blizzard' (d)	CBrk CSpe
broussonetii	CCan LHop NSty NWyt
callichrysum 'Etoile d'Or' ('Yellow Star')	CBrk EBre ECtt IHos LBre LHop
– 'Prado'	CB&S ECtt EDon
canariense hort.	See A. ***frutescens canariae***
'Cheek's Peach'	See A. 'Peach Cheeks'
'Chelsea Princess'	EOrc
¶ 'Cornish Gold'	CSpe
coronopifolium	CCan
double cream	CCan
double white	CCan ESma
'Edelweiss' (d)	CBar CBrk CCan EBar ECtt EDon ERav LHil LHop WEas WHal WHen
'Flamingo'	See RHODANTHEMUM ***gayanum***
foeniculaceum hort.	CCan CElw CHad CMHG CMer CSev ECha ELan ERav GMac LAbb LBlm NPer NSty NTow SDix SHer SIgm SMrm SUsu WHen WKif WOMN
– pink	See A. 'Petite Pink'
foeniculaceum 'Royal Haze' AGM	CB&S CCan CSpe GCal LHil NPer SFis
§ *frutescens*	CCla CGle CHEx EBre ECha ECtt EDon ELan EOrc ERea LAbb LBlm LBre LHil NFai WEas
* – 'Album Plenum'	EOrc
– ssp. *canariae* AGM	CBrk
§ – ssp. *frutescens*	CCan
– ssp. *pumilum*	GCal
– ssp. *succulentum* 'Margaret Lynch'	CBrk CCan EDon
'Gill's Pink'	CBrk CLTr CMer CSpe ECtt EDon NRar
§ *gracile*	CCan CMer CSev EBar ESma GCal LHil MFir SHer SUsu WEas WHal WKif
– 'Chelsea Girl' AGM	CBrk CCan CElw CLit ECtt ERav MArl MSte SIgm
'Hopleys Double Yellow'	LHil LHop NSty
§ 'Jamaica Primrose' AGM	Widely available
* 'Jamaica Snowstorm'	CB&S CBar CSpe NRoo SMrm WHal
* 'Lemon Meringue'	CBrk CElw CMer ECtt EOrc MArl
'Levada Cream'	ECtt EDon EOrc
'Leyton Treasure'	CBrk
§ *maderense* AGM	CB&S CBrk CCan CHad CLTr CLit CMHG CMer CSev CSpe EOrc ERav GCal IBlr LBlm LHil LHop MSte NFai NRoo NSty NTow SAxl SDix SFis SUsu WEas WOMN WPer WTyr
¶ – 'Forde Abbey'	SIng
¶ – pale form	CSpe
'Mary Cheek' AGM	CBrk CCan EOrc
'Mary Wootton' (d)	CBrk CCan CElw CGle CLit CSev ECtt ELan EOrc ERav GCal GMac LHil LHop MFir NSty NWyt SHer WHal
♦ 'Mini-Snowflake'	See A. 'Blizzard'
'Mrs F Sander' (d)	CBrk CCan ECtt EDon GGar NSty
'Nevada Cream'	See A. 'Qinta White'
ochroleucum	See A. ***maderense***
'Peach Cheeks'	CB&S CBrk CSev CSpe ECtt ERom MSte SIgm SMrm SRms
'Penny'	CBrk LHop
'Petite Pink' AGM	CB&S CBrk CMer CSpe ECtt EOrc MSte NPer SIgm SUsu WHen
'Pink Australian'	CBrk CLTr LHil
'Pink Break'	CCan
'Pink Delight'	See A. 'Petite Pink'
'Pink Silver Queen'	WEas
'Powder Puff' (d)	CBrk CCan CKni CLit CMer CSpe ECtt EDon EOrc LHop MRav MSte NFai SSte SUsu
§ 'Qinta White' AGM	CBrk CCan ECtt EDon
'Rollason's Red'	CBrk CCan CLit CSev ECtt EOrc LBlm LHop SHer
'Rosali' (d)	LHop
'Royal Haze'	See A. ***foeniculaceum*** Webb 'Royal Haze'
'Sark'	CCan CMer CSpe ECha GMac LHil LHop NSty NWyt SHer WEas
* 'Silver Queen'	WEas

single pink — CGle CLTr CLit CMer LHil NSty
'Snowflake' (d) — CB&S CBrk CCan CHEx CLit CMer CMil CSev CSpe ECtt EDon EOrc IHos LBlm LHil LHop MSte NPer SHer SMad SUsu WHen
'Stydd Rose' — NWyt
'Tony Holmes' — CCan
'Vancouver' AGM — Widely available
*'Vera' — IHos
'Wellwood Park' — CBrk CCan EBre ECtt GCal LBre LHop NFai
¶ 'White Spider' — CSpe

ARGYROCYTISUS See CYTISUS

ARISAEMA (Araceae)

amurense — CBro CRDP EPot GCLN GDra NHar NRog WChr WThu
candidissimum AGM — CBro CChu EBre ECha EPar EPot IMal LAma LBre NHar NHol NKay NRog NRoo SPou SWas WChr WCot WCru WHal WMar
¶ ***ciliatum*** — WCot
– CT 369 — SWas
concinnum — EBul NRog
consanguineum — CBro CChu CGle LAma NHol NRog WCru
costatum — CFil EBul GBuc NRog WChr
dracontium — LAma MSal NHol NRog SHer WChr WCru
erubescens — NRog
flavum — CBro EBul EPot GCal NNrd NRog WChr WCru WThu
griffithii — CBro GCra LAma NHol NRog WChr WCot WCru WHal
– var. ***pradhanii*** — WCru
helleborifolium — See A. ***tortuosum***
intermedium — NRog
jacquemontii — CBro EPot GBuc GDra LAma NHar NHol NRog
japonicum — See A. ***serratum***
¶ ***kelung-insularis***
B&SWJ 269 — WCru
§ ***nepenthoïdes*** — CBro GCra LAma NHol NRog SHer WChr WCot WCru
ochraceum — See A. ***nepenthoïdes***
propinquum — EPot NRog WCru
¶ ***quinatum*** — NRog
*– ***pusillum*** — NRog
*– ***zebrinum*** — NRog
ringens hort. — See A. ***robustum***
ringens (Thunberg) Schott — CBro LAma NHol WChr WCru
§ ***serratum*** — LAma NRog SBla
¶– GG 89394 — NHol
¶– GG 91200 — NHol
¶– GG 93168 — NHol
sikokianum — CBro CRDP EPot LAma LBow NHol NRog SHer WChr WCru
speciosum — ELan LAma LBow NHol WChr WCru
thunbergii ssp. ***urashima*** — LAma NHol NRog WCru
§ ***tortuosum*** — CRDP ECha LAma MBal NHol NRog WChr WCru WHal
triphyllum — CBro ECou EPar EPot LAma LBow MSal NHol NRog NRoo SHer WChr WCru
¶ ***urashima*** — WChr

ARISARUM (Araceae)

proboscideum — Widely available
– MS 958 — CMon EMar
vulgare — CB&S EPot LAma NGar
– ssp. ***simorrhinum***
SF 396/347 — CMon NGar
– ssp. ***vulgare*** JRM 1396 — CMon

ARISTEA (Iridaceae)

ecklonii — CAvo CBot CFee CHan CNic CTro EBar EBee LAbb SAxl WAbe WPer
ensifolia — ELan EMon WThi
– S&SH 88 — CHan

ARISTOLOCHIA (Aristolochiaceae)

¶ ***brasiliensis*** — CTro
clematitis — GPoy MBro MHew MSal NHex
§ ***durior*** — CB&S CBot CDoC CGre CHEx CSco ELan NPal SHBN SHer SHil
elegans — See A. ***littoralis***
¶ ***fimbriata*** — MSto
gigantea — CTro
§ ***littoralis*** AGM — SLMG
macrophylla — See A. ***durior***
¶ ***paucinervis*** SF 235 — MSto
sipho — See A. ***durior***
tomentosa — MSal

ARISTOTELIA (Elaeocarpaceae)

§ ***chilensis*** — CGre CPle MNes
– 'Variegata' — CAbb CBra CCla CGre CHan CPle CTre EPla LHop MMil WEas WPat WSHC
fruticosa (f) — ECou
– (m) — ECou
macqui — See A. ***chilensis***
peduncularis — GWht
serrata — ECou

ARMERIA (Plumbaginaceae)

§ ***alliacea*** — ECha GBar WPer
– Formosa hybrids — ECoo ELan IBlr NBar NCat NMir NOak SFis SIde WHoo WPbr
– f. ***leucantha*** — CBot NBro
alpina — NHol
'Bee's Ruby' AGM — CLew ECED GCal MFir MUlv WMer WPer
caespitosa — See A. ***juniperifolia***
§ ***girardii*** — EPot NHed NHol
§ ***juniperifolia*** AGM — CMHG EBre ECtt EMNN ESis LBee LBre LHop MBro MHig MPla MRPP MTho NKay NMen NNor NNrd NRoo NTow NWCA SBla SGil SHer SIng WCla WWin
– 'Alba' — CLew CRiv EBre ELan EPar ESis LBee LBre MCas MHig MPla NGre NHar NHed NNrd NRoo SGil SHer WHil WThu WWin
– 'Ardenholme' — NKay
– 'Beechwood' — NHol SBla SSmi WThu
– 'Bevan's Variety' AGM — CMHG CRiv CShe EBre ECha ELan EPar EPot LBre MBro MFir MHig MRav MWat NHar NHol NKay NMen NNrd NNrw NRoo NRya SHer WAbe WHil WHoo WPat WThu

– dark form	GDra
– rose	CLew EPot
– spiny dwarf form	EPot
leucocephala	GPlt
– 'Corsica'	ECha NBir
maritima	CArn CBow CKin CMHG CRow CShe EBre ECWi EPar GPlt LAbb LBre LGro LHol MBar MRav NCat NLan NMen NNor NRed SIde WByw WWye
– 'Alba'	CLTr CNic EBre ECha ECoo ELan EPar EPot ESis LBre MBal MBar MBri NHol NMir NNor NNrd NRoo NRya SSvw WAbe WByw WHen WHil WPat WPer WWin
– ssp. ***alpina***	See A. ***a.***
– 'Bloodstone'	CShe ECot ELan EPar LBee MWat SHer
– 'Düsseldorfer Stolz' ('D. Pride')	CMHG CShe CTom EBre ECha ELan LBre LHop MBri MBro MHig NHar NHol NMen NNrd NRoo SGil SHer SIng WHen WPat WWye
– 'Glory of Holland'	EPot
– 'Laucheana'	NNrd NOak WHoo
*– 'Pink Lusitanica'	WPer
– 'Ruby Glow'	LBuc NMen NNrd
– 'Snowball'	NOak
– 'Splendens'	EMNN GCHN NHar NMir NNrd SFis WCla WPer WWin
– 'Vindictive' AGM	ELan MBal SHer SRms WAbe
'Ornament'	ECtt ELan NRoo WCot WHen WTyr
plantaginea	See A. ***alliacea***
pseudarmeria	ELan WEas
setacea	See A. ***girardii***
¶ sp. ex Patagonia	WHil
tweedyi	CMea EPot EWes GTou SHer WHal
welwitschii	CMHG EWoo SRms

ARMORACIA (Cruciferae/Brassicaceae)

§ ***rusticana***	CArn CSFH CSev Effi GPoy IEde ILis LHol MBar MBri MSal NPri SIde WGwy WOak WWye
– 'Variegata'	CRDP EMar EMon EOrc GCal LHop NHol NSti WCHb

ARNEBIA (Boraginaceae)

echioïdes	See A. ***pulchra***
§ ***pulchra***	EBre ECED LBre

ARNICA (Compositae/Asteraceae)

* ***angustifolia*** 'Iljinni'	EBee NBir
chamissonis	GGar LHol MChe MHew MSal NRoo SIde WPer WWye
montana	CArn CSFH EBar GPoy GTou MChe MHew MSal NHol SHer SWat WPer WWye
¶ ***sachalinensis***	EBee

ARONIA (Rosaceae)

arbutifolia	CB&S CBow CGre CPle EPla GWht IJoh IOrc MBal NBar SHBN SHer SPer WAbe WBod WDin WWat
– 'Brilliant'	COtt ELan MUlv SHil SPer
– 'Erecta'	CCla EBre EHic ELan GWht LBre SRms WThu WWat
melanocarpa	CCla CHan CMHG EBre EHic LBre MBar MBlu MRav NHol NWyt SPer SReu WBod WDin WHCG WThu WWat
– 'Viking'	CCla LBuc MHlr MUlv WWes
x ***prunifolia***	CDoC CMHG CSco NHol SPer WHCG WWat

ARRHENATHERUM (Gramineae/Poaceae)

elatius ssp. ***bulbosum*** 'Variegatum'	CHan CNic EFol EFou EHoe ELan EMar EMon EPla ETPC LHil MCas NCat NRya SCob SFar SPla WEas WHal WRus

ARTEMISIA † (Compositae/Asteraceae)

§ ***abrotanum*** AGM	Widely available
absinthium	CArn CSFH CTom EEls EHer EWFC Effi GPoy LHol MBar MBri MChe MPit NNor NSti SHer SIde SPer WHal WNdy WOak WPer WWye
– 'Lambrook Silver' AGM	CB&S CCla CGle CLew CMea CSco CSev CShe EBre ECha EEls EGol ELan EPla LBre LHop NBro NFai NNor NRoo SBla SFis SHBN SPer SPla WAbe WDin WEas WRus WWin
§ ***alba***	CSev EEls EMon GBar ILis LHol NSti SIde SMad WBon WPer WTyr WWye
– 'Canescens' AGM	Widely available
annua	EEls MSal SIde WWye
arborescens	CArn CGle CGre CMHG CMer ECha EEls ELan EPla IJoh LBlm NFai NSti SDix SDry SGil SMad SPer WDin WHer
♦– 'Brass Band'	See A. 'Powis Castle'
– 'Faith Raven'	CMea CShe EBar EEls EGol ELan MBri NFai WHal WHer WMer WRus WSHC
– 'Porquerolles'	EEls LHop
¶ ***arctica***	EEls
¶ ***argyi***	EEls
armeniaca	EEls WWin
assoana	See A. ***caucasica***
atrata	EEls
brachyloba	CMHG EEls SHer WCHb
caerulescens	See SERIPHIDIUM ***c.***
campestris	EMon
– ssp. ***borealis***	EEls Effi GAbr LHol MBri MChe
– ssp. ***campestris***	CNat EEls
– ssp. ***maritima***	EEls
camphorata	See A. ***alba***
♦ ***cana***	See SERIPHIDIUM ***canum***
canariensis	See A. ***thuscula***
capillaris	EEls
§ ***caucasica*** AGM	CGle CMGP CPBP CShe EBre EEls EFol ESiP GCHN IDai LBre LGro LLWP MTol NKay NNrd NRed SHer SIng SMrm WCHb WEas WHer WHil WPer WWat
– ***caucasica***	SGil SIgm
chamaemelifolia	CArn EEls LHol NSti SIde WPer WWye
cretacea	See SERIPHIDIUM ***nutans***
discolor	See A. ***ludoviciana incompta***
¶ ***douglasiana***	EEls

– 'Valerie Finnis'	See A. ***ludoviciana*** 'V.F.'
dracunculus	CArn CGle CHad CRiv CSFH CSev ECha EEls EHer ELan Effi GAbr GBar GPoy IEde LHol MBar MBri MChe MHew NRoo SDix SIde WEas WOak WPer WWye
– ***dracunculoïdes***	EEls EJud MChe NPri
eriantha	EEls
♦***ferganensis***	See SERIPHIDIUM ***ferganense***
frigida AGM	EEls EOrc ILis MFir WEas WHCG WWin
glacialis	CMHG CRiv ECha EEls MRPP NRar NSti SIng
gmelinii	EEls
gnaphalodes	See A. ***ludoviciana***
gracilis	See A. ***scoparia***
granatensis	NSti WOMN
kitadakensis	EEls
– 'Guizhou'	See A. ***lactiflora*** Guizhou Group
laciniata	EEls
lactiflora AGM	CGle CHad CKel CSco ECha ECtt EEls EFou ELan EPar GCal IDai NKay NNor NSti SCro SDix SHer SPer WBon WWye
– dark form	See A. ***l.*** Guizhou Group
– Guizhou Group	Widely available
– ***purpurea***	See A. ***l.*** Guizhou Group
lanata Willdenow	See A. ***caucasica***
laxa	See A. ***umbelliformis***
§ ***ludoviciana***	CArn CBre CGle CSFH CSco CShe ECED EEls ELan ESiP IJoh LBlm LGro MWat NFai NNor NOak NOrc SIde WHil WOld WWin WWye
§ – var. ***incompta***	ECha EEls EFol MNFA NFai
– var. ***latifolia***	See A. ***l. latiloba***
§ – var. ***latiloba*** AGM	CBos CCla CHad CLew CMer CMil EEls EFol EHoe EOrc EPla LBlm LHop LLWP MBro MRav MTol NFai NOak NRoo WByw WCot WHal WHer WHoo WMer WPbr WPer
– 'Silver Queen' AGM	CCla CGle CKel CLew CMea CSco EBre ECtt EEls ELan ENot EPar LBre MBri NFai NHol NNor NSti SBla SPer SPla WHal WHen WHil WPbr WPer WWat
– 'Valerie Finnis' AGM	ECha EFou GCal WEas
maritima	See SERIPHIDIUM ***maritimum***
molinieri	EEls
mutellina	See A. ***umbelliformis***
niitakayamensis	EEls
nutans	See SERIPHIDIUM ***n.***
palmeri A Gray	See SERIPHIDIUM ***p.***
palmeri hort.	See A. ***ludoviciana***
pedemontana	See A. ***caucasica***
pontica AGM	Widely available
N 'Powis Castle' AGM	Widely available
¶ ***princeps***	EEls
procera	See A. ***abrotanum***
purshiana	See A. ***ludoviciana***
rupestris	EEls
¶ ***rutifolia***	EEls
schmidtiana AGM	ECha ECot EFou EPad EPot LHop MWat NRar SHer SPer WHen
– 'Nana' AGM	Widely available
§ ***scoparia***	EEls
¶ ***sieberi***	EEls
♦***splendens*** hort.	See A. ***alba*** 'Canescens'
splendens Willdenow	CMHG CShe EBre EFol ELan LBre MTol NSti SHer WEas WRus WSHC
– var. ***brachyphylla***	CHan
¶ sp. B&SWJ 088	WCru
sp. CLD 1531	EMon
♦sp. Guiz 137	See A. ***lactiflora*** Guizhou Group
stelleriana	CBrk CGle CLew CMer CShe CTom EBre ECha ESiP IJoh LAbb LBre LHop MNFA MTho NBro NMir NNor NSti SHer SIng SPer WHoo WPer WRus WSHC
– 'Boughton Silver'	See A. ***s.*** 'Mori'
§ – 'Mori's Form'	CCla CHad CLTr CMHG EEls EFou EHoe ELan EMNN LGre MBri NBar NHol NNrd NRar NSti NTow SCro SGil SMrm SPer WHen WMer WPer WWat WWeb WWye
– 'Nana'	ECha EEls GTou
– ***prostrata***	See A. ***s.*** 'Mori'
*– 'Silver Brocade'	ELan SHil
§ ***thuscula***	EEls
tridentata	See SERIPHIDIUM ***tridentatum***
§ ***umbelliformis***	EEls WDav WPer
vallesiaca	See SERIPHIDIUM ***vallesiacum***
verlotiorum	EEls GBar
* ***versicolor***	NNor
vulgaris	CArn CSFH EEls EWFC Effi GPoy IEde LHol MChe SIde WHer WOak WWye
– 'Cragg-Barber Eye' (v)	CNat
– 'Crispa'	SIde
– 'Variegata'	CBos CBre CElw CLTr CLew CRDP CWit EBee EEls EFol EHoe EMon GBar NRar WBon WHer
* ***wurzelli***	EEls

ARTHROPODIUM (Liliaceae/Anthericaceae)

candidum	CBot CHan CMea CRow EBar EBul ECha ECou EFol EPla EPot LHil MFir MPit NCat NMen NWCA SAxl SHer SUsu WEas WHal
– ***maculatum***	CNic MHig
– ***purpureum***	CRDP CRiv ELan EMon EPot GCal NHol WCot WCru
cirrhatum	CAbb CHol CPle CRDP CTre CTro EBee EBul ECou EOrc LHop
¶ – 'Three Knights'	WCot
¶ – 'White Knights'	WCot
milleflorum	EBul ECou ESma NSla NWCA SAxl WAbe

ARTICHOKE, Globe See **CYNARA *scolymus***

ARTICHOKE, Jerusalem See **HELIANTHUS *tuberosus***

ARUM (Araceae)

¶ ***albispathum***	WChr

§ ***concinnatum***	CFil CMon EPot WChr WHaw
♦ ***conophalloïdes***	See A. ***rupicola rupicola***
cornutum	See SAUROMATUM ***venosum***
creticum	CAvo CBot CBro CHan EBee ECha EPar EPot IBlr LAma NHol NRog NTow SWas
– FCC form	SPou WChr
– white	SPou
– yellow	NBir SDix
¶ ***cyrenaicum***	GCra WChr
♦ ***detruncatum*** var. ***detruncatum***	See A. ***rupicola rupicola***
§ ***dioscoridis***	CAvo CMon MTho NRog WChr
¶ – var. ***dioscoridis***	NRog
♦– var. ***smithii***	See A. ***d.***
dracunculus	See DRACUNCULUS ***vulgaris***
elongatum	EPot WChr
hygrophilum	CAvo WChr
idaeum	WChr
italicum	CBow CGle CLew ECro EOrc ETub LAma MBri NCat NNrd NRog SDeJ SHer WAbe WByw WOMN
– NL 1234	CMon
– ssp. ***albispathum***	CMon EMon EPot LAma NRog WChr
– 'Chameleon'	CHad CRDP EMon
– ssp. ***italicum***	WWat
§ – – 'Marmoratum' **AGM**	Widely available
§ – – 'Painted Lady'	EMon
– – 'Tiny'	SWas
§ – – 'White Winter'	EMon WRus
– ***marmoratum***	See A. ***i. i.*** 'Marmoratum'
– 'Nancy Lindsay'	EMon
– ***pictum***	See A. ***i. i.*** 'Marmoratum
korolkowii	EPot NRog WChr
maculatum	CKin ECWi EPar EPot EWFC GDra GPoy LAma LBlm MHew MSal NHex WWye
♦– 'Painted Lady'	See A. ***italicum italium*** 'P. L.'
– ***variegatum***	GPoy
nickelii	See A. ***concinnatum***
§ ***nigrum***	EMon WChr
orientale	EPot NHol
¶ – ssp. ***sintenisii***	WChr
palaestinum	CAvo
petteri hort.	See A. ***nigrum***
N ***pictum***	CAvo CRDP EBul EPot LAma NRog SPou WChr
– ACL 321/78	EMon
– CL 28	CMon
– 'Taff's Form'	See A. ***italicum italicum*** 'White Winter'
purpureospathum	CRDP
¶ ***rupicola***	WChr
§ – var. ***rupicola***	CAvo
¶ – var. ***virescens***	WChr

ARUNCUS (Rosaceae)

aethusifolius	Widely available
§ ***dioicus*** **AGM**	CCla CGle CHad CRDP CRow CSco EBar EBre ECha EFol EGol ELan ENot EOrc IDai LBre MBal NBro NDea NHol NNor SLon SMad SPer WOld
– 'Glasnevin'	CChu CCla CHol CRow CSco EBre ECtt EGol EOrc GAbr GCal LBre LGan MBri MUlv NHol SFis SHer WMer
– var. ***kamtschaticus***	NHol
– var. ***kamtschaticus*** AGSJ 59	NHol
– 'Kneiffii'	Widely available
– 'Zweiweltenkind' ('Child of Two Worlds')	COtt NHol WMer
japonicus AGSJ 238	NHol
plumosus	See A. ***dioicus***
sp. CLD 718	EMon
sylvester	See A. ***dioicus***

ARUNDINARIA † (Gramineae/Poaceae-Bambusoideae)

amabilis	See PSEUDOSASA ***a.***
anceps	See YUSHANIA ***a.***
angustifolia	See PLEIOBLASTUS ***chino a.***
auricoma	See PLEIOBLASTUS ***auricomus***
chino	See PLEIOBLASTUS ***c.***
disticha	See PLEIOBLASTUS ***pygmaeus distichus***
falconeri	See HIMALAYACALAMUS ***f.***
¶ ***fangiana***	EPla
fastuosa	See SEMIARUNDINARIA ***f.***
fortunei	See PLEIOBLASTUS ***variegatus***
funghomii	See SCHIZOSTACHYUM ***f.***
gigantea	SBam SDry WJun
hindsii	See PLEIOBLASTUS ***h.***
♦ ***hookeriana*** hort.	See HIMALAYACALAMUS ***falconeri*** 'Damarapa'
humilis	See PLEIOBLASTUS ***h.***
japonica	See PSEUDOSASA ***j.***
jaunsarensis	See YUSHANIA ***anceps***
maling	See YUSHANIA ***m.***
marmorea	See CHIMONOBAMBUSA ***m.***
murieliae	See FARGESIA ***m.***
nitida	See FARGESIA ***n.***
oedogonata	See CLAVINODUM ***oedogonatum***
palmata	See SASA ***p.***
pumila	See PLEIOBLASTUS ***humilis pumilus***
pygmaea	See PLEIOBLASTUS ***pygmaeus***
quadrangularis	See CHIMONOBAMBUSA ***q.***
simonii	See PLEIOBLASTUS ***s.***
spathiflora	See THAMNOCALAMUS ***spathiflorus***
§ ***tecta***	SDry
tessellata	See THAMNOCALAMUS ***tessellatus***
vagans	See SASAELLA ***ramosa***
variegata	See PLEIOBLASTUS ***variegatus***
veitchii	See SASA ***v.***
viridistriata	See PLEIOBLASTUS ***auricomus***
'Wang Tsai'	See BAMBUSA ***multiplex*** 'Fernleaf'

ARUNDO (Gramineae/Poaceae)

donax	CBen CHEx CRow CTro ECha EPla GAri GCal LBlm LMay LPan MUlv SArc SDix SMad
– 'Macrophylla'	CRow
– 'Variegata'	See A. ***d. versicolor***
§ – var. ***versicolor*** (v)	CB&S CBen CBot CBrk CHEx CRDP CRow CTro ECha EFol GCal IMal LBlm LHop MSta MSte MUlv SArc SMad SPer WOld

ASARINA (Scrophulariaceae)

♦***antirrhiniflora***	See MAURANDELLA ***a.***
barclayana	See MAURANDYA ***b.***
♦***erubescens***	See LOPHOSPERMUM ***e.***
hispanica	See ANTIRRHINUM ***h.***
lophantha	See LOPHOSPERMUM ***erubescens***
lophosperma	See LOPHOSPERMUM ***erubescens***
§ ***procumbens***	Widely available
– 'Alba'	SRms
¶ – dwarf form	CNic
♦***scandens***	See MAURANDYA ***s.***

ASARUM (Aristolochiaceae)

arifolium	EPar
canadense	GPoy MSal MTol WCru
caudatum	CHan CRDP CRow EMon EPla LHop MBri MSal SSvw WCru WHal
europaeum	CAvo CBos CBow CHEx CHan CRDP ECha EFol EFou ELan EMil EPar EPla GPoy LHop MFir MHew MSal MWat NGar NSti SAxl WCru WEas WHer WWye
hartwegii	CAvo CRDP ECha EPot MHig MSal MSto NBir WCru WMar
lemmonii	EPla

ASCLEPIAS (Asclepiadaceae)

¶ ***amplexicaulis***	MSal
'Cinderella'	SIgm
curassavica	CTro EBar LAbb MSal SLMG SLon
¶ ***exaltata***	MSal
♦***fruticosa***	See GOMPHOCARPUS ***fruticosus***
incarnata	CGre CHan CPle EBee ECro ELan GLil MRav MSal MUlv SAxl SFis SPer WPer
¶ – 'Alba'	EMon
♦***physocarpa***	See GOMPHOCARPUS ***physocarpus***
purpurascens	ECro EWoo LHop
¶ ***rubra***	MSal
speciosa	MSal
syriaca	CArn CGre ECro GCal GPlt MSal MSte WPer WPla
tuberosa	CArn CB&S CDoC EBar EBre ECED ECro EMil GPoy LAbb LBre MHew MRav MSal SFis SMrm WPer WWin
– Gay Butterflies Group	WHil

ASPARAGUS (Liliaceae/Asparagaceae)

asparagoïdes AGM	ERea SLMG
densiflorus 'Myers' AGM	ERea MBri
– Sprengeri Group AGM	MBri
falcatus	MBri
officinalis AGM	CHEx MHew WByw WNdy
– ***pseudoscaber*** 'Spitzenschleier'	GCal
setaceus AGM	MBri
– 'Pyramidalis'	MBri
verticillatus	GCal SRms

ASPENIUM

¶ ***scolopendrium*** 'Crispum Bolton's Nobile'	WRic
– Undulatum Cristatum Group	WRic

ASPERULA (Rubiaceae)

arcadiensis JCA 210.100	CPBP NTow WDav
aristata ssp. ***scabra***	ECha ELan EMon
– ssp. ***thessala***	See A. ***sintenisii***
gussonii	CLew CNic CRiv EPot ESis GAbr GArf GDra MBro MCas MHig MPit MTho MWat NHed NHol NKay NWCA SBla SIng SSmi WAbe WPat WThu
hexaphylla	ECED
hirta	CNic MCas MHig NHol NRed
§ ***lilaciflora***	LBee MHig NWCA SIng
– var. ***caespitosa***	See A. ***l. lilaciflora***
– ssp. ***lilaciflora***	CLew CMHG EBre ELan EPot LBre MTho NHar NHol NKay NMen NNrd SHer WPat WWin
nitida	ELan MCas MTho NNrd
– ssp. ***puberula***	See A. ***sintenisii***
odorata	See GALIUM ***odoratum***
§ ***perpusilla***	CShe
§ ***sintenisii*** AGM	EPot LBee MBro NHar NHol NKay NTow SBla SHer SIng SWas WAbe WDav WHoo WThu
suberosa hort.	EBre ELan EPot LBre MTho NHol NKay NMen SGil SHer SSmi WDav WOMN WThu
taurina ssp. ***caucasica***	EMon MHlr NSti SAxl WBon WCot WHal
tinctoria	GBar GPoy LHol MChe MHew MSal SIde SRms

ASPHODELINE (Liliaceae/Asphodelaceae)

brevicaulis	CMon SWas
liburnica	CChu CHol CMon CRDP ECha EMar MBro MNFA MWat NBro SDix WCot WRus
§ ***lutea***	Widely available
*– 'Gelbkerze' ('Yellow Candle')	EBar EPot

ASPHODELUS (Liliaceae/Asphodelaceae)

acaulis	ECha EWoo NGar SWas
– SF 37	CMon
§ ***aestivus***	CSam GCal SAxl
albus	CBot CChu EBul ECha EOrc ESma LGre
brevicaulis	See ASPHODELINE ***b.***
cerasiferus	See A. ***ramosus***
fistulosus	CAvo EFol ELan EMon EOrc ESis LGan LGre LHop MFir MTho NBir NBro WPer WWin
lusitanicus	See A. ***ramosus***

luteus	See ASPHODELINE ***lutea***
microcarpus	See A. ***aestivus***
§ ***ramosus***	CHan CMon EBee GAul LGre MNFA SAsh

ASPIDISTRA (Liliaceae/Convallariaceae)

elatior AGM	CHEx EBak ERav LHil MBri MHlr NRog SAxl SGil SHer SMad WMar WOak
– 'Variegata' AGM	LAbb MTho MUlv NBir
* ***lurida*** 'Irish Mist'	IBlr

ASPLENIUM † (Aspleniaceae)

adiantum-nigrum	CTom NHar
alternans	See A. ***dalhousieae***
bulbiferum AGM	CTro NMar WEas
§ ***ceterach***	EFer
cuneifolium	NKay
dareoïdes	GDra NHar NHol
§ ***delthiopicum***	EFou NBar
* ***fimbriatum***	MBri
flabellifolium	NMar
fontanum	NHar
furcatum Thunberg	See A. ***aethiopicum***
lepidum	NKay
marinum	NMar
nidus AGM	MBri
officinarum	See A. ***ceterach***
¶ ***platyneuron***	CFil
rhizophyllum	NMar
ruta-muraria	EFer SRms
– ssp. ***dolomiticum*** var. ***eberlei***	NKay
§ ***scolopendrium*** AGM	CFil CKin CWGN EBre ECha EFou EGol EHon EPar GPoy LBre LMay MBal MBri MSta NBro NGar NHol NKay NMar NOrc SArc SDix SMad SPer SRms WFib WWye
– 'Angustatum'	EFou NHar SMad SPla
– 'Conglomeratum'	SRms
– Crispum Group	CFil CRDP ECha EFer ELan EPla MBri MHlr NHar NHol NKay SApp WAbe WFib
– 'Crispum Nobile'	NBro NMar WEas WRic
– Cristatum Group	ELan IOrc MBal MBri MRav NHar NHol NKay NMar SMad SPer SPla SRms SWat WFib WHil
– 'Digitatum'	WFib
– 'Kaye's Lacerated'	EBee EGol ELan MBri NHar NHol NMar WRic
– Laceratum Group	SRms
– Marginatum Group	CWGN NMar SWat
– Marginatum Group 'Irregulare'	CRDP NHar NHol SRms WFib
– 'Muricatum'	CRDP NMar
– 'Ramocristatum'	NMar WRic
– 'Ramomarginatum Group'	CWGN ELan SRms WRic
– 'Sagittatocristatum'	NKay
– Undulatum Group	EGol EPla GGar NHar NMar SPla SRms SWat WAbe WRic
septentrionale	SRms
trichomanes	EBre EFer EFou ELan GGar LBre MBal MBri NHar NHol NKay NMar SApp SCob SLga WFib WHal WRic
– Cristatum Group	NMar
– Incisum Group	IOrc NHar NMar SMad
viride	SRms

ASTELIA (Liliaceae/Asteliaceae)

banksii	CB&S
cunninghamii	See A. ***solandri***
fragrans	CFil ECou
¶ ***graminea***	ECou
grandis	EBul
nervosa	CAbb CB&S CFil CHEx CTbh EBul ECou SArc
– var. ***chathamica***	GCal SArc WCot
– – 'Silver Spear'	CB&S CFee CFil CHEx EBee ERea EWri IBar IMal LHil LHop SDry WCru
nivicola 'Red Gem'	EWri WCot
§ ***solandri***	CHEx

ASTER † (Compositae/Asteraceae)

acris	See A. ***sedifolius***
♦ ***ageratoïdes***	See A. ***trinervius a.***
§ ***albescens***	CGre CPle CPou EMon EPla ISea MBal MPla WCru WSHC
alpigenus	CNic
alpinus AGM	CHol CWGN EBar EBre EMNN GCHN LBre MCas MFir MPit MWat NHol NKay NMen NNrw NWCA SBla SHer SIng WOMN WOld WPer WStI WWin
– var. ***albus***	CNic GBuc GCHN NCat NHol SIng WPer
– 'Beechwood'	NKay
– 'Dunkle Schöne' ('Dark Beauty')	EFou NOak WPer
– 'Happy End'	NHol NOak NRoo
– 'Roseus'	EPad
– 'Trimix'	ESis LAbb NBir NMir NRoo NVic SFis WHil
– violet	CBow WPer
– 'White Beauty'	CBow EFou MWil SIde
amelloïdes	See FELICIA ***amelloïdes***
amellus	NNor
– 'Blue King'	EFou SFis
– 'Breslau'	WOld
– 'Brilliant'	CAll CKel CLew CMGP CSco EBre ECtt EFou EGol EOrc LBre MNFA MWat NRoo SAxl SPer WByw WMer WOld
– 'Butzemann'	EFou
– 'Doktor Otto Petschek'	WMer
– 'Framfieldii' AGM	WOld
– 'Glücksfund' ('Empress')	WOld
– 'Jacqueline Genebrier' AGM	SMrm SWas WByw WOld
– 'King George' AGM	CAll CElw CHol CKel EBre ECED EFou ELan EOrc EPla ERav LBre MBel MWat NRoo SChu SPer SPla WAbe WEas WHoo WOld WPer
– 'Kobold'	WOld
– 'Lac de Genève'	CHol CSco CShe LRHS MBri WCot
– 'Lady Hindlip'	MUlv WEas
* – 'Marie Anne Neill'	SFis
– 'Moerheim Gem'	CAll WEas WOld
– 'Nocturne'	CAll ECED WByw WOld
– 'Peach Blossom'	CDoC EFou MUlv WOld

– 'Pink Pearl'	WOld
– 'Pink Zenith' ('Rosa Erfüllung')	Widely available
– 'Praecox Junifreude'	EFou
– 'Rudolph Goethe'	CCla EFou MUlv NPri SHBN WEas WMer WOld
– 'Schöne von Ronsdorf'	WOld
– 'September Glow'	ECha EFou EHal EOrc
– 'Sonia'	CAll ECha EFou SFis SUsu WByw WMer WOld
– 'Sonora'	WOld
– 'Sternkugel'	CShe WOld
– 'Ultramarine'	CAll EFou WAbb
N– 'Veilchenkönigin' ('Violet Queen') AGM	CAll CGle CKel CLew CMGP CVer EBar EBre ECha ECtt EFou ELan LBre MBri SBla SChu SDix SGil SUsu SWas WEas WHoo WOld WPer
– 'Weltfriede'	WOld
asper	See A. ***bakerianus***
§ ***bakerianus***	CHan NOak WOld WPer
'Barbara Worl'	SAsh
'Blue Star'	CBre EFou SChu WOld
canus	See A. ***sedifolius c.***
capensis 'Variegata '	See FELICIA ***amelloïdes*** variegated
§ ***carolinianus***	CHan
coelestis	See FELICIA ***amelloïdes***
'Coombe Fishacre' AGM	CAll CGle EFou GCal LGre LHil MBel MBri MNFA MTol MUlv NCat SFis SPla SWas WByw WEas WHer WOld
cordifolius 'Elegans'	CAll EFou NSti SHig WOld
– 'Ideal'	CDoC EFou LRHS WOld WPer
– 'Little Carlow'	See A. 'L. C.'
– 'Little Dorrit'	See A. 'Little Dorrit'
– 'Photograph'	See A. 'Photograph'
– 'Silver Queen'	CAll EOrc
– 'Silver Spray'	CAll CBre CCla CDoC EFou MBri MWat SFis WEas WHoo WMer WOld WPer
– 'Sweet Lavender' AGM	CAll GMac MNFA SFis WOld
corymbosus	See A. ***divaricatus***
'Deep Pink Star'	WOld
diffusus	See A. ***lateriflorus***
¶ ***diplostephioïdes***	GArf
§ ***divaricatus***	CAll CBos CBre CCla CElw CGle CHad CHan CLew CMea CRDP ECha EFol EFou ELan EOrc ESiP LHop MRav NHol NRar NSti SChu SHig SUsu WByw WOld WPer WWat WWin
N ***dumosus***	NKay WPer
ericoïdes	CGle CSam ERav SChu SIng WHil WWin
– 'Blue Heaven'	COtt
– 'Blue Star' AGM	GBuc NFai WOld
– 'Blue Wonder'	CGle MNFA WOld
– 'Brimstone' AGM	CAll EOrc MNFA WOld
– 'Cinderella'	CAll CTom CVer EHal EOrc EPad GMac MNFA NRoo NSti SPer SPla
– 'Constance'	CAll WOld
*– 'Dainty'	CLew CRDP
– 'Enchantress'	CAll
– 'Erlkönig'	CAll CMGP EFou EHic EJud GAbr LHil MBri MMil MSte SChu SHer WOld WPer
– 'Esther'	CAll CGle CLew ECha EFou EOrc ESma MNFA NBrk NSti SChu SDix SFis WOld
– 'Golden Spray' AGM	CAll CBre EFou MNFA NSti SPla WMer WOld
– 'Herbstmyrte'	GBuc
– 'Hon. Edith Gibbs'	CAll EOrc GMac WCot
– 'Hon. Vicary Gibbs'	See A. 'H. V. G.' (ericoïdes x)
– 'Ideal'	CAll
– 'Maidenhood'	SFis WOld
– 'Monte Cassino'	See A. ***pringlei*** 'M.C.'
¶– 'Novembermyrte'	CAll
– 'Perfection'	CAll
– 'Pink Cloud' AGM	CAll CBre CChu CGle CLew CTom CVer EFol EFou EOrc ESma MBro MNFA MSte MTol MUlv NFai NRoo SPla WHoo WOld WPer WRus
– prostrate form	EFol SCro
– 'Rosy Veil'	CAll GMac WByw WOld
– 'Schneegitter'	CAll EHic MSte
– 'Vimmer's Delight'	CAll
– 'White Heather'	CAll CBre CGle CSco CVer GMac LHil MHlr MNFA SFis SPla WByw WCot WEas WHoo WOld
– 'Yvette Richardson'	WOld
§ ***flaccidus***	GPlt MDHE
– ***albus***	WHil
foliaceus cusickii	EMon
x ***frikartii***	CAll CCla CLew CMea CSev EBre EFou EGol ELan ENot EOrc EPar GCHN LBre LHop MRav NBar NKay SBla SChu SGil SHBN SPer WByw WEas WOld WPer WWin
– 'Eiger'	WOld
– 'Flora's Delight'	EBre EOrc LBre NRoo
– 'Jungfrau'	MUlv NSti SAxl WOld
N– 'Mönch' AGM	Widely available
– 'Wunder von Stäfa' AGM	CCla CElw CMGP CSco ECot EFol EOrc MBri MUlv NSti SAxl SFis SHer WOld WStI WSun
'Herfstweelde'	CBre EMon GBuc SWas
¶ x ***herveyi***	EMon
himalaicus	GCHN GCra GTou
– BM&W 12	NHol
– C&Mc 145	GCHN WDav
– EMAK 0952	NHol
'Hon. Vicary Gibbs' (***ericoïdes*** x)	CAll CGle EOrc ESma MNFA MSte NBrk SFis WOld
hybridus luteus	See X SOLIDASTER ***luteus***
¶ ***ibericus***	EBee
§ 'Kylie' AGM	CBre EMon WCot WOld
laevis	CBre MSte
– 'Arcturus'	CBos CLTr LBlm
– 'Calliope'	EBar SWas WOld
lanceolatus 'Edwin Beckett'	CAll MNFA SFis WOld
lateriflorus	CGle EJud EOrc MNFA MNes WHow WOld WPer
– 'Delight'	CAll MUlv WOld
– 'Horizontalis' AGM	Widely available
– 'Lovely'	SFis
– 'Prince'	CAll CGle CLew CMil ECha EFou EHal EMon EPla MHlr SMad SPla SWas WCot

likiangensis	See A. ***asteroïdes***
§ ***linosyris***	CAll EPla SFis SPer WCot WMer
– 'Goldilocks'	See A. ***linosyris***
§ 'Little Carlow' (***cordifolius*** x) AGM	CAll CBre CGle EFou EHal EJud EOrc GCal LHil MNFA MRav NSti SBla SFis WEas WHal WOld WPer
§ 'Little Dorrit' (***cordifolius*** x)	CAll GMac NSti WCot WOld
macrophyllus	CAll CPou EBee ELan EMon NSti SPer WHaw WOld
– 'Albus'	EMon LRHS WCot
– 'Twilight'	CGle EBar EGle GMac MSte SUsu SWas WCot WOld
mongolicus	See KALIMERIS ***mongolica***
natalensis	See FELICIA ***rosulata***
* ***nepaulensis***	NWCA
novae-angliae	
'Andenken an Alma Pötschke' AGM	Widely available
– 'Andenken an Paul Gerber	EMon WMer
– 'Barr's Blue'	CGle EFou EMon MUlv SChu SHer WMer WOld
– 'Barr's Pink'	CAll CBre EFou EMon LHop SFis WEas WMer WOld WPer
– 'Barr's Violet'	CAll CGle SRms WCot WOld WPer
– 'Crimson Beauty'	CAll MWat WOld
– 'Ernie Moss'	SFis
– 'Festival'	SFis
– 'Forncett Jewel'	CAll EFou
– 'Harrington's Pink' AGM	CAll CBre CElw CGle CMea CSco CVer ECED EFou EMon EOrc IDai MWat NOak SChu SCro SGil SPer WByw WEas WOld WSun WWin
§ – 'Herbstschnee' ('Autumn Snow')	CAll CBre CGle CShe EBre EFou EMon EOrc GCHN GMac LBre LHop MBel MWat NFai NHol NSti SChu SGil SHer SPer WOld WPer WWin
– 'Lye End Beauty'	CAll CBre CGle EFou EMon EOrc MFir MNFA MSte MUlv MWat NOak SChu WOld
– 'Lye End Companion'	CAll CGle
– 'Mrs S T Wright'	CAll EFou EMon WByw WOld
*– 'Mrs S W Stern'	WOld
– 'Purple Cloud'	CAll EMon LHop
¶ – 'Purple Dome'	EMon
– 'Quinton Menzies'	CAll EMon EOrc MUlv WOld
– 'Red Cloud'	EFou
– 'Rosa Sieger'	EMon SChu WMer WOld
– 'Roter Stern'	EFou
– 'Rubinschatz'	CAll EFou
– 'Rudelsburg'	EFou EMon
– 'Sayer's Croft'	WCot
– 'Septemberrubin' ('September Ruby')	CAll CBre CMea EBre ECED ECtt EMon LBre LHop MRav MUlv NFai SChu SGil WByw WEas WOld WWin
– 'Treasure'	CAll CBre EFou EMon WOld
– 'Violetta'	CAll CBre EMon WOld
– 'W Bowman'	EMon
¶ ***novi-belgii***	WHer

N– 'Ada Ballard'	CAll CMGP CSco ECED ECas GCHN MBel SPer WOld
– 'Albanian'	CAll CElw EJud WOld
– 'Alderman Vokes'	CAll WOld
– 'Alex Norman'	CAll WOld
– 'Algar's Pride'	CAll MUlv WOld
– 'Alice Haslam'	CAll CBow CMGP ECas ECtt EFou MBal MBri MFir NBar NKay NOrc SPla WByw WHil WOld WPer
– 'Alpenglow'	CAll WOld
– 'Anita Ballard'	CAll WOld
– 'Anita Webb'	WEas WOld WPer
– 'Anneke'	WGor WHer
– 'Apollo'	CAll CB&S MBri
– 'Apple Blossom'	CAll WOld
– 'Archbishop'	WOld
– 'Arctic'	CAll WOld
– 'Audrey'	CAll CBow CBre CLew CMGP EBar ECED ECas ECtt EFou GCHN MBri MNFA NBar NBro NKay NOrc SPla WByw WMer WOld
– 'Autumn Beauty'	CAll WOld
– 'Autumn Days'	CAll WOld
– 'Autumn Glory'	CAll WOld
– 'Autumn Rose'	CAll WOld
– 'Autumn Snow'	See A. ***n-a*** 'Herbstschnee'
– 'Baby Climax'	CAll WOld
– 'Beechwood Beacon'	CAll
– 'Beechwood Challenger'	CAll CDoC NKay WMer WOld
– 'Beechwood Charm'	CAll MNFA WOld WSun
– 'Beechwood Rival'	WMer
– 'Beechwood Supreme'	CAll WOld
– 'Belmont Blue'	CAll
– 'Bewunderung'	EFou
– 'Blandie'	CAll CMGP CSco ECED ECas EFou MSte MWat NBro NVic WOld
– 'Blauglut'	EFou
– 'Blue Baby'	LHop SHer WPer
– 'Blue Bouquet'	CAll ECED SRms WByw WOld
– 'Blue Boy'	WOld
– 'Blue Danube'	CAll WOld
– 'Blue Eyes'	CAll EFou WOld
– 'Blue Gem'	CAll
– 'Blue Gown'	CAll CBre GCal MBri WOld
– 'Blue Patrol'	CAll WOld
– 'Blue Plume'	CAll
– 'Blue Radiance'	CAll MNFA WOld
– 'Blue Whirl'	CAll WOld
– 'Bonanza'	CAll MBal WOld
– 'Boningale Blue'	CAll WOld
– 'Boningale White'	CAll WOld
– 'Borealis'	CAll
– 'Bridesmaid'	CAll WOld
– 'Bridgette'	EFou
– 'Brightest and Best'	WOld
– 'Cameo'	CAll WOld
– 'Cantab'	WOld
– 'Carlingcot'	CAll WOld
– 'Carnival'	CAll CMGP CSco ECas EFou MBri MUlv NBar NOrc SFis SPer WCra WOld
– 'Cecily'	CAll WOld
– 'Charles Wilson'	WCot WOld

– 'Chatterbox' CAll CSco ECtt MNFA MWat SChu SRms WEas WOld
– 'Chelwood' CAll WOld
– 'Chequers' CAll ECED ECas ECot NBar WCra WGor WOld
– 'Chilcompton' CAll
– 'Choristers' CAll CShe CVer WOld
– 'Christina' See A. *n-b.* 'Kristina'
– 'Christine Soanes' EFou
– 'Cliff Lewis' CAll CShe WOld
– 'Climax' CAll CBre CSco ECha GCal GMac LBlm MBri MNFA MUlv NSti SPer WOld
– 'Climax Albus' See A. *n-b.* 'White Climax'
– 'Cloudy Blue' CAll CElw CVer EFou WOld
– 'Colin Bailey' CAll
– 'Colonel F R Durham' CAll WMer
– 'Coombe Gladys' WOld
– 'Coombe Joy' WOld
– 'Coombe Margaret' CAll WOld
– 'Coombe Queen' CAll WOld
– 'Coombe Radiance' WOld
– 'Coombe Ronald' MWat WOld
– 'Coombe Rosemary' CDec EBre ECtt LBre MUlv SGil WByw WCot WOld
– 'Coombe Violet' MWat WOld
– 'Countess of Dudley' CAll WOld WPer
– 'Court Herald' CAll CBow WOld
– 'Crimson Brocade' CAll CKel CSco ECED ELan ENot MBri MWat WMer WOld
– 'Crimson Velvet' CAll
– 'Dandy' CAll CTom EBee ECas ECot EFou ELan WByw WOld
– 'Daniela' EFou
– 'Daphne Anne' WOld
– 'Dauerblau' EFou WOld
– 'Davey's True Blue' EBee ECas WOld
– 'David Murray' WOld
– 'Dazzler' CAll EFou WOld
– 'Destiny' CAll WOld
– 'Diana' CNic WOld
– 'Diana Watts' CAll WOld
– 'Dietgard' WOld
– 'Dolly' EFou
– 'Dora Chiswell' CAll
– 'Dorothy Bailey' CAll
– 'Dusky Maid' CAll WOld
– 'Elizabeth' CAll WOld
– 'Elizabeth Bright' CAll WOld
– 'Elizabeth Hutton' CAll WOld
– 'Elsie Dale' CAll WOld
– 'Elta' WOld
– 'Erica' CAll CBow MWat WCot WOld
– 'Ernest Ballard' CAll MRav WOld
– 'Ernie Moss' EFou
– 'Eva' CAll WOld
– 'Eventide' CAll CB&S CElw ECED EFou ENot SPer WOld
– 'F M Simpson' ECas
– 'Fair Lady' CAll MWat WOld
– 'Faith' CAll WOld
– 'Farrington' CAll WOld
– 'Felicity' CAll
– 'Fellowship' CAll CB&S CElw CMGP ECED ECas EFou GCHN MBri MHlr MNFA MUlv MWat NCat NMir NVic SPer WEas WOld
– 'Flair' CAll
– 'Flamingo' CAll CSco
– 'Fontaine' WOld
– 'Freda Ballard' CAll EBee EBre ECED ECas EFou GCHN LBre MUlv MWat WOld
– 'Fuldatal' EFou
– 'Gayborder Beauty' CAll
– 'Gayborder Blue' CAll
– 'Gayborder Royal' CAll WOld
– 'Gayborder Spire' CAll
– 'Gayborder Splendour' WOld
– 'Goliath' CAll WOld
– 'Guardsman' CAll WOld
– 'Gulliver' EFou
– 'Gurney Slade' CAll CBre EJud MBri WOld
– 'Guy Ballard' CAll NNor
– 'Harrison's Blue' CAll WEas WOld WPer
– 'Heather' CAll
– 'Heinz Richard' CAll CMGP ECas ECha EFou ESma LHop MBri MUlv NBir SBla SChu WHil WOld
– 'Helen' WOld
– 'Helen Ballard' CAll CSco WOld
– 'Herbstpurzel' EFou WGor WMer
– 'Hey Day' CAll
– 'Hilda Ballard' CAll WOld
– 'Ilse Brensell' EFou
– 'Irene' CAll WOld
– 'Isabel Allen' WOld
– 'Janet McMullen' CAll EJud
– 'Janet Watts' CAll WOld
– 'Janice Stephenson' CAll
– 'Jean' CAll CSco MWat SChu SPla WEas WOld
– 'Jean Gyte' CAll WOld
– 'Jenny' CAll CBow CHol CKel CLew CSco EBre ECED ECas ECtt EFou ERav GCHN IDai LBre LHil LHop MBri MBro MRav MWat NBar SHBN SPer WByw WEas WHoo WOld WPer
– 'Jollity' CAll WOld
– 'Judith' EFou
– 'Julia' CAll WOld
– 'Juliet' CAll
– 'Karen' CAll
– 'Karminkuppel' CAll EFou
– 'King of the Belgians' CAll WOld
– 'King's College' CAll WOld
– 'Kristina' CAll EBre ECha ECtt EFol EFou LBre LHil MRav MUlv NBrk NCat WCot WHil WOld
– 'Lady Evelyn Drummond' WOld
– 'Lady Frances' CAll WHil WOld
– 'Lady in Blue' CAll CBow CLew CSco EBre ECas ECtt EFou ELan ENot EPla GCHN IHos LBre LHil MBro MWat NBar NMir NVic SPer SPla SSte WByw WHoo WOld WPer WWin
– 'Lady Paget' CAll WOld
– 'Lassie' CAll MWat SFis WOld
– 'Lavender Dream' CAll WOld
– 'Lawrence Chiswell' CAll WOld
– 'Leuchtfeuer' EFou
– 'Lilac Time' CAll WByw WOld
– 'Lisa Dawn' CAll WOld
– 'Little Blue Baby' CTom

– 'Little Boy Blue'	CAll CB&S SHBN WByw WMer WOld
– 'Little Pink Beauty'	CAll CBow CTom EBar ECas ECtt EFou ELan GCHN IHos LHop MBri MBro MWat NKay NMir NVic SHer SPer WEas WHil WHoo WOld WWin
– 'Little Pink Lady'	CAll CSco ECED
– 'Little Pink Pyramid'	CHol CSco SRms
– 'Little Red Boy'	CAll CB&S CSco MBel MTol WOld
– 'Little Treasure'	CAll WOld
– 'Lucy'	CAll WOld
– 'Mabel Reeves'	CAll CShe
– 'Madge Cato'	CAll WOld
– 'Mammoth'	CAll WOld
– 'Margaret Murray'	CAll
– 'Margaret Rose'	CAll ELan NKay NOrc WOld
– 'Margery Bennett'	CAll WOld
– 'Marie Ann Neil'	EFou
– 'Marie Ballard'	CAll CB&S CElw CKel CSco CShe EBre ECED ECas ENot GCal LBre LWad MBri MFir MWat NKay NOrc SChu SHBN SPer WEas WOld WPer
– 'Marie's Pretty Please'	EFou
– 'Marjorie'	CAll WOld
– 'Marjory Ballard'	WOld
– 'Mars'	CAll
– 'Martonie'	WOld WPer
– 'Mary'	CAll
– 'Mary Dean'	CAll WEas WOld WPer
– 'May Louise'	CAll
– 'Melbourne'	CAll
– 'Melbourne Belle'	CAll WOld
– 'Melbourne Lad'	CAll
– 'Melbourne Magnet'	WOld
– 'Melbourne Mauve'	CAll
– 'Melbourne Sparkler'	CAll
– 'Michael Watts'	CAll WOld
– 'Michelle'	CAll
– 'Miranda'	CAll
– 'Miss Muffet'	CAll
– 'Mistress Ford'	CAll
– 'Mistress Quickly'	CAll MBel WOld
– 'Mount Everest'	CAll CDoC WMer WOld WPer
– 'Mrs J Sangster'	CAll
– 'Mrs Leo Hunter'	CAll WOld
– 'My Smokey'	CAll
– 'Nancy'	CAll
– 'Nightfall'	CAll
– 'Niobe'	CAll CLew ELan WMer WOMN WOld
– 'Nobilis'	WOld
– 'Norman Thornely'	CAll
– 'Norman's Jubilee'	CAll WOld
– 'Norton Fayre'	CAll CShe
– 'Nursteed Charm'	CAll WOld
– 'Oktoberschneekuppel'	LRHS
– 'Orchid Pink'	CAll
– 'Orlando'	CAll WCot WOld
– 'Pacific Amarant'	SRos
– 'Pamela'	CAll WOld
– 'Patricia Ballard'	CAll CLew CMGP CSco CShe ECED ECas MBri MFir MWat NBro NKay NVic WOld WPer
– 'Peace'	CAll WOld
– 'Peerless'	CAll
– 'Pensford'	CAll
– 'Percy Thrower'	CAll ECas EFou WEas WOld
– 'Perry's White'	CAll
– 'Peter Chiswell'	MTol WOld
– 'Peter Harrison'	CAll GMac MBal MBri NBro WOld WPer
– 'Peter Pan'	CAll GPlt SHer WOld WSun
– 'Picture'	CAll WOld
– 'Pink Buttons'	CAll
– 'Pink Gown'	WOld
– 'Pink Lace'	CAll CSco EBar ECtt WByw WEas WOld WPer
– 'Pink Pyramid'	EJud WOld
– 'Plenty'	CBre WOld
– 'Pride of Colwall'	CSco
– 'Priory Blush'	CAll GMac WOld WSun
– 'Professor Anton Kippenberg'	CAll CSco CShe EBre ECtt EFou EJud GCHN GMac GPlt LBlm LBre MBri MBro SPer WAbe WOld
– 'Prosperity'	CAll WOld
– 'Prunella'	CAll WOld
– 'Purple Dome'	EFou WOld
– 'Purple Emperor'	CAll
– 'Queen Mary'	CAll WMer WOld
– 'Queen of Colwall'	CAll WOld
– 'Rachel Ballard'	CAll
– 'Ralph Picton'	WOld
– 'Raspberries and Cream'	CAll
– 'Raspberry Ripple'	CAll CMGP ECas ECot EFou MBri WOld
– 'Rector'	WOld
– 'Red Greetings'	CAll
– 'Red Robin'	MWat
– 'Red Sunset'	CAll CB&S WOld
– 'Rembrandt'	CAll CSco ECas
– 'Remembrance'	CAll EFou WOld
– 'Reverend Vincent Dale'	CAll WOld
– 'Richness'	CAll WOld
– 'Robert'	CAll
– 'Robin Adair'	CAll WOld
– 'Rose Bonnet'	CMGP CTom ECas EFou ENot IHos MMil MTol MWat NBar SChu SHBN SPla
– 'Rose Bouquet'	CAll CLew WOld
– 'Rosebud'	CAll ELan WEas WHoo WOld
– 'Rosemarie Sallman'	EFou
– 'Rosenwichtel'	CAll EFou EMar MBri NBar WOld
– 'Rosie Nutt'	CAll
– 'Royal Blue'	CAll WMer
– 'Royal Ruby'	CAll CSco ECtt WOld
– 'Royal Velvet'	CAll CSco ECED ENot WHil WOld
– 'Royal Violet'	CAll
– 'Royalty'	CAll
– 'Rozika'	EFou
– 'Rufus'	CAll WOld
– 'Sailing Light'	CAll
– 'Sailor Boy'	CAll CBre SFis WOld
– 'Saint Egwyn'	CAll WOld
– 'Sandford White Swan'	EJud MBel MTol WPer
– 'Sandford's Purple'	CAll
– 'Sarah Ballard'	CAll MUlv MWat WOld
– 'Saturn'	CAll

– 'Schneekissen' ('Snow Cushion')	CLew CSco EBre ECas ECtt EHal LBre LHop MBal MBri MBro NMir SBla SHer SPer WHil WOld
– 'Schöne von Dietlikon'	CAll CDoC EFou WMer WOld
– 'Schoolgirl'	CAll CShe MUlv WOld
– 'Sheena'	WCot WOld
– 'Silver Mist'	CAll
– 'Sir Edward Elgar'	CAll
– 'Snowdrift'	CAll EBee WOld
– 'Snowsprite'	CAll CB&S CBow CHol CKel CMGP CTom EBee EBre ECED ECas ELan IDai LBre MWat NBar NBro NOrc SPla WByw WHoo WOld
– 'Sonata'	CAll ECas EFou EJud LHil SPer WCra WOld
– 'Sophia'	CAll WOld
– 'Sputnik'	CAll
– 'Starlight'	CAll EFou ENot WOld
– 'Steinebrück'	EFou
– 'Stella Lewis'	CAll
– 'Sterling Silver'	CAll CShe WByw WOld
– 'Storm Clouds'	EFou SFis
– 'Strawberries and Cream'	CAll
– 'Sunset'	CAll WOld
– 'Sussex Violet'	CAll
– 'Sweet Briar'	WOld
– 'Symbol'	CAll
– 'Tapestry'	CAll WOld
– 'Terry's Pride'	CAll WOld
– 'The Archbishop'	CAll EFou
– 'The Bishop'	CAll WOld
– 'The Cardinal'	CAll ECED SFis WOld
– 'The Dean'	CAll WOld
– 'The Rector'	CAll
– 'The Sexton'	CAll WOld
– 'Thundercloud'	CAll WOld
– 'Timsbury'	CAll WOld
– 'Tony'	CAll WOld
– 'Tosca'	SFis
– 'Tovarich'	CAll GMac WOld
– 'Triumph'	SFis
– 'Trudi Ann'	EFou SFis
– 'True Blue'	CAll
– 'Twinkle'	EFou SFis
– 'Victor'	CAll MBal WOld
– 'Violet Lady'	CAll WOld
*– 'Violet Queen'	CBow EBre LBre LWad SFis WAbe
– 'Violetta'	CB&S EFou
– 'Waterperry'	MWat
– 'Weisse Wunder'	EFou
§ – 'White Climax'	CAll EFou MUlv WCot WOld
– 'White Ladies'	CAll EBee EBre ECas ECtt EFou LBre MUlv NOrc SPer
– 'White Swan'	CAll CBre CHol EMon NOak WEas WOld
– 'White Wings'	CAll MNFA WCot WOld
– 'Wickwar Crimson'	CAll
– 'Winford'	CAll
– 'Winston S Churchill'	CAll CBow CKel CRDP CSco ECED ELan ENot LWad MHFP MNFA MTol MWat NOrc SHBN SPer WEas WHil WOld
'Ochtendgloren' (*pringlei* x) AGM	EFou EMon GBuc MUlv
paniculatus hort.	See A. ***lanceolatus***
pappei	See FELICIA ***amoena***
'Pearl Star'	WOld
perfoliatus	NCat
petiolatus	See FELICIA ***petiolata***
§ 'Photograph' AGM	CAll CHan EFou MNFA MTol WOld
§ ***pilosus*** var. ***demotus*** AGM	CBre MSte SCro SGil SPla SWas
'Pink Star'	CBos CBre EFou GMac MHlr NSti WCot WOld
§ ***pringlei*** 'Monte Cassino' AGM	CChu CGle COtt EBre ECha EFou EHal ESma LBre LGre LHop MNFA MUlv NBrk NHol NRoo SChu SDix SGil SPla SWas WByw WCot WHil WOld
procumbens	CMer
ptarmicoïdes	CAll EFou EMon NPri WPer
pyrenaeus 'Lutetia'	CAll EBee ECha EFou GCal GMac MNFA MUlv NSti SHer WCot WOld
¶ ***radula***	GCal
'Ringdove' (***ericoïdes*** x) AGM	CAll CMGP EBee MMil NSti SChu SHer SPer WEas WOld
'Rosa Star'	WOld
rotundifolius 'Variegatus'	See FELICIA ***amelloïdes*** 'Variegata'
* ***sativus atrocaeruleus***	EBee ECro
scandens	See A. ***carolinianus***
§ ***sedifolius***	CAll EJud ELan EMon MTol MWat SDix SFis SPer SUsu WEas WOld WPer WSun
– 'Nanus'	CAll ECED ECha EFol EFou MBri NBir NSti SFis SSvw WByw WHow WOld
– 'Roseus'	CAll
'Snow Star'	WOld
spathulifolius	CHan CPle
spectabilis	CChu CLew WOld
sp. BM&W 18	See ERIGERON ***multiradiatus*** BM&W 18
¶ sp. CC&McK 145	NWCA
¶ sp. CLD 0494	NHol
¶ ***subspicatus***	WPer
thomsonii 'Nanus'	CGle COtt CSam CSco EBre ECha EFou EMon EOrc GCHN LBee LBre MNFA MRav NKay NRoo SBla SHBN WEas WHoo WMar WMer WOld WPer WSHC
tibeticus	See A. ***flaccidus***
§ ***tongolensis***	CHan MRav SRms WOMN WWin
– 'Berggarten'	EFou EOrc GCal MBri NRoo SCro SFis SPla WMer
– 'Lavender Star'	CLew EFou NMir SRms
– 'Napsbury'	CSco ECha EPla GCal GMac MBri NSti NVic SFis SPla
– 'Wartburgstern'	NPri SFis WPer
tradescantii hort.	See A. ***pilosus demotus***
tradescantii Linnaeus	CAll CGle CLTr EBar ECha EFou ELan LHil MFir MNFA MRav MUlv NOak NSti SAxl SMad WEas WOld
tripolium	CKin WHer WOld
turbinellus AGM	CAll EFou MHlr MNFA SChu WCot WOld
umbellatus	CBre EMon EOrc WOld
vahlii	ECou LHop WPer

vimineus 'Ptarmicoides'	See A. ***ptarmicoïdes***
vimineus Lamarck	See A. ***lateriflorus***
'Yvonne'	CBre

ASTERANTHERA (Gesneriaceae)

ovata	CGre ELan GGar MBal NSti SArc SHil WBod WSHC WWat

ASTERISCUS (Compositae/Asteraceae)

'Gold Coin'	See A. ***maritimus***
§ ***maritimus***	CB&S EHic EWes IHos LHop MPit NPri
spinosus	WHer

ASTILBE † (Saxifragaceae)

'Alba' (***simplicifolia***)	EFou GGar NHol SApp
'Amethyst' (x ***arendsii***)	CMGP CMHG CTom EGol NBar NRoo NTow SApp SHig SPer
'Anita Pfeifer' (x ***arendsii***)	MBri MUlv WMer
'Aphrodite' (***simplicifolia*** x)	COtt CSco EBee EBre EGol EPGN GCal LBre MBri MNFA NHol NMir NOrc WAbe WGor WTyr
x ***arendsii***	NNor SHer WPer
astilboïdes	NHol WCot
'Atrorosea' (***simplicifolia*** x)	CSco ECha
'Bergkristall' (x ***arendsii***)	CMHG
'Betsy Cuperus' (***thunbergii*** x)	CMHG EFou
biternata	WDav
'Bonn' (***japonica*** x)	CB&S CKel EPar SRms
'Brautschleier' ('Bridal Veil') (x ***arendsii***) AGM	CMHG EBee ECtt EFou EGol ENot EPGN EPla GAbr GCHN IDai MWat SGil
'Bressingham Beauty' (x ***arendsii***)	CMHG CSco CShe EBre ECtt EHon ELan ELun ENot EPGN EPar GCHN LBre MBri NBee NHol NRoo SChu SCro SGil SHig SPer
'Bronce Elegans' (***simplicifolia*** x) AGM	CBro COtt CSco EBar EBre ECha EFou EPGN EPar GPlt LBre MBal MBri MNFA NBar NHar NHol NKay NMir NOrc SChu SCro SPer WAbe
'Bumalda' (x ***arendsii***)	CDoC EPGN GCHN MBri MSte MUlv NBee NHol SApp WBon
* 'Carmine King'	SFis
¶ 'Carnea' (***simplicifolia*** x)	EGol
'Cattleya' (x ***arendsii***)	CMHG ECha EFou WGor
'Ceres' (x ***arendsii***)	CDoC CMHG MWat NHol NKay
♦ 'Cherry Ripe'	See A. 'Feuer'
chinensis	CMCN CMHG IBlr
– var. ***pumila*** AGM	Widely available
– ***taquetii*** 'Superba '	See A. 'Superba'
* 'Crimson Feather'	ECha
x ***crispa***	GAbr IBlr
'Deutschland' (***japonica*** x)	CB&S CBow CMHG CRDP EBre ECED EGol ELan EPGN EPla GAbr GCHN LBre MBri NHol NKay SApp SCro SHer SPer SPla WAbe WEas WHal WHoo WWin
'Diamant' ('Diamond') (x ***arendsii***)	CDoC CMHG MFir SFis
'Drayton Glory' (x ***arendsii***)	See A. 'Peach Blossom'
'Dunkellachs' (***simplicifolia*** x)	COtt EBre ECha EGol EPGN LBre LWad MBri MNFA NHol NOrc SHig SPla WAbe WMer
'Düsseldorf' (***japonica*** x)	CMGP CMHG EPla GGar SPer
'Elizabeth Bloom' (x ***arendsii***)	EPGN GCHN MArl
'Emden' (***japonica*** x)	MWat
'Erica' (x ***arendsii***)	CMHG GGar MBri
'Etna' (***japonica*** x)	CB&S CDoC CKni CMHG CSev EBee EGle EPGN GBri MBal SCro WTyr
'Europa' (***japonica*** x)	CMHG EPGN MBal NBar NOak SGil SHer
'Fanal' (x ***arendsii***) AGM	Widely available
'Federsee' (x ***arendsii***)	CB&S CMGP CMHG CSco EBre ECha ELan EPGN LBre LHop MBri NBar NKay NRoo SCro SHig SPer WAbe
§ 'Feuer' ('Fire') (x ***arendsii***)	CB&S CKni CMGP CMHG CSam CSco CShe EBre ECha ELan EPGN GCHN GGar LBre MBri NHol NRoo NTow NVic SGil SHer SPer SPla WPbr
'Finale' (***chinensis***)	CMHG CSco EGle EPGN NHol NKay NOrc SPer WEas
'Frankentroll' (***chinensis pumila***)	CMHG WHil
'Gertrud Brix' (x ***arendsii***)	CB&S CMHG COtt EPar WMer
glaberrima	EPar
– var. ***saxatilis*** AGM	CNic CRow ELan EPGN GCHN GCal MBal NHol NKay NOak NRoo NTow SChu SHer
– ***saxosa***	See A. 'Saxosa'
* – – ***minor***	NNrd
¶ 'Gladstone' (x ***arendsii***)	WGor
'Glenroy Elf'	MBal
'Gloria' (x ***arendsii***)	CMHG MBri
'Gloria Purpurea' (x ***arendsii***)	CKni CMHG MUlv NHol
'Glut' ('Glow') (x ***arendsii***)	CMHG EPGN EPar MBri NHol SCro SGil SHer SRms
'Gnom' (x ***crispa***)	CRow NHar
'Granat' (x ***arendsii***)	CDoC CMHG EPGN LHop MBal NHol NKay SDix SGil SHer WWin
grandis	CMHG EPGN GBur
'Grete Püngel' (x ***arendsii***)	MBri WMer
'Harmony' (x ***arendsii***)	CMHG
¶ 'Hennie Graafland' (***simplicifolia*** x)	EGol
'Hyazinth' ('Hyacinth') (x ***arendsii***)	CMHG CSco EGol ELan EPGN GAbr LWad NBee NFai NHol NOrc SCro SHer WTyr

'Inshriach Pink' (*simplicifolia* x)	CBro CMHG EBee EBre EGol ELan EPla GDra LBre MBri MUlv NHar NHol NNrd NOak SGil WHal
'Irrlicht' (x *arendsii*)	CBow CCla CGle CMHG CSco CShe EBre ECha EGol EHon ELan ELun EPGN EPla LBre LHop MBal MBri NBar NDea NHol NRoo SChu SCro SDix SPer
'Jo Ophorst' (*davidii* x)	CCla CMHG EBre ECha ECtt EPGN GCHN LBre MBel NDea SCro SGil SHer SPer
'Koblenz' (*japonica* x)	IDai NHol
'Köln' ('Cologne') (*japonica* x)	WAbe
'Kvele' (x *arendsii*)	MBri
'Lachskönigin' ('Salmon Queen') (x *arendsii*)	CMHG MWat
'Lilli Goos' (x *arendsii*)	CMHG
microphylla	CMCN CMHG NHol
– pink	CMHG NHol
*– ***saisuensis***	MHig
'Moerheimii (*thunbergii* x)	CMHG
'Montgomery' (*japonica* x)	CCla EBre ECha EPGN LBre NFai NHol
'Nana' (*simplicifolia* x)	CRow NNrd
'Obergärtner Jürgens' (x *arendsii*)	CMHG
'Peach Blossom' (x *rosea*)	CB&S CBow CCla CDoC CKni CMHG EPar GCHN MBal NBar NFai NHol WHoo WMer
'Perkeo' (x *crispa*) AGM	CHol CLew COtt CRDP CRow EBre ECha EGle EPGN GCHN GDra GGar LBre MBel MBri NBir NHar NKay NRoo SHig WStI
'Peter Barrow' (*glaberrima* x)	EPGN MBel SRms
'Pink Curtsy' (x *arendsii*)	EBre LBre
'Praecox Alba' (*simplicifolia*)	EBre ECha EGle EPGN LBre LWad MNFA NHol
'Professor van der Wielen' (*thunbergii* x)	CGle CMHG ECha EGle EMon EPGN GCHN GCal GGar LGre SPer SRms
'Purple Glory' (*chinensis*)	CMHG
'Purpurlanze' ('Purple Lance') (*chinensis taquetii*)	CMHG EBre ECha EFou EPGN GCHN LBre MBri MRav MUlv NBir NCat NOrc WCot WMer WTyr WWin
'Queen Alexandra' (x *rosea*)	SFis
'Red Admiral'	NNor
'Red Sentinel' (*japonica* x)	CB&S CTom EBre EFou ELun EPGN EPar EPla GCHN LBre NBee NHar NHol NOrc SGil SHer SPla WAbe
'Rheinland' (*japonica* x) AGM	CBow CMHG GCHN MBri WAbe WEas
rivularis	CCla CMHG
'Rosa Perle' ('Pink Pearl') (x *arendsii*)	CMHG ECha NHol
'Rosea' (*simplicifolia* x)	NHol
¶ 'Rosemary Bloom'	EPGN
'Rotlicht' ('Red Light') (x *arendsii*)	MBri
'Salmon Queen' (x *arendsii*)	See A. 'Lachskönigin'
§ 'Saxosa'	EPot ESis
'Serenade' (*chinensis pumila*)	CMHG SHig
simplicifolia AGM	CGle CRow GAul MHig MTho NHar NKay WCot WEas WHil WPer
– x ***glaberrima***	GDra NHar NHol
'Snow Queen' (x *crispa*)	NHar
'Snowdrift' (x *arendsii*)	CBow CMHG CSco EBar EBre ECha EFou EGol ELun EPGN EPla ERav GAri LBre LWad MUlv NMir NOak NOrc NRoo SApp
¶ 'Spätsommer' (*chinensis pumila*)	CMHG
* 'Spartan' (x *arendsii*)	ECot EHic EPGN LBuc NHol WGor
'Spinell' (x *arendsii*)	MWat
'Sprite' (*simplicifolia* x) AGM	Widely available
sp. CLD 1559	NHol
'Straussenfeder' ('Ostrich Plume') (*thunbergii* x) AGM	CSco EBre EFou ELun EPGN EPla GAbr GCHN GCal LBre NHol NTow SCro SHig WPbr WTyr
'Superba' (*chinensis taquetii*) AGM	CGle CMHG CRow CSco CTom EBre ECha ELan EPGN GCHN LBre MSte NDea NHol NNor NSti NTow SDix SHig SPer WAbe WEas WHil WOld WPbr
'Venus' (x *arendsii*)	CBow CCla CKel CMHG CSam CSco CShe CTom ECED ECha ECtt EFou EGol ELun EPGN MBel NHol NKay NOrc NVic SChu SCro SPer WPbr WTyr
'Veronica Klose' (*chinensis*)	CMHG MBri
'Vesuvius' (*japonica* x)	CB&S EPla MBel
'W E Gladstone' (*japonica* x)	CB&S CDoC EPGN WAbe WMer
¶ 'Washington' (x *arendsii*)	WMer
'Weisse Gloria' ('White Gloria') (x *arendsii*)	CCla CMHG ECha EPGN EPar MBel MBri NSti SCro SGil SPla
'Weisse Perle' (x *arendsii*)	CMHG
'White Queen' (x *arendsii*)	CElw NNrd
'William Buchanan' (*simplicifolia* x)	CBro CGle EBre ECtt EGol EMNN EPGN EPar EPot GCHN GGar GPlt LBre MBal MBar MBri MCas MHig MNFA NDea NHar NHol NKay NMen NRed SCro WTyr WWin
'William Reeves' (x *arendsii*)	CKni COtt MFir NHol
'Yakusima'	GCHN SRms

ASTILBOÏDES (Saxifragaceae)

§ *tabularis*	CChu CCla CGle CHEx CHad CRDP CRow CSco CWGN ECha EFol EFou EGol ELan EOrc GAbr MBro MSta NDea NHol NSti SBla SPer WHoo WWat

ASTRAGALUS (Leguminosae/Papilionaceae)

¶ *cicer*	EBee
glycyphyllos	EWFC MHew MSal WHaw
¶ *membranaceus*	MSal
utahensis	NHar WDav

ASTRANTIA (Umbelliferae/Apiaceae)

carniolica	NKay
– *major*	See A. *major*
– var. *rubra*	CB&S CBot CBro CCla CFee CKel CRDP CRow CSam EBre ECED ECro EPar GLil LBre LWad MFir NDea NFai SIng SPla WAbe WByw WCru WOMN WTyr WWat
– 'Variegata'	See A. *major* 'Sunningdale Variegated'
helleborifolia hort.	See A. *maxima*
§ *major*	Widely available
– *alba*	CRow ECha ECro EFol EGol NBir NCat NPer WPla
– *biebersteinii*	NBir
– 'Buckland'	CRDP SUsu SWas
¶ – 'Claret'	LGre SWas
– 'Hadspen Blood'	CBos CHad CMil MSta WMer WWeb
– 'Hillview Red'	WHil
– ssp. *involucrata*	CDec CLew GCHN NHol NVic WHow
– – 'Barrister'	CFil CRDP EBee MUlv SApp
– – 'Margery Fish'	See A. *m. i.* 'Shaggy'
– – 'Moira Reid'	WRus
§ – – 'Shaggy' AGM	CBre CChu CMGP CMHG CMea CShe ECro EFou ERav ESma NBee NDea NOak SHer SPer SPla WByw WCru WEas WPbr WRus WSun WWat
¶ – 'Lars'	MUlv
– 'Primadonna'	CSam EMar EOrc MSte SHer WPer
– 'Prockter's Seedling'	CBre WTyr
– *rosea*	CBre CCla CElw CGle CMGP CRDP ECro EFou EGol EMil LHop NBee NHol SGil SHer SPer
– 'Rosensinfonie'	CRDP EPar GCal WDav
– *rubra*	Widely available
– 'Ruby Wedding'	CGle EMon ESma LWad SWas WHoo WRus
§ – 'Sunningdale Variegated' AGM	Widely available
– 'Variegata'	See A. *m.* 'Sunningdale Variegated'
§ *maxima* AGM	Widely available
– 'Mark Fenwick'	NBir
minor	EPar LGre WCru
rubra	See A. *major r.*

ASYNEUMA (Campanulaceae)

canescens	EBar EPad WWin
limonifolium	GDra WDav
pulvinatum	SIng
– Mac&W 5880	EPot MHig NMen
¶ *trichostegium*	CNic

ASYSTASIA (Acanthaceae)

bella	See MACKAYA *bella*
§ *gangetica*	CNew CPle SLMG
violacea	See A. *gangetica*

ATHAMANTA (Umbelliferae/Apiaceae)

cretensis	NHol
macedonica	ESma
– ssp. *arachnoïdea*	SIgm

ATHEROSPERMA (Monimiaceae)

moschatum	CB&S CCla CGre CLan CPle CTre WBod

ATHROTAXIS (Taxodiaceae)

cupressoïdes	GAri MBar
x *laxifolia*	CMHG EBre LBre LCon MBar MBri WThu

ATHYRIUM † (Dryopteridaceae)

filix-femina AGM	CBar CFil CRow CTom EBre ECha EFer EFou ELan LBre MBal MBri MSta NBee NBro NEgg NHol NMar NOrc SPer SPla SWat WBon WFib
– 'Corymbiferum'	NHar NKay NMar SRms
– Cristatum Group	CWGN EFer ELan MBri NHol SCob SHer SPer SWat WFib WRic
– Cruciatum Group	EGol
– 'Fieldii'	CRow EFou NHar NHol WFib
– 'Frizelliae'	CBar CDoC CMil CRDP CWGN EFou ELan IOrc MBri NHar NHol NMar NOrc SApp SCob SMad SMrm SPla SRms WFib WHal WRic WWat
– 'Frizelliae Capitatum'	NKay SRms WFib
– 'Grandiceps'	NHar NMar SRms
– 'Minutissimum'	CBos CDec CFil CRDP CWGN ECha EFou EGol EHon ELan GCHN MBri NMar WRic
– Percristatum Group	NKay
– 'Plumosum Axminster'	CFil CRDP SMad SMrm
– 'Plumosum Cristatum'	NMar WRic
– Plumosum Group	CFil NMar
– 'Plumosum Percristatum'	NMar
– Ramocristatum Group	NMar
– 'Setigerum Cristatum'	NKay NMar
– 'Vernoniae Cristatum'	MBal NHar NHol NMar SPer WFib
– Vernoniae Group	ELan MBri WRic
– Victoriae Group & clone	CBar CRDP CRow EGol ELan GAri MBri NHar NHol SRms WAbe WFib WRic
frangulum	NMar
goeringianum 'Pictum'	See A. *niponicum pictum*
niponicum	EFer NMar
– *metallicum*	See A. *n. pictum*
§ – var. *pictum* AGM	Widely available
otophorum	EBee NHol NMar
– var. *okanum*	CFil ELan NHar SBla
palustre	NKay WRic
sp. ACL 290	SMrm

vidalii CFil

ATRAGENE See CLEMATIS

ATRAPHAXIS (Polygonaceae)
See Plant Deletions

ATRIPLEX (Chenopodiaceae)
canescens WDin
halimus CB&S CBot CCla CGle CHan COtt CPle CRow CShe EHoe ENot LAbb LHil MWat NBir NBrk SLon SPer SPla WDin WHCG WHer WKif WSHC WStI
hortensis MChe WWye
¶ – gold-leaved WCot
– var. *rubra* CArn CGle CRow ELan LHol MChe MHew MHlr NRar SIde SUsu WEas WHer WKif WOak WWye

ATROPA (Solanaceae)
bella-donna CArn ECWi GBar GPoy LHol MSal WWye
– *lutea* MSal
mandragora See MANDRAGORA *officinarum*

ATROPANTHE (Solanaceae)
sinensis MSal

AUBRIETA † (Cruciferae/Brassicaceae)
albomarginata See A. 'Argenteovariegata'
'Alida Vahli' EGle ELan
'Alix Brett' CLTr EBre ECtt ELan LBee LBre NHar NHol NPer SHer
'April Joy' CMHG ECot ELan MPla NHol SHer SRms
§ 'Argenteovariegata' CLTr ELan LHop NHol NRoo SBla SHer SSmi WAbe
'Astolat' (v) EFol ELan GCHN LBee NHar NHol SBla SHer WAbe WEas
§ 'Aureovariegata' CMea CNic CRiv EBar EBre ECha ECtt EFol EGle ELan LBre MHig MPla NHol NKay NPer NRoo NVic SBla SChu SHer SIng WAbe WHil
'Belisha Beacon' ECtt LBee MBri NGre NHol
Bengal hybrids GAbr
'Blaue Schönheit' ('Blue Beauty') EWes NHol
'Blue Cascade' ECtt WGor
'Blue Emperor' WMer
'Blue King' WMer
§ 'Bob Saunders' (d) CMHG CMea EBre ECtt ELan LBee LBre MCas NEgg NHol NVic SHer
'Bonfire' NHol NKay
* 'Bonsul' CShe
'Bordeaux' WMer
'Bressingham Pink' EBre ECtt ELan EPar LBre LHop MCas MHig NHol SHer
'Bressingham Red' EBre EWes LBre WMer
'Britannia' NKay
canescens SIgm
– JCA 225.150 CNic
'Carnival' See A. 'Hartswood Purple'
* *carnmenellis* EFol
'Church Knowle' NHol
cumulus NCat
* *deltoidea* 'Gloria' WPat
– 'Nana Variegata' EPot MPla MTho NGre WEas WGor WHil
– *rosea* MHig
– 'Tauricola' WMer
– 'Tauricola Variegata' CShe
– Variegata Group CRiv CShe ECtt EFol EPot ESis LHop MFir MHig MTho NGre NMen NTow SChu SIng WPat
– Variegata Group 'Shaw's Red' WDav
'Doctor Mules' AGM CDoC CLTr EBre ECtt EPot IHos LBee LBre MHig MPit NEgg NKay SHer SIng
'Doctor Mules Variegata' MHig NHol
'Dream' ECtt SIng
'Elsa Lancaster' CLew EPot MHig NGre WAbe
'Fire King' WMer
'Frühlingszauber' ('Spring Charm') SRms
'Gloriosa' CMHG CRiv NGre NHol SIng
'Godstone' EWes
'Golden Carpet' CMea NHol SHer SIng
'Golden King' See A. 'Aureovariegata'
gracilis ssp. *scardica* NTow
'Greencourt Purple' CMHG CRiv EBre ELan EPar EPot GAbr LBre MCas MHig NGre NHol NKay SHer SIng WEas
'Gurgedyke' ELan MHig NHol SHer SRms
'Hartswood' SIng
§ 'Hartswood Purple' CShe NHol
'Hendersonii' SRms
'Henslow Purple' EBre LBre
'Ina den Ouden' WMer
'J S Baker' SRms
'Joan Allen' CMHG ELan NGre NHar NHol NPri SHer
'Joy' NHol NRar SIng
'Lavender Gem' CMHG
* 'Lemon and Lime' EWes NHol
'Lilac Cascade' LBee
'Little Gem' MHig
'Lodge Crave' NHol SIng
'Lucy' NKay
macedonica EPot
'Magician' ECtt NHol NKay
'Mars' EFol EGle ELan SHer SRms
'Mary Poppins' MHig NHol NKay
'Maurice Prichard' ECtt
'Mrs Lloyd Edwards' ECtt
'Mrs Rodewald' CMHG CMea ECtt ELan MCas NGre NHol NKay NMen WAbe WHal
'Novalis Blue' AGM SRms
'Oakington Lavender' ELan EPar IHos LHop MPit NGre NHol
'Pennine Glory' CShe
'Pennine Heather' CShe
'Pike's Variegated' SRms
'Pink Gem' NKay
'Prichard's A1' WMer
'Purple Cascade' CNic ECtt EMNN GCHN LBee SRms WGor
'Purple Charm' SRms

'Red Carpet' CMHG CNic CRiv EBre EFol ELan EMNN EPar EPot IHos LBee LBre MCas MFir MHig MPla NEgg NGre NHol NKay NMen SChu SHer SIng WEas WHil
'Red Cascade' ECtt EMNN GAbr GCHN NMen
'Red Dyke' SIng
'Riverslea' NHol SIng
'Rosanna Miles' NHol SIng
'Rose Queen' CMea LBee
'Rosea Splendens' MPla
'Royal Blue' NRoo
'Royal Red' ESis LBee MCas MPit NRoo SRms WGor
'Royal Violet' ESis NRoo
'Schloss Eckberg' WMer
♦'Schofield's Double' See A. 'Bob Saunders'
'Silberrand' ECha ECtt SAxl
¶ 'Toby Saunders' SHer
'Triumphante' NEgg NMen
'Wanda' ELan IHos NHol SHer SIng
'Whitewell Gem' EBar SRms
Wisley hybrid WEas

AUCUBA (Aucubaceae)

japonica CB&S CChu CDoC CHEx EBre ELan ENot LBre SCob SPer SReu
– 'Crassifolia' (m) CHig MBal SArc WMar
– 'Crotonifolia' AGM CB&S CChe CDoC CHEx CSco EBre ENot IJoh LAbb LBre MBal MBar MBri MGos MRav MWat NWea SCob SDix SHBN SPer WDin WMar WStI
– 'Fructu Albo' CGre
– 'Gold Dust' (f/v) CLan CShe SHil WMar
– 'Golden King' (m/v) CB&S CDoC CSco CTrw EPla LNet MUlv SHer SPla
– 'Golden Spangles' (v) CB&S ECot MAll MBal SHer
– 'Hillieri' (f) CLan SHil
– 'Lance Leaf' (m/v) MUlv SHil
– 'Latiomaculata' (v) SCob
– f. *longifolia* AGM CHig SArc SDix SHil
– 'Maculata' (v) See A. *j.* 'Variegata'
– 'Nana Rotundifolia' (f) EPla MAsh MUlv SCob WMar
– 'Picturata' (m/v) CB&S CDoC CSco EBre EFol ELan ENot LBre MAll MBal MBri MGos NHol SCob SHBN SPer WAbe
– 'Rozannie' (m/f) CB&S CDoC COtt CSco ENot EPla MAsh MBal MBlu MBri MGos MUlv NBee SCob SPer SPla SReu WDin WStI
– 'Salicifolia' (f) ENot MBri MUlv SCob SHil SPer
– 'Sulphurea Marginata' (f/v) CB&S CSco EFol MBri MUlv
§ – 'Variegata' (f) CChe CPle ELan ENot GRei IDai IJoh ISea LBuc MBal MBar MBri MGos MRav MWat NBee NBir NNor SCob SHBN SHer SLon SPer SReu WAbe WBod WDin WStI
– 'Wykehurst' (v) LRHS
* 'Mr Goldstrike' (v) CSco LNet

AURINIA (Cruciferae/Brassicaceae)

§ *petraea* CNic
saxatilis AGM CShe EBre GAbr GDra IDai LBre MBar NKay NNrw SHer SIng SPer WWin
– var. *citrina* AGM CShe ECha ECtt MBel MPla MWat SDix SRms
– 'Compacta' CDoC EBre ECtt ENot LBre NEgg NMir NNor WHoo
– 'Dudley Nevill' CCMG CLew CRiv CShe EBre ECha EFol EMNN GAbr LBee LBre MPla MWat NEgg SBla SChu WDav
– 'Dudley Nevill Variegated' EBre ECED ERav EWes GAbr LBre MPla NBir NRoo SIng SUsu WOld WPer WRus
– 'Flore Pleno' NRoo SBla WEas WHil
– 'Gold Dust' EBee ECtt LGro NGre SRms WCot
– 'Golden Queen' CDoC ECtt NNrd
– 'Goldkugel' ('Gold Ball') ELan EMNN GAul LBee MPit NRoo NVic SHer SRms STre
– 'Silver Queen' ELan NRoo SPer WEas
– 'Variegata' CLew SBla

AUSTROCEDRUS (Cupressaceae)

§ *chilensis* CDoC CGre CKen GAri LCon MBal

AVENA (Gramineae/Poaceae)

candida See HELICTOTRICHON *sempervirens*
sterilis EHoe

AVENULA See HELICTOTRICHON

AVERRHOA (Oxalidaceae)

¶ *carambola* CTro

AVOCADO See PERSEA *americana*

AYAPANA See EUPATORIUM

AZALEA See RHODODENDRON Azalea

AZALEODENDRON See RHODODENDRON Azaleodendron

AZARA † (Flacourtiaceae)

dentata CB&S CGre CMCN CMac CMer CPle CTre CTrw ERea MBal WSHC
– 'Variegata' CBow CMac ERea LRHS
integrifolia CTre SArc
– 'Variegata' CB&S CGre CPle SHil
lanceolata CB&S CCla CPle IOrc ISea SLon SPer WBod WWat
microphylla AGM CB&S CBow CDoC CFee CGre CMCN CMHG CPle CSPN CSco CShe CTre EPla IBar IDai IOrc ISea LAbb MBal SArc SBra SDry SHil SPer WBod WStI
– 'Variegata' CAbb CDoC CHan CMac EHar EHoe ERav IDai IOrc ISea LHop MBal SArc WCru WWat
paraguayensis CGre CTre GAri
petiolaris CGre CPle IBar WCru WWat

serrata	CBot CBow CChu CCla CGre CHEx CHan CMCN CMHG CPle EBre EPla GWht ISea LAbb LBre SArc SBra SDix SLon SPer WBod WDin WPat
¶ sp. ex Chile	CGre

AZOLLA (Azollaceae)

♦***caroliniana*** auct. non Willdenow	See A. ***mexicana***
♦***caroliniana*** Willdenow	See A. ***filiculoïdes***
§ ***filiculoïdes***	CBen CHEx CRow CWGN ECoo EHon EMFW EWav IMal LMay MSta SHer SWat SWyc WHol WStI
§ ***mexicana***	SWat

AZORELLA (Umbelliferae/Apiaceae)

filamentosa	ECou
glebaria hort.	See A. ***trifurcata***
gummifera	See BOLAX ***g.***
lycopodioïdes	ECou GCHN
§ ***trifurcata***	CLew CRiv ELan EPot GAbr GAri GDra GTou MBro MTho NHol NKay NNrd NRoo SHer SSmi WAbe WByw WHil WPat WPer
– 'Nana'	CNic GArf GGar MHig MTho MWat NHol NMen NNrd SIng SSmi WOld WPat WThu

AZORINA (Campanulaceae)

§ ***vidalii***	CAbb CBot CGre CPle CSpe EPad GCal SGil WAbe WHal WOMN WPer
– 'Rosea'	EPad

BABIANA (Iridaceae)

ambigua	NRog
¶ ***angustifolia***	NRog
¶ 'Blue Gem'	NRog
cedarbergensis	LBow NRog
♦***disticha***	See B. ***plicata***
¶ ***dregei***	NRog
¶ ***ecklonii***	NRog
hybrids	LBow
¶ 'Laura'	NRog
¶ ***nana***	NRog
¶ ***odorata***	NRog
§ ***plicata***	NRog
¶ ***pulchra***	CFee LBow NRog
¶ ***pygmaea***	NRog
rubrocyanea	CMon NRog
¶ ***scabrifolia***	NRog
¶ ***secunda***	NRog
¶ ***striata***	NRog
stricta	NRog
– 'Purple Star'	ETub NRog
– 'Tubergen's Blue'	ETub NRog
tubulosa	NRog
villosa	LBow NRog
villosula	NRog
¶ 'White King'	NRog
¶ 'Zwanenburg's Glory'	NRog

BACCHARIS (Compositae/Asteraceae)

crispa	GCal
genistelloïdes	GCal
halimifolia	CPle
– 'Twin Peaks'	SDry
magellanica	ECou
patagonica	CAbb CBow CMHG CPle CTre LHop MAll SArc SDry SLon WBod

BACOPA (Scrophulariaceae)

* 'Snowflake'	CBar CBrk CSpe LHil

BAECKEA (Myrtaceae)

See Plant Deletions

BAILLONIA (Verbenaceae)

juncea	CGre CPle WSHC

BALDELLIA (Alismataceae)

¶ ***ranunculoïdes repens***	CRDP

BALLOTA (Labiatae/Lamiaceae)

acetabulosa	CDec CHan CWes ECha EFol EFou EHal EMar MBel SChu SDix SDry SPer WSHC
'All Hallows Green'	CChu CCla CGle CMGP CSam EBre ECro ECtt EFou EGol EMar EOrc GCal LBre LHop MBel MTol SAxl SChu SGil SUsu WHen WSun WWat
hirsuta	CHan
nigra	CArn LHol MHew MSal SHer SIde WWye
§ – 'Archer's Variegated' (v)	CGle CHan CRDP CSpe CWes EBar EFol EHal EJud EMon LBlm MBel NHex NPer SHer SIde WHer WRus
– 'Dingle Gold'	EFol
– 'Dingle Gold Variegated'	EFol
– ***variegata***	See B. ***n.*** 'Archer's Variegated'
– 'Zanzibar' (v)	EMon MBel
pseudodictamnus AGM	Widely available

BALSAMITA See TANACETUM

BAMBUSA † (Gramineae/Poaceae-Bambusoideae)

glaucescens	See B. ***multiplex***
* ***gracillima***	CB&S CBar COtt GAri SBam
§ ***multiplex***	EFul LBam SBam WJun
– 'Alphonse Karr'	CB&S CBra EFul EPla ISta SBam SCob SDry WJun
♦– 'Chinese Goddess'	See B. ***m. riviereorum***
§ – 'Fernleaf'	CBar COtt EFul GAri ISta LBam MUlv SBam SCob SDry WJun
– 'Wang Tsai'	See B. ***m.*** 'Fernleaf'
oldhamii	SBam
♦***pubescens***	See DENDROCALAMUS ***strictus***
tuldoïdes	GAri
ventricosa	LBam SBam SDry WJun
vulgaris	SBam
– 'Vittata'	SBam
– 'Wamin'	SBam WJun

BANANA See MUSA

BANKSIA (Proteaceae)

baueri	LBlm
baxteri	LBlm
blechnifolia	LBlm
dryandroïdes	LBlm
ericifolia	LBlm
grandis	LBlm
integrifolia	CB&S CTro LBlm NBar WDin
marginata	ECou
media	LBlm
quercifolia	CGre LBlm
robur	LBlm
saxicola	CTro
speciosa	LBlm SIgm
spinulosa collina	LBlm

BAPTISIA (Leguminosae/Papilionaceae)

australis AGM	CAbb CArn CBoy CCMG CCla CGle CHad CHan CPle CSco EBre ECha EFou ELan GCal LBre LGre MBri MSal NHol SDix SMad SPer SUsu WAbb WAbe WEas WPer WWin
– 'Exaltata'	ECro ELan LHop
§ ***bracteata***	ECro MSal NSti SMad
§ ***lactea***	CBot CBow CChu CPle ECro EHoe EOrc GCal MSal MUlv NBir
leucantha	See B. ***lactea***
leucophaea	See B. ***bracteata***
tinctoria	CPle GMac MSal WCot WHoo WThi

BARBAREA (Cruciferae/Brassicaceae)

praecox	See B. ***verna***
rupicola	WPer
§ ***verna***	CArn GPoy SIde WWye
vulgaris 'Variegata'	CGle CRow ECha ECro EFol EHoe ELan ELun EMar EPla ERav LHil MFir NBro NFai NOak NVic SUsu WHal WHil WPbr WWin

BARLERIA (Acanthaceae)

obtusa	CNew CTro
¶ ***repens*** 'Blue Prince'	CSpe
¶ – ***rosea***	CSpe
* ***suberecta***	CNew

BARTLETTINA See EUPATORIUM

BARTSIA (Scrophulariaceae)

See Plant Deletions

BASHANIA (Gramineae/Poaceae-Bambusoideae)

fargesii	EPla WJun

BAUERA (Cunoniaceae)

See Plant Deletions

BAUHINIA (Leguminosae/Papilionaceae)

¶ x ***blakeana***	CTro

BEAUCARNEA (Dracaenaceae)

recurvata AGM	LPal MBri

BEAUFORTIA (Myrtaceae)

sparsa	CTre

BEAUMONTIA (Apocynaceae)

grandiflora	CNew CTro

BEAUVERDIA See TRISTAGMA, IPHEION, LEUCOCORYNE

BECKMANNIA (Gramineae/Poaceae)

eruciformis	ETPC

BEDFORDIA (Compositae/Asteraceae)

salicina	ECou

BEGONIA † (Begoniaceae)

acerifolia	See B. ***vitifolia***
albopicta (C)	CHal CTro EBak ER&R
– 'Rosea'	CHal WDib
'Allan Langdon' (T)	CBla
'Alleryi' (C)	ER&R
'Amy' (T)	CBla
angularis	See B. ***stipulacea***
'Anita Roseanna' (C)	ER&R
'Anniversary' (T)	CBla
¶ 'Apollo' (T)	CBla
'Apricot Delight' (T)	CBla
'Argentea' (R)	EBak MBri
¶ x ***argenteoguttata*** (C)	CHal
'Baby Perfection'	WDib
'Barclay Griffiths'	ER&R
'Beatrice Haddrell'	WDib
'Bernat Klein' (T)	CBla
'Bertinii' (T)	MWBu
'Bethlehem Star'	ER&R WDib
'Billie Langdon' (T)	CBla
'Black Knight'	CHal
'Bokit'	ER&R
'Bonaire'	CHal
'Boomer' (C)	ER&R
'Bouton de Rose' (T)	MWBu NRog SDeJ
bowerae	CHal
'Burle Marx'	CNew ER&R WDib
'Bush Baby'	CHal
'Buttermilk' (T)	CBla
'Camelliiflora (T)	MWBu NRog
'Can-Can' (T)	CBla
'Carol Wilkins of Ballaarat' (T)	CBla
§ x ***carrierei***	MBri
x ***carrierei flore-pleno***	CHal LHop
'Cathedral'	ER&R
'Chantilly Lace'	CHal
'Clara' (R)	MBri
'Cleopatra'	CHal ER&R SLMG
coccinea (C)	ER&R
compta (C)	See B. ***stipulacea***
x ***corallina***	EBak
§ – 'Lucerna' (C)	CHal CTro EBak ER&R
– 'Lucerna Amazon' (C)	CHal IBlr
'Corbeille de Feu'	CHal

'Cowardly Lion' (R)	ER&R
'Crimson Cascade'	CBla
cubensis (C)	ER&R
cucullata	CHal ER&R
'Curly Locks' (S)	CHal
'Dannebo'	MBri
'Dawnal Meyer' (C)	ER&R WDib
♦***discolor***	See B. ***grandis evansiana***
'Di-anna' (C)	ER&R
'Druryi'	ER&R SLMG
echinosepala (C)	ER&R
'Elaine Wilkerson'	ER&R
¶ 'Emerald Giant' (R)	WDib
'Emma Watson'	CHal ER&R
epipsila	ER&R
x ***erythrophylla*** 'Bunchii'	ER&R SLMG
§ – 'Helix'	CHal ER&R
'Esther Albertine' (C)	ER&R
'Fairylight' (T)	CBla
feastii helix	See B. x ***erythrophylla*** 'Helix'
'Festiva' (T)	CBla
¶***fimbriata***	MWBu
'Fire Flush' (R)	ER&R WDib
'Five and Dime'	ER&R
'Florence Rita' (C)	ER&R
foliosa	ER&R WDib
– var. ***amplifolia***	ER&R
§ – var. ***miniata*** 'Rosea'	CHal
'Fred Bedson'	ER&R
fuchsioïdes AGM	CB&S CNew ER&R GCra MArl NPri WDib
– 'Rosea'	See B. ***foliosa miniata*** 'Rosea'
'Full Moon' (T)	CBla
gehrtii	CTro
glaucophylla	See B. ***procumbens***
'Gold Cascade'	CBla
'Goldilocks' (T)	CBla
¶ ***grandis***	SMrm
§ – var. ***evansiana***	CAvo CB&S CDec CGle CHEx CHal CRDP CTro ER&R ESma GCal LHil LHop MSte MTho NSti SChu SDix SIng SMad WCru
– – ***alba***	CAvo CHal CRDP EMon ER&R LHil MTho NBir SMad
griffithii	See B. ***annulata***
'Gustav Lind' (S)	CBrk CHal GCra SSad WEas
haageana	See B. ***scharffii***
'Honeysuckle' (C)	ER&R
incarnata (C)	ER&R
– 'Metallica'	SLMG
'Jean Blair' (T)	CBla
'Joe Hayden'	ER&R SLMG
'Lady Clare'	ER&R
'Lady France'	MBri
'Leopard'	ER&R MBri
'Libor' (C)	ER&R
limmingheana	See B. ***radicans***
lindeniana	ER&R
listada	CHal MBri WDib
'Little Darling'	ER&R
'Looking Glass' (C)	ER&R
'Lou Anne'	CBla
'Lubbergei' (C)	ER&R
'Lucerna'	See B. x ***corallina*** 'Lucerna'
luxurians	CTro ER&R
– 'Ziesenhenne	ER&R
maculata 'Wightii' (C)	ER&R
'Mac's Gold'	ER&R
'Majesty' (T)	CBla
manicata	ER&R
'Maphil'	MBri
'Marmorata' (T)	MWBu NRog
masoniana AGM	ER&R WDib
mazae	ER&R
'Medora' (C)	ER&R
'Melissa' (T)	CBla
metallica	CHal ER&R
'Mirage'	ER&R
natalensis (T)	ER&R
¶ 'Nell Gwynne' (T)	CBla
nigramarga	See B. ***bowerae*** 'Nigramarga'
'Norah Bedson'	ER&R
'Odorata Alba'	CNew CTro
'Old Gold' (T)	ER&R
'Ophelia' (T)	CBla
'Orange Cascade' (T)	CBla
'Orange Rubra' (C)	ER&R
partita	CTro
'Picotee' (T)	CSut NRog
'Pinafore' (C)	ER&R
polyantha	ER&R
'Président Carnot' (C)	ER&R SLMG
'Primrose' (T)	CBla
procumbens	See B. ***radicans***
¶ 'Purpurea' (R)	CHal
pustulata 'Argentea'	ER&R
'Queen Olympus'	WDib
§ ***radicans***	CHal CTro ER&R MBri
'Raquel Wood'	ER&R
'Raspberry Swirl' (R)	ER&R WDib
'Raymond George Nelson'	ER&R
'Red Planet'	ER&R WDib
rex	MBri
'Richard Robinson'	ER&R
'Richmondensis'	ER&R
'Ricky Minter'	ER&R SLMG
'Roy Hartley' (T)	CBla
'Royalty' (T)	CBla
'Sachsen'	ER&R
'Sandersonii'	WEas
sanguinea	ER&R
'Scarlet Pimpernel' (T)	CBla
'Scarlett O'Hara' (T)	CBla
'Sceptre' (T)	CBla
§ ***scharffii***	CHal CTro EBak ER&R
'Scherzo'	CHal ER&R
'Sea Coral' (T)	CBla
semperflorens hort.	See B. x ***carrierei***
serratipetala	EBak ER&R MBri
Skeezar	ER&R
Skeezar 'Brown Lake'	ER&R
solananthera	CHal ER&R WDib
sonderiana	ERea
'Sophie Cecile' (C)	ER&R
'Spellbound'	WDib
§ ***stipulacea***	CHal CTro ER&R
§ – 'Bat Wings'	SLMG
'Sugar Candy' (T)	CBla

sutherlandii **AGM**	CAvo CHal CRDP EBak ER&R LHil MBri NBir NPer SAxl SHer SLMG SSad SUsu
'Sweet Dreams' (T)	CBla
'Sweet Magic'	CHal ER&R
'Switzerland' (T)	LAma
'Tahiti' (T)	CBla
'Thrush' (R)	SLMG
'Thunderclap'	CHal
'Thurstonii'	CHal CTro ER&R LBlm
'Tiger Paws'	CHal ER&R MBri
'Tom Ment' (C)	ER&R
'Tom Ment II' (C)	ER&R
'Tondelayo' (R)	ER&R
tripartita (T)	ER&R
'Trout' (C)	SLMG
undulata (C)	ER&R
'Venus'	CHal
x ***verschaffeltii***	ER&R
¶ 'Vesuvius'	WDib
vitifolia	ER&R
'Weltoniensis'	ER&R
'Withlacoohee'	ER&R
¶ 'Yellow Sweety' (T)	CBla
'Zuensis'	ER&R
'Zulu' (T)	CBla

BELAMCANDA (Iridaceae)

chinensis	CBot CBoy CBro CDoC CHan CMHG EBar ECro LHop MHew MSal NBir NBro NRar NTow SLMG SMrm WHil WHoo WHow WOMN WOld WPer WWye
¶ – 'Dwarf Orange'	CHol EOrc WPer
– 'Hello Yellow'	MSte WPer

BELLEVALIA (Liliaceae/Hyacinthaceae)

dubia	CMon
forniculata	SPou
– JCA 227.770	CNic
hackelii MS 439	CMon
maura SF 387	CMon
nivalis CL 101	CMon
paradoxa	See B. ***pycnantha***
§ ***pycnantha***	ETub NHol NRog SIng
romana	NRog
– JCA 523	CMon
sessiliflora	CMon
sp. PD 20493	WOMN

BELLIS (Compositae/Asteraceae)

perennis	CKin ECWi EWFC MHew
– 'Alba Plena'	CMil CWes ELan NNrd NSti SHer SIng
– 'Alice'	CBos CGle CLTr CRDP NSti WHer
– 'Annie'	CGle
– 'Aucubifolia' (v)	EMon
– 'Dresden China' **AGM**	CCot CElw CMer CMil CTom ELan GAbr MCas MTho MWat SHer SIng SSvw WOMN WPer WRus
– 'Miss Mason'	CCot CGle EOrc GAbr WRus
– 'Monstrosa'	MWat
¶ – 'Odd Bod'	CBos
– 'Parkinson's Great White'	GAbr
– 'Pomponette' **AGM**	NRoo
– 'Prolifera' (Hen and Chickens)	CBos CCot CDec CGle CLTr CMil CRDP CRow GAbr MTho NSti
– 'Rob Roy' **AGM**	CGle CMil SIng
– 'Robert'	CMil GAbr
– 'Single Blue'	See B. ***rotundifolia*** 'Caerulescens'
– 'Stafford Pink'	CLTr GAbr WHer
– 'White Pearl'	MTho
rotundifolia	CLew CRiv
§ – 'Caerulescens'	CBos CCot CDec CNic EMar GAbr MCas MHig MTho NHol NMen NSti WEas WHer WOMN WPat WRus

BELLIUM (Compositae/Asteraceae)

bellidioïdes	EPla NHol
crassifolium canescens	WPer
minutum	CLew MHig MMil NGre NTow SMrm

BELOPERONE See JUSTICIA

BENSONIELLA (Saxifragaceae)

oregona	EBee EMon LRHS MHig

BERBERIDOPSIS (Flacourtiaceae)

corallina	Widely available

BERBERIS † (Berberidaceae)

aggregata	GAul MBal NBir SPer SRms WDin
x ***antoniana***	ESis MBri NHol WWeb
aquifolium	See MAHONIA ***aquifolium***
– ***fascicularis***	See MAHONIA ***pinnata***
N ***aristata***	CMCN EHal
bealei	See MAHONIA ***japonica*** Bealei Group
bergmanniae	CPle SLPl
'Blenheim'	LRHS NHol
brevipedunculata Bean	See B. ***prattii***
x ***bristolensis***	CSco EPla MBri NHol SLon SPla
buxifolia	MBal SCob SLon
§ – 'Nana'	CAbP CB&S CPle CSco ELan ENot IJoh MBal MBar MBri MPla NFai NHol NRoo SPer STre WStI
– 'Pygmaea'	See B. ***b.*** 'Nana'
calliantha **AGM**	CChu CSam CSco MBri NHol SGil SLPl WWat
candidula	CPle CSam EBre ELan ENot IJoh IOrc LBre MBal MBar MWat NHol NNor SBod SCob SLon SPer WBod WDin WStI WTyr WWat
x ***carminea*** 'Barbarossa'	CLan
– 'Buccaneer'	CDoC ENot NKay SBod SHer SPer
– 'Pirate King'	CDoC CSco CShe ENot MBal SCob SPer WWes
chrysosphaera	CChu WWat
congestiflora	CPle
coryi	See B. ***wilsoniae subcaulialata***
coxii	CB&S CPle CSam NTow
darwinii **AGM**	Widely available

dictyophylla **AGM**	CB&S CBot CCla CMHG CPle EBre EHar ELan LBre MBri MBrk SLon SMad SPer SSta WSHC WWat
dulcis 'Nana'	See B. ***buxifolia*** 'Nana'
empetrifolia	CGre CLew NNor SIng
♦***erythroclada***	See B. ***concinna***
x ***frikartii*** 'Amstelveen' **AGM**	CSam EBar ELan ENot IJoh SCob SLon WGor
– 'Telstar' **AGM**	CPle CSco ENot LBuc MBal MBri MRav SCob WStI
gagnepainii 'Fernspray'	MBri SBod SPer SRms
§ – var. ***lanceifolia***	CB&S CPle ENot EPla IOrc MBar MGos MWat NNor NWea SLPl SLon WHCG
– 'Purpurea	See B. x ***interposita*** 'Wallich's Purple'
gagnepainii hort.	See B. ***g. lanceifolia***
'Georgei'	CMHG SHil
glaucocarpa	LRHS
'Goldilocks' **AGM**	CAbP CDoC CMHG CPMA CTre EHar MBlu MBri SHil WWat
gracilis	WFro
hookeri	SCob
– var. ***latifolia***	See B. ***manipurana***
x ***hybridogagnepainii*** 'Chenault'	ELan SPer WAbe
hypokerina	CLan SHil
§ x ***interposita*** 'Wallich's Purple'	ENot MBal MBar MBri SGil SPer WGor WStI WTyr
jamesiana	CPle NTow
julianae	CB&S CBra CDoC CPle CSco EBre ELan ENot IOrc LBre MBal MBar MBri MGos MRav NBee NHol NNor NWea SCob SHBN SLPl SPer WDin WHCG WSHC
– 'Mary Poppins'	MBri MUlv
kawakamii	SLPl
knightii	See B. ***manipurana***
koreana	CMCN CSam ECtt EPla ERom SPer
¶ – 'Red Tears'	LRHS SPer
lempergiana	CB&S CMCN CMHG CPle
linearifolia	CBra GRei SLon WPat
– 'Orange King'	CAbP CB&S CChu CDoC CPMA CSco ELan ENot IJoh LHop MBri MGos MWat NBar NBee NKay SCob SDry SHBN SPer WDin WPat WStI
'Little Favourite'	See B. ***thunbergii*** 'Atropurpurea Nana'
x ***lologensis***	IOrc MGos SPla WDin
– 'Apricot Queen' **AGM**	CAbP CB&S CDoC CSco IJoh LHop MBal MBri SCob SDry SHBN SLon SPer WDin WStI WWeb
– 'Mystery Fire'	CAbP CBot CDoC CKni COtt CSco ECtt IOrc MAsh MBar MBlu MBri MGos MUlv SCob SPla
– 'Stapehill'	CB&S EBee EHar ENot MAsh MBri MUlv WWeb
lycium	EHal
§ ***manipurana***	CGre ENot
x ***media*** 'Parkjuweel' ('Park Jewel') **AGM**	CB&S CBra CDoC EBee EHal MAsh MRav NHol SGil SPer WWeb

– 'Red Jewel' **AGM**	CBra CChe CDoC CSco EBre IJoh LBre MBri MGos MWat SGil SHer SPer SPla WAbe WWeb
x ***ottawensis***	CSco GRei WStI
– 'Auricoma'	WWeb
– 'Decora'	SPer
– 'Lombart's Purple'	SLon
N x ***ottawensis purpurea***	EBee IJoh MBri SBod WDin
§ x ***ottawensis*** 'Silver Mile' (v)	CBot COtt CPle EFol ELan EPla LHop LNet MBel SApp SDry SGil SSta
N – 'Superba' **AGM**	CB&S CChe CDoC CPle CShe ELan ENot GWht IDai LHop MBal MBar MGos NBee NHol NNor NRoo SLon SPer SPla WDin
§ ***panlanensis***	ENot ESis MBar SCob SLon
patagonica	NNor
polyantha Hemsley	MRav
polyantha hort.	See B. ***prattii***
§ ***prattii***	CMHG MBri NHol NTow
pruinosa	CPle SLPl
'Red Tears'	CDoC CMHG COtt CPMA CSam MBlu MBri MGos WHCG WWes
replicata	CB&S SLPl SLon
'Rubrostilla' **AGM**	CDoC CSco ENot MBri SCob
sanguinea hort.	See B. ***panlanensis***
sargentiana	ELan ENot NNor SLPl SLon WWat
sherriffii	CLew CPle NHol NTow
sieboldii	CBot EHar WPat
¶ sp. C&S 1571	NMun
¶ sp. C&S 1651	NMun
x ***stenophylla*** **AGM**	CB&S CChe CPle CSco CShe ELan GRei IDai IJoh ISea LBuc MBar MBri MGos MWat NHol NKay NNor NRoo NWea SCob SHer SLon SPer SReu WBod WDin WHCG WPat WWin
– 'Autumnalis'	SCob
– 'Claret Cascade'	CCla CSco EHic ELan EWri MBri MGos SPer WWeb
– 'Coccinea'	EPla IBar
– 'Corallina'	WWeb
– 'Corallina Compacta' **AGM**	CLew ENot EPla EPot ESis IDai IMal MBal MBro MPla NHar NHol NKay SBla SBod SChu SHer SIng SPla WAbe WPat WThu
– 'Crawley Gem'	CMHG COtt CPle LNet MBar MBri MPla NHol NKay NRoo WStI WWin
– Cream Showers ®	See B. x ***s.*** 'Lemon Queen'
– 'Irwinii'	CMHG CSco CShe ENot EPla IOrc MBar MBri MGos MWat NKay SCob SIgm SLon SPer WDin WWeb
N – 'Lemon Queen'	CCla MAsh NHol SPer
– 'Nana'	EPla NHol
– 'Pink Pearl'	CBra CMHG CShe EFol EPla SHBN
temolaica	CCla CPMA CPle EBre EHar ELan LBre LGre SHil SLon SMad SPer SSta WWat
thunbergii **AGM**	ENot GRei IDai LBuc MBal NHol NKay NWea SPer WDin WStI
– f. ***atropurpurea***	Widely available
§ – 'Atropurpurea Nana' **AGM**	Widely available
– 'Atropurpurea Superba'	See B. x ***ottawensis*** 'Superba'

– 'Aurea'	Widely available
– 'Bagatelle' AGM	COtt ECtt ELan ENot EPot ESma IDai IOrc MBar MBri MGos MPla MRav NBee NHar NRoo SGil SHer SPer WAbe WDin WPat
– 'Carpetbagger'	IOrc MGos
– 'Crimson Pygmy'	See B. *t.* 'Atropurpurea Nana'
– 'Dart's Purple'	ENot MAsh MBri WWeb
– 'Dart's Red Lady'	CBot CCla EBre ECtt EHal ELan ENot EPla ESma IJoh IOrc LBre MBri MPla MRav NRoo SPer SPla WAbe
– 'Erecta'	ENot MAsh MBar MGos NHol SCob WDin
– 'Golden Ring'	CB&S CChe CCla CPMA CPle CSco EBar ECtt EFol EHoe ELan EPla LAbb LHop MBar MBri MGos MWat NHol NRoo SChu SHBN SPer SPla SReu WDin WHCG WPat WSHC
– 'Green Carpet'	EBre EHic ENot IOrc LBre MBal MBar NRoo SPer SSta
*– 'Green Mantle'	SBod
– 'Green Ornament'	MWat SPer
– 'Harlequin'	CB&S CChe CPle CSco EBre ECtt EHar EHoe ELan ENot EPla IJoh IOrc LBre MBal MBri MGos NBee NWyt SApp SCob SHBN SPer SPla WBod WDin WPat WStI
– 'Helmond Pillar'	CMHG CSco EBre EHoe ELan EMil ENot EPla IJoh IOrc LBre MBar MBlu MBri MPla NBee NFai NRoo SCob SGil SMad SPer SReu WEas WPat WSHC
– 'Kelleriis'	EBee EPla MBar MBri WStI
– 'Kobold'	ENot EPla MBar MBri MGos MPla NBee NRoo SPer WPat
¶– 'Pink Attraction'	LRHS
– 'Pink Queen'	CB&S MAsh MBri MGos SHer WWeb
– 'Red Chief' AGM	CMHG CSco CShe EBre ECtt EHar ELan ENot EPla GRei LBre LHop MBal MGos MRav MWat NBee NRoo SChu SCob SGil SHBN SLon SPer SPla SReu WDin WHCG WStI
– 'Red King'	WDin
– 'Red Pillar'	CB&S CLan CPle CSco EBre ECtt ELan LBre MBal MBar MBlu MBri MGos MWat NBee NHol SFis SHBN SPla WDin WStI WWeb
– 'Red Rocket'	EMil
– 'Robin Hood'	MBrk
– 'Rose Glow' AGM	Widely available
– 'Silver Beauty'	CB&S CCla CDoC CMHG CPle EHal ELan MBel MGos NFai SBod SPer WHCG WWeb
– 'Silver Mile'	See B. x *ottawensis* 'S.M.'
– 'Somerset'	CSco WWat
*– 'Tricolor' (v)	EHic EHoe MUlv WEas WPat WSHC WWeb
*– 'Variegata'	SReu
– 'Vermilion'	CSco
tsangpoensis	SLPl SLon
valdiviana	CBot EHar
veitchii	SLPl SRms
verruculosa AGM	CBra CLan CSco ELan ENot IDai LHop MBal MBar MBri MGos NHol NKay NNor NWea SCob SLon SPer SPla SReu SSta WBod WDin WWat
vulgaris	CArn MSal
wardii	CB&S
wilsoniae AGM	CBra CLan CSam CSco EBre EGol ELan ENot IOrc LBre MBar MPla MWat NFai NHol NKay NNor NTow NWea SCob SHBN SPer WDin WStI
¶– blue	MAsh MBri
– 'Graciella'	MBri NHol
– var. *guhtzunica*	EPla

BERCHEMIA (Rhamnaceae)

racemosa	SPer WSHC

BERGENIA † (Saxifragaceae)

'Abendglocken'	CLew CMil EBee ECha EHic MBri MNFA SFis SHig SPla
§ 'Abendglut'	CBow CGle CSco CShe EBar EBre ECha ECtt EGol ELan ELun EPla IBar LBre MBal MBri NDea NHol NKay NMir NOrc NSti SAxl SHig SPer SPla
****acanthifolia***	CRow
'Admiral'	ECha EGle MUlv
afghanica	CRow
'Apple Court White'	SApp
'Baby Doll'	CBow CCla CDoC COtt CSco EBre ECha EFou EGol EOrc EPla GCal IBar LBre LHop MBri MUlv NBir NHol NMir NOrc NPer NTow SApp SGil SHer SPla WAbe WRus
§ 'Ballawley'	CRow ECha IBlr IDai MUlv NDea SAxl SHig
N Ballawley hybrids	CB&S CBot CCla CMGP CMHG CShe EBre EGol EPar ERav LBre LGro MUlv NHol SDix SGil SHer SPer
'Bartok'	MUlv
beesiana	See B. ***purpurascens***
'Beethoven'	CHad CRow EBre ECha EGle EPla LBre
'Borodin'	MUlv
'Brahms'	CRow MUlv
'Bressingham Bountiful'	MUlv SPer
'Bressingham Ruby'	CDec COtt EBre EFol EPla ERav GAri LBre MHlr MUlv NRoo SPla WCot
'Bressingham Salmon'	CFee CMil CSco EBre ELan ERav LBre LWad MBri MHlr MMil NHol NMir SAxl SGil SHer SPer WCot WMer
'Bressingham White' AGM	CBot CBow CCla CMHG COtt CSco EBre ECha ECtt EGol ELan ELun EOrc ERav LBre LHop MBri MRav MUlv NCat NDea NFai NHol NRoo SApp SPer WRus WWin
'Britten'	CMil MBal MUlv
¶ 'Broica'	ECha
ciliata	CFee CHEx CHad CHan CMil CRow ECha EPla GAbr GCal GCra LGre MBal NBir NSti SAxl SDix SUsu WEas WPer WThu
¶– ***ficifolia***	EPla

– f. *ligulata*	ECha EMar EPla WHil WPer
♦– x *crassifolia*	See B. x *schmidtii*
cordifolia	CB&S CBow CGle CHEx CKel CMHG CSco EBre EHon ELan ENot EOrc EPar ERav GCal LBre MBal MFir MPit NBar NDea NFai NKay NNor SPer SReu WPer WStI WTyr WWin
– 'Purpurea' AGM	CB&S CSco CShe EBre ECha EGol EHal ELan ENot EPla LBre LBuc LGro LWad MBri MNFA MRav NKay SDix SHig SPer
– 'Redstart'	NMir NOak SGil
crassifolia	CB&S CGle CKel CWGN EBul EPla LGro MFir SHig SRms WByw
– DF 90028	EMon
– 'Autumn Red'	ECha EPla
– *orbicularis*	See B. x *schmidtii*
– var. *pacifica*	CFil
'Croesus'	IDai
delavayi	See B. *purpurascens*
'Delbees'	See B. 'Ballawley'
¶ 'Distinction'	IDai
'Eric Smith'	ECha EPla
'Evening Glow'	See B. 'Abendglut'
'Glockenturm' ('Bell Tower')	ECha EPla MUlv
'Jo Watanabe'	ECha EPla
'Lambrook'	See B. 'Margery Fish'
§ 'Margery Fish'	CMil COtt CSco CShe ECha EPla SPer SPla WDav
♦*milesii*	See B. *stracheyi*
'Morgenröte' ('Morning Red') AGM	CBow CCla CDoC COtt CSco CShe EBar ECha EPla MBri NDea NHol NKay SHig SPer SPla SRms WAbe
'Mrs Crawford'	ECha EPla
'Opal'	ECha EPla
'Profusion'	SPer
'Pugsley's Pink'	CMil ECha LHop MArl MUlv
§ *purpurascens* AGM	CDec CMHG CMil CRow CSco EBre ECha EPla ERav ESma GDra LBre MBal NHol SAxl SDix SPer WByw WWin
– var. *delavayi* CLD 1366	EMon WPer
'Purpurglocken'	ECha EPla
¶ 'Red Beauty'	NPri
'Rosette'	NFai
'Rosi Klose'	CGle EBee ECha EPla GCal LRHS SApp
'Rotblum'	ECtt EGol LRHS SFis WPer
§ x *schmidtii* AGM	CSco EPla LGro NBir SAxl SDix SHig
'Schneekissen'	EGle LRHS SGil
'Schneekönigin' ('Snow Queen')	CGle ECha EPla
'Silberlicht' ('Silverlight') AGM	Widely available
'Snowblush'	MBal
§ *stracheyi*	CBot CCla CLew CRow ECha EFol EGol EPla MNFA NHol SApp SAxl SDix SHig WDav WHil WHoo
– KBE 151	NHol
– KBE 209	EPla NHol
– *alba*	CChu ECha EPla GCal NDea SApp SDix SWas
'Summer Mountain'	MBri
'Sunningdale'	CB&S CMGP EBre ECha EGol EHal EPar EPla LBre MTol NBar NBir NSti SAxl SChu SPer SPla WMer
¶ 'Tubby Andrews'	NRar SPer
'Wintermärchen'	CBow ECha ECtt EFou EGol ELan EPla ERav IBar MBri MSte MUlv NBee NHol NOrc NSti SHer SPla WRus
¶ 'Winterzauber'	MUlv

BERKHEYA (Compositae/Asteraceae)

macrocephala	WCot

BERLANDIERA (Compositae/Asteraceae)

See Plant Deletions

BERULA (Umbelliferae/Apiaceae)

erecta	EHon

BESCHORNERIA (Agavaceae)

tubiflora	CHEx
yuccoïdes AGM	CB&S CHEx IBlr IFer SArc

BESSERA (Liliaceae/Alliaceae)

See Plant Deletions

BESSEYA (Scrophulariaceae)

See Plant Deletions

BETA (Chenopodiaceae)

trigyna	EMon
¶ *vulgaris*	WHer
¶ – 'Bull's Blood'	MHlr WCot

BETONICA See STACHYS

BETULA † (Betulaceae)

aetnensis	CSto
alba Linnaeus	See B. *pubescens*, B. *pendula*
albosinensis AGM	CB&S CGre ELan GAri WCoo WFro WMou WNor
– F 19505	CSto
– W 4106	CSto
– 'Conyngham'	CTho WWat
– var. *septentrionalis* AGM	CDoC CLnd CSto CTho EHar ENot GAri LNet MBri SEng SHil SPer WHCr WWat
§ *alleghaniensis*	CBow CDoC CGre CLnd CMCN CSam CSto IOrc MBal NWea WCoo WNor
apoiensis	CGre CSto
austrosinensis	MNes
borealis	CSto
x *caerulea*	CSto CTho
caerulea-grandis	See B. x *caerulea*
celtiberica	See B. *pubescens c.*
chichibuensis	CGre EPla MNes
chinensis	MNes
cordifolia	CSto MNes WHCr
costata hort.	See B. *ermanii* 'Blush'

costata Trautvetter	CCla CDoC CLnd CMCN COtt CSam CSco CSto CTho EBar EHar ELan ENot IBar IOrc WCoo WDin WFro WNor
davurica	CGre CLnd WCoo
¶ ***delavayi***	MNes
ermanii	CB&S CBra CGre CLnd CMCN CMHG COtt CSam CSco CSto CTho EHar ELan ENot IOrc MBal MBlu MBri MGos NWea SPer SReu WCoo WDin WFro WNor
– 'Blush'	MGos
– 'Grayswood Hill' **AGM**	CMHG CSto MBal SPer WWat
'Fetisowii'	CLnd CTho SHil SPer WHCr
§ ***fontinalis***	CSto WHCr
♦ ***fruticosa***	See B. ***humilis***
glandulifera	CLnd CSto EArb
glandulosa	EArb
¶ ***globispica***	MNes
grossa	CSto
'Hergest'	EHar WHCr
§ ***humilis***	CDoC
'Inverleith'	EHar MBri
jacquemontii	See B. ***utilis jacquemontii***
'Jermyns' **AGM**	CMHG CTho ECot EHar MUlv SHil
lenta	CFil CSto EHar MBal WCoo
litvinovii	WNor
luminifera	WHCr
lutea	See B. ***alleghaniensis***
maximowicziana	CB&S CBra CDoC CLnd CMCN EBar GAri MBal SSta WCoo WFro WNor
medwedewii **AGM**	CCla CGre CLnd CMCN CTho EBee GAri NHol SEng SSta WCoo
michauxii	NHol WAbe WPat
minor	CSto
nana	CLew CPle CSto EHar ELan EPla ESis GPlt IOrc MBal MBar MBro MPla NHol SHer SIng SSta STre WPer
– 'Glengarry'	EPot GAri NHol WDin
§ ***neoalaskana***	CSto
nigra **AGM**	CBra CDoC CGre CLnd CMCN CSto CTho EHar ENot IHos IOrc LMer MBal SHil SPer WCoo WDin WFro WMou WNor
¶ – 'Heritage'	EHar
occidentalis	See B. ***fontinalis***
papyrifera	CB&S CBra CLnd CMCN CSco CSto EHar ELan ENot IOrc ISea LBuc MBal MBar MGos NWea SHBN SPer SReu WCoo WDin WNor WWat
– var. ***commutata***	CLnd
– var. ***kenaica***	CDoC CTho SHil WHCr
– var. ***minor***	EArb
– 'Saint George'	CTho WWat
§ ***pendula*** **AGM**	CB&S CBra CKin CLnd CPer CSco CSto EBre EHar ELan ENot GRei IDai IJoh IOrc LBre LBuc MBal MBar MBri MGos NBee NWea SPer SReu WAbe WDin WMou
*– ***arvii***	EMil
– f. ***crispa***	See B. ***p.*** 'Laciniata'
N– 'Dalecarlica'	See B. ***p.*** 'Laciniata'
– 'Fastigiata'	CLnd CSco CTho EBre EHar ELan EMil ENot LBre LPan MGos SHil SPer SReu
– 'Golden Cloud'	CB&S CLnd EHar IOrc MBar MWat NBar SPer WDin
¶ – 'Gracilis'	EMil
§ – 'Laciniata' **AGM**	CLnd COtt CSco CTho EHar EMil ENot GRei IOrc MBar MBri MGos NBee NWea SHBN SPer SSta WDin WHCr WMou WWes
– var. ***pendula*** 'Dissecta'	WFro
– 'Purpurea'	CBra CLnd CSco CTho CWSG EBre EFol EHar ELan ENot IOrc LBre MBal MBar MBlu MBri MGos NBar NBee SEng SHBN SHil SPer SReu WDin
– 'Tristis' **AGM**	CDoC CLnd CSco CTho EHar EMil ENot GRei IOrc MBal MBar MBri NWea SPer WDin WHCr WMou
– 'Youngii' **AGM**	CB&S CBra CCla CLnd CSco EBre EGol EHar ELan ENot GRei IDai IJoh LBre LBuc LNet MBal MBar MBri MGos NBar NWea SHBN SPer SReu SSta WAbe WDin
platyphylla	CMCN CTho GAri LHop WFro
– var. ***japonica***	CLnd MBrk WFro WNor
populifolia	CSto GAri SEng
¶ ***potaninii***	CGre CMHG
§ ***pubescens***	CKin CLnd CPer CSto IOrc ISea LNet MBal NBar NWea WDin WMou
– 'Arnold Brembo'	CTho
– ssp. ***celtiberica***	CMHG CSto
pumila	CMCN CSto
¶ ***raddeana***	MNes
resinifera Britton	See B. ***neoalaskana***
saposhnikovii	WNor
schmidtii	CSto MNes WCoo WNor
¶ sp. CLD 407	WHCr
szechuanica	CSto SHil WAbe
– W 983	CSto
tatewakiana	See B. ***ovalifolia***
tianschanica	LMer
'Trost's Dwarf'	CB&S CChu CCla CWSG EFol EHal EHar ESis IJoh IOrc ISea LHop MBar MBro MGos MPla NBee NHar NHol NRoo SEng SPer WAbe WPat WWat
x ***utahensis***	CSto EArb
utilis	CBra CCla CLnd CMCN CMHG CTho EHar ELan EMil ENot GRei LNet MBal MBar MGos MRav NBar NBee NHol SPer WAbe WCoo WDin WFro WHCr WNor
– BL&M 100	CTho
– G-W&P 760	CSto
– PF 48	ISea
– SS&W 4382	CSto
– 'Buckland'	CTho
N– var. ***jacquemontii*** **AGM**	Widely available
– – 'Grayswood Ghost'	CTho
– – 'Silver Shadow' **AGM**	EHar WWat
♦– – wild origin	CSto
– 'Trinity College'	IMal
verrucosa	See B. ***pendula***

BIARUM (Araceae)

arundanum	CMon
bovei S&L 132	CMon
carduchorum	EPot LAma WChr
¶ ***carratracense***	WChr

– SF 233	CMon
davisii	EPot LAma WChr WCru
– ssp. ***davisii*** MS 785/735	CMon
– ssp. ***marmarisense***	CMon WChr
dispar	WChr
– AB&S 4455	CMon
– S&L 295	CMon
ditschianum	WChr
eximium FF 1024	CMon
– PD 26644	CMon
ochridense	WChr
– M&T 4629	CMon
pyrami PB	CMon
¶ – S&L 584	CMon
¶ ***spruneri*** S&L 229	CMon
tenuifolium	CBro CMon EPot LAma WChr
– AB&S 4356	CMon
¶ – var. ***abbreviatum***	WChr
– ssp. ***idomenaeum*** MS 758	CMon
– var. ***zeleborii***	CBro
¶ ***zeleborii***	WChr

BIDENS (Compositae/Asteraceae)

atrosanguinea	See COSMOS ***atrosanguineus***
aurea	CGle ECtt EPad GCal MSte NFai NPri
cernua	MHew MSal
ferulifolia AGM	CBrk CLTr CSev CSpe ECtt ERav ERea GCal GMac LHil LHop MFir NPer SBor SChu WEas WHal WOMN WPer
heterophylla CD&R 1230	CHan
ostruthioïdes	CBrk
sp. CD&R 1515	CHan
tripartita	EWFC MSal

BIGNONIA (Bignoniaceae)

capreolata	CBow EMil SBra SHil WSHC WWeb
lindleyana	See CLYTOSTOMA ***callistegioïdes***
unguis-cati	See MACFADYENA ***u-c.***

BILDERDYKIA See **FALLOPIA**

BILLARDIERA (Pittosporaceae)

¶ ***bicolor***	MSto
* ***cordata***	MSto
¶ ***erubescens***	MSto
longiflora	CAbb CB&S CGre CHan CMHG CMac CPle EBre ECou ELan EMil ERea IDai LBre LGre LHop MGos SApp SBra SHer SLMG SPer SSta SUsu WSHC WWat
– 'Cherry Berry'	ECou
– ***fructu-albo***	MBal SWas
– red berried	CSam EBul
– 'Rosea'	LBlm
scandens	ECou

BILLBERGIA (Bromeliaceae)

x ***albertii***	CTro
nutans	CHEx EBak ELan ERav IBlr LAbb LBlm MBri SArc SFar SLMG
pyramidalis var. ***striata*** (v)	SLMG
saundersii	See B. ***chlorosticta***
x ***windii*** AGM	EBak SLMG

BISCUTELLA (Cruciferae/Brassicaceae)

frutescens	MHig WWin

BISTORTA See **PERSICARIA**

BLACKBERRY See **RUBUS** ***fruticosus***

BLACKCURRANT See **RIBES** ***nigrum***

BLACKSTONIA (Gentianaceae)
See Plant Deletions

BLANDFORDIA (Liliaceae/Blandfordiaceae)

punicea	GCal SIgm

BLECHNUM (Blechnaceae)

alpinum	See B. ***penna-marina alpinum***
chilense	See B. ***tabulare***
gibbum	MBri
§ ***glandulosum***	NMar
magellanicum	See B. ***tabulare***
¶ ***nudum***	CFil SApp
occidentale nanum	See B. ***glandulosum***
penna-marina	CBos CBro CFil CTom EBul ECou EFer EPar GGar MBal MFos NGar NHar NMar SDix SHer SPer WAbe WEas WOMN WRic
§ – ssp. ***alpinum***	CFil NKay NMar
– ***cristatum***	CFil EBre GDra LBre MBal NHar NKay WRic
spicant AGM	CFil CKin GGar IOrc MBal NBro NMar SApp SArc SIng SPer SPla WRic
* – ***incisum***	SPer
– Serratum Group	CFil SApp
§ ***tabulare*** AGM	CB&S CBrd CFil CHEx EBul IBlr MBal NKay SArc SAxl SDix SHig

BLETILLA (Orchidaceae)

formosana	EFEx SWes WChr
hyacinthina	See B. ***striata***
ochracea	EFEx SWes WChr
§ ***striata***	CAvo COtt CRiv CSut ECtt EFEx EPot ERea GAbr IBlr LAma LHop MBri MTho MWBu NHol NRog NRya SHer SWes WAbe WChr
– ***alba***	See B. ***s. gebina***
– ***albostriata***	CBot EFEx ELan LAma NHol NRog SWes WChr
§ – f. ***gebina***	CAvo CBot ECtt EPot GAbr LAma MWBu NHol NNrd NRog NRya SWes WChr
szetschuanica	SWes
'Yokohama'	EFEx SWes WChr

BLOOMERIA (Liliaceae/Alliaceae)
crocea WChr

BLUEBERRY See **VACCINIUM *corymbosum***

BOCCONIA (Papaveraceae)
cordata See MACLEAYA *c.*
microcarpa See MACLEAYA *m.*

BOEHMERIA (Urticaceae)
See Plant Deletions

BOENNINGHAUSENIA (Rutaceae)
albiflora S&SH 108 CHan

BOISDUVALIA (Onagraceae)
¶ *densiflora* EBee

BOLAX (Umbelliferae/Apiaceae)
§ *gummifera* CFee GArf GCLN ITim NWCA

BOLTONIA (Compositae/Asteraceae)
asteroïdes CGle CHan CLew CSev EHal EMar EMon GMac NBrk NSti SHer WSun
– var. *latisquama* CBre CGle CHan CLew ECro EFou EHic EMon ESiP GCal GMac LRHS MSte NWyt SHer SMad SSvw
– – 'Nana' CBre ECha ELan GAul GBuc LHop NBrk NHol NPri SFis WPer
– 'Snowbank' EFol LHop MBel NWyt
incisa See KALIMERIS *incisa*

BOLUSANTHUS (Leguminosae/Papilionaceae)
See Plant Deletions

BOMAREA (Liliaceae/Alstroemeriaceae)
caldasii AGM CHEx CTro ERea
edulis ERea

BONGARDIA (Berberidaceae)
chrysogonum CAvo LAma LBow NRog

BORAGO † (Boraginaceae)
alba LHol MChe WCHb
laxiflora See B. *pygmaea*
officinalis CArn CSFH CSev EHer EWFC GPoy IEde LHol MBri MChe MHew NFai SHer SIde WEas WHal WHer WOak WPer WWye
– 'Alba' CBre CGle CMea CRDP EJud WHal WHer
§ *pygmaea* CElw CMil CRDP CSev EBre ECro ELan EMon ERav LBre LHol LHop MFir MPit MTho MTol NFai NSti SAxl SChu SIng WAbb WCru WHal WHer WOMN WOak WWin WWye

BORNMUELLERA (Cruciferae/Brassicaceae)
tymphaea SIgm

BORONIA (Rutaceae)
'Heaven Scent' CB&S EMil
heterophylla CB&S CMHG ERea LAbb LBlm LHop MUlv
megastigma CB&S EMil MAll

BOTHRIOCHLOA (Gramineae/Poaceae)
§ *bladhii* ETPC
caucasica See B. *bladhii*
ischaemum ETPC

BOTRYOSTEGE See **ELLIOTTIA**

BOUGAINVILLEA (Nyctaginaceae)
'Afterglow' ERea
'Albo d'Ora' CNew
'Alexandra' CNew MBri SLMG
'Amethyst' ERea MBri SLMG
'Apple Blossom' See B. 'Audrey Grey'
'Asia' (x *buttiana*) ERea
¶ 'Audrey Grey' (x *buttiana*) ERea
'Barbara Karst' ERea
¶ 'Begum Sikander' ERea
'Betty Lavers' ERea
'Brasiliensis' See B. 'Lateritia'
¶ 'Bridal Bouquet' See B. 'Mahara Off-White'
'Brilliance' ERea
♦ 'Brilliant' See B. 'Raspberry Ice'
'California Gold' See B. 'Golden Glow'
¶ Camarillo Fiesta ® (*spectabilis* x) ERea LAbb LBlm SLMG
¶ 'Chiang Mai Beauty' ERea
'Dania' LAbb MBri
'Danica Rouge' CNew SLMG
'Daphne Mason' ERea
¶ 'Dauphine' (v) ERea
¶ 'David Lemmer' ERea
'Dixie' ERea
'Doctor David Barry' CTro ERea
'Donyo' ERea
¶ 'Elizabeth' (*spectabilis* x) ERea
'Elizabeth Angus' ERea
♦ 'Flamingo Pink' See B. 'Chiang Mai Beauty'
'Gillian Greensmith' ERea
glabra AGM CB&S ERea LAbb MBri
– A ERea
¶ 'Gladys Hepburn' ERea
'Golden Dubloon' See B. 'Mahara Orange'
§ 'Golden Glow' (x *buttiana*) CNew CTro
'Harlequin' See B. 'Thimma'
'Harrissii' (*glabra*) (v) ERea LAbb
'Helen Johnson' ERea
¶ 'Indha' (*glabra* x) ERea
'Isobel Greensmith' CTro
N Jamaica White ® CB&S
'Jamaican Orange' ERea
'James Walker' ERea
'Jane Snook' ERea
'Jennifer Fernie' CNew ERea SLMG
'Juanita Hatten' CTro ERea
♦ 'Kauai Royal' See B. 'Purple Robe'
'Killie Campbell' AGM ERea MBri SLMG
'La Jolla' ERea

'Lady Mary Baring' (x ***buttiana***)	ERea
¶ 'Lavender Girl'	ERea
♦ 'Limberlost Beauty'	See B. 'Mahara Off-White'
¶ 'Lord Willingdon'	CTro ERea
'Magnifica'	ERea
'Magnifica Traillii'	See B. 'Magnifica'
'Mahara Double Red' (x ***buttiana***) (d)	ERea
§ 'Mahara Off-White' (x ***buttiana***) (d)	CTro ERea
§ 'Mahara Orange' (x ***buttiana***) (d)	CTro ERea
'Mahara Pink' (x ***buttiana***) (d)	ERea
¶ 'Makris'	ERea
'Mardi Gras' (x ***buttiana***) (v)	CTro ERea
'Mary Palmer' (Spectoperuviana Group)	CTro ERea
'Mary Palmer's Enchantment' (***peruviana*** x)	ERea
'Meriol Fitzpatrick' (***glabra***)	ERea SLMG
♦ 'Mini-Thai'	See B. 'Lord Willingdon'
¶ 'Miss Manila'	CTro
'Mrs Butt' (x ***buttiana***) AGM	ERea SLMG
'Mrs H C Buck' (Spectoperuviana Group)	ERea
§ 'Mrs Helen McLean' (x ***buttiana***)	ERea LBlm SLMG
¶ Natalii Group	ERea
'Nina Mitton'	ERea
¶ 'Ninja Turtle' (v)	ERea
'Orange Glow'	See B. Camarillo Fiesta ®
'Orange King'	See B. 'Mrs Helen McLean'
'Orange Stripe' (v)	ERea
♦ 'Pagoda Pink'	See B. 'Mahara Pink'
'Pearl'	ERea
'Pink Cluster'	ERea
'Pink Pixie'	See B. 'Lord Willingdon'
¶ 'Poultonii'	ERea
'Poultonii Special' AGM	CNew CTro ERea SLMG
¶ 'Poultonii Variegata'	ERea
¶ 'Pride of Singapore' (***glabra***)	ERea
¶ 'Purple Robe'	ERea
'Rainbow Gold'	ERea
'Raspberry Ice' (v)	CTro ERea
¶ 'Ratana Orange'	ERea
¶ 'Ratana Red'	ERea
'Red Diamond'	ERea LBlm SLMG
¶ 'Red Fantasy' (v)	ERea
¶ 'Red Glory'	ERea
'Rose Parme'	ERea
'Rosenka'	ERea
'Royal Bengal Orange' (***spectabilis***) (v)	ERea
'Royal Bengal Red' (v)	ERea
'Royal Purple'	ERea
'Rubyana'	CTro ERea
'San Diego Red'	See B. 'Scarlett O'Hara'
'Sanderiana' (***glabra***)	ERea NRog SLMG
'Sanderiana Variegata' (***glabra***)	MBri
¶ 'Scarlet Glory'	ERea
§ 'Scarlett O'Hara' (x ***buttiana***)	CNew CTro ERea LBlm SLMG
'Sea Foam'	CTro SLMG
♦ 'Smartipants'	See B. 'Lord Willingdon'
'Summer Snow'	CTro
Surprise ®	See B. 'Mary Palmer'
N Tahitian Maid ®	SLMG
'Tango'	See B. 'Miss Manila'
'Temple Fire'	CNew ERea
Texas Dawn ®	ERea
♦ 'Thai Gold'	See B. 'Mahara Orange'
'Thimma' (v)	CNew ERea
'Variegata' (***glabra***)	See B. 'Harrissii'
– (***spectabilis***)	CNew
¶ 'Vera Blakeman'	ERea
♦ 'Vicky'	See B. 'Thimma'
'Weeping Beauty'	CTro ERea
'White Empress'	CNew

BOUSSINGAULTIA (Basellaceae)

baselloïdes	See ANREDERA ***cordifolia***

BOUTELOUA (Gramineae/Poaceae)

curtipendula	EMon ETPC
gracilis	See CHONDROSUM ***gracile***

BOUVARDIA (Rubiaceae)

x ***domestica***	ERea
longiflora	CNew
scabrida	CPle LBlm
§ ***ternifolia***	CGre
triphylla	See B. ***ternifolia***

BOWENIA (Boweniaceae)

serrulata	LPal WNor

BOWIEA (Liliaceae/Hyacinthaceae)

See Plant Deletions

BOWKERIA (Scrophulariaceae)

citrina	CGre CPle
gerrardiana	CGre

BOYKINIA (Saxifragaceae)

aconitifolia	CGle CRDP CSam EBar ECro EFol ELan EMon GDra GTou MTol SApp WCru
♦ ***elata***	See B. ***occidentalis***
heucheriformis	See B. ***jamesii***
§ ***jamesii***	EPot LBee MBro MHig MRPP NHar NTow NWCA SIng WDav WThu
§ ***occidentalis***	GGar
rotundifolia	CSam ELan NHol NSti WCru
– JLS 86269LACA	EMon
tellimoïdes	See PELTOBOYKINIA ***t.***

BOYSENBERRY See **RUBUS**

BRACHYCHILUM See **HEDYCHIUM**

BRACHYGLOTTIS †
(Compositae/Asteraceae)

§ ***bidwillii*** CChu SDry WAbe WCru
§ ***buchananii*** CHan SDry WCru WSHC
§ ***compacta*** CDec EBee ECha ECou MAll MAsh MPla NRoo SDry SPer WCru WEas WWat
'Drysdale' MAll SDry WCru
§ Dunedin Hybrids Group
'Moira Read' (v) CPle CSco EFol ELan EPla ERav IMal LHop MAll MBal MUlv NPer SDry WCru WEas
§ – 'Sunshine' **AGM** CChe CDec CMHG ELan ENot IBlr LGro LHop MBal MBri MGos NPer SGil SPer SPla SSta WAbe WHen WWat
§ ***elaeagnifolia*** ISea MAll NNor SHil
N***greyi*** CLan CPle CSco CShe ERav GIsl GRei IDai IJoh ISea LAbb MBar NKay NNor NRoo SLon WEas WWin
§ ***hectorii*** LHop
§ ***huntii*** CAbb CBot CPle WCru
§ ***kirkii*** CGre CPle
N***laxifolia*** CLTr CLan LHop NNor WCru
§ 'Leonard Cockayne' CHEx SDry
§ ***monroi*** **AGM** CB&S CLan CMHG CPMA CPle CSam CSco ECou ELan EPla ERav IBlr IDai IOrc ISea LHop MBal MBar MRav NNor SLon SPer WAbe WCru WEas WSHC WWat
– 'Clarence' ECou
'New Zealand' CBot
repanda CHEx CPle
– 'Purpurea' CBot CHEx
– x ***greyi*** CPle SArc
§ ***rotundifolia*** CAbb CDoC CGre CPle IBlr IDai MAll MBlu WCru WEas
spedenii CFee GIsl GTou WCru
'Sunshine Variegated' See B. Dunedin Hybrids Group 'Moira Read'

BRACHYPODIUM (Gramineae/Poaceae)

phoenicoïdes ETPC
pinnatum CKin ETPC
sylvaticum CKin ECWi ETPC WPer

BRACHYSCOME (Compositae/Asteraceae)

'Harmony' IHos
iberidifolia CGre ELan NPri SHer
¶ ***melanocarpa*** CSpe
multifida CSpe IHos LHop MBri
nivalis var. ***alpina*** See B. ***tadgellii***
rigidula CRiv ECou MCas NNrd NTow
§ ***tadgellii*** WPer
'Tinkerbell' CBar IHos NRoo

BRACHYSTACHYUM
(Gramineae/Poaceae-Bambusoideae)

densiflorum SDry

BRACTEANTHA (Compositae/Asteraceae)

♦***acuminata*** De Candolle See B. ***subundulata***
bracteata 'Dargan Hill Monarch' CBrk CSev LHil LHop WEas WPer
– 'Skynet' CBrk GMac LHil LHop WPer

BRAHEA (Palmae/Arecaceae)

armata CTbh LPal NPal SArc
brandegeei LPal
edulis LPal

BRASSAIA See **SCHEFFLERA**

BRASSICA (Cruciferae/Brassicaceae)

japonica See B. ***juncea crispifolia***
§***juncea*** var. ***crispifolia*** CArn

BRAVOA (Agavaceae)

geminiflora See POLIANTHES ***g.***

BRAYA (Cruciferae/Brassicaceae)

alpina NMen WPer

BREYNEA

¶ ***nivosa*** 'Rosea Picta' CTro

BREYNIA (Euphorbiaceae)
See Plant Deletions

X BRIGANDRA (Gesneriaceae)

calliantha NTow

BRIGGSIA (Gesneriaceae)

muscicola MHig NTow

BRIMEURA (Liliaceae/Hyacinthaceae)

§ ***amethystina*** CAvo LRHS MHig WThu
– 'Alba' CAvo ETub LRHS MHig NHol NRog WHil WPer WThu

BRIZA (Gramineae/Poaceae)

maxima CSFH EHoe EJud EPla NSti SIng WWye
media CKin EBar ECWi EFou EHoe ELan EOrc EPla ETPC EWFC GAbr GCHN GCal LHop NBee NLan NMir SHer SPer WStI
– Elatior Group ETPC
– 'Limouzi' EGle EMon ETPC
minor CLew EHoe
triloba ETPC WHil

BROCCHINIA (Bromeliaceae)
See Plant Deletions

BRODIAEA (Liliaceae/Alliaceae)

capitata See DICHELOSTEMMA ***pulchellum***
elegans EBul ESma MFos WChr
ida-maia See DICHELOSTEMMA ***i.-m.***
laxa See TRITELEIA ***laxa***

peduncularis	See TRITELEIA *p.*
stellaris	WChr
terrestris	WChr
volubilis	WChr

BROMUS (Gramineae/Poaceae)

commutatus	ETPC
§ *lanceolatus*	ETPC
macrostachys	See B. *lanceolatus*
ramosus	EHoe ETPC

BROUSSONETIA (Moraceae)

papyrifera	CB&S CBot CCla CHEx CPle EArb EHar ELan LBuc SMad SPer WCoo WWat

BROWALLIA (Solanaceae)

speciosa 'Major'	MBri
– 'Silver Bells'	MBri

BRUCKENTHALIA (Ericaceae)

spiculifolia	CLew CNic EDen EPot GArf GPlt GWht IDai MBal MBar NHol WHil WThu WTyr
– 'Balkan Rose'	CNic EDen GCal

BRUGMANSIA (Solanaceae)

§ *arborea*	CArn CHEx NPal SLMG
aurea	CNew SLMG
x *candida*	EBak
– 'Grand Marnier' AGM	CBot ECot MBri SHil SLMG WEas WKif
§ – 'Knightii' AGM	CBot CBrk CHEx CNew CTro EBak ERea ERom
x *candida* x *aurea*	CTro
* *chlorantha*	CHEx CNew LHil MBri SLMG
– apricot	ERea
'Golden Queen'	CBrk ERea
x *insignis* 'Orange'	LBlm
§ – pink	CB&S CHEx CNew ERom LHil SHil
meteloïdes	See DATURA *inoxia*
'Panache'	CBot
rosei	See B. *sanguinea*
§ *sanguinea* AGM	CBrk CHEx CNew CTro ERea GCal ISea LHil MBri NRar SHil SLMG
♦– 'Rosea'	See B. x *insignis* pink
§ *suaveolens* AGM	CHEx EBar ELan ERea ISea SHil
– 'Flore Pleno'	SHil
– *rosea*	See B. x *insignis* pink
¶ – 'Variegata'	CNew ERea
§ *versicolor*	CBrk CNew CTro ERea LBlm SLMG

BRUNFELSIA (Solanaceae)

americana	CNew CPle CTro SLMG
calycina	See B. *pauciflora*
eximia	See B. *pauciflora*
¶ *latifolia*	CPle
pauciflora AGM	CNew CTro ELan LAbb MBri SLMG
– 'Floribunda'	CNew
– 'Macrantha'	CTro SLMG
undulata	CNew

BRUNNERA (Boraginaceae)

§ *macrophylla* AGM	Widely available
– *alba*	See B. *m.* 'Betty Bowring'
§ – 'Betty Bowring'	CBos CHad CRow EBee NCat SWas
§ – 'Dawson's White' (v)	CBot CCla CElw CGle CHEx CRow CSco EBre ECha EGol EOrc EPar EPla LBre LHop MBri MNes MTho NHol NRoo NSti SFis SHer SPer SUsu WPbr WRus
– 'Hadspen Cream' AGM	CBot CBro CFee CHad CRDP CRow CShe CSpe EBre ECha EFol EPar EPla LBre LGre MBri MRav MTho NBir NRoo WByw WCru WOld WRus
– 'Langtrees'	CElw CRow EBre ECha EFol EFou ELun EPar EPla GAbr LBre MTho MTol SAxl SFis WByw WCru WHer WPbr WRus
– 'Variegata'	See B. *m.* 'Dawson's White'

X BRUNSCRINUM (Liliaceae/Amaryllidaceae)

'Dorothy Hannibel'	CMon

BRUNSVIGIA (Liliaceae/Amaryllidaceae)

multiflora	See B. *orientalis*
§ *orientalis*	CMon NRog
– 'Alba'	CMon
rosea 'Minor'	See AMARYLLIS *bella-donna*

BRYANTHUS (Ericaceae)

gmelinii	GArf

BRYONIA (Cucurbitaceae)

dioica	EWFC GPoy MHew MSal

BRYOPHYLLUM See **KALANCHOË**

BRYUM (moss)

truncorum	LFle

BUCHLOË (Gramineae/Poaceae)

dactyloïdes	ETPC

BUDDLEJA † (Buddlejaceae)

agathosma	CBot CHan CPle WSHC
alternifolia AGM	Widely available
– 'Argentea'	CBot CBow CDoC CPMA CPle CSam CSco EBar ELan EPla ERav EWri LHol SGil SHBN SPer SPla WHCG WPat WSHC WWat WWeb
asiatica AGM	CBot CNew ERea ISea
auriculata	CAbb CB&S CBot CBow CCla CHan CMCN COtt CPle CTbh CWit ERea NSti SBor SDix SSta WCru WEas WHCG WWeb
¶ *australis*	CGre
bhutanica	CGre
* 'Butterfly Ball'	ERav GMac LHop WPer
caryopteridifolia	CCla EHar ENot
colvilei	CAbb CB&S CHEx CHan CPle CWit EWri GCal ISea MBal NBrk NSti SBor SPer WAbe WBod WCru WEas

– 'Kewensis'	CBot CCla CGre CSam IBlr MBlu MUlv SBla SHil WBod WSHC
¶ ***colvilei*** C&S 1577	NMun
¶ ***coriacea***	CPBP
§ ***crispa***	CBot CBow CDoC CPle ECha ELan ERav EWri LBlm LHop MSte SBor SDry SHBN SHil SPer SSta SUsu WCru WEas WHCG WKif WSHC WWat
– L 1544	NHex
davidii	CArn CKin LHol NRoo NWea WDin WWye
– 'African Queen'	ESma GAul SCob SMad SPer
– var. ***alba***	SHBN SLon
– 'Black Knight' **AGM**	Widely available
– 'Blue Horizon'	GCHN MHlr WCot
– 'Border Beauty'	CSco EHic ESma SBod SHer SPer SPla WWeb
– 'Calanadrina'	SBod
§ – 'Charming'	ELan SCob
– 'Dartmoor' **AGM**	CBot CMHG CRow ECtt EFol ELan ENot EPla GCal LAbb LHop MMil NBrk NPer SCob SDix SHBN SMad SPer SPla SSta WEas WHCG WSHC
– 'Dart's Blue Butterfly'	MBri MUlv
– 'Dart's Ornamental White'	EBee MBri MUlv
– 'Dart's Papillon Blue'	SLPl
– 'Dart's Purple Rain'	MBri MUlv
– 'Dubonnet'	SMad
– 'Empire Blue' **AGM**	CB&S CCla CSco CShe ECtt ELan ENot EPla GRei IDai IJoh MBal MUlv MWat NBee NPer NWea SCob SHBN SPer SPla WDin WStI
– 'Fascinating'	EPla GCal MAsh NPer SBod WHCG WWeb
– 'Fortune'	NNor
– 'Glasnevin'	SDix SHBN SPer
– 'Golden Sunset'	ECot
– 'Gonglepod'	ELan
– 'Harlequin' (v)	Widely available
– 'Ile de France'	CB&S EPla MGos MWat NWea SCob WHCG
– 'Les Kneale'	MBal
– 'Masquerade'	ENot MGos WWes
§ – 'Nanho Blue'	CBow CDoC CPle CSPN CSco EBre ECtt EFol EHar ELan ENot EPar EPla ESma GMac IOrc ISea LBre LHop MBar MGos NNor SBod SHBN WDin WHCG WSHC
– 'Nanho Petite Indigo'	See B. ***d.*** 'Nanho Blue'
– 'Nanho Petite Purple'	See B. ***d.*** 'Nanho Purple'
§ – 'Nanho Purple'	CDoC CSco EHar ELan ENot EPla GAri ISea LHol MBar MBri NRoo SPer SUsu WSHC WStI
– var. ***nanhoensis***	CHan CMHG CPle EBee MWat SLon SPer WHCG
– – ***alba***	EFol ELan LHop MMil SPla SRms WWat
– – blue	CShe IJoh MBri SPer SPla WEas WWat
– 'Operetta'	WDin
– 'Orchid Beauty'	SCob WWeb
– 'Peace'	CChe CLan CTre ECtt ENot ISea NPer SPer
– Petite Indigo ®	See B. ***d.*** 'Nanho Blue'
– Petite Plum ®	See B. ***d.*** 'Nanho Purple'
– 'Pink Beauty'	CLTr SCob SHBN WHCG
– 'Pink Charming'	See B. ***d.*** 'Charming'
*– 'Pixie Blue'	EPla
¶ – 'Pixie Red'	EPla
*– 'Pixie White'	EPla
– 'Purple Prince'	CB&S SCob
– 'Purple Rain'	SLPl
– 'Royal Purple'	MGos
– 'Royal Red' **AGM**	Widely available
¶ – 'Royal Red Variegated'	CRow
– 'Summer Beauty'	CPle SPer WPat
– 'Variegata'	NKay WWeb
– 'Variegated Royal Red'	EPla SCob SHBN
– 'White Bouquet'	CChe CPle EPla GRei MBal MBel MPla MRav MWat NBee NRoo NWea SBod SCob SPer SReu WWeb
– 'White Butterfly'	SPla
– 'White Cloud'	EPar IOrc ISea SMad
– 'White Harlequin' (v)	CLTr CRow EFol EMon EPla LHop WCot WCru WEas WWat
– 'White Perfection'	NKay
– 'White Profusion' **AGM**	CB&S CDoC CRow CSam CSco CShe ECtt ELan ESma GCHN IDai IJoh LAbb LBlm LHol MBal MBar MGos NBee NBrk NNor SCob SHBN SHer WDin WEas WHCG WStI WWin
¶ ***delavayi***	CPle
N***fallowiana***	CB&S CBow CGre CPle LAbb MAsh MSto NNor SReu
– var. ***alba*** **AGM**	CBot CBow CChu CDoC CGre CLan CPle CSco CTbh ELan ENot EPla ERav GCal GMac ISea LHop MBel NSti SHBN SHil SPer WCru WSHC WWat
farreri	CBot CPle SIgm WBod
forrestii	CBot CHEx CPle SArc
globosa **AGM**	Widely available
– 'Cannington Gold'	CPMA MUlv
– 'Lemon Ball'	SMad
heliophila	CGre CPle ERea WCru
japonica	CPle WCru
x ***lewisiana***	CPle
– 'Margaret Pike'	CBot WCru
x ***lewisiana*** x ***asiatica***	CNew
lindleyana	CAbb CB&S CBot CChu CDoC CGre CHan CMCN CMHG CPle CSPN CTre CTro ELan EOrc EPla ERea GCal GWht MBel NSti SBor SChu SPer SPla SUsu WCru WSHC
'Lochinch' **AGM**	Widely available
loricata	CBot CGre CHan CPle MSte
– CD&R 190	EPla
macrostachya SBEC 360	NHex
§ ***madagascariensis***	CB&S CGre CHEx CPle CTbh CTro LAbb LHop WWat
myriantha	CPle
nicodemia	See B. ***madagascariensis***
nivea	CBot CGre CMHG CPle ELan
– var. ***yunnanensis***	GCal MSte
officinalis	CBot CGre CPle CTro ERea
§ x ***pikei*** 'Hever'	CPle EHar SPer
'Pink Delight' **AGM**	Widely available
pterocaulis	CGre
saligna	CPle
salviifolia	CAbb CBot CBow CMHG CPle CTbh CTre ELan EPla GCal SDry SLon WCru
stenostachya	CPle

sterniana	See B. ***crispa***
♦*tibetica*	See B. ***crispa***
tubiflora	CBot CPle ERea
'West Hill'	CGre
x *weyeriana*	CBow CLTr CLan CPle CSam ECoo ECtt EFol ELan EPar EPla ESma IDai ISea MRav MSto MWat NBir SBod SHer WEas WHCG WSHC
– 'Golden Glow'	CB&S CBow CChe CDoC CHan CMCN CSco EBre GCHN LBre MBri MPla NKay NNor SGil SHil SMad WAbe WWeb WWin
– 'Lady de Ramsey'	WPer
– 'Moonlight'	CPle CRow EPla SCob SLon
– 'Sungold' AGM	CB&S CPle CRow ELan EWri IJoh IOrc MBal MBel MBlu MGos NBee SHBN SPer WTyr
– 'Trewithen'	CB&S CTrw

BUGLOSSOÏDES (Boraginaceae)

§ *purpurocaerulea*	CCla CKin CRDP ECha ELan EMon GCal MHew MSal MSte SAxl SFar SUsu WCru WEas WHal WOld WWin WWye

BULBINE (Liliaceae/Asphodelaceae)

¶ *alooides* S&SH 74	CHan
annua	EMon
bulbosa	WCot
caulescens	See B. ***frutescens***
§ *frutescens*	EBul
semibarbata	NBro WPer

BULBINELLA (Liliaceae/Asphodelaceae)

angustifolia	EPot NHol
hookeri	CRiv ECou ELan EPot GAbr GDra GGar ITim LBee MFir MTho NGre NHar NHed NHol SUsu WPer WThu
rossii	GDra

BULBINOPSIS See BULBINE

BULBOCODIUM (Liliaceae/Colchicaceae)

vernum	CAvo ETub LAma MBri NRog WChr WPat

BULLACE See PRUNUS *institia*

BUPHTHALMUM (Compositae/Asteraceae)

§ *salicifolium*	CBow CLew CSam CSev ELan EMon MBri NBro NOrc SPer SSvw WByw WMer WPer
¶ – 'Alpengold'	ECha
¶ – 'Dora'	NHol
– 'Golden Wonder' ('Golden Beauty')	SCro
speciosum	See TELEKIA ***speciosa***

BUPLEURUM (Umbelliferae/Apiaceae)

angulosum	CBos CRDP LGan LGre SIgm WCru WDav WPla
barceloi	SIgm
falcatum	CBos CGle CLTr ECha MUlv NBro NKay NSti SChu SFar WCru WWat
fruticosum	CAbb CB&S CBot CChu CCla CHad CHan CPle ECha ELan EMil ERav EWri LAbb LHop NRar SBla SChu SHil SIgm SPer SReu WCru WEas WSHC WWat
longifolium	CDoC CHan ECha GGar
rotundifolium	ECha MSal
stellatum	GArf LBee

BURCHARDIA (Liliaceae/Colchicaceae))

umbellata	CMon

BURSARIA (Pittosporaceae)

spinosa	CBot CGre CPle ECou

BUTIA (Palmae/Arecaceae)

capitata	CHEx CTbh CTro LPal NPal SArc
¶ *yatay*	CTrh

BUTOMUS (Butomaceae)

umbellatus AGM	CBen CRDP CRow CWGN ECha ECoo ECtt EHon ELan EMFW EWav LMay MHew MSta NDea SHig SWat SWyc WChe WHol
¶ – 'Schneeweisschen'	SWyc

BUXUS † (Buxaceae)

aurea 'Marginata'	See B. ***sempervirens*** 'Marginata'
balearica	EPla SDry SGil SLan WSHC WWat
bodinieri	EPla SLan
* 'David's Gold'	WEas WSHC
* 'Golden Frimley'	LHop
'Green Gem'	EHic NHar NWyt SLan
'Green Mountain'	SLan
'Green Velvet'	SLan
harlandii 'Richard'	SLan
harlandii hort.	EPla GAri SLan
japonica 'Nana'	See B. ***microphylla***
macowanii	SLan
§ *microphylla*	EHic GDra ISea LHol NHol SIng SLan STre
– 'Asiatic Winter'	MUlv SLPl
– 'Compacta'	CChu GPlt SLan WThu
– 'Curly Locks'	EPla GAri SLan
– 'Faulkner'	EBee ESma LHop MUlv SGil SLan
– 'Grace Hendrick Phillips'	SLan
– 'Green Pillow'	SLan
– 'Helen Whiting'	SLan
– var. *insularis*	See B. ***sinica insularis***
– var. *japonica*	SLan
– – 'Green Jade'	SLan
– – 'Morris Dwarf'	SLan
– – 'Morris Midget'	EHic SLan
– – 'National'	SLan
– – 'Variegata'	CMHG
– 'John Baldwin'	SLan
– var. *koreana*	See B. ***sinica insularis***
– var. *riparia*	See B. ***riparia***
– var. *sinica*	See B. ***sinica***
'Newport Blue'	MUlv
§ *riparia*	SLan
sempervirens AGM	Widely available

§ – 'Angustifolia'	EPla SGil SLan SMad
– 'Argentea'	See B. *s.* 'Argenteovariegata'
§ – 'Argenteovariegata'	MBal MRav SHig SLan WSHC
– 'Aurea'	See B. *s.* 'Aureovariegata'
– 'Aurea Maculata'	See B. *s.* 'Aureovariegata'
– 'Aurea Marginata'	See B. *s.* 'Marginata'
– 'Aurea Pendula' (v)	EHar EPla SLan SMad
§ – 'Aureovariegata'	CB&S CRow MBar MGos MRav MWat SChu SGil SIng SLan SPer WDin
– 'Blauer Heinz'	SLan
*– 'Blue Spire'	EHic
– clipped ball	CSco ERea NBee SPer
– clipped pyramid	CSco ERea MGos NBar SPer
§ – 'Elegantissima' **AGM**	CB&S CBot CBra CDec CMHG CSco CSev EFol ELan ERea ESis GPoy LBuc LHol LHop MBal MPla MWat NHar NKay NNor NNrd SIde SLan SLon SPer STre WDin WEas WWat
– 'Gold Tip'	See B. *s.* 'Notata'
– 'Greenpeace'	SLan
– 'Handsworthiensis'	SLan
– 'Handsworthii'	EHar ERea NWea SLon SPer
– ssp. ***hyrcana***	SLan
– 'Kingsville'	WCot
– 'Lace'	EBee NSti NWyt
I – 'Langley Pendula'	SLan
– 'Latifolia'	See B. *s.* 'Bullata'
– 'Latifolia Macrophylla' **AGM**	ELan EPla NWyt SLan
§ – 'Latifolia Maculata'	CAbP CSco EFol EPla ESma GDra ISea MBal MPla NHol NRoo SLan STre WOak
– 'Longifolia'	See B. *s.* 'Angustifolia'
§ – 'Marginata'	CSco ECtt GCHN LHop MRav NHol SHBN SLan SPla WStI
– 'Memorial'	SLan
– 'Myosotidifolia'	CMHG EPla NHar SLan WWat
– 'Myrtifolia'	CBot NHar NWyt SLan SLon
§ – 'Notata' (v)	CDec CRow ERea MAsh SGil
– 'Pendula'	CGre EHar NWyt SLan
*– 'Pendula Esveld'	SLan
– 'Prostrata'	EHic SLan
– 'Pyramidalis'	EBee EHic ENot NBee NWyt SLan
– 'Rosmarinifolia'	SLan
– 'Rotundifolia'	CLnd LHol SLan WDin
– 'Salicifolia Elata'	SLan
*– 'Silver Beauty' (v)	CB&S MGos
– 'Silver Variegated'	See B. *s.* 'Elegantissima'
– 'Suffruticosa' **AGM**	CArn CSco CSev CShe EHar ELan ERea ESis IEde LBuc LHol MBri MWat NRoo SCro SHer SLan SPer SPla STre WMou WOak
– 'Suffruticosa Variegata'	CB&S SRms
– 'Vardar Valley'	NHar NHol NWyt SLan
§ ***sinica***	SLan
– 'Filigree'	SLan
§ – var. ***insularis***	CLew EPla NHol
– – 'Justin Brouwers'	SLan
– – 'Pincushion'	SLan
– – 'Tide Hill'	SLan
– – 'Winter Beauty'	MUlv
wallichiana	SBor SLan WWat

CACCINIA (Boraginaceae)

See Plant Deletions

CAESALPINIA (Leguminosae/Caesalpiniaceae)

gilliesii	CBot CGre CHEx CPle EBee EMil ESma SHil SMad
¶ ***pulcherrima***	CTro

CAIOPHORA (Loasaceae)

See Plant Deletions

CALADIUM (Araceae)

§ ***bicolor*** (v)	MBri
– forms	NRog
x ***hortulanum***	See C. ***bicolor***
§ ***lindenii*** (v)	MBri

CALAMAGROSTIS (Gramineae/Poaceae)

§ x ***acutiflora*** 'Karl Foerster'	CDoC ECha EFol EPla ETPC GCal SApp SDix
– 'Overdam'	CElw EBre ECha EHoe EMon EPla ETPC LBre LRHS SApp SGil
– 'Stricta'	See C. x ***a.*** 'Karl Foerster'
epigejos	ETPC

CALAMINTHA † (Labiatae/Lamiaceae)

alpina	See ACINOS ***alpinus***
clinopodium	See CLINOPODIUM ***vulgare***
cretica	CSam EMon LHol LHop MTho NHol SIng WDav WHaw WHer WHil WPer WWye
§ ***grandiflora***	Widely available
– 'Variegata'	CDec CGle CRDP EFol EHoe ELan EMon LHop NPer NSti SMad WByw WCHb WHal WHer WHil WHoo WOld WPbr
§ ***nepeta***	CArn CBre CCla CHad CMGP CSFH ECha ECoo EMar EWFC IEde LAbb LGre MFir MRav MSte NBir NBro SBla SHer WEas WNdy WPer WWin WWye
– ssp. ***glandulosa*** ACL 1050/90	EMon WHoo
– – 'White Cloud'	CGle ECha EFou EMon GBuc GMac LGre MSte NTow SChu WPbr WRus
– ssp. ***nepeta***	CCla CGle CHan CSco CSev CShe EFou EGol ELan EMil EMon GBar GMac LHol LHop MBri MPla MRav MTho NOak SCro SIde SPer SUsu WHoo WRus WSHC WWat
– – 'Blue Cloud'	CGle ECha EFou LGre NTow SMrm SUsu WRus WWye
nepetoïdes	See C. ***nepeta nepeta***
§ ***sylvatica***	CNat WCla
– ssp. ***ascendens***	MHew MWil
♦ ***vulgaris***	See CLINOPODIUM ***vulgare***

CALAMONDIN See X CITROFORTUNELLA

CALANDRINIA (Portulacaceae)

caespitosa	MHig NGre NMen NWCA WPer
– P&W 6229	MSte
colchaguensis F&W 7210	MFos
compressa	WPer
grandiflora	ELan NWCA
megarhiza ssp. ***nivalis***	See CLAYTONIA ***m. n.***
rupestris	NGre NTow
sericea	NGre
sibirica	See CLAYTONIA ***sibirica***
skottsbergii	NGre
sp. JCA 12317	NGre
umbellata	CNic EBar ELan GCra LHop NGre NPri NTow NWCA SHer WOMN WPer WWin
*– ***amarantha***	WOMN

CALANTHE (Orchidaceae)

¶ ***arisanenesis***	EFEx
aristulifera	EFEx LAma NHol NRog SWes WChr
bicolor	See C. ***discolor flava***
¶ ***caudatilabella***	EFEx
discolor	EFEx LAma NHol NRog SWes WChr WCot
§ – var. ***flava***	LAma NHol
¶ ***japonica***	EFEx
¶ ***kintaroi***	EFEx
¶ ***nipponica***	EFEx
¶ ***okinawensis***	EFEx
reflexa	EFEx LAma NHol NRog SWes WChr
§ ***sieboldii***	EFEx LAma NHol NRog SWes WChr WCot WCru
striata	See C. ***sieboldii***
tricarinata	EFEx LAma NHol SWes WChr
¶ ***triplicata***	EFEx

CALATHEA † (Marantaceae)

albertii	MBri
albicans	See C. ***micans***
¶ ***bachemiana***	CTro
§ ***bella***	MBri
burle-marxii	MBri
crocata	MBri
'Exotica'	MBri
'Greystar'	MBri
♦ ***insignis*** hort.	See C. ***lancifolia***
kegeljanii	See C. ***bella***
lietzei	MBri
– 'Greenstar'	MBri
§ ***majestica***	CTro MBri
makoyana AGM	MBri
* 'Mavi Queen'	MBri
metallica	MBri
* 'Misto'	MBri
oppenheimiana	See CTENANTHE ***o.***
orbiculata	See C. ***truncata***
ornata	See C. ***majestica***
picturata 'Argentea'	MBri
– 'Vandenheckei'	MBri
roseopicta	MBri
§ ***truncata***	MBri
veitchiana	MBri
warscewiczii	MBri
'Wavestar'	MBri
zebrina AGM	MBri

CALCEOLARIA † (Scrophulariaceae)

acutifolia	See C. ***polyrhiza***
arachnoidea	EPot MSto NWCA WOMN
x ***banksii***	LBlm MFir
bicolor	GCal GCra
§ ***biflora***	CNic CRiv EBar ELan GCHN GDra GTou MBal NHol NKay NMen NMir NRed SHer WCla WHil WOMN WWin
– 'Goldcrest Amber'	GCra SRms WPer
'Camden Hero'	CBrk CKni LHop MAsh WOld WWat
chelidonioïdes	MTho
x ***clibranii***	CBrk
crenatiflora	GCra
¶ ***cymbiflora***	MSto
darwinii	GAbr GCra GTou MHig MSto NMen SIng WHoo
¶ ***ericoïdes*** JJA 13818	MSto
falklandica	CBoy ECtt ELan GTou LHop MPit NHol NRed NWCA SHer WHil WWin
fothergillii	GDra MHig MSto NTow
'Goldcrest'	GCHN NGre WDav
¶ ***helianthemoïdes*** JJA 13911	MSto
'Hort's Variety'	MTho
¶ ***hyssopifolia*** JJA 13648	MSto
§ ***integrifolia*** AGM	CAbb CB&S CDec CPBP CPle ELan EMar ERav ISea MBal MFir MSto NRog SChu SLon SPer SUsu WEas WOld WSHC WWat WWye
– var. ***angustifolia*** AGM	CGre SDry
– bronze	SPer WAbe
– 'Gaines' Yellow'	GCal
¶ – 'Sunshine' AGM	NPri
'John Innes'	EBur ELan ESis GAri GCal LHop NHol NMen NNrd NWCA SHer
'Kentish Hero'	CBot CBrk CDec CElw CMHG CPle ELan EMon GCal LHop MFir SChu WOMN WPat
mexicana	MSto SUsu WCru
¶ ***montana*** F&W 7225	WDav
¶ ***nivalis*** JJA 13888	MSto
¶ ***perfoliata*** JJA 13736	MSto
¶ ***picta***	MSto
plantaginea	See C. ***biflora***
§ ***polyrhiza***	CNic ELan MBal MSto NHol NRoo NRya NWCA SHer WAbe WCla
♦ ***rugosa***	See C. ***integrifolia***
scabiosifolia	See C. ***tripartita***
'Sir Daniel Hall'	SAsh
tenella	EBar ECtt EPot ESis GAri GDra MHig MSto MTho NHar NHol NTow NWCA SHer WAbe WWin
§ ***tripartita***	MSto
'Walter Shrimpton'	ECtt ELan EPot NHar NTow SBla SHer SIng

CALENDULA (Compositae/Asteraceae)

officinalis CArn CSFH GPoy LHol MChe MHew MSal SHer SIde WOak WWye
– 'Prolifera' WHer
– 'Variegata' MSal

CALLA (Araceae)

aethiopica See ZANTEDESCHIA ***aethiopica***
palustris CBen CHEx CRiv CRow CWGN EBre ECoo EHon EWav GAri GGar LBre LMay MSta NDea SHig SWat SWyc WChe WHol

CALLIANDRA (Leguminosae/Mimosaceae)

♦*brevipes* See C. ***selloi***
¶ *houstoniana* CTro
§ *selloi* CTro

CALLIANTHEMUM (Ranunculaceae)

coriandrifolium GDra

CALLICARPA (Verbenaceae)

bodinieri CBra NBir
– var. *giraldii* CDec CGre CShe MAsh MHlr MRav SLon SSta WBod WDin WWat WWeb
– – 'Profusion' AGM Widely available
cathayana CMCN
dichotoma CPle ELan EPla MNes WBod WSHC WWin
japonica WCoo
– 'Leucocarpa' CB&S CBow CMHG CPle EHic EPla SLon WWat
x *shirasawana* NBar

CALLIERGON (moss)

giganteum LFle

CALLIRHOË (Malvaceae)

involucrata WPer

CALLISIA (Commelinaceae)

repens MBri

CALLISTEMON (Myrtaceae)

'Burning Bush' CB&S LBlm
citrinus CBow CHan CLTr CPle CShe CTre EArb ECot ECou EMil ERav ERom GWht ISea LAbb MAll NPer SLMG SPer WWin
♦– *albus* See C. ***c.*** 'White Anzac'
– 'Mauve Mist' CB&S LBlm NPal
– 'Perth Pink' CB&S
– 'Red Clusters' CB&S ELan EMil ERea
– 'Splendens' AGM CB&S CBow CDoC CHEx CSam EBre ELan EMil EWri IOrc LBre NPal SDry SHBN SHil SLon SReu SSta WBod WStI WWat
§ – 'White Anzac' CGre GCHN
linearis AGM CBow CMac CTre ELan EMil IOrc ISea MAll MBal SLMG SLon
pallidus CBow CChu CMHG CMac CPle CWit ELan GWht MAll WBod
paludosus See C. ***sieberi***
'Perth Pink' CFee
phoeniceus IDai MAll
pinifolius IBar MAll
pityoïdes CGre
rigidus CB&S CBra CChe CDoC CHEx CLan CMHG CWSG ELan IBar ISea LBlm MAll MBlu MGos MUlv SHer SLMG SPer WBod WCru WDin
¶ 'Royal Sceptre' MAll
salignus AGM CChu CHEx CHan CMHG CSam CTre IOrc ISea MAll MBal MUlv SAxl SDry SHil SPer WSHC
sieberi AGM CBow CChu CGre ECou GWht IBar ISea LAbb MAll NBir WWat
speciosus See C. ***glaucus***
subulatus CMHG ECou MAll MBal SArc
viminalis MAll
– 'Captain Cook' AGM CB&S CBow EBre ECou LBre MUlv
– 'Hannah Ray' CB&S
– 'Little John ' CB&S CBow CFee
'Violaceus' CHan CPle
viridiflorus CChu CGre CPle ECou IBar IBlr

CALLITRICHE (Callitrichaceae)

autumnalis See C. ***hermaphroditica***
hermaphroditica EMFW
§ *palustris* CBen ECoo EHon SWyc
verna See C. ***palustris***

CALLITRIS (Cupressaceae)

oblonga CGre ECou
rhomboidea ECou

CALLUNA † (Ericaceae)

vulgaris CKin ECWi MGos
– 'Adrie' EDen
– 'Alba Argentea' EDen ENHC
– 'Alba Aurea' EDen ENHC MBar NWin
– 'Alba Carlton' EDen
– 'Alba Dumosa' EDen ENHC
– 'Alba Elata' CNCN EDen ENHC MBar
– 'Alba Elegans' EDen
– 'Alba Elongata' See C. ***v.*** 'Mair's Variety'
– 'Alba Erecta' EDen
– 'Alba Jae' EDen MBar
– 'Alba Minor' EDen
¶ – 'Alba Multiflora' EDen
¶ – 'Alba Pilosa' EDen
– 'Alba Plena' CB&S CMac CNCN EDen ENHC GPen GSpe IDai IJoh MBal MBar SBod WRid WStI
– 'Alba Praecox' EDen
– 'Alba Pumila' EDen MBar
§ – 'Alba Rigida' CMac CNCN EDen ENHC MBar MBri WGre WRid
– 'Alex Warwick' EDen SBod
– 'Alison Yates' EDen MBar
– 'Allegretto' EDen
– 'Allegro' AGM CMac EDen ENHC MBar MBri MOke NHol SBod WStI
– 'Alportii' EDen ENHC GAng GBla GDra GSpe IDai MBar MBri MOke SBod WGre WStI
– 'Alportii Praecox' CNCN EDen ENHC MBar SBod WGre
– 'Alys Sutcliffe' EDen

¶ – 'Amanda Wain' EDen
– 'Amilto' CNCN EDen WGre
– 'Andrew Proudley' EDen ENHC
– 'Angela Wain' EDen
– 'Anna' EDen
– 'Annabel' EDen
¶ – 'Anne Dobbin' EDen
– 'Anneke' EDen
– 'Annemarie' AGM EDen MBri MGos NBir SBod WGre
– 'Anthony Davis' AGM CNCN EDen ENHC GAng GAul GPen MBar MGos MOke NWin SBod WRid
– 'Anthony Wain' EDen MGos
– 'Anton' EDen
– 'Apollo' EDen
– 'Applecross' CNCN EDen SHBN
– 'Argentea' EDen MBar
– 'Ariadne' EDen
– 'Arina' EDen MBri MOke
– 'Arran Gold' CNCN EDen ENHC GBla GSpe MBar NRoo WGre
– 'Ashgarth Amber' EDen
¶ – 'Ashgarth Amethyst' EDen
– 'Asterix' EDen
– 'Atalanta' EDen
– 'August Beauty' CNCN EDen ENHC GBla MOke NWin WRid
– 'Aurea' EDen ENHC GSpe IJoh
– 'Autumn Glow' EDen
– 'Baby Ben' CMac CNCN EDen
– 'Barbara Fleur' EDen SBod
– 'Barja' EDen
– 'Barnett Anley' CNCN EDen ENHC GSpe MBal
– 'Battle of Arnhem' AGM CNCN EDen MBar WGre
– 'Beechwood Crimson' CNCN EDen ENHC
– 'Ben Nevis' EDen
– 'Beoley Crimson' CB&S CNCN EDen ENHC GAng GAri GDra MBar MGos NWin SBod WRid
– 'Beoley Gold' AGM Widely available
– 'Beoley Silver' EDen
– 'Bernadette' EDen
– 'Betty Baum' EDen
– 'Blazeaway' CMac CNCN EDen ENHC GAng GAul GBla GDra GRei GSpe IJoh MBal MBar MBri NBir NHar NHol NRoo SBod SHBN WBod WGre WRid WStI
– 'Blueness' EDen
– 'Bognie' CNCN EDen ENHC GRei WGre
– 'Bonfire Brilliance' CMHG CNCN EDen MBar NHar NRoo SBod
– 'Boreray' CNCN EDen
– 'Boskoop' CNCN EBre EDen ENHC LBre MBar MBri SBod WGre
– 'Braemar' EDen GBla
– 'Braeriach' EDen
– 'Bray Head' CNCN EDen GPen MBar SBod WGre
¶ – 'Brita Elisabeth' EDen
– 'Bud Lyle' EDen WGre
– 'Bunsall' CMac CNCN EDen
– 'Buxton Snowdrift' CMHG EDen
– 'C W Nix' CNCN EDen ENHC GPen GSpe IJoh MBar WRid
– 'Caerketton White' EDen ENHC GAng GBla GPen GSpe MBal
– 'Caleb Threlkeld' EDen
– 'Calf of Man' EDen ENHC
– 'Californian Midge' CNCN EDen ENHC EPot GAri GPen GSpe MBar MGos NBir NHol WGre
– 'Carl Röders' EDen
– 'Carmen' EDen
– 'Carole Chapman' CMHG EDen ENHC EPot GPen MBar MGos SBod SHBN WRid
– 'Carolyn' EDen
¶ – 'Catherine' EDen
– 'Catherine Anne' EDen
– 'Celtic Gold' EDen IDai
– 'Chindit' EDen
– 'Christina' EDen
– 'Citronella' EDen GPen
– 'Clare Carpet' EDen
– 'Coby' EDen
– 'Coccinea' CMac EDen ENHC MBal MBar SBod
– 'Colette' EDen
– 'Con Brio' EDen WGre
– 'Copper Glow' EDen
– 'Coral Island' EDen MBar MGos SBod
– 'Corries's White' EDen
– 'Cottswood Gold' EDen
– 'County Wicklow' AGM CMac CNCN EBre EDen ENHC GAng GBla GPen GSpe IJoh LBre MBal MBar MBri MGos MOke NHar NHol NRoo NWin SBod SHBN SPla WBod WGre WRid
– 'Craig Rossie' EDen
– 'Cramond' EDen ENHC GBla GDra MBar WGre
¶ – 'Cream Steving' EDen
– 'Crimson Glory' EDen GDra GSpe MBal MBar NWin WGre WStI
– 'Crimson Sunset' CNCN EDen SBod WStI
– 'Crowborough Beacon' EDen
– 'Cuprea' CMac CNCN EDen ENHC GAng GAul GBla GDra GRei GSpe MBal MBar MBri MOke NHol NWin SBod WGre WStI
¶ – 'Cuprea Select' EDen
– 'Dainty Bess' CNCN EDen MBar SBod WGre WStI
– 'Dark Beauty' EDen MGos NRoo WStI
– 'Dark Star' AGM EDen GSpe MOke NHar NRoo
– 'Darkness' AGM CB&S CMHG CNCN EDen ENHC GAng GAul GBla GPen GSpe IDai IJoh MBal MBar MBri MGos MOke NHar NHol NRoo NWin SBod SHBN SPla WGre WStI
– 'Darleyensis' EDen
– 'Dart's Amethyst' EDen
– 'Dart's Brilliant' EDen
– 'Dart's Flamboyant' CNCN EDen
– 'Dart's Gold' EDen EPot GBla MBar NHar NRoo
– 'Dart's Hedgehog' EDen WGre
– 'Dart's Parakeet' CNCN EDen
– 'Dart's Parrot' EDen NHar
– 'Dart's Silver Rocket' EDen GBla
– 'Dart's Squirrel' EDen
– 'David Eason' CNCN EDen ENHC MBal
– 'David Hutton' EDen MBar
– 'David Platt' EDen
– 'Desiree' EDen
– 'Dickson's Blazes' EDen GSpe

– 'Dirry' EDen GSpe
– 'Doctor Murray's White' See C. *v.* 'Mullardoch'
– 'Doris Rushworth' EDen
– 'Drum-ra' EDen ENHC GAng GBla GDra GSpe MBal MBar NRoo SBod WGre
– 'Dunnet Lime' EDen
– 'Dunnydeer' EDen ENHC
– 'Dunwood' EDen MBar
– 'Durfordii' EDen
– 'E F Brown' CNCN EDen ENHC
– 'E Hoare' EDen MBar
– 'Easter-bonfire' EDen NHol WGre
– 'Edith Godbolt' CNCN EDen ENHC
– 'Elegant Pearl' EDen MBar SBod
– 'Elegantissima' EDen ENHC GSpe MBri MOke
– 'Elegantissima Lilac' EDen
– 'Elegantissima Walter Ingwersen' See C. *v.* 'Walter Ingwersen'
– 'Elizabeth' SPla
– 'Elkstone' CNCN EDen ENHC MBal MBar SBod
¶ – 'Ellen' EDen
– 'Else Frye' EDen
– 'Elsie Purnell' **AGM** CMac CNCN EDen ENHC GAng GBla GPen GSpe MBal MBar MBri MGos MOke NHol SBod WBod WGre WRid WStI
– 'Emerald Jock' EDen SBod
¶ – 'Eric Easton' EDen
– 'Fairy' CMHG CMac EDen EPot MBri MOke NRoo
– 'Falling Star' EDen
¶ – 'Feuerwerk' EDen
§ – 'Finale' **AGM** CNCN EDen ENHC GPen MBar WGre
– 'Findling' EDen
– 'Fire King' EDen MBar
– 'Fire Star' EDen
– 'Firebreak' EDen MBar MBri
– 'Firefly' **AGM** CMac CNCN EBre EDen ENHC GAng GAul GBla GSpe LBre MBal MBar MBri MOke NHar NRoo NWin SBod SHBN SPla WBod WGre WRid WStI
– 'Flamingo' CMac CNCN EBre EDen LBre MBar MBri MOke NHar NHol WGre
– 'Flatling' EDen
– 'Flore Pleno' EDen ENHC MBar
– 'Foxhollow Wanderer' CNCN EDen ENHC GSpe MBal MBar MOke SBod
¶ – 'Foxii' EDen
– 'Foxii Floribunda' EDen ENHC GSpe MBar
– 'Foxii Lett's Form' See CC. *v.* 'Mousehole', 'Velvet Dome'
– 'Foxii Nana' CMac CNCN EDen ENHC GAng GBla GSpe MBal MBar NHar NHol SBod SPla WGre WRid
¶ – 'Foya' EDen
– 'Fred J Chapple' CNCN EDen ENHC GAng GAul GBla GDra GPen IDai MBal MBar MBri MOke SBod WBod WGre WStI
– 'Fréjus' EDen
– 'French Grey' CNCN EDen
– 'Gerda' EDen SPla
– 'Ginkels Glorie' EDen
– 'Glencoe' EDen ENHC GBla GSpe MBal MBar MBri MGos MOke NHar WGre
– 'Glendoick Silver' EDen
– 'Glenfiddich' EDen MBar MBri
– 'Glenlivet' EDen MBar
– 'Glenmorangie' EDen MBar
¶ – 'Gnome Pink' EDen
– 'Gold Charm' EDen
¶ – 'Gold Finch' EDen
– 'Gold Flame' EDen GAng MBar MBri SBod
¶ – 'Gold Hamilton' EDen
– 'Gold Haze' **AGM** CB&S CMac CNCN EBre EDen ENHC GAng GBla GSpe IJoh LBre MBal MBar MBri MOke NHol SBod WBod WGre WRid WStI
– 'Gold Knight' MBri SBod
– 'Gold Kup' EDen MBar
– 'Gold Mist' EDen
– 'Gold Spronk' EDen
– 'Goldcarmen' EDen
– 'Golden Carpet' CB&S CMac CNCN EDen ENHC EPot GAng GBla GDra GPen MBal MBar MBri MGos MOke NHar NRoo NWin WBod WGre WRid WStI
¶ – 'Golden Dream' EDen
– 'Golden Feather' CB&S CMHG CMac CNCN EDen ENHC EPot GAng GBla GDra GPen GRei IDai MBal MBar MGos NWin SBod SHBN WGre WRid
– 'Golden Fleece' EDen
– 'Golden Max' EDen NHar
– 'Golden Rivulet' CMac EDen ENHC MBar
– 'Golden Turret' EDen ENHC GBla GRei
– 'Goldsworth Crimson' EDen ENHC
– 'Goldsworth Crimson Variegated' CNCN EDen ENHC MBar SBod
– 'Grasmeriensis' EDen MBar
– 'Great Comp' EDen MBar
– 'Grey Carpet' CNCN EDen GBla MBar SBod
– 'Grijsje' EDen
– 'Grizzly' EDen
¶ – 'Grönsinka' EDen
– 'Guinea Gold' EDen MBar MBri WGre
§ – 'H E Beale' CB&S CMac CNCN EBre EDen ENHC GAng GBla GDra GPen GSpe IDai IJoh LBre MBal MBar MBri MGos MOke NHar NWin SBod SHBN WBod WGre WRid
– 'Hamlet Green' CNCN EDen MBar
– 'Hammondii' CNCN EDen GPen SBod WGre WStI
– 'Hammondii Aureifolia' CNCN EBre EDen GAng GAri GBla LBre MBal MBar MBri MOke
– 'Hammondii Rubrifolia' CNCN EDen GAng MBal MBar MBri MOke NHar
– 'Harlekin' EDen
¶ – 'Harry Gibbon' EDen
– 'Harten's Findling' EDen
¶ – 'Hatjes Herbstfeuer' EDen
– 'Hayesensis' EDen
– 'Heideberg' EDen
¶ – 'Heidepracht' EDen
¶ – 'Heidesinfonie' EDen

– 'Heideteppich'	EDen
– 'Heidezwerg'	EDen
– 'Herbert Mitchell'	EDen
– 'Hester'	EDen
– 'Hetty'	EDen
– 'Hibernica'	EDen GPen MBar WGre
– 'Hiemalis'	EDen ENHC MBar
– 'Hiemalis Southcote'	See C. *v.* 'Durfordii'
– 'Highland Rose'	EDen ESis GBla WGre
– 'Hilda Turberfield '	EDen
– 'Hillbrook Orange'	EDen MBar
¶ – 'Hillbrook Sparkler'	EDen
– f. ***hirsuta***	GPen NWin WGre WRid
– 'Hirsuta Albiflora'	EDen MBar
– 'Hirsuta Typica'	CNCN EDen WGre
– 'Hirta'	CNCN EDen MBar SBod WGre
– 'Hollandia'	EDen
– 'Holstein'	EDen
– 'Hookstone'	EDen GPen MBar WGre
¶ – 'Hoyerhagen'	EDen
§ – 'Hugh Nicholson'	CNCN EDen ENHC NHar
– 'Humpty Dumpty'	CNCN EDen ENHC NHol WRid
– 'Hypnoïdes'	EDen
– 'Ide's Double'	EDen SBod
– 'Inchcolme'	EDen GPen
– 'Ineke'	CNCN EDen ENHC MBar
– 'Ingrid Bouter'	EDen
– 'Inshriach Bronze'	CMac EDen ENHC EPot GDra GRei GSpe MBar NRoo SBod WGre WRid
¶ – 'Iris van Leyen'	EDen
¶ – 'Islay Mist'	EDen
– 'Isobel Frye'	EDen MBar
– 'Isobel Hughes'	EDen MBar
– 'J H Hamilton' **AGM**	CNCN EDen ENHC GAng GBla GDra GPen GSpe MBal MBar MBri MGos NHol SBod WGre WRid WStI
– 'Jan'	EDen
– 'Jan Dekker'	EDen SBod WGre
– 'Janice Chapman'	EDen MBar WGre
– 'Japanese White'	EDen
– 'Jenny'	EDen
– 'Jimmy Dyce' **AGM**	EDen SBod
– 'Joan Sparkes'	CMac CNCN EDen ENHC GBla GPen GRei IDai MBal MBar WGre WStI
¶ – 'Jochen'	EDen
– 'John F Letts'	CMac CNCN EDen ENHC GAng GBla GRei GSpe MBal MBar MGos NWin SBod SHBN WGre WStI
– 'Johnson's Variety'	CNCN EDen MBar WGre
– 'Joseph's Coat'	EDen
– 'Joy Vanstone' **AGM**	CMac CNCN EDen ENHC GAng GAul GBla MBal MBar MBri MGos MOke SHBN WGre WRid
– 'Julia'	CNCN EDen
– 'Karin Blum'	EDen
¶ – 'Kees Gouda'	EDen
– 'Kerstin'	EDen SPla
– 'Kinlochruel' **AGM**	CMHG CMac CNCN EDen ENHC GAng GBla GDra GPen GRei GSpe IJoh MBar MBri MGos MOke NHar NHol NRoo NWin SBod SHBN SPla WBod WGre WRid
– 'Kirby White'	CNCN EDen GAng GBla GPen MBar MBri NWin
– 'Kirsty Anderson'	EDen MBri MOke
– 'Kit Hill'	EDen MBar
– 'Kuphaldtii'	EDen MBar
– 'Kynance'	CNCN EDen ENHC MBar
¶ – 'Lady Maithe'	EDen
– 'Lambstails'	EDen MBal MBar MGos SBod
– 'LAncresse'	EDen
– 'Lemon Gem'	EDen
– 'Lemon Queen'	EDen
– 'Leslie Slinger'	EDen ENHC GBla MBar
– 'Lewis Lilac'	EDen WGre
– 'Llanbedrog Pride'	CNCN EDen MBar
– 'Loch Turret'	CNCN EDen ENHC GBla GSpe MBar MBri MOke NWin
– 'Loch-na-Seil'	EDen MBar
¶ – 'London Pride'	EDen
– 'Long White'	EDen GSpe MBar
¶ – 'Lüneberg Heath'	EDen
– 'Lyle's Late White'	CNCN EDen GPen
– 'Lyle's Surprise'	EDen MBar
– 'Lyndon Proudley'	EDen ENHC
§ – 'Mair's Variety' **AGM**	CNCN EDen ENHC GAng GBla GDra GSpe IDai MBal MBar NRoo SBod WGre WRid
– 'Manitoba'	EDen
– 'Marie'	EDen
– 'Marion Blum'	EDen MBar
– 'Marleen'	EDen SBod
– 'Masquerade'	EDen MBar NRoo
¶ – 'Matita'	EDen
– 'Mauvelyn'	EDen
– 'Mazurka'	EDen
– 'Mies'	EDen
– 'Minima'	EDen GPen MBar SBod
– 'Minima Smith's Variety'	EDen ENHC MBar WRid
– 'Minty'	EDen
– 'Mirelle'	CNCN EDen
– 'Miss Muffet'	NHol
– 'Molecule'	EDen MBar
¶ – 'Moon Glow'	EDen
§ – 'Mousehole'	CMac CNCN EDen ENHC GBla GSpe MBar MGos MOke NHol WGre WRid
– 'Mousehole Compact'	See C. *v.* 'Mousehole'
– 'Mrs Alf'	EDen
– 'Mrs E Wilson'	EDen
– 'Mrs Pat'	CNCN EDen ENHC GAri GPen MBar MOke NHol NRoo NWin WGre WRid
– 'Mrs Ronald Gray'	CMac CNCN EDen GDra IJoh MBar WGre WRid
– 'Mullach Mor'	EDen SBod
§ – 'Mullardoch'	EDen GPen MBar
– 'Mullion' **AGM**	CNCN EDen ENHC MBar MOke SBod
– 'Multicolor'	CB&S CMac CNCN EDen ENHC GAng GBla GDra GPen GSpe IDai MBal MBar MBri MOke NHol NRoo NWin SBod SPla WBod WGre WRid
– 'Murielle Dobson'	EDen MBar
§ – 'My Dream'	EBre EDen ENHC GSpe LBre MBar NHol WGre
– 'Nana'	ENHC
– 'Nana Compacta'	CMac CNCN EDen EPot GAng GPen GSpe MBal MBar MBri MOke NWin SBod WRid
¶ – 'Natasja'	EDen

– 'Naturpark'	EDen ENHC MBar
¶ – 'Nordlicht'	EDen
– 'October White'	CNCN EDen ENHC
– 'Oiseval'	EDen
– 'Old Rose'	EDen
– 'Olive Turner'	EDen
– 'Orange Carpet'	EDen
– 'Orange Max'	CNCN EDen GBla
– 'Orange Queen' **AGM**	CMac CNCN EDen ENHC GAng GBla GRei GSpe MBal MBar SBod WRid
– 'Öxabäck'	EDen MBar
– 'Oxshott Common'	CNCN EDen ENHC EPot MBar SBod WGre
– 'Pallida'	EDen
– 'Parsons' Gold'	EDen
¶ – 'Parsons' Grey Selected'	EDen
– 'Pearl Drop'	MBar
– 'Penhale'	EDen
– 'Penny Bun'	EDen
♦ – 'Pepper and Salt'	See C. *v.* 'Hugh Nicholson'
– 'Perestrojka'	EDen
– 'Peter Sparkes'	CB&S CMac CNCN EDen ENHC GAng GBla GDra GPen GSpe IDai IJoh MBal MBar MBri MGos MOke NHar NWin SBod WBod WGre WRid
– 'Petra'	EDen
– 'Pewter Plate'	EDen GPen MBar MBri NWin
– 'Pink Beale'	See C. *v.* 'H E Beale'
– 'Pink Dream'	EDen
– 'Pink Gown'	CNCN EDen
¶ – 'Plantarium'	EDen
– 'Platt's Surprise' (d)	EDen
– 'Prizewinner'	CNCN EDen
¶ – 'Prostrata Flagelliformis'	EDen
– 'Prostrate Orange'	CNCN EDen GSpe MBal MBar WRid
– 'Punch's Delight'	EDen
¶ – 'Punch's Dessert'	EDen
– 'Pygmaea'	EDen ENHC MBar
– 'Pyramidalis'	EDen ENHC
– 'Pyrenaica'	EDen GPen MBar
– 'Radnor' **AGM**	CMac CNCN EDen ENHC GAng GBla GSpe MBal MBar MBri MGos MOke NHar NRoo SBod WGre WRid
– 'Radnor Gold'	MBar
– 'Ralph Purnell'	CNCN EDen ENHC MBal MBar NHar SBod
¶ – 'Ralph's Pearl'	EDen
– 'Ralph's Red'	EDen
¶ – 'Randell's Crimson'	EDen
– 'Rannoch'	EDen
– 'Red Carpet'	CNCN EDen MBri MOke WBod WGre
– 'Red Favorit'	EDen NRoo SBod WGre
– 'Red Fred'	EDen MGos
– 'Red Haze'	CMHG CMac CNCN EDen ENHC GAng MBal MBar MBri MOke NHol SBod WBod WGre WStI
– 'Red Hugh'	IDai
– 'Red Max'	EDen
– 'Red Pimpernel'	EDen GSpe
¶ – 'Red Rug'	EDen
– 'Red Star' **AGM**	EDen GSpe MOke WGre
¶ – 'Redbud'	EDen
– 'Reini'	EDen
– 'Rica'	EDen
– 'Richard Cooper'	EDen MBar
– 'Rigida Prostrata'	See C. *v.* 'Alba Rigida'
– 'Rivington'	EDen
– 'Robber Knight'	EDen WGre
– 'Robert Chapman' **AGM**	CB&S CMac CNCN EBre EDen ENHC GAng GBla GDra GPen GRei GSpe IDai IJoh LBre MBal MBar MBri MGos MOke NHar NHol NWin SBod WBod WGre WRid
– 'Roland Haagen' **AGM**	EDen MBar MBri MOke NHar SBod WGre
– 'Roma'	EDen ENHC GPen MBar
¶ – 'Romina'	EDen
– 'Ronas Hill'	GDra
– 'Roodkapje'	EDen
– 'Rosalind'	CNCN EPot GBla GPen GSpe MBal MBar MOke NHol NRoo WGre
– 'Rosalind Underwood's Variety'	EDen
I – 'Rosalind, Crastock Heath Variety'	EDen
– 'Ross Hutton'	EDen GBla GPen
¶ – 'Rote Oktober'	EDen
– 'Ruby Slinger'	CNCN EBre EDen GAng GBla LBre MBar SBod WGre
– 'Rusty Triumph'	EDen SBod
– 'Ruth Sparkes'	CMac CNCN EDen ENHC GAng GPen MBal MBar MBri MOke NHol NWin SBod WRid
– 'Saint Kilda'	GPen GRei GSpe
– 'Saint Nick'	CNCN EDen ENHC MBar
¶ – 'Salland'	EDen
– 'Sally Anne Proudley'	CNCN EDen ENHC MBar SBod WGre
– 'Salmon Leap'	EDen GSpe MBar NHol NWin
¶ – 'Sam Hewitt'	EDen
– 'Sampford Sunset'	CSam
– 'Sandwood Bay'	EDen
¶ – 'Scaynes Hill'	EDen
– 'Schurig's Sensation'	EBre EDen GAri GBla GSpe LBre MBar MBri MOke NHar SBod
– 'Scotch Mist'	EDen
– 'Sedloñov'	EDen
– 'September Pink'	EDen
– 'Serlei'	EDen ENHC GPen MBal MBar MBri MOke SBod
– 'Serlei Aurea' **AGM**	CNCN EDen ENHC GAng GPen GSpe MBal MBar SBod WRid
– 'Serlei Grandiflora'	EDen GPen MBar
– 'Serlei Lavender'	EDen WGre WRid
– 'Serlei Rubra'	EDen
– 'Sesam'	EDen
– 'Shirley'	CMac EDen MBar
– 'Silver Cloud'	CNCN EDen MBar MBri NWin
– 'Silver King'	CMac CNCN EDen MBar
– 'Silver Knight'	CMHG CMac EBre EDen ENHC EPot GAng GBla GDra GPen GRei GSpe LBre MBal MBar MBri MGos MOke NHar NHol NRoo SBod SHBN WBod WGre WRid WStI
– 'Silver Queen' **AGM**	CMHG CMac CNCN EBre EDen ENHC GAng GAul GBla GRei GSpe IJoh LBre MBal MBar MBri MOke NHar NHol SBod WGre WRid

– 'Silver Rose' AGM	CNCN EDen ENHC GBla GSpe MBar NWin SBod WGre WRid
– 'Silver Sandra'	EDen
– 'Silver Spire'	CNCN EDen ENHC MBal MBar
– 'Silver Stream'	EDen ENHC MBar NWin SBod
– 'Sir John Charrington' AGM	CMac CNCN EBre EDen ENHC GAng GBla GDra GPen GSpe LBre MBal MBar MBri MGos MOke NHol SBod SHBN WGre WRid WStI
– 'Sirsson'	EDen MBri NWin
– 'Sister Anne' AGM	CMac CNCN EBre EDen ENHC EPot GAng GBla GDra LBre MBal MBri MGos MOke NHol SBod SHBN SPla WRid
– 'Skipper'	EDen MBar WGre
– 'Snowball'	See C. *v.* 'My Dream'
¶ – 'Snowflake'	EDen
– 'Soay'	EDen MBar SBod
– 'Sonja'	EDen
– 'Spicata'	EDen
– 'Spicata Aurea'	CNCN EDen MBar
– 'Spitfire'	CMac CNCN EDen ENHC GAng GPen GSpe MBal MBar WGre WRid WStI
– 'Spook'	EDen
– 'Spring Cream' AGM	CMHG CNCN EBre EDen ENHC ESis GAng GBla GSpe LBre MBar MBri MGos MOke NHar NHol SBod WGre WRid WStI
– 'Spring Glow'	CMac EDen GAng MBar MBri MOke NHar NWin SBod
– 'Spring Torch'	CB&S CMHG CNCN EBre EDen ENHC GAng GDra GSpe IJoh LBre MBal MBar MBri MGos MOke NHar NHol SBod SHBN WGre WRid WStI
– 'Springbank'	EDen MBar
– 'Stranger'	EDen
¶ – 'Strawberry Delight'	EDen
– 'Summer Elegance'	EDen
– 'Summer Orange'	CNCN EDen GAng GPen MBal MBar NHol
– 'Sunningdale'	See C. *v.* 'Finale'
– 'Sunrise'	EDen ENHC GAng MBar MGos MOke NHol SBod WGre WStI
– 'Sunset' AGM	CB&S CMHG CMac CNCN EBre EDen ENHC GAng GBla GDra GPen GRei GSpe LBre MBal MBar NHol NWin SBod SPla WGre WRid WStI
¶ – 'Sunset Glow'	EDen
– 'Tallisker'	EDen
¶ – 'Tenella'	EDen
– 'Tenuis'	CNCN EDen ENHC MBar NWin
– 'Terrick's Orange'	EDen
¶ – 'The Pygmy'	EDen
– 'Tib' AGM	CMHG CMac CNCN EDen ENHC GAng GBla GPen GSpe IJoh MBal MBar MBri MOke NWin SBod WGre WRid WStI
¶ – 'Tino'	EDen
– 'Tom Thumb'	EDen MBar
¶ – 'Tom's Fancy'	EDen
¶ – 'Torogay'	EDen
– 'Torulosa'	EDen ENHC GPen
– 'Tremans'	EDen
– 'Tricolorifolia'	CNCN EDen ENHC GAng GBla GDra IDai MBal SBod
– 'Underwoodii' AGM	EDen ENHC GBla GPen MBar
– 'Velvet Dome'	EDen MBal MBar SBod
– 'Velvet Fascination'	EDen NRoo
– 'Visser's Fancy'	EDen
§ – 'Walter Ingwersen'	EDen MBar
– 'White Carpet'	EDen GPen MBar
¶ – 'White Coral'	EDen
¶ – 'White Gold'	EDen
– 'White Gown'	EDen ENHC GDra WRid
– 'White Lawn' AGM	CMac CNCN EDen EPot MBar MGos NHol NWin SHBN
– 'White Mite'	EDen ENHC MBar
– 'White Princess'	See C. *v.* 'White Queen'
§ – 'White Queen'	EDen MBal MBar
¶ – 'White Star'	EDen
– 'Whiteness'	CNCN EDen WGre
– 'Wickwar Flame' AGM	CB&S CMac CNCN EBre EDen ENHC GAng GBla GDra GPen IJoh LBre MBal MBar MBri MOke NHar NHol NRoo SBod WBod WGre WRid WStI
– 'Wingates Gem'	EDen NWin
– 'Wingates Gold'	EDen NWin
– 'Winter Chocolate'	CMHG CMac CNCN EDen ENHC ESis GAng GBla GPen IDai MBal MBar MBri MGos MOke NHol NRoo SBod WGre WRid WStI
– 'Winter Fire'	EDen
– 'Winter Red'	EDen
¶ – 'Wood Close'	EDen
– 'Yellow One'	EDen
¶ – 'Yvonne Claire'	EDen

CALOCEDRUS (Cupressaceae)

§ ***decurrens*** AGM	CB&S CDoC CGre CMHG CMac CSco EHar EHul ENot IBar IDai IOrc LCon MBal MBar MBri MUlv NWea SGil SLim SPer WFro WMou WWat
– 'Aureovariegata'	CDoC CKen EHar IOrc LCon LLin LNet MAsh MBar MBlu MBri NHol SEng SHil SLim SMad WDin
– 'Berrima Gold'	CKen SHil
– 'Depressa'	CKen
– 'Intricata'	CKen
– 'Nana'	See C. ***d.*** 'Depressa'
– 'Pillar'	EHar
formosana	WBod

CALOCEPHALUS (Compositae/Asteraceae)

§ ***brownii***	CBrk ECou ERom MRav SChu SLon

CALOCHORTUS (Liliaceae/Liliaceae)

albus	WChr
amabilis	WChr
¶ ***amoenus***	WChr
barbatus	EBul MFos WOMN
¶ – ***chihuahuaensis***	WChr
luteus	EBul WChr
¶ ***monophyllos***	WChr
splendens	EPot WChr
superbus	WChr
uniflorus	EPot MFos WChr WOMN
venustus	WChr
vestae	WChr

CALOMERIA (Compositae/Asteraceae)

§ ***amaranthoïdes*** LHol

CALOPOGON (Orchidaceae)

¶ ***tuberosus*** NGar WChr

CALOSCORDUM (Liliaceae/Alliaceae)

§ ***neriniflorum*** EBur LBee SUsu SWas

CALOTHAMNUS (Myrtaceae)

validus CPle CTro

CALTHA † (Ranunculaceae)

'Auenwald' CRow
'Honeydew' CRDP CRow
introloba EPot SWat
laeta See C. ***palustris palustris***
leptosepala NGre SRms
natans CRDP CRow
palustris AGM CBen CFee CGle CHEx CKin CMHG CRDP CRiv CRow CWGN EBre EHon EPot EWFC GPoy LBre LMay MSta NDea NHol NMir SHig SLon SWat SWyc WByw WChe WCru WHol
– var. ***alba*** Widely available
– var. ***himalensis*** NGre WCot
¶ – 'Marilyn' CRDP
¶ – var. ***minor*** CRDP
§ – var. ***palustris*** CBen CRDP CRow CWGN EBre ECha EHon ELan EMFW EMon EPar EWav GAri GGar LBre LMay MSta NDea SHig SPer SWat WChe WHol
¶ – – 'Plena' CRow
– var. ***radicans*** CRDP CRow EMFW
– – 'Flore Pleno' AGM Widely available
* – 'Stagnatis' SWyc
– 'Tyermannii' CRow
– 'Wheatfen' CNat
polypetala See C. ***palustris palustris***
'Susan' CRow

CALYCANTHUS (Calycantheaceae)

fertilis CBot LBuc MUlv SEng WSHC
floridus CArn CB&S CBot CBow CChu CCla CPle EBar EGol ELan ENot IOrc SHil SPer WBod
– ***glaucus*** See C. ***fertilis laevigatus***
occidentalis CBow CCla ELan

CALYDOREA (Iridaceae)

speciosa See C. ***xiphioïdes***
xiphioïdes WPer

CALYPTRIDIUM (Portulacaceae)

umbellatum See SPRAGUEA ***umbellata***

CALYSTEGIA (Convolvulaceae)

§ ***hederacea*** 'Flore Pleno' CRDP ECha ELan EMon EOrc EPar GCal LHop MTho NGar NSti SAxl SFar SMad WCot WCru WHer WWin
japonica 'Flore Pleno' See C. ***hederacea*** 'F.P.'
silvatica 'Incarnata' CRDP EMon MBel
tuguriorum ECou

CALYTRIX (Myrtaceae)

See Plant Deletions

CAMASSIA † (Liliaceae/Hyacinthaceae)

cusickii CAvo CBro CCla CRDP ECha ELan EPar ETub LAma LBow MBri MTho NHol NRog SHer SIng WHal
esculenta See C. ***quamash***
fraseri See C. ***scilloïdes***
leichtlinii CAvo ECha EFou EPar ERav ETub LBow MUlv NCat NHol
– Alba Group AGM CAvo CBro CMon CVer EFou ELan ETub ISea LAma NCat NHol SIng
– 'Blauwe Donau' ('Blue Danube') LAma LBow
– Caerulea Group CBro CHad CRDP ELan EMon EPar ISea LAma MUlv NRog SIng
– 'Electra' ECha SWas
N – 'Plena' ECED ECha WCot WDav
– 'Semiplena' CAvo CBro CRDP EPar
§ ***quamash*** CAvo CBro CCla CMea ECha ELan EPar ETub LAma LBow MBri MTho NHol NRog SIng WBod WByw
– ***linearis*** NHol
– 'Orion' CBro EMon SApp
§ ***scilloïdes*** CMon MBri

CAMELLIA † (Theaceae)

'Aaron's Ruby' (***japonica***) CMHG CTre SCog
'Ada Pieper' (***japonica***) CTrh
'Adelina Patti' (***japonica***) CB&S CTre SCog
'Adolphe Audusson' (***japonica***) AGM CB&S CMac CSco CTre CTrh CTrw EBre ELan ENot IJoh IOrc LBre LHyd LNet MBal MBri MGos NKay SBod SCog SExb SHBN SHer SLon SPer SReu SSta WBod WStI
'Adolphe Audusson Special' (***japonica***) CB&S SCog
§ 'Akashigata' ('Lady Clare') (***japonica***) AGM CMac CSco CTre CTrw ELan ENot IHos SCog SExb SPla SReu SSta WBod WWat
§ 'Akebono' (***japonica***) CTrw
'Alba Plena' (***japonica***) CGre CMac CTre ENot IHos IOrc ISea LNet MGos SBod SCog SPer WFox
'Alba Simplex' (***japonica***) CB&S CGre CMac CSco CTre ELan IOrc LNet MBal SBod SCog SHBN SPer SSta WStI
'Alex Blackadder' (***japonica***) CMHG
'Alexander Hunter' (***japonica***) AGM CTre CTrh MAsh SBod SExb
'Alice Wood' (***japonica***) CTrh SCog
§ 'Althaeiflora' (***japonica***) CB&S CGre CMac CTre SCog
'Ama-no-gawa' (***japonica***) SCog
'Anemone Frill' (x ***williamsii***) CTrh

Name	Suppliers
'Anemoniflora' (*japonica*)	CB&S CTre ELan IHos ISea SBod SExb SPer WBod
'Angel' (*japonica*)	CMHG CTre SCog
'Ann Sothern' (*japonica*)	CB&S CTrh
'Annie Wylam' (*japonica*)	CTrh SCog
'Anticipation' (x *williamsii*) AGM	CB&S CGre CMHG CSam CSco CTre CTrh CTrw EBre GGGa GWht IDai IJoh IOrc ISea LBre LHyd MBri MGos SBod SCog SExb SGil SHBN SHer SPer WBod
'Anticipation Variegated' (x *williamsii*)	SCog
§ 'Apollo' (*japonica*)	CB&S CSam CTrh CTrw ELan IHos MAsh MBri SExb SHBN SLon SPer WBod
§ 'Apple Blossom' (*japonica*) AGM	CGre CMac MAsh MBal MBri
– (*saluenensis*)	See C. 'Shôwa-wabisuke'
– (*sasanqua*)	MAsh
'Arabella' (*japonica*)	SCog
'Arajishi' (*rusticana*)	CB&S CMac CTre ISea SCog SExb SPla WBod
'Arbutus Gum' (*reticulata* x *japonica*)	CTrh
'Arch of Triumph' (*reticulata*) AGM	CB&S CTrh
'Auburn White'	See C. 'Mrs Bertha A Harms'
* 'Augustine Supreme' (*japonica*)	CMac
'Augusto Leal de Gouveia Pinto' (*japonica*)	SCog
'Ave Maria' (*japonica*)	CTrh SCog
'Azurea' (*japonica*)	CGre
'Baby Face'	See C. 'Tongzimian'
'Ballet Dancer' (*japonica*) AGM	EHic MBri SCog SExb
'Ballet Queen' (x *williamsii*)	CB&S CTrh MBri MGos SExb WBod
'Ballet Queen Variegated' (x *williamsii*)	SCog
'Barbara Clark' (*saluenensis* x *reticulata*)	MBri MGos SExb
'Barbara Hillier' (*reticulata* x *japonica*)	CTre
'Barbara Woodroof' (*japonica*)	SCog
'Barchi'	See C. 'Contessa Samailoff'
'Baron Gomer' (*japonica*)	See C. 'Comte de Gomer'
'Baronesa de Soutelinho' (*saluenensis*)	SCog
'Bartley Number Five' (x *williamsii*)	CMac
'Beatrice Michael' (x *williamsii*)	CB&S CMac CTre SCog
¶ 'Beau Harp' (*japonica*)	SExb
'Bellbird'	SCog

Name	Suppliers
'Belle of the Ball' (*japonica*)	CMHG
'Ben' (*sasanqua*)	SCog
'Benten' (*japonica*)	CTrw MBri
'Benten-kagura' (*japonica*)	CTrh
'Berenice Boddy' (*japonica*) AGM	CB&S CTrh SCog SLon
'Berenice Perfection' (*japonica*)	CTrh SCog
'Bernadette Karsten' (*reticulata* x *japonica*)	CTrh
'Bert Jones' (*sasanqua*)	CTrh
'Bertha Harms Blush'	See C. 'Mrs Bertha A Harms'
'Bettie Patricia' (*sasanqua*)	SCog
'Betty Foy Sanders' (*japonica*)	CTrh
'Betty Sheffield' (*japonica*)	CGre CTre ISea SBod SCog SHBN WBod
'Betty Sheffield Coral' (*japonica*)	SCog
'Betty Sheffield Pink' (*japonica*)	CMHG
'Betty Sheffield Supreme' (*japonica*)	CB&S CGre CMac CTrh SCog SHer SPer
'Betty Sheffield White' (*japonica*)	SCog
'Bienville' (*japonica*)	SCog
¶ 'Billie McFarland' (*japonica*)	SExb
'Black Lace' (x *williamsii* x *reticulata*)	CTrh MBal SCog SExb SPer WStI
'Blackburnia' (*japonica*)	See C. 'Althaeiflora'
'Blaze of Glory' (*japonica*)	CGre CTrh SCog
§ 'Blood of China' (*japonica*)	CMac MAsh MBri SBod SCog SExb SPer WBod
'Blue Danube' (x *williamsii*)	CTrh
'Bob Hope' (*japonica*) AGM	CGre CTre CTrh MAsh SCog
'Bob's Tinsie' (*japonica*) AGM	CGre CTre CTrh CTrw MBri SCog SExb
'Bokuhan' (*japonica*)	CGre CTre CTrh MBri
'Bonnie Marie' (hybrid)	CGre CTre
'Bow Bells' (x *williamsii*)	CGre CMac CTre CTrh IJoh LHyd SCog WWat
'Bowen Bryant' (x *williamsii*) AGM	CGre CTre CTrh CTrw GGGa SCog
'Bridal Gown' (x *williamsii*)	CTrh SCog
'Brigadoon' (x *williamsii*) AGM	CMHG CTre CTrh CTrw GGGa IOrc ISea LHyd MAsh MBal SCog SExb
'Bright Buoy' (*japonica*)	CTrh
'Brilliant Butterfly' (*reticulata*)	CTrh

'Brushfield's Yellow' (*japonica*)	CB&S IMal MBal MBlu SGil
'Bryan Wright' (*japonica*)	CMHG
*'Burgundy Gem'	SExb
'Burncoose' (x *williamsii*)	CB&S
'Burncoose Apple Blossom' (x *williamsii*)	CB&S
'Bush Hill Beauty' (*japonica*)	See C. 'Lady de Saumarez'
'C F Coates' (x *williamsii*)	CTre MNes SCog
§ 'C M Hovey' (*japonica*) AGM	CMHG CMac CTrh MAsh MBal MNes SCog SExb SHBN WBod
'C M Wilson' (*japonica*) AGM	CMac CTre SCog
'Caerhays' (x *williamsii*)	CB&S CTre SCog SReu
'Caleb Cope' (*japonica*)	CMHG
N 'Campbellii' (*japonica*)	CMac
'Campsii Alba' (*japonica*)	ELan WStI
'Can Can' (*japonica*)	CMHG SCog SExb
'Captain Rawes' (*reticulata*) AGM	CMac CTre CTrh SHil
'Cara Mia' (*japonica*)	CB&S CTre
'Cardinal's Cap' (*japonica*)	CGre
¶ 'Carolyn Tuttle' (*japonica*)	SExb
'Carolyn Williams' (x *williamsii*)	CB&S
'Carter's Sunburst' (*japonica*) AGM	CB&S CTrh SCog SExb
*'Cascade' (*rosiflora*)	CTrh
caudata	CTrh
'Cécile Brunazzi' (*japonica*)	CMac SCog
'Chandleri Elegans' (*japonica*)	See C. 'Elegans'
'Chansonette' (*hiemalis*)	SCog SPla SSta
§ 'Charity' (x *williamsii*)	CTrh
'Charlean' (x *williamsii*)	SCog
'Charles Colbert' (x *williamsii*)	CTrh CTrw SCog
'Charles Michael' (x *williamsii*)	CB&S CGre CMac CTrh
'Charlotte de Rothschild' (*japonica*)	CTrh
'Charming Betty' (*japonica*)	See C. 'Funny Face Betty'
'Cheerio' (*japonica*)	SCog
'Cheryll Lynn' (*japonica*)	CTrh SCog
'China Clay' (x *williamsii*) AGM	CB&S CSam CTre SBod SCog
'China Lady' (*reticulata* x *granthamiana*)	SCog
chrysantha	See C. *nitidissima nitidissima*
'Cinderella' (*japonica*)	CTre SCog
§ 'Citation' (x *williamsii*)	CB&S CGre CMac CTrw SCog WBod
'Clarise Carleton' (*japonica*)	CMHG CTre CTrh SCog
'Clarrie Fawcett' (x *williamsii*)	CTre
N 'Cleopatra' (*japonica*)	CTrh SBor
'Colonel Firey' (*japonica*)	See C. 'C M Hovey'
'Colonial Dame' (*japonica*)	MBri SCog
'Commander Mulroy' (*japonica*)	CTrh
'Compton's Brow' (*japonica*)	See C. 'Gauntlettii'
§ 'Comte de Gomer' (*japonica*)	CGre MBri
'Conrad Hilton' (*japonica*)	SCog
'Contessa Lavinia Maggi'	See C. 'Lavinia Maggi'
§ 'Coquettii' (*japonica*) AGM	CTre MAsh
'Coral Delight' (x *williamsii*)	CTrh
'Cornish Clay'	ISea
'Cornish Snow' (*saluenensis* x *cuspidata*) AGM	CB&S CGre CMac CSam CTre CTrh GGGa IJoh IOrc ISea LNet MBal SHBN SMad SPer SReu SSta WWat
'Cornish Spring' (*japonica* x *cuspidata*) AGM	CTre CTrh WWat
'Coronation' (*japonica*)	WBod
*'Corsica'	SHBN
'Countess of Orkney' (*japonica*)	CTre
'Crimson King' (*sasanqua*) AGM	CGre MBal SBod SCog SHBN SPer WBod WStI
'Crinkles' (x *williamsii*)	CGre
cuspidata	CB&S CGre CTre
'Czar'	See C. 'The Czar'
'Daikagura' (*japonica*)	CMHG SCog SExb
'Daintiness' (x *williamsii*) AGM	CTre CTrh MBri SCog SExb
'Daitairin' (*japonica*)	See C. 'Dewatairin'
'Daphne du Maurier' (*japonica*)	SExb
'Dark Nite' (x *williamsii*)	CMHG
'Dawn'	See C. 'Ginryû'
'Dazzler' (*hiemalis*)	CTre CTrh SCog
'Dear Jenny' (*japonica*)	CB&S CTre SCog SExb
'Debbie' (x *williamsii*) AGM	CB&S CGre CMHG CMac CSam CSco CTre CTrh CTrw ELan ENot IJoh IOrc ISea LHyd MBal MBri MGos MRav SBod SCog SExb SHBN SPer SPla SSta WBod
'Debbie's Carnation' (x *williamsii*)	CMHG SCog
'Debut' (*reticulata* x *japonica*)	CTrh
'Debutante' (*japonica*)	CB&S CGre CMac CTre CTrh IDai MBri SCog SGil SHBN SReu SSta WBod
*'Deep Secret'	SExb
'Delia Williams'	See C. 'Citation'
'Desire' (*japonica*)	CMHG CTrh SCog SExb
'Devonia' (*japonica*)	CGre LHyd MBal MBri

§ 'Dewatairin' (***japonica***) CMac MNes SCog SSta WBod
'Diamond Head' (***japonica*** x ***reticulata***) SExb
'Dixie Knight' (***japonica***) SExb SSta
'Dobreei' (***japonica***) CMac
'Doctor Burnside' (***japonica***) CMHG CTrh SCog
'Doctor Clifford Parks' (***reticulata*** x ***japonica***) **AGM** CTre CTrh SCog
'Doctor Louis Polizzi' (***saluenensis*** x ***reticulata***) CTrh
'Doctor Tinsley' (***japonica***) **AGM** CGre CTrh SCog SExb
'Dona Herzilia de Freitas Magalhaes' (***japonica***) CTre SCog SExb SSta
'Dona Jane Andresson' (***japonica***) CMHG
'Donation' (x ***williamsii***) **AGM** Widely available
'Donckelaeri' See C. 'Masayoshi'
'Double Rose' (***japonica***) SCog
'Doutor Balthazar de Mello' (***japonica***) CMHG
'Drama Girl' (***japonica***) **AGM** CB&S CGre CTre CTrw IOrc MBal SBod SCog SExb WBod
'Dream Boat' (x ***williamsii***) CTrh SCog
'Dream Girl' (***sasanqua*** x ***reticulata***) CTrh SCog
* 'Dresden China' SExb
'Duc de Bretagne' (***japonica***) SCog SExb
'Duchesse Decazes' (***japonica***) CTre MGos SCog
'E G Waterhouse' (x ***williamsii***) CB&S CGre CMHG CTrh CTrw MAsh MBal SBod SCog SExb SSta WBod WWeb
'E T R Carlyon' (x ***williamsii***) **AGM** CB&S CTre ISea MBal MBri SCog WFox
'Eclipsis' See C. 'Press's Eclipse'
¶ 'Edelweiss' (***japonica***) SExb
'Eden Roc' (***reticulata***) CTrh
'Effendee' (***japonica***) See C. 'Rosea Plena'
'El Dorado' (***pitardii*** x ***japonica***) CTrh SCog SExb
§ 'Elegans' (***japonica***) **AGM** CB&S CGre CHig CMac CSco CTre CTrh ENot IHos IOrc ISea LHyd MBal NBee SBod SCog SExb SHBN SHer SReu SSta WBod
'Elegans Champagne' (***japonica***) CTrh SCog SExb
'Elegans Splendor' (***japonica***) CTre CTrh
'Elegans Supreme' (***japonica***) CGre CTre CTrh SCog
'Elegant Beauty' (x ***williamsii***) CB&S CTre CTrh CTrw IHos MBal MBri SBod SCog SExb SPer
'Elisabeth' (***japonica***) SCog
'Elizabeth Arden' (***japonica***) CTre
'Elizabeth Bolitho' CTre
'Elizabeth de Rothschild' (x ***williamsii***) SExb
'Elizabeth Dowd' (***japonica***) CB&S SCog
'Elizabeth Hawkins' (***japonica***) CTre
'Ella Drayton' (***japonica***) SCog
'Ellamine' (x ***williamsii***) CTrh
'Elsie Dryden' (***reticulata*** x ***japonica***) CTrh
'Elsie Jury' (x ***williamsii***) **AGM** CB&S CDoC CGre CMac CSam CSco CTrh CTrw IHos IOrc LHyd MBal MGos SBod SCog SExb SGil SHer SPer SSta WBod
Emmett Pfingstl ® (***japonica***) (v) SCog
* 'Emmy' SHBN
'Emperor of Russia' (***japonica***) MBri SCog SExb WBod
* 'Empire Rose' SExb
'Erin Farmer' (***japonica***) CB&S SCog
'Eugène Lizé' (***japonica***) WBod
euphlebia CTrh
'Exaltation' (x ***williamsii***) CB&S SCog
'Exbury Trumpet' (***saluenensis***) CTre
'Extravaganza' (***japonica*** x) CTrh SBod SCog
'Faith' (***japonica***) SCog
'Fascination' IDai
'Fatima' (***japonica***) CTre
§ 'Faustina' (***japonica***) SCog
'Faustina Lechi' See C. 'Faustina'
'Felice Harris' (***sasanqua*** x ***reticulata***) CTrh SCog
'Fimbriata Alba' (***japonica***) See C. 'Fimbriata'
'Finlandia Variegated' (***japonica***) SCog SSta
'Fire Dance' (***japonica***) CTrh
'Fire Falls' (***japonica***) CMHG
'Firebird' (***japonica***) CTrw
'First Flush' (***cuspidata*** x ***saluenensis***) SCog
* 'Fishtail White' SCog
'Flame' (***japonica***) CB&S SExb
'Flamingo' (***sasanqua***) See C. 'Fukuzutsumi'
'Fleur Dipater' (***japonica***) WBod
'Flora' (***japonica***) WBod
'Flore Pleno' (***reticulata***) See C. 'Songzilin'
'Flower Girl' (***sasanqua*** x ***reticulata***) CTrh
'Flowerwood' (***japonica***) SCog
'Forest Green' (***japonioca***) MAsh SCog
forrestii CTrh
'Forty-Niner' (***reticulata*** x ***japonica***) **AGM** SCog SExb
¶ 'Fragrans' (***sasanqua***) SSta
'Fragrant Pink' (***rusticana*** x ***lutchuensis***) CTrh

'Fran Homeyer' (*japonica*) CTrh
¶ 'Frances Council' (*japonica*) SExb
'Francie L' (***saluenensis*** x ***reticulata***) CGre CTre CTrh SCog
'Francis Hanger' (x ***williamsii***) CB&S CMac CSam CTre CTrh CTrw IJoh IOrc MBal MBri SBod SCog SPer WBod
fraterna CTrh
'Frau Minna Seidel' See C. 'Otome'
'Free Style' (x ***williamsii***) CTrh SCog
'Freedom Bell' (hybrid) CTre CTrh GGGa ISea SCog
'Frosty Morn' (***japonica***) SCog
§ 'Fukuzutsumi' (***sasanqua***) CB&S CBot SBod SPer
§ 'Funny Face Betty' (***japonica***) CMHG
'Furo-an' (***japonica***) MAsh
'Galaxie' (x ***williamsii***) **AGM** CB&S CTrh ISea
'Garden Glory' (x ***williamsii***) CTre CTrh
§ 'Gauntlettii' ('Lotus') (***japonica***) SCog
'Gay Time' (x ***williamsii***) CTre CTrh
'George Blandford' (x ***williamsii***) **AGM** CB&S CMac CTre CTrh
* 'George Orman' (***japonica***) CTrh
'Giardino Franchetti' (***japonica***) CGre
'Gigantea' (***japonica***) SCog
'Gigantea Red' (***japonica***) IOrc
'Gladys Wannamaker' (***japonica***) SCog
'Glen 40' (***japonica***) See C. 'Coquettii'
'Glenn's Orbit' (x ***williamsii***) **AGM** CB&S CGre CTre CTrw
'Gloire de Nantes' (***japonica***) **AGM** CGre CTrh MNes SCog SRms WBod
'Golden Spangles' (x ***williamsii***) (v) CB&S CTre ELan IJoh IOrc ISea LHyd MBal MBri MGos MNes SCog SDry SExb SPer SReu SSta
* 'Golden Wedding' (***japonica***) MAsh
'Grace Bunton' (***japonica***) EHic SCog
'Grace Caple' (***pitardii*** x ***japonica***) CMHG
'Granada' (***japonica***) SCog
'Grand Jury' (x ***williamsii***) CTre MGos SCog
'Grand Prix' (***japonica***) **AGM** CMHG CTrh CTrw SCog SSta
'Grand Slam' (***japonica***) **AGM** CMHG CMac CTre CTrh CTrw ISea MAsh SCog SExb
granthamiana CGre CTrh
grijsii CTrh
'Guest of Honor' (***japonica***) CB&S SCog SExb WStI
'Guilio Nuccio' (***japonica***) **AGM** CB&S CTre CTrh EBre LBre SCog SExb SPla
'Gwavas' (x ***williamsii***) CB&S CTre
'Gwenneth Morey' (***japonica***) CMHG CTre
'Hagoromo' (***japonica***) **AGM** CGre CMac EHic ELan ENot IHos MBal SPer WBod WFox WWat
'Hakurakuten' (***japonica***) **AGM** CTre CTrh ISea SBod SCog SLon
'Hanafûki' (***japonica***) CTre SCog
'Hanatachibana' (***japonica***) CTrh SExb
'Harold L Paige' (***japonica*** x ***reticulata***) CTrh
'Hassaku' (***japonica***) See C. 'Hassaku-shibori'
'Hatsuzakura' (***japonica***) See C. 'Dewatairin'
'Hawaii' (***japonica***) CB&S CMac CTre CTrh SCog WFox
'Henry Turnbull' (***japonica***) CTrh
'High Hat' (***japonica***) CTrw SCog SSta
'Hilo' (x ***williamsii***) CTrw
'Hinomaru' (***japonica***) CMac
'Hiraethlyn' (x ***williamsii***) **AGM** CTre WBod
'Hope' (x ***williamsii***) CTrh SCog
'Howard Asper' (***reticulata*** x ***japonica***) SCog
'Hugh Evans' (***sasanqua***) CB&S CBot CDoC CTre CTrh WFox
§ 'Imbricata' (***japonica***) CTre ENot IHos MGos SCog WBod
'Imbricata Alba' (***japonica***) SLon SPer SSta
'Imbricata Rubra' See C. 'Imbricata'
'In the Pink' (***japonica***) CMHG
'Innovation' (x ***williamsii*** x ***reticulata***) CB&S CTre CTrh GGGa IJoh ISea MGos SCog SExb
'Inspiration' (***reticulata*** x ***saluenensis***) **AGM** CB&S CGre CMac CSam CSco CTre CTrh GGGa IDai IJoh ISea LHyd MBri MGos SBod SCog SExb SGil SHBN WBod
'Interval' (***reticulata*** x) CTrh
'J C Williams' (x ***williamsii***) **AGM** CB&S CGre CMac CSam CTre CTrh CTrw GGGa GWht IDai IHos IJoh IOrc ISea LHyd MBal MBri MRav SBod SCog SPer WBod
'J J Whitfield' (***japonica***) CMac CTrh SCog
'Jack Jones Scented' (***japonica***) SCog
'James Allan' (***japonica***) SPer
'Janet Waterhouse' (***japonica***) CTrh SCog
japonica CTrh
'Jean Clere' (***japonica***) CTrh
'Jean Lyne' (***japonica***) SCog
'Jean May' (***sasanqua***) CB&S CDoC CTre SBod SCog
'Jenefer Carlyon' (x ***williamsii***) CTre SCog

'Jill Totty' (x *williamsii*) CTrh
'Jingle Bells' (*japonica*) CTrh SCog
'Joan Trehane' (x *williamsii*) AGM CTrh CTrw
'Joseph Pfingstl' (*japonica*) CGre CMHG CTre CTrh SCog
'Joshua E Youtz' (*japonica*) SCog
'Jovey Carlyon' (*japonica*) (hybrid) SCog
'Joy Sander' (*japonica*) See C. 'Apple Blossom'
'Joyful Bells' (x *williamsii*) CTrh
'Jubilation' (x *williamsii*) GGGa SCog
'Julia France' (*japonica*) CB&S SCog
'Julia Hamiter' (x *williamsii*) AGM CB&S CGre CTrh CTrw ELan SExb
'Juno' (*japonica*) SCog
'Jupiter' (*japonica*) AGM CB&S CMac CTre CTrh CTrw ISea LHyd LNet MBal MGos SExb SHBN WBod
'Jury's Charity' See C. 'Charity'
'Jury's Sunglow' (*williamsii*) SCog SExb
'Jury's Yellow' (x *williamsii* x *japonica*) CB&S CTrh CTrw IDai IJoh IOrc MAsh MBri MGos SBod SCog SExb SPer SSta
'Just Darling' (*japonica*) CTrh
'K O Hester' (*reticulata*) CTrh
'K Sawada' (*japonica*) SCog
'Katie' (*japonica*) SCog
'Kellingtoniana' (*japonica*) See C. 'Gigantea'
'Kenkyô' (*sasanqua*) SCog SPla SSta
'Kenny' (*japonica*) CB&S WBod
'Kewpie Doll' (*japonica*) CTrh SCog
'Kick-Off' (*japonica*) CTrh ELan SCog
'Kimberley' (*japonica*) WBod
§ 'Kingyo-tsubaki' (*japonica*) SBor SSta WBod
'King's Ransom' (*japonica*) CMac SExb
kissi CTrh
'Kitty' (*japonica*) CMHG SCog
§ 'Konronkoku' (*japonica*) AGM CTrh SBor SCog
'Kouron-jura' (*japonica*) See C. 'Konronkoku'
'Kramer's Beauty' (*japonica*) SCog SExb
'Kramer's Supreme' (*japonica*) CB&S CGre CMac CTre CTrh LNet MBal MGos SBod SCog SExb WBod WStI
§ 'Kumasaka' (*japonica*) CMac CSco WBod
'Kyô-nishiki' (x *vernalis*) SCog
'Lady Clare' See C. 'Akashigata'
§ 'Lady de Saumarez' (*japonica*) AGM CMac ELan LNet SBod SCog SExb WBod
'Lady Loch' (*japonica*) CTre CTrh MGos SCog
'Lady Marion' (*japonica*) See C. 'Kumasaka'
'Lady McCulloch' (*japonica*) SCog WStI
'Lady Vansittart' (*japonica*) CB&S CMac CSam CTre ELan ENot IHos ISea LNet MBal MBri SBod SCog SExb SGil SHer SPer WBod WStI
§ 'Lady Vansittart Pink' (*japonica*) CMac MGos MPla SBod SHBN
'Lady Vansittart Red' (*japonica*) See C. 'Lady Vansittart Pink'
'Lady's Maid' (x *williamsii*) CTrh
'Lalla Rookh' (*japonica*) See C. 'L'Avvenire'
'Lanarth' (*japonica*) CTre
'Lasca Beauty' (*reticulata* x *japonica*) AGM CTrh SCog
'Latifolia' (*japonica*) CTre ENot ISea SCog
'Laura Boscawen' (x *williamsii*) CTrh
¶ 'Laura Walker' (*japonica*) SExb
'Laurie Bray' (*japonica*) CGre CTrh SCog
§ 'Lavinia Maggi' (*japonica*) AGM CGre CMac CTre CTrh ELan GAri IHos IOrc LHyd MBri SBod SCog SExb SGil SHBN SLon SMad SPer SReu WBod WStI
'Lavinia Maggi Rosea' (*japonica*) SCog
'L'Avvenire' (*japonica*) CMac SCog
§ 'Le Lys' (*japonica*) CSco SCog
'Leonard Messel' (*reticulata* x *williamsii*) AGM CB&S CDoC CGre CMHG CSco CTre CTrh ENot GGGa IDai IHos IJoh ISea LHyd MBal MBri MGos SBod SCog SExb SHBN SPer SReu WBod WStI
* 'Les Jury' SExb
'Lila Naff' (*reticulata* x) CTre SCog
'Lily Pons' (*japonica*) CTrh SCog
'Little Bit' (*japonica*) CTrh SCog SSta
'Little Bo Peep' (*japonica*) CTrh
'Little Lavender' (x *williamsii*) (hybrid) SCog
'Little Pearl' (*sasanqua*) CTrh
'Look-Away' (*japonica*) SCog
'Lovelight' (*japonica*) CTrh
'Lucy Hester' (*japonica*) CTre MBal SCog
'Lulu Belle' (*japonica*) SCog SExb
lutchuensis CTrh
'Ma Belle' (*japonica*) CMHG SCog
'Madame de Strekaloff' (*japonica*) CMac
'Madame Lebois' (*japonica*) CB&S
'Madame Lourmand' (*japonica*) WBod
'Madame Martin Cachet' (*japonica*) CMHG SCog
'Madame Victor de Bisschop' See C. 'Le Lys'
'Madge Miller' (*japonica*) CTre ELan
'Magic City' (*japonica*) SCog
'Magnolia Queen' See C. 'Priscilla Brooks'

'Magnoliiflora' (*japonica*)	See C. 'Hagoromo'
'Maiden's Blush' (*japonica*)	CMac SCog SExb
maliflora	CB&S
'Man Size' (*japonica*)	SCog
'Mandalay Queen' (***reticulata***) **AGM**	CTrh
'Margaret Davis Picotee' (*japonica*)	CB&S CGre CMHG CTrh CTrw MGos SCog SExb SSta
'Margaret Short' (*japonica*)	SExb
'Margaret Waterhouse' (x ***williamsii***)	CTre SCog
'Margarete Hertrich' (*japonica*)	SCog
'Margherita Coleoni' (*japonica*)	CB&S SBod SHBN SPla WBod
'Marguérite Gouillon' (*japonica*)	ISea SCog
'Marinka' (*japonica*)	CB&S
* 'Mariottii' (*japonica*)	CMac
'Marjorie Magnificent' (*japonica*)	SExb
* 'Marjorie Miller'	SExb
'Mark Alan' (*japonica*)	SExb
'Maroon and Gold' (*japonica*)	SCog
'Mars' (*japonica*) **AGM**	CB&S CTre SExb WBod
'Martha Brice' (*japonica*)	CMHG
'Mary Christian' (x ***williamsii***) **AGM**	CB&S CSco CTre CTrh LHyd MBri WBod
'Mary Costa' (*japonica*)	CGre CTrh
'Mary J Wheeler' (*japonica*)	CTrw
'Mary Jobson' (x ***williamsii***)	CB&S CTre
'Mary Larcom' (x ***williamsii***)	CTre CTrh
'Mary Phoebe Taylor' (x ***williamsii***)	CB&S CTre CTrh CTrw IMal MBri SBod SCog SExb SHBN WBod WFox
§ 'Masayoshi' (*japonica*) **AGM**	CGre CMac ENot IOrc LHyd LNet SCog WBod
§ 'Mathotiana' (*japonica*)	CTrw MBal SCog WBod
'Mathotiana Alba' (*japonica*) **AGM**	CB&S MBal SCog SReu WBod
'Mathotiana Purple King' (*japonica*)	See C. 'Julia Drayton'
'Mathotiana Rosea' (*japonica*)	CB&S CMac CTre ELan ENot LNet SBod SCog SExb SGil SHBN SPer
'Mathotiana Supreme' (*japonica*)	SCog SExb
'Matterhorn' (*japonica*)	CTrh
'Mattie Cole' (*japonica*)	CGre CTre CTrh SCog
'Mattie O'Reilly' (*japonica*)	CTre
'Maud Messel' (x ***williamsii*** x ***reticulata***)	SPer
'Melinda Hackett' (*japonica*)	SCog
'Melody Lane' (*japonica*)	SCog
'Mercury' (*japonica*) **AGM**	CMac ENot GGGa NKay SExb SGil SHBN SLon SPer WBod
'Mercury Variegated' (*japonica*)	CMHG
'Midnight' (*japonica*)	CB&S CGre SCog SExb WStI
'Midnight Serenade' (*japonica*)	CTrh
'Midsummer's Day' (*japonica*)	CB&S
§ 'Mikenjaku' (*japonica*)	CMac CSco ENot LNet MAsh MGos SExb
'Mildred Veitch' (x ***williamsii***)	CGre CTre CTrh
'Mine-no-yuki' (***sasanqua***)	SCog
'Ming Temple' (***reticulata***)	CTre
'Minnie Maddern Fiske' (*japonica*)	SExb
'Mirage' (x ***williamsii***)	CTrh
'Miss Charleston' (*japonica*) **AGM**	CB&S SCog
'Miss Frankie' (*japonica*)	SCog
'Miss Tulare' (***reticulata***)	CTrh
'Miss Universe' (*japonica*)	CGre CTrh SCog SExb
'Momiji-gari' (*japonica*)	CTrh
'Mona Jury' (x ***williamsii***)	CTrh SCog
'Monica Dance' (x ***williamsii***)	CB&S
'Monstruosa Rubra' (*japonica*)	See C. 'Gigantea Red'
'Monte Carlo' (*japonica*)	SCog WBod
'Moonlight Bay' (*japonica*)	SCog
¶ 'Moonlight Sonata' (*japonica*)	SExb
'Morning Glow' (*japonica*)	WBod
§ 'Mrs Bertha A Harms' (*japonica*)	CGre SCog
'Mrs D W Davis' (*japonica*) **AGM**	CB&S CGre CTrh CTrw SCog SPer
'Muskoka' (x ***williamsii***) **AGM**	CB&S CMHG ISea
* 'Mutabilis' (*japonica*)	SCog
* 'Mywoods' (***sasanqua***)	CMac
'Nagasaki' (*japonica*)	See C. 'Mikenjaku'
'Nanbankô' (*japonica*)	CTrh
'Narumigata' (***sasanqua***) **AGM**	CBot CDoC CMac CTrh CTrw MAsh MBal MBlu SBod SCog SExb SLeo WBod
'Navajo' (***sasanqua***)	CTrh
'New Venture' (x ***williamsii***)	CB&S
'Nigra' (*japonica*)	See C. 'Konronkoku'
'Nijinski' (***reticulata*** x)	ISea
§ ***nitidissima*** var. ***nitidissima***	CGre CTrh
'Nobilissima' (*japonica*)	CB&S CMac CTre ELan IHos ISea SBod SCog SExb SHBN SPer WBod WWeb

'Nodami-ushiro' (*sasanqua*) CTrh
'November Pink' (x *williamsii*) CB&S CTre CTrh
'Nuccio's Gem' (*japonica*) AGM CB&S CTrh MBri SCog SExb SSta
'Nuccio's Jewel' (*japonica*) AGM CTre MGos SCog SExb SPer
'Nuccio's Pearl' (*japonica*) CTrh SCog SExb
'Nuccio's Ruby' (*reticulata*) CTrh
oleifera CSam CTre CTrh
¶ 'Olive Honnor' (*japonica*) SExb
'Onetia Holland' (*japonica*) CB&S CTre CTrw SCog
* 'Opal Princess' SExb
'Optima Rosea' (*japonica*) CTre
§ 'Otome' (*japonica*) CMac SLon WBod
'Otto Hopfer' (*reticulata* x *japonica*) CTrh
'Overture' (*reticulata*) CTrh
'Owen Henry' (*japonica*) CTrh
§ 'O-niji' (*japonica*) MBal WBod
'Painted Lady' (*japonica*) CMac
'Paolina' (*japonica*) SCog
'Paolina Maggi' (*japonica*) SCog
'Parkside' (*williamsii*) CTre
'Paul Jones Supreme' (*japonica*) SCog
'Pauline Winchester' (*japonica*) SCog
♦ 'Paul's Apollo' (*japonica*) See C. 'Apollo'
'Peachblossom' (*japonica*) See C. 'Fleur Dipater'
'Pensacola Red' (*japonica*) SCog
N 'Perfecta' (x *williamsii*) CTrh
'Phillippa Forward' (x *williamsii*) CMac WBod
'Pink Champagne' (*japonica*) CMHG CTre SBod SCog
'Pink Clouds' (*japonica*) SCog
'Pink Pagoda' (*japonica*) SCog
'Pink Perfection' (*japonica*) See C. 'Otome'
¶ 'Pink Snow' (*hiemalis*) SSta
'Pink Spangles' See C. 'Mathotiana Rosea'
'Pirate's Gold' (*japonica*) (v) SCog
pitardii* x *cuspidata SExb
'Plantation Pink' (*sasanqua*) CTrh SCog SPer
'Pompone' (*japonica*) SCog
'Pope Pius IX' (*japonica*) See C. 'Prince Eugène Napoléon'
'Powder Puff' (*japonica*) CTre SExb
§ 'Press's Eclipse' (*japonica*) SCog
'Preston Rose' (*japonica*) CB&S CGre CMac CTre ELan ISea MBal MGos SExb SPer WBod WWat
'Pride of Descanso' (*japonica*) See C. 'Yukibotan'
'Primavera' (*japonica*) CTrh SCog
§ 'Prince Eugène Napoléon' (*japonica*) SCog
* 'Princess du Mahe' (*japonica*) CMac
§ 'Priscilla Brooks' (*japonica*) SCog
'Professor Sargent' (*japonica*) SCog
'Purity' (*japonica*) See C. 'Shiragiku'
'Purple Emperor' (*japonica*) See C. 'Julia Drayton'
'Quercifolia' See C. 'Kingyo-tsubaki'
¶ 'Quintessence' (*japonica* x *lutchuensis*) SCog
'R L Wheeler' (*japonica*) AGM CB&S CGre CTre CTrh CTrw EBre LBre MBal SCog SExb
'Rainbow' (*japonica*) See C. 'O-niji'
'Red Cardinal' (*japonica*) SExb
'Red Dahlia' (x *williamsii*) SCog
'Red Dandy' (*japonica*) CTrh SCog
'Red Ensign' (*japonica*) SCog
'Red Rogue' (*japonica*) CTrh
'Reg Ragland' (*japonica*) SCog SExb
'Rendezvous' (x *williamsii*) SCog SPla
reticulata CGre CTre CTrh
'Robert Fortune' See C. 'Songzilin'
'Roger Hall' (*japonica*) SCog SExb
'Rôgetsu' (*japonica*) CGre
'Roman Soldier' (*japonica*) CB&S
¶ 'Rosa Perfecta' (*japonica*) SExb
'Rose Court' (x *williamsii*) WBod
'Rose Holland' (x *williamsii*) CMHG
'Rose Parade' (x *williamsii*) AGM CGre CTrh SCog SExb
'Rose Quartz' (x *williamsii*) ELan
§ 'Rosea Plena' (*sasanqua*) CB&S CMac CTre CTrw
'Rosemary Williams' (x *williamsii*) CB&S CTre CTrh CTrw
rosiflora CTre
'Royalty' (*japonica* x *reticulata*) CTre CTrh SCog
'Rubescens Major' (*japonica*) AGM CB&S CGre CMac CTrh ISea SCog SExb SReu WBod
'Rubra' (*sasanqua*) See C. 'Sasanqua Rubra'
'Ruby Bells' (x *williamsii*) CMHG
* 'Ruby Wedding' SExb
'Ruddigore' (*japonica*) CTrh
'Sabrina' (*japonica*) SCog
'Saint André' (*japonica*) CMac

'Saint Ewe' (x *williamsii*) AGM — CB&S CDoC CGre CMac CSam CTre CTrh CTrw ELan ENot GGGa GWht IJoh ISea MBal MBri MGos MRav SBod SCog SExb SHBN SPer SPla WBod
'Saint Michael' (x *williamsii*) — CB&S
'Salonica' — See C. 'Shimna'
saluenensis — CGre CTre CTrh SReu
– ***japonica*** — See C. x ***williamsii***
'Salutation' (***saluenensis*** x ***reticulata***) — CB&S CGre CSam CSco CTre ISea SCog WBod
'Samantha' (***reticulata***) — CTrh
'San Dimas' (***japonica***) — CTrh SCog
'Sarah Frost' (***japonica***) — SExb
sasanqua — CSam CTrh ISea SEng
'Sasanqua Rubra' — CMac
§ 'Sasanqua Variegata' (***sasanqua***) — SPla SSta WWat
'Satan's Robe' (***reticulata*** x) AGM — CMHG CTre CTrh SCog
'Saturnia' (***japonica***) — SCog WStI
'Sayonara' (x ***williamsii***) — CTre CTrh
'Scentsation' (***japonica***) AGM — CMHG CTre SCog
'Scentuous' (***japonica*** x ***lutchuensis***) — SCog
'Sea Foam' (***japonica***) — CMHG
'Sea Gull' (***japonica***) — CTrh
'Seiji' (***japonica***) — CMac
'Senator Duncan U Fletcher' (***japonica***) — CTrw
'Senorita' (x ***williamsii***) — CTrh
'Serenade' (***japonica***) — CMHG SCog
'Shinonome' (***sasanqua***) — CTrh
'Shin-akebono' (***japonica***) — See C. 'Akebono'
'Shirobotan' (***japonica***) — SCog SExb
'Shiro-daikagura' (***rusticana***) — SCog WBod
'Shiro-wabisuke' (Wabisuke) — CTrh
'Show Girl' (***sasanqua*** x ***reticulata***) — CTre CTrh SBod SCog SExb WBod
'Shôwa-no-sakae' (***hiemalis***) — SCog
'Shôwa-wabisuke' (Wabisuke) — CTrh
'Sierra Spring' (***japonica***) — SCog
'Silver Anniversary' (***japonica***) — CB&S CMHG ELan MAsh SBod SCog SExb SReu SSta
'Silver Waves' (***japonica***) — SCog
§ ***sinensis*** — CGre CTre CTrh EMil GAri
'Snow Goose' (***japonica***) — SCog
'Snowflake' (***sasanqua***) — CTrh SSta
'Songzilin' (***reticulata***) — SHil
'Souvenir de Bahuaud-Litou' (***japonica***) AGM — CGre CTre SCog SLon WBod WWat
'Sparkling Burgundy' (***hiemalis***) — CB&S CTre SCog WBod
'Speciosissima' (***japonica***) — SCog
'Spencer's Pink' (***japonica***) — CB&S CTre CTrw
'Splendens' — See C. 'Coccinea'
'Spring Festival' (***cuspidata*** x) AGM — CHig CTrh SCog SExb
'Spring Mist' (***japonica*** x ***lutchuensis***) — CMHG
'Spring Sonnet' (***japonica***) — SCog
'Stella Polare' — See C. 'Etoile Polaire'
* 'Strawberry Parfait' — SExb
'Strawberry Swirl' (***japonica***) — SCog
¶ 'Sundae' (***japonica***) — SExb
'Sunset Glory' (***japonica***) — SCog
'Swan Lake' (hybrid) — SCog SExb
'Sweet Delight' (***japonica***) — CMHG
'Sylvia' (***japonica***) — CMac WBod
taliensis — CGre CTre CTrh
'Tammia' (***japonica***) — SCog
'Tanya' (***sasanqua***) — CTrh
'Tarô'an' (***japonica***) — CTrh SCog
'Taylor's Perfection' (x ***williamsii***) — CDoC CTrw
'Teresa Ragland' (***japonica***) — SCog
'Teringa' (***japonica***) — CTre
'The Czar' (***japonica***) — CB&S CTre CTrw ISea MBri SCog WBod
I 'The Duchess of Cornwall' (x ***williamsii***) — CTre
'The Mikado' (***japonica***) — CTre
'The Pilgrim' (***japonica***) — SCog
thea — See C. ***sinensis***
'Thomas Cornelius Cole' (***japonica***) — CTre
'Tickled Pink' (***japonica***) — SCog
'Tiffany' (***japonica***) — CB&S CTre CTrh LNet SCog SExb SHBN SHer SPla
'Tinker Bell' (***japonica***) — CGre CTrh SCog
'Tinker Toy' (***japonica***) — CTrh
'Tiny Princess' (***japonica*** x ***fraterna***) — CGre CTrh
'Tiptoe' (x ***williamsii***) — CTrh SCog
'Tom Knudsen' (***reticulata*** x ***japonica***) — CTre CTrh SExb
'Tom Thumb' (***japonica***) — CTrh
'Tomorrow' (***japonica***) — CB&S CMHG CMac CSam CTre CTrh CTrw ISea MAsh SCog SExb WBod WFox
'Tomorrow Park Hill' (***japonica***) — CTrh SCog
'Tomorrow Supreme' — See C. 'Tomorrow Variegated'
§ 'Tomorrow Variegated' (***japonica***) — SCog
'Tomorrow's Dawn' (***japonica***) — CB&S CTrh SCog
transnokoensis — CTre
'Tregrehan' (x ***williamsii***) — ISea
'Tregye' (***japonica***) — CB&S
'Trewithen Red' (***saluenensis***) — CTrw

'Trewithen White' (*japonica*)	CSam CTrw
'Tricolor' (*japonica*) AGM	CB&S CGre CMac CTrh ENot IHos IJoh IOrc SCog SExb SHBN SPer WBod
'Tricolor Red' (*japonica*)	See C. 'Lady de Saumarez'
'Tricolor Sieboldii'	See C. 'Tricolor'
'Tricolor Superba' (*japonica*)	WBod
'Tristrem Carlyon' (*reticulata* x)	CB&S CTre MBri SCog SExb WBod WFox
tsaii AGM	CTrh
'Twilight' (*japonica*)	SCog
'Twinkle Star' (x *williamsii*)	SCog SExb
'Usu-ôtome'	See C. 'Otome'
'Valentine Day' (*reticulata* x *japonica*)	CTrh
'Valley Knudsen' (*saluenensis* x *reticulata*)	SCog
'Valtevareda' (*japonica*)	CGre
'Variegata' (*sasanqua*)	See C. 'Sasanqua Variegata'
'Victor de Bisschop' (*japonica*)	See C. 'Le Lys'
'Victor Emmanuel' (*japonica*)	See C. 'Blood of China'
'Virginia Carlyon' (*japonica*)	CB&S CTre
'Virginia Robinson' (*japonica*)	WBod
'Vittorio Emanuele II' (*japonica*)	CTrh
'Warrior' (*japonica*)	CTre SCog
'Water Lily' (x *williamsii*) AGM	CB&S CTre CTrh CTrw SExb
'Waterloo'	See C. 'Etherington White'
'White Nun' (*japonica*)	SCog
'White Swan' (*japonica*)	CB&S CMac CTre MAsh
'Wilamina' (*japonica*)	CTrh SExb
'Wilber Foss' (x *williamsii*)	CGre CTre CTrh CTrw SExb
'Wildfire' (*japonica*)	SCog
'William Bartlett' (*japonica*)	CTrh
'William Carylon' (*williamsii*)	CTre MBal
'William Hertrich' (*reticulata*)	CGre CTre
'William Honey' (*japonica*)	CMHG CTrh SCog
§ x ***williamsii***	CGre
'Winter Cheer' (*japonica*)	CTrh SCog
'Winton' (*cuspidata* x *saluenensis*)	CB&S
'Wood Nymph' (x *williamsii*)	CTre ISea MBal
'Woodville Red' (*japonica*)	CTre
'Yae-arare' (*sasanqua*)	CTrh
'Yesterday' (x *williamsii*)	CTre MAsh SCog
'Yoibijin' (*japonica*)	See C. 'Suibijin'
'Yours Truly' (*japonica*)	CMac CTre CTrh MGos SBod SCog
yuhsienensis	CTrh
§ 'Yukibotan' (*japonica*)	SCog
'Yukihaki'	See C. 'Yukishiro'
'Yukimi-guruma' (*japonica*)	SPla WBod
§ 'Yukishiro' (*japonica*)	CTrw
'Yuletide' (x *vernalis*)	CTrh
'Zoraide Vanzi' (*japonica*)	WBod

CAMPANULA † (Campanulaceae)

¶ ***aizoïdes***	EPad
alaskana	See C. ***rotundifolia alaskana***
§ ***alliariifolia***	Widely available
– 'Ivory Bells'	See C. ***alliariifolia***
allionii	See C. ***alpestris***
§ ***alpestris***	EPad GTou MBro
– 'Grandiflora'	EPad EPot WDav
– 'Rosea'	EPad
alpina	CMea EPad GDra GTou NNrd
– var. ***bucegiensis***	EPad NHar WDav
– ***orbelica***	See C. ***o.***
americana	EPad
anchusiflora	EPad MFos
andrewsii	EPad MFir MFos
– ssp. ***andrewsii***	EPad
– ssp. ***hirsutula***	EPad
argyrotricha	ECro EPad
¶ – C&Mc 477	GCHN
arvatica AGM	CLew EPad GCHN LBee MBro MHig MNFA MRPP NGre NHar NHol NMen NNrd NTow SHer SIng SSmi WAbe WDav
– 'Alba'	EPad LBee MHig NMen WHil
atlantis	EPad
aucheri	EBur EPad GArf GDra
autraniana	EPad
'Avalon'	EPad
'Balchiniana'	EPad ERav WEas WPbr
barbata	CNic ECro ELan EPad GCHN GDra GTou LHop MBro MCas MSte MSto MTol NMen NRya NWCA WCla WDav WHal WNdy WPer
– var. ***alba***	MBro MCas NNrd WDav
baumgartenii	EPad
bellidifolia	CNic EPad GDra NBir
bertolae	EPad
§ ***betulifolia*** AGM	CSam ECtt EPad EPot GCHN GDra MBro MRPP NGre NHar NRed NTow SIng SWas WDav WThu
– JCA 252.005	SBla
biebersteiniana	EPad
'Birch Hybrid' AGM	CMHG ECtt ELan EMNN EPad ESis GCHN GDra GMac MBal MBro MCas MNFA MRPP NHar NHol NMen NRoo SCro SHer SIng WCra WHil
bononiensis	EMon EPad SOkh WHaw WOld WPer
bornmuelleri	EPad
'Burghaltii' AGM	Widely available
§ ***buseri***	WThi
caespitosa	EPad NWCA
calaminthifolia	CLew EPad MSte NRed NWCA WAbe WOMN
§ ***carnica***	MBro NWCA

carpatha	EPad MRPP
carpatica AGM	CGle CRiv CShe GAri GDra LAbb MBar MBri MHig NBro NNor SIng SPer SUsu WHoo WKif WWin
– f. ***alba***	CGle CRiv CShe NNor NOak SIng SPer WEas WHoo
– 'Bees' Variety'	NKay
– 'Blaue Clips' ('Blue Clips')	CDoC CHol ECtt ELan EMNN EPad EPar ESis GTou LAbb MRPP NGre NHol NKay NMen NMir NRoo SHer SPer SPla WDav WPer
– 'Blue Moonlight'	EBre EOrc EPad GMac LBre NEgg NRoo
– 'Bressingham White'	EBre EPad GAri GCHN GDra LBee LBre NEgg NNrd SBla WHoo
– 'Caerulea'	CB&S
– 'Chewton Joy'	EBee EBre EOrc EPad ESis GAri GCHN LBre NRoo
– 'Ditton Blue'	EPad GDra MBel
– dwarf form	EPot
– 'Harvest Moon'	EPad
– 'Kathy'	SAsh SWas
– 'Lavender'	NKay WHil
– 'Maureen Haddon'	EBre EPad GAri GCHN GMac LBre NEgg NRoo
– 'Molly Pinsent'	CShe EPad WMar
– 'Queen of Sheba'	EPad
– 'Queen of Somerville'	EPad MBel NKay NNrd
– 'Riverslea'	EPad NKay
– 'Snowdrift'	EPad SFis
– 'Suzie'	EWes SBla
– var. ***turbinata***	GDra MTho WPer
– – f. ***alba***	ECha NNrd
– – 'Craven Bells'	EPad
– – 'Georg Arends'	SAsh
– – 'Hannah'	EBre EPad GCHN GDra LBee LBre SHer WMar
– – 'Isabel'	EPad GCHN MBel NKay NNrd
– – 'Jewel'	EPad LBee NNrd SSmi
– – 'Karl Foerster'	EBre EPad GBuc GCHN GMac LBre MBri MNFA NRoo WPer
– – 'Pallida'	GDra NHol NNrd SSmi
– – 'Snowsprite'	LRHS
– – 'Wheatley Violet'	EPad ESis GCHN MRPP NHol NMen NRoo SBla WPer
– 'Weisse Clips' ('White Clips')	CDoC ECtt ELan EMNN EPad EPar ESis GTou LAbb LHop NGre NHol NKay NMen NMir NNrd NRoo SHer SPer SPla WByw WPer
§ ***cashmeriana***	EBur EPad GCHN GCra GPlt ITim MFos NBir NTow NWCA SIng WAbe WOMN WThu
celsii	EPad
– ssp. ***carystea***	EPad
cephalenica	See C. ***garganica c.***
cervicaria	EPad NMir
§ ***chamissonis***	CNic EPad EPot MHig
§ – 'Major'	CPBP EMNN EPad EPot EWes SIng
– 'Oyobeni'	EPad NHar SUsu WDav
§ – 'Superba' AGM	CNic EGle GDra MBal MSto MTho NMen NNrd NTow SSmi WHil
§ ***cochleariifolia*** AGM	Widely available

– var. ***alba***	Widely available
– 'Annie Hall'	WHal
– 'Blue Tit'	EBre EPad GBuc LBre
– 'Cambridge Blue'	EBre EPad GCHN LBre NMen NNrd SSmi WAbe
– 'Elizabeth Oliver' (d)	Widely available
– 'Flore Pleno'	CMea ECtt EFol EPad NHar NHol NMen NNrd
– 'Miss Willmott'	EBur EPad EWes NBir SSmi
– 'Oakington Blue'	CElw EPad NHol NNrd SSmi
– var. ***pallida***	SRms
– – 'Miranda'	CNic CSpe EPad MHig NNrd SSmi
– 'R B Loder' (D)	EPad
– 'Silver Chimes'	EPad MSto NBir NNrd WPat WThu
– 'Temple Bells'	WPer
– 'Tubby'	CNic EPad GCHN GMac MTho NKay NNrd SHer SRms
– ***warleyensis***	See C. x ***haylodgensis*** 'Warley White'
collina	CRiv EPad GPlt MBro MCas MFir NHar SCro WAbe WHoo WPer
'Constellation'	EPad NCat NNrd
coriacea	WThu
– JCA 253.800	EPad
'Covadonga'	CPBP CTom EPad MDHE SHer WPat
crispa JCA 253.901	EPad
dasyantha	See C. ***chamissonis***
divaricata	EPad
'E K Toogood'	ECtt EPad GMac MDHE MWat NHar NHol NKay NNrd SBla SCro WHil
elatines	EPad NNrd
– var. ***elatinoïdes***	EPad
– var. ***elatinoïdes*** JCA 254.300	SBla
§ 'Elizabeth'	CBos CBro CElw CFee CHan CMea CSco ECro ECtt EFol EFou EMar EPad GBri LGre LHop MBel MBri MFir MSte NBrk NHar NSti SCro SFis SMad SMrm SUsu WBon WPbr
ephesia	CElw EPad EWoo
erinus	EPad
eriocarpa	See C. ***latifolia*** 'Eriocarpa'
excisa	EPad ITim MDHE NTow NWCA
'Faichem'	EPad GCra WPer
fenestrellata	EPad MDHE MNFA MTho NBro NCat NHol NNrd NSti SSmi
– ssp. ***fenestrellata***	EPad
– ssp. ***istriaca***	EPad
finitima	See C. ***betulifolia***
foliosa	EPad EWoo WHaw
formanekiana AGM	EBur EPad MFos NWCA
fragilis	CBow EBur ECro ELan EPad EPot GTou LLWP NPri SHer WPer
– ssp. ***cavolinii***	EPad
– 'Hirsuta'	ELan EPad SHer WPer
'G F Wilson' AGM	EGle EPad MBal NCat NHol NKay
garganica AGM	CBow CLew EFol ELan EOrc EPad ESis MBro MCas MFir MPit MTho NHar NKay NMen NNrd NRed NRoo SIde SIng WByw WCla WDav WHoo WPer
– 'Aurea'	See C. ***g.*** 'Dickson's Gold'

– 'Blue Diamond'	CRiv ELan EPad ESis LHop MPit NPri SHer SIng WAbe
§ – ssp. ***cephalenica***	EPad MDHE NHol NKay
§ – 'Dickson's Gold'	Widely available
– 'Hirsuta'	SRms
– 'W H Paine' **AGM**	EBre EPad LBre NCat SHer
'Glandore'	EPad NCat
glomerata	CB&S CBot CGle CKin CShe EBar EOrc EPad GTou MBal MFir MHew MTho MWat NBro NMir NRed NRya NSti SUsu WByw WEas WHal WNdy WTyn WWin
– var. ***acaulis***	CBow CDoC CHol CNic CRiv EBar ECro EPad EPot ESma GCHN LAbb MCas MPit NMen NOak NRoo SPla WHoo WPer WTyn WWin
– var. ***alba***	CBow CCla CSev EFol ELan EMon EPad MBal MBri MBro MNFA MUlv NBar NBro NFai SPer SPla SSvw WCot WHal WHil WHoo WNdy WPer
– 'Alba Nana'	EPad MBel
– var. ***dahurica***	CSco EPad LGan NNrd NOak WPer
– 'Joan Elliott'	ECha EPad GMac
– 'Purple Pixie'	EBre ECtt EPad LBre MBel
– 'Schneekrone' ('Crown of Snow')	CGle ECha ECro EFou EPad GMac NBrk NNor NOak NRoo WRus
– 'Superba' **AGM**	CBow CCla CGle CKel CRiv EFol EFou ELan ENot EPad EPar MBri MBro MNFA NBar NBrk NFai NHol NNor NOrc NRoo SCro SPer SPla SSvw WHoo WPer WTyr
– 'White Barn'	ECha
grossekii	EBee EPad EPot GBuc GTou MBel
grossheimii	EPad
hakkiarica	EPad
x ***hallii***	CNic EPad EPot ESis GMac MPla MRPP NGre NHol NRed NRoo WDav WPat
hawkinsiana	CPBP EMon
x ***haylodgensis***	CElw CNic CRiv CSpe ELan EPad EPot ESis IHos LLWP MBal MCas MHig NBro NHar NNrd NRoo SBla SIng SSmi SUsu WAbe WHal WHil WHoo WOMN WPat WThu
– 'Plena'	CLew CShe GMac LHop NHol SFis WEas WKif WPer
§ – 'Warley White' (d)	CGle CNic CRiv CSpe EBur ECro ELan EPad GDra LHop NNrd SGil SHer WOMN WPer
hemschinica	EPad
'Hemswell Starlight'	EPad NMen WPer
hercegovina	EPad EPot SIng
– 'Nana'	WAbe
herminii	EPad
heterophylla	EPad NTow
§ ***incurva***	CBot CGle CPou EPad GBuc GTou LGre LWad MRPP MRav NBrk NBro NHol SMad WByw WDav WPer
– JCA 256.800	MBro
innesii	See C. 'John Innes'
isophylla **AGM**	EPad EPot ERav LAbb MBri SGil SHer SIng SLMG WEas
– 'Alba' **AGM**	EPad LAbb SGil SHer SIng SLMG WEas
– 'Flore Pleno'	EPad
– 'Mayi' **AGM**	CSpe
– 'Pamela'	EPad
– 'Variegata'	See C. 'Balchiniana'
'Joe Elliott' **AGM**	CNic EPad LBee MHig SWas
§ 'John Innes'	CShe EPad
kemulariae	CNic EPad ESis GCHN MBro MCas NCat NHol NKay NNrd WDav WHil WPer
– ***alba***	EPad
'Kent Belle'	CElw LGre SUsu WCot WPla
kladniana	EPad
kolenatiana	EPad GCHN
laciniata	EPad
lactiflora	Widely available
– ***alba***	See C. *l.* white
¶ – 'Blue Avalanche'	SMrm
– 'Loddon Anna' **AGM**	Widely available
– 'Pouffe'	CDoC CKel CMGP CSco EBre ECha EFou ELan EOrc EPad LBre MNFA NBro NHol NRoo NSti SCro SPer SPla WHoo WPer WRus WWin
– 'Prichard's Variety' **AGM**	Widely available
– 'Violet'	WPer
– white **AGM**	CBot CKel CMGP EBre ECha EFou EOrc EPad LBre MBro NBir NBrk SPer SPla WEas WOld WPer
– 'White Pouffe'	CCla CLew EBre EFou EHal EOrc EPad GAbr GMac LBre NHol SCro SPer WByw WHoo WRus
lanata	ELan EPad WByw WTyn
lasiocarpa	EBur EPad GArf MHig WOMN
§ ***latifolia***	CBow CBre CElw CHan CKin CMea CSev ECWi ECha EFou EPad EPot GAbr LGan NMir NNor NOrc NRed NTow SPer WCla WEas
– 'Arthur Wood'	EPad
– 'Brantwood'	CChu CMGP CMil EMar EPad MFir MSte NBrk NHol NOak SChu SCro SFis SPer WPer
– 'Eriocarpa'	CHan
– 'Gloaming'	EPad MUlv SIde
– var. ***macrantha***	CHol CSco EFou EPad GLil MBri MNFA MSte NNrw NSti SMad SSvw WCot WHoo WOld WPer WTyn WWat
– – ***alba***	CChu CSco ECtt LGre LHop MBro SCro SSvw WPer WWat
– white	CChu CElw CGle CHan ECha EOrc EPad MBri MNFA MSte NNor NSti NTow SPer WCru WEas WHoo WNdy WRus
– 'White Ladies'	EBre EPad LBre
§ ***latiloba***	CGle CMea EBre EPad LBre LGro MFir WByw WEas WHoo WNdy WWin
– ***alba*** **AGM**	CBre CChu CElw CGle CHan CLew CMil EBre EFou EHal EMon EPad GCal GMac LBre LGre LHil LHop MBri MRav SCro WBon WEas WHer WMar WNdy WOld
– 'Hidcote Amethyst' **AGM**	Widely available

– 'Highcliffe Variety' AGM	CChu CMGP EBee ECha EFou EJud EPad MBri NHol SGil WEas WKif WNdy WOld WPer
– 'Percy Piper' AGM	CElw CSam ECED ECha EFou ELan EPad GCal GMac MBel MBri MRav NBrk NVic SCro SHer WByw WDav
ledebouriana pulvinata AGM	EPad
lingulata	EPad
linifolia	See C. ***carnica***
longestyla	EPad
'Lynchmere'	EPad EWes MNFA NKay SHer
lyrata	EPad
makaschvilii	EPad
'Marion Fisher'	EPad
mirabilis	EPad SIng
'Mist Maiden'	CFee CShe EPad EPot ESis LBee LLWP MCas MNFA NKay SHer WMar
moesiaca	EPad MBel WHaw
mollis	EPad
– var. ***gibraltarica***	EPad NTow WOMN
muralis	See C. ***portenschlagiana***
nitida	See C. ***persicifolia planiflora***
– var. ***planiflora***	See C. ***persicifolia planiflora***
'Norman Grove'	EGle EPad LBee MCas MHig NTow
ochroleuca	CMea EPad WHal
olympica Boissier	EPad GCra
olympica hort.	See C. ***rotundifolia*** 'Olympica'
orbelica	EPad
¶– JJH 919285	WDav
oreadum	CNic EPad
orphanidea	EPad MFos NHar NSla WDav
pallida	EPad
♦– ssp. ***tibetica***	See C. ***cashmeriana***
parryi	EPad
patula	CNat EPad MHew NRed WCla
– ssp. ***abietina***	EPad
¶ 'Paul Furse'	WHal WWin
pelviformis	EPad
peregrina	CHan
persicifolia	Widely available
– ***alba***	Widely available
§– 'Alba Coronata' (d)	CDec CElw EMon EPad LGan MBal MBel NBir NSti WRus
– 'Alba Plena'	See C. ***p.*** 'Alba Coronata'
– Ashfield double ice blue	NRar
– 'Bennett's Blue'	EOrc EPad MUlv
– blue	EOrc MBel WEas WPbr
– blue cup-in-cup	CElw WDav
– 'Boule de Neige' (d)	CDec CHad CHan CLew CPou CRDP ECha EMon EPad GAbr GCra GMac MBel NBrk NOak SPla WEas WHil WNdy WPer
– 'Caerulea Coronata'	See C. ***p.*** 'Coronata'
*– 'Caerulea Plena'	CBos EFol ELan NWyt WEas WPbr
¶– 'Capel Ulo' (v)	WHer
– 'Carillon'	CB&S CKel EPad NBrk
– 'Chettle Charm'	CBos CDec EFou MUlv
*– 'China Blue'	SFis
§– 'Coronata' (d)	EFou GAbr
N– cup & saucer white AGM	CElw ELan LGre MUlv NBrk NFai SAxl WBon WByw WMar WPer
– double blue	CElw CLew CTom EOrc LGre MBal NBro NFai NHol NSti WByw WEas WPla WRus
– double white	EFol ELan MBel NFai WByw WRus
– 'Fleur de Neige' AGM	CElw CGle CLew CSam MBri MUlv NCat WDav WHoo WRus
– 'Flore Pleno'	CHan EPad NBir SApp WNdy
– 'Frances'	CElw EMon WCot
– 'Frank Lawley'	EFou EMon MUlv
– 'Gawen' (d)	CBre CElw CGle GMac MHlr WCot
– 'George Chiswell'	CDec CElw CHad CHan CMil CRDP CSam CShe EFol ELan EOrc EPad GBri LGre LHop MUlv NBrk SAsh SAxl SBla SCro SMrm WAbb WEas
– 'Grandiflora'	NHol WDav WWat
– 'Grandiflora Alba'	GBuc SCro
– 'Grandiflora Caerulea'	SCro
§– 'Hampstead White' (d)	CDec CHan CPou ECha EFou EPad EPar GCal MBri MNFA NBir SBla WEas WHal WHoo WNdy
– 'Hetty'	See C. ***p.*** 'Hampstead White'
– 'Moerheimii' (d)	EOrc EPad EPar MBel MNFA MUlv NBir
– var. ***nitida***	See C. ***p. planiflora***
– – ***alba***	See C. ***p. planiflora alba***
*– 'Peach Bells'	EBar NOak
– 'Perry's Boyblue'	NPer
– 'Pike's Supremo'	LHop NBir
§ – var. ***planiflora***	CHan EPad MCas MNFA NHar NHol NNrd WAbe
§ – – f. ***alba***	EPad MCas MWat NHol WAbe WWin
– 'Pride of Exmouth'	CBre CElw CGle CLew CMil CPou CSam EFou EMon EPad GMac LHop MBel MNFA NBrk NNor NVic WDav WHal WHil WHoo WNdy WPbr WRus
– ssp. ***sessiliflora***	See C. ***latiloba***
– 'Telham Beauty'	CBow CDoC CHol CKel COtt ECED EFou ELan EOrc EPad GAbr LGan LHop LWad MFir NHol NWyt SMad SMrm SPer SSvw WCra WDav WPer WRus WWat
– 'Wedgwood'	MBal
N– 'White Cup and Saucer'	EMon GMac NCat WDav WRus
– 'White Queen'	CMGP ECro EFou EPad NFai NHol NVic SApp SMrm WEas WTyr
petraea	EPad WHil
pilosa	See C. ***chamissonis***
– ***superba***	See C. ***chamissonis*** 'Superba'
piperi	MHig MSto WHal
planiflora	See C. ***persicifolia p.***
§ ***portenschlagiana*** AGM	CElw CSco EBar ELan EPad EPar GAbr LGro MBro MCas MHig MWat NNor NRoo NRya SBla SDix SHer SIng SPer WAbe WEas WWin
– 'Bavarica'	IDai NHol
– 'Major'	CShe NKay SRms

– 'Resholdt's Variety'	CGle CLew CMea CNic CRiv CSam CShe EBre EFol EFou ELan EPad EPla GCHN LBre MPit MUlv NCat NHol NNrd WPer
poscharskyana	CBow CCla CElw ELan EPad ESis IDai LBlm LBuc LGro MBal MBri MCas MFir NBrk NGre NKay NMen NRoo SHer SIng SPer SPla SSmi WAbe WByw WPer
– 'Blauranke'	CNic EPad EWes GAri GCHN MDHE MNFA
– 'E H Frost'	CBre CElw CLew CShe ECtt EMNN EPad ESis LBlm LHop MBro MCas MHig MPla MWat NCat NHol NKay NMen NNrd NRed NRya SCro SIng SSmi WHil WPer WWin
– 'Glandore'	See C. 'G.'
– 'Lilacina'	CVer SIng WThi
– 'Lisduggan'	CElw CGle CNic EBur EPad ESis MBal MBro MCas MWat NCat NNrd SBla SUsu WAbe WDav WHil WPer
– 'Stella'	CShe EMNN EPad ESis GCHN MCas MNFA MRav NCat NMen NRed NRoo NVic SChu SDix SHer SIng WEas
– variegated	EHoe IBlr WCot
primulifolia	CNic CPou EBee ELan EPad GBuc GCra NHar SFis SSvw SUsu WByw WDav WHoo WHow WPer WPla WWin
x ***pseudoraineri***	ELan EPad EWes NGre SSmi
pulla	CLew CMea CRDP ELan EPad EPot ESis MBro MCas MHig MSto MTho NGre NHar NHol SHer SSmi WHal WPat WPer
– ***alba***	CRDP
x ***pulloïdes***	EBre EPad LBee LBre NMen NNrd SSmi
punctata	Widely available
– f. ***albiflora***	CHan EFol EPad GMac LGan LGre LHop MBri MNFA NCat NMen SApp WHal
– var. ***hondoensis***	ECro EPad MBel
– f. ***impunctata***	EPad
– 'Nana Alba'	GMac
– 'Pallida'	EPad
– pink	CChu CGle CMea LRHS MBri NKay SRms WHil
– 'Rubriflora'	CChu CCla CDec CHad ECro ECtt EGol ELan EMar EPad GCal GMac LHop MBro MNFA NBar NBrk NHol NOak NOrc NRoo SCro SPer WHal WHoo WPbr WPer WPla WRus
* 'Purple Dwarf'	NGre NNrd
pusilla	See C. ***cochleariifolia***
pyramidalis	CBot CBow CHan EFou EPad LWad NNrw NOrc NSti WByw WEas WHaw WPer WPla
– ***alba***	CBow CHol EFou EPad NNrw SIde WDav WPer WPla
*– ***rhomboidea***	WEas
x ***pyraversi***	EPad
radchensis	EPad
raddeana	CNic CRiv EPad GCHN MBro MNFA NGre NHar NMen NNrd NRed SSmi WCla WDav
raineri AGM	CFee EPad EPot GArf GCLN LBee NMen NWCA SHer WAbe WThu
§ ***rapunculoïdes***	CArn EBee EPad GTou SBla SSvw WHer WHil WPer WTyn
– 'Alba'	EMon EPad
rapunculus	EPad MWil
recurva	See C. ***incurva***
rhomboidalis	See C. ***rapunculoïdes***
rotundifolia	CArn CBos CBow CKin CLew CNic ECWi EPad GTou MHew NLan NMir NNrd NRoo NSti SSvw WCla WGwy WOak WPer WTyn
§ – var. ***alaskana***	EPad NBir NWCA
– ***alba***	CElw EPad MBro WHoo WPer
– ***caerulea plena***	See C. ***r.*** 'Flore Pleno'
§ – 'Flore Pleno'	CBos LBlm
§ – 'Olympica'	CHol CShe EBar EPad GCHN GMac MBro NPri SFis
¶ – 'Superba'	SCro
rupestris	CBot CNic EBur EPad EPot MFos NHol NWCA WAbe WThu
– NS 401	NWCA
rupicola	EPad WEas
– JCA 262.400	CNic SBla
samarkandensis	EPad
sarmatica	CGle CHan CNic EPad EPot GBuc MNFA NRoo NSti WCla WPer
sartorii	CNic EPad NWCA SIng
saxatilis AGM	EPad NRed WHal
– ssp. ***saxatilis***	EPad
saxifraga	EPad GCHN GTou NWCA
scabrella	EPad MFos
serrata	EPad
shetleri	CPBP EPad
sibirica	EPad WPer
– ssp. ***taurica***	EPad
'Southern Seedling'	EPad
spathulata	EPad
– ssp. ***spruneriana***	EPad
spatulata ssp. ***spatulata***	NWCA
speciosa	EPad GTou
spicata	EPad WHil
¶ ***sporadum***	EWoo
¶ – K 92.162	WDav
sp. ex Furze	WWat
sp. JCA 6872	EPad
sp. JCA 8363	EPad
sp. JJH 918638	EPad
'Stansfieldii'	EPad EPot NNrd NTow
sulphurea	EPad
takesimana	Widely available
– 'Elizabeth'	See C. 'Elizabeth '
thessala	EPad NWCA
thyrsoïdes	CBoy CMea CPou EPad GAbr GDra GTou MNFA NBro NSti NWCA WCla WHal WPer WPla
– ssp. ***carniolica***	EPad
tommasiniana	EPad LBee NHar SAsh SIng WOMN
topaliana	EPad
¶ – NS 407	NWCA
– ssp. ***cordifolia***	EPad
– ssp. ***cordifolia*** NS 409	NWCA

trachelium	CBoy CGle CKin EBar ECWi ECoo EJud EOrc EPad GMac MHew NCat NHol NSti WByw WCla WHer WPer WTyn
– var. ***alba***	CElw CGle EPad MFir WEas WNdy WPer
– 'Alba Flore Pleno'	CBos CBre CChu CElw CGle CRDP CRow ECha EFou ELan EMon EPad LGre MUlv SAxl WByw
– 'Bernice' (d)	CElw CGle CHad CMil CRDP CRow EFou ELan EMon EOrc EPad EPar GCHN MBri MUlv SCro SPer WByw WHal WHoo WNdy WRus
transsilvanica	EPad
tridentata	EPad
troegerae	EPad LBee LRHS MBro SBla
tubulosa	See C. ***buseri***
'Tymonsii'	EBur EPad ESis MCas MHig MMil NBir NKay NNrd NTow WHil
'Van-Houttei'	CHan CMea EMon EPad GCal MSte SBla WCot WPer WPla
versicolor	CHan EBee EPad MBel MHig NHol WEas WPer
– G&K 3347	EMon
vidalii	See AZORINA ***v.***
waldsteiniana	EPad EPot LBee MHig NNrd NTow SWas WOMN
– JCA 266.000	MBro
'Warley White'	See C. x ***haylodgensis*** 'W.W.'
'Warleyensis'	See C. x ***haylodgensis*** 'Warley White'
x ***wockei***	See C. x ***w.*** 'Puck'
§ – 'Puck'	CRiv EPad GDra MBro MCas NHar NMen NNrd SFis WHil WOMN WPat WPer
xylocarpa	EPad
* 'Yvonne'	CNic NEgg SFis WPer
zoysii	EPad MHig SBla

CAMPANULA X SYMPHYANDRA (Campanulaceae)

C. *punctata* x S. *ossetica*	EPad

CAMPHOROSMA (Chenopodiaceae)

monspeliaca	NHol

CAMPSIS (Bignoniaceae)

grandiflora	CB&S CBow CBra CGre CPle CSco EBre ELan ENot EPla LBre NPal SHil SPer SReu SSta WStI
radicans	CArn CBot CBow CDoC CGre CHEx CMac CPle CRHN ECtt ELan ENot EPla EWri GCHN MWat SHBN SPer SReu WDin
– 'Flamenco'	CB&S IOrc LHop MUlv NWyt WPat
§ – f. ***flava*** AGM	CDoC CMac ELan IHos IJoh IOrc LHop MBri MWat NPal SBra SHer SPer SSta
– 'Yellow Trumpet'	See C. ***r. flava***
x ***tagliabuana*** 'Guilfoylei'	NBar
– 'Madame Galen' AGM	CB&S CChu CCla CMac CSco EBre ECtt EMil EOrc EPla IJoh IOrc LBre LHop MBri MGos MRav NBar SBra SHBN SMad SPer SReu SSta WSHC

CAMPTOSORUS See ASPLENIUM

CAMPYLOTROPIS (Leguminosae/Papilionaceae)
See Plant Deletions

CANARINA (Campanulaceae)

canariensis AGM	CPle ERea WOMN

CANDOLLEA See HIBBERTIA

CANNA † (Cannaceae)

¶ 'Angele Martin'	CBrk
'Assaut'	CBrk LHil
'Black Knight'	CBrk GBuc LAma
¶ 'Champion'	CBrk
¶ 'China Lady'	LHil
¶ 'Chinese Coral'	LHil
coccinea	CBrk
Crozy hybrids	MHlr WCot
♦ ***edulis***	See C. ***indica***
x ***ehemanii***	CHEx CTro
'Endeavour'	CBrk MSta
'Erebus'	CBrk MSta
¶ 'Etoile du Feu'	CBrk
¶ 'Extase'	CBrk
'Fireside'	CBrk LHil
'General Eisenhower'	CBrk
x ***generalis***	CHEx
glauca	CBrk CMon SDix
'Golden Lucifer'	LAma MBri
¶ 'Hercule'	CBrk
hybrids	LBow
§ ***indica***	CBrk CChu CHEx CMon ERav GCra LBlm LBow LHil LHop SArc SLMG WCot
– 'Purpurea'	CBrk CChu CMon ECha ERav SDix WCot
– ***variegata***	LBow LHil
¶ – x ***generalis***	WHaw
iridiflora	CBrk CChu ECha LHil SArc SDix
¶ 'Jivago'	CBrk
'King Hakon'	CBrk
'King Midas'	CBrk LHil
¶ 'La Gloire'	CBrk
¶ 'Libération'	CBrk
'Louis Cayeux'	CBrk
'Lucifer'	CBrk LHil MWBu SLMG
lutea	WCot
malawiensis 'Variegata'	LHil LHop
¶ 'Meyerbeer'	CBrk
musifolia	CBrk LHil SDix
'Oiseau de Feu' ('Firebird')	MBri
'Oiseau d'Or'	CBrk
'Orchid'	CBrk LAma MBri
'Perkeo'	CBrk LHil
¶ 'Picadore'	CBrk
'Picasso'	CBrk LAma MWBu
'President'	LAma LHil MBri MWBu

¶ 'Professor Lorentz' CBrk
'Ra' CBrk MSta
¶ 'Richard Wallace' CBrk
'Roi Humbert' LHil SLMG
¶ 'Roi Soleil' CBrk
'Rosemond Coles' CBrk LHil MWBu SLMG
¶ 'Salmon' LHil
¶ 'Sémaphore' CBrk
'Shenandoah' CBrk
'Strasbourg' CBrk
striata CBrk
'Striped Beauty' CBrk
¶ 'Talisman' CBrk
¶ 'Taroudant' CBrk
'Tirol' CBrk
¶ 'Tropical Rose' LHil
'Verdi' CBrk LHil
warscewiczii CBrk SLMG
'Wyoming' CBrk LAma LHil MWBu
'Yellow Humbert' LAma LHil

CANTUA (Polemoniaceae)

buxifolia CB&S CFee CGre CPle CTro SHil SIgm

CAPPARIS (Capparaceae)

See Plant Deletions

CAPSICUM (Solanaceae)

annuum MBri
*– 'Janne' MBri

CARAGANA (Leguminosae/Papilionaceae)

arborescens CChu CPle ENot MBar SPer WDin WFro WStI WTyr
– 'Lorbergii' **AGM** CDoC CLnd CSco IOrc MBlu MPla MUlv NWyt SHil SPer WDin
– 'Pendula' CLnd CSco EBre ELan EMil GRei LBre MBar MBlu MUlv NBee SEng SPer WDin WStI
– 'Walker' CB&S CDoC COtt CPMA EBre EMil IOrc LBre MBlu MBri MGos MUlv NBar SMad SPer WStI
brevispina CPle GAul
franchetiana CLnd
frutex 'Globosa' SPer
¶ *jubata* MBlu

CARDAMINE (Cruciferae/Brassicaceae)

alba WEas
asarifolia hort. See PACHYPHRAGMA *macrophyllum*
asarifolia Linnaeus CRow WCru
bulbifera CHan CRDP CTom EMon
enneaphyllos ECha NGar
§ *heptaphylla* ELan EPar IBlr WHoo
§ *kitaibelii* EPar WCot
latifolia Vahl See C. *raphanifolia*
microphylla SWas
§ *pentaphyllos* CGle CRDP CWGN ECha ELan EPar EPla GAbr GArf GGar MRav NGar NSti SIgm WSHC
pratensis CArn CKin CRow CWGN ECWi EWFC MHew NDea NMir WCla WHer WOak
– 'Edith' (d) CGle CMil CRow EMon GBuc LRHS WCot WRus
– 'Flore Pleno' **AGM** CBre CChu CElw CFee CGle CLew CNic CRow CWGN ECha ELan EMon GArf LRHS MSta MTho NBro NNrd NSti SBla SUsu WByw WCla WEas WHoo WOMN WRus
– 'Improperly Dressed' EMon
– 'William' (d) CGle EMon GBuc LRHS WHal
quinquefolia CGle NCat SWas
§ *raphanifolia* CBre CGle CLew CRow CWGN ECha EMon GAbr GCal GGar NCat NVic WSun
trifolia CBos CCla CGle CRDP CWGN ECha EPar EPla GCal LGan MBar MHig NBro NGar NHol NKay NNor NRya NTow SBla SUsu WBon WByw WCru WEas WHal WHer WHil
*– *digitata* MTho
waldsteinii SWas WHal

CARDIOCRINUM (Liliaceae/Liliaceae)

cordatum EBul
– var. *glehnii* EBul
giganteum **AGM** CB&S CBot CBro CHEx CRDP EBul EPar EPla GGGa IBlr LAma MBal MBlu MSto NRog WChr WCru
– var. *yunnanense* CRDP EBul EPla GGGa

CARDIOSPERMUM (Sapindaceae)

grandiflorum CPle

CARDUNCELLUS (Compositae/Asteraceae)

rhaponticoïdes EPot

CARDUUS (Compositae/Asteraceae)

benedictus See CNICUS *b.*
nutans WPla

CAREX (Cyperaceae)

¶ *acutiformis* ECWi
albida CElw EGle EHoe EMon EPla ETPC MBal
¶ *arenaria* ECWi
atrata ECoo EHoe EMon EPla ETPC LHil SIng WPla
aurea ETPC
¶ *baccans* GCal
berggrenii CGle CMil CRDP CRow ECou EFou EHoe EMon EPar ESis GCHN LHil MNFA NCat NHar NHol NMir NNrd NSti NWyt WHil WPbr WPer
boottiana GGar
brunnea 'Variegata' GGar SCob WCot
buchananii Widely available
– 'Viridis' CB&S CBow EGol ELan EPla ETPC SPla WHer WPbr
caryophyllea 'The Beatles' EHoe ETPC GCal
comans CLew ECoo EFol EGol EHoe ELan EMon EPar EPla GCHN GCal GGar IBlr LHil MBal NBro NRya SIng SMrm WHal
– bronze Widely available

§ ***conica***	EFol LHil LHop MBri SIng WPbr
– 'Hime-kan-suge'	See C. ***c.*** 'Snowline'
§ – 'Snowline' (v)	Widely available
¶ ***crinata***	ETPC
crus-corvi	ETPC
dallii	ECou
demissa	EHoe EPla
depauperata	EMon EPla ETPC
digitata	WWye
dipsacea	CElw CRow ECou EHoe EMon EOrc EPla ETPC GCal NHar NHed NWCA SFar WHal WWye
§ ***elata*** 'Aurea' AGM	Widely available
¶ – 'Knightshayes' (v)	EMon WCot
firma	MHig NNrd
– 'Variegata'	CLew CRiv EHoe EPar MCas MDHE MTho NHar NMen NTow NWCA SGil SIng WRus
flagellifera	CB&S CHad CMHG CRow ECoo ECou EGol EHoe EMon EPar EPla ESiP ESma ETPC GGar LGan MFir NHol NWCA SHer SUsu WEas WPbr
flava	ETPC
forsteri	See C. ***pseudocyperus***
fortunei 'Variegata'	See C. ***morrowii*** 'V.'
'Frosted Curls'	Widely available
¶ ***fuscula***	ETPC
grayi	CHan EHoe EMon EPla ETPC GCal MTho
hachijoensis	EPla
– 'Evergold' AGM	Widely available
N 'Hime-kan-suge'	See C. ***conica***
hirta	CKin
hispida	ETPC
humilis 'Hexe'	ETPC
kaloïdes	ECou EHoe EPla LGan
macloviana	ETPC
morrowii Boott	EBre EOrc IBlr LBre MDHE NSti SPer
– 'Fisher's Form' (v)	CBow CBrd CFil CHan EFol EFou EGol EHoe EOrc EPla ESma ETPC GCHN LHil LHop MBri MUlv NHar SHer SMad WCot
*– 'Nana Variegata'	NBir
N– 'Variegata'	CElw CFil CGle CHan CMHG CRiv CRow EFol EHoe ELan ELun EMon EPla ETPC MBal MBar NEgg NHed NMir NNor SApp SCob SLon SPer WWat
morrowii hort.	See CC. ***oshimensis, hachijoensis***
muricata	CKin
muskingumensis	CB&S ECoo EFol EHoe EMon EPla ETPC GAbr LHil MBri NFai NSti SApp SDix SMad WPbr WWye
– 'Small Red'	CB&S
– 'Wachtposten'	EGle ETPC GCal MFir
nigra	CKin EHon ETPC GAbr
– ssp. ***tornata***	SIng
ornithopoda	CLew EPot LGan
– ***aurea***	See C. ***o.*** 'Variegata'
§ – 'Variegata'	CNic CRiv EBre ECoo ECtt EGol EHoe EMar EPar EPla ESiP ETPC EWri GCHN GCal LBre LHil MBal MCas NHar NHol NMir SCob SFar SPla SSmi WRus WWat WWye
oshimensis	IBlr
– 'Evergold'	See C. ***hachijoensis*** 'E.'
– 'Variegata'	CElw
otrubae	ETPC
pallescens	WWye
– 'Wood's Edge' (v)	CNat
panicea	ECWi ETPC
pendula	Widely available
¶ – 'Moonraker'	CBot
petriei	CBow CElw CNic CTom EBar ECha ECoo EGol EMon EPla ETPC GAbr GAri MHlr NHed NNrd NSti NVic SApp SFar
pilulifera 'Tinney's Princess' (v)	CFil EHoe EPot IBlr
plantaginea	CHan EHoe EMar EMon EPla ETPC
§ ***pseudocyperus***	CKin EHoe ETPC GCHN MSta SRms SWyc WWye
remota	WWye
riparia	EMFW
– 'Variegata'	CBen CGle CHan CMGP CRDP CRiv CRow CWGN EBre ECha EFol EHoe EHon EMFW EMon EPar EPla ESiP ETPC GCHN GCal LBre MBri MUlv NBro NFai SCro WAbb WByw
secta	EHoe ETPC NHol
– var. ***tenuiculmis***	EHoe ETPC
siderosticha	EPot GAri SMad WSHC
– 'Variegata'	Widely available
spicata	CKin
sp. ex Uganda	EPla GCal
stricta Goodenough	See C. ***elata***
– 'Bowles' Golden'	See C. ***elata*** 'Aurea'
¶ ***stricta*** Lamarck	ETPC
sylvatica	CKin ECWi ESiP WWye
testacea	CB&S CBow CMer ECoo ECou EFol EGol EHoe ELan ELun EMar EMon EPla ESiP ETPC LHil MBri NSti SFar WDav WPbr WStI WWye
trifida	CTom EFol EHoe EPla ETPC GAbr GCHN GCal NCat NMir SIng WHaw
uncifolia	ECou EHoe
vulpina	CKin ETPC

CARICA (Caricaceae)

chrysopetala	CTro

CARISSA (Apocynaceae)

bispinosa	SLMG
grandiflora	See C. ***macrocarpa***
F ***macrocarpa***	CNew CTro ERea

CARLINA (Compositae/Asteraceae)

acanthifolia	GCal SMad
acaulis	ECro ELan GLil MArl NBro NSti SFis SGil SHer WEas WPer
– bronze	LGre
– ***caulescens***	See C. ***a. simplex***
§ – ssp. ***simplex***	CDec EBee ECha ECro GBuc GCal MBri NHol NRar NRoo WHoo WPer
vulgaris	CKin WPer
¶ – 'Silver Star'	GCal

CARMICHAELIA
(Leguminosae/Papilionaceae)

aligera ECou
angustata ECou
¶ *appressa* ECou
§ *arborea* MAll WBod
arenaria ECou
astonii ECou
australis See C. ***arborea***
¶ *cunninghamii* ECou
curta ECou
enysii ITim
– var. *ambigua* ECou
– 'Pringle' ECou
exsul ECou
¶ *flagelliformis* ECou
glabrata CPle ECou NNor
kirkii ECou
– hybrid SIgm
– x *astonii* ECou
monroi ECou MAll MHig NHed
nigrans ECou
odorata ECou MAll
orbiculata ECou MAll
ovata ECou
¶ 'Parson's Tiny' ECou MAll
petriei ECou MAll
¶ *rivulata* ECou
¶ *robusta* ECou
¶ *solandri* ECou
¶ *suteri* ECou
uniflora ECou
violacea ECou
williamsii ECou

X CARMISPARTIUM
(Leguminosae/Papilionaceae)

astens See X C. ***hutchinsii***
§ *hutchinsii* ECou
– 'County Park' ECou MAll

CARPENTERIA (Hydrangeaceae)

californica AGM Widely available
– 'Bodnant' SHil
– 'Ladhams' Variety' CB&S LGre NWyt SHer

CARPINUS † (Corylaceae)

betulus AGM CB&S CBra CDoC CKin CLnd CPer EBre ELan ENot GRei IHos IJoh LBre LBuc LPan MBar MBri NBee NWea SPer SReu STre WDin WMou WNor WStI
– 'Columnaris' CLnd CTho ENot
§ – 'Fastigiata' AGM CDoC CLnd CSco CTho EBre ENot GRei IJoh IOrc LBre LPan MBar MBlu MGos NBee NWea SPer WDin WMou
– 'Frans Fontaine' CTho MBri SHil WMou
– 'Incisa' GAri LPan
– 'Pendula' CTho EBre GAri LBre WMou
– 'Purpurea' ENot MBlu
– 'Pyramidalis' See C. ***b.*** 'Fastigiata'
– 'Quercifolia' WMou
– 'Variegata' WMou
caroliniana CLnd CMCN GAri SHil WMou WNor
coreana WNor
fargesii See C. ***laxiflora macrostachya***
japonica GAri WCoo WMou
laxiflora CMCN ELan ISea WMou WNor
orientalis CMCN EArb EHal GAri WNor
x *schuschaensis* ELan
turczaninowii WNor

CARPOBROTUS (Aizoaceae)

§ *edulis* CHEx IBlr SLMG SMad WEas WHer

CARPODETUS (Escalloniaceae)

serratus CPle

CARTHAMUS (Compositae/Asteraceae)

tinctorius MChe MSal SIde

CARUM (Umbelliferae/Apiaceae)

carvi CArn CSFH EHer Effi GPoy IEde LHol MChe MHew SHer SIde WOak WPer WWye
petroselinum See PETROSELINUM ***crispum***

CARYA † (Juglandaceae)

cordiformis AGM CMCN EHar WCoo WWes
glabra CMCN WCoo
N *illinoinensis* CMCN EArb EHar
laciniosa CMCN
myristiciformis CMCN
ovata AGM CMCN EHar ESim MBrk SHil WCoo WWes
tomentosa CMCN

CARYOPTERIS † (Verbenaceae)

x *clandonensis* Widely available
– 'Arthur Simmonds' CDoC CSco ECha EGol EHal MBal MBri SFis SLon SPer SPla
– 'Ferndown' CArn CBow CDoC CSco EBre EGol ELan EMil LBre LHop NKay SPer SPla SReu SWas WDin WSHC WWeb
– 'Heavenly Blue' AGM CB&S CBra CSco CShe CTre EBre ECha EHoe ELan EMil ENot ERav IJoh LBre MBar MBri MGos MWat NKay NRoo NWyt SLon SMad SPer SPla SReu SSta WDin WHCG WRus
– 'Kew Blue' CB&S CBot CBow CBra CCla CDoC CLTr CShe CTre EBre EFou EGol ELan EMil ENot LAbb LBre LGre MGos SHBN SHer SPer SPla SSta WRus WSHC WWat WWeb WWye
– 'Worcester Gold' Widely available
§ *incana* CBow CDoC CPle CSco CShe ERav ISea LHop MSte SDry SFis SPer SPla WSHC
– weeping form GCal
♦ *mastacanthus* See C. ***incana***
odorata CPle

CARYOTA (Palmae/Arecaceae)

mitis CTro LPal

CASSANDRA See CHAMAEDAPHNE

CASSIA (Leguminosae/Caesalpiniaceae)

–	See also SENNA

CASSINIA (Compositae/Asteraceae)

leptophylla	CPle SPer WThu
– ssp. *fulvida*	CB&S CMHG CPle ECou EHoe EPla ESis IBar IOrc ISea MBar MBlu MPla MRav NNor NTow NWyt SBor SHil SPer STre WBod WDin WStI
– ssp. *vauvilliersii*	CKni CMHG NNor WSHC
– – var. *albida*	CB&S MAll SHil SPer WAbe WBod
N *retorta*	ECou IBar MAll NNor
'Ward Silver'	CBot ECou ESis EWes LGre MAll NNor

CASSINIA X HELICHRYSUM (Compositae/Asteraceae)

–	WKif

CASSIOPE † (Ericaceae)

'Askival'	ITim
'Badenoch'	CNic ESis GDra GGGa GWht MBal NHar
'Bearsden'	GAri GDra GGGa GWht MBal NHar NKay WPat WThu
'Edinburgh' AGM	CMHG EPot GAbr GDra GGGa GWht MBal MBar MBri NHar NHol SEng WAbe WDin WPat WThu
fastigiata	GGGa NHar
– B 542	MBal
– LS&H 17451	MBal
'George Taylor'	GArf WAbe WThu
'Inverleith'	WThu
'Kathleen Dryden'	GDra MBal
lycopodioïdes AGM	ESis GAbr GDra GGGa GWht MBal MBar MBri MGos NHar NHol NKay SIng SReu WAbe WThu
– 'Beatrice Lilley'	CRiv EPot GAri GGGa MBal MBar MHig NHar NHol WAbe WPat
– var. *globularis*	GArf GGGa
– *minima*	GArf
– 'Rokujo'	NHol
'Medusa'	EPot GDra GGGa MAsh MBal MHig SIng WPat WThu
mertensiana	CRiv ESis GGGa GWht MBal MBar NMen WAbe WThu
– *californica*	GArf
– dwarf form	MBal
– ssp. *gracilis*	CMHG CNic ELan GAbr GGGa MGos MHig NHar NHol
'Muirhead' AGM	EPot GDra GGGa GWht MBal MBar MHig NHar NHol NKay SHer SIng WAbe WDin WPat WThu
'Randle Cooke' AGM	ESis GDra GGGa MBal MBar MBri MHig NHar NKay WPat WThu
selaginoïdes	NHol
– LS&E 13284	GArf GAri GGGa
stelleriana	GArf SSta
tetragona	MAsh MBal MBar MBri NHol SRms
– var. *saximontana*	EPot GGGa MBal NHol

CASTANEA † (Fagaceae)

mollissima	EArb GAri ISea
sativa AGM	CB&S CBra CDoC CHEx CKin CLnd CPer ENot GRei IJoh IOrc ISea LBuc MBar MBri MWat NBee NRog NWea SHBN SKee SPer WDin WMou WStI WWes
§ – 'Albomarginata'	CDoC CSco EBre EHar LBre MBlu MBri MGos NBee SHil SMad SSta WWes
– 'Argenteovariegata'	See C. *s*. 'Albomarginata'
– 'Aureomarginata'	See C. *s*. 'Variegata'
F – 'Marron de Lyon'	ESim MBlu
§ – 'Variegata'	CB&S COtt ELan IMal SPer
– 'Vincent van Gogh'	SMad

CASTANOPSIS (Fagaceae)

cuspidata	SArc WCoo

CASUARINA (Casuarinaceae)

cunninghamiana	CGre ISea
equisetifolia	CGre CTro
¶ *glauca*	CGre
¶ *littoralis*	CGre
muelleriana	CGre
stricta	See ALLOCASUARINA *verticillata*

CATALPA † (Bignoniaceae)

bignonioïdes AGM	CB&S CBot CBow CBra CDoC CGre CHEx CLnd CSco ELan ENot IOrc ISea LPan MBri MWat NPal SPer WBod WCoo WDin
– 'Aurea' AGM	Widely available
– 'Purpurea'	See C. x *erubescens* 'P.'
– 'Variegata'	CWit LNet SPer SSta WPat
bungei	LPan SEng
– 'Purpurea'	ELan LPan
x *erubescens* 'Purpurea' AGM	CB&S CBot CBow CDoC CHEx CLnd EArb EBre EHar EMil IOrc LBre MBlu MBri SHBN SHil SMad SPer WPat
fargesii	CLnd
– f. *duclouxii*	EArb
ovata	CBot CGre CHEx EArb EHar NWyt WCoo
speciosa	CB&S CHEx CMCN EArb EHar WCoo WMou

CATANANCHE (Compositae/Asteraceae)

caerulea	CBow CDoC CMea CSco CSev EBre ECha EFol EFou LBre LHop MBri MBro MRav NBro NMir NRoo SChu SPer SSvw SUsu WHal WOld WPer WTyr WWin
– 'Alba'	CCla CGle CPou CSev ECha EFou EMar GCal LHop MUlv NBir NOak SAxl SChu SHer SPer SUsu WHal WRus WSun WTyr
– 'Bicolor'	EMon LCot SMad WElm
– 'Major' AGM	CShe ENot GCal MBri MWat SRms WEas

CATAPODIUM (Gramineae/Poaceae)

§ *rigidum*	ETPC

CATHARANTHUS (Apocynaceae)

roseus AGM MBri
– ***ocellatus*** MBri

CAULOPHYLLUM (Berberidaceae)

thalictroïdes MSal

CAUTLEYA (Zingiberaceae)

spicata CHEx IBlr
– 'Robusta' CAvo CCla CKni CRDP

CAYRATIA (Vitaceae)

See Plant Deletions

CEANOTHUS † (Rhamnaceae)

'A T Johnson' CMHG CMac CPle ENot EWri LNet NFai NKay SHBN SPer SPla SReu WAbe WBod WHCG WTyr WWeb
americanus CArn CMHG CPle MSal WWye
– 'Fincham' EPla
arboreus CGre SArc
– 'Trewithen Blue' AGM CB&S CChe CCla CGre CLan CMHG CMac CPle CSco CTre CTrw ELan IBar IDai IOrc ISea LHop LNet MRav NKay NSti SHer SLon SPer SReu WAbe WBod WSHC WStI WWat
'Autumnal Blue' AGM CB&S CCla CLTr CMHG CMac CPle CSco CShe EGol ELan ENot IDai IJoh MBri MGos MWat NFai NKay SHBN SHer SLon SPer SReu SSta WDin WEas WWat WWin
azureus See C. ***coeruleus***
'Basil Fox' EPla
*'Blue Cushion' CB&S CLan ECtt EHic ESis ESma LBuc LHop MGos MWat NWyt WAbe
'Blue Jeans' CAbP
'Blue Mound' AGM CDoC CGre CLTr CLan CPle CSco CShe CTre CTrw EBre EGol ERav ESma IBar IJoh LAbb LBre LHop MGos MRav NHol NNor NWyt SHer SPer SPla SReu WSHC WWat
'Burkwoodii' AGM CB&S CBra CDoC CGre CMac CPle CSco EBre GRei IDai IOrc LBre MBal MBri MPit NWea SHBN SLon SPer SReu
'Burtonensis' CGre CLan ENot
'Cascade' AGM CB&S CBra CDoC CLan CMHG CMac CSam CSco CShe ELan ENot IOrc ISea LAbb LNet MBri MWat NSti NWyt SHer SLon SPer SSta WAbe WBod WHCG WSHC WStI
§ ***coeruleus*** WBod
'Concha' CAbP CAbb CB&S CLTr CMHG CPle CSam CSco CTbh CTre EGol ELan ERav ESma IDai ISea LHop MBri MPla MUlv NWyt SHer SMad SPer SPla SReu SSta WEas WWat
cyaneus CGre CPle
'Cynthia Postan' CCla
'Dark Star' CBow CTbh EWll LRHS
'Delight' AGM EPla IDai IOrc LAbb NBrk NNor SChu SPer WAbe WBod WWat
x ***delileanus*** 'Gloire de Versailles' AGM Widely available
– 'Henri Desfossé' CPle CSco ELan SPer WDin WKif WStI
– 'Topaze' AGM CDoC CPle CSco CShe ENot NSti SLon
dentatus var. ***floribundus*** CSco ELan SDix
*– 'Prostratus' MBal
dentatus hort. See C. x ***lobbianus***
dentatus Torrey & A Gray CB&S CBra CMHG CMac CPle CSam CSco EBre EGol ELan ENot GRei IJoh IOrc LBre MBal MGos NKay NNor SChu SLon SPer WBod
depressus CPle
'Dignity' CGre CLan CSco WWeb
divergens CMac CPle MAll SPer WBod
'Edinburgh' AGM CMHG CMac ENot MArl MBri NBrk SGil SHer SPla WBod WKif WWeb
'Edward Stevens' CGre
¶ 'Eleanor Taylor' LRHS
fendleri CGre
foliosus CGre CPle
– ***austromontanus*** CB&S CLTr CLan CPle CTrw IDai
'Frosty Blue' MSta
gloriosus CCla CDoC CPMA CPle IOrc LHop MAll SDry WSHC WWat
¶ – 'Anchor Bay' CPle ELan
– 'Emily Brown' CB&S IJoh
griseus var. ***horizontalis*** SDry
– – 'Hurricane Point' CB&S
– – 'Yankee Point' CB&S CChe CMHG CMac CPle CSPN CSam CSco ECtt ERav LHop LNet MAsh MBel MBri MPit NFai SHBN SHer SLon SPer WWeb
¶ 'Hearstiorum' CPle
impressus CB&S CCla CDoC CGre CLan CMHG CPle CSco CShe ELan ENot IJoh MBal MBri MRav MWat SHer SLon SPer SPla SReu WAbe WBod WEas
integerrimus macrothyrsus CPle
N 'Italian Skies' AGM CDoC CGre CLan CMHG CMac CSam CSco EHal ELan ESma GMac LHop MBri MRav NWyt SHer SPla WBod WWeb
'Joyce Coulter' CB&S LRHS
'Julia Phelps' CMHG WEas
'Ken Taylor' CRos LRHS
x ***lobbianus*** CGre EBee NBee
– 'Russellianus' SHBN SLon WBod
'Mary Lake' CGre
x ***mendocinensis*** CPle
oliganthus CPle
x ***pallidus*** 'Marie Simon' CB&S CBot CPle CSco ELan ERav IJoh LHop MBri MRav NNor SHer SLon SPer WAbe WKif WSHC
– 'Perle Rose' CB&S CBot CChe CDoC CMac CPle EHal IOrc NWyt SGil SHBN SHer SPer SPla WAbe WKif
papillosus CBra CGre CLan CMac CPle ECtt
– var. ***roweanus*** CGre CMac CPle GAri LRHS SDry SHil WWat
– x ***thyrsiflorus*** CPle
'Percy Picton' CGre
'Pin Cushion' LRHS

'Point Millerton' LRHS
prostratus CDoC EPla IDai LGro MAsh SDry SHBN SHil WAbe WEas WWin
'Puget Blue' AGM CB&S CBra CCla CHad CLan CMHG CMac CPMA CPle CSam CSco CTbh EBre ELan LBre LHop MBri MGos MPla MWat NTow SDix SGil SHer SPer SSta WBod WKif WSHC
purpureus CGre CHan CPle EHic LBuc MAll SDry SGil WWeb
'Ray Hartman' CCla SMad
x ***regius*** LHop
repens See C. ***thyrsiflorus r.***
rigidus CBow CPle EBee MGos SDry SPla SRms WAbe WBod
'Sierra Blue' WBod
'Snow Flurries' CB&S CBow CMHG CPle CTre EHic ERav MSta SLon
sorediatus CPle
'Southmead' AGM CMac EBee IJoh IOrc ISea MBri WBod WWat
spinosus CPle
thyrsiflorus CB&S CMac CPle ELan IJoh LNet MBal MBri NBrk NFai NHol SArc SHBN WBod WDin
¶ – 'Millerton Point' CPle
§ – var. ***repens*** AGM Widely available
– 'Skylark' CPle CRos CTbh ELan LHop LRHS SReu
x ***veitchianus*** CB&S CBra CMac CSam CSco CShe EBre ELan ENot EWri LBre LNet MBar MWat NHol NPer SLon SPer WBod WTyr
verrucosus CPle
'White Cascade' EHic ELan LRHS MAll MSta NWyt

CEDRELA (Meliaceae)

sinensis See TOONA ***s.***

CEDRONELLA (Labiatae/Lamiaceae)

§ ***canariensis*** CArn CChu CGle CMer CSFH CSev CTre GCal GPoy IBlr ILis LBlm LHol MHew MSal SHer SIde SWat WHer WOMN WOak WPer WWye
mexicana See AGASTACHE ***m.***
triphylla See C. ***canariensis***

CEDRUS (Pinaceae)

atlantica See C. ***libani a.***
brevifolia See C. ***libani brevifolia***
deodara CBra CDoC CMac CSco EHar EHul ENHC ENot GRei IBar IDai IOrc ISea LBee LCon MBal MBar MBri MGos NWea SHBN SLim SLon SPer SReu STre WDin WMou WThu WWat
– 'Albospica' (v) LCon MAsh MBri
– 'Argentea' MBar MGos
– 'Aurea' AGM CBra CDoC CGre CSco EHar EHul IJoh LBee LCon LPan MAsh MBar MBri SEng SLim SPer SReu SSta WAbe WDin WFro WMou
I – 'Aurea Pendula' ENHC
– 'Blue Dwarf' CKen LCon
– 'Blue Triumph' LPan
– 'Cream Puff' EBre LBre LCon LLin MBri MGos
¶ – 'Deep Cove' MAsh
– 'Feelin' Blue' CDoC CKen COtt EBre LBee LBre LCon LLin LPan LRHS MAsh MBar MBri MGos MRPP NBar NHol SLim SPer
– 'Gold Cone' MGos
– 'Gold Mound' CKen GAri LCon MBri MPla
– 'Golden Horizon' CBra CDoC CGre CKen CMac CSco EBre EHar EHul ENHC IJoh IOrc LBee LBre LCon LLin MAsh MBar MBri MGos NBee NHol SHBN SLim SPer SSta WDin
– 'Karl Fuchs' EBre LBre LCon LRHS MAsh MBri WGor
– 'Kashmir' LCon MBri
– 'Klondyke' MAsh
– 'Lime Glow' CKen
*– 'MacPenny's Seedling' CMac
I – 'Nana Aurea' LCon
– 'Nivea' CKen
– 'Pendula' CMac EHul LPan MBar MBri MGos MWat SEng WGor WStI
– 'Pygmy' CKen
– 'Robusta' LCon
¶ – 'Roman Candle' SHBN
– 'Scott' CKen
– 'Verticillata Glauca' CDoC MBri SEng
§ ***libani*** ssp. ***atlantica*** CDoC CGre EHar EHul GAri ISea LCon MBar NWea SLim WDin WMou WWat
– – 'Aurea' CDoC CMac CSco EHar IBar LBee LCon LLin LPan MAsh MBar MBri MGos SHil SSta WDin
– – 'Fastigiata' CDoC CMac EHar EHul LCon LPan MBar MBri SLim WMou
I – – 'Glauca Fastigiata' CKen EHar LCon MBri SMad
– – Glauca Group AGM Widely available
– – 'Glauca Pendula' CBow CDoC CKen CSco EHar EHul IOrc LCon LNet LPan MBar MBri MGos SEng SHil SLim SMad SPer SSta WAbe WWes
– – 'Pendula' CMac EHar GAri NBee
§ – ssp. ***brevifolia*** AGM EHar ELan GAri ISea LCon MBar MBlu SSta
– – 'Epstein' MBar
– – 'Hillier Compact' CKen
– – 'Kenwith' CKen
– ssp. ***libani*** AGM CBow CBra CDoC CMac CSco EHar EHul ENot IJoh IOrc LCon MBar MBri NWea SHBN SPer STre WDin WFro WMou WNor WWat
– – 'Comte de Dijon' EHul LLin SHil SLim
– – 'De Creffe' CDoC
– – Nana Group CKen LCon MAsh SEng
– – 'Sargentii' CDoC CKen CMac CSco EHar EHul LCon LLin MAsh MBal MBar MBri MGos NHar SHil SLim SSta
– – 'Taurus' MBar

CELASTRUS (Celastraceae)

loeseneri (f) SBra
– (m) SBra
orbiculatus CB&S CBra CCla CHan CMCN CRHN CSco ELan EMil EMon GPlt MPla MRav NWyt SPer SReu SSta WBod WSHC

– 'Diana' (f)	EHic SSta
– hermaphrodite form AGM	CSam ELan EPla NHol SBra SDix SHil WWat
scandens	CMac ELan EOvi MSal
– (f)	SBra
– (m)	SBra

CELMISIA † (Compositae/Asteraceae)

alpina	WCru
¶ ***angustifolia***	EPot
argentea	EPot GArf GCHN GTou MHig NHar NHed
bellidioïdes	CRiv EMNN GArf GDra ITim NHar NHol NMen NNrd NRed WAbe WDav
brevifolia	IBlr
coriacea	GCal GCra IBlr NHar NNor WEas
dallii	WAbe
densiflora	GDra
¶ ***discolor***	MHig
gracilenta	GArf MFir MHig WDav
hectorii	IBlr ITim MHig NHed
incana	IBlr
Inshriach hybrids	GAbr MBal NHar
Jury hybrids	GCal
longifolia	EPla EPot GDra
lyallii	CFee
ramulosa	GArf GTou IBlr ITim MHig NHar
semicordata	WAbe
sessiliflora	GArf GTou ITim
– 'Mount Potts'	GDra WDav
¶ ***spectabilis*** ssp. ***magnifica***	GCLN
*– ***major***	CFee
traversii	WAbe
§ ***walkeri***	IBlr IDai WAbe
webbiana	See C. ***walkeri***

CELOSIA (Amaranthaceae)

argentea var. ***cristata***	MBri
– – Plumosa Group	MBri

CELSIA See VERBASCUM

X CELSIOVERBASCUM See VERBASCUM

CELTIS (Ulmaceae)

¶ ***africana***	CGre
australis	CB&S EHal LPan
bungeana	CMCN
jessoensis	CMCN
laevigata	CMCN
occidentalis	CPle EHar ELan WCoo
– var. ***pumila***	CMCN
reticulata	WCoo
sinensis	CMCN WCoo

CENOLOPHIUM (Umbelliferae/Apiaceae)

¶ ***denudatum***	SIgm

CENTAUREA (Compositae/Asteraceae)

¶ ***argentea***	CBot
atropurpurea	EMon
bella	Widely available
benoistii	EMar EMon
'Blue Dreams'	EMon
cana	See C. ***triumfettii cana***
candidissima hort.	See C. ***cineraria cineraria***
candidissima Lamarck	See C. ***rutifolia***
cheiranthifolia	ECha
§ – var. ***purpurascens***	EMon
¶ ***chrysantha***	WDav
§ ***cineraria*** ssp. ***cineraria*** AGM	CBrk CSpe IDai LBlm WPer
cyanus	CSFH ECWi EWFC MHew
cynaroïdes	See LEUZEA ***centauroïdes***
dealbata	CBot CHad CHan CHol CTom EBar ECtt GAbr LGan LLWP LWad MFir NBro NCat NFai NKay NMir NOak NOrc NRoo SChu SCro SHer SSvw SUsu WByw WHil WHoo WPer WWin
– 'Steenbergii'	CDoC CGle CMGP CPou CRDP CSco EBre ECED ELan EPad GCal LBre MBel MBri NOak NSti SCro SPer WByw WCot WHer
debeauxii ssp. ***nemoralis***	CKin
¶ ***drabifolia***	MSto
fischeri	See C. ***cheiranthifolia purpurascens***
glastifolia	EMon GCal
gymnocarpa	See C. ***cineraria cineraria***
hypoleuca 'John Coutts'	Widely available
jacea	NBir
macrocephala	Widely available
montana	CBow CBre EFol ELan ESma EWFC GAbr IDai LBlm LGan MBro MFir NBro NNor NOak NOrc NRar NRoo NVic SSvw WByw WCra WEas WHal WHen WOak WOld WPer WStI WWin
– ***alba***	CBow CBre CElw CGle CSev CTom ECha ECoo EFol EGol ELan EMar EMon EOrc EPar LGre MBri MFir MSte NCat NRar SChu SFis SPer SPla WByw WEas WHal WMer
§ – ***carnea***	CBre CElw CTom ECha EMon WBon WHal WWin
– 'Grandiflora'	MBri
– 'Ochroleuca'	CElw EMon
– 'Parham'	CBre CMGP CPou EBee EMon LBlm MUlv SChu SFis SMrm SPer
– ***purpurea***	CTom
– ***rosea***	See C. ***m. carnea***
– 'Violetta'	NBir
nigra	CArn CKin ECWi EWFC MHew NLan NMir SHer WCla
– var. ***alba***	CArn
– 'Breakaway' (v)	EMon
orientalis	ECha EMon NBro WPer
parilica NS 699	NWCA
pulcherrima	CBot ECha EFol EGle EMon
'Pulchra Major'	CGle CPou EBre ECha EGle EGol ELan GCal LBre LGre MUlv WByw WOMN
ruthenica	ECha MSte
§ ***rutifolia***	EBar
salonitana	EMon

scabiosa CArn CKin CNat ECWi ECoo EHal EWFC MChe MHew MTol NLan NPri SFis SHer SIde WCla WGwy WPer
¶ – 'Nell Hill' CNat
simplicicaulis CMea CNic CRDP LGan MFir MRav MTho NRoo NRya SFis SWas WAbe WCla WEas WHil WHoo WOMN WPer
§ *triumfettii* ssp. *cana* 'Rosea' CNic ECha EFol EMon NNrd WHil WWin
– ssp. *stricta* CTom ECoo EMar EMon GBuc LHil SUsu WOMN
– – 'Macedonia' SFis
uniflora ssp. *nervosa* NBro NPri WPer
– ssp. *nervosa* JCA 287.000 CLew EMon

CENTAURIUM (Gentianaceae)

♦*chloodes* See C. ***confertum***
§ *confertum* NNrw
erythraea CArn ECWi EWFC GPoy MChe MHew MSal SIde WCla WWye
scilloïdes CNic CRiv CSam CShe ELan MBro MCas MPit MPla MTho NGre NHol NMen NNrd NRoo NTow NWCA SHer WCla WHoo WOMN WWin

CENTELLA (Umbelliferae/Apiaceae)

asiatica CArn

CENTRADENIA (Melastomataceae)

§ *inaequilateralis* CTro
– 'Cascade' CB&S CLTr ECtt ERea IHos LHil LHop MBri NFai SFis SHer
♦*rosea* See C. ***inaequilateralis***

CENTRANTHUS (Valerianaceae)

§ *ruber* CArn CBot CBow CKin CLTr CSFH CTom EBre ECWi ECtt EFol EFou GAbr GPlt GPoy LBre LWad MChe MHew NMir NPer NRoo NSti SHer SSvw WByw WDin WHen WStI WWye
§ – *albus* Widely available
– *atrococcineus* CSco ECha SPer WPer
– *coccineus* CCla CDoC CLTr CMGP EBee ELan GBri MWat NFai NPri SMrm WHil WTyr

CEPHALANTHUS (Rubiaceae)

occidentalis CCla CPMA CPle EBar EHic ELan EMil ERav MBlu MPla MSal SPer WPat

CEPHALARIA (Dipsacaceae)

§ *alpina* CElw CGle ECha EPot ESis GCHN MPit NGre NHed NNrw NPri NRoo NTow SHer SUsu WAbe WPer WWin
– 'Nana' CShe NWCA WPat
¶ *ambrosioïdes* NPri
§ *gigantea* Widely available
leucantha EBee ECro SIgm WHer WPla
¶ *radiata* EBee
tatarica See C. ***gigantea***

CEPHALOTAXUS (Cephalotaxaceae)

fortunei CGre
– 'Prostrate Spreader' CGre SHil SMad
harringtonia var. *drupacea* CChu LCon WWat
– 'Fastigiata' CB&S CChu CDoC CKen EHul MBar MBri SHil SLim SMad
– 'Gimborn's Pillow' MBar
– 'Nana' CMCN

CEPHALOTUS (Cephalotaceae)

follicularis MHel MSte WHal WMEx

CERASTIUM (Caryophyllaceae)

alpinum ELan SRms WThi
– var. *lanatum* CNic GAul GTou MHig NGre NNrd NTow NWCA SHer SSmi WDav WHil WPer
tomentosum CBow CHol CRiv ELan GBur LGro NNor NPri NRoo SIng SPer WPer
– var. *columnae* CRiv EBre ECha EHoe GAul GGar LBre MHlr SHer SRms
– 'Silberteppich' SFis

CERATONIA (Leguminosae/Caesalpiniaceae)

See Plant Deletions

CERATOPHYLLUM (Ceratophyllaceae)

demersum CBen CRow EHon EMFW NDea SAWi SWat SWyc WChe

CERATOSTIGMA † (Plumbaginaceae)

abyssinicum CB&S ELan ERav LBlm
griffithii Widely available
– SF 149/150 ISea
larpentae See C. ***plumbaginoïdes***
§ *plumbaginoïdes* AGM Widely available
ulicinum LHop
willmottianum AGM Widely available

CERATOTHECA (Pedaliaceae)

See Plant Deletions

CERCIDIPHYLLUM † (Cercidiphyllaceae)

japonicum AGM Widely available
– var. *magnificum* AGM CMCN EHar MBlu MBri MGos SEng
– f. *pendulum* CBow CCla CDoC CPMA CSco EHar ELan ESma MBlu MBri NBar SHil SPer WWes
– 'Rotfuchs' WMou
– 'Ruby' CPMA

CERCIS (Leguminosae/Caesalpiniaceae)

canadensis CBot EMil MGos SPer WWes
– 'Forest Pansy' AGM CAbP CB&S CBow COtt CPMA CSco EHar ELan EMil LHop LRHS MBlu MBri MGos MUlv SHil SMad SPer WPat WWes
chinensis CBow CChu CSam SPer
– f. *alba* ELan
– 'Avondale' CB&S CPMA LNet MBri
griffithii CMCN
racemosa SHil

siliquastrum AGM — Widely available
– f. *albida* — CBot CBow CChu CCla CDoC CGre CLnd CMCN CPMA EHar IOrc LAbb MBlu MSta SHil SPer WBod

CERCOCARPUS (Rosaceae)

breviflorus — See C. ***montanus paucidentatus***
montanus — CB&S

CERINTHE (Boraginaceae)

glabra — WCru

CEROPEGIA (Asclepiadaceae)

armandii — SGil
lanceolata — See C. ***longifolia***
linearis ssp. *woodii* AGM — IBlr MBri SLMG
§ *longifolia* — SLMG
radicans — SLMG
stapeliiformis AGM — SLMG

CEROXYLON (Palmae/Arecaceae)

alpinum — LPal
quindiuense — LPal
utile — LPal

CESTRUM (Solanaceae)

aurantiacum — CB&S CPle CTro ERea GCal IBlr SLMG
§ *elegans* AGM — CBot CPle CSev CTre CTro IBlr ISea LHil MAll SHil SLMG
fasciculatum — CB&S CGre CPle IBlr NRar SLMG
'Newellii' AGM — CAbb CB&S CHEx CHan CPle CSev CTro ELan ERea ERom IBlr ISea LAbb LHop MAll MBal SCog SHil SLMG WAbe WSHC
nocturnum — CB&S CPle CTro ELan ERea LBlm LHil SLMG
parqui AGM — CAbb CBot CChu CDec CDoC CGre CMHG CPle ECha EFou EPla ERea GCal IBlr LHil LHop NNrw SDix SUsu WBod WOld WSHC
¶ – 'Cretian Purple' — CPle
psittacinum — CGre CPle SLMG
purpureum — See C. ***elegans***
roseum 'Ilnacullin' — CB&S CGre CPle ERea IBlr
violaceum — CB&S LBlm

CETERACH See ASPLENIUM

CHAENACTIS (Compositae/Asteraceae)

See Plant Deletions

CHAENOMELES (Rosaceae)

x *californica* 'Enchantress' — CShe
cathayensis — CPou
– var. *wilsonii* — CPle CTho
§ *japonica* — CDoC ENot GRei IJoh LBuc MAsh MBal MBar MPla NNor NRoo SHer WDin WWeb
– f. *alba* — CShe
– var. *alpina* — CSco MPla
– 'Sargentii' — COtt CShe
lagenaria — See C. ***speciosa***
maulei — See C. ***japonica***
sinensis — See PSEUDOCYDONIA ***s.***
§ *speciosa* — CSam ISea MBal MBar NNor NWea WFro WNor
– 'Apple Blossom' — See C. ***s.*** 'Moerloosei'
– 'Aurora' — LRHS MBar MBri
– 'Cardinalis' — CGre
– 'Choshan' — See C. x ***superba*** 'Yaegaki'
– 'Falconnet Charlet' — CShe LBuc
– 'Geisha Girl' — CDoC CPMA CRDP CSco EBre ECtt EPla ESis ESma LBre MAsh MBri MPla MRav MUlv NHol NWyt SHBN SHer SPer SPla STre WWat WWeb
– 'Knap Hill Radiance' — CShe SHer
§ – 'Moerloosei' AGM — CBow CChu CCla CPMA CSam CSco CShe EGol EHar ELan GWht MBri MPla MRav NSti SHBN SIng SPer SPla WWat WWeb
– 'Nivalis' — CB&S CBot CBow CCla CShe CTrc EBre EGol EHar ELan ENot GRei IJoh IOrc LBre LHop MBar MBri MPla SChu SHBN SPer SPla SReu SSta WBod WDin WWat
– 'Phylis Moore' — CLan
* – 'Port Eliot' — CDoC CGre MBal MBrk SHer WBod WWeb
– 'Rosea Plena' — CShe
– 'Rosemoor Seedling' — GAri
– 'Rubra Grandiflora' — CShe
– 'Simonii' — CPMA CSco ENot LHop MBal MBri MGos MPla SHer SPer WBod WWat
– 'Snow' — CSam ISea MBal MWat SHer WBod WStI WWeb
– 'Tortuosa' — CPMA EHic WWat
– 'Umbilicata' — CDoC CSco ENot MBel SPer SRms
x *superba* 'Boule de Feu' — CBra CDoC ECtt SCob SHer
– 'Cameo' — CAbP CBot CBow CDec EHar MBri SLPl
– 'Coral Sea' — CSco CShe NNor
– 'Crimson and Gold' AGM — CBra CChe CCla CPMA CSco EBre EHar ELan ENot IJoh IOrc LBre LHop MBal MBar MBri MGos MRav MWat NBee NKay NRoo SHBN SLon SPer SReu WBod WDin WStI
– 'Elly Mossel' — CB&S CDoC CSco CShe
– 'Etna' — CB&S SPla
– 'Fire Dance' — EBre ECtt ENot LBre MAsh SCob SPer
– 'Hever Castle' — CPMA CShe WWat
– 'Hollandia' — CDoC CSco CShe MBel MGos NEgg WStI
– 'Issai White' — MBri MUlv
– 'Jet Trail' — CB&S CPMA CSco EBee EBre ELan ENot EPla LBre MBri SCob SLPl
– 'Knap Hill Scarlet' AGM — CBow CLan CSam CShe CTre ECot IOrc LAbb LHop SHBN SHer SPer SPla STre WBod WDin WStI WWat
– 'Lemon and Lime' — CCla CPMA CSco EBee EGol ELan ENot SPer

– 'Nicoline' **AGM**	CSco EHar ENot GRei MBri MWat SCob WStI
– 'Ohio Red'	SCob WBod
– 'Pink Lady' **AGM**	CB&S CBot CBra CSam CSco CShe EBre EGol ELan ENot GRei IDai IJoh LBre LHop MBal MBar MBri MGos MPla MWat NEgg NNor NSti SHBN SLon SPer SReu SSta
– 'Rowallane' **AGM**	CSco EBee ENot GAri IDai MBal MRav MWat SHBN SPer WAbe
– 'Texas Scarlet'	MBri
§ – 'Yaegaki'	CDoC CSco CShe SPer

CHAENORHINUM (Scrophulariaceae)

'Blue Pygmy'	SChu
glareosum	CNic MCas MHig WCla WPer
§ ***origanifolium***	EPot ESis MFir NWCA WWin
– 'Blue Dream'	WPer
§ – 'Blue Sceptre'	MCas

CHAEROPHYLLUM (Umbelliferae/Apiaceae)

hirsutum	CRow ELan NBrk
– roseum	CBot CBre CChu CHan CLew CRDP ECha ECoo EFol EMar EPla MFir MRav MUlv NRoo NSti SMrm SPer SUsu WByw WEas WHal WSHC

CHAETACANTHUS (Acanthaceae)

See Plant Deletions

CHAMAEBATIARIA (Rosaceae)

millefolium	GCal LGre WThu

CHAMAECYPARIS † (Cupressaceae)

formosensis	CKen
§ ***funebris***	CMCN ISea
lawsoniana	CTre EHar EHul GAri GRei GWht IDai ISea MBar NWea WDin WFro WMou
– 'Albospica' (v)	CBra CMac EBre EHul LBre MBal MBar MBri MRav MWat SBod
– 'Albospica Nana' (v)	See C. *l.* 'Nana Albospica'
– 'Albovariegata'	EHul GPlt IDai LBee MBar
– 'Albrechii'	ENot WGor
– 'Allumii Aurea'	See C. *l.* 'Alumigold'
I – 'Allumii Green'	ISea
– 'Allumii Magnificent'	CB&S MAsh NBee WWeb
§ – 'Alumigold'	CB&S CDoC CKen EHar ENHC LBee LCon MAsh MBal MBar MBri MGos MWat SBod SLim SPer WDin WStI WWeb
– 'Alumii'	CDoC CMac EHar EHul ENot GRei IDai LBuc MBal MBar MGos NWea SLim SPer WDin WStI
– 'Argentea'	See C. *l.* 'Argenteovariegata'
§ – 'Argenteovariegata'	CMac LCon NEgg SLim WThu
I – 'Aurea Compacta'	GPlt
– 'Aurea Densa' **AGM**	CKen CMac CSco EBar EHar EHul GAri LCon MAsh MBar MBri MGos SBod SHer SLon
– 'Aureovariegata'	EBre IJoh LBre MBal MBar NRoo SIng
§ – 'Barabits' Globe'	MBar MWat
– 'Bleu Nantais'	CBra CKen CMHG CMac CSco EHul ENHC EPla LBee LCon LLin LNet MAsh MBal MBar MBri MGos MPla MWat NBee SBod SHBN SLim SSmi SSta WDin
– 'Blom'	CKen EHul MBri SLim
– 'Blue Gem'	LBee NHol
§ – 'Blue Gown'	EHul GRei LBee MBar MGos MPla SPer SRms WWeb
§ – 'Blue Jacket'	CSco MBar
– 'Blue Nantais'	See C. *l.* 'Bleu Nantais'
– 'Blue Surprise'	CBra CKen CMHG EHul EPla GPen LBee LCon LLin MAsh MBal MBar MBri MPla
– 'Bowleri'	LCon
¶ – 'Bregeon'	CKen
– 'Broomhill Gold'	CBra CDoC CMac CSco EBre EHul ENot LBre LCon LNet MAsh MBal MBar MBri MGos MPla MRav MWat NHol SBod SLim SPer WDin
* – 'Burkwood's Blue'	MBar
– 'Caudata'	CKen MBar
– 'Chantry Gold'	CKen EHul LCon SLim
– 'Chilworth Silver' **AGM**	CBra CDoC CKen CMHG EBre ENHC EPot IJoh LBee LBre LLin MBar MBri MCas MGos MPla MWat NRoo SBod SHBN SIng SLim SLon SPer WDin WStI WThu WWeb
– 'Chingii'	CDoC
– 'Columnaris'	CB&S CBra CDoC CMac EBre EHar ENHC ENot GRei GWht IDai IHos IOrc LBee LBre MBal MBar MBri MGos MOke NBee NWea SHBN SLim
– 'Columnaris Aurea'	See C. *l.* 'Golden Spire'
N – 'Columnaris Glauca'	EBre EHul IJoh LBre LCon LPan MAsh MGos MPla MWat NRoo SBod SGil SPer WBod WDin WStI WWeb
I – 'Cream Crackers'	EHul
– 'Croftway'	EHul SRms
– 'Dik's Weeping'	MBri
– 'Drummondii'	EHul
– 'Duncanii'	EHul LCon MBal
– 'Dutch Gold'	EHul GAri MAsh
– 'Dwarf Blue'	See C. *l.* 'Pick's Dwarf Blue'
¶ – 'Eclipse'	CKen
N – 'Elegantissima'	CKen CMac SHil
– 'Elfin'	EPla
– 'Ellwoodii' **AGM**	Widely available
– 'Ellwood's Empire'	ISea MBri
– 'Ellwood's Gold' **AGM**	Widely available
¶ – 'Ellwood's Gold Pillar'	EPla
§ – 'Ellwood's Nymph'	CKen CLew EBre LBre LCon MAsh MBar MBri MRPP NHol SHBN
– 'Ellwood's Pillar'	CBra CDoC CKen CMac CSco EBre EHul ENHC EPot LBee LBre LCon LLin MAsh MBar MBri MGos MPla MWat NBee NHol SBod SLim SSmi WAbe WDin
– 'Ellwood's Pygmy'	CMac EPot MBar
– 'Ellwood's Silver'	CGre MAsh WGor
– 'Ellwood's Variegata'	See C. *l.* 'Ellwood's White'
§ – 'Ellwood's White' (v)	CKen CMac EHul MAsh MBal MBar MBri MWat SHBN SSmi WAbe

I – 'Emerald'	CKen MBar MBri NHol
– 'Emerald Spire'	CDoC CMac MAsh
– 'Erecta'	See C. *l.* 'Erecta Viridis'
– 'Erecta Argenteovariegata'	MPla
– 'Erecta Aurea'	CKen EHul LBee SBod
– 'Erecta Filiformis'	MBar
§ – 'Erecta Viridis'	CB&S CDoC CMac EHar GRei LCon MBal MBar MPla MRav MWat NEgg NWea SBod SLim SPer WDin WWeb
– 'Ericoides'	EHul
– 'Erika'	LCon MBar MWat
– 'Fantail'	MWat
– 'Filiformis Compacta'	EBar WGor
– 'Fleckellwood'	CKen EHul GPen LBee LLin MBar MGos MPla SBod SLim SPla WStI
– 'Fletcheri' **AGM**	CB&S CBra CMac CSco EHar EHul ENHC ENot IDai LBee LCon MAsh MBar MGos MPla MRav NBee NWea SBod SHBN SLim SLon SPer SPla WBod WDin WStI WThu
– 'Fletcheri Aurea'	See C. *l.* 'Yellow Transparent'
– 'Fletcher's White'	EHul MBar
– 'Forsteckensis'	CKen CMac CNic EBar EHul ENHC ESis ISea LCon LLin MBar MGos MWat NBee NWea SLim SLon SSmi
I – 'Forsteckensis Aurea'	LCon
– 'Fraseri'	CMac EHar ENHC LCon MBar NWea WDin
– 'Gail's Gold'	CKen
– 'Gilt Edge'	CKen
– 'Gimbornii' **AGM**	CDoC CMHG CMac CSco EBar EBre EHul ENHC LBee LBre LCon LLin MAsh MBar MBri MPla NBee SBod SLim SLon
– 'Glauca Spek'	See C. *l.* 'Spek'
– 'Globus'	See C. *l.* 'Barabits' Globe'
– 'Gnome'	CDoC CLew CMac CNic EBre EHul ENHC EPot GAri LBre LCon MBal MBar MGos MPla NHar NHol SBod SHer SLim SPer
– 'Gold Flake'	MBar
– 'Gold Splash'	CKen MBar
¶ – 'Golden Guinea'	WGor
– 'Golden King'	MBar SRms
§ – 'Golden Pot'	CDoC CKen CMac EHul EPla GPlt LBee LCon LLin MBar MBri MGos MOke MPla MWat NRoo SBod SLim SPer WAbe
§ – 'Golden Queen'	CKen CMHG EHul
– 'Golden Showers'	CKen EHul
§ – 'Golden Spire'	CB&S MBar MBri SBod
– 'Golden Triumph'	CB&S EHul
– 'Golden Wonder'	CDoC CMHG CMac EHul IDai IOrc LBee LBuc LCon LNet MBal MBar MBri MGos MRav WStI
– 'Goldfinger'	CDoC CKen NHol
– 'Goldgren'	SMad
– 'Grayswood Feather'	CDoC CKen CMac CSco EHul ESma LBee LCon MAsh MBar MGos MPla SLim SLon WWeb
– 'Grayswood Gold'	CDoC CKen EBee EHul LBee MBar MPla
– 'Grayswood Pillar' **AGM**	CKen CMac LBee LCon MBal MBar MGos SIng
– 'Green Globe'	CDoC CKen EBre EHul EPot LBee LBre LCon LLin MAsh MBar MBri MCas MPla MRPP NHar NHol SBod WAbe WDin
§ – 'Green Hedger' **AGM**	CMac CSco EHar EHul ENot GRei LBuc MBar SBod WAbe WStI
§ – 'Green Pillar'	CKen CSco GAri GWht IJoh IOrc LBee LPan MBal MBar MBri MGos MWat SHBN SReu WStI WWeb
– 'Green Spire'	See C. *l.* 'Green Pillar'
– 'Green Wall'	EHul
– 'Grey Cone'	CKen LBee
– 'Hillieri'	MBar
– 'Hogger's Blue Gown'	See C. *l.* 'Blue Gown'
*– 'Hogger's Gold'	CMHG EHul WGor
– 'Howarth's Gold'	GAri MBri
I – 'Imbricata Pendula'	CKen SMad
– 'Intertexta' **AGM**	CMHG EHar EHul ISea SMad
– 'Jackman's Green Hedger'	See C. *l.* 'Green Hedger'
– 'Jackman's Variety'	See C. *l.* 'Green Pillar'
– 'Kelleriis Gold'	EHar EHul LPan
– 'Kilbogget Gold'	ISea
– 'Killiney Gold'	CMac
– 'Kilmacurragh' **AGM**	CMac EHar ENHC ENot GRei IDai MBal MBar SLim SPer
– 'Knowefieldensis'	CMHG CMac IDai LLin WWeb
§ – 'Lane' **AGM**	CBra CDoC CGre CKen CMHG CMac EHar EHul ENot GRei LCon MAsh MBal MBar MGos MRav NWea SLon WStI WTyr
– 'Lanei'	See C. *l.* 'Lane'
– 'Lanei Aurea'	See C. *l.* 'Lane'
– 'Lemon Flame'	NHol
– 'Lemon Queen'	EHul LBee LCon NBee
– 'Limelight'	CKen EHul
– 'Little Spire'	CDoC CMHG EBre EPla LBee LBre LCon LLin MBar MBri MGos MPla NHar NHol SLim
– 'Lombartsii'	CDoC CMHG EHul LCon
– 'Lutea' **AGM**	CMac EHar EHul LCon MBal MGos SBod SPer
§ – 'Lutea Nana' **AGM**	CKen CMac EHul IBar IDai MBar
– 'Luteocompacta'	CKen EHar LBee SHBN
– 'Lycopodioides'	CMHG EHul EPla MBar SSmi WThu
*– 'MacPenny's Gold'	CMac
– 'Magnifica Aurea'	ENHC
– 'Milford Blue Jacket'	See C. *l.* 'Blue Jacket'
§ – 'Minima'	MBar SRms WAbe
– 'Minima Aurea' **AGM**	Widely available
I – 'Minima Densa'	See C. *l.* 'Minima'
– 'Minima Glauca' **AGM**	Widely available
– 'Moonlight'	MBar MGos MPla NHol
– 'Naberi'	EHar LPan SHil
– 'Nana'	CMac MBar
§ – 'Nana Albospica'	CKen EHul ENHC LBee LCon LLin MAsh MBal MBar MGos MPla NBar NBee SGil SLim SPla
– 'Nana Argentea'	CKen CMHG EHul SGil WGor
– 'Nana Lutea'	See C. *l.* 'Lutea Nana'
§ – 'Nana Rogersii'	MBar SRms
– 'Nidiformis'	EHul GWht LBee MBal MBar SLim SLon
– 'Nivea'	MBar
– 'Nyewoods'	See C. *l.* 'Chilworth Silver'
– 'Nymph'	See C. *l.* 'Ellwood's Nymph'

– 'Parsons'	IHos SLon WDin
§ – 'Pelt's Blue' AGM	CB&S CBra CKen EHar EHul LBee LCon LPan MGos NBee NHol SHBN SLim SLon
– 'Pembury Blue' AGM	CBra CDoC CKen CMHG CMac CSco EBre EHar EHul ENHC ENot IDai LBee LBre LCon MAsh MBar MBri MPla MWat NBee NHol NRoo SBod SHBN SLim SLon SPer SReu WDin
– 'Pendula'	MBar
– 'Pendula Vera'	CBra
– 'Pick's Dwarf Blue'	EHul LCon MBar MBri NHol
– Pot of Gold ®	See C. *l.* 'Gold Pot'
– 'Pottenii'	CDoC CMac CSco EHar EHul ENHC IJoh IOrc LBee LCon MAsh MBal MBar MGos MPla MWat NBee NWea SBod SHBN SPer SReu WBod WDin WStI
– 'Pygmaea Argentea' AGM	CKen CMac EBar EBre EHar EHul ENHC EPla ESis GPen IDai LBee LBre LCon LLin MAsh MBal MBar MBri MPla MWat NBee NHol SBod SLim SPer SPla WAbe WDin WThu
– 'Pygmy'	CNic EBee EHul ESis GAri LBee LCon MBar MPla SLim
– 'Pyramidalis Lutea'	CKen
I – 'Reid's Own Number One'	GRei
– 'Rijnhof'	GAri MBar
– 'Rogersii'	See C. *l.* 'Nana Rogersii'
I – 'Romana'	MBri
– 'Royal Gold'	EHul
– 'Silver Queen' (v)	CKen EHar GRei IDai MBal MBar NWea
– 'Silver Threads' (v)	CBra CKen CMac EBre EHar EHoe EHul ENot EPla GPen IJoh LBee LBre LCon LLin MAsh MBar MBri MCas MGos MPla MWat NHol SBod SGil SHer SLim SLon
– 'Silver Tip'	EHul SLim
I – 'Slocockiana'	EHul SHBN
N– 'Smithii'	CMHG EHul ISea LCon MBar
– 'Snow Flurry' (v)	CKen EHul LBee
– 'Snow White' (v)	CDoC EBre EHul EPla IJoh LBee LBre LCon LLin MAsh MBar MBri MGos MPla NHol SLim
– 'Somerset'	CMHG CMac CSco IDai LCon MBar SLon WWeb
§ – 'Spek'	CB&S
– 'Stardust' AGM	CDoC CKen CMHG CMac ENHC ENot ESis GRei GWht IHos IJoh IOrc LCon MAsh MBal MBar MBri MGos MPla MWat NRoo SBod SHBN SIng SLim SPer SReu WDin
– 'Stewartii'	CMac MBal MBar MGos MPla NBee NWea SBod SGil SHBN SPer WStI
– 'Stilton Cheese'	MBar
*– 'Summer Cream'	EHul
– 'Summer Snow'	CDoC CMHG CMac EHoe EHul ENot IJoh IOrc LBee LCon LLin MAsh MBal MBar MBri MGos MPla MRav SBod SLim SPla SReu WAbe WWeb
– 'Sunkist'	CKen EBre LBre LCon MAsh
– 'Tamariscifolia'	CDoC EBre EHul ENHC IDai LBre LCon MBal MBar NBee SBod WDin
– 'Temple's White'	CKen
– 'Tharandtensis Caesia'	LCon MBar SLon
– 'Tilford'	EHul
– 'Treasure'	CDoC CKen CNic CRiv EBre EHoe EHul EPla LBee LBre LCon LLin MAsh MBar MBri MGos NHol
– 'Triomf van Boskoop'	EHul MBar
– 'Van Pelt's Blue'	See C. *l.* 'Pelt's Bue'
– 'Versicolor' (v)	EHul MBar
– 'Westermannii'	CMac EHar EHul LCon MAsh MBal SBod SHil SLim SLon SPer
– 'White Spot' (v)	CDoC CKen EBre EHar EHul ENHC IDai ISea LBee LBre LCon MAsh MBal MBar MBri SLim WStI
– 'Winston Churchill'	CMHG EHar LCon MAsh MBar MGos MPla SBod SLim SPer
– 'Wisselii' AGM	CDoC CKen CMac EHar EHul ENHC ENot IDai LBee LCon MAsh MBar NWea SBod SIng SLon SPer WDin
– 'Wisselii Nana'	CKen
– 'Witzeliana'	MBar MGos NBee
– 'Wyevale Silver'	MBar WGor
♦– 'Yellow Queen'	See C. *l.* 'Golden Queen'
– 'Yellow Success'	See C. *l.* 'Golden Queen'
§ – 'Yellow Transparent'	CMac EHul LCon LPan MBar MGos MWat SBod SHBN SLim SPer WGor
– 'Yvonne'	MBar MBri NHol
leylandii	See X CUPRESSOCYPARIS ***leylandii***
nootkatensis	EHar MBar WDin
– 'Aureovariegata'	EHar EHul EPla SLim
– 'Compacta'	LCon MBar
– 'Glauca'	ENHC MBar
– 'Gracilis'	EHul
– 'Jubilee'	WMou
– 'Lutea'	CDoC CMHG CMac IDai LCon MBal MBar NWea SHil
– 'Nidifera'	MBar
– 'Pendula' AGM	CDoC CSco EFol EHar ENHC ENot IJoh IOrc LCon LNet MAsh MBal MBar MBri MBrk MGos NBee NWea SLim SMad SPer WDin WMou
– 'Variegata'	EHar LCon MBar SLim
obtusa 'Albospica'	EHul
– 'Albovariegata'	CKen
– 'Aurea'	CDoC
I – 'Aureovariegata'	See C. ***o.*** 'Opaal'
– 'Aurora'	CKen SHil
*– 'Autumn Gold'	MBar
– 'Bambi'	CKen
– 'Bartley'	CKen EPot
– 'Bassett'	CKen
¶ – 'Bess'	CKen
– 'Caespitosa'	CKen EPot
– 'Chabo-yadori'	CDoC CMHG EPot LCon LLin MBal MBar MGos NHar NHol SBod SHer SLim
– 'Chilworth'	CKen LCon MBar MBri MRPP
– 'Chima-anihiba'	See C. *l.* 'Pygmea Densa'
– 'Contorta'	EPot LCon MAsh MBar MBri
– 'Coralliformis'	LLin MBal MBar NHol SLim

§ – 'Crippsii' **AGM**	CB&S CKen CMac EBar EHar EHul ENot EPot IDai LCon MBal MBar MBri MGos MPla SBod SHil SLim
– 'Crippsii Aurea'	See C. ***o.*** 'Crippsii'
– 'Dainty Doll'	CKen
– 'Densa'	See C. ***o.*** 'Nana Densa'
¶ – 'Draht'	MBar
I – 'Ellie B'	CKen
– 'Ericoides'	CKen
– 'Erika'	CDoC GPlt MPla
– 'Fernspray Gold'	CDoC CMHG CMac EHul ENot LCon LLin MAsh MBar MBri MPla NHar NHol SBod
– 'Filicoides'	LCon
– 'Flabelliformis'	CKen
– 'Gimborn Beauty'	LCon MBri
– 'Golden Fairy'	CKen LCon MRPP
– 'Golden Filament'	CKen
– 'Golden Nymph'	CKen LCon MBri
– 'Golden Sprite'	EBre EPot LBre LCon MAsh MBri MRPP
– 'Goldilocks'	EHul LCon MBri
– 'Gracilis Aurea'	CKen
– 'Graciosa'	See C. ***o.*** 'Loenik'
– 'Hage'	CKen EPot LCon MBri MPla MRPP
– 'Hypnoides Nana'	CKen
– 'Intermedia'	CKen EPot
¶ – 'Juniperoïdes'	CKen LCon
– 'Juniperoides Compacta'	CKen EPot LCon MAsh MBri
– 'Kamarachiba'	CKen
– 'Kanaamihiba'	MAsh MBar
– 'Kosteri'	CDoC CKen CMac CSco EBre EHul ENHC EPot ESis LBee LBre LCon LLin MBar MBri MGos MPla NHar NHed NHol SHBN SIng SLim WAbe
– 'Little Markey'	CKen
§ – 'Loenik'	CDoC EHul ENHC MBar NHol
– 'Lycopodioides'	CDoC EPot
§ – 'Mariesii' (v)	CKen LCon MAsh MBri SHBN
– 'Minima'	CKen EPot WTyr
– 'Nana' **AGM**	CKen CMHG CMac EPot GAri LBee LCon MBar MBri MPla MRav NHol SIng SLim SSmi
¶ – 'Nana Albospica'	MBar
– 'Nana Aurea' **AGM**	CDoC CMac CSco EBre EHul ENHC EPot LBre LLin MAsh MBar MBri MCas MRav MWat NHol SHBN SHil SIgm SIng SLon WStI
– 'Nana Compacta'	LCon MBri NHol
§ – 'Nana Densa'	CKen CMac
– 'Nana Gracilis' **AGM**	Widely available
I – 'Nana Gracilis Aurea'	EHul
I – 'Nana Lutea'	CKen CSco EBre EHul ENHC EPla EPot ESis LBee LBre LCon LLin MAsh MBar MBri MPla MRPP MRav NHol NRoo SBod SHer SLim SPla SSmi WAbe
– 'Nana Rigida'	See C. ***o.*** 'Rigid Dwarf'
– 'Nana Variegata'	See C. ***o.*** 'Mariesii'
§ – 'Opaal'	EPot LCon MBar MBri
– 'Pygmaea'	CDoC EBre EHul ENHC ENot EPot ESis IDai LBre LCon MBal MBar MPla NHar NHol SBod SLim SPer SPla
– 'Pygmaea Aurescens'	ENHC MBar MWat SIng
– 'Pygmaea Densa'	CKen MBri
– 'Reis Dwarf'	EPla LCon
§ – 'Rigid Dwarf'	CKen EHul EPot LBee MBar MBri
– 'Snowkist' (v)	CKen
– 'Spiralis'	CKen EPla MBar
– 'Stoneham'	CKen LCon MAsh MBar
– 'Tempelhof'	CDoC CKen EHar EHul EPot LCon MAsh MBar MBri MGos MPla NHar NHed SBod SLim SLon WWeb
– 'Tetragona Aurea' **AGM**	CDoC EHar EHul ENHC EPot GWht IDai LCon MBar MGos MWat SBod SLim
– 'Tonia' (v)	CKen EHul EPla ESis MBri SLim WWeb
– 'Verdon'	MBar MBri
¶ – 'Watchi'	LCon
– 'Wissel'	CKen
– 'Yellowtip' (v)	CKen LCon MBar MGos
pisifera	GAri LMer
– 'Aurea Nana'	See C. ***p.*** 'Strathmore'
– 'Avenue'	EHul LCon MPla NHol SPla
– 'Boulevard' **AGM**	Widely available
– 'Compacta'	NHed
– 'Compacta Variegata'	EHul MBar NHed
– 'Devon Cream'	EHoe GPen LCon MBar MPla NHol SBod
– 'Filifera'	CMac EBre LBre MBal MBar MRav SBod SLim SLon WBod
– 'Filifera Aurea' **AGM**	CBra CGre CKen CMHG CMac EBre EHul ENHC ENot GPen IDai IJoh LBre LCon LLin LNet MBal MBar MBri NBee NWea SBod SIng SLim SPer WDin WThu WWin
– 'Filifera Aureomarginata'	CMac EBre EPla GAri LBre MBal MBar MBri SLim
– 'Filifera Nana'	CDoC CGre EBar EBre EHul ENHC EPla LBre LCon MBal MBar MBri MWat NHed SPer SSmi WDin
I – 'Filifera Sungold'	See C. ***p.*** 'Sungold'
I – 'Filifera Variegata'	EHul LLin
– 'Gold Cushion'	CKen
– 'Gold Dust'	See C. ***p.*** 'Plumosa Aurea'
– 'Gold Spangle'	CMHG EPla MBar MGos SBod SLim SPla WBod WGor
*– 'Golden Dwarf'	SPla
– 'Golden Mop' **AGM**	CKen LCon MAsh MPla
– 'Hime-himuro'	CKen
– 'Hime-sawara'	CKen
– 'Nana'	CDoC CKen EBre EHul GAri GPen IOrc LBre LLin MAsh MBal MBar MBri MWat NHed NHol SBod SPer SSmi WThu
I – 'Nana Albovariegata'	CDoC CNic LBee MBar MBri SBod
♦– 'Nana Aurea'	See C. ***p.*** 'Strathmore'
§ – 'Nana Aureovariegata'	CDoC CMac EBar EHul EPot ESis GPlt IOrc LCon MAsh MBal MBar MBri MPla MWat NHed NHol SBod SIng SPer WWeb
I – 'Nana Compacta'	CMac IDai
I – 'Parslorii'	CKen EPot NHol
– 'Pici'	CKen
– 'Plumosa'	MBal SLon SPla SRms
– 'Plumosa Albopicta'	ENHC GPlt MBal MBar SBod SIng

§ – 'Plumosa Aurea'	CDoC CKen EHul ENHC GPen GWht IDai IJoh MAsh MBal MBar NWea WBod WDin
– 'Plumosa Aurea Compacta'	CKen CMHG CMac GAri GPlt LCon MPla NHed SLon WTyr
I – 'Plumosa Aurea Compacta Variegata'	CMac
– 'Plumosa Aurea Nana'	ENot MBal MBar MGos MPla NBee NHed
I – 'Plumosa Aurea Nana Compacta'	CMac SBod
– 'Plumosa Aurescens'	CMac
§ – 'Plumosa Compressa'	CDoC CKen CNic EHul EPot ESis GPen LBee LCon MAsh MBar MBri MCas MGos MRPP NHed SIng SLim WGor WThu
*– 'Plumosa Densa'	See C. *p.* 'Plumosa Compressa'
– 'Plumosa Flavescens'	CDoC CMac EHul MBar MPla MWat NHed SLon
I – 'Plumosa Juniperoides'	CKen EBre EHul GPlt ITim LBre LCon MBri MPla
– 'Plumosa Purple Dome'	See C. *p.* 'Purple Dome'
I – 'Plumosa Pygmaea'	EPot GPlt MGos SLon WGor
– 'Plumosa Rogersii'	CDoC EHul ENHC EPot MBar MCas MGos MPla SBod WThu
– 'Purple Dome'	EHul MBar MGos SBod
– 'Pygmaea'	See C. *p.* 'Plumosa Pygmaea'
– 'Rogersii'	See C. *p.* 'Plumosa Rogersii'
– 'Silver and Gold' (v)	MBar MCas
– 'Silver Lode' (v)	CKen
– 'Snow' (v)	CKen CMHG CMac EPot GAri GPen IDai LLin MBal MBar MBri MCas MPla SBod SIng SSmi WDin
– 'Snowflake'	EHul
§ – 'Squarrosa'	CDoC GAri GPen GWht MBal MBar NWea SLon WBod WDin WGor
N– 'Squarrosa Argentea'	MBal
I – 'Squarrosa Blue Globe'	CKen
– 'Squarrosa Dumosa'	CKen EHul MAsh MBar MWat
– 'Squarrosa Intermedia'	EHul LCon MBar MGos SLon
I – 'Squarrosa Lombarts'	CMac EBre EHul ENHC EPla LBre LCon LLin MAsh MBar MPla MWat NHed SBod SIng SPer SSmi
– 'Squarrosa Lutea'	EPla GPen MAsh MBar
– 'Squarrosa Sulphurea'	CMHG CMac CTre EBre EHul EPot GPen IDai LBee LBre LCon MAsh MBal MBar MPla MWat NBee SBod SLim WDin
– 'Squarrosa Veitchii'	See C. *p.* 'Squarrosa'
§ – 'Strathmore'	CKen EHul GPen IDai LBee LLin MBar MBri NHol SIng WGor
§ – 'Sungold'	CDoC CKen CMHG EHul ENot EPla GPen GPlt LBee LCon LLin MBar MBri MPla SBod SLim SPla
– 'Tama-himuro'	CKen EPot LLin MBri MGos SLim
– 'White Beauty'	CKen
*– 'White Brocade'	CMac
– 'White Pygmy'	EPot LCon MAsh MRPP
thyoïdes	SLim WThu
– 'Andelyensis' **AGM**	CDoC CMac CNic EHul ENHC GAri GPen LCon LLin MAsh MBal MBar MPla NHol SLim
– 'Andelyensis Nana' **AGM**	CKen
– 'Aurea'	EHul GPlt MBar
– 'Conica'	CKen LCon MAsh
– 'Ericoïdes' **AGM**	CDoC CKen CMHG CMac CSam EBar EHul ENHC GPen GWht LBee LCon LLin MAsh MBal MBar MWat NBee NHed SBod SLim SPer WBod WDin
§ – 'Glauca'	EHul
¶ – 'Heatherbun'	NHol
– 'Kewensis'	See C. *t.* 'Glauca'
♦– 'Red Star'	See C. *t.* 'Rubicon'
– 'Rubicon'	CDoC CKen CLew CMac EBre EHul ESis ESma GPen GPlt IBar IJoh LBee LBre LCon LLin MAsh MBar MBri MGos MPla MRav NHed NHol SBod SLim SPer SPla
– 'Schumaker's Blue Dwarf'	EPla MBar
*– 'Top Point'	IJoh SLim
– 'Variegata'	EHul MBar

CHAMAECYTISUS (Leguminosae/Papilionaceae)

§ ***albus***	ECtt ENot NNor SDix SPer WDin WStI
¶ ***glaber***	CPle
hirsutus	WDav
¶ ***proliferus***	MAll
§ ***purpureus***	CAbP CSco EBre EFol ELan IDai IOrc LBre LHop MBal MBar MBri MGos MPla NRoo SHBN SHil SPer SReu WAbe WBod WDin WOMN WRus WWin
– f. ***albus***	MBar MPla SHBN SHil SPer SUsu
§ – 'Atropurpureus' **AGM**	ENot MPla SHil SPer SSta
– ***incarnatus***	See C. *p.* 'Atropurpureus'
§ ***supinus***	LHop SRms

CHAMAEDAPHNE (Ericaceae)

§ ***calyculata***	CB&S CPle MUlv SHBN WBod
– 'Nana'	EHic MBal MBar MGos

CHAMAEDOREA (Palmae/Arecaceae)

costaricana	LPal
elegans **AGM**	LPal MBri
erumpens **AGM**	NPal
metallica **AGM**	LPal
¶ ***microspadix***	CTro
seifrizii **AGM**	CTro LPal MBri

CHAMAELIRIUM (Liliaceae/Melanthiaceae)

luteum	MSal

CHAMAEMELUM (Compositae/Asteraceae)

§ ***nobile***	CArn CHad CSFH CSev EHer EHal GPoy LHol MBar MBri NNrd NRoo SIde WOak WPer WWye
– 'Flore Pleno'	CGle CHan CMea CSFH CSev CShe CTom ECha ELan GMac GPoy LHol LHop MBri MCas NBro NCat NNrw NSti SChu SHer SIde SSvw SUsu WAbe WEas WHal WPer
– 'Treneague'	CArn CLew CSFH CSev CShe CTom ELan GAbr GPoy IEde LHol LMor MBri NNor NRoo NSti SHer SIde SIng WAbe WHal WOak WPer WWye

CHAMAENERION See **EPILOBIUM**

CHAMAEPERICLYMENUM See **CORNUS**

CHAMAEROPS (Palmae/Arecaceae)

excelsa hort.	See TRACHYCARPUS ***fortunei***
excelsa Thunberg	See RHAPIS ***excelsa***
humilis AGM	CHEx CTbh CTro GAri IOrc LPal NPal NRog SArc SDry SHil WCot

CHAMAESPARTIUM See **GENISTA**

CHAMELACIUM (Myrtaceae)
See Plant Deletions

CHAMELAUCIUM

¶ ***uncinatum***	CTro

CHAMOMILLA See **MATRICARIA**

CHARA (stonewort)
See Plant Deletions

CHASMANTHE (Iridaceae)

aethiopica	CHan GCal LHop MBel NRog WHaw
bicolor	CMon
floribunda	CFee NRog
– var. ***duckittii***	NRog

CHASMANTHIUM (Gramineae/Poaceae)

§ ***latifolium***	ECha EFou EHoe ELan EPla ESiP ETPC GAbr NHar NSti SDix SMad WBon WPer WWat

CHEILANTHES (Adiantaceae)

argentea	NMar
eatonii	SIgm
farinosa	NMar
hirta var. ***ellisiana***	NMar
lanosa	NHar NMar SIgm SMad
myriophylla	NMar
¶ ***pulchella***	CFil
¶ ***tomentosa***	CFil

CHEIRANTHUS See **ERYSIMUM**

CHELIDONIUM (Papaveraceae)

japonicum	CMea ECro NCat WPer
majus	CKin CRow CSFH ECWi EWFC GPoy GTou LHol MChe MHew MPit MSal NHex SIde WHer WWye
– 'Flore Pleno'	CGle CRow CWGN ELan GBar GCHN GCal NBrk NBro NSti WHaw
– var. ***laciniatum***	WHaw
– 'Laciniatum Flore Pleno'	CGre CRDP CRow GCal IBlr WHer WPer

CHELONE (Scrophulariaceae)

barbata	See PENSTEMON ***barbatus***
§ ***glabra***	CCla CHan CHol CRDP EBre ECha ECro EFol EFou EGol ELan GPoy LBre LHop MBri MHew MSal MUlv NHol SChu SCro SFis SPer WMer WOMN WOld WPer WRus WTyr WWat
lyonii	SHer
obliqua	CArn CChu CHan EBre ECha EFol EFou EGol ELan GCal GMac LBre LHop MBri MHew MRav NBro NSti NVic SFis SPer WHil WHoo WOld WPbr WPer WRus WWat WWin
– var. ***alba***	See C. ***glabra***

CHELONOPSIS (Labiatae/Lamiaceae)

¶ ***moschata***	ECha

CHENOPODIUM (Chenopodiaceae)

bonus-henricus	CArn CSev EHer EJud Effi GAbr GBar GPoy IEde ILis LHol MChe SIde WOak WPer WWye
botrys	MSal

CHERRY, Duke See **PRUNUS** x ***gondouinii***

CHERRY, Sour or Morello See **PRUNUS** ***cerasus***

CHERRY, Sweet See **PRUNUS** ***avium***

CHESTNUT, Sweet See **CASTANEA** ***sativa***

CHEVREULIA (Compositae/Asteraceae)
See Plant Deletions

CHIASTOPHYLLUM (Crassulaceae)

§ ***oppositifolium*** AGM	Widely available
– 'Frosted Jade'	See C. ***o.*** 'Jim's Pride'
§ – 'Jim's Pride' (v)	CBos CElw CLew CRDP CRow ECha EFol EMon EPla LAbb LBee LBlm LHop MCas MHlr MUlv NGre SMad WBon WCot WRus
simplicifolium	See C. ***oppositifolium***

CHILIOTRICHUM (Compositae/Asteraceae)

diffusum	CGre CPle ECou EHic GDra GWht IBar LBuc MAll MBlu SLon SPer

CHIMAPHILA (Ericaceae)
See Plant Deletions

CHIMONANTHUS (Calycanthaceae)

fragrans	See C. ***praecox***
§ ***praecox***	Widely available
– 'Grandiflorus' AGM	ENot
– 'Luteus' AGM	CPMA CSco MBlu SHil WWat
zhejiangensis	GCal

CHIMONOBABUSA

§ ***microphylla***	SBam SDry

CHIMONOBAMBUSA (Gramineae/Poaceae-Bambusoideae)

falcata	See DREPANOSTACHYUM ***falcatum***
hookeriana hort.	See DREPANOSTACHYUM 'Damarapa'
macrophylla f. ***intermedia***	SDry
§ ***marmorea***	EPla ISta LBam SBam SDry WJun
– 'Variegata'	EFul EPla ISta LBam SBam SDry WJun
§ ***quadrangularis***	EFul EPla GAri ISta SBam SDry WJun
– 'Svow' (v)	SDry
§ ***tumidissinoda***	EPla SBam SDry WJun

CHIOGENES See **GAULTHERIA**

CHIONANTHUS (Oleaceae)

retusus	SHil SSta
virginicus	CB&S CBow CCla CPMA EHar ELan IOrc MBri MUlv SEng SMad SSta WHCG WWat

CHIONOCHLOA (Gramineae/Poaceae)

conspicua	CElw CFil ETPC GAbr GCal MBal MFir NBir WHer
– 'Rubra'	See C. ***rubra***
flavescens	GCal
flavicans	EPla MUlv
§ ***rubra***	CElw EPla ETPC

CHIONODOXA † (Liliaceae/Hyacinthaceae)

cretica	See C. ***nana***
§ ***forbesii***	CAvo CBro CMon WPer
– 'Alba'	EPar ETub LAma NRog
– 'Pink Giant'	CAvo CBro CCla ELan LAma SIng WHil WPer
– 'Rosea'	EPar ETub LAma LBow NEgg NRog
§ – Siehei Group **AGM**	CBro
gigantea	See C. ***luciliae*** Gigantea Group
luciliae **AGM**	CAvo CBro CCla ELan EPar EPot ETub LAma LBow MBal MBri MWBu NEgg NMen NRog SIng WAbe
§ – Gigantea Group	ELan ETub LAma MWBu NEgg NRog SIng WHil
luciliae hort.	See C. ***forbesii***
* ***mariesii***	LAma
§ ***nana***	CBro CMon
sardensis **AGM**	CAvo CBro CCla EPar EPot ETub LAma LBow MBal NRog SIng WPer
siehei	See C. ***forbesii*** Siehei Group
tmolusi	See C. ***forbesii*** 'Tmoli'

CHIONOHEBE (Scrophulariaceae)

armstrongii	ITim
densifolia	ECou ITim NHed
x ***petrimea*** 'Margaret Pringle'	EPot
pulvinaris	ECou EPot ITim NHar NHol NSla NTow NWCA WDav WThu

X CHIONOSCILLA (Liliaceae/Hyacinthaceae)

§ ***allenii***	CMon LAma LRHS WChr

CHIRITA (Gesneriaceae)

sinensis **AGM**	WDib

CHIRONIA (Gentianaceae)

baccifera	CSpe

CHLIDANTHUS (Liliaceae/Amaryllidaceae)

fragrans	EOrc LBow NHol NRog WChr

CHLOROPHYTUM (Liliaceae/Anthericaceae)

comosum 'Variegatum' **AGM**	MBri NRog
– 'Vittatum' **AGM**	MBri

CHOISYA (Rutaceae)

arizonica	SDry
'Aztec Pearl' **AGM**	Widely available
mollis	CGre
ternata **AGM**	Widely available
– 'Moonsleeper'	NBee SHBN
– 'Sundance' **AGM**	Widely available

CHONDROPETALUM (Restionaceae)

¶ ***tectorum***	CTro

CHONDROSUM (Gramineae/Poaceae)

§ ***gracile***	EBee ECha EFou ELan EPla MMil NBro NSti SFar SMad SUsu

CHORDOSPARTIUM (Leguminosae/Papilionaceae)

muritai	ECou MAll
stevensonii	CBow CGre CHEx CPle ECou SMad
– 'Duncan'	ECou
– 'Kiwi'	ECou
– 'Miller'	ECou

CHORISIA (Bombacaceae)
See Plant Deletions

CHORIZEMA (Leguminosae/Papilionaceae)

ilicifolium	CB&S CSPN ERea

CHRYSALIDOCARPUS (Palmae/Arecaceae)

lutescens **AGM**	CTro LPal MBri

CHRYSANTHEMOPSIS See **RHODANTHEMUM**

CHRYSANTHEMUM (Compositae/Asteraceae)
See also ARGYRANTHEMUM, DENDRANTHEMA, RHODANTHEMUM

alpinum	See LEUCANTHEMOPSIS ***alpina***
arcticum Linnaeus	See ARCTANTHEMUM ***a.***
argenteum	See TANACETUM ***a.***
balsamita	See TANACETUM ***b.***
cinerariifolium	See TANACETUM ***c.***
clusii	See TANACETUM ***corymbosum c.***
coccineum	See TANACETUM ***c.***
coronarium	CArn
corymbosum	See TANACETUM ***c.***
foeniculaceum	See ARGYRANTHEMUM ***frutescens f.***
frutescens	See ARGYRANTHEMUM ***f.***
haradjanii	See TANACETUM ***h.***
hosmariense	See PYRETHROPSIS ***h.***
leucanthemum	See LEUCANTHEMUM ***vulgare***
macrophyllum	See TANACETUM ***m.***
mawii	See RHODANTHEMUM ***gayanum***
maximum hort.	See LEUCANTHEMUM × ***superbum***
maximum Ramond	See LEUCANTHEMUM ***m.***
nankingense	See DENDRANTHEMA ***n.***
nipponicum	See NIPPONANTHEMUM ***n.***
pacificum	See DENDRANTHEMA ***p.***
parthenium	See TANACETUM ***p.***
♦***praeteritium***	See TANACETUM ***p.***
ptarmiciflorum	See TANACETUM ***p.***
roseum	See TANACETUM ***coccineum***
rubellum	See DENDRANTHEMA ***zawadskii***
§ ***segetum***	ECWi EWFC MHew NMir WHer WOak WThu
uliginosum	See LEUCANTHEMELLA ***serotina***
welwitschii	See C. ***segetum***
weyrichii	See DENDRANTHEMA ***w.***
yezoense	See DENDRANTHEMA ***y.***

CHRYSOCOMA (Compositae/Asteraceae)
See Plant Deletions

CHRYSOGONUM (Compositae/Asteraceae)

virginianum	CRDP EBre ECha EFol EPla LBre LGan MRav SPer

CHRYSOLEPIS (Fagaceae)
See Plant Deletions

CHRYSOPOGON (Gramineae/Poaceae)

gryllus	EMon EPla ETPC

CHRYSOPSIS (Compositae/Asteraceae)

villosa	See HETEROTHECA ***v.***

CHRYSOSPLENIUM (Saxifragaceae)

davidianum	CBre CGle CRDP CTom ECha EPar EPot GCHN MNFA NBir NCat SBla WAbe WCru
– SBEC 231	NHol
oppositifolium	EMNN GDra GGar NKay WCla

CHRYSOTHAMNUS (Compositae/Asteraceae)
See Plant Deletions

CHRYSOTHEMIS (Gesneriaceae)
See Plant Deletions

CHUNIOPHOENIX (Palmae/Arecaceae)

hainanensis	LPal

CHUSQUEA † (Gramineae/Poaceae-Bambusoideae)

culeou AGM	CBot CDoC CFil CGre CHEx CMCN CTro EFul EHar ELan EPla GAbr GCal ISta LBam MBri MNes MUlv SArc SBam SDry SHer SSta WJun WNor
– ***breviglumis***	See C. ***c.*** 'Tenuis'
§ – 'Tenuis'	LBam SBam SDry WJun
montana	CFil SArc SBam WJun WWat
quila	CFil SArc SBam SDry WJun
ramosissima	SBam SDry WJun

CICERBITA (Compositae/Asteraceae)

plumieri	MHlr WCot

CICHORIUM (Compositae/Asteraceae)

intybus AGM	CKin CRDP CSFH EBre ECoo ECro EWFC Effi GAbr LBre LHol LHop MChe MHew NMir SChu SHer SIde WGwy WHer WOak WPer WWye
– ***album***	CPou ECha ECoo ECro EMon SChu SHer
– ***roseum***	CPou CRDP ECha ECoo ECot ECro ELan EMon LHop MRav MTho NRoo SHer SMrm SPer WHow
'Rosso di Verona'	ELan
spinosum	ELan EMon SIgm

CICUTA (Umbelliferae/Apiaceae)
See Plant Deletions

CIMICIFUGA † (Ranunculaceae)

acerina	See C. ***japonica***
§ ***americana***	MSal NHol SRms
♦***cordifolia*** Pursh	See C. ***americana***
♦***cordifolia*** Torrey & Gray	See C. ***rubifolia***
dahurica	CHan GCal MSal WPla
foetida	GPoy LGan NHol
§ ***japonica***	CHan CRow EBre GCal LBre LGre WCot WRus
racemosa AGM	CArn CChu CCla CRDP CRow CSam EBre EGol ELan ELun GAbr GCal GPoy LBre LGan MBal MRav MSal NDea NHol NSti SAxl SFis SPer WByw WWye
– var. ***cordifolia***	See C. ***rubifolia***
*– 'Purple Torch'	WEas
*– 'Purpurea'	CDoC CRDP EFol ELun MBel NBar SAxl SPer
ramosa	See C. ***simplex*** 'Prichard's Giant'
§ ***rubifolia***	CHan EBre LBre LGre MSal SBla SPer

simplex	CBot CSam LBre MBri MHlr NPri WCot WWat
– Atropurpurea Group	CAbb CB&S CBot CChu CCla CHan CRDP CRow EBre ECha EFou ELan EPar LBre LGre MBri MUlv NBar NOak NSti SBla SMad SMrm SPla SWas WCra WHoo WRus WWat
– 'Brunette'	MUlv
– 'Elstead' **AGM**	CRow EBee ECha ELun EPar GCal LGre MBri SBla
– 'Frau Herms'	LGre LRHS
§ – 'Prichard's Giant'	CHan GAri GBuc GCal LGre MBri NHol SHig SPer WCot
– 'White Pearl'	Widely available

CINERARIA (Compositae/Asteraceae)

maritima	See SENECIO ***cineraria***

CINNAMOMUM (Lauraceae)

camphora	CB&S CHEx ERea

CIONURA (Asclepiadaceae)

oreophila	GCal

CIRCAEA (Onagraceae)

lutetiana	CKin ECWi EWFC MHew MSal WHer
¶ – 'Caveat Emptor' (v)	CNat EMon

CIRSIUM (Compositae/Asteraceae)

acaule	CKin ECro
candelebrum	NWCA
diacantha	See PTILOSTEMON ***d.***
dissectum	CKin ECWi
eriophorum	CKin NMir
¶ – ssp. ***britannicum***	WPer
falconeri	EWoo
forrestii CLD 1000	NHol
helenioïdes	See C. ***heterophyllum***
§ ***heterophyllum***	CKin ECha ECro
japonicum	MFir
* – 'Pink Beauty'	CBow EGol ELan SHer WHil
– 'Rose Beauty'	CBow ELan GCal MBri NMir SHer SSvw WHil
– 'Snow Beauty'	GCal
¶ – 'White Victory'	SSvw
mexicanum	CRDP EMon
oleraceum	ECro GAul
palustre	CKin
rivulare atropurpureum	CBre CCla CElw COtt CRDP CSco ECha ECro EGol ELan MUlv NBir NSti SPer WByw WEas WHal WMer
spinosissimum	GCal
vulgare	CKin

CISSUS (Vitaceae)

antarctica **AGM**	MBri
rhombifolia **AGM**	MBri
– 'Ellen Danica' **AGM**	MBri
§ ***striata***	CB&S CGre CHEx CSPN EMil IBar WCru WWat

CISTUS † (Cistaceae)

x ***aguilarii***	CHan EPla LAbb NBrk SIgm SMrm WSHC
– 'Maculatus' **AGM**	CB&S CBot CDoC CHan CLTr CSco EBre ELan ENot LBre LGre MBri SDry SHil SLMG SPer SPla WAbe WHCG WKif WWin
albanicus	GCHN NTow
albidus	CRiv EBar NTow SDry WCru WEas
algarvensis	See HALIMIUM ***ocymoïdes***
'Anne Palmer'	CChu CDoC CHan CSco LHop NBrk SAxl SBla SChu WAbe WKif
atriplicifolius	See HALIMIUM ***atriplicifolium***
'Barnsley Pink'	See C. 'Grayswood Pink'
'Blanche'	CHan SIgm WKif
x ***canescens***	CB&S WAbe
– 'Albus'	CMHG CShe EPla LGre NBrk NSti SIgm WAbe WHCG
'Chelsea Bonnet'	WAbe
'Chelsea Pink'	EBar
§ ***clusii***	CKni CSam MAsh SAxl SCro
coeris	See C. x ***hybridus***
x ***corbariensis***	See C. x ***hybridus***
♦ ***creticus***	See C. ***incanus c.***
crispus 'Prostratus'	See C. ***c.*** Linnaeus
– 'Sunset'	See C. x ***pulverulentus*** 'S.'
crispus hort.	See C. x ***pulverulentus***
crispus Linnaeus	CHan ECha GAbr LGre NNor SIgm WAbe WCru WEas WRus WWeb
§ x ***cyprius*** **AGM**	CCla CMHG CSco CShe ECtt ELan ENot EPla IBar LHop MBel MBri MGos MWat NBrk NSti SDix SHBN SHil SMrm SPer SPla WBod WDin
– 'Albiflorus'	CDoC
§ x ***dansereaui***	CHan CShe IOrc SLMG WAbe WDin
– 'Decumbens' **AGM**	CB&S CCla CHan CMHG CSco EBre ELan GCal IJoh LBre MBal MBel MBri NFai NKay SHBN SIgm SPer SPla WAbe WHCG WStI WWat
'Elma' **AGM**	CGre CMHG ERav LGre MBri MHlr NTow SDix SDry SIgm SPer SPla WAbe WHCG WPla WWat
§ x ***florentinus***	CDoC CLTr EBee IOrc LAbb MRav NNor SAxl SChu WSHC
formosus	See HALIMIUM ***lasianthum***
§ 'Grayswood Pink'	CBow CDoC CMHG CMer ELan EPla ESma GMac MBri MPla MSte NBrk NSti SIgm SMrm WAbe WHCG WRus
halimifolius	See HALIMIUM ***halimifolium***
hirsutus	SDry WKif WWeb
N – var. ***psilosepalus***	EBar
§ x ***hybridus*** **AGM**	Widely available
§ ***incanus***	SChu SIde WHCG WPer WSHC
§ – ssp. ***creticus***	CMHG EBar ELan ERav LAbb LGre MBel MSte NTow SIgm SPer WAbe WSHC WWin
– ssp. ***incanus***	LGre SIgm
ingwerseniana	See X HALIMIOCISTUS ***ingwersenii***
ladanifer hort.	See C. x ***cyprius***

ladanifer AGM	CB&S CHan CSco EBre ECha ELan EWri IJoh IOrc LAbb LBre MBal MRav MSto NNor NSti NTow SChu SLon SPer WCru WEas WSHC
– Palhinhae Group AGM	LGre MSte NTow SDry SHil SIgm WAbe
– 'Pat'	CGre WEas
lasianthus	See HALIMIUM ***lasianthum***
laurifolius AGM	CCla CDec CHan CSco EBre ENot EPla LBre LGre MBal MBri MGos NSti NWyt SLPl SPer WEas WSHC WWat
x ***laxus*** 'Snow White'	CCla CHan EPla LGre LHop MBri MSte NPer NSti SChu SFar SSvw WKif
libanotis	CSam ELan NNor
Nx ***loretii*** Rouy & Fouc.	CBra CHan CMHG CSam ELan ENot LGre NSti SApp SDry SHBN SPer WCru WKif WPat WWat
x ***lusitanicus*** Maund.	See C. x ***dansereaui***
'Merrist Wood Cream'	See X HALIMIOCISTUS ***wintonensis*** 'Merrist Wood Cream'
monspeliensis	CHan CMHG CSev EPla GWht SChu SDry SPer
x ***obtusifolius***	CHan EFol EHic ELan ESiP EWes EWri MBel MBri NWyt SBla SLPl WTyr
ocymoïdes	See HALIMIUM ***ocymoïdes***
osbeckiifolius	GCal
palhinhae	See C. ***ladanifer*** Palhinhae Group
parviflorus hort.	See C. 'Grayswood Pink'
parviflorus Lamarck	CBot CCla CNic ECha LGre LHop NSti SChu SPer WSHC
'Peggy Sammons' AGM	CBot CDoC CLTr CSco CShe EBre ECha EGol ELan ERav IOrc LAbb LBre LHop MBri NBrk NSti SGil SHer SIgm SLon SPer SPla SSvw SUsu WBod WPat WSHC WTyr WWat
populifolius	CMHG EHic NCat SLon SMad SPer
– var. ***lasiocalyx*** AGM	CChu ERav IOrc LGre SHil SLon SMrm
– ssp. ***major***	CHan
§ x ***pulverulentus*** AGM	CCla CGre CHan CSco EPla ERav LAbb SChu SCro SPer WDin
§ – 'Sunset'	Widely available
– 'Warley Rose'	CDoC CSam CShe EBar EBre LBre SAxl SHBN SIgm WAbe
Nx ***purpureus*** AGM	Widely available
– 'Alan Fradd'	CBra CKni CSco EHic GMac NBrk SCro SGil SHer SIgm SMrm
– 'Betty Taudevin'	CB&S GMac LGre LHop LRHS MBri NCat NFai WAbe WCru WSHC
rosmarinifolius	See C. ***clusii***
sahucii	See X HALIMIOCISTUS ***sahucii***
salviifolius	CB&S CBow CDoC CHan CSam CSco EBee ERav WEas WHCG
– 'Avalanche'	WAbe WCru
– 'Prostratus'	CMHG ELan LGre LHop NTow WCru
– x ***monspeliensis***	See C. x ***florentinus***
'Silver Pink'	Widely available
x ***skanbergii*** AGM	CB&S CBra CCla CHan CLTr CMHG CSam CSco ELan ENot ERav EWri GMac LHop MGos MWat NBir NBrk NFai NSti SArc SDix SFis SHBN SLon SPer SPla WEas WWat WWin
¶ 'Snow Queen'	LRHS
symphytifolius	CGre GCal
tomentosus	See HELIANTHEMUM ***nummularium tomentosum***
x ***verguinii***	LGre LHop MBri SDix SIgm
¶ x ***verguinii albiflorus***	WAbe
villosus	See C. ***incanus***
wintonensis	See X HALIMIOCISTUS ***wintonensis***

CITHAREXYLUM (Verbenaceae)

ilicifolium	CGre
quadrangulare Jacquin	See C. ***spinosum***
§ ***spinosum***	CGre CPle

X CITROFORTUNELLA (Rutaceae)

F ***floridana*** 'Eustis'	ERea
F – 'Lakeland'	ERea
Limequat	See X C. ***floridana***
F ***microcarpa*** AGM	CGOG MBri WFou
F – 'Tiger' (v)	CB&S LHop
mitis	See X C. ***microcarpa***
F ***swinglei*** 'Tavares'	ERea

CITRON See CITRUS *medica*

X CITRONCIRUS (Rutaceae)

See Plant Deletions

CITRONELLA (Icacinaceae)

§ ***gongonha***	CAbb CPle
mucronata	See C. ***gongonha***

CITRUS † (Rutaceae)

F ***aurantiifolia*** 'Bearss'	CGOG ERea
F – x ***limon*** 'Indian Lime'	ERea
F – x ***limon*** 'La Valette'	ERea
F – 'Tahiti'	CB&S CNew ERea SPer
F ***aurantium*** 'Bouquet'	ERea
F – var. ***myrtifolia*** 'Chinotto'	ERea
– 'Seville'	CGOG ERea
Calamondin	See X CITROFORTUNELLA ***microcarpa***
F ***ichangensis***	SArc
japonica	See FORTUNELLA ***j.***
Kumquat	See FORTUNELLA ***margarita***
F ***limon***	LPan MBri
F – 'Fino'	CGOG
F – 'Garey's Eureka'	CGOG ERea MBri
F – 'Imperial'	ERea
F – 'Lemonade'	ERea
F – 'Lisbon'	CBow ERea
F – 'Quatre Saisons'	See C. ***l.*** 'Garey's Eureka'
F – x ***sinensis*** 'Meyer'	CB&S CBow CGOG CNew CTro GTwe LHop MBri NPal SEng SLMG SPer WFou WHig
F – 'Variegata'	ERea MBri
F – 'Verna'	CGOG

F – 'Villafranca' CNew ERea
F x *limonia* 'Rangpur' ERea
F *maxima* ERea
F *medica* 'Ethrog' ERea
F – var. *sarcodactylis* ERea
mitis See X CITROFORTUNELLA *microcarpa*
F x *nobilis* LPan
F – 'Blida' ERea
F – 'Murcott' ERea
F – Ortanique Group CTro
F – 'Silver Hill Owari' ERea
F – Tangor Group ERea
F x *paradisi* LPan
F – 'Foster ' ERea
F – 'Golden Special' CB&S CNew ERea IOrc SEng
F – 'Red Blush' CGOG
F – 'Wheeny' CNew
F 'Ponderosa' CNew ERea
¶ *reticulata* 'Variegata' CBow
reticulata x *paradisi* See C. x *tangelo*
F – Mandarin Group WFou
F – – 'Clementine' CB&S ERea IOrc SEng SPer
F – – 'Comun' CGOG
F – – 'De Nules' CGOG
F – – 'Encore' ERea
F – – 'Fortune' CGOG
F – – 'Nova' CGOG
F – – 'Tomatera' CGOG
F – Satsuma Group ERea
F – – 'Clausellina' CGOG
F – – 'Okitsu' CGOG
F – – 'Owari' CGOG
F *sinensis* LPan MBri
F – 'Arnci Alberetto' SEng
F – 'Egg' ERea
F – 'Embiguo' ERea
¶ – 'Harwood Late' ERea
F – 'Jaffa' See C. *s.* 'Shamouti'
F – 'Malta Blood' ERea
F – 'Moro Blood' ERea
F – 'Navelina' CGOG
F – 'Newhall' CGOG
¶ – 'Parson Brown' ERea
F – 'Prata' ERea
F – 'Ruby' ERea
F – 'Saint Michael' ERea
F – 'Salustiana' CGOG
F – 'Sanguinelli' CGOG ERea
F – 'Shamouti' ERea
F – 'Valencia' ECot ERea MBri
F – 'Valencia Late' CGOG ERea
F – 'Washington' CB&S CGOG CNew CTro ERea GTwe MBri NPal SPer
F x *tangelo* 'Mapo' WFou
F – 'Seminole' CTro ERea

CLADOTHAMNUS See ELLIOTTIA

CLADRASTIS (Leguminosae/Papilionaceae)

* *hirsuta* CSPN
lutea AGM CB&S CCla CLnd CMCN CPle EArb ELan GAul SHil WWat

CLARKIA (Onagraceae)

concinna WOMN

* *repens* CSpe

CLAVINODUM (Gramineae/Poaceae-Bambusoideae)

oedogonatum SDry

CLAYTONIA (Portulacaceae)

australasica See NEOPAXIA *australasica*
caroliniana LAma NRog
§ *megarhiza* var. *nivalis* GDra GTou MAsh NGre NTow NWCA WThu
§ *nevadensis* ELan EMar
♦ *parvifolia* See NAIOCRENE *p.*
§ *perfoliata* CArn EWFC GPoy WHer WWye
§ *sibirica* CLew CNic CRow ECoo ELan NGre WFox WHaw WHil WWye
virginica LAma NRog WEas

CLEMATIS † (Ranunculaceae)

'Abundance' (Vt) CBow CCla CDoC CPev CRHN CSCl CSPN EBre EHan EOvi ETho EVal IOrc LBre LPri MBea MBri MCad MRav NBea NHol SBra SDix SHBN SPer WSHC WTre
'Acton Pride' LPri
¶ 'Ada Sari' (L) MCad
addisonii EOvi MSto SBra WOMN
aethusifolia CHan CSCl CSPN EBre EOrc EOvi ERom EVal LBre LPri MBri MCad SBra
afoliata CPev ECou EOvi ETho MCad MFos MSto WCot
¶ 'Ajisai' (L x J) MCad
¶ 'Akaishi' MCad
akebioïdes CCla CHan CSCl ETho LRHS MCad SBra SHBN SPer
¶ 'Akemi' (L) MCad
¶ 'Akeshina' MCad
'Alabast' (F) MCad
'Alba Luxurians' AGM Widely available
albicoma CSCl
'Albiflora' CBow EVal MCad
I 'Albina Plena' (A) SPla
'Alice Fisk' (P) CSCl EOvi EVal LPri MCad NBea SBra WGor
'Aljonushka' EOvi MCad MGos
'Allanah' (J) CBow CRHN CSCl EHan EOvi EVal LPri MCad MGos NBea SBra
§ *alpina* AGM CBow CMac CPev CRDP CSCl CSco GDra GMac MBal MBar MBea MCad NBar NEgg NHol NPer NRoo SHBN SIng WAbe WStI WWat
¶ – 'Alice Belsay' EHan
– 'Blush Queen' CSCl NWyt
– 'Burford White' EOvi LPri MCad NBea WSHC
– 'Columbine' CBow CCMG CPev EOrc EOvi ETho EVal LPri MBea MCad NBea SBra SDix SPer
– 'Columbine White' AGM CHan EOvi ETho EVal MBri MCad NBea NRoo SPla
– 'Constance' CBow CSPN EHan EOrc ETho EVal LRHS NSti WTre
– 'Frances Rivis' AGM Widely available
– 'Frankie' CBow CDoC CSPN EHan ELan EOrc EOvi ETho EVal LRHS MBri MCad WGor WTre

– 'Inshriach'	MSte NHol
– 'Jacqueline du Pré'	CPev CSPN MCad MGos NBrk
– 'Jan Lindmark'	EBre LBre NBir
¶ – 'Linava'	NBrk
– 'Maria'	MCad
§ – 'Pamela Jackman'	CBow CCMG CCla CDoC CSCl CSPN EBre EHan ELan EOvi EVal IOrc LBre LPri MBea MBri MCad MGos NBar NBea NHol NRoo NSti SBra SDix SPer WTre
– 'Pink Flamingo'	CBow CSPN EHan EVal LRHS SBla WTre
– 'Ria'	MBea MCad
– 'Rosy Pagoda'	CBow CHan CSPN EOvi EVal LPri MCad NBea NBir NRoo SPla WWat
– 'Ruby'	Widely available
– ssp. ***sibirica***	CPev EOvi MCad NBea
§ – – 'White Moth'	CCMG CCla CMac CSCl CSPN CSco EBre ELan EOvi EVal LAbb LBre LPri MBri MCad MGos NBea NBrk NHol NRoo SBla SBra SHil SMad SPer WTre
– 'Tage Lundell'	See C. 'T. L.'
– 'Willy'	CBow CCMG CPev CSCl CSPN EGol EHan ELan EOrc EOvi ERom ETho EVal GMac LPri MBea MBri MCad MGos NBea SBod SBra SChu SDix SPer SPla WTre
¶ – 'Wisley Purple'	NBrk
'André Devillers' (P)	MCad
I 'Andromeda'	EVal
¶ 'Anita'	MCad
'Anna' (P)	EOvi EVal MCad
'Anna Louise'	CBow CSPN EHan ETho EVal LRHS MCad
'Annabel' (P)	MCad
* 'Anniversary'	LPri
apiifolia	CPev EHal EHan EOvi MCad SBra
– var. ***biternata*** GR 0008	SBra
'Arabella'	CPev EOvi
¶ 'Arctic Queen'	EVal
aristata	ECou MCad MSto
armandii	Widely available
– 'Apple Blossom'	CB&S CBow CCMG CCla CPev CRHN CSCl CSco EHan EHar ELan EOvi ETho EVal IOrc LPri MBea MBri MCad MGos NBea NHol SBra SHBN SPer SReu SSta WTre
– var. ***biondiana***	CMac EOvi MNes SBla
– 'Jeffries'	EBee EOrc EVal LRHS
– 'Snowdrift'	CB&S CPev CSCl CSam CSco EHan EOvi ETho LPri MCad MMea SBla SHil SPla SReu WStI
x ***aromatica***	EHan EOvi ETho MCad SBra SPla
¶ 'Asagasumi' (L)	MCad
'Asao' (P)	CBow CSCl CSPN EBre EHan ELan EOvi ERom ETho EVal LBre LPri MBea MCad NBea SBra SPer WWat
'Ascotiensis' **AGM**	CCMG CCla CPev CSCl CSPN EBre EHan EOvi ETho EVal LBre LPri MCad SBra SChu SDix SPer WTre
* ***atrata***	WCru
§ 'Aureolin' **AGM**	CDoC CSCl EBre EVal LBre MBar MBri MCad MGos NHol NWyt SBra WTre WWeb
'Aurora Borealis'	MCad
australis	MSto
¶ 'Bagatelle' (P)	MCad
'Barbara Dibley' (P)	CBow CCla CMac CPev CRHN CSCl EHan EOvi ETho EVal LPri MBea MBri MCad NBea SBod SBra SDix WBod WTre
'Barbara Jackman' (P)	CBow CCMG CCla CPev CSCl CSPN CSco ENot EOvi ERom ETho EVal LPri MBar MBea MBri MCad MRav NBar NBea SBra SDix SPer WBod WStI WTre
barbellata (A)	EOvi GDra MCad
– 'Pruinina'	See C. 'Pruinina'
¶ 'Beata' (L)	MCad
'Beauty of Richmond' (L)	EOvi ETho EVal MCad SBra SDix SPer
'Beauty of Worcester' (F/L)	CBow CCMG CCla CPev CSPN EBre EHan ELan EOvi ETho EVal LBre LPri MAsh MBar MBea MCad NBea SBra SDix SPer WMer WTre
'Bees' Jubilee' **AGM**	CB&S CMac CPev CSCl CSPN EBre EHan ELan ENot EOvi ERom ETho EVal IHos LBre LPri MBar MBea MBri MCad MGos NBar NBea NRoo SBra SDix SPer WBod WTre
¶ 'Bella' (J)	MCad
'Belle Nantaise' (L)	CPev CSCl CSPN EHan EOvi ETho EVal LPri MCad
'Belle of Woking' (F/P)	CBow CCMG CPev CSCl CSPN EBre EHan ELan EOvi ERom ETho EVal LBre LPri MBar MBea MBri MCad NBea SBra SDix SPer
'Benedictus'	EOvi
'Bessie Watkinson'	MCad
'Betty Corning' (Vt)	CSCl CSPN EHan EOvi ETho EVal LRHS MBri NBrk
§ 'Bill Mackenzie' **AGM**	Widely available
♦ 'Blue Angel'	See C. 'Błękitny Anioł'
'Blue Belle' (Vt)	CBar CSCl CSPN EHan ELan EOvi EVal LPri MBri MCad NBea NBrk SBra WGor
'Blue Bird' (A)	CCla CMac CSCl EOrc EOvi EVal IOrc LPri MBea MCad NBar NBea NHol SBod SBra SPer SPla WTre
'Blue Boy'	EVal MCad
'Blue Dancer'	CAbP MBal MWat
'Blue Gem' (L)	EOvi MCad NBrk SBra SHil WTre
x ***bonstedtii***	MCad
– 'Crépuscule'	CCla SRms
¶ 'Boskoop Beauty' (L)	EOvi NBrk
¶ 'Boskoop Glory'	MCad
'Bracebridge Star' (L/P)	CSCl EOvi ETho EVal MCad SBra
brachiata	CHan CPou CSCl EOvi LPri SBra SDix
brevicaudata	MCad WCru
'Broughton Star'	EOvi ETho MCad NBea SBra
'Brunette'	MGos
§ 'Błekitny Anioł'	MCad NBrk
buchananiana De Candolle	MCad
buchananiana Finet & Gagnepain	See C. ***rehderiana***
'Burford Variety' (Ta)	EGol EOrc EVal LPri MBri MCad NBea
'Burma Star'	CPev MCad
'C W Dowman' (P)	MCad SBra

calycina	See C. ***cirrhosa***
campaniflora	CBot CBow CCMG CCla CHan CPev CSCl CSPN EHan EOrc EOvi ERom ETho EVal LGan MBri MCad NBea SBra SDix
– 'Lisboa'	EOrc ETho EVal
¶ – x *viticella*	EHan
'Candy Stripe'	CSCl MCad
'Capitaine Thuilleaux'	See C. 'Souvenir du Capitaine Thuilleaux'
'Cardinal Wyszynski'	See C. 'Kardynal Wyszynski'
'Carmencita'	EOvi NBrk
'Carnaby' (L)	CBow CCMG CSPN EBre EHan ELan EOvi ERom ETho EVal LBre LPri MBar MBri MCad MRav SBod SBra WBod WTre WWeb
'Caroline'	CPev MCad
x ***cartmanii*** (Fo)	ECou
– 'Joe' (Fo)	EPot EVal MCad NHar WAbe
'Cassiopeia' (PxL)	EOvi
'Centre Attraction'	MCad
'Chalcedony' (FxL)	CPev CSCl EHan EOvi MCad NBrk WMer
'Charissima' (P)	CBow CMac CPev CSCl EHan EOvi ETho LPri MCad
'Cherry Brandy'	LPri
chiisanensis	EOvi MCad MSto NBea
chinensis	CSCl EVal LRHS MCad
¶ 'Christian Steven' (J)	MCad
chrysantha	EOvi
– var. ***paucidentata***	See C. ***hilariae***
N ***chrysocoma***	CBow CCMG CCla CHad CHan CPev CSCl EBar ELan EOvi ETho EVal GMac LPri MBar MBea MCad MGos MRav NHol SBla SBra SDix SPer SSta WCru WTre WWat
– B&L 12237	NBea SBra SWas
– B&L 12324	SBra
– hybrid	CSCl
– ***sericea***	See C. ***montana sericea***
– ***spooneri***	See C. ***montana sericea***
§ ***cirrhosa***	CBot CBow CHan CPev CSCl EBre EHan ELan EOvi ETho LBre LPri MCad SPer WSHC
– var. ***balearica*** AGM	Widely available
– – forms	CPev MCad WCru
– 'Freckles' AGM	CB&S CBow CCMG CCla CDoC COtt CSCl CSPN EBre EHan ELan EOrc EOvi ERav ETho EVal LBre LPri MBri MCad NBea NHol SBra SPer SPla WTre WWat
– 'Ourika Valley'	SBla
– 'Wisley Cream'	CB&S CCMG CSCl CSPN ECtt EGol EHan ELan EOrc ERom EVal LPri LRHS MAsh MCad NHol NSti SBra SPer SPla
coactilis	CSCl MCad
'Colette Deville' (J)	CSCl MCad NBrk SBra
columbiana	CNic MCad MSto SBla
¶ – var. ***columbiana***	MSto
'Comtesse de Bouchaud' AGM	Widely available
connata	CBot MCad MSto NBrk SBra
'Continuity'	EOvi EVal MBri MCad SBra WSHC
'Corona' (PxL)	CPev CSPN ELan EOvi ETho EVal LPri MBar MCad NBea WTre
'Corry' (Ta)	MCad NBea NBrk
'Countess of Lovelace' (P)	CB&S CCla CHan CMac CSCl CSPN EBre ELan EOvi ERom ETho EVal LBre LPri MBar MBea MBri MCad NBea SBod SBra SDix SPer WBod WTre
County Park hybrids (Fo)	ECou
'Crimson King' (L)	EOvi ETho EVal MAsh MBea MCad SBod SBra WGor WTre
crispa	CSCl EOvi MCad MSto SBra
§ – 'Cylindrica'	CSCl MCad MSto
I – 'Rosea'	See C. ***c.*** 'Cylindrica'
♦ ***cunninghamii***	See C. ***parviflora***
x ***cylindrica***	CSCl CSPN EHan EOrc EOvi ETho EVal LRHS MCad NBea SBra
'Daniel Deronda' AGM	CBow CCMG CPev CSCl CSPN EBre EHan ELan EOvi ERom ETho EVal LBre LPri MBea MBri MCad NBea SBod SBra SDix SPer SSta WBod WTre
'Darlene'	LPri
'Dawn' (L/P)	CBow CCMG CPev CSCl CSPN EBre EHan EOvi ERom ETho EVal LBre LPri MCad NBea SBra SChu SPer SPla WStI
'Debutante'	MCad
¶ ***delavayi*** var. ***spinescens*** KGB 283	MSto
'Denny's Double'	MCad NBrk
denticulata	WCru
– P&W 6287	MCad
* 'Dilly Dilly'	MCad
dioscoreifolia	See C. ***terniflora***
¶ 'Doctor Label'	MCad
'Doctor Ruppel' AGM	CBow CCMG CMac CPev CRHN CSCl CSPN EBre EHan ELan EOvi ERom ETho EVal LBre LPri MBar MBea MBri MCad MGos NBea NRoo SBod SBra SDix SHBN SPer WSHC WTre
'Donna'	MCad
'Dorothy Tolver'	ETho
'Dorothy Walton' (J)	EOvi ETho EVal LPri MCad SBra
douglasii	See C. ***hirsutissima***
drummondii	MCad
'Duchess of Albany' AGM	Widely available
'Duchess of Edinburgh' (F)	Widely available
'Duchess of Sutherland' (Vt)	CPev CSCl CSPN EHan EOvi ETho EVal LPri MAsh MBri MCad SBra SDix SPla WBod WSHC WTre
x ***durandii*** AGM	Widely available
'East Sunset'	MCad
'Ebba'	MCad
'Edith' AGM	CBow CCMG CSPN EHan EOvi ETho EVal LPri MAsh MBri MCad NBea NBrk WGor WWat
'Edomurasaki' (L)	CSPN EVal LPri LRHS
'Edouard Desfossé' (P)	MCad NBea
'Edward Prichard'	EHan EOvi MCad NBea NBrk SBra SDix
¶ 'Ellenbank White'	GMac
§ 'Elsa Späth' AGM	Widely available
'Elvan' (Vt)	CBar CHan CPev EHan EOvi GMac MCad NBea WSHC
'Emajogi' (L)	EOvi

Name	Suppliers
'Empress of India' (P)	EOvi EVal LPri MCad
§ x *eriostemon* (D)	CCla CRHN CSCl CSPN EHan EOvi ETho EVal MCad NWyt SBla SBra SChu SPer
– 'Blue Boy' (D)	MBri MCad SBra
§ – 'Hendersonii' (D)	CBow CCMG CCla CPev CSco EBre EGol EHan EHar ELan EOrc EOvi ETho LBre LHop MCad MRav MUlv NBea NBir NHol SBra SDix SHil SPer SPla WOMN WSHC WTre
'Ernest Markham' AGM	Widely available
'Esperanto' (J)	EOvi MCad
'Etoile de Malicorne' (P)	CSPN EHan EOvi ETho EVal MBri MCad NBea SBra WGor
'Etoile de Paris' (P)	EOvi ETho MCad SBra
'Etoile Rose' (T)	CBow CCla CHan CPev CSCl EBre EHan ELan EOrc EOvi ETho EVal IOrc LBre LPri MCad NBea SBla SBra SChu SHil SPer WSHC WTre
'Etoile Violette' AGM	Widely available
'Fair Rosamond' (L/P)	CCMG CPev CSCl CSPN EOvi ERom ETho EVal LPri MBri MCad NBea SBod SBra SDix WTre
'Fairy' (x *indivisa*) (Fo)	ECou
'Fairy Queen' (L)	EOvi ETho EVal LPri MCad SBra
fargesii	See C. ***potaninii***
x *fargesioïdes*	See C. 'Paul Farges'
'Farrago'	MCad
fasciculiflora	CBot CCMG CGre CHan CMHG CSCl EOrc MCad NBea NSti SMrm WCru WSHC
¶ – L 657	SBla
finetiana	MCad
'Fireworks' AGM	CBow COtt CSPN EBee EHan EOvi ERom ETho EVal MCad NBea WGor WTre
¶ 'Flamingo' (L)	EOvi MCad
flammula	Widely available
– 'Rubra Marginata'	See C. x ***triternata*** 'Rubromarginata'
'Floralia'	CSPN EBee EHan ELan EOvi EVal LRHS MBri MCad
florida	ETho
– *bicolor*	See C. *f.* 'Sieboldii'
– 'Flore Pleno'	CBow CCMG CCla CHan CPev CSCl CSPN EHan ELan EOrc EOvi ERom ETho EVal MCad NBea NHol SBla SBra SHBN SHil SMad SPer SPla WSHC WTre
§ – 'Sieboldii'	Widely available
foetida	ECou MCad MSto WAbe
forrestii	See C. ***napaulensis***
§ *forsteri*	CHan CSCl CSPN CSam EPot ERom EVal LPri MCad NBea SBod SBra WCru WOMN WSHC
'Four Star' (L)	LPri MCad
'Fuji-musume' (L)	EOvi LPri MCad SHil WMer
fusca hort.	See C. ***japonica***
fusca Turczaninow	MCad
§ – ssp. *fusca*	CSCl EHan
– var. *kamtschatica*	See C. ***fusca fusca***
– var. *mandshurica*	CSCl
– var. *violacea*	CSCl ETho MCad MSto SBra
'G Steffner' (A)	EOvi
¶ 'Gabrielle' (P)	WMer

Name	Suppliers
'Général Sikorski' AGM	CBow CCMG CMac CSCl CSPN CSam EBre EHan ELan EOvi ERom ETho EVal LBre LPri MBea MBri MCad MGos NBea SBra SDix SPer WBod WTre WWat
gentianoïdes	CSPN EVal GCHN MBri MCad
'Georg' (A)	EOvi
'Gillian Blades' AGM	CBow CSCl CSPN EBre EHan ELan EOvi ETho EVal LBre MBea MBri MCad NBea SBra WTre
'Gipsy Queen' AGM	Widely available
'Gladys Picard' (P)	MCad
glauca hort.	See C. ***intricata***
'Glynderek' (L)	EVal MCad
gouriana	CCla SBra
gracilifolia	EOvi EVal
'Grandiflora Sanguinea' (Vt)	CSPN EBre EHan EOvi EVal LBre MCad SBod SBra
grata hort.	See C. x ***jouiniana***
grata Wallich	CPev MBea MCad NBrk WEas
'Gravetye Beauty' (T)	Widely available
'Gravetye Seedling' (T)	EOvi
'Green Velvet' (Fo)	ECou
'Guernsey'	CSPN EHan EVal MCad
¶ 'Guernsey Cream'	CBow MCad WTre
'Guiding Star'	MCad
'H F Young' AGM	Widely available
'Hagley Hybrid' (J)	Widely available
'Hainton Ruby'	EVal
¶ 'Haku-no-hoshi'	EOvi
'Haku-ôkan' (L)	CPev CSCl CSPN EHan EOvi ETho EVal LPri MAsh MBea MCad SBod SBra WTre
¶ 'Halina Nell' (F)	NBrk
¶ 'Hanaguruma' (P)	MCad WMer
'Harlequin'	MCad
Havering hybrids (Fo)	ECou
'Heirloom'	MCad
¶ 'Helen Cropper'	NBrk
'Helios' (Ta)	CSCl EVal MBri MCad MGos NBrk SBra
'Helsingborg' AGM	CB&S CBow CSCl CSPN EBre EHan ELan EOrc EOvi ETho EVal LBre LPri MBri MCad NSti SBra SMad SPla WTre
♦ *hendersonii* Koch	See C. x ***eriostemon*** 'Hendersonii'
♦ *hendersonii* Standley	See C. x ***eriostemon***
'Henryi' AGM	CBow CCMG CCla CPev CRHN CSCl CSPN EBre EHan ELan EOvi ERom ETho EVal IOrc LBre LPri MBar MBea MBri MCad NBea SBra SDix SPer WBod WSHC WTre
heracleifolia	CBot CBow CPou CSCl EHan ETho MCad NRoo NWyt
N– 'Campanile'	CCla CPev CSCl EHan EOvi LPri MCad NBea NBir SBra SDix
N– 'Côte d'Azur'	CBot EBre EFol EOvi ETho LBre MCad NBea SHil
– var. *davidiana*	CHad CPev ELan EOvi NHol SPla WByw
– – 'Wyevale' AGM	CBot CBow CCla CHan CPev CSCl CSPN EGol ELan EVal IHos LHop LPri MBri MCad MUlv NBea NRoo SBra SDix SMad SPer WEas WHil WTre WWye
– 'Jaggards'	CBot

'Herbert Johnson' (P)	CMac CPev EOvi MCad SBra
hexapetala De Candolle	See C. ***forsteri***
hexapetala hort.	See C. ***recta recta lasiosepala***
'Hidcote Purple' (L)	MCad
¶ 'Hikarugengi'	MCad
§ ***hilariae***	CSCl EHan SBra
'Hint of Pink'	MCad
§ ***hirsuta***	EVal
hirsutissima	EPot LGre MSto
– var. ***scottii***	MCad MUlv NBea
¶ 'Honora'	MCad
hookeriana	MSto
'Horn of Plenty' **AGM**	CBow CCMG CSCl CSPN EHan EOvi ERom ETho EVal MBea MBri MCad SBra SDix
'Huldine' (Vt)	Widely available
§ 'Hybrida Sieboldii' (L)	CMac CRHN CSCl CSPN EHan EOvi EVal LPri MBea MCad NBea NBrk SBod SBra SPer
ianthina	See C. ***fusca violacea***
'Ilka' (P)	EOvi
§ ***indivisa***	CGre CPev ECou EHan EVal MCad WSHC
– (f)	CGre MCad NHar
– (m)	MCad
¶ – ***lobata***	EVal LRHS
integrifolia	CBow CHan CPou CSCl EHan EOrc EVal LGan LHop LPri MBri MBro MCad MGos NHol NPer NRoo NSti SFis SPer WCra WPer WTyr
§ – var. ***albiflora***	CBow EHan EOvi ETho EVal LPri MCad NBea NBir NBrk NRoo SBra
* – 'Finnis Form'	SChu WSHC
– 'Hendersonii' Koch	See C. x ***eriostemon*** 'H.'
– 'Olgae'	CCMG CCla CDoC CPev CRHN CSCl CSPN EHan EOvi ETho EVal LPri MCad NBea NBrk NWyt SBra SDix
– 'Pangbourne Pink'	EVal MCad SBra
– 'Pastel Blue'	CPev
– 'Pastel Pink'	CPev EHan ETho
– 'Rosea' **AGM**	CBot CBow CCla CDoC CPev CSCl CSPN EHan EOvi ETho EVal LGan LPri MBri MCad NBea NBrk NPer SHil
– 'Tapestry'	CPev MCad
– white	See C. ***i. albiflora***
§ ***intricata***	CGre CSCl CSPN EVal MCad MSto NSti WCru WWat
'Ishobel'	EOvi LPri MCad
ispahanica	See C. ***orientalis*** Linnaeus
'Jackmanii' **AGM**	CBra CMac CRHN CSCl EBre EHan ENot EOvi GRei IHos LBre MCad NBea NEgg NRoo NWea SBod SBra SChu SPer SPla
'Jackmanii Alba' (J)	CCMG CCla CPev CSCl CSPN EBre ELan EOvi ERom ETho EVal IJoh LBre LPri MBar MBea MBri MCad NBea NBrk SBra SDix SPer WTre
'Jackmanii Rubra' (J)	CPev CSCl EHan EOvi LPri MAsh MCad NBea SBra WTre
N 'Jackmanii Superba' (J)	Widely available
'James Mason'	CPev CSCl EHan ETho MCad WMer
§ 'Jan Pawel II' ('John Paul II') (J)	CBow CCla CSCl CSPN EBre EHan ELan EOvi EVal LBre LPri MCad NBea SBra SPer WTre
japonica	CPev CSCl EOvi ETho MCad NBea
¶ 'Jashio'	MCad
'Jim Hollis' (F)	EOvi MCad
'Joan Picton' (P)	CSCl EHan EOvi ETho LPri MAsh MBea MCad WTre
¶ 'Joanna' (f)	ECou
'John Gould Veitch' (F)	EOvi MCad
'John Huxtable' (J)	CDoC CPev EHan EOvi ETho EVal LPri MBri MCad NBea SBra SDix SPla WGor
'John Paul II'	See C. 'Jan Pawel II'
'John Warren' (L)	CCla CSCl EHan EOvi ETho EVal LPri MCad NBea SBod SBra SDix SPer WTre
¶ 'Jorma' (J)	MCad
§ x ***jouiniana***	CBow CPou EHan EOvi EVal ISea MBal MBea MCad MUlv SHil SPer WSHC
§ – 'Mrs Robert Brydon'	CBow CCMG CDoC CSco CShe EGol EVal GCal MCad NBea NBrk NHol NSti SPer
– 'Praecox' **AGM**	Widely available
¶ 'Jubileinyi 70'	EOvi
'Kacper' (L)	CSCl EOvi LPri MCad
§ 'Kakio' (P)	CSCl CSPN EHan ELan EOvi ETho EVal LPri MBri MCad SBra SPer WGor
'Kaleidoscope'	MCad
§ 'Kardynał Wyszyński' (J)	CBow CRHN CSCl EOvi LPri MBea MCad NBea SBra SPla
¶ 'Katherine'	MCad WMer
'Kathleen Dunford' (F)	CBow CSCl EHan EOvi ERom ETho EVal LPri MAsh MBea MCad NBea SBra WMer WTre
'Kathleen Wheeler' (P)	CBow CCMG CMac CPev CSco EHan EOvi ERom ETho EVal LPri MBri MCad NBea SBra SDix
'Keith Richardson' (P)	CPev CSCl EOvi LPri MCad SBra
'Ken Donson' **AGM**	CMac CSPN EOvi ETho EVal MCad NBrk SBod
§ 'Kermesina' (Vt)	CCla CMac CPev CSam CSco EBre EHan ELan EOvi ERav ETho EVal LBre LPri MBea MBri MCad MRav NBea NHol NSti SBra SDix SMad SPer SSta SUsu WSHC WWat
'King Edward VII' (L)	CSPN EHan EOvi ERom ETho EVal LPri MCad NBea SBra WGor
'King George V' (L)	EOvi ETho MBea MCad NBea SBra
'Kiri Te Kanawa'	CPev EHan MCad NBrk
kirilovii	SBra
koreana	CSCl EOvi MCad MSto SBra
– var. ***fragrans***	CSCl EOvi SPla
– f. ***lutea***	CSCl EOvi MCad MSto
'Kosmiczeskaja Melodija' (J)	MCad
ladakhiana	CHan CPev CSCl EHal EHan EOvi ETho MCad MSto NBea NBir SBra WEas WSHC

'Lady Betty Balfour' (J/Vt)	CBow CCMG CCla CMac CPev CRHN CSCl CSPN CSco EBre EHan ELan EOvi ERom EVal GRei LBre LPri MBea MBri MCad NBea NWyt SBra SDix WSHC WStI WTre
'Lady Caroline Nevill' (L)	CPev CRHN EOvi ETho EVal LPri MCad NBea SBra SChu WTre
'Lady Londesborough' (P)	CPev CSCl CSPN EGol EHan ELan EOvi ETho EVal LPri MCad NBea NBrk SBra SDix
'Lady Northcliffe' (L)	CBow CCMG CMac CPev CSCl EHan ELan EOvi ERom EVal LPri MAsh MCad NBea SBra SDix SPer WTre
'Ladybird Johnson' (T)	CPev CSCl EHan EOvi ETho MCad NBrk
'Lagoon'	See C. ***macropetala*** 'Maidwell Hall'
¶ ***lanuginosa*** 'Candida'	MCad
lasiandra	MBea
'Lasurstern' **AGM**	Widely available
¶ 'Laura' (L)	MCad
'Laura Denny'	EOvi MCad
'Lavender Lace'	MCad
'Lawsoniana' (L)	CCMG CMac CSCl EHan ETho LPri MAsh MBar MBea MCad NBea NBrk SBra WStI
¶ 'Lemon Chiffon'	EVal
§ ***ligusticifolia***	EVal MCad MSto NBea SBra
'Lilacina Floribunda' (L)	CSCl CSPN EHan ELan EOvi EVal LPri MBea MCad NBrk SBra WSHC WTre
* 'Lilactime'	EVal LPri
'Lincoln Star' (P)	CCMG CPev CSPN CSam CSco EHan ELan EOvi ERom ETho EVal LPri MBar MBea MBri MCad MRav NBea NBrk SBra SDix SPer WBod WTre
'Lincolnshire Lady'	EVal
'Little Nell' (Vt)	CBow CCMG CCla CPev CSCl CSPN EHan ELan EOvi EVal LPri MBea MBri MCad NBea NBrk NHol SBod SBra SDix SPer SReu SSta WSHC WTre
'Lord Nevill' **AGM**	CBow CCMG CPev CSCl EBre EOvi EVal LBre LPri MBea MBri MCad NBea SBod SBra SChu SDix SPer WStI WTre
'Louise Rowe' (F)	CSCl EHan EOvi ETho LPri MCad SBra WTre
'Lucie' (P)	MCad NBrk
¶ 'Lunar Lass' (Fo)	EPot
'Lunar Lass' x ***foetida***	ECou GCHN
'Luther Burbank' (J)	EOvi MCad
macropetala (A)	Widely available
– 'Alborosea'	EOvi
– 'Anders' (A)	EOvi EVal
– 'Ballerina' (A)	MCad
– 'Ballet Skirt' (A)	EOvi MCad MGos SPla
– 'Blue Lagoon' (A)	See C. ***m.*** 'Maidwell Hall'
– forms	CPev
– 'Harry Smith'	EVal LRHS
– 'Jan Lindmark' (A)	CSPN EBre EHan EOvi ETho EVal LBre LRHS MBri MCad MGos SPla WGor
§ – 'Maidwell Hall' **AGM**	CBow CCMG CCla CDoC CMac CSCl EBre EOvi ERom ETho EVal LBre LPri LRHS MBea MBri MCad MGos NHol NRoo SBla SBra SChu SHBN SPer SPla SSta WStI WTre
– 'Markham's Pink' **AGM**	Widely available
– 'Pauline' (A)	MCad SBra
– 'Pearl Rose' (A)	MCad
– 'Rödklokke (A)	MCad
I – 'Rosea'	EOvi
¶ – 'Salmonea'	EOvi
– 'Snowbird' (A)	CPev EOvi MCad NBea NHol NRoo
– 'Vicky'	CSCl
– 'Westleton'	NHol
– 'White Moth'	See C. ***alpina sibirica*** 'W. M.'
– 'White Swan'	See C. 'White Swan'
'Madame Baron Veillard' (J)	CPev CSCl CSPN EHan EOvi ERom ETho EVal LPri MBar MBea MCad NBea NBrk SBra SChu SDix WTre
'Madame Edouard André' **AGM**	CCMG CCla CDoC CMac CPev CSCl EHan EOvi ETho EVal LPri MBea MCad NBea SBra SDix WSHC WTre
'Madame Grangé' **AGM**	CPev CSPN CSco EOvi ERom ETho EVal LPri MBea MCad NBea NBrk SBod SBra SDix WTre
'Madame Julia Correvon' **AGM**	CBar CCla CHad CMac CSPN EBre EHan ELan EOrc EOvi ETho EVal LBre LPri MBar MBea MBri MCad MGos NBea NBir SBla SBra SChu SDix SPer SPla SSta WSHC WWat
'Madame le Coultre'	See C. 'Marie Boisselot'
¶ 'Madame van Houtte' (L)	MCad
mandschurica	CSCl MCad SBra
marata	NSla SBra WAbe
– 'Temple Prince' (m)	ECou
– 'Temple Queen' (f)	ECou
'Marcel Moser' (P)	CPev EHan EOvi EVal MCad NBea NBrk SBra SDix
'Margaret Hunt' (J)	CSCl CSPN EOvi ETho EVal LPri MCad NBrk SBra SPla WTre
¶ 'Margaret Jones'	EOvi
'Margot Koster' (Vt)	CDoC CSCl EBre EHan EOvi EVal LBre LPri MBea MCad NBea NWyt SBla SBra SSta WSHC WTre
§ 'Marie Boisselot' **AGM**	Widely available
'Marie Louise Jensen' (J)	EOvi MCad
¶ 'Marinka'	MCad
marmoraria **AGM**	ECou EPot GArf LBee MCad MSto NBir NHar NHol SBla WAbe
¶ – hybrid	CNic
¶ – x ***petriei*** (f)	CNic
¶ 'Maskarad' (Vt)	CSPN EVal LRHS
§ 'Matka Teresa'	MCad
'Matthais' (PxL)	EOvi
'Maureen' (L)	CBow CPev CSCl CSPN EHan EOvi ERom ETho EVal LPri MBri MCad NBea SBra SDix SPer WTre
maximowicziana	See C. ***terniflora***
¶ 'Meeli' (J)	MCad

microphylla	ECou MCad
'Minister' (P)	EOvi MCad
'Minuet' AGM	CCla CSCl CSPN EBre EHan EOvi ETho EVal IOrc LBre LPri MBea MBri MCad NBea NHol NRoo SBra SChu SDix SPer WSHC WTre
'Miriam Markham' (J)	CPev MCad
'Miss Bateman' AGM	Widely available
'Miss Crawshay' (P)	CBow CPev CSCl EOvi EVal MBea MCad NBea SBra SDix
N***montana***	Widely available
– ***alba***	See C. ***montana***
– 'Alexander'	CBow CCMG CDoC CSCl CSPN CSco EHan EOvi ERom EVal LPri MBea MBri MCad MGos SBra WCru
– 'Boughton Beauty'	EHan
– 'Elizabeth' AGM	Widely available
– 'Freda' AGM	CBow CSCl EBre EHan EOvi ETho EVal LBre LPri MBri MCad MGos NBea NHol SAxl SBra SDix SHBN SMad SPer SPla WBod
¶ – 'Gothenburg'	EVal
– f. ***grandiflora*** AGM	CBow CCMG CCla CMac CSco EBre ECtt EHan ELan EOvi ERom ETho GMac ISea LBre LPri MBea MBri MCad MGos NBea SBra SDix SPer SReu WBod WSHC WTre WWat
– 'Marjorie' (d)	CB&S CBow CDoC CSCl EBre ECtt EHan ELan EOvi ERom ETho EVal GMac LBre LPri MBal MBri MCad MRav NBea NHol NRoo SBra SHBN SPer SPla WSHC WTre
– 'Mayleen'	CBow CHad CSCl EHan EOvi ERom EVal LPri MBea MBri MCad MGos NBea SBra SHBN SPer
– 'Mrs Margaret Jones'	ERav ETho MCad SBra
– 'Odorata'	CDoC CSCl EOvi ERom ETho EVal LRHS MBea MCad MGos SBra WGor WWat
– 'Peveril'	CPev MCad
– 'Picton's Variety'	CBow CDoC CHan CPev CRHN CSCl EOrc EOvi ETho GMac LPri MBri MCad NBea SBra SHBN SPla WTre
– 'Pink Perfection'	CBow CCMG CDoC CSCl CSco EBre EHan ELan EOvi ERom ETho EVal LBre LPri MBea MBri MCad NBea NBrk NHol SBra WTre
¶ – 'Pleniflora'	MCad
– var. ***rubens*** AGM	Widely available
– 'Rubens Superba'	See C. ***m.*** 'Superba'
§ – var. ***sericea*** AGM	CBot CHan CPev EHan EOvi GMac LPri MCad NBea NBrk NHol SBra WTre WWat
– 'Snow'	EOvi
– 'Spooneri'	See C. ***montana sericea***
§ – 'Superba'	CSco ECtt GAri SHBN WTre
– 'Tetrarose' AGM	Widely available
– 'Veitch's Form'	CBot
– 'Vera'	CBow EHan EOvi EVal MCad NBea NBir SBra
– 'Warwickshire Rose'	CHan GMac
– var. ***wilsonii***	CBar CBot CBow CCMG CCla CLan CPev CSCl CSco EBre EHan ELan EOvi ETho EVal LBre LHol LPri MBar MBea MBri MCad MRav MWat NBea SDix SPer SPla WSHC
'Monte Cassino' (J)	CSCl MCad
§ 'Moonlight' (P)	CBow CPev CSCl EOvi ETho EVal MCad NBea SBra SDix SPer WTre
♦ 'Mother Therese'	See C. 'Matka Teresa'
'Mrs Bush' (L)	EOvi EVal LRHS MCad NBea
'Mrs Cholmondeley' AGM	Widely available
'Mrs George Jackman' AGM	CCla CPev CRHN EOvi ETho EVal LPri MBea MCad NBea SBra SDix WBod WTre
'Mrs Hope' (L)	CPev EOvi EVal MAsh MCad NBea SBra SChu SDix
'Mrs James Mason'	CPev EHan EOvi ETho EVal MCad SBra
'Mrs N Thompson' (P)	CBow CCMG CMac CPev CRHN CSCl CSPN EBre EHan ELan EOvi ERom ETho EVal LBre LPri MBar MBea MBri MCad NBea SBod SBra SDix SHBN SPla SSta WBod WStI WTre
'Mrs P B Truax' (P)	CSPN EHan EOvi ETho EVal LPri MCad NBea SBra SDix WTre
'Mrs Robert Brydon'	See C. x ***jouiniana*** 'Mrs R.B.'
'Mrs Spencer Castle' (Vt)	CPev CSCl EHan EOvi ETho EVal LPri MAsh MBea MCad NBea SBra SDix WTre
'Mrs T Lundell'	EOvi MCad NBrk
¶ 'Mukle'	MCad
'Multi Blue'	CSCl EBre EHan ELan EOvi ETho EVal LBre LPri MCad NBea SHil SMad WTre
¶ 'Muly'	MCad
¶ 'Musa China' (L)	MCad
'Myôjô' (P)	CSCl EOvi EVal LPri MBea MCad NBea WMer
¶ 'Myôkô'	MCad WMer
§ ***napaulensis***	CPev CSCl EHan EHic EOvi EVal IBlr LPri MBea MCad SBra
'Natacha'	MCad
'Negritjanka' (J)	EOvi
'Nelly Moser' AGM	Widely available
New Zealand hybrids	ECou
'Nikolaj Rubtzov'	EOvi MCad
'Niobe' AGM	Widely available
'North Star'	MCad
¶ 'Nuit de Chine'	MCad
occidentalis	MSto
– ssp. ***grosseserrata***	CSCl
orientalis 'Bill Mackenzie'	See C. 'Bill Mackenzie'
– 'Orange Peel'	See C. ***tibetana vernayi*** 'O.P.'
*– 'Rubromarginata'	CPev
– 'Sherriffii'	See C. ***tibetana vernayi*** LS&E 13342
orientalis hort.	See C. ***tibetana vernayi***
§ ***orientalis*** Linnaeus	EHan MCad NHol SBod SBra SReu
¶ – var. ***daurica***	CHan
'Otto Froebel' (L)	MCad
'Paddington'	MCad

'Pagoda' (Vt)	CBar CCla CDoC CPev CRHN CSCl CSam EHan EOvi ETho EVal MBea MCad SBra SPer SPla WSHC WWat
'Pamela Jackman'	See C. ***alpina*** 'P.J.'
paniculata Gmelin	See C. ***indivisa***
paniculata Thunberg	See C. ***ternifolia***
¶ 'Paola'	MCad
'Parasol'	MCad
§ ***parviflora***	MSto
'Pat Ann'	MCad
patens	CSPN EOvi EVal NBrk SBra
§ 'Paul Farges'	CSPN EVal SBra
'Pennell's Purity' (L)	MCad
'Percy Picton' (P)	MAsh MCad NBea
'Perle d'Azur' **AGM**	Widely available
¶ 'Perrin's Pride' (Vt)	CSPN EVal LRHS MCad NBrk WMer
petriei	ECou EOvi EPot WAbe
– 'Limelight' (m)	CSCl ECou
– 'Princess' (f)	ECou
petriei x ***foetida***	ECou
– x ***forsteri***	ECou
¶ – x ***marmoraria***	GCHN
– x ***parviflora***	ECou
'Peveril Pearl' (P)	CPev CSPN EHan ERom ETho EVal LPri MCad
'Pink Champagne'	See C. 'Kakio'
'Pink Fantasy' (J)	CMac CPev CSCl EBre EHan EOvi ETho EVal IJoh LBre LPri MAsh MCad WTre
'Pink Flamingo'	MBea
'Pink Pearl'	EOvi MCad
pitcheri	CBow CHan CPev CSCl EOrc EOvi ETho EVal MBri MCad NBea NBrk WSHC
¶ 'Pöhjanael' (J)	MCad
'Polish Spirit' **AGM**	CBow CDoC CSPN EBre EHan ELan EOrc EOvi EVal LBre MBri MCad NHol SBra SPer SPla WGor
§ ***potaninii***	CSCl ELan EOvi EVal MBri MCad NBea SBra
§ – var. ***potaninii***	CCla CGle CHan CMHG CPev EHan MBri MCad NBea SBra SDix SPer WSHC
– var. ***souliei***	See P. ***p. potaninii***
'Prince Charles' (J)	CBow CHad EHan EOvi ETho EVal LPri MCad NBea NBir NRoo SBra SDix
'Princess of Wales' (T)	CPev CSCl EOvi ETho EVal LPri MCad SApp SBra WSHC
'Prins Hendrik' (L/P)	CMac CSCl EHan EOvi EVal MBea MCad NBea SBra WGor
'Proteus' (F)	CB&S CBow CCMG CPev CSCl CSPN EBre EHan ELan EOvi ERom ETho EVal LBre LPri MCad NBea NWyt SBra SDix SPer SPla WSHC WTre
quadribracteolata	ECou EOvi NBea WAbe
¶ 'Queen Alexander'	MCad
'Radiant'	MCad
'Ramona'	See C. 'Hybrida Sieboldii'
¶ ***ranunculoïdes*** KGB 111	MSto
recta	CBow CHad CHan CPev CSPN EHan ELan EOvi ERom EVal LPri MBri MCad NBea NHol NRoo NWCA NWyt SAxl SPer WByw WHoo
– 'Grandiflora'	CSCl NHol
– 'Peveril'	CPev EHan

– 'Purpurea'	Widely available
§ – ssp. ***recta*** var. ***lasiosepala***	WWat
rehderiana **AGM**	Widely available
'Rhapsody'	CPev MCad WSHC
'Richard Pennell' **AGM**	CBow CCla CMac CPev CSCl CSPN EHan EOvi ERom ETho EVal LPri MBri MCad NBea SBra SDix WTre
'Rose Supreme'	MCad
'Rosie O'Grady' (A)	CSPN EHan ELan EOrc EOvi ETho EVal LPri MBar MBea MBri MCad NBea NHol NSti SBra SPer SPla
'Rouge Cardinal' (J)	Widely available
'Royal Velours' **AGM**	CCMG CCla CDoC CPev CSCl CSPN EHan ELan EOvi ETho EVal IOrc LPri MBea MCad NBea NHol SBla SBod SBra SChu SDix SHBN SHil WWat
'Royal Velvet'	CBow CSPN EHan EVal LRHS MCad WTre
'Royalty' **AGM**	CBow CSCl CSPN EBre EHan ELan EOvi ERom ETho EVal LBre LPri MBri MCad NBea NBir SBra SDix WBod WTre
'Ruby Anniversary'	MCad
'Ruby Glow' (L)	EOvi EVal MCad SBra
'Ruby Lady'	LPri
¶ 'Rüütel' (J)	MCad
'S Ruczehet'	MCad
'Sally Cadge' (P)	MCad
'Saturn' (Vt)	MCad SBra
'Scartho Gem' (P)	CMac CPev CSCl EHan EOvi EVal MCad SBra
¶ 'Schneeglanz'	MCad
'Sealand Gem' (L)	CCMG CPev CSCl CSPN EHan EOvi ETho EVal MBea MCad NBar NBea NWyt SBod SBra WTre
'Serenata' (J)	CRHN CSCl EHan EOvi ETho EVal LPri MBea MCad NBea NBir SBra
serratifolia	CCla CHan CPev CSCl CSPN EGol EHan EOvi EVal LPri MBea MBri MCad NBea NSti SBra SDix SPer SWas
'Shogun'	MCad
'Signe' (P)	MCad
'Silver Lining'	MCad
'Silver Moon' **AGM**	CBow CSCl CSPN EHan EOvi EVal LPri MAsh MCad NBea SBra SChu WMer WTre
¶ 'Simi'	MCad
¶ ***simsii***	EHan
'Sir Garnet Wolseley' (P)	CRHN EHan EOvi EVal MCad NBea NBrk SBod SBra SDix
'Sir Trevor Lawrence' (T)	CBow CCla CPev CSCl CSam EHan EOrc EOvi ETho EVal LPri MCad NBea SBod SBra SDix SPer WSHC WWat
'Sizaja Ptitsa' (T)	EOvi
'Snow Queen'	CBow CSCl CSPN EHan EOvi ETho EVal LPri MCad NBea SBra WTre
songarica	CSCl CSPN EOvi EVal GAul MBri MCad MSto SBra WSHC
¶ – 'Sundance'	EVal

'Souvenir de J L Delbard' (P)	MCad NBrk SBra
§ 'Souvenir du Capitaine Thuilleaux' (P)	CPev EHan EOvi ERom ETho EVal LPri MBea MBri MCad SBra SPer WTre
spooneri	See C. ***montana sericea***
– 'Rosea'	See C. x ***vedrariensis*** 'Rosea'
'Sputnik' (J)	MGos SBra
¶ sp. B&SWJ 292	WCru
sp. EMAK 1029	NHol
stans	CPou EHan ESis EVal SIng
¶ 'Star Fish' (L)	MCad
'Star of India' **AGM**	CBow CPev CSCl EHan ELan EOvi ETho EVal LPri MBri MCad NBea NWyt SBra SDix
'Strawberry Roan'	EOvi EVal
¶ 'Sugar Candy'	EVal
¶ 'Sunset' (J)	CSPN EVal LRHS MCad
'Susan Allsop' (L)	CPev EOvi MCad
'Sylvia Denny' (F)	CBow CCMG CCla CHad CSPN EBre EHan ELan EOvi ETho EVal LBre LPri MBar MBea MBri MCad MRav NBea SBod SBra SPer WTre
'Sympatia' (Vt)	CSCl MCad
'Tage Lundell' (A)	CSPN EOrc EOvi EVal GMac LRHS
¶ 'Tango' (T)	EHan ETho MCad
tangutica	Widely available
– 'Aureolin'	See C. 'Aureolin'
– 'Bill Mackenzie'	See C. 'B. M.'
– 'Gravetye Variety'	CCMG CSCl NHol
– 'Lambton Park'	EHan EOvi ETho EVal LPri MCad NBea NBir SBra SPla
– 'Warsaw'	EOrc MBri
§ ***ternifolia***	CPev CSCl EOrc EVal LPri MCad NBea NBrk SBra SPer WSHC
– Caddick's form	CHan
– ***mandshurica***	See C. ***m.***
♦– ***robusta***	See C. ***t. t.***
§ – var. ***ternifolia***	LRHS
'Teshio' (F)	EHan LPri MCad
¶ 'Tevia'	MCad
texensis	CGre CHan CSPN EOvi MCad MSto SReu
'The Comet'	LPri
'The President' **AGM**	Widely available
'The Vagabond'	LPri MCad
thunbergii hort.	See C. ***terniflora***
thunbergii Steudel	See C. ***hirsuta***
§ ***tibetana***	CMac CPev CSPN ELan EOrc ETho EVal MBal MBar MBea MCad MSto NHol NNor SPer WSHC WWat
§ – ssp. ***vernayi*** **AGM**	CCla CHan CMHG CSCl EBar EOvi EPot ESis LMer MCad MPla SBra WCru WWin
– ssp. ***vernayi*** C&Mc 193	NWCA
§ – ssp. ***vernayi*** LS&E 13342	CPev CSCl EHan EOrc EOvi ETho EVal MBri MCad NBea NBrk NHol SBla SBra SDix SPer WTre
– – var. ***laciniifolia***	WCru
§ – – 'Orange Peel'	ENot EVal IOrc MCad MGos
'Trianon' (P)	MCad
§ x ***triternata*** 'Rubromarginata' **AGM**	CBow CCla CDoC CPev CSCl CSPN CSco EHan EOrc ETho EVal GMac LPri MCad NBea NHol SBod SBra SDix SHil SPer SPla WCru WSHC WTre
'Tuczka' (J)	EOvi NBrk
'Twilight' (J)	CSCl CSPN EOvi ETho EVal MAsh MCad NBea SBra SPer WTre
uncinata	CPev EHan EOvi
¶ 'Valge Daam' (L)	MCad
'Vanilla Cream'	ECou
x ***vedrariensis***	EVal MCad SPer WAbe
– 'Dovedale'	CPev
– 'Highdown'	CCMG CCla CSCl LPri MBea MCad NBea NHol SBra
§ – 'Rosea'	CTrw EVal MCad MGos WSHC
'Venosa Violacea' **AGM**	CCla CSCl CSPN EHan ELan EOrc EOvi ERom ETho EVal LPri MBri MCad NBar NBea SBla SBra SDix SHil SPer SPla WTre
'Veronica's Choice' (L)	CBow CPev CRHN CSCl EHan EOvi ETho EVal MBri MCad MGos SBra
versicolor	CSCl EHan EOvi
'Victoria' (J)	CPev CSCl EBre EHan ELan EOvi ETho EVal LBre LPri MBea MCad NBea SBra SChu SDix
'Ville de Lyon' (Vt)	Widely available
'Vino' (J)	CBow CSPN EOvi ETho EVal MCad NBrk
'Violet Charm' (L)	CSPN EVal LRHS WTre
'Violet Elizabeth' (P)	CSCl MCad SBra
viorna	CSCl EHan LPri MSto NBea
virginiana Hooker	See C. ***ligusticifolia***
virginiana hort.	See C. ***vitalba***
§ ***vitalba***	CKin CPev CSCl ECWi EHan EVal MBar MBea MCad WHer
viticella	CHan CPev CSCl EHan EOvi EVal LAbb LGan LPri MCad SBra SDix WSHC WStI
¶ – 'Caerulea Luxurians'	EOvi
– 'Mary Rose' (d)	CPev EHan EOvi ETho MCad
– 'Purpurea Plena Elegans' **AGM**	Widely available
'Viticella Rubra' (Vt)	See C. 'Kermesina'
'Voluceau' (Vt)	CBow CRHN CSPN EHan EOvi EVal MBea MCad NBea SBra SPer WStI
'Vyvyan Pennell' **AGM**	Widely available
'W E Gladstone' (L)	CPev CRHN CSCl EHan EOvi EVal LPri MBea MCad NBea SBra SDix SPer WTre
'W S Callick'	MCad
'Wada's Primrose' (P)	CBow CCMG CCla CDoC CHad CSCl CSPN EBre EHan ELan EOvi ETho EVal LBre LPri MBea MBri MCad MRav NBea SBra SHil SPer SPla WSHC WTre
'Walter Pennell' (F/P)	CMac CPev CRHN EHan EOvi ETho LPri MCad SBra WGor WTre
'Warszawska Nike' (J)	CCMG CSCl EHan EOvi ETho EVal LPri MCad SBra WTre
§ 'White Swan' (A)	CBow CCMG CCla CSCl CSPN EHan EVal LPri MBri MCad MGos NHol SBra SChu SHil SPer
'White Tokyo' (A)	MGos
'Wilhemina Tull' (L)	CSCl EOvi MCad NBrk

'Will Goodwin' AGM — CB&S CSCl CSPN EHan ELan EOvi ERom ETho EVal LPri MBea MBri MCad NBea SBra WTre
'William Kennett' (L) — CBow CCMG CMac CPev CRHN CSCl CSPN CSco EHan ELan EOvi ERom ETho EVal LPri MBar MBea MBri MCad MGos MRav NBea NKay NRoo SBod SBra SChu SDix SPer WTre
¶ 'Wolga' — MCad
'Xerxes' — See C. 'Elsa Späth'
'Yellow Queen' — See C. 'Moonlight'
'Yorkshire Pride' — MCad
¶ 'Yukikomachi' (L x J) — MCad
'Yvette Houry' (L) — MCad WMer
'Zato' — MCad

CLEOME (Capparaceae)

§ ***hassleriana*** — SMrm
spinosa hort. — See C. ***hassleriana***

CLERODENDRUM (Verbenaceae)

bungei AGM — CAbb CB&S CBot CCla CGre CHEx CHad CPle CSco CWit ELan EPla ERea NPal SBor SDix SHil SLMG SMad SPer WBod WOMN WWat
fragrans var. ***pleniflorum*** — See C. ***philippinum***
myricoïdes 'Ugandense' — CNew CTro SLMG SSad
§ ***philippinum*** — ERea
x ***speciosum*** — CNew
¶ ***spectabile*** — CTro
¶ – 'Variegatum' — CTro
splendens AGM — CTro SLMG
thomsoniae AGM — CTro MBri SLMG
trichotomum — CB&S CBow CChu CCla CGre CHEx CTrw CWit EBar EBre EMil ENot ERom EWri IOrc ISea LBre NWyt SHer SMad SPer SReu SSta WBod WCoo WDin WFro WStI
– var. ***fargesii*** AGM — CAbb CBra CCla CPle CSco ELan EPla IOrc LHop MGos SHBN SLon SPer WEas WPat WWat
*– – 'Variegatum' — ELan

CLETHRA (Clethraceae)

alnifolia — CB&S CBot CChu CCla CGre CLan CMHG CSam CWSG ELan EMil EWri IBar IOrc MBar NBee SBor SHer SPer SReu WBod WDin WWin WWye
¶ – 'Alba' — EMil
– 'Fingle Dwarf' — SSta
– 'Paniculata' AGM — CCla CDoC EHic ENot MBri WWat
– 'Pink Spire' — CB&S CBow CCla CDoC CKni CWSG EHic ELan MPla MRav MUlv WStI
– 'Rosea' — CBot CChu CCla CSco EMil GWht IJoh IOrc MBal MBar MBlu MBri MGos SEng SHBN SPer WAbe WSHC WWat
arborea — CChu CHEx CPle CTre
barbinervis AGM — CBra CCla CGre CLan CWSG GGGa SHil SPer WCoo WSHC WWat
delavayi AGM — GGGa MBal NHol WWat
– CLD 1508 — NHol
fargesii — CCla EHal MGos SHil WWat
monostachya — GGGa

CLEYERA (Theaceae)

fortunei — See C. ***japonica*** 'Fortunei'
– 'Variegata' — See C. ***japonica*** 'Fortunei'
japonica 'Fortunei' — CBot WWat
– var. ***japonica*** — MBal
– 'Tricolor' (v) — CGre SHil

CLIANTHUS (Leguminosae/Papilionaceae)

§ ***puniceus*** AGM — CAbb CB&S CBot CGre CHEx CHan CMac CNew CPle CTro CTrw ECou ELan EMil ERea IDai IHos IJoh IOrc ISea LHop MBal SArc SLMG SPer WBod WCru WDin
§ – 'Albus' AGM — CB&S CBot CDoC CGre CHan CNew CPle CTro CTrw ELan EMil ERea IHos IMal IOrc ISea LHop MAll SDry SLMG SPer WBod
– 'Flamingo' — See C. ***p.*** 'Roseus'
– 'Red Admiral' — See C. ***p.***
– 'Red Cardinal' — See C. ***p.***
§ – 'Roseus' — CB&S ELan EMil ERea IHos LHop
– 'White Heron' — See C. ***p.*** 'Albus'

CLINOPODIUM (Labiatae/Lamiaceae)

§ ***acinos*** — CArn LHol MBri MChe MSal SIde WHer WWye
ascendens — See CALAMINTHA ***sylvatica***
calamintha — See CALAMINTHA ***nepeta***
grandiflorum — See CALAMINTHA ***grandiflora***
§ ***vulgare*** — CArn CKin ECWi EWFC GBar LHol MHew MSal NMir SIde WCla WNdy

CLINTONIA (Liliaceae/Convallariaceae)

andrewsiana — CBro GDra GGGa NKay WThi
borealis — EBul EPot MSal
umbellulata — EPot MSal SWas

CLITORIA (Leguminosae/Papilionaceae)

¶ ***mariana*** — MSto

CLIVIA (Liliaceae/Amaryllidaceae)

miniata hybrids — CElw CTro ERea LAma MBri NPal SLMG

CLUSIA (Guttiferae)

♦ ***rosea*** — See C. ***major***

CLYTOSTOMA (Bignoniaceae)

§ ***callistegioïdes*** — CTro ERea

CNEORUM (Cneoraceae)

tricoccon — WOMN

CNICUS (Compositae/Asteraceae)

§ ***benedictus*** — CArn CHan GPoy LHol MSal SIde WHer WWye

¶ ***diacantha*** WHaw

COBAEA (Cobaeaceae)

scandens AGM IBlr LAbb SMrm WGor WHal
– ***alba*** AGM ELan ERea IBlr LAbb SHer

COBNUT See CORYLUS *avellana*

COCCULUS (Menispermaceae)

♦***trilobus*** See C. ***orbiculatus***

COCHLEARIA (Cruciferae/Brassicaceae)

armoracia See ARMORACIA ***rusticana***
glastifolia EMon MSal
officinalis MSal WHer

COCONUT See COCOS *nucifera*

COCOS (Palmae/Arecaceae)

nucifera 'Dwarf Golden Malay' MBri
plumosa See SYAGRUS ***romanzoffiana***
weddelliana See LYTOCARYUM ***weddellianum***

CODIAEUM (Euphorbiaceae)

variegatum var. ***pictum*** 'Gold Moon' (v) MBri
– – 'Gold Sun' (v) MBri
– – 'Goldfinger' (v) MBri
– – 'Juliette' (v) MBri
– – 'Louise' (v) MBri
– – 'Mrs Iceton' (v) MBri
– – 'Petra' (v) MBri
– – 'Sunny Star' (v) MBri

CODONANTHE (Gesneriaceae)

gracilis CTro EBak WDib
paula WDib

X CODONATANTHUS (Gesneriaceae)

'Tambourine' MBri WDib

CODONOPSIS (Campanulaceae)

bhutanica EPad
bulleyana GCra WThu
cardiophylla GDra NHol WBon WDav WPla
clematidea Widely available
convolvulacea AGM CChu ESma GAbr GDra MBro MTho NHar NKay SDix WCru WHal WHoo WPer
– 'Alba' GDra NHar NHol SBla SWas
– Forrest's form See C. ***forrestii***
dicentrifolia MSto
§ ***forrestii*** GCra MSto NHol SBla WBod
handeliana See C. ***tubulosa***
§ ***lanceolata*** ECro GCra MSto NHar NHol WCru WDav
meleagris GCra GDra LGre NHar NHol
mollis ECro EPad MSto NHol
ovata CBot CGle EBar ECro ELan EPad ESma GCal GCra GDra MSto MTho NBro NHar NHol NWCA SBla SHer WEas WPer
– KBE 225 NHol
pilosula CNic ECro EPad GCra MTho NSti SBla WPla
rotundifolia angustifolia CDoC MSto NHol
subsimplex MSto NHol NWCA
tangshen CChu CGre EPad GPoy MSal MSto MTho NHar NHol NSti SBla WCru
§ ***tubulosa*** EPad
ussuriensis See C. ***lanceolata***
vinciflora CNic ECro GDra GTou LGre MSto SBla WCru
viridiflora ECro EPad NNrw WPer WThu
viridis C&Mc 618 GCHN

COFFEA (Rubiaceae)

arabica CTro

COFFEE See COFFEA *arabica*

COIX (Gramineae/Poaceae)

See Plant Deletions

COLCHICUM † (Liliaceae/Colchicaceae)

agrippinum AGM CAvo CBro CFee CMon ECha EPar EPot LAma LBow MBal NBir NRog WAbe WChr WThu
algeriense AB&S 4353 CMon
alpinum CMon SPou
'Antares' LAma
atropurpureum CBro EPot LAma WChr
'Attlee' LAma NRog WHil
'Autumn Herald' LAma
N 'Autumn Queen' AGM CBro LAma
§ ***autumnale*** CArn CAvo CBro CFee CMon ELan EPot ETub GPoy LAma LBow MBal NMen WShi
§ – 'Alboplenum' CBro EPot ETub LAma WChr
– ***album*** CAvo CBro CMon ECha EPar ETub GDra LAma LBow MBal NBir NHol SIng WHil
– ***major*** See C. ***byzantinum***
– ***minor*** See C. ***autumnale***
– – ***album plenum*** See C. ***a.*** 'Alboplenum'
– 'pannonicum' CBro
§ – 'Pleniflorum' CBro EPar ETub LAma NNrd WCot WHil
– ***roseum plenum*** See C. ***a.*** 'Pleniflorum'
baytopiorum EPot LAma SPou WChr
– PB 224 CMon
§ ***bivonae*** CBro EPot GCLN LAma SPou WChr
– S&L 467 CMon
§ ***boissieri*** CMon SPou
– CE&H 628 WChr
– S&L 468 CMon
bornmuelleri Freyn CAvo CBro EPar EPot ETub LAma NHol NNrd SIng
♦***bornmuelleri*** hort. See C. ***speciosum b.***
bowlesianum See C. ***bivonae***
burttii EPot WChr
§ ***byzantinum*** AGM CAvo CBro CMon ECha EPar EPot ETub LAma LBow MBri NRog SIng WChr WCot

– *album*	EPot SPou
chalcedonicum	EPot WChr
cilicicum	CBro EPot ETub LAma LBow WChr
– 'Purpureum'	LAma
'Conquest'	See C. 'Glory of Heemstede'
corsicum	EPar LAma WChr WThu
cupanii	CBro EPot LAma WChr
– MS 977	CMon
*– *glossophyllum*	CMon
'Daendels'	LAma
¶ *deserti-syriaci* SB&L 155	CMon
'Dick Trotter'	LAma NGar
doerfleri	See C. ***hungaricum***
'E A Bowles'	LAma
fasciculare	EPot LAma
§ *giganteum*	CMon EPot GCLN LAma SIng
– AC&W 2337	CMon
§ 'Glory of Heemstede'	LAma NGar
hierosolymitanum	EPot LAma WChr
§ *hungaricum*	LAma WChr
illyricum	See C. ***giganteum***
kesselringii	EPot
kotschyi	EPot LAma
laetum hort.	See C. ***parnassicum***
'Lilac Wonder'	CBro EPot ETub LAma LBuc MBri NHol NRog SIng WCot WHil
lingulatum	EPot LAma NRog
– S&L 217	CMon
§ *longiflorum*	EPot LAma
lusitanicum	LAma
– HC 2273	CMon
luteum	CBro ETub LAma NRog SIng WChr
macrophyllum	EPot LAma WChr
micranthum	EPot LAma
neapolitanum	See C. ***longiflorum***
¶ *parlatoris*	EPot
– Rix 2127	CMon
parnassicum	CMon EPot NGar
– CE&H 630	WChr
'Pink Goblet'	EPot LAma
polyphyllum	LAma
'Prinses Astrid'	CAvo LAma NGar
procurrens	See C. ***boissieri***
psaridis S&L 198	CMon
pusillum	CBro
– MS 803/833	CMon
'Rosy Dawn'	CBro ECha EPot LAma NGar WChr
sibthorpii	See C. ***bivonae***
speciosum AGM	CAvo CBro CMon CNic EPot ETub LAma LBow MBal MHlr NBir NGar NRar SIng WAbe
– 'Album' AGM	CAvo CBro ECha EPar EPot ETub LAma LBow MBri NBir NGar NHol SIng SPou WChr
– 'Atrorubens'	ECha EPot GDra LAma
– 'illyricum'	See C. ***giganteum***
– 'Maximum'	LAma
– 'Ordu'	LRHS
– *bornmuelleri* hort.	CMon
¶ *stevenii* SB&L 120	CMon
tenorei	LAma
'The Giant'	CAvo CBro ECha EPot LAma NRog SIng
troodii AGM	CMon EPot LAma
turcicum	EPot LAma WChr
umbrosum	CBro EPot
variegatum	CBro LAma SPou WChr
¶ – S&L 594	CMon
'Violet Queen'	CBro LAma SIng WHil
'Waterlily'	CAvo CBro ECha ELan EPar EPot ETub LAma LBow MBal MBri NBir NRog SIng WAbe WHil
'William Dykes'	LAma
'Zephyr'	LAma

COLEONEMA (Rutaceae)

¶ *aspalathoïdes*	CPle
pulchrum	CSpe CTro LBlm LHil LHop

COLEUS See SOLENOSTEMON, PLECTRANTHUS

COLLETIA (Rhamnaceae)

armata	See C. ***hystrix***
cruciata	See C. ***paradoxa***
¶ *ferox*	SMad
§ *hystrix*	CB&S COtt LAbb MAll SArc SLon SMad WAbe WBod WDin
– 'Rosea'	CAbb CGre CSco MBlu MPla SArc
§ *paradoxa*	CB&S CGre CHEx CTre EPla SArc SHil SMad

COLLINSONIA (Labiatae/Lamiaceae)

canadensis	ELan MSal

COLLOMIA (Polemoniaceae)

¶ *biflora*	WHaw
debilis	NWCA
¶ *grandiflora*	WHaw

COLOBANTHUS (Caryophyllaceae)

acicularis	EPot ITim
buchananii	ECou
canaliculatus	ECou EPot GPlt ITim NHed NHol
muscoïdes	NHol

COLOCASIA (Araceae)

♦ *antiquorum*	See C. ***esculenta***
§ *esculenta* AGM	CHEx

COLQUHOUNIA (Labiatae/Lamiaceae)

coccinea AGM	CAbb CArn CCla CHan EMil IMal MAll MBal MRav NTow SDry WBod WSHC
– *mollis*	See C. ***c. vestita***
§ – var. *vestita*	CB&S CDec CGre CPle EOrc IReg NHol SLon WPat

COLUMNEA (Gesneriaceae)

'Aladdin's Lamp'	NMos WDib
'Apollo'	WDib
x *banksii*	CTro MBri WDib
¶ 'Bold Venture'	WDib
§ 'Broget Stavanger' (v)	WDib
'Chanticleer' AGM	CTro MBri WDib
'Early Bird'	WDib
gloriosa	EBak

'Heidi'	MBri
hirta **AGM**	MBri WDib
– 'Variegata'	See C. 'Light Prince'
'Inferno'	WDib
'Katsura'	MBri WDib
I 'Kewensis Variegata' **AGM**	MBri
§ 'Light Prince' (v)	MBri
'Merkur'	WDib
* ***microphylla variegata***	MBri
I 'Midnight Lantern'	WDib
¶ 'Rising Sun'	WDib
schiedeana	MBri WDib
'Starburst'	NMos
'Stavanger' **AGM**	EBak MBri WDib
'Stavanger Variegated'	See C. 'Broget Stavanger'

COLUTEA (Leguminosae/Papilionaceae)

arborescens	CArn CB&S CPle EBre ELan EMil ENot GCHN IBlr IHos LBre MBlu MGos MSal NNor SHBN SPer WCru WDin WHer WWin
x ***media***	CGre EHal EMil MBlu WCru
– 'Copper Beauty'	CB&S CSco ELan MBri MGos SPer
multiflora	CPle
orientalis	SDry
persica	SLon

COLUTEOCARPUS (Cruciferae/Brassicaceae)

See Plant Deletions

COMARUM See POTENTILLA

COMBRETUM (Combretaceae)

¶ ***erythrophyllum***	CGre
¶ ***paniculatum***	CTro

COMMELINA (Commelinaceae)

coelestis	See C. ***tuberosa*** Coelestis Group
dianthifolia	CFee CGle CRDP GCal MCas MPit MSte MTho NGre NTow SSad WCru WPer
tuberosa	CAvo CHol EHic ELan GBuc MSto MWBu WFox WHaw WHow
– 'Alba'	CPou CRDP ELan EMon EOrc GCal LHop MSte MWBu NBro SAxl SCro SUsu WHer WPer
§ – Coelestis Group	CBow CGle CHan CMea CRDP ECha ECro EMon EOrc GCal LBlm LHop MWBu NBro SAxl SCro SIng SLMG SMrm SUsu WByw WCru WHal WHer WOMN WPer WWin WWye
– 'Snowmelt'	EMon
virginica hort.	See C. ***erecta***
virginica Linnaeus	EBee ECro IBlr WCru

COMPTONIA (Myricaceae)

peregrina	SHil

CONANTHERA (Liliaceae/Tecophilaeaceae)

¶ ***sabulosa***	WChr

CONIUM (Umbelliferae/Apiaceae)

See Plant Deletions

CONOCEPHALUM (liverwort)

supradecompositum	LFle

CONOPODIUM (Umbelliferae/Apiaceae)

majus	CKin

CONRADINA (Labiatae/Lamiaceae)

canescens	LGre
verticillata	CFee LGre

CONSOLIDA (Ranunculaceae)

§ ***ajacis***	CArn EWFC MSal WHaw
ambigua	See C. ***ajacis***
regalis	MSal

CONVALLARIA † (Liliaceae/Convallariaceae)

japonica	See OPHIOPOGON ***jaburan***
majalis **AGM**	Widely available
§ – 'Albostriata'	CBot CChu CRDP CRiv CRow ECha ELan EPar LGre MCas NBir NGar SAxl SPou WCru WEas WHer
– 'Fortin's Giant'	CBro CRDP CSco EBee ECro ELan EMon EPar EPla ERav NBrk
– 'Hardwick Hall' (v)	CRDP CRow EBul EFol EHoe
– 'Hofheim' (v)	CRow
– 'Prolificans'	CAvo CRDP CRow ELan EMon EPar EPot MCas NRar SPou
– var. ***rosea***	CAvo CBos CBro CCla CRDP CRiv CRow CSco CShe EBul EFou ELan EMon EPar EPot ERav NBir NGar NHol NSti SIng SPou WEas WHil
– ***variegata***	CAvo CRow
– 'Vic Pawlowski's Gold' (v)	CRow
montana	WChr

CONVOLVULUS (Convolvulaceae)

althaeoïdes	CBot CHad CHan CMil CPle CSam ECha LGre MNFA MNes MTho MTol NRar SBla SChu SCro SMad WAbb WCru WEas WHal WSun WWin
§ – ssp. ***tenuissimus***	CMer CRDP CSpe EOrc EWes GCal LHop MSto SAxl SUsu WCot
¶ ***assyricus***	MSto
§ ***boissieri***	MTho SBla SIng WAbe
cantabricus	MSto NRar
¶ ***cataonnicus***	WDav
¶ ***chilensis***	EWes
cneorum **AGM**	Widely available
¶ ***compactus***	MSto
elegantissimus	See C. ***althaeoïdes tenuissimus***
¶ ***humilis***	EBee
lineatus	ELan EPot LBee LHop MSto MTho NHar NMen NNrd NRar NWCA SBla SIng WDav
mauritanicus	See C. ***sabatius***
nitidus	See C. ***boissieri***
§ ***sabatius*** **AGM**	Widely available

– dark form CBrk CMHG CSpe ELan GCal LHil LHop MSte NBrk NRar SMrm SUsu WCru

X COOPERANTHES See ZEPHYRANTHES

COOPERIA See ZEPHYRANTHES

COPROSMA † (Rubiaceae)

acerosa (f) See C. *brunnea*
areolata ECou
atropurpurea (m) ECou ITim
baueri 'Picturata' See C. *repens* 'P.'
'Beatson's Gold' (f/v) CB&S CBra CBrk CDoC CLTr CMHG CMer CTrw ERea ESma GWht IBar IOrc ISea LHop MAll NFai SChu SGil STre WBod WSHC
§ *billardierei* GCal
'Blue Pearls' (f) ECou
'Brunette' (f) ECou
§ *brunnea* (f) ECou MHig
– x *kirkii* (m) ECou
cheesemanii ECou
¶ – 'Mack' MAll
¶ – 'Red Mack' MAll
'Chocolate Soldier' (m) ECou
'Coppershine' CB&S CMer ERea ESma MAll
repens (m) ECou
x *cunninghamii* (f) ECou
depressa ECou
foetidissima Forster ECou
'Green Girl' (f) ECou
'Hinerua' (f) ECou
'Indigo Lustre' (f) ECou
'Jewel' (f) ECou
x *kirkii* 'Kirkii' (f) CFee ECou
– 'Kirkii Variegata' (f) CB&S CBot CGre CHan CLTr CMer CPle ECou ERea ESma LAbb LHop MAll NTow STre WKif WSHC
'Kiwi-Gold' (v) CB&S CMer ECou ERea
¶ 'Lemon Drops' (f) ECou
linariifolia ECou
lucida ECou
macrocarpa ECou
nitida (m) ECou
parviflora (m) ECou
'Pearly Queen' (f) EBar ECou
'Pearl's Sister' (f) ECou
petriei CLTr ECou MHig NTow
– 'Don' (m) ECou
– 'Lyn' (f) ECou
propinqua EPla SDry WSHC
– (f) ECou
– (m) ECou
'Prostrata' (m) ECou
pumila ECou
quadrifida See C. *billardierei*
repens (f) CHEx ECou
– (m) CB&S ECou
– 'Apricot' (f) ECou
– 'Brownie' (f) ECou
– 'County Park Purple' (f) ECou ERea ESma
– 'Exotica' (f/v) ECou LHop SGil
– 'Marble King' (m/v) ECou ESma
– 'Marble Queen' (m/v) ECou ESma IBar LHil LHop SGil SLMG
– 'Orangeade' (f) ECou
§ – 'Picturata' (m/v) ECou ERea
– 'Pink Splendour' (v) CSpe ERea ESma LHop MAll
– 'Silver Queen' (m/v) ECou
– 'Variegata' (m) CPle ECou LHil
rhamnoïdes ECou
robusta (m&f) ECou EPla GWht SDry
– 'Williamsii Variegata' (m/f) LHop
rotundifolia (m&f) ECou
'Roy's Red' ECou
rugosa ECou IBar
tenuifolia (m) ECou
'Tuffet' (f) MUlv
'Violet Drops' (f) ECou
virescens (f) ECou
'Walter Brockie' CChu
¶ 'White Lady' (f) ECou

COPTIS (Ranunculaceae)

See Plant Deletions

CORALLOSPARTIUM (Leguminosae/Papilionaceae)

crassicaule ECou

CORALLOSPARTIUM X CARMICHAELIA (Leguminosae/Papilionaceae)

¶ 'County Park' ECou
kirkii ECou
¶ 'Essex' ECou
¶ 'Havering' ECou

CORDYLINE † (Agavaceae)

australis AGM Widely available
– 'Albertii' (v) CAbb CB&S CHEx CTro ERea IOrc LNet MBri NPal SArc SPla WCot
*– 'Black Tower' CBar COtt
– Purpurea Group CAbb CB&S CBot CBra CHEx EBre ENot ERea GAbr IBar IOrc ISea LBre NWyt SHBN SMad SPer WStI WWeb
– 'Red Star' CAbb CB&S CTor NPal WWes
– 'Sundance' CAbb CB&S CTor CTro CWit EBee IJoh ISea LHop MBri SArc SPla SSte WAbe WPat WStI WWes
– 'Torbay Dazzler' (v) CAbb CB&S CDoC CHEx COtt CTor CWit EBre ELan IJoh ISea LBre LHop MAsh MBal MBlu MBri NPal SHBN SHer SPla WWeb
– 'Torbay Green' CTor
– 'Torbay Red' CAbb CB&S COtt CTor CTro ELan IJoh ISea LHop MAsh MBri NPal SHer SPla SSte WAbe
– 'Torbay Sunset' CDoC CTor ELan IOrc
– 'Torbay Surprise' CTor
– 'Variegata' CBot CHEx
banksii CAbb ECou
fruticosa 'Atom' MBri
– 'Baby Ti' MBri
– 'Calypso Queen' MBri
– 'Kiwi' MBri
– 'Orange Prince' MBri

– 'Red Edge'	MBri
– 'Yellow King'	MBri
'Green Goddess'	CB&S NPal
§ *indivisa*	CHEx CLan EBak GAri MBri SArc
kaspar	CHEx ECou SArc
* *parryi purpurea*	NPal
'Purple Tower'	CB&S IBar WStI
stricta	CHEx MBri
terminalis	See C. ***fruticosa***

COREOPSIS † (Compositae/Asteraceae)

auriculata 'Schnittgold' ('Cutting Gold')	CSam EWll MWat NRoo SFis SSvw WPer
– 'Superba'	CTom EBre LBre SFis
'Gold Child'	SGil
'Goldfink'	EBre ECED ECha LBre MRav NKay SRms
grandiflora	CBow EHal MWil WOld
¶ – 'Astolat'	EMon
– 'Badengold'	CB&S CDoC NPri
– 'Early Sunrise'	CBot CBow CDoC CHol CSam ECtt LAbb LWad NBar NFai NMir NPer SFis SGil WElm WHen WHil WHoo WPer
– 'Mayfield Giant'	CBow EBee EWll LAbb MBel MWat NBar NPri NVic SHer SRms
– 'Rotkehlchen' ('Ruby Throat')	ECha
integrifolia	EMon WCot
¶ *lanceolata*	EBee
– 'Lichtstad'	MBri
– 'Sterntaler'	EFou EPar MBri NOrc NPri NRoo WHil
maximillion	WPer
¶ *palmata*	EBee
rosea	CLew CMea CRDP EPla ERav LAbb MBel WCot WOld
*– 'American Dream'	CLew CMGP EBee ECas ECtt EFou ELan EMar EMil EOrc EPar LHop MBri MMil NCat NFai NHol NPri SChu SFis SPer WAbe WMer WPbr WTyr
¶ – 'Nana'	SPla
'Sonnenkind' ('Baby Sun')	CMea ECtt EPar MBri MDHE MHig MPit NBro NMen NNor NNrd SFis
'Sunburst'	ECoo EJud NNor NOak SHer WFro
'Sunray'	CBow CKel CRiv ECtt EFol EFou LHil LWad MBel MBri MFir MPit NBar NMir NNor NOak NRoo SCro SFis SHer SSvw WByw WPer
tinctoria	MSal
– var. ***atkinsoniana***	WPer
tripteris	ECha EMon WCot
verticillata	CBow CLew CMea CShe ECha EFol ENot EOrc LHil MBal MFir MWat NFai NKay NPer SAxl SDix WAbe WEas WHal WOld WRus
– 'Golden Shower'	See C. ***v.*** 'Grandiflora'
§ – 'Grandiflora' **AGM**	CB&S CKel COtt CSco CTom EBre ECas EFou ELan EMon EPla LBre MBri NBar NHol NNor NOak NVic NWyt SChu SMad SPer SPla WPbr WWin
– 'Moonbeam'	Widely available
– 'Zagreb'	CCla CMGP COtt CSco ECas ECtt EFol EPar EPla GCal LHop MBri MUlv NBar NHol NRoo SPla WCra WMer WPbr WRus WTyr

CORETHROGYNE (Compositae/Asteraceae)

californica	CWes ESma LHil SLon WSHC

CORIANDRUM (Umbelliferae/Apiaceae)

sativum	CArn CSFH CSev EHer GPoy IEde ILis LHol MChe MHew SHer SIde WOak WPer WWye
– 'Cilantro'	CSev GAbr GPoy
– 'Morocco'	CSev

CORIARIA (Coriariaceae)

¶ *intermedia* B&SWJ 019	WCru
japonica	GCal SDry WCru WWat
kingiana	ECou WCru
§ *microphylla*	SDry WCru
myrtifolia	SDry WCru
nepalensis	CPle GCal WCru WWat
* 'Pictons'	WCru
terminalis var. ***xanthocarpa***	ECha GBuc GCal IBlr MBal MBel MHlr SDry WCot WCru
thymifolia	See C. ***microphylla***

CORIS (Primulaceae)

See Plant Deletions

CORNUS † (Cornaceae)

alba	CBow CDoC CKin CLnd CPer ENot IHos IJoh IOrc MBar MBri NWea WDin WMou WStI
*– 'Albovariegata'	CCla ENot
– 'Aurea'	CB&S CMCN CSco EBre ECtt EFol EGol EHar EHoe ELan EPla IJoh IOrc LBre MBar MBri MRav NBee NRoo SHBN SPer WAbe WDin WMou WPat
– 'Elegantissima' **AGM**	Widely available
– 'Gouchaultii' (v)	CB&S CDoC MBar NKay SRms WDin
– 'Kesselringii'	CAbP CB&S EBre EGol EHar EHoe ENot EPla IOrc LBre MBar MBri MWat SMad SPer SPla SSta WBod WDin
§ – 'Sibirica' **AGM**	Widely available
*– 'Sibirica Variegata'	CChu CDoC CPMA CSco EBre EPla IJoh IOrc LBre MBlu MBri MGos SHBN WPat
– 'Spaethii' **AGM**	Widely available
*– 'Variegata'	CB&S EFol SPer WWin
– 'Westonbirt'	See C. ***a.*** 'Sibirica'
alternifolia	CBow CCla CMHG COtt EHar ELan IJoh MSte MWat SPer WMou WWat
§ – 'Argentea' **AGM**	CBow CBra CCla CDoC CPMA CSco CShe EBre EGol EHar ELan IMal LBre MMor MWat SHil SLeo SMad SPer SReu SSta WDin WHCG WKif WPat WWat
– ***variegata***	See C. ***a.*** 'Argentea'
amomum	CB&S CChu CCla NHol
§ 'Ascona'	CB&S CBow CPMA ELan MBlu MBri SPer

australis	EPla
baileyi	See C. ***stolonifera*** 'B.'
§ ***canadensis*** AGM	Widely available
candidissima	See C. ***racemosa***
capitata	CB&S CChu CElw CGre CHan CPMA CPle CTbh ECtt ESma IOrc WAbe WCru
chinensis	CBra LPan
controversa	CAbP CB&S CBow CDoC CFee CMCN CPMA CPle CSam CSco EArb EHar ESma IJoh IOrc LPan MBar MBlu MBrk MSte NHed SEng SHBN SPer SReu SSta WCoo WDin WMou WWat
¶ – French variegated	SMad
– 'Pagoda'	CPMA CSco MBlu
– 'Variegata' AGM	Widely available
'Eddie's White Wonder' AGM	CB&S CBow CCla CPMA CSco EHar ELan ESma IMal MBal MBlu MBri MGos SHBN SHer SHil SPer SReu SSta WDin
florida	CBow CCla CGre EBre ELan IOrc LBre MSte SPer SReu SSta WCoo WHCG WNor
– 'Alba Plena'	CBow CPMA
– 'Apple Blossom'	CBow CPMA
– 'Cherokee Chief' AGM	CAbP CB&S CBow CDoC CPMA CSco LPan MBlu MGos SPer WAbe
– 'Cherokee Princess'	CBow CPMA CRos LPan MBlu SSta
– 'Clear Moon'	LPan
– 'Cloud Nine'	CB&S CDoC COtt CPMA CSco LPan MBal MGos
– 'Daybreak' (v)	CBow COtt CPMA MBlu
– 'First Lady'	CPMA LPan
– 'Fragrant Cloud'	LPan
– 'G H Ford' (v)	CPMA
¶ – 'Golden Nugget'	CPMA
¶ – 'Green Glow' (v)	CPMA
¶ – 'Junior Miss Variegated' (v)	CPMA
– 'Pendula'	CBow CPMA
– 'Purple Glory'	CBow CPMA
– 'Rainbow' (v)	CAbP CB&S CBow CCla CDoC COtt CPMA CSco ELan ESma LPan MBri MGos SEng SPer SSta WAbe
– 'Red Giant'	CPMA MGos SPer
– 'Royal Red'	CPMA
– f. ***rubra***	CB&S CBot CBow CDoC CSco ELan EWri IDai IJoh LPan MGos SHer SPer SReu SSta WNor
– 'Spring Song'	CBow CPMA MBri
– 'Stoke's Pink'	CPMA
– 'Sunset' (v)	CBow COtt CPMA MBlu
– 'Sweetwater'	CBow CCla CPMA
– 'Tricolor'	See C. ***f.*** 'Welchii'
§ – 'Welchii' (v)	CPMA SHil
– 'White Cloud'	SHil SPer
foemina	See C. ***stricta***
hemsleyi	EPla
§ ***hessei***	ELan MAsh NHol WPat
hongkongensis	SReu
'Kelsey's Dwarf'	See C. ***stolonifera*** 'Kelseyi'
kousa	CB&S CBow CBra CCla CDoC CMCN ELan ERom ISea LNet MBal MBar MWat NKay NNor SHBN SPer SReu SSta WAbe WCoo WDin WFro WHCG WStI WWat
– ***angustata***	CCla ELan MBal NHed SPer
– var. ***chinensis*** AGM	Widely available
– – 'Bodnant Form'	CPMA
– – 'China Girl'	CAbP CBow CDoC COtt CPMA CSco LPan MBri MGos SEng SHBN SMad SPla SSta
– – 'Milky Way'	CBow CPMA SPer
– – Spinners form	CBow CCla CPMA
– 'Gold Star' (v)	CAbP CBow CCla CPMA CSco ELan ESma IOrc MBri MGos SHBN SPer
– 'Madame Butterfly'	CPMA SPer
¶ – 'Radiant Rose'	CPMA
– 'Satomi' AGM	CBow CCla CDoC COtt CPMA CSco MBri SMad SPer SReu
– 'Snowboy' (v)	CPMA CSco ELan NEgg SMad SSta
¶ – 'Sunsplash' (v)	CPMA
¶ – 'Temple Jewel' (v)	CPMA
– 'Weaver's Weeping'	CBow CPMA
macrophylla	CMCN
mas AGM	Widely available
– 'Aurea' (v)	CBow CBra CCla CPMA EBre EGol EHar EPla ERav LBre MAsh MBri SHBN SPer SPla SSta WWat
§ – 'Aureoelegantissima' (v)	CPMA EHar ELan ERav MBri SPer SSta WPat WSHC
– 'Elegantissima' (v)	See C. ***m.*** 'Aureoelegantissima'
– 'Variegata' AGM	CBot CBra CCla CDoC CPMA EGol EHar ELan ERav IOrc MBri MGos NPal SHBN SHil SPer WDin WPat WWat
N 'Norman Hadden' AGM	CBot CCla CPMA CSam EHar MBlu MBri NKay SHil SPer SReu SSta WAbe WBod WThu WWat
nuttallii	CB&S CBot CBow CCla CSam CSco ELan LPan MBal MBri SEng SHBN SPer SSta WBod WCoo WDin WNor WWat
– 'Ascona'	See C. 'Ascona'
– 'Colrigo Giant'	CPMA SHil
– 'Gold Spot' (v)	CPMA IOrc
– 'Monarch'	CB&S CBow CPMA CSco
– 'North Star'	CBow CPMA MBri
– 'Portlemouth'	CBow CPMA SHil
obliqua	EPla
occidentalis	EPla
officinalis	CMCN EHal SHil WWat
'Ormonde'	CPMA SPer
paucinervis	CMCN EPla
pubescens	See C. ***occidentalis***
pumila	EPla NHol SPla
§ ***racemosa***	WWat
sanguinea	CKin CLnd CPer EBre ENot EPla LBre LBuc NNor NWea WDin
♦ – 'Compressa'	See C. ***hessei***
* – 'Midwinter Fire'	EGol EPla EWll LBuc MBar MGos MWat NBar NBee SMad SPla WPat
§ – 'Winter Beauty'	CB&S CDoC CSco EMil IJoh IOrc LHop MBri NHol SPer WWat
– 'Winter Flame'	See C. ***s.*** 'Winter Beauty'

¶ sp. CLD 613	EPla
stolonifera	CBow EGol MGos
– 'Baileyi'	CCla EHar
– 'Flaviramea' AGM	Widely available
§ – 'Kelseyi'	CB&S CBow CDoC CWit EBar EGol EPla ESis ESma IOrc LHop MBar NHol SEng SLPl SPer SPla WWat
§ – 'White Gold' (v)	CAbP ENot EPla IOrc MAsh MBri NHol SHil SPer WPat
– 'White Spot' (v)	See C. *s.* 'White Gold'
stricta	CLnd
walteri	CMCN

COROKIA (Escalloniaceae)

buddleioïdes	CB&S CChu CDoC CElw CMHG CPle ECou MAll WBod WCru
'Coppershine'	CB&S CMHG LAbb
cotoneaster	CDoC CLan CTrw ECou ELan ENot EPot IMal ISea LGre MBlu MUlv SDry SPer SReu SSta WBod WHCG WSHC WStI WWat WWes
– 'Little Prince'	CB&S ELan
– 'Ohau Scarlet'	ECou
– 'Ohau Yellow'	ECou
– 'Swale Stream'	ECou
– 'Wanaka'	ECou
macrocarpa	CDoC CPle ISea MAll SDix SPer WSHC
x ***virgata***	CAbP CB&S CBra CChu CDec CMHG CPle CTrw ECou ELan EMil GWht IBar IJoh IOrc ISea MAll MBlu MCas MUlv SArc SGil SPer WBod WSHC WStI
– 'Bronze King'	CTre CWit SPer
– 'Bronze Lady'	MAll MBal
– 'Cheesemanii'	ECou
– 'County Park Lemon'	ECou MAll
– 'County Park Purple'	ECou
– 'Havering'	ECou
– 'Red Wonder'	CB&S CBra CMHG EHal ERea IMal MAll SDry SHil WBod WWes
– 'Virgata'	ECou
– 'Yellow Wonder'	CB&S CMHG EBar ECot ECou EHic SHil WWes

CORONILLA (Leguminosae/Papilionaceae)

cappadocica	See C. ***orientalis***
♦***comosa***	See HIPPOCREPIS ***c.***
emerus	See HIPPOCREPIS ***e.***
glauca	See C. ***valentina g.***
globosa	SUsu
minima	NGar NTow SBla WAbe WOMN
§ ***orientalis***	NWCA WWin
valentina	CDoC CMac CNew CSPN CSam ECha EMil LHil LHop MHlr SBra SDix WCot WSHC
– 'Citrina' AGM	CAbb CB&S CBot CChu CCla CDoC CGre CMHG CSam CSco ECha ELan ERav LAbb LGre LHop MTho NPer SBla SChu SPer SUsu WAbe WHCG WKif WRus WSHC
§ – ssp. ***glauca*** AGM	CB&S CBot CBra CDoC CFee CGle CMac CPle CSam CSco ECha ELan ENot ERea EWri IJoh IOrc LBlm LHil MBal NTow NWyt SPer SUsu WAbe WBod WHCG WWin
– 'Variegata'	CAbb CB&S CBot CBra CGle CHan CLTr CMac CPle CSPN CSam CSco EBre ECha ELan EMil ERav ERea IBar LAbb LBre LHil LHop MTho SApp SBra SDix SPer SSta WEas
§ ***varia***	ECWi WCot

CORREA (Rutaceae)

alba	CGre CMHG CPle CSev ECou ERea MAll SDry
– 'Pinkie'	CPle ECou ERea LHop
backhouseana AGM	CAbb CB&S CCla CPle CSam GCal IBar IBlr IReg ISea LBlm LGre LHop MAll MBel SIgm SLMG WAbe WBod WSHC
calycina	CMHG ERea
decumbens	CGre CPle ECou ISea MAll WSHC
'Dusky Bells'	CHan CPle ECou ISea LHop MAll WOld
'Harrisii'	See C. 'Mannii'
lawrenceana	CAbb CB&S CBow CCla IBlr LHil MAll
– ***rosea***	CMHG MBel
§ 'Mannii' AGM	CBot CCla CGre CMHG CNew CSam CSev CWit ECou ERea IBar IMal IReg ISea LHil LHop MAll MNes NTow SHil SLMG WAbe WBod WEas WSHC WWat
¶ 'Marion's Marvel'	CB&S ERea
pulchella	CAbb CB&S CCla CGre CMHG CWit ERea GCal MAll MNes
§ ***reflexa***	CPle ECou LBlm MAll
– ***virens***	WEas
– 'Yanakie'	CPle
speciosa	See C. ***reflexa***

CORTADERIA † (Graminae/Poaceae)

argentea	See C. ***selloana***
fulvida	CGre EMon IBlr MUlv WCot WKif
richardii hort.	See C. ***fulvida***
§ ***richardii*** (Endlicher) Zotov	CAbb CElw CHEx CHan EBre EFou EHoe ELan ETPC GAri GGar IBlr LBre LHil MBal SArc
§ ***selloana***	CB&S CHEx CTre CWGN EBre ELan IBar ISea LBre LNet MBar NBee NEgg NHol NKay NNor SArc SPer WStI
§ – 'Albolineata' (v)	EMon EPla SMad
§ – 'Aureolineata' AGM	CB&S CCla CElw CSam CSco CWit EBre EGol EHar EHoe ELan EMon ENot EPla IHos LBre MBal MBri MGos MUlv NFai SAxl SCob SHBN SMad SPer SSta WPat
– 'Gold Band'	See C. *s* 'Aureolineata'
¶ – 'Monstrosa'	SMad
– 'Pink Feather'	EPla ESma NMir SRms WStI

– 'Pumila' AGM	CB&S CCla CDoC CSco ECtt EGol EHoe ELan EMon ENot EPla GAbr IDai ISea MBal MBri MGos MUlv NFai NHol NTow SCob SDix SHBN SMad SPer SPla WStI
– 'Rendatleri'	CB&S CDoC CGre CSco EHoe ELan GAbr GRei LHil MBal MUlv SCob SMad SPer
– 'Rosea'	CHEx EPla ISea MBal MBar MBri NBee
– 'Silver Fountain'	ELan MAsh SApp
– 'Silver Stripe'	See C. *s.* 'Albolineata'
– 'Sunningdale Silver' AGM	CB&S CBra CHol CSco EBre ECtt EGol EHoe ELan ENot EOrc EPla IBar IHos ISea LBre MBal MBri MGos MUlv MWat NFai NHol SCob SHBN SMad SPer
– 'White Feather'	CHEx CLan ECtt EPla NEgg NMir SFis
Toe Toe	See C. ***richardii***

CORTUSA (Primulaceae)

brotheri C&R	NHar
matthioli	CGle CNic GTou LBee LGan MBal MCas MFir MHig MSte NGre NMen NTow NWCA SAxl SHer WCla WCru
– ***alba***	GCal MBal NHar NWCA SAxl WDav
– ssp. ***pekinensis***	GCal GCra GDra LBlm MSte NHar NHol NTow
turkestanica	CNic NHar WDav

CORYDALIS (Papaveraceae)

ambigua hort.	EPot GDra LAma MTho NRog SMad WChr WCot WCru
angustifolia	EPot LAma SPou WChr
bracteata	EPot WChr
¶– ***alba***	WChr
bulbosa auct. non DC	See C. ***cava***
♦***bulbosa*** DC	See C. ***solida***
¶***buschii***	WChr
cashmeriana	EBre GArf GTou LAma LBre MHig NHar SBla SPou SWas
– 'Kailash'	SPou
caucasica	EPot GDra LAma NTow SPou WChr
♦– ***alba***	See C. ***malkensis***
§***cava*** AGM	CGle EPar EPot LAma MNFA
– ***albiflora***	EPar EPot SPou
– ***marschalliana***	EPot
cheilanthifolia	CAvo CLTr CLew CMea CNic CRDP CRiv CRow ECha EFol ELan EPar EPot GCHN LBlm MBri MBro MFir MRPP NBro NWCA SUsu WBon WCot WDav WEas WHil WHoo WKif WOMN
chionophila	EPot
decipiens	MTho SPou WChr
decumbens	EPot
ecristata	NHar
¶***elata***	MTho NHar
firouzii	EPot
flexuosa	Widely available
– CD&R 528	CAvo CGle CHad LGre MDHE NHar NRar NRya SHer SIng SMrm SUsu WCot WCru
– 'China Blue' CD&R 528c	CAvo CBro CDec CElw EOrc EPla EPot IBlr MBri MDHE NHar NRar SAxl SBla SMad SMrm SWas WAbe WBon WCot WCru WHal WOMN WRus
– 'Père David' CD&R 528b	CAvo CBos CChu CElw CGle CMea CRDP CVer ECha EOrc EPla GCHN IBlr MBel MBri MHlr MNFA SAxl SCro SMrm SPou WCot WCru WEas WHal WHoo
– 'Purple Leaf' CD&R 528a	CAvo CBos CDec CElw CMil CRDP CSco ECha EPla EPot GBuc IBlr MBri MDHE NHol SAxl SPer SUsu SWas WCot WCru WKif
¶***fumariifolia***	WChr
glauca	See C. ***sempervirens***
glaucescens	EPot WChr
integra	SPou WChr
intermedia	EPot WChr
kashgarica	EPot WChr
ledebouriana	CBro EPot WChr
lutea	See PSEUDOFUMARIA ***l.***
¶***macrocentra***	WChr
§***malkensis*** AGM	EPot NBir NHar SPou
¶***nevskii***	WChr
nobilis	MSto
ochroleuca	See PSEUDOFUMARIA ***alba***
ophiocarpa	CGle ELan EMar GAri GCal GGar IBlr MBel WCot WTyn
paczoskii	EPot LRHS WChr
¶***pallida*** B&SWJ 395	WCru
parnassica	See C. ***bulbosa***
¶***paschei***	SPou
¶***petrophila*** KGB 432	MSto
popovii	SPou
♦***pseudofumaria alba***	See PSEUDOFUMARIA ***alba***
pumila	EPot NTow WChr
¶– ***alba***	EPot
¶***ruksansii***	WChr
§***saxicola***	EBar EPot
§***sempervirens***	CBos SUsu WCru WEas WHer WOMN WPla WWin
¶– ***alba***	WChr
¶– 'Cream Beauty'	WChr
¶***shanginii***	EPot WChr
– ***shanginii***	WChr
solida AGM	CAvo CBro CGle CMea CRDP CRow EPar EPot ETub IBlr LAma LBow NGar NHar NMen NRog NRya SHer WAbe WCot WCru WHil
– MS 881	CMon
– ssp. ***densiflora***	MHig NGar
– forms	EPot SPou
– 'George Baker' AGM	CAvo CBro MTho SPou SWas WAbe
– ssp. ***incisa***	SPou
– f. ***transsylvanica***	EPot GArf NBir NHar NRya SPou WChr
¶– – 'George Baker'	NHar SPou WChr
¶– – 'Lahovice'	WChr
¶***speciosa***	GCLN WChr
sp. Gökce Beli	SPou

sp. Yayladag	SPou
thalictrifolia Franchet	See C. ***saxicola***
tomentella	EPot MSto NBro WAbe WPer WPla
wendelboi	SPou
– 'Kartal Tepe'	SPou WChr
wilsonii	CBot GCHN GDra GTou IBlr LGre MSto MTho NMen NTow NWCA SBla SIng WAbe WCru WEas WHal WOMN WThu

CORYLOPSIS † (Hamamelidaceae)

§ ***glabrescens***	CB&S CBow CDoC CMCN CPMA EBre LBre MBal SPer SReu SSta WNor
– var. ***gotoana***	CPMA ELan MAsh SPer
pauciflora AGM	CB&S CBow CCla CMCN CPMA CSco ECtt EHar ELan EMil ENot IBar IDai IJoh IOrc ISea MBal MBar MBri MGos MPla NBee NKay SHBN SPer SReu SSta WBod WRus WWat
platypetala	See C. ***sinensis calvescens***
– ***laevis***	See C. ***sinensis calvescens***
sinensis	EMil MBri SSta
§ – var. ***calvescens***	CPMA MBal MBri SSta
§ – – ***veitchiana*** AGM	CGre CMCN CPMA CSam MBal MBri SHil SSta WWat
§ – var. ***sinensis*** AGM	CCla CDoC CLan CWit ECtt ESma ISea MBal MBri MGos SPer SReu SSta WBod WWat
– – 'Spring Purple'	CAbP CBow CCla CDoC CPMA EHar ELan MBlu MBri SHBN SHil SPer SSta WWat
spicata	CB&S CDoC CPMA CSco ELan ENot IDai IHos IJoh ISea MBal MBar MBlu MBri MPla SPer SSta WHCG
veitchiana	See C. ***sinensis calvescens v.***
willmottiae	See C. ***sinensis sinensis***

CORYLUS † (Corylaceae)

F ***avellana*** (cobnut)	CBow CKin CLnd CPer EBre ENot ERea GRei LBre LBuc MBal MBar MBri NBee NRog NRoo NWea SHil SKee WDin WMou WStI
– 'Aurea'	COtt CSco ELan MBlu MGos MWat NBee SPer SSta WDin WMou
– 'Bollwyller	See C. ***maxima*** 'Halle'sche Riesennuss'
– 'Contorta' AGM	Widely available
F – 'Cosford Cob'	CDoC ERea ESim GTwe LBuc MBri MGos NRog SDea SKee SPer WHig
F – 'Fuscorubra'	CBow CMac CSco ELan ENot IOrc
– 'Halle Giant'	See C. ***maxima*** 'Halle'sche Riesennuss'
§ – 'Heterophylla'	EGol SSta WMou
– ***laciniata***	See C. ***a.*** 'Heterophylla'
– 'Merveille de Bollwiller'	See C. ***maxima*** 'Halle'sche Riesennuss'
– 'Nottingham Prolific'	See C. ***a.*** 'Pearson's Prolific'
F – 'Pearson's Prolific'	EHar ERea ESim GTwe LBuc MBri SDea
– 'Pendula'	WMou
– 'Purpurea'	See C. ***a.*** 'Fuscorubra'
F – 'Webb's Prize Cob'	ERea IJoh LHol MBri NRog SDea WMou
colurna AGM	CLnd CMCN EHar ENot ESim IOrc MGos NBee NWea SKee SMad SPer WDin WMou
*– 'Te Terra Red'	WMou
– variegated	WMou
– x ***avellana***	See C. x ***colurnoïdes***
§ x ***colurnoïdes***	ESim
F ***maxima*** (filbert)	CLnd GTwe SDea WDin
F – 'Butler'	ERea GTwe SKee
F – 'Ennis'	ERea GTwe SKee
– 'Fertile de Coutard'	See C. ***m.*** 'White Filbert'
F – 'Frizzled Filbert'	EBee ERea
– 'Frühe van Frauendorf'	See C. ***m.*** 'Red Filbert'
– 'Grote Lambertsnoot'	See C. ***m.*** 'Kentish Cob'
F – 'Gunslehert'	ERea GTwe SKee
F – 'Halle'sche Riesennuss'	ERea GTwe LBuc LHol SDea SKee
F – 'Kentish Cob'	CDoC CSam EHar ERea ESim GTwe LBuc MBri NRog SDea SFam SKee SPer WHig
– 'Lambert's Filbert'	See C. ***m.*** 'Kentish Cob'
– 'Longue d'Espagne'	ERea SKee
♦– 'Monsieur de Bouweller'	See C. ***m.*** 'Halle'sche Riesennuss'
– 'Purple Filbert'	See C. ***m.*** 'Purpurea'
F – 'Purpurea' AGM	Widely available
F – 'Red Filbert'	EHar ERea EWar GTwe MBlu MBri NBee NRog
– 'Red Zellernut'	See C. ***m.*** 'Red Filbert'
♦– 'Spanish White'	See C. ***m.*** 'White Filbert'
F – 'Tonda Giffon'	SKee
F – 'White Filbert'	ERea GTwe LBuc NRog SKee
– 'White Spanish Filbert'	See C. ***m.*** 'White Filbert'
– 'Witpit Lambertsnoot'	See C. ***m.*** 'White Filbert'
sieboldiana	WMou
x ***vilmorinii***	WMou

CORYNEPHORUS (Gramineae/Poaceae)

canescens	CTom EGle EHoe EPla ETPC LHil

CORYNOCARPUS (Corynocarpaceae)

laevigata	CGre CHEx ECou MBri
– 'Picturata'	CHEx
– 'Variegata'	CB&S CHEx

COSMOS (Compositae/Asteraceae)

§ ***atrosanguineus***	Widely available
¶ ***bipinnatus*** 'Sonata' AGM	WHaw

COSTUS (Costaceae)

curvibracteatus	CNew
§ ***cuspidatus***	CNew
igneus	See C. ***cuspidatus***
speciosus	CNew CTro NRog
spiralis	CNew

COTINUS † (Anacardiaceae)

americanus	See C. ***obovatus***
§ ***coggygria*** AGM	CBra CDoC CSco EBre ELan ENot IOrc LBre LHop MBar MBri MWat NBee NNor NRoo SHBN SPer WAbe WDin WFro WHCG WStI WWat WWes

– 'Foliis Purpureis'	See C. *c.* Rubrifolius Group
– 'Notcutt's Variety'	CCla ELan ENot SPla WWes
– Purpureus Group	CLan CSco
– 'Red Beauty'	COtt MBri
– 'Royal Purple' AGM	Widely available
§ – Rubrifolius Group	CCla MBal NNor SChu SDix SPer SPla WHCG WWeb
– 'Velvet Cloak'	CBow CCla CPMA CSam MBri MGos MUlv SHil SReu SSta WPat
'Flame' AGM	CDoC CPMA CSco CShe EHar SHil WBod WWes
'Grace' AGM	CAbP CB&S CBow CChu CDoC COtt CPMA CRos CSam CSco EBre ELan LBre MAsh MBri MGos MUlv SHil SPer SPla SReu SSta WDin WWes
§ *obovatus* AGM	CBow CChu CDoC CGre CKni CMHG CPMA CPle ELan ENot MBri MUlv SHBN SHil SPer SPla SSta WWat WWes

COTONEASTER † (Rosaceae)

adpressus AGM	CDoC CLew EPla GDra MGos MWat NHar NNor NWea SIng SPer
§ – 'Little Gem'	GAri MBri SRms WDav
– var. *praecox*	See C. *nanshan*
– 'Tom Thumb'	See C. *a.* 'Little Gem'
amoenus	SLPl SRms
§ *ascendens*	CMCN
assamensis	SRms
§ *astrophoros*	CDoC CSco NKay SIng SPer SRms WBod
atropurpureus	SRms
– 'Variegatus' AGM	CBot CBra CSco CTrw EHoe ELan ENot EPot GCal GRei IJoh IOrc LHop MBal MBar MBri MGos NHol NNor SHBN SLon SMad SPer SRms WAbe WDin WPat WSHC WWat WWin
¶ *bacillaris*	GAul
boisianus	SRms
§ *bullatus* AGM	CSam ELan ENot GRei IDai ISea MGos NNor SPer SRms WSHC WWat
– 'Firebird'	LBuc SRms
– f. *floribundus*	See C. *b.*
– var. *macrophyllus*	See C. *rehderi*
buxifolius f. *vellaeus*	See C. *astrophoros*
N *buxifolius* Wallich ex Lindley	EBee ESis
cashmiriensis AGM	LMer
cavei	SLon
chailaricus	SRms
§ *cochleatus* AGM	EPla EPot ESis GAri GDra MBal MBar MBro NMen SFis SReu SRms WDav WEas WWat
§ *congestus*	CFee CLew CMHG EPla IDai IJoh IOrc LHop MBal MBar MBri MBro MGos MRav NHol NKay NNor NNrd NRoo SBla WAbe WHal WWat WWeb WWin
– 'Menai'	CCla
– 'Nanus'	CDoC CMHG ELan IBar MPla NCat NHol SIng SPla SRms WHCG WPat
conspicuus	EPla IDai SRms
– 'Decorus' AGM	CLew CMHG CSco ELan ENot GDra GRei IOrc MBar MGos MRav NHol NNor NRoo NWea SPer SPla SReu WDin WStI WWes
– 'Flameburst'	ECtt MBal MBri SHBN
– 'Red Glory'	SRms
– 'Red Pearl'	SReu
cuspidatus	SRms
N *dammeri* AGM	CBra CMHG CSco EBre ELan ENot EPla EPot GRei IJoh ISea LBre LBuc LGro MBal MBar MGos NBee NNor NWea SLon SPer SReu SRms WDin WHCG WWat WWin
– 'Oakwood'	See C. *radicans* 'Eichholz'
– 'Streibs Findling'	See C. *procumbens*
– var. *radicans* hort.	CShe NKay SIng
– var. *radicans* Schneider	See C. *radicans*
declinatus	SRms
dielsianus	CCla NWea SRms
– 'Rubens'	SRms
distichus	See C. *nitidus*
– var. *tongolensis*	See C. *splendens*
divaricatus	ENot EPla GRei SPer
floccosus	ECtt EHal GRei IDai MBri NWea SPer WWat
franchetii	CB&S CChe CLan CMHG CSco EBre ELan ERom GCHN IDai IOrc LBre MBal MGos MRav MWat NBee NWea SHBN SPer SPla SRms WDin WMou WStI
– Yu 14144	MBal
frigidus	ENot GAri NKay NWea WBod
§ – 'Cornubia' AGM	CBra CChe CLan CLnd CSco EBre ELan ENot GCHN IDai LBre LHop LNet MBar MBri MGos MRav MWat NBee NKay NWea SHBN SLon SPer SRms WAbe WDin WStI WWat
– 'Fructu Luteo'	IBlr
– 'Notcutt's Variety'	ENot WWes
– 'Sherpa'	LMer
froebelii	SRms
giraldii	SRms
glaucophyllus	SRms
§ *glomerulatus*	ESis MBar SRms
harrovianus	SRms
henryanus	CDoC CSco WWat
§ *hjelmqvistii*	CDoC CSco ENot LBuc SPla
– 'Robustus'	See C. *h.*
– 'Rotundifolius'	See C. *h.*
horizontalis AGM	Widely available
– 'Variegatus'	See C. *atropurpureus* 'V.'
– var. *wilsonii*	See C. *ascendens*
humifusus	See C. *dammeri*
'Hybridus Pendulus'	See C. *salicifolius* 'Pendulus'
hylmoei	SRms
ignavus	CCla EHal
¶ *integerrimus*	CNat
§ *integrifolius*	CCla CHan CMHG CSam ELan EPla ESis IDai LNet MBal MBar MBri NKay NNor NRoo SRms STre WWat WWin
kitiabelii	SRms
lacteus AGM	CCla CMHG CSam CSco CShe ELan ENot LBuc MGos MRav SHBN SPer SPla SRms WDin WWat
laxiflorus	SRms
linearifolius	SRms
lucidus	EHar
marquandii	EPla NNor SRms
melanocarpus	SRms

melanotrichus	See C. ***cochleatus***
microphyllus AGM	CBow CChe CLan CMCN CSco EBre EFol ELan ENot GRei IJoh ISea LBre MBar MBri MGos NBee NNor NRoo SDix SHBN SLon SRms STre WAbe WBod WDav WDin
– 'Donard Gem'	See C. ***astrophoros***
– 'Teulon Porter'	See C. ***astrophoros***
– ***thymifolius***	See C. ***integrifolius***
mucronatus	SRms
multiflorus	NWea
nagaensis	SLPl
§ ***nanshan***	CDoC GRei LHop NWea SPer
– 'Boer'	MBri SPla
nitidifolius	See C. ***glomerulatus***
§ ***nitidus***	SLon SPer
nivalis	SRms
nummularius Mac&W 5916	NHol
pannosus	ESis WWat
parneyi	SRms
permutatus	SRms
perpusillus	GAri MBri
polyanthemus	SRms
§ ***procumbens***	EPla ESis GAri MAsh NRoo SRms
– 'Queen of Carpets'	ECtt MBri MGos NWyt SRms
prostratus 'Arnold Forster'	CDoC
pyrenaicus	See C. ***congestus***
radicans	SRms
§ – 'Eichholz'	CDoC ECtt ENot MBri MGos
§ ***rehderi***	SRms
rotundifolius	SRms
'Royal Beauty'	See C. x ***suecicus*** 'Coral Beauty'
rugosus	SLPl
salicifolius	CBra CLnd NBee NNor SPer WDin
– 'Elstead'	SPer
– 'Exburyensis'	CBra CSam CSco CTrw LNet MBri MGos MWat SHBN SPer SRms WAbe WDin WWat WWin
– 'Fructu Luteo'	EHal MBri WWes
– 'Gnom'	EHar EPla LNet MBal MBar MBri MGos NNor NRoo SLon SPer SRms WWat
– 'Herbstfeuer' ('Autumn Fire')	ECtt MBal MGos MRav MWat NKay NNor SPer SPla SRms WAbe
– 'Merriott Weeper'	CDoC CSco WWat
– 'Parkteppich' ('Park Carpet')	EBar NWea SLon SPer
§ – 'Pendulus'	CChe CSco CShe ELan EPot GRei IDai IJoh LNet LPan MBal MBar MBri MGos MRav MWat NBar NKay NWea SHBN SHer SPer SRms WAbe WStI
– 'Red Flare'	SPer
– 'Repens'	CChe CShe IDai MBal NNor NRoo NWea SPer SPla SRms WAbe
– 'Rothschildianus' AGM	CLan CShe EBre ECtt ELan ENot IJoh LBre LHop MBal MBar MRav NKay SPer
– 'Scarlet Leader'	MBri
salwinensis	SRms
schlechtendalii 'Blazovice'	SRms
– 'Brno'	SRms
serotinus AGM	CCla EPla SHil SLPl SRms
shansiensis	SRms
aff. ***sheriffii*** 'Highlight'	ECtt SRms
simonsii AGM	CChe CPer CSco EBre ELan IDai IOrc LBre LBuc MBar MBri MGos NBee NHol NWea SPer SRms WDin WStI
§ ***splendens*** AGM	CDoC CGre ECtt ELan SHil SRms
– 'Glasnevin'	SRms
– 'Sabrina'	See C. ***splendens***
sternianus AGM	CShe ENot MBar MBri SLPl SPer SRms
suavis	SRms
§ x ***suecicus*** 'Coral Beauty'	CChe CSco EBre ENot EPla ERom GRei IJoh IOrc LBre LBuc MBal MBar MBri MGos NBar NBee NHol NNor SPer SPla SReu SRms WDin WHCG WStI WWeb
– 'Skogholm'	CLew CSco GWht MBal MBar MGos MWat NRoo NWea SLon SPer SRms WDin WStI WWin
turbinatus	SRms
vestitus	SRms
wardii	CDoC CSco IDai IJoh IOrc NBee SPer
x ***watereri***	CShe ELan EPla LNet MGos NBar SHer SPla WDin WWat WWeb
– 'Cornubia'	See C. ***frigidus*** 'C.'
– 'Goscote'	MGos
– 'John Waterer' AGM	CBra SRms WBod
– 'Pendulus'	See C. ***salicifolius*** 'P'
– 'Pink Champagne'	CMer EHal MBri SHil SPer
zabelii	SRms

COTULA (Compositae/Asteraceae)

atrata	See LEPTINELLA ***a.***
– var. ***dendyi***	See LEPTINELLA ***dendyi***
coronopifolia	CBen CSev CWGN LMay MSta NDea SWat SWyc WChe
goyenii	See LEPTINELLA ***g.***
hispida	CMHG CNic CRDP CRiv EBar ECtt EFol EPot GCHN MBar MCas MHig MTho MWat NHol NMen NNor NNrd NRya NTow NWCA SBla SIgm SIng SSmi WAbe WCru WEas WHil WPer
lineariloba	CLew CPBP EWes LBee NNrd NSti
♦ ***minor***	See LEPTINELLA ***m.***
pectinata	See LEPTINELLA ***p.***
♦ ***perpusilla***	See LEPTINELLA ***pusilla***
potentilloïdes	See LEPTINELLA ***potentillina***
pyrethrifolia	See LEPTINELLA ***p.***
reptans	See LEPTINELLA ***scariosa***
rotundata	See LEPTINELLA ***r.***
scariosa	See LEPTINELLA ***s.***
sericea	See LEPTINELLA ***albida***
sp. C&H 452	MRPP
squalida	See LEPTINELLA ***s.***

COTYLEDON (Crassulaceae)

chrysantha	See ROSULARIA ***c.***
♦ ***gibbiflora*** var. ***metallica***	See ECHEVERIA ***g. m.***

oppositifolia — See CHIASTOPHYLLUM ***oppositifolium***
orbiculata S&SH 40 — CHan
¶ – var. *oblonga* — LGre
**pomedosa* — MBri
*– 'Variegata' — MBri
simplicifolia — See CHIASTOPHYLLUM ***oppositifolium***
undulata — WEas

COWANIA (Rosaceae)

See Plant Deletions

CRAB APPLE See MALUS

CRAIBIODENDRON (Ericaceae)

yunnanense — CTre MBal

CRAMBE (Cruciferae/Brassicaceae)

cordifolia AGM — Widely available
koktebelica — CHan ECha GCal
maritima — CGle CSco ECha ECoo EMar EPla ERav GAbr GPoy MSal NNor NSti WHoo
– 'Lilywhite' — ILis
orientalis — ECha

CRANBERRY See VACCINIUM *macrocarpon*

CRASPEDIA (Compositae/Asteraceae)

glauca — NHol
¶ *lanata* — GTou
richea — See C. ***glauca***
uniflora — GCLN

CRASSULA (Crassulaceae)

arborescens — CRDP GAri SLMG
argentea — See C. ***ovata***
coccinea — CHEx SLMG
dejecta x *coccinea* — CHEx
falcata AGM — CTro IBlr MBri WCot
**galanthea* — SLMG
§ *helmsii* — CBen EHon EMFW NDea WChe WHol
justi-corderoyi — CPle
§ *milfordiae* — CLew CNic EPot MCas MFir NGre NHar NHol NMen SBod SIng SSmi WPer
– *nana* — CLew
monstrosa — SLMG
moschata — ECou
multicaulis — ECou
muscosa 'Variegata' — SLMG
§ *ovata* AGM — EBak ELan MBri SLMG
– 'Basutoland' — MPla
– 'Hummel's Sunset' AGM — SLMG
– 'Variegata' — EBak SLMG
¶ *peploïdes* — NGre
perforata — SLMG
portulacea — See C. ***ovata***
recurva — See C. ***helmsii***
rupestris AGM — MBri
rupicola — GAri
§ *sarcocaulis* — CRiv CShe ELan EPot ESis GTou ITim MCas MPla MRPP MTho NGre NHar NHol NKay NMen NWCA SBod SHer SIng SSmi STre WAbe WEas WPat WPer WSHC WWin
– *alba* — CNic CRiv ELan NGre SIng STre WAbe WPer
– dark form — NHol
– 'Ken Aslet' — NGre NHol NNrd SIng
schmidtii — MBri
sedifolia — ELan MBar MRPP NBir WWin
sediformis — See C. ***milfordiae***
socialis — ITim
tetragona — SLMG

CRATAEGUS (Rosaceae)

arnoldiana — CTho EBee
'Autumn Glory' — CLnd CWSG EBre LBre MGos WJas
azarolus — WMou
F – 'White Italian' — ESim
champlainensis — CTho
chlorosarca — SHil
¶ *chungtienensis* CLD 117 — WHCr
N *coccinea* — NWea WDin
cordata — See C. ***phaenopyrum***
crus-galli hort. — See C. ***persimilis*** 'Prunifolia'
crus-galli Linnaeus — CB&S CDoC CLnd CTho LBuc SPer WDin WJas WMou
– var. *pyracanthifolia* Linneaus — CTho
x *durobrivensis* — CLnd CTho EArb WWat
eriocarpa — CLnd
gemmosa — CTho
x *grignonensis* — CB&S CLnd EBar ENot SPer WJas
§ *laciniata* — CLnd SHil STre WMou
§ *laevigata* — WMou
– 'Coccinea Plena' — See C. ***l.*** 'Paul's Scarlet'
– 'Crimson Cloud' — CLnd ENot MBri SPer
– 'Gireoudii' (v) — CCla CDoC CPMA EPla MGos WMou WPat
– 'Mutabilis' — CTho
§ – 'Paul's Scarlet' AGM — CB&S CBra CDoC CLnd CTho EBre ELan ENot GRei IDai IJoh IOrc LBre LBuc MBar MBri MGos MRav MWat NBee NWea SHBN SPer SReu WAbe WDin WJas WMou WStI
– 'Pink Corkscrew' — GAri
– 'Plena' — CB&S CDoC IHos MBri NWea SHBN SPer SPla WMou WTyn
– 'Rosea Flore Pleno' AGM — CB&S CDoC CLnd CTho EBre ELan ENot GRei LBre LBuc MBar MBri MGos MWat NWea SHBN SPer WAbe WDin WJas WMou WStI WTyn
x *lavallei* — CBra CLnd ENot MWat SPer WDin
– 'Carrierei' AGM — CDoC CSam CTho MBri NBee NWea
monogyna — CB&S CDoC CKin CLnd CPer EBre ELan ENot GRei LBre LBuc MBar MBri MGos NBee NWea SPer WDin WMou
– 'Biflora' — SHil WMou
– 'Compacta' — MBlu WMou
– 'Flexuosa' — WMou

– 'Pendula Rosea'	WMou
– 'Stricta'	CLnd CTho ENot MBri SHil
– 'Variegata'	EFol WMou
x ***mordenensis*** 'Toba' (d)	CDoC CTho ENot
orientalis	See C. ***laciniata***
oxyacantha	See C. ***laevigata***
pedicellata	CLnd CTho
§ ***persimilis***	
'Prunifolia' AGM	CB&S CBow CCla CDoC CSam CTho EBar ELan ENot IHos MBar MBri MGos NBee NWea SHBN SMad SPer WCoo WDin WMou WTyn
§ ***phaenopyrum***	CLnd CTho GAri MBrk SHil WWat
pinnatifida	WWat
– var. ***major***	SHil
prunifolia	See C. ***persimilis*** 'Prunifolia'
punctata	EArb
schraderiana	CTho
tanacetifolia	CLnd CTho EArb WMou
wattiana	CLnd CTho

X CRATAEMESPILUS (Rosaceae)

grandiflora	CTho

CRAWFURDIA (Gentianaceae)

speciosa	WCru

CREMANTHODIUM (Compositae/Asteraceae)

¶ ***pinnatifidum***	GArf

CREPIS (Compositae/Asteraceae)

aurea	CNic ECha EPar GAri GGar IBlr NMen NNrd SHer SPer
incana AGM	CFee CGle CLew CShe EBre ECha EPar LBre LHop MPit MTho NHol NKay SDix SIng SPer SUsu WAbe
¶ ***paludosa***	WHaw

CRINITARIA See ASTER

CRINODENDRON (Elaeocarpaceae)

§ ***hookerianum*** AGM	Widely available
patagua	CAbb CB&S CBot CDoC CGre CHan CLTr CPle CSam CTbh EPla GCal GWht IBar ISea LHop MAll MBal SHil SLon SPer WAbe WBod WSHC

CRINUM (Liliaceae/Amaryllidaceae)

amoenum	NRog WCot
aquaticum	See C. ***campanulatum***
§ ***bulbispermum***	ELan
– 'Album'	ECha
capense	See C. ***bulbispermum***
moorei	NRog
– f. ***album***	CTro
§ x ***powellii*** AGM	CAvo CB&S CCla CMil CMon CSco CTro EBak ECha ELan LAma LBow LHop MBal MBri MSta MUlv NRog SDix SGil SLMG SPer WCru WDav WHow
– 'Album'	CAvo CHEx CHan CSco ECha ELan ERav LBow MUlv NRog SApp SHig SLMG
– 'Longifolium'	See C. ***bulbispermum***
– 'Roseum'	See C. x ***powellii***
yemense	CMon

CRITHMUM (Umbelliferae/Apiaceae)

maritimum	GPoy MHew MSal SIgm

CROCOSMIA † (Iridaceae)

¶ 'Amberglow'	EWoo WCot
¶ ***aurea***	CGle
'Bressingham Beacon'	EBre GAri LBre MArl MUlv NBee SPer
'Bressingham Blaze'	GAri GCal IBlr NCat NOak
'Brightest and Best' (x ***crocosmiiflora***)	WCot
'Canary Bird' (x ***crocosmiiflora***)	CBro CRow EGol GAbr GAri GCHN GCal IBlr NBar NRoo
'Carmin Brillant' (x ***crocosmiiflora***)	CBos CRos CRow GCal IBlr LAma LRHS MBri SRms WCot
'Castle Ward Late'	CRow GCal IBlr MBel WCot
N 'Citronella' (x ***crocosmiiflora***)	CBot CBro CChu CGle CRow CSam ELun EOrc LAma LHop NNor NRoo NSti SApp SAxl SBla SDix SHer SUsu WAbe WDav WEas WHal WPer
¶ 'Croceus'	IBlr
x ***crocosmiiflora***	CBow CLTr CNic EPla IBlr MBel NOrc SRms WCot WHaw
¶ 'Darkleaf Apricot'	MBel WCot
¶ 'Donegal'	ECha
'Dusky Maiden'	WCot
'Eldorado'	GCal WCot
'Emberglow'	CBro CChu CMHG CRow CSam CTom EBre EFou GAri GCHN GCal LAma LBre MBal MBri NBar NHol NOrc SMad SPer WAbb
§ 'Emily McKenzie' (x ***crocosmiiflora***)	Widely available
'Fire King' (x ***crocosmiiflora***)	SAxl
'Firebird'	ECha GBuc SPer
'Firebrand'	WCot
'Flamenco'	CChu CShe MUlv SBla
'Flamethrower'	WCot
'George Davison' (x ***crocosmiiflora***)	CB&S ECha IBlr NHol SFis
'Golden Fleece'	CRos GCal GGar MBri NHol NRoo
¶ 'Golden Sheaf'	IBlr
'His Majesty' (x ***crocosmiiflora***)	COtt CRDP CRow GCal IBlr LRHS MBri WCot
N 'Honey Angels'	EWoo WCot
'Jackanapes' (x ***crocosmiiflora***)	CBos CBro CRow ECha EWoo GCal IBlr MBri NRoo SUsu WCot WHal

§ 'James Coey'	
(x *crocosmiiflora*)	CChu CFee CMHG CRow ECha EFou IBlr LAma LBlm LBow LHop MBel NHol NOrc NRog SApp SBla SWas WAbb WCot WHil
'Jenny Bloom'	CBro COtt EBre GCal LBre MArl MUlv NBir NRoo
* 'Jesse van Dyke'	CRow
'Jupiter'	LRHS MMil NFai
'Kiatschou'	ECha IBlr
'Lady Hamilton'	
(x *crocosmiiflora*)	CBos CChu CMHG CRow GAbr GCal IBlr MBri NRoo NTow SAxl SBla WMer
'Lady McKenzie'	
(x *crocosmiiflora*)	See C. 'Emily McKenzie'
'Lady Oxford'	
(x *crocosmiiflora*)	ECha IBlr
'Lady Wilson'	
(x *crocosmiiflora*)	CRow ECha EPar LAma NHol NOrc NRog
'Lana de Savary'	CRow IBlr
'Lucifer' **AGM**	Widely available
'Lutea'	IBlr
'Marcotijn'	EWoo IBlr
¶ 'Marjorie'	
(x *crocosmiiflora*)	WCot
'Mars'	GCal WCot
masoniorum **AGM**	CB&S CBro CHEx CKel CRow CSco CShe ECha EFou ELan EOrc EPar EWoo GAbr IDai LAma MWat NHol NNor NRog SFis SIng SPer SPla WAbb WAbe WByw WFox
– 'Dixter Flame'	SDix
– 'Firebird'	EBre LBre MUlv NRoo
'Morning Light'	WCot
'Mount Stewart'	GCal IBlr WCot
'Mount Usher'	IBlr
¶ 'Mr Bedford'	MBel
'Mrs Geoffrey Howard'	
(x *crocosmiiflora*)	CGle CRow IDai WCot
♦ 'Mrs Morrison'	
(x *crocosmiiflora*)	See C. 'James Coey'
'Norwich Canary'	
(x *crocosmiiflora*)	CSam ECha EFou ELan IBlr LAma LBlm LBow LHop MHlr MMil NOrc SFis WCot WHil WHoo WWin
* 'Orangeade'	CB&S
§ ***paniculata***	CAvo CSco EMar GAbr IDai MBal MUlv NHol NKay NOrc NRar NTow SArc SChu SIng WCot WHoo WOMN
– 'Major'	SPer
pottsii	CB&S CRow EPla IBlr WCot
¶ 'Princess'	
(x *crocosmiiflora*)	WCot
'Queen Alexandra'	
(x *crocosmiiflora*)	LAma LBlm LHop NFai WCot WHal
'Queen of Spain'	CRos IBlr LRHS MBri SUsu WMer
* 'Red Star'	CB&S NFai
'Rheingold'	
(x *crocosmiiflora*)	EPar IBlr WCot
rosea	See TRITONIA ***rubrolucens***
¶ 'Rowallane'	GCHN
'Rowden Bronze'	CRow
'Rowden Chrome'	CRow
¶ 'Saturn'	IBlr
'Severn Sunrise'	CMGP EBee EFou GCal IBlr LRHS MHlr NHol SApp WCot WMer
'Sir Matthew Wilson'	
(x *crocosmiiflora*)	IBlr
N 'Solfaterre'	
(x *crocosmiiflora*) **AGM**	Widely available
¶ 'Solfaterre Coleton Fishacre'	
(x *crocosmiiflora*)	IBlr
'Spitfire'	CBot CRow EBre ECha GAri IBlr LBre MBri MRav MSta NRoo WByw WEas
'Star of the East'	CBos CChu CMHG CRow ECha GCal IBlr MBel MBri SBla SMrm WCot
'Sultan'	WCot
'Venus'	
(x *crocosmiiflora*)	IBlr
'Vulcan'	CB&S EOrc EWoo SBla SPer
'Zeal Tan'	CChu

CROCUS † (Iridaceae)

abantensis	EPot LAma SPou WChr
'Advance'	CAvo CBro EPar EPot ETub EWal LAma MWBu NHol NNrd NRog SIng WShi
§ ***aerius***	LAma
– 'Cambridge'	WChr
alatavicus	CBro EPot
§ ***ancyrensis***	CAvo CBro EPar EPot ETub LAma LBow NRog SIng WChr WShi
– 'Golden Bunch'	See C. ***a.***
§ ***angustifolius*** **AGM**	CAvo CBro CMon EPot ETub LAma NRog SIng WChr
– 'Minor'	EPot LAma WChr
antalyensis	LAma WChr
asturicus	See C. ***serotinus salzmannii***
asumaniae	EPot LAma WChr
aureus	See C. ***flavus flavus***
banaticus **AGM**	CBro EPot LAma NGar NHol SPou WChr WThu
– JRM 3630	CMon
– 'John Marr'	SPou
baytopiorum	EPot LAma SPou WChr
biflorus	CBro EPar LAma NRog
– ssp. ***adamii***	EPot LAma WChr
– ssp. ***alexandri***	CAvo CBro EPot LAma NRog WChr
– 'Argenteus'	See C. ***b. biflorus***
§ – ssp. ***biflorus***	CMon LAma LBow
– ssp. ***biflorus*** MS 984/957	CMon
– ssp. ***crewei***	LAma WChr
– ssp. ***isauricus***	WChr
– ssp. ***melantherus*** S&L 226	CMon
– 'Miss Vain'	CAvo LAma NGar
– var. ***parkinsonii***	See C. ***b. biflorus***
– ssp. ***pulchricolor***	LAma SPou WChr
– sulphur	SPou
– ssp. ***tauri***	LRHS WChr
– ssp. ***weldenii*** 'Albus'	EPot LAma

– – 'Fairy'	CAvo CBro LAma LBow
biliottii	See C. ***aerius***
boryi AGM	CAvo EPot LAma SPou
– PJC 168	WChr
– VH 1546	CMon
cambessedesii	SPou
§ ***cancellatus***	
ssp. ***cancellatus***	CBro LAma LBow NHol
– var. ***cilicicus***	See C. ***c. cancellatus***
– ssp. ***mazziaricus***	CAvo CNic
– ssp. ***pamphylicus***	WChr
candidus var. ***subflavus***	See C. ***olivieri olivieri***
carpetanus B&S 399	CMon
cartwrightianus AGM	CBro LAma SPou
– CE&H 613	WChr
– S&L 484	CMon
N– 'Albus'	CMon EPot ETub SIng SPou
¶ ***caspius***	WChr
– PF 5036	CMon
chrysanthus AGM	WChr
– 'Ard Schenk'	EPot LAma
– 'Blue Bird'	EPar EPot EWal LAma LBow NNrd SIng
– 'Blue Giant'	LAma
– 'Blue Pearl' AGM	CAvo CBro EPar ETub LAma LBow MBri MWBu NRog SIng WShi
– 'Blue Peter'	CBro LAma
– 'Brass Band'	EPot LAma
– 'Canary Bird'	NRog
– 'Cream Beauty' AGM	CAvo CBro EPar EPot ETub EWal LAma LBow MBri MHlr MWBu NRog SIng WShi
– 'Dorothy'	LAma NRog
– 'E A Bowles' AGM	EPot LAma
– 'E P Bowles'	CAvo CBro CRiv LAma LBow MBri MWBu NRog SIng
– 'Elegance'	CBro LAma
– 'Eye-catcher'	EPot ETub LAma
– var. ***fuscotinctus***	CBro LAma MBri NRog SIng WShi
– 'Gipsy Girl'	CBro LAma MBri MWBu NRog SIng
– 'Gladstone'	LAma
– 'Goldilocks'	CBro LAma SIng
– 'Herald'	LAma
– 'Jeannine'	ETub
– 'Ladykiller' AGM	CAvo CBro EPar EPot LAma LBow MBri MWBu NRog SIng
– 'Moonlight'	EPot LAma NRog SIng
– 'Prins Claus'	EPot LAma SIng WShi
– 'Prinses Beatrix'	EPot LAma NRog SIng
– 'Romance'	EPot LAma
– 'Saturnus'	LAma NRog
– 'Sky Blue'	LAma
– 'Skyline'	CBro EPot MWBu
– 'Snow Bunting' AGM	CAvo CBro EPar EWal LAma LBow MWBu NRog SIng
– 'Spring Pearl'	CBro LAma
– 'Sunkist'	LAma
– 'Warley'	NRog
– 'White Beauty'	LAma
– 'White Triumphator'	EPot ETub LAma NRog
– 'Zenith'	LAma
– 'Zwanenburg Bronze' AGM	CAvo EPar ETub EWal LAma MWBu NRog SIng WShi
'Cloth of Gold'	See C. ***angustifolius***
clusii	See C. ***serotinus c.***
corsicus AGM	EPar EPot ETub LAma LBow SIng WChr
– PJC 657	SPou
cvijicii	WChr
– CE&H 560	SPou
dalmaticus	LAma
– CEH	SPou
danfordiae	LAma WChr
etruscus AGM	CAvo
¶– B&S 334	CMon
– 'Zwanenburg'	EPot ETub LAma
flavus	See C. ***f. flavus***
– M&T 4578	CMon
§ – ssp. ***flavus*** AGM	EPot GPlt LAma WChr
fleischeri	EPot LAma NMen WChr
gargaricus	EPot GCLN LAma WThu
– ssp. ***gargaricus***	SPou
– ssp. ***herbertii***	CBro SPou WChr
– ***minor*** JRM 3299/75	WThu
'Golden Mammoth'	See C. x ***luteus*** 'Golden Yellow'
goulimyi AGM	CAvo CBro EPar EPot ETub LAma LBow NHol SIng SPou WChr WThi
– S&L 197	CMon
♦– 'Albus'	See C. ***g.*** 'Mani White'
§ – 'Mani White'	SPou WChr
'Haarlem Gem'	ETub LAma
§ ***hadriaticus***	CAvo EPot LAma NHol SPou WChr
– BM 8124	CMon
– B&M 8039	WChr
– AM form	SPou
– var. ***chrysobelonicus***	See C. ***hadriaticus***
– f. ***hadriaticus***	CBro
heuffelianus	See C. ***vernus vernus*** Heuffelianus Group
¶ ***hyemalis*** S&L 50	CMon
imperati AGM	SIng SPou
– ssp. ***imperati*** MS 965	CMon
– – 'De Jager'	CAvo EPot LAma
– ssp. ***suaveolens***	SPou
– ssp. ***suaveolens*** MS 962	CMon
karduchorum	CBro LAma NRog WChr
'Keith Rattray'	SPou
korolkowii	CBro EPar EPot ETub LAma NHol SIng WChr
¶– 'Agalik'	WChr
¶– 'Dytiscus'	WChr
– 'Golden Nugget'	EPot WChr
– 'Kiss of Spring'	EPot LRHS WChr
¶– 'Varzob'	WChr
– 'Yellow Princess'	EPot
¶– 'Yellow Tiger'	WChr
kosaninii	WChr
kotschyanus AGM	CAvo SPou
– CM&W 2720	CMon
– 'Albus'	SPou SRms WChr
§ – ssp. ***kotschyanus***	CBro EPot LAma LBow NHol NRog SIng
– var. ***leucopharynx***	CMon NHol
laevigatus	WChr
– CE&H 612	CMon
– 'Fontenayi'	CAvo CBro EPot ETub LAma WChr
– form	LAma

– white	SPou
'Large Yellow'	See C. x ***luteus*** 'Golden Yellow'
lazicus	See C. ***scharojanii***
longiflorus	CAvo CBro EPot SPou WChr WThu
– MS 968/974/967	CMon
§ x ***luteus*** 'Golden Yellow' **AGM**	EPot ETub LAma MHlr WShi
§ – 'Stellaris'	CMon EPot ETub WChr
malyi **AGM**	CMon EPot LAma SPou
– CE&H 519	WChr
'Mammoth Yellow'	See C. x ***luteus*** 'Golden Yellow'
medius **AGM**	CBro CMon EPot LAma NMen NRog SPou
¶ ***michelsonii***	WChr
minimus	CAvo CBro CMea EPar EPot ETub LAma LBow SIng
nevadensis AB&S 4415	CMon
¶ – SB&L 62	CMon
niveus	CAvo CBro EPot LAma SPou
– PJC 164	WChr
– S&L 194	CMon
– blue	WChr
nudiflorus	CAvo CBro EPot LAma NHol WChr
– MS 872	CMon
ochroleucus	CBro EPot LAma LBow NHol NRog SIng WChr
olivieri	EPar EPot LAma
– ssp. ***balansae***	WChr
– ssp. ***istanbulensis***	EPot WChr
§ – ssp. ***olivieri***	CMon LAma WChr
oreocreticus	WChr
pallasii	EPot LAma WChr
pestalozzae	EPot LAma WChr
– var. ***caeruleus***	WChr
pulchellus **AGM**	CBro ETub LAma SPou
– CE&H 558	WChr
– M&T 4584	CMon
– ***albus***	SPou WChr
– 'Zephyr'	CBro EPot ETub ITim LAma NHol
'Purpureus'	See C. ***vernus*** 'Purpureus Grandiflorus'
reticulatus ssp. ***reticulatus***	EPot
robertianus	CAvo SPou WChr
sativus	CArn CAvo CBro CSFH ELan EPot ETub GPoy LAma LBow MBri MHew MSal NHol NRog SIde SIng WHil WShi
– ***cartwrightianus*** 'Albus'	See C. ***cartwrightianus*** 'Albus'
– var. ***cashmirianus***	CMon ETub
scardicus	WChr
§ ***scharojanii***	EPot WChr
– var. ***flavus***	EPot WChr
§ ***serotinus*** ssp. ***clusii***	CBro EPot LAma NHol WChr
§ – ssp. ***salzmanii***	CBro EPar EPot LAma
– ssp. ***salzmanii*** AB&S 4326	CMon
– ssp. ***salzmanii*** MS 343	CMon
– ssp. ***salzmanii*** SF 218	CMon
– ssp. ***salzmannii*** 'Albus'	WChr
sibiricus	See C. ***sieberi***
§ ***sieberi*** **AGM**	EPot LAma

§ – 'Albus' **AGM**	CAvo CBro EPot ETub LAma LBow
– ssp. ***atticus***	CBro EPot LAma LBow
– 'Bowles' White'	See C. ***s.*** 'Albus'
– 'Firefly'	CBro EPot LAma LBow NRog SIng
– 'Hubert Edelsten' **AGM**	CBro EPot LAma LBow
*– ***pallidus***	CMon
– ssp. ***sublimis*** 'Tricolor' **AGM**	CBro EPot ETub LAma LBow SIng SPou WChr
– 'Violet Queen'	CAvo CBro LAma MBri NRog
speciosus **AGM**	CAvo CBro ELan EPar ETub GCHN LAma LBow NHol NRog SIng WHil
– 'Aitchisonii'	CBro ETub LAma NHol SIng
– 'Albus'	CBro CMon ECha EPar EPot
– 'Artabir'	CBro EPot ETub SIng
– 'Cassiope'	EPot LAma
– 'Conqueror'	CBro LAma NHol SIng
– ssp. ***ilgazensis***	EPot
– 'Oxonian'	EPot ETub LAma
x ***stellaris***	See C. x ***luteus*** 'Stellaris'
susianus	See C. ***angustifolius***
suterianus	See C. ***olivieri olivieri***
thomasii B&S 364	CMon
– MS 978/982	CMon
tommasinianus **AGM**	CAvo CBro CMea CRiv EPar EPot ETub GPlt LAma LBow MBri MWBu SIng
– PF 6584	CMon
– f. ***albus***	CBro EPot LAma LBow WChr
– 'Barr's Purple'	LAma SIng
– 'Bobbo'	SPou WChr
– 'Eric Smith'	CAvo WChr
– 'Lilac Beauty'	EPot LAma
– var. ***pictus***	EPot LAma NGar WChr
– var. ***roseus***	CBro EPot LAma NGar SPou WChr
– 'Ruby Giant'	CAvo CBro CNic EPar EPot ETub LAma MWBu NRog SIng WShi
– 'Whitewell Purple'	CAvo CBro EPot LAma LBow MBri MHlr NRog
tournefortii **AGM**	CAvo CBro CMon EPot LAma SPou
vallicola	LAma
veluchensis	SPou WChr
§ ***vernus*** ssp. ***albiflorus***	EPot LAma WChr
– 'Enchantress'	ETub LAma
– 'Flower Record'	EPot
– 'Graecus'	EPot
– 'Grand Maître'	LAma NRog
– 'Jeanne d'Arc'	CBro EPot ETub LAma MWBu NRog WShi
– 'King of the Blues'	LAma NRog
– 'Little Dorrit'	LAma
– 'Negro Boy'	LAma
– 'Paulus Potter'	LAma NRog
– 'Peter Pan'	NRog
– 'Pickwick'	EPot ETub LAma MWBu NRog WShi
§ – 'Purpureus Grandiflorus'	CBro EPot ETub LAma NRog WShi
– 'Queen of the Blues'	CBro NRog
– 'Remembrance'	EPot ETub LAma MWBu NRog WShi
– 'Sky Blue'	NRog
– 'Snowstorm'	LAma

– 'Striped Beauty' LAma NRog WShi
– 'Vanguard' CBro ETub LAma NRog SIng
– ssp. ***vernus*** var. ***scepusiensis*** EPot
– – 'Grandiflorus' See C. *v.* 'Purpureus Grandiflorus'
§ – – Heuffelianus Group EPot NGar
– 'Victor Hugo' LAma NRog
versicolor MS 941/935 CMon
– S&B 384 CMon
– 'Picturatus' LAma
'Yellow Mammoth' See C. x ***luteus*** 'Golden Yellow'
zonatus See C. ***kotschyanus kotschyanus***

CROSSANDRA (Acanthaceae)

infundibuliformis MBri

CROTALARIA (Leguminosae/Papilionaceae)

capensis CPle

CROWEA (Rutaceae)

See Plant Deletions

CRUCIANELLA (Rubiaceae)

stylosa See PHUOPSIS ***stylosa***

CRUCIATA (Rubiaceae)

§ ***laevipes*** CKin EWFC NMir

CRYPTANTHUS (Bromeliaceae)

bivittatus 'Pink Starlight' AGM MBri
bromelioïdes MBri
* 'Red Starlight' (v) MBri
x ***roseus*** 'Le Rey' MBri
– 'Marian Oppenheimer' MBri

X CRYPTBERGIA (Bromeliaceae)

See Plant Deletions

CRYPTOGRAMMA (Adiantaceae)

crispa SRms

CRYPTOMERIA (Taxodiaceae)

fortunei See C. ***japonica sinensis***
japonica AGM CDoC EHar GAri GAul IOrc ISea MBar SPer WDin WFro WNor
§ – 'Araucarioïdes' EHul
– 'Aritaki' SLim
§ – 'Aurea' EPla
– 'Bandai-sugi' AGM CDoC CKen CMac EBar EHul IJoh LCon LLin MBar MGos MPla NHed SGil SIng SLim SLon SSmi WStI
– 'Compressa' CKen CSam EBar EHul LBee LCon LLin MBar MBri MPla NHar SLim
§ – 'Cristata' CDoC CMac EHar ELan ISea LCon LLin MBal MBar SEng SGil SHer SLim WBod
– 'Elegans' CB&S CDoC CHig CMac CSco EHar EHul ELan ENHC ENot GRei IDai IJoh ISea LCon LNet MBal MBar MWat SBod SHBN SLim SPer SReu SSta WDin WWin
– 'Elegans Aurea' CDoC CGre EHul LCon LLin MBal MBar MPla SBod SPer WDin
– 'Elegans Compacta' AGM CB&S CDoC CSco EBar EHul LBee LCon MBar MPla SLim WThu WWeb
– 'Elegans Nana' LBee SLim
– 'Elegans Viridis' EHar SLim
– 'Enko-sugi' See C. *j.* 'Araucarioïdes'
– 'Globosa' SRms
– 'Globosa Nana' LBee LCon LLin MBar NHed SHBN SLim WGor
– 'Jindai-sugi' CMac MBal MBar MPla NHed SIng
– 'Kilmacurragh' CKen MBar NHol SLim WThu
¶ – 'Kohui Yatsubusa' CKen
– 'Koshiji-yatsubusa' LCon MBar
¶ – 'Koshyi' CKen
– 'Little Diamond' CKen
– 'Lobbii' CDoC
– 'Lobbii Nana' See C. *j.* 'Nana'
– 'Midare-sugi' See C. *j.* 'Viridis'
– 'Monstrosa' CMHG MBar MGos SEng
– 'Monstrosa Nana' See C. *j.* 'Mankichi-sugi'
§ – 'Nana' CDoC CMac EBre EHul ENHC IJoh LBre LLin MBal MPla MWat SBod SLon SPer SReu
– 'Pygmaea' LCon NHol SRms
– 'Rasen-sugi' EHar GAri LCon
– 'Sekkan-sugi' CB&S CDoC CMHG EBre EHul EPla GAri LBee LBre LCon LLin MAsh MBar MBri MGos MPla NHol SHer SHil SLim SMad
– 'Sekka-sugi' See C. *j.* 'Cristata'
§ – var. ***sinensis*** CMCN
§ – 'Spiralis' CB&S CDoC CGre CKen CMHG CMac CSco EHar GWht IOrc LBee LCon LLin MBal MBar MBri MGos NHed SLim SPer SSmi WBod WWeb
– 'Tenzan-sugi' CKen
– 'Tilford Gold' EHul LLin NHed
– 'Vilmorin Gold' CKen
– 'Vilmorin Variegated' EPla
– 'Vilmoriniana' AGM Widely available
– 'Viminalis' NHol
¶ – 'Winter Bronze' CKen
– 'Wogon' See C. *j.* 'Aurea'
– 'Yatsubasa' See C. *j.* 'Tansu'
– 'Yokohama' EHul LCon MBar MRPP NHar NHol SLim
– 'Yore-sugi' See CC. *j.* 'Spiralis', j. 'Spiraliter Falcata'
– 'Yoshino' CKen

CRYPTOTAENIA (Umbelliferae/Apiaceae)

japonica CArn CPou GPoy SFis
– f. ***atropurpurea*** CBre CChu CElw CGle CRDP ECha ECoo ECro EFol EMar EMon GCal MHlr NPer WCot

CTENANTHE (Marantaceae)

§ ***amabilis*** **AGM** MBri
*'Greystar' MBri
lubbersiana **AGM** MBri
§ ***oppenheimiana*** MBri
setosa MBri
'Stripe Star' MBri

CUCUBALUS (Caryophyllaceae)

¶ ***baccifer*** EMon

CUMINUM (Umbelliferae/Apiaceae)

cyminum CArn EHer GPoy IEde MHew SIde

CUNILA (Labiatae/Lamiaceae)

See Plant Deletions

CUNNINGHAMIA (Taxodiaceae)

§ ***lanceolata*** CB&S CGre CMCN EFol EHar ISea LCon LLin MBar MPla MUlv SBor SEng SLim SMad WNor
§ – 'Bánó' CChu EBre EPla LBre MPla SMad
♦– 'Compacta' See C. *l.* 'Bánó'
sinensis See C. ***lanceolata***

CUPHEA (Lythraceae)

aequipetala WOMN
¶ ***bracteata*** CD&R 1205 LGre
caeciliae CBrk CKni CMHG LHil LHop SMrm
cyanaea CAbb CBrk CMHG CMer CSev CTre ESma GMac LHil LHop SBor SDix SLon SUsu
¶ – CD&R 1321 LGre
¶ – ***hirtella*** LHop
hyssopifolia **AGM** CBrk CFee CHan CMer CPle CSev CTre CTro EMil EOrc ERea ESma IBlr LAbb LHil LHop MBri NWyt SLon STre
– 'Alba' CBow CBrk CDoC CLTr CMer CPle LHop
– 'Riverdene Gold' CBrk LHop
– 'Rob's Mauve' CB&S CBow CMer
¶ – 'Rosea' LHop
§ ***ignea*** **AGM** CAbb CBrk CLTr ELan GCal IBlr ISea LHil MBri NWyt SLMG SUsu
– 'Variegata' CBrk LHil
♦ ***llavea*** See C. x ***purpurea***
macrophylla CBrk LHil
maculata CTro
♦ ***miniata*** hort. See C. x ***purpurea***
♦ ***platycentra*** See C. ***ignea***
§ x ***purpurea*** WBod
* ***signata variegata*** CMer IBlr LAbb

X CUPRESSOCYPARIS (Cupressaceae)

§ ***leylandii*** CB&S CBra CDoC CMac CSco EBre EHar EHul ENHC ENot IDai ISea LBre LBuc LCon LPan MBal MBar MBri MGos SBod SLim SPer WMou WStI
§ – 'Castlewellan' Widely available
– 'Galway Gold' See X C. *l.* 'Castlewellan'
– 'Golconda' EBre LBre
– 'Gold Rider' **AGM** CDoC EHul IOrc LBee MAsh MBar MBri MGos SLim SPer WStI
– 'Golden Sun' LCon
§ – 'Harlequin' (v) CMHG LCon MBar SEng WStI
– 'Hyde Hall' EHar EPla LBee MBar SBod SPla
¶ – 'Michellii' MBar
– 'Naylor's Blue' CMac
– 'New Ornament' SMad
¶ – 'Olive Green' IMal
– 'Robinson's Gold' **AGM** CBra CDoC CMHG CMac CSco EHar EHul GAri ISea LBee LCon MAsh MBal MBar MBri NWea SBod SLim WStI
– 'Silver Dust' (v) EHar ISea MBri SMad SRms
♦– 'Variegata' See X C. *l.* 'Harlequin'
ovensii CMHG

CUPRESSUS (Cupressaceae)

N ***arizonica*** var. ***arizonica*** CMCN CSco EHar ISea MBal SLon STre
– – 'Arctic' MBri
– var. ***bonito*** See C. ***a. a.***
– 'Conica Glauca' CMCN ENot MBar WDin
– var. ***glabra*** 'Aurea' EFol EHul LCon MAsh MBar SLim
– – 'Blue Ice' CB&S CDoC CKen CMHG EHar EHul LCon MBar MBri MGos SLim
– – 'Compacta' CKen LCon
– – 'Conica' CDoC CKen EHar SBod WWat
I – – 'Fastigiata' CB&S LCon LPan MBar
– 'Pyramidalis' **AGM** CMac CSco EHar IOrc SLim SPer
I – 'Sulfurea' CKen
bakeri CMHG WCoo
cashmeriana See C. ***torulosa*** 'Cashmeriana'
duclouxiana CMHG
funebris See CHAMAECYPARIS ***f.***
glabra See C. ***arizonica g.***
goveniana EArb GAri MBar
– var. ***abramsiana*** GWht
guadalupensis CMHG
lusitanica CMCN ISea
– 'Glauca Pendula' CKen LCon MAsh SHil
– 'Pygmy' CKen
macnabiana CMCN
macrocarpa CDoC EHar EHul GAul SArc
– 'Barnham Gold' SBod
I – 'Compacta' CKen CMac
§ – 'Crippsii' LCon
– 'Donard Gold' **AGM** CMac ISea MBal MBar
– 'Globe' See C. ***m.*** 'Compacta'
– 'Gold Spire' CMHG
– 'Gold Spread' **AGM** CDoC EHul LBee LCon SLim
– 'Goldcrest' **AGM** CB&S CBra CDoC CMac CSco EHar EHul ENot EPot IOrc LBee LCon LLin LPan MBal MBar MBri MGos MPla SBod SLim SLon SPer WAbe WDin
– 'Golden Cone' CMac MBal SHil
– 'Golden Pillar' CDoC CMac EHul LBee LCon MAsh MBar MPla MWat SLim WDin
– 'Greenstead Magnificent' EBre LBre LCon MAsh MBri
– 'Horizontalis Aurea' EHul MBar
¶ – 'Lohbrunner' CKen

– 'Lutea' CB&S CDoC CMac EHar EHul LCon MWat
– 'Pygmaea' CKen
– 'Sulphur Cushion' CKen
♦– 'Sulphurea' See C. ***m.*** 'Crippsii
¶– 'Woking' CKen
sargentii CMCN
sempervirens CB&S CMCN EHar EHul IOrc SArc SEng WCoo
– 'Green Pencil' See C. ***s.*** 'Green Spire'
§– 'Green Spire' SHil
– 'Pyramidalis' See C. ***s.*** 'Stricta'
– var. ***sempervirens*** See C. ***s.*** 'Stricta'
§– 'Stricta' **AGM** CArn CGre CSam CSco EHul GAri IJoh ISea LBee LCon LPan MPla SArc
– 'Swane's Gold' **AGM** CB&S CDoC CKen CMHG EBre EHar LBee LBre LCon LLin MAsh MPla SHil SLim
– 'Totem Pole' EHar MGos
¶sp. CLD 1031 MNes
§***torulosa*** 'Cashmeriana' **AGM** CAbb CDoC CGre CHEx ERea GAri ISea SHil SLim

CURCUMA (Zingiberaceae)

¶***zedoaria*** LBow

CURRANT, Black See RIBES *nigrum*

CURRANT, Pink See RIBES *rubrum* Pink Currant Group

CURRANT, Red See RIBES *rubrum* Red Currant Group

CURRANT, White See RIBES *rubrum* White Currant Group

CURTONUS See CROCOSMIA

CUSSONIA (Araliaceae)

¶***paniculata*** CTro
¶***spicata*** CTro

CYANANTHUS (Campanulaceae)

incanus EPad
¶***inflatus*** GCra
integer WAbe
– x ***lobatus*** 'Sherriff's Variety' GDra NBir NHar NHol WDav
lobatus **AGM** CMea CWes ELan EPad GBuc LBee MBel NGre NKay SBla SHer WCru
– 'Albus' EPot
– dark seedling GDra WDav
– giant form EPot GDra GTou NHar SBla WCru
– var. ***insignis*** CPBP WThi
– x ***microphyllus*** NWCA WCru
microphyllus **AGM** CLew CWes EPad GDra LBee SBla WCru
sherriffii NHar WThi

CYANELLA (Liliaceae/Tecophilaeaceae)

capensis See C. ***hyacinthoïdes***
hyacinthoïdes CMon
orchidiformis CMon LBow

CYANOTIS (Commelinaceae)

See Plant Deletions

CYATHEA (Cyatheaceae)

cooperi CB&S
dealbata CB&S CHEx NMar SArc
dealgardii WRic
medullaris CB&S CHEx NPal
smithii CHEx

CYATHODES (Epacridaceae)

§***colensoi*** CBow CMHG ECou GAbr GCal GGGa GWht IDai MBal MBar MBri MPla NHar SDry WAbe WBod WDav WPat WThu WWat
empetrifolia WThu
fasciculata See LEUCOPOGON ***fasciculatus***
fraseri See LEUCOPOGON ***fraseri***
juniperina ECou
§***parviflora*** ECou GWht

CYBISTETES (Liliaceae/Amaryllidaceae)

longifolia NRog

CYCAS (Cycadaceae)

cairnsiana LPal
circinalis LPal
kennedyana See C. ***papuana***
media LPal
&***papuana*** LPal
revoluta **AGM** CHEx LPal MBri SArc
§***rumphii*** CTro LPal
♦***thouarsii*** See C. ***rumphii***

CYCLAMEN † (Primulaceae)

africanum CAvo CBro CLCN CMon EBre EPot LAma LBre MAsh MSto NHol STil WMar
balearicum CAvo CBro CLCN CMon EBre EPot LAma LBre LCTD MAsh MBal MPhe MSto SBla STil WAbe WThu
cilicium **AGM** Widely available
– f. ***album*** CAvo CBro CLCN EBre LAma LBre MAsh STil WChr
¶'Coquette' LCTD
¶– 'Elsie Thomas ' LCTD
§***coum*** **AGM** Widely available
¶– BS 8927 LCTD
– M&T 4051 CMon
– var. ***abchasicum*** See C. ***c. caucasicum***
§– ssp. ***caucasicum*** CLCN EPot LAma STil
– ssp. ***coum*** CBro MBal
– – ***album*** CAvo CBot CDoC CRDP EPot LAma MAsh MBro MSto NGre NHol SDeJ SPou STil WChr WDav WHoo WNor
– – ***album*** (patterned leaved) STil
– – ***roseum*** CAvo LAma LBow MSto SDeJ STil WChr

– – ***roseum*** plain-leaved red	STil
– – 'Atkinsii'	CBro EPot GPlt MBro NHol
– – 'Nymans' ex EKB 371	EPot SBla SPou
¶ – – pewter-leaved	MAsh
– – pewter-leaved red	CBro CLCN CRDP LAma LCTD MSto SWas WChr WPat WThu
¶ – – silver-leaved bicolor	LCTD NHol NSla
– – silver-leaved red	CAvo EBre EPot LBre MSto MTho NHar NHol SIng STil WHoo WMar
¶ – 'Crimson King'	SDeJ
– dark pink	CAvo
¶ – 'Dusky Maid'	LCTD
– Elegans Group from Iran	SPou
– forms	CRDP LAma LCTD MBro MS&S SPou WWat
– ***ibericum album***	See C. ***c. caucasicum album***
– 'Maurice Dryden'	CAvo CBro CGle LCTD MAsh MSto NGar STil
¶ – plain-leaved	LCTD
– red	CRDP WChr
– from Russia	SPou
¶ – 'Sterling Silver'	LCTD
– 'Tile Barn Elizabeth'	SPou
– from Turkey	SPou
¶ – 'Turkish Princess'	LCTD
– 'Urfa'	EPot
creticum	CAvo CBro CLCN EPot LAma MAsh STil WMar WThu
¶ – x ***repandum***	CLCN EPot
cyprium	CAvo CBro CLCN CRiv EBre EPot ETub LAma LBre MAsh MFir MFos MSto SBla STil WAbe WChr WMar WThu
– 'E.S.'	SPou STil WThu
europaeum	See C. ***purpurascens***
fatrense	See C. ***purpurascens purpurascens***
graecum	CAvo CBro CFil CLCN CRiv EPot GPlt LAma MFos MSto STil WMar WThu
– f. ***album***	CBro LAma LRHS STil
§ ***hederifolium*** AGM	Widely available
– ***album***	Widely available
– 'Antiochus'	SPou
– 'Bowles' Apollo'	LCTD SBla STil
– 'Daley Thompson'	SPou
¶ – 'Fairy Rings'	LCTD
– forms	LAma LCTD MS&S NRed SPou WCru
*– ***minimum***	LCTD
– 'Perlenteppich'	NHol
– 'Rosenteppich'	NHol
– scented	CLCN LCTD SBla STil WMar
– 'Silver Cloud'	CLCN LCTD SPou
– silver leaved	EPot LCTD MAsh STil
– 'White Bowles' Apollo'	CLCN
ibericum	See C. ***coum caucasicum***
intaminatum	CAvo CBro CLCN CRiv EPot LAma MAsh MS&S MSto NHol NRya SBla SPou STil WAbe
– EKB 628	EPot
– 'E K Balls'	CAvo CBro
– patterned-leaved	LCTD NGre SPou STil WMar WThu
– plain-leaved	NGre STil WMar WThu
latifolium	See C. ***persicum***
libanoticum AGM	CAvo CBro CLCN EBre EPot LAma LBre LCTD MAsh MBal NGre SBla STil WChr WMar WThu
mirabile AGM	CAvo CBro CLCN EBre EPot LAma LBre MAsh MS&S MSto NGre STil WAbe WChr WMar WThu
neapolitanum	See C. ***hederifolium***
orbiculatum	See C. ***coum***
parviflorum	EPot LAma MSto
repandum ssp. ***peloponnesiacum peloponnesiacum*** AGM	CLCN EPot SPou STil
§ ***persicum***	CAvo CBro CFil CLCN CRiv CSam ESis LAma LBow MAsh STil
– RRL N8/65	CMon
– S&L 55	CMon
pseudibericum AGM	CAvo CBro CLCN CRiv EBre EPot ETub LAma LBow LBre LCTD MAsh MSto SBla SPou STil WChr WThu
– 'Roseum'	CLCN LCTD STil
¶ – scented form	LCTD
§ ***purpurascens*** AGM	CBro CFil CLCN EBre EPot ETub GDra LAma LBre MAsh MS&S MSto NHol SBla SIng SPou STil WChr WPat WThu WWat
– ***fatrense***	See C. ***purpurascens purpurascens***
– form	LAma SPou
– 'Lake Garda'	CFil
– Limone form	SBla
§ – ssp. ***purpurascens***	CAvo EPot LAma NGre STil
repandum	CAvo CBro CFil CLCN CRiv EBre ECop LAma LBre LCTD MAsh MBal MSto SBla SPou STil SWas WChr WThu
– 'Album'	EPot MAsh SBla SPou STil
♦ – 'Pelops'	See C. ***r. peloponnesiacum p.***
– ssp. ***rhodense***	CLCN LAma STil
– x ***balearicum***	CLCN
rohlfsianum	CAvo CBro CFil CLCN EPot MAsh MSto NGre STil WChr WThu
trochopteranthum	CAvo CBro CLCN EPot LAma LCTD MAsh MSto NHol NRog SBla SHer SPou STil WAbe WChr

CYCLOSORUS (Thelypteridaceae)

pennigerus	NMar

CYDISTA (Bignoniaceae)

aequinoctialis	CNew

CYDONIA (Rosaceae)

japonica	See CHAENOMELES ***speciosa***
F ***oblonga***	ESim LHol
♦ – 'Bereczcki'	See C. ***o.*** 'Vranja'
F – 'Champion'	CSco GTwe SFru WJas
– 'Early Prolific'	SKee
F – 'Le Bourgeault'	GTwe
¶ – 'Ludovic'	GTwe WJas

F – 'Meech's Prolific'	CDoC CSam CSco ERea ESim GTwe MWat SDea SFam SFru SIgm SKee WHig WMou
– pear shaped	EHar NRog
F – 'Portugal'	CSco GTwe NRog SIgm WJas
F – 'Vranja' AGM	CDoC CMac CSco EBre EHar ERea ESim EWar GChr GTwe LBre LBuc MBri MGos MMor NElm NRog SDea SFam SFru SIgm SKee SPer WHig WJas WMou
* *seibosa*	SKee

CYMBALARIA (Scrophulariaceae)

aequitriloba	WAbe
– *alba*	GGar WCru
§ *hepaticifolia*	CMea EFol EPot MDHE MTol NGre NMen NNrd WCru WHil WPer
– *alba*	CNic
§ *muralis*	CKin CMea EBar ECWi EPla EWFC GAbr MBar MPit MTol NMir SIde WGor WTyr
♦ – *albiflora*	See C. ***m. pallidior***
– 'Globosa Alba'	CRiv EPot
– 'Globosa Rosea'	CNic NNrd WCla
– 'Nana Alba'	CLew ELan GAbr GPlt LHop MDHE NMen NNrd NWCA WPer
§ – *pallidior*	CMea EPla ESis MBar NHar SHer WHil WOMN WWin
¶ – *rosea*	WHil
§ *pallida*	CElw CMea CNic LBee MCas NHar NKay SAxl SBla SHer WCla WCru WHil WPer
pilosa	CMGP CRDP ECtt EMNN GAbr MSto NGre NSti
¶ – *alba*	NGre

CYMBIDIUM (Orchidaceae)

See Plant Deletions

CYMBOPOGON (Gramineae/Poaceae)

citratus	CArn SHer SIde

CYMOPHYLLUS (Cyperaceae)

See Plant Deletions

CYMOPTERUS (Umbelliferae/Apiaceae)

¶ *terebinthinus*	SIgm

CYNARA (Compositae/Asteraceae)

baetica ssp. *maroccana*	ECha LGre
§ *cardunculus* AGM	Widely available
– ACL 380/78	EMon
¶ – 'Cardy'	CBot
cardunculus Scolymus Group	CB&S CCla CHad CSFH CSco EBre ECoo ERav GCal ILis LBre LHol MBri SMrm WByw WHer
¶ – – 'Gigante di Romagna'	WHer
– – 'Green Globe'	CBot CBow CSev NPer
– – 'Gros Camus de Bretagne'	WCot
– – 'Gros Vert de Lâon'	MBen WCot
– – 'Purple Globe'	CArn
¶ – – 'Violetto di Chioggia'	WHer
hystrix	See C. ***baetica maroccana***

CYNOGLOSSUM (Boraginaceae)

amabile AGM	EBar EBee ELan EMon WCot
– *roseum*	EMon
creticum	WHer
dioscoridis	CBot CGle MFir NBro WCot WPer
¶ *glochidiatum*	NBrk SAxl
¶ – CC 718	WCra
grande	SCro
nervosum	CBot CCla CGle CSco ECED ECoo EFou EGol ELan EPar GCal MRav MTol MUlv NMir NSti SPer SUsu WCra WRus WSun WTyr WWin
– *roseum*	CCla WCot WSun
officinale	CArn ECWi EWFC GBar LHol MChe MHew MSal NMir SIde WHer WNdy
zeylanicum	CBot WOMN

CYNOSURUS (Gramineae/Poaceae)

cristatus	MWil

CYPELLA (Iridaceae)

aquatilis	MSta
coelestis	CMon NTow WPer WThi
herbertii	CGle CMon LAma LBow MHig NWCA WCru WHil WThi
plumbea	See C. ***coelestis***

CYPERUS (Cyperaceae)

§ *albostriatus*	MBri
alternifolius	See C. ***involucratus***
§ *cyperoïdes*	MBri
diffusus	See C. ***albostriatus***
§ *eragrostis*	ECha EHoe EPla ETPC NBro SDix SWat WAbb
esculentus	GCal IBlr
haspan hort.	See C. ***papyrus*** 'Nanus'
§ *involucratus* AGM	CBen CHEx CKni CRDP CWGN EBak EMFW ERea ETPC LBlm MBri MSta SArc SWat SWyc WChe WWye
– 'Flabelliformis'	ETPC
– *gracilis*	EBak MBri
– 'Nanus'	ETPC
longus	CBen CRow CWGN EBre EHoe EHon EMFW EPla ETPC EWav LBre LMay MHew MSta NDea SMad SWat SWyc WChe WHol WNdy
nanus	CHEx CTro
papyrus	CHEx CTro ERea ETPC MBri MSta
§ – 'Nanus'	ERea
sumula hort.	See C. ***cyperoïdes***
* *variegatus*	ERea
vegetus	See C. ***eragrostis***

CYPHANTHERA (Solanaceae)

¶ *tasmanica*	CB&S

CYPHOMANDRA (Solanaceae)

betacea	See C. ***crassicaulis***
F *crassicaulis* 'Goldmine'	ERea SLMG

F– 'Oratia Red' — ERea

CYPRIPEDIUM (Orchidaceae)

acaule	MPhe
¶ x *barbeyi*	WChr
¶ *calceolus*	
var. *parviflorum*	WChr
debile	LAma SWes
formosanum	SWes
¶ 'Gisela'	WChr
guttatum	
var. *yatabeanum*	See C. ***guttatum***
¶ *henryi* x *flavum*	WChr
japonicum	LAma
¶ *kentuckiense*	WChr
¶ *macranthum*	WChr
¶ *reginae*	WChr

CYRILLA (Cyrillaceae)

racemiflora	WBod

CYRTANTHUS (Liliaceae/Amaryllidaceae)

brachyscyphus	CAvo EHic
§ *elatus* AGM	CAvo CBro ERea LAma LBow LHop MBri NGar NRog WChr
¶ – 'Delicatus'	WChr
falcatus	CMon WOMN
flavidus	LHop
luteus	SWas
mackenii	CTro NRog
– var. *cooperi*	WChr
parviflorus	See C. ***brachyscyphus***
purpureus	See C. ***elatus***
sanguineus	CMon
speciosus	See C. ***elatus***

CYRTOMIUM (Dryopteridaceae)

§ *caryotideum*	NMar SMad WRic
§ *falcatum* AGM	CHEx CRDP MBri NKay NOrc SArc WOMN WRic WWat
– 'Rochfordianum'	CRow WFib
§ *fortunei*	CFil EBee EBul EFer EFou IOrc NHar NHol NMar SApp SBla SIng WCot WFib WRic
¶ – var. *clivicola*	CBar NHar WRic

CYRTOSPERMA (Araceae)

See Plant Deletions

CYSTOPTERIS † (Dryopteridaceae)

bulbifera	CFil CMGP EFer EPot MNFA NMar NVic SBla SCob WEas
dickieana	CFil NHar NKay NMar
fragilis	CFil EBul EFer MBal NBro NKay NMar SRms WRic
– *sempervirens*	WRic
montana	NKay
regia	NKay

CYTISUS † (Leguminosae/Papilionaceae)

albus	See CHAMAECYTISUS ***a.***
♦ 'Andreanus'	See C. ***s. andreanus***
ardoinoi AGM	GDra MBal MBro MCas MHig MPla NHar NHol NKay NNrd NRoo WDav
battandieri AGM	Widely available
– 'Yellow Tail'	EHar SHil
x *beanii* AGM	CBow CMHG CPMA CSam ELan ENot ESis GDra GPlt MBal MBar MPla MWat NBee NNor NRya NTow SPer SPla SReu WAbe WDin WRus WWat
– 'Osiris'	NBar
'Boskoop Glory'	CSco ECtt GAul SPer
'Burkwoodii' AGM	CB&S CSco ENot GCHN IDai IJoh MBel MBlu MBri NBee SPla WStI
'Butterfly'	CB&S
canariensis	See GENISTA ***c.***
'College Girl'	NWyt
'Compact Crimson'	CDoC EBre LBre MAsh
'Cornish Cream' AGM	CB&S CSco ECot LHop MBri SPer SPla
'Cottage'	CPMA EHal EPot GDra MAsh MBri MBro MMil MPla NHar NHol SGil SIng SPla WAbe WDav
¶ 'Cottage Gold'	EHic
'Crimson King'	SPla
'Criterion'	MAll MBri MRav NBar
¶ 'Dainty'	MAll
'Daisy Hill'	IDai SPla
§ *decumbens*	CDoC CRiv EBee EPot IOrc MAsh MBro NHar NHol NKay WDav WHil WWin
demissus AGM	EPot GDra MHig NHol WAbe
'Dorothy Walpole'	CMHG CTrw EHal
'Dragonfly'	ELan IOrc
'Dukaat'	CDoC EBre LBre MAsh MBri NRoo SHBN
'Enchantress'	SPla
'Firefly'	MAsh MBal NWyt
'Fulgens'	CDoC CSco ELan IDai MAsh MBar MBri SPer WWeb
'Golden Cascade'	CB&S ELan MWat NNor WWeb
'Golden Showers'	MBal
'Golden Sunlight'	CDoC ECtt ELan ENot SHBN WStI
'Goldfinch'	CB&S CChe CDoC ENot MBri MWat WAbe WWeb
hirsutus	See CHAMAECYTISUS ***h.***
'Hollandia' AGM	CB&S CMHG CSco CShe EBre GCHN GRei LBre MAll MBar MGos MRav SHBN SPer WDin WStI WWeb WWin
x *kewensis* AGM	Widely available
– 'Niki'	CSco MBri SHBN SHil
'Killiney Red'	CDoC ENot GRei IJoh IOrc ISea MAll MBal MBri MWat NBee SHBN
'Killiney Salmon'	CSco EBee ENot MAll MAsh MGos MPla
'La Coquette'	CDoC CMHG MBar SHil
'Lena' AGM	CBow CMHG EBre ECtt EPla GAri IJoh LBre MAll MBar MBri MGos NHar NRoo SPla WStI
leucanthus	See C. ***albus***
'Lord Lambourne'	CChe LRHS
'Luna' AGM	ENot IJoh WStI
♦ *maderensis*	See GENISTA ***m.***
'Maria Burkwood'	CSco IDai NBee SHBN
¶ 'Miki'	MAll
'Minstead' AGM	CSco EBre ELan LBre MAll MBal SPer WAbe WDin
♦ *monspessulanus*	See GENISTA ***monspessulana***

'Moonlight'	MAll SPer
'Moyclare Pink'	CLan CMHG
'Mrs J Rodgers'	ISea
'Muldean'	NBar SPla WWeb
multiflorus AGM	CGre MBal SHil SPer WBod
– 'Toome's Variety'	SPla
– 'White Bouquet'	MBri
'Newry Seedling'	LRHS MBri
nigrescens	See C. ***nigricans***
§ ***nigricans***	CPle ENot SDry SHil SPer SReu
nubigenus	See C. ***supranubius***
'Palette'	CDoC CSco ECtt ELan SPer SPla
'Porlock' AGM	CDoC CLan CSPN CTre CWSG CWit ELan SHil SPla WBod WStI
x ***praecox***	See C. x ***p.*** 'Warminster'
– 'Albus'	CBow CCla CPMA CSco EBre ELan ENot GCHN GRei IJoh IOrc LBre MBar MBri MGos MWat NRoo SHBN SHil SPer SPla WAbe WWat
– 'Allgold' AGM	CB&S CBra CChe CCla CMHG CPMA CSam CSco CShe EBre ENot GRei IDai IJoh LAbb LBre MBar MBri MPla MRav NKay NRoo SHBN SPer SPla SReu SSta WAbe WBod WDin
– 'Canary Bird'	See C. x ***p.*** 'Goldspeer'
– 'Frisia'	CB&S GAri MBar
§ – 'Goldspeer'	ENot MAsh SPer
§ – 'Warminster' AGM	CCla CSco CShe ELan ENot GCHN GDra GRei IDai LHop MBal MBar MBri MGos MPla MWat NRoo NWea NWyt SHBN SPer SSta WAbe WWat WWin
'Princess'	MBri MPla
procumbens	LHop MBal SReu WWat
purgans	CDoC MAll MBal NNor SPer WBod
purpureus	See CHAMAECYTISUS ***p.***
racemosus	See CHAMAECYTISUS x ***spachianus***
'Red Wings'	CDoC EPot GCHN GDra IJoh MGos SPer WAbe WBod WStI
'Roter Favorit' ('Red Favourite')	MBar WGor
'Royal Standard'	NWyt
scoparius	CDoC CKin EBee ENot EWFC GRei LHol MHew NWea SReu WDin WWye
– f. ***andreanus*** AGM	ENot GRei IJoh MAll MGos MRav NNor SPer
– – 'Splendens'	CB&S CDoC CSco WStI
– f. ***indefessus***	EMon
§ – ssp. ***maritimus***	MBri NNor NTow WBod
– 'Pastel Delight'	CB&S
– var. ***prostratus***	See C. ***s. maritimus***
x ***spachianus***	See GENISTA x ***spachiana***
'Sunset'	ENot
supinus	See CHAMAECYTISUS ***s.***
'Windlesham Ruby'	CChe ELan GRei ISea MBar MPla SHBN SPer WBod WDin WWeb
'Zeelandia' AGM	CB&S EHic ENot MBar MRav SPla WAbe WTyr

DABOECIA † (Ericaceae)

§ ***cantabrica***	GAri GRei MBal
§ – f. ***alba***	CB&S CMac CNCN CNic COCH EBre ENHC ENot GAng GBla GDra GPen GRei GSpe IDai IJoh LBre MBal MBar MBri MOke NHol NRoo SBod SHBN SPla WBod WRid WStI
– 'Alba Globosa'	EDen ENHC MBar WGre
– 'Atropurpurea'	CNCN COCH EBre EDen ENHC ENot GAng GBla GPen GSpe IDai IJoh LBre MBal MBri MGos MOke NHol NWin SBod WBod WRid WStI
– 'Barbara Phillips'	EDen MBar
– 'Bicolor' AGM	CNCN COCH EDen ENHC GPen GRei GSpe MBal MBri MGos MOke NHar WGre WRid
– 'Blueless'	COCH EDen NWin
¶ – 'Celtic Star'	EDen
– 'Charles Nelson'	EDen MBar MOke
¶ – 'Cherub'	EDen
– 'Cinderella'	CNCN EDen GPen GSpe MBar
¶ – 'Cleggan'	EDen
¶ – 'Clifton'	EDen
– 'Covadonga'	CNCN COCH EDen ENHC MBar
– 'Creeping White'	EDen
– 'Cupido'	COCH EDen MGos NRoo
– 'David Moss' AGM	CMac EDen GAng GBla MBal MBar SBod WGre
– 'Donard Pink'	See D. ***c.*** 'Pink'
– 'Early Bride'	COCH EDen ENHC
– 'Eskdale Baron'	EDen ENHC
¶ – 'Eskdale Blea'	EDen
¶ – 'Eskdale Blonde'	EDen
– 'Globosa Pink'	EDen
– 'Harlequin'	EDen
– 'Heather Yates'	EDen ENHC GBla MBri MOke NWin SBod
– 'Hookstone Pink'	WBod
– 'Hookstone Purple'	COCH EDen ENHC GBla GPen MBar MBri MGos MOke NHol WGre
– 'Lilacina'	EDen ENHC GPen MBar WRid
§ – 'Pink'	COCH EDen GBla GPen MBar NMen
– 'Pink Blum'	EDen
– 'Pink Lady'	EDen MBar
– 'Polifolia'	CB&S EDen GBla GDra MBri MOke SBod SHBN SPla WRid
– 'Porter's Variety'	EDen GBla MBar MBri MOke NHar
– 'Praegerae'	CB&S CMac CNCN EDen ENHC GBla GPen GRei GSpe IDai MBal MBar MGos NHol NWin SBod WGre WRid
– 'Purpurea'	EDen GBla MBar
– 'Rainbow'	CNCN EDen MBar
– 'Rodeo'	EDen
– 'Rosea'	EDen MBar
– 'Snowdrift'	EDen GPen MBar
¶ – 'Tinkerbell'	NGar
– 'Waley's Red' AGM	COCH EDen ENHC GPen MBar NWin WRid
– 'White Blum'	COCH EDen
– 'White Carpet'	EDen
– 'Wijnie'	EDen
– 'William Buchanan'	See D. x ***scotica*** 'William Buchanan'
x ***scotica*** 'Bearsden'	EDen MBar
¶ – 'Ben'	EDen
– 'Cora'	ENHC GAng GSpe MBar

– 'Goscote' MGos
– 'Jack Drake' AGM EDen ENHC GDra GPen GSpe MBal MBar MBri MOke WGre WRid
– 'Red Imp' EDen
– 'Robin' EDen
– 'Silverwells' AGM CNCN EDen GAng MBar MBri MGos NHar NWin WRid
– 'Tabramhill' CNCN EDen MBar NWin
§ – 'William Buchanan' AGM CMac CNCN EDen ENHC GAng GBla GDra GSpe MBal MBar MBri MGos MOke NHar NHol NMen NRoo NWin SBod WGre WRid
– 'William Buchanan Gold' CNCN EDen MBar MBri NWin

DACRYCARPUS (Podocarpaceae)

§ *dacrydioïdes* ECou
– 'Dark Delight' ECou

DACRYDIUM (Podocarpaceae)

bidwillii See HALOCARPUS *bidwillii*
cupressinum ECou
franklinii See LAGAROSTROBOS *f.*
laxifolium See LEPIDOTHAMNUS *l.*

DACTYLIS (Gramineae/Poaceae)

glomerata 'Variegata' EGle ETPC IBlr NBro NCat NMir NSti

DACTYLORHIZA (Orchidaceae)

¶ x *braunii* ECha
¶ *cordigera* NHar
§ *elata* AGM EPar NHar WChr WThu
¶ *elata* x *majalis* NHar
§ *foliosa* AGM CBro CRDP MBri NGar NHar NHol WAbe WChr
¶ *foliosa* x *saccifera* CAvo
§ *fuchsii* ELan EPot NGar NHar SWes WChe WChr WCru WShi
– 'Bressingham Bonus' CRDP NGar NTow
¶ – 'Cruickshank' WChr
¶ *fuchsii* x *purpurella* EPot
incarnata EPot NGar SWes
¶ – *coccinea* x *elata* NHar
¶ – – x *majalis* NHar
¶ – – x *majalis praetermissa* NHar
¶ *incarnata* x *foliosa* EPot
¶ *larissa* x *maderensis* NHar
§ *maculata* EPar IBlr LAma MSta NHol NRog SWes SWyc WChe WCru WHer
¶ – ssp. *ericetorum* NHar
¶ *maderensis* x *majalis praetermissa* NHar
¶ – x *saccifera* NHar
§ *majalis* CCla EPot LAma WChr WCru
¶ – ssp. *praetermissa* CAvo NHar
¶ *majalis* x *elata* CAvo NHar
¶ – x *foliosa* CAvo
¶ – x *maderensis* NHar
mascula See ORCHIS *m.*
purpurella EPot NGar NRar
¶ *purpurella* x *incarnata coccinea* NHar
¶ sp. ex Armenia NHar
¶ *urvilleana* NHar

DAHLIA † (Compositae/Asteraceae)

'Abingdon Ace' (SD) NHal
'Abridge Bertie' (MinD) CSut
'Abridge Natalie' (SWL) NHal
'Alloway Cottage' (MD) NHal
'Alltami Apollo' (GSC) NHal
'Alltami Cherry' (SBa) NHal
'Alltami Classic' (MD) NHal
'Alltami Corsair' (MSC) NHal
'Alltami Cosmic' (LD) NHal
'Alstergruss' (Col) LAma NRog
'Alva's Supreme' (GD) NHal
'Amber Banker' (MC) NHal
'Anatol' CSut
'Apricot Honeymoon Dress' (SD) NHal
'Arabian Night' (SD) CHad LAma NRog SDeJ
'Athalie' (SC) NHal
'B J Beauty' (MD) NHal
'Banker' (MC) NHal
'Barbarry Banker' (MinD) NHal
'Barbarry Climax' (SB) NHal
'Barbarry Glamour' (SB) NHal
'Barbarry Lavender' (MinD) NHal
'Barbarry Pinky' (SD) NHal
'Barbarry Standard' (MinD) NHal
'Barbarry Trend' (MinD) NHal
'Bednall Beauty' (DwB) CBos CBrk CGle CRDP LHop MHlr NBir SMrm SUsu WCot WRus
'Berwick Wood' (MD) NHal
'Betty Bowen' (SD) ECtt
'Bill Homberg' (GD) NHal
'Bishop of Llandaff' (Misc) Widely available
¶ 'Black Fire' (SD) SMrm
'Black Monarch' (GD) NHal
'Bonaventure' (GD) NHal
'Bonny Blue' (SB) ECtt
'Border Princess' (SC) SDeJ
'Border Triumph' (DwB) NHal
¶ 'Brandaris' (MSC) SMrm
'Calgary' (SD) CSut
'Camano Choice' (SD) ECtt
'Candy Cupid' (MinB) NHal
'Candy Keene' (LSC) NHal
'Carstone Cobblers' (SBa) NHal
'Carstone Sunbeam' (SD) NHal
¶ 'Carter Bess' SMrm
'Catherine Ireland' (MinD) NHal
'Charlie Kenwood' (MinD) NHal
'Charlie Two' (MD) NHal

'Charmant' CSut
'Christopher Nickerson' (MSC) NHal
'Christopher Taylor' (SWL) NHal SMrm
'Clarion' (MC)(MSC) SDeJ
'Clint's Climax' (LD) NHal
'Cloverdale' (SD) NHal
coccinea (Misc) CAvo CBot ECha GCal LGre SUsu
– hybrids GCal
'Connie Bartlam' (MD) NHal
'Corona' (SSC)(DwB) NHal
'Cream Beauty' (SWL) NHal
'Crichton Honey' (SBa) NHal
'Cryfield Bryn' (SSC) NHal
'Cryfield Keene' (LSc) NHal
'Daleko Jupiter' (GSC) NHal
'Daleko National' (MD) NHal
'Dana Iris' (SSC) NHal
'Davenport Anita' (MinD) NHal
'Davenport Honey' (MinD) NHal
'Davenport Pride' (MSC) NHal
'Davenport Sunlight' (MSC) NHal
'David Howard' (MinD) CCMG CGle ELan LAma NHal
'Debra Anne Craven' (GSC) NHal
'Deepest Yellow' (MinBa) CSut
'Diana Nelson' (SD) ECtt
'Doc van Horn' (LSC) NHal
'Doris Day' (SC) LAma NHal NRog
'Duet' (MD) CSut LAma NRog
'Dusky Lilac' (SWL) NHal
¶ 'Easter Sunday' (Col) SMrm
'Eastwood Moonlight' (MSC) NHal
'Edinburgh' (SD) ECtt LAma NRog
'Edna C' (MD) NHal
'Ellen Houston' **AGM** CHad CRDP MBri
'Emmenthal' (SD) NHal
'Eveline' (SD) LAma SDeJ
'Evelyn Foster' (MD) NHal
'Evelyn Rumbold' (GD) CSut
'Evening Mail' **AGM** NHal
'Ezau' (GD) CSut
'Feu Céleste' (Col) LAma
'Figurine' (SWL) NHal
'Firebird' LAma NRog
¶ 'Fluttering' SMrm
'Frank Holmes' (Pom) ECtt
'Freestyle' (SC) NHal
* 'Friquolet' LAma
'G F Hemerik' (Sin) LAma
'Garden Festival' (SWL) NHal
'Gateshead Festival' (SD) NHal
'Gateshead Galaxy' (DwB) NHal
'Gerrie Hoek' (SWL) CSut LAma NRog
'Gina Lombaert' (MSC) LAma
'Glorie van Heemstede' **AGM** LAma NHal NRog
'Go American' (GD) NHal
'Gold Crown' (LSC) LAma NRog
'Golden Emblem' (MD) SDeJ
'Golden Impact' (MSC) NHal
'Good Earth' (MC) LAma
¶ 'Good Intent' (LD) LBlm
'Gordon Lockwood' (Pom) NHal
'Grenadier' MHlr WCot
'Grenidor Pastelle' (MSC) NHal
'Hamari Accord' (LSC) NHal
'Hamari Fiesta' (SD) NHal
'Hamari Girl' (GD) NHal
'Hamari Gold' **AGM** NHal
'Hamari Katrina' (LSC) CSut
'Hartenaas' LAma NRog
'Hayley Jane' (SSC) NHal
'Hazard' (MSC) LAma NRog
'Helga' (MSC) LAma
'Henriette' (Sin) CSut
'Herbert Smith' (D) LAma
'Hillcrest Albino' **AGM** NHal
'Hillcrest Blaze' **AGM** NHal
'Hillcrest Hillton' (LSC) NHal
'Hillcrest Royal' **AGM** NHal
'Hillcrest Suffusion' (SD) NHal
¶ 'Hinustan' CSut
'Hit Parade' (MSC) CSut LAma NRog
'Holland Festival' (GD) CSut
'Honey' (Anem/DwB) LAma NRog
'Honeymoon Dress' (SD) NHal
'House of Orange' (MD) SDeJ
imperialis (Misc) CMon GCal
'Inca Dambuster' (GSC) NHal
'Indian Summer' (SC) NHal
'Irene van der Zwet' (Sin) LAma
'Iris' (Pom) NHal
'Jeanette Carter' (MinD) NHal
'Jim Branigan' (LSC) NHal
'Jo Anne' (MSC) NHal
'Joan Beecham' (SWL) NHal
'Jocondo' (GD) NHal
'Johann' (Pom) NHal
'John Prior' (SD) NHal
'Karenglen' (MinD) NHal
'Kathleen's Alliance' **AGM** NHal
'Kathryn's Cupid' (MinBa) NHal
'Kelvin Floodlight' (GD) CSut
'Kenn Emerland' (MSC) LAma
'Kenora Challenger' (LSC) NHal
'Kenora Fireball' (MinB) NHal
'Key West' (MBa) CSut
'Kidd's Climax' (GD) NHal
'Kiwi Gloria' (SC) NHal
'Klankstad Kerkrade' (SC) ECtt NHal
'Kochelsee' (MinD) LAma

'Kym Willo' (Pom) ECtt
'La Gioconda' (Col) LAma
'Lady Kerkrade' (SC) NHal
'Lady Linda' (SD) NHal
'L'Ancresse' (MinBa) NHal
'Laura Marie' (MinBa) NHal
'Lavender Athalie' (SC) NHal
'Lavender Perfection' (GD) LAma
'Lavender Symbol' (MSC) NHal
'Lavengro' (GD) NHal
I 'Lemon Elegans' (SSC) NHal
'Lemon Puff' CSut
'Life Size' (LD) NHal
'Lilac Shadow' (SC) CSut
¶ 'Lilac Time' (MD) SDeJ
'Lilian Ingham' (SSC) NHal
'Lilianne Ballego' (MinD) NHal
'Linda's Cheter' (SC) NHal
'Lismore Peggy' (Pom) ECtt
¶ 'Little Dream' (SC) SDeJ
'Little Laura' (MinB) NHal
'Little Tiger' LAma NRog
'Majuba' (MD) LAma NRog SDeJ
'Mark Damp' (LSC) NHal
'Mark Hardwick' (GD) NHal
'Martin's Yellow' (Pom) NHal
merckii (Misc) Widely available
– ***alba*** CAvo CRDP ECha WCru WRus
– – 'Hadspen Star' CHad CRDP
'Mi Wong' (Pom) ECtt NHal
¶ 'Midnight Fire' (Misc) LHop
'Minley Carol' (Pom) NHal
'Minley Linda' (Pom) ECtt NHal
'Mistill Delight' (MinD) NHal
¶ 'Moonfire' (Misc) LHop WMer
'Moonlight' (SD) MBri
'Moor Place' (Pom) ECtt NHal
'Morning Dew' (SC) SDeJ
'Morning Kiss ' (LSD) SDeJ
¶ 'Mount Noddy' SMrm
'Mrs McDonald Quill' (LD) NHal
'Murillo' LAma NRog
'My Love' (SSC) ECtt LAma NRog
'Neal Gillson' (MD) NHal
'New Baby' (MinBa) LAma NRog
¶ 'Nicolette' (D) CSut
'Nina Chester' (SD) NHal
'Noreen' (Pom) ECtt NHal
'Nunton Harvest' (SD) ECtt
'Onslow Michelle' (SD) ECtt
'Orange Nugget' (MinBa) LAma
'Orfeo' (MC) LAma NRog
¶ 'Orion' CSut
'Park Princess' (DwB)(SC) LAma SDeJ
'Paul Chester' (SC) NHal
'Paul Damp' (MSC) NHal
'Pearl of Heemstede' **AGM** NHal
'Pensford Marion' (Pom) ECtt
'Periton' (MinB) NHal
'Peter' LAma
* 'Pink Cloud' (SSC) NHal
'Pink Honeymoon Dress' (SD) NHal
'Pink Jupiter' (GSC) NHal
'Pink Kerkrade' (SC) NHal
'Pink Pastelle' (MSC) NHal
'Pink Paul Chester' **AGM** NHal
'Pink Surprise' (LSC) SDeJ
'Pink Symbol' (MSC) ECtt
pinnata soft yellow CDec GCal
'Pop Willo' (Pom) NHal
'Potgieter' (MinBa) LAma NRog
'Preference' (SSC) LAma
'Preston Park' (Sin)(DwB) NHal
'Pride of Berlin' See D. 'Stolze von Berlin'
'Primrose Rustig' (MD) NHal
'Procyon' (SD) LAma
'Promotion' (MC) SDeJ
'Purple Gem' LAma NRog
'Queeny' (SSC) NHal
'Radfo' (SSC) NHal
'Raiser's Pride' (MC) NHal
'Red Diamond' (MD) NHal
'Red Sensation' (MD) NHal
'Reginald Keene' (LSC) NHal
¶ 'Requiem' (SD) ERom
'Reverend P Holian' (GSC) NHal
'Rhonda' (Pom) NHal
'Rhonda Suzanne' (Pom) ECtt
'Rose Jupiter' (GSC) NHal
'Rosella' (MD) LAma
'Rothesay Castle' (DwB) NHal
'Rothesay Robin' (SD) NHal
'Rotterdam' (MSC) NHal SDeJ
'Royal Ivory' (SWL) NHal
'Ruby Wedding' (MinD) NHal
rupicola SAxl
'Ruskin Diane' (SD) ECtt NHal
'Ruskin Dynasty' (SD) ECtt
'Rustig' (MD) NHal
'Safe Shot' (MD) LAma NRog
'Salmon Beauty' (D) SDeJ
'Salmon Keene' (LSC) NHal
'Satellite' (MD) SDeJ
'Scarlet Beauty' (SwL) NHal
'Scarlet Kokarde' (MinD) NHal
'Schweitzer's Kokarde' (MinD) NHal
'Scottish Relation' (SSC) NHal
'Scottish Rhapsody' (MSC) NHal
'Senzoe Ursula' (SD) NHal
'Shandy' (SSC) NHal
¶ ***sherffii*** CMon LGre
¶ – x ***coccinea*** CAvo
'Sherwood Standard' (MD) NHal
'Siemen Doorenbos' (Anem) LAma NRog

'Silver City' (LD)	CSut NHal
'Small World' (Pom)	ECtt NHal
'Sneezy' (Sin)	LAma
'Snowflake' (SWL)	LAma
'Snowstorm' (MD)	LAma SDeJ
'Sonia' (MinBa)	CSut
¶ 'Spacemaker'	SDeJ
§ 'Stolze von Berlin' (MinBa)	NRog
'Suffolk Bride' (MSC)	NHal
'Suffolk Punch' (MD)	SMrm
'Suffolk Spectacular' (MD)	NHal
'Summer Night' (MC)	CSut
'Sunney Boy'	CSut
'Sunray Glint' (MSC)	NHal
'Swanvale' (SD)	NHal
'Sweet Content' (SD)	ECtt
'Symbol' (MSC)	NHal
¶ 'Tally-Ho' (WL)	MBri
'Thomas A Edison' (MD)	CSut LAma
'Tommy Doc' (SSC)	NHal
'Top Choice' (GSC)	LAma SDeJ
'Trendy' (SD)	SDeJ
'Trengrove Jill' (MD)	NHal
'Trengrove Summer' (MD)	NHal
'Trengrove Tauranga' (MD)	NHal
'Vaguely Noble' (SBa)	NHal
'Vantage' (GSC)	NHal
'Veritable' (MSC)	SDeJ
'W J N' (Pom)	ECtt NHal
'Wanda's Capella' (GD)	NHal
'Welcome Guest' (MSC)	ECtt
'Wendy's Place' (Pom)	NHal
'White Alva's' (GD)	NHal
'White Hornsey' (SD)	ECtt
'White Kerkrade' (SC)	ECtt NHal
'White Linda' (SD)	NHal
'White Moonlight' (MSC)	NHal
'White Perfection' (GD)	SDeJ
'White Rustig' (MD)	NHal
'White Swallow' (SSC)	NHal
'William John' (Pom)	ECtt
'Willo's Flecks' (Pom)	ECtt
'Willo's Night' (Pom)	ECtt
'Willo's Surprise' (Pom)	ECtt NHal
'Willo's Violet' (Pom)	ECtt
'Wootton Cupid' AGM	CSut NHal
'Wootton Impact' (MSC)	NHal
'Yellow Cheer' (SD)(DwB)	SDeJ
'Yellow Frank Hornsey' (SD)	ECtt
'Yellow Hammer' (Sin)(DwB)	NHal SChu SMrm
'Yvonne'	CSut
¶ 'Zingaro'	CSut
'Zorro' (GD)	CSut NHal

DAISWA See **PARIS**

DAMPIERA (Goodeniaceae)

¶ ***diversifolia***	LGre

DAMSON See **PRUNUS *institia***

DANAË (Liliaceae/Ruscaceae)

§ ***racemosa*** AGM	CCla CFil CSco EBre ECro EMon EPla GCal IHos LBre MBri MUlv NTow SDry SEng SHil SPer

DAPHNE † (Thymelaeaceae)

acutiloba	CBow CCla CPMA EPot ERea MPla SBla SSta WCru
albowiana	CPMA SBla WCru
alpina	CPMA NHol SBla WOMN
¶ ***altaica***	CPMA
arbuscula AGM	EB&P EPot SBla SIgm WPat
bholua	CChu EB&P ELan ERea LHop SSta WCru WWat
– ***alba***	CB&S CChu LAbb SBla SSta WPat
– Darjeeling form	CBow CPMA SBla
– 'Gurkha' AGM	CBow CPMA CSco EHar SHil
– 'Jacqueline Postill' AGM	CBow CPMA CSco EHar LRHS MBri SGil SHil
blagayana	CShe EB&P EPot LGre MBal MBri MHig MPla NGar NHol NRar NRoo NSti SBla SHBN SLeo WDin WPat WWat
x ***burkwoodii*** AGM	CB&S CBot CBow CSam ELan IJoh IOrc MBal MWat SHBN SHer SPla WCru WDin WHCG WPat WWat
– 'Albert Burkwood'	CPMA NWea SBla
– 'Astrid' (v)	CB&S CBow COtt CPMA ELan MGos MUlv MWat WWes
§ – 'Carol Mackie' (v)	CAbb CBot CPMA EB&P ECha GAbr LHop MPla SGil SIgm SUsu WWat
– 'G K Argles'	CPMA MPla SBla WHCG WPat
– 'Somerset'	CB&S CPMA CShe EHar ELan ENot LAbb LHop MBar MBlu MGos MPla SBla SHBN SPer SPla SReu SSta WBod WDin WThu
– 'Somerset Gold Edge' (v)	CPMA CSco WCru
♦– 'Variegata' (broad cream edge)	See D. x ***b.*** 'Somerset Variegated'
– 'Variegata' (broad gold edge)	See D. x ***b.*** 'Somerset Gold Edge'
– 'Variegata' (narrow gold edge)	See D. x ***b.*** 'Carol Mackie'
caucasica	CBow CPMA WWat
– x ***petraea***	SBla
'Cheriton'	SBla
cneorum	CB&S CBow CCla EB&P IJoh MBal MBar MWat NBee SBla SHer SReu SSta WAbe WCru WDin WPat WWat WWin
– ***alba***	SBla

– 'Eximia' AGM	CDoC CPMA CPle EB&P ECha ELan EPot GAbr IMal IOrc LGre LNet MAsh MGos MPla SBla SGil SHBN SHer SSta WCru WWat
*– 'Poszta'	CPMA SBla
– var. *pygmaea*	SBla SIng WPat WThu
– – 'Alba'	SWas WPat
– 'Variegata'	CPMA EB&P EPot LGre MBar MPla NRar SBla SGil SHer SPer SPla SSta WAbe WCru WPat WRus WSHC WThu WWat
collina	See D. ***sericea*** Collina Group
genkwa	CPMA ELan MPla
giraldii	CBot EPot LGre SIgm
x ***hendersonii***	SBla
x ***houtteana***	CBot CPMA EB&P NBir SBla SSta WCru
x ***hybrida***	SBla
japonica 'Striata'	See D. ***odora*** 'Aureomarginata'
jasminea	EPot SBla WPat
jezoensis	SBla SSta
juliae	SBla
'Kilmeston'	SBla
laureola	CPMA ECot GPoy MGos MPla NPer WWat WWye
– var. ***cantabrica***	SChu
– 'Margaret Mathew'	EPot
– ssp. ***philippi***	CBow CDoC CPMA CShe EB&P ELan MPla SChu SGil SHBN SHer SSta WAbe WWat
longilobata 'Peter Moore'	SHil
x ***mantensiana***	SGil WCru WPat WThu
– 'Manten'	CPMA
mezereum	Widely available
– f. ***alba***	CBow CCla CSco CShe ELan IOrc LAbb MBar MCas MHig MPla MTho NHol SEng SHBN SHer SMad SPer SReu SSta SUsu WAbe WDin WThu WWat
– var. ***autumnalis***	ELan
– 'Bowles' Variety'	CBot CPMA EPot WOMN
– 'Grandiflora'	See D. ***m. autumnalis***
– 'Rosea'	MGos SRms
– var. ***rubra***	CB&S CBow CPMA CSco IOrc LNet MPla NBee SEng SReu WDin WTyr WWeb
x ***napolitana*** AGM	CChu CMHG CPMA EB&P ELan IOrc LNet MGos SChu WCru WEas WWat
odora	CBow CBra CChe CPle EB&P ERea LHol MGos SBla SChu SSta WAbe WCru
§ – f. ***alba***	CBot CPMA EB&P ERea NSti
§ – 'Aureomarginata'	Widely available
– var. ***leucantha***	See D. ***o. alba***
– 'Marginata'	See D. ***o.*** 'Aureomarginata'
– var. ***rubra***	CBow CPMA EB&P EBee ELan LHol SMrm
– 'Walburton' (v)	LRHS
oleoïdes	EHic GDra NHol NTow
papyracea	SBla
petraea	SBla
¶ – ***alba***	SBla
– 'Grandiflora' AGM	EPot SBla WPat
pontica AGM	CCla CPMA CPle CSco CTre EHar MPla SDix SMad SPer SSta SUsu WCru WPat WThu WWat
retusa	See D. ***tangutica*** Retusa Group
'Rosy Wave'	SBla
§ ***sericea*** AGM	CAlt CB&S CFil CPMA CSco EB&P ELan EPot MPla NTow NWyt SBla SHer SIng SPou WAbe WCru WThu
§ – Collina Group	NRar WWat
tangutica AGM	Widely available
¶ – 'Rajah'	SHer
– Retusa Group AGM	CB&S CBow CPMA CSco CShe EB&P ECha ELan EPot GAbr GDra IDai ITim LHop MAsh MBri MBro MHig MPla NHol NRar NSti SBla SHBN SReu SSta WBod WPat WThu WWat
x ***thauma***	SBla WPat
¶ ***tichtome***	SBla

DAPHNIPHYLLUM (Daphniphyllaceae)

humile JR 902	EMon
macropodum	CChu CFil CGre CHEx EHar GWht MUlv SArc SHil SPer

DARLINGTONIA (Sarraceniaceae)

californica AGM	EPot MHel MSte WHal WMEx

DARMERA (Saxifragaceae)

§ ***peltata*** AGM	Widely available
– 'Nana'	CCla ECha ECro NHar NHol SApp WOld

DASYLIRION (Dracaenaceae)

§ ***acrotrichum***	CHEx SArc
gracile Planchon	See D. ***acrotrichum***
¶ ***leiophyllum***	CTrh
longissimum	CTbh SIgm
¶ ***wheeleri***	CTrh CTro

DASYPHYLLUM (Compositae/Asteraceae)

dicanthoïdes	CGre

DASYPYRUM (Gramineae/Poaceae)

See Plant Deletions

DATE See PHOENIX *dactylifera*

DATISCA (Datiscaceae)

cannabina	EMon

DATURA (Solanaceae)

arborea	See BRUGMANSIA ***a.***
chlorantha	See BRUGMANSIA ***c.***
cornigera	See BRUGMANSIA ***c.***
§ ***inoxia***	CTro ERea LBlm MSal SMad
meteloïdes	See DATURA ***inoxia***
rosea	See BRUGMANSIA x ***insignis*** pink
rosei	See BRUGMANSIA ***sanguinea***
sanguinea	See BRUGMANSIA ***s.***
signata	LHil
stramonium	CArn GPoy MHew MSal SHer SIde WHer WWye
– Tatula Group	MSal

suaveolens	See BRUGMANSIA *s.*
versicolor	See BRUGMANSIA *v.*

DAUCUS (Umbelliferae/Apiaceae)

carota	CArn CKin ECWi EWFC MHew MSal MWil WHer

DAVALLIA (Davalliaceae)

bullata	See D. ***mariesii***
¶ ***canariensis***	CFil CTro
fejeenis	MBri
§ ***mariesii*** AGM	CBos CNic MBri SDix WRic
– var. ***stenolepis***	SDix
pyxidata	NMar
solida	NMar
trichomanoïdes	NMar
– ***lorrainei***	NMar
tyermannii	NMar

DAVIDIA (Cornaceae)

involucrata AGM	CBow CBra CChu CDoC CHan CSco CWSG EBre EHar ENot IDai IJoh IOrc ISea LBre LPan MBlu MBri NBar NPal NWea SHBN SHil SPer SReu WDin WNor WStI WWat
– var. ***vilmoriniana*** AGM	CChu CGre EHar ELan LNet MGos MWat NBee SPer SSta WCoo

DEBREGEASIA (Urticaceae)

longifolia	CAbb CPle

DECAISNEA (Lardizabalaceae)

fargesii	CBow CChu CGre CMHG CPle CSco EBar ELan EMil ENot EPla GCal ISea MGos MUlv SBla SHil SPer SReu SSta WCoo WDin WWat
¶ – 'Harlequin'	SMad

DECODON (Lythraceae)

verticillatus	EHon

DECUMARIA (Hydrangeaceae)

barbara	CBot CChu CCla CGre CHEx CMac EMil EOvi GCal IBar SBra SHBN SHil SPer WCru WSHC WWat
sinensis	CHEx SArc

DEGENIA (Cruciferae/Brassicaceae)

velebitica	CNic NTow NWCA SIng

DEINANTHE (Hydrangeaceae)

bifida	ECro NKay WCru
caerulea	CPou WCru

DELAIREA (Compositae/Asteraceae)

odorata	CHEx CTro

DELONIX (Leguminosae/Caesalpiniaceae)
See Plant Deletions

DELOSPERMA (Aizoaceae)

§ ***aberdeenense***	CHEx WEas WOMN
* ***album***	CHEx
ashtonii	WPer
'Basutoland'	See D. ***nubigenum***
cooperi	EBur EPot MHig NGre NMen NTow SIng WPat WPer
lineare	NBir
lydenburgense	IBlr
macellum	NGre
§ ***nubigenum***	CLew CMHG ELan GGar MFos NGre NNrd NRed SBod SHer SIng STre WAbe WHil WHoo WOMN WPer WThu WWin
sutherlandii	NGre NNrd NRed NTow WPat
'Wilson'	WWin

DELPHINIUM (Ranunculaceae)

'After Midnight'	LHar
'Agnes Brookes'	ERou
'Alice Artindale'	CBos ECha EGle LGre LHop MBri SChu SMrm
♦ ***ambiguum***	See CONSOLIDA ***ajacis***
'Ann Woodfield'	MWoo
'Anne Page'	ERou
Astolat Group	CB&S CBot CBow CDoC CHad CHol CMea CSco EBre ECED EFou ELan GAbr LAbb LBlm LBre MBri MRav MWat NNor NPri NRoo SHer SPer WEas
'Atholl'	LHar
Avon strain	MWoo
x ***belladonna*** 'Andenken an August Koeneman'	See D. B. 'Wendy'
¶ – 'Atlantis'	LGre
– 'Bellamosum'	CBot EFou SPla
– 'Casa Blanca'	CBow CDoC CMGP EFou SFis SSvw
– 'Cliveden Beauty'	CDoC CMGP EFou GBri NBar NRoo SMrm SPla SSvw SUsu
– hybrids	ELan
– 'Moerheimii'	EFou SPla WMer
– 'Peace'	EBre LBre
– 'Piccolo'	EFou SPla
– 'Pink Sensation'	See D. x ***ruysii*** 'P.S.'
– 'Völkerfrieden'	CRDP CSco EFou LGre LWad MUlv SApp SPla WMer
– 'Wendy'	ECED
x ***bellamosum***	GBri NBar SMrm
'Beryl Burton'	ERou
'Betty Baseley'	ERou
¶ ***biternatum***	MSto
Black Knight Group	CB&S CBow CDoC CHol CSco EBre ECtt EFou ELan GAbr LAbb LBre LWad MBri MRav MWat NMir NNor NPri NRoo NVic SHer SPer SPla WEas
'Blauwal'	EFou
'Blue Bird'	CB&S CBow CDoC CHol CMea GAbr LWad MBri MRav NMir NNor NPri NRoo NVic SHer SPer SPla
'Blue Butterfly'	See D. ***grandiflorum*** 'B. B.'
'Blue Dawn' AGM	CBla ERou SOgg

Blue Fountains Group	CBow CHol CMGP CSco ELan LAbb LHop MBri MPit MRav MWat NBee NMir NOak SHer SPer SPla WHil WStI WTyr
Blue Heaven Group	NOak
Blue Jade Group	CBla ERou NNor SOgg SPer
'Blue Jay'	CB&S CBow CDoC CHol CMGP EFou ENot NPri
'Blue Nile' **AGM**	CBla ERou MWoo SOgg
'Blue Tit'	CBla ERou SOgg
'Browne's Lavender'	SOgg
'Bruce' **AGM**	ERou LHar MWoo SOgg
brunonianum	LBee MSto MTho SBla WOMN
'Butterball'	CBla LHar SOgg
californicum	MSto WWin
Cameliard Group	CB&S CMGP EBre ECtt EFou ELan GAbr LBre LWad NPri SPer
'Can-Can'	ERou LHar
cardinale	CBot GCra LAbb LGre MSto NPri SFis WPer
'Carl Topping'	ERou MWoo
cashmerianum	CBot CHan ELan LGan MFos MHig MSto MTho NWCA SHer WOMN
'Cassius'	CBla ERou LHar SOgg
caucasicum	See D. ***speciosum***
'Chelsea Star'	CBla ERou LHar MWoo SOgg
'Cherub'	CBla ERou LHar MWoo SOgg
chinense	See D. ***grandiflorum***
'Circe'	ERou
'Clack's Choice'	ERou
'Clifford Lass'	MWoo SOgg
'Clifford Pink'	CBla LHar MWoo SOgg
'Clifford Sky'	MWoo SOgg
Connecticut Yankees Group	NMir NNor NOak
'Conspicuous' **AGM**	CBla ERou LHar MWoo SOgg
'Constance Rivett'	ERou SOgg
'Cressida'	ERou
'Cristella'	ERou
'Crown Jewel'	CBla ERou LHar SOgg
cryophilum	See D. ***elatum elatum***
'Cupid'	CBla ERou SOgg
'Daily Express'	ERou
'Darling Sue'	LHar SOgg
'David's Magnificent'	WEas
delavayi	MSto WDav
'Demavand'	ERou LHar
'Diana Grenfell'	LHar
'Dolly Bird'	CBla ERou SOgg
'Dora Larkan'	LHar SOgg
'Dorothy Ash'	LHar
'Duchess of Portland'	ERou
'Eamon Andrews'	ERou
* 'Eastgrove White'	WEas
elatum	SRms WHaw WOMN
'Emily Hawkins' **AGM**	ERou LHar SOgg
'Eva Gower'	ERou
'Evita'	LHar
'F W Smith'	EFou WMer
'Fanfare' **AGM**	CBla ERou LHar SOgg
'Father Thames'	ERou SOgg
'Faust' **AGM**	CBla ERou MWoo SOgg
'Fenella' **AGM**	CBla LHar MWoo SOgg
'Finsteraarhorn'	EFou
'Foxhill Lady'	LHar
'Foxhill Nina'	LHar
'Foxhill Oscar'	LHar
'Foxhill Pinta'	LHar
'Fred Yule'	ERou
Galahad Group	Widely available
'Garden Party'	CBla
'Gemma'	MWoo
geraniifolium	NTow WDav
'Gillian Dallas' **AGM**	CBla ERou LHar MWoo SOgg
'Giotto'	LHar
glaucum	CNic NHol
'Gordon Forsyth'	CBla ERou LHar MWoo SOgg
'Gossamer'	LHar
§ ***grandiflorum***	CBow CHad CNic EPad MSto SMrm
§ – 'Blue Butterfly'	CBot CBow CMea EBre EBur LBre LGan LHop SBla SPla WWin
Guinevere Group	CB&S CBow CMGP CMea ECtt GAbr LWad MBri MWat NBir NNor NPri NRoo NWyt SGil SHer SPer SPla WEas
'Guy Langdon'	ERou
'Harmony'	ERou SOgg
¶ ***hybridum***	MSto
'Iceman'	LHar
Ivory Towers Group	ECtt
'James Nuttall'	ECha
'Jill Curley'	LHar
'Joyce Roffey'	ERou
'Judy Knight'	ERou
'Kathleen Cooke'	LHar SOgg
'Kestrel'	ERou SOgg
King Arthur Group	CB&S CBow CDoC CSco ECtt ENot GAbr LWad MBri MRav MWat NNor NPri SHer WEas
'Lady Guinevere'	ERou
'Lady Hambleden'	See D. 'Patricia Lady Hambleden'
'Leonora'	ERou LHar SOgg
¶ ***likiangense***	MSto
'Lilian Bassett'	ERou LHar MWoo SOgg
'Loch Katrine'	LHar
'Loch Leven' **AGM**	CBla ERou LHar MWoo SOgg
'Loch Nevis'	SOgg
'Loch Torridon'	LHar
'Lord Butler' **AGM**	CBla LHar SOgg
'Lorna'	ERou SOgg
luteum	GCra
Magic Fountains	CBow EFou GAbr NPri NRoo WGor WPbr WRus
'Margaret Farrand'	ERou SOgg
'Marie Broan'	ERou
menziesii	MSto NWCA WPla
'Michael Ayres'	CBla ERou MWoo
'Mighty Atom' **AGM**	CBla ERou LHar MWoo SOgg
'Min'	ERou LHar
'Molly Buchanan'	CBla ERou SOgg
'Moonbeam'	CBla SOgg
'Morning Cloud'	ERou
'Mother Teresa'	ERou LHar
'Mrs Newton Lees'	EFou ERou
'Mrs T Carlile'	ERou
muscosum	WOMN
* 'Mystic'	LHar
* 'Mystique'	CBla ERou SOgg
New Century hybrids	CB&S EBre LBre
'Nicholas Woodfield'	MWoo SOgg
'Nimrod'	CBla ERou
'Nobility'	CBla ERou SOgg

nudicaule	CBot CBow ELan GDra LGan MSto NRoo NWCA SFis SSvw WOMN WPer
– ***luteum***	See D. *l.*
¶ ***nuttallianum***	MSto
'Olive Poppleton'	CBla MWoo SOgg
'Oliver'	ERou MWoo SOgg
'Our Deb'	MWoo SOgg
oxysepalum	MSto WHaw
Pacific hybrids	CKel EBre ENot LBre NOak SPer SRms WByw
parishii JJA 12737	MSto SIgm
'Patricia Johnson'	ERou LHar SOgg
Percival Group	NPri
'Pericles'	CBla LHar SOgg
'Pink Ruffles'	CBla ERou SOgg
'Polar Sun'	ERou
'Purity'	ERou
'Purple Ruffles'	ERou
'Purple Triumph'	ERou SOgg
pylzowii	CNic ESma GCra MSto NRoo SFis SSvw WPer
'Pyramus'	ERou SOgg
requienii	CBot CFee CMea ERav GCra LGan MSto SAxl SMrm WEas WHer
'Romany'	LHar
'Rosemary Brock' AGM	ERou LHar MWoo SOgg
'Royal Flush' AGM	CBla LHar MWoo SOgg
'Ruby'	CBla LHar
x ***ruysii*** 'Piccolo'	NBar
§ – 'Pink Sensation'	EBre EMon ERou GBri LBre MUlv NBar WMer WRus
'Sabrina'	CBla ERou
'Samantha'	ERou LHar
'Sandpiper' AGM	LHar SOgg
§ ***semibarbatum***	CBot MSto NPri SIgm
'Sentinel'	ERou
'Shimmer'	CBla ERou LHar SOgg
'Silver Jubilee'	ERou
'Silver Moon'	ERou SOgg
'Skyline'	CBla ERou SOgg
Snow White Group	NBir NOak SRms
'Snowdon'	LHar SOgg
'Solomon'	ERou
Southern Aristocrats Group	EBee LHar WHoo
Southern Consort Group	EBee LHar WHoo
Southern Countess Group	EBee LHar
Southern Countrymen Group	LHar
Southern Debutante Group	EBee LHar WHoo
Southern Jesters Group	EBee LHar WHoo
Southern Ladies Group	EBee LHar WHoo
Southern Maidens Group	EBee LHar
Southern Minstrels Group	EBee LHar
Southern Noblemen Group	LHar
Southern Royals Group	EBee LHar WHoo
§ ***speciosum***	WOMN
'Spindrift' AGM	LHar SOgg
staphisagria	GPoy MHew MSal WEas
'Strawberry Fair'	CBla ERou SOgg
'Summer Haze'	ERou
Summer Skies Group	CB&S CBow CMGP CNic CSco EBee ECtt EFou LWad MBri MWat NNor NPri NRoo SHer SPer SPla WEas
'Summerfield Miranda ' AGM	LHar SOgg
'Sungleam' AGM	CBla EFou ERou LHar SOgg
'Sunkissed'	MWoo SOgg
'Swan Lake'	ERou
tatsienense	CNic ECoo ELan GDra LHop MBro MSto MTho NWCA SHer SUsu WHoo WOMN
– 'Album'	MSto
'Tessa'	ERou
'Thamesmead'	LHar
'Thundercloud'	ERou SOgg
'Tiddles' AGM	CBla LHar SOgg
tricorne	MFos
¶ ***trolliifolium***	GTou
'Turkish Delight'	CBla ERou LHar SOgg
'Vespers'	ERou SOgg
'Walton Beauty'	MWoo
'Walton Gemstone'	MWoo SOgg
'Watkin Samuel'	ERou
yunnanense	GDra
zalil	See D. ***semibarbatum***

DENDRANTHEMA †
(Compositae/Asteraceae)

'Abbygates' (25b)	NHal
'Adorn' (22d)	MCol MRil
'Agnes Ann' (29K)	MCol
'Albert Broadhurst' (24b)	MWol NHal
'Albert's Yellow' (Rub)	MCol MMil
'Alexis' (5a)	MRil
'Alfreton Cream' (5b)	MRil
'Aline' (29K)	EHMN
'Alison' (29c)	EHMN
'Alison Kirk' (23b)	MCol NHal
'Allouise' AGM	MCol NHal
'Allure' (22d)	MRil
¶ 'Amber Enbee Wedding' (29d)	MRil
'Amy Shoesmith' (15a)	MCol
'Anastasia' (28)	CLTr CMil ECtt EOrc ERav GMac LHil LHop MCol MMil MNFA MRav NBrk NFai NRar NSti SChu SCro SPla SUsu WEas WPer WWin
N 'Anastasia Variegated' (28)	CSam EFol EMon ERav MBel NSti WCot
'Angelic' (28)	MCol
'Angora' (25b)	MCol
'Ann Brook' (23b)	MCol
'Anna Marie' AGM	EHMN MCol MWol
¶ 'Annapurna' (3b)	MWol
'Anne' (29K)	EHMN
'Anne, Lady Brockett'	EFou EMon GBuc NBro
¶ 'Apollo'	EMon
'Apricot' (Rub)	ECtt EFou MFir MMil MRav SFis SGil SMad SSvw
'Apricot Alexis' (5a)	MRil
'Apricot Cassandra' (5b)	NHal
'Apricot Chessington' (25a)	MRil NHal

'Apricot Courtier' (24a) MRil MWol NHal
'Apricot Enbee Wedding' (29d) MWol NHal
'Apricot Madeleine' (29c) NHal
'Apricot Margaret' (29c) EHMN
'Apricot Vedova' (6a) MCol
'Arthur Hawkins' (24b) NHal
¶ 'Artic Beauty' (4b) MWol
'Aucklander' (23b) NHal
'Audrey Shoesmith' (3a) NHal
'Aunt Millicent' (29K) MCol
'Aurora' (4a) MCol
'Autumn Days' (25b) MCol
'Babs' MMil
¶ 'Baden Locke' (24b) MWol
'Balcombe Perfection' (5a) MCol MRil MWol NHal
'Beacon' (5a) MRil NHal
'Belair' (9c) MCol
'Belle' (29K) EHMN
'Bertos' EHMN
'Bessie Rowe' (25a) MCol
'Betty' (29K) MCol
'Betty Wiggins' (25b) MCol
'Bill Bye' (1) MWol NHal
'Bill Wade' (25a) MCol MRil NHal
'Black Magic' (24b) MCol
¶ 'Bob Dear' (25a) MCol
'Bonnie Jean' (9d) MCol
'Bo-Peep' (28) EMon MCol WByw
'Bravo' NHal
'Brenda Rowe' (5a) MCol
'Bridget' (6b) MWol
'Brierton Festival' (7b) MWol
'Brietner' (24b) MCol
'Bright Eye' (28) MCol WPer
'Bright Golden Princess Anne' (4b) NHal
'Brightness' (29K) EHMN NFai SChu SUsu WEas
'Broadacre' (7a) MCol
'Bronze Belair' (9c) MCol
'Bronze Bornholm' (14b) MCol
'Bronze Bridget' (6b) MWol
'Bronze Cassandra' (5b) NHal
'Bronze Elegance' (28) CLTr CMil CSco EFou ELan EMon ERav LLWP SHer SIng SPer SPla SUsu WAbe WByw WEas WRus WWat
'Bronze Elite' (29d) EHMN
'Bronze Enbee Wedding' (29d) NHal
'Bronze Fairweather' (3b) MWol
'Bronze Fairy' (28a) MCol MWol
'Bronze Majestic' (2) MWol
'Bronze Margaret' **AGM** EHMN MCol MRil NHal
'Bronze Maria' (18a) MCol
¶ 'Bronze Matlock' (24b) MRil
¶ 'Bronze Max Riley' (23b) MRil
'Bronze Mayford Perfection' **AGM** MCol NHal
'Bronze Yvonne Arnaud (24b) MCol
'Bronzetti' EHMN
'Brown Eyes' (29K) EHMN
'Bruera' (24a) MWol NHal
'Bryan Kirk' (4b) MWol NHal
'Buff Peter Rowe' (23b) NHal
'Bullfinch' (12a) EHMN MWol
'Bunty' (28) ECha NBrk SMrm
'Cameo' (28a) EBar MCol
'Candid' (15b) MCol
'Candylite' (14b) MCol
'Canopy' (24a) NHal
'Carlene Welby' (25b) MRil NHal
'Cassandra' (5b) NHal
'Chaffinch' (22a) EHMN
'Charles Fraser' (25a) NHal
'Charles Tandy' (5a) MRil
'Cheddar' (13a) MCol
'Cherry Dynasty' (14a) MRil
'Cherry Margaret' (29c) EHMN MRil NHal
'Cherry Venice' (24b) MRil
'Chessington' (25a) MCol MRil NHal
'Chester Globe' (23b) NHal
'Christine Hall' (25a) MCol
'Christmas Carol' (5a) MWol
'Christmas Wine' (5a) MWol
I 'Citrus' (29K) EFou
'Clara Curtis' (Rub) Widely available
'Clare Dobson' (25b) MWol
'Clare Louise' (24b) MRil
'Claudia' (24c) EHMN MCol
'Cloudbank' (9a) MWol
'Columbine' (29K) EHMN
'Connie Meyhew' (5a) NHal
'Cooper Nob' (29K) EHMN
'Copeland' (14b) NHal
'Copper Margaret' (29c) MWol
'Coral Rynoon' (9d) MWol
¶ 'Cornetto' (25b) MRil
'Corngold' (5b) MWol NHal
'Cornish' (25b) MRil
'Cossack' (2) MWol
'Cottage Apricot' EWoo GMac LHop SMrm
'Cottage Pink' See D. 'Emperor of China'
'Cottingham' (25a) MCol NHal
'Courtier' (24a) MRil MWol NHal
'Cream Allouise' (25b) NHal
'Cream Elegance' (9c) NHal
'Cream John Hughes' (3b) MRil MWol NHal
'Cream Margaret' (29c) NHal
¶ 'Cream Pennine Thrill' (29) MRil
'Cream West Bromwich' (14a) MRil
'Creamist' (25b) MCol MWol
'Cricket' (25b) MCol
'Crimson Yvonne Arnaud' **AGM** MCol
'Cropthorne' EHMN
¶ 'Cygnet' (24b) MRil
'Daniel Cooper' (Rub) MCol
'Daphne' EHMN
'David Shoesmith' (25a) MCol MWol
'Debbie' (29K) EHMN
'Debonair' **AGM** MCol MRil NHal
'Dee Crimson' (29c) NHal
'Dee Lemon' (24c) MCol

'Dee Pink' (29c) MCol
'Denise' **AGM** MCol MWol
'Dennis Fletcher' (25a) MRil
'Derek Bircumshaw' (28a) MCol
'Deva Glow' (25a) MCol NHal
'Diamond Wedding' (25a) MWol
§ 'Doctor Tom Parr' (28) CGle EFou ELan EMon GCal LGre MBel MFir NBrk SMrm WByw
'Donna' (22f) MCol MRil
'Doreen Hall' (15a) MCol MRil
'Doris' (29K) EHMN
'Dorothy Stone' (25b) NHal
'Dorridge Beauty' (24a) MRil MWol NHal
'Dorridge Candy' (4b) MWol
'Dorridge Choice' (5b) MWol
'Dorridge Crystal' (24a) MRil MWol NHal
'Dorridge Flair' (3b) MWol
'Dorridge King' (4b) MWol
'Dorridge Velvet' (4b) MWol
¶ 'Dorridge Vulcan' MWol
'Duchess of Edinburgh' (Rub) CCla CDec CGle CSam CSco ECtt ELan EMon ERav GMac LGre LHop MBri MCol MFir MNFA MRav NFai SMad WEas WRus
'Duke of Kent' (1) MWol
'Dulverton' (24c) NHal
'East Riding' (25a) NHal
'Eastleigh' (24b) MWol
¶ 'Ed Hodgson' (25a) MRil
'Eddie Wilson' (25b) MRil
'Edelgard' EFou
'Edelweiss' (29K) EFou LHop
'Edwin Painter' (7b) MWol
¶ 'Egret' (23b) MRil
'Elegance' (9c) MCol NHal
'Elizabeth Burton' (5a) MWol
'Elizabeth Shoesmith' (1) NHal
'Ellen' (29c) NHal
'Emma Lou' (23a) MCol NHal
§ 'Emperor of China' (Rub) CDec CGle CMil CSam ECha EFou EHal EMon GAbr GCal GCra GMac LGre MBel MCol MRav MSte MUlv NBrk NFai SChu SFis SGil SHig SMad SSvw SUsu WEas WHoo WRus
'Enbee Dell' (29d) NHal
'Enbee Frill' (29d) MCol
'Enbee Wedding' **AGM** MRil MWol NHal
'Encore' NHal SFis
'Epic' (6b) MWol
'Ermine' (23a) MCol NHal
'Evelyn Bush' (25a) MCol
'Eye Level' (5a) MRil NHal
'Fairweather' (3b) MCol MRil MWol
'Fairy' (28) MCol MWol
'Fairy Rose' (4b) MCol MMil
'Fieldfare' EHMN
§ 'Fleet Margaret' **AGM** MRil MWol NHal
'Flying Saucer' (6a) MCol
'Formcast' (24a) NHal
'Fortune' (24b) MRil
'Fred Brocklehurst' (25a) MRil
'Fred Shoesmith' (5a) MRil MWol NHal
'Frolic' (25b) MCol MRil
'Gala Princess' (24b) MWol
'Galaxy' **AGM** MCol
'Gambit' (24a) MCol MRil NHal
¶ 'Gary Scothern' (25b) MWol
'Gay Anne' (4b) NHal
'Gazelle' (23a) MCol NHal
'George Griffiths' (24b) MRil NHal
'Gertrude' (19c) MCol
'Gigantic' (1) NHal
'Gingernut' (5b) MCol MRil NHal
'Gladys' (24b) EBee ELan EWoo MCol
'Gladys Homer' (24a) MWol
'Gloria' (25a) EHMN
– (30K) MCol
¶ 'Gold Enbee Wedding' (29d) MRil
'Gold Foil' (5a) MRil NHal
'Gold Margaret' See D. 'Golden Margaret'
'Golden Anemone' EHMN
'Golden Angora' (25b) MCol
'Golden Cassandra' (5b) NHal
'Golden Courtier' (24a) NHal
'Golden Creamist' **AGM** MCol
'Golden Elegance' (5a) MWol
'Golden Fred Shoesmith' (5a) NHal
'Golden Gigantic' (1) MWol
'Golden Honeyball' (15b) MCol
'Golden Ivy Garland' (5b) MCol NHal
'Golden Lady' (3b) MWol
§ 'Golden Margaret' **AGM** EHMN MCol MRil NHal
'Golden Mayford Perfection' **AGM** NHal
'Golden Orfe' (29c) MCol
'Golden Pamela' (29c) NHal
'Golden Pennine Pink' (29c) NHal
'Golden Pixton' (25b) MCol
'Golden Plover' EHMN
'Golden Quill Elegance' (9f) MWol
'Golden Saskia' (7b) MCol
'Golden Seal' (7b) EMon MCol
'Golden Taffeta' (9c) NHal
'Golden Treasure' (28a) MCol MWol
'Golden Wedding' (30K) MCol
'Goldmarianne' EFou
'Goldmine' NHal
'Goodlife Sombrero' (29a) NHal
'Gordon Taylor' (7b) MWol
'Grace Lovell' (25a) NHal
'Grace Riley' (24a) MCol MWol
'Grandchild' (29c) EHMN MCol
'Green Chartreuse' (5b) MWol
'Green Nightingale' (10) MWol
'Green Satin' (5b) MWol
'Grenadine' **AGM** MRil NHal
'Halloween' (4b) NHal
'Handford Pink' (29K) MCol

'Happy Geel' EHMN
'Hardwick Bronze' EHMN
'Hardwick Lemon' (29c) EHMN
'Hardwick Primrose' (29c) EHMN
'Hardwick Yellow' (19b) EHMN
'Harry Gee' (1) MWol
¶ 'Harry James' (25a) MCol
'Harry Woolman' (3b) MWol
'Harvest Dawn' (25) MCol
'Harvey' (29K) MCol
¶ 'Hayley Griffin' (25a) MWol
'Hazel' (30,K) EHMN
'Hazy Days' (25b) MCol NHal
'Heather James' (3b) MCol NHal
'Hedgerow' (7b) MCol
'Heide' **AGM** MCol NHal
'Hekla' (30) MCol
'Honey' (25b) EHMN
'Honeyball' (25b) MCol
'Illusion' MRil
'Imp' (28) MCol MWol
'Inkberrow' (24b) NHal
'Innocence' (Rub) CGle EBee EFou EHal ELan EMon GMac MUlv NFai NNrw SMad WEas
'Irene' (29K) EHMN SMad
'Iris Coupland' (5a) NHal
'Ivy Garland' (5b) MCol NHal
'James Kelway' NBir
'Jan Okum' (24b) MWol NHal
'Jan Wardle' (5a) MWol
'Jante Wells' (28) EMon MCol MFir WEas
¶ ***japonense***
var. ***ashizuriense*** EBee
'Jessie Cooper' (Rub) EOrc SChu
'Joan' (25b) EHMN
¶ 'John Austin' (25a) MRil
'John Hughes' (3b) MCol MRil MWol NHal
'John Lewis' (24b) MWol
'John Murray' NBir
'John Riley' (14a) MRil
'John Wingfield' (14b) MRil MWol NHal
'Jules la Graveur' EMon SMrm WByw
'Julia' EFou
'June Wakley' (25b) MCol
'Karen Riley' (25a) MRil
'Keystone' (25b) MCol MRil NHal
'Kimberley Marie' (15b) NHal
'Kingfisher' (12a) MWol
'Kismet' (4c) MWol
'Kleiner Bernstein' EFou
x ***koreanum*** See D. x ***grandiflorum***
'Lady Clara' (Rub) SPer
'Lady in Pink' (Rub) EMon
'Lakelanders' (3b) MWol NHal
'Leading Lady' (25b) MWol
'Lemon Blanket' EHMN
'Lemon Margaret' **AGM** EHMN MRil MWol NHal
'Lilian Hoek' (29c) EHMN MWol NHal
'Lilian Jackson' (7b) MCol
'Lilian Shoesmith' (5b) MRil
'Lindy' EFou
'L'Innocence' (29K) SMrm
'Little Dorrit' (29K) EHMN MCol
'Liverpool Festival' (23b) MCol NHal
'Long Island Beauty' **AGM** MCol
'Long Life' (25b) MCol
'Lorraine' (24b) MWol NHal
'Louise' (25b) EHMN
'Louise Etheridge' (23a) NHal
'Lucida' (29c) MWol
'Lucy Simpson' (29K) MCol MMil
'Lundy' (2) NHal
'Lyndale' (25b) MCol NHal
'Lynmal's Choice' (13b) MCol NHal
'Mac's Delight' (25b) MCol MRil
'Madeleine' **AGM** NHal
'Malcolm Perkins' (25a) MRil NHal
'Mandarin' CGle EFou
'Margaret' **AGM** EHMN MCol MRil MWol NHal
'Margaret Riley' (25b) NHal
'Maria' (28a) MCol
'Marion' (25a) EHMN
'Marlene Jones' (25b) MWol
'Martin Riley' (23b) MCol
'Martin Walker' (25b) MCol
'Mary' (29K) EHMN MCol
'Mary Stevenson' (25b) MCol
'Mary Stoker' (Rub) CGle CKel CMea CSco ECha ECtt EFou EHal ELan EMon GMac LGre MBel MBri MCol MNFA MRav NFai SChu SMad SPer WAbe WEas WRus
'Mason's Bronze' (7b) MCol
'Matlock' (24b) MRil NHal
¶ 'Matthew Woolman' (4a) MWol
¶ 'Maudie Hodgson' (24b) MRil
'Mauve Gem' (29K) EHMN
'Mavis' (28a) MCol MWol
'Max Riley' **AGM** MRil MWol NHal
'May Shoesmith' (5a) MCol NHal
'Mayford Perfection' **AGM** MCol NHal
'Megan Woolman' (3b) MWol
'Mei-kyo' (28) CGle CHol CLew CMea CMil CSam CSco ECtt ELan EMon EOrc ERav MRav NFai NHol NJap SHer SIng SPer SPla SSvw WAbe WEas WRus WWat
'Membury' (24b) MCol NHal
'Michelle Walker' (24b) MCol
'Midnight' (24b) MRil
'Minaret' (3b) MWol
'Minstrel Boy' (3b) MRil NHal
'Mirage' **AGM** MCol MRil NHal
'Moira' (29K) EHMN
'Molly Lambert' (36) MWol
'Moonlight' (29K) EHMN
'Morning Star' (12a) MWol
'Mottram Barleycorn' (29d) MCol
'Mottram Lady' (29d) MCol
'Mottram Melody' (29d) MCol
'Mottram Minstrel' (29d) MCol
'Mottram Sentinel' (29d) MCol

'Mottram Twotone' (29d) MCol
'Mrs Jessie Cooper' (Rub) EBee EFou ELan EMon
'Muriel Vipas' (25b) MRil
'Music' (23b) NHal
'My Love' (7a) MCol MWol
♦ *naktongense* See D. ***zawadskii latiloba***
'Nancy Perry' (Rub) CSam ELan EMon LGan MCol NCat SChu
§ ***nankingense*** EMon
'Nantyderry Sunshine' EFou SIng SUsu WEas WWat
'Naomi' (22f) MRil
'Nathalie' (19c) MWol
'Nell Gwyn' (Rub) MCol
'New Stylist' (24b) MRil
'Nicole' (22c) MRil
'Niederschlesien' EFou
'Nu Dazzler' (9d) MCol
¶ 'Nu Robin' (9d) MCol
'Nu-Rosemary' **AGM** NHal
'Oakfield Bride' (24b) NHal
'Ogmore Vale' (12a) MWol
'Olga Patterson' (5b) MWol
'Orange Allouise' (25b) MWol NHal
'Orange Fair Lady' (5a) NHal
'Orange Margaret' (29c) See D. 'Fleet Margaret'
'Orange Pennine Pink' (29c) NHal
'Orangeade' (24b) MCol
'Orno' (29b) MCol
'Overbury' EHMN
§ ***pacificum*** CB&S CCla CHan CMea COtt CTre ECha ECtt EFol EFou EHal ELan EPla ERav ESma GCal LGan LHop MFir MHlr NBir NBro NFai SBor SUsu WCot WEas WHer WHow
*– 'Hakai' SChu
♦– 'Silver and Gold' See D. ***p.***
'Packwell' (24b) MCol
'Pamela' (29c) NHal
'Panache' (5a) NHal
'Pat' (6b) EHMN
'Pat Addison' (24b) MWol NHal
'Patricia' EHMN
'Patricia Millar' (14b) NHal
'Paul Boissier' (Rub) CGle ELan EMon LGre MCol SMrm WByw WEas
¶ 'Pauline White' (15a) MRil
'Pavilion' (25a) MCol
'Payton Dale' (29c) MRil NHal
'Payton Glow' (29c) NHal
'Payton Lady' (29c) NHal
'Payton Plenty' (29c) NHal
'Payton Prince' (29c) NHal
'Payton Rose' (29c) NHal
'Peach Allouise' **AGM** NHal
'Peach Margaret' See D. 'Salmon Margaret'
'Pearl Celebration' (24a) MRil MWol NHal
'Peggy' (28a) EHMN
'Pelsall Imperial' (3a) MCol
'Pennine Amber' (29c) MRil NHal
'Pennine Brenda' (29d) MRil NHal
'Pennine Bride' (29c) MRil NHal
'Pennine Canary' **AGM** MRil
¶ 'Pennine Cheer' (29c) MRil
'Pennine Clarion' (29c) MRil
¶ 'Pennine Club' (29d) MRil
'Pennine Crimson' (29c) NHal
'Pennine Crystal' (29c) MCol
'Pennine Cupid' (29c) MWol
'Pennine Dell' (29d) MCol
'Pennine Dove' (29d) NHal
'Pennine Eagle' (29c) MCol
¶ 'Pennine Fizz' (29d) MRil
¶ 'Pennine Ginger' (29c) MRil
¶ 'Pennine Goal' (29c) MRil
'Pennine Hannah' (29d) NHal
'Pennine Harmony' (29f) MRil
'Pennine Jade' **AGM** MWol NHal
¶ 'Pennine Jessie' (29d) MRil
¶ 'Pennine Lace' (29f) MRil
¶ 'Pennine Magnet' (29a) MRil
¶ 'Pennine Marie' (29a) MRil
'Pennine Mavis' (29f) MRil
'Pennine Nectar' (29c) NHal
'Pennine Oriel' (29a) MCol MRil MWol NHal
'Pennine Pink' (29c) NHal
'Pennine Polo' (29d) NHal
'Pennine Punch' (29a) MCol
'Pennine Purple' (29c) EHMN MCol NHal
'Pennine Serene' (29d) MRil
'Pennine Sergeant' (29c) MWol
'Pennine Ski' (29c) MCol MRil
'Pennine Soldier' **AGM** MRil MWol NHal
¶ 'Pennine Sparkle' (29f) MRil
¶ 'Pennine Sprite' (29d) MRil
¶ 'Pennine Sugar' (29) MRil
¶ 'Pennine Swan' (29c) MRil
'Pennine Tango' (29d) NHal
¶ 'Pennine Thrill' (29d) MRil
'Pennine Trill' (29c) MWol
'Pennine Twinkle' (29a) MCol
'Pennine Waltz' (29c) EHMN
¶ 'Pennine Wax' (29) MRil
'Pennine Whistle' **AGM** MRil
'Pennine White' (29c) MWol
'Percy Salter' (24b) MCol
'Perry's Peach' NPer
'Peter Rowe' (23b) MCol NHal
'Peter Sare' GMac
'Peter White' (23a) MCol
'Peterkin' EBee ECtt EMar EMon GMac LGre MUlv SMrm WRus
'Phil Houghton' (1) MWol
'Piecas' EHMN
'Pink Champagne' (4b) NHal
'Pink Duke' (1) MWol NHal
¶ 'Pink Favorite' (5b) MCol
'Pink Gin' (9c) MWol NHal
¶ 'Pink Ice' (5b) MCol
'Pink Margaret' (29c) EHMN NHal
'Pink Overture' (15b) MCol
'Pink Progression' ECtt GMac NBir
'Pink World of Sport' (25a) MRil
'Pixton' (25b) MCol
'Playmate' (29K) MCol
'Plessey Snowflake' (29d) NHal
'Polar Gem' (3a) MCol MWol NHal

'Polaris' (9c) MCol
¶ 'Pomander' (25b) MRil
¶ 'Pot Black' (14b) MRil
'Primrose Alison Kirk' (23b) NHal
'Primrose Anemone' (29K) EHMN
'Primrose Angora' (25b) MCol
'Primrose Bill Wade' (25a) MRil NHal
'Primrose Chessington (25a) MRil NHal
'Primrose Cricket' (25b) MCol
'Primrose Ermine' (23a) NHal
'Primrose John Hughes' (3b) MRil MWol NHal
'Primrose Margaret' (29c) See D. 'Buff Margaret'
'Primrose Mayford Perfection' **AGM** MCol NHal
'Primrose Muriel Vipas' (25b) MRil
'Primrose Pennine Oriel' (29a) MRil
'Primrose Polaris' (9c) MCol
'Primrose Sam Vinter' (5a) MRil
'Primrose Tennis' (25b) NHal
'Primrose West Bromwich (14a) MRil NHal
'Princess' (29K) EHMN MCol
'Princess Anne' (4b) MCol NHal
'Promise' (25a) MCol
'Purleigh White' EFou SIng SUsu
'Purple Fairie' (28b) MCol
'Purple Gerrie Hoek' EHMN
'Purple Glow' (5a) NHal
'Purple Margaret' (29c) EHMN NHal
'Purple Payton Lady' (29c) NHal
'Queenswood' (5b) MCol
'Quill Elegance' (9f) MWol
'Rachel Fairweather' (3a) NHal
'Raquel' (29K) MCol
'Rayonnante' (11) MCol
'Red Admiral' (6b) MWol
'Red Balcombe Perfection' (5a) MWol NHal
'Red Claudia' (29c) EHMN
'Red Eye Level' (5a) MRil
'Red Formcast' (24a) NHal
'Red Gambit' (24a) MRil NHal
'Red Hoek' (29c) MWol
'Red Keystone' (25a) MRil
'Red Mayford Perfection' (5a) MCol
'Red Pamela' (29c) NHal
'Red Payton Dale' (29c) MRil
'Red Pheasant' EHMN
'Red Rosita' (29c) MCol
'Red Shirley Model' (3a) MWol NHal
¶ 'Red Shoesmith Salmon' (4a) MCol
'Red Wendy' **AGM** MCol NHal
¶ 'Red Windermere' (24a) MRil
'Redall' (4c) MCol
'Regal Mist' (25b) MCol
'Regalia' **AGM** MCol
'Remarkable' (30) MCol MRil NHal
'Riley's Dynasty' (14a) MRil NHal
'Ringdove' (12a) MWol
'Robeam' (9c) MWol
'Roblaze' (9c) MWol NHal
'Roblush' (9c) MWol
'Rockwell' (14b) NHal
'Rolass' (9c) NHal
'Romano Mauve' EHMN
'Romantika' EFou
'Romark' (9c) MWol NHal
¶ 'Ron Eldred' (15a) MRil
'Ron James' (4a) NHal
'Rose Enbee Wedding' (29d) MCol NHal
'Rose Mayford Perfection' **AGM** MCol
'Rose Payton Lady' (29c) NHal
¶ 'Rose Windermere' (24a) MRil
'Rosita' (28b) MCol
'Roy Coopland' (5b) MRil NHal
'Royal Command' (Rub) NBro SMad
'Rozette' EHMN
rubellum See D. ***zawadskii***
¶ 'Ruby Enbee Wedding' (29d) MRil
'Ruby Mound' (29K) EFou EHMN LGre LHop MCol NFai NHal SFis WEas
'Ruby Raynor' (Rub) MCol
'Rumpelstilzchen' EBee EMar
'Ryfinch' (9d) MCol
'Ryflare' (9c) MWol NHal
'Ryflash' (9d) MCol
'Rylands Gem' (24b) MCol NHal
'Rylands Victor' (23c) MCol
'Rynoon' (9d) MWol
¶ 'Ryred' MWol
'Rytorch' (9d) MCol
'Salmon Cassandra' (5b) NHal
¶ 'Salmon Enbee Wedding' (29d) MRil
'Salmon Fairie' (28) MCol
'Salmon Fairweather' (3b) MWol
§ 'Salmon Margaret' **AGM** MCol MRil
¶ 'Salmon Payton Dale' (29c) MRil
'Salmon Rylands Gem' (24b) MCol NHal
'Salmon Susan Rowe' (24b) MCol
'Salmon Tracy Waller' (24a) MRil
'Salmon Venice' (24b) MRil
'Salurose' EHMN
'Sam Oldham' (24a) MWol
'Sam Vinter' (5a) MRil NHal
'Sandra Burch' (24b) MWol NHal
'Sandy' (30) MCol MRil
'Sarah' MRil
'Sarah's Yellow' CSam

'Saskia' (7b) MCol
'Satin Pink Gin' (9c) NHal
'Sea Urchin' (29c) MCol
'Seagull' EHMN
'Seashell' (28b) MCol
'Sefton' (4a) NHal
'Setron' EHMN
'Sheila' (29K) EHMN
'Shining Light' (29K) EHMN MCol
'Shirley' (25b) MWol
'Shirley Glorious' (24a) MWol
'Shirley McMinn' (15a) MRil
'Shirley Model' (3a) MWol
'Shirley Primrose' (1) MWol
'Shoesmith's Salmon' AGM MWol
'Silver Gigantic' (1) MWol
'Silver Jubilee' (24a) MWol
'Silver Stan Addison' (5b) MWol
'Simon Mills' (2) NHal
'Snow Bunting' EHMN
'Snowbound' (30K) MCol
'Snowflake' (24a) CTre
'Snowshine' (5a) MWol
'Solarama' (9e) NHal
'Sonnenschein' LHop WHen
'Southway Sovereign' (29d) NHal
'Southway Sure' (29d) MRil NHal
¶ 'Spartan Crest' MWol
'Spartan Flame' (29c) MWol
'Spartan Glory' (25b) MWol
'Spartan Legend' (29c) MWol
'Spartan Leo' (29c) MWol
'Spartan Magic' (29d) MWol
'Spartan Moon' (25b) MWol
'Spartan Orange' (29d) MWol
¶ 'Spartan Pearl' MWol
'Spartan Rose' (29c) MWol
¶ 'Spartan Royal' MWol
'Spartan Sunrise' (29c) MWol
'Spartan Sunset' (29d) MWol
'Spartan White' (29c) MWol
'Spencer's Cottage' (13b) MCol
* 'Spoons' SCro
'Springtime' (24a) MCol
'Stan Addison' (5b) MWol NHal
'Stan's Choice' (29K) MCol
'Star Centenary' (3b) NHal
'Starlet' (29K) EHMN MCol
'Stockton' (3b) NHal
'Stoke Festival' (25b) MCol
'Sun Spider' (29K) EHMN
'Sun Valley' (5a) MCol
'Sunbeam' (25a) ECtt EFou
'Suncharm Bronze' (22a) MWol
'Suncharm Pink' (22a) MWol
'Suncharm Red' (22a) MWol
'Suncharm White' (22a) MWol
'Suncharm Yellow' (22a) MWol
'Sundora' (22d) MRil NHal
'Sunflight' (25b) MCol
'Sunny Margaret' (29c) NHal
'Susan Dobson' (25b) MWol
'Susan Riley' (23a) NHal
'Susan Rowe' (24b) MCol
'Sussex County' (15a) MWol NHal
'Swalwell' AGM NHal
'Swansdown' (25b) MWol
'Taffeta' (9c) MCol NHal
'Talbot Bolero' (29c) NHal
'Talbot Bouquet' AGM NHal
'Talbot Jo' (29d) NHal
'Talbot Parade' AGM NHal
'Tang' (12a) MWol
'Tapestry Rose' CGle EMon GMac
'Tapis Blanc' EHMN
'Target' (24b) MCol MRil
'Tenerife' (23b) MWol
'Tennis' (25b) MRil NHal
¶ 'Thacker's Joy' (24a) MRil
'The Favourite' (5b) MCol
'Tickled Pink' (29K) EHMN
'Tinkerbelle' (24b/12a) EHMN
'Toledo' (25a) MWol
'Tom Parr' See D. 'Doctor Tom Parr'
'Tommy Trout' (28) MCol
'Tracy Waller' (24b) NHal
'Triumph' NHal
'Truro' (24a) MWol
'Tundra' (4a) NHal
'Universiade' (25a) MRil NHal
'Vanity Pink' (7b) MCol
'Vanity Primrose' (7b) MCol
'Vedova' (6a) MCol
'Venice' (24b) MRil NHal
'Veria' EHMN
'Virginia' (29K) EHMN
'Vision On' (24b) MRil
'Wedding Day' EMon GBuc MFir MHlr SRms WCot WRus
'Wedding Sunshine' EHMN MUlv
'Wendy' AGM MCol NHal
'Wendy Tench' (29d) MCol
'Wessex Amber' (29d) NHal
'Wessex Cream' (29d) NHal
'Wessex Glory' (29d) NHal
'Wessex Gold' (29d) NHal
'Wessex Ivory' (29d) NHal
'Wessex Melody' (29d) NHal
'Wessex Solo' (29d) NHal
'Wessex Tang' (29d) NHal
'West Bromwich' (14a) MRil NHal
§ ***weyrichii*** CLew CNic EFol ELan LBee LHop MCas MHig MNFA MTho NHol NKay NMen SBla SBod SIng SSmi WAbe WOMN WPer WRus WThu
'White Allouise' AGM NHal
'White Bouquet' (28) MCol MWol
'White Cassandra' (5b) NHal
'White Fairweather' (3b) MRil MWol
'White Gem' (25b) EHMN
'White Gerrie Hoek' (29c) EHMN NHal
'White Gloss' (29K) EHMN
'White Lilac Prince' (1) MWol
'White Margaret' AGM EHMN MCol MRil MWol NHal

'White Margaret Riley (25b) NHal
'White Nu Rosemary' (9d) NHal
'White Pearl Celebration' (24a) MRil
¶ 'White Rayonnante' (11) MCol
'White Spider' (10) MCol
'White Taffeta' (9c) MCol NHal
'Win' (9c) NHal
'Winchcombe' (29c) EHMN
'Windermere' (24a) NHal
'Winnie Bramley' (23a) MRil MWol NHal
'Winning's Red' (Rub) NBro SMad
¶ 'Woolley Pride' (14b) MRil
'Woolman's Century' (1) MWol
'Woolman's Giant" (14a) MWol
'Woolman's Glory' (7a) MWol
¶ 'Woolman's Highlight' (3b) MWol
'Woolman's Perfecta' (3a) NHal
'Woolman's Prince' (3a) MWol
'Woolman's Queen' (24a) MWol
'Woolman's Star' (3a) MWol NHal
'World of Sport' (25a) MRil
'Yellow Alfreton Cream' (5b) MRil
'Yellow Balcombe Perfection' (5a) MWol
¶ 'Yellow Courtier' (24a) MRil
¶ 'Yellow Duke' (1) MWol
¶ 'Yellow Egret' (23b) MRil
'Yellow Fairweather' (3b) MWol
'Yellow Flying Saucer' (6a) MCol
'Yellow Fred Shoesmith' (5a) MWol
'Yellow Galaxy' **AGM** MCol
'Yellow Gingernut' (25b) MCol MRil NHal
'Yellow Hammer' EHMN
'Yellow Hazy Days' (25b) NHal
'Yellow Heather James' (3b) MCol
'Yellow Heide' **AGM** MCol NHal
'Yellow John Hughes' (3b) MCol MRil NHal
'Yellow John Wingfield' (14b) MRil NHal
'Yellow Lilian Hoek' (29c) EHMN MCol NHal
'Yellow Margaret' **AGM** EHMN MCol MRil MWol NHal
'Yellow Margaret Riley' (25b) NHal
'Yellow May Shoesmith' (5a) NHal
'Yellow Mayford Perfection' **AGM** MCol MRil
'Yellow Pennine Oriel' (29a) MCol MRil MWol NHal
¶ 'Yellow Percy Salter' (24b) MCol
'Yellow Polaris' (9c) MCol
'Yellow Spider' (10) MCol
'Yellow Starlet' (29K) EHMN MCol
'Yellow Taffeta' (9c) MCol
'Yellow Tennis' (25b) NHal
'Yellowmoor' (25b) MCol
§ ***yezoense*** **AGM** EBee EFou ELan EMon LHop MBel NKay SIng WCot WEas WRus
– 'Roseum' EBee NSti WRus
'Yvonne Arnaud' (24b) MCol MWol
zawadskii WRus
§ – var. ***latilobum*** EMon

DENDRIOPOTERIUM See SANGUISORBA

DENDROBENTHAMIA See CORNUS

DENDROCALAMUS (Gramineae/Poaceae-Bambusoideae)

giganteus SBam
§ ***strictus*** CB&S SBam

DENDROMECON (Papaveraceae)

rigida CB&S IMal SMad

DENDROSERIS (Compositae/Asteraceae)

littoralis CHEx

DENTARIA (Cruciferae/Brassicaceae)

californica EBee EPar
digitata See CARDAMINE ***pentaphyllos***
diphylla EPar LAma
pinnata See CARDAMINE ***heptaphylla***
polyphylla See CARDAMINE ***kitaibelii***

DERMATOBOTRYS (Scrophulariaceae)

See Plant Deletions

DERWENTIA See PARAHEBE

DESCHAMPSIA (Gramineae/Poaceae)

cespitosa CKin CNat CTom CWGN ESiP ETPC NHol WPer
– ssp. ***alpina*** EMon
– 'Bronzeschleier' ('Bronze Veil') CHan COtt EBre ECoo EFou EPla ETPC GAbr GCHN GCal IBlr LBre LGre MSte MUlv NBro NEgg NHar NMir SApp SMad SMrm SPer WAbe WCot WRus
– 'Fairy's Joke' See D. ***c. vivipara***
¶ – 'Golden Shower' ECtt NHol
– 'Goldgehänge' ('Golden Pendant') EHoe ETPC GCal IBlr NSti SAxl
– 'Goldschleier' ('Golden Veil') CElw CWGN EBre ECha EFou EHoe EMon EPla ETPC GAri GCHN IBlr LBre MUlv NHar

– 'Goldstaub' ('Gold Dust')	EFou ETPC GCal NCat
– 'Goldtau' ('Golden Dew')	CElw EHoe EMon EPla ETPC GCHN NBro NHar NMir NRoo SApp SUsu
– var. ***parviflora***	ETPC
§ – var. ***vivipara***	CRDP ECtt EHoe EMon ETPC NBro NCat NHol NSti SHer
flexuosa	EHoe EMon ETPC MBri SApp WPer
– 'Tatra Gold'	CDoC ECha ECoo EFol EHoe ELan EMon EPla ETPC GAbr LHop MBri MCas MNFA NCat NFai NHed NHol NMir NNor SAxl SGil SMad SUsu WHal WPat WPer
media	ETPC
¶ – bronze	ETPC

DESFONTAINIA (Loganiaceae)

§ ***spinosa*** **AGM**	Widely available
– 'Harold Comber'	MBal WBod WCru
– ***hookeri***	See D. ***spinosa***

DESMAZERIA (Gramineae/Poaceae)

rigida	See CATAPODIUM ***rigidum***

DESMODIUM (Leguminosae/Papilionaceae)

¶ ***callianthum***	CPle
§ ***elegans***	CChu CCla CGre CHan CMHG CPle EHal ELan EMil MArl WBod WSHC
praestans	See D. ***yunnanense***
tiliifolium	See D. ***elegans***
§ ***yunnanense***	CPle NRar WSHC

DESMOSCHOENUS (Cyperaceae)

¶ ***spiralis***	WCot

DEUTZIA † (Hydrangeaceae)

chunii	See D. ***ningpoensis***
compacta	CHan WBod WWat
– 'Lavender Time'	CCla CMHG CPle EHic ESma MPla NSti SHil WPat WSHC
corymbosa	CCla CFil
crenata 'Flore Pleno'	See D. ***scabra*** 'F. P.'
– var. ***nakaiana***	SIng
– – 'Nikko'	CB&S CCla CDoC CPle EFol EPla ESis LHop MBar MGos MHig MPla SEng SGil SHer SPla WOMN WRus WSHC
discolor 'Major'	CLan
x ***elegantissima***	CLan CMHG CSco CShe IDai MRav NKay NNor SPla SReu
– 'Fasciculata'	EHic SPer WWin
– 'Rosealind' **AGM**	CB&S CBow CCla CSco EBre ECtt ELan ENot IOrc LBre MBri MPla NSti SEng SLon SPer SReu SSta WBod WKif WSHC
¶ ***glomeruliflora***	CFil
gracilis	CBow GRei GWht MBal MBar MBel MPla MRav MWat NBee NNor SHBN SHer SPer WBod WDin WHCG WStI WWat
– 'Carminea'	See D. x ***rosea*** 'Carminea'
– 'Marmorata'	WHCG
*– 'Variegata'	CPMA ECro MPla
hookeriana	GGGa ISea WWat
¶ – KW 6393	SBor
x ***hybrida*** 'Contraste'	CDoC CLan SPer
– 'Joconde'	ECtt EHic
– 'Magicien'	CChu CLan CMHG CSam CShe EBre ECtt ELan ENot EPla LBre MBal SGil SHBN SLon SPer WHCG WPat
– 'Mont Rose' **AGM**	CB&S CBow CLan CShe ELan ENot GRei MBal MBar MGos MPla MRav NBee NRoo SHBN SPer SPla SReu SSta WDin WHCG WSHC WStI WWin
– 'Perle Rose'	CLan CSco
– 'Pink Pompon'	See D. x ***h.*** 'Rosea Plena'
§ – 'Rosea Plena'	CBow EHic ESma MBri MPla SSta STre WWeb
– 'Strawberry Fields'	MBri SHil
x ***kalmiiflora***	CB&S CLan CMHG CPMA CSco EBre EHar EPla LAbb LBre MBar MBri MGos MRav NKay NNor SLPl SPer SWas WAbe WDin WRus WWeb
longifolia	CLan
– 'Veitchii' **AGM**	MRav
x ***magnifica***	CDoC CSco ELan IOrc MRav SHil WStI WWeb WWin
¶ – 'Nancy'	MBri
*– 'Rubra'	EPla
monbeigii	ENot SBor WKif WWat
§ ***ningpoensis***	CChu CGre CWSG ECtt ESma NSti SLPl SPer WWat
– 'Pink Charm'	SHil
pulchra	CChu CFil CHan CLan CPle CShe EBre EHal ESma LBre NSti SHil SPer WHCG WWat
x ***rosea***	CBow CBra CMHG CTrw EBre ENot GRei IJoh LBre MBar MPla MWat NNor SHBN SHer WKif WStI WTyr WWin
– 'Campanulata'	ENot
§ – 'Carminea' **AGM**	CB&S CShe ELan LAbb MBal SDix SLon SPer SSta WDin
– 'Floribunda'	CBra ELan
scabra	CDoC CLan MGos
§ – 'Candidissima'	CMHG IDai MBri SPer SPla WBod
– 'Codsall Pink'	MGos
– 'Plena'	CB&S CPle EBee ECtt ELan ESma MSte NNor SEng SHBN SPer
– 'Pride of Rochester'	CBow CDoC CSco EHal ENot ESma GAul MBar MRav SHer SPla WDin
– 'Punctata' (v)	CMHG EFol EHoe WThu
– 'Variegata'	CPle EPla NSti
setchuenensis	CBow EPla GGGa SLon WPat WSHC
– var. ***corymbiflora*** **AGM**	CBot CCla CFil CLan SBla SDry WKif WWat
staminea	CLan
x ***wellsii***	See D. ***scabra*** 'Candidissima'
x ***wilsonii***	SRms

DIANELLA † (Liliaceae/Phormiaceae)

caerulea	EBul ECou GCal LHil WOld
– var. ***petasmatodes***	WCot
– 'Variegata'	See D. ***tasmanica*** 'V.'
intermedia	MUlv WCot WWat

nigra	CDoC EBul ECou GCal NHol
revoluta	ECou IBlr WCot
tasmanica	CChu CFee CGle CHan CHol CMon CRow ECou EMar EPla GCal GGar IBar IBlr LBlm MBri MUlv NOrc SArc SAxl SBor WWat
§ – 'Variegata'	ECou IBlr WOld

DIANTHUS † (Caryophyllaceae)

ACW 2116	EMFP GPlt LBee NMen NRed WPer
'Admiral Crompton' (pf)	MBel NPin SBai SHay
'Admiration' (b)	SHay
'Afton Water' (b)	SBai SHay
'Alan Titchmarsh' (p)	EBee SBai
'Albatross' (p)	SChu
'Alder House' (p)	NRoo WHil
'Aldersey Rose' (p)	WMar WWin
'Aldridge Yellow' (b)	SAll SBai
'Alfred Galbally' (b)	SBai
'Alice' (p)	CDoC CThr SAll SHay SSvw
'Alice Forbes' (b)	SAll SHay
'Alick Sparkes' (pf)	SHay
'Allen's Ballerina' (p)	NCra NPin
§ 'Allen's Huntsman' (p)	NCra NPin
§ 'Allen's Maria' (p)	CThr NCra NNrw SRms
'Alloway Star' (p)	EMFP WPer
'Allspice' (p)	CCot CLTr CMil CThr EMFP GAbr MBro NCra SChu SSvw WHoo WMar WPer
¶ Allwoodii Alpinus Group	CMea
'Allwood's Crimson' (pf)	SHay
alpinus AGM	CGle EMFP GDra GTou LAbb LBee MBal MFir MHig NGre NHol NKay NMen NWCA SBla SIgm SIng WHen WPer
– 'Adonis'	GCLN
– 'Albus'	LBee SBla
– Correvon's form	NHol
– 'Drake's Red'	NGre
– 'Joan's Blood' AGM	CRiv ECha EPot GAbr LHop NHar NHol NMen NRed SBla SIng WDav WHoo WMar
– 'Millstream Salmon'	GAbr
¶ – 'Rax Alpe'	EPot
– salmon	NGre
'Amarinth' (p)	EMar MBel WPer
amurensis	CNic EMon SUsu WCla WPer
anatolicus	EGle ELan LBee NHol SBla SSmi WPer
'Andrew' (p)	SHay
¶ 'Ann Unitt' (pf)	MWoo
'Anna Wyatt' (p)	NCra
'Annabelle' (p)	EMFP MCas MHig NKay SChu WHil
'Anniversay' (p)	NPin SBai
'Ann's Lass' (pf)	NPin
'Apricale' (pf)	SAll
'Apricot Sue' (pf)	NPin SHay
'Archfield'	CShe
arenarius	CLew CNic EMFP GCHN MCas MTol NPri SSvw WPer WWin
'Argus'	CMil WPer
'Ariel' (p)	NKay
armeria AGM	CKin EWFC GAul WOak WPer
arpadianus	GCLN MPla NGre NHol
'Arthur' (p)	EMFP
'Arthur Leslie' (b)	SAll
x ***arvernensis*** AGM	CMHG CNic CRiv ECha EPot GAbr GDra MBro MHig MPla NGre NHar NMen NRoo SHer SIng WPat
atrorubens	See D. ***carthusianorum*** Atrorubens Group
'Audrey Robinson' (pf)	MWoo NPin SBai
'Aurora' (b)	SHay
¶ 'Avon Dassett	LBuc
'Baby Treasure' (p)	GAbr NHol WHil
'Badenia' (p)	LBee MHig SBla
'Bailey's Apricot' (pf)	SHay
'Bailey's Splendour' (pf)	SBai
'Ballerina' (p)	EBee EBre LBre SBai SHay
barbatus Nigrescens Group AGM	CHad CRDP LBlm LGre LHil LHop MHlr SSvw WCot
– 'Wee Willie'	LHop
'Barleyfield Rose' (p)	GArf MTho
'Barlow' (pf)	SHay
§ 'Bat's Double Red' (p)	CCot CMil EMFP EMon NCra SHig SSvw WPer
'Beauty of Cambridge' (b)	SAll
'Beauty of Healey' (p)	CMil EMFP
'Becka Falls' (p)	CThr EBre LBre NCra SBai SHay
'Becky Robinson' AGM	CThr ELan EMFP MBel NPin SBai SHay SMrm SSvw WPbr
'Becky's Choice' (p)	EMFP
'Bet Gilroy' (b)	SHay
'Betty Buckle' (p)	SChu
'Betty Day' (b)	SHay
'Betty Norton' (p)	CShe EBee MBro MHig NCra SBla SMrm SSvw WHil WHoo WPer WThu
'Betty Tucker' (b)	SHay
'Betty Webber' (p)	SBai
'Bibby's Cerise' (pf)	SHay
'Binsey Red' (p)	SSvw
'Blaby Joy'	MUlv
* 'Blue Carpet'	WPer
'Blue Hills' (p)	ELan LBee MCas MWat SHer SIng
'Blue Ice' (b)	SHay
'Blush' (m)	See D. 'Souvenir de la Malmaison'
'Bobby' (p)	SAll
'Bobby Ames' (b)	SHay
'Bombadier' (p)	CTom NRoo WMar
'Bookham Fancy' (b)	SAll SHay
'Bookham Grand' (b)	SHay
'Bookham Lad' (b)	SAll SHay
'Bookham Lass' (b)	SHay
'Bookham Perfume' (b)	SBai SHay
'Bookham Sprite' (b)	SAll SHay
'Bourboule'	See D. 'La Bourboule'
'Bovey Belle' (p)	CLTr CSam CThr EBre ECot LBre NCra NPin SBai
'Boydii' (p)	NHol NTow
'Bransgore' (p)	WHoo
brevicaulis Mac&W 5849	WOMN
'Bridal Veil' (p)	CThr EMFP GAbr MBel NCra SChu SSvw
'Bridesmaid' (p)	SHay

'Brigadier' (p)	WPer WThu
'Brilliant'	See D. ***deltoïdes*** 'Brilliant'
'Brimstone' (b)	SHay
'Brymos' (p)	CMHG
'Brympton Red' (p)	CThr ECha EFou EMFP EOrc ERav NCra NSti SBla SChu SSvw WEas
'Bryony Lisa' (b)	MBel SBai
'Caesar's Mantle' (p)	CMil NGre SChu SSvw
caesius	See D. ***gratianopolitanus***
– 'Compactus'	See D. ***gratianopolitanus*** 'Compactus Eydangeri'
callizonus	CNic GArf LBee MHig NGre NKay NRed WAbe
'Calypso' (pf)	SHay
'Camelford' (p)	NCra WPer
'Camilla' (b)	CThr EMFP SSvw
'Candy Clove' (b)	SAll SHay
'Cannup's Pride' (pf)	SHay
'Can-Can' (pf)	SHay
'Carinda' (p)	SHay
'Carlotta' (p)	SHay
'Carmen' (b)	EBar SHay
¶ 'Carmine Letitia Wyatt' (p)	EBee
'Caroline Bone' (b)	SHay
'Caroline Clove' (b)	SHay
'Carolyn Hardy' (pf)	MWoo
carthusianorum	CSev EMFP GTou MBel NCat SSvw WHaw WHil WPer
– var. ***humilis***	WAbe
caryophyllus	CArn CSFH CSev SIde WElm WOak
'Casser's Pink' (p)	EMFP GBuc MPit MTho
'Catherine Glover' (b)	SAll SHay
* 'Catherine Tucker'	WEas
'Catherine's Choice'	See D. 'Rhyan's Choice'
§ 'Cedric's Oldest' (p)	ECha
'Charles' (p)	SAll
'Charles Musgrave' (p)	See D. 'Musgrave's Pink'
'Charm' (b)	SHay
'Chastity' (p)	GAbr MBro SChu SSvw WDav WHoo
§ 'Chelsea Pink' (p)	EMFP
'Cherry Clove' (b)	SAll
'Cherryripe' (p)	SHay
'Cheryl' (p)	See D. 'Houndspool Cheryl'
'Chetwyn Doris' (p)	NPin
chinensis (p,a)	MBri NNrw
'Chris Crew' (b)	SBai
'Christine Hough' (b)	SAll SBai
'Christopher' (p)	EBre GCHN LBre SAll SHay
'Cindy' (p)	LHop
cinnabarinus	See D. ***biflorus***
'Circular Saw' (p)	SHer
'Clara' (pf)	MWoo NPin SBai SHay
'Clara Lucinda' (pf)	NPin
'Clara's Choice' (pf)	NPin
'Clara's Flame' (pf)	NPin SHay
'Clara's Glow' (pf)	NPin
'Clara's Lass' (pf)	MWoo NPin SBai SHay
'Clare' (p)	MBel SAll SBai SHay
'Claret Joy' (p)	CThr CVer EBre ELan EMFP GAri LBre NCat NPin NRoo WPbr
'Clarinda' (b)	SAll
'Clunie' (b)	SAll SHay
§ 'Cockenzie Pink' (p)	CMil CThr EMFP SChu SSvw WEas WThu
'Cocomo Sim' (pf)	SHay
'Constance' (p)	EMFP SAll
'Constance Finnis' (p)	CThr ECha ELan NRoo SChu SMrm SSvw WEas WPer
'Consul' (b)	SAll
'Copperhead' (b)	SHay
'Cornish Snow' (p)	CMHG CSam
'Coste Budde' (p)	ECha WMar
'Cranmere Pool' (p)	CMea CThr CVer EBre ELan GAri LBre MWat NCra NHol NPin NRoo SHay SMrm WPbr WPer
'Cream Sue' (pf)	MWoo NPin SHay
'Crimson Ace' (p)	SHay
¶ 'Crimson Chance'	NSla
'Crimson Velvet' (b)	SHay
crinitus	CMil
'Crompton Classic' (pf)	NPin
'Crompton Princess' (pf)	MWoo NPin SBai
'Crossways' (p)	EGle GDra LBee MHig NHar SHer
'Crowley's Pink Sim' (pf)	SHay
* 'D D R'	LBee
'Dad's Choice' (p)	SBai
'Dad's Favourite' (p)	CGle CThr ECha ELan EMFP EOrc MBel NCra NPin SAll SBai SHay SSvw WEas WPer WTyr
'Daily Mail' (p)	EBee SBai SChu
'Dainty Clove' (b)	SHay
'Dainty Dame' (p)	NHol SIng
'Dainty Lady' (b)	SBai
'Daisy Hill Scarlet' (b)	IDai
'Damask Superb' (p)	EMFP MHig SSvw WHil WPer
'Dark Pierrot' (pf)	SBai
'Dartington Double' (p)	ELan NHol SGil SHer
'Dartington Laced'	CMil
'Dartmoor Forest' (p)	SBla
'David' (p)	SAll SHay
'David Saunders' (b)	SBai
'Dawlish Charm' (p)	CThr
'Dawn' (b)	SAll SHay
– (pf)	SAll
* 'Dazzler'	LHop MPla
'Debi's Choice' (p)	SBai
'Deep Purple' (pf)	SHay
deltoïdes AGM	CArn CKin CSev CShe CVer EBar ECha ELan IDai LGro LHol MBar MPla NGre NNor NRed WCla WOak WWin
– 'Albus'	CBow CGle CMea CRiv CSam CVer ECha EMFP LHop MBar MPla MTol NNor NNrd NOak NRed SSvw WByw WCla WPer
– 'Bright Eyes'	CTom MRav
§ – 'Brilliant'	CBow CHol CSev CTom LAbb LHop NNor NNrd NNrw NOak WGor WPbr
– 'Broughty Blaze'	GDra
– 'Erectus'	ELan SIde
– 'Leuchtfunk' ('Flashing Light')	CHol CMea CRiv CVer EBre EMNN EMar ESma GDra LBre LHop MPit NHar NKay NNrd WEas WHen WPbr WPer
– 'Microchip'	CDoC LAbb LBee MPit NHar NKay NOak WHaw
– 'Samos'	CDoC
– 'Wisley Variety'	WCla

¶ – 'Zwolle' WHaw
'Denis' (p) CThr EBre ELan LBre NCra NHol SRms WHil
'Devon Blossom' (p) CThr
'Devon Blush' (p) CLTr CThr EBre LBre NHol NPin NRoo
'Devon Cream' (p) CLTr CThr EBee EBre EMFP GAri LBre NHol NPin NRoo SSte
'Devon Dove' **AGM** CThr EBee EBre LBre NHol NPin NRoo SOkh
'Devon General' (p) CThr EBee EBre LBre NHol NPin NRoo
'Devon Glow' **AGM** CLTr CThr EBee EBre LBre NPin NRoo SFis
'Devon Maid' **AGM** CLTr CThr EBre LBre NHol NPin
'Devon Pearl' (p) CThr EBee NHol NRoo SSte
'Devon Pride' (p) EBre LBre NHol NPin SFis
¶ 'Devon Wizard' (p) EMFP NRoo
'Dewdrop' (p) CMea ESis GCHN LBee LBuc NHol NPri NRoo SChu WPer
'Diane' (p) CRiv CSam CSco CShe CThr EBre ELan EMFP LBre NCra NHol NPin SAll SBai SChu SFis SHay SMrm SPla SSvw WEas WPbr WPer
'Doctor Archie Cameron' (b) SHay
¶ 'Doctor Ramsey' MHig
'Dora' ESis NHol NNrw
'Doris' **AGM** CCla CMea CSco CShe CThr EBre ELan EMFP ENot GCHN LBre LHop MBel MWat NBro NCra NHol NPin NRoo SAll SAxl SBai SFis SHay SMrm SSvw WDav WEas WPbr WWin
'Doris Allwood' (pf) MBel NPin SHay
'Doris Elite' (p) SAll
'Doris Galbally' (b) MBel
'Doris Majestic' (p) SAll
'Doris Ruby' See D. 'Houndspool Ruby'
'Doris Supreme' (p) SAll
'Double Irish' (p) See D. 'Irish Pink'
'Downs Cerise' (b) SHay
'Dubarry' (p) MCas MHig NHol SBla WPer
'Duchess of Westminster' (m) SBor WMal
'Duke of Argyll' EMon
'Dunkirk' (b) MWoo
'Dusky' (p) NCra SChu
'E J Baldry' (b) SHay
'Earl of Essex' (p) CCot CMil CThr EMFP NCra SAll SHay WPer
'Ebor II' (b) SAll SHay
echiniformis MFos
'Edan Lady' (pf) NPin SHay
'Edenside Scarlet' (b) SHay
'Edenside White' (b) SBai
'Edith Johnson' (pf) NPin
'Edna' (p) SAll
'Edward' (p) SAll
'Eileen' (p) EMFP
'Eileen O'Connor' **AGM** MBel
'Elizabeth' (p) CElw CFee CGle LHop
'Elizabeth Anne' (pf) MWoo
'Ember Rose' (pf) See D. 'Le Rêve'
'Emile Paré' (p) ESis LHop MBel MTho SChu WMar
'Emma Sarah' (b) SBai
'Emperor' See D. 'Bat's Double Red'
'Enid Anderson' (p) NNrd SChu SHig SSvw
erinaceus CLew EMNN GCHN ITim LBee MBro MPla MSte NHar NHol NMen NRoo NWCA WAbe WDav WPer WThu WWin
– var. ***alpinus*** EPot SIng
'Erycina' (b) EBar SAll SHay
'Esperance' (pf) SAll SHay
* 'Ethel Hurford' WHoo
'Eudoxia' (b) SAll
'Eva Humphries' (b) SAll SBai SHay
'Excelsior' (p) CRiv CSco CThr EPad LCot NMir NNor NSti WThu
'Exquisite' (b) SBai SHay
'Fair Folly' (p) EMFP SSvw WHil WMar WPer
'Faith Raven' (p) EMon
'Fanal' (p) CRiv CShe NBir NNrd SAsh WAbe
'Farnham Rose' (p) CLTr MBel SChu
'Fascination' (b) SHay
'Fashino' (pf) SAll
'Favourite Lady' (p) SIng
'Fenbow Nutmeg Clove' (b) SChu
'Fettes Mount ' (p) CLTr EMon EPad GAbr MBel NSti SSvw
'Fiery Cross' (b) SAll SHay
'Fimbriatus' (p) WHoo
'Fingo Clove' (b) SAll
'Fiona' (p) SAll
'Firecrest Rose' CCot
'First Lady' (b) SAll
'Flame' (p) SHay
'Flame Sim' (pf) SHay
'Forest Glow' (b) SAll SBai
'Forest Sprite' (b) SAll SBai
'Forest Treasure' (b) SAll SBai
'Fortuna' (p) SAll
'Fountain's Abbey' (p) SSvw WMar
'Fragrant Ann' **AGM** MWoo NPin SBai SHay
'Fragrant Lace' (p) CThr
'Fragrant Rose' (pf) SBai SHay
'Frances Isabel' (p) NCra SAll
'Frances King' (pf) NPin
'Frances Sellars' (b) SHay
'Frank's Frilly' (p) CThr SSvw
'Freckles' (p) CThr SBai SHay
'Freda' (p) SAll SHay
'Freeland Crimson Clove' (b) SAll SHay
'French' CShe
freynii CLew CRiv EPot EWes MBro NGre NHed SHer
* 'Fringed Pink' See D. ***superbus***
furcatus NWCA
'Fusilier' (p) CMea CNic CSam ESis LBee MCas MRPP NHol NPri NRoo SChu SGil SHer WHoo
'G J Sim' (pf) SHay
'G W Hayward' (b) SHay
'Gail Tilsey' (b) SHay
Gala ® (pf) SBai
'Galil' (pf) SAll
'Garland' (p) CMea NHar NNrd NRoo WGor
'Garnet' (p) EFol SChu
giganteus EMFP IBlr MSto WCot
'Gingham Gown' (p) EMon NBir NCat NKay
'Gipsy Clove' (b) SHay

glacialis	GTou LBee MCas NHar NHol NMen NRed
– ssp. ***gelidus***	CPBP MRPP NGre NTow
¶ 'Glebe Cottage White'	CGle CVer
'Gloriosa' (p)	WPer
'Glorious' (p)	SHay
'Golden Cross' (b)	MBel SBai
'Golden Rain' (pf)	SHay
'Gran's Favourite' **AGM**	CElw CKel CLTr CSam CSco EBre ELan EMFP GAri LBre MBel MTho MWat NHol NPin NRoo SBai SChu SFis SHay SSvw WEas WMar WPer
§ ***gratianopolitanus*** **AGM**	CArn CSev EPad GCHN GTou LHol MBel MFir MHig NNrw NOak SIde SIng SSmi WOMN WOak WPer
– 'Albus'	EPad
– 'Flore Pleno'	EMFP
*– 'Karlik'	NWCA
– red	GAbr
¶ – 'Rosenfeder'	WPer
¶ – 'Splendens'	WPer
§ – 'Tiny Rubies'	WAbe
'Gravetye Gem' (b)	CRiv MBel NRoo SHer WPat
– (p)	NCra WHoo
'Grenadier' (p)	SGil SHer
'Gwendolen Read' (p)	SHay
* 'Gypsy Lass'	SFis
haematocalyx	EMFP ITim LHil NRed NWCA WDav WThu
– 'Alpinus'	See D. ***h. pindicola***
§ – ssp. ***pindicola***	EPot MFos WOMN
'Hannah Louise' (b)	MBel SBai
'Happiness' (b)	SBai
'Harlequin' (p)	ECtt EMFP EMNN NCra NHed NRoo WPer
'Harmony' (b)	SAll SBai SHay
'Haytor' (p)	See D. 'Haytor White'
'Haytor Rock' (p)	CThr EBee EBre GAri LBre NCra SHay SOkh WPer
§ 'Haytor White' **AGM**	CSam CThr EBre EMFP ERav GAri GCHN LBre MBel NCra NHol NNrw NPin NSti SAll SBai SChu SHay SSvw WEas WPbr
'Hazel Ruth' (b)	MBel SBai
'Heidi' (p)	SRms
'Helen' (p)	CThr SAll SHay WEas
'Henry of Essex' (p)	EMFP SSvw
'Hidcote' (p)	CNic CShe ELan EMFP MBel MHig NKay NMen NNrd SBla SHer WWin
'Highland Chieftain' (p)	NKay
'Highland Fraser' (p)	CNic CShe EMar GAbr MHig NHol NKay NRoo WEas WKif WPat WThu
'Highland Queen' (p)	CMil SAsh
hispanicus	See D. ***pungens***
'Hollycroft Fragrance' (p)	SAll
'Hope' (p)	CMer CThr EMFP ESis SChu SSvw WMar WPer WTyr
'Horsa' (b)	SHay
§ 'Houndspool Cheryl' (p)	CLTr CSco CThr ELan EMFP GAbr LCot NHol NPin SBai SSvw
§ 'Houndspool Ruby' **AGM**	CSam CThr EMFP MBel MWat NHol NOak NPin SBai SChu SSvw WEas
'Howard Hitchcock' (b)	SBai
'Huntsman'	See D. 'Allen's Huntsman'
'Ian' (p)	CLTr CThr NPin SHay
'Ibis' (p)	SHay
'Iceberg' (p)	EMFP
'Icomb' (p)	CLew CSam SRms WHoo WPer WWin
'Imperial Clove' (b)	SHay
'Ina' (p)	CMea GDra SRms
'Inchmery' (p)	CCot CLTr CMer CThr EMFP MBel NCra NKay NNor NSti SAll SChu SHay SIng SSvw WEas WHoo
'Indios' (pf)	SBai
¶ 'Inga Bowen' (p)	CThr
'Inglestone' (p)	CSam MCas NHar WDav
'Inshriach Dazzler' **AGM**	CMea EBre EMFP EPot ESis GCHN GDra ITim LBee LBre LHop MBro MSte NCra NHar NHed NHol NNrd NRoo SBla SHer WAbe WDav WHal WMar
'Inshriach Startler' (p)	GDra NRoo
§ ***integer minutiflorus***	GCHN
'Irene Della-Torré' **AGM**	SBai
'J M Bibby' (pf)	NPin SHay
'Jacqueline Ann' **AGM**	MWoo NPin SBai SHay
'Jaffa' (pf)	SAll
'James' (pf)	NPin
'Jane Austen' (p)	CLTr NCra SChu SSvw WMar WPer WSun
'Jane Coffey' (b)	SHay
'Jenny Wyatt' (p)	EBre LBre NCra SHay
'Jess Hewins' (pf)	MWoo NPin SHay
'Jessica' (pf)	SAll
¶ 'Joan Randall (pf)	MWoo
'Joanne' (pf)	NPin SHay
'Joanne's Highlight' (pf)	NPin SHay
'Joan's Blood'	See D. ***alpinus*** 'J. B.'
'Joe Vernon' (pf)	MWoo NPin SBai
'John Ball' (p)	EMFP
¶ 'John Faulkner' (pf)	MWoo
'John Gray' (p)	CMil
'Joker' (pf)	SHay
'Joy' (p)	CLTr CThr EBre EMFP LBre NCra NHol NPin SBai SHay WPbr
'Kesteven Chambery' (p)	WPer
'Kesteven Chamonix' (p)	EMFP NMen WPer WThu
'Kestor' (p)	CThr GCHN NCra
kitaibelii	See D. ***petraeus petraeus***
¶ 'Kiwi Pretty' (p)	CThr
knappii	CPou ECro EMFP EMon GCHN GLil LGan MSto NFai NOak SFar SUsu WCla WHil WPer WWin
§ 'La Bourboule' **AGM**	CNic CSam ELan EMNN EPot GDra LBee MBar MBel MHig MPla MWat NKay NMen NRed NRoo WAbe WDav WPat WPer WThu WWin
'La Bourboule Albus' (p)	CRiv CSam EMNN EPot ESis MHig NHol NRed NRoo SGil SHer WAbe WMar WPer WThu WWin
'Laced Hero' (p)	CMil MBel SChu WPer
laced hybrids	WCla
'Laced Joy' (p)	CGle CMHG CThr EMFP SAll SChu SHay WHoo WPer

'Laced Monarch' (p) CSam CThr CVer EMFP ESis GCHN MBel NBro NHol NPin NRoo SAll SBai SChu SSvw WDav WPer
'Laced Prudence' See D. 'Prudence'
'Laced Romeo' (p) CCot EMFP NCra SChu SHay SSvw WEas
'Laced Treasure' (p) CLTr CThr EPad SAll
'Lady Diana' (p) NKay
'Lady Granville' (p) CMil EMFP SSvw
'Lady Salisbury' (p) CMil EMFP
§ 'Lady Wharncliffe' (p) CMil EMFP MBel SSvw WMar WPer
'Lancing Lady' (b) SAll
'Lancing Monarch' (b) SAll SHay
¶ ***langeanus*** NS 255 NWCA
'Laura' (p) SAll SHay
'Lavender Clove' (b) SAll SBai SHay
'Lavender Lady' (pf) NPin
'Leatham Pastel' (pf) NPin
'Leiden' (b) SBai
'Lemsii' (p) CMHG CRiv CSam EMFP LBee MBal MCas NHar NMen NVic WHoo WPer
'Lena Sim' (pf) SHay
'Leslie Rennison' (b) SAll SHay
'Letitia Wyatt' (p) CThr NPin NRoo SFis
'Leuchtkugel' WAbe
'Lightning' (pf) SAll
'Lilac Clove' (b) SHay
'Little Diane' (p) MWoo
'Little Jock' (p) Widely available
'Little Miss Muffet' (p) SHer
'Little Old Lady' See D. 'Chelsea Pink'
'Liz Rigby' (b) SHay
'London Brocade' (p) EMFP NCra SChu WMar
'London Delight' (p) CCot CThr EMFP EOrc NCra SHay WPer WPla WTyr
'London Glow' (p) CLTr CThr SAll
* 'London Joy' WEas
'London Lovely' (p) CLTr EPad NCra SAll SSvw
'London Poppet' (p) CCot CRiv CThr EOrc SAll WHil WHoo
§ 'Lord Chatham' (b) EMon
'Loveliness' (p) CBre GAbr WEas
lumnitzeri EPot WPer
'Lustre' (b) SAll SBai SHay
'Madame Dubarry' (p) GAbr LBee
'Madonna' (p) CThr SHay SSvw
'Mandy' (p) SAll
'Manningtree Pink' (p) See D. 'Cedric's Oldest'
'Manon' (pf) SBai
'Marg's Choice' **AGM** EMFP
'Maria' See D. 'Allen's Maria'
'Mars' (p) CMHG ELan EPad GAbr GPlt ITim LBee NHed NRoo SAll SChu SHer WAbe WDav WHil
¶ 'Marshwood Melody' (p) CThr
'Marshwood Mystery' (p) CThr
* 'Martin Nest' ITim
'Mary Jane Birrel' (pf) MWoo NPin
'Mary Simister' (b) SAll SHay
* 'Mary's Gilliflower' SSvw
'Master Stuart' (b) SBai
'Matador' (b) SHay
'Maudie Hinds' (b) MBel SBai
'May Jones' (p) EMFP
'Maybole' (b) SAll SHay
'Maythorne' (p) SRms
'Mendip Hills' (b) SHay
¶ 'Mendlesham Maid' (p) EMFP
'Mercury' (p) SAll
'Merlin Clove' (b) SBai SHay
'Messines Pink' (p) SAll
'Michael Saunders' (b) SBai
'Microchip' (p) NRed SFis
microlepis ITim NMen NRed NWCA WAbe
– ***albus*** LBee SWas WAbe
– var. ***musalae*** EPot NHar WDav
'Mida' See D. 'Melody'
'Milley' (p) CRiv
'Miss Sinkins' (p) NCra
'Monica Wyatt' **AGM** CGle CThr EBee EBre LBre MRav NCra NPin NRoo SBai SChu SFis
monspessulanus EMon NWCA
– ssp. ***sternbergii*** NGre
'Montrose Pink' (p) See D. 'Cockenzie Pink'
'Mrs Clark' See D. 'Nellie Clark'
'Mrs Elmhurst' (p) NCra
'Mrs Jackson' (p) SAsh SBla
'Mrs Macbride' (p) CMil SSvw
'Mrs N Clark' See D. 'Nellie Clark'
'Mrs Shaw' (p) NCra
'Mrs Sinkins' (p) CBre CCla CGle CKel CSco CShe CThr CTom EBre ECha ELan EOrc GCHN LBre MBal MBel MHig MWat NCra NHol NPin NRoo NSti SAll SBai SHay WEas WThu
'Murcia' (pf) SBai
N 'Musgrave's Pink' (p) CGle CLTr CMer CShe CThr CTom ECha ELan EMFP EOrc LHop NCra SChu SSvw WDav WEas WHoo WMar WThu
'Musgrave's White' See D. 'Musgrave's Pink'
myrtinervius CBar CNic ECha ITim MFir NRoo NWCA WCla WHil WOMN WPer
'N M Goodall' (p) LHop
'Nan Bailey' (p) SBai
'Nancy Lindsay' (p) SSvw
'Napoleon III' (p) WKif
nardiformis WPer
'Nautilus' (b) SHay
neglectus See D. ***pavonius***
§ 'Nellie Clark' (p) CShe MBal NMen SChu SGil SHer WThu
'Neptune' (pf) SAll
'Nicola Jane Mannion' (pf) NPin
I 'Nina' (pf) SBai
nitidus EHic MRPP NBir NGre WOMN WPer
noeanus See D. ***petraeus n.***
'Nonsuch' (p) CMil EMFP
'Norman Hayward' (b) SHay
'Nyewood's Cream' (p) CMHG EMFP EMNN EPot GAbr GArf MBar MBro MFir MHig MPla MRPP MRav NCra NGre NHar NHol NMen NNrd NRed NRoo SHer SIng WDav WPat WPer
'Oakfield Clove' (b) SAll

§ 'Oakington' (p) CRiv CSam EBre EMNN GCHN LBre MBal MRav MWat NCra NKay NMen NNrd NRoo SChu WDav WHil
'Oakington Rose' See D. 'Oakington'
'Oakwood Billy Boole' (p) NPin
'Old Blush' See D. 'Souvenir de la Malmaison'
'Old Clove Red' (b) SFis WThu
'Old Dutch Pink' (p) CMil NCra SChu SSvw
'Old Fringed White' (p) EMFP SSvw
'Old Irish' (p) CMil NSti
'Old Mother Hubbard' AGM CFee ESis
¶ 'Old Red Clove' (p) EMFP
§ 'Old Square Eyes' (p) NNrw SBla SSvw WEas
'Old Velvet' (p) CLTr CMil CThr EFou GCal MBel SChu SSvw
'Oliver' (p) SAll
'Omagio' (pf) SAll
'Orange Maid' (b) SAll
'Orchid Beauty' (pf) SHay
'Oscar' (b) SAll
'Osprey' (b) SHay
'Paddington' (p) CThr EMFP NCra SChu SSvw
'Painted Beauty' (p) CThr EMFP NBir SIng
'Painted Lady' (p) CMer CThr MBel NHol SSvw WPat
'Paisley Gem' (p) CLTr CThr MBel NCra SChu SSvw
'Patchwork' SAsh
'Patricia' (b) SHay
'Patricia Bell' See D. ***turkestanicus*** 'P.B.'
'Paul' (p) EMFP MBel NPin
'Paul Hayward' (p) SHay
§ ***pavonius*** AGM CNic CSam GAbr GTou LBee MCas MRav NWCA SBla WAbe WDav WOMN WPer WWin
– 'Nancy Lindsay' See D. 'N.L.'
– ***roysii*** See D. 'Roysii'
'Peach' (p) SHay
'Perfect Clove' (b) SHay
§ ***petraeus*** LRHS NHol SIng WHaw
§ – ssp. ***noeanus*** WDav WHal WPer
§ – ssp. ***petraeus*** WPer
'Petticoat Lace' (p) SHay
'Phantom' (b) SHay
'Pheasant's Eye' (p) CMil CThr EMFP NCra WPer
'Philip Archer' (b) SHay
'Picture' (b) SHay
'Pierrot' See D. 'Kobusa'
'Pike's Pink' AGM Widely available
pindicola See D. ***haematocalyx p.***
pinifolius MSto
'Pink Bizarre' (b) SHay
'Pink Calypso' See D. 'Truly Yours'
'Pink Damask' (p) GAbr WPer
¶ 'Pink Devon Pearl' NRoo
'Pink Galil' (pf) SAll
'Pink Jewel' (p) CMHG CMea CSam ECha EPad ESis LBee MHig NHol NMen NRoo SChu SHer WEas
'Pink Mist Sim' (pf) SHay
'Pink Mrs Sinkins' (p) CLTr ECha EMFP SAll SChu WHoo
'Pink Pearl' (b) CThr EBee
'Pink Sim' (pf) SAll
'Pixie' (b) EMNN EPot ITim MCas NHol NNrd
plumarius NMir SRms WByw WGor WOak WPer
– 'Albiflorus' NOrc WHaw WPer
'Portsdown Fancy' (b) EBar SHay
'Portsdown Lass' (b) EBar SHay
'Portsdown Perfume' (b) SHay
preobrazhenskii NNrd
'Preston Pink' SChu
'Pretty Lady' (p) NRoo
'Prince Charming' (p) CRiv CSam ELan EMNN GAbr ITim MCas NHol NMen NNrd NRoo SIng WAbe WPer
'Prince of Wales' EPad
* 'Princess Charming' MHig
'Princess of Wales' (m) SBor WMal
'Priory Pink' (p) CLTr SAll
§ 'Prudence' (p) CThr EMFP NCra NSti SBai WHoo WMar
'Pummelchen' (p) EPot
§ ***pungens*** CNic
'Purley King' (p) CThr
'Purple Frosted' (pf) SHay
'Purple Jenny' (p) SAll
'Queen of Hearts' (p) ESis SGil WHil WPer
'Queen of Henri' (p) EBee ERav LBee NHol NRoo SChu SFis SHer WPla
'Queen of Sheba' (p) CLTr CMil CThr EMFP NCra SChu SSvw WMar
'Queen's Reward' (pf) SBai
'Raby Castle' See D. 'Lord Chatham'
'Rachel' (p) EBre LBre NRoo
'Raggio di Sole' (pf) SBai
'Rainbow Loveliness' (p,a) WCla WElm WHil
'Red and White' (p) WPer
'Red Emperor' (p) SAll WPer
'Red Penny' (p) ESis MBel MBro NBro NCat NRoo SAsh WHil WPat
'Red Velvet' SAsh
'Red-Edged Skyline' (pf) SHay
'Reiko' (pf) SAll
'Renoir' (b) SAll SHay
§ 'Revell's Lady Wharncliffe' See D. 'Lady Wharncliffe'
'Riccardo' (b) SBai
'Richard Gibbs' (p) MHig MRav NRoo WWin
'Rimon' (pf) SAll
¶ 'Rivendell' (p) WAbe
'Robert' (p) SAll
'Robert Allwood' (pf) SHay
'Robert Baden-Powell' (b) SHay
'Roberta' (pf) SAll
'Robin Thain' (b) EBar SAll SBai SHay
'Ron's Joanne' (pf) NPin SHay
'Roodkapje' (p) SSvw
'Rosalind Linda' (pf) MWoo
'Rose de Mai' (p) CLTr CMil CSam EMFP MMil NCra SChu SSvw
'Rose Joy' (p) CSam CThr NCra NHol NPin NRoo SBai SHay WPbr
'Rose Monica Wyatt' (p) CThr NRoo
'Rose Perfection' (pf) SHay

'Rosealie' (p)	SHay
'Royal Scot' (pf)	MWoo
'Royalty' (p)	SHay
§ 'Roysii' (p)	GPlt MPla NNrd WPer
'Rubin' (pf)	WEas
'Ruby' (p)	See D. 'Houndspool Ruby'
'Ruby Doris'	See D. 'Houndspool Ruby'
rupicola	CNic
'Russling Robin'	See D. 'Fair Maid of Kent '
'Ruth' (p)	SIng
'Sabra' (pf)	SAll
'Sahara' (pf)	SAll
'Saint Nicholas' (p)	NCra SHer SSvw WThu
'Sally Anne Hayward' (b)	SHay
'Salmon Clove' (b)	SAll SHay
'Sam Barlow' (p)	CLTr CMil CThr EMFP NCra SAll SChu SHay SIng SSvw WEas WMar WWin
'Sandra Neal' **AGM**	SBai
'Santa Claus' (b)	SAll SHay
'Sappho' (b)	SHay
'Scania' (pf)	SHay
'Scarlet Fragrance' (b)	SAll SHay
'Scarlet Joanne' (pf)	GBur MWoo NPin SHay
'Scaynes Hill' (p)	WSun
* ***scopulorum perplexans***	EPot
'Sean Hitchcock' (b)	SBai
seguieri	GAbr GCra MBro WPer
'Shaston' (b)	SHay
'Shaston Scarletta' (b)	SHay
'Shaston Superstar' (b)	SHay
'Shegange' (pf)	SAll
'Shocking Pink Sim' (pf)	SAll
'Show Aristocrat' (p)	SAll
'Show Portrait' (p)	NNor
'Sir Arthur Sim' (pf)	SAll SHay
'Sir Cedric Morris'	See D. 'Cedric's Oldest'
* 'Six Hills'	MBel MBro WPat
'Snow Clove' (b)	SHay
'Snowflake' (p)	NNrd
'Snowshill Manor (p)	WPer
'Solomon' (p)	SSvw WMar
'Sonata' (p)	MWil
'Sops-in-Wine' (p)	CLTr CSam CThr ECha EMFP GAbr MBel NCra SChu SHay SSvw WHil
'Southmead' (p)	EGle MHig
'Souvenir de la Malmaison' (m)	SBor WMal
'Spangle' (b)	SAll
'Spencer Bickham' (p)	EMFP EPot SSvw
¶ 'Spetchley'	WPer
'Spring Beauty' (p)	NBir NRoo WCla
'Square Eyes'	See D. 'Old Square Eyes'
squarrosus	EPot LBee MHig MSto NGre NNrd NWCA WDav
¶ – 'Nanus'	EWes
'Squeeks' (p)	SChu
'Stan Stroud' (b)	SHay
'Startler' (p)	SHay
'Storm' (pf)	SBai SHay
'Strathspey' (b)	SHay
'Strawberries and Cream' (p)	CThr EBre EMFP GAri LBre LHop MBel NHol NOrc NPin SBai SHay SMrm WPbr WTyr
strictus var. ***brachyanthus***	See D. ***integer minutiflorus***
§ ***subacaulis***	EPot GAbr MBro MMil MSto NWCA
suendermannii	See D. ***petraeus***
'Sunray' (b)	SHay
'Sunstar' (b)	SAll SHay
§ ***superbus***	CHad CTom GCra LWad MBel MTho WCla WOMN WPer WPla WSun WWin
¶ – 'Crimsonia'	WPer
– ***longicalycinus***	NNrw
I – 'Primadonna'	WPer
¶ – 'Snowdonia'	WPer WTyr
'Susan' (p)	EMFP IBar SAll
'Susannah' (p)	SAll
'Swanlake' (p)	SHay
'Swansdown' (p)	NNor
'Sway Belle' (p)	CThr MBel SBai SOkh
'Sway Candy' (p)	SBai
'Sway Gem' (p)	SBai
'Sway Mist' (p)	SBai
'Sway Pearl' (p)	SBai
'Sweet Sue' (b)	SAll SHay
¶ 'Sweetheart'	LHil
'Sweetheart Abbey' (p)	CCot CMil CThr EMFP NCra SChu SSvw WThu
sylvestris	EPot NNrd
¶ – 'Uniflorus'	MHig
'Tamsin Fifield' (b)	SBai
'Tangerine Sim' (pf)	SAll SHay
'Taunton' (p)	WPat
'Tayside Red' (m)	SBor WMal
'Telstar' (pf)	SHay
* ***tenerifa***	MBri
'Terry Sutcliffe' (p)	SSvw WMar WPer
'The Bloodie Pink'	See D. 'Caesar's Mantle'
'Thomas' (p)	CGle EFou NVic SAll SChu WEas
'Thomas Lee' (b)	SAll
'Thora'	EPad WMal
'Tiny Rubies'	See D. ***gratianopolitanus*** 'T. R.'
'Toledo' (p)	EMFP
'Tony Langford' (pf)	NPin SBai
'Torino' (pf)	SAll
'Tracy Barlow' (b)	SHay
'Treasure' (p)	SHay
turkestanicus	NBir
– 'Patricia Bell'	CSam SBla
'Uncle Teddy' (b)	SBai
uniflorus	MHig
'Unique' (p)	SSvw WMar
'Ursula Le Grove' (p)	CLTr SSvw WHoo WMar
'Valda Wyatt' **AGM**	CCla CLTr CSam CThr CVer ELan EMFP GCHN LHop MBel NCra NHol NPin NRoo NSti SBai SChu SSvw WPbr WTyr
'Valencia' (pf)	SBai
'Vera Woodfield' (pf)	MWoo NPin SHay
'Violet Carson' (b)	SAll
'Violet Clove' (b)	SHay
'Visa' (pf)	SAll
'W A Musgrave' (p)	See D. 'Musgrave's Pink'
'W H Brooks' (b)	SAll

'Waithman Beauty' (p) CCot CNic CTom ECha EMNN GAbr MBar MHig MPla NCra NNrd NRoo SAll SSvw WEas WHil WHoo WPat WPer
'Waithman's Jubilee' (p) CCot CRiv GCHN NBrk NCat NKay NSti WDav WPer
'Warden Hybrid' (p) CRiv EMNN ESis GAbr MHig NHol NRoo WAbe
'Warrior' (b) SAll SHay
'Weetwood Double' (p) CNic EHic WPer
'Welcome' (b) SHay
'Wells-next-the-Sea' (p) EOrc
weyrichii ITim NMen NNrd SIng WAbe WOMN WPer
'Whatfield Anona' (p) EGle ELan LBee SAll SHer
'Whatfield Beauty' ELan EPot LBee
'Whatfield Brilliant' LBee LRHS
¶ 'Whatfield Can-Can' NHol NRoo
'Whatfield Cyclops' EPot NHol SAll
'Whatfield Dorothy Man' (p) ELan SAll
'Whatfield Fuchsia' (p) SAll
'Whatfield Gem' (p) EBre ELan EMFP EPad GAbr LBre MCas MPit NHol NMen NNrd NRoo SAll SGil SHer WPer
'Whatfield Joy' (p) CLew ELan EPot ESis GAbr MCas MRPP NHol NMen NRoo NTow SAll SHer
'Whatfield Magenta' (p) EGle ELan EPad ESis GAbr LBee LRHS NHol SGil SHer WEas
'Whatfield Mini' (p) CSam LBee SAll WPer
'Whatfield Miss' (p) SAll
'Whatfield Peach' (p) SAll
'Whatfield Polly Anne' (p) SAll
'Whatfield Pom Pom' (p) SAll
'Whatfield Pretty Lady' (p) EPot SHer
'Whatfield Ruby' (p) EGle ELan EMFP LBee LRHS SAll SHer WPer
'Whatfield Supergem' ELan EPot
'Whatfield White' (p) ELan EPad LBee LRHS SHer SIng
¶ 'Whatfield Wink' EGle
'Whatfield Wisp' (p) CLew EGle EHic ELan EPad GAbr MPit NBir NMen SHer WMar
'White Barn' (p) ECha
¶ 'White Joy' (p) NRoo
'White Ladies' (p) CThr ELan ENot SSvw
'White Lighning' (pf) SAll
'White Sim' (pf) SAll SHay
'Whitecliff' (b) SAll SHay
'Whitehills' **AGM** CShe EPot NKay NMen NRoo NWCA WThu WWin
'Widecombe Fair' (p) CLTr CThr CVer EBre ERav LBre LHop MBel NCra NHol
'William Brownhill' (p) CMil EMFP SChu SSvw
'William Sim' (pf) SHay
'Winnie Lesurf' (b) MBel
'Winsome' (p) SHay
'Woodfield's Jewel' (p) MWoo
'Yellow Dusty Sim' (pf) SHay
'Yorkshireman' (b) SAll SHay
'Young Marie' (pf) NPin
'Zebra' (b) SAll SBai SHay
'Zodiac' (pf) SAll

DIAPENSIA (Diapensiaceae)
See Plant Deletions

DIARRHENA (Gramineae/Poaceae)
japonica ETPC

DIASCIA (Scrophulariaceae)
anastrepta CHan CLew CMHG CMer CVer ESma GAbr GCal LHop LLWP MCas MPit SChu SHer WCru WEas WPer WRus
¶ 'Appleby Apricot' CSpe
'Apricot' missapplied See DD. 'Hopley's Apricot, 'Blackthorn Apricot'
barberae EBre EHic ELan EMar ESis ESma GAri GCal LBre LHop MUlv SFis
'Blackthorn Apricot' CBot CElw CRDP GBuc LBee LBlm LGre MDHE SAxl SBla SIng SMrm SUsu SWas WByw WCru WPbr
¶ 'Blue Mist' SMrm
¶ 'Christine' NBra
§ *cordata* CGle CLew CMHG CShe EMNN EMar EMon EOrc ERav GDra IHos ITim MBal MPit MPla NHar NHol NMen SFis SUsu WEas WHil WPer WThu WWin
♦ *cordata* misapplied See D. ***barberae***
¶ *cordata* x 'Lilac Belle' WRus
¶ 'Dark Eyes' NBra
elegans See D. ***vigilis***
felthamii See D. ***fetcaniensis***
§ *fetcaniensis* Widely available
flanaganii See D. ***stachyoïdes***
¶ 'Frilly' NBra
'Hector Harrison' See D. 'Salmon Supreme'
§ 'Hopley's Apricot' CBot CBrk CLTr CMGP CSev CSpe ELan EOrc GCal LHop LLWP LRHS MHlr MMil NBrk NHol NPer SHer SMrm WCot WPbr
§ *integerrima* Widely available
– 'Harry Hay' CGle
integrifolia See D. ***integerrima***
'Jack Elliott' CB&S CLTr EHic ESma LHop MTho NBro NTow
¶ 'Jacqueline's Joy' CSpe
¶ 'Joyce's Choice' CBot CSpe EOrc LGre LLWP
'Katherine Sharman' (v) EMon
¶ 'Lady Valerie' CSpe
¶ 'Lavender Bell' EOrc
'Lilac Belle' CB&S CBar CBot CBrk CElw CLTr CSam CSpe ECtt ELan EMar EOrc EPot LHil LHop LLWP MBel MMil SChu SFis SMrm SUsu WCru WHil WPbr WRus
¶ 'Lilac Dream' NBra
¶ 'Lilac Lace' (v) NBra
¶ 'Lilac Mist' EOrc GCal LGre LHop NBra
lilacina CHan CLTr CLew CMHG CSev ECtt EMon EOrc ESis ESma GAbr GAri GCal LGan NCat SHer WEas WPer
megathura GCal SHer
¶ *mollis* CSpe
patens CBrk CDoC CSev EOrc ESis LHil NNrw SMrm WCru WPer
* *pentandra* CBot WPer

'Pink Queen' SFis WHil
'Pink Spot' EPot NBra
¶ ***purpurea*** NFai
rigescens **AGM** Widely available
– 'Forge Cottage' WPer
¶ – x ***integerrima*** SUsu
– – ***lilacina*** EHic NCat SIgm
'Ruby Field' **AGM** Widely available
'Ruby Field' x ***stachyoïdes*** SAxl SIgm
'Rupert Lambert' CBrk CLTr EMar EMon ESma GCal GMac LHop LLWP MBel NPer SChu SCro SUsu WCru WPbr WPer
§ 'Salmon Supreme' Widely available
§ ***stachyoïdes*** CLew CMHG EBar EHal ELan ERav ESma LBlm LHop LLWP NPer WPbr WPer WPla WRus
tugelensis CGle SWas
'Twinkle' CSpe EMar EPot LLWP NRar WPer
§ ***vigilis*** **AGM** Widely available
¶ – Jack Elliott 8955 SWas
¶ 'Wendy' EOrc

DIASCIA X LINARIA See NEMESIA *fruticans*

DICENTRA † (Papaveraceae)

'Adrian Bloom' CDoC CMea CSco GBur GCal MTho NCat NOak NSti SAxl SPla WCot WRus
'Adrian Bloom Variegated' WCot
'Bacchanal' CBos CMHG CRow CTom CWit EBre ECtt EFol EFou EPar EPla LBre LGre MBri MTho NBir NOak NRoo NSti SAxl SBla SChu SUsu WBon WCru WRus WSHC WWin
'Boothman's Variety' See D. ***formosa*** 'Stuart Boothman'
'Bountiful' CCla CGle CMHG CMil CRow CSco EGol MBro MHig MTho NNor NRoo NSti SChu SHer SPer WHoo
'Brownie' CWGN EMon MBel NCat SAxl SCro
canadensis CRDP EPot MSal MTho NHol NSti WChr
¶ ***chrysantha*** MSto
cucullaria CBre CRDP CRow ELun EPot GArf LGre MSal MTho NHar NHol NRya NSti NTow NWCA SIng SWas WAbe WChr WCru WDav WHil
eximia hort. See D. ***formosa***
eximia (Ker-Gawler) Torrey EBee MWat NSti
– 'Alba' See D. ***e.*** 'Snowdrift'
– 'Snowdrift' CLew CSpe SPou
§ ***formosa*** Widely available
§ – ***alba*** CBot CChu CGle CHad CHan CMil COtt CRDP CRow CSpe ECha ELan EOrc EPar LGre NBir NJap NNor NOak NRoo NVic SAxl SChu SUsu WAbe WByw WPbr WRus
– 'Furse's Form' EBre LBre NSti
– ssp. ***oregona*** CHan CRDP CRow CWGN EPar GCal MBal MFos NCat NOak NSti SChu WAbb WAbe WByw WCru WWin
– 'Paramount' NSti
§ – 'Stuart Boothman' **AGM** Widely available
'Langtrees' **AGM** Widely available
'Luxuriant' **AGM** CB&S CBow CCla CGle CRow CShe EBre ECtt EGol ELan ELun EOrc EPar LBre LGan MBri NBar NHol NJap NKay NOak NRoo NSti SPer WAbe WEas WRus
macrantha CBos CGle CHan CRDP CRow ECha EPot LGre LHil WCru WOMN
macrocapnos CB&S CHan CRDP CRow EBre LBre MSto MTho NRar NSti SMrm WCru WSHC
¶ 'Paramount' GBur NCat
'Pearl Drops' CBro CCla CDec CRow EBre EFol EGol ELan EOrc EPar GBur LBre MBri MRav MSte NOak NRoo SAxl SCro SPer WAbb WAbe WEas WHoo WMer WRus WSun WWin
peregrina MFos
§ ***scandens*** CBot CDec CGle CMHG CRHN CRow CVer EBul ELan MTho NBir NOak NRar WAbe WCru WHoo WSHC
'Silver Beads' SGil
'Snowflakes' COtt EBre EFol ELun GCHN LBre NRoo SPer
spectabilis **AGM** Widely available
– ***alba*** **AGM** Widely available
'Spring Morning' CBos CElw CGle CMHG CRow ECha EGle IBlr SChu WCot
thalictrifolia See D. ***scandens***
torulosa CLD 685 WCru
¶ 'Tsuneshige Rokujo' EMon
¶ ***uniflora*** MSto

DICHELOSTEMMA (Liliaceae/Alliaceae)

¶ ***congesta*** LBow
congestum CAvo ETub
§ ***ida-maia*** CMon
multiflorum WChr
§ ***pulchellum*** WChr
volubile WChr

DICHORISANDRA (Commelinaceae)

thyrsiflora CTro

DICHROA (Hydrangeaceae)

febrifuga CAbb CB&S CCla CGre LBlm LGre WCru
versicolor CDec CPle

DICKSONIA (Dicksoniaceae)

antarctica **AGM** CB&S CFil CHEx COtt CTre LPan MMea NHol NPal SArc WRic WWeb
fibrosa CB&S CHEx SArc WRic
lanata CFil
squarrosa CB&S CFil ERea SArc WRic

DICLIPTERA (Acanthaceae)

§ ***suberecta*** CBot ERea LBlm LHop

DICOMA (Compositae/Asteraceae)
See Plant Deletions

DICRANOSTIGMA (Papaveraceae)
See Plant Deletions

DICTAMNUS (Rutaceae)
albus AGM — Widely available
§ – var. ***purpureus*** AGM — Widely available
fraxinella — See D. ***albus purpureus***

DICTYOLIMON (Plumbaginaceae)
macrorrhabdos — NWCA

DICTYOSPERMA (Palmae/Arecaceae)
album — MBri

DIDYMOCHLAENA (Dryopteridaceae)
lunulata — See D. ***truncatula***
§ ***truncatula*** — MBri

DIDYMOSPERMA (Palmae/Arecaceae)
caudatum — See ARENGA ***caudata***

DIEFFENBACHIA (Araceae)
'Camille' (v) — MBri
'Candida' (v) — MBri
'Compacta' (v) — MBri
'Jeanette' (v) — MBri
'Jupiter' (v) — MBri
'Mars' (v) — MBri
'Neptune' (v) — MBri
'Saturnus' (v) — MBri
'Schott Gitte' (v) — MBri
seguine 'Amoena' (v) — MBri
– 'Carina' (v) — MBri
– 'Katherine' (v) — MBri
– 'Tropic Snow' (v) — MBri
'Triumph' (v) — MBri
'Tropic Sun' (v) — MBri
'Tropic White' (v) — MBri
'Veerie' (v) — MBri

DIERAMA (Iridaceae)
¶ ***ambiguum*** — CHan
cooperi — CHan
§ ***dracomontanum*** — CBro CGle CHan CPou CRDP ELan GAbr GCal LGre LHil NBir NRoo SBla SChu SPer WAbe WOMN
– dwarf lilac — GCal
– dwarf pale pink — EPla GCal
– dwarf pink — GCal
ensifolium — See D. ***pendulum***
igneum — CSam
– CD&R 278 — CHan
¶ ***jucundum*** — CHan
latifolium — GCal
¶ ***luteoalbidum*** CD&R 1025 — CHan
****ochroleucum*** — CGle
pauciflorum — CHan LGre
§ ***pendulum*** — CBot CFee CKel CMGP EBre EFou ELan EPla LAbb LBre MBri MFir NCat NHol SChu SMrm SPer WAbe WByw WHow WRus
– var. ***pumilum*** — See D. ***dracomontanum***
'Puck' — ECha GCal NCat SHig
pulcherrimum — Widely available
– 'Blackbird' — GAbr WDav
– dwarf forms — GCal LHop
– forms — ECha IBlr
– 'Peregrine' — GAbr
– Slieve Donard hybrids — GCal LHop MUlv
¶ – x ***dracomontanum*** — SMad
robustum — CHan
¶ sp. CD&R 192 — WAbe
sp. SH 20 — CHan
sp. SH 49 — CHan
sp. SH 63 — CHan
sp. SH 85 — CHan
'Titania' — MUlv NCat

DIERVILLA † (Caprifoliaceae)
lonicera — WWat
middendorffiana — See WEIGELA ***middendorffiana***
rivularis — SLon
sessilifolia — CB&S CCla CHan CPle CSco EBre EPar IOrc LBre MBel MUlv SChu SLPl WBod WHCG WKif WRus WSHC WTyr WWin
x ***splendens*** — CBow CBra CCla CDoC CMHG CPMA CPle EBar EBre ECha EHoe ELan EPla ERav GWht IJoh LBre MBar MPla MRav MUlv NHol SEng SLPl SPer SSta WAbe WDin WStI

DIETES (Iridaceae)
¶ ***bicolor*** — ERea
grandiflora — CMil CTro
§ ***iridioïdes*** — CGle WPer WThi

DIGITALIS † (Scrophulariaceae)
ambigua — See D. ***grandiflora***
apricot hybrids — See D. ***purpurea*** 'Sutton's Apricot'
ciliata — EBar EBee ELan GCra MSto NOak
cream hybrids — EFou NBrk
davisiana — CBot ECha ECro EHic EMar GCra LGre MSto NOak WHil WPer
dubia — CBot CMea ECro ECtt EMar NBir NPri SMrm
eriostachya — See D. ***lutea***
ferruginea — Widely available
– 'Gelber Herold' — CBot LBlm LGre NHol WBon WCra WDav
¶ – 'Gigantea' — CBot NHol
¶ – ***schischkinii*** — GMac
fontanesii — WHoo
x ***fulva*** — NBir
'Glory of Roundway' — CBot CHan
§ ***grandiflora*** AGM — Widely available
¶ – 'Carillon' — ECro WPer
– 'Temple Bells' — EHic EMar WCla WHer WHoo WPer WSun
heywoodii — See D. ***purpurea heywoodii***
¶ 'John Innes Tetra' — EBee EFou SHer

kishinskyi	See D. ***parviflora***
laevigata	CAbb CBot CHan CSam ECro EFou EPad ESma GTou LGre MSte MSto NBrk NBro NHol NMir NSti SBla SIng SUsu WCHb WCra WHer WPer
– ssp. ***graeca***	ECro EHic
lamarckii hort.	See D. ***lanata***
lamarckii Ivanina	MSto SIgm SWas
§ ***lanata*** AGM	Widely available
– x ***grandiflora*** 'John Innes Tetra'	SHer WPer
§ ***lutea***	Widely available
– Brickell's form	MSte
x ***mertonensis*** AGM	Widely available
obscura	CBot CGle CPle EBar ECro ECtt ELan EPad GCra LGan LHop MSto NOak NPri SBla SHer WHal WHil WPer
– dwarf form	MSto
♦ ***orientalis***	See D. ***grandiflora***
§ ***parviflora***	CBot CBow CChu CCla CHan EBar ECha ECro EFol EFou EPad EPar ESis LGan MFir MSto MWat NBrk NBro NOak NSti SHer SMrm SSvw SUsu WDav WEas WHil WMer WPer
purpurea	CArn CBow CKin EBre ECWi EFou ENot EWFC GPoy LBre LHol MPit NLan NMir NNor NPri SIde WCla WHal WNdy WOak WPer WWye
– f. ***albiflora*** AGM	CArn CB&S CBot CBre CCla CGle CHad CSFH EBre ECha EFol EFou ELan EMon LBre MWat NFai NSti SFis SPer SSvw WCla WEas WHal WPbr WPer WRus WSun WWye
– 'Chedglow' (v)	CNat
– Excelsior Hybrids Group AGM	CB&S CBot CBow CHol CKel CSam CSco EBre GAbr LAbb LBre LWad MBri MWat NBar NFai NMir NNor SPer WHen WHil
– Excelsior White Group	CKni
– Foxy Hybrids Group	CBot CBow EBar NFai NRoo SRms WHen WPer
– Giant Spotted Group	CMGP LBuc SSvw WPer WRus
– Glittering Prizes Group	CBow EHal WBon
– Gloxiniiflora Group 'The Shirley' AGM	ECtt EFou GCra SMad
§ – ssp. ***heywoodii***	CBot CSam ECro ELan EMar GBuc SFis SMrm WCHb WPbr WPer
– 'Isabelina'	CBot WPer
– ***nevadensis***	CBot WRus
– 'Sutton's Apricot' AGM	Widely available
sibirica	CBoy EBee ECro EMar MSto WHer WPer
thapsi	CBot ECro ELan EMon EPad MSto SBla WPer
¶ – JCA 410.000	WDav
trojana	CBoy ECro ECtt GAbr MSto NBrk NBro NRoo SFis SUsu WHer WHil WPer
¶ Vesuvius Hybrids	CBot
viridiflora	CAbb CArn EBar ECro ECtt EGol EPad ERav ESma GAul GCra MSto NBro NPri SFis SUsu WDav WHal WHer WHil WPer WPla WWye

DIMORPHOTHECA (Compositae/Asteraceae)

–	See also OSTEOSPERMUM

DIONAEA (Droseraceae)

muscipula	EFEx EPot MHel MSte WHal WMEx

DIONYSIA (Primulaceae)

aretioïdes AGM	CNic EPot GTou MCas NHar NTow SIgm WDav WThu
– 'Gravetye'	MRPP NHar NWCA SHer
– 'Phyllis Carter'	EPot MRPP NHar NMen NTow SHer
involucrata	CNic NWCA
tapetodes H 1164	MRPP
– 'Peter Edwards' (Hewer 1164)	WThu

DIOÖN (Zamiaceae)

edule	LPal NPal
mejiae	LPal
spinulosum	LPal

DIOSCOREA (Dioscoreaceae)

¶ ***deltoidea***	WCru
¶ ***quinqueloba***	WCru
villosa	MSal

DIOSMA (Rutaceae)

ericoïdes	CPle EPla IHos LBuc

DIOSPHAERA (Campanulaceae)

asperuloïdes	See TRACHELIUM ***asperuloïdes***

DIOSPYROS (Ebenaceae)

¶ ***duclouxii***	CFil
F ***kaki***	CB&S CBot CGre GWht
lotus	CB&S CFil EArb WWat
F ***virginiana***	EArb WCoo

DIPCADI (Liliaceae/Hyacinthaceae)

¶ ***fulvum***	WChr
lividum SF 1	CMon
¶ ***serotinum***	WChr
– MS 877	CMon

DIPELTA (Caprifoliaceae)

floribunda	CPMA MBlu SHil

DIPHYLLEIA (Berberidaceae)

cymosa	ECha LGre MSal WCru

DIPIDAX See ONIXOTIS

DIPLACUS See MIMULUS

DIPLADENIA See MANDEVILLA

DIPLARRHENA (Iridaceae)

§ ***latifolia***	CAvo LBee NSla WAbe

moraea CChu CDoC ECha ECou GCal GGar GWht IBar IBlr ILis ITim LHil MHig MTho NHol NOrc SAxl SBla WAbe WHal WOld WWin
– West Coast form See D. ***latifolia***

DIPLAZIUM (Dryopteridaceae)
See Plant Deletions

DIPLOTAXIS (Cruciferae/Brassicaceae)
tenuifolia WPer

DIPSACUS (Dipsacaceae)
§*fullonum* CArn CKin CLTr CSFH CWGN ECWi ECro EJud EWFC GCHN IEde LHol MChe MHew NBro NLan NMir SIde SMad SSvw WByw WNdy WOak WPer WWye
– ssp. *fullonum* MWil
inermis CHan ECro WCru
¶– C&Mc 567 GCHN
pilosus CKin ECro WHaw
sylvestris See D. ***fullonum***

DIPTERACANTHUS See **RUELLIA**

DIPTERONIA (Aceraceae)
sinensis CB&S CMCN CPle CSam EHar MBri WNor

DISANTHUS (Hamamelidaceae)
cercidifolius **AGM** CAbP CChu CSco MBlu MBri MGos SHil SMad SPer SReu WBod WWat

DISCARIA (Rhamnaceae)
See Plant Deletions

DISELMA (Cupressaceae)
archeri CKen CNic LCon MBar WThu

DISPOROPSIS (Liliaceae/Convallariaceae)
¶*arisanensis*
B&SWJ 1490 WCru
pernyi CRDP MNFA SAxl SBla SGil SPou SWas WCru

DISPORUM (Liliaceae/Convallariaceae)
flavens EPar SAxl SWas
hookeri WCru
– var. *oreganum* CBro CRow GTou IBlr LGre NHol
lanuginosum CBro
maculatum LGre
sessile EPla
– 'Variegatum' CAvo CBro CChu CHan CRDP CRow ECha ELan EPar EPla LGre SAxl SBla SGil SUsu SWas WCru WPbr WWin
smithii CHan EBul EPar EPot MSal NBir NHar NRya WCru WWat
trachycarpum EPla

DISTICTIS (Bignoniaceae)
buccinatoria CTro

¶ 'Mrs Rivers' CTro

DISTYLIUM (Hamamelidaceae)
racemosum CB&S CShe CTre ELan SHBN SReu SSta WBod WSHC WWat
§– *tutcheri* CWit

DIURANTHERA See **CHLOROPHYTUM**

DIURIS (Orchidaceae)
¶*longifolia* WThi

DIZYGOTHECA See **SCHEFFLERA**

DODECADENIA (Lauraceae)
grandiflora CTre

DODECATHEON † (Primulaceae)
alpinum CLew CNic CRDP GTou LBee MPhe NHar NRya WDav WThi
– JCA 11744 SBla
– JCA 9542 NHol
amethystinum See D. ***pulchellum***
clevelandii CBro GAbr NRed NTow
– ssp. *insulare* CNic LRHS MPhe NHol NWCA
– ssp. *patullum* LRHS
conjugens CNic NTow NWCA
cusickii See D. ***pulchellum cusickii***
dentatum CBro CElw CNic EPar GLil LBee LGre MBal MBro MCas MPhe MTho NMen NNrd NTow SWas WAbe WThi
– ssp. *dentatum* NHol
– ssp. *ellisiae* MBri NGre NRya
hendersonii **AGM** CBro EPar ESma LBee MBal MPhe NHol NNrd NSla SGil SIng
§*jeffreyi* CRDP EMil EPot GTou MPhe NHar NMen NSla NWCA SGil WAbe WCla
– 'Rotlicht' NHar NRoo WHil
*x *lemoinei* EPot SIng
meadia **AGM** Widely available
– f. *album* **AGM** CB&S CBro CLew ECha EFou ELan EOrc EPar GAbr GDra LAma LHop MTho NHol NRed NRoo NRya NSti SHer SPer WCru WHil WWat
– 'Alpenglow' NHol
– 'Millard's Clone' EPar NHol
– 'Rose Farben' NHol
pauciflorum See D. ***pulchellum***
poeticum EHic MBro NHar NTow WDav
§*pulchellum* **AGM** CNic CRDP EPar EPot GDra LBee MBal MPhe NGre NHar NHol NKay NRed NRya SBla SIng WAbe WDav WEas WHil
– JCA 9174 NHol
¶– *album* WDav
– ssp. *cusickii* CRDP GTou NWCA SIng
– ssp. *macrocarpum* NNrd
– ssp. *pulchellum* 'Red Wings' CNic CRDP EBar EBre EMar EPot GAbr GDra GTou LBre MBro MCas NHol NNrd NTow WHoo WRus
radicatum See D. ***pulchellum***
tetrandrum See D. ***jeffreyi***

DODONAEA (Sapindaceae)

humilis (f)	ECou
– (m)	ECou
viscosa	ECou IBlr
– ***angustifolia***	ISea
– 'Purpurea'	CB&S CGre CPle ECou ERea ISea LBlm MUlv SDry

DOLICHOS (Leguminosae/Papilionaceae)

lablab	See LABLAB ***purpureus***

DOLICOTHRIX (Compositae/Asteraceae)

§ ***ericoïdes***	SPer

DOMBEYA (Sterculiaceae)

burgessiae	CTro

DONDIA See HACQUETIA

DOODIA (Blechnaceae)

caudata	NMar
media	MMea NMar WRic

DORONICUM † (Compositae/Asteraceae)

austriacum	EBee ECro NCat WPer
caucasicum	See D. ***orientale***
§ ***columnae***	CB&S GDra NNrd NOak
cordatum	See D. ***columnae***
§ x ***excelsum*** 'Harpur Crewe'	CElw CGle ECED EFou MHlr MWat NKay SPer SPla WCot WEas
'Finesse'	ESma NOak
'Frühlingspracht' ('Spring Beauty')	CBow CElw CRDP CSam EBre ELan GDra LBre LWad NHar NHol SHer SPer SPla WEas WWin
'Miss Mason' **AGM**	CDoC CSco CShe ENot MBri MUlv NBro SPer
§ ***orientale***	CBow EHal GAbr GLil MBro NBar WByw WDav WHaw
– 'Goldzwerg'	CMGP CSco
– 'Magnificum'	CBow CHol CLew CMGP EBre ESma GAul LBre MFir MPit NFai NMir NOak NRoo SMrm WHil WPer WPla WWin
pardalianches	CMea ECha GCra MHew SAxl WByw WCot
plantagineum	ELan
♦– 'Excelsum'	See D. x ***excelsum*** 'H.C.'
'Riedels Goldkranz'	MBri NFai

DORYANTHES (Liliaceae/Doryanthaceae)

palmeri	CHEx

DORYCNIUM See LOTUS

DORYOPTERIS (Adiantaceae)

pedata	MBri

DOUGLASIA See ANDROSACE

DOXANTHA See MACFADYENA

DRABA (Cruciferae/Brassicaceae)

acaulis	WDav
aïzoïdes	CSam EBre ECha ELan EMil EPar GCHN GDra GPlt LBre MHig MPla NGre NKay NMen NMir SHer SIng WCla WDav WHoo WWin
– 'Compacta'	ELan
aïzoön	See D. ***lasiocarpa***
§ ***aspera***	GDra GTou NHol
aurea var. ***leiocarpa***	NHol
* ***balcanica***	NHol
bertolonii Boissier	See D. ***loiseleurii***
bertolonii Nyman	See D. ***aspera***
♦ ***bertolonii*** Thell.	See D. ***brachystemon***
breweri	ITim NHol
bruniifolia	EBre EBur EGle LBre MHig MTho NHol NWCA SHer SSmi WPer
¶ – ssp. ***heterocoma*** var. ***nana***	NHar WDav
bryoïdes	See D. ***rigida b.***
cappadocica JCA 419.500	CNic
♦ ***compacta***	See D. ***lasiocarpa***
crassifolia	NHol
cuspidata	EPot
♦ ***daurica***	See D. ***glabella***
dedeana	EWes MBro NGre WPer WWin
– ssp. ***mawii***	NNrd
densifolia	NGre NHol NTow SIng WDav
dubia	NWCA
haynaldii	NMen WDav
hispanica	NHol NWCA SIng
– ***brevistyla***	NTow
hoppeana	LHop NWCA
imbricata	See D. ***rigida imbricata***
§ ***incana***	MHig NNrd WPat WWin
incerta	CNic
kitadakensis	GCHN NHol
§ ***lasiocarpa***	MPit NHol NRoo NVic NWCA SIng WHal
¶ ***lonchocarpa***	MHig
longisiliqua **AGM**	MHig MRPP NTow NWCA SIng WHil
– EMR 2551	EPot
magellanica	CPBP GGar MDHE
mollissima	EPot GTou MHig MRPP NTow NWCA
§ ***norvegica***	CNic
oligosperma	CNic EPot MBro MFos NHol NTow NWCA WDav WThu
parnassica	CNic GCHN
paysonii	NGre NHol
– var. ***treleasii***	NHar SIng WDav
polytricha	GDra GTou WHil
repens	See D. ***sibirica***
rigida	GDra MBro MTho NHol NVic SSmi
§ – var. ***bryoides***	GDra MBro NGre NHar NHol NTow NWCA WThu
§ – var. ***imbricata***	EPot ITim MBro MFos NGre NHar NHol SSmi WThu

– – f. ***compacta*** EPot
¶ – var. ***rigida*** CNic WDav
rosularis GDra MHig SIng WHil
rupestris See D. ***norvegica***
sakuraii ESis GAbr WPer WWin
x ***salomonii*** EPot
sauteri GCHN
scardica See D. ***lasiocarpa***
¶ ***sierrae*** CNic
sp. CLD 348 NHol
streptocarpa MFos
♦ ***stylaris*** See D. ***incarna***
* ***thymbriphyrestus*** K 92.200 WDav
ussuriensis NHol WPer
ventosa GTou MHig NGre NTow
yunnanensis ex JJH 90856 WDav

DRACAENA (Dracaenaceae)

cincta 'Tricolor' (v) MBri
congesta See CORDYLINE ***stricta***
deremensis MBri
– 'Lemon Lime' (v) MBri
– 'Warneckei' AGM MBri
– 'Yellow Stripe' (v) MBri
fragrans MBri
*– ***glauca*** MBri
– 'Massangeana' AGM MBri
– Compacta Group 'Compacta Purpurea' MBri
– – 'Compacta Variegata' MBri
– – 'Janet Craig' (v) MBri
indivisa See CORDYLINE ***i.***
marginata AGM MBri
– 'Colorama' (v) MBri
sanderiana AGM MBri
* ***schrijveriana*** MBri
steudneri MBri
stricta See CORDYLINE ***s.***
surculosa 'Wit' (v) MBri
surculosa surculosa 'Florida Beauty' (v) MBri

DRACOCEPHALUM (Labiatae/Lamiaceae)

altaiense See D. ***imberbe***
argunense EBee LBee LGre LRHS MHig SCro SMrm SWas WHal WPer WWin
botryoïdes NWCA
bullatum NSti
calophyllum var. ***smithianum*** NGre WDav
forrestii EPot ESis SIng
grandiflorum CRDP MHig
hemsleyanum SIng
mairei See D. ***renatii***
moldavicum MSal SIde WWye
prattii See NEPETA ***p.***
§ ***renatii*** CPBP MHew MSal WPer
ruyschianum ELan EMon ESis LGan MBro MTol NOak NSti NWCA WPer
sibiricum See NEPETA ***sibirica***
virginicum See PHYSOSTEGIA ***virginiana***
¶ ***wendelboi*** GBri NPri WPer

DRACOPHYLLUM (Epacridaceae)

See Plant Deletions

DRACUNCULUS (Araceae)

canariensis GCra
– MS 934 CMon
§ ***vulgaris*** CGle CHEx CRDP CWit EBee EMon EPar EPot SDix SMad WCru WHal WPla

DRAPETES (Thymelaeaceae)

dieffenbachii GArf GDra
lyallii GDra

DREGEA (Asclepiadaceae)

§ ***sinensis*** CBot CChu CGre CMac CNew CSam CTro ELan ERav ERea SHBN SHil SPer WWat
– 'Variegata' CTro

DREPANOSTACHYUM (Gramineae/Poaceae-Bambusoideae)

§ ***falcatum*** WJun
falconeri hort. See HIMALAYACALAMUS ***falconeri*** 'Damarapa'
hookerianum WJun
khasianum ISta
* ***microphyllum*** WJun

DRIMIOPSIS (Liliaceae/Hyacinthaceae)

maculata CMon

DRIMYS (Winteraceae)

aromatica See D. ***lanceolata***
colorata See PSEUDOWINTERA ***c.***
§ ***lanceolata*** CAbb CBow CCla CGre CMHG CPle CTrw ECou ELan EMil GCal GWht IBar IDai ISea MBal MBlu SBor SDry SPer SReu SSta WAbe WBod WCru WSHC WWat
– (f) ECou
– (m) CTre ECou
winteri CAbb CB&S CBra CChu CCla CDoC CGre CHEx CPle CTrw GWht IDai IOrc ISea MUlv SArc SHBN SHil SPer SReu WDin WSHC
– var. ***andina*** CMHG CSam GGGa
§ – var. ***chilensis*** CB&S CGre CHEx CLan ISea MBal WBod
– 'Fastigiata' LBlm
– 'Glauca' ISea
– Latifolia Group See D. ***w. chilensis***
– ***punctata*** See D. ***w. winteri***

DROSANTHEMUM (Aizoaceae)

floribundum CHEx WEas
hispidum CHEx CRiv EBre ELan EPot LBre LHop MCas MHig MTho NGre NMen NNrd NNrw NTow NWCA SBod SHer SIng WCru WPat

DROSERA (Droseraceae)

adelae MHel WMEx
aliciae MHel WHal WMEx
andersoniana EFEx

anglica	WMEx
× ***badgerupii*** 'Lake Badgerup'	WMEx
'Beermullah'	MHel WMEx
§ × ***beleziana***	WMEx
* ***bicolor***	EFEx
§ ***binata***	EPot MHel MSte WHal WMEx
– 'Extremis'	MHel WHal
– 'Multifida'	EPot MHel WHal WMEx
browiana	EFEx
¶ ***bulbigena***	EFEx
bulbosa bulbosa	EFEx
– ***major***	EFEx
burmannii	WMEx
× ***californica*** 'Californian Sunset'	WMEx
¶ ***callistos***	MHel
capensis	EPot MHel MSte WHal WMEx
– ***alba***	MHel WHal WMEx
– narrow-leaved	WMEx
capillaris	MHel WMEx
¶ ***closterostigma***	MHel
cuneifolia	WMEx
dichotoma	See D. ***binata***
dielsiana	WMEx
* ***eriogyna***	EFEx
erythrorrhiza collina	EFEx
¶ – ssp. ***erythrorrhiza***	EFEx
– ***imbecilia***	EFEx
– ***magna***	EFEx
– ***squamosa***	EFEx
filiformis ssp. ***filiformis***	WHal WMEx
– ssp. ***tracyi***	WMEx
gigantea	EFEx
graniticola	EFEx
hamiltonii	WMEx
¶ ***heterophylla***	EFEx
indica	WMEx
intermedia	WMEx
♦ – × ***rotundifolia***	See D. × ***beleziana***
leucoblasta	WMEx
loureirii	EFEx
lovelliae	WMEx
macrantha ssp. ***eremaea***	EFEx
¶ – ssp. ***macrantha***	EFEx
macrophylla	EFEx
– ***marchantii***	EFEx
– ***monantha***	EFEx
– ***prophylla***	EFEx
'Marston Dragon'	WMEx
menziesii basifolia	EFEx
– ssp. ***menziesii***	EFEx
¶ ***modesta***	EFEx
× ***nagamotoi*** 'Nagamoto'	WMEx
– 'Watari'	WMEx
natalensis	WMEx
¶ ***neesii*** ssp. ***neesii***	EFEx
nitidula	WMEx
× ***obovata***	WMEx
¶ ***occindentalis***	MHel
orbiculata	EFEx
¶ ***oreopodion***	MHel
¶ ***peltata***	EFEx MHel
¶ – ssp. ***auriculata***	MHel
platypoda	EFEx MHel
prostratoscaposa	EFEx
pulchella	MHel WHal WMEx
– giant form	WMEx
¶ – × ***nitidula***	MHel
pygmaea	WMEx
radicans	EFEx
ramellosa	EFEx MHel
rosulata	EFEx
rotundifolia	CRDP EWFC GBar WHal WMEx
salina	EFEx
scorpioïdes	WMEx
slackii	MHel MSte WMEx
spathulata	WHal WMEx
– Kansai	WMEx
– Kanto	WMEx
¶ ***stolonifera***	MHel
– ssp. ***compacta***	EFEx
– ssp. ***humilis***	EFEx
– ***porrecta***	EFEx
– ssp. ***rupicola***	EFEx
– ssp. ***stolonifera***	EFEx
strictcaulis	EFEx MHel
tubaestylus	EFEx
¶ ***zonaria***	EFEx

DRYANDRA (Proteaceae)

¶ ***polycephala***	LBlm
praemorsa	LBlm
pteridifolia	LBlm

DRYAS (Rosaceae)

drummondii	NBir NHol SBla WAbe
– 'Grandiflora'	EPot GDra WThu
§ ***integrifolia***	CLew CMea EPot GDra MBro NHar NHol SIng WAbe WWin
octopetala AGM	CGle CSam CTom ECha EFol ELan GDra IDai LHop LLWP MBal MBro MHew MHig MWat NHar NHol NKay NNor NNrd SBla SIng SLon WAbe WDav WEas WHil WHoo WWin
– 'Minor' AGM	LBee MBro MHig NMen SHer WAbe WDav WHoo WPat
× ***suendermannii*** AGM	CMHG EBre ELan GAri GTou LBre MBal NHol NKay NNrd NRoo NWCA WAbe WEas WHoo WPat
tenella	See D. ***integrifolia***

DRYOPTERIS † (Dryopteridaceae)

¶ ***aemula***	NMar
§ ***affinis*** AGM	CFil CRow ECha EFou EPar GGar LWad MBal NHol NKay NMar WFib WHil
– 'Congesta Cristata'	EBre LBre NHar NHol WRic
¶ – 'Crispa Barnes'	WRic
§ – 'Crispa Congesta'	CBar CDoC CMil ELan NBir NKay SMrm SPla SRms
¶ – 'Crispa Gracilis'	WRic
– Crispa Group	IOrc NKay SCob

– 'Cristata Angustata' ELan IOrc NHol NKay NMar SPla SRms WFib
– 'Cristata Grandiceps Askew' NKay NMar WFib
– Cristata Group CRow NMar SMad SPla WFib WHer
– 'Cristata Ramosissima Wright' NKay
– 'Cristata The King' CBar CDoC CRDP EBre EFer EGol ELan IOrc LBre MBri NBro NCat NHar NHol NMar NOrc SCob SRms WAbe WRic
– 'Pinderi' EFou ELan
N– ***polydactyla*** NMar
atrata hort. See D. ***cycadina***
austriaca See D. ***dilatata***
¶ ***blandfordii*** CFil
♦***borreri*** See D. ***affinis b.***
carthusiana CBar CFil NHar NMar WRic
x ***complexa*** 'Stablerae' NMar WRic
crassirhizoma WRic
§ ***cycadina*** CFil CRDP CWGN ELan IOrc MBri MHlr NHol NMar SApp SMad WFib WRic WWat
¶ ***darjeelingensis*** CFil SApp
§ ***dilatata*** CKin CMGP CTom ECha EFer ELan MBal NHol NKay NMar SCob WFib WRic
– 'Crispa' NKay
– 'Crispa Whiteside' CBar ELan NHol SMad SMrm WRic
– 'Grandiceps' CRDP CRow NHar NHol WFib
– 'Lepidota Cristata' CRDP CWGN ELan IOrc NHol NMar SCob SPla SRms WFib WRic
– 'Lepidota Grandiceps' NMar
erythrosora **AGM** CBar CFil CRDP CWGN EBre EFer EGol ELan LBre MBri MRav NEgg NHar NHol NMar SApp SBla SCob SMad SPla WAbe WFib WHal WHil WRic WWat
– ***prolifera*** CMil CRDP NBir NHar NHol
filix-mas **AGM** CBar CFil CKin CRow CTom CWGN EBre ECha EFer EFou EHon ELan IOrc LBre LHol MBal MBri MSta NHol NKay NMar NOrc SCob SPer SWat WFib WRic WWye
– 'Barnesii' CBar EFer NHar NMar WRic
¶– 'Bollandiae' WRic
– 'Crispa' EHon NHol SCob WFib
– 'Crispa Congesta' See D. ***affinis*** 'C. C.'
– 'Crispa Cristata' CBar CMil CRDP EBre EGol ELan LBre MBri NBar NHol NMar SApp SPer SPla SWat WFib WRic
– Cristata Group EFer NMar SApp SCob WFib WRic
– Cristata Group 'Fred Jackson' NHol WFib
– 'Cristata Martindale' CRDP CRow NHol NKay NMar SRms WFib
– 'Depauperata' CFil CRDP SApp WFib
*– ***fluctuosa*** NKay SRms
– 'Grandiceps Wills' NHol NMar WFib WRic
– 'Linearis' CBar EBre EHon ELan IOrc LBre MBri SCob SRms
– 'Linearis Congesta' NKay
– 'Linearis Cristata' EBre LBre NKay NMar SApp WRic
– 'Linearis Polydactyla' NMar SMad
– 'Mapplebeck' CRDP CRow NHol WFib
– 'Multicristata' NMar
– 'Polydactyla Dadds' IOrc WFib
– Polydactyla Group NKay NMar WAbe WFib
****fructosa*** CFil SApp
fuscipes SBla
goldieana NMar WRic
¶ ***guanchica*** CFil
hirtipes See D. ***cycadina***
¶ ***hondoensis*** CFil
¶ ***lacera*** NHar
marginalis NKay NMar SCob SPla
¶ ***pallida*** CFil
pseudomas See D. ***affinis***
x ***remota*** SRms
shiroumensis NMar
sieboldii CFil NMar WRic
¶ ***stenolepis*** WRic
stewartii CBar NHar WRic
x ***tavelii*** IOrc WFib
¶ ***tokyoensis*** NHar
x ***uliginosa*** WRic
wallichiana **AGM** CFil CKni ECha EFer EFou MBri NHar NMar SApp SBla SCob SLga WFib WHal WRic

DRYPIS (Caryophyllaceae)
spinosa NWCA

DUCHESNEA (Rosaceae)
chrysantha See D. ***indica***
§ ***indica*** CLew CTom ECro EHic IBlr NSti
§– 'Harlequin' (v) EFol EMon EPla MTho NSti
– 'Variegata' See D. ***i.*** 'Harlequin.

DUDLEYA (Crassulaceae)
cymosa JCA 11777 CNic
farinosa CHEx IBlr

DUMORTIERA (liverwort)
hirsuta LFle

DUNALIA (Solanaceae)
§ ***australis*** CGre CHan CTro EMon LHil SMad
– blue EWll
– white CBot CHan

DURANTA (Verbenaceae)
§ ***erecta*** CPle CTro SLMG
plumieri See D. ***erecta***
repens See D. ***erecta***

DYCKIA (Bromeliaceae)
¶ ***remotiflora*** CTro

DYSCHORISTE (Acanthaceae)
¶ ***rogersii*** CSpe

EBENUS (Leguminosae/Papilionaceae)
cretica LGre SIgm

ECBALLIUM (Cucurbitaceae)

elaterium MHew MSal WHer

ECCREMOCARPUS (Bignoniaceae)

ruber SUsu
scaber AGM CB&S CGle CGre CMea CNic CRHN CSev ELan EMil ENot EOrc GAbr GCHN MBal MBri NBar NBro NNrw NPer SHer SLon SPer SUsu WCru WHal WHoo WWye
– *aurantiacus* CB&S CMHG ELan LHop NPer NTow
– *coccineus* CB&S CHan CMHG CMea EBar ELan GCHN WHoo WOMN
– *roseus* CB&S CBot CGle ELan WWin

ECHEVERIA † (Crassulaceae)

affinis MBri
agavoïdes AGM MRav
*– 'Metallica' MBri
*'Black Knight' SLMG
derenbergii AGM CHEx SLMG
*'Duchess of Nuremberg' SLMG
elegans AGM CHEx MBri SArc
gibbiflora var. *metallica* WEas
harmsii AGM WEas WOMN
'Imbricata' CHEx
secunda var. *glauca* ESma GBur IBlr NBir SLMG
setosa AGM CHEx SLMG WEas
'Warfield Wonder' AGM WEas

ECHINACEA (Compositae/Asteraceae)

angustifolia CArn GPoy MSal WWye
¶ *laevigata* EMon
pallida CBot CCMG CMil ESma LGan MSal SMad SOkh
paradoxa MSal
§ *purpurea* Widely available
– Bressingham hybrids EBre ELan LBre SPer
– dark stemmed form EFou
– 'Leuchtstern' SPla SSvw WHil WPer
– 'Magnus' CBot CHan CSco ESma LAbb LGre LHil LWad MBel MUlv NRoo SFis SMad SOkh SSvw SUsu WHen WHil WHoo WPer
– 'Robert Bloom' ECED LHop
– 'White Lustre' CSco EBre ECha EGol LBre MBri MRav MUlv SHer SPer SPla WCot WMer
– 'White Swan' Widely available
simulata MSal

ECHINOPS (Compositae/Asteraceae)

albus See E. 'Nivalis'
§ *bannaticus* 'Blue Globe' CHan CSco EBee EHic GCal NCat NRoo SFis WMer WPer
– 'Taplow Blue' AGM CB&S CHan CKel CSco EBre ECro ELan GAbr GCal IDai LBre LHop MUlv NHol NKay NPer SGil SPer SPla WMer
exaltatus NBir
giganteus LWad
humilis EMon
¶ *maracandicus* GCal
microcephalus EMon
§ 'Nivalis' CBre CCla CHan ECro EFou ELan EPla GCal NSti SGil SPer
¶ *niveus* EMon
**perringii* GCal MUlv
ritro hort. See E. ***bannaticus***
¶ – 'Charlotte' EMon
ritro AGM CB&S CBow CHan CMea CRow ECha ECtt EGol ELan ENot GCHN MArl MWat NBar NBee NBrk NBro NKay NMir NNor NRoo SPer SSvw WDav WEas WHil WOak WPer WWin
– ACL 149/75 EMon
– ssp. *ruthenicus* ECha EMon LGre
– 'Veitch's Blue' CCla CDoC CHad CMGP CSco EMon GCal GLil LWad MBri NCat SGil SHer SPla WMer
sphaerocephalus CHan ECha ECro ELan EMon IBlr MUlv WByw WPer

ECHINOSPARTUM See GENISTA

ECHIUM (Boraginaceae)

§ *candicans* CAbb CB&S CTro SArc WHal
fastuosum See E. ***candicans***
**nebrum* GBri
§ *pininana* CGre CHEx CHan CTre ISea LWad SArc WAbe
pinnifolium See E. ***pininana***
vulgare CArn CKin ECWi EWFC GPoy LHol MChe MHew MSal NMir SIde WHaw WHer WNdy WWye
webbii CGre CTro
wildpretii CBot CHEx CPle SArc WHal

EDGEWORTHIA (Thymelaeaceae)

§ *chrysantha* CB&S CPMA
¶ – 'Rubra' CPMA
papyrifera See E. ***chrysantha***

EDRAIANTHUS (Campanulaceae)

dalmaticus SBla WCru
dinaricus MCas NHol
graminifolius AGM EBur ECtt EPad GDra GTou NHar NHol NKay NWCA SSvw WDav WHil WPer WWin
– *albus* See E. ***g. niveus***
§ – ssp. *niveus* NKay
§ *pumilio* AGM CLew CNic EPad GTou MPit NGre NHar NHed NHol NKay NMen SBla WAbe WCru WDav WOMN
serbicus NBir
serpyllifolius CLew EPot
§ – 'Major' EPot WAbe
tenuifolius GPlt NHol

EGERIA (Hydrocharitaceae)

densa SWyc

EHRETIA (Boraginaceae)

§ *acuminata* CGre
dicksonii CB&S
ovalifolia See E. ***acuminata***
thyrsiflora See E. ***acuminata***

EICHHORNIA (Pontederiaceae)

crassipes CBen CHEx CWGN EMFW EWav LMay MSta NDea WHol

ELAEAGNUS † (Elaeagnaceae)

angustifolia AGM	CB&S CBot CCla CPle EHar LAbb MRav NTow SHBN SPer SSta WCoo WDin WEas WWat
– Caspica Group	See E. 'Quicksilver'
argentea	See E. ***commutata***
§ *commutata*	CBot CBow CCla CDoC CPle CSco EGol EHoe ELan ENot EPar IOrc LHop NNor NRoo NTow SHil SLPl SPer WDin WHCG WRus WStI WWat
x *ebbingei*	Widely available
I – 'Aurea'	LPan
– 'Coastal Gold'	CDoC EBee ENot MGos MUlv WWes
– 'Gilt Edge' AGM	Widely available
– 'Limelight' (v)	Widely available
– 'Salcombe Seedling'	EGol LHop MBri MUlv
– 'Southern Seedling'	CHEx
glabra 'Reflexa'	See E. x ***reflexa***
macrophylla	CChu CCla CLan CSam ENot NNor SDry SHil
multiflora	CChu MBlu SPer
– 'Gigantea'	ELan
parvifolia AGM	CChu CCla EBee ENot EPla WWes
pungens	CPle ERom NBir
– 'Argenteovariegata'	See E. ***p.*** 'Variegata'
– 'Aureovariegata'	See E. ***p.*** 'Maculata'
– 'Dicksonii' (v)	CDoC CLan CSco EHar IDai LNet SLon SPer SPla WHCG
– 'Frederici' (v)	CB&S CDoC CLan CMHG EBre EHar EHoe ELan EPla ERav LBre MBal MBri MPla MSta SCob SGil SHBN SHer SPer WHCG WPat WWat
– 'Goldrim' (v)	CKni COtt CSam EPla IJoh MBri MGos SCob SHBN SHil WDin
§ – 'Maculata' AGM	Widely available
§ – 'Variegata'	CB&S CCla CDoC CLan CSco EFol EGol EPla IOrc MBal MBri NBir SCob SHBN SPer WAbe WHCG
§ 'Quicksilver' AGM	CChu CCla CHad CPMA ECha EGol EHar ELan LGre SBla SMad SPla SSta SUsu WEas WHCG WSHC WWat
§ x *reflexa*	CChu CPle WWat
umbellata	CPle MBlu SMrm SPer WCoo WHCG WWat

ELAEOCARPUS (Elaeocarpaceae)

See Plant Deletions

ELATOSTEMA (Urticaceae)

daveauana	See E. ***repens***
pulchra	MBri

ELDERBERRY See SAMBUCUS *nigra*

ELEGIA (Restionaceae)

¶ *capensis*	CTro

ELEOCHARIS (Cyperaceae)

acicularis	CBen ELan EMFW NDea SWyc WChe
palustris	EMFW MSta SWyc

ELETTARIA (Zingiberaceae)

cardamomum	LBlm MBri

ELEUTHEROCOCCUS (Araliaceae)

pictus	See KALOPANAX ***septemlobus***
senticosus	GPoy
septemlobus	See KALOPANAX ***s.***
¶ *sieboldianus* 'Aureomarginatus'	CB&S
§ – 'Variegatus'	CBot CCla CHan EFol ELan IOrc LHop MBlu MGos NPal WSHC

ELINGAMITA (Myrsinaceae)

johnsonii	CHEx

ELISENA (Liliaceae/Amaryllidaceae)

longipetala	See HYMENOCALLIS ***l.***

ELLIOTTIA (Ericaceae)

bracteata	See TRIPETALEIA ***b.***

ELLISIOPHYLUM (Scrophulariaceae)

¶ *pinnatum* B&SWJ 197	WCru

ELMERA (Saxifragaceae)

racemosa	MFir NHol WPer

ELODEA (Hydrocharitaceae)

canadensis	EHon EMFW SAWi SWat SWyc WChe WHol
crispa	See LAGAROSIPHON ***major***
densa	See EGERIA ***d.***

ELSHOLTZIA (Labiatae/Lamiaceae)

fruticosa	CArn WWye
stauntonii	CArn CB&S CBot CBow CChu CCla CDoC ECha ENot LHop LWad SFis SHil WSHC WWye
– 'Alba'	CBot WSHC

ELYMUS (Gramineae/Poaceae)

arenarius	See LEYMUS ***a.***
canadensis	EHoe EPla ETPC
giganteus	See LEYMUS ***racemosus***
glaucus hort.	See E. ***hispidus***
§ *hispidus*	CHan ECoo EHoe EPla ETPC LHil LHop MBri MUlv SBla SPer SUsu WPla
N *magellanicus*	CElw CGle CHad CRDP CRow CSam CTom ECoo EFol EHoe ELan EOrc ERav GAbr GCHN GCal IBar MNFA NCat NFai NMir NSti SAxl WEas WPer WSun
¶ *nutans*	ETPC
§ *scabrus*	EMon ETPC

ELYTROPUS (Apocynaceae)

chilensis	CGre

EMBOTHRIUM † (Proteaceae)

coccineum	CB&S CBow CGre CHEx CSco ELan EMil IDai IOrc MBal SDry SHil SReu WNor WPat
– Longifolium Group	CB&S CDoC CTrw CWSG IBlr IJoh IOrc ISea SPer
coccineum Lanceolatum Group	CBra CCla CGre CSam ELan EMil IJoh MBal MUlv NHol NPal SArc SHBN SPer SSta WAbe WStI
– – 'Inca Flame'	CPMA CSco NPal WWat
– – 'Norquinco Form' **AGM**	CAbb CB&S CCla CDoC ELan IOrc MBal MBri SPer WAbe WBod WPat WWat

EMILIA (Compositae/Asteraceae)

javanica hort.	See E. ***coccinea***

EMINIUM (Araceae)

albertii	LAma
lehmannii	EPot
rauwolffii	LAma

EMMENOPTERYS (Rubiaceae)

henryi	CBrd EHar

EMPETRUM (Empetraceae)

luteum	MBar
nigrum	GAri GPoy MBal MBar MGos WDav
– var. ***japonicum***	GDra
– 'Lucia'	MGos NHol
rubrum	GArf WDav
– 'Tomentosum'	WThu

ENCEPHALARTOS (Zamiaceae)

lebomboensis	LPal
natalensis	LPal

ENDYMION See **HYACINTHOIDES**

ENGELMANNIA (Compositae/Asteraceae)
See Plant Deletions

ENKIANTHUS † (Ericaceae)

campanulatus **AGM**	Widely available
– f. ***albiflorus***	CB&S CCla CWSG ELan GGGa MBal MBri SPer WWeb
– var. ***palibinii***	CGre GAri GGGa MAll MBal MGos NHol WWat
– 'Red Bells'	CCla MBri SSta
– ***sikokianus***	GAri GGGa
cernuus var. ***matsudae***	GAri
– f. ***rubens*** **AGM**	CB&S CBow CCla CDoC CGre CPMA GAri GGGa MAsh MBal MBri NTow SHil SSta WDin WSHC WWat
chinensis	CB&S CBow CCla CGre CPMA EBre ELan GAri GCHN GGGa LBre MAsh MBar NHol SPer SReu WWat
perulatus **AGM**	CB&S CBra CWSG EMil GAri GAul MBar

ENSETE (Musaceae)

§ ***ventricosum***	CBot CHEx CTro LPal SArc

ENTELEA (Tiliaceae)

arborescens	CHEx CTro ECou

EOMECON (Papaveraceae)

chionantha	CBot CElw CHEx CHan CRDP CSam EBre ECha ELan EMar EMon EPar EPot GCal IBlr LBre MTho MUlv NGre NSti SApp SAxl SFar WAbe WCot WCru WHal WHer WWye

EPACRIS (Epacridaceae)
See Plant Deletions

EPHEDRA (Ephedraceae)

¶ ***americana*** var. ***andina***	SArc
distachya	GPoy NFai NNor
fragilis	EPla SDry
gerardiana	CNic EPla NHex
– var. ***sikkimensis***	EPla SDry WBod
§ ***major***	SDry WHer
minima	WDav WThu
nebrodensis	See E. ***major***
nevadensis	CArn GPoy MSal
viridis	CArn MSal

EPIDENDRUM (Orchidaceae)

criniferum	SLMG
ibaguense	CTro
radicans	See E. ***ibaguense***

EPIGAEA (Ericaceae)

asiatica	CNic MBal
gaultherioïdes	GGGa MBal
repens	MBal MSal

EPILOBIUM (Onagraceae)

§ ***angustifolium***	CGle CKin CRDP ECWi GBar NNrd
§ – ***album***	CBot CBre CElw CHan CLew CMHG CMea ECha EPot GCal LBlm MBri MTol NCat SAxl WCla WEas WHal WPer WRus WSHC WWat
¶ – 'Isobel'	WCot
– ***leucanthum***	See E. ***a. album***
– 'Stahl Rose'	EMon WCot
arizonicum K 92.460	WDav
* ***brunifolium***	CTom
♦ ***californicum*** Haussknecht	See ZAUSCHNERIA ***californica angustifolia***
♦ ***californicum*** hort.	See ZAUSCHNERIA ***californica***
♦ ***canum***	See ZAUSCHNERIA ***californica cana***
caucasicum	WDav WPat
§ ***chlorifolium***	CLew CTom ELan SUsu WOMN
– var. ***kaikourense***	See E. ***c.***
crassum	CLew EBar GPlt GTou NGre NMen NTow WCla WWin

§ ***dodonaei***	CGle CLew CNic EOrc LGan MTho NCat WCot WHaw WSHC WWin
fleischeri	CRDP MTho SSvw SUsu SWas WCru WPat WSHC
♦***garrettii***	See ZAUSCHNERIA ***californica g.***
N***glabellum***	CGle CLew CMea CSpe ECha ELan EMar EMon EOrc GMac LBlm LGre LHop MBel NBir NMen NRar SPer WAbe WDav WEas WHil WOMN WPat WPer WRus WWat WWin
– 'Sulphureum'	CNic CRDP EMar GCra GTou NCat SUsu
hirsutum	CKin ECWi WCla
¶– ***album***	NSti
¶– 'Will Creek'	ECha
luteum	WCla
microphyllum	See ZAUSCHNERIA ***californica cana***
montanum	CKin CNat
obcordatum	CLTr ELan EWoo GAul LHop NNrd NWCA
rosmarinifolium	See E. ***dodonaei***
rostratum	NGre
*****spathulifolium***	LHop
villosum	See ZAUSCHNERIA ***californica mexicana***
wilsonii misapplied	See E. ***chlorifolium***

EPIMEDIUM † (Berberidaceae)

¶***acuminatum***	GLil LGre WAbe
– L 575	CBos CChu CRDP SBla SWas
alpinum	CCla CMGP EPar MBal NGre NHol NJap SAxl SPer WCru WPbr WRus
¶ Asiatic hybrids	SWas
¶ 'Beni-chidori'	GLil
¶ 'Beni-kujaku'	GLil
x ***cantabrigiense***	CBro CCla CRDP CTom EBre ECtt ELun EOrc EPla GCHN GDra LBre MBal MBri NHol SPer WAbb WCru WPbr
davidii	CChu CRDP SWas WAbe WPbr
– EMR 4125	SBla
diphyllum	CChu CRDP LGre MCas SBla SWas WHal WPbr
¶– dwarf white	GLil
dolichostemon	SWas
elongatum	WAbe
'Enchantress'	GBuc SWas
§ ***grandiflorum*** AGM	CHan CTom ECha ELan EPar GDra MBal MBri NBir NMen SBla SPer SWas WCru WPbr WRus WThu
– 'Album'	EPot
¶– ***coelestre***	GLil
¶– ***cremeum***	GLil
– 'Crimson Beauty'	CChu LGre SBla SWas WHal
– ssp. ***koreanum***	CRDP ECha LGre SBla WAbe
– lilac seedling	CRDP LGre SAxl SBla SWas
– 'Lilafee'	ECha EMil LGre SWas WPbr
– 'Nanum' AGM	CBos CChu CRDP LGre NTow SBla SWas WAbe WCru
– 'Rose Queen' AGM	CBro EPla GGar LGre NRoo SBla SChu SHer SPla SWas WSHC
§ – 'Roseum'	CBow EBre LBre NKay NTow
– f. ***violaceum***	LGre WAbe
– 'White Queen' AGM	CBos ECha GLil LGre NOak SAxl SBla SWas WAbe WPbr
leptorrhizum	SBla SWas
¶– Y 44	SWas
macranthum	See E. ***grandiflorum***
x ***perralchicum*** AGM	CRDP MBal MBel SChu SCro SIng SPer WFox WSHC
– 'Frohnleiten'	CBro CCla CSco CTom EBre ECha ECtt ELun EOrc EPla EPot ERav GCHN LBre MBri MRav MSte MTol MUlv NBar NBrk NRoo SBla SMad SPer WAbb WAbe WCra WPbr
– 'Wisley'	MUlv SBla
perralderianum	CChu CCla CSam CWGN EBre EFou ELan ELun EPar EPot LBre LGro MBal MFir MRav SAxl SBla SHig WAbe WCru WHen WHil WPbr WWin
pinnatum	CChu CLew CMea MSta WHal
§ – ssp. ***colchicum*** AGM	CCla CRDP CSco EBee ELan ELun EPar EPot ERav MBal MBro NHol NKay NRoo NRya SDix SHig SPer WCru WHoo WPbr WRus
– ***elegans***	See E. ***p. colchicum***
pubigerum	ECha EGle EPla MBal
x ***rubrum*** AGM	Widely available
¶ ***sagittatum***	GLil
¶ 'Sasaki'	GLil
setosum	CChu ECha SBla SWas WAbe
¶ 'Sunset'	GLil
¶ 'Tamabotan'	GLil
x ***versicolor***	MBal WFox
– 'Cupreum'	SBla
– 'Neosulphureum'	CBro MTol
– 'Sulphureum' AGM	Widely available
– 'Versicolor'	LGre
x ***warleyense***	CBro CChu CCla CElw CRDP CSco ECha EFou ELan EPla EPot GCHN LGan LGre MArl MBal SAxl SBla SFis SWas WAbe WHal WPbr WRus WWin
– 'Orangekönigin'	SWas
x ***youngianum***	CB&S EGle EPot SBla
– 'Lilacinum'	See E. x ***y.*** 'Roseum'
– 'Merlin'	CChu EMon GLil SBla WAbe
– 'Niveum' AGM	Widely available
§ – 'Roseum'	CBow CCla CRDP CSco CTom EFou ELun EMil EPar LGan MBal MBri MTol MUlv NPri NSti NTow SBla SHer SPer SSte WHil WPbr
¶– 'Typicum'	WAbe

EPIPACTIS (Orchidaceae)

gigantea	CAvo CChu CFee ECha ELan EPar EPot MBal MTho NGar NHol SBla SIgm SWas SWes WChr
palustris	CAvo NGar NHar SWes WChe

EPIPREMNUM (Araceae)

§ ***aureum***	EBak MBri
§ ***pinnatum***	MBri

EPISCIA (Gesneriaceae)

§ ***dianthiflora***	CNew MBri WDib
* 'Iris August'	MBri
****primeria***	MBri
* 'San Miguel'	MBri WDib

EQUISETUM (Equisetaceae)

arvense MSal
hyemale CHEx CNat EBre LBre
§ – var. *affine* EBee ELan EPla
♦– var. *robustum* See E. *h. affinis*
ramosissimum CNat
scirpoïdes EBre EMFW LBre MCas
sylvaticum CNat

ERAGROSTIS (Gramineae/Poaceae)

chloromelas ETPC
curvula EHoe EMon ETPC
¶ *trichodes* ETPC WPer

ERANTHIS (Ranunculaceae)

§ *hyemalis* AGM CAvo CBro ELan EMon EPar ETub EWFC LAma LBow MBri MHew MHlr NGar NRog SIng WChr WCot WShi
§ – Cilicica Group CBro EPar EPot LAma LBow NMen NRog SIng WHil
– 'Flore Pleno' EPot
hyemalis Tubergenii Group 'Guinea Gold' AGM WChr

ERCILLA (Phytolaccaceae)

volubilis CChu CFee CGre CPle CSam ERav LHop WCru WSHC

EREMAEA (Myrtaceae)

See Plant Deletions

EREMURUS (Liliaceae/Asphodelaceae)

§ *aitchisonii* LAma
bungei See E. *stenophyllus stenophyllus*
elwesii See E. *aitchisonii*
himalaicus CBow EPar LAma LBow SMrm WCra
x *isabellinus* 'Cleopatra' LAma LBow SGil
– 'Pinokkio' ETub LAma
– Ruiter hybrids ECot EFou ELan EOrc EPar ETub LAma NFai NWyt SHer SPer
– Shelford hybrids CB&S ELan LAma LBow NOak SDeJ SPla
'Moneymaker' LAma
robustus CB&S CBot CBow CCMG CHEx EPar ETub LAma LBow NRog SGil SIgm SMad SPer WCra
stenophyllus ssp. *aurantiacus* SFis
§ – ssp. *stenophyllus* CMGP ELan EOrc EPar ETub LAma LBow NEgg NFai NNor NNrw NOak NRog NWyt SMrm SPer SPla

ERIANTHUS See SACCHARUM

ERICA † (Ericaceae)

arborea CAbb CBow CDoC CNCN MBal SArc SHBN
§ – 'Albert's Gold' AGM CB&S CNCN EBre EDen ELan ENHC GBla IDai IOrc LBre MBal MBar MBri MOke NHol SBod SPer SPla WGre WRid
– var. *alpina* AGM CMac CNCN EDen ENHC ENot GAbr GAng GBla GPen GPlt IDai IOrc MBal MBar MGos NHar NHol NWin SBod SLon SPer SReu SSta WBod WGre WRid WWat
*– 'Arbora Gold' See E. *a.* 'Albert's Gold'
– 'Arnold's Gold' See E. *a.* 'Albert's Gold'
– 'Estrella Gold' AGM CDoC CNCN EBre EDen ELan ENHC GAbr GPen LBre MBal MBar NBar NHar NHol NWin SBod SPer SPla SSta WGre WRid WStI
– 'Spring Smile' EDen
australis AGM CB&S ELan GAng GBla MBar SHBN SPer WRid
– *aragonensis* SRms
– 'Castellar Blush' CNCN
– 'Holehird' EDen
– 'Mr Robert' AGM CNCN EDen MBar SBod WGre
– 'Riverslea' AGM CNCN EDen ENHC GAng GAri GBla GPen IOrc MBal MBar MBri MOke NHol SBod WBod WGre
canaliculata CB&S CGre EDen MBal MUlv SReu SSta
carnea 'Accent' EDen
– 'Adrienne Duncan' AGM COCH EDen ENHC GAng GBla GPen MBar MBri MOke NHol NWin SBod SPla WGre
– 'Alan Coates' CMac CNCN COCH EDen ENHC MBal MBar WGre
– 'Alba' COCH EDen
– 'Altadena' CNCN COCH EDen MBar
– 'Amy Doncaster' See E. *c.* 'Treasure Trove'
– 'Ann Sparkes' AGM CMac CNCN COCH EBre EDen ENHC GAng GBla GPen LBre MBal MBar MBri MGos MOke MPla MWat NHol NWin SBod SPla WBod WGre WRid WThu
– 'Atrorubra' CMac COCH EDen ENHC MBal MBar
– 'Aurea' CB&S CMac CNCN COCH EDen ENHC ENot GAng GBla GPen LGro MBal MBar MBri MOke MPla NBar NHol SBod SLon WBod WGre WRid
– 'Barry Sellers' COCH EDen
¶ – 'Bell's Extra Special' NGar
– 'Beoley Pink' CNCN COCH EDen SBod
– 'C J Backhouse' COCH EDen ENHC GPen
– 'Carnea' COCH EDen ENHC MBar MBri MOke NBar NHol NWin WGre
– 'Cecilia M Beale' CNCN COCH EDen ENHC GBla MBar NHol NWin
– 'Challenger' AGM CNCN COCH EBre EDen LBre MBri MGos NBar NRoo SBod
– 'Christine Fletcher' COCH EDen WGre
– 'Clare Wilkinson' CNCN COCH EDen
– 'David's Seedling' COCH EDen
– 'December Red' CB&S CMac CNCN COCH EBre EDen ENHC ENot ESis GAng GBla GPen IJoh LBre MBar MBri MOke MPla MWat NBar NHol SBod SPla WBod WGre WRid
– 'Dommesmoen' EDen
– 'Early Red' COCH EDen
– 'Eileen Porter' CMac EDen ENHC GBla GDra IDai MBar MBri NWin WRid
– 'Foxhollow' AGM Widely available

– 'Foxhollow Fairy'	CB&S CNCN COCH EDen ENHC EPot GAng GPen MBar NWin WGre
– 'Gelber's Findling'	COCH EDen
– 'Golden Starlet' AGM	CNCN COCH EBre EDen LBre SPla WGre
– 'Gracilis'	EDen ENHC GPen MBar NWin WGre WRid
– 'Heathwood'	CB&S CNCN COCH EDen ENHC ENot GAng MBar MBri NHol SBod
– 'Hilletje'	COCH EDen
¶ – 'Ice Princess'	COCH EDen
– 'Isabell'	COCH EDen NRoo
– 'Jack Stitt'	COCH EDen MBar WGre
– 'James Backhouse'	CMac EDen MBri
– 'January Sun'	COCH EDen
– 'Jennifer Anne'	CNCN COCH EDen ENHC MBar
– 'John Kampa'	CNCN COCH EBre EDen ENHC LBre MBar MBri NHol WGre
– 'John Pook'	MGos
– 'King George'	CMac CNCN COCH EBre EDen GAng GBla GPen GRei GSpe IDai IJoh LBre MBar MGos MWat NBar NHar NHol NRoo NWin SBod SHBN SLon SPla WBod WGre WRid
¶ – 'Kramer's Rubin'	EDen
– 'Lake Garda'	COCH EDen SPla
– 'Late Pink'	COCH
– 'Lesley Sparkes'	COCH EDen ENHC GPen MBal MBar NWin WGre WRid
– 'Lohse's Rubin'	COCH EDen WGre
– 'Loughrigg' AGM	CMac CNCN COCH EDen ENHC ESis GAng GBla GDra GRei GSpe IJoh MBal MBar MBri MGos MOke NHol NRoo NWin SBod SPla WGre WStI
– 'March Seedling'	CB&S CNCN COCH EBre EDen ENHC ENot GAng GBla GDra GSpe LBre MBar MBri MGos MOke MPla NHol NRoo NWin SBod SPla WGre WRid WStI
– 'Margery Frearson'	EDen
¶ – 'Martin'	EDen
– 'Mrs Sam Doncaster'	CNCN COCH EDen MBar SBod
– 'Myretoun Ruby' AGM	Widely available
– 'Orient'	COCH EDen
– 'Pallida'	COCH EDen GPen
– 'Pink Beauty '	See E. *c.* 'Pink Pearl'
– 'Pink Cloud'	COCH EDen
§ – 'Pink Pearl'	COCH GPen MBar WGre
– 'Pink Spangles' AGM	CB&S CMac CNCN COCH EBre EDen ENHC ENot GAng GBla GDra GPen IJoh LBre MBal MBar MBri MGos MOke MPla NBar NHol NRoo NWin SBod WGre WRid
– 'Pirbright Rose'	COCH EDen ENHC MBri MPla SBod
– 'Polden Pride'	COCH EDen
– 'Porter's Red'	COCH EDen MBar WRid
– 'Praecox Rubra' AGM	CB&S COCH EDen ENHC GAng GBla GDra GPen IJoh LGro MBar MBri MGos MOke MPla NBar NHol NWin WRid
– 'Prince of Wales'	CNCN COCH EDen ENHC WRid
– 'Queen Mary'	CNCN EDen ENHC MPla SBod WRid
– 'Queen of Spain'	COCH EDen ENHC GPen MBri MOke
– 'R B Cooke' AGM	CNCN COCH EDen ENHC MBar MBri NWin SBod WGre WRid
– 'Red Jewel'	NRoo
– 'Red Rover'	COCH EDen
¶ – 'Robert Jan'	EDen
¶ – 'Rosalie'	COCH EDen
– 'Rosalinde Schorn'	COCH EDen
¶ – 'Rosantha'	NGar
– 'Rosea'	EDen
– 'Rosy Gem'	EDen MBar WRid
– 'Rosy Morn'	COCH EDen
¶ – 'Rotes Jewel'	COCH EDen
– 'Rubinteppich'	CNCN COCH EDen MBri SBod
¶ – 'Rubra'	EDen
– 'Ruby Glow'	CB&S CNCN COCH EDen ENHC ENot GAng GBla GPen GSpe IJoh LGro MBal MBar MBri MOke NHol
¶ – 'Schatzalp'	EDen
– 'Schneekuppe'	EDen
– 'Schneesturm'	COCH
§ – 'Sherwood Creeping'	EDen ENHC MBar
– 'Sherwoodii'	See E. *c.* 'Sherwood Creeping'
– 'Smart's Heath'	CNCN COCH EDen ENHC GPen
– 'Snow Queen'	CMac CNCN COCH EDen ENHC GPen MBar NBar NWin SBod SPla WGre
– 'Spring Cottage Crimson'	COCH EDen MBar
– 'Spring Day'	EDen WRid
– 'Springwood Pink'	CMHG CMac CNCN COCH EDen ENHC ENot GAng GBla GDra GPen GRei GSpe IDai LGro MBal MBar MBri MGos MOke MPla MWat NHol SBod SHBN WBod WGre WRid
– 'Springwood White' AGM	Widely available
– 'Startler'	COCH EDen ENHC MBar SBod SPla
– 'Sunshine Rambler' AGM	CNCN COCH EDen EPot GPen MBar MGos MPla NWin WGre
– 'Thomas Kingscote'	CNCN COCH EDen ENHC MBar WGre
– 'Treasure Trove'	COCH EDen
– 'Tybesta Gold'	CNCN COCH EDen
– 'Viking'	COCH EDen IJoh
– 'Vivellii' AGM	Widely available
– 'Vivellii Aurea'	COCH EDen WGre
– 'Walter Reisert'	CNCN COCH EDen
– 'Wanda'	COCH EDen MBar
– 'Wentwood Red'	COCH EDen
– 'Westwood Yellow' AGM	CNCN COCH EBre EDen ENHC GAng GBla LBre MBar MBri NHar NHol SBod SPla WGre WRid
¶ – 'White Glow'	WRid
¶ – 'White March Seedling'	NGar
– 'Winter Beauty'	CNCN COCH EDen GRei IDai IJoh MBri MOke MPla NBar NWin WGre
– 'Winter Gold'	COCH EDen
¶ – 'Winter Melody'	EDen
¶ – 'Winter Snow'	EDen
¶ – 'Wintersonne'	COCH EDen
ciliaris alba	EDen

– 'Aurea'	CMac CNCN EDen ENHC GPen MBar NWin WGre
– 'Camla'	EDen ENHC GPen MBar
– 'Corfe Castle' **AGM**	CMac CNCN EDen ENHC GPen MBar NWin SBod WGre WRid
– 'David McClintock' **AGM**	CMac CNCN EDen ENHC GPen MBar MGos NWin WGre
– 'Egdon Heath'	EDen
– 'Globosa'	CNCN EDen ENHC WGre
– 'Maweana'	EDen
– 'Mrs C H Gill' **AGM**	CMac CNCN EDen ENHC GPen MBal WGre
– 'Ram'	EDen
¶ – 'Rotundiflora'	EDen
– 'Stapehill'	EDen
– 'Stoborough' **AGM**	CMHG CNCN EDen ENHC MBal MBar
– 'White Wings'	CNCN EDen ENHC GPen
– 'Wych'	EDen GPen WRid
cinerea f. ***alba***	CMac GRei
– 'Alba Major'	EDen MBal MBar WGre
– 'Alba Minor' **AGM**	CNCN EBre EDen GAng GAul GPen GSpe LBre MBal MBar MBri MOke NHar NHol NRoo SBod WGre WRid
– 'Alette'	EDen
¶ – 'Alfred Bowerman'	EDen
– 'Angarrack'	EDen
– 'Anja Blum'	EDen
– 'Ann Berry'	CNCN EDen ENHC MBar SBod WGre
– 'Apple Blossom'	EDen WGre
– 'Apricot Charm'	EDen GAng GPen MBar SBod WGre
– 'Aquarel'	EDen
– 'Ashgarth Garnet'	EDen MBar WGre
– 'Atrococcinea'	CB&S
– 'Atropurpurea'	CNCN EDen MBar
– 'Atrorubens'	CMac EDen ENHC GPen GRei GSpe MBar NHar
– 'Atrorubens, Daisy Hill'	EDen
– 'Atrosanguinea'	CNCN ENHC GAng GBla GSpe MBar MGos NWin SBod WGre WRid
– 'Atrosanguinea Reuthe's Variety'	EDen
– 'Atrosanguinea Smith's Variety'	EDen GAri
– 'Baylay's Variety'	EDen MBar
– 'Blossom Time'	EDen MBar
¶ – 'Brick'	EDen
– 'Bucklebury Red'	EDen
– 'C D Eason' **AGM**	CMac CNCN EBre EDen ENHC ENot GAng GBla GDra GPen GRei GSpe IJoh LBre MBal MBar MBri MGos MOke NHol NWin SBod WBod WGre WRid
§ – 'C G Best' **AGM**	CMac CNCN EDen ENHC GBla GPen IDai MBal MBar SBod WGre
– 'Cairn Valley'	EDen GSpe
– 'Caldy Island'	EDen MBar NWin
– 'Carnea'	EDen
– 'Carnea Underwood's Variety'	EDen
– 'Cevennes' **AGM**	CMac CNCN EDen ENHC GAng GSpe IDai MBar MBri MGos MOke SBod WGre
¶ – 'Champs Hill'	EDen
– 'Cindy' **AGM**	CNCN EDen ENHC GSpe MBal MBar MBri MOke
– 'Coccinea'	EDen ENHC GRei IDai WGre
– 'Colligan Bridge'	EDen GPen MBar
– 'Constance'	EDen ENHC MBar
– 'Contrast'	EDen GSpe MBar WGre
– 'Daphne Maginess'	CNCN
– 'Discovery'	EDen
¶ – 'Doctor Small's Seedling'	EDen
– 'Domino'	CB&S CNCN EDen ENHC GBla GPen MBar MBri MGos MOke WBod
– 'Duncan Fraser'	CNCN EDen ENHC GSpe MBar
– 'Dunwood Sport'	EDen MBar
– 'Eden Valley' **AGM**	CMac CNCN EDen ENHC GAng GBla GPen GSpe MBar MGos SBod WGre WRid
– 'England'	EDen ENHC
¶ – 'Felthorpe'	EDen
– 'Fiddler's Gold' **AGM**	CNCN EDen ENHC GAng GAri GBla GPen MBar MBri MOke NHar NHol NWin
– 'Flamingo'	EDen
– 'Foxhollow Mahogany'	EDen ENHC GPen GSpe MBal MBar NWin WGre WRid
– 'Frances'	EDen ENHC GBla
¶ – 'Fred Corston'	EDen
– 'G Osmond'	EDen ENHC GPen MBar MOke
– 'Glasnevin Red'	EDen MBar NHar WGre
– 'Glencairn'	EDen GAng GPen MBar MBri NHol NWin
– 'Godrevy'	EDen SBod
– 'Golden Charm'	EDen NHol
– 'Golden Drop'	CMac CNCN EDen ENHC GAng GPen GSpe IJoh MBal MBar MBri MGos MOke NHol NWin SBod WGre WRid
– 'Golden Hue' **AGM**	CB&S CNCN EDen ENHC GAng GPen GSpe IJoh MBar MBri MOke WBod WGre WRid
– 'Golden Sport'	EDen MBri MGos NHar
¶ – 'Golden Tee'	EDen
– 'Graham Thomas'	See E. *c.* 'C G Best'
– 'Grandiflora'	EDen MBar
– 'Guernsey Lime'	EDen ENHC MBar SBod
– 'Guernsey Pink'	EDen
– 'Guernsey Plum'	EDen
– 'Guernsey Purple'	EDen SBod
– 'Hardwick's Rose'	CNCN EDen MBar
– 'Harry Fulcher'	CNCN EDen ENHC MBri MOke
– 'Heatherbank'	EDen
– 'Heathfield'	EDen
– 'Heidebrand'	EDen GPen MBar
– 'Hermann Dijkhuizen'	EDen
– 'Honeymoon'	EDen ENHC GSpe MBar
– 'Hookstone Lavender'	EDen ENHC GPen GSpe
– 'Hookstone White' **AGM**	CNCN EBre EDen ENHC GBla GDra GPen IJoh LBre MBal MBar SBod WGre WRid
– 'Hutton's Seedling'	EDen
– 'Iberian Beauty'	EDen
– 'Jack London'	CNCN EDen
– 'Janet'	EDen ENHC MBar MGos NWin WGre
¶ – 'Jim Hardy'	EDen
– 'John Ardron'	EDen SBod WGre
– 'John Eason'	EDen ENHC NHol

– 'Joseph Murphy'	EDen GAng GBla GSpe MBar WGre
– 'Josephine Ross'	EDen GSpe MBar NWin WGre
– 'Joyce Burfitt'	CNCN EDen ENHC
– 'Katinka'	CNCN EBre EDen ENHC GRei LBre MBar NHol WGre
– 'Kerry Cherry'	EDen
– 'Knap Hill Pink' AGM	CNCN EDen ENHC GAng GBla MBar
– 'Lady Skelton'	EDen MBar
– 'Lavender Lady'	EDen NWin
– 'Lilac Time'	EDen ENHC GAng GSpe MBar
– 'Lilacina'	EDen ENHC GSpe MBar MBri MOke
– 'Lime Soda'	CNCN EDen ENHC MBri
– 'Lorna Anne Hutton'	EDen
¶ – 'Maginess Pink'	CNCN
– 'Marina'	EDen
¶ – 'Mellie Dawson'	EDen
– 'Michael Hugo'	CNCN EDen
– 'Miss Waters'	EDen MBar NWin
– 'Mrs Dill'	EDen ENHC MBar
– 'Mrs E A Mitchell'	EDen MBri MGos MOke
– 'Mrs Ford'	EDen ENHC GAng GPen MBar
– 'My Love'	EDen ENHC IJoh MBar MBri MOke WBod
– 'Nell'	EDen GPen MBar
– 'Newick Lilac'	EDen MBar MBri MOke
– 'Novar'	EDen
– 'Old Rose'	EDen
– 'P S Patrick' AGM	CNCN EDen ENHC GAng GBla GPen GSpe MBal MBar MGos SBod WRid
– 'Pallas'	EDen GSpe IJoh
– 'Pallida'	EDen
¶ – 'Patricia Maginess'	CNCN
– 'Pentreath' AGM	EDen ENHC GPen MBar MBri MOke NWin WBod
– 'Peñaz'	EDen
– 'Pink Foam'	EDen GBla GPen MBar
– 'Pink Ice' AGM	CB&S CMac CNCN EBre EDen ENHC GAng GBla GDra GPen GRei GSpe IJoh LBre MBar MBri MGos MOke NHar NHol NRoo NWin SBod WBod WGre WRid
– 'Plummer's Seedling'	EDen GAng GBla GSpe MBar WRid
– 'Prostrate Lavender'	EDen ENHC GPen MBal
– 'Providence'	EDen
– 'Purple Beauty'	CB&S CNCN EDen ENHC GBla GSpe IJoh MBar MBri MGos MOke NHol NWin WGre
– 'Purple Robe'	CMac EDen ENHC
¶ – 'Purple Spreader'	EDen
– 'Purpurea'	EDen GPen
– 'Pygmaea'	EDen GBla MBar
– 'Red Pentreath'	EDen
– 'Rijneveld'	EDen
– 'Robert Michael'	EDen
– 'Rock Pool'	EDen GSpe MBal MBar NWin WGre
– 'Rock Ruth'	EDen
– 'Romiley'	EDen ENHC MBar MBri MOke
– 'Rosabella'	CNCN EDen ENHC MBar
– 'Rose Queen'	CMac EDen GSpe WGre WRid
– 'Rosea'	EDen ENHC GAng GPen GSpe WGre
– 'Rozanne Waterer'	CMac EDen NWin
– 'Ruby'	CMac CNCN EDen ENHC GAng GBla GSpe MBar

– 'Sandpit Hill'	EDen MBar WGre
– 'Schizopetala'	CNCN EDen GPen MBar
– 'Sea Foam'	CNCN EDen ENHC MBar
– 'Sherry'	CMac CNCN EDen ENHC GAng GBla GPen GRei GSpe MBar WGre
– 'Smith's Lawn'	EDen
– 'Snow Cream'	EDen GPen MBar
– 'Son of Cevennes'	MGos
– 'Spicata'	EDen
– 'Splendens'	EDen ENHC
– 'Startler'	CB&S EDen ENHC GSpe MBri MOke
– 'Stephen Davis' AGM	CNCN EBre EDen ENHC GAng GBla GPen GSpe LBre MBal MBar MBri MOke NHol NRoo SBod WBod WGre
– 'Strawberry'	EDen
– 'Sue Lloyd'	EDen WGre
– 'Summer Gold'	EBre EDen LBre
– 'Tilford'	EDen ENHC
– 'Tom Waterer'	EDen MBar
– 'Uschie Ziehmann'	EDen
– 'Velvet Night' AGM	CB&S CMac CNCN EDen ENHC GAng GBla GPen GSpe IDai IJoh MBal MBar MBri MOke NHar NHol NWin SBod WBod WGre WRid
– 'Victoria'	CMac EDen MBar WGre
– 'Violetta'	EDen
– 'Vivienne Patricia'	EDen ENHC GAng GBla GPen GSpe MBar NWin
– 'W G Notley'	EDen ENHC
¶ – 'West End'	EDen
– 'White Dale'	EDen MBar WGre
– 'Windlebrooke' AGM	EDen ENHC GPen MBar SBod WGre
– 'Wine'	EDen
– 'Yvonne'	EDen
cruenta	EDen
curviflora	EDen
x ***darleyensis*** 'Ada S Collings'	CNCN COCH EBre EDen ENHC GAng GBla LBre MBal MBar MPla NWin SBod SHBN
– 'Alba'	See E. x ***d.*** 'Silberschmelze'
– 'Archie Graham'	COCH EDen
§ – 'Arthur Johnson' AGM	CB&S CMac CNCN COCH EBre EDen ENHC ENot GAng GBla GPen GSpe LBre MBal MBar MBri MGos MOke MPla NHol NWin SBod SHBN SPla WGre WRid
– 'Cherry Stevens'	See E. x ***d.*** 'Furzey'
– 'Darley Dale'	CMac CNCN COCH EBre EDen ENHC ENot GBla GPen GSpe LBre MBal MBar MBri MOke MPla NGar NHol NRoo SBod WGre WRid
– 'Dunreggan'	COCH EDen
– 'Dunwood Splendour'	See E. x ***d.*** 'Arthur Johnson'
¶ – 'Epe'	COCH EDen
– 'Erecta'	COCH EDen
§ – 'Furzey' AGM	CB&S CMHG CMac CNCN COCH EDen ENHC ESis GAng GBla GPen GSpe MBal MBar MBri MGos MOke MPla NHar NHol NRoo SBod SHBN SPla WGre WRid

– 'George Rendall'	CB&S CMac CNCN COCH EDen ENHC GAng GDra GPen GSpe MBri MPla NHol SPla WGre WRid
– 'Ghost Hills' AGM	CNCN COCH EBre EDen ENHC ESis GAng GDra IDai LBre MBal MBar MBri MOke MPla NHol NWin SBod SHBN WBod WGre WRid
– 'J W Porter' AGM	CNCN COCH EDen ENHC GAng GBla GPen IJoh MBal MBar MBri MOke NHol NWin STre WGre WRid
§ – 'Jack H Brummage'	CB&S CMHG CMac CNCN COCH EBre EDen ENHC EPot GAng GBla GPen IJoh LBre MBal MBar MBri MGos MOke MPla NHar NHol NWin SBod SHBN SPla WGre WRid
– 'James Smith'	COCH EDen ENHC ESis MBar
– 'Jenny Porter' AGM	CMac CNCN COCH EDen ENHC GAul GPen MBar MBri MOke NHol NWin WGre WRid
– 'Kramer's Rote' AGM	CNCN COCH EBre EDen GPen LBre MBri MGos MOke NRoo SPla WGre
– 'Margaret Porter'	CB&S CMHG CNCN COCH EDen ENHC GAng IJoh MBri MPla NHol SBod WGre WRid
– 'Mary Helen'	CNCN COCH EDen NHol
– 'Norman R Webster'	COCH EDen GAul NWin
♦– 'Pink Perfection'	See E x *d.* 'Darley Dale'
§ – 'Silberschmelze' ('Molten Silver')	CB&S CNCN COCH EBre EDen ENHC ENot GAng GBla GDra GPen GSpe IDai LBre MBal MBar MBri MGos MOke MPla NHol NRoo NWin SBod SHBN WBod WGre WRid
– 'W G Pine'	COCH
– 'White Glow'	CNCN COCH EDen ENHC MBal MBri NHol SPla WGre WRid
– 'White Perfection' AGM	CNCN COCH EBre EDen GPen LBre MBar MBri SPla WGre WRid
densifolia	LBlm
discolor	CGre LBlm
doliiformis	EDen LBlm
§ ***erigena***	ELan ENot SHBN SPer
– 'Alba'	CMac COCH EDen ENHC MBar NWin
– 'Alba Compacta'	EDen GPen
– 'Brian Proudley' AGM	CNCN COCH EDen ENHC MBar SBod WRid
– 'Brightness'	CB&S CMac CNCN COCH EBre EDen ENHC EPot GAng GBla GPen LBre MBal MBar MBri MOke MWat NHar NHol NWin SBod WRid
– 'Coccinea'	COCH EDen ENHC NWin
– 'Ewan Jones'	CNCN COCH EDen ENHC IOrc MBar
– 'Glauca'	COCH EDen ENHC GPen
– 'Golden Lady' AGM	CMac CNCN COCH EBre EDen ENHC ESis GAng GPen LBre MBar MBri MGos MOke NHol SBod SPla WGre WRid
– 'Hibernica'	EDen GPen
– 'Hibernica Alba'	MBar
– 'Irish Dusk' AGM	CMHG CNCN COCH EBre EDen ENHC GAng GBla GPen IDai IJoh LBre MBar MBri MGos MOke NHar NHol NWin SBod SPla WGre WRid
– 'Irish Salmon'	CB&S CMac CNCN COCH EDen GPen IJoh MBal MBar NWin
– 'Irish Silver'	COCH EDen GPen MBar MBri NWin
– 'Ivory'	COCH EDen
– 'Mrs Parris' Lavender'	EDen WRid
– 'Mrs Parris' Red'	WRid
– 'Mrs Parris' White'	EDen WRid
¶ – 'Nana'	EDen
– 'Nana Alba'	CNCN COCH EDen GPen MBar
– 'Rosea'	EDen ENHC MBar NWin
¶ – 'Rosslare'	EDen
– 'Rubra'	EDen
– 'Rubra Compacta'	ENHC
– 'Superba'	CMac CNCN COCH EDen ENHC ENot GPen MBal MBar MGos MOke NHol NWin SBod WGre WRid
– 'W T Rackliff' AGM	CB&S CNCN COCH EBre EDen ENHC ENot EPot GAng GBla GPen LBre MBal MBar MBri MGos MOke NHol NWin SHBN SPla WGre WRid
– 'W T Rackliff Variegated'	ENHC
gracilis	MBri
herbacea	See E. ***carnea***
hibernica	See E. ***erigena***
lusitanica AGM	CB&S CMac CNCN COCH EDen ELan MBar NHol SBod SPer WBod WRid
– 'George Hunt'	CDoC CNCN EBre EDen ELan ENHC LBre MAsh NHol SBod SPer SPla
mackayana ssp. ***andevalensis***	EDen
– 'Ann D Frearson'	CNCN EDen
– 'Doctor Ronald Gray'	CNCN EDen ENHC GAng GPen MBar MBri MOke SBod WGre WRid
– 'Donegal'	EDen
¶ – 'Errigal Dusk'	EDen
– 'Galicia'	CNCN EDen
– 'Lawsoniana'	EDen ENHC
– 'Maura' AGM	EDen ENHC
– 'Plena'	CMHG CNCN EDen ENHC GPen MBal MBar MBri MOke SBod WGre
– 'Shining Light' AGM	EDen SPla
– 'William M'Calla'	ENHC
mammosa	EDen LBlm
manipuliflora	CDoC COCH GPen MBar SPla
– ssp. ***anthura*** 'Corfu'	COCH
– – 'Don Richards'	COCH EDen
– – 'Elegant Spike'	EDen
– – 'Heaven Scent' AGM	CNCN COCH EDen
– – 'Ian Cooper'	COCH EDen
– – 'Korcula'	COCH EDen
¶ – – 'Waterfall'	NGar
manipuliflora ssp. ***manipuliflora*** 'Aldburgh'	CNCN COCH
– x ***vagans*** 'Valerie Griffiths'	COCH EDen WGre
mediterranea	See E. ***erigena***
x ***praegeri***	See E. x ***stuartii***
scoparia azorica	EDen
§ – ssp. ***scoparia*** 'Minima'	EDen ENHC MBar
– – 'Pumila'	See E. ***s. s.*** 'Minima'

speciosa	EDen
§ x *stuartii*	CMHG ENHC GPen MBar SBod
– 'Charles Stuart '	See E. x *s.* 'Stuartii'
– 'Connemara'	EDen
– 'Irish Lemon' AGM	CMHG CNCN EBre EDen ENHC GAng GDra GPen GSpe LBre MBar MBri NHar NHol NWin SBod SPla WBod WGre WRid
– 'Irish Orange'	CNCN EDen ENHC GAng GSpe MBar MBri NBir NHol SBod SPla WGre WRid
– 'Nacung'	EDen
¶ – 'Pat Turpin'	EDen
§ – 'Stuartii'	CNCN EDen
subdivaricata	EDen
§ *terminalis* AGM	CNCN COCH EDen ENHC ENot EPot GAng IOrc MBal MBar NWin SBod SPer
– *stricta*	See E. *terminalis.*
– 'Thelma Woolner'	CMac CNCN COCH EDen ENHC MBar NHol WGre
tetralix	CKin ECWi WCla
– 'Afternoon'	EDen
– 'Alba'	EDen
– 'Alba Mollis' AGM	CMac CNCN EDen ENHC ENot GAng GBla GPen GSpe IJoh MBal MBar MBri MOke NHar NHol NRoo NWin SBod SPla WBod WGre WRid
– 'Alba Praecox'	EDen
– 'Ardy'	EDen ENHC
– 'Bala'	CNCN EDen
– 'Bartinney'	EDen MBar
– 'Con Underwood' AGM	CMac CNCN EBre EDen ENHC ENot GAng GBla GPen GSpe LBre MBal MBar MBri MOke NHol SBod SPla WBod WGre WRid
– 'Daphne Underwood'	EDen NWin WGre
– 'Darleyensis'	EDen
– 'Delta'	EDen ENHC MBar
– 'Foxhome'	EDen ENHC GPen MBar NWin
– 'Hailstones'	EDen ENHC MBar NWin
– 'Helma'	EDen ENHC
– 'Hookstone Pink'	CNCN EDen ENHC GAul GPen MBal MOke NHar NRoo NWin SBod SHBN WGre
– 'Humoresque'	EDen
– 'Ken Underwood'	CNCN EDen ENHC GPen MBar NWin SHBN WGre
– 'L E Underwood'	CMac EDen ENHC EPot GAng GPen MBal MBar NHol NWin WGre WRid
– 'Mary Grace'	EDen
– 'Melbury White'	CNCN EDen ENHC GPen MBar NWin
– 'Morning Glow'	See E. x *watsonii* 'F White'
– 'Pink Glow'	EDen
– 'Pink Star' AGM	CMac CNCN EBre EDen ENHC GAng GBla GSpe LBre MBal MBar NHol NWin SPla WGre WRid
– 'Rosea'	EDen
– 'Rubra'	EDen GPen
§ – 'Ruby's Variety'	EDen GPen MBar NWin
– 'Ruby's Velvet'	See E. *t.* 'Ruby's Variety'
– 'Ruth's Gold'	EDen MBar MBri NHol WGre
– 'Salmon Seedling'	EDen GPen
– 'Silver Bells'	CMac EDen ENHC GPen MBar WGre
– 'Swedish Yellow'	EDen
– 'Terschelling'	EDen
– 'Tina'	CNCN EDen
– 'White House'	EDen
umbellata	CNCN EDen ENHC GAng GPen MBal MBar NWin WAbe WGre WRid
vagans f. *alba*	MBal
– 'Birch Glow' AGM	EDen ENHC NWin SBod WGre
– 'Carnea'	EDen
– 'Cornish Cream' AGM	CNCN EDen ENHC GAri GPen MBar NHol NRoo NWin WBod
– 'Cream'	CNCN EDen ENHC IDai MOke NHar
– 'Diana Hornibrook'	CNCN EDen ENHC GAul GSpe MBal MBar MBri MOke NHar SHBN WGre
– 'Fiddlestone' AGM	CNCN EDen ENHC GPen GSpe MBar NWin SBod WGre
– 'French White'	CNCN EDen MBar SBod
– 'George Underwood'	EDen ENHC GPen MBar WBod WGre
– 'Grandiflora'	CNCN EDen GPen IJoh MBal MBar NWin SPla WGre
– 'Holden Pink'	CNCN EDen MBri MOke NHar SBod WBod
– 'Hookstone Rosea'	EDen MBar
– 'Ida M Britten'	EDen MBar
– 'J C Fletcher'	EDen
– 'Kevernensis Alba' AGM	EDen ENHC GPen IDai MBar NHol SBod
– 'Lilacina'	CMac CNCN EDen GSpe MBar
– 'Lyonesse' AGM	CB&S CMac CNCN EBre EDen ENHC ENot GAng GBla GPen GSpe IJoh LBre MBal MBar MBri MGos MOke NHol NRoo NWin SBod SPla WBod WGre WRid
– 'Miss Waterer'	EDen MBar
– 'Mrs D F Maxwell' AGM	CB&S CMac CNCN EBre EDen ENHC EPot GAng GBla GPen GSpe IDai IJoh LBre MBal MBar MBri MGos MOke NBar NHar NHol NRoo NWin SBod SPla WBod WGre WRid
– 'Mrs Donaldson'	EDen GPen
– 'Nana'	EDen MBal MBar
– 'Pallida'	EDen ENHC NHol
– 'Peach Blossom'	EDen MBar
– 'Pyrenees Pink'	CMac CNCN EDen GBla MBal MBar MBri MOke NHar WGre
– 'Rosea'	EDen
– 'Rubra'	CNCN EDen GBla MBal MBar
– 'Rubra Grandiflora'	ENHC
– 'Saint Keverne'	CB&S CMac CNCN EDen ENHC GAng GBla GPen MBal MBar MBri MGos MOke NHar NHol NRoo SBod WGre WRid
– 'Summertime'	CNCN EDen GPen MBar
– 'Valerie Proudley' AGM	CB&S CMac CNCN EBre EDen ENHC GAng GBla GDra GPen GSpe IJoh LBre MBal MBar MBri MGos MOke MWat NHar NHol NWin SBod SHBN SPla WGre WRid
– 'Viridiflora'	CNCN EDen MBar
– 'White Lady'	EDen ENHC MBar NWin
– 'White Rocket'	EDen MBar
– 'White Spire'	EDen
– 'Yellow John'	CNCN EDen GBla

x *veitchii* GPen MBal
– 'Exeter' CNCN COCH EDen GAri MAsh MBar WGre
– 'Gold Tips' AGM CNCN EDen ENHC GAng MBal MBar MBri MGos MOke NHar WGre WRid
– 'Pink Joy' EDen ENHC GAri MAsh MBal MBri MOke NBar NHar NHol WGre
versicolor LBlm
x *watsonii* 'Cherry Turpin' EDen SPla WGre
– 'Dawn' AGM CMHG CNCN EDen GAng GDra GPen GSpe MBal MBar MBri NHar NWin SBod SHBN WGre WRid
– 'Dorothy Metheny' EDen
§ – 'F White' EDen ENHC GPen MBar
– 'Gwen' CNCN EDen MBar
– 'H Maxwell' CNCN GPen GSpe MBal NWin
– 'Rachel' EDen MBal
– 'Truro' EDen
x *williamsii* 'David Coombe' EDen
– 'Gwavas' CNCN EDen EPot GAng GPen MBar SBod WGre
– 'P D Williams' AGM CNCN EDen MBal MBar NWin WGre WRid

ERIGERON † (Compositae/Asteraceae)

acer CKin EWFC MHew WCla WNdy
'Adria' GBuc SChu SPer
alpinus CNic GCHN GTou LBee LGan MCas NGre SFis
'Amity' CMGP EOrc GCHN SPer
atticus MHig WHaw
aurantiacus CBow CSam EBar LAbb LGan LHop MHlr MPit NBro NOak NSti SHer WCot WHil WPer
§ *aureus* EBur MHig SHer WAbe WDav WOMN
§ – 'Canary Bird' MSta NBir SHer SIng SWas WAbe WDav
'Azurfee' ('Azure Fairy') CBow CSam EFol ELan ESma LWad NFai NOak NRoo SPla SSvw WHen WHil WHoo WMer WPer WWin
'Birch Hybrid' SIng
¶ *bloomeri* MFos
'Blue Beauty' NMir
borealis CSam GCHN GTou WHil
'Charity' CGle CMGP CSco EBee EFou SChu SPer WTyr
chrysopsidis 'Grand Ridge' AGM EBur EPot WAbe
compositus CLew CNic ELan GCHN GTou MCas NGre NWCA WPer WThu
§ – var. *discoïdeus* CLew CNic EBur WPer
– 'Lavender Dwarf' NHol
¶ – 'Rocky' NNrw
'Dignity' CShe ECED EFou EGol ELan GCHN MWat NFai SChu SFis SPer WEas WPbr
'Dimity' CGle ECha EFou EHic GMac NCat SUsu WRus WWin
'Doctor Worth' SHer
'Dunkelste Aller' ('Darkest of All') AGM CGle CMGP CSco CSev ECED EFou ELan ENot GCHN MBri MRav NFai NSti SPer SSvw WEas WOld WRus WTyr WWin
elegantulus WDav
* *epirocticus* NS 462 NWCA
'Felicity' CShe EFou GAbr MMil SRms WOld
'Festivity ' SFis
flettii GCHN MFir SHer WDav WWin
'Foersters Liebling' AGM CSev EFou ENot MBri MHlr MUlv MWat NCat SFis SPla WCot WMer
¶ *formosissimus* EBee
'Four Winds' CLew CMil CShe EFou ELan EPad LHop MNFA NMen SHer SMad WCot WMer WPer
'Gaiety' CSco LHop SPer WTyr
glaucus CMer EPad IDai NCat NRed NVic SIng SMrm
– 'Albus' LHop WHil WPer WTyr
– 'Elstead Pink' CShe NFai SPla WByw WEas
– 'Roseus' CB&S CMer
¶ *howellii* ECha
hyssopifolius WHil
§ *karvinskianus* AGM CB&S CBos CGle CHan CLew CMea CNic ECha EMar IDai LGan LHop MWat NKay NMen NNrw NRar NRed NSti SAxl SDix SIng SPer SPla SUsu WAbe WCla WEas WHil WRus
leiomerus CNic MHig NKay NRed NTow NWCA WCla WOMN
'Mrs F H Beale' SCro
mucronatus See E. ***karvinskianus***
multiradiatus CLew WCot WPer
nanus SHer WPat WPer
peregrinus NHol WEas WPer
philadelphicus CElw CGle CLew ECha NBir NBro NSti SMrm WCot WRus
'Pink Jewel' See E. 'Rosa Juwel'
pinnatisectus CNic LBee NRed NWCA WPer
polymorphus NCat NHol WAbe
'Prosperity' CGle CShe EFou WOld
pumilis intermedius GDra
¶ *pygmaeus* MFos
'Quakeress' CElw CGle CLew CSam EBre ECha EFou EMon EOrc GAbr GCHN LBre MBel MNFA NCat SMrm SUsu SWas WCot
§ 'Rosa Juwel' ('Pink Jewel') CBow CSam EBar EFou EPad ESma GAbr GCHN LHil LHop LWad NBir NBro NMir NNrd NOak NRoo SPla SSvw WHen WHil WPbr WPer WTyr
'Rosa Triumph' ('Pink Triumph') EFou SPla
roseus ECha
'Rotes Meer' EFou ELan EMon MBri NCat
rotundifolius 'Caerulescens' See BELLIS ***rotundifolia*** 'C.'
N *salsuginosus* NOak
'Schneewittchen' ('Snow White') CGle CMGP EBee EFou ELan LHop LRHS MNFA NSti SChu SUsu WTyr
¶ 'Schöne Bläue' NBro

'Schwarzes Meer' ('Black Sea')	EFou EGol EHal LHop MUlv SPer SPla WCot WMer
'Serenity'	NCat SFis
simplex	GDra LBee LHop MCas MFir MWat NGre NHol NTow SHer WDav
'Sincerity'	CSco
'Sommerabend'	MUlv
'Sommerneuschnee'	CDoC NPri
speciosus	MPit MWil NNrd
sp. Bald Mountains	NWCA
'Strahlenmeer'	EOrc LRHS WCot
thunbergii	CLew
trifidus	See E. ***compositus discoïdeus***
¶ ***tweedyi***	NBro
uniflorus	CNic NHol NWCA
'Unity'	MWat
vagus	CLew CSam EBur NWCA
– JCA 8911	CNic MFos NRed
'White Quakeress'	LHil WCot
'Wuppertal'	EBee LRHS MMil NCat SFis

ERINACEA (Leguminosae/Papilionaceae)

§ ***anthyllis*** AGM	EPot SHer
pungens	See E. ***anthyllis***

ERINUS (Scrophulariaceae)

alpinus AGM	Widely available
– var. ***albus***	CBot CNic CRiv GGar GTou LBee LGan MBro MCas NHol NKay NMen NNrd NTow NWCA SIng WCla WDav WHoo WPat
– dark purple	NKay
– 'Dr Hähnle'	CNic EBre LBre MBro MCas MHig MPit NKay NMen NNrd NWCA SHer WHoo
– 'Mrs Charles Boyle' AGM	GDra MBro NKay SHer WHoo WOld

ERIOBOTRYA (Rosaceae)

deflexa	CB&S CDoC CPle EMil MUlv SMad
F ***japonica*** AGM	CAbb CB&S CBar CBot CChu CDoC CGre CHEx CLan CPle CWit EMil EPla ERea ERom ESim LPan SArc SDea SDry SEng SHil SLon SMad SPer SSta WSHC WWat
F – 'Benlehr'	ESim
F – 'Mrs Cookson'	ESim

ERIOCEPHALUS (Compositae/Asteraceae)

See Plant Deletions

ERIOGONUM (Polygonaceae)

brevicaule nanum	NWCA
caespitosum	MHig NTow NWCA SIgm
– ssp. ***douglasii***	NTow
¶ ***croceum***	SIgm
flavum	WPer
¶ ***gracilipes*** JCA 11718	WDav
jamesii	MHig WDav WHil WPat
¶ ***kelloggii***	WDav
¶ ***lobbii*** K 92.214	WDav
ovalifolium	MFos NWCA SIgm WDav
soredium	MFos
umbellatum	ECha EFol EPot MFir NHol NTow NWCA SIgm SIng
¶ – 'Kannah Creek'	WDav
– var. ***porteri***	NWCA
– var. ***subalpinum***	GArf MHig WDav
– var. ***torreyanum***	EPot GArf MBro MHig NHol SIng WAbe WDav WPat
¶ ***ursinum*** var. ***nervulosum***	WDav
¶ ***wrightii***	WOMN
¶ – ssp. ***wrightii*** K 92.224	WDav

ERIOPHORUM (Cyperaceae)

angustifolium	CBen ECWi EHon EMFW EPla ETPC EWav GCHN LMay MSta NDea SWat WChe WHol
latifolium	LMay MSta
vaginatum	See SCIRPUS ***fauriei vaginatus***

ERIOPHYLLUM (Compositae/Asteraceae)

lanatum	CHan CLew CNic CSam EBar ECha ECoo EMil EMon MFir MNFA MWat NCat NGre NSti NTow NVic SBla SChu SFis WAbe WHil WPla WWin WWye

ERITRICHIUM (Boraginaceae)

§ ***canum***	GTou MBro WCru WDav
rupestre	See E. ***canum***
¶ – var. ***pectinatum***	NWCA
strictum	See E. ***canum***

ERODIUM † (Geraniaceae)

absinthoïdes	GCHN LRHS SIng WThi
¶ – var. ***amanum***	GCHN
¶ – blue	GCHN
acaule	GCHN NRog NRoo
alnifolium	GCHN
balearicum	See E. x ***variabile*** 'Album'
battandierianum	GCHN SCou
'Bedderi'	WAbe
boissieri	GCHN
brachycarpum	GCHN
carvifolium	CBos CElw CLew GBur GCHN SCou WThu
§ ***castellanum***	EPad GCHN MBri NRog NRoo SCou SCro WMar
chamaedryoïdes	See E. ***reichardii***
§ ***cheilanthifolium***	CSam GCHN GGar SIng
chium Guitt 88042202	GCHN
chrysanthum	Widely available
¶ – pink	CGle LGre
– ***sulphureum***	CHan
ciconium Guitt 85051602	GCHN
¶ ***cicutarium***	EWFC
§ – ssp. ***cicutarium***	GCHN
corsicum	CGle CNic EBur MDHE MHig MTho NCat NGar NNrd NRog SHer SUsu WAbe WOMN
– 'Album'	CSam GCHN MMil WAbe
'County Park'	CLew ECou EWes SHer
crinitum	GCHN
daucoïdes hort.	See E. ***castellanum***
¶ 'Eileen Emmett'	GCHN
foetidum	GCHN MDHE NRog

N***glandulosum*** AGM	CMea CShe ELan EMon GCHN GCal LHop MBro NRog SBla SCou SWas WEas WHal WHoo WKif WPat WPbr WPer WSHC WThi
gruinum	CMea ECro EFol GCHN MTol SCou SUsu WPer
N***guttatum***	CGle CNic EPot LHop MPla MWat NKay NMen NTow SIng WAbe WHal WPer
¶ 'Helen'	GCHN
heteradenum	See E. ***petraeum***
x ***hybridum***	EFol EGle ELan EPar EWes NRoo WAbe WCru WHal WPbr
♦x ***hybridum*** misapplied	See E. 'Sara Francesca'
hymenodes hort.	See E. ***trifolium***
jahandierzianum	GCHN
'Katherine Joy'	MDHE NHed NRog
x ***kolbianum***	MDHE NHol
– 'Natasha'	CLew CNic CRiv EBur ELan EPot EWes GCHN MDHE MNFA NHol NRog NRoo SChu SGil SHer SIng SMrm
x ***lindavicum***	CLew
– 'Charter House'	GCHN
macradenum	See E. ***glandulosum***
malacoïdes	GCHN
malviflorum	SFis
manescaui	Widely available
'Merstham Pink'	CElw CLew ESis GCHN MDHE MMil MNFA NHed NRog NRoo SAxl SIng SUsu SWas WKif
moschatum Guitt 88041904	GCHN
munbyanum	GCHN
neuradifolium Guitt 86040601	GCHN
pelargoniiflorum	CBot CChu CGle CLew CMea ECro EFol ESis GCHN LGre MTho NBro NFai SCou SFis SUsu WCra WEas WHal WHil WHoo WOMN WPbr WPer WRus WWin
N***petraeum***	CWes NGre NMen NRoo SFis SIng WAbe WCra WOld WThu
– ssp. ***crispum***	See E. ***cheilanthifolium***
– ssp. ***glandulosum***	See E. ***glandulosum***
– hybrids	ECha
– 'Pallidum'	CElw CSam MNFA
– 'Roseum'	EGle GCal SBla SCro WAbe WMar WPer WRus
'Pickering Pink'	GCHN MDHE NRog
pimpinellifolium	GCHN
'Rachel'	GCHN
recorderi	GCHN
§ ***reichardii***	CBos CElw CLew CMea CRDP CRiv EPad ESis LBee MPla MTho NGre NHol NRog NRoo SBla SCou SIng SUsu WCla WHal WOMN
– cvs	See E. x ***variabile***
§ ***rupestre***	CBot CElw ECtt GCHN GCal NBrk NHed NKay NNor SIng
salzmannii	See E. ***cicutarium cicutarium***
§ 'Sara Francesca'	MDHE
saxatile	GCHN
x ***sebaceum*** 'Polly'	GCHN
'Stephanie'	GCHN MDHE
supracanum	See E. ***rupestre***
tordylioïdes	GCHN
trichomanifolium	SAsh SMrm WHil
§ ***trifolium***	CElw ELan GCal MMil NNrw NSti SCou SIng SUsu WCru WPla
– Guitt 85051701	GCHN
– var. ***montanum***	GCHN SCou
valentinum	GCHN NRog
¶ – 'Alicante'	MDHE
§ x ***variabile*** 'Album'	Widely available
– 'Bishop's Form'	Widely available
¶ – dwarf white	CNic
– 'Flore Pleno'	CLew CSpe ECtt ELan GArf LHop MCas MFir MHig MPla NCat NGre NNrd NRog NRoo SAxl SHer SIng WAbe WOld WPer
– 'Roseum' AGM	CBot CLew CSev ECro EFol ELan EPar EPot IDai MFir MHig NGre NHol NKay NNrw NRed NRog NWCA SFis SIng WAbe WHal WOld WPbr WPer WThu WWin
x ***wilkommianum***	NRog

ERPETION See VIOLA

ERUCA (Cruciferae/Brassicaceae)

vesicaria ssp. ***sativa***	CArn CSFH EHer GPoy LHol MChe SIde WHer WOak WWye

ERYNGIUM † (Umbelliferae/Apiaceae)

§ ***agavifolium***	Widely available
alpinum AGM	CB&S CChu CDec CGle CHad CHan CLew CRDP EBre ECha EFou ELan GDra LBre MBal MBro MTho NBir NSti SAxl SPer WEas WHal WHoo WHow
– 'Amethyst'	ELan GBuc GCal LGre MBri MUlv WMer
– 'Blue Star'	CBot EOrc ESma GCal GCra LGre LHop LWad NCat NRoo NWyt SFis SPla SSte WHoo WPer
– 'Holden Blue'	GCal
– 'Opal'	CShe ELan GCal LRHS MBri
– 'Slieve Donard'	GCal IBlr
– 'Superbum'	CBot ECro NRoo SBla SMad
amethystinum	CBot CBow CChu ECha EMon LGre MBri SGil SIgm
¶ ***aquifolium***	LGre
biebersteinianum	See E. ***caucasicum***
billardierei	EMon
bourgatii	CBot CBow CCla CGle CMea CSco CSev CShe ECas ECha EFou EGol ELan LHop MBal MTho NHar NHol NKay NNor NRoo NSti SAxl SBla SMad SPer WCHb WOld
– 'Forncett Ultra'	EFou
– 'Oxford Blue' AGM	CHan LGre NTow SMrm WEas
bromeliifolium hort.	See E. ***agavifolium***
caeruleum	CRDP SMad
campestre	CBot CRDP NHol
caucasicum	GBuc
creticum	ECro NBir NBro WHer
decaisneanum	See E. ***pandanifolium***
Delaroux	See E. ***proteiflorum***
dichotomum Caeruleum Group	ECro
ebracteatum	GCal
– var. ***poterioïdes***	EMon LWad

§ ***eburneum***	CBot CElw ECha ECro EMon GBuc NBro SAxl SMad
§ ***giganteum*** AGM	Widely available
– 'Silver Ghost'	EMon GCal SMrm
glaciale	LGre NWCA WThi
¶ – JJA 461.000	SBla
¶ ***horridum***	SArc WPer
maritimum	CArn CBot ECWi ECha ECoo GPoy LGre NTow SIde
Miss Willmott's Ghost	See E. ***giganteum***
x ***oliverianum*** AGM	CHan CRDP CSam EFou ELan GAbr IDai LHop MBri MBro NGar SDix SMad SPer SPla WByw WMer WSHC WWin
§ ***pandanifolium***	CElw CGre GCal IBlr LGre SArc SDix SMad
paniculatum	See E. ***eburneum***
planum	Widely available
– 'Blauer Zwerg' ('Blue Dwarf')	CCla CSco EFou GLil NBar SPla WMer
¶ – 'Blaukappe'	CBot EFou LGre NHol WHoo
– 'Flüela'	CGle CMGP EBee ECro EFou GCal LGre NCat NHol SApp SFis SGil SHer
– 'Seven Seas'	EBee NRoo SFis WPer
¶ – 'Tetra Petra'	WPer
¶ – violet blue	GCal
§ ***proteiflorum***	ECha GCal LGre SGil SRms WDav
serra	EBee
spinalba	CBot GAul GCal
– 'Silbermannstreu'	NHol
x ***tripartitum*** AGM	Widely available
– 'Variegatum'	EMon
variifolium	Widely available
yuccifolium	ECoo MSal SIgm WPer
x ***zabelii***	ECha ELan GCal MFir NBir
– 'Jewel'	MNFA MUlv SUsu
– 'Violetta'	CGle ELan GCal MBri MUlv

ERYSIMUM † (Cruciferae/Brassicaceae)

¶ ***alpestre***	NBro
alpinum hort.	See E. ***hieraciifolium***
amoenum	NWCA
arenicola	NHol
– ***torulosum***	See E. ***torulosum***
arkansanum	NPer NTow SMad
¶ ***asperum***	EBee
'Aunt May'	WRus
¶ 'Bowles Yellow'	SMrm
'Bowles' Mauve' AGM	Widely available
'Bredon' AGM	EFou ELan EOrc GAbr GCHN LAbb LHop MRav NBro NCat NFai NPer NSti NTow SAxl SHer SMrm SPla SUsu WKif WMar WRus
'Butterscotch'	CCMG CElw CFee CGle CLTr CLew CMHG CMil CSam ECoo EMar LHop SFis SGil SSvw SUsu WHil WKif WMar WMer WSun
capitatum	MDHE NKay SUsu WOMN WPer
¶ – ***capitatum***	NSla
¶ ***carniolicum***	WHaw
'Changeling'	LRHS
'Cheerfulness'	CHan
cheiri	CRow CSFH EWFC GPoy IBlr LHol SIde WEas WSun
N– 'Baden-Powell' (d)	ELan EOrc LHop WPer
– 'Bloody Warrior' (d)	CBot CCot CDec CElw CLew ELan EOrc GAbr GCal GCra MFir MPla MTho NPer WHer WHil
– 'Chevithorne'	SHBN
– 'Deben'	CBot
– 'Harpur Crewe' AGM	Widely available
– 'Jane's Derision'	CNat
– 'Malmesbury' (v)	CNat
'Chelsea Jacket' AGM	CMil EFou EHic GAbr LHop NSti WMar WRus
'Chequers'	CElw ELan WMer WPer WRus
concinnum	See E. ***suffrutescens***
'Constant Cheer' AGM	CCot CElw CSam CShe GAbr GMac NFai NPer SAxl SPer SUsu WEas WHil WKif WMar WMer WOMN WPer WRus WSun
'Devon Gold'	CPla
'Devon Sunset'	CElw CMil CPla CSam
'Dorothy Elmhirst'	See E. 'Mrs L K Elmhirst'
'Emm's Variety'	NCat
¶ 'Glowing Embers'	CRos ELan
'Gold Flame'	MCas MWat NMen
'Golden Gem'	EHic GGar MDHE NHed SBla WHaw WPer
'Golden Jubilee'	NTow SHer WByw WSun
§ ***helveticum***	CNic ESis GAbr GCra GTou LHil MHig NCat NTow
§ ***hieraciifolium***	CRiv CSam MBal NBee NBro SIde SIng WHil
'Jacob's Jacket'	CCot CElw CFee CGle CMil CSam EBar EFou EPot GAbr GCHN LAbb LHop NNrw NPer NRoo SAxl SChu WMer WPer WRus WSun WWin
'John Codrington'	CCMG CGle CHan CMHG EMar LBlm MBel NBro NPer NSti SBla SChu SHBN SMad SUsu WSun
'Joseph's Coat'	CCot LBlm
'Jubilee Gold'	EJud ELan MCas NCat SIng
'Julian Orchard'	CElw CLew SAxl SUsu
kotschyanum	MCas MHig NTow SBla WHil
'Lady Roborough'	CElw CMil GBuc
linifolium	EBur MDHE NBee NCat NPri NWCA SHer SRms WGor
§ – 'Variegatum'	CBar CCla CGle CMer CSam EFol ELan EOrc IMal LBlm LHil LHop MBri MRav NBro NPer NRoo NSti SAxl SCro SPer SUsu WAbe WEas WHal WHil WHoo WPer WSun
¶ 'Mayflower'	MBel
'Miss Hopton'	CCot NTow WEas WHil
'Moonlight'	CB&S CCot CElw CGre CMHG CMer CSam EFou EMar EOrc GCHN LAbb LBee MTho NBrk NBro NNor SChu SDix SFis SPer SUsu WAbe WDav WEas WHil WPer WRus WSun
§ 'Mrs L K Elmhirst'	CVer EHal LHop NCat NPer NSti
mutabile	CB&S CCot CMHG CRiv CShe EOrc GAbr GCHN NBir NBro NCat NPer NRar NSti NWyt SPla SSvw SUsu WEas WKif
– 'Variegatum'	CBot CElw EFol ELan LHop WEas WHoo
¶ 'New Zealand Limelight'	WCot
¶ 'Onslow Seedling'	GCHN SUsu

'Orange Flame'	CLew CMHG CNic CRiv CSam EFol ELan EMar EPad EPot ESis GAbr LAbb LHop MBro MHig MPla MRav NBro NHol NKay NRoo NTow SHer SMad WDav WPer
perofskianum	NPri WEas
¶ 'Perry's Peculiar'	NPer
'Perry's Pumpkin'	NPer
'Primrose'	CMHG ECoo EFol GCHN LHop SSvw WPer
pulchellum	CRiv MWat SUsu WEas WElm WHaw WHil WPat
pumilum De Candolle	See E. ***helveticum***
¶ *pusillum* NS 727	EBee
'Rufus'	CCot CMHG CSam ELan EOrc GAbr GCHN GMac LBlm LHop MBel MRav MTho NSti SSvw WEas WHil WMar WRus
rupestre	See E. ***pulchellum***
§ *scoparium*	LHop NBro NGar NPer NTow WHil
semperflorens	NPer SMrm
'Sissinghurst Variegated'	See E. ***linifolium*** 'Variegatum'
'Sprite'	CLew CMHG CMea CShe EMar EOrc EPot GAbr MFir MHig MPla NCat NHol NKay NMen NNrd NPer WHil
§ *suffrutescens*	ESis GPlt LHop NPer
'Sunbright'	MCas NCat NMen NNrd NRoo
'Sunshine'	ELan
§ *torulosum*	EPad NPer WHaw
N 'Variegatum'	CB&S EBee SHBN SPla WRus WWin
'Wenlock Beauty' AGM	CCot CMHG CSam ELan GAbr GCHN LBlm MTho NBro NCat NFai NPer SAxl SChu SHer SSvw SUsu WDav WHil WMar WMer WPer WRus
'Wenlock Beauty Variegated'	CMil
wheeleri	NPer SFis SUsu
witmannii	WPer

ERYTHRAEA See CENTAURIUM

ERYTHRINA (Leguminosae/Papilionaceae)

crista-galli AGM	CAbb CB&S CBot CBow CGre CHEx CPle CTro ELan ERea ESma LAbb MUlv SHil SMad
humeana	CGre
♦ *indica*	See E. ***variegata***
lysistemon	CGre CPle CTro
§ *variegata*	CTro

ERYTHRONIUM † (Liliaceae/Liliaceae)

albidum	LAma NRog
americanum	CArn CAvo CBro CHEx CRDP ECha EPot GDra LAma LBow MNFA MPhe MSal NRog WAbe WChr WCru
californicum	CAvo CHEx MPhe MS&S NRog WChr
– 'White Beauty' AGM	CAvo CB&S CBos CBro CNic CRiv CWGN ECha ELan EPar EPot ETub ITim LAma LBow MBal MHig MTho NHar NHol SHer SIng WAbe WChr WCru WKif
caucasicum	CBro EPot LBow NHol NRog WChr
citrinum	EPot MPhe
'Citronella'	CBro EPar LAma LBow NGar NHar NHol NRog SHer SIng WAbe WChr WCru WHil
cliftonii	See E. ***multiscapoideum*** Cliftonii Group
dens-canis AGM	CAvo CBro CHEx CMea CRDP CRiv ECha ELan EPar EPot ETub LAma LBee LBow MBal MBri MHig MS&S MTho NHol NRog SIng SPou SWas WAbe WChr WPat
– 'Frans Hals'	EPar EPot LAma NHol NRog WChr WHil
– 'Lilac Wonder'	CBro EPar EPot LAma NHol NRog SIng WChr
– *niveum*	EPot LAma WChr
– 'Old Aberdeen'	WChr
– 'Pink Perfection'	EPar LAma NHol NRog SHer WChr WHil
– 'Purple King'	EPar EPot LAma MNFA NHol NRog WChr
– 'Rose Queen'	CRDP ELan EPar EPot ETub LAma MNFA MTho NHol NRog WAbe WChr
– 'Snowflake'	ECha EPar EPot LAma MNFA NHol NRog WAbe WChr
– 'White Splendour'	CBro WChr
¶ *elegans*	CFil
grandiflorum	CAvo MS&S NHar WChr
helenae	CFil
hendersonii	LAma WChr
¶ – JCA 11116	CNic
¶ *howellii*	CFil
japonicum	CBro CRDP CWGN EOrc EPar EPot LAma LBow NHol NRog SIng WAbe WChr
'Jeannine'	CBro LAma LRHS WChr
'Kondo'	EPot LAma MHig MNFA MS&S NHar NHol NRog NRoo SIng WAbe WCru
* *moerheimii* 'Semiplena'	EPot
§ *multiscapoideum*	MPhe MS&S WChr
§ – Cliftonii Group	MPhe WChr
oregonum	EPar EPot MPhe MS&S
'Pagoda' AGM	CAvo CB&S CBro CCla CMea CMon CRDP CWGN ECha ELan EOrc EPar EPot ETub LAma LBow MS&S MUlv NEgg NHar NHol NRog NWCA SHig SIng WAbe WChr WDav
purdyi	See E. ***multiscapoideum***
revolutum AGM	CBro CFil EPot GGar IBlr LAma MS&S
– Johnsonii Group	CFil MBal WChr
– 'Rose Beauty'	CBro LAma
¶ *sibiricum*	WChr
'Sundisc'	EPot NRog WChr
tuolumnense AGM	CAvo CBro CRiv EPar EPot LAma LBow MBal NHar NHol NRog SIng WAbe WChr
umbilicatum	MS&S WChr

ESCALLONIA † (Escalloniaceae)

'Alice'	CGre MBri SPer
§ *alpina*	CGre CPle
'Apple Blossom' AGM	Widely available
§ *bifida*	CBot CGre CPle WSHC WWat

'C F Ball'	CSco CTre ELan ENot GCHN GRei IOrc LBuc MGos NRoo NWea WAbe WDin WStI
'Compacta Coccinea'	CLan CMer
'Dart's Rosy Red'	LRHS MBri
'Donard Beauty'	CChe CDoC CMer CSco MBel SRms
'Donard Brilliance'	CMer ISea MGos
'Donard Radiance' AGM	CB&S CDoC CSco CShe ELan ENot IDai IJoh ISea LHop MGos MRav MWat NKay SBod SGil SHer SPer WBod WDin WSHC
'Donard Scarlet'	CMer SRms
'Donard Seedling'	CB&S CBow CDoC CLan CMer CPle CSco EBre ECtt ELan ENot IDai LBre LBuc MBal MBel MBri MRav NBee NNor NNrw NRoo NWea SBod SHBN SPla SRms STre WAbe
'Donard Star'	CShe ENot IOrc MGos
'Donard Suprise'	NNor
'Donard White'	IDai ISea SRms
'Edinensis' AGM	CMHG CSco ECtt ENot ISea MBar NNor WDin WWat
'Erecta'	CBow
x ***exoniensis***	SRms
fonkii	See E. ***alpina***
'Glasnevin Hybrid'	IDai
'Glory of Donard'	CDoC CSco ENot
gracilis alba	CPle
'Gwendolyn Anley'	CDoC CLTr CMHG CMer CSco ESis MAsh MGos NTow SBod SGil SHer SPer WTyr WWat WWeb
'Hopleys Gold'	See E. ***laevis*** 'Gold Brian'
illinita	CGre CMer CPle
'Iveyi' AGM	Widely available
§ ***laevis***	CGre SDry
– 'Gold Brian'	CB&S CMHG EBee MSta WStI
– 'Gold Ellen'	EFol LHop
'Lanarth Hybrid'	CMer
'Langleyensis' AGM	CB&S CDoC CMer IJoh MWat NNor NWea SBod SPla WDin WSHC
leucantha	CGre CMer CPle
littoralis	CPle
macrantha	See E. ***rubra m.***
mexicana	CBot CHan
montevidensis	See E. ***bifida***
'Newryensis'	SPer
organensis	See E. ***laevis***
'Peach Blossom' AGM	CDoC CPle CSco EBar EBee ELan ENot MGos SHBN SPer WHCG
'Pink Elf'	ECtt LRHS MBri
'Pink Pearl'	CMer SRms
'Pride of Donard' AGM	CB&S CDoC CLan CSco IDai IOrc ISea LHop MAsh SGil WWeb
pulverulenta	CGre
punctata	See E. ***rubra***
'Rebecca'	CMer ESma
'Red Dwarf'	WAbe
'Red Elf'	CMHG CMer EBre ECtt ELan ESma IJoh ISea LBre MBar MBri MGos MPla MWat NHol SLPl SLon SPer SPla WHen WPat
'Red Hedger'	CDoC CMer
resinosa	CPle SArc
revoluta	CGre CPle SDry
'Rose Queen'	IDai
rosea	CGre CPle
§ ***rubra***	CGre SPer
– 'Crimson Spire' AGM	CB&S CChe CDoC CLan CSco CShe EBar EBre ENot GRei LBre MGos MRav MWat NNor SBod SHBN SHer SLon SPer SPla SRms WHen WStI WTyr
¶ – 'Hybrida'	CPle
– 'Ingramii'	CChe CMHG CMer CSco SBod SHBN
§ – var. ***macrantha***	CB&S CBow CHEx CSco CTre GRei GWht IDai IJoh ISea SArc SLon SPer SPla WAbe WBod WDin WPat WStI WTyr
– 'Pubescens'	CMer SLon
– 'Pygmaea'	See E. ***r.*** 'Woodside'
– var. ***uniflora***	SDry
§ – 'Woodside'	CPle EHic ESis GAbr IDai LHop MGos NHol SHer SIng WHCG
'Saint Keverne'	CMer
'Silver Anniversary'	CGre CPMA CPle EFol ELan LHop LRHS MAsh SApp SMad SPer SPla
'Slieve Donard'	CMer ENot GRei MGos MRav SLPl
x ***stricta*** 'Harold Comber'	CMer MUlv SDry
tucumanensis	CGre CPle
virgata	CGre CMer CPle SDix WWat

EUCALYPTUS † (Myrtaceae)

acaciiformis	CArn
aggregata	CArn SArc WCel
approximans approximans	WCel
archeri	CGre CMHG MBal WCel
¶ ***barberi***	CGre
¶ ***brookeriana***	CGre
caesia	GCHN
camphora	CMHG WCel
cinerea	IOrc WCel
citriodora	CTro GBar LWad SHer SIde WCel
coccifera AGM	CAbb CB&S CDoC CGre CHEx CSco GAri IOrc MBal WCel WNor WWeb
consideniana	CArn
cordata	CGre MBal WCel
crenulata	WCel
dalrympleana AGM	CB&S CBow CDoC CMHG CSam CSco EBre ELan ENot IOrc LBre MBal MGos MUlv SHil SPer SPla WCel WDin WWeb
deanei	WCel
delegatensis	CMHG GAri IOrc WCel
divaricata	See E. ***gunnii***
ficifolia	CGre SLon
foecunda	CGre
fraxinoïdes	WCel
glaucescens	CBow CGre CMHG EBar SArc WCel
globulus AGM	CB&S CGre CHEx GAri MBal
– ***bicostata***	IOrc
goniocalyx	WCel
§ ***gregsoniana***	CMHG ISea WCel WWeb
§ ***gunnii*** AGM	Widely available
– ***divaricata***	WCel
johnstonii	IOrc ISea WCel WWeb
kitsoniana	MBal WCel
kybeanensis	WCel

leucoxylon	WCel
macarthurii	WCel
mannifera ssp. ***elliptica***	WCel
mitchelliana	WCel
moorei nana	WNor WPat
muelleriana	CArn
neglecta	WCel
nicholii	CMHG WCel
niphophila	See E. ***pauciflora n.***
nitens	CMHG GAri MBal WCel
§ ***nitida***	CArn CGre CMHG WCel WNor
nova-anglica	CMHG
ovata	CGre
parvifolia AGM	CB&S CDoC CLnd GAri SDry SHil WCel
pauciflora	CBow CDoC EBre ERav GAri IBar LBre MBal MUlv SArc SPer WBod WCel WNor
– ssp. ***debeuzevillei***	CMHG SArc WCel
– ***nana***	See E. ***gregsoniana***
§ – ssp. ***niphophila*** AGM	Widely available
– – 'Pendula'	CMHG GAri WCel WWeb
perriniana	CB&S CBow CDoC CHEx CMHG ELan ENot IBlr MBal MUlv NRoo SArc SDry SPer SPla WCel WNor WWeb
pulchella	CGre
pulverulenta	CGre WCel
regnans	CGre ISea MBal
risdonii	WNor
rubida	CGre CMHG ESis IOrc WCel
simmondsii	See E. ***nitida***
stellulata	CMHG IOrc WCel
stuartiana	See E. ***bridgesiana***
sturgissiana	GCHN
subcrenulata	CMHG WCel
tenuiramis	CGre
urnigera	CDoC CGre GAri ISea SPla WBod WCel WWeb
vernicosa	CGre WCel
viminalis	CArn IOrc ISea WCel

EUCHARIDIUM (Onagraceae)

¶ ***breweri***	WHaw

EUCHARIS (Liliaceae/Amaryllidaceae)

§ ***amazonica***	CTro LAma NRog SDeJ SGil
grandiflora hort.	See E. ***amazonica***
x ***grandiflora*** Plan. & Lind.	CTro LBow WChr

EUCODONIA (Gesneriaceae)

'Adele'	NMos
andrieuxii	NMos
– 'Naomi'	NMos WDib
♦ 'Cornell Gem'	See X ACHICODONIA 'C.G.'
'Tintacoma'	NMos
verticillata 'Frances'	NMos

EUCOMIS (Liliaceae/Hyacinthaceae)

§ ***autumnalis***	CAvo EMon LAma
bicolor	CAvo CBow CChu CCla CHEx EBak LAma LBlm LBow MHlr NRog SChu SDix SGil WCru WEas
– hybrids	EFou
§ ***comosa***	CAvo CB&S CChu CHEx EBul LAma LBlm LBow NRog SGil WCru
– purple-leaved	EMon
¶ 'Frank Lawley'	LGre
pole-evansii	CAvo
punctata	See E. ***comosa***
undulata	See E. ***autumnalis autumnalis***
zambesiaca	CFee CMon EBul LBow
¶ 'Zeal Bronze'	LGre

EUCOMMIA (Eucommiaceae)

ulmoïdes	CMCN CPle WCoo

EUCROSIA (Liliaceae/Amaryllidaceae)

¶ ***bicolor***	WChr

EUCRYPHIA † (Eucryphiaceae)

'Castlewellan'	ISea
cordifolia	CB&S CGre CLan ISea MBal SCog WBod
– x ***lucida***	CB&S CCla CDoC CGre IOrc ISea MBal SCog SPer WAbe WDin
glutinosa AGM	CB&S CCla CGre CLan CSam EHar ELan IBar ISea LHyd MBal MBri NBir NPal SCog SHBN SHil SPer SReu SSta WAbe WBod WCoo WDin WNor WWat
– Plena Group	ISea
x ***hillieri*** 'Winton'	CAbb CGre ISea MBal
x ***intermedia***	CCla CDoC CGre CSam ELan GCHN GGGa IDai NPal SCog SHBN SPer WAbe WDin WWat
– 'Rostrevor' AGM	CB&S CBow CLan CMHG CSco ELan GAbr GWht IBar ISea MBal SHil SLon SPer SReu SSta WBod WSHC
lucida	CCla CMHG GWht ISea LHyd MBal SCob SSta WBod WCoo WNor WWat
– 'Pink Cloud'	CMHG CPMA IBar ISea
milliganii	CB&S CBow CCla CDoC CGre CMHG ELan GWht ISea MBal MBrk MUlv NPal SCob SCog SHBN SHil SPer SSta WAbe WBod WSHC WWat
moorei	CB&S CCla ELan ISea MBal SSta WBod
x ***nymansensis***	CB&S CBow EBre ECtt EMil IBar LAbb LBre MBal SArc SBor SCog SReu WHCG WStI
– 'George Graham'	ISea MBal
– 'Mount Usher'	CGre IOrc ISea
– 'Nymansay' AGM	Widely available
N 'Penwith'	ISea MBal

EUGENIA (Myrtaceae)

myrtifolia	CPle STre
smithii	CTro

EUMORPHIA (Compositae/Asteraceae)

* ***canescens***	WHer
¶ ***prostrata***	CSpe
sericea	CHan CNic GAbr NNor NSti

EUNOMIA See AETHIONEMA

EUODIA (Rutaceae)

daniellii	See TETRADIUM ***d.***
hupehensis	See TETRADIUM ***daniellii*** Hupehense Group

EUONYMUS † (Celastraceae)

alatus AGM	Widely available
– var. ***apterus***	MUlv SHBN
– 'Ciliodentatus'	See E. ***a.*** 'Compactus'
§ – 'Compactus' AGM	CChu CDoC CPMA EBre EHar EPla ESis LBre LNet MBlu MBri MPla MUlv WDin WWat
bungeanus	CCla CMCN EPla
cornutus var. ***quinquecornutus***	EPla SWas WMou WOMN
europaeus	CArn CBow CBra CDoC CKin CLew CLnd CPer CShe EBre ELan EPla LBre LBuc NWea SPer WCoo WDin WMou
– f. ***albus***	CBow CMCN CPle ELan EPla NWyt WWat
– 'Atrorubens'	CPMA MPla
– 'Aucubifolius' (v)	EPla
– var. ***intermedius***	ENot EPla
– 'Red Cascade' AGM	Widely available
* ***farreri***	CLew
fimbriatus	CB&S
¶ ***fortunei*** 'Blondy'	MAsh MBri SPer WWes
– 'Canadale Gold' (v)	CCla CDoC EPla MBri MGos NBee NFai NHol SPer
– 'Coloratus'	CLan ENot MBar SHBN SPer WDin
– 'Croftway'	SCro
– 'Dart's Blanket'	CCla ELan ENot EPla MRav SLPl SPer WDin
¶ – 'Dart's Cardinal'	EPla
– 'Emerald Cushion'	EHic ENot ESis NTow SPer
– Emerald Gaiety® AGM	Widely available
– 'Emerald Surprise'	MBri SHBN
– Emerald 'n' Gold® AGM	Widely available
– 'Gold Spot'	See E. ***f.*** 'Sunspot'
– 'Gold Tip' (v)	See E. ***f.*** Golden Prince®
– 'Golden Pillar' (v)	GWht NHol
§ – Golden Prince® (v)	CB&S CCla CPle EFol ENot EPla IJoh MBar NFai NHol SPer SReu SSta WStI
– 'Harlequin' (v)	COtt CPMA CSam ELan EPla LBuc LHop MAll MAsh MBlu MCas NHol NRar SApp SHBN SHil SMad SPer SPla SSta
* – 'Highdown'	EMon
– 'Hort's Blaze'	MGos
– 'Kewensis'	CLew CMGP CMHG CMer CNic CPle CRiv ENot MBar MCas MPla MRav MWat NBee NTow SArc SBod SPer WCru WWat
– 'Minimus'	CDoC EGol EHal EHic EPla ESis GAri NHol NNrd SPla WPer
– 'Sheridan Gold'	ECtt EGol EHoe EPla MPla MRav NHol NWyt SHBN SPer
– 'Silver Gem'	See E. ***f.*** 'Variegatus'
– 'Silver Pillar' (v)	EBar EHic ENot ERav ESis
– 'Silver Queen' AGM	Widely available
– 'Sunshine' (v)	CPMA CSco ELan EPla MAll MBri MGos NHol
§ – 'Sunspot' (v)	CBow CMHG CSco EBre ECtt EGol ELan EPla ERav ESis GWht ISea LAbb LBre LHop MBar MBri MGos MRav NFai NHol NTow SChu SLon SPla SSta WDin WPat WStI
– 'Tustin'	SLPl
§ – 'Variegatus'	CBow CMHG EFol ELan ENot MAll MBar MCas NKay NNor SPer STre WBod WDin WPat
– 'Variegatus' EM '85	MBri MUlv
– var. ***vegetus***	EPla NNor
hamiltonianus	CMCN SLon
– ssp. ***hians***	See E. ***h. sieboldianus***
§ – ssp. ***sieboldianus***	CCla CMCN CPMA EBee EGol LHop MBal MGos WWat
– – 'Coral Charm'	EGol SHil WWes
– – Semiexsertus Group	EHar
– ***yedoensis***	See E. ***h. sieboldianus***
* ***hibarimisake***	SBla
japonicus	ENot SArc WDin
– 'Albomarginatus'	CB&S MBar MPla NBrk WSHC
– 'Aureopictus'	See E. ***j.*** 'Aureus'
– 'Aureovariegatus'	See E. ***j.*** 'Ovatus Aureus'
§ – 'Aureus' (v)	CB&S CSco ELan ENot EPla IDai IJoh LPan MBal MBri SHBN SLon WDin
¶ – 'Bravo'	NHol
– 'Duc d'Anjou' (v)	CB&S CRow EBre EFol EHoe ELan EPla LBre LPan SDry SHil SMad
– 'Golden Pillar' (v)	ESis ESma
§ – 'Latifolius Albomarginatus' AGM	CCla EBre EHoe LBre SPer
– 'Luna'	See E. ***j.*** 'Aureus'
– 'Macrophyllus'	GAri
– 'Macrophyllus Albus'	See E. ***j.*** 'Latifolius Albomarginatus'
– 'Marieke' (v)	See E. ***j.*** 'Ovatus Aureus'
– 'Mediopictus'	MBri
– 'Microphyllus'	EMil MBal MUlv NHol SArc
§ – 'Microphyllus Albovariegatus'	CLTr CMHG CNic CSco ECtt EFol ELan EMil EPla EPot ESiP ISea MBal MBar MGos MRav NHol SHBN SHer SLon SPla WAbe WHCG WPat WThu WWat
– 'Microphyllus Aureovariegatus'	EMil WPat WThu WWin
– 'Microphyllus Aureus'	See E. ***j.*** 'Microphyllus Pulchellus'
§ – 'Microphyllus Pulchellus' (v)	CB&S CMHG CNic EFol EPla EPot ESis IJoh LHop MBar MRav SHer SLon WHCG WWeb
– 'Microphyllus Variegatus'	See E. ***j.*** 'Microphyllus Albovariegatus'
§ – 'Ovatus Albus' (v)	CPle
§ – 'Ovatus Aureus' AGM	CChe CLan CSco EFol ELan ENot ERav ISea LPan MBal MBar MGos MPla MRav SPer SReu WDin WPat WStI
– 'Président Gauthier' (v)	CDoC CRow EBee EFol LHop LPan
– 'Robustus'	CDoC CSco EPla
* – 'Silver Princess'	SHBN
kiautschovicus	EPla
latifolius	CMCN WMou
– x ***hamiltonianus***	CMCN

§ ***lucidus*** CChu CGre
¶ ***macropterus*** EPla
myrianthus WWat
§ ***nanus*** CPle EPla ESis MBal NHol WPat WSHC WWat
– var. ***turkestanicus*** CBrd EPla ESis NWyt SPer SRms WWat
¶ ***obovatus*** CHan
oxyphyllus CCla CMCN WMou WThu WWat
pendulus See E. ***lucidus***
phellomanus CSco EBar EHic EPla GDra LHop LNet MAsh MBar MBlu MUlv WWat
§ ***planipes*** AGM CCla CGre CMHG CPle CSco EBar EHar ELan ENot EPla MBri NHol SHil SPer WMou WWat
radicans See E. ***fortunei radicans***
'Rokojo' NHol WPat
rosmarinifolius See E. ***nanus***
sachalinensis hort. See E. ***planipes***
sp. B&L 12543 EPla
¶ ***tingens*** CFil
velutinus CChu CGre
verrucosus EPla
yedoensis See E. ***hamiltonianus sieboldianus***

EUPATORIUM (Compositae/Asteraceae)

album CLew GBar MHew WPer
altissimum CBot CGle CHan ELan EPar GCal MSal NSti SChu SPer WCHb WDav WEas WOld
– JLS 88029 EMon
– 'Braunlaub' EFou MHlr MUlv NPri WCot
aromaticum CArn CMGP CSev EBee ECro ELan EMon NBro SCro SFis SSvw WCHb WPer WWye
cannabinum CArn CKin CSam CWGN ECED ECWi ECoo EHon ELan EMFW EWFC GPoy LHol MHew MSal MSta NMir NSti WGwy WNdy WOak WPer WWye
– 'Album' EMon GBar GCal
– 'Flore Pleno' CCla CSev ECha ECro EFou EHic EMon EOrc MHlr MSte MUlv NBrk NSti SCro SFis WCot WHer
¶ – 'Spraypaint' CNat
¶ ***coelestinum*** EMon
– forms WCot
fortunei EMon
glechonophyllum CGre
hildalgense CGre
§ ***ligustrinum*** CB&S CCla CDec CDoC CGle CHan CLan CPle CTre CWit ECha ELan ERom IOrc ISea LGre LHop SDix SMad SMrm SPer SUsu WBod WCHb WPer WSHC
¶ ***madrense*** CLTr
micranthum See E. ***ligustrinum***
perfoliatum CArn ECha GBar GPoy LHol MHew MSal NWyt SIde WWye
purpureum Widely available
– ssp. ***maculatum*** EMon GCal MUlv SFis
– – 'Atropurpureum' AGM CBos CChu CCla CGre CHad CHan CHol CSco CSev EBre ECha EFol EFou ELan EOrc GCal LBre LHol MBri MFir NBir NPri NSti NWyt SAxl SFis SUsu
– – 'Berggarten' GCal
¶ – 'Purple Bush' ECha
¶ ***rugosum*** SIde
– ***album*** See E. ***album***
sordidum CNew CTro ERea SLMG
triplinerve CTom LHol MSte
weinmannianum See E. ***ligustrinum***
§ ***xylorhizum*** JJH 95059 LGre WDav

EUPHORBIA † (Euphorbiaceae)

acanthothamnos LGre
amygdaloïdes CKin CRow ECWi EWFC WTyr WWye
– 'Purpurea' See E. ***a.*** 'Rubra'
§ – var. ***robbiae*** AGM Widely available
§ – 'Rubra' Widely available
– 'Variegata' CRDP CRow ELan EMon EOrc LGre MTho NRar SMad SUsu WRus
biglandulosa See E. ***rigida***
* ***britzensis*** WRus
capitata WDav
capitulata CLew EFol ELan EPot EWes LHop MCas MHig MTho NMen NNrd WThu WWin
ceratocarpa CB&S CMHG CMil EMon EPla GCal NHol NSti NWyt SUsu
characias AGM CB&S CBot CBow CGle CHol CMer CRow CWGN ECtt ELun EMon MBri NBar NHol NNor NOak NPer NPri NSti WByw WHoo WTyr WWat
– JCA 475.500 CMil GCal
– 'Blue Hills' EFou EMon GCal IBlr LHop
¶ – ssp. ***characias*** AGM LGre
– – 'H E Bates' NBir
– – 'Humpty Dumpty' EBre LBre LHop LRHS NPer
¶ – dwarf ELan
– 'Forescate' GCal NWyt
– 'Jenetta' NCat
¶ – 'Portuguese Velvet' SWas
– 'Variegata' CRow
– ssp. ***wulfenii*** AGM Widely available
– ssp. ***wulfenii*** JCA 475.603 CMil GCal
– – var. ***sibthorpii*** MUlv NBrk WCot WOld
– – 'Bosahan' (v) GCal NRar SMad
– – 'Emmer Green' (v) CMil SBla
– – 'Jayne's Golden Giant' EMon
§ – – 'John Tomlinson' AGM CMHG ECha EHic EPla MUlv NHol NSti NWyt WEas
– – Kew form See E. ***c. w.*** 'John Tomlinson'
– – 'Lambrook Gold' AGM CHad CMHG CRow CSam ECtt EGol ELan EMon EOrc EPar GCal LHop MRav NPer SChu SMad SPer WHoo WRus
– – 'Lambrook Yellow' CCla CMil EMon EWll MWat
– – Margery Fish Group EFou EPla NCat WMer
– – 'Minuet' CHan CShe
– – 'Perry's Tangerine' NPer
– – 'Perry's Winter Blusher' NPer
§ – – 'Purple and Gold' NSti SAxl SChu WRus
♦ – – 'Purpurea' See E. ***c. w.*** 'Purple and Gold'
¶ – – Ulverscroft form MUlv
cognata C&Mc 607 GCHN

¶– C&Mc 724 — EBee
¶ *conifera* — CB&S NWyt
coralliöides — CArn CLew CSco ECha IBlr MFir NPer SFar SPer WCru WHer WHil
cornigera — CElw CMHG EHic EMon GCal GMac IBlr NHol SAxl WSHC
cyparissias — Widely available
– Ashfield form — NRar
– 'Betten' — See E. x *gayeri* 'B.'
– 'Bush Boy' — IBlr WCot
– 'Clarice Howard' — ECha NRar
¶– 'Fens Ruby' — EMon
– 'Orange Man' — EBee EFou EMon IBlr NBrk
– 'Tall Boy' — IBlr
N*donii* — CLew ECha EFou ELan EPla IBlr LHop MMil NSti SBor SDix SFis SUsu WAbb
dulcis — CGle CLew CRow CTom ECha EFol EFou ELun EOrc GAbr LGan NBrk NBro NHol NOak NSti SUsu WByw WCot WEas WHen WOld WRus WWat
– 'Chameleon' — Widely available
*– 'Nana' — EHic NHol
epithymoïdes — See E. *polychroma*
esula — CGle
¶*franchetii* — GCal
fulgens — CBow
glauca — ECou IBlr WCot
griffithii — CBow CRow ISea NBrk NBro NCat NWyt SBor WAbb WCru
– 'Dixter' AGM — Widely available
– 'Fern Cottage' — SWas
– 'Fireglow' — Widely available
– 'Wickstead' — CHol EPla GCal LHop SAxl
horrida — SLMG
hyberna — CTom IBlr MFir MTho MUlv NHol NWyt
jacquemontii — GCal LGan MRav SFis
x *keysii* — MBri
lathyris — CRow CSFH ELan ERav LHol MHew NPer SIng WEas WFox WWye
♦*longifolia* D Don — See E. *donii*
longifolia hort. — See E. *cornigera*
♦*longifolia* Lamarck — See E. *mellifera*
macrostegia — SChu
mammillaris — SLMG
x *martinii* AGM — Widely available
§ *mellifera* — Widely available
milii AGM — EBak
– 'Koenigers Aalbäumle' — MBri
myrsinites AGM — Widely available
nicaeënsis — CB&S CCMG CChu CCla CFil CMea EMon EOrc EPla GAbr GCal LGre LHop MRav NGar NSti SBla SBod SChu SCro SFar SMrm SUsu WWat
oblongata — CB&S CBow CMil EBee EFou ELan EMon EPla IBlr LHop LRHS NBrk NHol NSti SBod
palustris AGM — CChu CHad CHan CMHG CMer CRDP CRow CSco CShe EFou EGol ELan ELun ERav GCal LHop LMay MSta NDea NHol NSti SAxl SBla SDix SMad SPer SUsu WEas WWat WWin
– 'Walenburg's Glorie' — GCal NRoo SMad
pilosa — CNat ERav NSti
– *major* — See E. *polychroma* 'Major'
pithyusa — CBot CGle CHan ECha EMon EPla GCal LHop MMil SMad SMrm SUsu WRus
§ *polychroma* AGM — Widely available
– 'Emerald Jade' — IBlr
§ – 'Major' — CMHG CTom ECha GCal MUlv NCat SLga SPer WCot WEas
– 'Midas' — EMon
– 'Purpurea' — Widely available
– 'Sonnengold' — ECha EHic EPla GCal NHol NWyt SMad WSHC
*– 'Variegata' — EFol EPla MMil NBir WPbr
portlandica — CB&S EFol EHic ELan GAbr NHol NWyt SUsu WHer
§ x *pseudovirgata* — CMHG CMil EHal EMon IBlr SAxl SFar SUsu
pugniformis — MBri
pulcherrima — EWes MBri
'Red Dwarf' — EHic EOrc NWyt
reflexa — See E. *seguieriana niciciana*
resinifera — SLMG
§ *rigida* — CBot CFil CHan CMil EFol EPla ERav GCal SAxl SBla SGil SWas
robbiae — See E. *amygdaloïdes r.*
schillingii AGM — Widely available
seguieriana — EBee ECha EGle EPot NCat
§ – ssp. *niciciana* — Widely available
serrulata — See E. *stricta*
sikkimensis — Widely available
¶ *spinosa* — SIgm SMad SUsu
§ *stricta* — CRow CTom IBlr NCat NRar NSti WWat
* *submammillaris* 'Variegata' — MBri
uralensis — See E. x *pseudovirgata*
§ *virgata* — EMon
x *waldsteinii* — See E. *virgata*
N*wallichii* — CChu CHad CMGP CSam CSco ECha EFou EGol ELan EOrc IBlr MBri MUlv NHol NOrc NRoo NSti NWyt SChu SMad SMrm WAbb WRus WTyr WWat

EUPTELEA (Eupteleaceae)

franchetii — See E. *pleiosperma*
polyandra — CCla CGre EHar WCoo

EURYA (Theaceae)

japonica 'Variegata' — See CLEYERA *japonica* 'Fortunei'

EURYOPS (Compositae/Asteraceae)

abrotanifolius — CMHG EPla WPer
§ *acraeus* AGM — Widely available
§ *chrysanthemoïdes* — CB&S CBrk CMHG CPle CSam CSpe EBar ERea IBlr LHil MSte NTow WPer
evansii — See E. *acraeus*
* *grandiflorus* — CBot
pectinatus AGM — CB&S CBra CBrk CCla CHan CMHG CMer CPle CSam CTre CTro ERea ERom GCal IBlr IDai LHil LHop MFir MRav NSty SDry SHBN SIgm SLon SMrm SUsu WEas WPer
sericeus — See URSINIA *sericea*
tenuissimus — CPle
tysonii — CPle GGar

virgineus	CB&S CMHG CMer CPle CSam CTre CTro ESma IBlr

EUSTEPHIA (Liliaceae/Amaryllidaceae)

jujuyensis	LBow WChr

EUSTOMA (Gentianaceae)

§ *grandiflorum*	MBri
russellianum	See E. *grandiflorum*

EUSTREPHUS (Liliaceae/Philesiaceae)

¶ *latifolius*	ECou

EVOLVULUS (Convolvulaceae)

convolvuloïdes	ERea
glomeratus 'Blue Daze'	See E. *pilosus* 'B. D.'
§ *pilosus* 'Blue Daze'	ERea SSad

EWARTIA (Compositae/Asteraceae)

nubigena	NWCA

EXACUM (Gentianceae)

affine	MBri
– 'Rococo'	MBri

EXOCHORDA (Rosaceae)

giraldii var. *wilsonii*	CBow CCla CDoC CPMA CSam CSco EBar EHar LAbb MPla MUlv WWat
korolkowii	SHil WWat
x *macrantha* 'The Bride' AGM	Widely available
racemosa	CBow CDoC CGre CPMA EHal GCal ISea LAbb LHop MBal MGos NNor SEng SHBN SLon SPer WWat

FABIANA (Solanaceae)

imbricata	CBot CBra CLan CPle EBar EMil ERav IDai LAbb MAll MBar SHil SLon SPer SReu SSta WAbe WBod
– *alba*	WThu
– 'Prostrata'	CBow CPle EBar GCal MUlv SDry SHil WDin WWat WWin
– f. *violacea* AGM	CB&S CFee CGre CPle EMil EPla LAbb MBar SHil SLon SReu SSta WBod

FAGOPYRUM (Polygonaceae)

cymosum	See F. *dibotrys*
§ *dibotrys*	ELan NSti

FAGUS † (Fagaceae)

crenata	CMCN WCoo WNor
engleriana	CMCN CSco CTho SHil
grandifolia	CMCN WCoo WMou
sylvatica AGM	CB&S CDoC CKin CLnd CPer ELan ENot GRei IDai IOrc ISea LBuc LPan MBar MBri MGos NBee NWea SHBN SPer SReu WDin WMou WNor WStI
§ – 'Albomarginata'	IOrc MBlu SHil
– 'Albovariegata'	See F. *s.* 'Albomarginata'
– 'Ansorgei'	CMCN CTho MBlu MBri
– 'Atropunicea'	See F. *s.* Purpurea Group
– 'Aurea Pendula'	CMCN EHar SHil
– 'Black Swan'	CMCN MBlu MBri WMou
– 'Bornyensis'	EHar
– 'Cochleata'	CMCN
– 'Cockleshell'	CMCN
– Copper Group	WMou
– 'Cristata'	CMCN GAri
– 'Cuprea'	See F. *s.* Copper Group
§ – 'Dawyck' AGM	CB&S CDoC CLnd CMCN COtt CSco CTho EBre EHar ELan EMil ENot IHos IOrc ISea LBre MBal MBar NWea SPer WDin
– 'Dawyck Gold' AGM	CAbP CDoC CMCN COtt CSco EHar IOrc ISea LPan MBar MBlu MBri SHil SMad WMou
– 'Dawyck Purple' AGM	CAbP CDoC CMCN COtt CSco EHar IOrc LPan MBlu MBri SHil SMad SPer
– 'Fastigiata'	See F. *s.* 'Dawyck'
– 'Frisio'	CMCN
– var. *heterophylla*	CLnd CTho EHar GAri ISea
– – f. *laciniata*	CMCN
– – 'Aspleniifolia' AGM	CB&S CBra CDoC CMCN COtt CPMA CSco ELan EMil ENot IOrc LPan MBal MBri SPer WDin WMou WNor
– 'Luteovariegata'	CMCN
– 'Mercedes'	CMCN
– 'Nana'	CMCN
N – 'Pendula' AGM	CB&S CBra CDoC CLnd CMCN CTho EHar ELan ENot GRei IJoh IOrc ISea MBal MBar MBri NWea SMad SPer WDin WMou WStI
– 'Prince George of Crete'	CMCN ISea
– 'Purple Fountain' AGM	CDoC CMCN COtt CSco EHar IJoh IOrc LPan MBlu MBri MGos MUlv SMad SPer
N – Purple Group	CB&S CBra CDoC CKin EHar ELan EMil ENot GRei IDai IOrc LBuc MBal MBar MBri MGos NBee NHol NWea SHBN SPer WCoo WDin WMou WStI
– 'Purpurea Pendula'	CCla CMCN CPer CSco CTho EHar ELan EMil ENot GRei IJoh IOrc ISea LPan MBal MBar MBlu MGos NBee NWea SPer WStI
§ – 'Purpurea Tricolor'	CBow CDoC CMCN CSco EFol EHar IOrc LPan MBar MGos NBee SHBN SHil SPer WDin
– 'Quercifolia'	CMCN
– 'Quercina'	CMCN
¶ – 'Red Obelisk'	MBlu
– 'Riversii' AGM	CB&S CDoC CLnd CMCN CSco EHar ELan EMil ENot IDai IJoh IOrc LPan MBal MBri NWea SHBN SPer SSta WDin WStI
– 'Rohan Gold'	CMCN EBee MBri WMou
– 'Rohan Obelisk'	EBee MBlu
* – 'Rohan Trompenburg'	CMCN
– 'Rohanii'	CAbP CB&S CDoC CLnd CMCN COtt CPMA CSco CTho CWSG EHar ELan EMil IHos IOrc ISea LPan MBal MBlu MBri NBee SEng SHBN SHil SPer WDin WMou WNor
– 'Roseomarginata'	See F. *s.* 'Purpurea Tricolor'
– 'Rotundifolia'	CDoC NWea SPer
* – 'Silver Wood'	CMCN MBri
– 'Spaethiana'	MBri
– f. *tortuosa*	EHar
– 'Tortuosa Purpurea'	CMCN

♦– 'Tricolor' misapplied — See F. *s.* 'Purpurea Tricolor'
– 'Tricolor' (v) — CB&S CLnd COtt CPMA ELan ENot IJoh LBuc MBal MBri MUlv WDin
– 'Zlatia' — CB&S CDoC CLnd CMCN COtt CSco CTho EHar ELan EMil ENot IOrc MBal MBar MBri MGos NBee SEng SHBN SHil SPer WDin WMou WStI

FALLOPIA † (Polygonaceae)

aubertii — See F. ***baldschuanica***
§ ***baldschuanica*** AGM — CCla CMac CSco CShe ELan ENot GRei IDai IHos ISea LBuc MBar MGos MPla MRav MWat NEgg NHol NKay NRoo SBra SHBN SLon SPer WBod
§ ***japonica*** — CRow ELan
§ – var. ***compacta*** — CHan CRow EPla MFir MUlv
– 'Spectabilis' — CRow EFol EGol ELan MUlv
– 'Variegata' — CRow EPla IBlr SMad
sachalinensis — CRow ELan EMon

FALLUGIA (Rosaceae)

See Plant Deletions

FARFUGIUM (Compositae/Asteraceae)

¶ ***japonicum nokozanense***
B&SWJ 298 — WCru
§ ***tussilagineum*** — CHEx MTho
– 'Argenteum' (v) — CBos CHEx CHan CRDP
– 'Aureomaculatum' AGM — CAbb CB&S CBos CHEx CHan CRDP CTro MTho SApp SAxl WHal

FARGESIA (Gramineae/Poaceae-Bambusoideae)

dracocephala — EPla ISta SArc SBam SDry WJun
§ ***murieliae*** AGM — CB&S CCla CHEx CHan CLew ECha EFul EHar ELan ENot EPla ISta LNet MBar MBri NBee NJap SBam SCob SDry SPer WHow WJun
*– ***dana*** — WJun
§ – 'Leda' (v) — SDry
– 'Simba' — CDoC EBee EPla ESiP ISta MAsh SCob WJun
§ ***nitida*** AGM — CBra CHEx CSco CShe EFul EHar ENot EPla ESiP ETPC IOrc ISea ISta LBam MBri MGos MUlv NJap NKay SBam SCob SDry SHig SPer WDin WHow WJun
– 'Eisenach' — ISta
– 'Nymphenburg' — CPMA EPla
robusta — EPla SBam SDry WJun
♦ ***spathacea*** misapplied — See F. ***murieliae***
utilis — EPla SBam SDry WJun

FARSETIA (Cruciferae/Brassicaceae)

clypeata — See FIBIGIA ***clypeata***

FASCICULARIA (Bromeliaceae)

andina — See F. ***bicolor***
§ ***bicolor*** — CGre CHEx CWGN IBlr IJoh LHil LHop MTho MUlv SArc SLMG WEas
kirchhoffiana — SLMG
pitcairniifolia — CGre CHEx CTro EBak EBul GGar IBlr MUlv SArc SLMG

X FATSHEDERA (Araliaceae)

lizei AGM — CB&S CBot CBow CDoC CHEx CLan CRow CSam CSco EPla IBlr MAll MBal MBri NNor NRog SArc SBra SDry SPla SReu WDin WStI WWat
– 'Annemieke' AGM — CBot CDec EPla IBlr LRHS MBri
– 'Aurea' (v) — SDry
– 'Aureopicta' — See X F. *l.* 'Aurea'
♦– 'Lemon and Lime' — See X F. *l.* 'Annemieke'
♦– ***maculata*** — See X F. *l.* 'Annemieke'
– 'Pia' — MBri
– 'Variegata' AGM — CB&S CBow CDoC CGre CHEx CMHG CRow CSco IBlr MBal MBri SDry SGil SHer WStI WWat

FATSIA (Araliaceae)

§ ***japonica*** AGM — Widely available
– 'Variegata' AGM — CB&S CBot MBri MGos MUlv NPal SArc SHBN SHil SPer WDin
papyrifera — See TETRAPANAX ***papyrifer***

FAUCARIA (Aizoaceae)

tigrina — MBri

FAURIA See NEPHROPHYLLIDIUM

FEIJOA See ACCA

FELICIA (Compositae/Asteraceae)

§ ***amelloïdes*** — CBow CCan CLTr CMer CRiv CSam CSev CTro ERea ERom ESis ESma GCal LAbb MPit NRar NTow SChu WHal WPer
– 'Astrid Thomas' — CBrk CSpe LHop SHer
¶ – 'Blue Eyes' — NRar
– 'Read's Blue' — CCan GMac LHil LHop MArl
– 'Read's White' — CBrk CCan CSpe CTro EDon EOrc ERav ERea ESis ESma GMac LHil LHop MSte
§ – 'Santa Anita' AGM — CBrk CCan CSev CSpe ECtt EDon EOrc ERea LHil LHop WEas WHal
– 'Santa Anita' (large flowered) — LBlm LHil
– 'Santa Anita Variegated' AGM — LHop
§ – variegated — CBar CBot CBrk CCan CCla CHan CRiv CSev CTro EBar ECha ECtt EDon ELan ERav ERea ERom ESis IBlr LHil LHop MBri MSte NPer NRar SAxl WEas WHal WPer WRus
amethystina — See F. 'Snowmass'
§ ***amoena*** — CBrk CCla CHad CHan CMer EDon ELan LHil LHop MTho NRar SChu SLon WEas WHal WPer WWin
– 'Variegata' — CMer EOrc LAbb MCas MPit SChu
bergeriana — WOMN
capensis — See F. ***amelloïdes***
– 'Variegata' — See F. ***amelloïdes*** variegated
coelestis — See F. ***amelloïdes***

drakensbergensis NTow
echinata WPer
natalensis See F. ***rosulata***
pappei See F. ***amoena***
§ ***petiolata*** CAll CBrk CElw CHan CRiv ECha EMon ERav ERea ESma IBlr LHil LHop MMil NSti WCru WHow WOMN WPer WWin
****plena ensbergensis*** MPit
§ ***rosulata*** CHan CWes ELan EMon GArf GAri GDra LHop MCas MHig MPit MRPP MTho NKay NMen NNrd NRoo NSti NTow SIng SSmi WHil WWin
'Snowmass' CBot WWin
uliginosa CFee CRiv GGar LBee MDHE MTho NBir NRar NTow WEas WHil

FERRARIA (Iridaceae)

§ ***crispa*** CMon CTro LBow WMar
¶ ***uncinata*** CMon
undulata See F. ***crispa***

FERREYRANTHUS (Compositae/Asteraceae)

excelsus CB&S

FERULA (Umbelliferae/Apiaceae)

assa-foetida CArn MHew MSal
*'Cedric Morris' ECha SMad
communis CWes LGan LHol SDix SMrm WCot WHal WHer WPla WWye
– 'Gigantea' CHad ECha LGre
'Giant Bronze' See FOENICULUM ***vulgare*** 'G.B.'

FESTUCA (Gramineae/Poaceae)

alpina ETPC
amethystina CLew EHoe EMon ETPC LGan MBro NBee NHol NMir NSti WCra WPer
– 'Aprilgrün' EHoe
– 'Bronzeglanz' ETPC
ampla ETPC
arundinacea CKin
californica ETPC
curvula ssp. ***crassifolia*** EPla
dalmatica ETPC
dumetorum ETPC
elatior 'Demeter' ETPC
elegans ETPC
erecta EHoe
eskia CElw EHoe EPla ETPC NHol
extremiorientalis ETPC
filiformis EMon EPla ETPC LRHS
§ ***gautieri*** ECED ELan EPla ESiP ETPC LHil MFir MUlv NOrc SCob
– 'Pic Carlit' ETPC
gigantea ETPC
glacialis EHoe EPla ETPC MBal MDHE NHol NNrd NRed
¶ – 'Czakor' ETPC
glauca Widely available
– 'Azurit' EFou EMon EPla ETPC LRHS
– 'Blaufuchs' ('Blue Fox') **AGM** CDoC CElw ECot EHoe EPla ETPC MBri MSte WWat
– 'Blauglut' ('Blue Glow') EBre EPla LBre NHar NMir
– 'Harz' CElw EHoe EPla ETPC IBlr
– 'Meerblau' ('Sea Blue') CElw
*– ***minima*** EFol ESis NHol NNrd
– 'Pallens' See F. ***longifolia***
– 'Seeigel' ('Sea Urchin') EBee EGle EHoe EPla ETPC LHil
– 'Seven Seas' See F. ***valesiaca*** 'Silbersee'
heterophylla ETPC
¶ ***juncifolia*** ETPC
§ ***longifolia*** EFou ETPC
mairei EHoe ETPC IBlr SApp
ochroleuca ETPC
ovina CElw ECha EHic EHoe EPla ESis GAbr LHil SIng SMad SPla WFox WPer
– ssp. ***coxii*** EHoe ETPC MHlr WCot
paniculata CElw EHoe EMon EPla ETPC
¶ ***pulchella*** ETPC
punctoria CLew CTom ECha EFol EHoe EPla ETPC MDHE NHol SBla SGil SSmi
¶ ***rubra*** 'Variegata' WDav
– var. ***viridis*** NHol SIng
sclerophylla ETPC
scoparia See F. ***gautieri***
tenuifolia ETPC
valesiaca var. ***glaucantha*** ETPC NHol WWat
§ – 'Silbersee' ('Silver Sea') CLew EBre ECha EFol EFou EHoe EPla ETPC IBlr LBre MBar MBri MCas MSte NCat NHol NNrd SGil SHer SIng
vivipara EHoe EMon NHol

FIBIGIA (Cruciferae/Brassicaceae)

§ ***clypeata*** ELan EMar ESis NSti SHer WCru WEas

FICUS † (Moraceae)

¶ ***aspera*** CTro
australis hort. See F. ***rubiginosa*** 'Australis'
benghalensis MBri
benjamina **AGM** MBri
– 'Exotica' MBri
– 'Flandriana' MBri
– 'Golden King' MBri
– 'Golden Princess' MBri
– 'Green Gem' MBri
– var. ***nuda*** MBri
– 'Starlight' (v) MBri
capensis CTro
F ***carica*** **AGM** MBri
F – 'Adam' ERea
F – 'Angélique' ERea
F – 'Bellone' ERea
F – 'Bifere' ERea
F – 'Black Ischia' ERea
F – 'Black Mission' ERea
F – 'Boule d'Or' ERea
F – 'Bourjassotte Grise' ERea
F – 'Brown Turkey' **AGM** CB&S CBow CCla CHEx CHad CMac CSam ELan ERea ESim GBon GTwe IJoh ISea LBuc LHol MBri MRav MWat NBee NPer NRog SArc SDea SFam SHBN SMad SPer WDin WHig

F – 'Brunswick' CDoC ERea ESim GBon GTwe WCot
F – 'Castle Kennedy' ERea
F – 'Col de Dame' ERea
F – 'Figue d'Or' ERea
F – 'Goutte d'Or' ERea
F – 'Grise de Saint Jean' ERea
F – 'Grise Ronde ' ERea
F – 'Grosse Grise' ERea
F – 'Kaape Bruin' ERea
F – 'Lisa' ERea
F – 'Longue d'Août' ERea
F – 'Malcolm's Giant' ERea
F – 'Malta' ERea
F – 'Marseillaise' ERea ESim GTwe SDea
F – 'Negro Largo' ERea
F – 'Osborn's Prolific' ERea
F – 'Panachée' ERea
F – 'Petite Grise' ERea
F – 'Pied de Boeuf' ERea
F – 'Pittaluse' ERea
F – 'Précoce Ronde de Bordeaux' ERea
F – 'Rouge de Bordeaux' ERea
F – 'Saint Johns' ERea
F – 'San Pedro Miro' ERea
F – 'Sollies Pont' ERea
F – 'Sugar 12' ERea
F – 'Verte d'Argenteuil' ERea
F – 'Violette de Sollies' ERea
F – 'Violette Sepor' ERea
♦– 'White Genoa' See F. *c.* 'White Marseilles'
F – 'White Ischia' ERea
F – 'White Marseilles' ERea
cyathistipula MBri
deltoidea diversifolia CTro MBri
elastica 'Robusta' MBri
– 'Zulu Shield' MBri
♦*foveolata* Wallich See F. *sarmentosa*
lyrata AGM MBri
microcarpa STre
– 'Hawaii' (v) MBri
natalensis leprieurii 'Westland' MBri
palmata CGre SMad
pumila AGM CB&S CHEx EBak MBri NHol SArc
– 'Minima' MCas MHig
– 'Sonny' (v) MBri
– 'Variegata' CHEx MBri
radicans See F. *sagittata*
¶ *rubiginosa* CTro
§ – 'Australis' CTro MBri
§ *sagittata* 'Variegata' MBri
§ *sarmentosa* MBri
triangularis See F. *natalensis leprieurii*

FIG See FICUS *carica*

FILBERT See CORYLUS *maxima*

FILIPENDULA (Rosaceae)

alnifolia 'Variegata' See F. *ulmaria* 'Variegata'
digitata 'Nana' See F. *palmata* 'Nana'
hexapetala See F. *vulgaris*
– 'Flore Pleno' See F. *vulgaris* 'Multiplex'
'Kahome' EGol EOrc GAbr NHol NMir NOrc NRoo NSti NTow SFis SMrm WCra
kamtschatica CRow CWGN ECoo ELan NDea NMir
– *rosea* IBlr LHop NBrk
palmata CBre CWGN ECha WByw
– 'Alba' ECha GCal
– 'Digitata Nana' See F. *p.* 'Nana'
§ – 'Elegantissima' CChu CRow EBee ECha GGar MTol
¶ – miniature GCal
§ – 'Nana' CRow ECha ECro EPla GCal MBal MBro WHoo
– *purpurea* See F. *purpurea*
– 'Rosea' CGle NBir NCat WCHb
– 'Rubra' CSco
§ *purpurea* AGM CDoC CRow CWGN ECha EFou ELun GGar LGan MBel MUlv SMad WAbe WEas
– *alba* CBre EGol MUlv
– 'Elegans' NFai WHil
*– *splendens* NKay
rubra CHan CRow CWGN ECED WCra WHaw
§ – 'Venusta' AGM Widely available
– 'Venusta Magnifica' See F. *r.* 'Venusta'
sp. CLD 360 NHol
§ *ulmaria* CArn CKin CSFH CWGN ECWi ECoo EHon EMar EPla EWFC Effi GPoy LHol MChe MHew MTho MTol NHol NLan NMir NOak SIde WCla WNdy WOak WPer WWye
– 'Aurea' Widely available
– 'Flore Pleno' CBre CRDP CRow CWGN EBre LBre NHol NSti SHer SHig SPer
– 'Rosea' CLew CTom EPla MUlv SPer
§ – 'Variegata' Widely available
§ *vulgaris* CBow CFee CKin CWGN ECWi ECtt EWFC LGan LHol LMay MChe MHew MSal MTol NBee NBro NLan NMir NNor NOrc NPri SIde WByw WChe WCla WNdy WPer WWye
– 'Grandiflora' EOrc NCat
§ – 'Multiplex' CCla CDoC CGle CHan CLew CSco ECha EGol ELan EOrc EPar EPla LHop LWad MBal MFir MTho MUlv NDea NHol NRar NSti SPer WEas WHal WRus WWat
– 'Plena' See F. *v.* 'Multiplex'

FINGERHUTHIA (Gramineae/Poaceae)

sesleriiformis S&SH 1 CHan

FIRMIANA (Sterculiaceae)

simplex CHEx

FITTONIA (Acanthaceae)

albivenis Argyroneura Group AGM MBri
– – 'Nana' MBri

FITZROYA (Cupressaceae)

cupressoïdes CB&S CMac GAri IOrc LCon MBal MBar SIng WThu

FOENICULUM (Umbelliferae/Apiaceae)

vulgare	CArn CHad CTom ECWi ECha EEls ELan Effi GBar GPoy IEde LAbb LHol MChe MHew MSal NMir NRoo SHer SIde WByw WOak WPer WWye
– 'Bronze'	See F. *v.* 'Purpureum'
– var. *dulce*	CArn CSev EHer EPla IEde MChe WWye
§ – 'Giant Bronze'	CGle CSco ELan LAbb SPer
§ – 'Purpureum'	CArn CFee CGle CHad CMea CSev ECha EEls EHoe GPoy LGan LHol MChe MFir MPit MSal NBro NMir NOak NRoo NSti SUsu WEas WHal WOak WPer WSun WWye
– 'Smokey'	CWit EFou ESma

FOKIENIA (Cupressaceae)

hodginsii	CKen CMCN

FONTINALIS (moss)

antipyretica	SAWi

FORSYTHIA (Oleaceae)

'Arnold Dwarf'	CBow EHal SRms WWeb
N 'Beatrix Farrand'	CLTr ECtt ELan ESma MGos MPla MWat NGar NHol NNor SHer SPer SPla WWeb
¶ Boucle d'Or ®	COtt
europaea	WWeb
'Fiesta' (v)	CPMA CSam EFol ELan EPla IJoh MBel MBlu MBri MBrk MHlr MPla NBar NHol SFai SHil SPla WCot WHer WPat
giraldiana	SRms WBod WWeb
'Golden Nugget'	EBre ELan ESis IOrc LBre MAsh NRoo SHBN SLon SPer WStI
x *intermedia*	CBow WWeb
– 'Arnold Giant'	CShe WBod WWeb
– 'Densiflora'	WWeb
– Goldzauber®	WWeb
– 'Karl Sax'	CBow CBra SCob WWeb
– 'Lynwood' AGM	CB&S CBra CChe CSco CShe ELan ENot GRei IDai IJoh ISea LHop MBal MBar MBri MGos NBee NHol NKay NNor NRoo SDix SLon SPer SReu SSta WBod WDin WWeb
¶ – 'Lynwood' LA '79	MUlv SPla
– 'Mertensiana'	WWeb
– 'Minigold'	CB&S CBow CBra ECtt EPla ESma IDai IJoh MAsh MGos MUlv MWat SHBN SPer SPla WPat WStI WWeb
– 'Spectabilis'	CDoC CLTr ELan IOrc LBuc MBar NWea SHBN SPer WBod WDin WWeb
– 'Spectabilis Variegated'	CPle EFol EPla LHop MPla SDry SHer WCot WWeb
– 'Spring Glory'	EBee ECtt ENot MBri MRav WWeb
– 'Variegata'	CPMA EWri GAul MUlv NHol NSti NWyt SPer SSta
– 'Vitellina'	WWeb
japonica saxatilis	WWeb
Marée d'Or ® ('Courtasol')	COtt EBee IJoh MBri SPer
I 'Melissa'	WDin
'Northern Gold'	CB&S WWeb
ovata	EBre EPla LBre
– forms	MUlv WWeb
– 'Tetragold'	CB&S CBow CMer CSco MBal MBar MBel NBee NHol SHBN WWeb
'Paulina'	CBow ESis GAri
* 'Spring Beauty'	EHal WWeb
suspensa AGM	CB&S CBra CSco CShe ENot IJoh IOrc MBar MWat SHBN SPer WStI WWeb
– L 275	WWeb
– f. *atrocaulis*	CPle EMon GAri SGil WWeb
– 'Decipiens'	WBod WWeb
– var. *fortunei*	WWeb
¶ – 'Hewitt's Gold'	EMon
– 'Nymans'	CBra CDoC CSco MBri MUlv WWeb
– var. *sieboldii*	WWeb
§ – 'Taff's Arnold' (v)	ELan EMon
– 'Variegata'	See F. *s.* 'Taff's Arnold'
'Tremonia'	CMer EHal EHar MAsh MBal MGos MPla NNor WWeb
viridissima	EHal NNor WWeb
– 'Bronxensis'	CLew ELan EPar EPot ESis MHig MPla NBir SHer SIng SMad WOMN WPat WWeb
– var. *koreana*	EPla WWeb
* – – 'Variegata'	CPMA
– 'Weber's Bronx'	MBar
Week-End ®	CDoC ENot MBri

FORTUNEARIA (Hamamelidaceae)

See Plant Deletions

FORTUNELLA (Rutaceae)

F x *crassifolia* 'Meiwa'	ERea
F *japonica*	LPan
F *margarita*	CGOG MBri WFou WHig
F – 'Nagami'	ERea WFou

FOTHERGILLA (Hamamelidaceae)

gardenii	CPMA EBre ELan IOrc LBre MBri MPla MUlv NBar SPer SPla SSta WDin WWat
– 'Blue Mist'	CAbP CBow CPMA ELan LRHS MAsh MBri SMad SPer SPla SReu SSta
* 'Hunstman'	CCla MUlv SReu SSta
major AGM	CB&S CBow CBra CGre CPMA CSco EBre ECtt ELan IJoh LBre MBal MBri MGos MUlv NBar NBee NHol NTow SChu SHBN SPer SReu WDin WNor WPat WStI WWat
– Monticola Group	CBra CChu CPMA CSam CSco ELan ENot IBar IHos ISea MBal MBar MBri MPla NHed SChu SHBN SHer SPer SPla SSta WBod

FRAGARIA † (Rosaceae)

alpina	See F. *vesca* 'Semperflorens'
– *alba*	See F. *vesca* 'Semperflorens Alba'
F x *ananassa* 'Aromel' AGM	CWSG GTwe MBri NBar SDea WHig WWeb
F – Bogota ®	ECas GRei GTwe NBar NBee
F – 'Bounty'	GTwe SDea
F – 'Calypso'	CSut ECas GTwe WHig

F – 'Cambridge Favourite' **AGM** — CMac CSut CWSG ECas ESha GRei GTwe IJoh MBri MMor NBar NElm NRog SDea WHig WWeb
F – 'Cambridge Late Pine' — CWSG GTwe
F – 'Cambridge Rival' — GTwe NEgg
F – 'Cambridge Vigour' — ECas GTwe IJoh MMor NBar NBee NRog SDea
F – Elsanta ® — CDoC CWSG ECas GRei GTwe NBar SDea WHig
F – Elvira ® — CSut
– 'Fraise des Bois' — See F. ***vesca***
F – 'Gorella' — ECas NBar SDea WWeb
F – 'Hapil' — ECas GTwe
F – 'Harvester' — NEgg
F – 'Honeoye' **AGM** — ECas GTwe WHig
F – 'Idil' — GTwe
F – Korona ® — GTwe
F – 'Kouril' — NBar
F – Mara des Bois ® — ECas
F – 'Melody' — GTwe
F – 'Ostara' — GTwe
F – 'Pandora' — ECas GTwe SDea WWeb
F – 'Pantagruella' — GTwe SDea
F – 'Pegasus' — CSut ECas GTwe WHig
F – Rapella ® — GTwe
F – 'Redgauntlet' — NBar NRog SDea
F – 'Rhapsody' — ECas GTwe WHig
F – 'Royal Sovereign' — CMac GTwe SDea
F – 'Talisman' — GTwe
F – 'Tamella' — ECas GTwe SDea
F – 'Tenira' — GTwe
F – 'Totem' — GTwe
F – 'Variegata' — CGle CLTr CMea CMil CRiv CSFH CSev CShe ECro EFol ELan EOrc EPla LHop MRav NRoo NSti SCro SIng SPer WRus WThu WWin
F 'Baron Solemacher' — EJud WHer WHig
'Bowles' Double' — See F. ***vesca*** 'Multiplex'
F ***chiloensis*** — EMon
– 'Chaval' — ECha EMon
N – 'Variegata' — CAbb GCal WByw WEas
– x ***virginiana*** — CArn
daltoniana — NHol SIng
¶ – C&Mc 559 — GCHN
indica — See DUCHESNEA ***indica***
nipponica — EPla
F 'Pink Panda' — CHan EBre LBre MArl MBri NBar NBir NRoo SHer SPer WElm
'Variegata' — See F. x ***ananassa*** 'V.'
F ***vesca*** — CArn CKin ECWi ECoo EWFC GPoy LHol MHew NMir SHer SIde WCla WNdy WOak WPer WSun WWye
F – 'Alexandria' — GAbr MChe NHol NRog WCHb
– 'Flore Pleno' — See F. ***v.*** 'Multiplex'
F – 'Fructu Albo' — WPer
F – 'Mara des Bois' — GTwe WHig
F – 'Monophylla' — CRow CTom ELan EMon MFir NHol SIde WHer
§ – 'Multiplex' — CGle CRow CSFH CSev CTom ELan EMon EOrc ERav ESma GAbr NHol NSti NWyt SSvw WByw WCHb WHer
§ – 'Muricata' — CBos CFee CLTr CMil CPou CRow EMon GAbr NBrk NSti WHer WSun
– 'Plymouth Strawberry' — See F. ***v.*** 'Muricata'
F – 'Rügen' — WHoo
F – 'Semperflorens' — IEde ILis NBrk
F – 'Semperflorens Alba' — NHol
– 'Variegata' — ECha EPar NFai NMir SUsu WCru WHal WPbr WPer

FRANCOA (Saxifragaceae)

appendiculata — See F. ***sonchifolia***
¶ 'Purple Spike' — WCot
§ ***ramosa*** — CGle CGre CHan CLew CRDP CSam ECro GAbr IBar IBlr ITim LHop MHlr MTol NBro NNrw NRog NRoo NSti WCru WHal
– ***alba*** — See F. ***r.***
§ ***sonchifolia*** — Widely available
– Rogerson's form — CGle ECha

FRANKENIA (Frankeniaceae)

laevis — CNic CShe GGar MBro NVic SRms WWin
thymifolia — CLew CMHG CMer ELan EPot ESis GCHN IDai MBar MPla MRPP MWat NHol NKay NNrd NRed NRoo SBod SHer SIng SSmi WHoo WPer WWin

FRANKLINIA (Theaceae)

alatamaha — CGre CMCN WNor

FRASERA (Gentianaceae)

See Plant Deletions

FRAXINUS † (Oleaceae)

americana — CMCN CTho EArb EHar
– 'Autumn Purple' — SHil
angustifolia — CMCN EArb
– var. ***lentiscifolia*** — CTho EHar
§ – 'Raywood' **AGM** — CB&S CDoC CLnd COtt CTho EHar ELan ENot IOrc MBlu MBri MGos NWea SPer WDin WJas WMou
chinensis — CChu CLnd CMCN CTho EArb EHar
– ssp. ***rhyncophylla*** — WMou
excelsior **AGM** — CB&S CDoC CKin CLnd CPer ENot GRei IJoh LBuc LPan MBar MGos MWat NBee NWea SHBN SPer SPla WDin WMou WStI
– 'Allgold' — SMad WMou
– 'Aurea Pendula' — LMer WMou
– 'Crispa' — EMon WMou
– f. ***diversifolia*** — EMon WMou
– 'Diversifolia Pendula' — See F. ***e.*** 'Hetrophylla Pendula'
– 'Geesink' — ENot IHos
– 'Heterophylla Pendula' — WMou
– 'Jaspidea' **AGM** — CB&S CDoC CLnd COtt CSco CTho EHar ENot GRei IDai IJoh IOrc MBar MBlu MBri MGos MRav SHBN SHil SPer SSta WDin WJas WMou WStI WWat
– 'Pendula' **AGM** — CBow CDoC CLnd CPMA CSco CTho EBre EHar ELan ENot GRei IJoh IOrc LBre LPan MBlu MBri NBee SHBN SPer WDin WJas WMou WStI
– 'Pendula Wentworthii' — WMou
– 'R E Davey' — CTho
¶ – 'Stanway Gold' — EMon

– 'Stripey'	EMon
– 'Westhof's Glorie' AGM	CDoC CLnd CSco EBee ENot WJas
lanuginosa Koidz 0131	WHCr
§ ***latifolia***	ISea WCoo
mandshurica	WCoo
mariesii	See F. ***sieboldiana***
nigra	CFil LPan
♦***oregona***	See F. ***latifolia***
ornus AGM	CBot CLnd CSco CTho CWit EBar EHar ELan ENot IOrc ISea MBri SPer WCoo WDin WMou WWat
– 'Arie Peters'	LPan WStI
– 'Messek'	LPan
oxycarpa	See F. ***angustifolia***
pennsylvanica	EArb EHar
– 'Aucubifolia'	CTho
– var. ***lanceolata***	See F. ***p. subintegerrima***
– 'Variegata'	CLnd CTho SHil WMou
§ ***sieboldiana***	CFil CPMA IOrc SHil WCoo WMou
sogdiana Potamophila Group	CMCN
spaethiana	WMou
velutina	CBot CSto CTho EArb EHar ISea SHil WMou

FREESIA (Iridaceae)

N***alba***	LAma NRog
¶ 'Ballerina'	MWBu
'Diana'	LAma
'Fantasy' (d)	LAma
hybrids	CSut NRog
¶ 'Melanie' (d)	MWBu
¶ 'Oberon'	MWBu
'Romany' (d)	LAma
¶ 'Royal Blue'	MWBu
¶ 'Royal Gold'	MWBu
'White Swan'	LAma
xanthospila	LBow

FREMONTODENDRON (Sterculiaceae)

'California Glory' AGM	Widely available
californicum	Widely available
'Ken Taylor'	ERea
mexicanum	CBot CChu CGre
'Pacific Sunset'	CBow CCla CPMA ENot LHop SMad SPer

FREYLINIA (Scrophulariaceae)

cestroïdes	See F. ***lanceolata***
§ ***lanceolata***	CB&S CHan CPle CTre
* ***rosmarinifolia***	CB&S

FRITILLARIA † (Liliaceae/Liliaceae)

acmopetala AGM	CAvo CBro CMon CNic CRiv ECha ELan EPar EPot ETub EWal ITim LAma LBow MBal MHig MS&S MTho NRog SIng WAbe WChr WDav
– ssp. ***wendelboi***	EPot LAma WChr
§ ***affinis***	CBro EBul EPot EWal LAma MS&S WDav
§ – var. ***gracilis***	LAma WChr WDav
– ***tristulis***	WChr
alburyana	LRHS
alfredae ssp. ***glaucoviridis***	WChr
arabica	See F. ***persica***
armena	EPot LAma WChr
assyriaca	EBur ELan EPar EPot ETub EWal ITim SIng WDav
¶ ***atropurpurea***	MSto
aurea	EPot LAma
biflora	WChr
– 'Martha Roderick'	CBro EWal
§ ***bithynica***	CBro EPot LAma MSto NMen WChr WDav
brandegeei	EWal LAma
bucharica	CBro EPot WChr
camschatcensis	CAvo CBro CRDP ECha ELan EOrc EPar EPot ETub LAma LBow MS&S MSto NHar NRog SIng WAbe WChr
– black	MSto NHol
– ***multiflora***	WDav
carduchorum	See F. ***minuta***
carica	EPot WChr
– ssp. ***serpenticola***	EPot
caucasica	LAma WChr
citrina	See F. ***bithynica***
§ ***collina***	EPot
conica	LAma
crassifolia	CRiv EPot LAma WDav
– ssp. ***crassifolia***	WChr
§ – ssp. ***kurdica***	EPot WChr WDav
davisii	CBro EBul EPot ETub LAma MSto WChr
delphinensis	See F. ***tubiformis***
drenovskyi	LAma
eastwoodiae	LAma
ehrhartii	EPot MSto
elwesii	CBro MSto WChr
epirotica	LAma
glauca	LAma
graeca	CBro EPot ETub MSto
– ssp. ***graeca***	WChr
– ***ionica***	See F. ***g. thessala***
§ – ssp. ***thessala***	LAma MSto WChr WDav
§ ***grayana***	LAma WChr
gussichiae	LAma
hermonis ssp. ***amana***	EPot LAma WChr
hispanica	See F. ***lusitanica***
imperialis	CAvo CB&S CHEx MBal MBri MWBu NRog
– 'Argenteovariegata'	CBot
– 'Aureomarginata'	EPar LAma LBow MBri NRog
– 'Aurora'	CAvo EPar LAma LBow MHlr MWBu NRog SIng WCru
– 'Crown upon Crown'	See F. ***i.*** 'Prolifera'
– 'Lutea Maxima'	See F. ***i.*** 'Maxima Lutea'
– 'Maxima'	See F. ***i.*** 'Rubra Maxima'
§ – 'Maxima Lutea' AGM	CBow CBro CHEx CMea ELan EPar ETub LAma LBow MWBu NEgg NRog SIng SMad WCru
§ – 'Prolifera'	EPar ETub LAma LBow LRHS
– 'Rubra'	CBow CMea ELan EPar ETub LAma LBow LBuc MWBu NBir NRog WHil
§ – 'Rubra Maxima'	CBro LAma SIng WCru
– 'The Premier'	EPar LAma LBow SIng SMad
involucrata	CBro EPot LAma MS&S MSto SIng WChr
ionica	See F. ***graeca thessala***

karadaghensis	See F. ***crassifolia kurdica***
kotschyana	WChr
lanceolata	See F. ***affinis***
latakiensis	LAma WChr
§ ***latifolia***	EPot LAma WChr
– var. ***nobilis***	See F. ***latifolia***
liliacea	CBro EPot LAma WCot
§ ***lusitanica***	LAma MS&S
– MS 440	CMon
lutea	See F. ***collina***
meleagris AGM	Widely available
– ***alba*** AGM	CBro ECtt ELan EPot ETub LAma LBow MBri MBro MHig MS&S NHar NRya SHer SIng WCru
– 'Aphrodite'	CAvo EPot MHlr NHol WChr WCot
messanensis	CMon ECha LAma MBal MS&S WChr
– ssp. ***gracilis***	LAma MBal MS&S MSto
– ssp. ***messanensis***	CBro
michailovskyi AGM	CAvo CBro CRDP ECtt ELan EPar EPot ETub EWal GCra LAma LBow MBri MSto MTho NRog SHer SIng SUsu WAbe WChr WCla WCru WHil WPat
micrantha	LAma
§ ***minuta***	EPot
nigra	See F. ***pyrenaica***
olivieri	WChr
pallidiflora AGM	CAvo CBro EPar EPot ETub EWal ITim LAma MBal MS&S MSto NEgg NHar NSla WAbe WChr WCru WDav
§ ***persica***	CB&S CWes ECha EOrc EPar EPot LAma LBuc MBri MWBu SUsu WHow
– S&L 118	CMon
– 'Adiyaman'	CAvo CBro CRDP ELan ETub LBow NEgg NRog SIng
phaeanthera	See F. ***affinis gracilis***
pinardii	CBro EPot WChr
pontica	CAvo CBro CMon ECha EPar EPot EWal ITim LAma LBow MBal MS&S NHar SBla WChr WCru WDav
– Pras 1276	LRHS
pudica	EPot ITim LAma MS&S MSto WDav
§ ***pyrenaica*** AGM	CAvo CBro CMon EBul ECha EPot LAma LBow MBal MS&S NHar NHol SChu WChr WDav
raddeana	LAma
roderickii	See F. ***grayana***
rubra major	See F. ***imperialis*** 'Rubra Maxima'
ruthenica	EBul MS&S WChr
sewerzowii	EPot LAma MSto WChr
sibthorpiana	CBro EPot LAma WChr
stenanthera	CAvo CBro EPot LAma MSto WChr
stribrnyi	WChr
tenella	See F. ***orientalis***
thunbergii	CRiv
§ ***tubiformis***	WChr
tuntasia hybrids	ECha
uva-vulpis	CAvo CBro CRDP EBul LAma LBow MS&S MSto WAbe WHil
verticillata	CAvo CBro ECha EPar EPot ETub LAma MTho NHar SPou WChr WCru
walujewii	EPot WChr
whittallii	EPot LAma MSto WChr
¶ ***zagrica***	MSto

FUCHSIA † (Onagraceae)

N 'A M Larwick'	EBak
'A W Taylor'	EBak
'Abbé Farges'	CCla CLit CLoc EBak EBly ECtt EKMF GPen LCla MAsk MSmi MWhe NMGN NPor SKen SLBF SOld SPla
¶ 'Abbey Kilner'	MLab
'Abigail'	EKMF SLBF
'Achievement' AGM	CLoc EBly GPen LCla MAsk MJac MLab SKen SOld
'Ada Perry'	ECtt EKMF MAsk MSmi
'Adagio'	CLoc
'Adrian Young'	SLBF
'Ailsa Garnett'	EBak
'Aintree'	CLit NPor
'Airedale'	MAsk MJac
'Ajax'	EGou
'Alabama Improved'	MAsk MSmi SKen
'Aladna's Sander'	EGou
'Alan Ayckbourn'	EBly LCla MWar NPor
'Alan Stilwell'	NPor SLBF
'Alaska'	EBak EKMF MAsk SKen SOld
'Albion'	CCla
'Alde'	EBly EGou
'Alf Thornley'	EKMF MAsk MWar MWhe NPor
'Alfred Rambaud'	NMGN
'Alice Ashton'	CLit EBak EKMF NMGN
'Alice Hoffman'	CCla CLit CLoc CSco EBak EBly EGou EKMF GMon GPen LCla LVer MAsk MBar MBri MGos MJac MLab MSmi MWat MWhe NKay NMGN NPor SHer SIng SKen SLBF SOld SPer
'Alice Mary'	EBak EBly SLBF
'Alice Rowell'	EKMF
¶ 'Alice Stringer'	ECtt
'Alice Travis'	CLit EBak EGou
'Alison Ewart'	CLit CLoc EBak EKMF LCla MWhe NPor SKen SOld
'Alison June'	MBri
'Alison Patricia'	EKMF LCla MWar MWhe NPor SLBF
'Alison Reynolds'	LCla MBri
'Alison Ryle'	EBak
'Alison Sweetman'	EKMF MJac MWhe SKen
¶ 'Allure'	EGou
'Alma Hulscher'	EGou
§ ***alpestris***	EBak EKMF GMon
'Alton Water'	EGou EKMF
'Alwin'	CLit MWhe
'Alyce Larson'	EBak ECtt MAsk MJac MWhe NMGN NPor
'Amanda Bridgland'	EKMF LCla
'Amanda Jones'	EKMF MAsk MWhe
'Ambassador'	CLit EBak ECtt MAsk SKen
'Amber Supreme'	SKen
'Amelie Aubin'	CLoc EBak EKMF
'America'	EBak EGou
'American Dream'	MLab
'American Spirit'	MLab
'Amethyst Fire'	CCla
'Amigo'	CLit EBak
§ ***ampliata***	EBak EGou LCla

'Amy Lye'	CLoc EBak EKMF MAsk MSmi NMGN NPor SKen
§ 'Andenken an Heinrich Henkel'	CLoc EBak EKMF LCla MAsk MWhe NMGN SOld
'André Le Nostre'	EBak
andrei	EKMF
'Andrew'	EBak MAsk
'Andrew Carnegie'	CLoc
'Andrew George'	MJac
'Andrew Hadfield'	EKMF LCla MAsk MSmi MWar NPor SLBF
N 'Andromeda'	CCla
'Angela Leslie'	CLoc EBak EKMF
'Angela Rippon'	CLit MJac MWhe SKen SOld
'Angeline'	EGou
'Angel's Dream'	MAsk
'Angel's Flight'	CLoc EBak MSmi SOld
'Anjo'	NPor
'Ann Adams'	MJac
'Ann Howard Tripp'	CLoc LVer MAsk MBri MJac MWhe NMGN NPor
'Ann Lee'	CLoc EBak
'Ann Porter'	NPor
'Ann Roots'	EGou
'Anna of Longleat'	CLoc EBak EBly LVer SKen SLBF
'Annabel' **AGM**	CLit CLoc EBak EBly EGou EKMF LVer MAsk MBri MJac MLab MSmi MWar MWhe NFai NMGN NPor NPri SFar SHer SKen SLBF SOld
'Annie Johnson'	MLab
'Anthea Day'	CLoc
'Antigone'	SLBF
'Aphrodite'	CLoc EBak
N 'Apollo'	SOld
'Applause'	CLoc EBak EBly ECtt EGou EKMF LCla LVer MAsk MSmi NMGN NPor SOld
aprica hort.	See F. × ***bacillaris***
aprica Lundell	See F. ***microphylla aprica***
'Aquarius'	MWhe
'Arabella Improved'	EGou EKMF
arborea	See F. ***arborescens***
arborescens	CLit CLoc CPle CTro EBak EGou EKMF ERea LCla MAsk SBor SLBF SOld
'Arcadia'	MWar
'Arcadia Gold'	ECtt EKMF
'Arcadia Lady'	CLit MAsk MJac
'Arcady'	CLoc
'Archie Owen'	MSmi
'Ariel'	NMGN
'Army Nurse' **AGM**	CCla CLoc GCHN GPen MAsk MLab MWhe NPor SLBF SOld WWeb
'Art Deco'	EGou
'Art Nouveau'	MSmi
'Ashwell'	MLab
'Athela'	EBak
'Atlantic Star'	EBly MBri MJac NPor SOld
'Atlantis'	CLit MAsk MJac
'Atomic Glow'	EBak
'Aubergine'	EKMF MSmi NPor SLBF
¶ 'Audray'	MAsk
'Audrey Hepburn'	EKMF
'Aunt Juliana'	CLit EBak
'Auntie Jinks'	CLit EBak EGou EKMF LCla LVer MAsk MJac MSmi MWar MWhe NMGN NPor SKen SLBF SOld
'Aurora Superba'	CLoc EBak EKMF LCla NMGN NPor SLBF
'Australia Fair'	CLoc EBak
§ ***austromontana***	EBak
'Autumnale'	CLoc EBak EBly EFol EKMF LCla MAsk MBri MLab MSmi MWhe NMGN NPor NPri SKen SLBF SOld
'Avalanche'	CLoc EBak MAsk
'Avocet'	CLoc EBak
'Avon Celebration'	CLoc
'Avon Gem'	CLoc
'Avon Gold'	CLoc
ayavacensis	EKMF
'Azure Sky'	EKMF
¶ 'Babs'	MAsk
'Baby Blue Eyes'	CLit SLBF
'Baby Bright'	NPor SLBF
'Baby Chang'	MWhe SLBF
'Baby Neerman'	EKMF
'Baby Pink'	CLit EBly
¶ 'Baby Thumb'	EKMF SOld
§ × ***bacillaris***	CGre CMHG CRDP CSam CWit EBak LCla MBlu SBor SLBF
§ – 'Cottinghamii'	ESma IMal ITim WSHC
§ – 'Oosje'	EGou EKMF
'Bagworthy Water'	CLoc
'Baker's Tri'	EBak
'Bali Hi'	MSmi
'Balkonkönigin'	CLoc EBak MAsk SKen
'Ballet Girl'	CCla CLit CLoc EBak ECtt EKMF LCla MSmi SLBF SOld
'Bambini'	EBly NPor
'Banstead Bell'	SLBF
¶ 'Banzai'	EKMF
'Barbara'	CLit CLoc EBak EKMF LCla MAsk MJac MWar MWhe NPor SKen SOld WEas
'Barbara Hallett'	MLab
'Barbara Pountain'	MJac
'Barnsdale'	MLab
'Baron de Ketteler'	EKMF
'Baroness van Dedem'	NPor SLBF
'Baroque Pearl'	EKMF
¶ 'Barry M Cox'	EGou
'Barry's Queen'	EBak MAsk SKen SOld
'Bashful'	CCla EBly LCla MAsk MBri SIng SKen SOld WWeb
'Basketfull'	CLit
'Beacon'	CCla CLoc EBak EGou EKMF IHos LCla LVer MAsk MBri MJac MLab MSmi MWhe NMGN NPor SKen SOld WStI
'Beacon Rosa'	CLoc EBly EGou EKMF LCla LVer MAsk MBri MJac MLab MSmi MWar MWhe NPor SKen SLBF SOld
'Bealings'	CLit EBly ECtt EGou LCla LVer MAsk MJac MWar MWhe NPor NPri SHer SOld
'Beatrice Burtoff'	EKMF
'Beau Nash'	CLoc
'Beauty of Bath'	CLoc EBak
'Beauty of Clyffe Hall'	EBak
'Beauty of Exeter'	CCla CLit EBak EKMF SKen
'Beauty of Prussia'	CLoc ECtt GPen

'Beauty of Swanley' EBak
'Beauty of Trowbridge' NPor SKen
¶ 'Becky' EGou
'Begame Kiekeboe' EKMF
'Bella' CGle
'Bella Forbes' CLoc EBak MAsk SOld
'Bella Rosella' MSmi
'Belle de Lisse' EGou
'Belsay Beauty' MJac NPor
'Belvoir Beauty' CLoc MJac
'Ben's Ruby' SLBF
N 'Beranger' EBak
'Berba's Coronation' EKMF
'Berba's Happiness' EGou
'Berba's Inge Mariel' EGou
'Bergnimf' LCla
'Berliner Kind' EBak
'Bermuda' CLit EKMF
'Bernadette' CLTr
'Bertha Gadsby' EKMF
'Beryl's Choice' CLit
'Beth Robley' CLit MAsk NPor
'Betsy Ross' EBak
'Bette Sibley' LCla
'Beverley' EBak EBly GPen SLBF
'Bewitched' CLit EBak
'Bianca' SOld
'Bicentennial' CLoc EBak EBly ECtt EGou EKMF LCla LVer MAsk MJac MLab MSmi MWar MWhe NMGN NPor SKen SOld
'Big Charles' EGou
'Bill Gilbert' MSmi NPor SLBF
¶ 'Bill Stevens' EKMF
'Billie Roe' NMGN
'Billy Green' AGM CLit CLoc EBak EBly ECtt EKMF LCla MAsk MJac MSmi MWar MWhe NMGN NPor SKen SLBF SOld
'Bishop's Bells' MAsk MJac SKen
'Bittersweet' CLit MAsk
'Black Prince' MAsk MBri MWar
'Blackberry Ripple' MLab
I 'Blanche Regina' MJac MWhe NPor
'Bland's New Striped' EBak EKMF SLBF
'Blowick' EGou MAsk MLab NMGN NPor
¶ 'Blue Anne' SOld
'Blue Beauty' EBak
'Blue Bush' EKMF GPen MAsk MJac NMGN NPor
'Blue Butterfly' EBak
'Blue Gown' CLoc EBak EBly EKMF GPen LCla LVer MAsk MLab MSmi MWar SKen
'Blue Ice' MWhe
'Blue Lace' CCla LVer
N 'Blue Lagoon' MAsk MLab
'Blue Lake' MAsk MLab
'Blue Mink' EBak
'Blue Mirage' EGou MAsk MLab NMGN
'Blue Mist' EBak
'Blue Pearl' CLit EBak MAsk NMGN
'Blue Petticoat' CLoc
'Blue Pinwheel' EBak
'Blue Satin' LVer MSmi
'Blue Tit' SKen
'Blue Veil' ECtt EKMF MAsk MJac MSmi NMGN NPor SKen SLBF
'Blue Waves' CLit CLoc EBak EBly ECtt EGou EKMF LCla LVer MAsk MJac MWar MWhe NMGN NPor SOld
'Blush of Dawn' CLit CLoc EBak EBly EGou EKMF LCla LVer MAsk MSmi MWar NMGN SKen SLBF SOld
'Blythe' EBly EGou
'Bob Brown' LCla NPor SLBF
'Bob Pacey' MJac
'Bob Paisley' MBri
'Bobby Boy' EBak
'Bobby Dazzler' ECtt EKMF MJac
'Bobby Shaftoe' EBak EKMF MAsk MWhe
'Bobby Wingrove' EBak
'Bobolink' EBak
'Bob's Best' EBly MJac SLBF
'Bob's Choice' MAsk
'Boerhaave' EBak MAsk
'Börnemanns Beste' CLoc EBak EGou EKMF LCla MAsk NPor SKen
'Bohémienne' MAsk MSmi
boliviana Britton See F. ***sanctae-rosae***
boliviana Carrière CTro EBak EKMF GCra MWhe
§ – var. ***alba*** AGM CLoc EBak EGou EKMF LCla MAsk MWhe SLBF
– var. ***boliviana*** EGou
♦– var. ***luxurians*** See F. ***b. alba***
– ***puberulenta*** See F. ***b.***
'Bon Accorde' CLoc EBak EBly EKMF LCla MAsk NPor SKen SLBF SOld
'Bon Bon' CLit EBak
'Bonita' CLit MAsk MJac MSmi
'Bonnie Berrycloth' SOld
'Bonnie Lass' CLit EBak
'Bonny' CLoc
'Bora Bora' EBak EKMF
'Border Princess' EBak LCla
'Border Queen' AGM CLit CLoc EBak EBly EGou EKMF LCla MAsk MJac MLab MWhe NPor SKen SLBF
'Border Reiver' CLit EBak
'Bouffant' CLoc EBak MAsk MJac
'Bountiful' CLit CLoc EGou EKMF MAsk MWhe NMGN NPor SKen SOld
'Bouquet' EKMF SKen
'Bow Bells' CLoc ECtt MAsk MJac MWhe NMGN NPor
'Brain C Morrison' EGou EKMF
'Brandt's Five Hundred Club' CLoc EBak
'Breckland' EBak MJac
'Breeders' Delight' MBri
'Breeder's Dream' EBak
'Brenda' EBak EGou LCla
'Brenda Megan Hill' EBly
'Brenda Pritchard' ECtt
'Brenda White' CLit EKMF LCla MAsk MWar NMGN NPor SLBF
'Brentwood' EBak
brevilobis EKMF
'Brian Stannard' EGou
'Bridal Veil' EBak
'Bridesmaid' CLit EBak EKMF MAsk MSmi
'Brigadoon' CLoc EBak
'Brightling' MSmi
'Brighton Belle' EBly EGou LCla
N 'Brilliant' CCla CLoc EBak GPen LHil MAsk MGos MLab MPla MWat MWhe NPor SKen

'Briony Caunt'	EKMF
'British Jubilee'	EBly EKMF MAsk NMGN NPor
'Brodsworth'	MAsk MLab NMGN
'Brookwood Belle' AGM	EBly EGou MJac NPor SLBF
¶ 'Brookwood Dale'	MWhe
'Brookwood Joy'	EGou MAsk MJac SLBF SOld
'Brutus' AGM	CCla CLit CLoc EBak EBly EKMF ESma GMon GPen ISea LCla LVer MAsk MBel MSmi MWat MWhe NPor SKen SOld WStI
'Buddha'	EBak
'Bunny'	EBak NPor
'Buttercup'	CLoc EBak MAsk MWhe SKen SOld
¶ 'Butterfly'	MAsk
'Buttons and Bows'	NMGN
'C J Howlett'	EBak
'Caballero'	EBak
'Caesar'	EBak EKMF MAsk SOld
'Caledonia'	EBak NMGN
'Callaly Pink'	NPor
¶ 'Calverley'	SOld
'Cambridge Louie'	CLit EBak GPen LCla MAsk MBri MLab MWar MWhe NMGN NPor SKen SOld
'Camelot'	EBak
campos-portoi	EKMF
¶ 'Cancun'	MJac
'Candlelight'	CLoc EBak NPor
¶ 'Candy Kisses'	CLit
'Candy Stripe'	CLoc
canescens Bentham	EBak EKMF
canescens Munz	See F. ***ampliata***
'Capri'	EBak
'Cara Mia'	CLoc NPor SKen
¶ 'Cardinal'	CLoc
'Cardinal Farges'	CCla CLoc EKMF GPen LCla MSte NMGN SKen SLBF SOld
'Carioca'	EBak
'Carl Drude'	LCla
'Carl Wallace'	EKMF MJac
'Carla Johnson'	CLTr CLit CLoc EBly ECtt EKMF LCla MAsk MBri MJac MLab MWar MWhe NPor SLBF SOld
'Carlisle Bells'	MAsk
'Carmel Blue'	CLTr CLit CLoc MAsk MWhe SKen SOld
'Carmen Maria'	CLit LCla MJac SKen
'Carmine Bell'	EKMF
'Carnea'	GPen
'Carnival'	EGou LCla SOld
'Carnoustie'	EBak EGou MAsk
'Carol Grase'	CLoc
'Carol Nash'	CLoc
'Carol Roe'	EKMF SOld
'Carole Hardwick'	MLab
'Carole Scott'	MLab
'Caroline'	CLoc EBak EBly EKMF MAsk MSmi NMGN SKen SOld
'Cascade'	CLit CLoc ECtt EGou EKMF LCla LVer MAsk MBri MJac MLab MSmi MWar MWhe NMGN NPor SKen SOld WEas
'Casper Hauser'	EGou EKMF MAsk NPor
'Catherine Bartlett'	EKMF
'Cathie MacDougall'	EBak
'Cecile'	EBly ECtt EKMF LVer MAsk MLab MSmi SLBF
'Celadore'	CLit EKMF LCla MAsk MJac NMGN NPor SKen
'Celebration'	EGou ESma LCla
'Celia Smedley' AGM	CLit CLoc EBak EBly EGou EKMF LCla LVer MAsk MBri MJac MWar MWhe NMGN NPor SKen SLBF SOld
'Centenary'	SOld
'Centerpiece'	EBak
'Ceri'	CLoc
'Champagne Celebration'	CLoc
'Chandleri'	EKMF NPor SLBF
'Chang'	CLit CLoc CMHG EBak EKMF LBlm LCla MAsk MWar MWhe NMGN NPor SLBF
¶ 'Chantry Park'	EGou
'Chaos'	EGou
'Charisma'	LCla SOld
'Charlie Gardiner'	EBak EGou MWhe NMGN
'Charlie Girl'	EBak
'Charming'	CCla CLoc EBak GCHN GPen MAsk MJac MWar MWhe NMGN SOld
'Checkerboard' AGM	CLit CLoc EBak EGou EKMF LCla LVer MAsk MJac MLab MSmi MSte MWar MWhe NPor SKen SLBF SOld
'Cheers'	EBly EGou EKMF MAsk MSte MWar MWhe NMGN NPor SOld
'Chessboard'	CLoc
'Chillerton Beauty' AGM	CCla CLit CLoc CSco ECtt EKMF GMon GPen IDai LCla MAsk MJac MWhe SLBF SOld SPer
'China Doll'	CLit EBak MWhe SKen
'China Lantern'	CLoc EBak MAsk
'Chiquita Maria'	EKMF MSmi
'Christ Driessen'	EGou
'Christina Becker'	EGou
'Christine Shaffery'	EGou LCla
'Christine Truman'	EBly
'Christmas Ribbons'	EGou MSmi
'Churchtown'	NPor
cinerea	EKMF LCla
'Cinnabarrina'	SLBF
'Circe'	CLit EBak EKMF MAsk
'Circus'	EBak
'Citation'	CLoc EBak EKMF MJac MSmi NMGN NPor SOld
'City of Adelaide'	CLoc MWhe SKen
'City of Leicester'	LCla MAsk MBri MLab NPor
'Claire de Lune'	EBak MAsk NPor SLBF
'Claire Evans'	CLoc
'Classic Jean'	MWhe
'Clifford Gadsby'	EBak
'Cliff's Hardy'	EKMF LCla MAsk
'Cliff's Unique'	EBly MAsk NPor
'Clifton Beauty'	MAsk MJac
'Clifton Belle'	MJac
'Clifton Charm'	EBly MJac
'Cloth of Gold'	CLit CLoc EBak MAsk MJac MLab MSte MWhe NMGN NPor SKen SLBF SOld
'Clouds'	CCla
'Cloverdale Delight'	SKen
'Cloverdale Jewel'	EBak LCla MJac MLab MWhe SKen
'Cloverdale Joy'	EBak MAsk

'Cloverdale Pearl' AGM — CLit EBak EKMF ENot LCla MJac MWhe NPor SKen SLBF SOld
'Cloverdale Pride' — MAsk
'Cloverdale Star' — SKen
'Coachman' — CLoc EBak EBly EKMF LCla LVer MAsk MLab MSmi MWar MWhe NMGN NPor SKen SLBF SOld SPla
coccinea — CGre EKMF
¶ 'Col' — MAsk
x ***colensoi*** — CTre ECou EGou EKMF ESma
'Collingwood' — CLit CLoc EBak MAsk
'Come Dancing' — ECtt LVer MAsk MLab SKen SLBF
N 'Comet' — CLit CLoc EBak LCla
'Conchilla' — EBak
'Concorde' — CLoc
'Confection' — MSmi NMGN
¶ 'Congreve Road' — EGou
'Connie' — CCla EBak
'Conspicua' — EBak EGou EKMF ELan SKen
'Constable Country' — CLit
'Constance' — CCla CLit CLoc EGou EKMF GPen LCla MAsk MJac MSmi MWar MWhe SKen SLBF SOld
N 'Constellation' — CLoc EBak MAsk MJac MWhe NPor SKen SOld
'Continental' — CLit EBly EGou
'Coquet Bell' — EBak MAsk NPor
'Coquet Dale' — EBak ECtt EGou EKMF LCla MAsk MJac MWhe NMGN NPor
'Coquet Gold' — ECtt NMGN
'Coral Seas' — EBak
§ 'Coralle' AGM — CLit CLoc EBak EBly EGou EKMF LBlm LCla MAsk MJac MLab MWar MWhe NPor SKen SLBF SOld
'Corallina' AGM — CBra CCla CLit CLoc CMHG EBak EKMF GPen IHos MAsk MWhe NMGN SKen SLBF WEas
cordifolia Bentham — CB&S CBrk CTre EBak MAsk
cordifolia hort. — See F. ***splendens***
'Core'ngrato' — CLoc EBak
'Cornelian Fire' — CCla
'Corsair' — EBak EKMF MSmi NMGN SLBF
§ ***corymbiflora*** — EBak EGou EKMF LCla
– ***alba*** — See F. ***boliviana luxurians alba***
'Cosmopolitan' — EBak
'Costa Brava' — CLoc EBak
'Cotta Bella' — EGou EKMF MJac NPor
¶ 'Cotta Bright Star' — EKMF
'Cotta Fairy' — EKMF
'Cotta Princess' — ECtt EKMF
¶ 'Cotta Vino' — EKMF
'Cottinghamii' — See F. x ***bacillaris*** 'C.'
'Cotton Candy' — CLit CLoc EBly EGou MAsk MBri MLab MWhe SLBF SOld
'Countess of Aberdeen' — CLoc EBak EGou EKMF MAsk NPor SLBF SOld
'Countess of Maritza' — CLoc
'Court Jester' — CLoc EBak
'Cover Girl' — EBak MSmi MWhe
'Coverdale Jewel' — ECtt
'Coxeen' — EBak
'Crackerjack' — CLoc EBak MSmi
crassistipula — EKMF
'Crescendo' — CLoc SKen
¶ 'Crinkley Bottom' — EBly
'Crinoline' — EBak
¶ 'Crosby Serendipidy' — CLoc
'Crosby Soroptimist' — CLit EBly LCla MWar MWhe NPor
'Cross Check' — MAsk MBri MJac MLab SLBF
'Crusader' — NMGN
'Crystal Blue' — EBak MAsk
'Crystal Stars' — SKen
'Cupcake' — CLit
'Cupid' — EBak
'Curly Q' — EBak EKMF MAsk
'Curtain Call' — CLit CLoc EBak EGou SKen
cylindracea — EKMF
'Cymon' — MAsk MWhe
'Daffodil Dolly' — MLab
'Dainty' — EBak
'Dainty Lady' — EBak
'Daisy Bell' — CLit CLoc EBak ECtt EGou EKMF LCla LVer MAsk MJac MSte MWhe NPor SKen SLBF SOld
'Dalton' — EBak
'Dancing Flame' — CLit CLoc EBly EGou EKMF LCla LVer MAsk MJac MLab MSmi MWar MWhe NMGN NPor NPri SKen SLBF SOld
¶ 'Danielle' — MAsk
'Danny Boy' — CLoc EBak MAsk MWhe NMGN SOld
'Dark Eyes' AGM — CLoc EBak ECtt EGou EKMF LCla LVer MAsk MJac MLab MSmi MWhe NFai NMGN NPri SKen SLBF SOld
'Dark Secret' — EBak
'Darreen Dawn' — SLBF
'David' — EKMF ERav GMon LCla MAsk MPla SKen SLBF
'David Alston' — CLoc EBak
'David Lockyer' — CLoc
'David Ward' — EGou EKMF LCla
'Dawn' — EBak LCla SKen SOld
'Dawn Redfern' — MJac
'Dawn Sky' — EBak
'Dawn Star' — EBly MJac MLab MWhe
'Dawn Thunder' — MSmi
¶ 'Dawning' — EGou
'Day by Day' — MAsk
'Day Star' — EBak
'Daytime Live' — EBly
'Debby' — EBak
'Deben' — EGou
'Deben Rose' — MAsk
'Deborah' — MSmi
¶ 'Deborah Street' — CLoc
'Debra Hampson' — MLab
N ***decussata*** — CGle EBak EKMF
'Dee Copley' — EBak
'Deep Purple' — EGou EKMF MLab MSmi
'Delaval Lady' — CLit
'Delilah' — EKMF MJac
'Denis Bolton' — SLBF
§ ***denticulata*** — CLit CLoc CMHG EBak EKMF IBar LCla MAsk SLBF SOld
dependens — See F. ***corymbiflora***
'Derby Imp' — CLit MAsk MWar NMGN SKen
¶ 'Desmond Davey' — SOld
¶ 'Deutsche Perle' — CLit

'Devonshire Dumpling'	CGre CLTr CLoc EBak EBly ECtt EGou EKMF LVer MAsk MBri MJac MLab MWar MWhe NMGN SKen SLBF SOld
'Diablo'	EBak EGou
'Diamond Fire'	CCla
'Diamond Wedding'	SOld
'Diana'	EBak
'Diana Wills'	MSte MWhe SKen
'Diane Brown'	CLit EKMF MJac
'Diann Goodwin'	EGou
'Dick Swinbank'	SLBF
'Dilly-Dilly'	MAsk MJac
'Dimples'	MAsk NMGN
'Dipton Dainty'	CLoc EBak LCla
'Display' **AGM**	CCla CLit CLoc EBak ECtt EGou EKMF IHos LCla MAsk MBri MJac MLab MWar MWhe NMGN NPor NPri SHer SKen SLBF SOld WStI
'Doc'	CCla LCla MAsh MAsk SOld WWeb
'Docteur Topinard'	CLoc EBak
'Doctor'	See F. 'The Doctor'
'Doctor Brendan Freeman'	MJac
'Doctor Foster'	CCla CLoc CMHG CSco EBak ENot EPla LCla MSmi SOld WEas
'Doctor Olson'	CLoc EBak
'Doctor Robert'	EBly EKMF MBri MJac MWhe NPor SLBF
§ 'Dollar Princess' **AGM**	Widely available
'Dolly Daydream'	EGou EKMF SLBF
'Domacin'	EGou MSmi MWhe NMGN
'Dominyana'	EBak EKMF LCla SLBF
'Don Peralta'	EBak
'Dopey'	CCla LCla MAsk SOld
'Doreen Redfern'	CLit CLoc EKMF MAsk MJac MWhe NPor SOld
'Doris Birchell'	MBri
'Doris Coleman'	LCla SOld
¶ 'Doris Deaves'	EBly
'Doris Hobbs'	EKMF
¶ 'Doris Yvonne'	SOld
'Dorothea Flower'	CLoc EBak
'Dorothy'	SLBF
'Dorothy Day'	CLoc
'Dorothy M Goldsmith'	LCla
'Dorothy Shields'	EBly MJac NPor
¶ 'Dorrien Brogdale'	EGou
'Drake 400'	CLoc
'Drame'	CCla CLit EBak ECtt EKMF GMon GPen LCla LHil MAsk MSmi NMGN SKen SOld
'Dreamy Days'	EGou
¶ 'Drifter'	EGou
'Drum Major'	EBak
'Du Barry'	EBak
'Duchess of Albany'	CLit CLoc EBak MAsk
'Duet'	CLit MSmi
N 'Duke of Wellington'	CLoc
'Dulcie Elizabeth'	CLit EBak EKMF LCla MJac MWar MWhe SOld
'Dunrobin Bedder'	GMon
'Dusky Beauty'	CLit EKMF MJac MWar NPor SLBF
'Dusky Rose'	CLoc EBak EGou MAsk MJac MLab MWar MWhe
'Dutch Girl'	CCla
'Dutch Mill'	CLoc EBak
'Earl of Beaconsfield'	See F. 'Laing's Hybrid'
'Earre Barre'	CLit
'East Anglian'	CLoc EBak
'Easter Bonnet'	CLoc
'Easterling'	LCla
'Ebbtide'	CLoc EBak
¶ 'Echo'	CLit
'Ecstasy'	SOld
'Ed Largarde'	EBak EKMF MAsk NPor
'Edale'	MSmi
'Eden Lady'	CLoc MWar MWhe SOld
'Eden Princess'	MJac MWhe SKen
¶ 'Edie Lester'	SOld
'Edith'	EKMF GMon LCla SLBF
'Edith Hall'	EGou EKMF
'Edith Jack'	GPen
'Edith of Kimbolton'	MLab
'Edna May'	MWar NPor
'Edna W Smith'	ECtt
'Edwin J Goulding'	EGou EKMF SOld
'Eileen Raffill'	EBak
'Eileen Saunders'	EBak
'El Camino'	CLit ECtt MAsk MWhe NFai NPri
'El Cid'	CLoc EBak EKMF GPen MAsk
'Elaine Ann'	EBly MJac NPor
'Eleanor Clark'	EKMF LCla NPor
'Eleanor Leytham'	CLit EBak EKMF LCla MAsk NMGN SOld
'Eleanor Rawlins'	EBak EKMF GPen MLab NMGN NPor SKen SOld
'Elf'	CCla
'Elfin Glade'	CLoc EBak NBir
'Elfrida'	EKMF NMGN SKen
'Elfriede Ott'	CLit CLoc EBak EKMF MWhe SLBF SOld
N 'Elizabeth'	EBak
¶ 'Elizabeth Anne'	MLab
'Elizabeth Broughton'	EKMF
'Elizabeth Travis'	EBak
'Ellen Morgan'	EBak
'Elsa'	ECtt
'Elsie Mitchell'	CLit MAsk MSte MWar MWhe NMGN NPor
§ 'Emile de Wildeman'	EBak EGou EKMF LCla MWar MWhe NPor
'Emily Austen'	EGou EKMF
'Emma Louise'	NPor SLBF
'Emma Rowell'	EKMF
'Empress of Prussia' **AGM**	CCla CLoc EBak EKMF GPen MAsk MLab SKen SLBF SSte
'Enchanted'	EBak MWar
encliandra	
ssp. ***encliandra***	EGou EKMF
– ***tetradactyla***	EKMF
§ 'Enfant Prodigue'	CCla CLoc EKMF GMon SLBF
'English Rose'	MAsk
'Eric Cooper Taylor'	MLab
'Erica Julie'	LCla
'Ernest Rankin'	EKMF
'Ernestine'	EBly EGou MWhe SOld
'Ernie Bromley'	EGou
'Errol'	CLoc
'Esme Tabraham'	CCla
'Estelle Marie'	CLit CLoc EBak EGou EKMF MAsk MJac MWar MWhe NPor SKen SLBF SOld

'Esther Devine'	MAsk
'Eternal Flame'	EBak MBri MWhe NMGN NPor SKen
'Ethel May Lester'	SOld
'Eurydice'	CLoc
'Eusebia'	EGou EKMF MAsk MJac MSmi NMGN SLBF SOld
'Eva Boerg'	CCla CLit CLoc CSco EBak ECtt EKMF IHos LCla LVer MAsk MBri MLab MSmi MWar MWhe NFai NMGN NPor NPri SKen SOld WKif
'Evanson's Choice'	SKen
¶ 'Eve Hollands'	EGou
'Evelyn Steele Little'	EBak
'Evening Sky'	EBak
'Evensong'	CLoc EBak EBly NMGN SOld
'Excalibur'	CLit EGou
excorticata	CB&S CGre CTre CTrw ECou EKMF SBor WSHC
'Exeter'	EBly
'Expo '86'	MSmi
'Exton Beauty'	MLab
¶ 'Fabian Frank'	EGou
'Fairytales'	EKMF
¶ 'Falklands'	MAsk
'Falling Stars'	CLoc EBak MWhe NPor
'Fan Dancer'	EBak
'Fan Tan'	MSmi
'Fancy Pants'	CLoc EBak EGou MAsk MBri
'Fanfare'	EBak
'Fascination'	See F. 'Emile de Wildeman'
'Fashion'	EBak
'Favourite'	EBak
'Fenman'	EBly EGou MJac
'Fergie'	LCla SOld
'Festival'	MAsk
'Festoon'	EBak
'Fey'	CLit EGou EKMF MAsk
'Fiery Spider'	EBak EKMF
'Filigraan' ('Filigree')	CCla
'Finn'	EBly EGou LCla LVer
'Fiona'	CLit CLoc EBak EGou MAsk
'Fiona Jane'	EKMF
'Fire Mountain'	CLoc EGou MWhe NMGN NPor SKen
'Firecracker'	MLab
'Firefly'	CBow
'Firefox'	MLab
'Firelite'	EBak
'Firenza'	MWar SLBF
'First Lady'	CLit MAsk MSmi
'First Success'	EKMF MAsk NPor
'Flair'	CLit CLoc
'Flame'	EBak
'Flash' **AGM**	CCla CLoc EBak ECtt EKMF GPen LCla LVer MAsk MJac MWhe NMGN SIng SLBF SOld WStI
'Flashlight'	ELan
'Flat Jack o'Lancashire'	ECtt EKMF
'Flavia'	EBak SOld
'Flirtation Waltz'	CLit CLoc EBak EGou EKMF LCla MAsk MBri MJac MSmi MWhe NMGN NPor SKen SOld
'Flocon de Neige'	EBak
'Floral City'	CLoc EBak
'Florence Mary Abbott'	EBly EGou LCla MWar NMGN SOld
'Florence Turner'	EBak EBly EKMF LCla MAsk MWhe SKen
'Florentina'	CLoc EBak EGou EKMF MWar NPor SLBF
'Flowerdream'	MJac
¶ 'Fluffy Frills'	CLit SLBF
'Flyaway'	EBak NPor
'Flying Cloud' **AGM**	CLoc EBak EKMF MAsk MBri MWhe NMGN
'Flying Scotsman'	CLoc EBak EBly EGou LVer MAsk SLBF SOld
'Folies Bergères'	EBak
'Foline'	MSmi
'Fondant Cream'	MLab
'Foolke'	EBak EBly LCla
¶ 'Forest King'	CLit
N 'Forget Me Not'	CLoc EBak EKMF GMon MAsk MWhe SLBF
'Fort Bragg'	EBak MSmi SKen
'Forward Look'	MWhe SKen
'Fountains Abbey'	NPor
¶ 'Foxgrove Wood'	EBak EBly SLBF
¶ 'Foxwood Grove'	EGou
'Frank Saunders'	LCla SLBF
'Frank Unsworth'	ECtt EKMF MAsk MWar MWhe NMGN NPor SOld
'Frau Hilde Rademacher'	CCla CLit EBak EBee EBly EKMF MPla SLBF
'Fred Swales'	EKMF
'Freefall'	EBak
'Freeland Ballerina'	EBly MJac
'Friendly Fire'	EKMF
'Frosted Flame'	CLit CLoc EKMF LCla LVer MAsk MJac MWar MWhe NPor SLBF SOld
'Frühling'	EBak
I 'Fuchsia Fan'	EBly
'Fuchsiade '88'	EBak EGou LCla LVer MWhe SLBF SOld
'Fuchsiarama '91'	EGou EKMF MSmi
¶ 'Fudzi San'	EGou
'Für Elise'	EBak
'Fuksie Foetsie'	EGou EKMF MAsk
fulgens **AGM**	CMHG EKMF LCla LHil MAsk MBal MSte MWhe NWyt SOld
– ***rubra grandiflora***	See F. 'Rubra Grandiflora'
'Gala'	EBak
'Galadriel'	CLit EGou
'Galahad'	EBak
'Garden News' **AGM**	CCla CLit CLoc EBly ECtt EGou EKMF GMon GPen LCla LVer MAsk MJac MPla MSmi MWar MWhe NMGN NPor SKen SLBF SOld SPla
'Garden Week'	MAsk MWhe SOld
'Gartenmeister Bonstedt' **AGM**	CLoc EBak EBly EKMF LCla MAsk NMGN NPor SKen SMad SOld WEas
'Gay Anne'	EKMF
'Gay Fandango'	CLit CLoc EBak ECtt EGou LCla MAsk MWar NMGN SKen SLBF SOld
'Gay Future'	EKMF
'Gay Parasol'	CLit CLoc EGou LVer MAsk MSmi MWhe
'Gay Paree'	EBak MAsk
'Gay Senorita'	EBak
'Gay Spinner'	CLoc
'Gazebo'	MSmi

gehrigeri	EBak EKMF
¶ 'Général Charles de Gaulle'	EGou
'Général Monk'	CLit EBak ECtt EKMF MBri MJac MPla SKen SOld
'Général Voyron'	MPla
'General Wavell'	CLit
'Genii' AGM	Widely available
'Geoffrey Smith'	ECtt EKMF
'Georgana'	ECtt MSmi MWhe
'George Barr'	EKMF SKen
'George Humphrey'	SOld
'George Travis'	EBak MBri
'Gerda Manthey'	EKMF
¶ 'Gerharda's Aubergine'	EGou
'Gesneriana'	CLoc EBak
'Giant Falls'	CLoc MSmi
'Giant Pink Enchanted'	CLoc EBak
'Gilda'	EGou MAsk MJac NPor
'Gilt Edge'	CLoc
¶ 'Gina's Gold'	MAsk
'Gipping'	EGou
'Girls Brigade'	EKMF
'Gladiator'	EBak LCla SKen
'Gladys Lorimer'	NPor SLBF
'Gladys Miller'	CLoc
'Glenby'	CLit NPor
'Glitters'	EBak ECtt EKMF LCla NMGN NPor
'Globosa'	CCla EBak GMon SKen
¶ 'Gloria Johnson'	EKMF
'Glow'	EBak
'Glowing Embers'	EBak MAsk
Glowing Lilac ®	EKMF MSmi
'Glyn Jones'	EKMF
'Gold Brocade'	CCla CLit SKen
'Gold Crest'	EBak
'Gold Foil'	EGou
'Gold Leaf'	CLit
'Golden Anniversary'	CLoc EBak EBly EGou EKMF MAsk MJac MSmi NMGN SOld
'Golden Arrow'	EGou
'Golden Border Queen'	CLoc
'Golden Dawn'	CLoc EBak ECtt LVer NPor SKen SOld
¶ 'Golden Drame'	MAsk
'Golden Eden Lady'	MWhe
¶ 'Golden Guinea Pig'	SOld
¶ 'Golden Herald'	SLBF
'Golden Jessimae'	MAsk MLab
'Golden La Campanella'	CLoc ECtt SOld
'Golden Lena'	EKMF MAsk SOld
'Golden Marinka' AGM	CLit CLoc EBak ECtt EKMF ESma LCla LVer MAsk MBri MJac MSmi MWar MWhe NMGN NPor SOld
'Golden Melody'	CCla
¶ 'Golden Penny Askew'	MAsk
'Golden Runner'	LVer MAsk MJac NPor
'Golden Spangles'	CB&S
'Golden Spring Classic'	MLab
'Golden Swingtime'	EGou LCla LVer MAsk MBri MLab MWar MWhe NMGN NPor SOld
'Golden Tolling Bell'	MAsk MLab
'Golden Treasure'	CLit CLoc CSco ECtt EKMF LCla MBri NMGN NPor
'Golden Wedding'	EKMF
'Goldsworth Beauty'	GPen LCla
'Golondrina'	EBak MWhe
'Goody Goody'	EBak
'Gordon Thorley'	EBly EKMF MWhe NPor SLBF
'Gordon's China Rose'	LCla SKen
'Göttingen'	EBak
'Governor 'Pat' Brown'	EBak MAsk
'Grace Darling'	EBak MWhe
'Grace Durham'	EBak
gracilis	See F. ***magellanica gracilis***
'Graf Spee'	EGou
'Graf Witte'	CCla CLTr CLit EGou GPen MWhe
¶ 'Grand Duchess'	EGou LCla
'Grand Prix'	MAsk MLab SKen SOld
'Grand Slam'	SKen SOld
'Grandma Sinton'	CLoc EBly LCla MBri MJac MWar MWhe NPor
'Grandpa George'	SOld
'Grasmere'	NPor
¶ 'Great Ouse'	EBly
'Great Scott'	CLoc SKen
'Green 'n' Gold'	EBak
'Greenpeace'	EKMF MAsk SLBF
'Greg Walker'	CLit
'Gretna Chase'	MBri MWhe
'Grey Lady'	SOld
'Groene Kan's Glorie'	EKMF SLBF
'Grumpy'	EBly LCla MAsk MBri NPor SKen SOld WWeb
'Gruss aus dem Bodethal'	CLoc EBak EBly EKMF LCla SKen
'Guinevere'	EBak
'Gustave Doré'	EBak
'Guy Dauphine'	EBak
'Gwen Dodge'	MSmi
'Gwen Wakelin'	MLab
'Gypsy Girl'	CLit MAsk SKen
'Gypsy Prince'	CLoc
'H G Brown'	EBak MWhe NPor
'Halsall Beauty'	MBri
'Halsall Pride'	MBri
'Hampshire Beauty'	MJac SOld
'Hampshire Blue'	SLBF
'Hanna'	CCla
'Hannah Williams'	CLTr MAsk MLab
'Happiness'	NMGN
'Happy'	CCla EBly LCla MAsk SIng SOld
'Happy Anniversary'	EKMF MAsk MWar
'Happy Fellow'	CLoc EBak
'Happy Wedding Day'	CLoc EKMF LCla MAsk MLab MWhe SLBF
'Hapsburgh'	EBak
'Harlow Car'	CLit EKMF MAsk MWar
N 'Harmony'	EBak
'Harnser's Flight'	EGou LCla
¶ 'Harold Smith'	SOld
'Harriett'	MAsk MSmi
'Harrow Pride'	SKen
'Harry Dunnett'	EBak
'Harry Gray'	CLit CLoc EBak EBly ECtt EGou LCla MAsk MBri MJac MLab MSmi MWar MWhe NMGN NPor NPri SHer SKen SLBF SOld
'Harry Lye'	EBly EGou
hartwegii	EGou EKMF LCla MAsk
'Hathersage'	EBak

	Cultivar	Suppliers
	'Hathor'	EGou
	'Hatschbachii'	EKMF GMon
	'Haute Cuisine'	EGou EKMF MAsk MSmi SLBF
	'Hawaiian Night'	CLit
	'Hawaiian Princess'	ECtt
¶	'Hawaiian Sunset'	SLBF
	'Hawkshead'	CCla CDec EGou EKMF ELan GMon GPen LCla LGre LHil MAsk MJac MWhe NPor SAxl SChu SMrm SOld WCru
	'Hazel'	EKMF MAsk MWhe
	'Heart Throb'	EBak MBri
	'Heathfield'	GPen
	'Hebe'	EBak MWhe
	'Heidi Ann' **AGM**	CLit CLoc EBak EBly EGou EKMF IHos LCla LVer MAsk MBri MJac MLab MSmi MWar MWhe NMGN NPor NPri SKen SLBF SOld
	'Heidi Weiss'	NMGN SKen SOld
♦	'Heinrich Henkel'	See F. 'Andenken an Heinrich Henkel'
	'Heirloom'	ECtt EKMF MSmi NMGN
	'Helen Clare'	CLoc EBak
	'Helen Elizabeth'	MBri
	'Helen Spence'	MLab
	'Hellan Devine'	MJac
	'Hello Dolly'	CLoc
	'Hemsleyana'	See F. ***microphylla hemsleyana***
	'Henri Poincaré'	EBak EKMF MSmi
	'Herald' **AGM**	CLit EBak NMGN SLBF SOld
	'Herbe de Jacques'	SKen
	'Heritage'	CLoc EBak
	'Hermiena'	CLoc EGou EKMF MWar NPor SLBF
	'Heron'	EBak EKMF GMon NMGN SKen
	'Hessett Festival'	EBak EBly EGou LVer
	'Heston Blue'	EKMF NMGN
	'Hi Jinks'	EBak MAsk MSmi
	hidalgensis	See F. ***microphylla hidalgensis***
	'Hidcote Beauty'	CLit CLoc EBak EKMF MAsk MWhe NPor SKen SLBF
	'Hidden Beauty'	MLab
	'Highland Pipes'	EKMF LCla MAsk MSmi
	'Hindu Belle'	EBak EKMF MSmi
	'Hinnerike'	EGou MAsk SLBF
	'His Excellency'	EBak
	'Hobson's Choice'	LCla LVer MWar SLBF SOld
¶	'Hokusai'	EKMF
	'Hollywood Park'	EBak
	'Horatio'	ECtt MJac
	'Howlett's Hardy'	CLit CLoc EBak EBee ECtt EKMF GCHN MAsk MBal MBri MSmi NMGN NPor
	'Hula Girl'	CLit EBak ECtt EGou EKMF LCla MAsk MJac MLab MWar MWhe NMGN NPor SKen SLBF
	'Humboldt Holiday'	ECtt EKMF MAsk MLab MSmi NMGN
	'Hungarton'	MLab
	'Ian Brazewell'	CLoc
	'Ian Leedham'	EBak EKMF NPor
	'Ice Cream Soda'	EBak
	'Iceberg'	EBak EBly
	'Icecap'	EKMF
	'Iced Champagne'	CLoc EBak MAsk MJac MWar NPor SKen
	'Ichiban'	CLoc SKen
	'Ida'	EBak
	'Igloo Maid'	CLoc EBak EKMF MAsk MJac MLab MWhe NPor SKen SOld
	'Imagination'	MLab
¶	'Impala'	EGou
	'Imperial Fantasy'	SLBF
	'Impudence'	CLoc EBak MAsk NMGN
	'Impulse'	CLoc ECtt EKMF SKen SLBF
¶	'Ina'	MAsk
	'Independence'	NPor
	'Indian Maid'	EBak EBly ECtt EKMF MAsk MBri MJac NMGN SKen SOld
	'Inferno'	EKMF MSmi
	'Ingleore'	EKMF
	'Ingram Maid'	MAsk
	'Insulinde'	EGou
	'Intercity'	EKMF
	'Interlude'	EBak
	'Irene L Peartree'	EGou
	'Iris Amer'	CLoc EBak NPor SLBF
	'Isabel Ryan'	CCla
	'Isis'	CCla EKMF SKen
	'Isle of Mull'	CLit EGou LCla SKen
	'Isle of Purbeck'	MJac
	'Italiano'	MJac NPor
	'Jack Acland'	ECtt EGou NPor SKen
	'Jack Coast'	SOld
	'Jack Shahan' **AGM**	CLoc EBak EBly EKMF IHos LCla LVer MAsk MBri MJac MSmi MWar MWhe NFai NMGN SKen SLBF SOld
	'Jack Stanway'	CCla EGou MAsk
	'Jackie Bull'	EBak
	'Jackpot'	EBak
	'Jackqueline'	EGou EKMF MAsk SOld
	'Jam Roll'	MAsk SLBF
	'Jamboree'	EBak MAsk
	'James Lye'	EBak GMon MAsk SKen
	'James Travis'	EBak GMon LCla NPor SKen
	'Jandel'	MSmi
	'Jane Humber'	EKMF LCla
	'Jane Lye'	EBak
	'Janet Goodwin'	MLab
¶	'Janice Ann'	SOld
	'Janice Revell'	MJac
	'Jaunty'	CTre
	'Jayne Rowell'	NPor SKen
	'Jean'	EKMF
	'Jean Campbell'	EBak
	'Jean Clark'	SLBF
	'Jean Dawes'	EGou
	'Jean Muir'	MLab
	'Jean Pidcock'	MLab
¶	'Jennette Marwood'	SOld
	'Jennie Rachael'	NMGN
¶	'Jennifer Haslam'	EGou
	'Jenny Sorensen'	EBly EKMF LCla LVer MAsk MWar NPor SLBF
	'Jess'	LCla SLBF
	'Jessimae'	CLit MAsk
N	'Jester'	CLoc
	'Jet Fire'	EBak
	'Jezebel'	MSmi
	'Jill Whitworth'	NMGN
	'Jim Coleman'	EBly LCla MWhe NPor SLBF SOld
¶	'Jim Dodge'	SLBF
	'Jim Muncaster'	CLit EKMF MAsk

jimenezii EKMF
'Jimmy Carr' EKMF SOld
'Joan Cooper' CCla CLoc EBak EKMF GPen NPor
'Joan Goy' EBly EKMF MAsk MJac MWar NPor
¶ 'Joan Knight' CLoc
'Joan Leach' CCla
¶ 'Joan Margaret' MJac
'Joan Pacey' EBak MAsk SKen
'Joan Smith' CLit EBak NPor
¶ 'Joan Young' EGou
'Joe Browning' CCla
'Joe Kusber' EBak EKMF MAsk NMGN SKen SOld
'John Lockyer' CLoc EBak
'John Maynard Scales' CMer EBly EGou MAsk MJac MWhe
'John Suckley' EBak
'John Yardell' MJac
'Johnny' CLoc
'Jomam' EBly LCla MAsk MWhe NPor SLBF
'Jon Oram' CLoc
'Jose's Joan' CLit MAsk MLab MWhe NMGN
'Joy Bielby' EGou EKMF NPor
'Joy Patmore' AGM CLit CLoc EBak EBly EKMF LCla MAsk MWhe NPor SKen SLBF SOld
'Joy White' CCla
'Joyce Sinton' EKMF MBri NPor
'Jo-Anne Fisher' EBly
'Judi Spiers' EBly
'Judith Alison Castle' GCHN
'Judith Coupland' LCla NPor SLBF
'Judith Mitchell' MLab
'Jules Daloges' EBak
'Julia' EKMF
¶ 'Julie' MAsk
'Julie Marie' EBly LCla MJac SLBF
'June Gardner' EKMF
N 'Juno' EBak
'Jupiter Seventy' EBak
'Justin's Pride' CLit EKMF MAsk MLab NMGN
'Kaboutertje' EKMF
'Kaleidoscope' EBak MSmi
'Karen Bielby' EKMF
'Karen Louise' CLoc
'Karin de Groot' EKMF MSmi
'Kathleen Colville' CLoc
'Kathleen Muncaster' EKMF MWar
'Kathleen Saunders' LCla
'Kathleen Smith' ECtt EKMF
'Kathryn Maidment' EKMF
¶ 'Kathy Scott' EBly
'Kathy's Prince' ECtt EKMF
'Kathy's Sparkler' EKMF
'Katrina' CLoc EBak
'Katrina Thompsen' EKMF LCla NPor SLBF
¶ 'Keele '92' EKMF
'Keepsake' CLoc EBak
¶ 'Kegworth Beauty' MAsk
'Kegworth Carnival' CLit LCla MAsk MJac MLab NPor SKen SOld
'Kegworth Delight' CLit LCla NPor
'Kegworth Supreme' MJac MWhe
'Ken Goldsmith' EBly EGou
'Ken Jennings' MJac NPor
'Ken Sharp' CLit MJac
'Kenny Dalglish' EKMF
'Kernan Robson' CLoc EBak EGou
'Kerry Anne' EBly EKMF
'Keystone' EBak MAsk
'Khada' EKMF MWhe
'Kim Wright' MWhe
'Kimberly' EBak
'King of Bath' EBak
'King of Hearts' EBak
'King's Ransom' CLit CLoc EBak MAsk MWhe NMGN NPor SKen SLBF SOld
'Kiss 'n' Tell' MJac MWhe
'Kit Oxtoby' ECtt EKMF LCla SKen
'Kiwi' EBak MAsk NMGN SKen SLBF
'Knight Errant' SLBF
'Knockout' CLit EGou EKMF MAsk MSmi NPor
'Kolding Perle' SOld
'Kon-Tiki' CLit EKMF NMGN
'Koralle' See F. 'Coralle'
'Kwintet' EBak LCla MJac NPor SKen
'Kyoto' EKMF
'La Apache' EBak
'La Bianca' EBak
'La Campanella' AGM CLoc EBak EBly ECtt EGou EKMF LCla LVer MAsk MBri MJac MLab MSmi MSte MWar MWhe NFai NMGN NPor NPri SHer SKen SLBF SOld
'La Fiesta' CLit EBak MSmi NMGN
'La France' EBak
N 'La Neige' EBak MAsk MSmi SKen SOld
'La Porte' CLit CLoc
'La Rosita' EBak MAsk MSmi SLBF
N 'La Traviata' EBak
'Lace Petticoats' EBak EKMF MSmi
'Lady Boothby' CBow CCla CHEx CLit CPle EBak EKMF MAsk NMGN NPor SKen SOld SPla
'Lady in Grey' EKMF SLBF
'Lady Isobel Barnett' CLit CLoc EBak EBly EKMF IHos LCla LVer MAsk MBri MJac MSmi MWar MWhe NPor SKen SOld
'Lady Kathleen Spence' CLit EBak EKMF MAsk MJac MWhe NMGN NPor SKen SOld
'Lady Love' MBri
'Lady Pamela Mountbatten' MAsk
'Lady Patricia Mountbatten' EBly ECtt EKMF LCla MBri MJac MLab MWhe NPor SOld
'Lady Ramsey' CLit EBak MJac NMGN
'Lady Rebecca' CLoc
'Lady Thumb' AGM CChe CCla CLit CLoc CMHG CSco CShe EBak EBly EKMF GPen LCla LVer MAsk MBal MBar MBri MJac MLab MPla MSmi MWar MWat MWhe NKay NMGN SKen SLBF SOld SPer
'Lady's Smock' EKMF
§ 'Laing's Hybrid' EGou
'Lakeland Princess' EBak
'Lakeside' CLoc EBak
'Lancashire Lass' MBri NPor
'Lancelot' CLit EBak EBly EGou LCla NMGN SKen
'Land van Beveren' MSmi NPor
'Lark' EBly EGou

'L'Arlésienne'	CLoc EBly
'Lassie'	CLoc EBak MJac MSmi
N 'Laura'	CLoc EKMF MSmi MWhe NMGN SLBF
'Laura Amanda'	EBly
'Laurie'	SOld
'Lavender Blue'	CCla
'Lavender Kate'	CLoc EBak MJac
¶ 'Lavender Lace'	MWhe
'Lazy Lady'	EBak
'Le Berger'	EKMF
'Lechlade Apache'	EGou LCla
'Lechlade Chinaman'	EKMF
'Lechlade Fire-Eater'	EGou
'Lechlade Gorgon'	EKMF LCla
'Lechlade Magician'	CMer EKMF
'Lechlade Marchioness'	EGou EKMF
'Lechlade Potentate'	MAsk
'Lechlade Rocket'	EKMF
'Lechlade Tinkerbell'	EGou
'Lechlade Violet'	EKMF
¶ 'Lee Anthony'	EGou
'Leica'	EKMF
'Leicestershire Silver'	MJac
'Len Bielby'	EKMF
'Lena' AGM	CCla CLit CLoc CMHG EBak EBly EGou EKMF GPen LCla LVer MAsk MBal MBri MJac MLab MPla MSmi MWhe NFai NMGN NPor SHer SKen SOld SPer WEas
'Lena Dalton'	CLit CLoc EBak EKMF IHos MAsk MBri MJac MSmi MWar MWhe SKen SOld
'Leonora' AGM	CLoc EBak EBly EKMF LCla LVer MAsk MBri MLab MSmi MWar MWhe NPor SKen SLBF SOld
'Letty Lye'	EBak
'Lett's Delight'	EBly
'Leverhulme'	See F. 'Leverkusen'
§ 'Leverkusen'	CLoc EBak ECtt EKMF MJac MWhe SKen SLBF SOld
'Libra'	MSmi
N 'Liebesträume'	EBak
'Liebriez'	EBak EBly EKMF LCla SOld
'Lilac'	EBak
'Lilac Dainty'	GPen
'Lilac Lady'	MJac
'Lilac Lustre'	CLoc EBak EKMF MBri
'Lilac Princess'	MJac SKen
'Lilac Queen'	EBak
'Lillibet'	CLoc EBak SKen
'Lillydale'	CLit
'Linda Goulding'	EBak EBly EGou LCla MAsk MWhe NMGN SOld
'Lindisfarne'	CLit EBak EGou EKMF LCla MAsk MJac MWar NPor SKen SOld
'Linet'	EBak
¶ 'Linsey Brown'	NPor
'Lisa'	EBly MSmi SLBF
'Lisi'	EKMF NPor
'Little Beauty'	EKMF MLab MWhe NPor SLBF
'Little Gene'	EBak
'Little Jewel'	SKen
'Little Ouse'	EGou LCla
'Little Ronnie'	MWhe
'Little Witch'	EGou EKMF
'Liz'	EBak SOld
'Lochinver'	MJac MWar MWhe
'Loeky'	EBak LCla NPor SLBF SOld
'Logan Garden'	SLBF
'Lolita'	EBak MAsk SKen
'Lonely Ballerina'	CLoc
'Long Wings'	EKMF MAsk NMGN SLBF
'Lord Byron'	CLoc EBak LCla SOld
'Lord Lonsdale'	EBak EBly LCla MAsk MWhe NMGN SKen SOld WEas
'Lord Roberts'	CLit CLoc SKen
'Lorna Swinbank'	CLoc SLBF
'Lorraine's Delight'	CLit
'Lottie Hobby'	CLoc CMGP CMil CNic EBly ECtt EKMF GMon GPen ISea LBlm MAsk SKen WBod WPat WThu
'Louise Emershaw'	EBak MAsk MJac NMGN
'Lovable'	EBak MAsk
'Love Knot'	MSmi
'Loveliness'	CLoc EBak EKMF MAsk MWhe
'Love's Reward'	EBly LCla MJac MWar MWhe NPor SLBF
N ***loxensis***	ERav LCla MAsk
I 'Loxensis' AGM	EBak EKMF LCla SKen SOld
'Loxhore Calypso'	EKMF
'Loxhore Cancan'	EKMF
¶ 'Lucille'	CLit
'Lucky Strike'	CLit CLoc EBak SKen
'Lumière'	EGou
'Lustre'	EBak NPor
lycioïdes Andrews	EBak EGou EKMF
lycioïdes hort.	See F. 'Lycioïdes'
'Lye's Excelsior'	EBak LCla
'Lye's Favourite'	NMGN
'Lye's Own'	EBak LCla MAsk NMGN SLBF
'Lye's Unique'	CLTr CLoc EBak EBly EGou EKMF LCla MAsk MJac MWar MWhe NMGN NPor SKen SLBF SOld
'Lylac Sunsa'	EKMF
'Lynette'	CLoc
'Lynn Ellen'	EBak
'Lynne Marshall'	CCla
'Mabel Greaves'	LCla MAsk NPor
'Machu Picchu'	CLoc EBly EKMF LCla
macrophylla	EKMF
'Madame Butterfly'	CLoc
'Madame Cornelissen' AGM	CCla CLoc CSco EBak EBly EKMF ENot EPla GMon GPen IJoh LVer MAsk MBar MBri MJac MLab MWhe NKay NMGN NPor SHer SOld SPer SPla
'Madame Eva Boye'	EBak
'Madelaine Sweeney'	MBri
'Maes-y-Groes'	EKMF
magellanica	CGle CMHG EKMF GMon LHil NNor NPer SKen WCru WWat
– 'Alba'	See F. ***m. molinae***
I – 'Alba Aureovariegata'	CBow CRDP LHop MBel MBri SApp WCru
– 'Alba Variegata'	CMHG EKMF WEas
§ – var. ***gracilis*** AGM	CCla CLit CLoc EKMF ESma GMon MAsk SLon

– – 'Aurea'	CBot CCla CMHG CTre EGol EGou EHar EHoe EKMF ELan ENot ERav GCHN GMon GPen ISea LCla LHop MAsk MWat MWhe NPor SIng SKen SLBF SPer SPla WCru WRus WWat
§ – – 'Tricolor' (v)	GMon LCla SLBF
– – 'Variegata' **AGM**	Widely available
– 'Longipedunculata'	GMon
– var. ***macrostema***	GMon
– – 'Variegata'	EGou
§ – var. ***molinae***	Widely available
§ – – 'Sharpitor' (v)	CB&S CCla CDec CTre ECha EGou EHoe EKMF ELan EMon LHop MAsk MBar MBri MPla NSti SDix SMrm SPer SPla WCru WRus WSHC
– var. ***pumila***	GCal GMon NPor SChu SIng
– ***purpurea***	GMon
– 'Riccartonii'	See F. 'Riccartonii'
§ – 'Versicolor' **AGM**	Widely available
'Magenta Flush'	MJac
'Magic Flute'	CLoc MJac SOld
'Maharaja'	EBak
'Major Heaphy'	CCla EBak MAsk MWar MWhe NMGN NPor
'Malibu Mist'	EGou EKMF LCla MAsk MSmi
'Mama Bleuss'	EBak
'Mancunian'	ECtt EGou MAsk
N 'Mandarin'	EBak
'Mantilla'	CLoc EBak EGou EKMF MAsk MJac MLab MSmi MWhe NMGN SOld
'Maori Pipes'	EGou
'Marbled Sky'	MJac
'Marcus Graham'	CLoc EGou EKMF MAsk MSmi MWar MWhe SLBF
'Marcus Hanton'	ECtt EKMF LCla MAsk MWar NPor
'Mardale'	MLab
'Mardi Gras'	EBak
'Margaret' **AGM**	CLit CLoc CSco EBak EGou EKMF ENot EPla ERav GCHN GPen ISea LCla LVer MAsk MBal MWar MWhe NMGN SKen SLBF SLon SMrm SOld WStI
'Margaret Brown' **AGM**	CCla CLTr CLoc EBak EKMF LCla LVer MAsk MPla MSte MWhe NMGN NPor SKen SLBF WStI
'Margaret Davidson'	CLoc
'Margaret Pilkington'	EKMF LCla MAsk MLab MWar NPor
'Margaret Roe'	CLit EBak EKMF LCla MJac MWhe NPor SKen SOld
'Margaret Rose'	MJac
'Margaret Susan'	EBak
'Margaret Tebbit'	NPor SLBF
'Margarita'	CCla
¶ 'Margarite Dawson'	CLit
'Margery Blake'	CCla EBak
'Maria Landy'	EKMF MAsk MWar NPor SLBF
'Maria Merrills'	EKMF
'Marilyn Olsen'	EBly EKMF LCla MWar NPor SLBF
'Marin Belle'	EBak LCla
'Marin Glow' **AGM**	CLoc EBak EKMF LCla MAsk MBri NMGN NPor SLBF SOld
'Marinka' **AGM**	CLit CLoc EBak ECtt EGou EKMF IHos LCla LVer MAsk MBri MJac MLab MSmi MWar MWhe NFai NMGN NPor NPri SKen SLBF SOld
¶ 'Marjorie Coast'	SOld
'Mark Kirby'	EKMF
'Marlene Gilbee'	CLit ECtt
'Marshside'	NPor
'Martha Brown'	MLab
'Martin Hayward'	SKen
'Martin's Midnight'	NMGN
'Marton Smith'	MWhe
'Marty'	EBak
'Mary' **AGM**	CLoc EBly EGou EKMF LCla MAsk MSmi MWar MWhe NPor SKen SLBF SOld
'Mary Joan'	EKMF MAsk NMGN
'Mary Lockyer'	CLoc EBak
'Mary Poppins'	SLBF
'Mary Reynolds'	MWar
'Mary Rose'	EKMF
¶ 'Mary Stilwell'	SLBF
'Mary Thorne'	EBak
'Mary Wright'	MWhe
'Masquerade'	EBak EKMF MWhe
mathewsii	EKMF
'Maureen Munro'	NMGN
'Maureen Ward'	EKMF
'Mauve Beauty'	EGou EKMF
'Mauve Lace'	CCla
'Mauve Wisp'	SOld WWeb
'Max Jaffa'	MAsk
'Mayblossom'	EBly ECtt EGou LVer SLBF
'Mayfayre'	CLoc
'Mayfield'	MJac MWhe SKen
'Mazda'	MWhe
'Meadowlark'	CLit EBak ECtt EKMF
'Medalist'	NMGN
'Meditation'	CLoc
'Meike Meursing'	NMGN SKen
'Melody'	EBak MAsk MWhe SKen
'Melody Ann'	EBak
'Melting Moments'	EKMF
'Mendocino Mini'	EGou EKMF
'Meols Cop'	MWhe NPor
'Merry England'	MAsk
'Merry Mary'	EBak EKMF NPor
'Mexicali Rose'	CLoc
'Michael'	EBly MAsk
'Michele Wallace'	SOld
'Micky Goult'	CLoc EBly EKMF LCla LVer MAsk MJac MWar MWhe NMGN NPor SLBF SOld
'Microchip'	SLBF
microphylla	CB&S CCla CElw CGle CLit CLoc CMHG CNic CTre EBak EBar EKMF ERav ERea GRei LVer MBel SFar SLon STre SUsu WCru WEas
– ssp. ***aprica***	CGre EGou EKMF MAsk
§ – ssp. ***hemsleyana***	CBar CCla EKMF LCla MLab MWhe SKen SLBF SOld
§ – ssp. ***hidalgensis***	EGou EKMF SLBF
– ssp. ***microphylla***	EGou
'Midas'	MAsk MBri MSmi NPor
'Midnight Sun'	EBak EBly SKen

'Mieke Meursing'	CLit CLoc EBak ECtt EKMF LCla MJac MWar MWhe NPor SLBF SOld
'Miep Aalhuizen'	EGou EKMF LCla
N 'Mikado'	EGou
'Mike Oxtoby'	EKMF MAsk
'Millrace'	EGou
'Ming'	CLoc
¶ 'Miniature Jewels'	SLBF
N ***minimiflora***	CLit GAri LHil SRms
'Minirose'	EKMF LCla MAsk MWar MWhe NPor SKen SLBF
'Minnesota'	EBak
'Mipan'	SLBF
'Mischief'	CCla WWeb
'Miss California'	CLTr CLit CLoc EBak EBly ECtt EKMF MAsk MBri MLab MSmi MWar NMGN SKen SOld
'Miss Great Britain'	MAsk SOld
'Miss Vallejo'	EBak
'Mission Bells'	CCla CLit CLoc EBak EKMF LVer MAsk MJac MSmi MWhe NMGN SKen SLBF SOld
'Misty Blue'	EKMF
'Misty Morn'	EGou SLBF
'Misty Pink'	EKMF MSmi
¶ 'Moira Ann'	ECtt
'Molesworth'	EBak MJac MLab MWhe NPor SKen SOld
'Mollie Beulah'	ECtt EKMF
'Money Spinner'	CLoc EBak MSmi
'Monsieur Thibaut'	CCla ENot GMon LCla SKen SOld SPer
'Monte Rosa'	CLoc SKen
'Monterey'	MWhe
'Montevideo'	EGou
'Montezuma'	SOld
'Montrose Village'	MWhe SLBF
'Mood Indigo'	EGou MWar NPor SLBF
'Moonbeam'	CLoc EBly MAsk MLab MWhe NPor
'Moonlight Sonata'	CLit CLoc EBak LVer MAsk MJac MSmi SKen
'Moonraker'	ECtt LVer
'Moonshot'	NMGN SKen
'Morcott'	MLab
¶ 'More Applause'	CLoc EKMF MWhe SLBF
'Morning Light'	CLoc EBak MSmi NPor
'Morning Mist'	EBak
'Morning Star'	MBri
'Morrells'	EBak
'Moth Blue'	CLit EBak NPor
'Mount Stewart'	CBow CCla
'Mountain Mist'	EKMF MJac NPor
'Moyra'	EKMF
'Mr A Huggett'	CLit CLoc EBly EGou LCla MAsk MWhe NPor SLBF SOld
'Mr P D Lee'	MWhe
'Mr W Rundle'	CLit EBak EBly
'Mrs Churchill'	CLoc
'Mrs Lawrence Lyon'	EBak
'Mrs Lovell Swisher'	CLit EBak EKMF LCla MBri MJac MWar MWhe NPor SKen SLBF SOld
'Mrs Marshall'	EBak ECtt MAsk SLBF SOld
'Mrs Minnie Pugh'	CLoc
'Mrs Popple' **AGM**	Widely available
'Mrs Susan Brookfield'	LCla NPor SLBF
'Mrs W Castle'	NPor
'Mrs W P Wood' **AGM**	CLoc
'Mrs W Rundle'	CLoc EBak EBly EKMF MWhe NPor SLBF
'Muirfield'	EGou
'Muriel'	CLoc EBak ECtt EKMF MWhe SKen
'My Beauty'	MSmi
'My Dear'	CLoc
'My Fair Lady'	CLoc EBak
'My Honey'	MAsk
¶ 'Mystique'	CLit MAsk
'Nancy Lou'	CLit CLoc EBly EGou EKMF LCla LVer MAsk MJac MSmi MWar MWhe NMGN NPor SKen SLBF SOld
'Nanny Ed'	MBri
'Natalie Jones'	EGou
'Natasha Sinton'	ECtt MBri MJac MWar NPor NPri SLBF SOld
'Native Dancer'	EBak
'Nautilus'	EBak
'Navy Blue'	CCla
'Neapolitan'	EGou EKMF MAsk MWhe SKen SLBF
'Neil Clyne'	MWhe
'Nell Gwyn'	CLoc EBak NPor
'Nellie Nuttall' **AGM**	CLit CLoc EBak EBly EGou EKMF LCla LVer MAsk MBri MJac MSte MWar MWhe NMGN NPor SLBF SOld
'Neopolitan'	CCla EKMF NPor SOld
'Nettala'	CLit
'Neue Welt'	EBak
'New Fascination'	EBak SKen
'Nice 'n' Easy'	LVer MBri MWhe
'Nicholas Hughes'	NPor
'Nickis Findling'	EGou EKMF MSmi
'Nicola'	CLoc EBak
N 'Nicola Claire'	EGou NPor
'Nicola Jane'	CCla CLit EBak EBly EKMF GPen LCla MAsk MBri MJac MSmi MWhe NMGN NPor SLBF
'Nicolette'	MJac
'Nightingale'	CLoc EBak
§ ***nigricans***	EGou EKMF
– x ***gehrigeri***	EKMF
'Nikki'	SKen
'Nimue'	MAsk
'Nina Wills'	EBak
'Niobe'	EBak
'No Name'	EBak
'Norah Henderson'	CLit MLab
'Norma Nield'	LCla
'Norman Greenhill'	SLBF
'Normandy Bell'	EBak MSmi
¶ 'North Cascades'	MAsk
'Northern Pride'	MAsk NMGN SOld
'Northumbrian Belle'	EBak MJac SOld
'Northway'	CLoc LCla MAsk MJac MWhe NPor
'Norvell Gillespie'	EBak
'Novato'	EBak
'Novella'	EBak MSmi NPor
'O Sole Mio'	SKen
'Oakham'	MLab
'Obergärtner Koch'	EKMF SKen SOld
'Ocean Beach'	EBly MAsk MSmi
'Old Somerset'	CLit MAsk MWhe SOld
'Oldbury'	SOld

'Oldbury Delight'	SOld
'Oldbury Galore'	SOld
'Oldbury Gem'	SOld
'Oldbury Pearl'	SOld
'Olive Moon'	EBly SLBF
'Olive Smith'	EBly LCla LVer MAsk MJac MLab NMGN
'Olympic Lass'	EBak
'Omeomy'	NPor
¶ 'Onna'	NPor
'Oosje'	See F. x ***bacillaris*** 'Oosje'
'Opalescent'	CLoc
'Orange Bell'	NMGN
'Orange Crush'	CLoc EBak MAsk MWar MWhe SLBF
'Orange Crystal'	CLit EBak EKMF IHos MAsk MBri MJac MLab MWhe NFai NMGN SHer SKen SOld
'Orange Drops'	CLoc EBak EBly ECtt EKMF MAsk MWhe NPor SKen SOld
'Orange Flame'	LVer
'Orange Flare'	CLit CLoc EBak EKMF LCla MJac MSmi MWhe NMGN SLBF SOld
'Orange Flash'	SOld
'Orange King'	EGou NMGN
'Orange Mirage'	CLit CLoc EBak EBly LCla LVer MAsk MBri MLab MSmi SKen SLBF SOld
'Orangeblossom'	LCla SLBF
'Oranje Boven'	EKMF
'Oranje van Os'	MJac MWhe NPor
¶ 'Orchid Princess'	MLab
'Orient Express'	CLit EGou EKMF MAsk MWhe
Oriental Flame ®	CLit EKMF
'Oriental Sunrise'	MAsk MSmi MWhe NPor SKen
'Orientalis'	EKMF
'Ornamental Pearl'	CLoc EBak ECtt LCla SKen SLBF SOld
'Orwell'	CLit EGou
'Other Fellow'	CLit EBak EBly EKMF LCla MAsk MLab NMGN NPor SKen SLBF SOld
'Our Darling'	EBly MWhe NPor
'Our Ted'	SOld
'Ovation'	MSmi
'Overbecks'	See F. ***magellanica molinae*** 'Sharpitor'
'Overbecks Ruby'	EMon GBuc GMon
'P J B'	SLBF
'Pacific Grove'	EBak
'Pacific Queen'	CLoc EBak EKMF
'Pacquesa' **AGM**	CLit EBak EBly EKMF IHos LVer MAsk MJac MLab MWar MWhe NMGN NPor SKen SLBF SOld
'Padre Pio'	MJac
'Pale Flame'	MSmi MWhe
'Palford'	EBak
pallescens	EKMF
'Pamela Knights '	EBak EGou
'Pan America'	EBak
paniculata	CBot EBak EGou EKMF LCla LHop MAsk SLBF SMrm
'Pantaloons'	EBak
'Papa Bleuss'	CLoc EBak NMGN SOld
'Papoose'	CCla EBak EKMF GPen MAsk MPla NMGN SLBF SOld
'Party Frock'	CLoc EBak LCla NMGN SOld
parviflora hort.	See F. x ***bacillaris***
parviflora Lindley	EBak
'Passing Cloud'	SKen
'Pastel'	EBak
'Pat Meara'	CLoc EBak
'Pathetique'	CLoc
'Patience'	EBak EBly EGou EKMF LCla NMGN SLBF SOld
'Patio Party'	MBri
'Patio Princess'	LCla MBri MJac MWar NPor
N 'Patricia'	EBak GPen
'Patricia Ann'	EKMF MWar SLBF
'Patty Evans'	EBak MBri
'Patty Sue'	MBri
¶ 'Paul Berry'	EKMF
'Paul Cambon'	EBak EKMF
¶ 'Paul Pini'	SOld
'Paul Roe'	MJac NPor
'Paula Jane' **AGM**	CLit LCla MJac MWhe SLBF SOld
'Paula Johnson'	MJac
'Pauline Rawlins'	CLoc EBak
'Pa's Princess'	MLab
'Peace'	EBak
'Peachy Keen'	EBak
'Peacock'	CLoc
'Pebble Mill'	MLab
'Pee Wee Rose'	EBak EKMF GMon
'Peggy King'	EBak LCla
'Peloria'	CLoc EBak MAsk
'Pennine'	MBri MWar
'Peper Harow'	EBak
'Pepi'	CLoc EBak SOld
'Peppermint Candy'	MSmi
'Peppermint Stick'	CLit CLoc EBak EBly EKMF LCla LVer MAsk MBri MJac MSmi MWhe NMGN NPor SHer SKen SOld
'Perestroika'	MSmi
'Perky Pink'	CLit EBak EBly LCla MAsk MLab MWhe NMGN SKen SOld
'Perry Park'	CLit EBak GMon MAsk MBri MJac
'Perry's Jumbo'	NPer
perscandens	ECou EGou EKMF GIsl ISea SLBF
'Personality'	EBak MSmi
'Peter Bielby'	EGou EKMF MWar SLBF
'Peter Crooks'	EGou EKMF MAsk MJac NPor
'Peter Pan'	CLit EBly SIng SPer
'Peter Sanderson'	EKMF LCla
petiolaris	EKMF
'Petite'	EBak
'Petronella'	MAsk MWar SOld
'Pharaoh'	CLoc
'Phénoménal'	EBak EBly EKMF MAsk SKen SOld
'Phyllis' **AGM**	CCla CLit CLoc EBak EBly EGou EKMF GMon GPen LCla MAsk MBal MJac MSmi NFai NMGN SHer SKen SLBF SOld SPla
'Phyrne'	EBak
'Piet Hein'	MSmi
'Pinch Me'	CLTr CLit EBak EKMF MAsk NMGN NPor SKen SOld
'Pink Aurora'	CLoc
'Pink Ballet Girl'	CLoc EBak ECtt
'Pink Bon Accord'	CLoc
'Pink Bouquet'	MJac
'Pink Campanella'	MLab
'Pink Chiffon'	EKMF MSmi

'Pink Claws'	CCla
'Pink Cloud'	CLoc EBak
'Pink Darling'	CLit CLoc EBak MWhe SKen
'Pink Dessert'	EBak SKen
'Pink Fairy'	CLit EBak NMGN NPor
'Pink Fandango'	CLoc
'Pink Fantasia'	CLoc EBak EBly EGou EKMF LCla MAsk MJac MWar MWhe NPor
'Pink Flamingo'	CLoc EBak NMGN SKen
'Pink Galaxy'	MJac
'Pink Galore'	CLit CLoc EBak EBly EGou EKMF IHos LCla LVer MAsk MBri MJac MSmi MWhe NFai NMGN NPor NPri SKen SLBF SOld
'Pink Goon'	EKMF LCla MAsk SLBF
'Pink Jade'	EBak NPor
'Pink La Campanella'	EKMF LVer MAsk MJac MWhe NMGN NPor NPri
'Pink Lace'	CCla SOld
N 'Pink Lady'	MWhe NPor
'Pink Marshmallow'	CLit CLoc EBak EBly EGou EKMF LCla MAsk MJac MSmi MWar MWhe NPor NPri SHer SKen SLBF SOld
'Pink Most'	EKMF
'Pink Panther'	ECtt EKMF LCla
N 'Pink Pearl'	EBak EKMF
'Pink Picotee'	MJac
'Pink Pineapple'	MLab
'Pink Profusion'	EBak
'Pink Quartet'	CLoc EBak LCla NMGN SOld
'Pink Rain'	EGou EKMF
¶ 'Pink Slippers'	CLoc
'Pink Spangles'	CLit IHos LVer MAsk MBri NPri
'Pink Surprise'	MJac
'Pink Temptation'	CLit CLoc EBak SOld
'Pinkmost'	ECtt
'Pinwheel'	CLoc EBak
'Piper'	MWar
'Piper's Vale'	EGou EKMF SLBF
'Pirbright'	EKMF
'Pixie'	CCla CLoc EBak EGou EKMF GMon GPen MAsk MJac NMGN SKen SLBF SOld
'Pixie Bells'	CMHG
'Playford'	EBak
'Plenty'	CLoc EBak LCla NPor
'Ploughman'	EGou
'Plumb-bob'	EGou EKMF SLBF
'Pluto'	CCla
¶ 'Poacher'	EGou
'Pop Whitlock'	CCla EKMF SKen
'Poppet'	SOld
¶ 'Popsie Girl'	SLBF
'Port Arthur'	EBak
'Postiljon'	EBak EKMF MAsk NPor SLBF
N 'Powder Puff'	CLoc EBly ECtt EKMF LVer MAsk MBri MSmi NMGN SKen SOld WWeb
N 'Prelude'	CLoc EBak
'President'	EBak SKen
'President B W Rawlins'	EBak
§ 'President Elliot'	MWhe
'President Leo Boullemier'	EBak ECtt EKMF LCla MAsk MJac SKen
'President Margaret Slater'	CLit CLoc EBak LVer MAsk MJac MLab MSte MWhe SLBF
'President Norman Hobbs'	EKMF MWar
'President Roosevelt'	ECtt
'President Stanley Wilson'	CLit EBak EBly ECtt MAsk
'President Wilf Sharp'	SKen
'Preston Guild'	CLoc EBak EGou EKMF LVer MAsk MWhe NMGN NPer NPor SKen SLBF SOld
¶ 'Pride and Joy'	MLab
'Pride of the West'	EBak
'Prince of Orange'	CLoc EBak LCla NPor SOld
'Prince of Peace'	MSmi NMGN
'Princess Dollar'	See F. 'Dollar Princess'
'Princess of Bath'	CLoc
'Princess Pamela'	SLBF
'Princess Pat'	EKMF
'Princessita'	CLit EBak ECtt EKMF LCla LVer MAsk MBri MJac MLab MSmi MWar MWhe NPri SKen SLBF
procumbens	Widely available
'Prodigy'	See F. 'Enfant Prodigue'
'Prosperity' **AGM**	CLoc EBak EBly EGou EKMF GPen LCla MAsk MJac MLab MSmi MWar MWhe NMGN SLon SOld
N 'Pumila'	CCla EGou EKMF ELan EPla GPen LCla MAsk MBal MPla SLBF
'Purperklokje'	EBak EKMF MAsk SLBF
'Purple Ann'	NMGN
'Purple Emperor'	CLoc
¶ 'Purple Graseing'	MAsk
'Purple Heart'	CLoc EBak NMGN SKen
'Purple Lace'	CCla
'Purple Pride'	MBri
'Purple Rain'	EKMF MSmi
'Purple Splendour'	CSco
'Pussy Cat'	CLoc EBak EKMF NMGN SKen
¶ 'Putney Pride'	EBly
putumayensis	EBak LCla SLBF
'Put's Folly'	EBak MJac SKen
'Quaser'	CLoc EKMF MAsk MWhe NMGN SLBF SOld
'Queen Mabs'	EBak
'Queen Mary'	CLoc EBak EKMF
'Queen of Bath'	EBak
'Queen of Derby'	MAsk
'Queen's Park'	EBak
'Query'	EBak GPen SKen
'R A F'	CLoc EBak EBly ECtt EKMF LCla MAsk MJac MWar SKen SLBF SOld
'Rachel Sinton'	MBri
'Radcliffe Beauty'	MWhe
'Radcliffe Bedder'	EKMF NMGN SKen
'Rading's Inge'	EGou EKMF
'Rading's Karin'	EGou EKMF
'Rahnee'	MJac NPor
'Rainbow'	EGou
'Rambling Rose'	CLoc EBak ECtt EGou MAsk MJac MLab MWar SKen SOld
'Rams Royal'	LVer MAsk MJac MLab
'Raspberry'	CLit CLoc EBak LCla MAsk MWar MWhe NMGN SKen
'Ratatouille'	EGou EKMF MAsk MSmi SLBF

ravenii	EGou EKMF LCla
'Ravenslaw'	EKMF
'Ray Redfern'	MJac
'Razzle Dazzle'	EBak
'Reading Show'	EBly SLBF
'Rebecca Williamson'	EGou MJac NMGN NPor SLBF
'Rebekah Sinton'	MBri
'Red Imp'	CCla NPor WWeb
'Red Jacket'	EBak
'Red Ribbons'	EBak
'Red Shadows'	CLit CLoc EBak EBly MBri MJac MWhe NMGN SLBF
'Red Spider'	CLoc EBak EGou EKMF LVer MAsk MLab MSmi MWar MWhe NMGN NPor SKen SLBF SOld
'Red Wing'	CLoc
'Reg Dickenson'	MJac MWhe
'Reg Gubler'	SLBF
'Regal'	CLoc
regia alpestris	See F. ***alpestris***
– var. ***regia***	EKMF
– ssp. ***reitzii***	EGou EKMF GMon
– ssp. ***serrae***	EKMF
'Remus'	EKMF LCla MAsk MBri
¶ 'Renate'	EGou
'Requiem'	CLoc IHos
'Reverend Doctor Brown'	EBak
'Reverend Elliott'	See F. 'President Elliot'
N 'Rhapsody'	CLoc
'Ri Mia'	EGou
¶ 'Riant'	SLBF
§ 'Riccartonii' AGM	CB&S CChe CCla CLoc CSco EBak EGou EKMF ELan ENot GPen IDai IJoh ISea LCla LHil MBar MBel MBri MLab NBee NMGN NPer NWea SMrm WBod WCru WEas WStI
'Riccartonii Variegated'	WEas
'Ridestar'	CLit CLoc EBak LCla MAsk MJac MSmi MWhe NMGN SLBF
'Rina Felix'	EGou
'Ringwood Gold'	LVer SOld
'Ringwood Market'	CLit EBly ECtt EKMF LCla LVer MWhe NMGN SHer SKen SOld
'River Plate'	EGou
'Robbie'	CLit EKMF NMGN SLBF
'Robert Bruce'	EKMF
¶ 'Rodeo'	EGou
'Rolla'	EBak
'Roman City'	CLoc
'Romance'	EKMF NMGN
¶ 'Romany Rose'	CLoc
'Ron Ewart'	EKMF MWhe NPor
'Ron Holmes'	LCla
'Ronald L Lockerbie'	CLit CLoc EKMF MAsk MSmi MWhe
¶ 'Roos Breytenbach'	EGou LCla
'Rosamunda'	CLoc
'Rose Aylett'	EBak
'Rose Bower'	NMGN
'Rose Bradwardine'	EBak
'Rose Churchill'	CLit EKMF LCla LVer MBri MJac MSmi
¶ 'Rose Fantasia'	SLBF
'Rose Lace'	CLit
'Rose Marie'	CLit CLoc
'Rose of Castile' AGM	CCla CLit CLoc EBak EKMF GPen MAsk MJac MWhe NMGN
'Rose of Castile Improved'	CCla EBak EBly EKMF LCla MAsk MJac MWar NPor SKen SOld
'Rose of Denmark'	CLTr CLoc EBak MAsk MJac MLab MSmi MWar MWhe NPri SLBF SOld
'Rose Reverie'	EBak
'Rose Winston'	EKMF MWhe NPri
'Rosebud'	EBak
'Rosecroft Beauty'	EBak EBly GPen MAsk MWhe SKen SLBF SOld
'Rosemary Day'	CLoc
'Rosy Frills'	EGou EKMF LCla MJac MWhe NMGN NPor SOld
'Rosy Morn'	CLoc EBak
Rosy Ruffles ®	EKMF MSmi
'Rothbury Beauty'	MAsk
'Rough Silk'	CLoc EBak LCla SOld
'Roy Walker'	CLit CLoc EGou EKMF LVer MAsk MJac MLab MWar MWhe NMGN NPor SKen SOld
'Royal and Ancient'	CLTr EGou
'Royal Orchid'	EBak
'Royal Purple'	CLit EBak EKMF MAsk MBri
'Royal Touch'	EBak
'Royal Velvet' AGM	CLTr CLit CLoc EBak EBly EGou EKMF LCla LVer MAsk MJac MLab MSmi MWar MWhe NMGN NPor SKen SLBF SOld
'Royal Wedding'	LVer
'Rubens'	MWar
§ 'Rubra Grandiflora'	EBak EKMF LCla SLBF
'Ruby'	CLit SOld
'Ruby Wedding'	CLit LCla SLBF
'Ruddigore'	EBly ESma MAsk SLBF SOld
'Ruffles'	CLit EBak MSmi
§ 'Rufus'	CCla CLoc CMHG EBak EBly EKMF EPla GPen LCla LVer MAsk MBel MJac MWar MWhe NMGN SKen SLBF
'Rufus the Red'	See F. 'Rufus'
¶ 'Ruth'	CLit
'Ruth Brazewell'	CLoc
'Ruth King'	CLit EBak ECtt NMGN NPor SKen SOld
'Rutland Water'	MAsk
'Sahara'	NMGN
¶ 'Sailor'	MJac
'Sally Ann'	NPor
'Sally Gunell'	MLab
'Salmon Cascade'	EBak ECtt EKMF MAsk MJac MWar SLBF
'Salmon Glow'	MJac MWhe
'Sampson's Delight'	MAsk
'Samson'	EBak
'Sam's Song'	MJac
'San Diego'	CLit MSmi
'San Francisco'	EBak
'San Leandro'	EBak NMGN
'San Mateo'	EBak
§ ***sanctae-rosae***	EBak EGou EKMF LBlm LCla
'Sandboy'	EBak SOld
'Sangria'	SLBF
'Sanrina'	EKMF
'Santa Barbara'	NMGN
'Santa Cruz'	CCla EBak EGou EKMF GMon LCla MAsk MWhe SOld
'Santa Lucia'	CLoc EBak

'Santa Monica'	EBak
'Sapphire'	EBak MSmi
'Sara Helen'	CLoc EBak NPor
'Sarah Ann'	MWar
'Sarah Greensmith'	EKMF
'Sarah Jayne'	EBak LCla
'Sarah Louise'	EKMF
'Sarong'	EBak
'Saskia'	EKMF
'Satchmo'	EGou
'Satellite'	CLoc EBak EKMF MAsk MJac MSmi
'Saturnus'	EBak SOld
scandens	See F. ***decussata***
'Scarborough Rosette'	EGou
'Scarcity'	CLit EBak GMon SKen
¶ 'Scarlet Ribbons'	EKMF
'Schneeball'	EBak EKMF
'Schneewittchen'	EBak EKMF
'Schneewittcher'	EBly
'Schönbrunner Schuljubiläum	EBak SLBF
'Scotch Heather'	MSmi
'Sea Shell'	EBak MAsk
'Seaforth'	EBak
'Sealand Prince'	CCla ECtt GPen MAsk
'Sebastopol'	CLoc ECtt EKMF MSmi NPor
serratifolia Hooker	See F. ***austromontana***
serratifolia Ruiz & Pavón	See F. ***denticulata***
sessilifolia	EKMF LCla
'Seventh Heaven'	CLoc EGou MAsk MSmi MWar NMGN
'Shangri-La'	EBak
'Sharon Allsop'	MWhe
'Sharon Caunt'	EKMF
'Sharpitor'	See F. ***magellanica molinae*** 'Sharpitor'
'Shawna Ree'	EKMF
'Sheila Crooks'	EBak MWhe NPor
'Sheila Kirby'	MJac
'Shelford' AGM	CLoc EBak EBly EKMF LCla MAsk MWar MWhe NPor SLBF SOld
'Shell Pink'	GPen
'Shelley Lyn'	SKen
'Shooting Star'	EBak
'Shy Lady'	MWhe SKen
'Sierra Blue'	CLoc EBak EKMF SKen
'Silver Anniversary'	EGou EKMF MSmi
'Silver Dawn'	EBly EKMF MAsk MWhe NMGN NPor SLBF
'Silver Dollar'	MWhe NMGN NPor SKen
'Silver Pink'	CCla
'Silverdale'	EKMF GMon MAsk MWhe
'Simon J Rowell'	EKMF LCla
simplicicaulis	EBak EGou EKMF LCla MAsk SOld
'Sincerity'	CLoc MWhe
'Siobhan'	MJac
'Sir Alfred Ramsey'	EBak MJac MWhe
N 'Siren'	EBak
'Sister Ann Haley'	EBly EKMF MWar
'Skylight'	MLab
'Sleepy'	CCla GPen LCla MAsk MBri SKen SOld
'Sleigh Bells'	CLoc EBak EKMF MAsk MWhe NMGN SKen SOld
'Small Pipes'	EGou EKMF
'Smokey Mountain'	EKMF MSmi
'Smoky'	EGou
'Sneezy'	CCla MAsk SKen WWeb
'Snow Burner'	MSmi
¶ 'Snow Goose'	EGou
'Snow White'	LVer MAsk NMGN SKen
§ 'Snowcap' AGM	CCla CLit CLoc CMHG EBak EBly EGou EKMF GPen IHos LCla LVer MAsk MBri MJac MLab MSmi MSte MWar MWhe NFai NMGN NPer NPri SHer SKen SLBF SOld WStI
'Snowdon'	MWar
N 'Snowdrift'	CLoc EBak MWhe NMGN
'Snowfire'	CLoc EBly ECtt EGou EKMF LCla MAsk MSmi MWhe NMGN SKen
'Snowstorm'	CMHG ECtt NMGN
'Snowy Summit'	MSmi
'So Big'	EKMF
Software ®	MSmi
'Son of Thumb' AGM	CCla CLit CLoc EBly EKMF ELan GAri GMon GPen LCla MAsk MBri MJac MWhe SKen SLBF SOld
'Sonota'	CLoc EBak MSmi NMGN SOld
'Sophie Claire'	EGou EKMF
'Sophie's Surprise'	EGou EKMF
'Sophisticated Lady'	CLoc EBak EBly ECtt EKMF LCla LVer MAsk MJac MSmi MWar NMGN SOld
¶ 'South Lakeland'	CLit
'South Seas'	EBak
'Southgate'	CLit CLoc EBak EBly EGou EKMF LVer MAsk MWar NMGN NPor NPri
'Southlanders'	EBak
'Southwell Minster'	EKMF NMGN
'Space Shuttle'	EKMF LCla MAsk
'Speciosa'	CTre EBak EKMF LCla
'Spion Kop'	CLit EBak EKMF LVer MAsk MJac MLab MWar MWhe NFai NMGN NPri SHer SKen SLBF
splendens AGM	CLoc EBak EGou EKMF LCla NPer SMrm SOld
– 'Karl Hartweg'	LBlm
'Spring Classic'	MLab
'Springtime'	CSco
'Squadron Leader'	EBak EBly EGou SOld
'Stad Elburg'	MJac
'Stanley Cash'	CLit CLoc EKMF LCla LVer MAsk MBri MJac MWar MWhe NMGN NPor SKen SOld
'Star of Pink'	MSmi MWhe
'Star Rose'	EKMF
'Stardust'	EBak MJac MWhe NPor SKen SOld
'Steeley'	CLit MSmi MWhe
'Stella Ann'	CLit EBak EBly EGou LCla MWhe
'Stella Marina'	CLoc EBak
¶ 'Sterretje'	EGou
'Stormy Sunset'	EGou
'Strawberry Delight'	CLit CLoc CMHG EBak ECtt EGou EKMF LCla LVer MAsk MJac MLab MWhe NPor SKen SOld
'Strawberry Fizz'	MSmi
'Strawberry Sundae'	CLoc EBak NMGN SLBF
'Strawberry Supreme'	EKMF LCla MAsk

'String of Pearls'	ECtt EKMF LCla LVer MAsk MBri MJac NPor SKen SLBF SOld
'Sugar Almond'	MJac NPor
'Sugar Blues'	EBak
'Suikerbossie' ('Sugarbush')	MJac
'Sunkissed'	EBak
'Sunlight Path'	LCla
'Sunningdale'	EGou LCla
'Sunny'	SKen
'Sunny Smiles'	NMGN NPor
'Sunray'	CBrd CLit CLoc EBak EFol EGou EKMF GPen LHop MAsk MSmi NMGN SKen SLBF SOld
'Sunset'	CLit CLoc EBak MAsk MWhe NPor SKen SPer
'Supernova'	NMGN NPor
'Superstar'	EBly LCla MBri MSmi NPor
'Susan'	LCla
¶ 'Susan Arnold'	MAsk
'Susan Daley'	NPor
'Susan Ford'	EKMF MAsk NPor SKen
'Susan Green'	EGou EKMF LCla MWhe NMGN NPor NPri SLBF
'Susan Joy'	MLab
'Susan McMaster'	CLoc
'Susan Travis'	CCla CLit CLoc EBak EKMF EPla GMon GPen MAsk MWhe NMGN SKen SOld
'Susie Olcese'	EBak NPor
'Suzy'	MSmi
'Swanland Candy'	ECtt
'Swanley Gem' AGM	CLoc EBak EKMF LCla MAsk NMGN NPor SKen SLBF
'Swanley Pendula'	CLoc
'Swanley Yellow'	EBak SKen SOld
'Sweet Leilani'	CLoc EBak NMGN SKen
'Sweet Sixteen'	CLoc
N 'Sweetheart'	EBak
'Swingtime' AGM	CLit CLoc CMHG EBak EBly EKMF IHos LCla LVer MAsk MJac MLab MSmi MWar MWhe NFai NMGN NPor NPri SHer SKen SLBF SOld
'S'Wonderful'	CLoc EBak MSmi
sylvatica	See F. ***nigricans***
'Sylvia Barker'	EGou
¶ 'Sylvia Dyos'	SLBF
'Sylvy'	CLit LCla
'Symphony'	CLit CLoc EBak MAsk
'Tabatha'	MLab
'Taddle'	EBly EKMF MJac NPor SLBF
'Taffeta Bow'	CLoc EKMF MAsk
'Taffy'	EBak
'Tamworth'	CLit CLoc EBak LCla MAsk MJac NPor
'Tangerine'	CLit CLoc EBak MWhe NPor
'Tania Leanne'	CLit
'Tanya'	CLoc
'Tanya Bridger'	EBak
'Tarra Valley'	EGou LCla SLBF
'Tartan'	MLab
'Task Force'	CLit MAsk NMGN SKen
'Tausendschön'	CLoc ECtt EKMF
¶ 'Tear Fund'	EGou
'Ted Perry'	NMGN
'Television'	CLoc MAsk
'Tempo Doelo'	CLit
N 'Temptation'	CLit CLoc EBak ECtt MBri NPor
'Tennessee Waltz' AGM	CCla CLit CLoc CMHG EBak EBly EGou EKMF GMon LCla LVer MAsk MBel MJac MLab MSmi MWar MWhe NMGN NPor SChu SKen SLBF SOld SPer SPla WEas
'Terrysue'	EKMF
'Texas Longhorn'	CLoc EBak EKMF MSmi NMGN SOld
'Thalia' AGM	CLit CLoc EBak EBly ECtt EGou EKMF ERea IHos LBlm LCla LHil LVer MAsk MBri MJac MLab MSmi MWar MWhe NMGN NPor NPri NWyt SKen SLBF SOld SPla SUsu WEas
'Thamar'	EGou EKMF MWar NPor SLBF
'Thames Valley'	EGou
'That's It'	EBak
'The Aristocrat'	CLoc EBak NPor
§ 'The Doctor'	CLoc EBak EKMF MAsk MWhe
'The Jester'	EBak
'The Madame'	EBak MAsk
'The Red Arrows'	MLab
'The Rival'	EKMF MSmi NMGN
'The Spoiler'	MSmi
'The Tarns'	CLit EBak EKMF GPen MAsk MBel WCru
'Therese Dupois'	EKMF
'Théroigne de Méricourt'	EBak
¶ 'Think Pink'	SLBF
'Thompsonii' AGM	EKMF EMon GMon GPen SKen
'Thornley's Hardy'	CLit EKMF GPen MAsk MBri NMGN NPor SOld
'Three Cheers'	CLoc EBak
'Three Counties'	EBak
'Thunderbird'	CLoc EBak EGou
thymifolia	CBow CMil EBur ELan EMon ESis ESma GCra GMac LHil LHop MAsk MBal MPla NRar SMrm WKif WPer
– ssp. ***minimiflora***	EKMF
– ***thymifolia***	EKMF
'Tiara'	EBak
N 'Tiffany'	EBak
tillettiana	EKMF
'Tillmouth Lass'	MAsk
'Timlin Brened'	EBak LCla MAsk MWhe
'Ting-a-Ling'	CLoc EBak EBly EKMF LVer MAsk MBri MWhe NMGN NPor SKen SLBF SOld
N 'Tinker Bell'	EBak EKMF SOld
'Tintern Abbey'	NPor
'Toby Bridger'	CLoc EBak
'Tolling Bell'	CLit EBak EKMF LCla MAsk MJac MSmi MWhe NMGN NPor SKen SOld
'Tom H Oliver'	EBak
'Tom Knights'	EBak EGou EKMF MAsk MWhe SLBF SOld
'Tom Redfern'	MJac
'Tom Thorne'	EBak
'Tom Thumb' AGM	Widely available
'Tom West' (v)	CLit CLoc CMHG EBak EFol EGou EKMF ERav LBlm LCla LHil MAsk MLab MSmi MWhe NMGN NPor SKen SLBF SMrm SOld SPla SUsu WEas
'Tom Woods'	LCla MLab MSmi MWhe NPor
'Top Score'	NMGN
'Topaz'	CLoc EBak
'Topper'	ECtt SLBF

'Torch'	CLoc EBak EKMF MJac MSmi NMGN
'Torchlight'	EBly MAsk MJac
'Torville and Dean'	CLoc EBly EGou EKMF MAsk MJac MLab MSmi MWar MWhe NMGN NPor SKen SLBF SOld
'Tour Eiffel'	EGou
'Tower of London'	SKen
'Towi'	EGou SLBF
'Tracid'	CLoc
'Tracie Ann'	EKMF
'Tradewinds'	MSmi
'Trail Blazer'	CLit CLoc EBak LCla MJac MLab NPor SKen
'Trailing Queen'	EBak EKMF MAsk MJac
'Tranquility'	MSmi
'Trase'	EBak EBly EKMF MAsk MLab NMGN NPor
'Traudchen Bonstedt'	CLoc EBak EBly LCla MAsk MWhe NMGN SLBF SOld
'Treasure'	EBak
'Trewince Twilight'	LVer MAsk MLab
'Tricolor'	See F. ***magellanica gracilis*** 'Tricolor'
'Tricolorii' (v)	EBly EKMF MAsk
'Trio'	CLoc
triphylla	EBak EKMF IReg SOld
'Trish Dewey'	MLab
'Tristesse'	CLoc EBak MAsk MJac MWhe NMGN
'Troika'	EBak EKMF SLBF
'Troon'	MAsk
'Tropic Sunset'	MAsk MBri MSmi MWhe SKen
'Tropicana'	CLit CLoc EBak NPor
'Troubadour'	CLoc
'Trudy'	CCla EBak EKMF GPen MAsk NMGN SKen
N 'Trumpeter'	CLit CLoc EBak EBly EGou EKMF LCla MAsk MJac MSmi MWhe NMGN NPor SKen SLBF SOld
'Tsjiep'	MAsk NPor
'Tuonela'	CLoc EBak EKMF MAsk MWhe NMGN NPor SKen
'Tutone'	MAsk MJac
'Tutti-Frutti'	CLoc MWhe
'Tutu'	EKMF
¶ 'Twink'	EGou
'Twinkling Stars'	EKMF LCla MJac
'Twotiers'	EKMF LCla NPor
'Ullswater'	EBak MAsk
'Ultramar'	EBak LVer
'Uncle Charley'	CLoc EBak EKMF WEas
'Uncle Steve'	EBak
'Uppingham Lass'	MLab
'Upward Look'	EBak EKMF MAsk
'Valentine'	EBak
'Valerie Ann'	EBak SKen SOld
'Valiant'	EBak
'Vanessa'	CLoc
'Vanessa Jackson'	CLoc MAsk MJac MWar MWhe NPor SKen SLBF
'Vanity Fair'	CLoc EBak
vargarsiana	EKMF
¶ 'Variegated Brenda White'	EKMF
'Variegated Snowcap'	CCla MWhe
'Variegated Swingtime'	EBak NPri
'Variegated Vivienne Thompson'	MBri
'Variegated White Joy'	EKMF
'Varty's Pride'	NPor
N 'Venus'	CCla
'Venus Victrix'	EBak EKMF MAsk SLBF
venusta	EBak EGou EKMF LCla
'Vera Wilding'	LCla SLBF
'Versicolor'	See F. ***magellanica*** 'Versicolor'
'Victory'	EBak
'Vincent van Gogh'	EGou
I 'Violacea'	MSmi
'Violet Bassett-Burr'	CLoc EBak
'Violet Gem'	CLoc
'Violet Rosette'	EBak SLBF
'Viva Ireland'	EBak ECtt MAsk MJac
'Vivien Colville'	CLoc
'Vivienne Davis'	EGou
'Vivienne Thompson'	SLBF
'Vobeglo'	EKMF
'Vogue'	EBak
'Voltaire'	EBak GPen
'Voodoo'	CLoc EBak EBly ECtt EKMF MAsk MWar NMGN NPor SKen SLBF SOld
vulcanica	See F. ***ampliata***
'Vyvian Miller'	MJac
¶ 'W P Wood'	MAsk
'Waldfee'	CCla EKMF MAsk MWhe
'Walsingham'	CLit EBak EGou LCla MJac MWhe NMGN NPor SKen SLBF
'Waltzing Matilda'	CLit
¶ 'Walz Bella'	SLBF
'Walz Freule'	EKMF MJac
'Walz Harp'	EGou SLBF
¶ 'Walz Jubelteen'	EGou EKMF MWar
'Walz Lucifer'	EGou SLBF
'Walz Luit'	EGou
'Walz Mandoline'	EGou
'Walz Parasol'	EGou
'Walz Triangel'	EKMF
'Walz Waterval'	EGou
'Wapenfeld's Bloei'	EGou LCla
'War Dance'	MWhe
'War Paint'	CLoc EBak
'Warton Crag'	NPor
'Waternymph'	CLoc SLBF
'Wave of Life'	EKMF MAsk MWhe SKen
'Waveney Gem'	EBak EGou EKMF LCla MAsk MJac MWar NMGN SLBF SOld
'Waveney Queen'	MJac
'Waveney Sunrise'	ECtt EGou EKMF LCla MAsk MJac MSte MWar
'Waveney Valley'	EBak MJac NMGN
'Waveney Waltz'	EBak EKMF LCla MAsk MJac MWhe SLBF
'Wedding Bells'	LCla SOld
'Welsh Dragon'	CLoc EBak MAsk SLBF
'Wendy'	See F. 'Snowcap'
'Wendy Atkinson'	EKMF LCla
'Wendy Harris'	MJac
'Wendy Leedham'	ECtt EKMF
'Wendy's Beauty'	CLoc MLab MSmi
'Wentworth'	EGou
'Wessex Belle'	LCla
'Westgate'	ECtt EKMF

'Westminster Chimes' AGM	CLit CLoc EKMF LVer MAsk MJac MLab MWhe NMGN NPor SOld
¶ 'Whickham Beauty'	SLBF
'Whirlaway'	CLoc EBak EKMF MAsk NMGN SOld
'White Ann'	CLit CLoc LCla MBri SLBF
'White Falls'	MAsk
'White Galore'	EBak EKMF LVer MAsk MSmi SKen SOld
'White Gold'	EBak
'White Heidi Ann'	LVer MAsk MLab
'White Joy'	CLit EBak EKMF MAsk MWhe SKen
'White King'	CLit CLoc EBak EKMF MAsk MSmi MWhe NMGN NPor SLBF SOld
'White Lace'	CCla
'White Pixie'	CCla EBly EKMF ELan GMon LCla LVer MAsk MJac MPla SHer SKen SOld SPer
'White Pixie' Wagtails	EBak MWhe
N 'White Queen'	EBak MJac MWhe NPor
'White Spider'	CLit CLoc EBak EKMF MAsk MWhe SKen SOld
'White Surprise'	SOld
'Whiteknights Amethyst'	SKen
'Whiteknights Blush'	CBow CCla GMon MBel SKen
'Whiteknights Cheeky'	EBak EGou EKMF
'Whiteknights Goblin'	See F. ***denticulata*** 'W.G.'
'Whiteknights Pearl'	CLit ECtt EKMF GMon GPen MAsk SLBF
'Whiteknights Ruby'	SLBF
'Wicked Queen'	CCla LCla
'Wickham Blue'	LCla NPor SLBF
'Wiebe Becker'	EKMF
'Wild and Beautiful'	CLit EKMF MAsk SLBF
'Wildfire'	CLit
'William Caunt'	EKMF
'Wilson's Colours'	EBly
'Wilson's Pearls'	CLit MWar SLBF SOld
'Wilson's Sugar Pink'	EBly LCla
'Win Oxtoby'	EKMF
'Wine and Roses'	EBak MSmi
'Wingrove's Mammoth'	MAsk
'Wings of Song'	EBak
'Winston Churchill' AGM	CLit CLoc EBak EBly EKMF IHos LCla LVer MAsk MBri MJac MLab MSmi MWar MWhe NFai NMGN NPor NPri SHer SKen SOld
¶ 'Wm's Lass	MLab
'Woodnook'	MAsk
wurdackii	EGou MAsk SLBF
¶ 'Xmas Tree'	MAsk
'Yorkshire Rally'	MJac NPor
'Yuletide'	EBly SKen
'Zara'	MWhe NPor
'Ziegfield Girl'	EBak
'Zulu Queen'	EKMF MSmi

FUMARIA (Papaveraceae)

lutea	See PSEUDOFUMARIA ***lutea***
officinalis	GPoy MSal

FURCRAEA (Agavaceae)

§ ***foetida***	CGre
§ – var. ***mediopicta***	CB&S CTro
♦ – 'Variegata'	See F. ***f. mediopicta***
♦ ***gigantea***	See F. ***foetida***
longaeva	CAbb CHEx CTbh SArc
selloa	CHEx
– var. ***marginata***	CHEx

GAGEA (Liliaceae/Liliaceae)

lutea	EPot
pratensis	EPot

GAHNIA (Cyperaceae)

setifolia	EPla

GAILLARDIA (Compositae/Asteraceae)

aristata hort.	See G. x ***grandiflora***
aristata Pursch JCA 11449	EMon
'Bremen'	CBot
'Burgunder'	CBow CDoC CMGP ECtt ELan GCal MBri NBro NFai NMir NOak SHer SPer WGor WRus WSun WTyr
'Dazzler' AGM	CBow EBre ECtt ELan ENot GAul LBre LWad MBri MWat NHol NNor SHer WStI WTyr
'Goldkobold' ('Yellow Goblin')	CBow CMGP ELan MPit
§ x ***grandiflora***	CGle CSco GAri MBel NOak NVic WSun
¶ – 'Aurea Plena'	CMGP NPri
Kelway's hybrids	CKel
'Kobold' ('Goblin')	CB&S CDoC CHol EBre ECtt EPar GAbr LBre MBri MRav NPri NRoo SPer WHen WHil WTyr WWin
'Mandarin'	EBre ECot LBre SRms WTyr
'Summer Sun'	NFai
'Wirral Flame'	EPar WEas

GALACTITES (Compositae/Asteraceae)

tomentosa	CBos CPle CRow ECha ELan EMar EMon LAbb MHlr SMrm SUsu WEas WPer

GALANTHUS † (Liliaceae/Amaryllidaceae)

allenii	CAvo WChr
alpinus	EPot LAma WChr
¶ 'Armine'	LFox
'Atkinsii' AGM	CAvo CBro EMor EOrc EPot ERav LAma LFox MBri NGar WChr WWat
'Augustus'	EMor LFox
¶ 'Benhall Beauty'	LFox
¶ 'Bertram Anderson'	LFox
'Bitton'	CBro LFox
¶ 'Blewbury Tart'	CMea LFox
bortkewitschianus	CBro LFox
'Brenda Troyle'	CBro EPot LFox WChr
byzantinus	See G. ***plicatus b.***
cabardensis	See G. ***transcaucasicus***
caucasicus AGM	CAvo CBro CMea CRDP ECha EPot ERav LAma LFox NGar WCru WMar
– early form	WChr
– var. ***hiemalis***	CBro ECha EMor

corcyrensis (Spring flw)	See G. ***reginae-olgae vernalis***
– (Winter flw)	See G. ***reginae-olgae*** Winter-flowering Group
'Cordelia' (d)	LFox
'Desdemona'	LFox
'Dionysus' (d)	CBro EBul EMor LFox LRHS NGar WChr
elwesii AGM	CBro CMon EMor LAma LBow LFox MBri NBir NGar NRog SIng
¶ – 'Flore Pleno'	LFox
¶ – ***poculiformis***	LFox
'Ermine Street'	EPot
fosteri	CAvo CBro EPot LAma
– PD 256830	EMor
'Galatea'	EMor LFox
§ ***gracilis***	CBro EBul EMor EPot LFox NGar WOld WThu
– Highdown form	SWas
graecus Boissier	See G. ***elwesii***
graecus hort.	See G. ***gracilis***
'Hill Poë' (d)	CBro ECha ERav LFox
'Hippolyta' (d)	CBro ECha EMor LAma LFox
ikariae ssp. ***ikariae*** AGM	EOrc EPot ERav LAma
§ – Latifolius Group	CAvo CBro EBul EMor EOrc EPot LAma LFox NGar WChr WOld
– Woronowii Group	EPot LAma LRHS WChr
'Jacquenetta' (d)	CBro EMor NGar
'John Gray'	EMor LFox
kemulariae	See G. ***transcaucasicus***
♦ ***ketskovelii***	See G. ***transcaucasicus***
'Ketton'	CBro EOrc LFox
'Kite'	CBro
'Lady Beatrix Stanley' (d)	CBro ECha EMor EPot ERav LAma LFox NGar WChr
lagodechanus	See G. ***transcaucasicus***
latifolius	See G. ***ikariae*** Latifolius Group
'Lime Tree'	EMor LFox
lutescens	See G. ***nivalis*** 'Lutescens'
'Magnet' AGM	CAvo CBro EBul EMor EPot ERav LAma LFox NGar NHar SWas WChr WThu
'Maidwell L'	EMor WChr
'Merlin'	EMor EOrc LFox NGar SWas
'Mighty Atom'	CMea LFox
'Moccas'	WOld
'Neill Fraser'	LFox
'Nerissa' (d)	EPot NGar
nivalis AGM	CAvo CBro CKin CRiv CRow ECWi ELan EMor EPar EPot ERav ETub LAma LBow LFox LHop MBar MBri NGar NLan NRog SIng WPer WShi
– ***angustifolius***	CBro EPot
¶ – 'Appleby One'	EPot
¶ – 'April Fool'	LFox
– 'Boyd's Double'	EMor
– dwarf form	LFox
– 'Flore Pleno' AGM	CAvo CBro CMon CRiv CRow EPar EPot ERav ETub LAma LBow LFox MFos NGar NRog NRya SIng WCru WHal WHen WPer WShi WWye
– 'Humberts Orchard'	LFox
– ssp. ***imperati***	CBro EPot
– – 'Ginns'	EMor LFox
– 'Lady Elphinstone' (d)	CAvo CBro CRow ECha EMor EPot ERav LFox NGar WChr
§ – 'Lutescens'	CBro EMor EPot LAma LFox NGar SWas WChr
– Poculiformis Group 'Sandhill Gate'	EMor NGar
– 'Pusey Green Tip' (d)	CBro EBul EMor EPot ERav ITim LFox NGar WChr
§ – Scharlockii Group	CBro EMor EOrc EPot LAma LFox NGar NHar SWas WChr
– 'Tiny'	EMor NGar NHar SIng
§ – 'Virescens'	EMor
– 'Viridapicis'	CAvo CBro EBul ECha EMor EPar EPot ERav ETub LAma LBow LFox NGar SIng WChr
¶ – 'Warei'	LFox
'Ophelia' (d)	CAvo CBro ECha EPar ERav LAma LFox NGar WChr
'Peg Sharples'	EPot
'Pewsey Vale'	EMor
platyphyllus	See G. ***ikariae*** Latifolius Group
plicatus AGM	CAvo CMea EBul LFox NGar WChr WOMN
§ – ssp. ***byzantinus*** AGM	CAvo CBro CMea EBul EMor EOrc EPot ERav LFox NGar WChr
¶ – – 'Greenpeace'	EBul
¶ – – 'Trym'	LFox
¶ – Ginn's ex Turkey	LFox
– large form	EOrc
– 'Warham'	CBro EOrc SWas WOld
reginae-olgae	CBro CMea CMon EMor EPot LAma NGar WChr
– ***reginae-olgae*** Winter-flowering Group	CAvo CBro EBul ECha EMor LAma LFox
§ – ssp. ***vernalis***	EMor LFox NGar
– ssp. ***vernalis*** AJM 75	EMor
– ssp. ***vernalis*** CE&H 541	EMor
rizehensis	CBro EPot
'Robin Hood'	EMor LFox WChr
'S Arnott' AGM	CAvo CBro CMea EMor EPot ERav LAma LFox NBir NGar NHar SIng WChr WOld WThu
¶ 'Sally Anne'	LFox
'Scharlockii'	See G. ***nivalis*** Scharlockii Group
'Straffan'	CAvo CBro EMor EOrc EPot ERav LAma LFox NHar WOld
'Tiny Tim'	NBir
'Titania' (d)	NGar
§ ***transcaucasicus***	CBro EHic EPot LFox NGar WChr
'Trotter's Merlin'	EMor
¶ 'W Thomas'	LFox
'Warley Belles'	EBul
'Warley Duo'	EBul
'Warley Longbow'	EBul
'Winifrede Mathias'	CBro LFox

GALAX (Diapensiaceae)

aphylla	See G. ***urceolata***
§ ***urceolata***	CRDP IBlr MBal SReu WThi

GALEGA (Leguminosae/Papilionaceae)

bicolor	CCla CWit EBee ECro EMar IBlr MSte NBrk NBro WCot WHaw WHer WTyr

'Duchess of Bedford'	EMon
x ***hartlandii***	IBlr
– 'Alba' AGM	EMon GBar GCal IBlr NBro WCot
– 'Candida'	CGle GCal NTow SPer
* 'His Majesty'	EBee EMon GCal LRHS NBrk
'Lady Wilson'	CGle NBrk SFis WCot WRus
officinalis	CArn CBot CCla CHad CHan CSev EBar ECro EFou ELan EOrc Effi GMac GPoy IBlr LHil LHol MChe MTol NBir NBro NSti SIde WByw WEas WHoo WMer WOak WWin WWye
– 'Alba'	CBot CElw CHad CHan ECED ECro EFol EMon ERav GMac IBlr SUsu WAbb WByw WCHb WEas WHer WHoo WRus
orientalis	CGle CHad CHan ECha EFol EMar GCal MArl WAbb WCot WRus

GALEOBDOLON See LAMIUM

GALEOPSIS (Labiatae/Lamiaceae)

* ***setiferum***	EBee
¶ ***speciosa***	ECWi

GALIUM (Rubiaceae)

arenarium	SHer WPer
aureum	See G. ***firmum***
cruciatum	See CRUCIATA ***laevipes***
mollugo	CArn CKin ECWi MHew MSal NLan SIde WCHb WNdy
§ ***odoratum***	CArn CBre CGle CKin CSFH EEls EFol EFou EHer ELan EOrc EWFC Effi GPoy IEde LHol MBar MBri MSal NLan NMir NSti SIde SUsu WBon WHer WMer WNdy WOak
palustre	CKin
perpusillum	See ASPERULA ***perpusilla***
verum	CArn CKin ECWi EJud EWFC MChe MHew MSal NLan NMir SIde WCHb WGwy WNdy WOak WPer WWye

GALPHIMIA (Malpighiaceae)

See Plant Deletions

GALTONIA (Liliaceae/Hyacinthaceae)

candicans	CAvo CB&S CBro CChu CCla CHol CMHG ECha ECro ELan GMac LAma LBow LHop MBri NFai SDeJ SDix SFar SPer WDav WEas WPer WWat
princeps	CAvo ECha ECro ECtt EPla GCra MFir NRoo SAxl SDix WEas
¶ ***regalis***	CHan
viridiflora AGM	CAvo CBot CBro CRDP ECha ECro ECtt ELan ESma GCHN GCal MHFP MHlr NRoo SAxl SDix SIgm SMrm WOMN WPer
– S&SH 3	CHan

GAMOCHAETA (Compositae/Asteraceae)

¶ ***nivalis***	MHig

GAMOLEPIS See STEIRODISCUS

GARDENIA (Rubiaceae)

§ ***augusta***	CB&S CBow CNew CTro EBak LAbb MBri SHer SLMG
¶ – 'Gold Magic'	CTro
– 'Prostrata Variegata'	See G. ***a.*** 'Radicans Variegata'
– 'Radicans Variegata'	CNew
– 'Veitchiana'	ERea
cornuta	CTro
florida	See G. ***augusta***
globosa	See ROTHMANNIA ***g.***
grandiflora	See G. ***augusta***
jasminoïdes	See G. ***augusta***
thunbergia	CNew CTro

GARRYA † (Garryaceae)

elliptica	Widely available
– 'James Roof' AGM	Widely available
fremontii	CB&S CBow CKni ELan ISea WStI
x ***issaquahensis*** 'Glasnevin Wine'	ELan LRHS MAsh MBlu SMad SPla SReu SSta
– 'Pat Ballard' (m)	ELan IOrc LRHS MAsh SReu SSta

X GAULNETTYA See GAULTHERIA

GAULTHERIA † (Ericaceae)

adenothrix	EPot GDra GPlt MBal MBar NHar WAbe
antipoda	MBal NHar NHol
¶ – x ***macrostigma***	CMHG
crassa	GArf MHig NHol
cuneata AGM	ELan EPot GDra GWht IBar IDai MBal MBar MBri MGos MHig NNrd SPer SReu SSta WAbe WThu
¶ – 'Pinkie'	CRos
depressa	GArf MBal NHar
– pink	NHol
– – ***crassa***	MBal
forrestii	CTrw
fragrantissima	NHol
furiens	See G. ***insana***
'Glenroy Maureen'	MBal
griffithiana BM&W 69	MBal
¶ – KEKE 854	NHol
§ ***hispida***	EBro GArf GDra MBal MGos NHar NHol
hispidula	See G. ***hispida***
hookeri	IBlr MBri NHar NHol
– B 547	MBal
humifusa	MBal
§ ***insana***	LMer MBal
itoana	CMHG GAbr GArf GDra GPlt MBal MBar MGos MHig WAbe
leucocarpa	NHol
littoralis	MBal
macrostigma	MBal
miqueliana	EBar GArf IBar MBal MBar MDHE MGos NHar SPla SReu SSta WAbe WThu WWat
mucronata AGM	CMHG CPle ELan ENot IDai ISea MBal MBar NNor NWea

– (m)	CPMA CSco ELan GRei MBar MBri MGos MRav MUlv NKay SPer SReu SRms WPat
– P&W 6273	EPot
– 'Alba' (f)	CSco GRei GWht MAsh MGos MRav
– 'Atrococcinea' (f)	SRms WPat
– 'Barry Lock' (f)	WPat
– 'Bell's Seedling' AGM	CChe CDoC CSco ENot GRei MBri MGos NKay SHBN SPer SReu SSta WAbe WPat
– 'Cherry Ripe' (f)	CDoC CSco GPlt IOrc NHol SHBN SPer
– 'Crimsonia' AGM	CChe ELan GPlt MAsh MGos NHol SHBN SLon SPer SPla SReu SRms WPat
– 'Indian Lake'	CDoC GPlt NHol
– 'Lilacina' (f)	MAsh MBal MBri MGos NKay
– 'Lilian' (f)	MAsh MBri NHol SHBN SPer SPla WWeb
– 'Mulberry Wine' AGM	CDoC IOrc NHol
– 'October Red' (f)	GPlt WWeb
– 'Parelmoer' ('Mother of Pearl') (f)	CChe CPMA ELan ENot GPlt MBri NHol NKay SPer WPat WWeb
– 'Pink Pearl' AGM	MAsh MBri SRms
– 'Rosalind' (f)	GPlt WWeb
– 'Rosea' (f)	CSco GRei
– 'Rosie' (f)	MBri
– 'Sea Shell' AGM	IOrc MBri NHol
– 'Signaal' ('Signal') (f)	CPMA ELan ENot GPlt MAsh MBri MGos MPla SPer SReu WPat WWeb
– 'Sneeuwwitje' ('Snow White') (f)	CPMA ENot GPlt MAsh MBri SHBN SPla SReu
– 'Stag River' (f)	GDra NHar WDav
– 'Thymifolia' (m)	CChe GAri MAsh SHBN SPer SPla
– 'White Magic' (f)	SLon
– 'White Pearl' (f)	IOrc MBri NHol
– 'Wintertime' AGM	ELan MAsh SRms WWeb
§ ***myrsinoïdes***	GAri GDra MBal
– 'Geoffrey Herklots'	MBri
nana Colenso	See G. ***parvula***
nummularioïdes	GAri GTou MHig NHar NHol NMen
– B 673	MBal
– TW	GWht
§ – ***elliptica***	SSta
– ***minor***	MBal
– 'Minuta'	See G. ***n. elliptica***
ovalifolia	See G. ***fragrantissima***
I ***paraguayensis***	MBal
§ ***parvula***	ECou
phillyreifolia	SSta
poeppigii	NHol WPat
– ***racemosa***	SSta
procumbens AGM	Widely available
prostrata	See G. ***myrsinoïdes***
– ssp. ***pentlandii***	MBal NHar
* – ***purpurea***	See G. ***myrsinoïdes***
pumila	ECou GAri GWht MBal MBar MBri NHar
§ – C&W 5226	MBal NHol
– 'E K Balls'	EPot GPlt NHar NHol WDav WThu
pyroloïdes	MBal NHol WThu
– BM&W 5	MBal
rupestris	GDra MBal
shallon	CB&S CDoC CLan CTom ENot GAul GRei IDai IJoh MBar MBri MGos MPla SHBN SLon SPer SReu SSta WDin WFro WStI
– dwarf form	MBal
sinensis	MBal MHig WThi
sp. P&W 6142	NHol
sp. Wr 8710	NHol
tasmanica	ECou GDra GWht MBal MBar NHol
– white-berried	GDra WDav
– yellow-berried	MBal
– x ***pumila***	MBal
thymifolia	MBal NHol
trichophylla	GArf GDra MBal WAbe WDav WWin
willisiana	See G. ***eriophylla***
x ***wisleyensis***	CLan MBal MUlv SLon SPer SSta WAbe WBod WPat
– 'Pink Pixie'	CCla CMHG ECro EPla IDai MAsh MBar MBri SIng SPer SSta WAbe
– 'Wisley Pearl'	CB&S GDra GWht IBlr IDai MBar MBri MGos NHar SDry SIng SReu WPat WThu
yunnanensis	EPla

GAURA (Onagraceae)

lindheimeri AGM	Widely available
– 'Corrie's Gold' (v)	EBar ECha ECtt EMon LGre LHop SAxl SChu SMad SUsu
¶ – 'Jo Adella'	ECha LHop
– 'The Bride'	EFou NFai
– 'Whirling Butterflies'	ECha EMon SMrm SOkh WCot WMer

GAYLUSSACIA (Ericaceae)

brachycera	GGGa
ursinum	SReu SSta

GAZANIA (Compositae/Asteraceae)

'Aztec' AGM	CBrk LBlm LHil
¶ 'Blackberry Ripple'	CB&S
'Brodick'	GCal
'Christopher'	CSpe LHil WPer
'Cookei' AGM	CBrk ELan LHil LHop SAxl WEas
'Cornish Pixie'	LHop
cream	LHop MRav
'Cream Beauty'	CHad EOrc GCal LBlm LHil MSte NTow SAxl SChu SHer SUsu
cream & purple	CHad ELan LHop SAxl SChu SUsu WPer
crimson and green	MSte
'Daybreak Bronze'	NRoo
'Dorothy'	LHil
♦ double yellow	See G. 'Yellow Buttons'
'Flash'	WEas
* 'Flore Pleno'	WPer
'Freddie'	SMrm
'Hazel'	GCal
hybrids	ELan LHop SDix SHer WPer
krebsiana	LBlm WPer
¶ 'Lemon Beauty'	WCot
* ***madeira***	LHop
'Magenta'	LBlm LHop SAxl
'Michael'	GCal

'Mini Star White' NFai WHen
'Mini Star Yellow' WHen
'Northbourne' GCal
'Orange Beauty' EHic ELan
¶ 'Patricia Morrow' CSpe
'Red Velvet' LHil LHop
§ ***rigens*** CB&S CSam MBri
– 'Aureovariegata' LHop SAxl
– var. ***uniflora*** CBrk EOrc GCal LHop MSte WEas
– – 'Variegata' CBot
– 'Variegata' AGM CB&S CBrk CRiv EBee ELan EOrc MPit NSti WPer
'Silver Beauty' CBot ERom LAbb NTow SChu
'Slate' EHic SMrm
'Snuggle Bunny' NTow
splendens See G. ***rigens***
'Talent' AGM NRoo
¶ 'Tiger' EOrc
§ 'Yellow Buttons' (d) EHic EMon LHil LHop

GEISSORHIZA (Iridaceae)

aspera CMon NRog
inflexa NRog
monantha NRog
radians NRog

GELASINE (Iridaceae)

azurea See G. ***caerulea***
§ ***coerulea*** WThi

GELIDOCALAMUS (Gramineae/Poaceae-Bambusoideae)

♦***fangianus*** See CHIMONOBAMBUSA ***microphylla***

GELSEMIUM (Loganiaceae)

rankinii CChu CMCN CPle
sempervirens AGM CAbb CB&S CMCN CNew CSPN CTro EBee ERea IBar MSal
– 'Flore Pleno' CB&S ERea LHop
– 'Pride of Augusta' CMCN

GENISTA (Leguminosae/Papilionaceae)

aetnensis AGM CB&S CBow CCla CLan CMHG CSam CSco EBre EHar ELan ENot IOrc LBre LHop LNet MBal MBri MWat SArc SDix SHBN SMad SPer SSta WBod WDin WOMN WSHC WWat
¶ ***albida*** WDav
anglica CKin
– 'Cloth of Gold' CNic MPla WDav
§ ***canariensis*** CGre CTre ERea LAbb MBri
cinerea CDoC CShe MAll SPer
decumbens See CYTISUS ***d.***
delphinensis See G. ***sagittalis delphinensis***
'Emerald Spreader' See G. ***pilosa*** 'Yellow Spreader'
fragrans See G. ***canariensis***
hispanica CB&S CSco EBre ELan ENot IDai IJoh IOrc LBre MBal MBar MGos MRav MWat NHol NNor SHBN SLon SPer SPla SReu WAbe WDin WStI
– 'Compacta' CLew SIng SPer
humifusa See G. ***villarsii***
¶ ***involucrata*** Spach WDav
lydia AGM Widely available
monosperma See RETAMA ***m.***
§ ***monspessulana*** EMon
pilosa CLan ENot EPot IDai ISea LNet MBar MBro MCas MGos MHew MPla NHar NMen NNor NRoo SBla SIng SPer WAbe WBod WEas WWin
– 'Goldilocks' CBow CBra CDoC CPMA ECtt ESis GPlt MAll MAsh MBar MBri NHar SSta WBod WStI
– 'Lemon Spreader' See G. ***p.*** 'Yellow Spreader'
*– ***major*** MHig
– ***minor*** GTou WAbe
– 'Procumbens' CLew CNic GDra MBal NHol SIng WEas WPat
– 'Superba' NNrd
– 'Vancouver Gold' CB&S COtt CSco EBre EHal ELan EPla EPot IHos IJoh IOrc LBre LHop MBri MGos MRav NBee NHar NHol NNrw NTow SBla SLon SPer SReu WGor WSHC WStI WWat WWeb
§ – 'Yellow Spreader' CB&S CBow CBra CLTr CMHG CPMA EBre ECtt ESis GPlt LBre MBal MBri MRav MWat NHol NNrd SHer WBod WWat WWeb
'Porlock' CDoC ELan
sagittalis CHan CLew CMHG CWGN LHop MAll MBal MBro NHol NNor NNrd SBla SPer WDin WWat
§ – ssp. ***delphinensis*** AGM CLew ELan EPla MCas MHig NHol NKay NNrd
– ***minor*** See G. ***s. delphinensis***
§ x ***spachianus*** AGM CGre MBri
¶ ***subcapitata*** dwarf form NWCA
tenera SPer
– 'Golden Shower' AGM CDoC CSco SHil
tinctoria CArn CKin CRDP EWFC GBar GPoy ILis MBar MChe MHew MSal NFai NNor SHer SIde WDin WHer WNdy WOak WWye
– 'Flore Pleno' AGM CMHG ELan EMon EPla ESis GPlt MBal MBar MPla NHar NHol NKay NMen NRar SHer SPer WBod WHil
– 'Humifusa' NHar NWCA
*– ***humilis*** MHig NHol
– 'Moesiaca' CNic
– var. ***prostrata*** WOak
– 'Royal Gold' AGM CBra CSco ECtt ENot MAll MBri MGos MPla MRav MWat NNor SHBN SHer SPer SPla WBod WWeb
– var. ***virgata*** CHan
tournefortii CShe MBal WPat
¶ ***umbellata*** SMad
§ ***villarsii*** EPot MBro MHig NHol NKay WDav

GENNARIA (Orchidaceae)

¶ ***diphylla*** EPot

GENTIANA † (Gentianaceae)

§ ***acaulis*** AGM Widely available
– ***alba*** WThu
– Andorra form GDra
– 'Belvedere' EMNN GCLN MHig WAbe WThu

– 'Coelestina'	GAng
– 'Dinarica'	See G. ***dinarica***
¶ – Excisa Group	WDav
– 'Gedanensis'	GAng
– 'Harlin'	NNrd
– 'Holzmannii'	EPot GAng NNrd
– 'Krumrey'	EMNN EPot GDra NNrd WThu
– 'Rannoch'	EMNN EPot NMen NNrd WThu
– 'Trotter's Variety'	GAng
– 'Undulatifolia'	NHar WDav WThu
¶ – 'Velkokvensis'	WAbe
affinis	CNic
algida	CPla
'Alpha'	See G. x ***hexafarreri*** 'A.'
alpina	GAng
¶ 'Amythyst'	WAbe
andrewsii	CLew CPla CRiv WHil
angustifolia	CNic GAng NHol NTow SIgm WAbe WThu
'Ann's Special'	GAng MDHE NHar NHol NRoo
asclepiadea AGM	CCla CGle CPla CRDP CWGN EBul ECha ELan GAng GCHN GDra IDai MBri MBro MTho NEgg NHol NRar NRoo SBla SIng SPer SUsu WAbe WHoo WWat
– ***alba***	CBot CCla CPla CRDP CRiv ELan ELun GAng IBar LHop MBri MBro MTho NHol NRar NRoo SBla SPer SUsu WAbe WHoo WOMN WWat
– 'Knightshayes'	EGle GAng LHop MBri MBro SHer SWas WHoo WRus
– 'Nymans'	ELan SHer
– pale blue	NRoo WOMN
– 'Phyllis'	MBro MTho WHoo WRus
– 'Rosea'	CNic WOMN
'Barbara Lyle'	GAng NRoo WAbe
¶ ***bellidifolia***	WAbe
x ***bernardii***	See G. x ***stevenagensis*** 'Bernardii'
bisetaea	SRms WDav
'Blauer Diamant'	GAng
'Blauer Edelstein'	GAng
'Blue Flame'	GAng GDra MSte
'Blue Heaven'	CLew GAng GCHN GCra GDra NHar WAbe
brachyphylla	NHol
– ssp. ***favratii***	WDav
§ ***burseri*** var. ***villarsii***	CNic
N ***cachemirica***	GTou MTho NGre WDav
calycosa	NHol
Cambrian hybrids	WAbe
x ***caroli***	GAng GAri NKay NWCA SBla WAbe WPat
'Christine Jean'	GAbr NHar NMen WDav
clusii	CNic EPot GAng GArf WAbe WPer
– ***costei***	NHol WAbe
– ***rochelii***	SIgm WDav
¶ 'Compact Gem'	WAbe
¶ ***crassicaulis***	GCra
– CLD 424	NHol
crinita	See GENTIANOPSIS ***crinita***
§ ***cruciata***	CPla GAbr GTou LHop MTho NHol WPer
§ ***dahurica***	ELan GAbr GCal GDra LBee SBla WPer
decumbens	CNic GCal MSto WHal WPer
dendrologi	NHol
depressa	GArf MTho WAbe WThi
'Devonhall'	WAbe
§ ***dinarica***	GAng GDra MBro MTho WAbe WDav WThu
Drake's strain	GAng GDra MSte NGre WAbe
'Dumpy'	WAbe
'Dusk'	GAng GDra NHar
'Eleanor'	GAng NHar
'Elizabeth'	GAng NHar NNrd WDav
'Excelsior'	NHol
'Exploi'	GAng
x ***farorna***	GAng NRoo
farreri	GArf NKay NWCA WAbe
'Fasta Highlands'	GAng
freyniana	GAng NWCA
gelida	NGre NHol
– JCA 518.400	NHol
'Glendevon'	GAng
§ ***gracilipes***	ELan MSte MWat NWCA SHer SIgm SRms
– 'Yuatensis'	See G. ***wutaiensis***
gracilis	CPla
grossheimii	MSto NHol
x ***hascombensis***	See G. ***septemfida lagodechiana*** 'Hascombensis'
x ***hexafarreri***	GAng NHar
§ – 'Alpha'	GAng GCHN WAbe
hexaphylla	GAng NHar
'Ida K'	GAng
'Indigo'	WAbe
Inshriach hybrids	GDra NHar NHol NNrd
'Inverleith' AGM	CNic ELan GAng MBri MBro NHar NHol NKay NRoo WGor WPat WThu
¶ ***kauffmanniana***	NHol
kesselringii	See G. ***walujewii***
kochiana	See G. ***acaulis***
¶ ***kolalowskyi***	NHol
kurroo	ELan NNrd SHer WOMN
– ***brevidens***	See G. ***dahurica***
lagodechiana	See G. ***septemfida l.***
'Leslie Delaney'	GAng
¶ ***loderi***	CVer
¶ ***lucerna***	NHar
lutea	CArn CBot CPla CRDP ECha GCra GDra GPoy GTou LGan LHop MSte NHar NHol NSti SDix SIgm WKif WPer WWye
x ***macaulayi*** AGM	CLew CPla CRiv GAng MBri MHig MSte NHol NKay NRoo SIng
– 'Blue Bonnets'	GAng NHar
– 'Edinburgh' AGM	GAng MDHE NNrd NRoo
– 'Elata'	ELan MBri MDHE NHar NHol
– 'Kidbrooke Seedling'	ELan NGre NHar NHol NKay NRya WAbe WStI
– 'Kingfisher'	CLew CMHG CPla CRiv ELan GAng GCra GDra MHig MSte NHar NMen NNor NNrd NRoo NWCA SBla SBod SIng WHil WStI
§ – 'Praecox'	ELan GAng GCHN MBri NHar NHol
§ – 'Wells's Variety'	GAbr MBri MHig NKay WAbe
macrophylla	See G. ***burseri villarsii***
'Magnificent'	GAng
makinoi	GAbr GAng GCLN MSto NGre NWCA

¶ – *alba*	GCLN
¶ – 'Royal Blue'	GCLN
'Maryfield'	GAng
'Midnight'	GAng
'Multiflora'	GAng
ochroleuca	See G. ***villosa***
x ***oliviana***	NHol
oreodoxa	EPot WAbe
pannonica	GDra
– hybrids	GDra
paradoxa	CLew CNic GArf GCHN GCra LBee MFos NGre NHar WDav WOMN
parryi	CNic EPot WDav
¶ ***patula***	CPBP
phlogifolia	See G. ***cruciata***
pneumonanthe	CRDP CRiv LHop NHol NRoo
prolata	WAbe
– K 214	GArf
– RH 61	WThu
przewalskii	GAbr
¶ ***puberulenta***	NHol
pumila	WAbe
punctata	GTou NHol
purdomii	See G. ***gracilipes***
purpurea	CVer WPer
robusta	CRDP ELan EMon GAbr NWCA
'Royal Highlander'	GAng MDHE NHar
saxosa	CNic CRDP ECou GAng GTou ITim LHop MBro MFos MSte MTho NBir NGre NHar NHol NMen NNrd NRed NWCA SGil SHer SWas WAbe WDav WOMN
scabra	NSla WWye
§ – var. ***buergeri***	LBee
– var. ***saxatilis***	See G. ***s. buergeri***
'Sensation'	GAng
septemfida AGM	CCla CPla ELan EMNN GAng GDra LHop MBar MBri MBro MCas MPla MTho MWat NEgg NGre NHol NKay NRoo SBla SIng WCla WDav WHoo WPat
– var. ***lagodechiana*** AGM	CLew CSam LAbb NGre NRoo NVic NWCA SHer SIng SRms WPer
§ – – 'Doeringiana'	GCHN NMen NRoo SIng
§ – – 'Hascombensis'	CPla ELan GCHN NGre NWCA
– – 'Latifolia'	CNic WHil
'Shot Silk'	WAbe
¶ ***sikokiana***	MSto
sino-ornata AGM	CPla ELan EMNN GAng GCHN GDra IDai LHop MBar MBri MFos MHig NEgg NHar NHol NKay NNrd NRoo NWCA SBla SFis SHer SIng WAbe WDav WPat
– ***alba***	CPla GAbr GDra NHar NHol NKay NRoo WDav WHil WWin
– 'Angel's Wings'	ELan GAng MBri NHar NHol WAbe WCru
– 'Blauer Dom'	GAng
– 'Brin Form'	CRiv NKay NNor NNrd NRoo SBod SIng WAbe WHil
– 'Downfield'	NHar NHol
– 'Edith Sarah'	CMea ELan EPot GAng MBri MHig NHar NHol NKay NNrd NRoo SBla WAbe WHil
– 'Lapis'	CMGP NHol
– 'Mary Lyle'	GAng GGar MBri MTho NHar NHol NRoo WAbe WThu
– 'Praecox'	See G. x ***macaulayi*** 'P.'
– 'Trogg's Form'	MDHE NHar NHol
– 'White Wings'	ELan NHar NHol
– 'Woolgreaves'	EPot WAbe
sp. SBEL 220	MSte
x ***stevenagensis*** AGM	CPla CRiv EMNN GAng MBri MFir MHig NHar NRoo SIng WHoo WPat WSun WThu
§ – 'Bernardii'	GAng MBri SIng WAbe
– dark form	NRoo WAbe
– 'Frank Barker'	GAng MBri WAbe
'Strathmore'	CRDP ELan GAng MBri MDHE NHar NHol NRoo SIng WAbe
'Susan'	GAng
'Susan Jane'	GAng MSte
ternifolia	ELan EPot GAng GDra MSte NKay NRoo SIng WDav
– SBEC 1053	GGGa NHol
– 'Cangshan' ex SBEC 1053	NHar WAbe
– 'Dali' ex SBEC 1053	GCLN MBri NBir NHar NHol WAbe
thunbergii	NHol WHil
'Thunersee'	GAng
tibetica	CBot CMea CNic CPla CRiv EBar GAbr GCal GTou NHol NRoo NSti WEas WHil WPer
– CLD 592	NHol
trichotoma CLD 429	NHol
triflora	GBuc MSto NHol
– var. ***japonica***	GBuc NGre SIng
– var. ***montana***	GDra
– 'Royal Blue'	GCal
¶ ***trinervis***	MSto
veitchiorum	MBri NRoo
verna	CGle CLew CNic CSam ELan GAng GTou LBee LGan LHop MBro MPla MTho MWat NKay NRoo NTow WAbe WDav WOMN WPat WPer
– ***alba***	WPat
– ***angulosa***	See G. ***v. balcanica***
§ – ssp. ***balcanica***	CNic CPla ELan EPot GAng GDra MBro MCas MHig MTho NGre NHar NHol NRed SBla SHer SIng WHoo WPat
waltonii	ELan SHer
§ ***walujewii***	CCla MSto
wellsii	See G. x ***macaulayi*** 'Wells's Variety'
§ ***wutaiensis***	CNic ELan GAbr GDra MSto NRed SHer
'Zauberland'	GAng

GENTIANELLA (Gentianaceae)

See Plant Deletions

GENTIANOPSIS (Gentianaceae)

See Plant Deletions

GEOGENANTHUS (Commelinaceae)

See Plant Deletions

GERANIUM † (Geraniaceae)

aconitifolium L'Héritier	See G. ***rivulare***
albanum	CElw CHan EMon EMou EOrc GCHN MHFP MNFA MUlv NCat SAxl SCou SDix WByw WCra WCru
albiflorum	GCHN MHFP MNFA NCat SAxl

anemonifolium	See G. ***palmatum***
'Ann Folkard'	Widely available
¶ 'Ann Folkard' × ***psilostemon***	CElw
'Anne Thomson'	EOrc GCHN SAxl
antrorsum	WEas
argenteum	ELan MDHE SCou
– 'Purpureum'	See G. × ***lindavicum*** 'Alanah'
aristatum	CElw EOrc GCHN SCou WCra WCru
armenum	See G. ***psilostemon***
asphodeloïdes	CElw CGle CHil CHol CLew EBar ECro EMon EMou EOrc ESma GAbr GCHN NCat NSti SUsu WBon WByw WCra WCru WEas WHCG WHal WHen WNdy WPbr WRus WSun WToa
§ – ssp. ***asphodeloïdes*** white	CHan EBre EOrc LBre MNFA SCou WRus
¶ – ssp. ***crenophilum***	WCru
– forms	MHFP NCat SCou WCru WHal WHen
– 'Prince Regent'	CBre GCHN GCal NRoo SAxl SCou WCot
¶ – ssp. ***sintenisii***	WCru
– 'Starlight'	GCHN GCal NCat SAxl SCou WCru
atlanticum Hooker f.	See G. ***malviflorum***
'Baby Blue'	SAxl
biuncinatum	SCou
'Black Ice'	GCHN SAxl WCru
¶ 'Blue Cloud'	SAxl
'Blue Pearl'	SAxl
bohemicum	CHil EBar GCHN GCal MDHE MNFA NCat NVic SCou SFis WByw WCra WCru WEas WHal WHen WHer WNdy WToa
'Brookside'	CElw CHil ECha EMou EOrc EPla GAbr GCHN MBel MNFA NBir NBrk SAxl SCou WCra WHen WToa
brutium	GCHN SCou SUsu WCra WCru WHen WToa
¶ ***brycei***	EMon
'Buxton's Blue'	See G. ***wallichianum*** 'Buxton's Variety'
caffrum	CElw CHan EMar EOrc GBuc GCHN NCat SAxl SCou WCru WEas WHal
canariense	CGre NCat SCou WCru WHal
candicans hort.	See G. ***lambertii***
§ × ***cantabrigiense***	Widely available
– 'Biokovo'	Widely available
– 'Cambridge'	CBos CDoC CElw CHil CMHG EBre ECoo ECtt EFou ELan ERav LBre MRav NCat NFai NHol NVic SAxl SCro WCra WHen WHer WPbr
– 'Karmina'	CElw CHil EPla NRoo SAxl SCou WHoo
– 'Saint Ola'	CElw GBuc GCHN SAxl WCru
¶ – 'Show Time'	SCro
cataractarum	EFou EMon GCHN NCat SCou SUsu WCra WCru WHal
– ssp. ***pitardii***	SAxl
'Chantilly'	CElw GAbr SAxl
cinereum	CGle CSev GAbr GBur WToa
– 'Apple Blossom'	See G. × ***lindavicum*** 'A.B.'
– 'Ballerina' AGM	Widely available
– var. ***cinereum***	GCHN WHil
– – 'Album'	GCHN MBal SCou
– 'Lawrence Flatman'	Widely available
– var. ***subcaulescens*** AGM	Widely available
– – 'Giuseppii'	CHil CLew CWGN EBre EFou GCHN LBre MBro MNFA NCat NRoo SAxl SCou WCra WCru WHoo WRus WToa
– – 'Splendens' AGM	CHil CLew CRDP EBre ECha EFou ELan GCHN GMac LBre MBal MBri NRoo NSti WCru WHoo WRus WToa
'Claridge Druce'	See G. × ***oxonianum*** 'Claridge Druce'
¶ ***clarkei*** Raina 82.83	SCou
– 'Kashmir Blue'	GCHN SAxl
– 'Kashmir Pink'	CElw CGle CMea CPou GBur GCHN MHFP NBir SAxl SBla SCro SMrm SOkh SWas WHCG WHal WHen WToa
§ – 'Kashmir Purple'	Widely available
§ – 'Kashmir White'	Widely available
collinum	CElw GCHN GMac NCat SAxl SCou SUsu WByw WCru WHen WNdy WToa
columbinum	NCat SCou
'Coombeland White'	NCat SAxl WCru
dahuricum	SCou
dalmaticum AGM	Widely available
– 'Album'	Widely available
– × ***macrorrhizum***	See G. × ***cantabrigiense***
delavayi Franchet	CBot CChu
'Dilys'	GCHN NCat SAxl WCru WHen
dissectum	EWFC MSal SCou
¶ 'Diva'	WCru
donianum	SCou
endressii AGM	Widely available
¶ – 'Castle Drogo'	CHil NCat
– dark form	CMea NCat WCru
♦ – 'Prestbury White'	See G. 'Prestbury Blush'
– 'Priestling's Red'	SMrm
– 'Rose'	GBur LBlm WPer WToa
erianthum	CElw EMou GBuc GCHN NCat SAxl SCou WCru WNdy
– 'Calm Sea'	GCHN NCat SAxl WCru
– 'Neptune'	NCat SAxl
♦ ***eriostemon*** Fischer	See G. ***platyanthum***
farreri AGM	CBot CElw CHil CLew EBre GCHN GMac LBre MHFP MNFA NCat NGre NKay NRoo NTow NWCA SBla SCou WCru WEas WHal WToa
flanaganii	CElw EBee GCHN WCru
fremontii	CRDP GCHN NCat SAxl SCou WCru
gracile	CElw CHil EMou GCHN GMac MHFP MNFA NBir NSti NVic SAxl SCou SUsu WCru WHal WHer
– pale form	CElw SCou
grandiflorum	See G. ***himalayense***
– var. ***alpinum***	See G. ***himalayense*** 'Gravetye'
¶ ***grandistipulatum***	SCou
¶ ***harveyi***	CHan
¶ ***hayatanum*** B&SWJ 164	WCru

§ ***himalayense***	CElw CFee CWGN EBar ECha ELan EMou GCHN LBlm MTho MWat NBir NBrk NBro NHol NNor NSti SMrm SUsu WBon WCra WCru WHCG WHen WMer WPer
♦– ***alpinum***	See G. ***h.*** 'Gravetye'
– 'Birch Double'	See G. ***h.*** 'Plenum'
§ – 'Gravetye' AGM	Widely available
– 'Irish Blue'	CElw CHil GCHN GCal MBel MHFP MNFA SAxl SCou SCro WAbb WCru WHen WToa
§ – 'Plenum'	Widely available
ibericum	CBow CCla CElw CHol CKel CShe ECED EPad EPla MBal MTol MWat NRoo SCou SPer WByw WCra WCru WEas WHen WNdy WToa WWin
– ssp. ***jubatum***	CElw EGle GCHN GCal MNFA SAxl
– var. ***platypetalum*** Boissier	See G. ***platypetalum***
– var. ***platypetalum*** hort.	See G. x ***magnificum***
incanum	CElw CHan CMHG CSev CShe CSpe EMon EOrc GCHN GCal LBlm LHop NBir SAxl SBor SCou SCro SMrm WCra WToa
– var. ***incanum***	GCHN WCru
– ***multifidum***	CElw GCHN MBel SAxl SUsu WCru
¶ 'Ivan'	SWas
'Johnson's Blue' AGM	Widely available
'Joy'	CElw GCHN LGre SAxl SCou SUsu WCru
§ 'Kate'	CElw GCHN SAxl SCou WCru
'Kate Folkard'	See G. 'Kate'
kishtvariense	CElw GCHN GCal MNFA SAxl SBla SCou WCru WHal
koreanum	CChu CFil CHan EBee GCHN MNFA WCru
kotschyi	WCru
– var. ***charlesii***	GCal WCru
¶ ***krameri***	CElw
§ ***lambertii***	CLew NBir NBrk NSti SCou WEas WHal WHoo
– 'Coombland White'	SCou
– 'Swansdown'	CElw GCHN GCal NBrk NTow SCou WCru
lanuginosum	SCou
libani	CChu CElw CHan EMou GCHN GCal MBel MHFP MHlr MNFA NSti SAxl SCou SCro WCot WCra WCru WEas WHal
¶ 'Libretto'	NCat
x ***lindavicum*** 'Alanah'	EMon
§ – 'Apple Blossom'	MNFA NRoo WMar
'Little Gem'	GCHN SAxl
lucidum	ECWi EJud EWFC GCHN GCra MHew MSal NCat NSti SCou WHaw
§ ***macrorrhizum***	Widely available
– 'Album' AGM	Widely available
– 'Bevan's Variety'	Widely available
– 'Czakor'	Widely available
– 'Ingwersen's Variety' AGM	Widely available
– 'Lohfelden'	CElw GCHN SAxl SWas WCru
– ***macrorrhizum***	CElw SRms
– 'Pindus'	CElw GCHN SAxl SWas WCru
– 'Ridsko'	CElw CHil GCHN GCal NCat SAxl SCou WCru WHen
– ***roseum***	See G. ***m.***
– 'Spessart'	CCla CDoC CElw CLTr CMGP CRos ERav MBel MUlv NSti SCou SHig WCru
– 'Variegatum'	CElw CGle CHan CRDP CShe ECha EFol EFou EGol ELan EPar EPla ERav GBur LHop MBri MTho NBir NRoo NSti SAxl WByw WHCG WHen WHer WNdy WOld WWin
– 'Velebit'	GCHN SAxl
macrostylum	CElw GCHN MBro WCot WCru WPer
maculatum	CBow CChu CElw CHan CSev ECha ELan EMou GCHN GCal GMac GPoy MBro MHFP MNFA MRav MSal NRoo SAxl SCou SCro SFis SMrm SUsu WCra WCru WHal WHen WHoo
– f. ***albiflorum***	CBow CElw CGle CHil GCHN GCal MBel MHFP MNFA SAxl SCou SUsu WCra WHal WSun WToa
maderense AGM	CBoy CHEx CPla CPle CSam CTbh CTro ECro EMon GAbr GCHN GCal IBlr MHFP NBrk NPer SAxl SCou SDix WCru WEas WHal WKif WPer
§ x ***magnificum*** AGM	Widely available
– 'Wisley Variety'	GAbr
magniflorum	GCHN NCat SCou WCru
– S&SH 32	CHan
§ ***malviflorum***	CBos CElw CHan CMon ECha EFou ELan EMar EMou EPla EPot GCHN LGre LHop MBro MTho NSti SAxl SBor SCou SFis SUsu WCru WHal WHoo WKif WOMN WOld WToa
¶ – pink	SBla
'Mary Mottram'	WEas
molle	EWFC MSal
§ x ***monacense***	CBos CBow CBre CElw CHil CSam EFou ELan EMar GGar MBel MWat NFai NRoo NSti SAxl SCou SCro SUsu WByw WCra WCru WHer WNdy WPbr WSun WToa
x ***monacense anglicum***	EGle EOrc GCHN MBel MNFA NSti SAxl SCou SCro WToa
x ***monacense monacense***	CElw WHen
x ***monacense*** 'Muldoon'	CMHG CSev ECha EMon EPla GAbr GCal LHil MBri MFir MHFP MUlv NBrk NOak NRoo SPer WCra WCru WHCG WNdy WPbr
– 'Variegatum'	EFou EGol ELan NSti SCou WCru WEas WRus WToa
'Mourning Widow'	See G. ***phaeum***
multisectum	CElw CHan WCru
napuligerum	NSla
nepalense	CTom NCat SCou WHer
nervosum	CElw MNFA SAxl SCou WCru
¶ 'Nicola'	NCat
'Nimbus'	CElw EOrc GCHN MNFA SAxl SWas WToa
nodosum	Widely available
– dark form	CBos CElw CLew WCru WHen
– pale form	CElw CLew MHFP SCou SMrm WCru
– 'Svelte Lilac'	EMon EPla LRHS
– 'Swish Purple'	EMon
– 'Whiteleaf'	CElw EMon WCru
ocellatum	CBre NCat

oreganum	GCHN SCou WCru
§ ***orientalitibeticum***	Widely available
¶ 'Orkney Pink'	GCal MBel WCru
x ***oxonianum***	SAxl SCou WCru WEas
– 'A T Johnson' AGM	Widely available
¶ – 'Armitage'	NCat
¶ – 'Bregover Pearl'	CBre
§ – 'Claridge Druce'	Widely available
¶ – 'David McClintock'	EMon
¶ – 'Frank Lawley'	SAxl
– 'Hollywood'	CElw EBee ELan EMon EOrc GCHN SAxl SCro SMrm WToa
¶ – 'Julie Brennan'	NCat
¶ – 'Kate Moss'	GCHN
– 'Lace Time'	EBee SCro SOkh
– 'Lady Moore'	CHil EBre GBuc GCHN LBre LGan SAxl SCro WToa
– 'Miriam Rundle'	EOrc NCat SAxl WCru
– 'Old Rose'	CElw GCHN SAxl WCru
– pale form	EOrc
♦– 'Prestbury White'	See G. 'Prestbury Blush'
¶ – 'Rebecca Moss'	CElw GCHN NCat WCru
¶ – 'Rohina Moss'	SCou
– 'Rose Clair'	CElw CHil CShe EBre EOrc LBlm LBre MNFA NFai NHol SAxl SChu SCou WCru WEas WElm WHen WPer
– 'Rosenlicht'	SAxl SUsu WCru WToa
– 'Sherwood'	CElw CHil CLew EBee EOrc GCHN GCal MHFP MTho NCat NRoo SAxl SCou SCro SMrm
– 'Southcombe Double'	CBre CElw CMil CWGN EBre EGle EMou LBre MFir MNFA MUlv NCat NRoo SAxl SChu SLga SUsu WByw WCra WCru WHal WHen WToa WWin
§ – 'Southcombe Star'	CElw EBee EHal GCal MBel MHFP NBrk NSti SAxl SCou WCru WHal WNdy
§ – 'Thurstonianum'	Widely available
– 'Wageningen'	CBre EPla GCal GMac NCat NRoo SAxl SCou WCru
– 'Walter's Gift'	CElw CGle CHan ECoo EFou EMar EMon GAbr GCal GMac MBel MNFA MTho NCat NRoo SAxl SCou SCro SUsu WCot WCru WHen WHer WToa
– 'Wargrave Pink' AGM	Widely available
¶ – 'Waystradi'	SCou
– 'Winscombe'	CElw CHil EBre EFou EMou EOrc GAbr GCHN GCal LBlm LBre MNFA MTho NCat NHol NRoo NSti SApp SAxl SCou SCro SMrm WHen WRus WToa
x ***oxonianum*** x ***sessiliflorum nigricans***	CHil WToa
'Pagoda'	EOrc SAxl
§ ***palmatum*** AGM	CAbb CBos CBot CElw CHad CHan CPle CRDP CSpe EMar EPad LHil MFir NBro NCat NFai NPer SCou SCro SMad SMrm SUsu WCru WEas WHal WHer WKif WPer WToa
palustre	CElw CHil EMon EMou GCHN GCal MBel MHFP MNFA NSti SAxl SCou WByw WCru WHal WToa
papuanum	GCHN NCat SBla WCru WToa
'Patricia'	SAxl
Pelargonium	See PELARGONIUM
§ ***phaeum***	Widely available
– 'Album'	Widely available
*– ***aureum***	NCat
♦– black	See G. ***p.*** 'Mourning Widow'
¶ – 'Calligrapher'	SAxl
– forms	CBos EMou
*– ***hungaricum***	CChu CHil EBee GCal MFir NCat SCou
– 'Joan Baker'	CBos CGle CMil EBee NCat SAxl SCro
– 'Langthorn's Blue'	ELan MHFP NCat SMrm WPbr
§ – 'Lily Lovell'	Widely available
– var. ***lividum***	CBre CChu CElw CFee CGle CHil CMea EBre EMou GCHN LBre MUlv SChu SCou SFis SPer SWas WByw WCra WCru WHal WHen WHer WSun WWin
– – 'Majus'	CElw EBre EGle GCal LBre LGre MNFA NCat SAxl SCou
¶ – 'Mierhausen'	CGle
§ – 'Mourning Widow'	CElw LGre NCat SAxl WCru WHen WPbr
– Mrs Gardener's Selection	SUsu
¶ – 'Night Time'	SCro
¶ – 'Samobor'	CBos CElw SWas WHal
– 'Taff's Jester' (v)	CElw CHad CRDP GCal MTol NSti SCou SCro WHer
– 'Variegatum'	CElw CHan CMil CRDP EBar EBre ECro EGol ELan EMon EMou ERav GBur LBre MFir MRav NCat NSti SAxl WCru WHer WNdy
§ ***platyanthum***	CBos CElw CGle CHil CLew EMon EMou EPla GCHN GCal LGre MBri MNFA MTol NNor NSti SAxl SCou WByw WCra WCru WHal WHen WPer
platypetalum Fischer & Meyer	CElw CHan CHol EBre EHal ELan ENot GAbr GAri GBur GCHN LBre MHFP MNFA MPit NBir NKay SCou WCru WToa WTyr
¶ – 'Album'	CLTr
¶ – 'Georgia Blue'	CFil
♦***platypetalum*** Franchet	See G. ***sinense***
pogonanthum	GBuc GCHN GCal GMac MNFA NBro SAxl SCou WCru WHal
polyanthes	CElw CTom GAbr GAri GDra GTou NSti NTow SCou WCra WCru WHal
potentilloïdes	GCHN NBir NCat SAxl SCou WCru
pratense	CArn CBow CBre CHol CKin CWGN ECWi ECro EFou ELan EMou EOrc EWFC GBur GCHN LHol MHew MSal NLan NMir SCou WCla WCru WHen WNdy WPer WToa WTyr WWye
– f. ***albiflorum***	Widely available
– 'Bittersweet'	EMon
– 'Blue Chip'	EMon
– 'Cluden Ruby'	GCHN
– 'Cluden Sapphire'	GCHN WCru
– 'Flore Pleno'	See G. ***p.*** 'Plenum Violaceum'
– forms	GCHN SCou
– 'Galactic'	CHan EMon NCat SAxl WCru WHoo WNdy WOMN
– 'Mrs Kendall Clark' AGM	Widely available

– pale form	MHFP
– 'Plenum Album'	CElw CHil SCou
§ – 'Plenum Caeruleum'	CBos CCla CElw CGle COtt EOrc GCHN GCal MBri MWat NNor SCou SPer WCra WCru WEas WHCG WHoo WToa
– 'Plenum Purpureum'	See G. ***p.*** 'Plenum Violaceum'
§ – 'Plenum Violaceum' **AGM**	CB&S CBot COtt CRDP ELan EOrc GAbr GCHN MUlv NNor SChu SCou SDix WCra WCru WHoo WKif WNdy WOld WRus WToa WWin
– ***rectum album***	See G. ***clarkei*** 'Kashmir White'
– 'Rose Queen'	SAxl WCru
– ***roseum***	CGle CHil ELan EOrc GBur LHop NBir NHol NSti WByw WCru WHoo WToa
– 'Silver Queen'	CBre CGle CHil CSco EBee ELan EOrc GCHN GGar MHFP NBrk NRoo SAxl SCou WCra WCru WHen WToa
– ssp. ***stewartianum***	SAxl WCru
– 'Striatum'	CChu CElw CHil CLew CMil EBre ECha EMon EMou LBre LGre MHFP MNFA NCat NFai NNrw SAxl SCou SUsu WCra WCru WEas WElm WHal WHoo WKif WWin
– 'Wisley Blue'	SCou SCro SOkh
– x ***himalayense***	WCru
§ 'Prestbury Blush'	EMon GCHN SCou WSun
procurrens	Widely available
¶ ***pseudosibiricum***	SCou
§ ***psilostemon*** **AGM**	Widely available
– 'Bressingham Flair'	Widely available
– 'Gold Leaf'	WCot
pulchrum	CElw EMon EOrc GCHN GCal NCat SAxl SCou WCru
punctatum hort.	See G. x ***monacense*** 'Muldoon'
– ***variegatum***	See G. x ***monacense*** 'Variegatum'
pusillum	CKin MSal
pylzowianum	CElw CLew CNic CRiv CShe EPla GBur MBri MNFA NGre NHol NMen NNrd NRoo NRya NVic SAxl SBor SChu SCou SSmi WCra WCru WHal WHer WToa
pyrenaicum	CBre CElw CKin CRDP ECWi EOrc ESma EWFC GAbr GCHN MHew MSal NNrw NSti NVic SCou SUsu WCru WHal WHen WToa
– f. ***albiflorum***	CElw CHil CLew EFol EJud EOrc GCHN MHFP MTho NBir NNrw NSti NVic SAxl SCou SUsu WCla WCra WCru WHen WToa
– 'Bill Wallis'	CLew EFol EOrc LGan MHFP MHlr MTho MUlv NCat SAxl WCot WCru
rectum	SAxl WCru
– 'Album'	See G. ***clarkei*** 'Kashmir White'
'Red Dwarf'	GCHN
reflexum	CBre CChu CElw CSev EGol GBur GCHN MHFP MNFA NCat SAxl SCou SCro WEas WHCG WHal WToa
renardii **AGM**	Widely available
– blue	See G. ***r.*** 'Whiteknights'
– 'Philippe Vapelle'	CElw GCHN NBir SAxl SCou SCro
§ – 'Whiteknights'	EGol EPla MNFA NBir NSti SCou WCru WEas
– 'Zetterland'	EBre LBre SAxl
richardsonii	GCHN GCal MNFA NBir SCou WCru
x ***riversleaianum***	ECas GBur SCou WCru
– 'Jean Armour'	GCHN WCru
– 'Mavis Simpson'	CCla CElw CHil CLew CMHG CRos EBre EFou EGol EMon EPla GCHN LBre LGre MBri MNFA NRoo SAxl SCou SCro SMrm SUsu WByw WCra WCru WHal WHen WNdy WRus WToa
– 'Russell Prichard' **AGM**	Widely available
§ ***rivulare***	GCHN MNFA WCru WHCG WHer WToa
– 'Album'	CBre
'Robert Burns'	GCHN
robertianum	CKin ECWi EFol EWFC LHol MChe NCat SHer SIde WHen
§ – 'Album'	NCat NSti NVic SCou WElm WNdy WSun
– f. ***bernettii***	See G. ***r.*** 'Album'
– 'Celtic White'	CBre CTom EFol EMon GCal MHFP NCat NSti WHal
robustum	CElw CGle CHan EMon GCHN GCal GMac MNFA NCat NSti SAxl SCou SUsu WByw WCra WCru WEas WHal WNdy WSun WToa
– S&SH 14	CHan CMea WCru WToa
¶ – 'Norman Warrington'	CElw
¶ – x ***incanum***	WCru
rubescens	GBur GGar MFir MNFA NBir NBro NCat NNrw SAxl SCou WCra WCru WEas WHal WNdy WToa
rubicaule	NCat
rubifolium	MHFP SAxl SCou SUsu WCra WCru WToa
ruprechtii	CElw GCHN SCou WCru
* 'Sally'	NRar
'Salome'	CElw CGle CMHG CMil CRDP SBla SCou SMrm SWas WCru
sanguineum	Widely available
– 'Alan Bloom'	LRHS
– 'Album' **AGM**	Widely available
– 'Ankum's Pride'	CGle
¶ – 'Barnsley'	SCou
¶ – 'Bloody Graham'	EMon
– 'Cedric Morris'	CElw CFil ECha MHFP MNFA SAxl SCou SWas WCru
¶ – 'Elliott's Variety'	SIng
– 'Elsbeth'	CElw CHil GCHN SAxl SCou SWas WCru
¶ – 'Farrer's Form'	WCru
– 'Glenluce'	CGle CHil EMou EPla GCHN GCal MBel MHFP MNFA NCat NOrc NRoo SAxl SChu SCou SCro SMrm SRms WCra WCru WHCG WHal WPer WToa
¶ – 'Holden'	WCru
¶ – 'John Elsley'	CHil WCra
– 'Jubilee Pink'	CHil SBla SCou WCru WToa
– var. ***lancastrense***	See G. ***s. striatum***

– 'Max Frei'	CElw CGle CHil CLew CMGP CSev EBre EFou EGol ELan EPla GCHN GCal LBre MHFP MNFA NBar NBir NHol SAxl SChu SCou WCru WHow WMer WRus WToa WTyr
– 'Minutum'	SCou WCru
– 'Nanum'	EPar NHol NKay NNrd WCru
– 'Nyewood'	GCHN MHFP SAxl WCru
– var. ***prostratum***	See G. ***s. striatum***
– 'Shepherd's Warning' AGM	CCla CHil CLew CMea CSco CSev CShe EBre ECtt EPla GAbr GCHN LBre LHop MRav NEgg NRoo SCou SIng WByw WCra WCru WHCG WHal WHoo WPat WRus WToa
§ – var. ***striatum*** AGM	Widely available
– – deep pink	SCro
I – – 'Splendens'	CCla CElw CKel CLew CSco ECha EGol EHar ELan EPla GDra IDai LHop MWat NKay NNor NRoo SAxl SCou SSmi WCru WEas WOld WSun
¶ – x ***swatense***	SAxl
schlechteri	WCru
'Sea Fire'	CElw GCHN SAxl WCru
'Sea Pink'	CElw GCHN SAxl SUsu WCru
'Sea Spray'	CElw GCHN SAxl SUsu WCru WToa
sessiliflorum	ECou EPar GBur SCou WCru WElm WToa
– ssp. ***brevicaule*** var. Glabrum Group	SUsu
– ssp. ***novae-zelandiae*** green-leaved	CElw GCHN
– – 'Nigricans'	Widely available
– – 'Nigricans' x ***traversii elegans***	CBos CHan CRDP ESis GCHN NCat NGar SAxl WCot WCru
– – 'Nigricans' x ***traversii elegans*** Crûg strain	NCat WCru WToa
§ – – 'Porter's Pass'	CBos CElw CLew EFol EHoe EWes GCHN GCal MHFP MPit NBir SCou WCru
♦ – – red-leaved	See G. ***s. n-z.*** 'Porter's Pass'
shikokianum	SCou
¶ – var. ***yoshiianum***	GLil
sibiricum	GBur GCHN SCou WToa
¶ 'Silver Pink'	SAxl
sinense	CBre CHan EMar EPla GCHN GCal GMac LBlm LGre NRoo SCou SUsu SWas WCra WCru WHCG WHal WHer WHoo
soboliferum	GBuc NBir SAxl SCou WCru
¶ 'Sonata'	NCat
'Southcombe Star'	See G. x ***oxonianum*** 'S. S.'
'Spinners'	CBre CElw CMil CSam EOrc GBuc GCHN GCal MBri NCat SAxl SCou SMrm WCru WHen WHoo
'Stanhoe'	EFol NSti SCou SUsu WCru WToa
stapfianum roseum	See G. ***orientalitibeticum***
subulatostipulatum	WCru
'Sue Crûg'	WCru
¶ ***suzukii*** B&SWJ 016	WCru
swatense	CElw NCat SAxl SCou WCru WHal
– SEP 131	GCHN WCru
sylvaticum	CBow CBre CSev EMou EWFC GMac MBal MNFA MSal SCou WBon WCra WCru WHal WHen WNdy WPer
– f. ***albiflorum***	CBot CBre CElw CHan CMil CSco EFol EGol ELan EMou EPad GCHN MBro NRoo NSti SCou SUsu WCru WOld WToa WWin
– 'Album' AGM	CBow CCla CFil CGle CLew CMGP CTom ECas ECha EFou GAbr LBlm LHop MBel MBri MHFP MWat NHol NNrw SApp SCro SPer WBon WCra WEas WHal WHoo WRus WWat
– 'Amy Doncaster'	CBos CElw CMea CMil ECha ELan GCHN MBri MHFP MNFA NCat SAxl SCou SPer SWas WHal
– 'Angulatum'	SCou
– 'Baker's Pink'	CElw CFil CHil CMil EMou GCHN MHFP MNFA SAxl SBla SWas WHCG
– 'Birch Lilac'	GCal NCat NRoo SAxl SCou
– 'Mayflower' AGM	Widely available
– 'Meran'	SCou
– f. ***roseum***	CElw EGle GCHN MHFP NCat SCro SPer WCra
– 'Silva'	CGle GCHN GCal SAxl SCou
– ssp. ***sylvaticum*** var. ***wanneri***	CGle CHil GCHN LBlm LGre NCat SCou WCra WCru WHal WHoo
thunbergii	CHan CLTr CLew EMon EPla GAbr GCHN MTol NHol NMir NOak SCou SCro WCra WCru WHal WHen WHer WNdy WPer WToa
– ***roseum***	WCru
thurstonianum	See G. x ***oxonianum*** 'Thurstonianum'
transbaicalicum	CElw GCHN MBri MHFP MNFA WCru WHal
traversii	CBot EPot MDHE
– var. ***elegans***	CBos CCla CElw CHad CLew CSpe ELan GCHN GCal GMac LGan LGre MHFP MTho SAxl SCou SMad SUsu SWas WCra WCru WEas WHCG WHal WHer WNdy WOMN
– 'Seaspray'	GCal SCou
– 'Sugar Pink'	NBir
tuberosum	Widely available
– M&T 4032	CMon
– S&L 99	CMon
– var. ***charlesii***	See G. ***kotschyi c.***
versicolor	CElw CHad CHil CRDP CShe CTom EMar EMou GBur GCal GMac MNFA NVic SAxl SCou SCro SUsu WByw WCru WEas WHCG WHal WNdy WToa WWin
– ***album***	CElw CHan MHFP NCat WCru WHer WToa
– 'Snow White'	SAxl SMrm
¶ – 'White Lady'	WCru
violareum	See PELARGONIUM 'Splendide'
viscosissimum	EPla GCal GMac MBel MFir SAxl SCou SUsu WCra WOMN
– var. ***viscosissimum***	MHFP
wallichianum	ECas NMir NSti WCra WDav WHal WHen WNdy WToa
§ – 'Buxton's Variety' AGM	Widely available
– 'Syabru'	CBos MHFP SWas WCru

wilfordii hort.	See G. ***thunbergii***
wilfordii Maximowicz	WThi
¶ 'Wisley Hybrid'	WCru
wlassovianum	CElw CHil CMil CSco EGol EMou EPla GCHN LGre MHFP MNFA MTho MTol NBir NHol SAxl SCou SPer WCra WCru WHal WHoo WNdy WToa
yesoense	CElw GCHN MHFP NBir SCou SWas WCra WCru WHal WNdy
yunnanense	CHan GGar SCou

GERBERA (Compositae/Asteraceae)

jamesonii	CB&S

GESNERIA (Gesneriaceae)

cardinalis	See SINNINGIA ***c.***
x ***cardosa***	See SINNINGIA x ***c.***

GEUM † (Rosaceae)

aleppicum CLD 610	EMon EPla
alpinum	See G. ***montanum***
'Beech House Apricot'	CGle EBee LGre MBel SUsu SWas
¶ 'Birkhead's Creamy Lemon'	NBir
N 'Borisii'	Widely available
'Borisii' x ***montanum***	LHop
bulgaricum	LRHS NFai NHol WByw WMer WSun
canadense	ECro
capense S&SH 33	CHan
¶ 'Carlskaer'	SWas
§ ***chiloense***	EBar NHol
– P&W 6513	CHan MSte
– 'Dolly North'	CGle ECED EFou GGar MBri NBro NCat NFai NHol WMer
– 'Fire Opal' AGM	CHol CSco GCal MBel MNFA NBir SPer WTyr
– 'Georgenberg'	CB&S CElw CGle CKel CSco EBre ECtt ELun LBlm LBre LHil NBar NBir NFai NHol NOak SAxl SChu SPer WAbb WByw WDav WHal WMer WNdy WOld
– 'Lady Stratheden' AGM	CB&S CDoC CKel CSco EBre ECtt ELan ENot GCHN LAbb LBre MBri MFir MRav MWat NBro NFai NMir NNor NRoo SPer SPla SSvw WEas WHen WHil WPer WTyr
– 'Mrs J Bradshaw' AGM	CB&S CHad CKel CSco CShe EBre ECtt ELan ENot GCHN GMac LAbb LBre LHop MBri MBro MFir MRav MWat NBro NFai NMir NNor NRoo SPer SSvw SUsu WEas WHil WWin
– 'Prinses Juliana'	CBos EFou GCal MUlv NCat WMer
– 'Sigiswang'	MBel
coccineum hort.	See G. ***chiloense***
coccineum Sibthorp & Smith 'Feuermeer'	LHop MBel SAxl SUsu
– 'Prince of Orange'	ECha LBlm SHer
– 'Red Wings'	GCal WMer
– 'Werner Arends'	MBri NFai
'Coppertone'	CChu CGle CMil CRDP EBar ECha ECtt EHal ELan GAbr GCal GMac IBlr MMil MNFA NBir NBro NCat SAxl SHer SPer SUsu SWas WAbb WElm WHal
x ***heldreichii***	WAbb
* ***hybrida luteum***	MBel NSti
x ***intermedium***	CBre CChu CElw CRow CTom EMon EPla SChu SCro SUsu WCot
leiospermum	ECou
'Lemon Drops'	CGle CMil ECha EGol GMac MNFA SAxl
macrophyllum	GTou
– var. ***sachalinense***	EWoo
magellanicum	See G. ***parviflorum***
§ ***montanum*** AGM	CGle CHan CLew CSam ECha ELan GDra GTou LBee MBro MCas MFir NBir NBro NHol NKay NNrd NRoo SWas WCla WHal WPer WWin
parviflorum	EWes EWoo MBro MSto NBrk WBon
pentapetalum	GArf WAbe
pseudochinense	SUsu
pyrenaicum	EWoo MSto WDav
quellyon	See G. ***chiloense***
reptans	See SIEVERSIA ***r.***
x ***rhaeticum***	NKay NTow
'Rijnstroom'	MBel MUlv NFai
rivale	Widely available
– 'Album'	Widely available
– 'Dingle Apricot'	EFol NBir
– 'Leonard's Variety'	Widely available
– 'Leonard's Variety Double'	ECtt
– 'Lionel Cox'	Widely available
– 'Marika'	CBre CRow NBrk
– 'Variegatum'	WNdy
'Rubin'	WRus
'Tangerine'	EPla GGar MRav NRoo SUsu
x ***tirolense***	NKay
triflorum	EBee EPla GTou LGre
* 'Two Ladies'	NBar
urbanum	CArn CKin ECWi EWFC GPoy LHol MChe MHew NLan SIde SWat WCla WHer
– 'Checkmate' (v)	EMon EPla

GEVUINA (Proteaceae)

avellana	CB&S CGre CHEx CTrw ISea SArc

GIBASIS (Commelinaceae)

See Plant Deletions

GIGASPERMUM (moss)

repens	LFle

GILIA (Polemoniaceae)

aggregata	See IPOMOPSIS ***a.***
♦ ***californica***	See LEPTODACTYLON ***californicum***

GILLENIA (Rosaceae)

stipulata	EBee EMon LGre MSal
trifoliata AGM	Widely available

GINKGO (Ginkgoaceae)

biloba AGM	Widely available
– 'Autumn Gold' (m)	WMou
– 'Fairmount'	WMou

– 'Fastigiata' WMou
– 'Heksenbezen Leiden' WMou
– 'Horizontalis' WMou
– 'King of Dongting' (f) MBlu WMou
– 'Ohazuki' (f) WMou
– 'Pendula' CMCN LPan LRHS MBri WMou
– 'Princeton Sentry' (m) WMou
I – 'Prostrata' CBow CPMA
– 'Saratoga' (m) COtt CPMA LNet MBri WMou
– 'Tremonia' MBlu SHil WMou
– 'Tubifolia' WMou
– 'Umbrella' WMou
– 'Variegata' (f) CMCN EPla SMad WMou

GLADIOLUS † (Iridaceae)

alatus NRog
'Alice' (Min) LAma
'Amanda Mahy' (N) CBro GCra LAma LBow MUlv NCat NRog
'Anitra' (P) LAma
'Applause' (L) LAma NRog
'Apricot Queen' (L) LAma
'Atom' (P) CBro LAma NRog
¶ ***atroviolaceus*** SPou
'Avalanche' (B) LAma
'Bell Boy' (B) LAma
'Blackpool' (M) LAma NRog
♦ ***blandus*** var. ***carneus*** See G. ***carneus***
Butterfly hybrids LBow
byzantinus See G. ***communis byzantinus***
callianthus AGM CRDP CWes LBlm
§ – 'Murieliae' AGM CAvo CBro CSut LAma LBow NRog SDeJ
'Cambourne' (Min) LAma NRog
cardinalis IBlr
carinatus NRog
carmineus CMon EPot LBow
§ ***carneus*** CAvo CBro ETub LBow MSto NRog
'Charm' (N) CAvo CBro LAma MWBu
'Charming Beauty' (Tub) NRog
'Chartres' (B) LAma
'Chiquita' (M) CSut
'Christabel' (L) LBow
'Cindy' (B) LAma
'Columbine' (P) LAma NRog
'Comet' (N) LBow NRog
communis LAma
§ – ssp. ***byzantinus*** AGM CB&S CBro CFee CGle CHEx CHad CSam CTom ECha ELan EPar EPla ETub LAma LBow LGan MBri MUlv NRog NSti SIng WEas WHil WOMN WShi
¶ 'Dancing Doll' MWBu
¶ 'Don Juan' CSut
'Dyanito' (B) LAma
'Edward van Beinum' (L) LAma
'Elvira' (N) LAma NRog
'Essex' (P/S) MWBu
'Esta Bonita' (G) CSut
'Fair Lady' (Tub) NRog
'Fidelio' (L) LAma MWBu
'Firebird' LAma
floribundus LBow
'Flower Song' (L) LAma
'Friendship' (L) MWBu
garnieri CAvo CMon
'Georgette' (B) LAma MWBu
¶ 'Giallo Antico' CSut
'Gillian' (L) LBow
'Good Luck' (N) CBro
grandis See G. ***liliaceus***
'Green Woodpecker' AGM LAma MWBu NRog
'Guernsey Glory' (N) LAma MWBu NRog
'Halley' CBro
'Helene' (P/B) LAma
'Her Majesty' (L) CSut LAma
'High Style' (L) CSut
'Holland Pearl' (B) LAma NRog
'Hunting Song' (L) LAma NRog
'Hypnose' (B) LAma
illyricus CMon
¶ – ssp. ***kotschyanus*** MSto
'Impressive' (N) LAma MWBu NRog
§ ***italicus*** MSto
'Jacksonville Gold' (L) LAma
'Jessica' (L) LAma
¶ 'Jupiter' MWBu
'Lady Godiva' (P/Min) LAma NRog
'Leonore' (P) LAma MWBu
¶ 'Liebelei' MWBu
§ ***liliaceus*** LBow WThi
¶ 'Lowland Queen' (L) CSut
¶ 'Marvinka' CSut
'Mary Housley' (L) LAma
'Mascagni' (M) LAma
'Mirella' (N) NRog
'Murieliae' See G. ***callianthus*** 'M.'
'My Love' (G) LAma MWBu
§ ***natalensis*** GCal IBlr WCot
'Nicole' LAma
'Nova Lux' (L) LAma MWBu NRog
'Nymph' (N) CAvo LAma LBow NRog SIng
'Obelisk' (P) LAma NRog
'Oscar' (G) LAma NRog
'Ovation' (L) CSut
papilio CAvo CChu CFee CHad ECha EHal EOrc GCal GMac MUlv NCat SAxl SBla SChu SMad SMrm WAbb WEas WHal WOMN
– 'Grey Ghost' WEas
§ – Purpureoauratus Group CBro CGle CSam EBee IBlr MFir MSto SOkh
'Passion' (L) CSut
'Pegasus' (P/Min) LAma
'Perky' (Min) LAma
'Perseus' (P/Min) LAma
'Peter Pears' (L) LAma MWBu NRog
'Picture' (P) LAma
'Picturesque' (P) LAma NRog
'Piquant' (P) LAma
'Praha' (L) LAma MWBu NRog
primulinus See G. ***natalensis***
Primulinus hybrids LBow SDeJ
'Princess Margaret Rose' (Min) LAma
'Prins Claus' (N) CBro LAma NRog
priorii NRog
'Priscilla' LAma MWBu
purpureoauratus See G. ***papilio*** Purpureoauratus Group

'Red Beauty'	CSut
'Red Jewel' (B)	LAma
'Richmond' (B)	NRog
¶ 'Robin' (P)	MWBu
'Robinetta' (***recurvus*** x) **AGM**	LAma MWBu NCat NRog
¶ 'Rose Delight'	CSut
'Rose Supreme' (G)	LAma
'Rougex'	NRog
'Royal Dutch' (L)	MWBu
¶ 'Sabu'	MWBu
'Saxony' (P)	MWBu
scullyi	NRog
segetum	See G. ***italicus***
'Shakespeare' (L)	LAma
'Spic and Span' (L)	LAma MWBu
'The Bride' **AGM**	CAvo CBro CGle CMil LAma LBow MUlv NCat NRog
'Trader Horn' (G)	LAma MWBu NRog
tristis	CBro CRDP ECha ELan EPot LBow NRog SDix SWas WAbe WThi
– var. ***concolor***	WHer WThu
undulatus	ETub LBow
'Velvet Joy' (P)	LAma
¶ 'Vera Lynn'	CSut
'Victor Borge' (L)	LAma NRog
'Violetta' (M)	LAma
'White City' (P/B)	LAma MWBu
'White Friendship' (L)	LAma MWBu NRog
'White Prosperity' (L)	LAma
'Wind Song' (L)	LAma
'Wine and Roses' (L)	CSut
¶ 'Wise Cracks'	MWBu
'Ziegennerbaum'	CSut

GLANDULARIA (Verbenaceae)

bipinnatifida	See VERBENA ***b.***
pulchella	See VERBENA ***tenera***

GLAUCIDIUM (Glaucidiaceae)

palmatum **AGM**	ECha GDra MBal WCot
– 'Album'	See G. ***p. leucanthum***
§ – ***leucanthum***	NSla

GLAUCIUM (Papaveraceae)

§ ***corniculatum***	CBot CGle CSpe LGan LGre SMad SUsu WCru WEas WHoo
flavum	CGle CHan CRDP CSpe EBar ECWi ECha EFol EWFC GAbr LGan NBro NHex SMrm WCru WHer WOld WPer WWin
– ***aurantiacum***	See G. ***f. fulvum***
§ – f. ***fulvum***	CBos ECha LHop MBel
– orange	See G. ***f. fulvum***
– red	CRDP
phoenicium	See G. ***corniculatum***

GLAUX (Primulaceae)

maritima	ELan NCat SHer WPer
– dwarf form	NWCA

GLECHOMA (Labiatae/Lamiaceae)

hederacea	CArn CKin ECWi EWFC GBar GPoy IHos NBro NMir SIde WHer WWye
– 'Rosea'	EMon LRHS
§ – 'Variegata'	CRow CTom ECro EFol EJud ELan ILis MBri MRav NHol SIde SLMG SPla
hirsuta AL&JS 90069YU	EMon

GLEDITSIA (Leguminosae/Caesalpiniaceae)

caspica	CB&S
triacanthos	CPle EArb ENot GAri IOrc LPan NWea WDin WFox WNor
– 'Elegantissima' (v)	SPer
– 'Emerald Cascade'	SEng
– f. ***inermis***	ENot LHil
– 'Rubylace'	CBow CBra CDoC COtt CSco CWSG EHar ELan EMil LPan MBar MBlu MGos SEng SHBN SHer SMad SSta WDin
– 'Skyline'	LPan SEng
– 'Sunburst' **AGM**	CB&S CBra CCla CLnd CSPN CSco CWSG EHar ELan EMil ENot IDai IJoh IOrc LNet MBar MBlu MBri MGos MWat NBee SHBN SMad SPer SPla SReu SSta WDin WWat

GLOBBA (Zingiberaceae)

¶ ***winitii***	CNew LBow

GLOBULARIA (Globulariaceae)

albiflora	WAbe
bellidifolia	See G. ***meridionalis***
bisnagarica	NHar SIgm WDav
¶ – NS 695	NWCA
cordifolia **AGM**	CLew CMHG CNic CRiv MBro MTho NHar NHol NTow WHoo WOld WPer
– NS 696	NWCA
incanescens	LBee SHer SIgm WCla WWin
§ ***meridionalis***	EWes ITim LBee MBro MHig MWat NHar NNrd NWCA SBla SIng WHal
– 'Hort's Variety'	NNrd WAbe
nana	See G. ***repens***
nudicaulis	CLew GCHN MBro NHar WDav WPer
punctata	CNic LBee MBro NHol NTow NWCA SHer SRms WHoo WPer
pygmaea	See G. ***meridionalis***
repens	CNic MBro SIgm
trichosantha	CLew GAbr LBee MHig NHol SRms WDav
vulgaris	ELan

GLORIOSA (Liliaceae/Colchicaceae)

caramii	LBow
carsonii	See G. ***superba*** 'Carsonii'
lutea	See G. ***superba superba***
rothschildiana	See G. ***superba*** 'Rothschildiana'
§ ***superba*** **AGM**	CB&S EOrc IBlr LAma LBow LHop MBri NRog SDeJ SLMG WChr WCru
– 'Carsonii'	LBow
– 'Rothschildiana'	CB&S LAma LBow SLMG
§ – ***superba***	LAma LBow NRog WChr

GLOXINIA (Gesneriaceae)

See also SINNINGIA

'Chic' NMos
perennis NMos
sylvatica WDib

GLYCERIA (Gramineae/Poaceae)
aquatica variegata See G. ***maxima v.***
maxima ECWi WChe
§ – var. *variegata* Widely available
plicata See G. ***notata***
spectabilis 'Variegata' See G. ***maxima variegata***

GLYCYRRHIZA (Leguminosae/Papilionaceae)
echinata CArn MSal
§ *glabra* CArn LHol MHew MSal SIde WWye
– 'Poznan' GPoy
glandulifera See G. ***glabra***
lepidota MSal
¶ *uralensis* MSal

GLYPTOSTROBUS (Taxodiaceae)
lineatus See G. ***pensilis***
§ *pensilis* LRHS

GMELINA (Verbenaceae)
See Plant Deletions

GNAPHALIUM (Compositae/Asteraceae)
'Fairy Gold' See HELICHRYSUM ***thianschanicum*** 'Goldkind'
keriense See ANAPHALIS ***keriensis***
subrigidum See ANAPHALIS ***subrigida***
trinerve See ANAPHALIS ***trinervis***

GODETIA See **CLARKIA**

GOMPHOCARPUS (Asclepiadaceae)
§ *fruticosus* WHer
§ *physocarpus* CArn CPle
¶ – S&SH 67 CHan

GONIOLIMON (Plumbaginaceae)
§ *tataricum*
var. *angustifolium* CCla ELan GLil NFai NMir SRms WByw WHil WPer
¶ – 'Woodcreek' WPer

GOODENIA (Goodeniaceae)
humilis ECou

GOODIA (Leguminosae/Papilionaceae)
lotifolia CHan CPle

GOODYERA (Orchidaceae)
pubescens MPhe

GOOSEBERRY See **RIBES** ***uva-crispa***

GOOSEBERRY, Cape See **PHYSALIS** ***peruviana***

GORDONIA (Theaceae)
axillaris CB&S CHEx

GOSSYPIUM (Malvaceae)
See Plant Deletions

GRANADILLA See **PASSIFLORA** ***quadrangularis***

GRAPE See **VITIS** ***vinifera***

GRAPEFRUIT See **CITRUS** ***paradisi***

GRAPTOPETALUM (Crassulaceae)
bellum SLMG
– 'Super Star' SLMG
bellus MBri SHer
§ *paraguayense* CNic SLMG

GRATIOLA (Scrophulariaceae)
officinalis CArn EHon GPoy LHol MHew MSal SIde WHer WWye

GREENOVIA (Crassulaceae)
§ *aurea* SIng WCot

GREVILLEA † (Proteaceae)
alpina CBow EMil SBla
– 'Olympic Flame' CB&S CBar CDoC
* 'Apricot Queen' CB&S
'Canberra Gem' **AGM** CGre CHan CTro ECou LBlm LHop MAll MBal SDry SIgm WCru
'Desert Flame' CB&S
juniperina CHan
¶ – 'Rubra' CTro
– f. *sulphurea* **AGM** CBow CCla CDoC CHEx COtt CTre EMil SHil SIgm SPer WAbe WBod WPat WSHC
¶ *prostrata* 'Aurea' CB&S
robusta **AGM** MBri
rosmarinifolia **AGM** CBow CBra CCla CHEx COtt CTre CTrw CWSG EMil MAll MBal SArc SHil SIgm SLon SPer WAbe WBod WCru WPat WSHC
– 'Jenkinsii' CB&S CTro
x *semperflorens* CGre
thelemanniana CPle ECou MAll
thyrsoïdes CB&S MAll SDry
* *tolminsis* LBlm MAll

GREWIA (Tiliaceae)
§ *biloba* CMCN
parviflora See G. ***biloba***

GREYIA (Greyiaceae)
radlkoferi CHEx
sutherlandii CHEx

GRINDELIA (Compositae/Asteraceae)

chiloensis	CAbb CGre CHan CPle ECha MHlr SAxl SBor SDix SDry SHil WCot WPat WPer
robusta	MHlr WCot
sp. G&K 4423	CGre
squarrosa	SCro WCot
stricta	CArn

GRISELINIA † (Griseliniaceae)

* 'Crinkles'	SDry
littoralis AGM	CB&S CBot CBra CChe CGre CHEx CLan CSco CTre EBre ENot GRei IDai ISea LBre MBal MBri MGos NNor SArc SDix SLon SPer WAbe WBod WDin WSHC WWin
– 'Bantry Bay' (v)	CAbP CChu CDoC CGre CLan EBre ECtt EPla IMal IOrc LBre MAll MBal SGil SMad SPer SPla WAbe
– 'Dixon's Cream' (v)	CAbb CB&S CDec CGre MAll SDry SGil SLon SPla
– 'Green Jewel' (v)	CB&S CDoC CTre MAll SDry
– 'Variegata'	CB&S CBot CBra CChe CLan CSco CTre CTrw EHoe ELan ENot GRei IDai IJoh IOrc ISea MBal NKay NNor SHBN SLon SPer SPla SSta WAbe WDin WSHC WThu
lucida	CHEx MUlv
¶ ***racemosa***	CGre
ruscifolia	CGre CMCN ISea
scandens	CGre WSHC

GUAVA See **PSIDIUM**

GUICHENOTIA (Sterculiaceae)
See Plant Deletions

GUNNERA (Gunneraceae)

arenaria	GAri GGar IBlr
chilensis	See G. ***tinctoria***
dentata	CFee GCal NHol
flavida	CFee CRow GGar WCot
fulvida	IBlr
hamiltonii	CHEx ECha ECou GGar IBlr SWas WCot WCru
magellanica	CB&S CFee CHEx CRow CTom CWGN EBre ECha ECoo EPot ESis GWht IBar IBlr LBre MBal NDea NHol NMen NNor NWCA SPer SWat SWyc WCru WHal WWat
¶ ***magellanica*** (f)	GCal
manicata AGM	Widely available
¶ x ***mixta***	WCot
monoica	CElw CRow GCal WCot
prorepens	CFee CTre EPot IBlr SWat WCru WWye
¶ – small form	WCot
scabra	See G. ***tinctoria***
§ ***tinctoria***	CHEx CRow CWGN ECha EFou ELun GAbr MSta SDix WStI

GUZMANIA (Bromeliaceae)

'Amaranth'	MBri
'Cherry'	MBri
'Claret'	See NEOREGELIA Claret
dissitiflora	MBri
'Exodus'	MBri
Festival	MBri
'Gran Prix'	MBri
lindenii	MBri
lingulata AGM	MBri
– 'Empire'	MBri
– var. ***minor*** AGM	MBri
Marlebeca	MBri
monostachya AGM	MBri
'Orangeade'	MBri
sanguinea AGM	MBri
* 'Surprise'	MBri
'Vulkan'	MBri
* 'Witten Lila'	MBri

GYMNADENIA (Orchidaceae)

¶ ***camtschatica***	EFEx
¶ ***conopsea***	EFEx

GYMNOCARPIUM (Dryopteridaceae)

dryopteris AGM	CBos EBul EFer EPar EPot MBri NGar NKay NMar NWCA SAxl SDix WAbe WRic
– 'Plumosum'	NHar NHol NKay NMar WFib WRic
robertianum	EFer NKay NMar WRic

GYMNOCLADUS (Leguminosae/Caesalpiniaceae)

dioica	CB&S CChu CCla CGre EArb ELan LGre MBlu MBri NPal SHil SMad SPer WCoo WDin

GYMNOSPERMIUM (Berberidaceae)

albertii	CAvo EPot LAma WCot

GYNANDRIRIS (Iridaceae)

setifolia	CMon WThi
sisyrinchium	CAvo ETub WThi
– MS 416	CMon
– ***purpureum*** AB&S 4447	CMon

GYNERIUM (Gramineae/Poaceae)

argenteum	See CORTADERIA ***selloana***

GYNURA (Compositae/Asteraceae)

§ ***aurantiaca*** 'Purple Passion' AGM	MBri
sarmentosa hort.	See G. ***aurantiaca*** 'Purple Passion'

GYPSOPHILA (Caryophyllaceae)

acutifolia	ELan
altissima	CPou SSvw
aretioïdes	NHol NNrd NSla
§ – 'Caucasica'	EBur EPot MHig NHar NHed NHol SIng WDav
– ***compacta***	See G. ***a.*** 'Caucasica'
briquetiana	LBee NTow
– Mac&W 5920	EPot WDav

cerastioïdes	CMHG CMea ELan EMNN ESis GArf GTou LBee MCas MFir MHig MTol NKay NMen NNrd NRed NTow NWCA SHer WHal WHoo WPbr WPer WWin
– ***farreri***	WEas
dubia	See G. ***repens*** 'Dubia'
¶***fastigiata***	WHow WPer
¶ 'Festival'	CB&S
nana	SIng
– 'Compacta'	CNic CPBP
oldhamiana	EMar SFis
pacifica	EBee ECoo ECro ECtt EFou NBro NOak SSvw WCot WHer
§ ***paniculata***	CBow CHol EHic MWat NMir NNor SRms WEas WPla WWin
– 'Bristol Fairy' **AGM**	CB&S CMer CRDP CSam CSco CShe EBre EFou ENot ERav IBar IDai LBre MBri NBar NFai NOrc NRoo SChu SHer SMad SPer SPla
– 'Compacta Plena'	CCla EFou ELan GCal LHop MMil NHol NRoo SRms WPer
– 'Flamingo' (b)	CB&S CBow CSco EBre ECot ECtt EFou IDai LBre MBri MUlv NFai SHer SPer
– 'Pink Star' (b)	CSco
– 'Schneeflocke' ('Snowflake') (b)	CBow CCla EBre ECtt ESma GAul LBre NPri NRoo SFis SPla SSvw WHil WHoo
– 'Snow White'	LHop LWad NOrc
petraea	WDav
repens **AGM**	CBow CLew EPad IDai MHig MPla MTho MWat WHil WPer
– ***alba***	CLew EFou ELan EPad ESis GLil MPla NNor NNrd SHer WAbe WDav WPer
– 'Dorothy Teacher' **AGM**	CShe EMNN LHop MCas MHig MPit NHol SIng WAbe WEas WPat
§ – 'Dubia'	CMHG CShe ECha EFol ELan EMNN EPot ESis MHig MPla NHol SBod SHer SIgm WAbe WDav WPer WWin
– ***fratensis***	ELan EMNN ESis GArf MPla NHol NKay NMen SHer WDav
– 'Letchworth Rose'	EWes MCas
– 'Rosa Schönheit' ('Pink Beauty')	ECha ESma EWes MMil NRoo SHer SMrm
– 'Rose Fountain'	SFis WPat WThu
– 'Rosea'	CMHG EFou EMNN ESis GLil LAbb LBuc LWad MCas MWat NFai NHar NKay NMen NNor NOak NRed NRoo NTow NWCA SBla SFis WHal
'Rosenschleier' ('Veil of Roses') **AGM**	CCla CHad CLew EBre ECha EFou ELan ESma LBre NBar NHol NKay NMen NNrd NRoo SFis SIgm SPer WBod WByw WEas WHoo WOld
'Rosy Veil'	See G. 'Rosenschleier'
tenuifolia	CNic EPot ITim LBee MBro MCas MHig MPla MWat NGre NHed NHol NNrd NRed NTow NVic NWCA WAbe WDav WThu WWin
transylvanica	See G. ***petraea***

HAASTIA (Compositae/Asteraceae)

See Plant Deletions

HABENARIA (Orchidaceae)

radiata	See PECTEILIS ***r.***

HABERLEA (Gesneriaceae)

ferdinandi-coburgi	CGle EPot MFos NHol NKay NWCA SHer SIgm SIng SPou SWas WCru
rhodopensis **AGM**	CChu CNic CRiv EPar IDai MBal MBro MCas MHig MSte MWat NHar NNrd NSla NTow NWCA SBla SIng SPou WAbe WCru WOMN WOld WThu
– 'Virginalis'	CChu EPot GDra NHar SIng SWas WCru WOMN WThu

HABRANTHUS (Liliaceae/Amaryllidaceae)

andersonii	See H. ***tubispathus***
gracilifolius	CBro CMon WChr
martinezii	CBro
§ ***robustus***	CBro CMon GCra LAma MBri NRog WAbe
texanus	CBro CMon SIng WChr WThu
§ ***tubispathus***	CBro CMon ESma NWCA SIng WChr WThu

HACQUETIA (Umbelliferae/Apiaceae)

§ ***epipactis*** **AGM**	Widely available

HAEMANTHUS (Liliaceae/Amaryllidaceae)

albiflos	CMon CTro EBul SLMG WChr
coccineus	CMon
humilis hirsutus S&SH 72	CHan
kalbreyeri	See SCADOXUS ***multiflorus multiflorus***
katherinae	See SCADOXUS ***multiflorus katherinae***
natalensis	See SCADOXUS ***puniceus***
sanguineus	NRog

HAKEA (Proteaceae)

lissosperma	SArc SHil
microcarpa	CB&S
sericea	CChu CHan SArc
suaveolens	SArc

HAKONECHLOA (Gramineae/Poaceae)

macra	CFil EHoe NFai
§ – 'Alboaurea'	CB&S CFee CFil CHad CPMA CRiv CShe EBre ECha EGol ELan ELun EPar EPla ERav ETPC LBre LHil MBar MCas MUlv NKay SApp SGil SMrm SPer SPla WRus WWin
– 'Aureola' **AGM**	CAbb CBos CChu CElw CFil CHan CLew CRDP EBul ECha ECtt EHoe EPla LHop MBal MBri NGar NRya SAxl SCob SDix SIng SWas WAbe WCot WEas WPat WPer WWat
– ***variegata***	See H. ***m.*** 'Alboaurea'

HALENIA (Gentianaceae)

¶ ***elliptica***	GCra GTou

HALESIA (Styracaceae)

carolina	See H. *tetraptera*
diptera var. *magniflora*	WFro
monticola	CB&S CBow COtt EArb EBre ELan IJoh LBre MBal MBri SHil SPer WFro WNor WWat
– f. *rosea*	CPMA ELan MSta SHil
– var. *vestita* AGM	CAbP CBra CChu CCla CMHG CPMA CSam CSco CWSG CWit IOrc MBlu SHBN SHil SPer SSta WBod WHig WWat
§ *tetraptera*	CCla CDoC CLnd CPMA CSam EHar ELan GWht IOrc MBri MGos MUlv SPer SSta WBod WSHC WWat

X HALIMIOCISTUS (Cistaceae)

algarvensis	See HALIMIUM *ocymoïdes*
§ 'Ingwersenii'	CB&S CLTr CLew CMHG CSco EWri IDai LHop NBro NHol NRya NSti SIng SPer WAbe WBod WDav WPer WSHC
revolii Dansereau	EBar ERav LGan LHop WCru WKif
revolii hort.	See H. *sahucii*
§ *sahucii* AGM	CAbb CCla CPle CSco CShe ECha ERav GAbr GCHN LHop MBal MBel MPla MRav MSto MWat NBro NKay NSti SHBN SPer WCru WDav WHil WRus WSHC WWin
'Susan'	See HALIMIUM *ocymoïdes* 'S.'
§ *wintonensis* AGM	CB&S CFee CHan CMHG CSco EBre ECtt ELan EOrc EPla ERav LBre LHop MBri MRav MWat NSti NWyt SAxl SHBN SPer WAbe WCru WRus WSHC WWat
§ – 'Merrist Wood Cream' AGM	Widely available

HALIMIUM † (Cistaceae)

N *alyssoïdes*	CSam GCHN WBod
§ *atriplicifolium*	LHop SChu WStI
§ *commutatum*	ELan GCHN MBel SIgm WAbe
formosum	See H. *lasianthum*
N *halimifolium*	GCal SIgm WCru WSHC
§ *lasianthum*	CB&S CDoC CShe CWit ECha ELan ENot EPla EWri GAbr GCHN LAbb LGre MBal MBel NSti NWyt SChu SLon SMrm SPer WAbe WBod WEas WWin
– f. *concolor*	LHop NTow SDry SSta WAbe WCru WDin WWin
– ssp. *formosum*	CKni GCal MBri NTow SDix WCru WSHC
– 'Sandling'	ELan NTow SPla WCru
libanotis	See H. *commutatum*
§ *ocymoïdes* AGM	CB&S CCla CDoC CSco ELan ENot EWri LGre MBal MBel MPla MWat NKay NRar NWyt SIgm SLon SPer WBod WCru WSHC WWat
– 'Susan' AGM	CBra CDoC CLew CMHG EBre ELan ERav LAbb LBre LHop MBri MPla NHex NMen NNor NSti NWyt SHer SPer SUsu WAbe WPat WPer
§ *umbellatum*	CSam GAbr LGre LHop MBri NHol NSti SPer WAbe WCru WDin WKif WSHC
wintonens	See X HALIMIOCISTUS *wintonensis*

HALIMODENDRON (Leguminosae/Papilionaceae)

halodendron	CB&S CCla CPle ELan MBlu

HALLERIA (Scrophulariaceae)

lucida	CGre

HALOCARPUS (Podocarpaceae)

§ *bidwillii*	ECou LCon

HALORAGIS (Haloradigaceae)

¶ *colensoi*	ECou
¶ *erecta*	CPle ECou
¶ – 'Rubra'	WCot

HAMAMELIS † (Hamamelidaceae)

§ 'Brevipetala'	CB&S IOrc MAsh MBri NHol SSta
x *intermedia* 'Advent'	SSta
– 'Allgold'	SSta
– 'Arnold Promise' AGM	CBow CDoC COtt CPMA CSco EBre ELan IOrc LBre MAsh MBal MBri NHol SPer SPla SReu SSta
– 'Aurora'	SSta WDin
– 'Barmstedt Gold'	EBre LBre LRHS MAsh MBri MGos NHol SReu SSta
– 'Boskoop'	SSta
– 'Carmine Red'	CBra SSta WNor
– 'Copper Beauty'	See H. x *i.* 'Jelena'
– 'Diane' AGM	CB&S CBow CDoC CPMA CSco EBre EHar ELan IOrc LBre MBar MBri MBrk MGos NHol SHil SLon SMad SPer SReu SSta WDin
– 'Feuerzauber' ('Magic Fire')	IOrc NBar SPer SSta
– Hillier's clone	SSta
– 'Hiltingbury'	LRHS SSta
§ – 'Jelena' AGM	CAlt CB&S CBow CBra CDoC CPMA CSam CSco EBre EHar ELan ENot IHos IOrc LBre LNet MBal MBri MGos SHil SLon SPer SPla SReu SSta WDin WWat
– 'Luna'	SSta
– 'Moonlight'	CAlt CPMA SSta
– 'Orange Beauty'	CB&S CPMA MBal MGos NBar SReu SSta
– 'Pallida' AGM	CAlt CArn CBow CBra CPMA CSco EGol EHar ELan ENot IBar IHos IJoh IOrc LNet MBal MBri MGos NRoo SHBN SHer SHil SPer SReu SSta WDin WPat WStI WWat
– 'Primavera'	CDoC IOrc MAsh MBal MBri NHol SSta
– 'Ruby Glow'	CB&S CCla EGol ELan MBal SPer SSta
– 'Sunburst'	MBri SHil SSta
– 'Vezna'	MBlu MBri SSta
§ – 'Westerstede'	EBee IOrc LBuc MAsh MGos NHol SSta WDin
– 'Winter Beauty'	SHil SSta
japonica	MBal WFro WWat
– 'Arborea'	SSta WNor
– var. *flavopurpurascens*	SSta
– 'Sulphurea'	SSta

- 'Zuccariniana' CB&S SSta
mollis **AGM** CArn CB&S CBra CSco CShe ELan ENot GRei IDai IJoh LNet MBal MBar MBri MGos NBar NBee NHol NKay NWea SHBN SMad SPer SReu SSta WDin WWat
- 'Brevipetala' See H. 'Brevipetala'
- 'Coombe Wood' CAbP SSta
- 'Goldcrest' CBra CPMA SSta
- Henry form SSta
- 'James Wells' SSta
- 'Jermyns Gold' SHil
- 'Nymans' CAbP
- Renken form SSta
- 'Select' See H. x ***intermedia*** 'Westerstede'
- 'Superba' SSta
- Wilson Clone SSta
vernalis 'Carnea' SSta
- 'Christmas Cheer' SSta
- Compact form SSta
- 'January Pride' SSta
- 'Lombart's Weeping' SSta
- 'New Year's Gold' SSta
- 'Orange Glow' SSta
- 'Pendula' SSta
- 'Red Imp' SSta
- 'Sandra' **AGM** CAbP EHar MAsh MBri NHol SReu SSta WWat
- 'Squib' SSta
- f. ***tomentella*** SSta
virginiana CB&S EBee GPoy ISea LHol SHer WCoo WWat

HANNONIA (Liliaceae/Amaryllidaceae)

hesperidum SF 21 CMon

HAPLOCARPHA (Compositae/Asteraceae)

****cheilanthifolia*** MHig
rueppellii CTom NNrd SIng SRms WHil WPer

HAPLOPAPPUS (Compositae/Asteraceae)

acaulis See STENOTUS ***a.***
brandegeei See ERIGERON ***aureus***
coronopifolius See H. ***glutinosus***
foliosus CGre
§ ***glutinosus*** CHan CLew CMHG CRiv ECha ECtt EFol EPot LBee LHop MHig MMil MTho MWat NWCA SChu SFar SIng SSmi WEas
lyallii See TONESTUS ***l.***
¶ ***microcephalus*** WPer
¶- AJW 93/559 NWCA
prunelloïdes NNrd
rehderi GLil
sp. P&W 6545 MSte
suffruticosus CPle

HARDENBERGIA (Leguminosae/Papilionaceae)

comptoniana **AGM** CGre CPle LBlm LHil
- ***rosea*** ERea
violacea **AGM** CAbb CSam ELan EMil ERea IBlr IReg LAbb LBlm WBod
- 'Alba' See H. ***v.*** 'White Crystal'
- 'Happy Wanderer' CB&S EMil ERea
§ - 'White Crystal' CGre ERea

HARRIMANELLA See CASSIOPE

HAWORTHIA (Liliaceae/Aloëaceae)

x ***cuspidata*** SLMG

HAYNALDIA See DASYPYRUM

HEBE † (Scrophulariaceae)

See also PARAHEBE
albicans **AGM** CCla CLan CSco CSea CShe ECou EFol ELan ENot ESis GIsl IJoh MAll MBal MBar MBel MBri MGos MWat NNor NSti SHBN SPer SSmi STre WBod WEas WHCG WWin
- 'Cobb' ECou
- 'Cranleigh Gem' ECou GIsl NFai NHed SSmi
- 'Pewter Dome' See H. 'P.D.'
- prostrate form See H. ***a.*** 'Snow Cover'
- 'Red Edge' See H. 'R.E.'
§ - 'Snow Cover' CSea ECou GIsl
¶ - 'Snow Drift' NHed
- 'Snow Mound' ECou
§ - 'Sussex Carpet' ECou EPla ESis MFir
§ 'Alicia Amherst' **AGM** CLTr CLan CSam CSea ECou ECtt ENot GCHN LHop SGil
♦ ***allanii*** See H. ***amplexicaulis hirta***
'Amanda Cook' (v) CSea ECou EHoe EPla ESis LHop MPla MUlv NHed NHol NPer SDry
amplexicaulis CNic GIsl MAll NHed
§ - var. ***hirta*** ECou GDra GIsl MAll MBro NHed NNor NTow
§ 'Amy' Widely available
x ***andersonii***
'Argenteovariegata' See H. x ***a.*** 'Variegata'
- 'Aureovariegata' ECou SDry
x ***andersonii compacta*** GIsl
*x ***andersonii*** 'Heida' MBri
§ - 'Variegata' CB&S CMer CPle ECou IDai IOrc MAll MBri MSte NSti NTow SDry WEas
*- 'White Summer' MBri
anomala hort. See H. 'Imposter'
anomala (J B Armstr.) Ckn. See H. ***odora***
'Aoira' See H. ***recurva*** 'A.'
*'April Joy' MUlv
§ ***armstrongii*** CBot CMHG CSea ECou EHoe ELan ENot GAbr IDai IJoh MBar NHed NNor SHer SPer WDin WEas WPer WStI
'Autumn Blush' MPla
'Autumn Glory' Widely available
'Autumn Joy' EBar MPla SHer
*'Autumn Queen' NNor
'Azurea' ELan MBri MRav SMrm WBod WPer
'Baby Marie' CAbP CMHG CSea ECot ECou ELan EPla ESis GIsl MAll NFai NHed NPer SGil SHer SHil WPer
'Balfouriana' CSea GIsl MAll NHed
barkeri ECou
'Beatrice' ECou NHed
x ***bishopiana*** ECou MAll

'Blonde'	NNor
'Blue Clouds' AGM	CElw ECou EHal ELan EPla GIsl GMac MFir NHed SIgm SPla WEas WPat WRus
'Blue Diamond'	WEas
* 'Blue Streak'	ELan
'Blue Wand'	MBal
'Bluebell'	ECou
'Blush Wand'	CAbb CSea GIsl WAbe
bollonsoi	CSea ECou GIsl MSte
¶ 'Bowles' Variety'	CNic CSea
'Bowles's Hybrid'	CMHG CSco CSea CShe ECou GIsl IJoh LHil MGos MPla MRav NBee NFai NGre NNor SChu SGil WAbe WEas
brachysiphon	ECou ENot ISea MGos MPla SLon SPer WDin WHCG WTyr
breviracemosa	CSea ECou
'Brill Blue'	EMNN ESis NMen NNrd NRed NTow WWin
'Brockiei'	ECou GIsl
buchananii	ECou EMNN ESis GAbr GDra GIsl GTou MAll MFir MGos MTho NBee NFai NHed NHol NNor NPer WBod WPer
– 'Christchurch'	ECou
– 'Minima'	CDoC MNFA
– 'Minor'	CLew ECou EPot GAbr GAri GCHN MBar MBri MFir MHig MRav NBir NHar NHed NHol NMen NNrd SChu SIng
– 'Nana'	See H. ***b.*** 'Minor'
– 'Ohau'	ECou
– 'Otago'	ECou
§ – 'Sir George Fenwick'	ECou SHer
– 'Wanaka'	ECou
buxifolia hort.	See H. ***odora***
buxifolia (Benth.) Ckn.& Allan	CMHG CSco EBre ELan ENot GAbr GCHN GIsl IHos IJoh LBre LHil MAll MBal NSti NWea SHer SPer WDin WHil WStI
– 'Nana'	CSam CSco EHar EPad EPla ESis GIsl MBri MHig NPer WWin
* – ***patens***	MGos WHCG
N 'C P Raffill'	CSea ECou GIsl MUlv
§ 'Caledonia'	CDec CLew CNic CSea CShe ECou ERav ESis GAbr GIsl MBri MFir MGos MHig MSte NFai NHed NHol NPer NTow SBla SChu SPer WEas WHoo WOMN WPat WPer WSHC
'Candy'	ECou
§ ***canterburiensis***	ECou EHal GIsl
N 'Carl Teschner'	See H. 'Youngii'
'Carnea'	CElw CSea
'Carnea Variegata'	CAbb CSea ECou GIsl LHop SBod SHil SPer
carnosula	CMHG ECou EHoe EPla GIsl IJoh MAll MFir MGos NNor SPer WPer WTyr
'Cassinioïdes'	ESis MAll
catarractae	See PARAHEBE ***catarractae***
I 'Chalk's Buchananii'	CNic
chathamica	CLew CMHG CNic CSea ECou EMNN ESis GAbr GCal GPlt MBal MCas MPla NTow SDry WSHC
cheesemanii	ECou GDra GIsl MHig
'Christabel'	CSea ECou GIsl MAll SIgm
'Christensenii'	ECou GIsl MAll

ciliolata	ECou
coarctata	CNic CSea ECou GIsl MAll
cockayneana	CSea ECou GIsl
colensoi	ECou
– 'Glauca'	See H. 'Leonard Cockayne'
'Colwall'	EBee EHic ESis LHop NHed SHer WAbe WHen WOMN
'Cookiana'	See H. ***stricta macroura*** 'C.'
corrigana	ECou
corstorphinensis	GIsl
'County Park'	ECou ECtt EMNN ESis ESma GAbr MAll MBal MGos MHig MMil MUlv NTow SBod WAbe WSHC
'Craigpark'	GIsl
'Cranleighensis'	EBar ECou ELan SBod SFai
'Cressit'	GIsl
'Cupins'	CLew CNic
cupressoïdes	CMHG CSco ECou ELan GIsl IDai LHil MAll MBal MBar MFir MGos NHed NNor WDin
– 'Boughton Dome' AGM	ECha ECou EHoe EMNN ESis GAbr GCHN GPlt GTou LAbb MBri MBro MGos MHig MPla MTho NMen NNrd NTow SDix SIng WEas WHoo WOld WPer
– 'Golden Dome'	CB&S EPla ESis MAll NHed NHol WAbe
– 'Nana'	ECou NNrd SPer
darwiniana	See H. ***glaucophylla***
¶ 'David Hughes'	NFai
'Debbie'	ECou
decumbens	CNic ECou EHic ESis GDra GIsl MAll
'Diamond'	CSea
'Diana'	CAbb CNic CSea
dieffenbachii	CSea ECou GIsl SDry
diosmifolia	CBot CDoC CLan CNic CSea ECou ESis GIsl ISea WSHC
– 'Marie'	ECou ESis GIsl MAll
divaricata	ECou
x ***divergens***	CLan NHed
'Dorothy Peach'	See H. 'Watson's Pink'
'Douglasii'	GIsl NHed
'E A Bowles'	ECou
'E B Anderson'	See H. 'Caledonia'
¶ 'Early Blue'	GIsl NBir WTyr
'Edinensis'	CMHG CMer CNic CSea ECou ESma GAbr GIsl NNor WPer WSHC WTyr WWin
'Edington'	CElw CNic CSea ECou MFir
¶ 'Ellen'	WRus
elliptica	ECou GIsl IBlr SFis
– 'Anatoki'	CSea ECou
– 'Bleaker'	ECou
– 'Charleston'	ECou
– 'Kapiti'	ECou
– 'Variegata'	See H. x ***franciscana*** 'Variegata'
'Emerald Dome'	GAbr NGre NMen WPer
'Emerald Gem'	See H. 'Emerald Green'
§ 'Emerald Green' AGM	CChe CMHG CNic CRiv CSam ECou EGol ELan EPot ESis GAbr GIsl IJoh LHop MAll MBar MBri MBro MGos MPla MWat NHed NHol NSti SIng WAbe WPat WPer
epacridea	ECou EWes GAbr GDra GIsl GTou MHig NHed NHol NMen WAbe

§ 'Eveline'	CAbb CPle CSco CSea EBee ELan MBal NBir SChu SPla WEas WSHC
'Evelyn'	CSea GIsl
evenosa	CSea ECou GIsl MAll
'Eversley Seedling'	See H. 'Bowles's Hybrid'
'Fairfieldii'	CSea IBlr IDai NMen SDry WSHC
'Fairlane'	CNic ECou
formosa	LBlm
'Fragrant Jewel'	CChu CPle CSco EBre ELan LBre SFai SMrm WRus
x ***franciscana***	CSea ECou WTyr
– 'Blue Gem' AGM	CLan CSco CSea EHal ENot ESis GIsl IDai IJoh MAll NBir NFai NPer SPer WBod WWin
– 'Jura'	ECou
– 'Red Gem'	GIsl
– 'Tresco Magenta'	ECou
§ – 'Variegata' AGM	CB&S CChe CMer CSco CSea EBre ECou ELan ENot ERav GIsl GRei IBar IDai IJoh LBre MAll MBal MGos MRav NFai NHol NPer NRoo NSti SHBN SLon SPer WBod WStI
– 'White Gem'	ESiP GIsl
'Franjo'	ECou SSmi
¶ ***fruticeti***	GIsl
'Gauntlettii'	See H. 'Eveline'
gibbsii	ECou
'Gibby'	ECou
glaucophylla	GIsl SBod
– 'Clarence'	ECou NHed
N 'Glaucophylla'	CSco ECou
'Glaucophylla Variegata'	CAbb CB&S CNic ECou ESis GAbr GIsl MAll MBel MHig NFai NHol NRoo NSti SBod SMad SPer WHer WKif WPer WRus WSHC
'Glengarriff'	CChu MAll NHol
§ 'Gloriosa'	CAbb CSam IOrc SPla WBod
'Gnome'	ECou GIsl
'Godefroyana'	CNic GIsl
gracillima	CMHG ECou GCal GIsl
'Gran's Favourite'	ECou
'Great Orme' AGM	Widely available
'Green Globe'	See H. 'Emerald Green'
'Greensleeves'	CMHG CSam EBee ECou GAbr GIsl MGos NHed
'Gruninard's Seedling'	GIsl
haastii	ECou GDra GIsl MHig NHol NNor
'Hagley Park'	CNic CSam ECou EOrc ERav ESis LGre LHil LHop MMil MPla SGil SMrm SUsu WEas WHCG WKif WPat WSHC
'Hartii'	CSea GIsl
'Havering Green'	ECou MHig NTow
'Headfortii'	CSea IDai SGil
hectorii	CSco EPla GIsl GTou IJoh LBuc MAll MBal MFir MHig NBee
– var. ***demissa***	ECou GIsl NHed
¶ 'Heidi'	GIsl
'Hidcote'	WTyr
'Hielan Lassie'	CSea GIsl
'Highdownensis'	CPle CSea ECou GIsl
¶ 'Hinderwell'	NPer
'Hinerua'	ECou
hookeriana	See PARAHEBE ***h.***
hulkeana AGM	CBot CSam ECou ELan ERom GIsl LGre MBel MHig MPla MUlv NBir NTow SGil SHil SMad SMrm SUsu WAbe WEas WHCG WHil WKif WPer WSHC WWat
– 'Averil'	ECou
– 'Lilac Hint'	ECou
– 'Sally Blunt'	ECou
§ 'Imposter'	CSea ECou NFai SRms
'Inspiration'	CSea ECou
insularis	ECou SFis
'Jack's Surprise'	ECou
'James Platt'	ECou NHed WAbe
'James Stirling'	See H. ***ochracea*** 'James Stirling'
'Jane Holden'	CDoC CElw CSco CSea SBla SFar WSHC
'Jasper'	ECou ESis MAll
¶ 'Jewel'	CSea SDix
'Joan Lewis'	ECou NHed
'Joyce Parker'	ECou
¶ 'Judy'	ECou
'June Small'	CNic
'Kewensis'	CSea
'Killiney Variety'	CLan ECou MBal
'Kirkii'	ECou MUlv SGil SPer
'Knightshayes'	See H. 'Caledonia'
§ 'La Séduisante' AGM	CB&S CSco EBar ECou ENot IDai IOrc MAll NRoo SHBN SPer WBod WSHC
'Lady Ardilaun'	See H. 'Amy'
laevis	See H. ***venustula***
laingii	CSea ECou GIsl NHed
lapidosa	See H. ***rupicola***
* ***latifolia***	NNor
lavaudiana	ECou ESis WWat
'Lavender Queen'	CAbb CSea
leiophylla	CAbb GIsl
§ 'Leonard Cockayne'	CDoC CGre GIsl NSti WSHC
'Lewisii'	CSea
ligustrifolia	ECou
'Lilac Haze'	MAll
'Lilac Wand'	CMer
'Lindsayi'	CNic CPle ECou IDai MAll MUlv NHed
'Loganioïdes'	CLew CRiv ECou EMNN ESis GAbr GPlt MAll MBal NMen NNor SBod SSmi WPer
'Long Acre Variety'	ECou
'Lopen' (v)	ECou GIsl
lyallii	See PARAHEBE ***lyallii***
lycopodioïdes	CMHG ECou NHed WThu
– 'Aurea'	See H. ***armstrongii***
– var. ***patula***	ECou
– 'Peter Pan'	ECou GAbr SRms WPat
§ 'Macewanii'	CMHG ECou EPla ESis GIsl MAll NHed WHCG
mackenii	See H. 'Emerald Green'
macrantha AGM	CShe ECou EMon ERav ESis GAbr GCHN GRei ITim LGre MAll MBal MHig MPla NHed NHol NNor NPer SBla SGil SIng SPer WAbe WBod WOMN WSHC WWin
– var. ***brachyphylla***	ECou
macrocarpa	ECou
– var. ***brevifolia***	ECou
– var. ***latisepala***	ECou GIsl

'Margery Fish'	See H. 'Primley Gem'
'Margret'	EBar EBre GRei LBre MAsh MGos MWat NRoo SMrm SPer WStI
'Marjorie'	CChu CMHG CPle CSco ECou ENot EOrc GAbr GIsl MAll MBal MBel MGos MPla MRav NFai NHed NNor NPer NRoo SBod SLon SPer WDin WTyr
matthewsii	ECou NNor
¶ 'Mauve Queen'	CSea WRus
'McEwanii'	See H. 'Macewanii'
'McKean'	ECou NHed
'Megan'	ECou
¶ 'Melanie'	WRus
'Menzies Bay'	GIsl
'Mercury'	ECou
'Midsummer Beauty' AGM	CB&S CSco CSea EBre ECou ELan ENot GIsl IOrc ISea LBre LGro MAll MFir MGos MRav MWat NFai NHol NNor NTow SBod SDix SHBN SPer SPla WAbe WDin WStI
'Milmont Emerald'	See H. 'Emerald Green'
'Mini'	ECou
'Miss E Fittall'	CSea ECou
'Mist Maiden'	CNic ESis NHed
'Monica'	CNic ECou GCHN NHed NHol
'Morning Clouds'	ECou NHol
'Mrs E Tennant'	CSco
§ 'Mrs Winder' AGM	Widely available
x ***myrtifolia***	SHer
'Mystery'	ECou
¶ 'Nantyderry'	WEas WWat
'Neil's Choice'	CSea ECou GIsl MSte SHer
'Netta Dick'	ECou
'Nicola's Blush'	CAbb CElw CLTr CNic CSam EBar ECou EFol ESis GIsl GMac LAbb LHop LLWP MBel MPla MRav NFai SFai SHer SIng SMrm SSta WRus
'Northumbria Beauty'	NNor
'Northumbria Gem'	NNor
obtusata	ECou
§ ***ochracea***	ECou LAbb MAll MGos NSti SLon SPer STre
§ – 'James Stirling' AGM	Widely available
¶ 'Oddity'	ECou
§ ***odora***	CChe CDoC CSea EBee ECou ENot EPla GIsl MFir NNor
– 'New Zealand Gold'	CMHG CNic CSam EBee ECou EGol GIsl MAll NFai NHed SLon
– prostrate form	CSea ECou GIsl
– 'Stewart'	ECou
– 'Wintergreen'	GAul GIsl
'Oratio Beauty'	IBar
¶ 'Orientale'	CSea NHed
'Otari Delight'	CMHG
'Pageboy'	ECou NHed
parviflora var. ***angustifolia*** AGM	ECou EPla IDai SArc
– 'Palmerstone'	ECou
parviflora hort.	See H. 'Bowles's Hybrid'
'Pauciflora'	EFol GPlt NHed NHol NMen SBod
pauciramosa	CSea ECou EPla GIsl MAll NTow SRms
'Penny Day'	ECou
perfoliata	See DERWENTIA ***p.***
'Perryhill Lilac'	SPer
'Perryhill White'	SPer
'Perry's Bluey'	NPer
¶ 'Perry's Rubyleaf'	NPer
'Petra's Pink'	ECou ESis MAll MFir WEas
§ 'Pewter Dome' AGM	Widely available
'Pimeba'	NHol
pimeleoïdes	CSea ECou EPad ESma MFir NCat NHed NNor
– 'Glauca'	GIsl NPer SHBN WWin
– 'Glaucocaerulea'	CMHG ECou EGol ESis GIsl MBar MFir MPla NHed SHil SPer WAbe WKif
– var. ***minor***	ECou ESis GDra
– – 'Elf'	ECou
– – 'Imp'	ECou
– 'Quicksilver' AGM	Widely available
– var. ***rupestris***	CSea ECou ESis
pinguifolia	ECou GIsl NHed
– 'Godefroyana'	ECou
– 'Hutt'	CSea ECou
– 'Mount Dobson'	CNic ECou GIsl NHol
– 'Pagei' AGM	Widely available
– 'Sutherlandii'	CDoC CNic CSco ECou ESma GCHN GDra GIsl IJoh MAll MFir NHed NSti SLon
* 'Pink Payne'	LHop
♦ 'Pink Pearl'	See H. 'Gloriosa'
'Pink Wand'	CB&S CLTr CSea GIsl IJoh
'Polly Moore'	CLew MBal NTow WAbe
poppelwellii	ITim
'Porlock Purple'	See PARAHEBE ***catarractae*** 'Delight'
§ 'Primley Gem'	CLan CNic EBar MFir NNor SHer WAbe WSHC
'Princess'	ECou
propinqua	ECou ESis ESma
§ – 'Aurea'	MBal
– 'Minor'	GIsl NHed
'Prostrata'	ECou MAll
* ***pulchella***	CSam
¶ 'Purple Emperor'	SHil
'Purple Picture'	ECou ECtt NFai SDry SGil
'Purple Prince'	GIsl
'Purple Queen'	See H. 'Amy'
'Purple Tips' misapplied	See H. ***speciosa*** 'Tricolor'
rakaiensis AGM	Widely available
ramosissima	GIsl NHed
raoulii	CShe ECou MCas WHCG WHoo
– var. ***maccaskillii***	ECou ESis
– var. ***pentasepala***	ECou ESis
§ ***recurva***	CMHG CNic CPle ECou EFol EPla ESis GAbr LAbb LHop MBri MFir NBee NNor SPla SWas WAbe WDin WPer WRus
§ – 'Aoira'	ECou NHed NTow SPer
* – 'Boughton Silver' AGM	SDry
¶ – green-leaved	NHed
– 'White Torrent'	ECou
§ 'Red Edge' AGM	Widely available
'Red Ruth'	See H. 'Eveline'
rigidula	ECou ESis GIsl MAll NHed
'Ronda'	ECou SGil
'Royal Purple'	See H. 'Alicia Amherst'
salicifolia	CChe CCla CLTr CMer CPle CSea ECou ELan ENot GAbr GCHN GIsl LGro MFir NNor SHBN SPer WDav WHCG
– 'Snow Wreath' (v)	ECou IBlr

– 'Variegata'	CNic CPle
salicornioïdes	ECou
– 'Aurea'	See H. ***propinqua*** 'A.'
'Sapphire'	CDoC CSea ECou ESis GIsl MAll MGos NTow SPla
'Sarana'	ECou
'Silver Gilt'	CBot
'Silver Wings'	NFai
'Simon Delaux' AGM	CB&S CChu CDec CSam CSco ECou EPad GAbr GIsl LHop MAll MBal NTow SHBN SHer SPer WAbe WBod WEas WRus
speciosa 'Dial Rocks'	ECou
– 'Johny Day'	ECou
– 'Kapiti'	CSea
– 'Rangatira'	ECou
– 'Ruddigore'	See H. 'La Séduisante'
§ – 'Tricolor' (v)	ECou IBlr IDai LAbb NHol NPer NSti SDry SHer WEas
'Spender's Seedling' AGM	CDoC CLan CMer CSco CSea ECou GIsl MAll NSti SPer
♦ 'Spender's Seedling' misapplied	See H. ***parviflora angustifolia***
¶ 'Spring Glory'	MAll
stricta	ECou
– ***cookiana***	See H. ***s. macroura*** 'C.'
– var. ***macroura***	CSea ECou EPla GIsl SDry
– – 'Cookiana'	CSea
subalpina	CDoC CLan CSea CShe EBee EBre ECou LBre NHed NWea
subsimilis var. ***astonii***	ESis MHig WThi
'Sussex Carpet'	See H. ***albicans*** 'Sussex Carpet'
tetrasticha	WAbe
'Tiny Tot'	ECou ESma GIsl MTho NHol
'Tom Marshall'	See H. ***canterburiensis***
topiaria	CAbP CNic COtt CSea EBre ECou EGol EPla ESiP ESis ESma GIsl GPlt LBre LHop MAll MBri MWat NHed NHol NNor SFai SGil SMrm SPer SPla SSta WAbe WEas
'Torlesse'	ECou
townsonii	CSea ECou MAll
traversii	CSea ECou GAbr GIsl MSte SPla SRms WTyr
– 'Mason'	ECou
– 'Woodside'	ECou
¶ 'Trenchant Rose'	WHil
'Tricolor'	See H. ***speciosa*** 'Tricolor'
'Trixie'	CNic ECou MUlv
tumida	ECou
urvilleana	ECou GIsl
'Veitchii'	See H. 'Alicia Amherst'
§ ***venustula***	CMHG CSea ECou MBel NHed
– 'Blue Skies'	CSea ECou WPer
– 'Patricia Davies'	ECou
vernicosa	CLew CMHG CMer CNic ECou EFol EGol EPla ESis GDra GIsl GRei LHop MAll MBar MBri MCas MHig NHed NHol NNor NPer NTow SFis SIgm SPer WAbe WHCG WHil
'Violet Queen'	CAbb
'Violet Wand'	CSea
'Waikiki'	See H. 'Mrs Winder'
'Walter Buccleugh'	ECou GIsl MFir WOMN WSHC
'Wardiensis'	CMHG CSco ECou MBar
'Warleyensis'	See H. 'Mrs Winder'
§ 'Watson's Pink'	CLTr CNic ECou ESma GAbr GAri GIsl MAll MBel SChu SPer SUsu WAbe WKif
'White Gem'	CMer ECou ECtt ESis ESma GRei MAll MBal MGos NNor NPer WStI
¶ 'White Heather'	GIsl NHed
'White Wand'	CB&S NFai
'Willcoxii'	See H. ***buchananii*** 'Sir George Fenwick'
'Wingletye'	CAbP CLew CMHG CNic CSco EBre ECou ECtt EHoe EPla ESma GAbr GIsl LBre LHop MBal MBri MCas MGos NHed NTow SGil WAbe WPat WPer
'Winter Glow'	CMHG ECou ELan
* 'Wootten'	WPer
§ 'Youngii'	CMea CSam CSco CShe ECha ECou ELan EMNN ESis GDra GIsl GRei MBal MBar MBro MCas MGos MPla NHol NWCA SBla SPer SSmi WEas WSHC WThu WWat WWin

HEBENSTRETIA (Scrophulariaceea)

See Plant Deletions

HECHTIA (Bromeliaceae)

¶ ***montana***	CTbh

HECTORELLA (Hectorellaceae)

See Plant Deletions

HEDEOMA (Labiatae/Lamiaceae)

See Plant Deletions

HEDERA † (Araliaceae)

§ ***algeriensis***	CHEx CSco SArc SHil WFib
– 'Argyle Street'	WFib
§ – 'Gloire de Marengo' AGM	Widely available
– 'Marginomaculata' AGM	EPla LHop MUlv WFib
– 'Montgomery'	NRar WFib
– 'Ravensholst' AGM	CB&S CMac EHic WFib WWat
¶ ***arizonica*** 'Aurea'	EMon
azorica	EWhi WCot WFib WWat
– 'Pico'	EWhi WFib
§ – 'Saõ Miguel'	EWhi WFib
– typica	See H. ***a.*** 'Saõ Miguel'
canariensis 'Algeriensis'	See H. ***algeriensis***
♦ – 'Cantabrian'	See H. ***maroccana*** 'Spanish Canary'
– 'Gloire de Marengo' (v)	See H. ***algeriensis*** 'G. de M.'
– 'Variegata'	See H. ***algeriensis*** 'Gloire de Marengo'
canariensis hort.	See H. ***algeriensis***
canariensis Willdenow	CDoC WFib WTyr
chinensis typica	See H. ***nepalensis sinensis***
colchica AGM	CHEx CTom ENot SPer WDin WFib
– 'Dentata' AGM	CHEx EPla EWhi LBuc LPri MBal NKay SHil WFib
– 'Dentata Aurea'	See H. ***c.*** 'Dentata Variegata'

§ – 'Dentata Variegata' AGM	CB&S CMac CSco ELan ENot EPla EWhi GRei IDai IJoh MBal MBar MBri MWat NHol SBra SDix SHBN SLon SPer SSta STre WFib WPat WWat
– 'Paddy's Pride'	See H. *c.* 'Sulphur Heart'
§ – 'Sulphur Heart' AGM	CB&S CCla CHEx CMHG CMac CSco EHoe ELan ENot EWhi IHos IJoh LPri MBal MBar MBri MGos MWat NHol NKay SBra SHBN SMad SPer SSta WDin WEas WFib WWat
– *variegata*	See H. *c.* 'Dentata Variegata'
cristata	See H. ***helix helix*** 'Parsley Crested'
cypria	EPla
helix 'Hispanica'	See H. ***maderensis iberica***
– 'Pallida'	See H. ***hibernica*** 'Hibernica Variegata'
– 'Poetica'	See H. ***h. poetarum***
¶ – ssp. ***rhizomatifera***	EPla
helix f. ***caucasigena***	WFib
– ssp. ***helix***	CKin EWFC EWhi MBar MGos NWea WFib WHer
– – '238th Street'	EWhi
– – 'Abundance'	EWhi
– – 'Adam' (v)	EMon ESis LHop MBri MGos MTho SGil STre WByw WFib WWat WWeb
– – 'Ahorn'	EWhi WFib
– – 'Albany'	EWhi
– – 'Alpha'	EWhi
– – 'Alt Heidelberg'	EWhi WFib
– – 'Alte Brucken'	EWhi WFib
– – 'Ambrosia' (v)	EWhi WFib
– – 'Anchor'	EWhi
– – 'Angularis'	ECot
– – 'Angularis Aurea' AGM	CSco EFol EHoe EPla EWhi MPla NBir SHBN SMad WFib
– – 'Anne Borch'	See H. ***hibernica*** 'Anne Marie'
– – 'Annette'	See H. ***h. h.*** 'California'
– – 'Apaloosa'	WFib
– – 'Aran'	See H. ***hibernica*** 'A.'
♦ – – 'Aran' misapplied	See H. ***h. h.*** 'Rutherford's Arran'
– – 'Arapahoe'	WFib
– – 'Arborescens'	CNat EPla EWhi SArc
– – 'Arborescens Variegata'	EPla MAsh
– – 'Ardingly' (v)	EMon EWhi SPer WFib
– – 'Asterisk'	EPla EWhi NBrk WFib
– – 'Astin'	EWhi WFib
– – 'Atropurpurea' AGM	EPla EWhi MBar WFib
– – 'Aurea Variegata'	CMac EWhi WFib
– – 'Avon' (v)	WFib
– – 'Baby Face'	EWhi
– – 'Baccifera'	EWhi WFib
– – 'Baden-Baden'	EWhi WFib
– – 'Baltica'	EWhi WFib
– – 'Bates'	EWhi
– – 'Big Deal'	EWhi
– – 'Bill Archer'	EPla EWhi WFib
– – 'Bird's Foot'	See H. ***h. h.*** 'Pedata'
– – 'Blodwen'	WFib
– – 'Bodil' (v)	WFib
– – 'Boskoop'	EPla EWhi WFib
– – 'Bowles Ox Heart'	WFib
– – 'Brigette'	MBri
– – 'Brightstone'	WFib
– – 'Brokamp'	EWhi MMil SLPl WFib
– – 'Buttercup' AGM	CBra CCla CMac CSco ECha EHoe ELan EPla ESiP EWhi GDra LHop MBal MBar MBri MGos MPla MTho NBrk NNor SBra SHBN SLon SPer WEas WFib WWat
§ – – 'Caecilia' (v)	COtt EFol ELan EPla ESiP ESis EWhi LHop MGos NSti WDin WFib
– – 'Caenwoodiana'	WFib
– – 'Caenwoodiana Aurea'	EPla EWhi
§ – – 'Calico' (v)	EHal WFib
§ – – 'California'	EWhi MBri WFib
– – 'California Fan'	EWhi SGil
– – 'California Gold' (v)	EBre ESis EWhi LBre WFib
– – 'Carolina Crinkle'	EPla EWhi WFib
– – 'Cascade'	WFib
– – 'Cathedral Wall'	WFib
§ – – 'Cavendishii' AGM	EPla ESiP EWhi MPla NBrk WFib
– – 'Ceridiwen'	CRDP EWhi WFib
– – 'Chester' (v)	EWhi MBri WFib WWat
– – 'Chicago'	EBee EWhi WFib
– – 'Chicago Variegata'	EWhi WFib
– – 'Chrysanna'	WFib
– – 'Chrysophylla'	EPla EWhi WFib
– – 'Clotted Cream'	See H. ***h. h.*** 'Caecilia'
– – 'Clouded Gold'	SPer
– – 'Cockle Shell'	EWhi
– – 'Congesta' AGM	EPla EWhi GDra GPlt MBal MTho SSmi STre WEas WFib
– – 'Conglomerata'	CLew CSam ELan EPla EWhi MAsh MBal MBar MBri NBir NNor NRya SMad SPer SSmi WDin WEas WFib WPat
– – 'Conglomerata Erecta'	WFib
– – 'Crenata'	EWhi
– – 'Crispa'	NNor
– – 'Cristata'	See H. ***h. h.*** 'Parsley Crested'
– – 'Cristata Melanie'	See H. ***h. h.*** 'Melanie'
– – 'Curleylocks'	See H. ***h. h.*** 'Manda's Crested'
– – 'Curley-Q'	EMon
– – 'Curvaceous' (v)	EWhi
– – 'Cuspidata Major'	EWhi
– – 'Cuspidata Minor'	EWhi
– – 'Cyprus'	See H. ***cypria***
– – 'Denmark'	WFib
– – 'Denticulata'	EWhi WFib
– – 'Diana'	EWhi
– – 'Dicke von Stauss'	EWhi
– – 'Direktor Badke'	EWhi WFib
– – 'Discolor' (v)	See H. ***h. h.*** 'Minor Marmorata'
– – 'Domino' (v)	EFol EPla EWhi WFib
§ – – 'Donerailensis'	EWhi GAri SHer WFib
– – 'Dragon Claw'	EHic EPla EWhi SMad WCot WCru WFib
– – 'Duckfoot'	CLew EWhi IReg MNFA MTho NSti WFib WWat
– – 'Edison'	EWhi
– – 'Elegance'	EWhi WFib
– – 'Elfenbein' (v)	EWhi WFib

– – 'Emerald Gem'	EWhi
– – 'Emerald Globe'	EPla EWhi WFib
– – 'Erecta' AGM	CMac EPla ESis EWhi GAri MBar MBri MTho NHol NRya SIng SPer WFib WPat WThu
– – 'Ester' (v)	CDoC EWhi MBri WFib
– – 'Eugen Hahn' (v)	EPla EWhi WCot WFib WHer
– – 'Eva' AGM	CMac EWhi MBal MBri MGos NBir WFib WWeb
– – 'Evesham'	WFib
– – 'Fallen Angel'	WFib
– – 'Fan'	EWhi
– – 'Fantasia' (v)	CMac EWhi
– – 'Ferney'	WFib
– – 'Fiesta'	WFib
– – 'Filigran'	EPla EWhi SMad WFib WHer
– – 'Flamenco'	EPla EWhi WFib
– – 'Flava'	EWhi
– – 'Fleur de Lis'	EWhi WFib
– – 'Fluffy Ruffles'	EPla EWhi
*– – 'Francis'	MBri
§ – – 'Frank Wood'	EWhi
– – 'Fringette'	EWhi MTho WFib
– – 'Frosty' (v)	EHic
– – 'Garland'	EWhi
– – 'Gavotte'	EPla EWhi MTho WFib
– – 'Gertrude Stauss' (v)	EWhi MBri
– – 'Glache' (v)	EWhi WFib
– – 'Glacier' AGM	CBra CMac CSam CSco EBre EHoe ELan ESis EWhi IHos LBre LPri MBal MBar MBri MGos NKay NNor NSti SHBN SLon SPer WBod WFib WHen
§ – – 'Glymii'	EPla EWhi WFib
*– – 'Gold Harald'	MBri
– – 'Gold Knight'	EFol
– – 'Gold Nugget'	EWhi
– – 'Goldchild' AGM	CB&S CSam EBre ELan EPla EWhi LBre MBar MBri MGos MTho NBir NCat WByw WFib
– – 'Goldcraft' (v)	EPla EWhi
*– – 'Golden Ann'	MBri
– – 'Golden Ester'	EWhi MBri
– – 'Golden Gate'	EWhi MBri
– – 'Golden Ingot'	ELan EWhi MGos WFib
– – 'Golden Kolibri'	MBri
– – 'Golden Medal'	EWhi WFib
– – 'Golden Pittsburgh'	EWhi
– – 'Golden Shamrock'	SGil
– – 'Golden Snow'	MBri
– – 'Goldfinger' (v)	WFib
– – 'Goldheart' (v)	See H. ***h. h.*** 'Oro di Bogliasco'
– – 'Goldstern' (v)	CNat EWhi LHop NGar WFib WWat
– – 'Gracilis'	EWhi
§ – – 'Green Feather'	ESis EWhi WFib WHer
– – 'Green Finger'	See H. ***h. h.*** 'Très Coupé'
– – 'Green Ripple'	CB&S CMac CSam CSco EWhi IJoh IOrc MBar NCat NNor SPer SSta WAbe WFib WHen
– – 'Green Spear'	WFib
– – 'Hahn's Green Ripple'	See H. ***h. h.*** 'Green Ripple'
– – 'Hamilton'	See H. ***hibernica*** 'H.'
*– – 'Harald' (v)	EBar EWhi MBal MBri SGil WEas WFib WPat WWeb
– – 'Harlequin'	WFib
– – 'Harrison'	EWhi
– – 'Harry Wood'	EWhi
– – 'Hazel' (v)	WFib
– – 'Heise' (v)	EWhi WFib
– – 'Helvig'	See H. ***h. h.*** 'White Knight'
– – 'Heron'	ELan EMon WFib
– – 'Hite's Miniature'	EWhi
– – 'Humpty Dumpty'	CDoC MBar
– – 'Ingelise'	See H. ***h. h.*** 'Sagittifolia Variegata'
– – 'Ingrid' (v)	See H. ***h. h.*** 'Hamilton'
– – 'Ivalace' AGM	CB&S CTom ECha EFol ELan EPla ESiP ESis EWhi LHop MBal MGos MNFA MRav NNrw NSti SGil WAbe WEas WFib WHen
– – 'Jack Frost' (v)	NWyt WFib
*– – 'Jane's Findling' (v)	CNat
– – 'Jasper'	WFib
*– – 'Jerusalem'	WFib
– – 'Jubilee' (v)	CSco ELan EWhi MNFA WFib
– – 'Knulch'	EPla EWhi WFib
– – 'Königers Auslese'	EFol EPla ESiP EWhi SLPl WFib
– – 'Kolibri' AGM	CDoC CSam EHar EMil EWhi MBri WFib
– – 'Kurios'	EWhi
– – 'La Plata'	EWhi
– – 'Lady Kay'	See H. ***h. h.*** 'Lucy Kay'
– – 'Lalla Rookh'	CRDP EWhi WFib
– – 'Lemon Swirl' (v)	EWhi WFib
– – 'Leo Swicegood'	EPla EWhi WFib
– – 'Light Fingers'	SPer WFib
*– – 'Limelight'	NRar
– – 'Little Diamond' AGM	CLTr CSam EHoe EPla EWhi MBar MBri MGos SHBN WFib WThu WWat WWye
– – 'Little Gem'	EWhi WFib
– – 'Little Luzii' (v)	EFol EHal WFib
– – 'Little Picture'	ESis WFib
– – 'Liz' (v)	WFib
§ – – 'Lucy Kay'	EWhi WFib
§ – – 'Luzii' (v)	EFol EHoe EPla EWhi MBar MGos NNor NSti SGil SHBN SPer WByw WFib
– – 'Maculata'	See H. ***h. h.*** 'Minor Marmorata'
§ – – 'Manda's Crested' AGM	CDec ELan ESis MBal SLon WFib WWeb
– – 'Manda's Fan'	WFib
– – 'Manda's Fringette'	EWhi
– – 'Maple Leaf'	EPla EWhi WFib
– – 'Maple Queen'	EWhi MBri
– – 'Marginata'	SRms
– – 'Marginata Elegantissima'	See H. ***h. h.*** 'Tricolor'
– – 'Marginata Major'	EWhi WFib
– – 'Marginata Minor'	See H. ***h. h.*** 'Cavendishii'
– – 'Marie Luise'	EWhi
– – 'Marilyn'	EWhi
– – 'Marmorata'	See H. ***h. h.*** 'Luzii'
– – 'Masquerade' (v)	CCla EWhi WGor
– – 'Mathilde'	EWhi WFib
– – 'Meagheri'	See H. ***h. h.*** 'Green Feather'
– – 'Mein Herz'	See H. ***hibernica*** 'Deltoidea'
§ – – 'Melanie'	ECha ELan EPla NBrk WFib
– – 'Merion Beauty'	EPla EWhi GAri WFib
– – 'Microphylla Picta' (v)	EWhi
– – 'Midas Touch' AGM	EFol EPla EWhi LHop LPri

-- 'Midget'	WEas WFib
-- 'Mini Ester' (v)	EWhi MBri
-- 'Mini Heron'	MBri
-- 'Miniature Knight'	EWhi
-- 'Minima'	See H. ***h. h.*** 'Donerailensis'
§ -- 'Minor Marmorata' (v)	EHal EPla EWhi MBal MTho WEas WFib
-- 'Mint Kolibri'	EFol EHoe MBri
-- 'Miss Maroc'	EWhi WFib
-- 'Misty'	EWhi WFib
-- 'Mrs Pollock' (v)	EWhi WFib
-- 'Mrs Ulin'	EWhi
-- 'Needlepoint'	IOrc
-- 'Neilson'	CLTr EWhi SPer STre WFib
-- 'Neptune'	EWhi
-- 'New Ripples'	EHal EWhi NBrk WFib
-- 'Nigra'	EWhi
-- 'Nigra Aurea'	EWhi WFib
-- 'Northington Gold'	WFib
-- 'Olive Rose'	EPla EWhi MTho WCot WFib
§ -- 'Oro di Bogliasco' (v)	CMac CSam ELan ENot ISea LPri MBal MBar MBri NBrk NKay NNor NSti NWea SBra SIng SLon SPer WAbe WEas WFib WPat WThu WWat
-- 'Pallida'	See H. ***hibernica*** 'Hibernica Variegata'
-- 'Paper Doll' (v)	EWhi
-- 'Parasol' (v)	EPla WFib
§ -- 'Parsley Crested'	ECha ELan EPla ESis EWhi MBal MBar MGos NKay NSti SPer WEas WFib WTyr WWat WWye
-- 'Pedata' AGM	ELan ENot EPla EWhi MAsh WFib
-- 'Pedata Heron'	WFib
-- 'Pencil Point'	EWhi
-- 'Pennsylvanian'	EWhi
-- 'Perkeo'	EPla EWhi WFib
-- 'Perle' (v)	EPla EWhi NBir WFib
-- 'Persian Carpet'	EWhi LMer WFib
-- 'Peter' (v)	EFol EPla EWhi WFib
-- 'Pin Oak'	EPla EWhi ISea MNFA SIng
* -- 'Pink 'n' Curley'	EPla WCot
-- 'Pirouette'	WFib
§ -- 'Pittsburgh'	WFib
-- 'Pixie'	EWhi WFib
-- 'Plume d'Or'	CSam EPla MTho WFib
-- 'Preston Tiny'	NBir
-- 'Professor H Tobler'	EPla EWhi WFib
-- 'Quatermas'	EWhi WFib
-- 'Ralf'	EPla EWhi WFib
-- 'Rambler'	NBir
-- 'Rauschgold'	EWhi
-- 'Ray's Supreme'	See H. ***h. h.*** 'Pittsburgh'
-- 'Reef Shell' (v)	WFib
-- 'Regency'	EWhi
-- 'Ritterkreutz'	EWhi WFib
-- 'Romanze' (v)	EWhi WFib
-- 'Rusche'	EPla EWhi WFib
-- 'Russell's Gold'	WFib
§ -- 'Rutherford's Arran'	EPla WFib
-- 'Sagittifolia'	CLTr CMac CNic CSco ELan EPla EWhi MBal NNor SPer WAbe WEas WFib WWat
§ -- 'Sagittifolia Variegata'	CMac EBre EFol EHal EMil EPla ESis EWhi LBre MBri SIng SPer WAbe WFib
-- 'Sally' (v)	EPla EWhi
-- 'Salt and Pepper'	See H. ***h. h.*** 'Minor Marmorata'
-- 'Schafer One' (v)	MMil WFib
-- 'Schafer Three'	See H. ***h. h.*** 'Calico'
-- 'Schafer Two' (v)	WFib
-- 'Scutifolia'	See H. ***h. h.*** 'Glymii'
-- 'Serenade' (v)	EPla
-- 'Shamrock' AGM	EPla EWhi MBri MNFA SPer WCot WFib
-- 'Shannon'	EWhi
-- 'Silver King' (v)	EPla EWhi NBir WFib
-- 'Silver Queen'	See H. ***h. h.*** 'Tricolor'
-- 'Sinclair Silverleaf'	WFib
-- 'Small Deal'	EWhi
-- 'Spear Point'	EWhi
-- 'Spectabilis Aurea'	WFib
-- 'Spectre' (v)	CNat EFol ELan EPla EWhi MTho WFib WHer
-- 'Spetchley' AGM	CLew CNic EFol EMon EPla ESis EWhi MBar MNFA MTho NHar SMad
-- 'Spinosa'	EPla EWhi WFib
-- 'Staghorn'	EPla EWhi
-- 'Stift Neuberg' (v)	WFib
-- 'Stuttgart'	EPla EWhi WFib
-- 'Succinata'	EPla EWhi
-- 'Sulphurea' (v)	EWhi WFib
-- 'Suzanne'	See H. ***nepalensis nepalensis*** 'S.'
-- 'Sylvanian'	WFib
-- 'Symmetry'	EWhi
-- 'Tango'	MNFA WFib
-- 'Telecurl'	EPla EWhi WFib
-- 'Tenerife'	ELan
-- 'Tiger Eye'	EPla EWhi
§ -- 'Très Coupé'	CB&S EWhi ISea MBal MGos MNFA MTho NHol SPer WDin WFib
§ -- 'Tricolor' (v)	CB&S CDoC CMac CSco ELan EPla EWhi IDai ISea SBra SHBN SHil SPer SReu
-- 'Trinity' (v)	NHol WByw WFib
-- 'Tristram'	EWhi WFib
-- 'Triton'	EPla EWhi MBal MTho WFib WHer
-- 'Trustee'	EWhi
-- 'Tussie Mussie'	EWhi WFib
-- 'Ustler'	EWhi
-- 'Walthamensis'	EWhi WFib
§ -- 'White Knight' (v)	EPla EWhi MBri WFib
-- 'White Kolibri'	MBri
-- 'Wichtel'	EWhi
-- 'William Kennedy' (v)	EWhi WEas WFib
-- 'Williamsiana' (v)	EWhi WFib
-- 'Woener'	EWhi WFib
♦ -- 'Woodsii'	See H. ***h. h.*** 'Frank Wood'
-- 'Zebra' (v)	EWhi WFib
– ssp. ***hibernica***	See H. ***hibernica***
§ – ssp. ***poetarum***	EPla EWhi IOrc WFib
-- 'Poetica Arborea'	ECha SDix WFib
§ ***hibernica*** AGM	CB&S ELan LBuc MBar MBri MRav NNor SBra SPer WFib WStI WWat

– 'Albany' EWhi WFib
§– 'Anne Marie' (v) CMac ESis EWhi MBri WEas WFib WWin
– 'Aran' EWhi
– 'Cuspidata Major' EWhi WFib
– 'Cuspidata Minor' EWhi WFib
– 'Dealbata' CMac EWhi WFib
– 'Deltoidea' EMon EPla EWhi MBal MBri NHol WCot WFib
– 'Digitata' EPla WFib
– 'Gracilis' EWhi WFib
– 'Hamilton' ESis EWhi WFib
– 'Helena' EPla EWhi WFib
– 'Helford River' WFib
– 'Hibernica Variegata' WFib
– 'Lobata Major' SRms WFib
– 'Maculata' (v) EPla
– 'Palmata' EWhi WFib
– 'Rona' EWhi WFib
– 'Rottingdean' EWhi WFib
– 'Sark' WFib
– 'Tess' EPla EWhi
– 'Variegata' EWhi WFib
§ ***maderensis*** ssp. ***iberica*** WFib
§ ***maroccana*** 'Spanish Canary' WFib
nepalensis ISea MBal MBlu WFib
– var. ***nepalensis*** 'Suzanne' EWhi WFib
§– var. ***sinensis*** EWhi WFib
pastuchovii EFol EMon EWhi WFib
– 'Cyprus Taxon Troodos' See H. ***cypria***
rhombea EWhi WCot WFib
– 'Japonica' See H. ***r. rhombea***
§– var. ***rhombea*** EWhi
–– 'Variegata' EWhi WFib

HEDYCHIUM † (Zingiberaceae)

aurantiacum EBul NRog SLMG
chrysoleucum LAma NRog
coccineum AGM CB&S LAma LBow MUlv NRog SLMG
– var. ***aurantiacum*** CNew LAma LBow
– 'Tara' AGM CChu SArc SLMG
coronarium CAvo CBrk CNew CTro EOrc GGar LBow MSte NFai SAxl SLMG WPer
densiflorum CBrk CTre CTro EBul SDix
– 'Assam Orange' CB&S CBrk CChu CHEx CNew GCal MSte SArc
ellipticum LAma LBow NRog SHer
flavescens CNew CTro LAma NRog SArc
forrestii CChu CHEx CTre SArc
gardnerianum CGre CHEx CNew CTro ERea LAma LBow MSte MUlv NRog SArc SDix SHer SLMG
greenei CGle CHEx LBow NRog SLMG
horsfieldii CTro
longicornutum CNew
¶ ***pradhanii*** CNew
* 'Shamshiri' CNew
spicatum CHEx CHan CMon LHil MSte NRog SLMG
villosum LAma LBow NRog

HEDYOTIS (Rubiaceae)

– See also HOUSTONIA

HEDYSARUM (Leguminosae/Papilionaceae)

coronarium CArn CGle CHan CPle CSpe ELan GCra MHlr MSte NWyt SFis SUsu WCot WCra WEas WHil WOMN WWin
– 'Album' CBot
multijugum CB&S CDoC CSco ENot SDry SHil SPer
– var. ***apiculatum*** ELan
¶ ***nitidum*** SIgm
¶ ***varium*** WDav

HEDYSCEPE (Palmae/Arecaceae)

§ ***canterburyana*** NPal

HEIMERLIODENDRON See PISONIA

HEIMIA (Lythraceae)

salicifolia CArn CGre CHan CPle CSam ELan MAll MSal NSti WWin WWye

HELENIUM † (Compositae/Asteraceae)

autumnale CLew EBar EHal MBel MPit MSal NMir SHer SSvw
¶– JLS 88007WI EMon
¶– 'All Gold' WPer
'Baudirektor Linne' CSam ECED
bigelovii WByw WDav
'Bruno' CMGP ELan MMil NCat SMrm SPer WCra
'Butterpat' CB&S CSco ECED EFou EHic LBuc MBel MMil NFai SChu SHer SMrm SPer
'Chipperfield Orange' EBee EFou LRHS SGil SHer
'Coppelia' CKel CSam CShe ECED MUlv
'Crimson Beauty' ELan MBri MRav NBar NFai NRoo WMer
'Croftway Variety' SCro
'Dunkelpracht' ('Dark Beauty') LRHS
'Feuersiegel' EFou
'Gold Fox' CSam WMer
'Goldene Jugend' ('Golden Youth') EFou ELan NRoo WCot WEas
'Goldrausch' EFou EJud
hoopesii CBow CHol CShe EBar EFou EMon GCal LWad MFir MNFA NBro NOak NPri NSti SCro SHer SMrm SPla SSvw WCra WDav WHil WPer
'Kupfersprudel' ('Copper Spray') MRav
'Kupferzwerg' EFou
'Margot' EFou
'Moerheim Beauty' Widely available
'Pumilum Magnificum' CDoC CMGP CSam CSco EPar MBri MWat NKay NRoo SCro SPer WByw
'Riverton Gem' ECtt
'Rotgold' ('Red and Gold') CBow CDoC ECtt NOak WFro WHil WPer
'Sonnenwunder' ECha EFou
'Sunshine' GCHN

'The Bishop'	CBow CMGP CSam CSco EFou MBri MNFA MRav NBar NSti WMer
'Waldtraut'	CKel CMGP ECot EFou ELan MUlv NBar NCat NOak SCro SGil SHer SPer WDav WMer
'Wyndley'	CB&S COtt CSam CSco ECED EFou EGle MArl MBel MNFA MRav NRoo WCra WMer
'Zimbelstern'	ECha EFou EGle

HELIAMPHORA (Sarraceniaceae)

¶ ***heterodoxa***	EFEx
nutans	MHel MSte WMEx

HELIANTHELLA (Compositae/Asteraceae)

§ ***quinquenervis***	GCal MSte NTow

HELIANTHEMUM † (Cistaceae)

'Alice Howarth'	CShe CVer ESis MDHE SIng WHCG WHoo WPer
alpestre serpyllifolium	See H. ***nummularium glabrum***
amabile 'Plenum' (d)	EBar GDra SIgm
'Amabile Plenum'	GCal
'Amy Baring' AGM	EBre EGle EMNN GAbr GAri GDra GPlt LBee LBre LHop MHig NCat NKay NMen NRoo SBod SIng WPer WSHC
'Annabel'	CCla CElw CRiv EBar EFol EOrc GAbr GCHN MFir MPit MPla NBrk NEgg NRoo NSti SAxl SChu SGil SHer WHCG WPer
apenninum	MBro WCla WPer
– var. ***roseum***	WCla
'Apricot'	SBod SHer
'Baby Buttercup'	CRiv GAbr LBuc NHol SIng WPat
'Beech Park Red'	CRiv CShe ESis GAbr LBee LBuc MBro MDHE MMil MWat SAsh SChu SIgm SIng WHoo WKif
'Ben Afflick'	CRiv EBar GAbr IDai LBee NHol NKay NSty SBod SGil SHer SIgm SIng
'Ben Alder'	MDHE NHol NSty
'Ben Attow'	NKay
'Ben Dearg'	ECtt EGle EMNN ESis GAbr GPlt NHol NKay NSty SBod SIng
'Ben Fhada'	CMGP CMHG CMea CRiv EGle ELan EMNN GAbr GDra LBee MBal MFir MHig NHol NKay NSti NSty SBod SHer SSvw WAbe WEas WPer WWin
'Ben Heckla'	CHad CHol CMHG CRiv CSam GAbr GCHN GPlt MSte NEgg NMen NRoo SAxl WEas WPer
'Ben Hope'	CVer EBar EMNN GAbr GDra MBal NHol NKay NMen NRoo NSty SChu SHer SIng WPer WWin
'Ben Lawers'	NHol
'Ben Ledi'	CHol CMea CRiv CVer EFol ELan EMNN ESis GAbr GCHN GDra GPlt LBee MBal NKay NNrd NSty SBod SHer WAbe WHoo WPer WTyr WWin
'Ben Lomond'	CRiv GAbr MBal
'Ben Macdui'	GAbr LBee
'Ben More'	CB&S CRiv EGle ELan EMNN ESis GAbr GDra IDai IHos LBee LBuc MBal MCas MFir MPla MWat NKay NMen NSti SBod SIng SSmi WPat WWin
'Ben Nevis'	CBow CRiv CShe ECha ELan GAbr GDra LHop MDHE SHer WHoo WWin
'Ben Vane'	CRiv EGle EMNN MDHE NHol NKay SIng
'Birch White'	NHol SIng
'Bishopsthorpe'	CShe
'Boughton Double Primrose' (d)	CGle EFol ELan GAbr GCal GMac LBee LHop NHol NSti SChu SIgm SSvw WEas WSHC
'Broughty Beacon'	GAbr GDra WGor
'Broughty Sunset'	GAbr MBro MDHE NBir SIgm WHoo
'Brown Gold' (d)	EOrc
¶ 'Bunbury'	GAbr
'Butter and Eggs' (d)	SRms
'Butterball' (d)	MDHE NKay SIng
canum	MSto NHol SIng WPer
– ssp. ***balcanicum***	NTow
– ssp. ***piloselloïdes***	WAbe WWin
'Captivation'	EFol
'Cerise Queen' (d)	CRiv EBre ECha GAbr GMac LBre LHop MBel MCas MPla NKay SAxl SDix SGil SHer SIgm SIng WCla WHoo WPer
chamaecistus	See H. ***nummularium***
'Cheviot'	MDHE NHol WEas WHoo WPer WWat
'Chocolate Blotch'	EBar ECtt ELan EMNN GAbr LBuc MTho NMen NRoo NSty SChu SFis SIng WPer
'Coppernob'	SRms
'Cornish Cream'	CVer EWes SIng
croceum	NTow
cupreum	EFou NHol
'Doctor Phillips'	CShe WHCG WPer WSun
double apricot	CRiv CShe EGle GAbr NHol WHil
double cream	CMGP CMea CNic ECha ECtt EMNN EOrc ESis MBel MDHE MFir NSti SGil SHer WPer
'Double Orange'	EBar LHop MWat WPer
double pink	CMGP ECha GAbr
'Double Primrose'	SIng
double red	ECha MPla
double yellow	ECha MPla NSti SUsu
'Fairy'	EGle ESis
§ 'Fire Dragon' AGM	CSam ECtt EGle ELan ESma GAbr GAri GCHN LBee LBuc NRoo NWCA SChu SIgm SIng WAbe
'Fireball' (d)	See H. 'Mrs C W Earle'
'Firegold'	WAbe
'Gaiety'	CRiv GAbr WPer
'Georgeham'	CMHG CRiv CShe CVer ELan GAbr LBee LHop MDHE NCat SIng WDav WEas WHCG WPer
globulariifolium	See TUBERARIA ***globulariifolia***
'Gloiriette'	SIng
§ 'Golden Queen'	CVer ECtt LLWP NHol NMen NSty SChu SGil SIng WCla WPer
'Henfield Brilliant' AGM	CCla CHad CMHG CRiv CShe EBre EGle GAbr GDra LAbb LBee LBre LHop MBro MCas MPit NHol NRoo SIng SSmi WDav WEas WHoo WPer WSHC WWat
'Highdown'	GAbr MCas SRms WAbe
'Honeymoon'	SAxl SIde
'John Lanyon'	LBee SIng

'Jubilee' AGM	CMHG EBre EGle ELan EMNN EOrc GAbr IDai LBre LBuc LHop NHol NNor NRoo NSti NSty SChu SIng SSvw WAbe WCla WEas WHCG WHil WHoo WPer WWin
I 'Jubilee Variegatum'	GAbr MPla SIgm
'Kathleen Druce' (d)	CMea EWes GMac LHop MCas MWat NHol SIng
ledifolium	WPer
'Lucy Elizabeth'	GAbr
lunulatum	CLew EMon ESis LBee MBro MCas MPla MSto NHol NKay NMen NNrd NTow SIgm WAbe WPat
'Magnificum'	MWat
'Moonbeam'	WWin
§ 'Mrs C W Earle' AGM	CHol CMHG CRiv ELan EMNN EOrc ESis GAbr GPlt IDai LHop NKay NNrd NRoo NSti NSty SBod SDix SFis SIng WAbe WHil WPer WSun WWin
'Mrs C W Earle Variegated' (d)	EFol ELan LHop WWin
'Mrs Clay'	See H. 'Fire Dragon'
¶ 'Mrs Hays'	GMac
'Mrs Jenkinson'	CMHG
'Mrs Lake'	EMNN NSty
'Mrs Moules'	SRms
'Mrs Mountstewart Jenkinson'	LHop MBro
mutabile	WPer
§ ***nummularium***	CKin EWFC GPoy MHew NMir NWCA SHer WCla WNdy WPat
§ – ssp. ***glabrum***	CLew CMHG EMNN GAbr MBro NHol NKay NNrd NRoo NTow SIng WHoo WPat WPer
– ssp. ***grandiflorum*** 'Variegatum'	MWat
§ – ssp. ***tomentosum***	MWat
oelandicum ssp. ***alpestre***	MBro NKay SRms SSmi WPer
– – 'Baby Buttercup'	CMea MPla
– ***piloselloïdes***	MHig
'Old Gold'	CRiv EBre LBee LBre MHig NHol NRoo SIgm WAbe WDav WPer
ovatum	See H. ***nummularium obscurum***
¶ ***pilosum***	LBee
'Pink Glow'	WPer
'Pink Perfection'	CMHG CSam
'Praecox'	CMea ESis LBee MBal MCas MPla NRoo NSty SIng WHoo WPer
'Prostrate Orange'	SRms
'Raspberry Ripple'	CCla CShe EBre EFol EGle ELan EOrc ESis GAbr GCHN ITim LBre LBuc LHop MPla MRav MSte MTho NEgg NHol NRoo SAxl SChu SFis SIng WHoo WPat WPer WRus WWin
'Red Orient'	See H. 'Supreme'
§ 'Rhodanthe Carneum' AGM	Widely available
'Rosa Königin' ('Rose Queen')	EMNN LBee MDHE NKay NMen NSty WAbe
'Rose of Leeswood' (d)	CMea CShe ELan EOrc GAbr GMac LHop MBro NKay SChu SFis SIgm SIng SMrm SSvw WEas WHCG WHil WHoo WKif WSHC WWin
'Rose Perfection'	CHol
'Roxburgh Gold'	SRms
'Rushfield's White'	WHCG WRus
'Saint John's College Yellow'	CMHG CSam EBar EHal GAbr SSmi WHCG WPer
'Salmon Bee'	CShe MDHE
'Salmon Queen'	CMHG CRiv EMNN ESis ITim LBee MCas NCat NKay NRoo SIng WPer WWin
* ***scardicum***	NHol
serpyllifolium	See H. ***nummularium glabrum***
'Shot Silk'	NRoo SIng
'Silvery Salmon'	WAbe
'Snow Queen'	See H. 'The Bride'
'Snowball'	ECha EMon SIng
'Southmead'	GAbr
'Sterntaler'	GAbr GDra NHol SIng SRms WDav
'Sudbury Gem'	CRiv EBre ECha GAbr GAri LBre LHop NHol NRoo WDav WSHC
x ***sulphureum***	GCal
'Sunbeam'	CRiv CSam EMNN GAbr MCas NSty SRms
§ 'Supreme'	CRiv CShe ELan GAbr IDai LBee LHop MWat NKay SChu SDix SIgm SIng SSvw WHCG WPer
§ 'The Bride' AGM	CElw CMea EBre ECha EFou EGle ELan EOrc ESis GCHN LBre LBuc LHop MSte MWat NMen NSty SChu SDix SHer SIng SSvw WAbe WPer WSHC
'Tigrinum Plenum' (d)	ESis EWes LBee MDHE NRoo SHer WPer WWin
'Tomato Red'	ECha SMrm
umbellatum	See HALIMIUM ***umbellatum***
'Venustum Plenum' (d)	MBro WEas
'Voltaire'	EMNN ESma GAbr MDHE NHol NKay NRoo SIng WWin
'Watergate Rose'	MDHE MWat NBir NKay SIng
'Westfield Wonder'	CBot
'White Queen'	WPer
'Windermere'	SIgm
'Wisley Pink'	See H. 'Rhodanthe Carneum'
'Wisley Primrose' AGM	Widely available
'Wisley White'	CRiv CSam ECha EFol GAbr GCal LHop MBal MBro NRoo SAxl SChu SIgm SIng WHCG WHoo WRus
'Yellow Queen'	See H. 'Golden Queen'

HELIANTHUS † (Compositae/Asteraceae)

atrorubens	CBow CDoC EPla MBri WHaw
'Capenoch Star' AGM	CBow ECha EFou MUlv SDix WByw
* ***decapetalus*** 'Kastle Kobena'	CFee
– 'Maximus'	SRms
– 'Morning Sun'	CBre EMon
¶ – 'Soleil d'Or	ECtt EHic
– 'Triomphe de Gand'	CBos CBre EMon MWat WOld
'Gullick's Variety'	EMon LLWP NBro
x ***kellermanii***	EMon
§ x ***laetiflorus***	ELan EMon NOrc WCot
'Lemon Queen'	CBre CShe ECha ECtt EFou EHal EMon EPar GBuc MHlr WCot WOld

§ 'Loddon Gold' AGM — CSco ECED ECtt EFou ELan ENot MHlr NVic SFis WCot WWye
¶ *maximilianii* — EMon NPri
'Monarch' AGM — ECED EMon MFir WCot WOld
nuttallii — EMon WCot
orgyalis — See H. ***salicifolius***
quinquenervis — See HELIANTHELLA ***q.***
rigidus — See H. x ***laetiflorus***
§ *salicifolius* — ECED ECha EMon EPla MBri MHlr MSte MUlv SDix SFis SMad WHer WOld
scaberrimus — See H. ***laetiflorus***
tuberosus — NRog

HELICHRYSUM † (Compositae/Asteraceae)

acuminata — See BRACTEANTHA ***subundulata***
§ *aggregatum* — ECou
alveolatum — See H. ***splendidum***
ambiguum — LHop MPla NHar NNor NOak WDav
angustifolium — See H. ***italicum***
– Cretan Form — See H. ***italicum microphyllum***
arenarium — SSmi WHil
¶ – ssp. *aucheri* — NHar WDav
§ *argyrophyllum* — CBrk CSpe MAll SIng
§ *arwae* — EPot ESis GTou ITim LHop MHig NHed NTow SBla
asperum — See OZOTHAMNUS ***purpurascens***
basalticum — NHar SIng WDav
¶ *baxteri* — WCot
bellidioïdes — CLew CNic CShe ECha ECou ELan EPot IDai MBal MHig MTho NGre NKay NNrd WCru WOMN
bellum — LHop
bracteatum — See BRACTEANTHA ***bracteata***
* 'Coco' — IHos
confertum — ITim MHig
coralloïdes AGM — GArf MHig NWCA SIng WEas
'County Park Silver' — CMHG CRiv CSam ECou EPot ESis MSto NHar NHed NHol NTow NWCA SBla SIng WDav
dasyanthum — MHig
depressum — ECou
doerfleri — MHig
'Elmstead' — See H. ***stoechas*** 'White Barn'
ericifolium — See OZOTHAMHUS ***purpurascens***
ericoïdes — See DOLICOTHRIX ***ericoïdes***
foetidum — CHan
fontanesii — EBee EPot LHil NKay SMrm SPer WPla
frigidum — EPot ITim LBee MHig NMen NNrd NTow NWCA SBla SIng WOMN
glomeratum — See H. ***aggregratum***
gmelinii — CHan LBlm
gunnii — CSco
hookeri — ECou MHig SChu
§ *italicum* AGM — CArn CHan CShe ECha ECoo EHer ENot Effi GAbr GCHN GPoy IEde LGro LHol MBri MHew MPla NHol NKay NSti SDry WDin WEas WHCG WWat WWin
§ – ssp. *microphyllum* — CSam ECha EFol ELan ESis GBar NPri SIde SIgm WEas
– 'Nanum' — See H. ***i. microphyllum***
§ – ssp. *serotinum* — CDoC COtt EBee GPoy LHop NRar SPer SPla WAbe WPer WWeb
lanatum — See H. ***thianschanicum***
ledifolium — See OZOTHAMNUS ***ledifolius***
lobbii — ELan NGre
marginatum — See H. ***milfordiae***
microphyllum — See PLECOSTACHYS ***serpyllifolia***
§ *milfordiae* AGM — CMHG EBur EPot IDai ITim MBal MHig MWat NHar NHol NKay NNor NWCA SBla SGil SIng WAbe WOld WPat WThu
'Mo's Gold' — See H. ***argyrophyllum***
orientale — CHan NHol NKay NTow SIng WSun WThu
pagophilum — CPBP EPot
§ *petiolare* AGM — CB&S CBow CCla CHad CTre EBak ECtt ERom IHos LAbb MRav NRoo WEas WHal
– 'Aureum' — See H. ***p.*** 'Limelight'
– 'Goring Silver' — CBrk LHil LHop NPri
§ – 'Limelight' — CB&S CBow CBrk CCla CTre ECtt ERom ESma IHos LAbb MRav MUlv NPri NRoo SLon WEas WHal WWye
– 'Roundabout' (v) — CBrk ESma LHil LHop MRav NPri WEas
– 'Variegatum' AGM — CB&S CCla CTre ECtt ERom ESma IHos LAbb MRav NPri NRoo WEas WHal
petiolatum — See H. ***petiolare***
plicatum — CBrk EBar LHol WCra
plumeum — ITim MHig NWCA
populifolium — CBrk CKni EMon
praecurrens — EWes ITim NHol
rosmarinifolium — See OZOTHAMNUS ***rosmarinifolius***
'Schweffellicht' ('Sulphur Light') — CHad CMGP CSam CSco CShe CTom ECED ECha EFol EFou EOrc EPla ESis MBri MRav NFai NHol NRoo SPer SPla WEas WHal WSHC
scorpioïdes — ECou NWCA
selago — See OZOTHAMNUS ***s.***
serotinum — See H. ***italicum serotinum***
serpyllifolium — See PLECOSTACHYS ***serpyllifolia***
sessile — See H. ***sessilioïdes***
sessilioïdes — EPot ITim MHig NHar NHol NTow NWCA SBla SIng WDav
§ *sibthorpii* — EPot ITim MHig NHed NTow WAbe
siculum — See H. ***stoechas barrelieri***
§ *splendidum* AGM — CFee CHan CSco CShe ECha EOrc GAbr GCHN LHil LHol NBro NHol NNor SDix SMrm SPer SUsu WDin WEas WHer WHil WPer WWat
sp. from Drakensburg Mountains — CLew CRiv GAbr NHol NKay

stoechas	IDai
§ – ssp. ***barrelieri***	CNic
§ – 'White Barn'	ECha
'Sussex Silver'	EPla WKif
§ ***thianschanicum***	EWri NHol WPla
§ – 'Goldkind' ('Golden Baby')	NBir NMen NNrd NPri SFis WHil
thyrsoideum	See OZOTHAMNUS ***thyrsoideus***
trilineatum	See H. ***splendidum***
tumidum	See OZOTHAMNUS ***s. t.***
virgineum	See H. ***sibthorpii***
woodii	See H. ***arwae***

HELICHRYSUM X RAOULIA (Compositae/Asteraceae)

'Rivulet'	ECou
'Silver Streams'	ECou

HELICODICEROS (Araceae)

muscivorus	CMon WChr

HELICONIA (Heliconiaceae)

bihai	CTro
mariae	CNew
rostrata	CNew
stricta 'Dwarf Jamaican'	CNew

HELICTOTRICHON (Gramineae/Poaceae)

* ***alopecuroïdes***	EPla
filifolium	EPla ETPC
pratense	EMon EPla ETPC
§ ***sempervirens*** AGM	CBot CHan CKel CRow CSco ECas ECha EFol EFou EHoe ELan ERav ESiP GCal IHos MBri NBro NEgg NHol NKay NNor NSti SApp SAxl SCob SDix WEas WRus WWat WWin
– var. ***pendulum***	EMon EPla MUlv
* ***splendens***	EHic

HELIOPHILA (Cruciferae/Brassicaceae)

See Plant Deletions

HELIOPSIS † (Compositae/Asteraceae)

¶ ***helianthoïdes***	EMon
– 'Gigantea'	WCot
– 'Hohlspiegel '	ECha GCal
*– 'Limelight'	LHil SDix WEas
¶ – var. ***scabra***	WHil
– – 'Ballerina'	NBee
– – 'Goldgrünherz'	ECED EPla WCot
– – 'Light of Loddon'	MWat
– – 'Sommersonne' ('Summer Sun')	CBow CHol CMGP CSco EBre ECtt EFou GAul LBre LHop LWad MFir NFai NMir SCro SHer SPer SPla SSvw WHoo WPer WWin
– 'Sonnenglut'	MBri

HELIOTROPIUM (Boraginaceae)

amplexicaule	SWas
anchusifolium	See H. ***amplexicaule***
§ ***arborescens***	CArn CKni CSev MPit
'Chatsworth'	CBar CBrk CCla CHad CPle ERea LBlm LHil SAxl SHer SIde SSad SUsu WEas
'Gatton Park'	ERea LHil SMrm SSad
'Lord Roberts'	ERea EWoo
'Netherhall White'	ERea
'P K Lowther'	CBrk ERea WEas
peruvianum	See H. ***arborescens***
'Princess Marina'	CBrk ERea LHil SSad WEas
'The Speaker'	CBrk
'W H Lowther'	CNew
'White Lady'	CBrk ERea SSad
¶ 'White Queen'	LHil

HELIPTERUM (Compositae/Asteraceae)

albicans ssp. ***albicans incanum***	GDra
– ssp. ***alpinum***	NTow
anthemoïdes	EBee ECou

HELLEBORUS † (Ranunculaceae)

§ ***argutifolius*** AGM	Widely available
– x ***sternii***	CLCN LHil
atrorubens hort.	See H. ***orientalis abchasicus*** Early Purple Group
¶ ***atrorubens*** Waldst. & Kit WM 9317/19	MPhe
atrorubens Waldst. & Kit.	NRar WStI
– WM 9028/9101/9216	MPhe
colchicus	See H. ***orientalis abchasicus***
corsicus	See H. ***argutifolius***
cyclophyllus	CFil CRos GCal NRoo SBla SPou WAbe
¶ – JCA 560.625	CLCN
dumetorum	CFil NRar
– Croatia WM 9025	MPhe
– Hungary WM 9209/9307	MPhe
– Slovenia WM 9214/9301	MPhe
§ x ***ericsmithii***	CRDP SBla
foetidus	Widely available
– Bowles' form	CBro MPhe
– 'Chedglow'	CNat
– 'Green Giant'	CMil MPhe WCru
– Italian form	NHol WRus
¶ – 'Pontarlier'	MPhe
¶ – scented form	MPhe
– 'Sopron'	MPhe WCru
¶ – 'Tros-os-Montes'	MPhe
– Wester Flisk Group	CAvo CBos CBot CBro CRDP CSco ELan EMar EPar EPla ERav LGre MBri MFir MPhe NHol NRar NSti SBla SPer WAbb WAbe WCru WDav WFib WHoo WRus WWat
lividus AGM	CAvo CBot CBow CBro CChu CGle CHan CLCN CRDP ELan GCal GCra MUlv NHar SAxl SBla SHer WAbb
– ***corsicus***	See H. ***argutifolius***
– dwarf	SPou
multifidus	CRos NBir
– ssp. ***bocconei***	SBla WOMN
¶ – ssp. ***hercegovinus***	CAvo
– ssp. ***hercegovinus*** WM 9011/9105	MPhe

– ssp. ***istriacus***	CAvo CBro SBla
– ssp. ***istriacus*** WM 9002/9222	MPhe
¶ – ssp. ***istriacus*** WM 9321/22/24	MPhe
– ssp. ***multifidus***	SBla
– ssp. ***multifidus*** WM 9010/9104	MPhe
niger AGM	Widely available
¶ – WM 9223/27	MPhe
– Blackthorn Group	SBla SWas
– Harvington hybrids	LRHS
– 'Higham's Variety'	CGle
– 'Louis Cobbett'	CBro
– ssp. ***macranthus***	CMil NHol
– ssp. ***macranthus*** WM 9030	WCru
– 'Madame Fourcade'	MBri
– ***major***	See H. ***n. macranthus***
– 'Potter's Wheel'	CBro CChu CCla CHan CPMA ECot ELan EPad GCal MBri MHig MUlv NRar SBla SHer SPer WCru WWat
– 'Saint Brigid'	NRar
– Sunset Group WM 9113	MPhe SPla
– 'Trotter's Form'	SPou
– 'White Magic'	CPMA GDra NHol SBla SWas
x ***nigercors*** AGM	SBla
x ***nigristern***	See H. x ***ericsmithii***
odorus	CAvo CDec CFil CLCN CRos EBar GCal NRar SBla
¶ – JCA 562004	SWas
– WM 9016/9103	MPhe
– WM 9202	MPhe
– ***laxus***	See H. ***multifidus istriacus***
N ***orientalis*** hort.	Widely available
– 'Agnes Brook'	WFib
– 'Albin Otto'	EBre LBre
– 'Amethyst'	CHol
– Anderson's Red Hybrids	CLCN
– 'Angela Tandy'	WFib
– 'Baby Black'	ECot
– Ballard's Group	ECha NRar WRus
– black seedlings	CGle GDra WCru
– 'Carlton Hall'	WFib
¶ – 'Chartreuse'	MUlv
– 'Cheerful'	NBir
¶ – 'Cygnus'	ECha
– Draco strain	CLCN
– 'Elizabeth Coburn'	WFib
– 'Eric's Best'	ECha
– 'Fred Whitsey'	WFib
– Galaxy Group	SHig
– 'Gertrude Raithby'	WFib
– 'Gladys Burrow'	WFib
– ssp. ***guttatus***	CAvo CChu CHol CLCN COtt ELun MUlv SBla SHig WCot WCru
– – cream	ECha
¶ – – light purple	ECha
– – pink	ECha WCru
– 'Hades'	NBir
– Hadspen hybrids	CHad
– 'Hercules'	MUlv
– 'Ian Raithby'	WFib
– ivory	CLCN
– 'John Raithby'	WFib
– Kochii Group	ECha ELun MUlv NRar NRoo WCru WRus
– 'Lady Charlotte Bonham-Carter'	WFib
– 'Lavinia Ward'	WFib
– 'Leo'	MUlv
– 'Limelight'	ECha
– 'Little Black'	SBla WAbe WFib
– 'Mary Petit'	WFib
– 'Maureen Key'	WFib
– Midnight Sky Group	WWat
– 'Pebworth White'	WFib
– 'Philip Ballard'	CHol
– 'Philip Wilson'	CHol
– pink	CLCN CPMA CRDP WCru
– 'Plum Stippled'	ECha
– purple	CLCN CRDP ECha NHol WCru
¶ – 'Queen of the Night'	CRDP
– 'Sirius'	SHig
– 'Trotter's Spotted'	GDra
– 'Victoria Raithby'	WFib
– white	CGle ECha MBal WCru
– Zodiac Group	CLCN SHig
orientalis Lamarck	MPhe SPou SWas
– JCA 562.402	CLCN
§ – ssp. ***abchasicus***	CAvo CDec GCra MBri NRoo WCru
– – Early Purple Group	CBow CLCN CSco ECha ELun IDai LBuc NBee SCro SHig
– ***olympicus***	See H. ***o. orientalis***
– ssp. ***orientalis***	SPou WWat
purpurascens	CAvo CBow CHad CRos ECha LWad NBir NRar SPou SWas WSHC
¶ – WM 9303	MPhe
– Hungary WM 9208/9211	MPhe
x ***sternii***	CBos CBot CBow CChu CCla CElw CHol CLCN CRDP EGol ELan EPot GCal MBal MFir NBar NHar NHol SBla SBod SMad SUsu SWas WAbe WEas WHal WRus WWat
– Blackthorn Group AGM	CChu CDec CPMA CRos ECha EHar MBri MUlv NRar SBla WByw WCru WWat
– 'Boughton Beauty'	CAvo CB&S CBro ECha LGre MTho NHol NRar SFar WCot
– Boughton Group	CBot MUlv WCru
– dwarf form	SWas
torquatus	CAvo CBro CFil CLCN CRos NRar SPou WCot WDav WMer
– BM 5279	SPou
– Bosnia WM 9003/9111	MPhe
– hybrids	SBla WCru
– Montenegro WM 9106	MPhe
– Party Dress Group (d)	SBla
¶ – Wolverton Hybrids	SBla
viridis	ECha LWad SBla SRms WCot WCru WStI
– ssp. ***occidentalis***	CAvo CBro MPhe SBla

HELONIOPSIS (Liliaceae/Melanthiaceae)

japonica	See H. ***orientalis***
§ ***orientalis***	CTom EPot WCru
§ – var. ***breviscapa***	CFil SWas WCru WThi
– var. ***yakusimensis***	See H. ***o. breviscapa***

HELWINGIA (Helwingiaceae)

himalaica EMon
japonica CBot GWht LGre WWat

HELXINE See SOLEIROLIA

HEMEROCALLIS †
(Liliaceae/Hemerocallidaceae)

'Added Dimensions' SApp
¶ 'Addie Branch Smith' EGol
'Admiral' MAus
'Adoration' SPer
'Alan' CKel SCro SHig
¶ 'Albany' SApp
¶ 'Alec Allen' SRos
¶ *altissima* EMon
'Amadeus' SApp
'Ambassador' CKel
'Amber Star' LMay
¶ 'American Revolution' EBee SApp
*x *andersonii* 'Nancy Saunders' SMrm
'Angel Flight' MAus
'Anne Welch' EPla
'Anzac' CB&S ECha ECtt EPla ERou GAri MBlu MSta NBee NHol NMir WCot WTyr
'Apricot Beauty' NPri WHil WTyr
¶ 'Apricotta' CKel
'Artistic Gold' EGol
¶ 'Asian Pheasant' SApp
'Atalanta Bouquet' SApp SRos
'Aurora' WAbe
'Autumn Red' CBow ERou NCat NFai
'Back Bay' MAus
'Ballet Dancer' ERou
'Baroni' ECha
'Battle Hymn' MAus
'Beauty Bright' MAus
¶ 'Beauty to Behold' SApp SRos
'Bejewelled' EGol EPla MSta
'Beloved Returns' MAus
¶ 'Bertie Ferris' SSte
'Bess Ross' CMHG MAus
'Bess Vestale' EBee ECas ERou MWat NHol
¶ 'Betty Woods' (d) SApp SRos SSte
'Bibury' SCro
'Black Knight' SRms
'Black Magic' CBro CHad CMGP CSev ECED ECas EGol ELan EPla ERou GMac LHop MAus MBri MRav NHol SHer SPer WHal
'Black Prince' CBow
'Blushing Belle' WWin
'Bold Courtier' CKel EFol MAus
¶ 'Bold One' SRos
'Bonanza' CBro CCla CKel CMGP CSco CTom EBre ECas ECha ECtt EHon ELan EPla ERou LBre MAus MBri MRav NBee NBro NCat NFai NHol SChu SHig SPer WAbe WTyr WWin
'Bourbon King' EGol EPla ERou MBel
§ 'Brass Buckles' EGol
'Brass Cup' MAus
'Bright Banner' MAus
'Bright Spangles' SApp SRos
'Brunette' SApp
'Burlesque' CKel
'Burning Daylight' CB&S CMGP CSco EBre EPla ERou LBre LHop MAus MBel MHlr NBar NHol NVic SPer WOld
'Buttons' CShe
'Buzz Bomb' CCla ECas SHig SPer SRos SSte
'By Jove' MAus
¶ 'California Sunshine' SRos
¶ 'Camden Gold Dollar' SApp
'Canary Glow' EBre LBre NCat SRos WWat
'Captured Heart' MAus
'Caramea' NFai WHil
'Cartwheels' **AGM** CRiv EBee ECha MAus MBel MMil NFai SApp SPer
¶ 'Casino Gold' SRos
'Catherine Wheel' NBir
'Catherine Woodbery' CCla CLew COtt CSev EBre ECtt EGol ELan EPla LBre MRav MSta NBar NCat NFai SApp SAxl SPer SSte WCot WCra
¶ 'Caviar' SSte
¶ 'Charles Johnston' SRos
¶ 'Charlie Brown' SSte
¶ 'Charlie Pierce Memorial' MBel
'Chartreuse Magic' CRiv EGol EPla NHol SPer
¶ 'Cheek to Cheek' CB&S
'Cherry Cheeks' CB&S CKel EBre ECtt EGol ELan EPla ERou LBre MAus MRav SRos SSte WCot WCra WTyr
¶ 'Cherry Kiss' SRos
'Chic Bonnet' SPer
'Chicago Apache' MBel SApp SRos SSte
¶ 'Chicago Fire' EGol
'Chicago Petticoats' EGol
'Chicago Picotee Queen' LRHS MBri MTol
'Chicago Royal Robe' EGol EPla MBel MSta MUlv WCot WWin
'Chicago Sunrise' EGol EPla LWad MSta NHol NOrc SMrm SRos SSte WMer
'Chief Sarcoxie' MAus
'Children's Festival' CHad CMGP CWes EBee ECtt EGol LWad MBel NHol SMrm SRos WAbe WHil WRus
¶ 'Chinese Autumn' SRos
'Chinese Coral' CKel
'Chloe's Child' SCro
'Chorus Line' MBel SRos
'Christmas Candles' MAus
citrina ELan EMon SPla
'Classic Simplicity' MAus
¶ 'Claudine' SApp
'Colonial Dame' CKel
¶ 'Coming up Roses' SRos
'Conspicua' CShe CWGN
'Constitutional Island' MAus
'Contessa' CBro ELan SCro SPer
¶ 'Cool Jazz' SRos
'Corky' **AGM** EBul ECha GCal MBel SChu SDix SPer
'Countess Zora' MAus
'Cream Drop' CBow CHad CMGP CWes ECtt EFou EGol LWad MBel NHol NOrc SMrm WAbe WHow WMer WRus
'Crimson Pirate' ERou
'Croesus' MAus NHol SCro SRms

'Croftway'	SCro
'Crumpet'	SApp
¶ 'Curly Ripples'	SApp
¶ 'Dainty Pink'	CB&S
¶ 'Dance Ballerina Dance'	SRos
'Dark Elf'	SSte
'Dawn Play'	CKel
'Decatur Imp'	EGol
¶ 'Decatur Piecrust'	MBel
'Devon Cream'	SPer
¶ 'Devonshire'	SRos
'Diamond Dust'	CRiv SApp SPer
'Dido'	CSco ERou GBuc
¶ 'Display'	CKel
'Dominic'	SApp SRos
'Dorcas'	MAus
¶ 'Dorethe Louise'	SSte
'Dorothy McDade'	EGol
'Double Cutie'	SApp
¶ 'Double Oh Seven'	SSte
'Double Pleasure'	MBel
'Down Town'	MAus
'Dresden Doll'	SPer
'Dresden Gleam'	CRiv
§ 'Dubloon'	CKel CMGP EBul ERou GAbr GBuc MAus NHol
dumortieri	CAvo CBot CBro CCla CDec EBre EBul ECha EFou EGol ELan EMon EOrc EPla LBre MAus MUlv MWat NHol NSti NVic SHig SPer
¶ 'Ed Murray'	SRos
'Edna Spalding'	SRos
'Eenie Weenie'	CB&S CBow CBro CFee CKel CWes ECtt EGol LWad MBel NHol NOrc SApp SMrm SSte WMer WRus
¶ 'Eenie Weenie Non-stop'	ECha SWas
'Elaine Strutt'	WCot
'Esther Walker'	CKel
'Evelyn Claar'	CKel SCro
¶ 'Fairy Frosting'	SSte
¶ 'Fairy Tale Pink'	MBel SApp SRos
'Fairy Wings'	SAxl
¶ 'Faith Nabor'	SRos
'Fandango'	SPer
'Fashion Model'	CKel
'Feelings'	SApp
'Felicity'	CKel
¶ 'Femme Osage'	SRos
'Fire Dance'	SCro
¶ 'Fire Music'	SApp
'First Formal'	SPer
¶ 'Flames of Fantasy'	CKel SRos
flava	See H. ***lilioasphodelus***
'Folklore'	MAus
'Frances Fay'	SRos
¶ 'Francis Russell'	CKel
'Frans Hals'	CBre COtt EPla ERou MBri MRav NFai NPri SPer SPla SRos WHal WHil WHoo WTyr
'Fresh Air'	SApp
¶ 'Frosty White'	SApp
'Full Reward'	MAus
fulva	CBos CRow CWGN ELan EPla NCat NHol SChu SHig WWin
N– 'Flore Pleno'	Widely available
N– 'Green Kwanso'	EMon
– 'Kwanzo Variegata'	CBot CChu CGle ELan EMon EPla LHop MTho NBir WCot WFox
'Garnet Garland'	CKel
'Gateway'	MAus
* 'Gay Nineteen'	CKel
¶ 'Gay Nineties'	CKel
'Gay Rapture'	SPer
'Gay Troubadour'	CKel
¶ 'Gemini'	SSte
¶ 'Gentle Country Breeze'	SRos
'Gentle Shepherd'	SApp SRos
'George Cunningham'	CLew CMGP CRiv CSev EBre ECas ECtt EFol EGol ELan EPla ERou LBre MAus MBri SChu SGil WAbb
'Giant Moon'	EBre EGol ELan EPla ERou LBre MBri MUlv SAxl SPer WHal WRus
'Gingerbread Man'	SSte
'Glowing Gold'	MAus
'Gold Imperial'	CBow CShe
'Golden Bell'	NHol SChu
'Golden Chance'	CCla MAus
'Golden Chimes' **AGM**	Widely available
'Golden Gate'	SHig
'Golden Ginko'	LRHS MBri
'Golden Orchid'	See H. 'Dubloon'
'Golden Peace'	SApp
'Golden Prize'	EBre EPla LBre SApp SRos
¶ 'Golden Scroll'	SRos
¶ 'Grape Magic'	EGol
'Green Chartreuse'	ECha
'Green Drop'	WTyr
'Green Flutter'	CSev ECas EWll NBir SApp SAsh SRos SSte
'Green Magic'	EPla MAus NSti
'Grumbly'	EBee ELan
'Gusto'	MAus
'Halo Light'	CKel SPer
¶ 'Happy Returns'	ECha EGol SApp
¶ 'Hawaian Punch'	EGol
'Heartthrob'	MAus
'Heaven Knows'	MAus
'Heirloom Lace'	MAus
'Helios'	CSco SHig
¶ 'Helle Berlinerin'	SApp
'Her Majesty'	CKel
¶ 'Hey There'	SRos
'High Time'	SMrm
¶ 'High Tor'	GCal
'Holiday Mood'	ELan ERou SGil
¶ 'Honey Redhead'	CKel
¶ 'Hope Diamond'	SSte
'Hornby Castle'	CBro EBre LBre NHol NVic
¶ 'Hot Ticket'	SRos
¶ 'Humdinger'	SRos
'Hyperion'	CCla CMGP CShe EBre ECED ECtt EGol GAri LBre LHop MRav NBar NHol NRoo SChu SPer SUsu WOld
'Ice Castles'	SSte
'Ice Cool'	SApp
'Imperator'	CWGN EPla LMay NHol
¶ 'Imperial Blush'	CKel
¶ 'Inspired Word'	SRos
¶ 'Invictus'	SRos
'Iron Gate Glacier'	EPla

'Iron Gate Iceberg'	SSte
¶ 'Jedi Dot Pearce'	SRos
'Jo Jo'	MAus WWin
'Joan Senior'	EGol EPla MBel SApp SRos SSte
'Judah'	SApp SRos
'Kelly's Girl'	SRos SSte
'Kelway's Gold'	CKel
¶ 'Kindly Light'	SRos
N 'Kwanso Flore Pleno'	See H. ***fulva*** 'Green Kwanso'
N 'Kwanso Flore Pleno Variegata'	See H. ***fulva*** 'Kwanzo Variegata'
¶ 'Lady Cynthia'	CKel
'Lady Inora Cubiles'	MAus
¶ 'Lady Mischief'	SSte
¶ 'Lady of Leisure'	MBel
'Lark Song'	CKel COtt EGol
'Lavender Bonanza'	MAus
'Lemon Bells'	SApp
¶ 'Lemon Ice'	CKel
¶ 'Lenox'	SRos
'Lilac Wine'	ECha NHol WMer
§ ***lilioasphodelus*** AGM	CAvo CBos CBre CGle CHad CHan CRDP CTom EBul ECha ELan EMon EPla GCal LGan MBro MFir NHol NTow SApp SAxl SDix SHig SMad SPer SPla SUsu WHal WHil WHoo
'Linda'	CMGP ERou MAus NHol
'Little Beige Magic'	EGol
¶ 'Little Big Man'	SSte
¶ 'Little Bumble Bee'	EGol
¶ 'Little Business'	SSte
'Little Cameo'	EGol
'Little Cranberry Cove'	EGol
¶ 'Little Dandy'	EGol
¶ 'Little Dart'	ECha
'Little Deeke'	SApp SRos
'Little Fat Dazzler'	SApp
'Little Grapette'	EGol SApp SRos
'Little Gypsy Vagabond'	SRos SSte
'Little Lavender Princess'	EGol
'Little Maggie'	SSte
'Little Men'	MAus
'Little Sally'	EGol
¶ 'Little Toddler'	SSte
'Little Wart'	EGol
'Little Wine Cup'	CBow ECtt EFou EGol LWad MAus MBel NHol NOrc SApp SSte WHil WTyr
¶ 'Little Zinger'	SSte
'Lotus Land'	CKel
'Lowenstine'	SApp
¶ 'Lukey Boy'	CMHG
'Lullaby Baby'	EGol SRos
¶ ***luna***	GMac WFox
'Lusty Leland'	SApp
'Luxury Lace'	CDec COtt EBre EFol EFou EGol ELan EOrc EPla LBre MAus MBel MSta MUlv SPer
'Lynn Hall'	EGol
'Mabel Fuller'	SCro SPer
¶ 'Malaysian Monarch'	MBel
'Mallard'	COtt EBre ECtt EGol EPla LBre MBri MRav MUlv SApp SRos WCot WCra WMer
¶ 'Manchurian Apricot'	SRos
¶ 'Marion Moss'	CKel
'Marion Vaughn' AGM	CCla CLew CMGP EBre ECas ECot EGol EPla LBre MMil MUlv NSti SChu SDix WCot
'Mary Todd'	EGol
'Mavoureen Nesmith'	SCro
'May Colven'	EGol
¶ 'Meadow Gold'	CKel
'Meadow Sprite'	SSte
'Melody Lane'	EGol
'Meno'	EGol
middendorffii	EBul EMon GDra MAus
'Mikado'	GAul
¶ 'Millie Schlumpf'	SRos
'Ming Porcelain'	SRos
'Mini Pearl'	EGol
'Mini Stella'	CBro EPla SApp SSte
Miniature hybrids	SRms WPer
minor	CBro CCla EGol SApp SPla SRms
¶ 'Missenden'	SMrm
¶ 'Missouri Beauty'	CRos
'Misty'	MAus
¶ 'Monica Marie'	SRos
¶ 'Moonlight Mist'	SApp SSte
'Morocco Red'	CBro CCla COtt CWGN EFol ELan GGar MAus WWat
¶ 'Mosel'	SSte
'Mount Joy'	SPer
'Mountain Laurel'	LRHS MBri MUlv
'Mrs David Hall'	CKel SCro SMrm
'Mrs Hugh Johnson'	CHad CMGP ECas ECot EHon NHol SUsu
'Mrs John J Tigert'	CSco ERou
'Mrs Lester'	CKel
multiflora	CCla NHol SHig
'My Happy Valentine'	SApp
¶ 'Naomi Ruth'	EGol
'Nashville'	CBro ELan ERou SGil
'Neyron Rose' AGM	EGol EPla ERou SPer
'Night Raider'	SApp SRos
'Nigrette'	LMay MUlv MWat NHol
'Nina Winegar'	SApp
'Nob Hill'	EGol SRos
¶ 'Norton Beauté'	MBel
¶ 'Nova'	SApp
'Olive Bailey Langdon'	EGol SRos
¶ 'Oom-pa-pa'	ECha
'Open Hearth'	SApp
¶ 'Optic Elegance'	SAsh
'Orangeman'	CBow CDoC EBee SMrm
'Orford'	WWin
'Ozark Lass'	MAus
'Paige Parker'	EGol
'Painted Lady'	CKel
'Pandora's Box'	EGol SApp SSte
'Paradise Prince'	EGol
'Pardon Me'	EGol SApp SSte
'Party Partner'	MAus
'Pastel Accent'	SApp
¶ 'Pastel Ballerina'	SRos
'Peaceful'	MAus
¶ 'Penelope Vestey'	SApp
¶ 'Penny's Worth'	EGol SSte
'Persian Princess'	CKel
'Persian Shrine'	EGol
¶ 'Piccadilly Princess'	MBel

'Pink Charm'	CCla CMGP CWGN ECas LMay MAus MBal MWat NHol NOrc WCra WHil WTyr
'Pink Damask' AGM	CBow CCla CKel CSco CShe CTom CWGN EBre EBul ECED ECha EFou EHon ELan LBre LGro MAus MBel MBri MFir MWat NHol SAxl SChu SCro SPer SRos WEas WHal
'Pink Dream'	ECas NHol
'Pink Heaven'	EGol
¶ 'Pink Interlude'	CKel
'Pink Lady'	ERou SPer SRms
¶ 'Pink Opal'	CKel
'Pink Prelude'	EWll NHol SChu
¶ 'Pink Salute'	SRos
'Pink Snowflake'	MAus
'Pink Sundae'	ECha
¶ 'Pink Super Spider'	SRos
¶ 'Piquante'	EBee
'Pixie Pipestone'	SApp
'Pojo'	SSte
'Pony'	EGol
'Prairie Bells'	NFai WHoo
'Prairie Blue Eyes'	CB&S EGol SSte
'Premier'	MAus
'Prima Donna'	CKel SCro
'Primrose Mascotte'	NBir WCot
♦ 'Puddin'	See H. 'Brass Buckles'
¶ 'Pumkin Kid'	SRos
¶ 'Pumpkin Face'	EGol
¶ 'Purple Rain'	SApp
¶ 'Pursuit of Excellence'	SRos
'Queen of May'	WCot
¶ 'Quick Results'	SRos
¶ 'Quietness'	SRos
¶ 'Raindrop'	EGol
'Rajah'	GAul MBel NBro NCat WFox
'Rare China'	CMHG
¶ 'Raspberry Sundae'	CB&S
¶ 'Raspberry Wine'	ECha
'Red Joy'	SApp
'Red Precious' AGM	EGol MBel SAsh
'Red Torch'	CKel CSco
'Revolute'	MAus
'Romany'	LMay
¶ 'Rosavel'	CB&S
¶ 'Rose Emily'	SRos
¶ 'Royal Corduroy'	MBel
'Royal Ruby'	CSco
'Royalty'	CKel EBul
'Ruffled Apricot'	SRos
'Ruffled Pinafore'	CCla
'Russell Prichard'	ERou
'Saladin'	EBul
'Salmon Sheen'	CKel
'Sammy Russell'	CMGP CWGN ECas EGol EOrc EPla GMac LHop MAus MBal MBro NBro NFai NHol SBod WCra WFox WHer
'Sandra Walker'	EGol
¶ 'Satin Clouds'	EGol
¶ 'Satin Glow'	ECha
'Scarlet Flame'	ECha
¶ 'Scarlet Orbit'	SRos
'Scarlet Tanager'	LRHS MUlv WMer
'Screech Owl'	LRHS WMer
¶ 'Searcy Marsh'	EGol
¶ 'Sebastian'	SRos
¶ 'Serena Sunburst'	MBel
'Shooting Star'	EGol SPla
'Silent World'	MAus
'Silken Fairy'	EGol
¶ 'Siloam Angel Blush'	SSte
'Siloam Baby Talk'	EGol SSte
'Siloam Bo Peep'	EGol SApp SSte
'Siloam Button Box'	EGol
'Siloam Byelo'	EGol
¶ 'Siloam Cinderella'	EGol
¶ 'Siloam Double Classic'	MBel
¶ 'Siloam Ethel Smith'	SSte
'Siloam Fairy Tale'	EGol SSte
¶ 'Siloam Little Girl'	EGol
¶ 'Siloam Pee Wee'	EGol
'Siloam Pink Glow'	EGol
¶ 'Siloam Pink Petite'	EGol
'Siloam Prissy'	EGol SApp
'Siloam Purple Plum'	EGol
¶ 'Siloam Queen's Toy'	SApp
¶ 'Siloam Red Toy'	EGol
¶ 'Siloam Red Velvet'	EGol
¶ 'Siloam Ribbon Candy'	EGol
'Siloam Rose Dawn'	SRos
¶ 'Siloam Show Girl'	EGol
'Siloam Sugar Time'	EGol
¶ 'Siloam Tee Tiny'	EGol
'Siloam Tiny Mite'	EGol
¶ 'Siloam Toddler'	EGol
'Siloam Tom Thumb'	EGol
'Siloam Ury Winniford'	EGol SApp SSte
'Siloam Virginia Henson'	EGol
¶ 'Silver Veil'	SApp
'Sirius'	MWat NHol
'Snow Elf'	SApp
¶ 'Solano Bulls Eye'	SApp
'Solid Scarlet'	CSco
'Song Sparrow'	CBro SApp
'Sound of Music'	MAus
'Spanish Gold'	CSco
¶ 'Sparkling Dawn'	MBel
¶ 'Spiderman'	SRos
'Stafford'	CMGP CSco EBre ECED ECtt EFou ELan EPla ERou LBre LGro LHop MBel MBri NBrk NHol NOrc SApp SChu SGil SHig SPer SRos WCra
'Starling'	EGol
'Stella de Oro' AGM	Widely available
¶ 'Sugar Cookie'	SSte
'Summer Interlude'	MAus
'Summer Wine'	CMGP CRos EBee EGol EPla LRHS MUlv NFai NPri WCot WCra WHoo
¶ 'Superlative'	SRos
'Sweet Refrain'	CBot
'Tasmania'	SPer
¶ 'Techny Spider'	SRos
¶ 'Teenager'	EGol
'Tejas'	CSco EBee
'Telstar'	CSco
'Thumbelina'	ECha
§ ***thunbergii***	EBul EPla MAus SApp
'Tom Collins'	SApp
¶ 'Tom Wise'	SRos
¶ 'Tonia Gay'	SApp SRos SSte

¶ 'Tootsie Rose'	SApp
'Towhead'	EGol LRHS MAus MUlv WMer
'Toyland'	CMGP CRDP EBee LRHS
'Triple Treat'	CCla MAus
'Twenty Third Psalm'	WHal
'Varsity'	COtt EBre EGol LBre NBir SApp SPer SRos
¶ 'Vesper Song'	SApp
vespertina	See H. ***thunbergii***
'Vicountess Byng'	SFis SHig
'Victoria Aden'	CBro
'Virgin's Blush'	SPer
'Wally Nance'	LRHS
'Water Witch'	EGol
'Waxwing'	CKel
¶ 'Wee Chalice'	EGol
'Whichford' AGM	CBro EBre ECtt EGol ELan LBre NHol SGil SHig WWin
¶ 'Whiskey on Ice'	SApp
¶ 'White Dish'	EGol
¶ 'White Temptation'	MBel
¶ 'Whooperie'	MBel
'Wild Welcome'	MAus
¶ 'Windsong'	SApp
'Windsor Tan'	MAus
¶ 'Wine Bubbles'	EGol
'Winnetka'	MAus
'Winnie the Pooh'	MAus SApp
¶ 'Winsome Lady'	ECha
'Wishing Well'	SChu WCot
'Woodbury'	WRus
'World of Peace'	MAus
¶ 'Wynn'	MBel
¶ 'Yellow Petticoats'	SApp
'Yellow Rain'	SAsh WCot
'Young Countess'	MAus
'Zara'	CRiv SPer

HEMIPHRAGMA (Scrophulariaceae)

See Plant Deletions

HEMIZYGIA (Labiatae/Lamiaceae)

¶ *obermeyerae*	CSpe

HEPATICA † (Ranunculaceae)

acutiloba	CBro EPar LAma NGar NHol NKay WChr WCru
americana	CArn CBro CRDP LAma NGar NHol WChr WCru
angulosa	See H. ***transsilvanica***
¶ *maxima*	EPot
x *media* 'Ballardii' AGM	IBlr NBir NGar SPou
§ *nobilis* AGM	Widely available
– blue	MS&S NGar NHar NSla SBla SPou SRms SWas WAbe
– double pink	See H. ***n.*** 'Rubra Plena'
– 'Elkofener Heidi'	SPou
¶ – 'Elkofener Micky'	SPou
¶ – 'Elkofener Resi'	SPou
¶ – 'Elkofener Schrei'	SPou
– var. *japonica*	CBro CRDP EPar LAma NGar NHol SHer WChr WOMN WWat
– lilac	NSla SWas
– pink	CNic ELan MS&S NGar SBla SPou SWas WChr
§ – 'Rubra Plena'	LHop MBri NBir NGar SPou
– white	CNic ELan MHig MS&S NGar NHol SBla SPou
§ *transsilvanica* AGM	CAvo CBro CCMG CHad CRDP EBre ELan EPar EPla EPot GDra LBee LBre LHop MBri MBro MS&S MWat NGar NHar NHol NKay SBla SPou WChr WCru
– *alba*	NGar SPou
¶ – 'Buis'	CAvo
¶ – 'Eisvogel'	NGar
– 'Elison Spence'	NGar
¶ – forms	SPou
– 'Lilacina'	NGar
– 'Loddon Blue'	NGar
– 'Nivea'	NGar
– pink	SPou
triloba	See H. ***nobilis***

X HEPPIMENES (Gesneriaceae)

I 'Purple Queen '	NMos

HEPTACODIUM (Caprifoliaceae)

jasminoïdes	CBot CChu CFil CPle ERav GCal SMad
¶ *miconioïdes*	COtt

HEPTAPLEURUM See SCHEFFLERA

HERACLEUM (Umbelliferae/Apiaceae)

mantegazzianum	CRow MFir WOak
minimum roseum	ELan MSte MTho NGre SIgm WEas WOMN WPat

HERBERTIA (Iridaceae)

lahue	LBee WThi
pulchella	WThi

HERMANNIA (Sterculiaceae)

candicans	See H. ***incana***
§ *depressa* S&SH 12	CHan
♦ *erodioïdes*	See H. ***depressa***
incana	CBrk
§ *pinnata*	LHop SSad
♦ *verticillata*	See H. ***pinnata***

HERMODACTYLUS (Iridaceae)

§ *tuberosus*	CAvo CBro CChu CCla CMea CMil CMon ECha ELan ERav LAma LBow MSto NRog SCro SIng SUsu WHal WHil
– MS 976/762	CMon

HERNIARIA (Illecebraceae)

glabra	CLew EPar GBar GPoy LHol MHew MSal NCat NHol NPri WHer WWye

HERPOLIRION (Liliaceae/Anthericaceae)

See Plant Deletions

HERTIA See OTHONNA

HESPERALOË (Agavaceae)

¶ *funifera*	CTbh
¶ *parviflora*	CTbh SIgm

– 'Rubra' SArc

HESPERANTHA (Iridaceae)

buhrii See H. ***cucullata*** 'Rubra'
§ *cucullata* 'Rubra' NWCA SUsu
huttonii GBuc GCal MFir
moysii WHal

HESPERIS † (Cruciferae/Brassicaceae)

lutea See SISYMBRIUM ***luteum***
matronalis CArn CCMG CCla CGle CHol CRow CSFH CSev EBar ECWi ECoo EEls EFou EHer ELan EWFC LHol MHew NBee NBrk SIde SSte SSvw WBon WCla WHer WOak WPer WWye
♦– *alba* See H. ***m. candida***
§– *candida* CBot CCMG CCla CLew CRDP EFou EMar EPad MFir SMrm SPer SSvw WCot
– – 'Alba Plena' CRDP LHol MHlr SMrm WCot WRus
– double form ELan MBri WCru
– 'Lilacina Flore Pleno' CBos CBot CBow CGle CHad CMil CRDP CSco EMon LBlm MBel NBir NBrk NSti
* *sylviniana* WPer

HETEROCENTRON (Melastomataceae)

§ *elegans* CB&S CTre

HETEROMELES See PHOTINIA

HETEROPAPPUS (Compositae/Asteraceae)

altaicus WPer

HETEROTHECA (Compositae/Asteraceae)

villosa CRDP ECha EMon

HEUCHERA † (Saxifragaceae)

§ *americana* CBow CRDP CRow CShe EBar ECha EFol EFou EOrc EPar GBar LHil MNFA MSal MUlv NBir SCro SHer WDav WEas WHal WThu WWat
'Apple Blossom' CSco
Bressingham hybrids CBow CMGP EBre EFou GDra LBre LHil LWad MBri MUlv NBir NHol NMir NOak SCro SFis SHer SPer SPla WHoo WPer WWin
x *brizoïdes* 'Gracillima' CGle
'Cherry Red' ECha
chlorantha NHol
Coral Bells See H. ***sanguinea***
'Coral Cloud' CB&S CKel EBre ENot GCHN IDai LBre
cylindrica EBar GCHN GCra LBlm MBel MSte WWin
– var. *alpina* CLew NGre NHol
– 'Chartreuse' CGle
– 'Greenfinch' CB&S CGle CKel CRow CSco CWGN ECha ECtt EFol EGol ELan EPla GCal GTou NBro NCat NHol NOrc NSti SApp SMad WCla WEas WHal WHer WKif WPbr WWat
– 'Hyperion' CSco EBre LBre MBal MNFA MUlv
♦'Dennis Davidson' See H. 'Huntsman'
'Dingle Mint Chocolate' EFol
'Firebird' CKel CSco ELan MBal MNFA NVic
'Firefly' CBow CCla CHol ECha EFou EPla ESis ESma GAul MFir MRav NBar NBrk NFai NMir NOrc NRoo NWyt SCro SFis SPer SPla WHoo WPer
glauca See H. ***americana***
'Green Ivory' CCla CGle CMil CWGN EBre EFou EGol EHal ELan ELun GCHN LBre MBal MBel MBri MNFA MRav MUlv NCat SHer SPer
grossulariifolia EPla LBuc MTho NHar NPri SGil WCot WPer
¶ *hallii* NHol
hispida LRHS MSte NHol SMad WBon WCra
§ 'Huntsman' CGle ECha ELan EPla SMad
* *maritima* SIng
'Mary Rose' CSco
* *micans* NHar SIng WDav WThi WThu
micrantha CTom ELan GGar LBlm SRms WHaw
– JLS 86275CLOR EMon
– var. *diversifolia* NHol
– – 'Bressingham Bronze' CDoC
N– – 'Palace Purple' **AGM** Widely available
¶ – 'Eco Magnifica' WCot
¶ – 'Persian Carpet' WCot
¶ – 'Pewter Veil' WCot
* 'Moondrops' CRow
'Mother of Pearl' ECha
¶ 'Painted Lady' COtt SPla
parvifolia GCal
'Pewter Moon' Widely available
pilosissima GPlt WCot
'Pluie de Feu' GCal WTyr
'Pretty Polly' ENot MHFP
pringlei WHil WPer
pubescens GCHN LBee
– 'Alba' GBur WCot WHoo WSun WThi
pulchella ESis LGre MFir NRed NSla SBla
– JCA 9508 CRDP NHol
'Rachel' Widely available
'Red Spangles' **AGM** CBow CGle CKel EBre EPla GCHN LBre NBir SRms
richardsonii ECED
rubescens ELan GArf MTho NHar WWin
¶ *rubra* 'Redstart' SUsu
'Ruffles' CRow
§ *sanguinea* CGle CMea CNic GCHN MBal NBar NNor NRoo SPla WByw WHal WPer WPla
¶ – 'Alba' EMon
¶ – 'White Cloud' WHil
'Schneewittchen' (v) ECha EFou EPla WMer
'Scintillation' **AGM** CB&S CKel CSco EBre ECED GCHN LBre SRms
'Silver Veil' CRow
'Snow Storm' (v) Widely available
'Sparkler' (v) CKel
'Taff's Joy' (v) CRow EFol LHop MBel MHlr MTho WCot
versicolor GCal
villosa CElw ECha GCHN MRav

¶ – 'Royal Red'	ECha
'Widar'	NHol SAxl

X HEUCHERELLA (Saxifragaceae)

alba 'Bridget Bloom'	Widely available
– 'Rosalie'	CBos CDec CGle CLew CMHG CSco ECha MBri SUsu SWas WHal
tiarelloïdes AGM	CMGP EBar EBee EFol ELan MNFA NCat NFai NNor NSti SAxl SPer

X HIBANOBAMBUSA (Gramineae/Poaceae-Bambusoideae)

tranquillans	EFul EPla SDry WJun
– 'Shiroshima' (v)	EPla ISta SDry WJun

HIBBERTIA (Dilleniaceae)

aspera	CGre CPle LBlm LHil
cuneiformis	CGre CPle ERea
dentata	SLMG
procumbens	ESis ITim SBla
§ *scandens* AGM	CGre CHEx CPle CSpe CTro ECou ERea LAbb LBlm WBod
tetrandra	See H. ***cuneiformis***
volubilis	See H. ***scandens***

HIBISCUS † (Malvaceae)

¶ *biseptus*	MSto
¶ *cardiophyllus*	MSto
coccineus	MSte MSto
fallax	CTro
geranioïdes	LBlm
¶ 'Hawaian Girl'	CTro
huegelii	See ALYOGYNE ***h.***
leopoldii	SRms
* *moesiana*	MBri
'Morning Glory'	CNew
moscheutos	CArn CHan MSte MSto
¶ *pedunculatus*	CTro
rosa-sinensis	EBak MBri SLMG
¶ – 'American Beauty'	CTro
¶ – 'Brilliant'	CTro
– 'Casablanca'	MBri
– 'Cooperi'	CNew CTro
– 'El Capitolio'	CNew
– 'Full Moon'	CNew
– 'Helene'	MBri
– 'Herm Geller'	CNew
– 'Holiday'	MBri
– 'Kardinal'	MBri
– 'Koeniger'	MBri
– 'Rose of China'	MBri
¶ – 'Ross Estey'	CTro
– 'Tivoli'	MBri
– 'Weekend'	CNew MBri
rubis	ELan
schizopetalus AGM	CNew CTro SLMG
sinosyriacus 'Autumn Surprise'	SHil
– 'Lilac Queen'	SHil
* – 'Red Centre'	CBot
– 'Ruby Glow'	MGos
¶ *storckii*	CTro
syriacus	CHEx WOMN
– 'Admiral Dewey'	CCla
– 'Ardens' (d)	ELan MRav SGil SPer
– 'Blue Bird'	See H. ***s.*** 'Oiseau Bleu'
– 'Coelestis'	SPer
– 'Diana' AGM	CSco EPla
– 'Dixie Belle'	LHop
– 'Dorothy Crane'	ENot
– 'Duc de Brabant' (d)	CBow SHBN SRms
– 'Elegantissimus'	See H. ***s.*** 'Lady Stanley'
– 'Hamabo' AGM	CBow CBra CDoC ELan ENot IHos MBri MGos MRav MWat SGil SHBN SPer SPla SReu WStI
– 'Jeanne d'Arc' (d)	CBot
§ – 'Lady Stanley' (d)	ECtt EHic NWyt SGil SPer SPla
– 'Meehanii' (v)	EGol NWyt
– 'Monstrosus'	IOrc
§ – 'Oiseau Bleu' ('Blue Bird') AGM	CB&S CBow CBra CCla CDoC CSco CShe ELan ENot EPla IHos IOrc MBri MGos MWat NBee NWyt SChu SGil SHBN SHer SPer SPla SReu WDin WStI WTyr
– Pink Giant ® AGM	CB&S CBow EBee ELan NWyt SGil SHer SPer WDin
– 'Red Heart' AGM	CBow CCla CDoC CSco ECtt ELan MRav MWat NWyt SHer SPer WDin WStI WWeb
– 'Russian Violet'	CBow CBra CCla CDoC CSco ELan MRav NWyt SGil SHer WWeb
– 'Speciosus'	SPer
– 'Totus Albus'	SPla
* – 'Variegatus'	CBot MBri
– 'William R Smith'	CCla EBee ELan ENot SHBN SPer WWeb
– 'Woodbridge' AGM	CB&S CBow CBra CSco ELan ENot IHos MBri MGos MRav MWat SChu SHBN SHer SPer SPla SReu WStI
¶ *tiliaceus*	CTro
trionum	CArn CHad ECou LCot LHop MSto SLMG
– 'Spirits Bay'	ECou
– 'Sunny Day'	ELan

HIERACIUM (Compositae/Asteraceae)

alpinum	CTom
aurantiacum	See PILOSELLA ***aurantiaca***
bombycinum	See H. ***mixtum***
brunneocroceum	See PILOSELLA ***aurantiaca carpathicola***
glabrum	WPer
§ *glaucum*	CRiv MTol NHol WByw WEas WWin
§ *lanatum*	CGle CMea CNic EBar ECro NBir NBro NHol NWCA SUsu WCru WEas WHal WPer WWin
maculatum	CRow ECoo ECro EFol EHoe ELan EMar EPar EPla GGar MFir MUlv MWat NCat NFai NSti SIng WCru WDav WOak WPer WWye
§ *mixtum*	NWCA
murorum	NWCA
pannosum NS 399	NWCA
pilosella	See PILOSELLA ***officinarum***
praecox	See H. ***glaucum***
scotostictum	EMon LRHS
sp. from Afghanistan	NKay
x *stoloniflorum*	See PILOSELLA ***stoloniflora***

variegatum	See HYPOCHAERIS *variegata*
villosum	CBot CChu CNic CRow CSam EFol EHoe GAul MSte NBro NNor SIng WCru WDav WEas WHer WPer WWin
waldsteinii	NHol NNor
welwitschii	See H. *lanatum*

HIEROCHLOË (Gramineae/Poaceae)

odorata	ETPC
redolens	ETPC GAbr

HILDABERRY See RUBUS 'Hildaberry'

HIMALAYACALAMUS (Gramineae/Poaceae-Bambusoideae)

§ *falconeri*	EFul EPla ISta LBam SBam SCob
§ – 'Damarapa'	EPla ISta LBam SArc SBam SCob SDix WJun

X HIPPEASPREKELIA (Liliaceae/Amaryllidaceae)

¶ 'Mystique'	WChr

HIPPEASTRUM (Liliaceae/Amaryllidaceae)

'Apple Blossom'	LAma MWBu NRog
'Beautiful Lady'	LAma
'Bestseller' AGM	LAma
bifidum	See RHODOPHIALA *bifida*
'Bouquet'	LAma
'Byjou'	NRog
'Dutch Belle'	LAma
'Fantastica'	LAma
'Fire Dance'	LAma
gracile 'Donau'	ETub
– 'Pamela'	ETub
'King of the Stripes'	LAma
'Lady Jane'	ETub
'Lucky Strike'	LAma
'Ludwig's Goliath'	LAma
'Maria Goretti'	LAma
'Oskar'	LAma NRog
papilio	LAma NRog WChr
'Papillon'	LAma
phycelloïdes	CHan
'Picotee'	LAma
¶ 'Red Lion'	MWBu
roseum	See RHODOPHIALA *rosea*
'Striped Vlammenspel'	LAma
'United Nations'	LAma
'Vera'	LAma
'White Dazzler'	LAma
¶ 'White Snow'	MWBu
'Wonderland'	LAma
'Yellow Pioneer'	LAma

HIPPOBROMA See LAURENTIA

HIPPOCREPIS (Leguminosae/Papilionaceae)

§ *comosa*	CKin ECWi EWFC MWil WGwy WHaw
– 'E R Janes'	EFol MPla
§ *emerus*	CHan CMHG CPle CSco ECro EHal ELan ERea EWri IMal MBal SHil WAbe WHCG WKif WSHC

HIPPOLYTIA (Compositae/Asteraceae)

§ *herderi*	EFol EHoe EMon LHop LLWP NBro SChu SGil

HIPPOPHAË (Elaeagnaceae)

rhamnoïdes AGM	CB&S CBow CBra CKin CLnd CSco EBre ELan EMil ENot GPoy GRei IHos IOrc LBre LBuc MBar MWat NWea SPer WDin WHCG WStI WWat
– 'Leikora' (f)	EPla MGos SPer
– 'Pollmix' (m)	MGos SPer
salicifolia	CLnd CPle

HIPPURIS (Hippuridaceae)

vulgaris	CBen CRDP ECWi EHon EMFW MHew WHol WWye

HIRPICIUM (Compositae/Asteraceae)

armerioïdes S&SH 6	CHan

HISTIOPTERIS (Dennstaedtiaceae)

incisa	CFil EBul

HOHERIA (Malvaceae)

§ *angustifolia*	CB&S CBot CChu CCla CHan ECou WSHC
glabrata AGM	CB&S CBot CSco ECou ISea MBal MBar SHil
'Glory of Amlwch' AGM	CChu CGre CMHG CSam GCal MRav WSHC
§ *lyallii* AGM	CB&S CBow CChu CCla CDoC CMHG CSam CWSG ECou ELan IDai IOrc ISea SHBN SPer SReu SSta WBod WDin
microphylla	See H. *angustifolia*
populnea	CBot
sexstylosa AGM	CBot CBow CCla CDoC CFee CPle CTbh EHar ELan EPla EWri IOrc ISea MUlv NNor NTow SHil SSta WOMN
– var. *crataegifolia*	CGre
*– *pendula*	CB&S
– 'Stardust'	CPMA MAsh SReu

HOLBOELLIA (Lardizabalaceae)

coriacea	CBot CChu MGos SArc SBra SHil WBod
latifolia	CGre CSam SArc

HOLCUS (Gramineae/Poaceae)

lanatus	MWil
mollis 'Albovariegatus'	CLew CNic CShe ECha EFol EHoe ELan EMon EPar EPla ETPC GCHN MBar MFir NBro NHol NNrd NRed NRya NSti SCob SPer WEas WHil WWat

HOLODISCUS (Rosaceae)

discolor	CBow CCla CDoC CGre CLew CPle EBar ELan EMil GCal MBlu SHBN SHil SLon SPla SSta WDin WHCG WSHC
¶ – var. *ariifolius*	EMil

HOMALOCLADIUM (Polygonaceae)
See Plant Deletions

HOMALOTHECA (Compositae/Asteraceae)
¶ *supina* NWCA

HOMERIA (Iridaceae)
breyniana See H. *collina*
– var. *aurantiaca* See H. *flaccida*
§ *collina* CFee EPot WThi
comptonii EPot
§ *flaccida* LAma LBow NRog
marlothii CMon WThi
ochroleuca EPot LAma LBow NRog

HOMOGLOSSUM See **GLADIOLUS**

HOMOGYNE (Compositae/Asteraceae)
alpina NGar

HOOKERIA (moss)
lucens LFle

HORDEUM (Gramineae/Poaceae)
jubatum CFee EHoe ETPC NSti SAxl WHil
murinum CKin

HORMINUM (Labiatae/Lamiaceae)
pyrenaicum CLew CRiv ELan GDra MBro MFir MHig MTho NGre NHol NSti SBla SIng SSmi SUsu WAbe WCla WHil WPat WPer WThu WWin
– pale blue MSte WDav

HOSTA † (Liliaceae/Hostaceae) ¢ FUNKIA
aequinoctiiantha EBul EGol
'Aksarben' EMic
'Alba' (*sieboldiana*) See H. 'Elegans Alba'
albomarginata See H. *sieboldii*
'Albomarginata' (*fortunei*) CB&S CRDP CWGN EBul EGol EMic EPGN MBar NFai SFis SHer WCru WHoo
'Allan P McConnell' (v) CBdn EGol EMic EPGN
'Alpine Aire' EMic
'Amanuma' EGol EMic
¶ 'Amber Maiden' (v) EGol
'Antioch' (*fortunei*) (v) CBdn EGol EMic
'Aoki' (*fortunei*) EMic EPGN NHol
'Aphrodite' (*plantaginea*) (d) EGol EMon EPGN
'Apple Green' EMic
¶ 'Apple Pie' SApp
¶ 'Aqua Velva' EGol
'Argentea Variegata' (*undulata*) See H. *undulata undulata*
'Aspen Gold' (*tokudama* x) EMic
'August Moon' Widely available
'Aurea' (*sieboldii*) See H. *sieboldii subcrocea*
aureafolia See H. 'Starker Yellow Leaf'
'Aureoalba' (*fortunei*) See H. 'Spinners'
'Aureomaculata' (*fortunei*) See H. *fortunei albopicta*
§ 'Aureomarginata' (*montana*) CBdn CBow EFou EGol EHoe EMic EPGN SApp WRus
– (*rohdeifolia*) See H. *rohdeifolia aureomarginata*
§ – (*ventricosa*) AGM CBdn CBro CHad EBre ECha EGol EMic EPGN LBre NHol NRoo NSti SDix SHig SPer SPla WRus
¶ 'Aurora Borealis' (*sieboldiana*) (v) EPGN
'Banyai's Dancing Girl' EMic
'Barbara White' EGol
bella See H. *fortunei obscura*
'Bennie McRae' EGol
¶ 'Betcher's Blue' EGol
'Betsy King' EPGN WMer
¶ 'Big Boy' (*montana*) EGol
'Big Daddy' (*sieboldiana* x) CBdn CBow CBro COtt CRDP EBre ECtt EGol ELan EMic EOrc EPGN EPla ERav ESma LBre LGre MBri NBir NFai NHol NSti SApp SMad SPla WAbe WCra WCru WRus
'Big Mama' (*sieboldiana* x) EGol EMic LRHS
§ 'Birchwood Parky's Gold' CBdn CBos CHan CRiv CTom EGol EMic EPGN NHol SApp SAxl WCru
'Birchwood Ruffled Queen' EGol EMic
§ 'Blonde Elf' EGol EMic
'Blue Angel' (*sieboldiana*) AGM CB&S CBdn CCMG ECha EGol EHoe ELan EMic EOrc EPGN MBal MTol MWat NHol NOrc SApp SFis WHoo
¶ 'Blue Arrow' EGol
'Blue Belle' (Tardiana) CBdn ECha EGol EMic
'Blue Blush' (Tardiana) EGol
'Blue Boy' CHad EGol EMic EPGN NHol
'Blue Cadet' CBdn CHad ECha EGol EMic MBar WStI
'Blue Danube' (Tardiana) CBdn ECha EGol EMic
'Blue Diamond' (Tardiana) CHad EGol EMic NFai
'Blue Dimples' (Tardiana) EGol EMic LRHS
'Blue Edger' ECha
'Blue Heart' (*sieboldiana elegans*) ECha EMic
'Blue Lake' SGil
'Blue Mammoth' (*sieboldiana*) EGol EMic
'Blue Moon' (Tardiana) CB&S CBro CHad CMHG EBar EBre EFou EGol ELan EMic EOrc EPGN ESma LBre LGre LWad MBri NFai NHol SApp SHer SMad SPla WCru WEas WWat
'Blue Seer' (*sieboldiana*) EGol
'Blue Skies' (Tardiana) EGol ELan EMic EPGN
'Blue Umbrellas' (*sieboldiana* x) CBdn EGol ELan EMic EOrc EPGN EPla NHol NJap
¶ 'Blue Velvet' CBdn
'Blue Vision' EPGN

'Blue Wedgwood' (Tardiana) CBdn CBow CBro CMHG CRow EGol ELan EMic EOrc EPGN EPla MTol NHol SApp WCru WRus WWat
'Bold Ribbons' (v) EGol EMic
'Bold Ruffles' ***(sieboldiana)*** EGol EMic LRHS
'Bonanza' ***(fortunei)*** EMic
'Bountiful' EGol EMic
'Bouquet' EGol
'Bressingham Blue' EBre ECtt EGol EMic EPla LBre NDea NMir SApp SAxl SPer
'Bright Glow' (Tardiana) CBdn EGol EMic
'Bright Lights' ***(tokudama)*** (v) EGol EPGN
'Brim Cup' (v) CBdn EGol EPGN
'Brooke' EMic
'Brother Ronald' (Tardiana) EGol
'Bruces Blue' EGol
'Buckshaw Blue' CBdn EGol EMic EPGN MBal NBir SApp SDix WCot
'Butter Rim' ***(sieboldii)*** (v) EGol
'Camelot' (Tardiana) EGol EMic
'Candy Hearts' CBdn CHan EGol EMic EPGN WMer
capitata EBul EMic
¶ – MSF 850 CFil
caput-avis See H. ***kikutii c-a.***
'Carol' ***(fortunei)*** (v) CBdn EGol EMic
'Carrie' ***(sieboldii)*** (v) EGol EMic
'Celebration' (v) EGol ELan EMic EPGN
'Challenger' EMic
'Change of Tradition' (v) EMic
'Chartreuse Wiggles' ***(sieboldii)*** EGol
'Chinese Sunrise' ***(cathayana)*** (v) CBdn EGol EMic EPGN NHol WMer
'Chiquita' EGol
¶ 'Choko Nishiki' ***(montana)*** (v) EGol
'Christmas Tree' (v) CBdn EGol EMic EPGN LRHS
clausa EMic
– var. ***normalis*** EGol EMic GCal
'Color Glory' ***(sieboldiana)*** (v) EGol EPGN
'Colossal' EGol EMic LRHS
'County Park' EGol
'Cream Delight' ***(undulata)*** See H. ***undulata undulata***
♦ 'Cream Edge' See H. 'Fisher Cream Edge'
¶ 'Crepe Suzette' (v) EGol
'Crested Reef' EGol EMic
§ ***crispula*** **AGM** CB&S CHad CRow CSco CShe EGol EHon EMic EOrc EPGN EPar GGar MBal NFai NHol SHig WHil WTyr
'Crown Jewel' EMic EPGN
'Crown Prince' EMic
§ 'Crowned Imperial' ***(fortunei)*** (v) CBdn EMic EPGN NHol SApp
'Curlew' (Tardiana) ECha EMic
'Dawn' EGol SApp
'Daybreak' EGol
decorata (v) EGol EMic LGro WPat
'Devon Blue' (Tardiana) CBdn CWGN EGol EMic
'Devon Cream' CBdn
¶ 'Devon Green' CBdn
'Devon Tor' CBdn EPGN
'Diamond Tiara' (v) EGol
'Dimple' ECha
'Dorothy' EMic
'Dorset Blue' (Tardiana) EMic
'Dorset Charm' (Tardiana) EGol EMic MBal
'Dorset Flair' (Tardiana) EMic
'Drummer Boy' EMic
¶ 'Du Page Delight' ***(sieboldiana)*** (v) EGol
¶ 'El Capitan' (v) EGol
elata EMic ISea MUlv WWat
'Eldorado' See H. 'Frances Williams'
'Elegans' See H. ***sieboldiana elegans***
§ 'Elegans Alba' ***(sieboldiana)*** EGol
'Elfin Power' ***(sieboldii)*** (v) EGol EMic
¶ 'Elisabeth' CBdn
'Elizabeth Campbell' ***(fortunei)*** (v) CBdn
'Ellen' EMic
'Ellerbroek' ***(fortunei)*** (v) EGol EMic
'Emerald Carpet' EMic
'Emerald Skies' EGol
'Emerald Tiara' EGol LRHS
'Emma Foster' ***(montana)*** EGol
'Eric Smith' (Tardiana) EGol EMic EPGN MUlv
'Eunice Choice' EMic
'Evening Magic' (v) EGol EMic
'Excitation' EGol EMic
'Fall Bouquet' ***(longipes hypoglauca)*** EGol
'Fall Emerald' EMic
'Feather Boa' EMic EPGN
* 'Fenman's Fascination' EMic
§ 'Fisher Cream Edge' ***(fortunei)*** WMer
'Floradora' CBdn EGol EMic
'Flower Power' EGol
fluctuans EMic NHol
§ – 'Variegated' **AGM** CBdn EGol EMic EPGN LRHS
'Fortis' See H. ***lancifolia***
fortunei CBow CCla CHad CMHG CRow CWGN EGol EMic EOrc EPGN MBal NDea NHol SChu SHig SPer WCru WEas
§ – var. ***albopicta*** **AGM** Widely available
§ – – ***aurea*** **AGM** CBdn CCla CHad CKel CMGP CMHG CRow ECha EGol EHoe ELan EMic EPGN EPla LHyd MBal SChu SHig SPer SPla WRus
– f. ***aurea*** See H. ***fortunei albopicta aurea***
§ – var. ***aureomarginata*** **AGM** Widely available
– var. ***gigantea*** See H. ***montana***
§ – var. ***hyacinthina*** **AGM** CBdn CCla CGle CSco EGol EMic EOrc EPGN EPla GCal GGar MBal MBar NBar NDea NSti WCru WRus WWin

– – variegated	See H. 'Crowned Imperial'
§ – var. ***obscura***	CShe EGol EMic LHyd WCru
– var. ***rugosa***	CHad EMic
'Fountain'	EMic NHol
¶ 'Fragrant Blue'	EGol
'Fragrant Gold'	CBdn EGol EMic
'Francee' (***fortunei***) **AGM**	Widely available
§ 'Frances Williams' (***sieboldiana***) **AGM**	Widely available
'Frances Williams Improved' (***sieboldiana***) (v)	EGol
'Fresh' (v)	EGol EPGN
'Fringe Benefit' (v)	CBdn EBre EGol EMic EPGN LBre NHar NHol WMer
'Frosted Jade' (v)	CBdn EGol EMic EPGN LRHS
¶ 'Gaiety' (v)	EGol
'Geisha' (v)	EGol EPGN
'Gene's Joy'	EPGN
'Gilt Edge' (***sieboldiana***) (v)	EMic
'Gingee'	EMic
'Ginko Craig' (v)	Widely available
glauca	See H. ***sieboldiana elegans***
'Gloriosa' (***fortunei***) (v)	EGol EMic
'Gold Drop'	EGol EMic
'Gold Edger'	CBdn CBow CBro CHan CMHG CRDP CRiv EBar EBre EGol ELan EMar EMic EOrc EPGN LBre MBri MNFA MSte NBar NFai NHol NJap NNrd SApp SChu SPer SPla WRus WWat
'Gold Flush' (***ventricosa***)	EMic
§ 'Gold Haze' (***fortunei***)	CHad EGol EMic EOrc EPGN NHol WCru
'Gold Leaf' (***fortunei***)	EGol
'Gold Regal'	CBdn EGol EMic
'Gold Standard' (***fortunei***) (v)	CBdn ECha EGol ELan EMic EPGN EPla LGre MNFA MWat NFai SApp SGil SWas WRus
'Goldbrook' (***fortunei***) (v)	EGol
'Goldbrook Genie'	EGol
'Goldbrook Glimmer' (Tardiana)(v)	EGol
'Goldbrook Gold'	EGol
'Goldbrook Grace'	EGol
'Golden' (***nakaiana***)	See H. 'Birchwood Parky's Gold'
'Golden Age'	See H. 'Gold Haze'
'Golden Bullion' (***tokudama***)	EMic
'Golden Circles'	See H. 'Frances Williams'
* 'Golden Giboshi'	WCru
'Golden Isle'	EGol
'Golden Medallion' (***tokudama***)	CB&S CBdn CBow CBro EBar EBre EGol ELan EMic EOrc EPGN LBre MBel MNFA NFai NHol NJap NSti SApp SMad WWat
'Golden Nakaiana'	See H. 'Birchwood Parky's Gold'
'Golden Prayers' (***tokudama***)	CAbb CB&S CBdn CBow CBro CCMG CHad CHol CRDP EGol ELan EMic EOrc EPGN LGre MBri NBar NFai NHol NOrc SApp SChu SHer SIng SPer SPla SUsu WAbe WHow WRus
'Golden Scepter' (***nakaiana***)	CBdn EGol EMic EPGN
'Golden Sculpture' (***sieboldiana***)	EGol
'Golden Spider'	EMic
'Golden Sunburst' (***sieboldiana***)	CHad CSco ECha EGol ELan EMic EPGN GGar MBal MBri NBar NHol NJap NRoo SGil WCru WRus
'Golden Tiara' **AGM**	CB&S CBdn CHan EGol ELan EMic EPGN EPla LWad MBar MNFA NFai NHar NHol NJap NSti SApp WCru WHow WRus
'Goldsmith'	EGol
'Good as Gold'	EMic
gracillima	CRow EBul EPGN EPar LHyd MNFA NHar NHol NKay WCru
'Granary Gold' (***fortunei***)	EPGN
'Grand Master'	EGol EPGN
'Great Expectations' (***sieboldiana***) (v)	CBdn EGol EPGN
'Green Acres' (***montana***)	EMic
'Green Fountain' (***kikutii***)	CBdn EGol EMic EPGN EPla
'Green Gold' (***fortunei***) (v)	CBdn EMic WMer
'Green Piecrust'	EGol EMic EPGN
'Green Sheen'	EGol EMic
'Green Smash'	EMic
¶ 'Green Velveteen'	EGol
'Greenwood'	EMic
'Ground Master' (v)	Widely available
'Ground Sulphur'	EGol EMic
'Gum Drop'	EMic
'Hadspen Blue' (Tardiana)	CBdn CCla CDoC CHad CMHG EBar EBre ECha EGol EMic EOrc EPGN EPla LBre NBro NHol NJap NSti SApp SMrm WHow WRus WWat
'Hadspen Blue Jay' (Tardiana)	CBro
¶ 'Hadspen Hawk' (Tardiana)	EGol LGre
'Hadspen Heron' (Tardiana)	CHad ECha EGol EMic EPGN MBal
'Hadspen Samphire'	CHad CHan EGol EMic EPGN
'Hadspen Seersucker'	CHad
'Hadspen White' (***fortunei***)	EPGN
'Hakujima' (***sieboldii***)	EGol LGre
§ 'Halcyon' **AGM**	Widely available
'Happiness' (Tardiana)	CBdn ECha EHoe EMic EPGN WCot
'Happy Hearts'	EGol
'Harmony' (Tardiana)	EGol EMic
'Harrison'	EMic
'Harvest Glow'	EGol
'Hazel'	EMic
'Heartleaf'	EMic
¶ 'Heartsong' (v)	EGol

'Helen Doriot' (*sieboldiana*) EGol EMic LRHS
helonioides f. ***albopicta*** hort. See H. ***rohdeifolia***
'Herifu' (v) EGol
¶ 'Hirao Majesty' EGol
¶ 'Hirao Supreme' EGol
'Hoarfrost' EMic
'Holstein' See H. 'Halcyon'
§ 'Honeybells' AGM CB&S CBdn CBro CCla CHad CMHG CRow CSco EBre ECha EGol ELan EMic EOrc EPGN EPar LBre LGro LHop LHyd LMay MBal MBar NHol NJap NSti SPer WAbe WDav
'Hydon Gleam' EPGN
'Hydon Sunset' (*nakaiana*) CBdn CCMG CHan CMHG EGol EMic EOrc EPGN LHyd MBal MBri NFai NHol NOrc NSti SApp SIng WAbe WWat
hypoleuca EGol
§ 'Inaho' EGol EMic EPGN
'Invincible' CBdn EGol EMic EPGN SApp
'Iona' (*fortunei*) CBdn EGol
¶ 'Iron Gate Glamor' EGol
'Jade Scepter' (*nakaiana*) EGol EMic
'Janet' (*fortunei*) (v) EGol EMic EOrc NHol WMer
'Japan Boy' See H. 'Montreal'
'Japan Girl' See H. 'Mount Royal'
¶ 'Joker' (*fortunei*) (v) CBdn
'Julie Morss' EGol EMic EPGN
'Jumbo' (*sieboldiana*) EMic
'June' (Tardiana)(v) CBdn EBee EGol EPGN SApp SMad SPer
'Kabitan' See H. ***sieboldii kabitan***
'Kath's Gold' CBdn EMic
'Kelly' SApp
'Kelsey' EMic
kikutii EGol EMic
– var. ***caput-avis*** EGol EMic
– var. ***polyneuron*** EBul EGol
– var. ***pruinosa*** EGol LRHS
– var. ***yakusimensis*** CRDP EGol EMic GDra
'Kirishima' EPGN NKay
kiyosumiensis CRow EBul NHol
'Klopping Variegated' (*fortunei*) EMic
'Krinkled Joy' EMic
'Krossa Regal' AGM Widely available
'Lady Helen' EMic
§ ***lancifolia*** AGM CBro CHad CKel CMCN CMHG CRow CSco CWGN EBre EBul ECha EGol ELan EMic EPGN EPar LBre LGro LHyd MBal NHol NJap SFis SPer WDav WThu WWat
'Leather Sheen' EGol EMic
'Lemon Lime' CBdn CRiv CWGN EGol EMic SApp WMer
'Leola Fraim' (v) EGol
* ***lilacina*** SCro
'Little Aurora' CBdn EGol EMic MBal
'Little Blue' (*ventricosa*) CBdn EGol EMic
'Little Razor' EGol EMic
'Little White Lines' (v) EGol EMic
longipes EGol
– var. ***longipes*** EBul
longissima EBul EGol EPla LHyd NHol WCru WWin
– var. ***longissima*** EMic LHyd
'Louisa' (*sieboldii*) (v) ECha EGol EPGN MSte NHol NNrd
'Love Pat' (*tokudama*) AGM CBdn EGol EMic
'Lucky Charm' EMic
'Lunar Eclipse' (v) EGol EMic
'Maculata' EMic
'Maculata Aurea' SCro
'Maekawa' EGol
N 'Marginata Alba' (*fortunei*) CBdn CBot CHad CKel ECha LMay NDea SPer WAbe WWin
'Marilyn' EGol EMic
'Mary Jo' EMic
'Mary Marie Ann' (*fortunei*) (v) EMic
'Mediovariegata' (*undulata*) See H. ***undulata undulata***
'Mentor Gold' EGol EMic
'Midas Touch' (*tokudama* x) EGol EMic EPGN EPla ESma NBar NFai NHol NJap NVic WRus
'Middle Ridge' EMic
§ 'Midwest Gold' EGol
'Mildred Seaver' CBdn EGol LRHS
'Minnie Klopping' EMic
§ ***minor*** CBro CTom EGol ELan EMic EPot GDra MTho NHol NTow SPou WBon WWin
¶ – Goldbrook form EGol
– f. ***alba*** hort. See H. ***sieboldii alba***
* 'Minuta' (*undulata*) WMer
'Misty Waters' (*sieboldiana*) EMic
'Moerheim' (*fortunei*) (v) EGol EPGN EPar MBar MBri NHol SApp WCru WMer
N ***montana*** CHad ECha EGol EMic NHol SApp
'Montreal' EMic
'Moon Glow' (v) EGol EMic EPGN LRHS
'Moonlight' (*fortunei*) (v) EGol EMic
¶ 'Moscow Blue' EGol
'Mount Kirishima' (*sieboldii*) See H. 'Kirishima'
'Mount Royal' (*sieboldii*) EMic
'Mountain Snow' (*montana*) (v) EGol EMic
nakaiana EMic NHol WCru
'Nakaimo' EMic NHol WCru
'Nameoki' NHol
'Nana' (*ventricosa*) See H. ***minor***
§ 'Nancy Lindsay' (*fortunei*) (v) EBee EGol EMic EPGN SMrm
'Neat Splash Rim' (v) EMic
'New Wave' EGol EMic
'Nicola' (Tardiana) EGol EMic EPGN WCot
nigrescens EGol EMic EPGN GCal LRHS
'Nokogiryama' EGol EMic
'North Hills' (*fortunei*) (v) CBdn EGol EMic EPGN NBir
'Northern Halo' (*sieboldiana*) (v) EGol ELan EMic SApp

'Northern Lights' (*sieboldiana*)	EGol LRHS
'Northern Sunray' (*sieboldiana*) (v)	EMic
'Obscura Marginata' (*fortunei*)	See H. *f. aureomarginata*
'Olga's Shiny Leaf'	EGol EMic
'Oriana' (*fortunei*)	CBdn EGol EMic
'Osprey' (Tardiana)	EGol
'Oxheart'	EMic
pachyscapa	EMic
'Pacific Blue Edger'	SApp
'Parker Jervis Blue'	NFai
'Pastures New'	CBdn EGol EMic EPGN NHol SApp
¶ 'Patriot' (v)	EGol EPGN
'Paul's Glory' (v)	EGol EMic
'Pearl Lake'	CBdn EGol EMic LGre NHol
'Pelham Blue Tump'	EGol
'Perry's True Blue'	EMic
'Peter Pan'	EMic
'Phyllis Campbell' (*fortunei*)	See H. 'Sharmon'
'Picta' (*fortunei*)	See H. *f. albopicta*
'Piedmont Gold'	CBdn EGol EMic EPGN EPla
'Pineapple Poll'	CBdn EMic EPGN
'Pizzazz' (v)	EGol EPGN
plantaginea	CBdn CBrd CWGN EBee EGol EMic ERav SApp WDav
♦ – var. *grandiflora*	See H. *p. japonica*
§ – var. *japonica*	CBot CGle CHan CSco ECha EMic EPar SApp SWas WPat WWat
¶ 'Popo'	EGol
'Purple Dwarf'	NHol WBon WCra WCru
'Purple Profusion'	CBdn EMic
¶ *pycnophylla*	EGol
¶ 'Radiant Edger' (v)	EGol
¶ 'Raleigh Remembrance'	EGol
rectifolia	CMHG EMic NHol WKif
'Regal Splendor' (v)	EGol EMic
'Resonance' (v)	EMic SApp
'Reversed' (v)	ELan EMic EPGN NHol
'Richland Gold' (*fortunei*)	CBdn EGol EMic LRHS
'Rippling Waves'	EMic
'Robusta' (*fortunei*)	See H. *sieboldiana elegans*
§ *rohdeifolia* (v)	EGol EMic
§ – f. *albopicta*	CBdn EGol ELan EPGN EPar NHol
'Rosanne'	EMic
'Royal Standard' AGM	CBdn CBos CBro CCla CHad CRow CSco ECha EGol ELan EMic ENot EPGN EPla LHyd MBal NHol NJap SPer SPla WAbe WRus WTyr
'Royalty	EGol
rupifraga	EGol EMic
'Russell's Form' (*ventricosa*)	EMic
'Ryan's Big One'	EMic
♦ 'Sagae'	See H. *fluctuans* 'Variegated'
§ 'Saishu Jima' (*sieboldii spathulata*)	EGol NHol WCru
'Samual Blue'	EMic
'Samurai' (*sieboldiana*) (v)	CBdn EGol EMic
'Sazanami' (*crispula*)	See H. *crispula*
'Sea Dream' (v)	EGol EPGN
'Sea Drift'	EGol EMic
'Sea Fire'	EGol
'Sea Gold Star'	EGol EMic LRHS
'Sea Lotus Leaf'	EGol LRHS
'Sea Monster'	EGol LRHS
'Sea Octopus'	EGol EMic
'Sea Sapphire'	EGol
'Sea Yellow Sunrise'	EGol EMic
'See Saw' (*undulata*)	EGol EMic
'September Sun' (v)	CBdn EGol
'Serendipity'	CBdn EGol EMic
'Shade Fanfare' AGM	CBdn CBro COtt EBre ECha EGol ELan EMic EOrc EPGN LBre MBal MBri MNFA MRav MWat NFai NJap NRoo SCro SPer WHoo
'Shade Master'	EMic NHol
'Sharmon' (*fortunei*) (v)	CBdn EGol EMic EPGN EPla NHol SPer WCru
'Sherbourne Profusion' (Tardiana)	EMic
'Sherbourne Songbird' (Tardiana)	EMic
'Sherbourne Swan' (Tardiana)	EMic
'Sherbourne Swift' (Tardiana)	CBdn EMic
'Shining Tot'	CBdn EGol EPGN
* 'Shirofukurin'	CBdn EPGN SIng
'Shogun' (v)	EGol
sieboldiana	CHad CHan CKel CMHG CRow CShe EBar EGol ELan EMic EOrc EPot IBar IDai LHyd MBal NBar NHol NNor SFis SHig SPer WAbe WHil WWat
§ – var. *elegans* AGM	Widely available
§ *sieboldii* AGM	CMGP EBre EBul ECha EGol EMic EPGN IDai LBre LHyd MBal MBar MFir MRav NKay SApp SBla SFis WPer
§ – var. *alba*	CBos CCla CHad CHan CMGP CRiv EGol ELan EMic
– f. *kabitan* (v)	CBdn EGol EMic EPGN EPla
– f. *shiro-kabitan* (v)	EGol EMic EPGN
– var. *thunbergiana*	See H. *sieboldii spathulata*
'Silver Lance' (v)	EGol EMic
'Snow Cap' (v)	EGol
'Snow Crust' (*elata*) (v)	EMic
'Snowden'	CBdn CHad COtt EBre ECha EGol EMic EPGN LBre MBal NBir NHol SApp WRus
'Snowflakes' (*sieboldii*)	EGol EPGN GCal MBar MBri NHol SPer WMer
'So Sweet'	CBdn EGol EMic EPGN
'Special Gift'	EMic
§ 'Spinners ' (*fortunei*) (v)	CBdn CHad ECha EGol EMic SApp
'Spritzer' (v)	CBdn EGol EPGN
'Squiggles' (v)	EGol
'Starker Yellow Leaf'	EMic
'Stenantha Aureomarginata' (*fortunei*)	EMic WMer
¶ 'Stiletto' (v)	EGol
'Sugar and Cream' (v)	CBdn EGol EMic EPGN SApp SGil
'Sugar Plum Fairy' (*gracillima*)	EGol EMic

'Sum and Substance' AGM	CB&S CBdn EBre EGol ELan EMic EPGN ESma LBre MUlv NHol SApp
'Summer Fragrance'	EGol EMic EPGN LRHS SApp
'Sun Glow'	EMic
'Sun Power'	CBdn CBro EGol EMic EPGN MWat NJap SPer WRus
'Sundance' (*fortunei*) (v)	CBdn EGol EMic
'Super Bowl'	EGol
'Suzuki Thumbnail'	EMic
¶ 'Sweet Standard'	SApp
'Sweet Susan'	EMic MUlv SPer
'Sweetheart'	EMic
'Tall Boy'	CBdn EBee ECha EGol EMic EPGN GCal NHol SApp SPer
'Tall Twister'	EMic
x *tardiana*	CBro CCla CMGP CRiv CShe EGol ELan EPla MBal NHol SHig SPer WAbe WKif
tardiflora	CBos CSco EGol EMic EPla MBal MHig NHol NKay SPer
tardiva 'Aureostriata'	See H. 'Inaho'
'The Twister'	EMic
'Thomas Hogg'	See H. ***undulata albomarginata***
¶ 'Thumb Nail'	ECha EGol
tibae	EMic
'Tiny Tears' (*venusta*)	EGol EMic
tokudama	CBdn CHad EGol ELan EPGN ERav IHos MBri NBar NFai NHol NSti SApp SChu SPer SPla WAbe WCru WKif WWat
§ – f. *aureonebulosa*	CBdn EGol EMic EPGN LGre
– f. *flavocircinalis* (v)	CBdn ECha EGol EMic EPGN
'Tot Tot'	EMic
'Trail's End'	EMic
'True Blue'	CBdn EMic EPGN SApp
'Twinkle Toes'	EMic
undulata (v)	CBow CMGP EMic GAul NDea SApp SFis WGor
§ – var. *albomarginata*	Widely available
– var. *erromena* AGM	CBow CCla CHad CHan CMGP CWGN EHon EMic EPGN EPla GPlt LMay MNFA NHol NKay SChu SFis SPer WAbe WCot
§ – var. *undulata* AGM	Widely available
– var. *univittata* AGM	CRow ECha EGol EMic EPGN EPla LHop LHyd NFai SApp SPla WKif
'Valentine Lace'	EGol EMic
'Vanilla Cream' (*cathayana*)	EGol EMic
'Variegata' (*gracillima*)	See H. 'Shirofukurin'
– (*tokudama*)	See H. ***tokudama aureonebulosa***
– (*undulata*)	See H. ***undulata undulata***
– (*ventricosa*)	See H. 'Aureomarginata' (*ventricosa*)
ventricosa AGM	CB&S CBdn CBro CHad CKel CSco CTom EBre EGol EMic EPGN ERav GDra LBre LHyd LMay NHar NHol SHig WWat
– var. *aureomaculata*	CCla CHad EBee EGol EMic EPGN SPla WCru WRus
– *minor*	See H. ***minor***
I 'Venucosa'	EMic GCal
venusta AGM	Widely available
– dwarf form	LGre
– x *sieboldiana*	CHan
– *yakusimensis*	See H. ***kikutii y.***
N 'Venusta Variegated'	CBdn EGol
'Vera Verde' (v)	See H. 'Shirofukurin'
'Vilmoriniana'	EMic
'Viridis Marginata'	See H. ***sieboldii kabitan***
'Wagtail' (Tardiana)	EMic
'Wayside Blue'	EMic
'Wayside Perfection'	See H. 'Royal Standard'
'Weihenstephan' (*sieboldii*)	CBdn
'White Gold'	EGol EPGN
¶ 'White Tacchi'	EMon
'Wide Brim' AGM	Widely available
'Wind River Gold'	SApp
'Windsor Gold'	See H. 'Nancy Lindsay'
'Wogon' (*sieboldii*)	CBdn CRDP CRow ECha EFou EGol EMic EPGN EPar EPla NHol SApp WCru
'Wogon Giboshi'	See H. 'Wogon'
'Wrinkles and Crinkles'	LRHS
'Yellow Boa'	EMic
'Yellow Edge' (*fortunei*)	See H. ***f. aureomarginata***
– (*sieboldiana*)	See H. 'Frances Williams'
'Yellow River' (*montana*) (v)	EGol
'Yellow Splash' (v)	CBdn ECha EPGN
'Yellow Splash Rim' (v)	EGol EMic
¶ *yingeri*	EGol
'Zager Blue'	EMic
'Zager Green'	EMic
'Zounds'	Widely available

HOTTONIA (Primulaceae)

palustris	CBen CWGN ECoo EHon ELan EMFW LMay MSta NDea SWat SWyc

HOUSTONIA (Rubiceae)

caerulea hort.	See H. ***michauxii***
caerulea Linnaeus	CLew CRiv CSam ELan GGar MPit MPla NGre NMen NPri WAbe WWin
– var. *alba*	CLew EWes NTow WAbe WPer
'Fred Millard'	CNic EPot EWes NHol NNrd SHer SIng
michauxii	NNrd

HOUTTUYNIA (Saururaceae)

cordata	CBow CHan CTom IBlr MUlv NSti SWat
– 'Chameleon' (v)	Widely available
– 'Flore Pleno'	CBen CBro CGle CRow CWGN ECha EFol EHon ELan EOrc EPar LMay MBal MSta NBar NBir NBro SIde SIng SPer SWat SWyc WAbe WByw WChe WHol WOld WRus WWin
– 'Tricolor' (v)	See H. ***c.*** 'Chameleon'
– *variegata*	IBar IBlr MPit NDea NVic WByw WChe WHol

HOVENIA (Rhamnaceae)

acerba	CMCN
dulcis	CB&S CMCN CPle ELan

HOWEA (Palmae/Arecaceae)

§ *belmoreana*	CTro

forsteriana **AGM** CTro LPal MBri

HOYA † (Asclepiadaceae)

angustifolia CNew
archboldiana CNew
arnottiana SLMG
§ ***australis*** CNew CTro SLMG
bandaensis CTro SLMG
bilobata CNew
carnosa **AGM** CB&S CMer CNew CTro EBak ELan ERea LAbb NRog SHer SLMG
– 'Compacta' MBri SLMG
– 'Exotica' **AGM** SLMG
*– 'Jungle Garden' SLMG
– 'Krinkle Eight' SLMG
– 'Prolifica' SLMG
– 'Red Princess' MBri
– 'Rubra' SLMG
– 'Variegata' CTro MBri SLMG
crassicaulis CNew
cumingiana CNew
curtisii CNew
darwinii hort. See H. ***australis***
engleriana SLMG
fusca 'Silver Knight' SLMG
fuscomarginata See H. ***pottsii***
imperialis CNew SLMG
ischnopus CNew
kenejiana CNew
kerrii CNew
lacunosa CNew
lanceolata ssp. ***bella*** **AGM** CB&S ERea MBri NRog SLMG
linearis CNew
longifolia CNew
macgillivrayi CNew
meredithii CNew
motoskei CNew CTro
multiflora CNew MBri WHCG
neocaledonica CTro LAbb SLMG
nicholsoniae CNew
obovata CNew
parasitica var. ***citrina*** CNew
pauciflora CNew
polyneura CNew CTro SLMG
pottsii CNew
pubicalyx 'Red Buttons' CNew CTro SLMG
purpureofusca CTro
serpens CNew
shepherdii CNew
'Shibata' CNew
uncinata CNew

HUGUENINIA (Cruciferae/Brassicaceae)

alpina See H. ***tanacetifolia***

HUMATA See DAVALLIA

HUMEA (Compositae/Asteraceae)

elegans See CALOMERIA ***amaranthoïdes***

HUMULUS (Cannabaceae)

japonicus MSal NHex
lupulus CArn CB&S CBow CSFH ECoo GAri GBar GPoy ILis LHol MHew MSal SIde WHer WWye
¶– (f) WWat
¶– (m) WWat
– 'Aureus' **AGM** Widely available
– 'Fuggle' GPoy
– 'Hip-Hop' EMon
– 'Wye Challenger' GPoy

HUTCHINSIA See THLASPI

HYACINTHELLA (Liliaceae/Hyacinthaceae)

acutiloba EPot LAma WChr
heldreichii WChr
lineata WChr
– M&T 5048 CMon
millingenii WChr
pallens ETub

HYACINTHOÏDES (Liliaceae/Hyacinthaceae)

§ ***hispanica*** CAvo CBro EWFC IBlr MBri MWBu NHol SIng WHaw WWye
– ***algeriensis*** AB&S 4337 CMon
– 'Danube' ('Donau') LBow
– 'Excelsior' ETub
– 'La Grandesse' CBro
– 'Queen of the Pinks' LBow
– 'Rosabella' CBro
– 'White City' LBow
italica CMon
– ***vicentina alba*** WChr
§ ***non-scripta*** CAvo CBro CKin ECWi EPar EPot ERav ETub EWFC GDra IBlr LAma LBow LFox MBri MWBu NLan NMir NRog SIng WCla WShi

HYACINTHUS † (Liliaceae/Hyacinthaceae)

amethystinus See BRIMEURA ***amethystina***
azureus See MUSCARI ***azureum***
comosus 'Plumosus' See MUSCARI ***comosum*** 'Plumosum'
¶ ***orientalis*** WChr
– 'Amethyst' LAma MWBu NRog
– 'Amsterdam' ETub LAma MWBu NRog
– 'Anna Liza' NRog
– 'Anna Marie' **AGM** CBro ETub LAma MBri MWBu NRog
– 'Ben Nevis' (d) LAma MBri NRog
– 'Bismarck' LAma MWBu NRog
– 'Blue Giant' LAma NRog
– 'Blue Jacket' **AGM** CBro ETub LAma MWBu NRog
– 'Blue Magic' LAma NRog
– 'Blue Orchid' (d) LAma
– 'Blue Star' LAma
– 'Borah' **AGM** LAma NRog
– 'Carnegie' CBro ETub LAma MWBu NRog
– 'Chestnut Flower' (d) ETub
– 'City of Haarlem' **AGM** CBro ETub LAma MWBu NRog
– 'Colosseum' LAma
– 'Concorde' LAma
– 'Delft Blue' **AGM** CBro ETub LAma MBri MWBu NRog
– 'Distinction' LAma

– 'Edelweiss' LAma
– 'Fondant' LAma
– 'Gipsy Queen' **AGM** LAma MBri MWBu NRog
– 'Hollyhock' (d) ETub LAma MBri NRog
– 'Jan Bos' ETub LAma MWBu NRog
– 'King Codro' (d) LAma MBri NRog
– 'King of the Blues' LAma NRog
– 'La Victoire' LAma NRog
– 'Lady Derby' LAma MWBu
– 'Lord Balfour' LAma
– 'L'Innocence' **AGM** CBro LAma MWBu NRog
– 'Madame Krüger' LAma
– 'Marconi' (d) LAma NRog
– 'Marie' LAma NRog
– 'Mulberry Rose' LAma NRog
– 'Myosotis' LAma
– 'Oranje Boven' ETub LAma
– 'Ostara' **AGM** CBro ETub LAma MBri MWBu NRog
– 'Peter Stuyvesant' NRog
– 'Pink Pearl' **AGM** CBro ETub LAma MWBu NRog
– 'Pink Royal' (d) LAma NRog
– 'Pink Surprise' ETub MWBu
– 'Princess Margaret' LAma
– 'Prins Hendrik' LAma
– 'Queen of the Pinks' LAma NRog
– 'Queen of the Violets' NRog
– 'Rosalie' NRog
– 'Rosette' (d) LAma NRog
– 'Salmonetta' See H. ***o.*** 'Oranje Boven'
– 'Sneeuwwitje' ('Snow White') LAma NRog
– 'Violet Pearl' CBro ETub LAma NRog
– 'Vuurbaak' LAma
– 'White Pearl' LAma NRog

HYDRANGEA † (Hydrangeaceae)

anomala CChu
§ – ssp. ***petiolaris*** **AGM** Widely available
§ – – ***cordifolia*** CChu CHan EBar EPla MBrk SReu SSta WWeb
– – ***tiliifolia*** MBlu WSHC
– – dwarf form See H. ***a. p. cordifolia***
§ ***arborescens*** CArn NNor WWeb
– 'Annabelle' **AGM** Widely available
– ssp. ***discolor*** 'Sterilis' CFil EPla SGil SPla
– 'Grandiflora' **AGM** CB&S CBot CBow CCla CSco ELan IJoh SBod SPer SReu WBod WDin WSHC WWin
– 'Hills of Snow' SMad
– ssp. ***radiata*** CFil CHan ELan MAsh NHlc SMad WCru WWat
aspera CBow CFil CGre CSco IOrc SChu SDry SSta WCru
– Kawakamii Group CFil EPla
♦– ***macrophylla*** hort. See H. ***a.*** 'Macrophylla'
§ – 'Macrophylla' **AGM** CBow CCla CFil EPla MBri NRar
– 'Mauvette' CBow CFil MBlu SSta
– ssp. ***robusta*** EPla GAri SDry WCru
§ – ssp. ***sargentiana*** **AGM** CAbP CB&S CBot CBow CChu CCla CFil CHEx COtt CSco EHar ELan LNet MBal MBlu MBri SArc SBor SHBN SHil SMad SPer SSta WCru WDin WKif WWat
– ssp. ***strigosa*** CDoC ELan
– 'Taiwan' NHlc
§ – Villosa Group **AGM** Widely available

§ 'Blue Deckle' (L) CCla CFil CMHG EBar EPla NHlc SPla SWas
♦ 'Blue Tit' See H. ***macrophylla*** 'Blaumeise'
cinerea See H. ***arborescens discolor***
§ 'Grant's Choice' (L) NHlc NHol
heteromalla CBot CMHG SMrm SPer WAbe
– Bretschneideri Group **AGM** CB&S CChu CMCN EHal GAri NHlc SPer WBod WWat
– 'Snowcap' EHar NHlc SHil
– f. ***xanthoneura*** CBot GAri WSHC
– 'Yelung Ridge' NHlc
hirta CPle
integerrima See H. ***serratifolia***
involucrata CBow CSco MBal MPla NHlc SDry SHil SMrm WCru
– 'Hortensis' **AGM** CBow CHan CPle IOrc SHer SHil WBod WKif WSHC
macrophylla
'Alpenglühen' ('Alpen Glow') (H) CB&S ELan ENot ESis IOrc NHar NHlc SBod SHBN SHer SPla
– 'Altona' **AGM** CB&S CSco EPla GAri IOrc ISea MBal MGos MRav NHlc NKay NRoo SBod SPer SReu WStI
– 'Ami Pasquier' **AGM** CB&S CSco EPla IOrc NHlc SHer
– 'Aureovariegata' ELan SMad
– 'Ayesha' **AGM** CAbb CB&S CBot CBra CChu CCla CDec CGre CHan CMHG CPle CSco CTrw EBre EPla LBre MRav SBod SChu SDix SHBN SMad SPer SPla WBod WHil
– 'Beauté Vendômoise' (H) CFil
– 'Belzonii' (L) NHlc
– 'Benelux' (H) CB&S IJoh
– 'Beni-gaku' CB&S CFil
– 'Blauer Prinz' ('Blue Prince') (H) CB&S EBre GCHN IJoh IOrc LBre MAll NHlc SHBN
§ – 'Blaumeise' (L) CFil LRHS NHlc
¶ – 'Blue Bird' CFil
– 'Blue Bonnet' (H) MAsh SPer WHen
¶ – 'Blue Sky' NHlc
– 'Blue Wave' (L) See H. ***m.*** 'Mariesii Perfecta'
– 'Bodensee' (H) ELan MRav SBod SHer SPla WStI WWeb
– 'Bouquet Rose' (H) CSco ECtt EHal MGos
– 'Cordata' See H. ***arborescens***
– 'Covent Garden' MAll
– 'Deutschland' (H) IOrc
– 'Domotoi' (H) EPla
*– 'Dwaag Pink' WWeb
– 'Enziandom' ('Gentian Dome') (H) CB&S CFil EPla SMrm WAbe
– 'Europa' **AGM** CB&S CTrw IOrc MAsh MGos NHlc SBod SGil WStI
– 'Forever Pink' EPla MAsh
– 'Frillibet' (H) CFil EPla
– 'Générale Vicomtesse de Vibraye' **AGM** CB&S CBot CFil CMHG CSco GCHN IDai ISea MBal MBar MBri NHlc SHBN SLon SPer SReu WBod WWin
– 'Geoffrey Chadbund' **AGM** CB&S CBow CCla CFil CSco ECtt EPla GAul IHos MBri NHlc SAxl SBod SChu SDix SHer SMad SPer SSta SUsu WWeb

¶– 'Gerda Steiniger' CB&S
– 'Gertrude Glahn' (H) CB&S
– 'Glowing Embers' CFil
– 'Goliath' (H) CFil MBri
– 'Hamburg' (H) CB&S CSco ECtt ENot IDai IOrc MGos MPla NBee NHlc NKay SDix SLon WAbe WStI
– 'Harry's Pink Topper' (H) MAsh
– 'Hatfield Rose' (H) CB&S CDoC
– 'Heinrich Seidel' (H) CB&S CDoC NHlc
– 'Holstein' (H) COtt IDai MAsh NBee NRoo
– 'Intermezzo' MAll WWeb
– 'James Grant' See H. 'Grant's Choice'
¶– 'Kardinal' CFil
*– 'Khudnert' WWeb
– 'King George' (H) CB&S CSco EBre IDai IOrc LBre MBar MGos MRav NHlc SPer WStI WWeb
– 'Kluis Superba' (H) CB&S CPle CSco IOrc MRav NHlc WAbe
– 'Koningin Wilhelmina' ('Queen Wilhelmina') (H) CDoC CFil
– 'La France' (H) CB&S EBee EHal MBar SGil WWeb
– 'Lanarth White' AGM CB&S CCla CFil CSco ELan MPla MRav NHlc SDix SHBN SLon SPer SReu WBod WWeb
§– 'Le Cygne' (H) MBri MGos WBod
§– 'Libelle' (L) CB&S CCla CFil EBee EHic MBri NBar NHlc NSti SPer WKif
– 'Lilacina' (L) CCla CFil CGre EHic EPla NHlc SPer SWas
§– 'Maculata' (L) CPle EFol ELan EPla IOrc LAbb LHop NKay WWat
– 'Madame A Riverain' (H) COtt MAll SBod
– 'Madame Emile Mouillère' AGM CB&S CBot CCla CFil CHan CSco ENot IDai IOrc MBri MPla NHlc SAxl SBod SChu SDix SGil SHBN SHer SLon SMad SPer SPla SSta WBod
*– 'Magic Light' MBri
– 'Maréchal Foch' (H) IOrc
– 'Mariesii' (L) CBot CCla CMHG ELan ENot EPla IDai ISea MBal NBee NHlc NKay SAxl SDix SHil SLon SPer WKif WStI WWat
§– 'Mariesii Perfecta' AGM CBot CCla CMHG CPle CSco ELan IDai IJoh ISea MBri MGos MRav NKay SAxl SDix SPer WBod WHen WStI WWat
– 'Masja' (H) CB&S COtt IHos IOrc MBri MGos SHBN
– 'Mathilda Gutges' (H) CFil EHic WAbe WStI WWeb
– 'Miss Belgium' (H) IDai IOrc MBal MBri MUlv SBod
– 'Miss Hepburn' COtt SPer
– 'Niedersachsen' (H) CDoC CFil EPla MRav
– 'Nigra' AGM CChu CCla CGre CHan CPle CTre ELan EPla IOrc ISea MBal SDix SHBN SLon SPer SSta WStI
– 'Nikko Blue' CB&S CFil
– var. ***normalis*** NHlc
§– 'Otaksa' (H) CSco NHlc
– 'Parzival' AGM CB&S CSco CTrw MBri NHlc WBod
– 'Pia' (H) CB&S CDec CLew EFol ELan EPla ESis IOrc LHop MAsh MBal MCas MHig MPla MTho MUlv NHar SBod SIng SMad SMrm SPer SPla WAbe WOMN WPat WThu WWat
– 'Pink Wave' (L) CB&S
– 'Prinses Beatrix' CChe
– 'Quadricolor' (L/v) CAbb CChu CCla CDec CFil CMil CPle EHoe EPla GCal IJoh MBri MRav MUlv NRar SDix SHBN SMad SPer SPla WCru WSHC
– 'R F Felton' CB&S
– 'Red Lacecap' CDoC
– 'Regula' (H) CTrw
– 'Rosita' (H) MAsh
¶– 'Rotkehlchen' ('Redbreast') LRHS
– 'Saint Claire' CB&S
– 'Sea Foam' (L) EPla IJoh IOrc NHlc
– 'Seascape' NHlc
– 'Sibylla' (H) CB&S MAll NHlc WAbe
– 'Sir Joseph Banks' See H. ***m.*** 'Otaksa'
– 'Soeur Thérèse' ('Sister Therese') (H) CB&S CPle GAri IOrc MAll MAsh MGos WStI WWeb
– 'Souvenir du Président Paul Doumer' (H) CB&S CSco
– 'Taube' CB&S
*– 'Teller's Blue' MBri NHlc WDin
*– 'Teller's Red' CB&S IHos MBri WDin
– 'Teller's Variegated' See H. ***m.*** 'Tricolor'
– 'Teller's White' See H. ***m.*** 'Libelle'
– 'Tokyo Delight' CB&S CBrd CFil CMer IOrc NHlc SBla
– 'Tovelit' COtt EPla GAri MBri
§– 'Tricolor' AGM CB&S CBot CBow CBra CCla CSco EPla ERav ISea MAsh MBri MGos MTho SBod SChu SLon SPer SReu WCru WKif
¶– 'Twilight' NHlc
– 'Variegata' See H. ***m.*** 'Maculata'
– 'Veitchii' AGM CB&S CBot CCla CFil CGre CHan CMHG CSco ENot IJoh MBri SAxl SBod SDix WBod WWat
– 'Vicomte de Vibraye' See H. ***macrophylla*** 'Générale Vicomtesse de Vibraye'
– 'Westfalen' AGM NHlc SDix SPla
– 'White Lace' (L) ELan
– 'White Swan' (H) See H. ***m.*** 'Le Cygne'
– 'White Wave' AGM CCla CFil CPle CSco ENot MBar SBod SHBN SPer WDin WStI
– 'Wryneck' (H) NHlc
paniculata CFil CMCN CPle CTrw SLon
– 'Brussels Lace' CKni MAsh SMad SPla
– 'Floribunda' AGM CCla SPer
– 'Grandiflora' AGM CBot CBow CCla CPMA CSco ELan ENot GCHN GRei IOrc MBal MBar MBri MGos MWat NHlc NKay NNor NRoo SBod SHBN SLon SMad SPer SReu SSta WAbe WBod WDin
– 'Kyushu' AGM CAbb CB&S CBow CCla COtt CPMA CSco EBre ECtt ELan EPla ERav GCHN IOrc LBre MBlu MBri MGos MWat NBee NHar NHlc NRoo SPer SPla SSta WBod WHen WPat WWat

– 'Pink Diamond' CPMA EBee EBre EHar LBre LHop LRHS MAsh SMad
– 'Praecox' AGM CCla CSco ENot IDai NKay SDix SPer WPat WWin
– 'Tardiva' CB&S CBot CBow CSam CSco EHar EPla MRav NHlc SDix SHil SPer SPla WPat
– 'Touchard' CSco
– 'Unique' AGM CB&S CBow CCla CDoC CPMA EHar EPla IJoh LHop MBri NHlc SPla
– 'Vera' ENot
– 'White Moth' CKni CPMA EHar MAsh MBri MUlv
petiolaris See H. ***anomala p.***
'Preziosa' AGM Widely available
quelpartensis CB&S CChu CHan CPle CTre
quercifolia AGM Widely available
– 'Flore Pleno' See H. ***q.*** Snow Flake ®
– Snow Flake ® (d) CB&S CBow CChu COtt CPMA CSPN ELan EPla ERav MBri MUlv NBar SMad SPer SSta WWat
– Snow Queen ® CB&S CDoC CPMA CSco MAsh MBal MBri SPla WWat
¶ – 'Stardust' CRos
sargentiana See H. ***aspera s.***
scandens CGre CPle
– ssp. ***chinensis*** SPer
seemannii CB&S CBot CBow CChu CFil CHEx CMac CPle CSam CTrw EPla ISea LHop NHlc SArc WCru WSHC WWat
serrata CBow CDoC CTrw NHlc
– 'Acuminata' See H. ***s.*** 'Bluebird'
– 'Belle Deckle' See H. 'Blue Deckle'
§ – 'Bluebird' AGM CBot CBra CCla CFil CSco EBre ELan ISea LBre MBal MBri MGos NBee NHlc NKay SBod SDix SHBN SMad SPer SPla SSta WStI
– ***chinensis*** NHlc
– 'Diadem' CBrd CFil CPle EPla NHlc NSti SBod SDix SHBN WHil
– 'Grayswood' AGM CBot CCla CGre CHig CPle CSam CSco ECtt ENot LHop MBal NHlc NKay SDix SPer WKif WWat
– 'Intermedia' CCla ENot
– 'Macrosepala' CPle EHic
– 'Miranda' (L) CBrd CFil CMHG EHic EPla MUlv NHlc
– 'Preziosa' See H. 'P.'
– 'Rosalba' AGM EPla MRav SChu SPer SPla WSHC
– var. ***thunbergii*** CB&S CMHG CPle
§ ***serratifolia*** CBot CChu CGre EPla LHop SArc SHil WCru WSHC
sinensis See H. ***scandens chinensis***
tiliifolia See H. ***anomala petiolaris***
umbellata See H. ***scandens chinensis***
villosa See H. ***aspera*** Villosa Group

HYDRASTIS (Ranunculaceae)
canadensis CArn GPoy MSal

HYDROCHARIS (Hydrocharitaceae)
morsus-ranae CBen CRDP CWGN EHon EMFW IMal LMay MSta NDea SWat WChe

HYDROCLEYS (Limnocharitaceae)
See Plant Deletions

HYDROCOTYLE (Umbelliferae/Apiaceae)
§ ***americana*** NHol
asiatica See CENTELLA ***a.***
moschata CRiv GAri NHol WPer WWin
ranunculoïdes See H. ***americanum***
vulgaris MSta WChe WHol

HYDROPHYLLUM (Hydrophyllaceae)
appendiculatum MSal
canadense EMar EMon
virginianum MSal WEas

HYLOMECON (Papaveraceae)
japonica CLew CRDP EBar EPar MBri MSte MTho MTol MUlv NBir NKay NRya WCru WOMN

HYLOTELEPHIUM See SEDUM

HYMENANTHERA See MELICYTUS

HYMENOCALLIS (Liliaceae/Amaryllidaceae)
'Advance' LAma LBow
amancaes WChr
§ ***caroliniana*** LAma WChr
x ***festalis*** CMon CSut ERea LAma LBow MBri NRog SDeJ SLMG WChr
harrisiana LBow WChr
littoralis NRog
longipetala LBow WChr
narcissiflora WChr
occidentalis See H. ***caroliniana***
'Sulphur Queen' LBow NRog SDeJ SLMG WChr

HYMENOSPORUM (Pittosporaceae)
flavum CGre

HYMENOXYS (Compositae/Asteraceae)
See also TETRANEURIS
subintegra WPer

HYOPHORBE (Palmae/Arecaceae)
§ ***lagenicaulis*** LPal
¶ ***verschaffeltii*** CTro

HYOSCYAMUS (Solanaceae)
albus GBar MSal WWye
niger CArn CSFH EWFC GPoy MChe MSal WHer WWye

HYPERICUM † (Guttiferae)
acmosepalum SBEC 93 CChu
addingtonii CCla EPla
adenotrichum CNic GCHN
aegypticum CRiv CSam ELan EPad EPot ESis GCHN MHig MRPP NMen NWCA SGil SHer SIng WAbe WPat WPer
amblycalyx EWes SIgm

androsaemum	CArn CKin ECha ELan ENot EWFC MFir MHew MSal NMir NRoo SLon WDin WNdy
*– 'Autumn Blaze'	MBal MBel
– 'Dart's Golden Penny'	SLPl SPer
§ – 'Gladys Brabazon' (v)	EFol EMon EPla ERav MBel MUlv WCot WDin
– 'Orange Flair'	CDoC MGos
– 'Variegatum'	See H. ***a.*** 'Gladys Brabazon'
§ ***annulatum***	EFol ELan EMon ERav
athoum	ESis GCHN LHop MBro MHig MPla NHol NTow WPer
augustinii	CChu CPle CTre
balearicum	CHan CPle EPad EPla MAll MCas MPla MTho SChu SDry SIgm SSta WHil WPer
beanii	CChu EBar EMon LRHS
bellum	EMon GCal
– ssp. ***latisepalum***	CChu
¶ – pale form	EMon
buckleyi	GCHN MDHE MHig SIng
calycinum	CB&S CLan CPle CSco ELan ENot IDai ISea LBuc LGro MBal MBar MFir MGos MWat NNor NRoo NWea SHBN SLon SPer SReu STre WDin
§ ***cerastioïdes***	CLew CMHG CSam ESis GCHN MBro MPla NTow SChu SIgm SIng SUsu WAbe WHil WHoo WPer WWin
choisyanum B&L 12469	CChu
coris	CLew CSam CShe ECha EPot ESis LHil MBro MCas MTho MWat NMen NTow WCla WHoo
cuneatum	See H. ***pallens***
x ***cyathiflorum*** 'Gold Cup'	CTre MBal
x ***dummeri*** 'Peter Dummer'	CChu CCla MBri WWat
elatum	See H. x ***inodorum***
elodeoïdes	MSta SRms
elongatum	EMon ESis
empetrifolium	CLew EWes MCas MHig
§ – ssp. ***oliganthum***	ECha ESis ESma EWes GCHN NHar WOMN WPer
– 'Prostatum'	See H. ***e. oliganthum***
¶ ***erectum*** 'Gemo'	EBee
§ ***forrestii*** AGM	CBot CCla CLan CPle EHar ELan ENot GAul MBal MGos WWat
N ***fragile*** hort.	See H. ***olympicum minus***
frondosum	CLTr
– 'Buttercup'	EMil SPla
– Sunburst ®	EPla MBri MGos
'Gold Penny'	See H. ***androsaemum*** 'Dart's Golden Penny'
grandiflorum	See H. ***kouytchense***
henryi L 753	CChu
¶ – ssp. ***hancockii*** FSP 047	ISea
'Hidcote' AGM	Widely available
'Hidcote Variegated'	CMHG CMer COtt EBre EHar ELan EMon GCHN IJoh LBre MBal MUlv NWyt SPer WCru WWeb
hircinum ssp. ***cambessedesii***	EMon LRHS
– ssp. ***majus***	EMon
hirsutum	CKin
hookerianum	CLan GWht
humifusum	ECWi WCla
x ***inodorum***	SHer
– 'Albury Purple'	EBee EFol EPla LMer MHlr SHer WCot WDin
– 'Elstead'	CB&S CLan CShe ECtt ELan IDai LHop MBal MBar MBel MGos MWat NKay NNor NRoo SHBN SHer SPer SUsu WDin WEas WHCG WSHC WWin
– 'Summergold'	IBar SUsu
– 'Ysella'	CMer CRow ECha ECoo ECtt EFol ELan EPla NSti SDry SPla
¶ ***japonicum***	ECou
kalmianum	CBot CDoC EHar
kamtschaticum	CChu
kelleri	CLew GCHN NHol
§ ***kouytchense*** AGM	CLan CPle CSco EMon EPla IBar MBri SDry SPla WKif WPat WWeb
lagarocladum	CChu ELan
lancasteri	EMon LRHS
– L 750	CChu
N ***leschenaultii***	CLan
linarioïdes	WDav
¶ ***linoïdes***	CNat
¶ ***maclarenii***	WBod
– L 863	CChu CPle
manolatum	See H. ***annulatum***
montanum	MSal
x ***moserianum*** AGM	CB&S CLan CMHG CSco CShe EBre ENot IDai IJoh LBre MBal MBar MBri NNor NRoo SHBN SHer SPer WAbe WStI
§ – 'Tricolor' (v)	Widely available
– 'Variegatum'	See H. x ***m.*** 'Tricolor'
'Mrs Brabazon'	See H. ***androsaemum*** 'Gladys Brabazon'
nummularium	NWCA
olympicum AGM	CArn CMea CShe ECha ELan EPot GCHN GDra GLil GPlt IDai MFir MPla MWat NMen NNor SBla SIng SLon SPer SPla SSmi WHen
– 'Edith'	CLew NCat NHol SAsh WPat
– 'Grandiflorum'	See H. ***o. uniflorum***
§ – f. ***minus***	CNic ECha ECtt ELan EMNN ESis GCHN GDra GPlt IDai LBee MCas MRav NHol NKay NRoo SGil SHer SIgm STre WHil WPer WStI WWin
§ – – 'Sulphureum'	CBot CChu CRiv ESis MRav NRoo SGil SPer SUsu WSHC WWin
§ – – 'Variegatum'	CRDP EFol ELan MHig NRoo SIng WPat
§ – f. ***uniflorum***	CVer EBar EBre GAri GAul LBre MBal MBar MBro NBro NHol NPri NRoo NVic WAbe WCla WHoo
– – 'Citrinum' AGM	CLew CMea CNic ECha ECtt EFol EPot GCHN LBee LHop MBal MWat NBro NKay NRoo SBla SIgm WAbe WCla WDav WEas WOMN WWat
orientale	CLew CMHG CNic ECoo EMNN ESis GCHN GPlt MBro MPla NRoo NWCA SChu WCla WOld WPer
patulum var. ***forrestii***	See H. ***forrestii***
– var. ***henryi***	See H. ***pseudohenryi***
– 'Variegatum'	CMHG EFol EPla LHop MUlv SPer

perforatum	CArn CKin CSFH ECWi EWFC Effi GPoy LHol MChe MHew NLan NMir SIde WCla WHer WNdy WOak WPbr WWye
polyphyllum	See H. ***olympicum minus***
– ***citrinum***	See H. ***olympicum minus*** 'Sulphureum'
– 'Grandiflorum'	See H. ***olympicum uniflorum***
– 'Sulphureum'	See H. ***olympicum minus*** 'Sulphureum'
– 'Variegatum'	See H. ***olympicum minus*** 'Variegatum'
prolificum	CChu CCla CSco ECtt ELan EPla GCHN SChu SUsu
§ ***pseudohenryi***	EBar EMon
– B&L 12009	CChu
– L 1029	CChu
pseudopetiolatum	GTou
– var. ***yakusimense***	See H. ***y.***
pulchrum	CKin ECWi
quadrangulum Linnaeus	See H. ***tetrapterum***
reptans misapplied	See H. ***olympicum minus***
rhodoppeum	See H. ***cerastioïdes meuselianum***
'Rowallane' AGM	CB&S CBot CLTr CLan CPle CSco CTre CTrw IDai ISea LHop MArl MBri NBrk SDix SHBN SHer SPer WAbe WBod
stellatum	CGre EPla ESis SLon WWat
subsessile	ELan EMon
'Sungold'	See H. ***kouytchense***
tenuicaule KR 743	ISea
§ ***tetrapterum***	CKin CRDP ECWi EWFC MHew MSal MWil NLan
tomentosum	GCHN WPer
trichocaulon	CLew CMea ELan EMNN EPot GCHN LBee MBro MPit NHol NRoo SHer SIng WAbe WOMN WPat WPer WThu
uralum	EPla MBal
wilsonii	CChu
yakusimense	GCHN MBar MFir MTho NGre NTow NWCA SIng WCla WPer

HYPOCHAERIS (Compositae/Asteraceae)

¶ ***acaulis*** F&W 7208	MFos WDav
radicata	CKin ECWi NMir
¶ sp. JCA 3948	MFos
uniflora	CNic NGre WDav
§ ***variegata***	CLTr

HYPOCYRTA See NEMATANTHUS

HYPOËSTES (Acanthaceae)

¶ ***aristata***	CSpe
phyllostachya AGM	MBri
– 'Bettina' (v)	MBri
– 'Carmina' (v)	MBri
– 'Purpuriana' (v)	MBri
– 'Wit' (v)	MBri
sanguinolenta	See H. ***phyllostachya***

HYPOLEPIS (Dennstaedtiaceae)

millefolium	CFil CRDP GAri
punctata beddomei	WRic

HYPOXIS (Liliaceae/Hypoxidaceae)

hygrometrica	CRDP ECou NHol WAbe WPer WThu
krebsii	LHil

HYPOXIS X RHODOHYPOXIS (Liliaceae/Hypoxidaceae)

	See also RHODOHYPOXIS X HYPOXIS
parvula x ***baurii***	CRDP EPot NHar SBla SIng

HYPSELA (Campanulaceae)

longiflora	See H. ***reniformis***
§ ***reniformis***	CNic EBre ELan EMNN EPar EPot LBee LBre MCas MHig MPit NGre NHar NMen NNrd NOak NRed NWCA SSmi WPer WWin
– 'Greencourt White'	GAri GGar MCas NHar WPer

HYSSOPUS (Labiatae/Lamiaceae)

officinalis	CArn CBow CHan CSFH CSev ECha EHer ELan Effi GPoy IEde LAbb LBuc LHol MBri MChe MHew NRoo SChu SIde SSvw WCHb WEas WHer WHil WOak WPer WSun WWye
– f. ***albus***	CSFH ECED ECha EMon GPoy MChe NNor SChu SIde WCHb WHer WMar WPer WSun WWin WWye
– ssp. ***angustifolius***	See H. ***o. officinalis***
– ssp. ***aristatus***	CLew CSFH CSco EBre EMon ESis GPlt GPoy LBre LHol LLWP MChe NRoo SHer SIde WCHb WEas WPer WWin WWye
– ***decussatus***	MBar
§ – ***purpurascens***	LLWP
– ***roseus***	CRDP CSFH ECha EMon GPoy LAbb MChe NNor NSti SChu SIde WCHb WHer WKif WMar WPer WSun WWin WWye
– f. ***ruber***	See H. ***o. purpurascens***
seravshanicus	EMon
¶ ***tianschanicus***	MFos

HYSTRIX (Gramineae/Poaceae)

patula	EBee EHoe EMon EPla ETPC GAbr GCal NBro NCat NHol WHal WPer

IBERIS (Cruciferae/Brassicaceae)

amara	EWFC GPoy MSal
candolleana	See I. ***pruitii***
commutata	See I. ***sempervirens***
'Correvoniana'	WEas
gibraltarica	CLew CRiv ELan GAul LAbb NNor NPri NTow SRms WGor
jordanii	See I. ***pruitii***
§ ***pruitii***	CRiv EBur MBal NHol NKay SBla WCla
saxatilis	NHol WPat
– ***candolleana***	See I. ***pruitii***
semperflorens	NGar
§ ***sempervirens*** AGM	CB&S CMHG CNic CRiv ELan LAbb LGro LHop MBal MPit MWat NBro NGre NNor NOrc WCot WPer WTyr
– 'Little Gem'	See I. ***s.*** 'Weisser Zwerg'

– 'Pygmaea'	EMNN EWes MWat NHar NMen WDav WHil
– 'Schneeflocke' ('Snowflake') AGM	CHol CShe ENot GAri IDai MCas MFir SHer SIng SPer WHoo WPla
¶ – 'Starkers'	EMon
§ – 'Weisser Zwerg'	CLew CMea CShe EBre ECha EFou ELan EMNN EPla GLil LBee LBre MBro MCas MHig MPla MTho NGre NHar NHol NKay NMen NTow SBla SHer SIng WHoo WOld WWin

IDESIA (Flacourtiaceae)

polycarpa	CB&S CMCN EHar SHil WCoo WWat

ILEX † (Aquifoliaceae)

¶ x ***altaclerensis***	SHHo
– 'Atkinsonii' (m)	CRos
N– 'Belgica Aurea' AGM	CB&S CMHG CRos CSam EHar ELan LNet MBal MBar MBri MWat NHol SGil SHBN SHHo SHil
– 'Camelliifolia' AGM	CChu CMCN CMHG CRos ELan GWht MMea MRav MUlv MWat SBod SGil SHHo SHil SMad SPer WWat
– 'Camelliifolia Variegata' (f)	CChu
– 'Golden King' AGM	Widely available
– 'Hendersonii' (f)	SBod
– 'Hodginsii' AGM	CDoC CRos ECot IOrc IReg MBar
– 'Lady Valerie' (f/v)	IReg SHHo
– 'Lawsoniana' AGM	CB&S CDec CMHG CPle CRos CSam EBre EHoe ELan LAbb LBre LNet MBal MBar MBri MGos MMea MWat NHol NWea SBod SGil SHHo SHil SLon SMad SPer WDin WPat WThu
– 'Maderensis Variegata'	See I. ***aquifolium*** 'M.V.'
– 'Nigrescens' (m)	MWat
– 'Ripley Gold' (v/f)	CBow SHHo
– 'Silver Sentinel'	See I. x ***a.*** 'Belgica Aurea'
– 'Wilsonii' AGM	CMHG IOrc IReg MMea MWat SBod SMad
aquifolium AGM	CB&S CKin CPer CSam CSco GRei LNet MBar MBri MGos MWat SHBN SLon WDin WMou WStI
– 'Alaska' (f)	CDoC CMCN CRos EBre IHos LBre LBuc MBal MMea MWat SHHo WMou
– 'Alcicornis' (m)	CMCN
– 'Amber' (f)	COtt LHop MWat SHHo SHil SMad
– 'Angustifolia' (m or f)	CB&S EHar EPla GAri IOrc MBar MWat SArc SHHo WPat WThu WWeb
§ – 'Argentea Marginata' AGM	CB&S CBra CSam CSco CShe EBre ECtt ENot ISea LBre LPan MBri MGos MMea MRav NBee NWea SHHo SPer SReu WAbe WDin WPat WStI
§ – 'Argentea Marginata Pendula' (f)	CSco CShe EHar ELan LPan MBal MBri NHol SBod SHHo SHil SLon SPer SReu WPat WWat WWeb
– 'Argentea Pendula' (f)	See I. ***a.*** 'Argentea Marginata Pendula'
– 'Argentea Variegata' (f)	See I. ***a.*** 'Argentea Marginata'
– 'Atlas' (m)	CB&S CDoC CRos LBuc
– 'Aurea Marginata' (f)	CMHG ECtt EHoe ELan LHop LPan MMea SBod SHBN SHHo WAbe WPat
– 'Aurea Marginata Pendula' (f)	CDoC CRos EBee NHol WPat
– 'Aurea Ovata'	See I. ***a.*** 'Ovata Aurea'
– 'Aurea Regina'	See I. ***a.*** 'Golden Queen'
– 'Aurifodina' (f)	IReg
§ – 'Bacciflava' (f)	CPle CSam ECtt EHar ELan EPla GCHN IOrc IReg ISea MBal MBlu MGos MMea MRav MWat NBee SPer WDin
– 'Crassifolia' (m)	EPla
– 'Crispa' (m)	CRos EPla ISea MBal NHol SHHo WPat
– 'Ferox' (m)	CBra CLan EHal EHar ELan LPan MBal SHHo SMad
– 'Ferox Argentea' AGM	CCla CMHG CRos EBre ECtt EHar ELan IJoh IOrc ISea LBre LNet MBal MBar MBri MMea MRav MWat NHol NKay SHBN SHHo SMad SPer SPla SReu WAbe WPat WSHC
– 'Ferox Aurea' (m/v)	CBra CCla CMHG CPle EHar ELan EPla MWat NBee NHol SGil SHHo SPer WPat
– 'Flavescens' (f)	CBot EHar EPla SHil
– 'Fructu Luteo'	See I. ***a.*** 'Bacciflava'
– 'Gold Flash' (f/v)	ECtt EMil MBri NBee NHol
– 'Golden Milkboy' AGM	CB&S CBow CCla CLan CRos ECtt ELan ENot IHos LNet MBal MWat NHol SHHo SPla WPat
– 'Golden Milkmaid' (f/v)	CRos IOrc
§ – 'Golden Queen' AGM	CB&S CRos ELan ENot IJoh LNet MBal SHil SPer SReu
* – 'Golden Tears'	SHHo
– 'Golden van Tol' (f/v)	CB&S CBra CRos CSco EBre ECtt ENot IJoh IOrc ISea LBre LHol LNet MBal MBar MBri SGil SHBN SHHo WStI
– 'Green Pillar' AGM	MMea SHHo
– 'Handsworth New Silver' AGM	Widely available
§ – 'Hascombensis'	CLew CRos GDra LGre LHop MBal MGos MPla NHar NHol SAxl WPat WWat
– 'Hastata' (m)	CMHG SHHo SMad
– 'Ingramii' (m/v)	CRos EHar SHHo
– 'J C van Tol' AGM	CSco EBre ECtt ELan ENot IDai IJoh IOrc LBre MBal MBar MBri MGos MWat NBee NHol NRoo NWea SBod SHBN SHHo SPer SReu SSta WDin WMou WStI WTyr WWat
– 'Lichtenthalii' (f)	SHHo
– 'Madame Briot' AGM	CDoC CMHG CRos CSco EHar ELan ENot IOrc LHol MBal MBar MBri MMea NHol NRoo SBod SGil SHHo SHer SPer SPla SReu WAbe WDin
§ – 'Maderensis Variegata' (m)	SHHo
– moonlight holly	See I. ***a.*** 'Flavescens'
– 'Myrtifolia' (m)	CDoC CSam ELan EPla GAri IBar MBar MBri NHol SGil

– 'Myrtifolia Aurea Maculata' AGM — CDoC CLan CMHG CRos EBar EHar EHoe ELan LNet MBal MBri MWat NHol NWea SChu SMad WPat
§ – 'Ovata Aurea' (m/v) — CBra CRos SSta
– 'Pendula' (f) — CDoC CRos MBri SBod SHHo
– 'Pendula Mediopicta' — See I. *a.* 'Weeping Golden Milkmaid'
§ – 'Pyramidalis' AGM — CSco EBre ELan ENot GCHN GRei IHos LBre MBar MBri NBee NHol NWea SHHo SPer SPla SReu WAbe WDin
– 'Pyramidalis Aureomarginata' (f) — CDoC
– 'Pyramidalis Fructu Luteo' AGM — CSco EHar MBar SHHo
– 'Recurva' (m) — EPla MWat WWeb
– 'Rubricaulis Aurea' (f/v) — MBal
– 'Silver King' — See I. *a.* 'Silver Queen'
– 'Silver Milkboy' (f/v) — CB&S CMHG ELan MBal MBri
– 'Silver Milkmaid' AGM — CB&S CCla CMHG IJoh MBar MRav MWat SHBN SHHo SHer SPer SPla SSta
§ – 'Silver Queen' AGM — CB&S CLan CSco EBre ELan GRei IDai IJoh ISea LBre LHol MBal MBar MBri MGos MMea MWat NBee NHol NRoo NWea SHHo SPer SPla WHen WStI
– 'Silver Sentinel' — See I. x ***altaclerensis*** 'Belgica Aurea'
– 'Silver van Tol' (f/v) — EHar MBri SHHo WAbe WStI
§ – 'Watereriana' (m/v) — CLan ISea MAsh MBal SBod SGil
– 'Waterer's Gold' — See I. *a.* 'Watereriana'
x ***attenuata*** — CRos SMad
– 'Sunny Foster' (f) — CRos EBee EHar EPla
bioritsensis — MMea
cassine — IReg
*– yellow-berried — CMCN
ciliospinosa — CMCN CRos GWht
'Clusterberry' (f) — CRos
colchica — CRos
cornuta — CLan CLew CMCN CRos EPla GAri SHHo
*– 'Aurea' — SHHo
– 'Burfordii' (f) — CRos SHil
¶ – Korean form — EPla
– 'O'Spring' (f/v) — CMHG CRos EPla SHHo SMad
– 'Rotunda' (f) — EPla
crenata — CMCN MBar MGos SArc SReu STre WBod WCru WWat
– 'Aureovariegata' — See I. *c.* 'Variegata'
§ – 'Bennett's Compact' (m) — CMHG
♦– 'Compacta' — See I. *c.* 'Bennett's Compact'
– 'Convexa' AGM — CB&S CDoC ENot GDra GWht MBal MBar MBri NHol NWea SHHo WPat WWat
– 'Fastigiata' — LHol SHHo
– 'Fukarin' — See I. *c.* 'Shiro-fukurin'
– 'Golden Gem' AGM — Widely available
¶ – 'Green Dragon' — EPla
– 'Green Island' (m) — CRos EPla LRHS
– 'Helleri' (f) — MBar NHol WPat
– 'Ivory Hall' (f) — CRos EPla
– 'Luteovariegata' — See I. *c.* 'Variegata'
– 'Mariesii' (f) — GWht MBlu MHig MPla NHed NHol SBla SIng WPat
– f. ***microphylla*** — CMHG
– 'Mount Halla' (f) — CMCN
I – 'Pyramidalis' (f) — EHic NHar
I – 'Rotundifolia' — EPla
– 'Sentinel' (f) — CLew CMHG CSam
§ – 'Shiro-fukurin' (f/v) — CMCN CMHG EHic ELan EPla LGre NHar NHol SHHo SPla WEas WPat
– 'Snowflake' — See I. *c.* 'Shiro-fukurin'
– 'Stokes' (m) — GAri NHol WPat
– 'Twiggy' (f) — CLew
– upright form — CMCN
§ – 'Variegata' — CDoC CMHG CSam EBre ELan EPla GAri LBre MBar MBlu SHHo
'Dazzler' — SHHo
decidua — CMCN
– 'Warren Red' (f) — CMCN
dimorphophylla — CChu SGil SHHo
'Doctor Kassab' (f) — CMCN
'Drace' (f) — ELan EPla
Dragon Lady ® (f) — EPla SGil
'Elegance' (f) — CRos MBlu
ficoidea — CMCN
glabra 'Ivory Queen' (f) — CRos
– 'Snow White' (f) — MBal
'Good Taste' (f) — CRos
hascombensis — See I. ***aquifolium*** 'Hascombensis'
hookeri — CMHG
'Indian Chief' (f) — CMHG CSam MBri SMad WWat
insignis — See I. ***kingiana***
*'Jim' — LRHS
'John T Morris' (m) — CRos MBal
§ ***kingiana*** — CB&S SHil WWat
x ***koehneana*** — CBot
– 'Chestnut Leaf' AGM — CCla CMCN CMHG EHar EPla MMea MRav SHHo SHil SMad
§ ***kusanoi*** — CMCN
latifolia — CB&S CHEx CMCN EHar SArc SHHo SHil SMad
longipes — CMCN
'Lydia Morris' (f) — CMHG CSam EPla SHHo WWat
macropoda — CMCN
x ***makinoi*** — CMCN
x ***meserveae*** Blue Angel ® AGM — COtt CRos CSam ECtt EHoe ENot IOrc LHol MBal MBri MMea MWat NHol NNor SHer SPer SReu SSta WDin WPat WStI WWat
– 'Blue Boy' (m) — CRos
– 'Blue Girl' (f) — CRos
– 'Blue Prince' (m) — CB&S CBow CMHG COtt CRos EHoe IOrc LBuc LHol MBal MBar MMea NBee NHed NHol SHBN SHHo SHer SPer WDin WStI
– Blue Princess® AGM — CB&S CBow CDec CMHG COtt CRos ENot LBuc LHop LPan MBal MBar MMea NHol SHBN SHHo SPer SReu SSta WDin WStI
*– 'Glenroy Purple' — MBal
– 'Goliath' (f) — CRos
*– 'Red Darling' (f) — COtt CSco
muchagara — CB&S CMCN
myrtifolia — CMCN CSco ECot NHar SPer
– yellow-berried — CMCN
'Nellie R Stevens' (f) — CRos ENot IHos
nothofagifolia C&H 424 — GAri GGGa

opaca	CMCN EArb
pedunculosa	CMCN SHHo
perado latifolia	See I. ***p. platyphylla***
§ – ssp. ***platyphylla***	CB&S CHEx CMCN CMHG SHHo
pernyi	CB&S IOrc IReg LBuc MBal MBri NHol SHHo SHil SLon SPla WThu WWat WWeb
– var. ***veitchii***	CRos EPla NWea
poneantha	See I. ***kusanoi***
pringlei	CMCN
'Pyramidalis'	See I. ***aquifolium*** 'Pyramidalis'
rotunda	CMCN
rugosa	CMCN
'September Gem' (f)	CMCN CRos
serrata	CMCN IReg WWes
'Sparkleberry' (f)	CRos
verticillata (f)	CPle CRos ELan GAri SPer
– (m)	ELan GAri
– 'Afterglow' (f)	MBlu
– f. ***aurantiaca*** (f)	MBlu
– 'Christmas Cheer' (f)	SHil
– dwarf male early-flowering	MBlu
– early male late-flowering	MBlu
§ – 'Nana' (f)	MBlu
– 'Red Sprite'	See I. ***v.*** 'Nana'
– 'Winter Red' (f)	MBlu
x ***wandoensis***	CMCN
'Washington' (f)	EPla NHol WPat
yunnanensis	CMCN CRos GAri GWht

ILIAMNA See SPHAERALCEA

ILLICIUM (Illiciaceae)

anisatum	CArn CChu CCla CHan CPle CTre EPla NHol SBor SHil SSta WPat WSHC WWat WWye
floridanum	CBow CChu CCla MBal NRar SPer SSta WBod WCoo WSHC WWat
henryi	SHil WSHC
verum	MSal

ILYSANTHES (Scrophulariaceae)

****floribunda***	CSpe

IMPATIENS (Balsaminaceae)

auricoma	EBak
burtonii	CGre
double flowered forms	EBak
glandulifera 'Candida'	CBre EMon
hawkeri	EBak
New Guinea hybrids	EBak MBri
niamniamensis	EBak ERea GCra
– 'Congo Cockatoo'	CTro
pseudoviola	CSpe
¶ ***sodenii***	LBlm
tinctoria	CChu CFil CGre CTre EMon GCal LHil SBor
¶ – ssp. ***elegantissima***	CFee
walleriana	EBak MBri

IMPERATA (Gramineae/Poaceae)

cylindrica	EPar EPla GCal MHlr NRar NSti WCot
– 'Red Baron'	See I. ***c.*** 'Rubra'
§ – 'Rubra'	CAbb CBow CDec CDoC CFil CLew CRDP ECha EFou EHoe ELan ETPC GAbr LHil LHop MBri SBla SChu SFar SHer SPer SPla SWas WHal WPat WPbr WPer WRus WWat WWye

INCARVILLEA (Bignoniaceae)

§ ***arguta***	CBot CChu CHad CHan CNic ECro EMon GCal GCra GMac LGre NSti SAxl SMrm SUsu WHil WOld WPer WThi WWin
– C&Mc 117	GCHN
brevipes	See I. ***mairei***
compacta	MSto WHoo WThu
delavayi	Widely available
– 'Bees' Pink'	CAvo ELan GBuc GCra
¶ ***forrestii*** KGB 43	MSto
¶ ***lutea*** L 1986	SBla
§ ***mairei***	ECro ESma GDra LHop MTho NHol WDav WPer
– 'Frank Ludlow'	GDra NHar NSla
– var. ***grandiflora***	ELan EPot MTho SBla
– 'Nyoto Sama'	GDra SBla
– pink	NCat
§ ***olgae***	CBot CSam EBee ELan EMon MSto SMrm WHoo
sinensis	WPer
– 'Alba'	MSto SUsu WCru
sp. CLD 0233	NHol

INDIGOFERA (Leguminosae/Papilionaceae)

amblyantha AGM	CBow CChu CPle EHar EMil ESma GAbr GCal NSti SDry WCru WKif WSHC
dielsiana	CB&S CChu CPle ESma GCal WSHC
gerardiana	See I. ***heterantha***
hebepetala	WBod WDin WSHC
§ ***heterantha*** AGM	CB&S CBot CBra CCla CGre CPle CSco EHar ELan ENot ERav ESis IJoh IOrc LHop MPla NBar NKay SBla SHBN SLon SPer SReu SSta WBod WDin WSHC WWat
kirilowii	CGre
potaninii	CDoC CSco SHBN SHil WCru WOMN
pseudotinctoria	CChu ESma GCal SRms

INDOCALAMUS (Gramineae/Poaceae-Bambusoideae)

hamadae	EPla SDry
latifolius	EPla SBam SDry WJun
longiauritus	SBam SDry
solidus	EPla SBam SDry WJun
¶ ***tessellatus***	EPla

INULA † (Compositae/Asteraceae)

acaulis	MTho
conyzae	CKin MHew MSal
crithmoïdes	WHer
♦ ***dysenterica***	See PULICARIA ***d.***

ensifolia	CBow CHan CLew CSam ECro ELan IBlr LHop MPit MRav MTho NDea NHol SFis SSvw WEas WHoo WMer
– 'Compacta'	MBri
– 'Gold Star'	CBow CHol CMGP ECtt ESma LHil NBir NHol NNor NOak NRoo NVic WPer WTyr
glandulosa	See I. ***orientalis***
'Golden Beauty'	See BUPHTHALMUM ***salicifolium*** 'G.B.'
helenium	CArn CKin CRDP CSFH CSev ECWi ECro EWFC Effi GAbr GPoy ILis LHol MChe MFir MHew MSal NMir SIde WByw WHal WHer WOak WPer WWye
hookeri	CBre CMea CRDP CSev EBar ECha ELan EMar EMon EPla GMac IBlr LHop MBel MBri MFir MSte NDea NHol NSti SDix WAbb WByw WDav WEas WHal WOld WTyr
magnifica	CHan CLew CSam EBre ECha ECro EFol ELan EMon ESma GAbr GGar LBre MBri MBro MFir MRav MUlv NDea NHol SDix SFis SMrm SSvw WHal WHoo WMer WOld WPer WWin
* 'Mediterranean Sun'	NNrd SIde WHil
¶ ***oculus-christi***	EBee ECro SFis
§ ***orientalis***	CDoC CSco ECro EFou ESma GAbr GCra LHop MArl MBri MBro NCat NMir NNor NRoo WHoo WOld WPer
racemosa	ECha ECro EMon ESma GCal MBel MSte SRms
– C&Mc 620	GCHN
rhizocephala	CSam EWoo
royleana	CSam ECha EPla GCal GCra MBel MBri MBro MSte NSti SUsu
sp. CLD 658	EMon
verbascifolia	GCal

IOCHROMA (Solanaceae)

cyanea	CGre CPle CTro ERea LHil
grandiflora	CHEx SLMG
violacea	CPle CSPN ERea LBlm LHil
warscewiczii	CTro

IPHEION (Liliaceae/Alliaceae)

'Alberto Castello'	CBro WChr
dialystemon	CMon
§ 'Rolf Fiedler' **AGM**	CAvo CBro CMon EBul ELan EPar EPot MTho NGar NHol SBla SHer SWas WChr WOMN WThu
uniflorum	CAvo CBro CHan CNic CRiv ECha EFol ETub LAma MBri MBro MTol NGar NMen NNrd NRog NWCA SIng WAbb WCla WHoo WPer
– ***album***	CAvo CBro CMon EBul ECha ELan EPar EPot GDra MTho NGar SBla SIng WChr
– 'Froyle Mill' **AGM**	CAvo CBro CRiv EBur EPar EPot GDra LBow MTho NGar NHol NNrd SBla SHer SIng WChr
– 'Wisley Blue' **AGM**	CAvo CBro CMea CNic CRiv ECha ELan EPar EPot ETub GPlt LAma LBow LHil LHop MFos MTho NGar NHol NNrd SBla SIng WChr WCru WHil WHoo WWat

IPOMOEA (Convolvulaceae)

acuminata	See I. ***indica***
§ ***cairica***	ECou
carnea	CNew
¶ ***hederacea***	WHaw
§ ***indica*** **AGM**	CB&S CHEx CKni CLTr CMer CNew CTro ERea GCal LAbb SLMG SSad WHaw
learii	See I. ***indica***
palmata	See I. ***cairica***
purpurea	CTro WHer
quamoclit	WHaw
¶ 'Scarlett O'Hara'	WGor
tuberosa	See MERREMIA ***t.***

IPOMOPSIS (Polemoniaceae)

¶ ***aggregata arizonica***	WDav
rubra	WPer
¶ – K 92.249	WDav

IRESINE (Amaranthaceae)

herbstii	EBak ERea GBur IBlr NWyt SLMG
– 'Brilliantissima'	CBrk
lindenii **AGM**	CBrk SLMG
¶ – 'Formosa'	CTro

IRIS † (Iridaceae)

'A W Tait' (***spuria***)	GCal
'Abracadabra' (SDB)	LBro MRob MS&S
'Abridged Version' (MTB)	NZep
'Acapulco Gold' (TB)	SCro
'Ace of Clubs' (SDB)	NZep
'Action Front' (TB)	CKel ECas ERou NFai SChu SGil SHer WTyr
'Actress' (TB)	EFou
acutiloba	EPot LAma
'Adobe Sunset' (Spuria)	LBro MS&S
'Adrienne Taylor' **AGM**	LBro MAus WWin
'Ain't She Sweet' (IB)	SCro
aitchisonii chrysantha	NHol
'Alastor' (TB)	CKel MS&S
'Alba' (***sibirica***)	CRDP CRow ECha EHic EWav GDra MNFA NKay SBla
'Albatross' (TB)	CKel
albicans	CMon MAus
¶ 'Alcazar' (TB)	GLil
'Alenette' (TB)	MAus
'Alien' (IB)	LBro
'All Right' (IB)	NZep
¶ 'All the Way' (AB)	LBro
'Allegiance' (TB)	MAus WEas
'Alpine Lake' (MDB)	NZep
'Amadora' (TB)	LBro
'Amaranth Gem' (SDB)	LBro
'Amas' (***germanica***)	MAus
'Amazon Princess' (SDB)	NZep
'Ambassadeur' (TB)	CKel ERou
'Amber Blaze' (SDB)	NZep
'Amber Queen' (DB)	CMGP EBee ECas ECtt ELan LHil NMen SChu SPer
'American Heritage' (TB)	NZep
'Amethyst Crystal' (CH)	LBro

'Amethyst Flame' (TB)	CKel EBre ERou LBre LHil MAus MS&S
'Amethyst Sunset' (MTB)	LBro
'Amphora' (SDB)	CBro NNrd
¶ 'Amsterdam' (TB)	CKel
¶ 'Anastasia' (TB)	CKel
'Ancilla' (Aril)	CMon EPot
'Angel Unawares' (TB)	MAus
'Angelic' (SDB)	LBro MAus
'Angel's Kiss' (SDB)	NZep
'Angel's Tears'	See I. ***histrioïdes*** 'Angel's Eye'
¶ 'Anglesey' (***sibirica***)	LBro
anglica	See I. ***latifolia***
'Ann Dasch' (***sibirica***)	EFou LBro
'Anna Belle Babson' (TB)	SCro
'Annabel Jane' (TB)	LBro MAus SCro
'Anne Elizabeth' (SDB)	CBro
'Annemarie Troeger' (***sibirica***)	LBro
'Annikins' (IB)	NZep
'Anniversary' (***sibirica***)	LBro MAus SCro
'Antarctic' (TB)	CKel CMGP
'Apache Warrior' (IB)	LBro
aphylla	MAus NOrc WThu
'Appledore' (SDB)	CBro MRob
'April Accent' (MDB)	MRob
'April Ballet' (MDB)	NZep
'Apropos' (TB)	MAus
¶ 'Aquilifer' (AB)	LBro
'Arab Chief' (TB)	CKel
'Arabi Pasha' (TB)	MAus SMrm SPer WGor
'Arabi Treasure' (IB)	LBro
'Arabic Night' (IB)	MAus
'Archie Owen' (Spuria)	LBro MAus
'Arctic Fancy' **AGM**	CKel LBro SCro
'Arctic Star' (TB)	CKel CShe
'Arctic Tern' (TB)	LBro
'Arctic Wine' (TB)	MAus
'Arden' (BB)	LBro
arenaria	See I. ***humilis***
'Arnold Sunrise' **AGM**	LBro
'Arnold Velvet' (SDB)	LBro MRob
'Art Gallery' (IB)	NZep
'Ask Alma' (IB)	LBro NZep
¶ 'Attention Please' (TB)	CKel
§ ***attica***	CBro CMon EPot LAma LBee MHig MSto WThu
– S&L 486	CMon
§ ***aucheri***	CBro EPot LAma WChr
'Audacious' (BB)	NZep
'Austrian Sky' (SDB)	CBot CHad CSam EGol ELan LBro MAus MBri MBro MMil MRob
'Autumn Leaves' (TB)	MAus MMil
'Avanelle' (IB)	EFou ERou LBro
'Az Ap' (IB)	NZep SCro
'Aztec Star' (SDB)	LBro
'Azure Excho' (IB)	LBro
'Babe' (SDB)	NZep
¶ 'Baby Bibs' (MTB)	NZep
'Baby Blessed' (SDB)	CBro NSti NZep
'Baby Face' (TB)	MMil
'Baccarat' (TB)	CKel
'Baked Alaska' (TB)	MMil
bakeriana	LAma LRHS
'Ballerina Blue' (TB)	ERou
'Ballyhoo' (TB)	MAus
'Banbury Beauty' (CH)	LBro NSti
'Banbury Fair' (CH)	LBro
'Banbury Melody' (CH)	LBro
'Banbury Ruffles' (SDB)	CKel MAus NSti WHil
'Banbury Welcome' (CH)	IBlr
'Bang' (TB)	CKel
'Barbara's Kiss' (Spuria)	LBro
'Barbushka' (SDB)	LBro
'Baria' (SDB)	CBot EPot LBro
'Barletta' (TB)	CKel MAus
barnumae polakii (Oncocyclus)	See I. ***polakii***
'Baroque Prelude' (TB)	CKel MMil
'Basso' (IB)	SCro
'Batik' (BB)	SCro
'Batsford' (SDB)	CBro
'Baxteri' (***sibirica***)	CRow
'Bay Ruffles' (SDB)	NZep
'Be Dazzled' (SDB)	EFou LBro
¶ 'Be Happy' (SDB)	NZep
¶ 'Beaumaris' (***sibirica***)	LBro
'Beauty Mark' (SDB)	NSti NZep
¶ 'Beckon' (TB)	CKel
'Bedtime Story' (IB)	LBro
'Bee Wings' (MDB)	MRob NZep WEas
'Belise' (Spuria)	LBro
'Benton Arundel' (TB)	SCro
'Benton Cordelia' (TB)	SCro
'Benton Dierdre' (TB)	SCro SRms
'Benton Lorna' (TB)	SCro
'Benton Nigel' (TB)	MAus
'Benton Sheila' (TB)	SCro
'Berkeley Gold' (TB)	CMGP CSco ECas ECtt ERav LHil NOrc SPer
¶ 'Berliner Runde' (***sibirica***)	LBro
'Berry Rich' (BB)	SCro
'Betsey Boo' (SDB)	CKel MRob NZep
'Betty Chatten' (TB)	MHig NMen NNrd
'Betty Cooper' (Spuria)	LBro MS&S
'Betty Wood' (SDB)	LBro
'Beverly Sills' (TB)	CKel EFou
'Beyond' (TB)	SCro
'Bibury' (SDB)	EGle LBro MAus MMil
'Big Day' (TB)	CKel
'Big Wheel' (CH)	LBro
biliottii	CBro
'Black Dragon' (TB)	SCro
¶ 'Black Flag' (TB)	LBro
'Black Hills' (TB)	CKel MAus MUlv
'Black Lady' (MTB)	LBro
'Black Swan' (TB)	EBre ECtt ELan ERav GCHN LBre MAus MRav MRob SMrm SPer
'Black Watch' (IB)	CKel NZep
'Blackberry Brandy' (BB)	LBro
* 'Blackfoot'	ESma
'Blazing Saddles' (TB)	NZep
'Blenheim Royal' (TB)	SCro
'Blitz' (SDB)	NZep
'Blue Asterisk' (IB)	LBro

'Blue Ballerina' **AGM** LBro
¶ 'Blue Burgee' (***sibirica***) ECha SCro
¶ 'Blue Chip Pink' (TB) LBro
'Blue Denim' (SDB) CBro CSco CSpe EBar EBre ECtt EGle EGol ENot GCHN LBre LBro LHil MRob MS&S WCra WMar WMer
'Blue Doll' (MDB) MRob MS&S NZep
'Blue Duchess' (TB) CKel LHil
'Blue Elegance' (Dutch) LAma
'Blue Eyed Blond' (IB) SCro
'Blue Eyed Brunette' **AGM** LHil MAus
'Blue Hendred' (SDB) LBro MAus NBir
¶ 'Blue Horizon' NMen
'Blue Icing' (IB) NZep
'Blue King' (***sibirica***) CKel
'Blue Line' (SDB) NZep
'Blue Luster' **AGM** LBro SCro
'Blue Magic' (Dutch) LAma NRog
'Blue Mascara' (SDB) SCro
'Blue Mere' (***sibirica***) LBro
'Blue Moss' (SDB) LBro
'Blue Neon' (SDB) NZep
'Blue Owl' (TB) CKel
'Blue Pigmy' (SDB) CGle CMGP CSco EBre ECas LBre NBar NMen NNrd SCro SPer
'Blue Pools' (SDB) EFou EGle LBro MHFP NZep SCro
'Blue Reflections' (TB) MMil
'Blue Rhythm' (TB) CKel CMGP CSco EBee ECas EHal ERou LBuc MAus NFai NPri SCro SMrm SPer
'Blue Sapphire' (TB) MAus
'Blue Shimmer' (TB) EBee EBre ECas ELan ENot LBre MAus MRav NFai SCro SPer
'Blue Smoke' (TB) CKel
'Blue Sparks' (SDB) LBro
'Blue Staccato' (TB) CKel SCro
'Blue Zephyr' (Spuria) LBro
'Bluebird in Flight' (IB) LBro
'Bluebird Wine' (TB) MAus
'Blushes' (IB) SCro
'Blushing Pink' (TB) SCro
'Bodderlecker' (SDB) EFou
'Bold Lassie' (SDB) LRHS WHer
'Bold Print' (IB) NZep SCro
'Bonny' (MDB) CBro
'Boo' (SDB) CKel LRHS MAus NZep
'Bracknell' (***sibirica***) CWGN
bracteata CFil CNic EBul EPot MHig SIng WPer
'Braithwaite' (TB) CKel EHic ELan ERou LBro LBuc LHil MAus SMrm SRms
brandzae See I. ***sintenisii b.***
'Brannigan' (SDB) CBro EGol LBro LHil MMil MRob NBir NNrd
'Brass Tacks' (SDB) LBro MAus NZep
'Brassie' (SDB) CBro CKel CRiv LBro LHil MRob NNrd SIng
¶ 'Breakers' (TB) LBro
'Bridal Crown' (TB) SCro
'Bride' (DB) CSpe LHil
'Bride's Halo' (TB) SCro
¶ 'Bright Button' (DB) CKel
'Bright Chic' (SDB) NZep
'Bright Moment' (SDB) LBro NZep
'Bright Vision' (SDB) MRob NZep
'Bright White' (MDB) CBro CKel EPot LBro MRob NMen NNrd WHil
'Bright Yellow' (DB) EBre GCHN LBre MRav
'Brighteyes' (IB) CSco EBre ELan ENot ESis LBre LBro LHil MHig MRob MS&S MTho SChu SCro WHil WPer
'Brilliant Excuse' (TB) NZep
'Brindisi' (TB) CKel SCro
'Bristo Magic' (TB) SCro
'Bristol Gem' (TB) SCro
'Broad Grin' (SDB) LBro NZep
'Broadleigh Ann' (CH) CBro
'Broadleigh Dorothy' (CH) CBro
'Broadleigh Elizabeth' (CH) CBro
'Broadleigh Emily' (CH) CBro
'Broadleigh Florence' (CH) CBro EGle
'Broadleigh Joan' (CH) CBro
'Broadleigh Lavinia' (CH) CBro
'Broadleigh Mitre' (CH) CBro
'Broadleigh Nancy' (CH) CBro
'Broadleigh Peacock' (CH) CBro
'Broadleigh Rose' (CH) CBro EOrc LGre SMrm
'Broadleigh Sybil' (CH) CBro WCru
'Broadleigh Victoria' (CH) CBro LBro WCru
'Broadway' (TB) NZep SCro
'Bromyard' (SDB) CBro MAus
'Bronze Beauty' (***hoogiana*** x) EPot
'Bronze Bird' (TB) CKel
'Bronze Charm' (TB) CKel
'Bronze Cloud' (TB) CKel
'Bronze Perfection' (Dutch) LAma
'Bronze Queen' (Dutch) LAma
'Broseley' (TB) LBro
'Brown Doll' (IB) NZep
'Brown Lasso' (BB) EFou LBro SCro
'Brown Trout' (TB) CKel
'Brummit's Mauve' MAus
¶ 'Bryngwyn' (TB) LBro
¶ 'Brynmawr' (***sibirica***) LBro
'Bubbling Over' (TB) SCro
'Bubbly Blue' (IB) NZep
bucharica x ***aucheri*** EPot
bucharica Foster CAvo CBro CMon EPar EPot ETub GCra LAma LBow MBro NHar NRog WChr WHil WThu
bucharica hort. See I. ***orchioïdes***
bulleyana SRms SWas
'Bumblebee Deelite' (MTB) NZep
'Bunny Hop' (SDB) NZep
'Burgundy Brown' (TB) NZep
¶ 'Burmese Dawn' (TB) CKel
'Butter and Sugar' (***sibirica***) CRos LBro NFai NSti WTyr
'Butter Pecan' (IB) NZep SCro
'Buttercup Bower' (TB) MAus

'Buttercup Charm' (MDB) NZep
'Buttered Chocolate' (Spuria) LBro
'Buttermere' (TB) SRms
'Buttermilk' LGre
'Butterpat' (IB) NZep
'Butterscotch Kiss' (TB) EBre ELan ERou LBre MMil SMrm
'Button Box' (SDB) NZep
'Byword' (SDB) LBro
caerulea See I. ***albomarginata***
'Caesar' (***sibirica***) CKel LBro MHlr MNFA WCot
'Caesar's Brother' (***sibirica***) CMGP IBlr MAus MSta MUlv SPer WWin
'Caliente' (TB) MAus
'California Style' (IB) NZep
§ Californian hybrids CChu CGle CWGN ELan EMon EOrc GAbr GCra LHil MBal NSti SChu WBon
'Calypso Mood' (TB) SCro
'Cambridge' (***sibirica***) **AGM** EFou LBro MAus MNFA NHol
'Camelot Rose' (TB) MAus
'Campbellii' See I. ***lutescens*** 'C.'
'Canary Bird' (TB) CKel LHil
¶ 'Canary Frills' (TB) CKel
'Cannington Bluebird' (TB) LBro
¶ 'Cannington Sweet Puff' (TB) LBro
'Cantab' (Reticulata) CAvo CBro ELan EPar EPot ETub LAma LBow MWBu NHar NRog SIng WHil WPer
'Can't Stop' (SDB) NZep
'Capricious' (TB) SCro
'Captive Heart' (SDB) NZep
'Caramba' (TB) NZep SCro
¶ 'Cardew' (TB) LBro
'Caress' (SDB) MRob NZep
¶ 'Carey' (TB) CKel
'Carilla' (SDB) LBro LGre
'Carnaby' (TB) EFou LBro
'Carnival Glass' (BB) LBro
'Carnival Time' (TB) EFou
'Carnton' (TB) CKel MAus WEas
'Carolina Gold' (TB) SCro
'Carolyn Rose' (MTB) LBro MS&S NZep
'Casbah' (TB) SCro
'Cascadian Skies' (TB) ERou
'Catalyst' (TB) SCro
caucasica EPot
'Cayenne Capers' (TB) MMil
'Celestial Glory' (TB) MAus
¶ 'Center Ring' (TB) CKel
'Centre Court' (TB) NZep SCro
'Centrepiece' (SDB) LBro
chamaeiris See I. ***lutescens***
¶ 'Champagne Elegance' (TB) LBro
'Champagne Music' (TB) MAus
'Change of Pace' (TB) SCro
'Chantilly' (TB) EBee ECas ELan NOrc SCro SGil SHer
'Chapeau' (TB) MAus NSti
'Chapel Hill' (SDB) LBro
'Char True' (Spuria) MAus
¶ 'Charger' (TB) MMil
'Charm Song' (IB) LBro
¶ 'Charmaine' (TB) CKel
'Charming' (TB) CKel
'Chartreuse Ruffles' (TB) SCro
'Cheers' (IB) LBro NZep
'Cherry Falls' (TB) LBro
'Cherry Garden' (SDB) CBro CKel EBar EBre ECtt EFol EGol ELan GCHN LBre LGre LHil MBri MRav MRob MS&S NBir NHar NNrd WCra
'Cherry Orchard' (TB) NNor
'Cherry Pop' (SDB) NZep
'Cherry Smoke' (TB) SCro
'Cherub Tears' (SDB) MRob NZep
'Cherub's Smile' (TB) SCro
'Chicken Little' (MDB) CBro
'Chief Chickasaw' (TB) LBro
'Chief Moses' (TB) MAus
'Chief Quinaby' (TB) SCro
'Chief Waukesha' (TB) SCro
'Chieftain' (TB) CKel MAus NSti
¶ 'Childsong' (AB) LBro
'Chinese Coral' (TB) MAus
'Chivalry' (TB) MAus SCro
¶ 'Chorus Girl' (TB) CKel
¶ 'Christening Party' (TB) CKel
'Christmas Angel' (TB) ERou MAus
'Christmas Time' (TB) NZep
Chrysofor Group NHol
chrysographes CCla CGle EBar ELan ELun GCra LBro MBal MTho NHol NNor SIng SUsu WWin
– B&L 12617 EMon
– ***alba*** NBir
– black Widely available
– 'Black Beauty' NHol
– 'Black Knight' CBot CSpe CVer ECha EFol ELan GCal MS&S NNor NOrc NPri SPer WWin
– 'Black Velvet' ECha
– crimson CRDP NCat NHol SIng
– 'Inshriach' GDra NHol WDav
– 'Mandarin Purple' CWGN GCal NCat SPer SWyc WThi
– 'Margot Holmes' (Cal-Sib) GCal GDra IBlr SChu
¶ – 'Martyn Rix' CRDP
– purple CRDP
– red CRDP MBal SHer
§ – var. ***rubella*** CRow GDra GMac LGre NHol SCro SWas SWyc
♦ – 'Rubra' See I. ***c. rubella***
¶ – x ***forrestii*** SIng
chrysophylla EPot MSto
'Church Stoke' (SDB) SCro
'Cider Haze' (TB) CKel
'Circus Stripes' (TB) NPri
'Cirrus' (TB) LHil
'City Girl' (SDB) NZep
'City of David' (TB) SCro
'Clairette' (Reticulata) CAvo CBro ELan EPar LAma SIng
'Clap Hands' (SDB) LBro NZep
'Clarke Cosgrove' (Spuria) LBro

clarkei CHan ELan GAbr LGan LHop NNrd NSti NTow NWCA WDav
'Classy Babe' (SDB) NZep
'Clay's Caper' (SDB) EFou LBro MS&S
¶ 'Clementine' (Sibirica) NRar
'Cleo' (TB) CKel NBir
'Cliffs of Dover' (TB) CKel LBro MS&S SRms
'Climbing Gold' NPri WHil
'Closed Circuit' (TB) NZep
'Clotted Cream' ECha
'Cloud Cap' (TB) SRms
'Cloudless Sunrise' (TB) ERou
'Colonial Gold' (TB) MAus
'Color Brite' (BB) SCro
'Color Splash' (TB) SCro
'Columbia Blue' (TB) SCro
'Colwall' (TB) LBro
'Combo' (SDB) CKel
'Comma' (SDB) NZep
'Concord Touch' (SDB) NZep
'Condottiere' (TB) SCro
'Confederate Soldier' (IB) LBro
confusa CAvo CGle CHEx CHan CRDP EBee ECha EPla GCal LHil MTho MUlv SArc
'Connoisseur' (Spuria) LBro
¶ 'Constant Wattez' (IB) CKel
'Consummation' (MTB) NZep
'Cool Spring' (***sibirica***) WThi
'Copper Classic' (TB) NZep SCro
'Coral Chalice' ERou
¶ 'Coral Joy' (TB) LBro
'Coral Wings' (SDB) NZep
'Corn Harvest' (TB) MMil NZep
'Cotati' (BB) LBro
'Cote d'Or' (TB) SCro
'Cotton Blossom' (SDB) EGol LBro NZep
'Court Magician' (SDB) NZep
'Cozy Calico' (TB) SCro
'Cracklin Burgundy' (TB) SCro
'Cranberry Ice' (TB) CKel SCro
¶ 'Cream Cake' (SDB) NZep
'Creative Stitchery' (TB) SCro
¶ 'Cregrina' (TB) LBro
¶ 'Crème Chantilly' (***sibirica***) LBro SCro
cretensis See I. ***unguicularis*** Cretensis
'Cricket Lane' (SDB) NZep
'Crispen Rouge' (TB) CKel
'Crispin' (SDB) NZep
cristata CAvo CBro ECha EPot ITim LAma SIng WCru WThu
– ***alba*** CBro LBee MBal MDHE NHar SCro SIng SWas WAbe
¶ – x ***gracilipes*** EPot
– – ***lacustris*** CHan GArf
croatica See I. ***germanica***
crocea GCra MSto WDav
'Crocus' (MDB) NZep
'Croftway Lemon' (TB) SCro
'Cross Stitch' (TB) MMil NZep
'Crown Sterling' (TB) SCro
'Crushed Velvet' (TB) MAus
'Cum Laude' (IB) SCro
'Cup Race' (TB) MAus NSti NZep
'Curio' (MDB) LBro
'Curlew' (IB) LBro SCro
'Cutie' (IB) NZep
'Cyanea' (DB) CKel
'Cycles' (TB) NZep
'Daisy Fresh' (MDB) LBro
'Dale Dennis' (DB) LBro
'Dame Judy' (TB) CKel
¶ 'Dance Ballerina' (***sibirica***) LBro
'Dancer's Veil' **AGM** CKel EBre ECtt EFou ELan ERou LBre LBro MAus NVic SCro SPer
'Dancing Eyes' (SDB) LBro
'Dancing Gold' (MTB) NZep
'Dancin'' (IB) NZep
danfordiae CAvo CB&S CBro ELan EPar EPot ETub LAma LBow MBri MWBu NRog SIng WPer
'Dante' (TB) CKel LHil
'Dappled Pony' (MTB) NZep
'Dardanus' (Aril) EPot ETub
'Daring Eyes' (MDB) NZep
'Dark Blizzard' (IB) NZep
'Dark Bury' (TB) LBro
* 'Dark Lavender' (***sibirica***) GMac
'Dark Rosaleen' (TB) LBro
'Dark Spark' (SDB) MAus NSti
'Dark Vader' (SDB) NZep
'Darkover' (SDB) LBro MAus
'Darkside' (TB) SCro
¶ 'David Chapman' (TB) LBro
'Dawn Candle' (Spuria) LBro
'Dawn Favour' (SDB) LBro
'Dawn Glory' (TB) SCro
'Dazzling Gold' (TB) SCro
§ ***decora*** CBro GAul MAus WDav
'Deep Black' (TB) CHad CMGP CRDP CSco EBee ECas MAus SCro SPer
'Deep Fire' (TB) SCro
'Deep Pacific' (TB) MAus MBri
'Deep Space' (TB) LHil MAus
'Deft Touch' (TB) MAus
delavayi WCot
'Delicate Air' (SDB) EGol LBro MS&S
'Delphi' (TB) SCro
¶ 'Demelza' (TB) LBro
'Demon' (SDB) CKel EFou LBro
¶ 'Denys Humphries' (TB) LBro
'Deputé Nomblot' (TB) CKel CShe LHil
'Derring Do' (SDB) LBro MS&S
'Derry Down' (SDB) LBro
'Derwentwater' (TB) CKel CWes SRms
'Desert Dream' (AB) GDra SWyc
'Desert Echo' (TB) EFou
'Desert Quail' (MTB) LBro
'Desert Song' (TB) CKel SGil
'Designer Gown' (TB) ERou
¶ 'Designers Choice' (TB) LBro
'Dew Point' (IB) LBro SCro
'Die Braut' (DB) See I. 'Bride'
'Diligence' (SDB) NZep
'Disco Jewel' (MTB) NZep
'Discretion' (TB) SCro
'Ditto' (MDB) NZep

'Dixie Pixie' (SDB)	NZep
¶ 'Doctor Behenna' (TB)	LBro
'Doll Dear' (SDB)	LBro NZep
'Doll House' (MDB)	CMea
'Doll Ribbons' (MTB)	NZep
'Doll Type' (IB)	EFou LBro
'DoSiDo' (SDB)	SCro
'Dotted Doll' (MTB)	NZep
'Double Lament' AGM	CBro LBro MRob SCro
'Douglas 402' (TB)	SCro
douglasiana	CBre EBul EPar EPla EPot GDra IBlr LBro LGan NSti WChe
¶ 'Dovedale' (TB)	LBro
'Doxa' (IB)	LBro SCro
'Dragonfly' (***sibirica***)	MAus
'Dream Builder' (TB)	NZep
'Dreamcastle' (TB)	CKel
¶ 'Dreaming Green' (***sibirica***)	ECha
'Dreaming Spires' (***sibirica***)	LBro MAus
'Dreaming Yellow' (***sibirica***)	CTom EBre ECha EFou EGle LBre LBro MArl MUlv NBro NRoo SCro SPer WRus
'Dresden Candleglow' (IB)	CHad CKel CWGN
'Dresden China' (TB)	CRow
¶ 'Dualtone' (TB)	CKel
'Dundee' (TB)	SCro
'Dunlin' (MDB)	CBro LHil MRob NMen NNrd
'Dusky Challenger' (TB)	LBro SCro
'Dutch Lament' (SDB)	MMil
dykesii	CRow
'Eagle's Flight' (TB)	LBro NZep
'Eardisland' (IB)	LBro
'Earl' (TB)	MMil
'Earl of Essex' (TB)	MAus MMil
'Early Edition' (IB)	LBro LHil
¶ 'Early Frost' (IB)	CKel
'Early Light' AGM	LBro
'East Indies' (TB)	MAus
'Easy Grace' (TB)	MAus
'Easy Strolling' (SDB)	LBro
'Eccentric' (SDB)	NZep
¶ 'Edale' (TB)	LBro
¶ 'Edge of Winter' (TB)	CKel
'Edith Wolford' (TB)	SCro
'Edward' (Reticulata)	LAma WPer
'Edward of Windsor' (TB)	CHad CRDP ECas ELan ERou GLil NOrc SChu SCro
'Ego' (***sibirica***)	CDoC CWGN ECha ELun GCal LBro LWad MBri MUlv NHol WHal WThi WWat
¶ 'Eirian' (TB)	LBro
'Eleanor's Pride' (TB)	CKel MAus MMil
'Elegans' (TB)	LHil
elegantissima	See I. ***iberica e.***
'Elixir' (Spuria)	LBro
'Elizabeth Arden' (TB)	CKel
'Elizabeth Poldark' (TB)	LBro
'Ellesmere' (***sibirica***)	GCal
'Elvinhall'	CBro
¶ 'Ember Days' (TB)	MMil
'Emperor' (***sibirica***)	CB&S CBre CKel CRow ERou LMay MNFA MS&S NHol NPri WElm
'Emphasis' (TB)	NZep
'Empress of India' (TB)	LWad
'Encanto' (SDB)	MAus
'Enchanted Blue' (SDB)	LBro MRob NZep
'Enchanted Gold' (SDB)	NZep
'English Cottage' (TB)	GCal LHil MMil SCro
'Ennerdale' (TB)	MAus SRms
§ ***ensata***	CBen CCla CKel CMHG CRDP CWGN ELan EPot LBro LHil LMay LWad MAus MBri MSta NBro NRoo SHig SWat WDav WHol WPer WWin
– 'Alba'	CBot CGle CWGN ECha
– 'Aoigata'	WThi
– 'Apollo'	CRow
– 'Benokohji'	EHon
– 'Blue Peter'	CRow
¶ – 'Caprician Butterfly'	SWyc
– 'Chitose-no-tomo'	CRow
– 'Dancing Waves'	CRow
– 'Enchanting Melody'	CRow
– 'Freckled Geisha'	CRow
– 'Galatea'	CRow CWGN EHon
– 'Gei-sho-ui'	CWGN
¶ – 'Ghost'	CGle
– 'Gipsey'	CKel CRiv
– 'Glitter and Gaiety'	CRow
– 'Hakug-yokuro'	CRow
– 'Hana-aoi'	CRow IBlr WThi
¶ – 'Happy Awakening'	SWyc
– 'Hatsu-shimo'	CRow IBlr
– 'Hercule'	CRow CWGN
– Higo hybrids	CRow IBlr LHop MSta SCro SPer WThi
– 'Hokkaido'	CGle CRow CWGN EHon
¶ – 'Iso-no-obi'	WMer
– 'Komo-no-obi'	CKel CRiv
– 'Kuma-funjin'	CWGN
– 'Laced'	SPer
– 'Landscape at Dawn'	EHon
¶ – 'Lilac Blotch'	SPer
– 'Magic Opal'	CRow
– 'Mandarin'	CGle CRow EHon
– 'Midsummer Reverie'	CRow
§ – 'Moonlight Waves'	CCla CDoC CMGP CRow CWGN EGol EHon ELan GCal MAus MFir NBrk NRoo SApp SCro WElm WRus WWat
– 'Narihiri'	CRow
– 'Oku-banri'	CWGN
– pale mauve	SPer
– 'Pink Frost'	CHad
– purple	SPer
– 'Purple East'	CDoC CKni CRow CWGN
– 'Rampo'	CRow
– 'Red Dawn'	EHon
§ – 'Rose Queen'	CRDP CRow CSco CWGN EBre ECha EGle ELan ELun EMFW EPar ERou EWav GCal LBre LMay MSta NBrk NBro NKay NRoo SChu WChe WRus
– 'Rowden'	CRow
– 'Royal Crown'	CRow
– 'Royal Purple'	CGle NHol
– 'Ruby King'	CRiv
– 'Shihainami'	IBlr

¶ – 'Summer Storm' SWyc
– 'Tago-sode' CRow
¶ – 'The Great Mogul' SWyc
– 'Umi-botaro' CRow
– 'Valiant Prince' CRow
– 'Variegata' CBen CMil CRDP CRow CTom CWGN ECha EGol EHon IBlr LMay MSta MUlv SCro WByw WHol WRus
– 'Waka-muasaki' WMer WRus
– 'Worley Park' CRow
– 'Yako-no-tami' CRow
– 'Yusho' CRow
'Eric the Red' (*sibirica*) CB&S
'Erleen Richeson' (TB) SCro
'Essay' (Spuria) LBro
'Evening Magic' (TB) SCro
'Evening Pond' (MTB) NZep
'Everything Plus' ERou
ewbankiana EPot
'Ewen' (*sibirica*) EFou LBro SCro
'Excelsior' (DB) CSco CShe
'Exotic Gem' (TB) MAus
'Exotic Isle' (TB) NZep
'Exotic Shadow' (SDB) LBro
'Eye Shadow' (SDB) MAus
'Eyebright' (SDB) CBro EFou LBro LHil MAus WThi
'Fairy Time' (IB) LBro
'Fall Primrose' (TB) LBro
'Fancy Capers' (IB) MAus
'Fancy Tales' (TB) NZep
¶ 'Fantaisie' (TB) CKel
'Fantasy World' (IB) LBro
'Farolito' (Spuria) LBro
'Fashion Fling' (TB) MAus
'Fashion Lady' (MDB) CBro NNrd WThi
'Favorite Angel' (SDB) NZep
¶ 'Feathered Giant' (*sibirica*) LBro
'Feminine Charm' (TB) CKel MAus
'Feminist' (TB) SCro
fernaldii EPot MSto
¶ 'Festival Crown' (TB) LBro
'Festive Skirt' (TB) CKel MAus
'Fiery Song' (TB) CKel
filifolia CBro
– MS 437 CMon
– var. ***latifolia*** SF 332 CMon
'Fire and Flame' (TB) NBir
'Fire One' (SDB) LBro
'Fire Siren' (TB) MMil
'Firecracker' (TB) EBre ERou LBre MAus MBri MRav SCro SPer
'First Interstate' (TB) SCro
'First Lilac' (IB) LBro
'First Violet' (TB) MAus
'Five Star Admiral' (TB) SCro
¶ 'Flaming Dragon' CKel NPri
'Flamingo' (TB) CKel
¶ 'Flammenschwert' (TB) CKel
¶ 'Flash' NHol
'Flashing Beacon' (MTB) NZep
flavescens MAus NSti
'Flea Circus' (MDB) MRob NZep
'Flight of Butterflies' (*sibirica*) CRDP CRow CTom EBre EFou EGle EGol ELan ERou GAbr GMac LBre MNFA MRav NBrk NCat NRar SPer SWas WRus
'Flight of Cavalry' (IB) CGle
'Flirty Mary' (SDB) EGle MAus
'Florentina' (IB) CArn CBro CRow EBre ECha EFou ERav Effi GAbr GPoy IBlr LBre LBro LHil LHol MChe MHew MRav SCro SIde WSun WWye
¶ 'Focal Point' NPri
'Focus' (TB) NZep SCro
§ ***foetidissima*** Widely available
– ***aurea*** MS 902 CMon
– 'Aurea' CMon WDav
– ***chinensis*** See I. *f.* ***citrina***
§ – var. ***citrina*** CChu CMea CRDP CRow EBul ECha EFou EGle EGol EPla GAbr GCal LBro MBal MBro MNFA NSti SChu SUsu WAbe WHoo WOMN WRus WWin
– 'Fructu Albo' CRow EGol
– var. ***lutescens*** CMil EMon
– 'Moonshy Seedling' EGol
– 'Variegata' CBro CChu CGle CRDP CRow CSam EFol EGle EGol ELan EOrc EPar EPla ERav ESiP MBri NDea NHol NPer NRar NRoo NSti SPla WAbe WEas WRus WThu WWat
– yellow seeded EFou
'Forest Hill' (TB) CKel
'Forest Light' (SDB) CBro LBro MRob NNrd
formosana CHEx
'Forncett Moon' (*sibirica*) EFou
forrestii CHan CNic CRow CWGN EFol EOrc EPar GCal GDra GPlt LHop LMay MBri NBro NHed NHol NSla NSti NWyt SUsu WAbe WCla WDav WHal WHer WHil WHol WWat
– hybrids NHol WDav
– x ***chrysographes*** GDra NBir
'Fort Apache' (TB) SCro
'Fort Regent' (TB) LBro
¶ 'Fourfold Lavender' (*sibirica*) LBro
'Fourfold White' (*sibirica*) LBro
¶ 'Foxcote' (IB) LBro
'Foxfire' (TB) MAus
* 'Foxtor' (TB) CKel
'Frank Elder' (Reticulata) CBro LAma MTho
'French Gown' (TB) EFou
'Fresno Flash' (TB) NZep SCro
'Friendly Welcome' (*sibirica*) LBro
¶ 'Frontier Marshall' (TB) CKel
'Frost and Flame' (TB) CMGP EBre ECtt ELan ERav ERou LBre MMil MRav MRob NOrc SChu SCro SPer
¶ 'Frosted Angel' (SDB) LBro
'Frosty Crown' (SDB) NZep
'Full Tide' (TB) MAus SCro
fulva CRDP ECha EPla GCal IBlr MUlv NBro NSti WChe WEas

x *fulvala*	CHan CRDP EPla GCal IBlr MAus NSti SWyc WChe WRus WWat
'Funny Face' (MDB)	NZep
'Furnaceman' (SDB)	CBro
'Fuzzy' (MDB)	LBro
'Gala Gown' (TB)	MAus
§ *galatica*	EPot LAma
'Galleon Gold' (SDB)	NZep
gatesii	EPot LAma
'Gatineau' (*sibirica*)	GDra WThi
¶ 'Gay Parasol' (TB)	LBro
'Gay Prince' (TB)	CKel MS&S
'Gay Trip' (TB)	CKel
§ 'Gelbe Mantel' (Chrysographes)	EHic GCra NBir NSti
¶ 'Gelee Royal' (AB)	LBro
'George' (Reticulata)	CAvo CBro EPar EPot ETub LBow MHlr SIng WCot
'George Barr' (*stolonifera*)	ETub SIng
'Gerald Darby' (x *robusta*)	CBro CRDP CRow CWGN ECha EFol EGol ELun EPar GCal IBlr MAus MUlv NSti SCro SHig SUsu SWyc WChe WEas WRus
germanica	LBro MAus NNor
– 'Kharput'	EGol LBro
¶ 'Germantet' (*sibirica*)	LBro
'Gibson Girl' (TB)	MMil
'Gigglepot' (SDB)	LBro MRob NZep
'Gilston Gulf' (TB)	MAus
'Ginger Swirl' (TB)	SCro
'Gingerbread Man' (SDB)	CBro EFou EGle LBro LGre LHil MAus MRob
'Glad Rags' (TB)	NZep
¶ 'Glaslyn' (*sibirica*)	LBro
'Gleaming Gold' (SDB)	CKel
'Glee Club' (IB)	NZep
'Glen' (TB)	CKel
'Godfrey Owen' (TB)	MAus
'Going My Way' (TB)	NZep SCro
'Gold Burst' (TB)	NZep SCro
'Gold Canary' (MDB)	NZep
'Gold Flake' (TB)	CKel
'Gold Galore' (TB)	NZep SCro
'Gold Intensity' (BB)	LBro
¶ 'Gold of Autumn' (TB)	CKel
'Golden Alps' (TB)	ENot MAus
* 'Golden Bow' (TB)	CKel
'Golden Dewdrops' (SDB)	LBro
'Golden Encore' (TB)	CKel MAus
'Golden Eyelet' (MDB)	NZep
'Golden Fair' (SDB)	LHil NBir SIng
'Golden Harvest' (Dutch)	CB&S EPot LAma MWBu
'Golden Lady' (Spuria)	LBro
'Golden Muffin' (IB)	LBro NZep
'Golden Planet' (TB)	CKel
'Golden Ruby' (SDB)	LBro MRob NZep
'Golden Spice' (TB)	LBro
'Golden Starlet' (SDB)	LBro
* 'Golden Surprise' (TB)	CKel
'Golden Veil' (TB)	CKel
'Golden Waves' (Cal-Sib)	LBro
* 'Goldfinder' (TB)	CKel
'Goldilocks' (TB)	CKel
'Good and True' (IB)	SCro
'Good Morning America' (TB)	NZep
'Good Nature' (Spuria)	LBro
'Gordon' (Reticulata)	EPot LAma LBow
'Goring Ace' (CH)	LBro
gormanii	See I. ***tenax***
gracilipes	CRiv GArf MBal
– 'Alba'	SWas
graeberiana	EPot WChr
graminea	CAvo CBro CHan CMon CRow CSco ECha EFou EGol ELan EPar LBee LBro MAus NHol NNrd NSti SAxl WOMN WPer WRus WWat
– 'Hort's Variety'	GCal NHol
– var. *pseudocyperus*	CMon CRow
♦ *graminifolia*	See I. ***kerneriana***
'Granada Gold' (TB)	SRms
'Grand Baroque' (TB)	MMil
'Grand Waltz' (TB)	SCro
'Grandpa's Girl' (MTB)	LBro NZep
'Grape Orbit' (SDB)	NZep
'Grapelet' (MDB)	LBro NZep
'Grapesicle' (SDB)	NZep
'Graphic Arts' (TB)	NZep
'Grecian Skies' (TB)	SCro
'Green Halo' (DB)	EGle EGol LBro
'Green Ice' (TB)	CKel MS&S
'Green Jungle' (TB)	LBro
* 'Green Little' (DB)	CKel
'Green Spot' (IB)	Widely available
'Greenstuff' (SDB)	LBro MMil
'Gringo' (TB)	MAus
'Gypsy Boy' (SDB)	NZep
¶ 'Gypsy Caravan' (TB)	CKel
'H C van Vliet' (Dutch)	EPot LAma NRog
'Hagar's Helmet' (IB)	LBro
'Hallowed Thoughts' (TB)	MMil
¶ 'Halo in Pink' (TB)	LBro
¶ 'Halo in Yellow' (TB)	LBro
halophila	See I. ***spuria h.***
'Happening' (SDB)	NZep
'Happy Choice' (Spuria)	LBro
'Happy Mood' **AGM**	LBro
'Happy Song' (BB)	LBro
'Happy Thought' (IB)	CKel
'Harbor Blue' (TB)	CKel MAus MWat
'Harleqinade' (BB)	LBro
'Harlow Gold' (IB)	NZep
'Harmony' (Reticulata)	CAvo CBro EPot ETub LAma LBow MBri MHlr MWBu NRog SIng
¶ 'Harpswell Happiness' (*sibirica*)	LBro
¶ 'Harpswell Haze' (*sibirica*)	ECha
¶ 'Harriette Halloway' (TB)	SMrm
hartwegii	EPot WDav
– ssp. *columbiana*	WDav
¶ – ssp. *pinetorum*	WDav
'Harvest Festival' (SDB)	LBro
'Hazy Skies' (MTB)	LBro

'Headlines' (TB) CKel
'Heavenly Blue' (*sibirica*) CSco EHon LMay
'Heavenly Days' (TB) MAus
'Hedge' CDoC
'Helen Astor' (*sibirica*) CCla CMea CRow CSco CWGN GAbr GDra SWyc WCot
'Helen Boehm' (TB) SCro
'Helen McGregor' (TB) CKel
'Helen Proctor' (IB) NZep SCro
'Helge' (IB) CKel LWad NFai
'Hellcat' (IB) NZep
'Hell's Fire' (TB) SCro
'Hercules' (Reticulata) LAma
'Hers' (IB) SCro
'High Barbaree' (TB) MAus
'High Command' (TB) CKel LHil SCro
'Highland Cascade' (TB) MAus
'Hildegarde' (Dutch) LAma
'Hills of Lafayette' (IB) NZep
'His' (IB) SCro
histrio ssp. ***aintabensis*** EPot LAma
¶ – var. ***histrio*** EPot
histrioïdes EPot
§ – 'Angel's Eye' EPot
– 'Angel's Tears' See I. *h.* 'Angel's Eye'
– 'Major' **AGM** CBro LAma MBal MBri NRog
¶ – 'Reine Immaculée' GCLN
– 'Sheila Ann Germaney' EPot
¶ 'Hoar Edge' (*sibirica*) LBro
'Hocus Pocus' (SDB) EFou LBro
'Holden Clough' CAvo CBot CCla CGle CRDP CWGN ELan ELun EMFW EOrc GCal LBro MAus MFir MHFP MMil MNFA MUlv NHol NSti SHig SMrm SUsu SWyc WAbb WChe WEas WOld WRus WWin
'Holiday Flame' (IB) NZep
'Honey Glazed' (IB) EFou LBro MAus NZep
¶ 'Honey Pot' (MDB) CKel
'Honeydip' (SDB) NZep
'Honington' (SDB) LRHS MAus MMil
'Honorabile' (MTB) CKel MAus
'Hoodwink' (SDB) LBro NZep
hoogiana EPot ETub LAma LBow MTho SIng WChr WThu
– 'Alba' EPot ETub
– 'Purpurea' EPot LRHS WChr
'Hopscotch' (BB) SCro
'Hot Fudge' (IB) NZep
'Hot Spice' (IB) NZep
¶ 'Howard Weed' (TB) CKel
'Hubbard' (*sibirica*) SCro
'Hubbub' (IB) SCro
'Hula Doll' (MDB) EGle MRob
§ ***humilis*** EPot WAbe WThu
hyrcana CBro EPot LAma
'I Do' (TB) MMil NZep
§ ***iberica*** EPot WChr
§ – ssp. ***elegantissima*** EPot
¶ – ssp. ***iberica*** WThi
'Ice Chip' (SDB) LBro NZep
'Ida' (Reticulata) LAma
'Ideal' (Dutch) LAma
illyrica JCA 589.800 See I. ***pallida***
imbricata MAus
'Imperator' (Dutch) CB&S
'Imperial Bronze' (Spuria) MAus WCot
'Imperial Sun' (Spuria) LBro
'Impetuous' (BB) LBro
'Indeed' (IB) LBro NZep
'Indian Chief' (TB) CKel ENot LBro
'Indian Jewel' (SDB) EGle LBro
'Indian Pow Wow' (SDB) LBro
* 'Indian Sunset' (TB) CKel
'Indigo Flight' (IB) EFou LBro
'Infinite Grace' (TB) SCro
'Ingenuity' (SDB) LBro
'Innocent Heart' (TB) MAus
innominata CCla CFil CGle CMea CRDP CRow CSam EBar ECha EPot GAbr LBee MFir MHig MSto MTho NBro NHar NHol NMen NSti NTow SMrm SUsu WCla WDav WEas WWat
¶ – JCA 13227 CNic
– 'Alba' EPot
– 'Doctor Riddle's Form' CGle CRDP EPla GDra MBal NHol
– rose CNic
– 'Spinners' SHer SWas WDav
'Inscription' (SDB) EGle LBro NZep
'Interpol' (TB) MAus
'Irish Doll' (MDB) CKel EGle LBro LHil MAus MRob
'Irish Tune' (TB) SCro
'Ishmael' (SDB) EGle LBro
'Ivor Knowles' (CH) LBro
'Ivory Gown' (TB) MAus
'J S Dijt' (Reticulata) CAvo CBro EPar EPot LAma LBow MBri MWBu NRog SIng WHil WPer
'Jack o' Hearts' (SDB) CMea LBro
'Jade Mist' (SDB) EGle LBro
'Jan Reagan' (SDB) NZep
'Jana White' (MTB) MAus
'Jane Phillips' (TB) CHad CKel CMGP CRDP CSco CShe ECas ECtt EGle ELan ENot ERou LBro LGre MAus MHFP MMil MRav NOrc SChu SCro SMrm SPer SWat
'Jane Taylor' (SDB) CBro EGle
'Janice Chesnik' (Spuria) LBro MS&S
'Janice Ruth' (TB) MAus
japonica LHil NPer WThu
– L 638 SCro
– 'Ledger's Variety' CAvo CBro CHad CHan CMon CRDP CRow CSco ECha ELan EPar GCal LGan MAus MBro MUlv NHol SCro SUsu WAbe WEas WHoo WRus WWat
– 'Variegata' CBot CHan CMon CRDP CRow ECha EFol EPar GCal LBro LHop MBal MUlv NHol NOrc NPer SArc SBla SCro WHer
'Jasper Gem' (MDB) EGle LBro MMil MRob MS&S
'Java Charm' (TB) MMil
¶ 'Jay Kenneth' (IB) LBro
'Jazzebel' (TB) SCro
'Jean Guymer' (TB) LBro MMil NBir
'Jeannine' (Reticulata) LAma
'Jeremy Brian' **AGM** LBro MAus NZep
'Jersey Lilli' (SDB) EFol LRHS MAus NSti
'Jesse's Song' (TB) NZep SCro
'Jewel Baby' (SDB) CBro NZep

'Jewel Bright' (SDB) EFou MAus
'Jillaroo' (SDB) SCro
¶ 'Jitterbug' (TB) LBro
¶ 'Jo Jo' (TB) CKel
'Joan Lay' (TB) CSco
'Joanna Taylor' (MDB) CBro MAus NZep WMar
¶ 'Joe Elliott' (CH) EGle
'Joette' (MTB) LBro
'John' (IB) SCro
'Jolly Fellow' (SDB) EGle LBro WThi
jordana S&L 38 CMon
'Joyce' (Reticulata) CAvo CBro ELan EPar EPot LAma MBri MWBu NRog SIng WPer
¶ 'Joyce McBride' (SDB) NZep
'Joyce Terry' (TB) CKel MBri
'Joyful' (SDB) LBro NZep
'Joyous Isle' (SDB) LBro NZep
'Jubilee Gem' (TB) CKel
'Juliet' (TB) CKel
juncea CMon
'June Prom' (IB) SCro
¶ 'Juneau' (TB) WCot
'Jungle Fires' (TB) MAus
'Jungle Shadows' (BB) LGre MAus
'Jungle Warrior' (SDB) NZep
'Just Jennifer' (BB) LBro MAus
kaempferi See I. ***ensata***
kamaonensis GDra WOMN
¶ 'Kansas' (TB) CKel
'Karen Christine' (TB) SCro
'Karen Maddock' (TB) LBro
'Kashmir White' (TB) EGol LAma
'Kate Izzard' (TB) LHil
'Katharine Hodgkin' (Reticulata) CAvo CBro CRDP EOrc EPot GArf LAma LBow MTho NGar NHar NRog SIng WAbe WCru
'Katinka' (CH) LBro
'Katy Petts' (SDB) EFou LBro LRHS MAus NZep
'Kayo' (SDB) CHad EFou EGle LBro MAus MRob MS&S NSti NZep
'Kent Pride' (TB) CMGP CSco EBee EFou ERav ERou LBro MRav SGil SHer SMrm SPer
'Kentucky Bluegrass' (SDB) EFou LBro MMil MRob NZep WWin
'Kentucky Derby' (TB) SCro
'Kermit' (IB) SCro
§ ***kerneriana*** CBro CMil CRiv ELan EPot LGre SBla WEas WOMN
'Keyhaven' (SDB) LBro
'Kildonan' (TB) MAus
'Kilt Lilt' (TB) SCro
'Kirkstone' (TB) MAus
kirkwoodii EPot
'Kissing Circle' (BB) LBro
'Kista' (SDB) LRHS MAus
'Kiwi Capers' (SDB) NZep
¶ 'Kiwi Slices' (SDB) NZep
klattii See I. ***spuria musulmanica***
'Knick Knack' (MDB) CBro CGle CMGP ECas EGle ELan LGre LHil MAus MHig MRob NMen NNrd SChu SGil SHer SIng WWin
'Knotty Pine' (SDB) MAus
kolpakowskiana EPot
kopetdagensis EPot WChr
korolkowii f. ***violacea*** WChr
kuschakewiczii EPot
'La Nina Rosa' (BB) MAus
'Laced Cotton' (TB) SCro
'Laced Lemonade' (SDB) EFou LBro
lactea SCro WThi
lacustris CRDP CRiv ELan EPot MBro MHig MSto NCat NHar NKay NMen NTow NWCA WAbe WOMN WPat
– x ***gracilipes*** CRDP EPot GDra LGre SWas WAbe WOMN
'Lady Bell' (MTB) LBro
'Lady Friend' (TB) ERou SCro
'Lady Ilse' (TB) MAus
'Lady Madonna' (TB) SCro
'Lady Mohr' (AB) CKel MAus
'Lady of Nepal' (IB) LBro
¶ 'Lady of Quality' (***sibirica***) LBro SCro
¶ 'Lady Vanessa' (***sibirica***) SCro
§ ***laevigata*** **AGM** CBen CRDP CRow EBre ECha EGle EGol EHon ELan LBre LHil LMay MAus MSta NBar NBrk NBro NDea SHig SPer SWat SWyc WChe WDav WHol
– 'Alba' CBen CRDP CRow CWGN ECha EGol LMay SWyc WChe
– 'Atropurpurea' CRDP CRow EGol IBlr LMay MSta
– 'Colchesterensis' CBen CRDP CRow CWGN EBre EGol EHon LBre LMay MSta SCro SWat SWyc WChe
– 'Dorothy' CWGN CWes MSta SCro WChe
– 'Elegante' CRow CWGN EGol SWyc
– 'Midnight' CBen CRow CWGN EGol EHon SCro SWat SWyc
– 'Monstrosa' SWyc
– 'Mottled Beauty' CBen CRow MSta SWyc
¶ – 'Plena' SWyc
¶ – 'Plum Purple' EGle
¶ – 'Regal' SWyc
¶ – 'Reveille' EGle
– 'Richard Greany' CRow
– 'Rose Queen' See I. ***ensata*** 'R.Q.'
– 'Snowdrift' See I. 'Snowdrift'
– 'Variegata' CBot CChu CRDP CWGN ECha EGol EHon EMFW EWav LMay MAus MSta NDea SCro SWat SWyc WChe WHol WWat
– 'Violet Garth' CRow
– 'Weymouth' CRDP CRow CWGN EGol SCro SWyc
'Lake Placid' (TB) SCro
¶ 'Lamorna' (TB) LBro
'Land o' Lakes' (TB) SCro
'Langport Chapter' (IB) CKel
'Langport Chief' (IB) CKel MS&S
'Langport Chimes' (IB) CKel
¶ 'Langport Claret' (IB) CKel
¶ 'Langport Curlew' (IB) CKel
¶ 'Langport Dawn' (IB) CKel
¶ 'Langport Dolly' (IB) CKel
'Langport Duchess' (IB) CKel
¶ 'Langport Duke' (IB) CKel
'Langport Fairy' (IB) CKel
'Langport Fashion' (IB) CKel

'Langport Finch' (IB) CKel NZep
'Langport Flame' (IB) CKel MMil
'Langport Flash' (IB) CKel
'Langport Flush' (IB) CKel SCro
'Langport Girl' (IB) CKel
¶ 'Langport Haze' (IB) CKel
¶ 'Langport Hero' (IB) CKel
'Langport Honey' (IB) CKel
¶ 'Langport Hope' (IB) CKel
'Langport Jane' (IB) CKel
'Langport Judy' (IB) CKel
¶ 'Langport Kestrel' (IB) CKel
'Langport Lady' (IB) CKel LHil
¶ 'Langport Lord' (IB) CKel
'Langport Magic' (IB) CKel
'Langport Minstrel' (IB) CKel NZep
¶ 'Langport Myth' (IB) CKel
'Langport Pagan' (IB) CKel
'Langport Pansy' (IB) CKel
'Langport Pearl' (IB) CKel
¶ 'Langport Phoebe' (IB) CKel
'Langport Pinnacle' (IB) CKel
¶ 'Langport Pleasure' (IB) CKel
'Langport Prince' (IB) CKel
¶ 'Langport Robe' (IB) CKel
'Langport Robin' (IB) CKel
'Langport Romance' (IB) CKel
'Langport Secret' (IB) CKel
'Langport Smoke' (IB) CKel
'Langport Snow' (IB) CKel
'Langport Song' (IB) CKel MMil
'Langport Star' (IB) CKel
'Langport Storm' (IB) CKel EFou
'Langport Sultan' (IB) CKel
'Langport Sun' (IB) CKel LHil
¶ 'Langport Sunbeam' (IB) CKel
¶ 'Langport Swift' (IB) CKel
'Langport Tartan' (IB) CKel MS&S
¶ 'Langport Tempest' (IB) CKel
'Langport Vale' (IB) CKel
'Langport Violet' (IB) CKel
'Langport Vista' (IB) CKel
'Langport Warrior' (IB) CKel MS&S
'Langport Wren' (IB) CBro CKel LBro LGre LHil LHop MMil
'Langthorn's Pink' (*sibirica*) ELan
'Las Olas' (CH) LBro
§ ***latifolia*** AGM WCot WDav
– ***alba*** ELan
'Latin Rock' (TB) SCro
'Laurenbuhl' (***sibirica***) LBro SCro
'Lavanesque' (TB) CKel
'Lavendula Plicatee' CKel MRob
§ ***lazica*** CAvo CBro CMon EPot IBlr MAus MBel MUlv NSti SChu SCro SHer WCot WEas WRus
'Leda's Lover' (TB) SCro
'Lemon Blossom' (SDB) NZep
'Lemon Brocade' (TB) MAus
'Lemon Drop' (TB) CKel
'Lemon Flare' (SDB) CMGP EBre ECtt EGol LBre LBro MAus MBri MS&S NHar NRoo
'Lemon Flurry' (IB) LBro
'Lemon Glitter' (TB) EFou
'Lemon Ice' (TB) MMil
'Lemon Mist' (TB) MMil
'Lemon Puff' (MDB) CBro LBro MRob
'Lemon Reflection' (TB) MMil
'Lemon Tree' (TB) MAus
'Lena' (SDB) CBro SHer WCot WCra
¶ 'Lenzschnee' (TB) CKel
'Letitia' (***sibirica***) WThu
'Libation' (MDB) LBro
'Licorice Stick' (TB) MAus
'Light Cavalry' (IB) NZep
'Light Laughter' (IB) LBro
'Lighted Window' (TB) SCro
¶ 'Likiang' (Chrysographes) LBro
'Lilac and Lavender' (SDB) MMil NZep
'Lilac Lulu' (SDB) NZep
'Lilli-White' (SDB) CHad CKel EBre EFol EGle EGol ESma LBre LBro MAus MBri MRob NHar WCra
'Lime Grove' (SDB) SCro
'Limeheart' (***sibirica***) EGle ELan ERou LBro NHol NRoo NSti SPer WHal
'Limelight' (***sibirica***) SRms
'Limpid Pools' (SDB) SCro
¶ 'Lindis' (AB) LBro
'Liquid Smoke' (TB) EFou
'Listowell' (IB) LBro
'Little Amigo' (SDB) NZep
'Little Annie' (SDB) NZep
'Little Bill' (SDB) EFou EGle WThi
'Little Bishop' (SDB) NZep
'Little Black Belt' (SDB) EFou LBro MRob MS&S NZep
'Little Blackfoot' (SDB) CHad LRHS MAus WWin
'Little Blue' (TB) SCro
'Little Chestnut' (SDB) LBro MAus
'Little Cottage' (IB) SCro
'Little Dandy' (SDB) EGle MAus
'Little Dogie' (SDB) EGle LBro
'Little Dream' (SDB) NZep
'Little Episode' (SDB) NZep
¶ 'Little Jewel' (DB) CKel
'Little Miss' (BB) SCro
'Little Paul' (MTB) LBro
'Little Pearl' (MDB) NZep
'Little Rosy Wings' (SDB) CBro LBro LGre MMil SCro
¶ 'Little Sapphire' (SDB) CKel
'Little Shadow' (IB) CKel EBre ECtt LBre LBro MRav MRob NHar SHer WCra
'Little Sir Echo' (BB) MAus
'Little Snow Lemon' (IB) NZep
'Little Suki' (SDB) EFou
'Little Vanessa' (SDB) MAus NSti
'Live Jazz' (SDB) MRob NZep
'Lively Rose' (MTB) LBro
¶ 'Llangors' (***sibirica***) LBro
'Llanthony' (SDB) MAus
¶ 'Llyn Brianne' (***sibirica***) LBro
'Lodestar' (TB) LBro MS&S
'Lodore' (TB) CKel MAus SRms
'Lollipop' (SDB) NZep
longipetala NBir

'Lookin' Good' (IB) NZep
¶ 'Loop the Loop' (TB) CKel
'Lord Baltimore' (TB) SCro
'Lord Warden' (TB) EFou
'Lord Wolsely' (Spuria) LBro
'Lorilee' (TB) SCro
'Lorna Lee' (TB) MAus
'Lothario' (TB) CKel MS&S
'Loud Mouth' (AB) LBro
'Loud Music' (TB) MAus
'Louise Hopper' (MTB) NZep
'Louvois' (TB) CKel
¶ 'Love Chant' (TB) CKel
'Love Lisa' (SDB) NZep
'Loveday' (TB) LBro
'Lovely Again' (TB) MAus
'Lovely Kay' (TB) SCro
'Lovely Light' (TB) MAus
'Lovely Me' (SDB) NZep
'Loveshine' (SDB) NSti NZep
'Love's Tune' (IB) SCro
'Low Snow' (SDB) NZep
'Lucky Charm' (MTB) LBro
'Lucky Duck' (SDB) NZep
'Lugano' (TB) MMil
'Luscious One' (SDB) LBro
lutescens LBro LHil MAus
§ – 'Campbellii' CBro EBee EBre EGol LBre LGre MBro MHig MSto NBar NMen NNrd SIng WMar
– ***cyanea*** NKay
– 'Jackanapes' NKay
– ***lutescens*** CMon
'Lydia Jane' (Spuria) LBro
'Lynwood Gold' (IB) EFou
¶ ***maackii*** GAul
macrosiphon EPot
'Madeira Belle' (TB) MAus
'Maestro' (TB) CKel
'Magenta and Peach' (TB) MAus
¶ 'Magharee' (TB) LBro
'Magic Carpet' (TB) CKel
'Magic Flute' (MDB) EGle LBro MRob
'Magic Hills' (TB) CKel
'Magic Man' (TB) LBro
magnifica EPot ETub WChr WThu
'Mahogany Snow' (SDB) NZep
'Maiden Blush' (TB) LHil
'Mama Hoohoo' (IB) SCro
'Mandarin' (TB) CKel GDra
¶ 'Maori King' (TB) ELan
maracandica EPot
'Maranja' (TB) LHil
'Marcus Perry' (***sibirica***) CRow MSte
'Marhaba' (MDB) CBro
¶ 'Mariachi' (TB) CKel
¶ 'Marilyn Holmes (***sibirica***) WCot
'Marmalade Skies' (BB) LBro NZep
'Marmot' (MDB) MAus
'Maroon Caper' (IB) MAus
'Marshlander' (TB) EFou SCro
'Marty' (IB) LBro
'Mary Frances' (TB) LBro SCro
'Mary McIlroy' (SDB) CBro LBro
'Mary Randall' (TB) MS&S
'Master Touch' (TB) SCro
'Matchpoint' (TB) LBro
¶ 'Matinata' (TB) CKel
'Maui Moonlight' (IB) NZep
'May Melody' (TB) CKel MBri
'Meadow Court' (SDB) CBro CHad CKel MAus MRob WMer
'Meadow Moss' (SDB) EGol
'Media Luz' (Spuria) LBro WCot
¶ 'Meg's Mantle' (TB) LBro
'Melbreak' (TB) CKel EBre LBre MAus
'Melissa Sue' (TB) SCro
mellita See I. ***suaveolens***
– ***rubromarginata*** See I. ***suaveolens***
'Melon Honey' (SDB) CKel EGle LBro MAus MRob MS&S NZep WWin
'Menton' (SDB) LBro
'Merry Day' (IB) CKel
'Merseyside' (SDB) EGle LBro LHil
'Metaphor' (TB) MAus MMil
'Michael Paul' (SDB) LBro NZep
'Midas Kiss' (IB) LBro
'Midnight Fire' (TB) ERou
'Midnight Madness' (SDB) NZep
¶ 'Mikiko' (***sibirica***) LBro
milesii CHan CPou NBir SCro WPer
¶ – CR 346 WPer
¶ – C&Mc 741 GCHN
'Mini Dynamo' (SDB) NZep
'Minnie Colquitt' (TB) SCro
'Mirror Image' (TB) NZep
'Miss Carla' **AGM** LBro
¶ 'Mission Ridge' (TB) CKel
'Mission Sunset' (TB) MAus
'Missouri Gal' (Spuria) LBro
missouriensis CRow ESma IBlr MSto
– ***arizonica*** WDav
'Mister Roberts' (SDB) LBro NZep
'Monaco' (TB) EFou
monnieri CMil CMon SDix
Monspur Group (Spuria) GCal MAus
'Moon Shadows' (SDB) MAus
¶ 'Moon Sparkle' (IB) CKel
'Moonlight' (TB) EGol EPot ESma LBro MAus MRav NNor
'Moonlight Waves' See I. ***ensata*** 'M.W.'
'Morning Hymn' (TB) SCro
'Morning Show' (IB) SCro
'Morocco' (TB) SCro
'Morwenna' (TB) LBro MAus
'Mrs Nate Rudolph' (SDB) EFou EGle LBro LHil WThi
'Mrs Rowe' (***sibirica***) CRow EFou LBro MAus MNFA WCot
'Mrs Saunders' (***sibirica***) CBre CRow
munzii EPot
'Muriel Neville' (TB) MAus
'Music Box' (SDB) NZep
'Music Caper' (SDB) LBro
¶ 'Mute Swan' (TB) LBro
'My Honeycomb' (TB) MAus
'My Mary' (TB) CKel
'My Seedling' (DB) CBro NMen NNrd
'My Smoky' (TB) CKel

'Myra's Child' (SDB) MAus
'Mystique' (TB) SCro
'Nambe' (MTB) LBro
'Nampara' (TB) LBro
'Nancy Hardy ' (MDB) CBro
'Nancy Lindsey' See I. ***lutescens*** 'N.L.'
'Nashborough' (TB) CKel MS&S
'Natascha' (Reticulata) ELan EPot ETub LAma SIng WHil
'Navajo Blanket' (TB) SCro
¶ 'Navy Brass' (***sibirica***) LBro
'Navy Doll' (MDB) CKel NZep
'Nectar' (TB) CKel MS&S
'Needlecraft' (TB) CKel MMil
'Needlepoint' (TB) SCro
'Neon Pixie' (SDB) NZep
'Neophyte' (Spuria) LBro
nepalensis See I. ***decora***
nertschinskia See I. ***sanguinea***
'New Idea' (MTB) CKel LBro MAus MS&S
'New Snow' (TB) CWes ENot MAus
'New Wave' (MTB) NZep
'Nice 'n' Nifty' (IB) NZep
nicolaii EPot LRHS WChr
'Niebelungen' (TB) CKel NFai NPri
'Night Owl' (TB) LHil SCro
'Night Shift' (IB) NZep
nigricans S&L 148 CMon
'Nineveh' (AB) MAus NSti
'Nora Distin' (sibirica) MAus
'Normandie' (TB) MAus
'Norton Sunlight' (Spuria) LBro
'Nottingham Lace' (***sibirica***) LBro NBrk SWyc
'No-name' NSti
'Nuggets' (MDB) NZep
nusairiensis EPot WChr
'Nylon Ruffles' (SDB) EGol LBro
¶ 'Oban' (***sibirica***) LBro
'Ochraurea' GCal
ochroleuca See I. ***orientalis***
'Offenham' (TB) LBro
'Oh Jay' (SDB) NZep
'Ohio Belle' (SDB) NZep
'Oklahoma Bandit' (IB) LBro
'Ola Kala' (TB) CMGP EBee ECas ERou MAus SCro
'Old Flame' (TB) NZep
'Oliver' (SDB) LBro MAus
¶ 'Olympic Challenger' (TB) LBro
'Olympic Torch' (TB) CKel LHil MAus
'On Fire' (SDB) MRob NZep
'One Accord' (SDB) SCro
'One Desire' (TB) MAus NZep
'Open Sky' (SDB) NZep
'Orange Blaze' (SDB) CBro CKel
'Orange Caper' (SDB) MBri NHar NZep
'Orange Dawn' (TB) LBro
'Orange Maid' (Spuria) LBro
'Orange Plaza' WHil
'Orange Tiger' (SDB) NZep
'Orchardist' (TB) CKel
'Orchid Flare' (MDB) LHil
¶ 'Orchidarium' (TB) CKel
§ ***orchioïdes*** EPot
'Oregold' (SDB) NZep
'Oregon Skles' (TB) SCro
¶ 'Oriental Baby' (IB) CKel
'Oriental Blush' (SDB) LBro
'Oriental Glory' (TB) MAus
§ ***orientalis*** CAvo CBot CHan CMil CRiv CRow ELan EPla LBro LMay MAus MBal NSti SChu SDix SHig WWat WWin
– 'Alba' See I. ***sanguinea*** 'A.'
'Oritam' (TB) SCro
'Ornament' (SDB) LBro MS&S NZep
'Oroville' (Spuria) LBro
'Orville Fay' (***sibirica***) AGM EFou GCal LBro SAxl SCro
'Ottawa' (***sibirica***) CCla CHad CLTr CRiv CRow CWGN ELan ERou EWav MS&S NRoo SChu SCro
'Ouija' AGM LBro
'Out Yonder' (TB) MAus
'Outstep' (SDB) NZep
'Ovation' (TB) SCro
'Pacer' (IB) NZep
'Pacific Coast Hyb' See I. Californian hybrids
'Pacific Mist' (TB) SCro
'Pagan Princess' (TB) MAus
'Painted Rose' (MTB) LBro
'Pale Primrose' (TB) MAus WEas
'Pale Suede' (SDB) LBro
§ ***pallida*** CMGP EBee EFou LHol MAus NSti
– 'Argentea Variegata' CCla CGle CHad CMGP CRDP ECas EFol LHop MUlv NRoo NSti SCro WHoo WHow WRus WWat
– 'Aurea' See I. ***p.*** 'Variegata'
– 'Aurea Variegata' See I. ***p.*** 'Variegata'
– ssp. ***cengialtii*** CMon WThi
– var. ***dalmatica*** See I. ***pallida pallida***
§ – ssp. ***pallida*** CBot CCla EBre ECha EGol ELan LBre LBro LHil MBri MUlv NSti SCro SDix SMrm SPer
N– 'Variegata' Widely available
'Palomino' (TB) MAus
'Paltec' LGre SCro
'Pandora's Purple' (TB) SCro
'Papil' (***sibirica***) NCat
'Papillon' (***sibirica***) CCla CHad CLTr CMGP EBre EGle ELan ERou LBre LHop MAus MBro MUlv NBro NHol NRoo NSti SChu SMrm SPer SUsu WRus WSun WWat
'Paradise' (TB) LBro SCro
'Paradise Bird' (TB) LBro
'Paradise Pink' (TB) CSco
paradoxa EPot WChr
'Parakeet' (MTB) LBro
'Paricutin' (SDB) CBro EBar EGle NNrd
'Party Dress' (TB) CMGP EBre ECtt ELan ENot EPla ERou LBre LBro MRav MRob MS&S NOrc SChu SMrm SPer WTyr
¶ 'Pascoe' (TB) LBro
'Passport' (BB) MAus
¶ 'Pastel Charm' (SDB) CKel
'Pastel Delight' (SDB) NZep
'Path of Gold' (DB) CBro CKel LBro MRob WHil
'Patterdale' (TB) LBro MAus MS&S NBar NVic
'Pauline' (Reticulata) CAvo CBro EPot LAma NRog SIng WPer
'Peach ala Mode' (BB) MAus

'Peach Band' (TB) ERou
'Peach Eyes' (SDB) LBro
'Peach Petals' (BB) LBro NZep
'Peach Picotee' (TB) SCro
'Peach Spot' (TB) MAus
'Peaches 'n' Topping' (BB) LBro
'Peachy Face' (IB) LBro NZep
'Peacock' ECha LGre SChu SUsu WSHC
'Pearly Dawn' (TB) CCla CMGP EBre ECas ECtt GCHN LBre MS&S NVic SGil SHer SPer
'Pecan Spot' (SDB) NZep
'Pegasus' (TB) SCro
'Peggy Chambers' (IB) EFou LBro
'Peking Summer' (TB) SCro
'Pennies' (MDB) NZep
'Penny Bunker' (Spuria) LBro
'Penny Candy' (MDB) NZep
'Pennyworth' (IB) SCro
¶ 'Penrhyn' (TB) LBro
'People Pleaser' (SDB) SCro
'Peppermint Twist' (SDB) NZep
'Perry's Blue' (***sibirica***) CArn CB&S CCla CWGN EBre EFou EPar ERou ESma GAbr GDra LBre MNFA NBrk NKay NNrd NPer SCro SPer SUsu WHal WRus WSun WWat
'Perry's Favourite' (***sibirica***) CBre CRow
'Perry's Pygmy' (***sibirica***) CRow CSpe
'Persian Doll' (MDB) NZep
persica LAma
'Persimmon' (***sibirica***) CRos EBre EGle ERou LBre MArl SMrm SPer
'Pet' (SDB) NSti NZep
¶ 'Petite Polka' (SDB) CKel
'Pied Pretty' (SDB) SCro
¶ 'Pigeon' (SDB) NZep
'Pigmy Gold' (IB) LBro
'Pinewood Amethyst' (CH) LBro
'Pink Angel' (TB) SCro
'Pink Bubbles' (BB) LBro NZep
'Pink Clover' (TB) LBro
'Pink Confetti' (TB) SCro
¶ 'Pink Divinity' (TB) MMil
'Pink Haze' (***sibirica***) SCro
¶ 'Pink Horizon' (TB) CKel NPri
'Pink Kitten' (IB) NZep
'Pink Lamb' (BB) LBro
'Pink Lavender' (TB) SCro
'Pink Pleasure' (TB) NZep
'Pink Randall' (TB) SCro
'Pink Ruffles' (IB) CKel
'Pink Taffeta' (TB) CKel SCro
'Pink 'n' Mint' (TB) SCro
'Piper's Tune' (IB) NZep
'Pipes of Pan' (TB) MAus
'Pippi Longstockings' (SDB) NZep
¶ 'Piquant Lass' (MTB) NZep
'Pirate Prince' (***sibirica***) LBro NPer
¶ 'Piroska' (TB) CKel
'Pixie' (DB) CKel
'Pixie Flirt' (MDB) LBro
'Pixie Plum' (SDB) MAus
'Pixie Princess' (SDB) MAus
planifolia EBul
– AB&S 4609 CMon
– S&L 301 CMon
'Pledge Allegiance' (TB) SCro
plicata MAus
'Plickadee' (SDB) MMil NNrd
'Plum Perfect' (SDB) ECha SCro
'Pogo' (SDB) EBre ECtt EGle EGol ELan ENot LBre MBri MMil MRav NHar NNrd NZep SCro WCra
'Pogo Doll' (AB) LBro
§ ***polakii*** WThi
'Polly Dodge' (***sibirica***) LBro
¶ 'Pontypool' (***sibirica***) LBro
'Pony' (IB) LBro
'Popinjay' (CH) LBro
'Port of Call' (Spuria) LBro
'Post Time' (TB) SCro
'Pot Luck' (IB) LBro MS&S
'Prairie Warbler' (Chrysographes) CRow
'Praise the Lord' (TB) LBro
'Prancing Pony' (TB) CKel SCro
'Pretender' (TB) MAus MBri
'Prettie Print' (TB) SCro
'Pride of Ireland' (TB) SCro
'Prince' (SDB) EFou EGle LBro
¶ 'Princess' (TB) CKel
'Princess Beatrice' See I. ***pallida pallida***
prismatica CBre CMon ECha EPot
– ***alba*** GAbr
'Prodigy' (MDB) LBro
'Professor Blaauw' (Dutch) LAma
'Prophetic Message' (AB) LBro
'Protégé' (Spuria) LBro
'Proud Tradition' (TB) SCro
¶ 'Provencal' (TB) CKel
pseudacorus Widely available
– 'Alba' GCal SWyc
– var. ***bastardii*** CChu CRDP CRow CWGN ECha EGol EMFW MS&S MUlv SPer SWyc WChe
– cream EGol MUlv NBir
– dwarf form NSti
– 'Ecru' CRow
¶ – 'Esk' GCal
– 'Flore Pleno' CRow EMFW SWyc
– 'Golden Fleece' SPer
– 'Golden Queen' CRow MSta MUlv SWyc
– 'Ivory' CRow
¶ – Tangarewa Cream Group SWyc
– 'Turnispeed' GCal
– 'Variegata' Widely available
– x ***versicolor*** SCro
pseudopumila WThu
– MS 986/975 CMon
pumila CChu CMon EPla MAus MBro NKay NNor NWCA SPla WAbe WCla WDav
– ***aequiloba*** EPot
– ***atroviolacea*** CKel MBro MCas MNFA NTow

– ssp. ***attica***	See I. ***attica***
– ***aurea***	CBow MBro MCas MNFA NTow
– ***lutea***	WHil
– 'Violacea'	MBro SCro SPer
'Pumpkin Center' (SDB)	NZep
'Puppet' (SDB)	EGle EGol LBro NZep
'Puppet Baby' (MDB)	NZep
'Puppy Love' (MTB)	NZep
purdyi	EPot NSti
¶ 'Purpeller' (***sibirica***)	LBro
'Purple Cloak' (***sibirica***)	LBro MSte
'Purple Dream' (CH)	LBro
'Purple Gem' (Reticulata)	CBro EPot LAma
'Purple Mere' (***sibirica***)	LBro
'Purple Sensation' (Dutch)	CB&S EPot LAma MWBu
'Purple Song' (TB)	MS&S
'Purple Streaker' (TB)	SCro
purpurea	See I. ***galatica***
¶ ***purpureobractea***	EPot
'Pussytoes' (MDB)	NZep
'Queechee' (TB)	ERou MRav MS&S SCro
'Queen in Calico' (TB)	SCro
'Queen of Hearts' (TB)	SCro
'Queen's Ivory' (SDB)	MAus
'Queen's Pawn' (SDB)	LBro NZep
'Quiet Lagoon' (SDB)	NZep
'Quiet Thought' (TB)	LBro
'Quintana' (CH)	LBro
'Quip' (MDB)	NZep
'Rabbit's Foot' (SDB)	NZep
¶ 'Rabelais' (TB)	CKel
'Radiant Summer' (TB)	SCro
'Rain Dance' (SDB)	MAus NZep
'Rainbow Trout' (TB)	LBro
'Raindance Kid' (IB)	NZep
'Rajah' (TB)	CMGP EBre ECas ERou LBre LBro LHil NOrc WHer
'Rancho Rose' (TB)	CKel SCro
'Ranger' (TB)	CKel LHil
'Rare Edition' (IB)	CKel EFou LBro MRob MS&S NZep SCro
'Rare Treat' (TB)	NZep
'Raspberry Acres' (IB)	MAus MBri MS&S
'Raspberry Blush' (IB)	CKel LBro NZep
'Raspberry Jam' (SDB)	EFou EGle LBro MS&S NZep
'Raspberry Rose' (IB)	NZep
'Raspberry Sundae' (BB)	LBro NZep
'Rathe Primrose' (IB)	SCro
'Raven Hill' (TB)	MAus
'Real Jazzy' (MTB)	CKel NZep SHer
'Red Flag' (***sibirica***)	NHol
'Red Flare' (***sibirica***)	EGle EHon ELan LBro LHop MS&S
'Red Flash' (TB)	CKel
'Red Heart' (SDB)	ECtt MRav NHar
¶ 'Red Kite' (TB)	LBro
'Red Lion' (TB)	NZep
'Red Orchid' (IB)	CBow CDoC CKel
'Red Revival' (TB)	MAus
'Red Rufus' (TB)	LBro
'Red Rum' (TB)	CKel
'Red Tempest' (IB)	NZep
'Red Zinger' (IB)	NZep SCro
'Reddy Maid' (***sibirica***)	LBro SCro
'Redwing' (TB)	MWat WPer
'Redwood Supreme' (Spuria)	LBro MS&S
'Regards' (SDB)	CBro CKel EGle LBro MRob
'Reginae'	MAus
¶ ***regis-uzziae*** S&L 133	CMon
reichenbachii	LBee
– Balkana Group	SIng
'Repartee' (TB)	SCro
§ ***reticulata*** AGM	CB&S CBro CMon EPar EPot ERav ETub GPlt NRog SIng
– cvs.	See under cultivar name
'Riches' (SDB)	NZep
'Rickshaw' (SDB)	LBro
* 'Ride Joy' (TB)	CKel
'Right Royal' (TB)	MAus
'Rime Frost' (TB)	MAus MMil
'Rimouski' (***sibirica***)	LBro
'Ringo' (TB)	CKel NZep SCro
'Ripple Chip' (SDB)	NZep
'Rippling Waters' (TB)	MAus
'Rising Moon' (TB)	SCro
¶ 'Ritz' (SDB)	CKel
'River Hawk' (TB)	SCro
'River Patrol' (TB)	EFou
'Robert Graves' (TB)	MAus
§ 'Rocket' (TB)	CKel CMGP ECas NBir SCro SMrm SPer
'Roger Perry' (***sibirica***)	CRow
'Roman Emperor' (TB)	EFou
'Romance' (TB)	ERou
'Ron' (TB)	SCro
¶ 'Rose Caress' (TB)	LBro
'Rose Queen'	See I. ***ensata*** 'R.Q.'
'Rose Violet' (TB)	MAus
'Roselene' (TB)	SCro
'Rosemary's Dream' (MTB)	CKel NZep
rosenbachiana	WChr
'Rosie Lulu' (SDB)	NZep
'Rosy Air' (SDB)	NZep
'Rosy Wings' (TB)	EGol
'Roustabout' (SDB)	EFou LBro MS&S
'Roy Elliott'	NHol WPer
'Royal Ascot' (TB)	LBro
'Royal Blue' (Reticulata)	LAma
– (***sibirica***)	ECha SBla
'Royal Contrast' (SDB)	LBro
'Royal Elf' (SDB)	NZep
'Royal Eyelash' (SDB)	NZep
'Royal Intrigue' (TB)	SCro
'Royal Midget' (SDB)	LBro
'Royal Regency' (TB)	SCro
'Royal Ruffles' (TB)	MAus
'Royal Toss' (TB)	CKel
'Royal Touch' (TB)	EFou
'Royal Velours'	LHil
'Royal Yellow' (Dutch)	LAma NRog
'Ruby Chimes' (IB)	CHad MAus MS&S
'Ruby Contrast' (TB)	MAus MS&S NSti
'Ruby Gem' (TB)	CKel
'Ruby Locket' (SDB)	LBro
'Ruby Mine' (TB)	MAus
rudskyi	See I. ***variegata***
'Ruffled Ballet' (TB)	SCro
'Ruffled Surprise' (TB)	SCro
'Ruffled Velvet' (***sibirica***)	LBro SCro WTyr

'Ruffles and Lace' (TB) SCro
¶ 'Ruffles Plus' (*sibirica*) LBro
'Rustam' (TB) CKel
'Rustic Jewel' (TB) CKel
'Rusty Dusty' (SDB) NZep
'Ruth Couffer' (BB) LBro MS&S
¶ 'Ruth Knowles' (SDB) LBro
¶ 'Ruth Margaret' (TB) CKel
'Ruth Nies Cabeen' (Spuria) LBro
ruthenica GArf NKay NNrd WOMN WPer
¶ – var. ***nana*** L 1280 SBla
'Sable' (TB) EBre ECas EPla LBre MAus NOrc SMrm SPer WGor
'Sable Night' (TB) CKel ERou MAus
'Saint Crispin' (TB) CHad CMGP CSco EBee EBre ECas ERou LBre LBuc MRav MUlv MWat SChu SMrm SPer WTyr
¶ 'Sally Kerlin' (*sibirica*) SCro
'Salonique' (TB) CKel NFai
'Saltwood' (SDB) CBro LBro
'Sam' (SDB) NZep
'Sam Carne' MAus
'Samurai Warrior' (TB) SCro
'San Jose' (TB) NZep
'Sand and Sea' (TB) LBro
'Sandy Caper' (IB) MAus
¶ 'Sangreal' (IB) CKel
§ ***sanguinea*** CAvo CWGN WDav
§ – 'Alba' CRow GCHN WThi
– x ***laevigata*** SCro
'Santana' (TB) SCro
'Sapphire Beauty' (Dutch) LAma NRog
¶ 'Sapphire Gem' (SDB) CKel
'Sapphire Hills' (TB) SCro
'Sapphire Jewel' (SDB) NZep
'Sarah Taylor' (SDB) CBro EFou LBro MAus
sari EPot LAma WChr
'Sass with Class' (SDB) NZep
'Saturnus' (Dutch) LAma
'Saucy Peach' (BB) LBro
'Savoir Faire' (*sibirica*) CWGN ECha EGle LBro
'Saxon Princess' (TB) LBro
¶ 'Scarlet Ribbon' (TB) CKel
schachtii WChr
'Schortman's Garnet Ruffles' (TB) SCro
'Scintilla' (IB) MMil SCro
'Scintillation' (TB) SCro
'Scribe' (MDB) CBro EGle LHil LRHS MAus NZep
'Scrimmage' (SDB) NZep
¶ 'Sea Double' (TB) MMil
'Sea Fret' (SDB) CBro
'Sea Horse' (*sibirica*) NCat
'Sea of Joy' (TB) SCro
'Sea Shadows' (*sibirica*) NBir
'Sea Urchin' (SDB) NZep
¶ 'Second Opinion' (MTB) NZep
¶ 'Senlac' (TB) CKel GLil
serbica See I. ***reichenbachii***
'Serenity Prayer' (SDB) NZep
setosa CBro CCla CMea CRDP CRiv CRow ECha EGle EGol EMNN GAbr GCra ITim LGan LHil MHig MSta NHed NKay NNrd SCro WCru WHil
– ***alba*** CRow LGan WDav
§ – var. ***arctica*** CCla CNic CRDP CRow ELan ELun EMon EPot GCHN GDra LBee MBal MBro NGre NHol NTow NWCA SBla SCro SHer SIng SPer SUsu WAbe WHoo WOMN WPer
– dwarf form See I. ***s. arctica***
¶ – 'Hondoensis' EMon
– 'Hookeri' See I. ***s. canadensis***
*– ***major*** SIng
– ***nana*** See I. ***s. arctica***
'Shaft of Gold' (TB) SCro
'Shampoo' (IB) EFou NZep
'Sheer Class' (SDB) NZep
'Sheik' (AB) SCro
'Shelford Giant' (Spuria) CRow LBro
¶ 'Shirley Pope' (*sibirica*) LBro
'Short Distance' (IB) LBro
'Show Me Yellow' (SDB) NZep
'Showcase' (TB) NZep
'Showdown' (*sibirica*) CB&S ECtt LBro LWad MBri MUlv NHar NHol WHal WWat
'Showman' (TB) ERou
'Shrawley' (*sibirica*) MAus
♦ ***shrevei*** See I. ***virginica s.***
'Shrinking Violet' (MTB) LBro
'Shy Violet' (SDB) NZep
sibirica CMHG CMea CNic CRDP CShe CTom CWGN EGle EHon LAma LHil MBro MFir MWat NDea NNor SMad WEas WHer WHol WHoo WWin
– cream WCot
*– white EGle
'Sierra Nevada' (Spuria) EFou LBro
¶ 'Signals Blue' (*sibirica*) ECha
'Silent Strings' (IB) LBro
'Silver Edge' (*sibirica*) CRos CSpe EFou MAus NFai SCro WTyr
'Silver Tide' (TB) WEas
'Silvery Moon' (TB) SCro
sindjarensis See I. ***aucheri***
'Sing Again' (IB) CWes MAus
sintenisii CBro CHan EPar SIng
¶ 'Sister Helen' (TB) MMil
'Siva Siva' (TB) EBre ERou LBre WHer
'Skating Party' (TB) SCro
'Skier's Delight' (TB) SCro
'Skip Stitch' (SDB) LBro MAus
'Sky and Snow' (SDB) NZep
'Sky Hooks' (TB) SCro
'Sky Wings' (*sibirica*) CB&S CWGN EBee ECha EGle MNFA
'Skyfire' (TB) SCro
'Slap Bang' (SDB) NZep
'Sleepy Time' (MDB) NZep
'Slim Jim' (MTB) LBro
'Small Sky' (SDB) CBro LBro MRob
'Small Wonder' (SDB) LBro
'Smart Girl' (TB) CKel
'Smarty Pants' (MTB) LBro

'Smell the Roses' (SDB) NZep
'Smoke Rings' (TB) SCro
'Smokey Dream' (TB) CKel
'Smoky Valley' (BB) LBro
'Smooth Orange' (TB) MAus
'Sneak Preview' (TB) NZep
'Snow Crest' (***sibirica***) CCla NHol
'Snow Elf' (SDB) LBro
'Snow Festival' (IB) NZep
'Snow Fiddler' (MTB) NZep
'Snow Gambit' (MTB) NZep
'Snow Jo' NCat
'Snow Mound' (TB) SCro
'Snow Queen' (***sibirica***) CCla CHad CKel CRow CWGN EGle EHon ELan EPot ERou EWav LGan LMay MAus MBro NSti SCro SPer
¶ 'Snow Tree' (SDB) NZep
'Snow Troll' (SDB) LRHS MAus WHer
'Snowcone' (IB) NZep
'Snowcrest' (***sibirica***) MAus
§ 'Snowdrift' CRow CWGN EGol EHon EMFW EWav LMay MSta NDea SCro SHig SPer SWyc WChe WHol
'Snowshill' (TB) LBro
'Snowy Owl' (TB) LBro MAus
'Snowy River' (MDB) NZep
'Snowy Wonderland' (TB) NZep
'Soaring Kite' (TB) LBro
'Soft Blue' (sibirica) LBro
'Soft Breeze' (SDB) NZep
'Solar Song' (SDB) NZep SCro
'Solid Gold' (TB) CKel
'Solid Mahogany' (TB) MAus MMil MUlv
'Somerset Vale' (TB) CKel MS&S
'Song of Norway' (TB) NZep SCro
'Soul Power' (TB) ERou
'Sounder' (BB) LBro
'Southcombe White' (***sibirica***) CRow CVer GBuc GCal SWas
'Southern Clipper' (SDB) LRHS MBri
'Space Odyssey' (TB) NZep
'Spanish Coins' (MTB) LBro NZep
'Sparkling Cloud' (SDB) EGle MAus
'Sparkling Rosé' (***sibirica***) CBot CTom CWGN EBre ECtt EFou EGol LBre LBro LWad MBri NHar NHol WHal WHoo WRus
'Specify' (TB) CKel
'Spirit of Memphis' (TB) MMil
'Splash of Red' (SDB) LBro NZep
¶ 'Split Decision' (SDB) NZep
'Spring Bells' (SDB) EFou
'Spring Dancer' (IB) SCro
'Spring Festival' (TB) CKel MAus
'Spring Signal' (TB) LBro
'Spring Wine' (IB) LBro
'Springtime' (Reticulata) CAvo EPot LAma NRog SIng WCru
spuria ELan MSto SWyc WHaw
– ssp. ***carthaliniae*** EHic WPer
– ssp. ***demetrii*** ESma
– ssp. ***halophila*** CMon EHic LBro MAus
– ssp. ***maritima*** NNrd SIng
§ – ssp. ***musulmanica*** EHic LBro MBri WThi
– ***ochroleuca*** See I. ***orientalis***
¶ – ssp. ***sogdiana*** EHic
¶ 'Spuria Alba' SWyc
sp. AGSJ 431 EWoo NGre WBon WDav
¶ sp. CLD 0180 NHol
sp. CLD 0495 NHol
sp. CLD 0566 NHol
sp. CLD 1399 NHol
sp. CLD 1541 NHol
x ***squalens*** MAus
'Squeaky Clean' (SDB) NZep
'Stability' (Spuria) LBro
'Stapleford' (SDB) CBro EGle
¶ 'Star Shower' (SDB) NZep
'Starcrest' (TB) SCro
'Starlit River' (TB) EFou
'Starry Eyed' (SDB) EGle LBro
'Starshine' (TB) CKel MAus
'Startler' (TB) SCro
'Staten Island' (TB) CKel ELan ENot LHil MAus MMil MS&S SRms
'Stella Polaris' (TB) SCro
§ ***stenophylla*** EPot
'Stepping Little' (BB) NZep
'Stepping Out' AGM EBre EFou LBre MAus SCro
'Stitch in Time' (TB) SCro
'Stockholm' (SDB) CKel LBro NZep
stolonifera CMon EPot
– 'Bronze Beauty' CMon
'Stop the Music' (TB) SCro
'Storrington' (TB) SCro
'Strange Child' (SDB) NZep
'Strawberry Love' (IB) MAus NSti NZep
'Strawberry Sensation' (TB) NZep
'Stylish' (DB) CKel
stylosa See I. ***unguicularis***
'Suave' (TB) SCro
§ ***suaveolens*** CBro ELan EPot MSto SIng WMar
subbiflora WDav
'Sudeley' (SDB) SCro
'Sugar' (IB) CHad MAus NSti
'Sugar Candy' (CH) LBro
'Sugar Please' (SDB) NZep
'Sullom Voe' (TB) LBro
¶ 'Sultan's Palace' (TB) CKel
'Summer Luxury' (TB) NZep
'Sumptuous' (TB) SCro
'Sun Dappled' ERou
'Sun Doll' (SDB) NZep
'Sun Symbol' (SDB) MRob
'Sunbrella' (SDB) NZep
'Sunday Chimes' (TB) SCro
'Sunlit Sea' (Spuria) LBro
'Sunlit Trail' (SDB) MAus
'Sunny Dawn' (IB) LBro NZep
'Sunny Day' (Spuria) LBro
'Sunny Heart' (SDB) CKel
'Sunny Honey' (IB) NZep SCro
'Sunnyside' (Spuria) LBro
¶ 'Sunset Sky' (TB) CKel
'Sunshine Isle' (SDB) NZep
'Superlation' (TB) SCro
'Superstition' (TB) SCro
'Surprise Blue' (MTB) NZep

'Surprise Orange' (MDB)	NZep
'Susan Bliss' (TB)	CKel ELan NFai
susiana	ETub LAma SIng
'Suspense' (Spuria)	LBro
'Svelte' (IB)	LBro
'Swahili' (TB)	MAus
'Swank' (***sibirica***)	LBro
'Swazi Princess' (TB)	CKel SCro
¶ 'Sweertii '	WThi
'Sweet and Neat' (SDB)	SCro
'Sweet Lavender' (TB)	SCro
'Sweet Musette' (TB)	SCro
'Sweet Treat' (SDB)	NZep
'Swizzle' (IB)	LBro MS&S
'Syllable' (SDB)	NZep
'Sylvia Murray' (TB)	MAus
'Symphony' (Dutch)	MWBu
'Syncopation' (TB)	LBro
'Tall Chief' (TB)	CWes EBre LBre MAus NBrk NSti SCro
'Tanex'	MAus
'Tangerine Sky' (TB)	SCro
'Tangerine Sunrise' (TB)	LBro
'Tantara' (SDB)	MRob NZep SCro
'Tarheel Elf' (SDB)	LBro
'Tarn Hows' (TB)	SRms
'Taupkin' (SDB)	LBro
tauri	See I. ***stenophylla***
¶ 'Teal Velvet' (***sibirica***)	LBro
'Tease' (SDB)	LBro
tectorum	CMon CRDP GCra LGre WOMN
– 'Alba'	CChu CMea CPou CRDP EHic WThi WThu
– Burma form	WThi
– 'Variegata'	GAbr MBri SPer WHal
'Tell Fibs' (SDB)	NZep
'Ten' (SDB)	NZep SCro
tenax	CMil CNic EBul EPot LBee MBal MHig WChe
– 'Alba'	EPot
tenuis	MHig NNrd
'The Bride'	See I. 'Bride'
'The Citadel' (TB)	CKel SCro
'The Monarch' (TB)	CKel
'The Rocket'	See I. 'Rocket'
'Theatre' (TB)	NZep SCro
'Theda Clark' (IB)	SCro
'Thelma Perry' (***sibirica***)	WCot
'Theseus' (Aril)	EPot
'Third Charm' (SDB)	CBro
'Third World' (SDB)	CBro
'Thor' (Aril)	EPot
'Three Cherries' (MDB)	CBro EGle
'Threepio' (SDB)	NZep
'Thrice Blessed' (SDB)	NZep
'Thriller' (TB)	NZep
thunbergii	See I. ***sanguinea***
'Thundercloud' (TB)	MAus
'Tidbit' (DB)	LBro
'Tiddle de Winks' (BB)	LBro
'Tide's In' (TB)	ERou SCro
'Time for Love' (TB)	NZep
'Timeless Moment' (TB)	SCro
'Timmie Too' (BB)	LBro
tingitana	CMil
– var. ***fontanesii*** AB&S 4452	CMon
'Tinkerbell' (SDB)	CKel ECas EGle EGol LBro LGre MBri MRob NRoo SChu SHer WCra
¶ 'Tintinara' (TB)	LBro
'Tiny Freckles' (MDB)	NZep
¶ 'Tirra Lirra' (SDB)	LBro
'Titan's Glory' (TB)	CKel LBro MHlr SCro WCot
'Toasty' (SDB)	NZep
'Tom Tit' (TB)	MAus
'Tomingo' (SDB)	LRHS MAus
'Tomorrow's Child' (TB)	SCro
'Toni Lynn' (MDB)	NNrd
'Toots' (SDB)	EGle LBro
'Top Flight' (TB)	CMGP ENot ERou SHer SPer WGor
'Topolino' (TB)	CKel
'Topsy Turvy' (MTB)	LBro NZep
'Torchlight' (TB)	CKel MS&S
'Torchy' (SDB)	NZep
'Total Eclipse'	SRms
'Touch of Spring' (TB)	MMil
'Toy Boat' (SDB)	NZep
'Transcribe' (SDB)	NZep
'Treasure' (TB)	MAus
'Trevaunance Cove' (TB)	LBro
'Triplicata' (IB)	LGre
trojana	CMon
'Tropic Night' (***sibirica***)	CCla CRiv CSco CWGN EBre EFou ERou GAbr LAbb LBre MBri MRav MSta NBrk NHol NRoo NRya SCro SMad SPer WRus WWat
'Truly' (SDB)	CKel MAus
'Tu Tu Turquoise' (SDB)	NZep
tuberosa	See HERMODACTYLUS ***tuberosus***
'Tumbleweeds' (SDB)	NZep
'Tupelo Honey' (TB)	NZep
'Tuscan' (TB)	CKel
'Tut's Gold' (TB)	SCro
'Twist of Fate' (TB)	SCro
'Two Rubies' (SDB)	NZep
'Tycoon' (***sibirica***)	CWGN NHol SPer
'Tyke' (MTB)	NZep
¶ ***typhifolia***	WThi
§ ***unguicularis*** AGM	Widely available
¶ – L&R 65	CMon
¶ – MS 720	CMon
¶ – S&L 478	CMon
¶ – S&L 550	CMon
– 'Abington Purple'	CAvo CBro
– ***alba***	CAvo CBro ECha
– f. ***angustifolia***	CAvo IBlr SWas
– 'Bob Thompson'	CAvo CMil ECha WCot
– broken form	MHlr WCot
§ – ssp. ***cretensis***	ECha NHol SPou
– 'Francis Wormsley'	ECha
– var. ***lazica***	See I. ***lazica***
– 'Marginata'	LBro

– 'Mary Barnard' CAvo CBro CHan CMon CPou CRDP CRiv CSam CSco ECha GAbr GCHN LBro MUlv SBla SChu SCro SPer SPou SWas WAbe WDav WRus WSun
– 'Oxford Dwarf' CBro SPer SPou
– 'Walter Butt' CAvo ECha GCal NBir SBla SChu SWas WRus
¶ ***uniflora caricina*** WCot
urmiensis See I. ***barnumae u.***
uromovii CMil WHoo
'Ursula Vahl' (TB) LBro
'Vanity' (TB) NZep SCro
'Vanity's Child' (TB) ERou
§ ***variegata*** EPar GCal NHol SWas
– ***alba*** EPar
*– ***pontica*** SCro
'Vegas Showgirl' (SDB) NZep
'Velvet Bouquet' (MTB) LBro
'Velvet Robe' (TB) SRms
'Vera' (Aril) EPot ETub WChr
verna CGle CNic NHol WThi
versicolor CArn CBow CCla CRow CWGN EGol EHon EMFW EPar EPot EWav LGan LMay MAus MHew MSal MSta NDea NHol NRoo SIng SWyc WHol
– 'Blue Light' CBow WChe
– 'Dottie's Double' CRow
– 'Goldbrook' EGol
– 'Kermesina' CRDP CRow CWGN ECha EGol EHon ELan EMFW EPar GCal GGar MSta NDea SHig WChe WRus
– purple CRow
– ***rosea*** CRow
– 'Version' CRow
'Vi Luihn' (***sibirica***) CB&S ECha LBro
'Victor Herbert' (TB) SCro
'Victoria Falls' (TB) NZep SCro
'Vim' (SDB) LBro
'Vintage Year' (Spuria) LBro
violacea See I. ***spuria musulmanica***
'Violet Beauty' (Reticulata) EPot LAma SIng WPer
'Violet Classic' (TB) EFou MAus MMil
¶ 'Violet Icing' (TB) LBro
'Violet Lass' (SDB) NZep
'Violet Lulu' (SDB) NZep
'Violet Miracle' (TB) MMil
'Violet Zephyr' (Spuria) LBro
'Violetmere' (***sibirica***) LBro
'Violetta' (DB) CKel
virginica var. ***shrevei*** MAus MSto WThi
viscaria EPot
'Visual Arts' (TB) SCro
'Vitality' (IB) SCro
'Vivien' (TB) SCro
'Voila' (IB) EFou LBro NZep
'Wabash' (TB) CSco EBre EPla ERou LBre LBro MAus
'Wake Up' (SDB) NZep
'Walter Butt' See I. ***unguicularis*** 'W.B.'
'Wampum' (IB) SCro
'War Sails' (TB) SCro
¶ 'Warleggan' (TB) LBro
'Warlsind' (Juno) EPot
¶ 'Watchman' (AB) LBro
'Waterboy' (SDB) NZep
'Watercolor' (SDB) NZep
wattii CHEx
'Webelos' (SDB) LBro LGre LHil
'Wedding Candles' (TB) SCro
¶ 'Wedding Vow' (TB) CKel
'Wedgwood' (Dutch) MWBu
'Wee Doll' (MDB) NZep
¶ 'Welcome Return' (***sibirica***) LBro
'Well Endowed' (TB) SCro
'Well Suited' (SDB) NZep
'Wenlock' (IB) MAus
'Westar' (SDB) LBro NZep
'Westwell' (SDB) LRHS MAus
'What Again' (SDB) SCro
'White Bridge' (Dutch) LAma NRog
'White Canary' (MTB) LBro
'White City' (TB) CMGP CSco ECas EGle EHal ERav LBro LHil MAus MBro MMil NPer SCro SRms SWat
'White Excelsior' (Dutch) CB&S EPot LAma
'White Gem' (SDB) NZep WWin
'White Heron' (Spuria) LBro
'White Knight' (TB) CBow ELan SCro
* 'White Pearl' CRow
'White Queen' (***sibirica***) LBro
¶ 'White Superior' (Dutch) MWBu
'White Swirl' (***sibirica***) CB&S CBot EBar EBre ECtt EGol EPla ERou LBre LBro MBri MBro MUlv MWat NBro NRoo SCro SPer SWyc WHoo WWat WWin
'White van Vliet' (Dutch) NRog
'White Wedgwood' (Dutch) LAma
'Whiteladies' (IB) LBro LHil
'Whoop 'em Up' (BB) LBro NZep
'Why Not' (IB) LBro NZep
'Widecombe Fair' (SDB) EPar
'Widget' (MTB) LBro
'Wild Echo' (TB) CKel
¶ 'Wild West' (TB) NPri
willmottiana WChr
– 'Alba' EPot WChr
'Willow Mist' (SDB) NZep
'Willow Ware' (IB) SCro
¶ ***wilsonii*** WThi
♦– 'Gelbe Mantel' See I. 'Gelbe Mantel'
'Windsor Rose' (TB) CKel SCro
winogradowii ECha EPot GArf SDix
'Winter Olympics' (TB) EFou
'Wisley White' (***sibirica***) CSco LBro NFai NPri WTyr
'Wisteria Sachet' (IB) MAus NSti
'Witch of Endor' (TB) MMil
'Wizard of Id' (SDB) EGle LBro NZep
'Woodling' (SDB) NZep
'World News' (TB) SCro
'Wow' (SDB) LBro MRob
'Wrights Pink' (SDB) MAus
xiphioïdes See I. ***latifolia***
xiphium WThi
'Yellow Apricot' (Chrysographes) CRow

'Yellow Court' (Chrysographes) CRow
'Yellow Girl' (SDB) NZep
'Yo-Yo' (SDB) NZep
'Zantha' (TB) CKel
'Zeeland' (BB) LBro
'Zink Pink' (BB) SCro
'Zipper' (MDB) NZep
'Zowie' (SDB) NZep
'Zua' (IB) MUlv

ISATIS (Cruciferae/Brassicaceae)
tinctoria CArn CSFH ELan EWFC GPoy IEde ILis LHol MChe MHew MSal SHer SIde SSvw WHer WNdy WOak WPer WWye

ISCHYROLEPIS (Restionaceae)
§ *subverticillata* CHEx

ISMENE See **HYMENOCALLIS**

ISOCOMA (Compositae/Asteraceae)
See Plant Deletions

ISOLEPIS (Cyperaceae)
§ *cernua* MBri

ISOLOMA See **KOHLERIA**

ISOPLEXIS (Scrophulariaceae)
canariensis CBot CHEx GCra SArc WEas
sceptrum CBot

ISOPOGON (Proteaceae)
See Plant Deletions

ISOPYRUM (Ranunculaceae)
§ *nipponicum* var. *sarmentosum* NTow
ohwianum See I. ***nipponicum sarmentosum***
thalictroïdes CRDP SPou

ISOTOMASee **SOLENOPSIS, LAURENTIA**

ITEA (Escalloniaceae)
ilicifolia AGM Widely available
japonica 'Beppu' MGos SLPl
virginica CB&S CCla CDoC CLTr CPle CWit ECro ELan LHop MBal MBlu MGos MUlv SEng SPer SReu SSta WBod WDin WHCG WSHC WWat
– Swarthmore form LMer
yunnanensis CGre IOrc

IVESIA (Rosaceae)
gordonii NWCA WPer

IXIA (Iridaceae)
'Blue Bird' LAma
flexuosa NRog
'Hogarth' LAma
hybrids SDeJ
'Mabel' ETub NRog
maculata NRog
'Marquette' NRog
paniculata ETub LBow NRog
'Paradijsvogel' ('Bird of Paradise') LAma
polystachya NRog
'Rose Emperor' ETub LAma NRog
'Venus' LAma
viridiflora NRog

IXIOLIRION (Liliaceae/Ixioliriaceae)
pallasii See I. ***tataricum***
§ *tataricum* ETub LAma LBow MBri NRog
– Ledebourii Group CAvo LAma LBow

JABOROSA (Solanaceae)
integrifolia EBee ELan EMon GCal WCru

JACARANDA (Bignoniaceae)
acutifolia HBK MBri
acutifolia hort. See J. ***mimosifolia***
mimosifolia CB&S CPle

JACOBINIA See **JUSTICIA**

JAMESIA (Hydrangeaceae)
americana CCla

JASIONE (Campanulaceae)
§ *crispa* ECro NHol
§ *heldreichii* CHan CRiv LGan MHig NKay NMir NNrd NRoo SBla SChu SFar SIng WCra WHoo WWin
humilis See J. ***crispa***
jankae See J. ***heldreichii***
§ *laevis* CBow EBre ECoo ECot EHal ELan GMac LBre LGan MUlv NBro NMir SRms WHal WTyr WWin
– 'Blaulicht' ('Blue Light') EBar ECha ESis MBri MRav NBrk NOak NRed SUsu WHil WPer WRus
montana CKin CSam ECWi EWFC MChe WCla WHer
perennis See J. ***laevis***

JASMINUM † (Oleaceae)
angulare CAbb CBow CGre CRHN CTro ERea LBlm
azoricum AGM CB&S CNew CTro ERea
beesianum CArn CB&S CBot CBra CHan CPle CSco EPla GCal LHol MBea MPla MRav NEgg SBra SHBN SLon SPer SSvw WBod WDin WHCG WHer WSHC
floridum IOrc
fruticans CDoC CMac ECro ELan EPla GAri LHop MAll MWat NKay
grandiflorum 'De Grasse' ERea
humile IBlr SHer SLon WBod WKif
– B&L 12086 CBot

– KR 709	ISea
§ – 'Revolutum' AGM	Widely available
– f. ***wallichianum***	EHal
§ ***mesnyi*** AGM	Widely available
nitidum	ERea
nudiflorum AGM	Widely available
– 'Aureum'	CDec CDoC CMer EFol EHar ELan EPla EWri MRav NHol NSti SApp SPer SPla WEas WHCG WPat WRus
¶ – 'Mystique' (v)	CPMA LRHS SPla
– 'Nanum'	ELan WPat
odoratissimum	ERea
officinale AGM	Widely available
§ – f. ***affine***	CB&S CPle EBre ELan ENot EOrc EPla ERea GCal IBar IDai IOrc LBre LPri SDix SMad WCru
§ – 'Argenteovariegatum' AGM	CArn CB&S CBot CDec CPle ECha EFol EHar ELan EPla IBar LHop MBri MSta NHol NSti SApp SBra SEng SHBN SHil SMad SPer SPla SSta WPat WRus WSHC WWat
– 'Aureovariegatum'	See J. *o.* 'Aureum'
§ – 'Aureum'	CB&S CBot CCla CMac EBre ECtt EFol EHal EHar ELan EPla ERav IJoh LBre LPri MBri MWat NBir NHol SApp SHBN SHil SMad SPer SSta WHCG WPat WSHC WWat
– 'Grandiflorum'	See J. *o. affine*
– 'Variegatum'	See J. *o.* 'Argenteovariegatum'
parkeri	CB&S CBot CFee EBar EPla EPot ESis IDai LHop MBro MCas MPla MSto NHar NHol NKay SHBN SIng WAbe WCru WDav WOMN WPat WThu WWat
polyanthum AGM	CArn CB&S CPle CTre CTro CTrw CWit EBak ELan ERav ERea ERom IReg ISea LAbb LBlm LHop MBea MBri NRog NTow SGil SLon
primulinum	See J. ***mesnyi***
reevesii	See J. ***humile*** 'Revolutum'
sambac	CNew CTro ELan LAbb SHil
– 'Maid of Orleans'	ERea
simplicifolium suavissimum	CNew SHil
x ***stephanense*** AGM	Widely available
– 'Variegatum'	CHan

JATROPHA (Euphorbiaceae)

¶ ***multifida***	CTro

JEFFERSONIA (Berberidaceae)

diphylla	CArn CBro CChu CElw CGle CRDP EPar LAma MSal MTho NBir NHar NHol NRog NRya SBla WAbe WChr WCru WHil WWat
dubia	EWes NBir NHol NRog SBla SWas WOMN

JOVELLANA (Scrophulariaceae)

punctata	CDec CGre CHan CPle
¶ ***repens***	WCot
sinclairii	CGle CNic CRDP EBee ECha ECou ELan GCal NGre SWas WBod WCru
violacea AGM	CAbP CAbb CB&S CDec CGle CGre CHan CMHG CMer CPle CSam CWit EMil ERea GCal ISea ITim LHop MAll MBal MPla MTho NHol SArc SDry SHil SLon SMad WBod WSHC

JOVIBARBA (Crassulaceae)

§ ***allionii***	CMea CWil EPad EPot GAri LBee MCas NKay NNor NNrd SIng SMit SSmi WAbe WHil WThu
– from Estang x ***hirta*** from Biele	SMit
– x ***hirta glabrescens*** from Smeryouka	SMit
– x ***hirta***	CWil NHol SSmi
– x ***hirta*** 'Oki'	CWil NHed
– x ***sobolifera***	SMit SSmi
§ ***arenaria***	CWil ESis GCHN MDHE MRPP NKay NMen SIng SSmi
– from Murtal	CWil MDHE SSmi
– 'Opiz'	MCas
'Emerald Spring'	CWil
§ ***heuffelii***	CWil MCas NBra NMen NWCA SMit
¶ – 'Aga'	SSmi
¶ – 'Alemene'	SSmi
– 'Almkroon'	SSmi
– 'Angel Wings'	SSmi
– 'Apache'	SSmi
– 'Aquarius'	CWil SSmi
– 'Artemis'	SSmi
– 'Beacon Hill'	CWil SMit SSmi
– 'Belcore'	CWil SSmi
– 'Bermuda'	CWil SSmi
– 'Bermuda Sunset'	SSmi
– 'Brandaris'	SSmi
– 'Brocade'	SMit
– 'Bronze Ingot'	CWil
– 'Bronze King'	CWil SMit
¶ – 'Bros'	SSmi
– 'Chocoleto'	CWil
¶ – 'Cleopatra'	SSmi
– 'Cloverdale'	SMit
– 'Copper King'	SSmi
– 'Cythera'	SSmi
– 'Fandango'	CWil SSmi
– 'Gento'	CWil SSmi
– 'Giuseppi Spiny'	CWil SSmi
– var. ***glabra***	NGre
– – fr. Kosova x ***hirta glabra*** fr. Smeryouka	SMit
– – from Anabakanak	CWil SMit
– – from Anthoborio	CWil SSmi
– – from Backovo	SSmi
– – from Bansko Vihren	SSmi
– – from Galicica	SSmi
– – from Haila	CWil SMit
– – from Jakupica	CWil
– – from Kapaenianum	SSmi
– – from Koprovnik	CWil
– – from Kosovo	SSmi
– – from Ljubotin	CWil NGre SMit SSmi
– – from Osljak	SSmi
– – from Pasina Glava	CWil

– – from Pelister SSmi
– – from Rhodope CWil GAri NGre SSmi
– – from Stogovo SSmi
– – from Treska Gorge CWil SMit
– – from Vitse CWil SMit
– 'Goya' SSmi
– 'Grand Slam' CWil SSmi
– 'Greenstone' CWil SMit SSmi
¶ – 'Harmony' SSmi
¶ – 'Helena' SSmi
– 'Henry Correvon' CWil SMit SSmi
– 'Hystyle' SMit
– 'Iason' SSmi
¶ – 'Ikaros' SSmi
– 'Inferno' CWil SMit
– 'Iole' SSmi
¶ – 'Iuno' SSmi
– 'Jade' SSmi
– 'Kapo' SMit SSmi
– var. ***kopaonikensis*** CWil
¶ – 'Mary Ann' SSmi
– 'Miller's Violet' CWil SMit
– 'Minuta' CWil SSmi
– 'Mont Rose' SSmi
– 'Mystique' CWil
– 'Nannette' SSmi
– 'Nobel' SSmi
– 'Orion' CWil SMit SSmi
¶ – 'Pampero' SSmi
– 'Passat' SSmi
– 'Pink Skies' SSmi
– 'Prisma' CWil SSmi
– 'Purple Haze' CWil SSmi
¶ – 'Pyrope' SSmi
¶ – 'Red Rose' SSmi
– 'Springael's Choice' SSmi
– 'Sundancer' CWil SMit
– 'Suntan' CWil SSmi
– 'Tan' CWil SMit SSmi
– 'Tancredi' SMit SSmi
– 'Torrid Zone' CWil SMit SSmi
– 'Tuxedo' CWil SMit SSmi
¶ – 'Vesta' SSmi
– 'Violet' CWil SSmi
– 'Vulcan' CWil SSmi
§ ***hirta*** CRiv CWil MCas MDHE NHol NMen SIng STre
– ssp. ***borealis*** CWil MBro NHed
– from Col d'Aubisque SMit
– ssp. ***glabrescens*** ESis
– – from Belansky Tatra CWil GCHN NGre NHed SSmi
– – from High Tatra MDHE
– – from Smeryouka CWil SIng SSmi
– – var. ***neilreichii*** SIng
– 'Preissiana' CWil NHed NMen
x ***mitchellii*** 'Sandy' SSmi
– 'Suzan' SSmi
x ***nixonii*** 'Jowan' SMit SSmi
§ ***sobolifera*** CNic CRiv CWil EPot ESis GAri GCHN NGre NHol NKay SIng SMit SSmi
– 'Green Globe' CWil MDHE NGre SSmi

JUANIA (Palmae/Arecaceae)

See Plant Deletions

JUANULLOA (Solanaceae)

aurantiaca See J. ***mexicana***
mexicana 'Gold Finger' CTro

JUBAEA (Palmae/Arecaceae)

§ ***chilensis*** CHEx CTbh LPal NPal SArc
spectabilis See J. ***chilensis***

JUGLANS † (Juglandaceae)

§ ***ailanthifolia*** CHEx ESim SHil SSta WCoo
– var. ***cordiformis*** EArb
x ***bixbyi*** ESim
F ***cinerea*** EArb ESim SHil SSta WCoo
– x ***ailanthifolia*** See J. x ***bixbyi***
microcarpa EArb
F ***nigra*** AGM CB&S CBow CBra CLnd EArb EHar ESim GTwe IOrc LHol LNet NRog SDea SHBN SKee SPer SSta WCoo WDin WMou WStI
F ***regia*** AGM Widely available
F – 'Broadview' CDoC ERea ESim GTwe MBri SDea SKee WMou
F – 'Buccaneer' ESim GTwe SDea SHil WHig WMou
– 'Franquette' CDoC EBee EHar GTwe SKee WMou
– 'Laciniata' EHar WMou
– 'Lara' SKee
– 'Red Leaf' WMou
sieboldiana See J. ***ailanthifolia***

JUNCUS (Juncaceae)

acutus ETPC
articulatus CKin
compressus CKin
conglomeratus EHoe ETPC
§ ***decipiens*** 'Curly-Wurly' CRDP EHoe EMon EPla ETPC GCal MFir MUlv NCat SHer SWat WHal
– 'Spiralis' See J. ***d.*** 'Curly-Wurly'
effusus CKin ECWi EMFW ETPC SWat WHol
¶ – 'Cuckoo' (v) CNat
§ – 'Spiralis' CLew CRDP CRow CWGN EHoe EHon ELan EMon EPla ETPC GCal GDra IBlr LMay MBal MSta NDea NNrd WChe WHal WHol WPbr
ensifolius CRow MSta SGil
inflexus CKin EHon SWat
– 'Afro' CRDP EMon EPla LRHS SApp
pallidus ETPC
tenuis ETPC
xiphioïdes
JLS 86161LACA EMon

JUNIPERUS † (Cupressaceae)

ashei CMCN
chinensis CMac NWea
– 'Aurea' AGM CDoC CKen CMHG CMac EBre EHar EHul EPla GPen IJoh LBre LCon LLin LNet MAsh MBal MBar MBri MGos SLon WThu

– 'Blaauw' AGM	CDoC CMac EHul ENHC ENot EPla GAri IHos LCon LLin MBar MGos SHBN SHil SLim STre WStI
– 'Blue Alps'	CDoC CMHG EBre EHar EHul EPla GPen IJoh LBre LCon LNet LPan MAsh MBal MBar MBri MGos NHol SLim WStI
– 'Blue Point'	EHul MBar
– 'Densa Spartan'	See J. *c.* 'Spartan'
– 'Echiniformis'	CKen CMac
– 'Expansa Aureospicata'	CBra CDoC CKen CMac EBre EHar EHul ENHC LBre LCon LLin MBar SBod SLim SSmi
§ – 'Expansa Variegata'	CBra CMac EBre EHar EHul GAri GPen LBre LCon LLin MAsh MBal MBar MGos MPla NBee NHol SBod SLim SLon SSmi WAbe WDin WStI
– 'Globosa Cinerea'	MBar
– 'Iowa'	CMHG
– 'Japonica'	MBar
– 'Japonica Variegata'	EBre LBre
– 'Kaizuka' AGM	CDoC CMHG EBre EHul ENHC GAri LBre LCon MBal MBar SLim
– 'Kaizuka Variegata'	See J. *c.* 'Variegated Kaizuka'
– 'Keteleeri'	LCon
– 'Kuriwao Gold'	CDoC CMHG CMac EBre EHul ENHC GRei GWht LBee LBre LCon LLin LNet MBar MGos MRav MWat NHol NRoo SBod SLim SPer SPla WAbe WStI
– 'Kuriwao Sunbeam'	NHol
– 'Mas'	MAsh
– 'Obelisk' AGM	CDoC EBar EBee LBee LCon MBar MGos NHol SBod SLim
– 'Oblonga'	EHul EPla LCon LLin MBar
– 'Parsonsii'	CMac EHul MBar SHBN STre
– 'Plumosa'	MBar SHil
– 'Plumosa Albovariegata'	LCon MBar
– 'Plumosa Aurea' AGM	CDoC EHar EHul ENHC ENot LCon MBar SHil WDin
– 'Plumosa Aureovariegata'	CKen EPla LCon MAsh MBar
– 'Pyramidalis' AGM	CDoC CMac EBar EBre EHar EHul ENHC ENot GAri GWht LBre LCon LLin MGos MWat NRoo SBod SLim SRms
– 'Pyramidalis Variegata'	See J. *c.* 'Variegata'
I – 'Robusta Green'	LCon SLim
– 'San José'	CDoC EBar EHul ESis GAri LCon LLin LPan MAsh MBar MPla SLim WWeb
– 'Shimpaku'	CKen EPla LCon LLin MBar
§ – 'Spartan'	EHul LBee
– 'Stricta'	CKen EHul ENHC GPen IHos LBee MAsh MBal MBar MBri MPla NBee SLim STre WDin WStI
– 'Stricta Variegata'	See J. *c* 'Variegata'
♦– 'Sulphur Spray'	See J. ***virginiana*** 'S. S.'
§ – 'Variegata'	EHul LLin MBar MPla SLim
§ – 'Variegated Kaizuka'	EHul EPla MBar NHol
communis	CArn CKin CSev EHul GAri GPoy GRei ITim LHol MPla MSal NHex NWea SIde SPer WMou
– 'Arnold'	LCon MGos
– 'Atholl'	CKen GAbr
I – 'Aureopicta'	LCon MBar
– 'Barton'	LLin MPla NHol
– 'Berkshire'	CKen EPla LCon MAsh
– 'Brien'	CKen
– 'Clywd'	LBee WThu
– 'Compressa' AGM	Widely available
– 'Constance Franklin' (v)	EHul EPla MBar MCas
– 'Corrielagen'	CKen MBar MCas MGos MPla MWat
– 'Cracovia'	EHul
– var. ***depressa***	GPoy MBal MBar
– 'Depressa Aurea'	Widely available
– 'Depressed Star'	CDoC MBar
♦– 'Gelb'	See J. *c.* 'Schneverdingen Goldmachandel'
§ – 'Gold Cone'	CDoC CKen EBre EHul EPla ESis LBee LBre LCon LLin MAsh MBar MBri MCas MPla NHed NHol SGil SHil SLim SPla WAbe WGor
♦– 'Golden Showers'	See J. *c.* 'Schneverdingen Goldmachandel'
– 'Goldenrod'	SHil
– 'Green Carpet' AGM	CDoC CKen EBre EPla EPot LBre LCon LLin MAsh MBar MBri SLim WStI
– 'Greenmantle'	SPla
– var. ***hemispherica***	MBar NHed SRms
– 'Hibernica' AGM	Widely available
– 'Hornibrookii' AGM	CDoC CMac CSco EBar EHul ENot GDra GWht IDai LLin MBal MBar MGos MPla MWat NWea SBod SHBN SLim SLon SPla SReu SSmi STre WDin WWin
– 'Horstmann'	EBre EPla GAri LBre MBar MBri SSmi
– 'Mayer'	SLim
§ – 'Minima'	ENHC LCon SBod
§ – var. ***montana***	EHul EPot SSta
– 'Pyramidalis'	LLin WGor
– 'Repanda' AGM	Widely available
§ – 'Schneverdingen Goldmachandel'	EBre EPla LBre NEgg SLim WAbe
– 'Sentinel'	CBra CDoC EBre EHul ENHC IHos IJoh IOrc LBee LBre LCon LPan MBar MBri MPla NBee SLim WBod WWeb
¶ – 'Sieben Steinhauser'	CKen
– 'Spotty Spreader' (v)	SLim
– f. ***suecica***	EHul ENot IHos LCon LPan MBar NWea SBod
– 'Zeal'	CKen EPla
conferta	CBra CDoC EHar EHul IDai LBee LLin MBar MBri MWat SBod SLim SLon SPer
– 'Blue Pacific'	CDoC CMac GAri LCon MBar SLim
– 'Emerald Sea'	EHul
– ***maritima***	See J. ***taxifolia lutchuensis***
davurica	EHul
– 'Expansa'	See J. ***chinensis*** 'Parsonsii'
– 'Expansa Albopicta'	See J. ***chinensis*** 'Expansa Variegata'
deppeana var. ***pachyphlaea***	GAri
– 'Silver Spire'	MBar MGos MPla SMad
§ ***excelsa*** var. ***polycarpos***	LMer
horizontalis	NRar NWea
– 'Alpina'	CKen

§ – 'Andorra Compact'	CKen CMac ESis LBee LCon MBar
– 'Banff'	CKen MBar
– 'Bar Harbor'	CB&S CKen CMac ENHC GPlt LPan MBar MGos MPla NHol SBod WGor
§ – 'Blue Chip'	CDoC CKen CMac EBre EHar EHul ENHC ENot EPla LBee LBre MAsh MBar MBri MGos MPla NHol NRoo SBod SLim SPer SPla SSmi
– 'Blue Moon'	See J. *h.* 'Blue Chip'
– 'Blue Rug'	See J. *h.* 'Wiltonii'
– 'Douglasii'	CMac EHul MBal MBar WGor
– 'Emerald Spreader'	CKen EBar EHul ENHC ENot LPan MBar MGos SLim SSmi
¶ – 'Glacier'	CKen
– Glauca Group	CMac EBee EHul ENHC ENot GDra IDai LGro LLin MBal MBar MGos WWin
– 'Glomerata'	CKen EPla MBar
¶ – 'Golden Spreader	CDoC
– 'Grey Pearl'	CDoC CKen EBre EHul EPla ESis LBre LCon LLin MBri NHed NHol SBod SLim SPer WWeb
– 'Hughes'	CDoC CKen CMac CSco EBar EBre ENot EPla IHos LBee LBre LCon LLin MAsh MBar MBri MGos MPla MRav NBee NHed NRoo SBod SLim
– 'Jade River'	CKen LRHS MBri SLim
– ***montana***	See J. ***communis m.***
– 'Neumänn'	CKen
– 'Plumosa' **AGM**	GPen NHed SSmi
– 'Plumosa Compacta'	See J. *h.* 'Andorra Compact'
– 'Prince of Wales'	CDoC CKen EBar EBre EHul GRei LBee LBre LCon MAsh MGos NHol SLim WGor
– var. ***saxatalis***	See J. ***communis montana***
– 'Turquoise Spreader'	CKen EHul MBar MPla
– 'Variegata'	EPla MBar
– 'Venusta'	CKen LCon
– 'Webberi'	LCon MAsh MBar SLim WWeb
– 'Wilms'	EPla
– 'Wiltonii' **AGM**	CKen EHul ENot IHos LLin MBal MGos MPla MWat WThu WTyr
– 'Winter Blue'	ENHC LBee SLim
– 'Youngstown'	CMac EBre LBre LCon MBar NHol SBod SPla SSta WGor
– 'Yukon Belle'	CKen
♦ ***macropoda***	See J. ***excelsa polycarpos***
x ***media*** 'Armstrongii'	EHul
♦ – 'Blaauw'	See J. ***chinensis*** 'B.'
– 'Blue and Gold'	CDoC CKen EPla ESis GPen MBri SHBN SLim SPer
§ – 'Carbery Gold'	CDoC CMac CSam EBar EHul GPen LBee LCon LLin LPan MAsh MBar MGos NHol SHer SLim
– 'Gold Coast'	CDoC CKen CMac EBre EHul ENHC ENot IHos LBee LBre LCon MBar MBri MGos MWat NBee SLim
– 'Gold Sovereign'	EBre LBre MAsh MGos NBar
– 'Golden Saucer'	LCon MAsh MBri NHol SBod
– 'Goldkissen'	MBri
– 'Milky Way' (v)	MWat
§ – 'Mint Julep'	CDoC CMac CSco EBar EBre EHul ENHC ENot EPla GPlt GRei IDai IJoh LBee LBre LCon LLin LPan MAsh MBar MGos MPla NBee NHol NRoo SLim SPer
– 'Mordigan Gold'	EHul LPan
* – 'Nelson's Compact'	NHol
– 'Old Gold' **AGM**	Widely available
– 'Old Gold Carbery'	See J. 'Carbery Gold'
– 'Pfitzeriana' **AGM**	CBra CMac EHar EHul ENHC ENot LLin MBal MBar MBri MGos NWea SBod SLim SLon SPer WDin WStI WWin
– 'Pfitzeriana Aurea'	CB&S CDoC CMac CSco EHar EHul ENHC ENot EPot GDra GPen IHos LCon MBal MBar MBri MGos MPla MWat NWea SBod SHBN SLim SLon SPer
– 'Pfitzeriana Compacta' **AGM**	CDoC CMac EHul MBar SLim WStI
– 'Pfitzeriana Glauca'	CDoC CSco EHul LCon LPan MWat NEgg SLim WGor
– 'Richeson'	MBar
♦ – 'Sea Green'	See J. x *m.* 'Mint Julep'
– 'Silver Cascade'	EHul
– 'Winter Surprise'	LCon NBee SLim
oxycedrus	CMHG GAri
pingii 'Glassell'	CLew LCon MBar NHol
– 'Loderi'	CKen EHar EHul LCon MBar SSta WGor
§ – 'Pygmaea'	CDoC LCon MBar MPla SLim
§ – 'Wilsonii'	CKen MBar WGor
procera	CGre
procumbens	MBri SLon WAbe WBod
– 'Bonin Isles'	CSam LLin MBal MBar MGos SLim SRms WAbe
– 'Nana' **AGM**	CDoC CKen CLew CMac EHar EHul ISea LBee LCon LLin MAsh MBal MBri MGos MPla MWat NHar NHol NKay SHBN SLim SPla SSmi SSta
recurva	GWht
– 'Castlewellan'	EBre LBre MGos SMad
– var. ***coxii***	CChu CDoC CMac EHar EHul EPla ISea LBee LCon MBri MGos SLim SLon SMad WThu
§ – 'Densa'	CKen EHul EPla GAri LCon LLin MBar NHol SHBN SPla STre
– 'Embley Park'	EHul LCon MAsh MBar MBri SHil SLim
– 'Nana'	See J. *r.* 'Densa'
rigida	GAri MBar SIng
sabina	GPoy LHol
– 'Arcadia'	CMac SRms
– 'Blaue Donau' ('Blue Danube')	CMac EHul IDai LPan MBar MGos SLim SRms WGor
– 'Broadmoor'	SLim
– 'Buffalo'	EHul
– 'Cupressifolia'	MBar
– 'Hicksii'	CMac MBar MGos NWea
– 'Rockery Gem'	EHul SLim WGor
– 'Skandia'	CKen
– 'Tamariscifolia'	CB&S CBra CDoC CMac EBre EHul ENot GPen IDai LBee LBre LCon LGro MAsh MBal MBar MBri MGos MPla MWat NBee NRoo NWea SBod SHBN SLim SLon SPer SSmi WSHC
– 'Tripartita'	MBar
– 'Variegata'	CMac EHul GWht LBee MBar SLim
sargentii	EHul GAri LCon MBal WWeb
– 'Glauca'	GAri
– 'Viridis'	EHul GAri

scopulorum 'Blue Arrow'	CKen LLin MGos MWat
¶ – 'Blue Banff'	CKen
– 'Blue Heaven' AGM	EBre EHar EHul ENHC ENot GAri LBre LCon MBal MBar SLim
– 'Boothman'	EHul
– 'Gray Gleam'	EHul ENHC
– 'Moonglow'	EBre LBre MBar MBri
– 'Mrs Marriage'	CKen
– 'Repens'	MBar MGos SRms
– 'Silver Globe'	LCon
– 'Silver Star'	CKen EHar EHul EPla MBar MGos
– 'Skyrocket'	Widely available
– 'Springbank'	CMac EHar ENHC LBee LCon MBar SLim
– 'Table Top'	MBar
– 'Wichita Blue'	LCon WGor
♦ ***seravshanica***	See J. ***excelsa polycarpos***
squamata	NWea
– 'Blue Carpet' AGM	Widely available
– 'Blue Spider'	CKen LCon LLin MBar MBri
– 'Blue Star' AGM	Widely available
– 'Blue Star Variegated'	See J. ***s.*** 'Golden Flame'
– 'Blue Swede'	See J. ***s.*** 'Hunnetorp'
– 'Chinese Silver'	CDoC CMHG EHul LCon MBar
– 'Filborna'	CDoC CKen LBee MBar MWat NHol SLim
– 'Glassell'	See J. ***pingii*** 'G.'
§ – 'Golden Flame'	CKen EPla
– 'Holger' AGM	CDoC CKen CMac EBre EHul EPla ESis GAri IDai LBee LBre LCon LLin MAsh MBar MBri MGos MPla MWat NHol SBod SGil SLim WStI
– 'Hunnetorp'	EHul GPlt LCon LPan MBar MBri MGos
♦ – 'Loderi'	See J. ***pingii*** 'L.'
– 'Meyeri'	CBra CMac CSco EHul ENHC ENot GDra GPen IDai LCon LLin MBal MBar MWat NWea SBod SLim SLon SPer WStI WTyr WWin
♦ – 'Pygmaea'	See J. ***pingii*** 'P.'
♦ – 'Wilsonii'	See J. ***pingii*** 'W.'
§ ***taxifolia*** var. ***lutchuensis***	EHar EPot LBee LCon MBal MPla MWat
virginiana	CMCN GWht NWea
– 'Blue Cloud'	CDoC EHul LCon LLin MBar SLim
– 'Burkii'	EHar EHul LCon MBal
– 'Canaertii'	LPan
– 'Frosty Morn'	CKen EHul LCon MBar
– 'Glauca'	EHul NBee NWea SLon
– 'Golden Spring'	CKen
– 'Grey Owl' AGM	CBra CDoC CMHG CMac EHar EHul ENot GRei LCon LLin MBal MBar MBri MGos MPla NBee SLim SLon SPer SPla STre WDin WGor WTyr
– 'Helle'	See J. ***chinensis*** 'Spartan'
– 'Hetz'	CB&S CBra CMac EHar EHul ENHC GWht LCon LPan MAsh MBal MBar MBri MGos NWea SBod
– 'Hillii'	MBar
– 'Hillspire'	EHul
– 'Nana Compacta'	MBar
– 'Pendula'	EPla
I – 'Robusta Green'	ENHC
– 'Silver Spreader'	EHul LCon LLin MGos SPer
– 'Staver Blue'	EHul
§ – 'Sulphur Spray' AGM	CDoC CKen CMHG CMac EBre EHul ENHC EPla GPen GRei GWht IJoh LBee LBre LCon MBar MBri MGos MPla MWat NHol SLim SPer SSmi

JURINEA (Compositae/Asteraceae)

ceratocarpa	See SAUSSUREA ***c.***
¶ ***mollis***	ECro GBuc
moschus ssp. ***moschus***	NWCA

JURINELLA See JURINEA

JUSSIAEA See LUDWIGIA

JUSTICIA (Acanthaceae)

§ ***brandegeeana*** AGM	MBri SLMG
– ***lutea***	See J. ***b.*** 'Yellow Queen'
§ – 'Yellow Queen'	SLMG
§ ***carnea***	CSev CTro EBak ERea MBri
floribunda	See J. ***rizzinii***
guttata	See J. ***brandegeeana***
* 'Norgard's Favourite'	MBri
pauciflora	See J. ***rizzinii***
pohliana	See J. ***carnea***
polianthor robusta	CTro
§ ***rizzinii*** AGM	CAbb CKni CPle CSpe CTre CTro ERav ERea IBlr LBlm LHil LHop
spicigera	ERea
suberecta	See DICLIPTERA ***s.***

KADSURA (Schisandraceae)

japonica	CGre CHan CPle EMil WSHC
– 'Variegata'	CPle EMil SSta WSHC
suromi	EMil

KAEMPFERIA (Zingiberaceae)

♦ ***ovalifolia***	See K. ***parishii***
§ ***parishii***	LBow
¶ ***rotunda***	CNew

KALANCHOË (Crassulaceae)

beharensis	MBri SLMG
¶ ***daigremontiana***	GBur
marmorata	SGil
pumila AGM	EWoo IBlr SGil WEas
synsepala	SGil
– ***laciniata***	SGil
'Tessa' AGM	MBri SHer SLMG
tomentosa AGM	SLMG WEas
'Wendy' AGM	MBri SHer

KALIMERIS (Compositae/Asteraceae)

§ ***incisa***	EMil EMon SMrm
¶ – 'Alba'	EMon
integrifolia	ECha NBrk WCot
§ ***mongolica***	WPer
yomena 'Shogun' (v)	CBos CElw CRDP ECha ECoo EFol EHal EHoe EMon EPla NBir SOkh WCot
– 'Variegata'	See K. ***y.*** 'Shogun'

KALMIA † (Ericaceae)

angustifolia AGM	CBow CLan GAul IJoh ISea LNet MBar WDin
– f. ***candida***	GGGa
– f. ***rubra***	CB&S CBow CBra CCla CDoC CMHG CSco ELan GGGa GWht ISea LAbb MBal MGos NBar NBee NHol NKay NRoo SHBN SPer SReu SSta WBod WPat WThu WWeb
cuneata	SSta
latifolia AGM	CB&S CBow CBra CLan CSco ELan EMil ENot GAul GGGa GRei ISea LAbb LHyd LNet MBal MBar MGos NWea SPer SReu SSta WAbe WDin WStI WWat
– 'Alpine Pink'	MLea
– 'Bullseye'	LNet
– 'Carousel'	CAbP LMil LNet MAsh MGos MLea SHBN
– 'Clementine Churchill'	CCla ECot
– 'Elf'	EMil MAsh
– 'Freckles'	LMil LNet MAsh MLea
– 'Fresca'	SHer
– 'Goodrich'	CB&S MGos SPer WWeb
– 'Heart of Fire'	CAbP LMil
– 'Minuet'	CAbP CPMA EB&P MAsh SHer
– 'Nipmuck'	LHyd MGos MLea
– 'Olympic Fire'	ELan EMil IOrc LNet MAsh MBal MGos MLea NHed
– 'Ostbo Red' AGM	CB&S CBra CChu EHar ELan EMil ENot IOrc LHyd LNet MBal MBri MGos MLea NHed SHBN SHer SReu SSta WBod
– 'Pink Charm'	MAsh MBal MGos MLea SHBN
– 'Pink Frost'	CB&S CCla LNet MGos MLea SHBN WWat WWeb
– 'Pink Star'	MLea SHBN
– 'Pinwheel'	MLea
– 'Richard Jaynes'	GGGa
– 'Sarah'	GGGa
– 'Shooting Star'	MGos
– 'Silver Dollar'	ELan MAsh
– 'Snowdrift'	MAsh
§ ***microphylla***	GGGa MBal WPat WThu
– 'Mount Shasta'	GGGa
– var. ***occidentalis***	GGGa
polifolia	CB&S CDoC GGGa MBar MRav SReu SSta WPat
– ***compacta***	GArf
– 'Glauca'	See K. ***microphylla***
– f. ***leucantha***	GGGa
****pygmaea***	GGGa

KALMIOPSIS (Ericaceae)

leachiana AGM	CNic EPot GArf GTou MBal MGos WAbe
– 'Glendoick'	GGGa MAsh WPat WThu
– 'La Piniec'	GGGa MGos
– Umpqua Valley form	EPot

X KALMIOTHAMNUS (Ericaceae)

ornithomma	GGGa WAbe

KALOPANAX (Araliaceae)

pictus	See K. ***septemlobus***
§ ***septemlobus***	CB&S CBot CHEx EArb EHar ELan MBri SArc SHil SPla
– var. ***maximowiczii***	CHEx MBlu MBri NBee SMad

KECKIELLA (Scrophulariaceae)

§ ***cordifolia***	CMHG LGre LHop SIgm
corymbosa JCA 11618	CMHG LGre NWCA WDav
¶ ***lemmonii*** JCA 13004	WDav
§ ***ternata*** JLS 86304LACA	EMon

KELSEYA (Rosaceae)

See Plant Deletions

KENNEDIA (Leguminosae/Papilionaceae)

coccinea	CB&S CTro SLMG
nigricans	CTro LHop

KENTIA (Palmae/Arecaceae)

belmoreana	See HOWEA ***b.***
canterburyana	See HEDYSCEPE ***c.***

KENTRANTHUS See **CENTRANTHUS**

KERNERA (Cruciferae/Brassicaceae)

See Plant Deletions

KERRIA (Rosaceae)

japonica	CB&S CTrw IOrc NBee NKay SDix WDin WTyr WWin
– 'Golden Guinea' AGM	CChu CDoC EBre ECtt ELan ESma IOrc LBre LRHS MBri MRav NHol SGil SPla WWat WWeb
§ – 'Picta' (v)	CB&S CChe CPle CSco CShe EBre EHoe ELan ESis IJoh IOrc ISea LAbb LBre MBar MBri MGos MPla MWat NBar NKay NNor SPer WDin WEas WPbr WSHC WWat WWin
– 'Pleniflora' AGM	CB&S CBra CChe CPle CSco CShe EBre ELan ENot GRei IDai IJoh ISea LBre MBar MBri MGos MPla MRav MWat NHol NNor NRoo NWea SHBN SLon SPer STre WDin
– 'Simplex'	CSco ELan ENot IDai ISea NWea
– 'Variegata'	See K. ***j.*** 'Picta'

KICKXIA (Scrophulariaceae)

spuria	MHew MSal

KIRENGESHOMA (Hydrangeaceae)

palmata AGM	Widely available
§ – Koreana Group	CCla CRDP CSco ECha ECro ELan EPar MBel MBri NSti SAxl SPer WAbe WMer

KITAIBELA (Malvaceae)

vitifolia	CGle CHan CSam CTom ECoo ECro ELan EMar EMon EOrc GAul GCal LGan LHop MTol NBro NSti NWyt SFis SMad SSvw WCot WDav WPer

KITCHINGIA See KALANCHOË

KIWI FRUIT See ACTINIDIA *deliciosa*

KLEINIA (Compositae/Asteraceae)

♦*articulata*	See SENECIO *articulatus*
senecioïdes	WEas

KNAUTIA (Dipsacaceae)

arvensis	CArn CKin CRiv ECWi ECoo EWFC LHol MChe NLan NMir WCla WGwy WHer WNdy WOak
dipsacifolia	WCot
**jankiae*	WHer
§ *macedonica*	Widely available
– pink	CBos SWas

KNIGHTIA (Proteaceae)

excelsa	CHEx

KNIPHOFIA † (Liliaceae/Asphodelaceae)

'Ada'	EBre ERou GCHN LBre WCot
'Alcazar'	CBow CDoC CMGP ECot EFou EPar MHFP WMer
'Apple Court'	SApp
'Apricot'	SWas
'Apricot Souffle'	ECha MHlr WCot
'Atlanta'	EBre EMon GCal IBlr LBre
'Bees' Lemon'	IBlr
'Bees' Sunset' AGM	SHig SPer WCot WHal
'Border Ballet'	CBow CMHG ECtt LHop LWad MFir MPit NBro NFai NMir WBon WByw WGor WHil
'Bressingham Comet'	CGle EGle SBla
Bressingham hybrids	COtt EBre IBlr LBre NBir NKay
'Brimstone' AGM	EPla WCot
'Buttercup' AGM	CChu CGle CMHG EBul
'C M Prichard' hort.	See K. *rooperi*
'Candlelight'	WWin
'Catherine's Orange'	EFou
caulescens AGM	CBot CHEx CHan CPou CRDP CSam EBre EBul EMon GCra LBre MUlv SBla SCro SDix SHig WCot
– BH 5020	ECha
citrina	CB&S CBot EBee EFou MBal SAxl SIgm SMrm WWat
'Cobra'	COtt CPou ERou GCHN
'Corallina'	LRHS WCot
'Cream Flame'	SApp
'Dr E M Mills'	COtt SPer
'Early Buttercup'	CMGP CWGN ECot EFou EGol EOrc MMil MNFA MUlv NCat SPer
elegans	WCot
¶ 'Ernest Mitchell'	WCot
'Fairyland'	WCot
'Fiery Fred'	CMHG COtt EBre EFou EGle ELan LBre MHFP WCot
'Fireking'	LRHS
galpinii AGM	CAbb CBot CChu CGle CMGP ENot EPla MBal NBir NSti WCot WHil WWat
galpinii hort.	See K. *triangularis triangularis*
'Goldelse'	CChu ECha EOrc IBlr NBir SBla
'Goldfinch'	SMrm
'Green Jade'	CLew CRow ECha EGol EPar LGre MNFA MUlv NBir SIgm SMrm
'H E Beale'	GCal
hirsuta H&B 16444	EMon
'Ice Queen'	COtt CRDP EBre EFou EGle EGol EOrc LBre MRav MUlv SPer WCot WRus
ichopensis	CHan
'Innocence'	CChu EGle LRHS SApp
'Jenny Bloom'	MHFP SBla SHig SMrm SWas WCot
late orange	EBul MUlv
'Limelight'	EOrc
'Little Elf'	SBla SWas
'Little Maid' AGM	Widely available
¶ 'Lord Roberts'	SDix
macowanii	See K. *triangularis triangularis*
'Maid of Orleans'	IBlr WCot
'Mermaiden'	CMHG GCal LRHS
'Modesta'	EGle GCal IBlr SUsu WCot
'Mount Etna'	CGle WAbe WCot
'Nancy's Red'	ECha SMrm SWas
nelsonii	See K. *triangularis triangularis*
'Nobilis'	See K. *uvaria* 'N.'
northiae	CBot
'Painted Lady'	MHlr WCot
'Percy's Pride'	CSam EBre EBul EOrc LBre MHlr SApp WCot
'Pfitzeri'	SRms
'Primrose Beauty'	WMer
'Prince Igor'	CRiv ECha EFou GAbr MBal SApp
pumila	WCot
§ *rooperi*	CBot MBal WCot
'Royal Caste'	CBow EBee NOrc
'Royal Standard' AGM	CB&S CChu CHEx CMHG ELan ENot GAbr IBlr IDai LHop LWad NMir SBla SCro SPla
rufa	GCal
'Samuel's Sensation' AGM	WCot
'September Sunshine'	EFou
'Shining Sceptre'	CChu CMHG COtt EBre ECtt LBre MUlv WCot WMer
'Sir C K Butler'	IBlr
sp. ex Ethiopia	GCal
'Star of Baden-Baden'	LRHS NBir
'Strawberries and Cream'	SBla SUsu SWas
'Sunningdale Yellow' AGM	CPou ECha SChu SRms WEas
§ *thomsonii* var. *snowdenii*	CBot CChu CHan CMon ECha IBlr LBlm LHil MSte SAxl SBla WCot
'Toasted Corn'	ECha
'Toffee Nosed' AGM	EFou ERou GCal
'Torchbearer'	WCot
triangularis AGM	CBot CMon SBla
§ – ssp. *triangularis*	CBot CChu CGle IBlr MNFA NBro SHig SIgm WCot
'Tuckii'	CGre CHol LBlm LGan MBal SIgm SMrm WCot
uvaria	CHEx CHol CShe LRHS MHFP NBir NCat NFai SIgm SRms WByw WHoo
§ – 'Nobilis' AGM	EBul MHlr SDix WCot
'Wrexham Buttercup'	CBos
'Yellow Hammer'	CBot EGol GAbr GCal IBlr NCat

¶ 'Zululandiae' WCot

KNOWLTONIA (Ranunculaceae)
See Plant Deletions

KOBRESIA (Cyperaceae)
See Plant Deletions

KOELERIA (Gramineae/Poaceae)
glauca EBar ECha EHoe EMon EOrc EPla ESiP ESis ETPC GAbr GAul GCHN MBri NFai NHol NMir NSti WCot WHal WPer WWat
macrantha ETPC MWil
vallesiana EHoe EMon EPla ETPC LRHS

KOELLIKERIA (Gesneriaceae)
'Red Satin' NMos

KOELREUTERIA (Sapindaceae)
bipinnata CGre
paniculata **AGM** Widely available
– ***apiculata*** CMHG MBri
– 'Fastigiata' EBre LBre MBlu MBri

KOHLERIA (Gesneriaceae)
'Clytie' MBri
¶ 'Dark Velvet' WDib
♦***digitaliflora*** See K. ***warscewiczii***
eriantha **AGM** CPle MBri SLMG WDib
'Hanna Roberts' WDib
hirsuta CPle
*x ***hybrida*** NMos
'Strawberry Fields' **AGM** MBri NMos
¶ 'Success' CTro
§ ***warscewiezii*** CTro WDib

KOLKWITZIA (Caprifoliaceae)
amabilis CB&S CGre CSco CTrw ELan GRei IDai IJoh LAbb MGos MPla MWat NBee NHol NNor NWea SSta WCru WDin WHCG WStI WWin
– 'Pink Cloud' **AGM** CB&S CBra CCla CPle CShe CTrw EBre EHar ENot IOrc ISea LBre LHop MBal MBar MBri MGos NBar NHol NKay SHBN SLon SPer SPla SReu SSta WBod WDin WSHC WWat

KUMMEROWIA
(Leguminosae/Papilionaceae)
See Plant Deletions

KUNZEA (Myrtaceae)
ambigua CB&S CGre CMer
§ ***ericoïdes*** ECou
parvifolia CB&S

LABICHEA (Leguminosae/Caesalpiniaceae)
See Plant Deletions

LABLAB (Leguminosae/Caesalpiniaceae)
§ ***purpureus*** WHaw

+ LABURNOCYTISUS
(Leguminosae/Papilionaceae)
adamii CBow CBra CDoC COtt CSco CWSG EHar ELan GAri IOrc LBuc MNes SHBN SHil SPer

LABURNUM †
(Leguminosae/Papilionaceae)
alpinum CNic GAri NWea
– 'Pendulum' CDoC CPMA EBre ELan EMil IJoh IOrc LBre LNet MBri MGos MRav NBar NBee SHBN SMad SPer WDin WStI
§ ***anagyroïdes*** GAri GRei NWea WDin
– 'Pendulum' CLnd
vulgare See L. ***anagyroïdes***
x ***watereri*** 'Alford's Weeping' MBar MGos
– 'Vossii' **AGM** CB&S CLnd CSco EBre ELan EMil ENot GRei IJoh IOrc LBre LBuc LNet MBar MBri MGos MRav NBar NBee NWea SFam SHBN SPer SReu SSta WAbe WDin WJas

LACCOSPADIX (Palmae/Arecaceae)
See Plant Deletions

LACHENALIA (Liliaceae/Hyacinthaceae)
§ ***aloïdes*** EBul ETub LBow MBri WOMN WThi
– var. ***aurea*** **AGM** CMea ETub LBow SHer
– var. ***luteola*** LBow
– 'Nelsonii' LBow
– 'Pearsonii' SHer
– var. ***quadricolor*** **AGM** LBow
– var. ***vanzyliae*** LBow
§ ***bulbifera*** LBow MBri NRog SHer
– 'George' LBow
contaminata LBow
hybrid Lac. 213 LBow
mediana LBow
pallida NRog
pendula See L. ***bulbifera***
pustulata NRog
reflexa WThi
¶ x ***regeliana*** LBow
rubida NRog
tricolor See L. ***aloïdes***
zeyheri EBul

LACTUCA (Compositae/Asteraceae)
alpina See CICERBITA ***alpina***
perennis CElw CLew SChu WPer
virosa MSal

LAGAROSIPHON (Hydrocharitaceae)
§ ***major*** CBen CRow EHon ELan EMFW NDea SAWi SRms SWyc WChe WHol

LAGAROSTROBOS (Podocarpaceae)
§ ***franklinii*** CB&S IOrc LLin WBod

LAGENOPHORA (Compositae/Asteraceae)
pinnatifida WPer

LAGERSTROEMIA (Lythraceae)

chekiangensis	EArb
indica AGM	CPle CTro SEng SLMG
¶ – 'forms'	CTro
– 'Rosea'	CB&S CTro
¶ ***subcostata***	CB&S

LAGUNARIA (Malvaceae)

patersonii	CNew CTro
– 'Royal Purple'	ERea

LALLEMANTIA (Labiatae/Lamiaceae)

See Plant Deletions

LAMARCKIA (Gramineae/Poaceae)

See Plant Deletions

LAMIASTRUM See LAMIUM

LAMIUM † (Labiatae/Lamiaceae)

¶ ***album***	CKin ECWi
¶ – 'Ashfield Variegated'	NRar
– ***aureovariegatum***	See L. ***a.*** 'Goldflake'
¶ – 'Brightstone Gem'	EMon
– 'Friday' (v)	EFol EHoe EMon LRHS MBel MTho NRar SApp WCHb WCot WCru WHer
¶ – 'Golden Halo'	EMon
§ – 'Goldflake' (v)	EFol EMon MBel WCHb
– 'Pale Peril'	EMon
¶ ***armenum***	EWes
flexuosum	EMon MBel
§ ***galeobdolon***	CArn CGle CKin EBre ECWi EMon EWFC LBre LGro LHil MHew MSal MWat NFai SPer WCru WNdy WOak
¶ – 'Canford Wood'	EPla
§ – 'Florentinum'	CGle CHol CRow CSFH CSco CShe CTom ECha ECro EFol EHoe ELan ENot EPar NHol NNor SIng SSvw STre WPer
– 'Hermann's Pride'	CBos CHan CLew CMHG COtt CRDP CWit EBre ECtt EHal EMon GAbr GCal GCra LBre LHil LHop MBel MBri MUlv NFai NMir SPer WByw WCru WWye
¶ – 'Purple Heart'	EMon
– 'Silberteppich' ('Silver Carpet')	CBow CRow ECha EFol EFou ELan EMar EMon EOrc EPla ERav GGar LHop MTho NHol NKay NNor NSti NWyt SBla SHer SIng SMad SMrm WCru WPer WWat
– 'Silver Angel'	EMon ESma MBel NSti WCru
¶ – 'Silver Spangled'	EMon
– 'Variegatum'	See L. ***g.*** 'Florentinum'
garganicum ssp. ***garganicum***	CBre CElw CGle CHan CSev EFol EMon NRar NSti WCru WWye
– 'Laevigatum'	EMon MBel
– ***pictum***	See L. ***g. striatum***
– ***reniforme***	See L. ***g. striatum***
§ – ssp. ***striatum***	EFol ELan SHer
– ssp. ***striatum*** DS&T 89011T	EMon
maculatum	CArn CBow CMer CRow CTom EMon NBee WByw WCru WWye
– ***album***	CBow CGle CLew CMea CNic CRow EFou ELan EMon LGro MHig MTol NHol SPer WBon WByw WCru WWat
§ – 'Aureum'	CB&S CCla CGle CLew CMer EBre ECha EFol EHoe ELan EMon EOrc EPla LBre LGro LHop MBel MTho NFai NHol NKay NMir NNor SMad WBon WEas WHil WOak
– 'Beacon Silver'	Widely available
– 'Beedham's White'	EPla NSti SCro SUsu WCru WRus
– 'Cannon's Gold'	EBee ECha ECtt EFol EHoe ELan EMon EPla ESma GBuc WCru
N – 'Chequers'	CBow CDoC CSFH CSco EBre ELan EMon ENot EPla LBre NHol SPer
– 'Dingle Candy'	EFol EMon
¶ – 'Edinburgh Broadstripes'	EPla
– 'Elizabeth de Haas' (v)	EFol EHoe EMon ESma LHil LHop WCot WCru
– 'Gold Leaf'	See L. ***m.*** 'Aureum'
– 'Golden Nuggets'	LWad NPri SFis
– 'Hatfield'	ELan EMon GBuc
¶ – 'Ickwell Beauty' (v)	EMon
– 'Immaculate'	EMon EPla
– 'James Boyd Parselle'	CLTr EMon MHlr WCHb WCot
– 'Margery Fish'	SRms WEas
– 'Pink Nancy'	CBot CMea CSpe MTho WAbb
– 'Pink Pewter'	CGle CLTr ECha ECtt EFou EMon EPla MBel MTol NBrk NSti SCro SMrm SUsu WBon WByw WCHb WCru WHoo
¶ – 'Purple Winter'	EPla
– 'Red Nancy'	CBre EBee EMar EMon EPla EPot GCal WCru
§ – ***roseum***	CBre CGle CLew CMea CMer CRow CShe CTom EFol EFou EGol ELan EPla GCal LGro LHop MWat NFai NHol NMir NNor SIng SPer WBon WHer WHil WPer WTyr WWat
– 'Shell Pink'	See L. ***m. roseum***
– 'Silver Dollar'	EMon EPla MBri
– 'Sterling Silver'	EMon EPla
– 'White Nancy' AGM	Widely available
¶ – 'Wild White'	EPla
– 'Wootton Pink'	CBos CLTr GMac WCra WEas
orvala	CBot CGle CHan EBre ECha ECro EFol EMon EPla LBre MFir NGar SAxl SIng WBon WByw WHal WWat
– 'Album'	CBot CHan ECha ECro EFol ELan EMon EPla SIng WCot

LAMPRANTHUS (Aizoaceae)

aberdeenensis	See DELOSPERMA ***aberdeenense***
¶ ***amoenus***	CTbh
aurantiacus	CB&S CHEx NBrk
¶ ***aureus***	CTbh
blandus	CB&S CHEx CTbh
§ ***brownii***	CB&S CHEx ELan EPot SHer WCru
* 'Carn Brae'	CB&S
§ ***deltoïdes***	CHEx MRav SLMG WEas
edulis	See CARPOBROTUS ***e.***
falcatus	SLMG

falciformis WPer
glaucus CB&S CHEx
haworthii SLMG
lehmannii See DELOSPERMA ***l.***
¶ *multiradiatus* CTbh
oscularis See L. ***deltoïdes***
pallidus See DELOSPERMA ***pallidum***
¶ *primavernus* CTbh
¶ *roseus* CTbh
spectabilis CB&S CTbh SLMG
– 'Tresco Apricot' CB&S
– 'Tresco Brilliant' CB&S
– 'Tresco Fire' CBrk
– 'Tresco Red' CB&S WPer
¶ *stayneri* CTbh
zeyheri CB&S

LANTANA (Verbenaceae)

camara CPle CTro ERea LAbb MBri
– 'Brasier' ERea
¶ – 'Cocktail' NPri
– 'Feston Rose' ERea
– 'Firebrand' SLMG
– forms ERea IBlr
– 'Mine d'Or' ERea
– 'Mr Bessieres' ERea
– 'Snow White' ERea SLMG
'Gold Dust' SLMG
* *montevidensis* CBar CBrk CPle CTro ERea LBlm LHop SLMG WEas
*– *alba* ERea
– 'Boston Gold' CBrk
¶ – 'Malans Gold' ERea
*– 'White Lightening' LHop
'Radiation' ERea
sellowiana See L. ***montevidensis***

LAPAGERIA (Liliaceae/Philesiaceae)

rosea **AGM** CB&S CBow CGre CHEx CMac CNew CTro ERea LAbb LHop MBal SArc SHBN SHer SPer SReu WNor WWat
– var. *albiflora* CNew
– – 'White Cloud' CGre
– 'Flesh Pink' **AGM** CB&S CGre CNew ERav
– 'Nash Court' **AGM** CB&S CBot CChu CGre CMac CSam ECot ELan EMil ERav ERea IBar IOrc ISea LHop SHer WSHC WStI
– 'Penheale' CB&S

LAPEIROUSIA (Iridaceae)

cruenta See ANOMATHECA ***laxa***
laxa See ANOMATHECA ***laxa***

LAPIEDRA (Liliaceae/Amaryllidaceae)

martinezii MS 423 CMon

LAPSANA (Compositae/Asteraceae)

communis 'Inky' CNat

LARDIZABALA (Lardizabalaceae)

biternata CGre

LARIX (Pinaceae)

decidua **AGM** CB&S CDoC EHar ENHC ENot GAul GRei IDai IHos LCon LPan MBal MBar NWea SHBN SPer WDin WMou WStI
– 'Corley' CKen EBre LBre MAsh
– 'Little Bogle' CKen
¶ – 'Oberförster Karsten' CKen
– 'Pendula' CB&S EBre EHar LBre
x *eurolepis* See L. x ***marschlinsii***
gmelinii GAri ISea WThu
– var. *olgensis* CMCN
§ *kaempferi* **AGM** CBow CDoC CLnd CPer CSco CTre EHar ENHC ENot GRei IJoh LBuc LCon LNet MBar MGos NWea SLim SPer WFro WMou WNor WStI
– 'Bambino' CKen
– 'Blue Ball' CKen LLin
– 'Blue Dwarf' CDoC CKen EBre LBre LCon LLin LNet LPan MAsh MBri SLim
– 'Blue Rabbit Weeping' LPan SLim
– 'Cruwys Morchard' CKen
– 'Dervaes' EHar
– 'Diane' CKen EBre GAri LBre LLin MBlu
¶ – 'Elizabeth Rehder' CKen
– 'Grant Haddow' CKen
¶ – 'Green Pearl' CKen
¶ – 'Grey Pearl' CKen
¶ – 'Hobbit' CKen
*– 'Jacobsen' SMad
– 'Little Blue Star' CDoC
– 'Nana' CKen GAri MAsh
I – *nana prostrata* CKen
– 'Pendula' CBra CDoC EHar IBar IJoh IOrc MBar MBlu MBri MGos MUlv SHil SLim
– 'Varley' CKen
¶ – 'Wehlen' CKen
– 'Wolterdingen' CKen
laricina GAri
– 'Arethusa Bog' CKen
leptolepis See L. ***kaempferi***
§ x *marschlinsii* EHar ENot GRei MBar NWea WMou
– 'Domino' CKen LLin
– 'Gail' CKen
– 'Julie' CKen
x *pendula* 'Pendulina' GAri
¶ *potaninii* CLD 123 WHCr
russica See L. ***sibirica***
§ *sibirica* GAri LCon MBar WNor
sukaczevii See L. ***sibirica***

LASER (Umbelliferae/Apiaceae)

¶ *trilobum* SIgm

LASERPITIUM (Umbelliferae/Apiaceae)

See Plant Deletions

LASIAGROSTIS See STIPA

LATHYRUS † (Leguminosae/Papilionaceae)

¶ *amphicarpos* MSto
¶ *annuus* MSto
aphaca MSto
§ *articulatus* MSto

aureus Brândză	MSto
♦***aureus*** hort.	See L. ***gmelinii*** 'Aureus'
azureus	See L. ***sativus***
chloranthus	MSto SSad
¶ ***chrysanthus***	MSto
¶ ***cicera***	MSto SSad
¶ ***clymenum***	SSad
♦– ***articulatus***	See L. ***a.***
¶ ***cyaneus***	MSto
– ***alboroseus***	MTho
davidii	MSto
¶ ***filiformis***	MSto
*****fremontii***	CSpe MTho SSad WWin
¶ ***gmelinii***	MSto
§ – 'Aureus'	CBos ECha GCal GCra MTho NCat NHol NSti SBla SFar SSad SUsu WEas WOMN
¶ ***gorgonii***	SSad
grandiflorus	CGle CRDP CSev ECha EMon LGre MSto NSti SSad WOak
heterophyllus	GAul MSto WCot WHal WHil
¶ ***hierosolymitanus***	MSto SSad
¶ ***hirsutus***	MSto
¶ ***hookeri***	MSto
inermis	See L. ***laxiflorus***
japonicus	MSto MWil WGwy
¶ ***laevigatus***	CBot
latifolius AGM	CBow CCla CGle CMea CTom EBre ELan ERav GCHN GCal GPlt LBre LGan MFir NHol NPer NSti SIng SUsu WCot WEas WFro WHal WHer WNdy WOak WPer WStI WWin WWye
– 'Albus'	CBot CHad CRDP ELan EMon GDra LGre LWad MSte SAxl SGil SUsu WCot WEas WHal WSun
– 'Blushing Bride'	WCot
– deep pink	NSti
– pale pink	CSam NSti WEas WHal
– 'Red Pearl'	CDoC EBre ECro ECtt EFou LBre MBri SPer SSvw WPer WTyr
– 'Rosa Perle' ('Pink Pearl')	CDoC ECro ECtt EFou GAbr LAbb LGan MBri MSte NWyt SPer SSvw WRus
¶ – 'Rose Queen'	CB&S
¶ – 'Splendens'	CB&S
– 'White Pearl' ('Weisse Perle') AGM	CB&S CChu CCla CDoC CGle CMea EBre ECha ECro EFou EOrc GAbr GCal LAbb LBre MBri MSte NHol NPer NSti SBla SFis SMad SPer SSvw WCra WHer WPer WRus WWat
§ ***laxiflorus***	EOrc MSto NCat NTow SAxl SUsu WCru
linifolius montanus	CKin WNdy
♦***luteus*** 'Aureus'	See L. ***gmelinii*** 'Aureus'
magellanicus	See L. ***nervosus***
¶ ***multiceps*** F&W 7192	CRDP MSto
§ ***nervosus***	CBot CPla CPou CRDP CSpe EBre ECro GCal LBre MSto MTho SAxl SBla SFis SIgm SMad SMrm SSad SUsu WEas WHal WOMN WRus
neurolobus	CNic SSad
niger	EMon
nissolia	ELan MSto MWil
¶ ***ochrus***	MSto
odoratus AGM	CGle CHan
– 'Bicolor'	ELan
– 'Painted Lady'	EJud
¶ ***palustris***	LGre MSto
pannonicus	MFir MSto
pratensis	CKin ECWi EWFC MSto MWil WGwy WNdy
pubescens	CRDP GCra MSto WCot
rotundifolius	ECoo EPad ERav GCal GDra LGre MHlr MSto MTho NSti SSad SUsu SWas WBon WCot WHal WHoo WOMN
¶ – hybrids	LGre MSto
§ ***sativus***	CHad CMea CSpe ELan GAul MSto SMrm SSad SUsu WEas WSun WWye
¶ – ***alboazureus***	MSto
¶ – ***albus***	MSto
– ***azureus***	See L. ***s.***
¶ ***sphaericus***	MSto
sylvestris	CKin ECro ELan EMon LGre MSto MWil WNdy
tingitanus	WEas WHer
¶ – 'Flame'	MSto
¶ – salmon pink	MSto
tuberosus	EMon
¶ ***undulatus***	MSto
vernus AGM	CBot CHad CHan CTom EFou ELan GAbr LGre MFir MTho NOak NSti SSad SUsu WDav WHal WKif WPer WRus WThu WWye
– 'Alboroseus'	EFol EFou ELan GCal LGre MBri MNFA MSto NHol NTow SBla SFar SIng SMrm SSad SUsu WCot WHoo WKif WOMN WRus WThu
– ***albus***	SSad
♦– ***aurantiacus***	See L. ***gmelinii*** 'Aureus'
– 'Caeruleus'	LGre SMrm
– ***cyaneus***	CHad NTow SSad WRus
– 'Flaccidus'	EMon WKif
¶ – 'Rosenelfe'	CBot GCal WHil
– f. ***roseus***	CRDP ECha GPlt NTow
– 'Spring Melody'	WCot

LAURELIA (Monimiaceae)

§ ***sempervirens***	CAbb CB&S CGre CTrw SArc SBor
serrata	See L. ***sempervirens***

LAURENTIA (Campanulaceae)

See Plant Deletions

LAURUS (Lauraceae)

§ ***azorica***	CB&S CGre CTre GCal
canariensis	See L. ***azorica***
nobilis AGM	Widely available
– f. ***angustifolia***	CPle EHar EPla LAbb LHol MBlu SArc SDry SLon
– 'Aurea' AGM	CB&S CBow CDec CGre CMHG CPle CSco CSev EBre EHar ELan ERav EWri IOrc LBre LHol LNet MBlu MChe SHil SMad SPer WCHb WPat WWat

LAVANDULA † (Labiatae/Lamiaceae)

N 'Alba'	CArn CB&S CBot CJer CSco CSev EFol EFou ELan EOrc ERav GCHN LHol MPla SBla SLon SMad SPer WEas WHal WOak WPer WSHC WWye
x ***allardii***	CJer ENor NHHG
§ ***angustifolia*** AGM	CArn CBow CLan CSFH CShe EHer ENot GPoy LBuc MBar MBri MChe MGos MPla MWat NHar NNor NPer NWyt SHBN SLon WAbe WHil WWye
– 'Alba'	CChe CMer CPMA EBar EHic ENor GPoy LHop MChe NFai WPbr
– 'Alba Nana'	See L. ***a.*** 'Nana Alba'
§ – 'Bowles' Early'	CJer CPMA CSam CSco MChe NHHG
– 'Bowles' Variety'	See L. ***a.*** 'Bowles' Early'
– 'Dwarf Blue'	EFol LHop NBee NHHG
– 'Folgate'	CAbb CB&S CBow CDoC CHad CJer CPMA CSco EFou LHol LHop MChe NFai NHHG SIde WPer
– 'Fring Favourite'	CJer NHHG
– 'Heacham Blue'	CJer NHHG
§ – 'Hidcote' AGM	Widely available
– 'Hidcote Pink'	Widely available
– 'Imperial Gem'	CBow CCla CJer EBee EHic ENor ESis GBar LGre MChe NHHG NHar NPer SIde
– 'Jean Davis'	CJer MHFP NHHG
– 'Loddon Blue'	CJer CPMA LHol NHHG SIde
– 'Loddon Pink'	CBow CJer GBar GCra IEde MChe NHHG WAbe WStI
– 'Maillette'	CJer
– 'Munstead'	Widely available
§ – 'Nana Alba'	Widely available
– 'Nana Atropurpurea'	CJer
– 'Norfolk'	LRHS
– No. 9	CJer NHHG
– 'Princess Blue'	CJer ENor ESis NHar NWyt SHer SIde
§ – 'Rosea'	Widely available
– 'Royal Purple'	CArn CJer CSev ENor EWes GBar LHol NHHG NHar NWyt SGil SIde WWye
– 'Twickel Purple' AGM	CDoC CJer EBar EBee GCHN LHop MChe NHHG SAxl
canariensis	MSto NHHG
dentata	CArn CHan CJer CMHG CMer CSev ELan ENor ERav LAbb LBlm LHol MChe NBrk NFai NHHG SDry SFis SHer SUsu WAbe WEas WHal WHer WOMN WOak WPer WWye
§ – var. ***candicans***	CGle CJer EBar EOrc ESma GCal LGre LHil LHol LHop MAll MChe NHHG SGil SIde SMrm SSad WCHb WHal WPer WWye
– silver	See L. ***d. candicans***
¶ 'Fragrant Memories'	LRHS
'Hidcote Blue'	See L. ***angustifolia*** 'Hidcote'
x ***intermedia*** 'Alba'	NHHG
§ – Dutch Group AGM	CArn CJer EFou ELan EMon ENot MBar MBri MChe SChu SPer WHen WHer WHil WPer
– 'Grappenhall'	CAbb CArn CBow CCla CJer CPMA CSco CShe EBar EBre ENor EOrc GAbr IEde LBre LHol LHop MChe NFai NHHG SChu SHer SPer WOak WPer WSun WTyr WWat WWye
– 'Grey Hedge'	LHol NHHG
– 'Grosso'	CJer LHol NHHG NHex
– 'Hidcote Giant'	CJer EHal NPer
– 'Lullingstone Castle'	SIde
– Old English Group	CArn CBow ELan NBrk WEas WOak WWat WWeb
– 'Seal'	CArn CJer CPMA GBar GCHN LHol MChe NHHG NSti SApp SGil SHer SIde SPla WPer WWat WWye
N – 'Twickel Purple'	CArn CBow CCla CMHG CPMA CSco CSev EMon ENot EWes GCHN LHol NFai NHHG SChu SFis WAbe WOak WPer WWat WWye
'Jean Davis'	See L. ***angustifolia*** 'Rosea'
lanata AGM	CAbb CArn CBot CGle CHan CJer ECha ELan EMon ENor ERav GCal GPoy LHol MBro MChe MPla NHHG NSti SDry SMad SSvw WEas WHal WOMN WPer WWye
– x ***angustifolia***	CJer NHHG
latifolia	CArn CJer EBee LGre MHew
'Loddon Pink'	See L. ***angustifolia*** 'L. P.'
multifida	CAbb CArn CJer ENor ERav ERea ERom LHol NHHG SIde SSad SUsu WHer WPer
officinalis	See L. ***angustifolia***
§ ***pinnata***	CArn CJer ENor EWes LHol NHHG SDry SSad WCHb WPer
– var. ***buchii***	NHHG
♦ ***pterostoechas pinnata***	See L. ***pinnata***
'Richard Gray'	EFol EMon LHop
'Rosea'	See L. ***angustifolia*** 'Rosea'
'Sawyers'	EHic ENor ESis LGre MBri MChe NPer NSti SBod
N ***spica*** nom. rejic.	See LL. ***angustifolia, latifolia,*** x ***intermedia***
stoechas AGM	Widely available
– ***albiflora***	See L. ***s. leucantha***
§ – f. ***leucantha***	Widely available
* – 'Nana'	CArn ESma
– 'Papillon'	See L. ***s. pedunculata***
§ – ssp. ***pendunculata*** AGM	Widely available
– – 'James Compton'	CB&S CSev ECha EHic EMon LHop MPla NHHG NHar NSti NWyt SMad
* – 'Snowman'	CSam
¶ – 'Willow Vale'	LGre
vera De Candolle	See L. ***angustifolia***
vera hort.	See L. x ***i.*** Dutch Group
viridis	Widely available

LAVATERA (Malvaceae)

arborea	CArn GBar ISea WHer
– 'Ile d'Hyères'	NPer
– ***rosea***	See L. 'Rosea'
– 'Variegata'	CB&S CHan ECro ELan GBar LHil LHop MHlr NFai NPer SGil WCru WEas WHer
assurgentiflora	EMon GBri LHil LHop NRar
'Barnsley' AGM	Widely available
'Barnsley Perry's Dwarf'	NFai NPer
bicolor	See L. ***maritima***

¶ 'Blushing Bride' SHBN WHil
'Bredon Springs' CB&S ECha ELan EMil EMon GBri GMac LHop MBri MGos NBrk NHol SAxl SFis SHer SMrm WStI
* 'Bressingham Pink' LHop SMad
'Burgundy Wine' Widely available
cachemiriana CGle CHan CHol ELan GMac LBlm MFir NPer NRoo NSti NWyt WDav WPer WRus
'Candy Floss' CB&S CBow CCla CDoC CKni CSco EBar EBre EDon ELan ERav ESma GPlt IJoh LBre LHop MBri MGos MRav NHol NPer SAxl SHBN SMrm SPer SPla WDin WOld WRus WStI
'Kew Rose' CB&S CKni EDon EOrc LHop NPer SMad SMrm
§ ***maritima*** AGM Widely available
– ***bicolor*** See L. ***m.***
¶ 'Mary Hope' CHan
oblongifolia CBot SMad
N***olbia*** CBot CGle EMon MPla MWat NFai SDix WCru WHaw
'Peppermint Ice' See L. 'Ice Cool'
* 'Pink Frills' CBot CCla CSam EBre ELan EPla ERav LBre LHop MArl MHlr NBrk SAxl SDry SFai SHBN SMad SUsu WHil WRus WStI
§ 'Rosea' AGM Widely available
'Shorty' EFol ELan EMon NBrk
tauricensis WCot
N***thuringiaca*** EMon NBro NPri
– AL&JS 90100YU EMon
§ – 'Ice Cool' Widely available
'Variegata' See L. 'Wembdon Variegated'
§ 'Wembdon Variegated' CBow ECoo EDon EFol ELan EMar EMon MHlr NPer NWyt SHBN SHer SMad WCot

LAWSONIA (Lythraceae)

See Plant Deletions

LEDEBOURIA (Liliaceae/Hyacinthaceae)

adlamii See L. ***cooperi***
§ ***cooperi*** CMon CRDP EBul ELan ESis GCal IBlr NGar SIng WOMN
§ ***ovalifolia*** EBul
§ ***socialis*** CHEx CMon CRDP CTro IBlr NGar NRog
violacea See L. ***socialis***

X LEDODENDRON (Ericaceae)

§ 'Arctic Tern' AGM CDoC CSam GGGa IDai ITim LHyd LMil MBal NHar NHol SLeo SPer SReu WAbe WThu

LEDUM (Ericaceae)

columbianum GWht MBal
glandulosum GWht NHol SPer
groenlandicum MBar NHol NTow SPer WSHC
– 'Compactum' LRHS MAsh MBal
palustre EPot GPoy MBal MGos WThu
§ – f. ***dilatatum*** CLew GGGa
– ***hypoleucum*** See R. ***p. dilatatum***
– 'Minus' GGGa

LEEA (Leeaceae)

coccinea MBri

LEGOUSIA (Campanulaceae)

¶ ***hybrida*** EWFC

LEIBNITZIA (Compositae/Asteraceae)

anandria NWCA

LEIOPHYLLUM (Ericaceae)

buxifolium AGM GGGa GWht MBal MHig SIng WCru
*– 'Compactum' WThu
– ***hugeri*** NHar WDav
– var. ***prostratum*** WPat

LEMBOTROPIS See CYTISUS

LEMNA (Lemnaceae)

gibba CBen LMay MSta SAWi
minor CBen EHon EMFW EWav LMay MSta SAWi SWat WHol
polyrhiza See SPIRODELA ***polyrhiza***
trisulca EHon EMFW LMay MSta SAWi SWat

LEMON See CITRUS *limon*

LEONOTIS (Labiatae/Lamiaceae)

dysophylla LHil
leonurus See L. ***ocymifolia***
§ ***ocymifolia*** CAbb CFee CMer CPle CTre CTro GCra LBlm LHil LHop SLMG SMad WHer WWye
– var. ***ocymifolia*** LHil

LEONTICE (Berberidaceae)

albertii See GYMNOSPERMIUM ***a.***

LEONTODON (Compositae/Asteraceae)

autumnalis CKin
hispidus CKin MWil NMir

LEONTOPODIUM (Compositae/Asteraceae)

alpinum CKel EBre ELan EMil GAbr GCHN GLil GTou IDai LBre MBal MHew MPit MRav NHol NKay NMen NNor NRoo SIng WHoo WPer WWin
– 'Mignon' CLew CRiv ELan EMNN EPad GDra GTou MBro MCas MHig NHol NKay NMen NNrd NRoo NRya NVic SHer SIng SSmi WHil WHoo WPer
– ssp. ***nivale*** CNic
¶ – ***pirinicum*** WDav
hayachinense miyabeanum WHoo
himalayanum EMAK 605 NHol
§ ***ochroleucum*** var. ***campestre*** WPer
palibinianum See L. ***ochroleucum campestre***
sibiricum See L. ***leontopodioïdes***

souliei WHil
tataricum See L. ***discolor***
wilsonii ECha

LEONURUS (Labiatae/Lamiaceae)

cardiaca CArn CSev ECoo EFol EMon EPla EWFC Effi GBar GPoy LHol MChe MHew MSal SIde WHer WOak WPer WWye
sibiricus CGre GBar MHew MSal

LEOPOLDIA (Liliaceae/Hyacinthaceae)

brevipedicellata CMon
comosa See MUSCARI ***comosum***
spreitzenhofera See MUSCARI ***s.***
tenuiflora See MUSCARI ***tenuiflorum***

LEPECHINIA (Labiatae/Lamiaceae)

floribunda CGre

LEPIDIUM (Cruciferae/Brassicaceae)

nanum MFos MRPP NSla NWCA WDav

LEPIDOTHAMNUS (Podocarpaceae)

§ *laxifolius* WThu

LEPIDOZAMIA (Zamiaceae)

hopei LPal
peroffskyana LPal

LEPTINELLA (Compositae/Asteraceae)

§ *atrata* NMen
– ssp. *luteola* GGar MCas MHig NGre NMen NNrd
§ *dendyi* ECou ESis NHol
– forms ECou
¶ – 'Southley' WCru
maniototo ECou
§ *minor* ECou NHol WCru
§ *pectinata* ECou NGre WCru
– var. *sericea* See L. ***albida***
¶ – ssp. *villosa* NWCA
perpusilla See COTULA ***p.***
§ *potentillina* EBar ECha EFol EHoe ELan EMon ESis MMil NHol NKay NNrd NRya SChu SIng WCru WPer WWin
§ *pusilla* SSmi
pyrethrifolia CNic GAri GGar GTou
– var. *linearifolia* CLew ELan ESis ESma SFar SIng
reptans See L. ***scariosa***
§ *rotundata* CKni ECou NCat WCru WPer
§ *scariosa* ECou LHop
serrulata GCHN GCLN NHol WCru
§ *squalida* CLew CNic CRiv ECha ECou ESis IBlr MBar MCas NCat NHol NNrd NVic SIng SSmi WByw WPer

LEPTODACTYLON (Polemoniaceae)

§ *californicum* LGre

LEPTOSPERMUM † (Myrtaceae)

¶ *argenteum* CB&S
citratum See L. ***petersonii***
cunninghamii See L. ***lanigerum***
ericoïdes See KUNZEA ***ericoïdes***
N *flavescens* See L. ***polygalifolium***
§ *grandiflorum* CHan CPle ELan ISea WSHC
humifusum See L. ***rupestre***
juniperinum CB&S CPle
laevigatum ISea
§ *lanigerum* AGM CB&S CFee CGre CMHG CPle ECou GCHN IOrc ISea MAll NHol SLon SPer WBod WSHC WWin
– 'Citratum' ECou
§ – 'Cunninghamii' CAbb CCla CDoC CPMA CRos CSco ECou ELan EPla IBar LGre SDry SPer SPla SSta WPat
– 'Silver Sheen' See L. *l.* 'Cunninghamii'
– 'Wellington' ECou
liversidgei CPle GAri
macrocarpum ISea
minutifolium
x *scoparium* 'Green Eyes' ECou
– – *scoparium* 'Pink Surprise' ECou
nitidum ECou
obovatum CMHG
§ *petersonii* CPle ECou
phylicoïdes See KUNZEA ***ericoïdes***
polygalifolium SRms
prostratum See L. ***rupestre***
pubescens See L. ***lanigerum***
rodwayanum See L. ***grandiflorum***
§ *rupestre* AGM CB&S CChu CMHG CPle ECou EPot GTou IBar IDai ISea LHop MBal MBar MGos NHar SDry WBod WCru WDav WPat WSHC WWat
scoparium CDoC CLan ECou EMil GAri GWht IOrc NHed WDin
– 'Autumn Glory' MAll NHed WStI
– 'Avocet' ECou
– 'Blossom' CB&S ECou
– 'Bunting' ECou EWes
– 'Burgundy Queen' CB&S ECou EMil
– 'Chapmanii' CB&S CMHG
– 'Charmer' CB&S
– 'Cherry Brandy' CB&S EPot
– 'Chiff Chaff' ECou
¶ – 'Coral Candy' CB&S EMil
– 'Elizabeth Jane' CB&S CDoC EMil GCHN SHer
– 'Fascination' CB&S CGre
– 'Firecrest' ECou
– 'Gaiety Girl' (d) CGre
– 'Grandiflorum' CTrw GCHN
– 'Jubilee' CB&S
– 'Keatleyi' AGM CGre CMHG ECou LAbb WBod
– 'Leonard Wilson' ECou LBlm
– 'Lyndon' ECou
– 'Martinii' CB&S WBod
– 'McLean' ECou
– *nanum* CRiv NHol SBod SHBN SHer SIng WPat WThu
– – 'Huia' CB&S CDoC ECou EMil ENot IOrc
– – 'Kea' CLew ECou EPot ESis MHig NHol WPat WThu
– – 'Kiwi' AGM CB&S ECou ELan ENot EPot EWes IOrc ITim SHer SLon SPla WPat

– – 'Kotoku'	EPot WAbe
¶ – – 'Pipit'	EWes
– – 'Tui'	CDoC MAll
– 'Nichollsii' AGM	CB&S CGre CMHG CSco ENot EPot ITim SLon WAbe WOld WSHC
– 'Nichollsii Grandiflorum'	IDai
– 'Nichollsii Nanum' AGM	MHig SIng
– 'Pink Cascade'	CB&S MBal NHed WAbe
– 'Pink Champagne'	ECou LAbb
¶ – 'Pink Damask'	SPer
– var. *prostratum*	See L. ***rupestre***
– 'Red Damask' AGM	CB&S CChe CGre CLan CSam CSco CTre ELan ENot ESis EWri IBar IDai IOrc LAbb LHop MRav NHed SBod SHBN SHer SIgm SPer SPla WAbe WDin WSHC WStI
– 'Red Ensign'	ENot EWri MAll SBod
– 'Red Falls '	ECou
– 'Redpoll'	ECou
– 'Redstart'	ECou
– 'Robin'	ECou
– 'Ruby Glow' (d)	WBod
– 'Snow Flurry'	CB&S CDoC CGre ENot NHed SHer SIgm WBod WDin
– 'Sunraysia'	CDoC CSam CTrw LBlm
– 'Winter Cheer'	CB&S

LESCHENAULTIA (Goodeniaceae)

¶ ***biloba***	LGre
¶ ***formosa***	LGre
¶ – orange	LGre

LESPEDEZA (Leguminosae/Papilionaceae)

bicolor	CB&S CBow CCla CSco CWit ECro EHal EOrc ESma LHop SLPl WDin
buergeri	CB&S ELan LRHS
floribunda	CCla CPle WSHC
hedysaroïdes	See L. ***juncea***
thunbergii AGM	CB&S CBow CCla CGre CSco EHar ELan LHop MBlu MBri MGos MPla SBla SHil SMad SPer SReu SSta WCru WDin
– 'Albiflora'	WThi
tiliifolia	See DESMODIUM ***elegans***
yakushima	MPla

LESQUERELLA (Cruciferae/Brassicaceae)

alpina	NWCA WDav
¶ ***arctica*** var. ***purshii***	WHil
arizonica	WHil
fendleri	NTow WDav

LEUCADENDRON (Proteaceae)

argenteum	CHEx SIgm
tinctum	LBlm

LEUCAENA (Leguminosae/Mimosaceae)

§ ***latisiliqua***	CPle
leucocephala	See L. ***latisiliqua***

LEUCANTHEMELLA
(Compositae/Asteraceae)

§ ***serotina*** AGM	CBre CGle CHan CLew ECha EJud ELan ESiP LCot MHlr MSte NSti SApp SPer SPla WBon WEas WHoo WPla WWin

LEUCANTHEMOPSIS
(Compositae/Asteraceae)

§ ***alpina***	MDHE NNrd
hosmariensis	See RHODANTHEMUM ***hosmariense***
§ ***pectinata***	NSla
¶ – JCA 627.801	CPBP
♦ ***radicans***	See L. ***pectinata***

LEUCANTHEMUM †
(Compositae/Asteraceae)

discoïdeum	EMon
'Fringe Benefit'	EMon EPla
♦ ***hosmariense***	See RHODANTHEMUM ***h.***
♦ ***mawii***	See RHODANTHEMUM ***gayanum***
§ ***maximum***	CNic GAbr GCHN NBro NNor NPer SApp SPla WByw WOak WWin
– ***uliginosum***	See LEUCANTHEMELLA ***serotina***
nipponicum	See NIPPONANTHEMUM ***nipponicum***
'Sonnenschein'	ECha EMon GBuc MHlr WCot
¶ x ***superbum***	WHil
– 'Aglaia' AGM	EMon LRHS MBri MUlv SFis WCot WHal
– 'Alaska'	CDoC CMGP EOrc NFai NOak SPer WPer
– 'Antwerp Star'	MFir
– 'Beauté Nivelloise'	CBre CKel CMil CShe ECha WCot
– 'Bishopstone'	CDec CMil ELan LHil MUlv WEas
– 'Christine Hagemann'	MBri
– 'Cobham Gold' (d)	EMon EPla ERea NOrc
– 'Esther Read' (d)	CGle CShe ECED ELan ERea NNor NRoo SFis SHer SPla WByw WTyr
– 'Everest'	NOak
– 'Fiona Coghill'	IBlr WCot
– 'Flore Pleno'	GAbr
– 'H Seibert'	CKel CMil CSam ECED SMrm
– 'Horace Read' (d)	CMil ECED ECha EFol ELan EMon EPla ERea LHil NPer SChu SPla WEas
– 'John Murray'	LRHS MBri MUlv
– 'Little Miss Muffet'	MBri NFai
– 'Little Princess'	See L. x ***s.*** 'Silberprinzesschen'
– 'Manhattan'	EMon LRHS
– 'Mount Everest'	SRms WCot
– 'Phyllis Smith'	CGle CHan CSco ECha EJud EPla GAbr MBel MBri NFai SFis SMrm WAbb WDav WHal
– 'Polaris'	NFai NOak WPla
– 'Shaggy'	CRDP WSHC
§ – 'Silberprinzesschen'	CDoC CShe EJud GAbr MFir NHol NMir NOak NPri NRoo SHer WCot WHal WHen WPer
– 'Snow Lady'	GCHN LAbb MPit NMir NRoo WHen
– 'Snowcap'	CCla EBee ECha ENot EPla GAri MBri NBar SApp SMrm SPer SPla

– 'Sonnenschein' ('Sunshine')	LRHS NBrk NFai SMrm
– 'Starburst' (d)	EFou MBri NMir NRoo WHen
– 'T E Killin' AGM	CGle CSco ECha EJud EPla
§ – 'Wirral Supreme' AGM	CCla CHol CKel ECED EFou ELan ENot EOrc EPla GAbr IDai MBro MFir MWat NFai NNor NWyt SApp SFis SHer SPer SPla WByw WEas
§ *vulgare*	CArn CKin ECWi ECoo EWFC NLan NMir WCla WEas WHen WHer WOak WWye
– 'Corinne Tremaine'	WHer
– 'Maikönigin' ('May Queen')	EMon GCal
– 'Maistern'	EMon EPla
– 'Woodpecker's'	WCot
♦ 'Tizi-n-Test'	See RHODANTHEMUM ***gayanum*** 'T. T'

LEUCOCORYNE (Liliaceae/Alliaceae)

¶ *coquimbensis*	CMon
ixioïdes	LBow

LEUCOGENES (Compositae/Asteraceae)

aclandii	EPot GArf
grandiceps	GArf ITim NHar SBla WAbe
leontopodium	GArf GGar GTou ITim MHig NHar NRoo NWCA WAbe

LEUCOJUM † (Liliaceae/Amaryllidaceae)

aestivum	CB&S CBro CFee ECWi ELun EOrc LAma LBow MBri MWBu NEgg NLan NRog WCla WCru WGwy WShi
– 'Gravetye Giant' AGM	CAvo CBro CHad CRDP ECha ELan EPar EPot ERav ETub LAma LBow LFox LHop MBro NEgg NHol NRog SIng WThu
autumnale AGM	CAvo CBos CBro CFee CNic CRDP CTom ELan ESis GPlt ITim LAma LBee LBow MPit NGar NMen SAxl SPou SWas WChr WCru WOMN WThu
– 'Cobb's Variety'	LHop
– var. *oporanthum*	CMon EPot NRog
– var. *pulchellum*	CBro CMon CRiv CVer EPot
longifolium	CMon EBul
nicaeënse AGM	CAvo CBro CRDP EBul EBur EPot GArf LBow LHop NGar WChr WOMN WThu
roseum	CAvo CBos CRDP EBur LAma SPou SWas WChr
tingitanum	CMon
trichophyllum	CBro CMon WChr
– *purpurascens*	EPot WChr
valentinum	CAvo CBro WChr
vernum AGM	CBro ELan EPar EPot ERav ETub GDra LAma LBow MBri MWBu SGil SHer SIng WAbe WBod WShi
– var. *carpathicum*	EBul ECha EPot LAma WChr
¶ – 'Podpozje'	WChr
– var. *vagneri*	EBul ECha LFox WChr

LEUCOPHYTA (Compositae/Asteraceae)

♦ *brownii*	See CALOCEPHALUS ***b.***

LEUCOPOGON (Epacridaceae)

ericoïdes	MBar
§ *fasciculatus*	ECou
§ *fraseri*	ECou GArf IBar
parviflorus	See CYATHODES ***parviflora***

X LEUCORAOULIA (Compositae/Asteraceae)

§ *loganii*	EPot GArf GDra GTou ITim MHig NHar NWCA
§ R. *hectorii* x L. *grandiceps*	EPot GTou MHig NHol NMir SIng

LEUCOSCEPTRUM (Labiatae/Lamiaceae)

¶ *canum*	CGre

LEUCOSPERMUM (Proteaceae)

See Plant Deletions

LEUCOTHOË (Ericaceae)

axillaris	SSta
¶ *catesbyi*	GCHN
davisiae	GGGa MBal SSta WAbe
fontanesiana AGM	CCla GWht MBal MGos SPer SReu WStI WWat
– 'Lovita'	GCal MBri MRav MUlv SSta
– 'Nana'	MAsh
– 'Rainbow'	CAbb CB&S CBra CCla CLan CSco CTrw EHar ELan ENot GRei IBar IDai IJoh IOrc LHop LNet MAsh MBal MBar MGos NBee NHol SHBN SLon SPer SReu SSta WDin WThu
– 'Rollissonii' AGM	GWht MBal MBar NHol SPla SReu SSta WBod
grayana	MBal NHol
keiskei	WAbe
– 'Royal Ruby'	WDin
populifolia	See AGARISTA ***p.***
'Scarletta'	CB&S CBow CChu CCla CKni CMHG COtt CPMA CSam IBar IJoh LBuc LHop MAsh MBal MBar MBri MGos MUlv NHol SHer SPer SPla SReu SSta WDin WWeb

LEUZEA (Compositae/Asteraceae)

§ *centauroïdes*	MFir
conifera macrocephala	WOMN

LEVISTICUM (Umbelliferae/Apiaceae)

officinale	CArn CSFH CSev ECha EHer EJud ELan Effi GPoy LHol MBar MChe MHew SDix SFar SHer SIde SWat WHer WOak WPer WTyr WWye

LEWISIA † (Portulacaceae)

'Archangel'	NRya
'Ashwood Pearl'	MAsh
'Ben Chace'	MAsh
Birch strain	CB&S ELan EPad SIng
brachycalyx AGM	EPot GAbr GArf GDra GTou MAsh MBal MTho NGre NHar WDav
cantelovii	MAsh NGre NNrd WThu
columbiana	CNic CPla ESis GTou MAsh NGre NHar NNrd NTow WHal WHil
– 'Alba'	GCHN GDra MAsh

– 'Rosea'	CLew MAsh MCas MHig NGre NNrd WAbe WGor WThu
– ssp. ***rupicola***	CNic EPot GCHN MAsh NGre NMen NWCA WGor
– ssp. ***wallowensis***	CLew CNic EPot MAsh NMen NNrd WGor WThu
congdonii	MAsh NGre
cotyledon **AGM**	CNic CPla ESis MAsh MFir NEgg NNrd NWCA WHil WPat
– f. ***alba***	CPla ESis GAbr GDra GTou LHop MAsh MBro NGre NTow SBla SHer WAbe WCla WDav WHoo WThu
– Ashwood Ruby Group	MAsh NHar
– Ashwood strain	CNic EBre ESis EWes LBee LBlm LBre MAsh MBri NRoo NRya WAbe WGor WHoo
– 'Harold Judd'	CRiv
– var. ***heckneri*** **AGM**	CNic ESis GDra MAsh
– var. ***howellii***	CPla ELan SHer SRms
– hybrids	CBow CCla CFee CMHG CMea CNic EMNN EPad EPot GAul GDra GTou ITim LGan LHop MBro MFos MHig NGre NHar NHol NMen NRed WAbe WDav WGor WThu WWin
– 'John's Special'	GCHN GDra
– magenta strain	GAbr MAsh WDav WGor
– 'Rose Splendour'	CNic ELan EPad EPar EPot MAsh SHer WGor
– 'Sundance'	GDra MAsh
– Sunset Group **AGM**	CSam ELan GAbr GCHN GDra LAbb MBal MBri NGre NHar NKay NTow SBla SHer WCla WDav WPer
– 'White Splendour'	MAsh WGor
'Edithiae'	WAbe
'George Henley'	CRiv EBre ESis EWes LBre LHop MAsh NHar NHed NNrd NRya SHer SIng WAbe WDav WThu
* 'L W Brown'	SIng
leeana	CNic MAsh WGor WThu
¶ 'Little Plum'	GCHN
longifolia	See L. ***cotyledon cotyledon***
§ ***longipetala***	EBar ESis GCHN GDra GTou MAsh MHig NGre NNrd NTow NWCA WAbe WHal WThu
* ***longiscapa***	ESis MAsh NGre
§ ***nevadensis***	CMea CNic CPla ELan EPar EPot ESis GCHN GDra GTou ITim LAma LHop MAsh MBri MFir MTho NGre NKay NNrd NRed NRoo NWCA SHer SSmi WAbe WCla WDav WThu
– ***bernardina***	See L. ***n.***
oppositifolia	CMea LBee MAsh NNrd NWCA
¶ – ex JCA 11835	CNic
'Oxstalls Lane'	WThu
'Paula'	CNic SIng
'Phyllellia '	MAsh
'Pinkie'	CRiv EPot GCLN MAsh MCas SIng
pygmaea	CNic CRiv EPot ESis GCHN GTou ITim LBee LGan MAsh MBri MBro MFos NBir NGre NHar NNrd NRoo NWCA SIng WAbe WPer WThu
– ssp. ***longipetala***	See L. ***longipetala***
rediviva	GCHN GDra GTou ITim MAsh MBro MFos NGre NHar NWCA WAbe WDav
– Jolon strain	MAsh WGor
– white	MAsh NGre NWCA
'Regensbergen'	CNic WPer
serrata	GTou MAsh NGre WHil
sierrae	EPot MAsh NGre NNrd NRed WThu
'Trevosia'	CRiv EPot MAsh MCas MHig SIng WAbe WThu
triphylla	MAsh NGre NNrd NWCA
tweedyi **AGM**	EBre EPad EPot ESis GDra GTou LBre LHop MAsh NGre NHar NHol NWCA SIng WAbe WDav
– 'Alba'	GDra MAsh NGre WGor
– 'Elliott's Variety'	ESis MAsh
– 'Rosea'	ESis GDra MAsh NGre NHed NNrd NTow WAbe WGor WThu

LEYCESTERIA (Caprifoliaceae)

crocothyrsos	CAbb CBot CDec CGre CPle MFir WWat
formosa	Widely available

LEYMUS (Gramineae/Poaceae)

§ ***arenarius***	CElw CHad CHan CRDP CWGN ECha EFol EHoe ELan EOrc EPla ETPC GBur GCal LHil MUlv NBro NFai NOrc NSti SApp WEas WRus WWat
hispidus	See ELYMUS ***hispidus***
racemosus	ETPC

LHOTZKYA See CALYTRIX

LIATRIS (Compositae/Asteraceae)

aspera	ECro
¶ ***ligulistylis***	EMon
pycnostachya	EBar ECro WWin
scariosa 'Magnifica'	CB&S
§ ***spicata***	Widely available
– 'Alba'	CCla ECha ECro EFol EFou EGol ELan EOrc GGar LAma LBow LHol LHop NBar NFai SDeJ SPer WFox WHal WHoo WPer
– ***callilepis***	See L. ***s.***
– 'Floristan Violett'	CBow CSam GAbr NRoo NWyt WHil
– 'Floristan Weiss'	CArn CBow CHol CMGP CSam EBre ECro GAbr GBuc GCHN LBre LGan MRav NOak NRoo NWyt SApp SMrm SPla WAbe WHil
– 'Kobold' ('Goblin')	CB&S EBre ECED ECtt EMil ENot EOrc IDai LBre MBri MRav NRoo SPla WCra WHoo WMer WPer

LIBERTIA † (Iridaceae)

'Amazing Grace'	IBlr SAxl
¶ Ballyrogan Hybrid	IBlr
* ***breunioïdes***	IBlr
caerulescens	CHan CLew CPou ECro IBlr MFir NCat
chilensis	See L. ***formosa***
elegans	CGre GBuc IBlr WCot
§ ***formosa***	Widely available
– form	IBlr
grandiflora	Widely available
ixioïdes	CAvo CCla CElw CHan CSam ECou ESis GGar IBar NHol SIng WHoo

– 'Tricolor'	IBlr
'Nelson Dwarf'	ECou
paniculata	CHan EGol IBlr
peregrinans	CAbb CChu CCla CDoC CFee CHan CNic CRDP ECha EPla GCal IBlr MFir SChu SDix SPer SUsu WAbe WHal WPat WThi
– East Cape form	IBlr
– 'Gold Leaf'	CB&S WCot
****procera***	CGre IBlr WCot
pulchella	CGle IBlr NTow
¶ Shackleton Hybrid	IBlr
sp. ex New Zealand	EPla GCal
stolonifera	NHol
****umbellata***	IBlr

LIBOCEDRUS (Cupressaceae)

chilensis	See AUSTROCEDRUS ***c.***
decurrens	See CALOCEDRUS ***decurrens***

LIBONIA See JUSTICIA

LICUALA (Palmae/Arecaceae)

grandis	LPal MBri

LIGULARIA (Compositae/Asteraceae)

amplexicaulis	CRow GCra
calthifolia	CRow
clivorum	See L. ***dentata***
§ ***dentata***	CHEx CHan CRDP CRow ELun LWad MFir NBro SPla SWat WCru WHaw WOld
– 'Desdemona' **AGM**	Widely available
– 'Orange Princess'	CSco WPer
– 'Othello'	CCla CRow CSco MBal MBri NFai NKay SCro SSte SWat WCot WCra WMer
– 'Rubrifolia'	GDra
*– 'Sonnengold'	ECha SPer
¶ ***fischeri***	GCra
glabrescens	CRow
§ 'Gregynog Gold' **AGM**	CDoC CHad CHan CRow CSco EBre ECha EGol ELun ENot LBre MBri MRav NBro NDea NKay NMir NOrc SCro SMrm SPer WCru WHoo WMer
x ***hessei***	CHan CRow ECha SWat
hodgsonii	CSam CSco MBri NHol NNrw NSti WCru WMer WPer
jacquemoniana	CRow
japonica	CRow CSco
macrophylla	CHan CRow ECro
moorcroftiana	CRow
oblongata	See CREMANTHODIUM ***oblongatum***
x ***palmatiloba***	ECha EGol EPar EPla GCal NDea WCot
§ ***przewalskii***	Widely available
reniformis	See CREMANTHODIUM ***reniforme***
smithii	See SENECIO ***smithii***
stenocephala	CHEx CRow EGol NBro NDea
¶– B&SWJ 283	WCru
tangutica	See SINACALIA ***tangutica***
'The Rocket' **AGM**	Widely available
tussilaginea	See FARFUGIUM ***tussilagineum***
veitchiana	CCla CHan CHol CRow CSco EOrc GCal GDra LGan MSte NDea SApp SFis SWat WCru
'Weihenstephan'	LRHS MBri MUlv WMer
wilsoniana	CHan CRow EBee ECtt SFis

LIGUSTICUM (Umbelliferae/Apiaceae)

ferulaceum	SIgm
¶ ***lucidum***	SIgm
porteri	MSal
scoticum	GBar GPoy ILis MHew MSal

LIGUSTRUM † (Oleaceae)

chenaultii	WWat
¶ ***compactum***	CPle
delavayanum	CB&S GAri SArc WWat
x ***ibolium*** 'Midas'	CMHG
japonicum	EHar ENot ISea WBod WDin WWat
– 'Coriaceum'	See L. ***j.*** 'Rotundifolium'
§ – 'Rotundifolium'	CCla CDec CDoC CPle EHar EPla EWri GAri LNet MUlv SDry SGil SHil SReu
– 'Texanum'	CDec SEng
lucidum **AGM**	CBow CBra CChu CCla CDoC CMCN CPle CShe EHar ELan ENot MBar MGos MUlv SArc SMad SPer WDin WMou WWat
– 'Aureovariegatum'	EHar
– 'Excelsum Superbum' **AGM**	CAbP CBow CDoC CPMA CSco ECtt EHar ELan LPan MBar MBri MMea SHil SPer
– 'Golden Wax'	LRHS MUlv
– 'Latifolium'	MUlv SHil
– 'Tricolor' (v)	CBow CLan CPMA CSco EHar ELan IOrc MBal MBri SChu SHBN SMad SPer SPla WWat
obtusifolium 'Dart's Elite'	SLPl
– var. ***regelianum***	CDoC
ovalifolium	CB&S CBra CChe CDoC CLnd CSco EBre GRei IDai ISea LBre LBuc LPan MBar MBri MGos NBee NNor NWea SPer WDin WMou
§ – 'Argenteum' (v)	CB&S CBra CDoC CGle CLan CSco EFol EHoe EPla ERav ISea MBar MBri NBee NHol SGil SLon SPer SPla SReu WEas WPat WWin
– 'Aureomarginatum'	See L. ***o.*** 'Aureum'
§ – 'Aureum' **AGM**	Widely available
*– 'Lemon and Lime' (v)	SPla
– 'Variegatum'	See L. ***o.*** 'Argenteum'
quihoui **AGM**	CCla CDoC CHan EHar ELan EPla MGos SDix SHil SPer WWat
§ ***sempervirens***	CPle SSta
¶– B&L 12033	EPla
sinense	CHan CMCN CMHG ISea WWat
– 'Pendulum'	EHar EPla NHol
– 'Variegatum'	CMHG CPMA CRow EBar EFol EHar EHic EPla IDai WWat
– 'Wimbei'	CPMA EPla ESis WWat
strongylophyllum	SArc
tschonoskii	SLPl
'Vicaryi'	EBre EHar ELan EPla ERav LBre MBar NHol SPer WPat WWat

vulgare CKin CPer EBre EWFC GRei LBre LBuc WDin WHer WMou WNdy

LILAEOPSIS (Umbelliferae/Apiaceae)

macloviana NHol

LILIUM (Liliaceae/Liliaceae)

¶ 'Admiration' (Ia) MWBu
African Queen (VIa) CKel ECot EFEx LAma MCed MWBu NRog SDeJ SRms
¶ 'Aladdin' (Ia) MWBu
'Alliance' (VII) CB&S
¶ 'Allright' (VIIb/d) MWBu
'Angela North' (Ic) EBul
'Apeldoorn' (Ie) EFEx LAma LBuc
'Apollo' (Ia) EFEx ETub LRHS MBri MCed SDeJ
* ***argenteum*** CHEx
'Aristo' See L. 'Orange Aristo'
Asiatic hybrids (VI/VII) LAma SDeJ
'Attila' (Ib) SDeJ
auratum (IX) CB&S CBro LAma LBow LGre SDeJ
– 'Crimson Beauty' (IX) LAma SDeJ
♦– 'Gold Band' See L. ***a. platyphyllum***
¶ – 'Golden Ray' MCed
§ – var. ***platyphyllum*** AGM CB&S EFEx GCra MWBu
'Avignon' (Ia) EFEx LAma
'Barcelona' (Ia) CB&S EFEx ETub WHil
Bellingham hybrids AGM EBul
'Bellona' (Ia) NRog
'Black Beauty' (VIId) EBul
'Black Dragon' AGM EFEx GAul LAma
Black Magic (VIa) SDeJ
¶ 'Blitz' (Ia) MWBu
'Bonfire' (VIIb) SDeJ
'Brandywine' (Ib) SRms
'Bright Star' (VIb) CBro EFEx ETub LAma MCed SDeJ SRms
'Bronwen North' (Ic) EBul
bulbiferum (IX) MSto
Bullwood hybrids (IV) EBul
§ ***canadense*** (IX) CRDP EBul LAma MBal NRog SDeJ WChr WCru
– var. ***editorum*** LAma
– ***flavum*** See L. ***canadense***
candidum AGM CArn CAvo CB&S CBro CHEx ECha ECtt ELan EMon ETub GAbr GCra LAma LBow MBri MBro MCed MWBu NRog SDeJ
– 'Plenum' EMon
'Capitol' (VII) CB&S
'Carmen' (VIIc) CB&S
¶ ***carniolicum*** (IX) WChr
'Casa Blanca' AGM CB&S ETub LAma MCed MWBu NRog SDeJ
cernuum (IX) SDeJ
chalcedonicum AGM MS&S WChr
'Charisma' (Ia) LRHS MBri
¶ 'Charmer' MCed MWBu
'Cherrywood' (IV) EBul
'Chinook' (Ia) EFEx LAma NRog
Citronella (Ic) CBro LAma MS&S NRog SRms
'Coachella' (IV) EBul
'Cocktail' (Ia) MCed
¶ 'Commodore' (Ia) MCed
¶ 'Compass' (Ia) MCed
concolor
var. ***partheneion*** (IX) EPot MSto
'Concorde' (Ia) SDeJ
'Connecticut King' (Ia) CB&S CBro EFEx ETub LAma MCed MHlr MWBu NBrk NRog SDeJ
¶ 'Connection' (Ia) MWBu
'Corina' (Ia) EFEx MBri MS&S NCat SDeJ
'Corsage' (Ib) CAvo NRog
'Côte d'Azur' (Ia) EFEx ETub LAma LBuc MCed MWBu SDeJ WHil
§ x ***dalhansonii***
'Marhan' AGM LAma
¶ 'Dandy' (Ia) MCed MWBu
dauricum CNic
§ ***davidii*** var. ***willmottiae*** (IX) LAma SRms
♦ 'Delta' See L. ***leichtlinii*** 'D.'
'Destiny' (Ia) LAma NRog SRms
¶ 'Domination' MWBu
'Dominique' (VII) LAma NRog
'Dream' (Ia) CSut
'Dreamland' (Ia) EBul
duchartrei (IX) CBro
* 'Elvin's Son' CB&S ETub LAma LRHS MCed WHil
'Enchantment' AGM CB&S CBro EFEx LAma LBow LBuc MBri MCed MHlr NCat NEgg NRog SDeJ
¶ Everest (VIId) EFEx
'Exception' (Ib) LAma
'Festival' (Ia) CB&S LAma MCed
¶ 'Fiesta Gitana' (Ia) MWBu
'Fire King' (Ib) EFEx ETub LAma MCed NRog SDeJ SRms
¶ 'Fire Star' (VIIc/d) MWBu
§ 'Firebrand' (I) LAma
'Firecracker' (Ia) LAma
'Flamenco' (Ib) MS&S
formosanum (IX) EBul SHer WHal
– var. ***pricei*** AGM CMea COtt CRDP CRiv CSam EBul ELan EPar EPot ITim LBee LGre LHop MBal MBri MCas MFir MHig MSto MTho NHol NMen NNrd NWCA SBla SUsu WAbe WHoo WHow WPer
'Fresco' (VII) CB&S
'Friendship' (VII) CB&S
'Furore' (VIIc) CB&S
'Geisha' (VII) CB&S
¶ 'Golden Melody' (Ia) EFEx
Golden Splendor (VIa) EFEx LAma MCed MWBu NRog SRms
'Gran Cru' (Ia) CB&S EFEx
'Gran Paradiso' (Ia) CB&S EBul LAma
¶ 'Gran Sasso' (Ia) MCed
'Grand Cru' MCed SDeJ
grayi (IX) EBul WChr
'Green Dragon' AGM LAma
Green Magic (VIa) EFEx LAma
'Hannah North' (Ic) EBul LGre
hansonii AGM LAma NRog
Harlequin Hybrids (Ic) SDeJ
¶ 'Harmony' (Ia) EFEx
'Harvest' (Ia) ETub
henryi AGM CAvo EFEx LAma LBow LHop MCed MWBu NRog SDeJ WPla
¶ 'Her Grace' (Ia) MWBu

'Hornback's Gold' (Ic) EBul
Imperial Gold (VIIc) LAma SDeJ
Imperial Silver (VIIc) LAma SDeJ
'Iona' (Ic) EBul
§ 'Jacques S Dijt' (II) LAma
Jamboree (VIId) SDeJ
¶ 'Jan de Graaf' MCed
¶ 'Jazz' (Ia) MCed MWBu
'Jetfire' (Ia) CB&S LAma SDeJ
'Journey's End' (VIId) CB&S EBul EFEx ETub LAma MCed NRog SDeJ
§ 'Joy' (VIIb) CB&S EFEx LAma
'Karen North' AGM EBul
kelleyanum (IX) WChr
'King Pete' (Ib) EFEx SDeJ WHil
¶ 'Kiss Proof' (VIIb) MCed MWBu
¶ 'Kyoto' (VIId) MCed MWBu
'Lady Ann' (VIb) SDeJ
'Lady Bowes Lyon' (Ic) EBul
'Ladykiller' (Ia) EFEx LAma NRog
'Lake Tahoe' (IV) EBul
'Lake Tulare' (IV) EBul
§ ***lancifolium*** (IX) CLTr LAma LBow SDeJ SRms
– var. ***flaviflorum*** SRms
– 'Flore Pleno' (IX) CAvo CRDP EMon WCot
§ – var. ***splendens*** (IX) CBro EMon ETub LAma LBow SDeJ
'Laura' (VII) CB&S
'Le Rêve' See L. 'Joy'
leichtlinii 'Delta' (IX) MCed MWBu
'Levant' (Ic) LAma
'Liberation' (I) LAma NBir
'Lilliput' (Ia) LRHS
'Limelight' AGM LAma
¶ 'Little Girl' (VIIb) MWBu
'Little Snow White' (v) NOak
longiflorum AGM CAvo CB&S LAma MHlr NRog WCot WCru WHal
– 'Casa Rosa' MCed MWBu
– 'Gelria' (IX) SDeJ
– 'White American' (IX) EFEx MBri MCed
¶ ***lophophorum*** (IX) WChr
'Lotus' (VI) LRHS
'Luxor' (Ib) CB&S CSut EFEx MCed NBir
mackliniae AGM ECha GGGa IBlr MBal MSto NBir NHar NHol WAbe
maculatum davuricum See L. ***dauricum***
¶ 'Magic Eye' (Ia) MCed
'Marhan' (II) See L. x ***dalhansonii*** 'M.'
x ***marhan*** 'J S Dijt' See L. 'Jacques S Dijt'
'Maria Callas' (Ia) CSut
'Marie North' (Ic) EBul
martagon (IX) CAvo CBro ECha EFou ELun EMon ETub LAma LBow MBal MS&S MWBu NBir NRog SDeJ SUsu WShi WWat
– var. ***album*** AGM CAvo CBro ECha EFou EPot ETub LAma LBow MS&S MTho SDeJ SHig SUsu WChr
– var. ***cattaniae*** AGM EMon
– 'Netherhall Pink' (IX) EMon
– 'Netherhall White' (IX) EMon
– 'Plenum' (IX) EMon
'Medaillon' (Ia) LAma NRog
¶ 'Milano' (Ia) EFEx WHil
'Mona Lisa' (VIIb/d) CB&S LRHS MBri
§ ***monadelphum*** AGM EFEx LAma NRog WChr
'Mont Blanc' (Ia) CB&S CBro EFEx LAma MCed NBir SDeJ
'Monte Rosa' (Ic) MWBu SDeJ
'Montreux' (Ia) CB&S EBul EFEx LAma NCat
'Moonflower' (Ia) CB&S
Moonlight (VIa) SDeJ
'Moulin Rouge' (Ib) NRog
'Mrs R O Backhouse' AGM CBro LAma
§ ***nanum*** (IX) CAvo GArf GGGa GTou NHol NRog WChr
¶ – CH&M WChr
– deep purple (IX) NKay
– var. ***flavidum*** (IX) WChr
– 'Len's Lilac' (IX) GDra MSto NHol NKay WChr
– McBeath's form (IX) NKay
nepalense (IX) CBro LAma MS&S NRog SDeJ WCot WCru
'New Yellow' LRHS MBri
I 'Nivea' (I) MWBu
'Olivia' (Ia) CSut EFEx ETub LAma SDeJ
Olympic Hybrids (VIa) EFEx LAma SDeJ
'Omega' (VII) CB&S LAma SDeJ
§ 'Orange Aristo' (Ia) MBri MCed
'Orange Pixie' (Ia) CBro LRHS MBri
'Orange Triumph' (Ia) LAma SRms
'Orange Wattle ' (Ic) EBul
'Orchid Beauty' (Ia) MBri
oxypetalum (IX) CAvo GGGa NHol WChr
– var. ***insigne*** (IX) GDra GGGa NHol NTow WAbe WChr
Paisley hybrids (II) CBro
'Pandora' (Ia) CB&S
pardalinum (IX) CAvo CGle ECha ELan
– var. ***giganteum*** AGM CBro EBul
¶ 'Parisienne' (Ia) MCed MWBu
¶ ***parryi*** dwarf form (IX) WAbe
¶ 'Passage' (VIIc) MWBu
'Peachblush' (Ia) CB&S LAma
'Peggy North' (Ic) EBul
'Perugia' (VIId) EFEx
philippinense (IX) ESma WHil
¶ 'Picture' (VIId) MCed MWBu
'Pink Beauty' (VIIc) CBro
Pink Perfection AGM CAvo CB&S CBro EFEx LAma MCed MWBu NRog SDeJ
'Pink Sunburst' (VId) SDeJ
'Pirate' (Ia) LAma SRms
¶ ***pitkinense*** (IX) EMon
¶ 'Polka' MWBu
pomponium (IX) MSto
¶ 'Preference' (Ia) MCed
¶ 'Primavera' (Ia) MCed
'Prominence' See L. 'Firebrand'
¶ 'Providence' MS&S
§ ***pumilum*** AGM CAvo CBro ETub LAma LHop MHlr MSto MTho NBir SDeJ WCru
pyrenaicum AGM ELan GDra LHop MS&S MSto WByw WChr WCot
– var. ***aureum*** See L. ***p. pyrenaicum***
'Rangoon' (Ia) EBul
'Red Carpet' (Ia) CBro EFEx ETub MBri NBir WHil
Red Jewels (Ic) LAma
'Red Lion' (Ia) CSut SDeJ
'Red Night' (I) EFEx NRog

regale **AGM**	CArn CAvo CB&S CBro CCla CHad CHol CSam CSut EBul EFEx EFou ETub LAma LBow LGre LHop MBal MCed MS&S MWBu NEgg NRog SDeJ WCru WEas WHal WWat
– Album Group (IX)	CAvo EFEx EFou LAma LBow MCed MWBu NRog SDeJ WCru
§ – Royal Gold (IX)	CB&S EFEx LAma MCed NEgg SDeJ SRms
'Roma' (Ia)	EBul EFEx ETub LAma LBuc LGre NBir WHil
'Rosefire' (Ia)	EFEx LAma MS&S
'Rosemary North' **AGM**	EBul
'Rosita' (Ia)	EFEx LAma MBri NRog
Royal Gold strain	See L. ***regale*** Royal Gold
¶ 'Sahara' (Ia)	MWBu
'Sans Pareil' (Ia)	SDeJ
'Sans Souci' (VIId)	LRHS MBri MCed MWBu
'Scentwood' (IV)	EBul
shastense	See L. ***kelleyanum***
'Shuksan' (IV)	CBro
¶ 'Silhouette' (Ia)	MWBu
'Simoen' (Ia)	SDeJ
'Snow Princess'	LAma
'Snow Trumpet' (v)	CSam
¶ 'Snowstar' (Ia)	MCed
¶ 'Sorisso' (Ia)	MWBu
'Sorrento' (Ia)	CSut
speciosum var. ***album*** (IX)	CBro EFEx LAma NBir SDeJ
– 'Grand Commander' (IX)	LAma SDeJ
– var. ***roseum*** (IX)	EFEx LAma SDeJ
– var. ***rubrum*** (IX)	CAvo CB&S CBro ECha EFEx LAma LBow MCed MWBu NBir NRog SDeJ WCot WCru
§ – 'Uchida' (IX)	CSut LAma SDeJ
'Star Gazer' (VIIc)	CB&S CBro CSut ECot EFEx LAma MCed MHlr MWBu NRog SDeJ WHil
'Stardrift' (VIId)	CSut
'Starfish' (I)	SRms
* 'Sterling Silver'	LAma
'Sterling Star' (Ia)	CB&S EFEx ETub LAma MCed NCat NRog SDeJ
'Sun Ray' (Ia)	EFEx LAma LRHS MWBu NCat NRog
superbum **AGM**	LAma NRog WChr
¶ 'Symphony' (Ib)	MCed MWBu
szovitsianum	See L. ***monadelphum***
'Tamara' (Ib)	CSut LAma MBri NRog
¶ 'Taptoe' (Ia)	MCed MWBu
tenuifolium	See L. ***pumilum***
x ***testaceum*** **AGM**	CAvo CBro EFEx ETub LAma NRog SDeJ
tigrinum	See L. ***lancifolium***
'Trance' (VIIb)	CB&S LRHS MBri MCed MWBu
♦ 'Uchida Kanoka'	See L. ***speciosum*** 'Uchida'
¶ 'Vino' (VII)	MCed
wallichianum (IX)	LAma NRog SDeJ WChr
'Walter Bentley' (Ic)	SRms
'Wattle Bird' (Ia)	EBul
¶ 'White Cloud' (Ia)	MCed
'White Happiness' (Ia)	LAma
'White Henryi' (VId)	EFEx
'White Journey's End' (VIId)	CB&S
'White Mountain' (VIIc)	SDeJ
¶ 'White Star Gazer' (VII)	MWBu
¶ ***wigginsii*** (IX)	WChr
willmottiae	See L. ***davidii willmottiae***
Yellow Blaze (Ia)	LAma NRog SDeJ
'Yellow Giant'	See L. 'Joanna'
'Yellow Present'	SDeJ
¶ 'Yellow Star' (Ib)	MCed

LIME See CITRUS *aurantiifolia*

LIMNANTHES (Limnanthaceae)

douglasii **AGM**	CDoC CFee CKni CMea CRiv ELan IBlr MPit SHer SIng WBod WEas WFox WHal WHer

LIMONIUM (Plumbaginaceae)

bellidifolium	CElw CLew CShe EBre ECha ELan ESis LBre MHig NHol NMen NTow SBla SHer WCla WEas WHoo WPer
¶ ***binervosum***	MWil
cosyrense	CLew CMea NHol NMen SRms WPer WWin
§ ***dregeanum***	WThu
dumosum	See GONIOLIMON ***tataricum angustifolium***
globulariifolium	See L. ***ramosissimum***
gmelinii	SFis SSvw WPer
– 'Perestrojka'	MHlr NMir SIgm WCot WSun
gougetianum	MCas NTow
latifolium	See L. ***platyphyllum***
minutum	ELan MHig SHer
paradoxum	CLew ELan SHer
¶ ***peregrinum***	CSpe
§ ***platyphyllum***	CBow CCla CGle CSco CSpe EFou EGol GLil IDai LHil MBel MFir MTol MWat NBee NMir NRar NWyt SCro SDix SMad SPer SSvw WEas WHoo WOld WPer WSun
– 'Robert Butler'	EOrc GCal MMil MRav
– 'True Blue'	LRHS
– 'Violetta'	CBot CDoC CSco EBre ECha EFol ELan LBre MBri MRav MUlv SPer WHoo WSun
§ ***ramosissimum***	WThu
tataricum	See GONIOLIMON ***t.***
tetragonum	See L. ***dregeanum***
vulgare	WGwy

LINANTHASTRUM See LINANTHUS

LINANTHUS (Polemoniaceae)

nuttallii	CPBP

LINARIA (Scrophulariaceae)

¶ ***aeruginea***	NMir
– ssp. ***nevadensis***	WCla WHil
alpina	CMea CRiv CTom ECro ELan LBee MBro MPit MTho NKay NMen NOak NWCA SHer WCla WPer
¶ – 'Purpurea'	WCru
– 'Rosea'	NKay WCla WCru
anticaria	WDav
¶ 'Antique Silver'	SWas
§ ***bipunctata***	WHer

* 'Blue Pygmy'	MPit
¶ ***canadensis***	WOMN
cymbalaria	See CYMBALARIA ***muralis***
dalmatica	CDec CGle CHan CSev CTom ECha ELan EMon LBlm LGan MFir MTol NBro NCat NSti SAxl SChu SMrm WKif WPer WRus
x ***dominii*** 'Carnforth'	EJud EMar EMon ERav LGre LRHS NSti
– 'Yuppie Surprise'	EMon NBir SMad SUsu
genistifolia	GAbr GDra NCat SFis
♦***glutinosa***	See L. ***bipunctata***
hepaticifolia	See CYMBALARIA ***h.***
****lobata alba***	SHer
¶ 'Natalie'	LGre
origanifolia	See CHAENORHINUM ***origanifolium***
pallida	See CYMBALARIA ***pallida***
pilosa	See CYMBALARIA ***pilosa***
purpurea	CGle CHol CKin CRiv CWGN ECro EFou ELan EWFC LHol MChe MFir NBro NCat NFai NMir NNor NPer WCla WCra WHal WHen WPer WWin
– 'Alba'	See L. ***p.*** 'Springside White'
– 'Canon Went'	CBre CCMG CCla CElw CGle CHan CLew CSev ECha ECro EFol EFou ELan EOrc ERav LGre LHop MFir NBro NFai NNor NRoo NSti SPer SUsu WCla WCot WEas WHer WKif
– 'Dwarf Canon Went'	WCot
– 'Radcliffe Innocence'	See L. ***p.*** 'Springside White'
§ – 'Springside White'	CBre ECha ECro EMon LGre LRHS MSte SUsu WRus
repens	CKin EWFC WCot WHer
supina	MWat NKay WCla WHer
triornithophora	CElw CGle ECha ECoo ECro EMar ERav GCra LGan MFir MNFA SFis SUsu WCot WHil WWin
– pink	CBot CGle CHan WEas WPer
– purple	CHan ELan
tristis 'Toubkal'	WOMN WWin
vulgaris	CArn CKin CRiv ECWi EJud EWFC LHol MChe MHew NLan NMir SIde WHer WNdy WPer
– peloric form	CNat

LINDELOFIA (Boraginaceae)

anchusoïdes hort.	See L. ***longiflora***
§ ***anchusoïdes*** Lehmann	CHan EBar EBee ECro GCal NSti WCru WDav
longiflora	ECro GBuc GCal WCru WPer
¶ – 'Alba'	ECha

LINDERA (Lauraceae)

benzoin	CB&S SHil
erythrocarpa	CMCN WCoo
megaphylla	CB&S
obtusiloba AGM	SHil WCoo
umbellata	WCoo

LINNAEA (Caprifoliaceae)

borealis	CRDP GAri GDra MBal NGre NNrd WAbe WOMN
– var. ***americana***	NHar NMen NNrd NWCA

LINUM † (Linaceae)

arboreum AGM	ECha MBro MPla MSto NHol NMen SBla SUsu SWas WOMN WPat WThu WWat
bienne	CKin
♦***bulgaricum***	See L. ***tauricum***
capitatum	MHig NTow WAbe WOMN
flavum	CBow CGle CLew EPot MBro NMen SHer WHoo WPbr
– 'Compactum'	CCla CDoC ECha EFou ELan GAul LAbb LGan LHop MPit MRav NHol NKay NMen NRoo SBla SPer SSvw WDav WHal WHil WMer WOld WPer WWin
'Gemmell's Hybrid' AGM	CLew CRDP CShe EPot LBee MBro MCas MHig NHar NHol NWCA SBla SWas WAbe WDav WPat WThu
leonii	EMon WRus
mongolicum	WPer
monogynum	ECou LGre MTho NTow NWCA SBla SChu SFis WDav WOld WPla
§ – ***diffusum***	ECou NHol
– dwarf form	CLew MSto MTho
– 'Nelson'	See L. ***m. diffusum***
narbonense	CSam CShe ECha LGre LGro MBri MBro MFir MRav MUlv NBro NHol NOak SIgm SMrm WCra WHoo WKif WMer WOld WPer
– 'Heavenly Blue' AGM	ELan LHop SUsu WEas WHen
perenne	CArn CHan CMea ECWi ECha EFol ELan EWFC GCal LAbb LHol MBri MChe MHew MPit MPla NMir NNor SHer SIde SPer WHer WPer WWin WWye
– ***album***	CDoC CGle CHad CSco ECha EFou ELan LHol LHop SGil SHer SMrm SPer SSvw WHen WHer WPer WRus
– ssp. ***alpinum***	LGre MBro WPer
– – 'Alice Blue'	NHar SBla WDav
– ssp. ***anglicum***	NMir
– 'Blau Saphir' ('Blue Sapphire')	CBow CDoC CSam EFou EOrc ESis MPit NFai NHol NOrc NRoo SSvw WHen WPbr
– 'Diamant'	CBow NFai NPri NRoo WPbr
– ***lewisii***	LHop MHig MSto NBir NHol NTow NWCA
– 'White Diamond'	ESis LGre WCot WHen
rubrum	MChe
sibiricum	See L. ***perenne***
****spathulatum***	MSto
suffruticosum ssp. ***salsoloïdes*** 'Nanum'	MBro NTow NWCA WPat WThu
– – 'Prostratum'	ECha GBuc SIgm
§ ***tauricum***	MSto
tenuifolium	ESis MSto

LIPPIA (Verbenaceae)

canescens	See PHYLA ***c.***
chamaedrifolia	See VERBENA ***peruviana***
citriodora	See ALOYSIA ***triphylla***
nodiflora	See PHYLA ***nodiflora***
repens	See PHYLA ***nodiflora***

LIQUIDAMBAR (Hamamelidaceae)

acalycina	WPat
formosana	CGre CMCN EArb ELan GAri GWht MBlu MBri SSta WCoo WNor
– Monticola Group	SHil SSta
orientalis	CMCN LMer MGos SSta
styraciflua	Widely available
¶ – 'Andrew Hewson'	CPMA SSta
– 'Aurea'	CLnd COtt IOrc LNet NHol SSta WPat
¶ – 'Aurea Variegata'	CPMA
– 'Burgundy'	COtt CPMA NHol WPat
* – ***festeri***	SSta
– 'Golden Treasure' (v)	CBow CPMA CSco LNet SMad SSta
– 'Gumball'	CPMA EHar SSta
– 'Kia'	CPMA SSta
– 'Lane Roberts' AGM	CCla CDoC CPMA CSco EHar LBuc LPan MUlv NHol SHil SMad SReu SSta WDin WPat
– 'Moonbeam' (v)	NHol SSta WPat
– 'Moraine'	SSta
– 'Palo Alto'	LPan NHol SSta WPat
¶ – 'Parasol'	CPMA
– 'Pendula'	CPMA EHar SSta
– 'Silver King' (v)	CPMA
¶ – 'Stared'	CPMA
– 'Variegata'	CPMA LNet SEng SSta WPat
– 'Worplesdon' AGM	CB&S CCla CDoC COtt CSco EBre EHar ELan ENot ESma IHos LBre LMer LNet MBri SMad SPer SReu SSta WAbe WWat

LIRIODENDRON † (Magnoliaceae)

chinense	CAbP CChu CGre CMCN CPle EArb EHar ELan ISea MBlu MBri WCoo WWat
tulipifera AGM	Widely available
¶ – 'Arnold'	COtt
– 'Aureomarginatum' AGM	Widely available
– 'Fastigiatum' AGM	CB&S COtt CSco CTho EBre EHar ELan ENot LBre LPan MBlu MBri SHil SPer SSta
– 'Mediopictum'	ELan MBlu SMad

LIRIOPE † (Liliaceae/Convallariaceae)

exiliflora 'Ariaka-janshige' ('Silvery Sunproof') (v)	ECha EGol MUlv WCot WRus WThu
gigantea	SApp
graminifolia	See LL. ***spicata, muscari***
hyacinthifolia	See REINECKEA ***carnea***
§ ***muscari*** AGM	Widely available
– ***alba***	See L. ***m.*** 'Monroe White'
– 'Gold-banded'	EGol GCal NOrc WCot
– 'John Burch' (v)	EGol NOrc WCot
– 'Majestic'	GCal SApp WCot
§ – 'Monroe White'	CMea EPla GCal MUlv NFai NOrc SApp SHer SLMG SPer WCot WRus
– 'Purple Bouquet'	SApp
– 'Royal Purple'	NOrc WCot
– 'Silvery Midget' (v)	WCot
– 'Superba'	WCot
– ***variegata***	CRow ELan EPla MHlr NOrc WCot
– variegated white bloom	WCot
– 'Webster Wideleaf'	WCot
platyphylla	ECro SApp
§ ***spicata***	CAvo NFai NOrc WHoo
– 'Alba'	CCla CHad CRow EBre ECro EGol EPla GCal LBre MRav MTho MUlv SAxl WWin
– 'Silver Dragon' (v)	CAvo EGol WCot

LISTERA (Orchidaceae)

¶ ***ovata***	WThi

LITHOCARPUS † (Fagaceae)

densiflorus	WCoo
edulis	CHEx SArc
§ ***glaber***	CHEx SBor
pachyphyllus	CB&S

LITHODORA (Boraginaceae)

§ ***diffusa***	CNic EMil MPit NBro NKay SBla
– 'Alba'	CLew CMHG EMil EPot GAri GWht LBee LHop MBri MBro MPla NEgg NHar NHol NMen NRoo SHer SIng SUsu WAbe
– 'Cambridge Blue'	LAbb LHop MPla
– 'Compacta'	EWes LBee LHop SAxl
¶ – 'Grace Farwell'	EGle
– 'Grace Ward' AGM	CCla CGle EPot IDai MPla NHar NHol NRar NRoo SBod SIng WAbe WDav WPat WThu
– 'Heavenly Blue' AGM	Widely available
– 'Inverleith'	EWes LBee LHop LRHS SAxl SHer
– 'Picos'	EPot GArf GTou SIgm WDav WPat
graminifolia	See MOLTKIA ***suffruticosa***
hispidula	ELan NMen SHer WCru
x ***intermedia***	See MOLTKIA x ***i.***
§ ***oleifolia*** AGM	CShe ELan EPot MBro MFos MHig MTho MWat NHol NKay NMen SHer WCru WDav WPat
rosmarinifolia	CSpe ELan
zahnii	ELan EPad LHop NTow SHer SIgm SIng SMrm WAbe WHil

LITHOPHRAGMA (Saxifragaceae)

bulbiferum	See L. ***glabrum***
glabrum JCA 10514	CNic
parviflora	EPot GArf GDra MHig MTho NBir NHol NMen NRya SIng WDav WOMN

LITHOSPERMUM (Boraginaceae)

diffusum	See LITHODORA ***diffusa***
doerfleri	See MOLTKIA ***doerfleri***
officinale	GBar GPoy MHew MSal WCla WHer
oleifolium	See LITHODORA ***oleifolia***
purpureocaeruleum	See BUGLOSSOIDES ***purpurocaerulea***

LITSEA (Lauraceae)

japonica	CHEx

LITTONIA (Liliaceae/Colchicaceae)

modesta	CGre CMon LBow SLMG WChr WCru

LIVISTONA (Palmae/Arecaceae)

australis	CHEx CTbh CTro LPal NPal
chinensis AGM	CTro LPal NPal
decipiens	CTbh NPal

LOASA (Loasaceae)

lateritia	See CAIOPHORA *l.*
triphylla var. *volcanica*	GCal

LOBELIA (Campanulaceae)

anatina	ESma GCal LAbb SGil
♦*angulata*	See PRATIA *a.*
'Bees' Flame'	CRos CRow EBre LBre MTho
'Brightness'	CRos CRow EBee EBre ELan LBre SAxl
'Butterfly Blue'	CAbb CB&S CBow GBuc GCal NWyt WWat
'Butterfly Rose'	CAbb CB&S CBow EOrc GBuc GCal NWyt SBla SFis
cardinalis AGM	CArn CRDP CRow CWGN EHon EPot EWav GCHN GCal GMac LHol LMay MHew MSal MSta MSte NDea SChu SUsu SWyc WChe WCru WHol WMer WOld WWin WWye
– JLS 88010WI	EMon
– *multiflora*	GCal
'Cherry Ripe'	CGle CRDP CRiv CWGN ELan LHil MSte MTho SAxl SChu SHer SUsu WCHb
'Cinnabar Rose'	CAbb CB&S CBow CChu EMil EOrc MHlr NCat SRms WCot WHil WPer WRus WWin WWye
'Complexion'	CBoy ESma GCHN SMad
'Compliment Scarlet' AGM	CBow CHol CRos CRow EBar EBre EMil GCHN LBre NBro NCat NPer WHil WPer
'Dark Crusader'	CBos CChu CElw CHad CMHG CRDP CRiv CRow CWGN ECha ECtt EFou ELan GCal LHil MBri MTho NBro NDea NHol NOrc NSti SAxl SChu SMrm WCra WEas
erinus 'Kathleen Mallard' (d)	CElw CFee CGle CSev CSpe ELan EOrc ERav GCal LHop NPri SFis SHer WOMN
'Eulalia Berridge'	CGle CRDP CRos EFou ESma GBuc SAxl SMrm SWas
excelsa	CGre CHEx
'Fan Deep Red'	CHad CHol GBuc GCHN GMac WHil
'Flamingo'	See L. 'Pink Flamingo'
fulgens	CWGN IBlr MHlr SCro WByw WCot WEas
– 'Illumination'	GMac
'Galen'	CRow
x *gerardii*	NHol
– 'Eastgrove Pink'	WEas
§ – 'Vedrariensis'	Widely available
gibberoa	CHEx
'Hadspen Royal Purple'	CHad
inflata	CArn MSal SIde WWye
'Jack McMaster'	CBos CChu CWGN LHop MBel MSte MTho
¶ *kalmii*	MSto WPer
¶ 'Kimbridge Beet'	SHig
laxiflora	CBot MTho SMrm WHer
– var. *angustifolia*	CBos CBow CChu CGre CHEx CHan CHol CMHG CPle CRDP ELan EPla ERea GCal IBlr LHil LHop MSte SMrm SUsu WAbb WHal WMar WPer WWye
lindblomii	CLTr CRiv CTom EHic GAri GGar LBee NCat WAbe WHal WHil
linnaeoïdes	EPot GArf GCHN LBee MTho NGre NMen NTow NWCA WAbe WCru WEas WOMN
macrodon	NGre SIng
§ *oligodon*	GAri NBro NKay
pedunculata	See PRATIA *p.*
♦*perpusilla*	See PRATIA *p.*
'Pink Elephant'	EFou SWas WCot
§ 'Pink Flamingo'	CBoy CChu CDec CGre CHad CRDP CRow CWGN ECha EFol EFou EMFW GCHN GCal GMac LBlm LHop MBel MTho MTol NFai NNor SAxl SChu SFis SMrm WCra WHal WPer
'Queen Victoria' AGM	Widely available
♦*repens*	See PRATIA *r.*
richardsonii	CBrk LHil LHop SDix SFis SHer WEas
'Rowden Magenta'	CRow
'Royal Robe'	CRow
N 'Russian Princess'	CBrk CChu CGle CRDP CRow CSam CSco CWGN ESma LHil LHop MBel MBri MTho NBee NBrk NHol NOrc NSti SAxl SChu SMad WCra WMer
sessilifolia	GBuc MBel NGre SRms WChe WPer WWye
– B&L 12396	EMon
siphilitica	Widely available
– *alba*	CB&S CBow CBre CRow ECro GCal GMac LAbb LGan LHil NSti WByw WCra WEas WHoo WPer WWye
– 'Nana'	GCal
'Sonia'	CGle
x *speciosa*	CRow
– dark form	CRos CRow EMil SMrm
sp. CLD 1007	NHol
surrepens	ECou
'Tania'	CChu CGle CRDP CRow EFou ESma IBlr LHil MSte MUlv SAxl SChu SCro SHig SMad WByw WRus
♦*treadwellii*	See PRATIA *t.*
tupa	CB&S CBot CBow CChu CDoC CHEx CHan CMHG CRDP CRow CSam ECha ELan EOrc GCal GGar IBlr ISea LGre LHil LHop NGar SFis SMad SSte WCHb WCru WPer WWat WWin
– G&K 4253	CCla
– dark orange form	GCal SArc
valida	ELan GBuc NBro WPer
vedrariensis	See L. x *gerardii* 'Vedrariensis'
'Will Scarlet'	CChu CRos EBre LBre MBel MTho SAxl
'Zinnoberrosa'	SMad

LOBOSTEMON (Boraginaceae)

¶ ***montanus*** CSpe

LOGANBERRY See RUBUS

LOISELEURIA (Ericaceae)

procumbens WAbe

LOMANDRA (Lomandraceae)

longifolia ECou GWht

LOMARIA See BLECHNUM

LOMATIA (Proteaceae)

dentata CB&S
ferruginea CAbb CHEx CLan ISea MBal SArc WBod
longifolia See L. ***myricoïdes***
§ ***myricoïdes*** CAbb CCla CHEx CLan CTrw ELan LAbb SArc SDry SHil WBod WWat
silaifolia SArc SDry SHil
§ ***tinctoria*** CB&S CHEx CLan CPle CTrw SArc

LOMATIUM (Umbelliferae/Apiaceae)

¶ ***canbyi*** SIgm
¶ ***columbianum*** SIgm
¶ ***grayi*** SIgm
¶ ***macrocarpum*** SIgm
utriculatum MSal

LONICERA † (Caprifoliaceae)

albertii EHic WHCG
alseuosmoïdes CChu SBra SLon WWeb
altmannii CPle
N x ***americana*** hort. See L. x ***italica***
x ***americana*** AGM CSPN EOrc LHop NHol SAxl SBla SBra SHil SReu SSta WCru
arizonica SBra
x ***brownii*** CMac CRHN IDai
§ – 'Dropmore Scarlet' Widely available
N – 'Fuchsioides' CBow CCla ELan MUlv NBrk NHol NSti SAxl SBra SPer WPat WSHC WWat WWeb
caerulea CPle EHal WHCG
– var. ***edulis*** ESim
caprifolium AGM CDoC CRHN CSco CShe EBre ELan EOrc EPla LBre LGre LHol LHop LPri MBar MBri NSti SBra SHBN SPer WWat
– 'Anna Fletcher' EBar ELan MUlv SBra WEas WWeb
– f. ***pauciflora*** See L. x ***italica***
chaetocarpa CBot CMHG NHol WPat
chrysantha CMCN CPle
ciliosa CGre MSto SBra
'Clavey's Dwarf' IOrc MPla NBrk SPer
¶ ***cyanocarpa*** KGB 438 MSto
¶ ***deflexicalyx*** KGB 165 MSto
dioica SBra
'Early Cream' See L. ***caprifolium***
etrusca CHan CSco CWit EHal EPla LHol LHop LPri SBra SHil WWeb
– 'Donald Waterer' EHic MUlv NHol SBra SPer WGor WWat
– 'Michael Rosse' SBra
– 'Superba' CRHN EBre ECtt ELan ESma EWri GCal LBre MUlv NSti NWyt SBla SBra WCru WSHC WWat
flexuosa See L. ***japonica repens***
fragrantissima Widely available
giraldii hort. See L. ***acuminata***
giraldii Rehder CB&S CBot CChu CHan EBre EOrc LBre LPri NHol SBra WSHC
glabrata SBra
glaucescens SBra
glaucohirta See L. ***periclymenum g.***
grata See L. x ***americana*** (Miller) K. Koch
x ***heckrottii*** CDoC CMac CMer CMil CRHN ECtt ISea LPri MBar NBar NKay NRoo NSti SPer WDin WStI WWat
– 'Gold Flame' CB&S CBow CSco EBre ELan EPla GAri IDai LBre LHop MBal MBar MBea MBri MGos MWat NHol SBra SHBN WAbe WSHC WStI WWat
§ ***henryi*** CB&S CBow CChu CCla CMac CRHN CSco EBre EGol ELan EOrc EPla IOrc LBre LHop LPri MBar MBri MWat NBrk NHol SBra SHBN SLon SPer WBod WDin WSHC
– var. ***subcoriacea*** See L. ***henryi***
* 'Hidcote' CMac
hildebrandtiana CGre CHEx
hirsuta SBra
hispidula SBra
implexa EFol ELan EPla GCal LGre SBra WSHC
insularis CMCN CPle
involucrata CB&S CChu CCla CHan CMCN CMHG CPMA CPle EBar LHil LHop MBar MRav WDin WHCG
– var. ***ledebourii*** CHan CSPN ELan EPla GRei MBel MWat NHol WPat WTyr WWin
§ x ***italica*** CBot CBow CChu CCla CMac CSco CShe EBre EHar ELan ENot ESma LAbb LBre LHol LPri MGos MWat NSti SBla SBra SHil SLon SPer SPla SSta WSHC WWat
§ ***japonica*** 'Aureoreticulata' CB&S CCla CMac CShe EBre EGol EHoe ELan ENot IDai IJoh ISea LBre LPri MBal MBar MBea MBri NHol NKay NNor SBra SHBN SPer SSta WEas WWat WWin
– 'Dart's Acumen' SLPl
– 'Dart's World' SBra SLPl
– 'Halliana' AGM Widely available
– 'Hall's Prolific' CSam EBee ECtt EHic EOrc EWll LBuc MAsh MBri MGos MUlv NHol SBra SPla WWat WWeb
¶ – 'Horwood Gem' ECtt EHic NHol
– 'Peter Adams' MGos
§ – var. ***repens*** CDoC CMac CSco CShe CTre EBar EBre ECtt ELan ENot EOrc EPla IHos LBre LPri MPla SBra SHBN SPer SPla WCru WWat WWeb
– 'Soja' SBra
– 'Variegata' See L. ***j.*** 'Aureoreticulata'

korolkowii	CBow CChu CCla CMCN CPle CSam EBee EHic MUlv MWat NBir
– var. ***zabelii***	EFol ELan
¶ ***lanceolata*** KGB 488	MSto
maackii	CHan CMCN CPMA WHCG
¶ – f. ***podocarpa***	CPle
x ***muscaviensis***	CPle
¶ ***myrtillus*** KGB 298	MSto
nigra	EPla
nitida	CB&S CKin CLan CSco EBre ELan EMar ESma ISea LBre MRav NNor SHBN SLon SPer WDin WHen WMou WStI
– 'Baggesen's Gold' **AGM**	Widely available
– 'Elegant'	CDoC ELan IOrc LBuc
– 'Ernest Wilson'	MBar SRms
– 'Fertilis'	SPer SRms
– 'Hohenheimer Findling'	MUlv
– 'Maigrün' ('Maygreen')	EPla MBri SPer
– 'Silver Beauty'	CAbb CDec CPMA CPle EBee EFol MGos
*– 'Silver Lining'	EPla
periclymenum	CArn CBow CKin ECWi EPla EWFC GPoy MHew NMir NNor NWea WDin WHCG WMou WOak WWin
N– 'Belgica' **AGM**	Widely available
– ***clarkii***	SBra
– 'Cornish Cream'	EBre EGol LAbb LBre
– 'Florida'	See L. ***p.*** 'Serotina'
– ***glaucohirta***	SBra
– 'Graham Thomas' **AGM**	Widely available
– 'Harlequin' (v)	CBot EBee EMil ENot MGos MUlv NRoo NSti SMad SPer
– 'Heaven Scent'	EMil
– 'La Gasnerie'	GAri NHol SMad
– 'Liden'	SBra
– 'Munster'	SBra
*– 'Red Gables'	MHlr NHol WGor WPat
N– 'Serotina' **AGM**	Widely available
– 'Serotina' EM '85	MBri MUlv
– 'Serpentine'	SBra
– ***sulphurea***	EPla EWll
¶ – 'Sweet Sue'	SBla
– yellow	SPer
pileata	CB&S CChe CCla CLan CMer CSco CShe EBre EGol ELan EMar ENot GRei IJoh LBre LBuc MBar MGos NBee NHol NNor SLon SPer SPla SUsu WDin WStI WWat WWin
– 'Moss Green'	CDoC MUlv SLPl WHCG WWat
– 'Stockholm'	SLPl
♦***pilosa***	See L. ***strophiophora***
praeflorens	CChu
x ***purpusii***	CBra CHan CPle CSam EBre LAbb LBre LHol MBar MBel MPla WBod WCru WEas WHCG WSHC WWin
– 'Winter Beauty' **AGM**	CBow CCla CDoC CPMA CSam CSco EBre ECoo ECtt ELan LBre MBlu MBri MBrk MPla MRav NBrk NHol NSti SLon SPla SSta WWat
pyrenaica	CPle LGre SHil
quinquelocularis	CPle EHal EPla
reflexa	EHar LHop NBrk
§ ***rupicola*** var. ***syringantha***	CBra CChu CCla CHan CMHG COtt CPle CSam EFol EHar ELan LHol LHop MGos MWat NHol SHBN SLon SPer SPla SUsu WHCG WSHC WWat WWin
– – 'Grandiflora'	MPla WAbe
ruprechtiana	CPle
segreziensis	CPle
sempervirens **AGM**	CBot CRHN EGol GAri LPri MRav SBra SHil
♦– 'Dropmore Scarlet'	See L. x ***brownii*** 'D.S.'
N– f. ***sulphurea***	CMCN SBra WWeb
¶ ***serotina*** 'Honeybush'	CPle
setifera	CBot SHil
similis var. ***delavayi***	CBot CDoC CHan CLTr CSPN SBra SWas WSHC
'Simonet'	SBra
splendida	CBot SBra WCru WEas
¶ sp. CLD 315	CPle
¶ sp. KBE 062	NHol
standishii	CB&S CPle LHol MBea MBel MGos MRav MUlv SPer WDin WRus WThu WWat WWin WWye
§ ***strophiophora***	SBra
– CD&R 1216	CHan
syringantha	See L. ***rupicola s.***
¶ ***tangutica*** KGB 535	MSto
tatarica	CMCN CPle LPri WCru WHCG
¶ – 'Alba'	CPMA
– 'Arnold's Red'	CB&S CBot CBow CDoC CPle CSco EHal ELan MBal MBlu MPla SMrm WAbe
– 'Hack's Red'	CB&S CBra CCla CPMA MPla NKay SPer STre WHCG
– 'Rosea'	CPMA
– f. ***sibirica***	EHal SPer
– 'Zabelii'	CChu MGos SMrm
x ***tellmanniana*** **AGM**	Widely available
– 'Joan Sayer'	EHic EPla LHop MUlv
thibetica	CPle MBlu WWat
tragophylla **AGM**	CB&S CChu CCla CMac EBar EBre EHar ELan IOrc LBre LHop LPri MBri NSti SBla SBra SHil SPer SReu SSta WCru WDin WSHC WWat
¶ ***trichosantha*** KGB 404	MSto
¶ ***vesicaria***	CPle
x ***xylosteoïdes*** 'Clavey's Dwarf'	MBel MGos SLPl
– 'Miniglobe'	EPla ESis SPer
* ***yunnanensis*** 'Variegata'	ESis

LOPHOMYRTUS (Myrtaceae)

§ ***bullata***	CChu CGre CPle CTre ECou EPla WCHb
'Gloriosa'	CB&S CDoC CGre CPle WCHb
§ ***obcordata***	CGre WWat
§ x ***ralphii***	WCHb WWat
§ – 'Kathryn'	CB&S CHan CPle CTre ERea GAri ISea MAll WCHb WSHC
§ – 'Traversii'	CGre
– 'Variegata'	EBre ERea LBre MAll
¶ 'Sundae'	MAll
'Tricolor'	CPle CTre GAri MAll
'Versicolor'	CB&S CDoC CMer LAbb LBlm

LOPHOSORIA (Lophosoriaceae)

¶ ***quadripinnata***	CFil

LOPHOSPERMUM (Scrophulariaceae)

erubescens CBot CHEx CRHN CSam CTbh CWes LHop MSte NSti SLMG WOMN WOld WPer
§ ***scandens*** LBlm WOMN

LOQUAT See ERIOBOTRYA *japonica*

LOROPETALUM (Hamamelidaceae)

chinense CCla CMCN CPle

LOTUS (Leguminosae/Papilionaceae)

berthelotii AGM CBar CBrk CFee CGle CHEx CSev CTro ELan ERav ERea ERom IHos LAbb LBlm LHil MUlv SAxl SChu SIgm SLMG SUsu WEas WKif WPer
– Kew form GCal LHil LHop
– x ***maculatus*** CBar CBrk CLTr CSpe ERav LHil LHop SAxl SMrm WPer
corniculatus CArn CKin EWFC GAbr MHew MWil NLan SIde
– 'Plenus' CLew CMer CMil CRiv ELan EPot GCal IBlr LAbb NHol SFis SIng WPer WTyr
'Gold Flash' IHos
§ ***hirsutus*** CBot CChu CCla CGle CHad CHan CLTr CMea CSam CSco CSev CShe ELan EMil ENot GMac LAbb LHop NRar NSti SAxl SDix SFis SIng SPer WEas WOld WSHC WWat WWin
¶ – dwarf form CHan
jacobaeus LHil
maculatus AGM CBar CBrk CGle CSpe CTro ESma LBlm LHil LHop SIgm
maritimus NGre
mascaensis hort. See L. ***sessilifolius***
pedunculatus See L. ***uliginosus***
§ ***pentaphyllus pentaphyllus*** MTol NBrk
§ ***rectus*** EBee
§ ***sessilifolius*** CBrk CSpe ERea LHil SIgm SUsu
suffruticosus See L. ***pentaphyllus pentaphyllus***
uliginosus MWil NMir

LOXOSTYLIS (Anacardiaceae)

¶ ***alata*** CTro

LUCULIA (Rubiaceae)

gratissima AGM CB&S CBot CHEx CHan LHop SHil

LUDWIGIA (Onagraceae)

grandiflora CRow

LUETKEA (Rosaceae)

pectinata CLew GCHN GDra MHig NHol NMen SIng WAbe WThu

LUMA (Myrtaceae)

§ ***apiculata*** AGM CAbb CHan CMHG CPle CSam CTre CTrw EBre ISea LBre LHol MBal SArc SDix SHil SPer STre WBod WCHb WSHC WWat WWye
§ – 'Glanleam Gold' (v) Widely available
– 'Variegata' CMHG ISea NHol WWat WWye
§ ***chequen*** CChu COtt CPle CTre GAri LHol MAll WCHb WWat

LUNARIA (Cruciferae/Brassicaceae)

§ ***annua*** ECWi NCat SHer WByw WHaw WHer WOak
– ***alba*** AGM CCMG EFol NBir NCat NHol SIde WHer WOak
I – 'Alba Variegata' CSpe EMon MSto SUsu WByw WCru WPla
– 'Croftacre Purple Pod' ECro
¶ – 'Golden Spire' WHil
– 'Ken Aslet' NHol
*– 'Stella' GCal WHen
– ***variegata*** CCMG CSFH CTom EFol GCal IBlr MTho NBir SPla WEas WHal WHer WHil WOMN WOld
– violet NBir
biennis See L. ***annua***
rediviva ECha ECoo EJud EMon GAri GCHN GCra GGar IBlr MNFA MTol NBro NSti SAxl SUsu WCot WCru WEas WHen WHer

LUPINUS † (Leguminosae/Papilionaceae)

'Alan Titchmarsh' MWoo
albifrons SIgm
– var. ***douglasii*** LGre
'Ann Gregg' AGM MWoo
arboreus AGM Widely available
¶ – ***albus*** SUsu
– cream SMad
– 'Golden Spire' GWht NBee NBrk SMad WDin
– 'Mauve Queen' CB&S CRDP NBee NBrk
– 'Snow Queen' CB&S CCla WDin
'Band of Nobles' AGM ECtt GAbr LAbb NVic
'Barnsdale' MWoo
'Beryl, Viscountess Cowdray' EMon
'Blushing Bride' EMon
¶ ***breweri*** MSto
¶ ***caespitosus*** MSto
chamissonis CBos CBrk EWes LGre LHop MTho NTow SAxl SDry SIgm SMrm SUsu WPla
'Chandelier' CBow CHad CHol CSco EBre ECtt EFou ELan GAbr GAri GCHN LBre LWad MBri NBar NBrk NMir NRoo SHer SPer SPla WPer WTyr
'Chelsea Pensioner' MWoo
'Clifford Star' MWoo
'Deborah Woodfield' AGM MWoo
Dwarf Gallery hybrids NOak
'Dwarf Lulu' See L. 'Lulu'
'Esmerelder' AGM MWoo
Gallery series CBow NPri NRoo
¶ 'Garden Gnome' WPer
'Helen Sharman' AGM MWoo
'Household Brigade' MWoo
'Judith Chalmers' MWoo
'Kayleigh Ann Savage' AGM MWoo
lepidus MSto
¶ – var. ***lobbii*** NWCA WAbe
¶ ***leucophyllus*** SIgm

'Little Eugenie' MWoo
littoralis CMea GDra NCat
§ 'Lulu' CBow EBre ECtt ELan LBre MPit MRav NMir NOak SFis SHer SPer WPer
¶ ***microphyllus*** MSto
Minarette Group CBow ECtt MBri SPla SRms WGor
Mirakel hybrids SFis WHil
'Misty' MWoo
'Moonraker' MWoo
'My Castle' CBow CHol CSco EBre ECtt EFou ELan GAbr GAri GCHN LBre LWad MBri MRav NBar NBrk NMir NOak NRoo SHer SPer SPla WHil WPer WTyr
'Noble Maiden' CBow CHol EBre ECtt EFou ELan GAbr GAri GCHN LBre MBri NBar NBrk NMir NOak NRoo SPer WHen WHil WPer
nootkatensis WPat
'Olive Tolley' **AGM** MWoo
oreophilus F&W 7353 SIgm
'Party Dress' MWoo
perennis CGle EMon
pilosus See L. ***varius orientalis***
'Pope John Paul' **AGM** MWoo
princei ELan
'Royal Wedding' MWoo
Russell hybrids CB&S CBow CKel CSco ELan NMir SGil SHer WHer
sericatus SIgm
'Sunset' MWoo
'Sunshine' CGle
'The Chatelaine' CBow CHad CHol CSco EBre ECtt EFou ELan GAbr GAri GCHN LBre LWad MBri MRav NBar NBrk NMir NRoo SHer SPer SPla WHen WHil WPer WTyr
'The Governor' CBow CHol CSco EBre ECtt ELan GAbr GAri GCHN LAbb LBre LWad MBri MRav NBar NBrk NMir NRoo SHer SPer SPla WPer WTyr
'The Page' CBow CDoC CHol EBre EFou ELan GAbr GAri LAbb LBre LWad MBri MRav NBar NBrk NMir NRoo SHer SPer SPla WHil WPer WTyr
'Thundercloud' CHad
'Troop the Colour' **AGM** MWoo
varius ssp. ***orientalis*** WCot
'Walton Lad' MWoo
'Yellow Boy' CB&S NBrk

LUZULA (Juncaceae)

alopecurus ECou
alpinopilosa ssp. ***candollei*** ETPC
x ***borreri*** 'Botany Bay' (v) EHoe EMon EPla
campestris CKin
celata ECou
forsteri ETPC
lactea ETPC
luzuloïdes 'Schneehäschen' EMon EPla ETPC
maxima See L. ***sylvatica***
multiflora EHoe
* ***nivalis*** CHan
nivea CBow CBre ECha EFol EFou EHoe EOrc EPla ETPC GAbr GCal LGan MBri MFir NCat NHar NHol NSti SAxl SFar SGil SUsu WByw WDav WOMN WWye
pilosa GCal IBlr
plumosa ETPC
pumila ECou
purpureosplendens ETPC
rufa ECou
sibirica ETPC
§ ***sylvatica*** CKin CRow ECWi EFou EPla ETPC GBur MFir NBro NOrc WHer
♦– 'A Rutherford' See L. *s.* 'Taggart's Cream'
– 'Aurea' ECha EPla ETPC GAbr NSti SMad SPla WCot WRus WWat
♦– 'Aureomarginata' See L. *s.* 'Marginata'
I – 'Auslese' ETPC
– 'Hohe Tatra' CElw EFol EHoe
§ – 'Marginata' CB&S CElw CHEx CRow EBar ECha EFol EGol EHoe EMon EPla ETPC GAbr LGan MBal NBro NRar NSti SArc SFar WByw WRus WWat WWin
§ – 'Taggart's Cream' (v) CRow
¶ – 'Tatra Gold' EMon
– 'Tauernpass' EHoe EMon EPla ETPC WRus
ulophylla ECou EHoe NHol

LUZURIAGA (Liliaceae/Philesiaceae)

radicans CGre WCru WSHC

X LYCENE (Caryophyllaceae)

§ ***kubotae*** EPot NBro

LYCHNIS † (Caryophyllaceae)

alpina CMHG ECoo ECro ELan EWFC GAul GDra GTou LAbb NHol NKay NMen NMir NNor NNrw NPri NRoo SHer SMrm WCla WHil WPer WWin
– 'Alba' NBir
– ***americana*** NTow
¶ – compact form WPat WPer
– ***rosea*** CHan SIng SRms
x ***arkwrightii*** CBow CGle CKel CRow EBre ECha ECoo EFou EHoe ELan EPot LBee LBre LGan MBri MPit NMen NOak NSti SIng SPer WCla WOMN WWin
– 'Vesuvius' CB&S CBow CDoC CGle EBre ESma GGar LBlm LBre LHop NBar NBir NNrw NRoo SFis SSvw WCot WHoo WHow WMer WPbr WPer WTyr
chalcedonica **AGM** Widely available
– 'Alba' CBos CSam ECha ECro EFou ELan EMon ERav IBlr LGan MBri MFir NBro NCat NFai NOak NSti NWyt SFis SHer SPer WDav WEas WHen WHoo WPer
– 'Carnea' EMon GCal MUlv NCat
– 'Flore Pleno' CBos CMil ECha ELan EMon GBuc GCal MHlr MUlv NHol NSti SFis SSvw WCot WOld WPer
– 'Rosea' CGle CHad CLew CTom ECro EFou EHal MUlv NFai NHol NMir WByw WHen WPer
¶ – 'Rosea Plena' CBot

¶ ***cognata***	CGle
§ ***coronaria***	CArn CGle CRow EBar EBre ECha EHoe ELan EPar LBre MBri MFir MHew NKay NMir NNor NOak NSti SMrm SPer SSvw WByw WCla WDav WEas WOld
– 'Abbotswood Rose'	See L. x ***walkeri*** 'A.R.'
– Alba Group **AGM**	Widely available
– 'Angel's Blush'	CCla ECro GCHN NMir SPer WPbr WPer WTyr
– Atrosanguinea Group	CBow CBre ECro EFou EPad EPla GCHN IBlr LHil NFai NHol SCro WPer
– 'Cerise'	ESma MArl
– Oculata Group	CBro CGle CHan CLew CMHG CMil ELan EMar EMon ESma GCHN IBlr LAbb LHop MFir MMil MTho NFai NOak NSti SSvw WDav WEas WHen WHer WHoo
dioica	See SILENE ***dioica***
flos-cuculi	CArn CKin CNic CRow CSFH CWGN EBre ECro EHon EMFW EPar EWFC GCHN LBre LGan MHew MSal MSta MTol NDea NLan NMir NOrc WBon WCla WHen WHer WNdy WWye
– ***albiflora***	CBre CRow CSFH CSam CTom ECro EMon EPar LGan NBro NDea NSti SIde WCla WHer
– 'Nana'	CNic CRDP ELan EMon EPla GArf GGar LHop MBro MFir MTol NMen NMir WCla WHil WOMN WPat WPer
flos-jovis	CGle CLew CSco ECha ECro ELan EMon GPlt LHop MFir NOak SHer SSvw WByw WEas WPat WPer WSun
– 'Alba'	MRav
– 'Hort's Variety'	CDec CKel CLTr CMil ECoo EFou EJud MBel MHig MHlr MUlv NSti NTow SBla SPer WCla
– 'Minor'	See L. ***f-j.*** 'Nana'
§ – 'Nana'	CNic CRow ECro GCHN LHop MCas MNFA MTol NFai NRed WHoo WOMN
x ***haageana***	CMil ECoo EOrc LBlm LHil LWad MBri MSto NMir NWCA SIng
¶ ***kiusiana***	ECoo
kubotae	See X LYCENE ***k.***
lagascae	See PETROCOPTIS ***glaucifolia***
miqueliana	CChu CPou EBar EMon LGan MFir MHlr MSto NBrk NCat SFis WCot
'Molten Lava'	EBee LHop NOrc WHow WPer WTyr
nutans	MHew MSal
¶ ***punctata*** dwarf	EHic
§ ***viscaria***	CBow CGle CKin ECha ECro MHew MSal NLan NNor NNrd NSti WCla
– ***alba***	ECha ECro GCal NBro NNrd
– ***alpina***	See L. ***a.***
– ssp. ***atropurpurea***	GCal
– 'Firebird'	EFou
– 'Plena'	CDoC CMil CSco EFou NCat NSti SFis WHil WOld WPbr
– 'Snowbird'	EFou
– 'Splendens Plena' **AGM**	CGle ECha EFol ELan EMar EMon EPla GMac IDai MBal MBri NBro NKay NVic WEas WPbr
– 'Splendens Rosea'	SLga
¶ – ssp. ***viscaria***	GLil
§ x ***walkeri*** 'Abbotswood Rose' **AGM**	EMon ESma NBar NCat
wilfordii	CBot CLew CPou ECoo EHic NRed SUsu
yunnanensis	CSam ECro EMon GCHN LGan MFir MSte NHol NOak WGwy WOld WPer

LYCIANTHES (Solanaceae)

§ ***rantonnetii***	CBar CBrk CHad CHan CSpe CTro ERea LBlm LHop

LYCIUM (Solanaceae)

barbarum	CPle ELan WWye
¶ ***europaeum***	WTyr

LYCOPODIUM (Lycopodiaceae)

clavatum	GPoy

LYCOPSIS See ANCHUSA

LYCOPUS (Labiatae/Lamiaceae)

europaeus	CArn CSFH ECWi GBar GPoy MChe MHew MSal WChe WHer WNdy WWye
sp. JLS 88040	EMon

LYCORIS (Liliaceae/Amaryllidaceae)

albiflora	SDeJ
aurea	CGre

LYGODIUM (Schizaeaceae)

See Plant Deletions

LYONIA (Ericaceae)

ligustrina	CChu CCla ELan

LYONOTHAMNUS (Rosaceae)

floribundus	
ssp. ***aspleniifolius***	CAbb CChu CGre SArc SHil

LYSICHITON (Araceae)

americanus **AGM**	CB&S CBen CCla CHEx CHad CRow CWGN EBul ECha EHon ELan EMFW EPar EWav GDra IBar LMay MRav MSta MUlv NDea SPer SWat WBod WChe WHol WWat
camtschatcensis **AGM**	CB&S CBen CCla CHEx CRDP CRiv CRow CWGN ECha EHon ELan EMFW EPar IBar LMay MSta NDea SHig SPer SWat WChe WHol

LYSIMACHIA † (Primulaceae)

atropurpurea	MHlr NNrw NPri SFis WCot WPer
barystachys	CRow GCHN MRav SLga WCot
ciliata	Widely available
– 'Firecracker'	CDec COtt ECha MHlr NFai SFis SPla SSte WCot WPer WRus

clethroïdes AGM Widely available
¶ *congestiflora* CMer CTro LHil LHop NNrw NPer NPri
ephemerum Widely available
fortunei EMon LGre MHlr MUlv WCot
henryi CRDP GBuc GCal LHil NCat WCru WEas
japonica 'Minutissima' GCHN MTho NGre NKay WAbe WCru WHil WPer
lanceolata WCot
¶ *lichiangensis* NBro
– B&L 12317 CGle EMon EPla
– B&L 12464 CRow NSti WCot WThi
♦ *lyssii* See L. ***congestiflora***
mauritiana WCot
minoricensis CBot CHan CRDP CRow EPla MFir NBro SCro SMad SUsu SWat WBon WByw WCot WDav WPer
nemorum ECWi EWFC WCot WPer WTyr
nummularia Widely available
– 'Aurea' AGM Widely available
*– *nana* MPit
ovata NHol
pseudohenryi LHop WCot
punctata Widely available
¶ – 'Alexander's' EMon WCot
– *verticillata* See L. ***verticillaris***
thyrsiflora CBen CRow EBre LBre MSta NDea SWat WChe WCot WHer
verticillaris WCot
vulgaris CArn CWGN ECWi EHon EWFC MHew SIde WChe WCru WGwy WHaw WHil WWye
– var. *davurica* WCot

LYSIONOTUS (Gesneriaceae)

pauciflora WCru

LYTHRUM (Lythraceae)

'Croftway' CDoC
salicaria CArn CKin CRDP CRow CWGN ECWi ECoo EHon EWFC GCHN MChe MFir MHew MSal NBee NBro NLan NMir NNor SUsu SWat WByw WChe WCla WHer WHil WPbr WWye
– 'Brightness' CSco NCat NHol
– 'Feuerkerze' ('Firecandle') AGM CMGP CRow EBre EFou EHal ELan EPad LBre MBel MNFA MRav MUlv NCat NFai NHol NSti SChu SFis SHer SMrm SPer WPer
– 'Florarose' EFou
– 'Happy' GCal
– 'Lady Sackville' EFou GBuc GCal GGar SAxl SFis WAbe
– 'Morden's Pink' CDoC EFou MBri
– 'Robert' CDoC CMGP CRow CSco CShe EBre ECha ELan EPar LBre MWat NHol NOak SChu SPer WChe WEas
– 'Rose' ELan
– 'The Beacon' CDoC CRow LWad MHlr SFis SRms WCot
– Ulverscroft form MUlv
virgatum 'Dropmore Purple' MBri NSti SMad
– 'Rose Queen' ECha EFol GCal SPer WPer
– 'Rosy Gem' CBow CRow ECtt EMar EPad MFir MWat NOak NPri NTow SFis SSvw WHal WHoo WPer
– 'The Rocket" CMGP CRow CSco EBre LBre NCat NHol NSti SFis SHer SPer WWin

LYTOCARYUM (Palmae/Arecaceae)

§ *weddellianum* AGM CTro MBri

MAACKIA (Leguminosae/Papilionaceae)

amurensis CB&S CChu CCla EHar ELan WCoo

MACFADYENA (Bignoniaceae)

§ *unguis-cati* CGre CTro

MACHAERANTHERA (Compositae/Asteraceae)

glabriuscula CNic
pattersonii See M. ***bigelovii***

MACHILUS See PERSEA

MACKAYA (Acanthaceae)

§ *bella* AGM CTro ERea LHop

MACLEAYA (Papaveraceae)

N *cordata* AGM CArn CBow CHEx CWGN EBee ECoo EFou ELan EPar ESma LAbb MRav MTol MWat NOrc SFis SPer WEas WHal WHoo WKif WSun WWin
– 'Flamingo' EBre ECas ECha EFou EOrc GCHN GCal LBre MNFA MRav MUlv NWyt SGil SMrm WWye
x *kewensis* WHoo
microcarpa EHal EPla ESma SUsu WHer
– 'Kelway's Coral Plume' AGM CB&S CBow CGle CHEx CHad CShe CSpe CWGN EBre ECha EFol EFou ELan EOrc GMac LBre MBri NBar NBro NSti SGil SPer WEas WOld WWat

MACLURA (Moraceae)

pomifera CB&S CLnd CPle EArb EHar WDin

MACRODIERVILLA See WEIGELA

MACROPIPER (Piperaceae)

crocatum See PIPER ***ornatum***
excelsum CHEx ECou
– 'Aureopictum' CHEx

MACROZAMIA (Zamiaceae)

communis LPal WNor
miquelii LPal
moorei LPal
reidlei LPal WNor

MAGNOLIA † (Magnoliaceae)

acuminata CB&S CFil CMCN MBal SHil
¶ – 'Golden Glow' CPMA

§ – var. ***subcordata***	LRHS SHil
– – 'Miss Honeybee'	ELan
'Ann' AGM	CTrh
'Apollo'	CB&S CBow CPMA
'Athene'	CB&S CBow CMHG CPMA
'Atlas'	CB&S CBow CPMA
'Betty' AGM	CB&S CTrh IOrc LNet MGos SReu SSta WBod WDin WStI
x ***brooklynensis*** 'Woodsman'	CB&S CBow CPMA SSta
'Caerhays Belle'	CB&S CBow CPMA
campbellii	CAbb CB&S CBow CMCN CRos CSam ELan IOrc ISea SPer
– var. ***alba***	CB&S CBow CPMA SPer SSta
– ssp. ***mollicomata***	CB&S CBow CDoC CPMA CTrh CTrw IBar SHil
– – 'Lanarth'	CB&S CBow CPMA
¶ – 'Strybing White'	CPMA
campbellii Raffillii Group 'Charles Raffill' AGM	CB&S CBow CPMA EHar IBar MUlv SHBN
– – 'Kew's Surprise'	CB&S CGre
'Charles Coates'	CBow CCla CLan LHyd
cordata	See M. ***acuminata subcordata***
cylindrica AGM	CB&S CMCN IOrc SSta
dawsoniana	CB&S CMCN SHil
delavayi	CB&S CFil CHEx CTre SArc SHil SMad WBod
§ ***denudata*** AGM	CB&S CCla CMCN CTrh CTrw EHar IOrc ISea LPan MBal SEng SHil SPer SReu SSta WBod WNor WWat
– 'Forrest's Pink'	CPMA
– var. ***purpurascens***	See M. ***sprengeri diva***
'Elizabeth' AGM	CFil ELan
fraseri	WCoo
'Galaxy' AGM	CB&S CBow CPMA
'George Henry Kern'	CMHG COtt CPMA EB&P IOrc MGos SEng WBod WDin
globosa	CB&S CMCN ISea WWat
grandiflora	CBow CHEx CMCN EArb EBre IJoh ISea LBre MRav MWat SArc SLon SSta WDin WNor WWat
– 'Exmouth' AGM	CB&S CBot CBow CBra CChu CGre CLan CMCN CSco CTrh ECtt EHar ELan ENot IOrc ISea LNet MBal MBri SHBN SMad SPer SPla SReu SSta WAbe WBod WStI WWat
– 'Ferruginea'	CLan
– 'Galissonière'	CDoC IOrc ISea LPan SEng
I – 'Galissonière Nana'	LPan
– 'Goliath' AGM	CB&S CBow CHEx CLan EHar ELan IOrc ISea LNet MBal SArc SHil SPer SSta WBod
– 'Little Gem'	CBow CPMA
– 'Russet'	CBow CPMA LNet
– 'Saint Mary'	CBow CPMA
– 'Samuel Sommer'	CBow CMCN CPMA LNet LRHS
– 'Undulata'	IOrc
– 'Victoria'	ELan MAsh MBri SSta
'Heaven Scent' AGM	CAbP CB&S CBow CMCN COtt CSam CTre EHar IDai IOrc LPan MBal MBar MBri MGos SPer SSta
heptapeta	See M. ***denudata***
hypoleuca AGM	CB&S CBow CDoC CFil CHEx SHBN SReu SSta WThu
'Iolanthe' AGM	CB&S CBow CMCN CPMA EHar MBri SPer SSta
'Jane' AGM	CDoC COtt CTrh EBre ELan IOrc LBre MBri MGos NHol SPer SSta WBod
'Judy' AGM	CTrh
x ***kewensis*** 'Kewensis'	CB&S SHil
– 'Wada's Memory' AGM	CB&S CBow CCla CMCN CMHG CSco CTrh LHyd LRHS MBri SHil SPer SSta WBod WWeb
kobus	CB&S CBot CBow CBra CGre CMCN EHar IOrc LHyd LPan SEng SHBN SLeo SPer WBod WNor WWat
§ – 'Norman Gould'	CMCN
'Lilenny'	WBod
§ ***liliiflora***	CSco CTrh CTrw MAsh MBar
§ – 'Nigra' AGM	CB&S CBow CGre CLan CMHG EBre ELan ENot IJoh IOrc ISea LBre LPan MGos MRav MWat NBar SDix SHBN SPer SPla SReu WBod WDin WStI WWat
x ***loebneri***	CB&S CBow CLan CTrh EHal ELan LHyd
– 'Ballerina'	CMCN MBri
– 'Leonard Messel' AGM	Widely available
– 'Merrill' AGM	CB&S CBow CCla CMCN CMHG CPMA CSam CSco CTrh EBre ECtt EHar ELan IOrc ISea LBre LPan MBal MBri SPer SReu SSta WBod WDin WWat
– 'Neil McEacharn'	IOrc
– 'Snowdrift'	CMCN
– 'Star Bright'	CLan CMCN
macrophylla	CFil CMCN SArc SHil
– 'Sara Gladney'	CHEx
'Manchu Fan'	CPMA IOrc LRHS MBri
'Mark Jury'	CB&S CBow CMCN CPMA
'Maryland' AGM	CPMA
'Milky Way'	CB&S CBow CPMA
N ***obovata***	CTre WBod
'Peppermint Stick' AGM	CPMA MGos SSta
'Peter Smithers'	IOrc
'Pickard's Coral'	MBal WWeb
'Pickard's Firefly'	WWeb
'Pickard's Garnet'	WWeb
'Pickard's Glow'	WWeb
'Pickard's Schmetterling'	See M. 'Schmetterling'
'Pinkie' AGM	IOrc MAsh MBri
x ***proctoriana*** AGM	CDec IOrc SReu
– 'Proctoriana'	EBre LBre LHyd SLeo SPer SPla
quinquepeta	See M. ***liliiflora***
'Raspberry Ice'	CRos MBal SSta WBod
'Ricki' AGM	CMCN COtt CPMA CTrh EB&P IOrc LRHS MBri MGos
'Royal Crown'	CKni EHar MBri SSta WBod
'Ruby'	CPMA
salicifolia AGM	ISea SHil SPer SSta
– 'Jermyns'	LHyd SLeo
sargentiana	CFil CGre IOrc
– var. ***robusta***	CB&S CTrw EHar ELan NHlc SReu SSta
– – ***alba***	CTrw
'Sayonara' AGM	CB&S CBow COtt CPMA IOrc
§ 'Schmetterling'	SSta
'Serene'	CB&S CBow CPMA
sieboldii AGM	CAbb CB&S CBra CCla CGre CMCN CSco CTrh EHar ELan IOrc MBal MBar MBri MGos SHBN SHil SPla SReu SSta WAbe WBod WCoo WNor

– ssp. ***sinensis*** **AGM**	CB&S CDoC CMCN CSam CSco ELan ISea SHil SPer WSHC WWat
x ***soulangeana***	CB&S CBra CLan CSco CShe CTrh CTrw EBre ELan ENot IBar IDai IJoh ISea LBre LHyd MBal MBar MBri MGos MWat NBar SHBN SPer SReu WAbe WDin WNor
– 'Alba'	See M. x *s.* 'Alba Superba'
§ – 'Alba Superba'	CB&S CBra CGre COtt CSco ENot IOrc ISea MGos SPer SReu WBod
– 'Alexandrina' **AGM**	CBow CDoC CTrh ELan IOrc MBri SPer WBod WWeb
– 'Amabilis'	CDoC IOrc WBod
– 'Brozzoni' **AGM**	CB&S CBow CGre CMCN CMHG CPMA CSam CTrh IOrc ISea WBod
N– 'Burgundy'	CB&S CBot EBre ISea LBre SSta WBod
– 'Lennei' **AGM**	CB&S CBow CBra CMCN CMHG CSco CTrh EHar ENot GWht IOrc MGos NKay SHBN SPer SReu WBod WNor WStI
– 'Lennei Alba' **AGM**	CMCN CSco ELan IOrc WBod
– 'Nigra'	See M. ***liliiflora*** 'Nigra'
– 'Pickard's Sundew'	CB&S CMCN CPMA EB&P IOrc MBri MGos SEng SHBN WBod WWeb
– 'Picture'	CDoC CGre CMCN CSco CTrh IOrc WBod
– 'Rubra'	See M. x *s.* 'Rustica Rubra'
§ – 'Rustica Rubra' **AGM**	CB&S CBow CBra CLan CMCN CPMA CSam CSco CTrh EBre ECtt EHar ELan ENot IOrc LBre LNet LPan MBri SHBN SPer SReu SSta WBod
– 'San José'	CCla CMCN CRos EB&P IOrc MBri SPer SSta
– 'Verbanica'	CCla LRHS
'Spectrum'	CPMA
sprengeri	CTrw
§ – var. ***diva***	CB&S CMCN
– – 'Burncoose'	CB&S
– ***elongata***	ISea
'Star Wars'	CB&S CBow CPMA EHar SSta
§ ***stellata*** **AGM**	Widely available
– 'Chrysanthemiflora'	CMCN LRHS SPer
– f. ***keiskei***	CDoC COtt
– 'King Rose'	CB&S CTrh ISea MBlu MBri SPer SPla SSta WBod
– 'Massey'	ISea WBod
♦– 'Norman Gould'	See M. ***kobus*** 'N. G.'
– 'Rosea'	CDoC EHar ELan IOrc ISea MGos MPla SHBN WBod
– 'Royal Star'	CB&S CBot CLan CMCN CSco CTrw EBre ECtt ENot IOrc ISea LBre LPan MBri MGos NHol SPer SPla SSta WAbe WBod WStI
– 'Water Lily' **AGM**	CB&S CBot CBow CMCN CRos CSam CSco EHar ELan IOrc ISea SPer SSta WBod WWeb
'Susan' **AGM**	CAbP CB&S CCla CMCN COtt EBre ELan IJoh IOrc LBre MBal MBri MGos MWat NHol SEng SHBN SHer SMad SPer SPla SReu SSta WAbe WBod WDin WStI WWeb
x ***thompsoniana***	CBow CMCN WBod
tripetala	CAbb CB&S CGre CHEx CMCN SHBN SHer WWat
x ***veitchii***	CGre
– 'Isca'	WBod
– 'Peter Veitch'	CGre
virginiana	CGre CMCN WOMN
'Vulcan'	CB&S CBow CMHG CPMA SSta
x ***watsonii***	See M. x ***wiesneri***
§ x ***wiesneri***	CB&S ELan MBlu WBod
wilsonii **AGM**	CB&S CBow CGre CMCN CSam CSco EHar ELan GGGa IOrc ISea MBal SAxl SHBN SHil SPer SReu SSta WCoo WDin WNor WWat
'Yellow Bird'	CFil
'Yellow Fever'	CFil

MAGNOLIA X MICHELIA (Magnoliaceae)

See Plant Deletions

X MAHOBERBERIS (Berberidaceae)

aquisargentii	CAbP CBra CSam EHar ENot EPla EWri GWht LHop MGos MPla MRav NHol SLon SPer WPat WWat
'Dart's Treasure'	EPla MBri
'Magic'	LBuc MGos MWat WWeb
miethkeana	CDoC CMHG CSam MBar

MAHONIA † (Berberidaceae)

acanthifolia	See M. ***napaulensis***
§ ***aquifolium***	CB&S CBra CPer ELan ENot GCHN GRei IDai IJoh MBal MBar MBri MGos MHew MWat NKay NNor NRoo NWea SHBN SLon SPer SPla SReu WDin WHCG WStI WWin
– 'Apollo' **AGM**	CSco CShe ECtt EGol EHar ELan ENot EPla IOrc MBar MBri MGos NBee NHol SHBN SPer SReu SSta WPat WWat
– 'Atropurpurea'	CDoC CSco EHar ENot EPla IDai NKay SHBN SPla WPat WWat
– 'Fascicularis'	See M. x ***wagneri*** 'Pinnacle'
– 'Green Ripple'	MBri NBar SPla
– 'Smaragd'	CCla CDoC CSco EBre EPla LBre MBlu MUlv NBee NHol SEng WHCG WPat
¶ – 'Versicolor'	MBlu
bealei	See M. ***japonica*** Bealei Group
confusa	CFil
eutriphylla	EPla SGil
fortunei	CBot EPla MBal WSHC
fremontii	LGre
gracilipes	LRHS MBlu
japonica **AGM**	CBot CHEx CSco CShe CTre CTrw EGol ELan ENot IDai IJoh MBal MBar MBri MWat NHol NKay SDix SHBN SPer SReu SSta WBod WDin WHCG WPat WSHC WThu WTyr WWat
§ – Bealei Group	CB&S CCla CLan EBre ELan GRei IOrc LBre MBar MGos NWyt SLon SPla WDin WStI WWeb
– 'Hiemalis'	See M. *j.* 'Hivernant'
§ – 'Hivernant'	EHar EPla MBri NHol WAbe WWat
lomariifolia **AGM**	CAbb CB&S CBot CBow CHEx CLan CSco ENot GCal IHos IOrc MBal MRav MUlv NSti SArc SDry SPer SPla SReu SSta WSHC

x *media* 'Buckland' AGM — CAbP CB&S CBra CChu CMHG CSam CSco CTrw ECtt ENot ISea MBal MBri NHol SGil SHer SLon SPer WPat WWat
– 'Charity' AGM — Widely available
– 'Charity's Sister' — MBri
– 'Faith' — EPla
– 'Lionel Fortescue' AGM — CB&S CChu CMHG COtt CSam CSco CTre CTrw EHar ELan GCHN LHop MBal MBri NHol SBla SGil SMad SPer SReu SSta WAbe WHCG WWat
– 'Underway' AGM — CSam ELan MBri SPla WAbe WWes
– 'Winter Sun' AGM — CB&S CBot CBow COtt CSco EBre EHar ELan EPla IOrc ISea LBre MBal MBlu MBri MGos MWat NHol SGil SHBN SHer SPer SSta WAbe WDin WWat WWin
§ *napaulensis* — IDai
nervosa — CChu CDoC CSam CSco EPla GGGa MBlu MBri MUlv NHol SHBN SHil SPer SSta WPat WWat
¶ *pallida* — CFil
– T&K 553 — CChu
N *pinnata* — CWit ELan ENot EPla IOrc MAsh MBal MBar NWea SPer WDin WPat WStI
piperiana — MUlv
pumila — EPla
repens — CPle EGol EPla GCal SRms WWat
– 'Rotundifolia' — EPla
siamensis — CGre
trifoliolata var. *glauca* — SHil
x *wagneri* 'Fireflame' — MUlv
– 'Moseri' — MUlv SPla
§ – 'Pinnacle' AGM — CSco MBri MGos
– 'Undulata' AGM — CSco ECtt EGol ENot IHos MUlv NHol SDix SPer

MAIANTHEMUM (Liliaceae/Convallariaceae)

bifolium — CBre CNic CRDP CRow EBul ELan ELun EMon EPar EPot MBal MCas NBro NGar NKay SAxl SFar WCru WDav WWat
– British form — WThu
§ – var. *kamtschaticum* — CRDP EBul ECro EMon EPar
canadense — GCal MSal
dilatatum — See M. *bifolium kamtschaticum*

MAIHUENIA (Cactaceae)

¶ *poeppigii* JCA 1253 — GCHN

MALEPHORA (Aizoaceae)

lutea — CNic MHig NMen

MALLOTUS (Euphorbiaceae)

japonicus — CGre

MALPIGHIA (Malpighiaceae)

See Plant Deletions

MALUS † (Rosaceae)

x *adstringens* 'Almey' — SIgm SKee
– 'Hopa' — GTwe
– 'Purple Wave' — GTwe MBri SIgm WTyn
– 'Simcoe' — CDoC CLnd EBee GChr GTwe MBri SKee
'Aldenhamensis' — See M. x *purpurea* 'A.'
x *atrosanguinea* — NWea
baccata — CMCN GTwe MBri MBrk WNor
¶ – 'Dolgo' — SKee
– 'Gracilis' — MBri
– 'Lady Northcliffe' — CLnd SFam
– var. *mandshurica* — EHar
'Butterball' — EHar MBri SKee
'Cheal's Weeping' — MBar WStI
coronaria 'Charlottae' — CDoC CLnd COtt CSam CSco CTho EHar ENot SHil SIgm SPer WTyn
'Crittenden' — IMal SHil
F *domestica* — MGos
F – 'Acme' (D) — CSco SDea SKee
F – 'Adam's Pearmain' (D) — CSco GTwe SDea SFam SFru SIgm SKee WHow WJas
F – 'Advance' (D) — CSco SKee
F – 'Akane' (D) — SDea
F – 'Alderman' (C) — CSco
F – 'Alexander' (C) — GTwe
F – 'Alford' (Cider) — SKee
F – 'Alfriston' (C) — CSco SKee
F – 'Alkmene' (D) — GTwe SKee
F – 'Allen's Everlasting' (D) — CSco GTwe SDea SKee
F – 'Allington Pippin' (D) — CSam CSco NRog SDea SFru SKee WHow WJas
F – 'American Mother' — See M. *d.* 'Mother'
F – 'Ananas Reinette' (D) — CSco SKee
F – 'Anna Boelens' (D) — SDea
F – 'Anne-Marie' (C) — SKee
F – 'Annie Elizabeth' (C) — CSco GTwe MMor SDea SFam SFru SKee WHig WJas
F – 'Api Noir' (D) — SKee
F – 'Api Rose' (D) — SKee WJas
F – 'Ard Cairn Russet' (D) — CSco GTwe SDea SKee
F – 'Aromatic Russet' (D) — CSco SKee
F – 'Arthur Turner' AGM — CDoC CSco GTwe LBuc MGos NRog SDea SFam SKee WJas WStI
F – 'Arthur W Barnes' (C) — CSco
F – 'Ashmead's Kernel' AGM — CSam CSco EBre ECas ERea GTwe LBre LBuc MWat NRog SDea SFam SFru SIgm SKee WHig WHow WJas
F – 'Ashton Bitter' — CSam
F – 'Autumn Pearmain' (D) — CSco SDea WJas
F – 'Backwell Red' (Cider) — CSco
F – 'Baker's Delicious' (D) — CSco SDea SIgm SKee
F – 'Balsam' — See M. *d.* 'Green Balsam'
F – 'Barnack Beauty' (D) — CSco SKee
F – 'Barnack Orange' (D) — SKee
F – 'Baron Ward' (C) — SKee
F – 'Baumann's Reinette' (D) — CSco SKee

F – 'Baxter's Pearmain' (C/D) SKee
F – 'Beachamwell' (D) WJas
F – 'Beauty of Bath' (D) CDoC CSam CSco ECas EHar GTwe IJoh IOrc MBea NRog SFam SKee WJas
F – 'Beauty of Hants' (D) SKee
F – 'Beauty of Kent' (C) SDea SKee
F – 'Beauty of Moray' (C) SKee
F – 'Beauty of Stoke' (C) SKee
F – 'Beeley Pippin' (D) GTwe SDea SKee
F – 'Belle de Boskoop' **AGM** CSco SKee
F – 'Belle-Fille Normande' (C) SKee
F – 'Belle-Fleur de France' (C) SIgm
F – 'Bembridge Beauty' SDea
F – 'Ben's Red' (D) CDoC SKee
F – 'Bess Pool' (D) CSco SKee
F – 'Bismarck' (C) CSco SKee
F – 'Blaze' (D) GTwe
F – 'Blenheim Orange' **AGM** CDoC CSam CSco ECas EHar EWar GBon GTwe LBuc MBri MMor MWat NRog SDea SFam SFru SIgm SKee SPer WHig WHow WJas WStI
F – 'Blenheim Red' See M. *d.* 'Red Blenheim'
F – 'Bloody Ploughman' SKee
F – 'Blue Pearmain' (D) SKee
F – Bolero ®/ 'Tuscan (D/Ball) EBal MGos NBar SDea WWeb
F – 'Boston Russet' See M. *d.* 'Roxbury Russet'
F – 'Bountiful' (C) CDoC CSco GTwe MGos SFru SIgm WHig WStI
F – 'Bow Hill Pippin' (D) SKee
F – 'Box Apple' (D) SKee
F – 'Braddick Nonpareil' (D) CSco SKee
F – 'Braeburn' (D) SDea SKee
F – 'Bramley's Seedling' **AGM** Widely available
F – 'Bread Fruit' (C/D) CDoC SKee
F – 'Breakwell Seedling' (Cider) CSco
F – 'Bridgwater Pippin' (C) WJas
F – 'Broad-Eyed Pippin' (C) SKee
F – 'Brownlees Russet' (D) CSco GTwe NRog SDea SFam SFru SKee WJas
F – 'Brown's Apple' (Cider) CSco
F – 'Broxwood Foxwhelp' (Cider) CSco
F – 'Bulmer's Chisel Jersey' (Cider) CSco
F – 'Bulmer's Crimson King' (Cider) CSco
F – 'Bulmer's Fillbarrel' (Cider) CSco
F – 'Bulmer's Foxwhelp' (Cider) CSco
F – 'Bulmer's Norman' (Cider) CSco SKee
F – 'Bushey Grove' (C) SDea SKee
F – 'Buxted Favorite' (F) SKee
F – 'Calagolden Elbee' (D) SKee
F – 'Calville Blanc d'Hiver' (D) CSco SKee
F – 'Calville des Femmes' (C) SKee
F – 'Cambusnethan Pippin' (D) SKee
F – 'Carlisle Codlin' (C) CSco
F – 'Caroline' (D) WJas
F – 'Carswell's Orange' (D) SKee
F – 'Catherine' (C) SKee
F – 'Catshead' (C) CSco SDea SKee WJas
F – 'Cellini' (C) CSco SDea SKee
F – 'Charles Eyre' (C) CSco SKee
F – 'Charles Ross' **AGM** CMac CSam CSco EBre ECas EWar GBon GRei GTwe LBre MBea MWat NRog SDea SFam SIgm SKee WHow WJas WWeb
F – Charlotte ® (C/Ball) EBal MGos NBar
F – 'Cheddar Cross' (D) CSco SKee
F – 'Chelmsford Wonder' (C) SKee
F – 'Chiver's Delight' (D) CSco GTwe MMor SDea SFru SIgm SKee WHig WJas
F – 'Christmas Pearmain' (D) CSco GTwe SDea SKee WHig WHow WJas
F – 'Cinderella' CDoC
F – 'Claygate Pearmain' **AGM** CSco GTwe SDea SFam SFru SIgm SKee WJas
F – 'Cockle Pippin' (D) CSco GTwe SDea SIgm SKee
F – 'Coeur de Boeuf' (C) SKee
F – 'Colloget Pippin' (C/Cider) CDoC
F – 'Colonel Vaughan' (C) SIgm SKee
F – 'Cornish Aromatic' (D) CDoC CSam CSco GTwe SDea SFam SIgm SKee WJas
F – 'Cornish Crimson Queen' GTwe
F – 'Cornish Gilliflower' (D) CDoC CSco SDea SFam SIgm SKee WJas
F – 'Cornish Longstem' (D) CDoC
F – 'Cornish Pine' (D) CDoC SDea SKee
F – 'Coronation' (D) SDea SKee
F – 'Cortland' (C) CSco SKee
F – 'Costard' (C) GTwe SKee
F – 'Cottenham Seedling' (C) SKee
F – 'Coul Blush' (D) SKee
F – 'Court of Wick' (D) CSco SKee
F – 'Court Pendu Plat' (D) CSco MWat NRog SDea SFam SIgm SKee WJas
F – 'Cox's Orange Pippin' (D) CB&S CMac CSco EBre ECas EHar ELan EWar GTwe IJoh LBre LBuc MBea MBri MMor MWat NElm NRog SDea SFam SFru SKee SPer WHig WJas WWeb
F – 'Cox's Pomona' (C/D) CSco SDea SKee
F – 'Cox's Red Sport' (D) SKee
F – 'Cox's Rouge de Flandres' (D) SKee
F – 'Cox's Selfing' (F) GTwe SKee

F– 'Crawley Beauty' (C) CSco GTwe SDea SFam SFru SKee WHow WJas
F– 'Crimson Bramley' (C) CSam CSco SKee
F– 'Crimson Cox' (D) SDea
F– 'Crimson Peasgood' (C) SKee
F– 'Crimson Queening' (D) SKee WJas
F– 'Crispin' See M. *d.* 'Mutsu'
F– 'Crown Gold' CSco ERea GBon
F– 'Curl Tail' (D) SKee
F– 'Dabinett' (Cider) CSco SDea SKee
F– 'DArcy Spice' (D) CSco SDea SFam SFru SIgm SKee WHig
F– 'Dawn' (D) SKee
F– 'Deacon's Blushing Beauty' (C/D) SDea
F– 'Decio' (D) SFru SKee
F– 'Delkid' GTwe
F– 'Devonshire Buckland' (C) WJas
F– 'Devonshire Quarrenden' (D) CSam CSco SDea SFam SKee WJas
F– 'Dewdney's Seedling' (C) GTwe
F– 'Diamond Jubilee' (D) SKee WJas
F– 'Discovery' **AGM** CB&S CSam CSco EBre ECas EWar GBon GChr GRei GTwe IOrc LBre LBuc MBea MBri MMor MWat NBee NElm NRog SDea SFam SFru SIgm SKee SPer WHig WJas WWeb
F– 'Doctor Hare's' (C) WJas
F– 'Doctor Harvey' (C) EHar
F– 'Doctor Kidd's Orange Red' (D) SDea
F– 'Domino' (C) SKee
F– 'Downton Pippin' (D) SKee WJas
F– 'Duchess of Oldenburg' (C/D) CSco SKee
F– 'Duchess's Favourite' (D) CSco SKee WJas
F– 'Duke of Devonshire' (D) CSam CSco SDea SFam SKee WJas
N– 'Dumeller's Seedling' (C) GTwe SDea SFru SKee
F– 'Dunn's Seedling' (D) SDea
F– 'Dutch Mignonne' (D) SKee
F– 'Early Crimson' CSco
F– 'Early Julyan' (C) SKee WJas
F– 'Early Victoria' See M. *d.* 'Emneth Early'
F– 'Early Worcester' See M. *d.* 'Tydeman's E. W.'
F– 'Easter Orange' (D) CSco GTwe SKee WJas
F– 'Ecklinville' (C) SDea SKee
F– 'Edward VII' **AGM** CDoC CSco EBre GTwe LBre SDea SFam SFru SKee WJas
F– 'Edwin Beckett' (D) SKee
F– 'Egremont Russet' **AGM** CMac CSam CSco EBre ECas EWar GBon GChr GTwe IOrc LBre LBuc MBea MBri MMor MWat NBee NElm NRog SDea SFam SFru SIgm SKee SPer WHig WJas WWeb
F– 'Ellison's Orange' **AGM** CSam CSco ECas EWar GBon GTwe MBri MMor NBar NRog SDea SFam SFru SIgm SKee WJas WStI
F– 'Elstar' **AGM** CSco GTwe IOrc SDea SFru SIgm SKee WHig
F– 'Elton Beauty' (D) SDea SKee
F– 'Emneth Early' **AGM** CSam GTwe MMor NRog SDea SFam SFru SKee WHow WJas
F– 'Empire' (D) SKee
F– 'Encore' (C) CSco SDea SFru SKee
F– 'Epicure' **AGM** CDoC CSam CSco GBon GTwe IOrc NElm NRog SFam SFru SIgm SKee
F– 'Ernie's Russet' (D) SDea
F– 'Evening Gold' (C) SDea
F– 'Eve's Delight' (D) SDea
F– 'Exeter Cross' (D) CSco SDea SFam SKee
F– 'Fall Russet' (D) GTwe
F– 'Falstaff' **AGM** CDoC CSco GTwe MGos SFru SIgm SKee
F– 'Fameuse' (D) SKee
F– 'Fearn's Pippin' (D) CSco SKee
F– 'Feltham Beauty' (D) CSco
F– 'Feuillemorte' (D) SKee
F– 'Fiesta' **AGM** CDoC CSam CSco EBre ECas GBon GTwe LBre LBuc MBri MGos NBar SDea SFam SFru SIgm SKee WHig
F– 'Fillbarrel' (Cider) CSco
F– 'Fireside' SIgm
F– 'Firmgold' (D) SDea
F– 'First and Last' (D) CSco
F– 'Five Crowns' SKee
F– Flamenco ® (D/Ball) EBal EBee MGos NBar
F– 'Flower of Kent' (C) CSco SDea SFru SIgm SKee
F– 'Flower of the Town' (D) WJas
F– 'Folkestone' (D) SKee
F– 'Forge' (D) CSco SDea SKee
F– 'Formosa Nonpareil' (C) WJas
F– 'Fortune' **AGM** CDoC CMac CSam ECas GChr GRei GTwe MGos NElm NRog SDea SFam SFru SIgm SKee SPer WHow WJas
F– 'Foster's Seedling' (D) SKee
F– 'Franklyn's Golden Pippin' (D) CSco
F– 'Frederick' (Cider) CSco
F– 'French Crab' (C) CSco SDea
F– 'Freyberg' (D) SKee
F– 'Friandise' (D) CSco
F– 'Frogmore Prolific' (C) CSco WJas
F– 'Fuji' (D) SDea SKee
F– 'Gala' (D) CSam CSco GBon GTwe MBri SDea SFam SFru SIgm SKee
F– 'Gala Mondial' SKee
F– 'Gala Royal' SKee
F– 'Galloway Pippin' (C) GTwe SKee
F– 'Gascoyne's Scarlet' (D) CSco SDea SFam SKee
F– 'Gavin' (D) GTwe SDea SKee
F– 'Genesis II' (D/C) SDea
F– 'Geneva' (Crab) SKee
F– 'Gennet Moyle' (C) WJas
F– 'George Carpenter' (D) SKee
F– 'George Cave' (D) CSco GChr GTwe NBee NRog SDea SFam SFru SIgm SKee WJas
F– 'George Neal' **AGM** CSco SDea SFam SFru SIgm SKee
F– 'Gladstone' (D) SIgm SKee WJas

F– 'Glass Apple' (C/D)	CDoC
F– 'Gloria Mundi' (C)	SDea SKee
F– 'Glory of England' (C)	WJas
F– 'Gloster '69' (D)	CSco GTwe SDea SIgm SKee
F– 'Gloucester Cross' (D)	SKee
F– 'Golden Delicious' AGM	CB&S CMac CSco EBre ECas ELan EWar GBon IJoh LBre MBea MBri MMor NElm NRog SDea SKee SPer WStI WWeb
F– 'Golden Harvey' (D)	CSco
F– 'Golden Knob' (D)	SKee WJas
F– 'Golden Noble' AGM	CDoC CSco GTwe SDea SFam SFru SIgm SKee WJas
F– 'Golden Nonpareil' (D)	CSco
F– 'Golden Nugget' (D)	SIgm SKee
F– 'Golden Pearmain' (D)	SIgm
F– 'Golden Pippin' (C)	CSco SKee
F– 'Golden Reinette' (D)	CSco GTwe SKee
F– 'Golden Russet' (D)	CSco GTwe SDea SKee WJas
F– 'Golden Spire' (C)	CSco NRog SDea SKee
F– 'Goldilocks'	CDoC CSco GTwe SKee
F– 'Gooseberry' (C)	CSco SKee
F– 'Grange's Pearmain' (C)	CSco
F– 'Granny Smith' (D)	CSco ECas GTwe MBea SDea SIgm SKee SPer WWeb
F– 'Gravenstein' (D)	SDea SFam SFru SKee
F– 'Green Balsam' (C)	NRog
F– 'Green Roland'	See M. *d.* 'Greenup's Pippin'
F– 'Greensleeves' AGM	CDoC CSam CSco EBre ECas GTwe LBre MBea MBri MGos NBee NRog SDea SFam SFru SIgm SKee SPer WHig WJas
F– 'Greenup's Pippin' (D)	SKee
F– 'Grenadier' AGM	CDoC CSco EBre EWar GChr GRei GTwe IJoh IOrc LBre MBri MGos MMor NBee NElm NRog SDea SFru SIgm SKee SPer WHig WStI
F– 'Gulval Seedling'	SKee
F– 'Hambledon Deux Ans' (C)	CSco SDea SKee WJas
F– 'Hambling's Seedling' (C)	CSco SKee
F– 'Haralson' (D)	SIgm
F– 'Harry Masters Jersey' (Cider)	CSco SDea
F– 'Harry Master's Dove' (Cider)	CSco
F– 'Harry Master's Lambrook' (Cider)	CSco
F– 'Harry Master's Red Streak' (Cider)	CSco
F– 'Harvey ' (C)	CSco SDea SKee
F– 'Hawthornden' (C)	SKee
F– 'Hereford Cross' (D)	CSco SKee
F– 'Herefordshire Beefing' (C)	SKee WJas
F– 'Herring's Pippin' (D)	CSco GTwe SDea SKee
F– 'Heusgen's Golden Reinette' (D)	CSco SKee
F– 'High View Pippin' (D)	SKee
F– 'Hills Seedling'	SKee
F– 'Histon Favourite' (D)	SKee
F– 'Hoary Morning' (C)	SDea SKee
F– 'Hocking's Green' (C/D)	CDoC
F– 'Holland Pippin' (C)	SKee
F– 'Holstein' (D)	CSam CSco GTwe SDea SIgm SKee
F– 'Hormead Pearmain' (C)	CSco SKee
F– 'Horneburger Pfannkuchen' (C)	SKee
F– 'Houblon' (D)	SKee
F– 'Howgate Wonder' (C)	CDoC CSam CSco ECas GBon GChr GTwe IJoh IOrc LBuc MBri MGos MMor NBee NElm NRog SDea SFam SFru SIgm SKee SPer WHig WJas
F– 'Hubbard's Pearmain' (D)	SKee
F– 'Idared' AGM	CSco GBon GTwe MGos NBar SDea SFru SKee
F– 'Improved Cockpit' (D)	NRog
F– 'Improved Keswick' (C/D)	CDoC
F– 'Ingrid Marie' (D)	CSco SDea SIgm SKee WJas
F– 'Irish Peach' (D)	CSco GTwe SDea SFam SFru SIgm SKee WHig WHow WJas
F– 'Isaac Newton's Tree'	See M. *d.* 'Flower of Kent'
F– 'Isle of Wight Pippin' (D)	SDea
F– 'Isle of Wight Russet' (D)	SDea
F– 'James Grieve' AGM	CMac CSam CSco ECas EWar GBon GChr GRei GTwe IJoh IOrc LBuc MBea MBri MMor MWat NBar NBee NElm NRog SDea SFam SFru SIgm SKee SPer WHig WJas WWeb
F– 'James Lawson' (D)	SKee
F– 'Jerseymac' (D)	CSco SDea
F– 'Jester' (D)	CSco GTwe SDea SIgm SKee WHig
F– 'John Apple' (C)	SKee
F– 'John Broad'	CDoC
F– 'John Standish' (D)	GTwe SDea
F– 'Jonagold' (D)	CSco ECas GTwe IJoh MBea MBri SDea SFam SIgm SKee SPer WHig WWeb
F– 'Jonagold Crowngold' (D)	GTwe
F– 'Jonagored' AGM	CSco SFru SKee
F– 'Jonared' (D)	GTwe
F– 'Jonathan' (D)	CSco SDea SKee
F– 'Jordan's Weeping'	GTwe SDea WJas
F– 'Josephine' (D)	SDea
F– 'Joybells' (D)	CSco SKee
F– 'Jubilee'	See M. *d.* 'Royal Jubilee'
F– 'Jupiter' AGM	CDoC CSam CSco GBon GTwe IOrc LBuc MBea MBri MGos MWat NBar NRog SDea SFam SFru SIgm SKee WHig WJas WWeb
F– 'Kapai Red Jonathan' (D)	SDea
F– 'Karmijn de Sonnaville' (D)	SDea SFru SKee
F– 'Katja' (D)	CDoC CSam CSco ECas GBon GChr GTwe IJoh IOrc LBuc MBea MBri NBar NBee SDea SFam SFru SIgm SKee SPer WHig
F– 'Katy'	See M. *d.* 'Katja'

F– 'Kent' (D)	GTwe SDea SKee
F– 'Kentish Fillbasket' (C)	SIgm SKee
F– 'Kentish Pippin'	See M. *d.* 'Colonel Vaughan'
F– 'Kentish Quarrenden' (D)	SKee
F– 'Kerry Pippin' (D)	CSco SKee
F– 'Keswick Codling' (C)	CSam CSco NRog SDea SIgm SKee WJas
F– 'Kidd's Orange Red' **AGM**	CSco EBre ECas GTwe LBre MMor SFam SFru SIgm SKee WHig
F– 'Kilkenny Pippin'	GTwe
F– 'King Byerd' (C/D)	CDoC
F– 'King Charles' Pearmain' (D)	SKee
F– 'King George V' (D)	CSco SKee WJas
F– 'King Luscious' (D)	SDea
F– 'King of the Pippins' **AGM**	CSam CSco ECas GTwe LBuc SDea SFru SKee WJas
F– 'King of Tompkins County' (D)	CSco SKee
F– 'King Russet' **AGM**	SDea SFru
F– 'Kingston Black' (Cider)	CSam CSco SDea SKee
F– 'King's Acre Bountiful' (C)	CSco SKee WJas
F– 'King's Acre Pippin' (D)	CSco SDea SFam SFru SKee WHow WJas
F– 'Knobby Russet' (D)	SKee
F– 'Lady Bacon'	SKee
F– 'Lady Henniker' (D)	CSco GTwe SDea SKee WJas
F– 'Lady of the Wemyss' (C)	SKee
F– 'Lady Stanley' (D)	SDea
F– 'Lady Sudeley' (D)	CSco SDea SFru SKee
F– 'Lady Williams' (D)	SKee
F– 'Lady's Delight' (C)	WJas
F– 'Lady's Finger' (C/D)	CDoC
F– 'Lady's Finger of Hereford' (D)	WJas
F– 'Lady's Finger of Lancashire' (C/D)	SKee
F– 'Lady's Finger of Offaly' (D)	SDea SKee
F– 'Lamb Abbey Pearmain' (D)	SKee WJas
F– 'Landsberger Reinette' (D)	SKee
F– 'Lane's Prince Albert' **AGM**	CSam CSco EBre EHar EWar GBon GTwe IJoh LBre MGos MWat NRog SDea SFru SIgm SKee WJas
F– 'Langley Pippin' (D)	SDea SKee
F– 'Lass o' Gowrie' (C)	CSco SKee
F– 'Laxton's Fortune'	See M. *d.* 'Fortune'
F– 'Laxton's Pearmain' (D)	CSco
F– 'Laxton's Rearguard' (D)	CSco SKee WJas
F– 'Laxton's Reward' (D)	CSco
F– 'Laxton's Royalty' (D)	CSco SDea SFam
F– 'Laxton's Superb' (D)	CB&S CSam CSco EBre ECas EHar ELan EWar GBon GTwe IJoh IOrc LBre LBuc MBea MBri MMor NBee NElm NRog SDea SFru SIgm SKee SPer WJas WWeb
F– 'Leathercoat Russet' (D)	SKee
F– 'Leeder's Perfection'	SKee
F– 'Lemon Pippin' (C)	CSco SDea SKee WJas
F– 'Lewis's Incomparable' (C)	SKee
F– 'Liberty' (D)	SDea
F– 'Linda' (D)	CSco SKee
F– 'Loddington' (C)	CSco SKee
F– 'Lodgemore Nonpareil' (D)	CSco
F– 'Lodi' (C)	SDea SKee
F– 'Lord Burghley' (D)	GTwe SDea SKee
F– 'Lord Derby' (C)	CDoC CMac CSam CSco EBre ECas GTwe LBre MBri MWat NBar NBee NRog SDea SKee WHig WJas
F– 'Lord Grosvenor' (C)	CSco GTwe SKee
F– 'Lord Hindlip' (D)	CSco GTwe SDea SKee WJas
F– 'Lord Lambourne' **AGM**	CDoC CSam CSco EBre ECas EHar EWar GChr GTwe IOrc LBre MMor MWat NRog SFam SFru SIgm SKee SPer WHig WJas
F– 'Lord of the Isles'	CDoC
F– 'Lord Rosebery' (D)	SKee
F– 'Lord Stradbroke' (C)	SKee
F– 'Lord Suffield' (C)	CSco SIgm SKee WJas
F– 'Lucombe's Seedling' (D)	SKee
F– 'Mabbott's Pearmain' (D)	CSco SIgm
F– 'Madresfield Court' (D)	CSco SDea SKee WJas
F– 'Maiden's Blush' (D)	WJas
F– 'Maidstone Favourite' (D)	SKee
F– 'Major' (Cider)	CSco
F– 'Malling Kent' (D)	CSam CSco SDea SFam
F– 'Maltster' (D)	GTwe SKee WJas
F– 'Manaccan Primrose' (C/D)	CDoC
F– 'Manks Codlin' (C)	SKee
F– 'Mannington's Pearmain' (D)	SKee
F– 'Margil' (D)	CSco GTwe SDea SFam SIgm SKee
F– 'Marriage-Maker' (D)	SKee
F– 'May Queen' (D)	CSco SDea SFam SKee WJas
F– 'Maypole' (D/Ball)	CWSG EBal MGos NBar SDea WWeb
F– 'McCutcheon'	SIgm
F– 'McIntosh Red' (D)	SKee WJas
F– 'Mead's Broading' (C)	SKee
F– 'Medina' (D)	GTwe
F– 'Melba' (D)	CSam SKee
F– 'Melon' (D)	SDea
F– 'Melrose' (D)	CSco GTwe SKee
F– 'Mère de Ménage' (C)	CSco SIgm
F– 'Merton Beauty' (D)	CSco SFru
F– 'Merton Charm' **AGM**	CSco SFam SKee
F– 'Merton Joy' (D)	CSco
F– 'Merton Knave' (D)	CSco GTwe MGos SDea SFru
F– 'Merton Russet' (D)	CSco SDea SKee

F– 'Merton Worcester' (D) CSco SDea SKee
F– 'Michaelmas Red' (D) CSco GTwe SKee WJas
F– 'Michelin' (Cider) CSco SDea
F– 'Miel d'Or' SKee
F– 'Miller's Seedling' (D) GTwe SIgm SKee WHow WJas
F– 'Millicent Barnes' (D) SDea
F– 'Mollie's Delicious' (D) GTwe
F– 'Monarch' (C) CSco GTwe MMor NRog SDea SFam SKee WHow WJas
F– 'Morgan's Sweet' (C/Cider) CSco SDea SKee
F– 'Moss's Seedling' (D) CSco GTwe SDea
F– 'Mother' AGM CDoC GTwe LBuc SDea SFam SFru SKee WJas
F– 'Mrs Phillimore' (D) SKee
F– 'Muscadet de Dieppe' CSam
F– 'Mutsu' (D) GTwe MMor NRog SDea SFru SIgm SKee
F– 'Neasdale Favorite' SKee
F– 'Nehou' (Cider) CSco
F– 'Nettlestone Pippin' (D) SDea
F– 'New German' (D) WJas
F– 'Newton Wonder' AGM CDoC CMac CSam CSco ECas EWar GTwe IJoh MMor NElm NRog SDea SFam SFru SIgm SKee WHig WStI
F– 'Newtown Pippin' (D) SDea
F– 'Niemans Neiburger' CSco
F– 'Nittany Red' (D) SDea
F– 'Nobby Russet' GTwe
F– 'Nonpareil' (D) CSco SKee
F– 'Norfolk Beauty' (C) CSco SKee
F– 'Norfolk Beefing' (C) CSco SKee WJas
F– 'Norfolk Royal' (D) CDoC CSco ECas EHar GTwe MGos SDea SFam SIgm SKee WHig
F– 'Norfolk Royal Russet' (D) WHig
F– 'Norfolk Summer Broadend' (F) SKee
F– 'Norfolk Winter Coleman' SKee
F– 'Norman's Pippin' (D) CSco
F– 'Northern Greening' (C) GTwe SKee
F– 'Northwood' (Cider) CSco
F– 'Nutmeg Pippin' (D) CSco SKee
F– 'Old Pearmain' (D) SDea SKee
F– 'Opalescent' (D) CSco SKee
F– 'Orange Goff' (D) SKee
F– 'Orkney Apple' SKee
F– 'Orleans Reinette' (D) CSco GTwe LBuc MWat SDea SFam SFru SIgm SKee WHig WHow WJas
F– 'Oslin' (D) SKee
F– 'Owen Thomas' (D) CSco SKee
F– 'Paroquet' (D) SKee
F– 'Patricia' (D) SKee
F– 'Paulared' (D) SDea SKee
F– 'Peacemaker' (D) SKee
F– 'Pear Apple' (D) CDoC
F– 'Pearl' (D) CSco SDea
F– 'Peasgood's Nonsuch' AGM CSco GTwe SDea SFam SFru SKee WHig WJas
F– 'Peck's Pleasant' (D) SKee
F– 'Pickering's Seedling' (D) SKee
F– 'Pig's Nose Pippin' (D) CDoC SKee
F– 'Pine Golden Pippin ' (D) SKee
F– 'Pitmaston Pine Apple' (D) LBuc SDea SFam SFru SKee WJas
F– 'Pitmaston Pippin Nonpareil' CSco SKee
F– 'Pixie' AGM CSam CSco GTwe LBuc SFru SIgm SKee WJas
F– Polka ®/ 'Trajan (D/Ball) CWSG EBal MGos NBar SDea WWeb
F– 'Polly Prosser' (D) SKee
F– 'Polly Whitehair' SDea SKee
F– 'Ponsford' (C) CSco SKee
F– 'Porter Pefection' (Cider) CSco
F– 'Pott's Seedling' (C) SKee
F– 'Powell's Russet' (D) CSco
F– 'Priscilla' (D) GTwe
F– 'Puckrupp Pippin' (D) WJas
F– 'Queen' (C) CSco SKee
F– 'Queen Caroline' (C) SKee
F– 'Queen Cox' (D) CSco CWSG GBon MBri MRav SDea SFru SIgm SKee
F– 'Queenie' (D) CDoC
F– 'Racky Down' SKee
F– 'Red Astrachan' (D) SKee
F– 'Red Blenheim' (C/D) SKee
F– 'Red Charles Ross' (C/D) SDea SFru
F– 'Red Devil' (D) CWSG ECas GTwe MBri SIgm SKee WHig
F– 'Red Ellison' (D) CSco GTwe NRog SDea
F– 'Red Fuji' SDea
F– 'Red James Grieve' (D) SDea
F– 'Red Joaneting' (D) CSco SKee
F– 'Red Melba' (D) CSco
F– 'Red Miller's Seedling' (D) CSco SDea
F– 'Red Siberian' (Crab) SDea
F– 'Red Superb' (D) SKee
F– 'Red Victoria' (C) CSco GTwe WJas
F– 'Redfree' GTwe
F– 'Redsleeves' (C) CSco GTwe SDea SIgm WHig
F– 'Reinette Doreé de Boediker' (D) GTwe
F– 'Reinette du Canada' (D) CSco SFru SIgm SKee
F– 'Reinette d'Obry' (Cider) CSco
F– 'Reinette Rouge Etoilée' (D) SDea SKee
F– 'Reverend Greeves' SDea
F– 'Reverend W Wilks' (C) CDoC CSco EBre LBre MWat NRog SFam SFru SIgm SKee WJas
F– 'Ribston Pippin' AGM CSco EBre GTwe LBre LBuc MWat SDea SFam SFru SIgm SKee WJas
F– 'Rival' (D) CSco SDea SKee WJas
F– 'Robin Pippin' (D) GTwe

F– 'Rome Beauty' (D) SDea
F– 'Rosamund' (D) SKee
F– 'Rosemary Russet' **AGM** CSam CSco GTwe SDea SFam SFru SIgm SKee WHig WHow WJas
F– 'Ross Nonpareil' (D) CSco GTwe SDea SKee
F– 'Roundway Magnum Bonum' (D) CSco SDea SKee
F– 'Roxbury Russet' (D) CSco SKee
F– 'Royal Gala' **AGM** SDea
F– 'Royal Jubilee' (C) SKee
F– 'Royal Russet' (C) SDea
F– 'Royal Snow' (D) SKee
F– 'Rubens' (D) SKee
F– 'Rubinette' CDoC CWSG ECas GTwe MBri MGos NBar WHig WHow WJas
F– 'S T Wright' (C) SKee
F– 'Saint Albans Pippin' (D) SKee
F– 'Saint Augustine's Orange' SKee
F– 'Saint Cecilia' (D) CSco SDea SKee WJas
F– 'Saint Edmund's Pippin' **AGM** CSam CSco ERea GTwe LBuc SDea SFam SFru SIgm SKee WHig WJas
♦– 'Saint Edmund's Russet' See M. *d.* 'Saint Edmund's Pippin'
F– 'Saint Everard' (D) CSco SFru SKee
F– 'Saint Magdalen' SKee
F– 'Saltcote Pippin' (D) CSco SKee
F– 'Sam Young' (D) CSco SKee
F– 'Sandringham' (C) SKee
F– 'Sanspareil' (D) SKee
F– 'Saw Pits' SKee
F– 'Scarlet Crofton' (D) CSco SKee
F– 'Scarlet Nonpareil' (D) CSco SKee
F– 'Scarlet Pimpernel' (D) CSco WJas
F– 'Schweizer Orange' ('Swiss Orange') CSco
F– 'Scotch Bridget' (C) SKee WHow WJas
F– 'Scotch Dumpling' (C) GTwe
F– 'Seaton House' (C) SKee
F– 'Shakespeare' (D) WJas
F– 'Sheep's Nose' (C) SDea SKee
F– 'Shenandoah' (C) SKee
F– 'Shoesmith' (C) SIgm
F– 'Shortymac' (D) SKee
F– 'Sir Isaac Newton's' See M. *d.* 'Flower of Kent'
F– 'Sir John Thornycroft' (D) SDea
F– 'Smart's Prince Arthur' (C) SDea
F– 'Somerset Red Streak' (Cider) CSco
F– 'Sops in Wine' (C/Cider) CDoC SKee
F– 'Spartan' (D) CDoC CSam CSco EBre ECas GBon GTwe LBre LBuc MBri MGos MMor NBar NRog SDea SFam SFru SIgm SKee SPer WHig WJas WStI
F– 'Spencer' (D) SKee
F– 'Spur Mac' (D) SDea
F– 'Star of Devon' (D) SDea
F– 'Stark' (D) SDea
F– 'Starking' (D) SKee
F– 'Starking Red Delicious' (D) CSco
F– 'Starkrimson' (D) SKee
F– 'Starkspur Golden Delicious' (D) SKee
F– 'Stark's Earliest' (D) SKee
F– 'Stembridge' (Cider) CSco
F– 'Stembridge Jersey' (Cider) CSco
F– 'Steyne Seedling' (D) SDea
F– 'Stirling Castle' (C) CSco GTwe SKee
F– 'Stobo Castle' SKee
F– 'Stoke Edith Pippin' (D) SKee WJas
F– 'Stoke Red' (Cider) CSco
F– 'Stone's' See M. *d.* 'Loddington'
F– 'Striped Beefing' (C) CSco SKee
F– 'Stub Nose' SKee
F– 'Sturmer Pippin' (D) CSam CSco GTwe MWat SDea SFam SFru SIgm SKee
F– 'Summer Golden Pippin' (D) SKee
F– 'Summer Granny' SDea
F– 'Summergold' CSco
F– 'Summerred' (D) CSco CWSG SKee WStI
F– 'Sunburn' (D) SIgm SKee
F– 'Sunset' **AGM** CDoC CMac CSam CSco CWSG ECas GTwe LBuc MBea MBri NBee NRog SDea SFam SFru SIgm SKee SPer WHig
F– 'Suntan' **AGM** CSam CSco GBon GTwe MWat NBee SDea SFru SIgm SKee WHig
F– 'Superb' See M. *d.* 'Laxton's Superb'
F– 'Surprise' (D) GTwe
F– 'Sweet Alford' (Cider) CSco
F– 'Sweet Coppin' (Cider) CSco
F– 'Taunton Cream' CSco
F– 'Taylor's' (Cider) CSco SDea
F– 'Ten Commandments' (D) SDea WJas
F– 'The Queen' CSco
F– 'Thomas Rivers' (C) SDea SKee
F– 'Thorle Pippin' (D) SKee
F– 'Tillington Court' (C) WJas
F– 'Tom Putt' (C) CDoC CSam CSco CWSG GTwe SDea SIgm SKee WHow WJas

F– 'Tommy Knight' (D) CDoC
F– 'Tower of Glamis' (C) SKee
F– 'Transparente de Bois Guillaume' (D) SKee
F– 'Transparente de Croncels' (C) SKee
F– 'Tregoana King' (C/D) CDoC
F– 'Tremlett's Bitter' (Cider) CSco SDea
F– 'Twenty Ounce' (C) GTwe SKee WJas
F– 'Twinings Pippin' (D) SKee
F– 'Tydeman's Early Worcester' (D) CSco EBee GRei GTwe NBee NRog SDea SKee WHow WJas
F– 'Tydeman's Late Orange' (D) CSco GTwe MMor NRog SDea SFam SFru SKee
F– 'Tyler's Kernel' (C) SKee
F– 'Underleaf' (D) CSco
F– 'Upton Pyne' (D) CSam CSco SDea SKee
F– 'Venus Pippin' (C/D) CDoC
F– 'Vetch's Perfection' SKee
F– 'Vickey's Delight' (D) SDea
F– 'Vilberie' (Cider) CSco
F– 'Vista-Bella' (D) CSco GTwe NBee SDea SKee
F– 'Wagener' (D) CSco SDea SFam SKee
F– Waltz ®/ 'Telamon (D/Ball) CWSG EBal MGos NBar SDea WWeb
F– 'Wanstall Pippin' (D) SKee
F– 'Warner's King' AGM CSco SDea SFru SKee WJas
F– 'Wealthy' (D) SDea SKee
F– 'Wellington' See M. *d.* 'Dumeller's Seedling'
F– 'Wellspur Delicious' (D) CSco WJas
F– 'Wellspur Red Delicious' GTwe
F– 'Welsh Russet' (D) SDea
F– 'White Jersey' (Cider) CSco
F– 'White Joaneting' (D) CSco
F– 'White Melrose' (C) CSco GTwe SDea SKee
F– 'White Paradise' (C) SKee
F– 'White Transparent' (C/D) CSco GTwe SDea SKee
F– 'William Crump' (D) SDea SFru SKee WHig WHow WJas
F– 'Winston' AGM CSco GTwe NRog SDea SFam SIgm SKee WJas
F– 'Winter Banana' (D) SDea SKee
F– 'Winter Pearmain' (D) CSco SKee
F– 'Winter Quarrenden' (D) SDea SKee
F– 'Winter Queening' (D/C) SDea
F– 'Woolbrook Pippin' (D) CSco
F– 'Woolbrook Russet' (C) CSco SFru SKee
F– 'Worcester Pearmain' AGM CSam CSco ECas EWar GBon GChr GRei GTwe IJoh LBuc MBea MBri MMor MWat NBar NElm NRog SDea SFam SFru SIgm SKee SPer WHig WJas WStI WWeb
F– 'Wormsley Pippin' (D) SKee WJas
F– 'Wyken Pippin' (D) CSco GTwe SDea SFam SKee WJas
F– 'Yarlington Mill' (Cider) CSco SDea SKee
F– 'Yellow Ingestrie' (D) CSco SKee WJas
F– 'Yellowspur' (D) SKee
F– 'Young America' SIgm
F– 'Zabergäu Renette' (D) SKee
'Echtermeyer' See M. x ***gloriosa*** 'Oekonomierat Echtermeyer'
'Elk River' GTwe
'Evereste' AGM CBar CDoC CLnd CSco EBar GChr GTwe MBlu MBri SIgm SKee WAbe WDin WJas WTyn
florentina WMou
floribunda AGM CBra CDoC CLnd CSam CSco CTho ELan ENot GTwe IDai IHos IOrc LBuc MBri MGos MRav NBee SChu SHBN SIgm SKee SPer WDin WJas WMou WTyn
'Gardener's Gold' MBri
§ x ***gloriosa*** 'Oekonomierat Echtermeyer' EBee WDin
'Golden Gem' GTwe SIgm WJas
'Golden Hornet' See M. x ***zumi*** 'G. H.'
'Goldsworth Purple' CTho
halliana CMCN
x ***hartwigii*** 'Katherine' AGM COtt
'Hillieri' See M. x ***schiedeckeri*** 'H.'
hupehensis AGM CB&S CCla CLnd CMCN CTho EHar ENot GAul GTwe IHos MBri SFam SHBN SIgm SKee SPer WJas WMou WNor WWat
F 'John Downie' AGM Widely available
'Kaido' See M. x ***micromalus***
kansuensis CLnd WMou
x ***magdeburgensis*** CLnd SIgm
§ x ***micromalus*** CLnd GAri
x ***moerlandsii*** CLnd
– 'Liset' CLnd EBar EBee EBre ECtt ENot GChr LBre NBar SIgm SPer WJas WStI
– 'Profusion' CBra CLnd CSco CTho EBar EBre ELan ENot GRei IDai IOrc LBre MBar MBri MGos NBee NWea SHBN SIgm SKee SPer SPla WAbe WDin WJas WStI
orthocarpa CLnd SKee
'Pink Perfection' CLnd ENot SHBN SHil SPer
'Prince Georges' SHil
prunifolia 'Cheal's Crimson' NRog
– 'Pendula' GAri
pumila 'Cowichan' GTwe LRHS MBri SPer WTyn
– 'Dartmouth' CLnd CSco CTho NRog SFam SKee SPer
– 'Montreal Beauty' MBri WJas
– 'Niedzwetzkyana' CLnd
x ***purpurea*** 'Aldenhamensis' CLnd SDea SKee WDin
– 'Eleyi' CLnd EBar ENot GTwe MGos NWea SKee WDin
– 'Lemoinei' CTho EBee GRei GTwe IOrc SDea
– 'Neville Copeman' AGM CAbP CDoC CLnd WJas WTyn

– 'Pendula'	See M. x ***gloriosa*** 'Oekonomierat Echtermeyer'
'Red Glow'	CDoC CLnd COtt CSco MBri SKee WJas
x ***robusta***	CDoC CLnd EBee GTwe MBal NWea SPla
– 'Red Sentinel' **AGM**	CDoC CLnd COtt CSco EBre ELan ENot LBre LNet MBar MBri NBee SFam SIgm SKee SPer WJas
– 'Red Siberian' **AGM**	SHBN SHil SPer
– 'Yellow Siberian' **AGM**	CLnd SHil
'Royal Beauty' **AGM**	CBar COtt CSco EBre GTwe LBre MBri SKee
'Royalty'	CB&S CBra CDoC CLnd CSco CTho EBar EBre ELan ENot GRei GTwe IHos LBre LBuc LNet MBar MBri MGos MRav SFam SHBN SIgm SKee SPer SSta WJas WStI WTyn
'Rudolph'	ENot
sargentii	See M. ***toringo s.***
x ***schiedeckeri*** 'Exzellenz Thiel'	SIgm SKee
– 'Hillieri'	CLnd CTho EBar IDai SFam SKee
– 'Red Jade'	CLnd CSco EBre ECtt ELan ENot GTwe IJoh IOrc LBre LBuc MBar MBri MGos MRav NBee SHBN SIgm SKee SPer SPla WAbe WDin WJas WStI
sieboldii	See M. ***toringo***
– 'Gorgeous'	CLnd COtt CSco GTwe MBri SIgm WJas
'Snowcloud'	CLnd ENot MBri SHBN SHil SPer
spectabilis	CLnd
sp. CLD 417	EMon
¶ 'Stellata'	SKee
'Strathmore'	GTwe
sylvestris	CKin CLnd CPer GAri GChr LBuc NRog NWea SKee WDin
§ ***toringo***	CSto GTwe WJas
¶ – 'Rosea'	GTwe
§ – ssp. ***sargentii***	ECtt ENot GTwe MBri MGos SFam SIgm SKee SPer WNor WThu WWat
– 'Wintergold'	CDoC CLnd CSam ECtt MRav SIgm SKee WStI
toringoïdes	CLnd CMCN CTho GTwe MBri SFam SHBN SIgm SPer WMou WNor WWat
transitoria **AGM**	CLnd CTho SHil SKee WWat
– 'R J Fulcher'	CTho
trilobata	CLnd GTwe SHil SKee WMou
tschonoskii **AGM**	CDoC CLnd CSam CTho EBar EBre ELan ENot GTwe IOrc LBre MBal MBri MGos MRav NBar NBee NWea SHBN SIgm SKee SPer SSta WAbe WDin WJas WStI WTyn WWat
'Van Eseltine'	CBar CBra CLnd EBee EBre ENot GChr GTwe LBre MBri SIgm
'Veitch's Scarlet'	CLnd CTho GTwe NRog SFam SIgm
'Wisley'	CLnd GTwe SDea SFam SKee
x ***zumi*** 'Golden Hornet' **AGM**	Widely available
– 'Professor Sprenger'	CLnd

MALVA (Malvaceae)

alcea	CShe
– var. ***fastigiata***	CArn CGle CHan CMGP EBre ECED ECoo ECro ELan EMon LBre LGan MBri MNFA MRav NBro NCat NHol NRoo NVic SPer WEas WHal WPer
bicolor	See LAVATERA ***maritima***
crispa	See M. ***verticillata***
hispida	CNat
moschata	Widely available
– ***alba*** **AGM**	Widely available
– – 'Pirouette'	WHen WPbr
– 'Romney Marsh'	GCal MRav MTol SAxl SGil WSHC
– ***rosea***	ECha ESma LAbb MHFP NBee NNor NPer SFis WByw WPbr
¶ ***neglecta***	EWFC WPer
sylvestris	CGle CKin CLew CTom ECWi EHer EWFC GCHN MChe MPit NBro NLan NOak NRoo SMad SWat WEas WHer WPer WWin WWye
– 'Brave Heart'	CB&S EOrc LRHS NPer
– 'Cottenham Blue'	ELan EMon LRHS NRar WPbr
– ***mauritiana***	ECro ELan EMar EPad GBri LBlm LHop MFir MPit NFai NNor NPer SHer WHer WPbr WRus
¶ – 'Perry's Blue'	NPer
– 'Primley Blue'	CB&S CBot CElw CGle CHad CHan ECha EFol ELan ERav GBri GMac LAbb LGre LHop MTho NBrk NFai NPer NRar NRoo NSti SHer SMad SMrm SUsu WHal WOld WWin
– 'Zebrina'	CB&S ECro EJud EMar NBrk NFai NPer NRoo SMad WHaw WPbr
§ ***verticillata***	ELan
– 'Crispa'	EMon MChe

MALVASTRUM (Malvaceae)

x ***hypomandarum***	See ANISODONTEA x ***hypomandarum***
lateritium	Widely available
– 'Eastgrove Silver' (v)	CMea GBri LHil WCot
– 'Hopley's Variegated'	SUsu
– 'Variegatum'	WPer
* ***latifolium***	SPer WByw
peruvianum	See MODIOLASTRUM ***p.***

MALVAVISCUS (Malvaceae)

arboreus var. ***mexicanus*** LHil

MANDARIN See CITRUS *reticulata* Mandarin Group

MANDEVILLA (Apocynaceae)

x ***amoena*** 'Alice du Pont' **AGM**	CB&S CHEx CNew CRHN CTro ELan EMil ERea IHos IOrc SHil SLMG
boliviensis	CNew
§ ***laxa***	CAbb CBot CChu CHEx CMer CNew CPle CSPN CSam CTro ELan EMil ERea GCal IHos IOrc LBlm LHil LHop NPal SBra SHil SMad WBod WOMN
sanderi	EMil MBri
¶ – 'Rosea'	ERea

splendens	CGre CTro EBak LHil SLMG
suaveolens	See M. ***laxa***

MANDRAGORA (Solanaceae)

autumnalis	GPoy MSal WThi
§ ***officinarum***	CRDP GPoy LGre MSal WHer

MANETTIA (Rubiaceae)

inflata	See M. ***luteorubra***
§ ***luteorubra***	CTro LHil LHop SLMG

MANGIFERA (Anacardiaceae)

* 'Heidi'	CTro

MANGLIETIA (Magnoliaceae)
See Plant Deletions

MANGO See **MANGIFERA**

MANIHOT (Euphorbiaceae)

¶ ***esculenta***	CTro

MARANTA (Marantaceae)

bicolor	EBak
leuconeura	
var. ***erythroneura***	MBri
– var. ***kerchoveana*** **AGM**	MBri

MARCHANTIA (liverwort)

calcarea	LFle
palmatoïdes	LFle
sp. from Tristan da Cunha	LFle

MARGYRICARPUS (Rosaceae)

§ ***pinnatus***	CLew CRiv ELan ESis GCal MCas NMen NWCA SFar SHer WAbe WPer WTyr
setosus	See M. ***pinnatus***

MARISCUS See **CYPERUS**

MARKHAMIA (Bignoniaceae)

lutea	CPle
platycalyx	See M. ***lutea***

MARRUBIUM (Labiatae/Lamiaceae)

candidissimum	See M. ***incanum***
catariifolium	EMon
cylleneum	ECha ECro EFol EMar EMon SAxl WPer WWin
*– 'Velvetissimum'	CHad CMGP ECoo EGle EMar EOrc ESma LHop SChu SCro SFis
'Gold Leaf'	EBar ECha EFol ESma NSti
§ ***incanum***	CGle CHan CMHG EBee EHal EMon LBlm NTow SFis SLga WEas
libanoticum	EMon MSte WPer
supinum	EMon GCal GLil NSti
velutinum	CGle EMon
vulgare	CArn CSev EEls EHer EJud EMar Effi GBar GPoy IEde LHol MChe MHew NMir SHer SIde WHer WOak WPer WWye

MARSDENIA (Asclepiadaceae)

erecta	See CIONURA ***e.***

MARSILEA (Marsileaceae)

¶ ***mutica***	SWyc
¶ ***quadrifolia***	SWyc
* ***schelpiana***	SWyc

MASCARENA See **HYOPHORBE**

MATELEA (Asclepiadaceae)
See Plant Deletions

MATRICARIA (Compositae/Asteraceae)

chamomilla	See M. ***recutita***
♦ ***maritima***	See TRIPLEUROSPERMUM ***maritimum***
parthenium	See TANACETUM ***parthenium***
§ ***recutita***	EJud GPoy IEde LHol MChe MHew SIde

MATTEUCCIA (Dryopteridaceae)

orientalis	NHar NMar NOrc
pensylvanica	NHar SMad
struthiopteris **AGM**	CBot CFil CRow CWGN ECha ECoo EGol EHon ELan EPar MBri NBar NDea NEgg NHol NMar NOrc SAxl SCob SHig SPer SWat WFib WHal WHoo WRic WWat

MATTHIOLA (Cruciferae/Brassicaceae)

¶ ***arborescens***	WPer
§ ***fruticulosa***	CArn
¶ – 'Alba'	EMon
– ssp. ***perennis***	NSti NWCA
incana	WRus
'Les Merriennes' (d)	WOMN
pink perennial	WRus
scapifera	NTow
sinuata	CNat
♦ ***thessala***	See M. ***fruticulosa***
white perennial	CArn CGle CHad CHan CRDP CSpe MTol NBrk NPer NTow SSvw WEas WHoo WSun

MAURANDELLA (Scrophulariaceae)

antirrhiniflora	CSpe SFis

MAURANDYA (Scrophulariaceae)

§ ***barclayana***	CBot CFee CRHN CSpe CTbh GCra MBri SLMG SUsu
– ***alba***	CBot
erubescens	See LOPHOSPERMUM ***e.***
lophantha	See LOPHOSPERMUM ***s.***
♦ ***lophospermum***	See LOPHOSPERMUM ***scandens***
* 'Pink Ice'	CLTr CRHN SLMG WHaw
§ ***scandens***	CRHN ELan EWes SLMG WHaw WPer
* 'Victoria Falls'	SLMG
¶ ***wislizenii***	CTbh

MAYTENUS (Celastraceae)

boaria	CBot CGre CMCN EHar SArc SHil WWat
– 'Worplesdon Fastigiate'	LMer

MAZUS (Scrophulariaceae)

¶ *alpinus* B&SWJ 119	WCru
pumilio	EBur ECou NKay WCru
radicans	CRiv ECou NKay WCru WThi
reptans	CNic CRow CTom ELan EPar EPot MPit NMen NRoo NWCA SBla WHoo WPer
– 'Albus'	CMer CNic CRiv CRow CTom ECha ELan LHop SBla SHer WCru WHoo

MECONOPSIS † (Papaveraceae)

aculeata	GBuc GCra GTou MSto WOMN
baileyi	See M. ***betonicifolia***
x *beamishii*	CNic GGar NRoo
§ *betonicifolia* AGM	Widely available
– var. *alba*	CB&S CCla EBre EFou ELan EPot GArf GCra LBre MBal MBri NHar NHol NLin NRoo SBla SPer WPer
– Harlow Carr strain	GMac
cambrica	CBow CCla CGle CKin CMea CNic CRDP EBar ECWi EJud ELan EMar EWFC GTou MPit NCat NHol NLan NMir SChu SIng WAbe WBon WCru WHal WHer WPer WTyr WWye
– var. *aurantiaca*	ELan EMon NBir WAbe WBon WPer
– *flore-pleno*	CGle CRDP ECha EMon EPar ESma GBuc MFir MTho NBro NCat NVic WAbe WHil WOMN WPer
– 'Frances Perry'	CNat CRDP ESma GBuc IBlr NHol WCru WPer
¶ – 'Muriel Brown'	WPer
chelidoniifolia	EBre LBre WCru
dhwojii	CB&S GCra MNes MSto NBir WAbe WDav
grandis AGM	CB&S CBow CCla CElw CGle CHol CMea CNic CSam ELan EPot ESma GArf GCra ISea MBri MSto NHar NLin NRoo SBla SIgm WEas WOMN WSHC
– GS 600	GCra NBir NWCA
– PS&W 5423	GDra
¶ – Balruddry form	GGGa
horridula	CNic CSam EPot GCra GGGa MBri MSto MTho NKay WPer
– CLD 1070	NHol
– CLD 1202	NHol
– Rudis Group	GCra
¶ *impedita* KGB 303	MSto
integrifolia	GCra GDra GGGa
Kingsbarns hybrids	GArf
¶ *lancifolia* KGB 824	MSto
§ *napaulensis*	CB&S CNic CRiv CSam ELan EPot GArf GCra GDra GGGa MBal MBri MNes NCat NHar NKay NRoo NVic WCru WEas WHal WHil WOMN WPer WThu WWin
– forms	GArf NHar
– red	CRiv NBir NWCA
nudicaulis	See PAPAVER ***nudicaule***
paniculata	GBuc GCra GGGa NBir NLin
– C&Mc 296	GTou
¶ – compact form	GCra
¶ *punicea*	GGGa MSto
quintuplinervia AGM	EBre ECha GArf GCra GDra GGGa LBre NBir NRoo NRya SBla WHal
regia	CB&S CBot CSam ELan GAbr GArf GCra NHar NHol NRoo SIgm WPer
– hybrids	CAbP GTou WDav
¶ *robusta*	GGGa
x *sarsonsii*	CNic NBir NRoo
x *sheldonii* AGM	CSam GBuc GGGa MArl MFir MSto NBir NHar NLin NRoo NVic WOld
– 'Branklyn'	GAbr IBlr
– Crewdson hybrids	EPot GArf GBuc GCra GDra MBri MNes WEas
¶ – 'Lingholm'	GGar
– 'Ormswell'	GArf NKay SRms
– 'Slieve Donard' AGM	EBre GDra GGar IBar IBlr LBre MNes MUlv NHar
simplicifolia	MSto
¶ *speciosa* KGB 316	MSto
¶ sp. CH&M 1013	GCra
sp. CLD 704	NHol
¶ sp. C&Mc 1056	GTou
superba	CB&S GBuc GCra GGGa MBal MNes MSto NRoo SIgm
villosa	CSam GArf GGGa GTou IBlr MSto NBir SIgm WPer
♦ *wallichii*	See M. ***napaulensis***

MEDEOLA (Liliaceae/Convallariaceae)

virginica	LAma WCru WThi

MEDICAGO (Leguminosae/Papilionaceae)

arborea	CPle ELan IBlr WHer
echinus	See M. ***intertexta***
sativa	CKin EWFC WHer
– ssp. *sativa*	IBlr

MEDINILLA (Melastomataceae)

magnifica	MBri

MEDLAR See MESPILUS *germanica*

MEEHANIA (Labiatae/Lamiaceae)

urticifolia	CRDP EMon MBel WCot WHer WOMN

MEGACARPAEA (Cruciferae/Brassicaceae)

polyandra	GDra NHol

MELALEUCA (Myrtaceae)

acuminata	CB&S
armillaris	CPle
¶ *bracteata*	CTro
¶ – 'Golden Revolution'	CTro
decussata	ECou
* *ericifolia*	MAll
erubescens	See M. ***diosmatifolia***
gibbosa	CPle GCal MAll
hypericifolia	CGre ECou GWht MAll
¶ *linariifolia*	ECou

¶ ***nesophylla***	ECou
pauciflora	See M. ***biconvexa***
pulchella	LBlm LHil MAll WThi
pustulata	ECou MAll
¶ ***quinqenervia***	ECou
rosmarinifolia	ECou
squamea	ECou GWht
squarrosa	CGre CLTr CMer ECou GWht
thymifolia	CB&S
viridiflora	CB&S MAll

MELANDRIUM See **SILENE**

MELANOSELINUM (Umbelliferae/Apiaceae)

decipiens	CHEx

MELANTHIUM (Liliaceae/Melanthiaceae)

virginicum	MSal

MELASPHAERULA (Iridaceae)

graminea	See M. ***ramosa***
§ ***ramosa***	CAvo CMon EBee EHic ELan NRog WThi

MELIA (Meliaceae)

§ ***azedarach***	CB&S CPle
– var. ***japonica***	See M. ***azedarach***

MELIANTHUS (Melianthaceae)

major AGM	Widely available
minor	CHEx NWyt

MELICA (Gramineae/Poaceae)

altissima	ETPC
– 'Atropurpurea'	CDec CElw CHan ECha EHoe EMon EPla ESis ETPC LBlm LGre LHil LLWP MSte NHol NNrw NSti WCot WPer
ciliata	CElw CSam EHoe EMon EPla ETPC GCHN WPer
– bronze	ETPC
– ssp. ***magnolii***	ETPC
– ***taurica***	ETPC
macra	EHoe ETPC
* ***minima***	ETPC
nutans	EHoe EMon EPla ETPC NHol NLan WHal
picta	ETPC
subulata	ETPC
transsilvanica	EHoe ETPC
– 'Atropurpurea'	ETPC NHol
uniflora	CKin
– f. ***albida***	CFil EHoe EMon EPla ETPC
– 'Variegata'	CBre CFil EFol EHoe EMon EPla ETPC SApp WCot

MELICOPE (Rutaceae)

ternata	ECou

MELICYTUS (Violaceae)

alpinus	CLew ECou
angustifolius	ECou MAll MHig SDry
crassifolius	CBot CChu CPle ECou EMon MAll NHol WHCG WSHC
obovatus	CPle ECou
ramiflorus	CPle ECou

MELILOTUS (Leguminosae/Papilionaceae)

altissima	NMir
officinalis	CArn CKin CSFH ECWi Effi GPoy MChe MHew SIde WHer WNdy
– ***albus***	MHew SIde

MELINIS (Gramineae/Poaceae)

repens	EHoe

MELIOSMA (Meliosmaceae)

§ ***dilleniifolia*** ssp. ***flexuosa***	WBod
– ssp. ***tenuis***	WCoo
myriantha	WCoo
pendens	See M. ***dilleniifolia flexuosa***
¶ ***simplicifolia*** ssp. ***pungens***	CB&S
veitchiorum	CB&S CHEx

MELISSA (Labiatae/Lamiaceae)

officinalis	CArn CBow CSFH CTom EHer EJud Effi GPoy LHol MBal MBar MBri MChe MHew MPit SIde WEas WOak WPer WTyr WWye
– 'All Gold'	CLew CMea CRiv CSev ECha EFou EHoe EJud ELan EMon LHol MBri MChe NFai NHol NSti SHer SPer WEas WWye
§ – 'Aurea' (v)	Widely available
N– 'Variegata' misapplied	See M. ***o.*** 'Aurea'

MELITTIS (Labiatae/Lamiaceae)

melissophyllum	EBee ECha SIng SRms
– pink	EMon

MENISPERMUM (Menispermaceae)

canadense	GPoy LAbb SHBN

MENTHA † (Labiatae/Lamiaceae)

aquatica	CBen CKin CRDP CRow CWGN EBre ECWi ECoo EHon EJud EWFC EWav GAbr GPoy LBre LMay MChe MSta SHer SWat SWyc WChe WHer WHol WOak
arvensis	CArn MHew MSal SIde WHer
asiatica	SIde
cervina	MSta WChe
citrata	See M. x ***piperata c.***
cordifolia	See M. x ***villosa***
♦ ***corsica***	See M. ***requienii***
'Eau de Cologne'	See M. x ***piperita citrata***
x ***gentilis***	See M. x ***gracilis***
§ x ***gracilis***	CArn CBow EHer EOrc Effi GBar LHol MChe NDea NPri SHer SIde WOak WSun WWye
– 'Aurea'	See M. x ***g.*** 'Variegata'
§ – 'Variegata'	CDec CSFH CSev CTom CWGN ECha ECoo EHoe ELan EMar EPar ESma GPoy ILis MBal MFir NFai NNor NRoo NSti WEas WHal WHer WHil WOak WPer
Lavender Mint	NFai

§ ***longifolia***	CRDP ECha ECoo ELan EMar EOrc ESma GBar LHop NSti SAxl WEas WHer WOak WPer WWye
– Buddleia Mint Group	EWes GAbr
*– 'Variegata'	NCat NSti
x ***piperita***	CArn CRiv CSFH CSev ECha EHoe EJud Effi GPoy ILis LHop MBri MChe MHew MPit NHol NNor NRoo WHal WOak WPer WWye
§ x ***piperita citrata***	CArn CSFH ECha EHer Effi GAbr GPoy LHol MBri MChe MFir NFai NSti SHer SIde WEas WOak WPer WWye
I – 'Basil'	EJud
– 'Lemon'	EHer GAbr MBri SIde WPer
pulegium	CArn CRiv CRow CSFH CSev CWGN EBar ECha EHer EPar EWFC Effi GPoy LHol MChe MHew MPit SHer SIde WHer WOak WPer WWye
– Greek form	WHer
– 'Upright'	MWil SIde WPer
§ ***requienii***	Widely available
rotundifolia 'Bowles'	See M. x ***villosa alopecuroïdes***
rotundifolia hort.	See M. ***suaveolens***
rubra raripila	See M. x ***smithiana***
§ x ***smithiana***	CArn EJud GAbr GBar GPoy ILis MChe NFai NPri SIde WChe WHer WPer WWye
– 'Capel Ulo'	WHer
§ ***spicata***	CArn CSFH CSev CTom ELan Effi GPoy ILis LHol MBal MBri MChe MHew MPit NFai NNor NRoo SHer WEas WHal WHer WOak WWye
– 'Crispa'	CBre EJud EMon GAbr GAri GBar NFai NPri NRoo WPer
– 'Moroccan'	CArn CSev GAbr NPri SHer SIde WHer WOak WPer WWye
sp. Nile Valley Mint	CArn
§ ***suaveolens***	CArn CSFH CWGN EHer EJud ESma Effi GBar GPoy ILis LHol MBal MBri MFir MHew MPit NRoo SHer WHal WHer WOak WPer
§ – 'Variegata'	CArn CDec CNic CRow CSFH CShe CWGN EBar ECha EFol EHer EHoe EOrc EPar Effi GAbr MBal MBri MChe NFai NHol NNor WEas WHer WOak WPer WTyr
sylvestris	See M. ***longifolia***
§ x ***villosa alopecuroïdes*** Bowles' Mint	CBre EHer GBar GPoy ILis LHol MChe NFai SHer SIde WEas WHer WOak WWye
viridis	See M. ***spicata***

MENYANTHES (Menyanthaceae)

trifoliata	CBen CNic CRDP CRiv CRow CWGN EBre ECWi ECha ECoo EHon EMFW EWav GPoy LBre LMay MHew MSta NDea SLon SWyc WChe WHol WWye

MENZIESIA (Ericaceae)

alba	See DABOECIA ***cantabrica alba***
ciliicalyx	MBlu
– dwarf form	CNic SSta
– ***lasiophylla***	See M. ***c. purpurea***
– var. ***multiflora***	GDra GGGa MBal NHar WDav WThu
§ – var. ***purpurea***	GDra GGGa MBal SHil WBod
¶ – 'Spring Morning'	SSta
ferruginea	MBal
¶ ***pentandra*** AGS J 317	WDav
polifolia	See DABOECIA ***cantabrica***

MERCURIALIS (Euphorbiaceae)

perennis	CKin CNat GPoy

MERENDERA (Liliaceae/Colchicaceae)

attica	EPot WChr
eichleri	See M. ***trigyna***
filifolia AB&S 4665	CMon
hissarica	WChr
kurdica	EPot LAma
montana	WMar
– MS 900/913	CMon
– SF 221	CMon
nivalis	WChr
raddeana	See M. ***trigyna***
sobolifera	EPot WChr WThu
– BSBE 806	CMon
§ ***trigyna***	EPot LAma WChr

MERREMIA (Convolvulaceae)

§ ***tuberosa***	CNew

MERTENSIA (Boraginaceae)

ciliata	CHan EBee EBre ELan EOrc LBre MRav MTol SPer
echioïdes	NTow SRms WCru
franciscana	GCal WCru
maritima	ECha EPad GPoy NTow NWCA WCru WOMN WWin
– ssp. ***asiatica***	See M. ***simplicissima***
primuloïdes	GCal WCru
pterocarpa	See M. ***sibirica***
§ ***pulmonarioïdes*** AGM	CBot CBro CGle CRDP CRiv EFol ELan EPot GDra GGar LAma LHop MTho NHol NSti SPer WByw WCru WWat
§ ***sibirica***	CCMG CRDP EPot GCal LGre MBel NHar NKay NTow WDav
simplicissima	CBos CBot CCMG CHad CHan COtt CRDP ELan LBee LGre MMil MPit MTho NBir NGre NHar NPer NWCA SBla SMad SPer SWas WAbe WCru WDav WHoo WOMN
virginica	See M. ***pulmonarioïdes***

MERYTA (Araliaceae)

sinclairii	CHEx
– 'Variegata'	See M. ***s.*** 'Moonlight'

MESEMBRYANTHEMUM (Aizoaceae)

'Basutoland'	See DELOSPERMA ***nubigenum***
brownii	See LAMPRANTHUS ***brownii***
§ ***hispidum***	GAbr

ornatulum	See DELOSPERMA ***ornatulum***
putterillii	See RUSCHIA ***p.***

MESPILUS (Rosaceae)

F ***germanica***	CB&S CBra CDoC CLnd ELan IJoh IOrc LHol MWat SHBN WDin WMou
F – 'Autumn Blaze'	SFru
– 'Breda Giant'	GTwe
F – 'Dutch'	SDea SKee
F – 'Large Russian'	ERea ESim SKee
F – 'Monstrous'	GTwe SDea
F – 'Nottingham'	CBow CDoC CWSG EHar ERea ESim EWar GChr GTwe LBuc MBea MMor NBee SDea SFru SHil SIgm SKee SPer WHig WJas WMou
F – 'Royal'	SFru

METAPANAX See **PSEUDOPANAX**

METASEQUOIA (Taxodiaceae)

glyptostroboïdes AGM	Widely available
– 'Fastigiata'	See M. ***g.*** 'National'
* – 'Green Mantle'	EHul
§ – 'National'	CSam
– 'Sheridan Spire'	CB&S LNet
– 'Waasland'	WMou

METROSIDEROS (Myrtaceae)

carmineus	CHEx
– 'Carousel'	ERea
– 'Ferris Wheel'	ERea
¶ ***collinus***	ECou
§ ***excelsus***	CAbb CHEx CTro ECou
– 'Aureus'	ECou
– 'Scarlet Pimpernel'	NPal SLon
¶ – 'Spring Fire'	CB&S
fulgens	ECou
'Goldfinger'	ERea NPal
kermadecensis	CTro ECou LHil
– 'Radiant' (v)	LHop NPal
– 'Variegatus'	CB&S CTro ECou ERea LGre LHil LHop
lucidus	See M. ***umbellatus***
robustus	CB&S CHEx ISea
♦ ***tomentosus***	See M. ***excelsus***
§ ***umbellatus***	CGre CHEx ECou
¶ ***villosus*** 'Tahiti'	CB&S

MEUM (Umbelliferae/Apiaceae)

athamanticum	CLew COtt CRDP EFou EGol EPla GCal GPoy LHop MHew MSal MTho MUlv NBrk NRoo SMrm WPer

MIBORA (Gramineae/Poaceae)

See Plant Deletions

MICHAUXIA (Campanulaceae)

campanuloïdes	EPad ESma
laevigata	EPad
tchihatchewii	CBot ECro EPad ESma LHop

MICHELIA (Magnoliaceae)

compressa	CGre
doltsopa	CB&S CGre CHEx SHil
– 'Silver Cloud'	CB&S
figo	CBow CGre CTro ERea

MICRANTHUS (Iridaceae)

alopecuroïdes	NRog

MICROBIOTA (Cupressaceae)

decussata AGM	CDoC CKen CMHG CMac EBar EBre EHar EHul ENHC EPla EPot ESis GRei IBar LBee LBre LCon LLin MBar MBri MGos MWat NHol SLon SSmi WBod WWat
¶ – 'Jakobsen'	CKen
– 'Trompenburg'	CKen

MICROCACHRYS (Podocarpaceae)

tetragona	ECou EPla ESis LCon SIng WThu

MICROCOELUM See **LYTOCARYUM**

MICROGLOSSA (Compositae/Asteraceae)

albescens	See ASTER ***albescens***

MICROLEPIA (Dennstaedtiaceae)

speluncae	MBri

MICROMERIA (Labiatae/Lamiaceae)

* ***caerulea***	CNic
corsica	See ACINOS ***corsicus***
croatica	WThi
rupestris	See M. ***thymifolia***
§ ***thymifolia***	MPla
varia	ELan MCas WDav

MICROSERIS (Compositae/Asteraceae)

ringens	EBre ECha LBre
– 'Girandole'	WPer

MICROSORUM (Polypodiaceae)

diversifolium	CFil CHEx EBul SArc

MICROSTROBOS (Podocarpaceae)

fitzgeraldii	CKen LCon WThu

MIKANIA (Compositae/Asteraceae)

dentata	MBri
scandens	MSal
ternata	See M. ***dentata***

MILIUM (Gramineae/Poaceae)

effusum	CKin
– 'Aureum'	Widely available

MILLIGANIA (Liliaceae/Asteliaceae)
See Plant Deletions

MIMOSA (Leguminosae/Mimosaceae)
See Plant Deletions

MIMULUS (Scrophulariaceae)

'A T Johnson'	GCHN NVic SIng
§ 'Andean Nymph' AGM	CMea EBre ELan EPot ESis GCHN GTou LBre MBal MFos MSte NKay SHer SIng WCla WOMN
'Andean Nymph' forms	CGle CNic CRDP NTow
§ ***aurantiacus*** AGM	Widely available
¶ – JCA 13208	WDav
§ – var. ***puniceus***	CBar CBot CBrk CCla CGre CLTr CPle CTro ELan LHil LHop SDry SLMG SMrm SUsu WEas WOMN WPer
x ***bartonianus***	ELun NVic
'Bees' Scarlet'	NFai
bifidus	EOrc LGre LHop SMrm
– 'Verity Buff'	LHil
boydii	NKay
'Burgess'	CBen
x ***burnetii***	CNic LMay MFir NVic SRms
californicus	CHan
Calypso hybrids AGM	SRms
cardinalis AGM	CWGN EHon ELan LHop MFir MNFA MTho NCat NDea NHol NNor SIng WHer WPer WWin
¶ – 'Dark Throat'	WPer
cupreus	MBal WHil
– 'Minor'	SHer
– 'Whitecroft Scarlet' AGM	CBen CNic CWGN EBre ECha ELan EPot GDra LBre LMay NGre NHar SBod SHer SIng WPer WWin
glutinosus	See M. ***aurantiacus***
– ***atrosanguineus***	See M. ***aurantiacus puniceus***
– ***luteus***	See M. ***aurantiacus***
§ ***guttatus***	CBen CKin CRow EBre ECWi EWFC GAbr GAri GBar LBre MFir NDea NHol NKay NRar WChe WPer
– variegated	WCot
'Highland Orange'	CBow GAri GCHN NHar NMen WGor WPer
'Highland Pink'	ECtt NHar NRoo SBod WGor WPer
'Highland Red' AGM	ECtt GCHN GDra MArl MBar MBel MPit NHol NMen SHer WHal WOMN WPat WPer WWin
'Highland Yellow'	CRiv ECtt GAri GCHN MPit NMen NRoo SBod SHer WHal WPat WPer
hose in hose	CLTr CMer CRow ECha GCal MTho NCat NDea NFai WHer
¶ 'Inca Sunset'	EWes WOMN
'Inshriach Crimson'	GAri GCHN GDra
langsdorffii	See M. ***guttatus***
lewisii AGM	CNic CRDP CRiv ELan GCra GDra GMac GTou LGan MSte MTho NHol NOak NWCA SFis WHal WOMN WPer
longiflorus	CBot CLTr CSpe LGre LHil LHop WCot
¶ – ***saccharatus***	SMrm
¶ – 'Santa Barbara'	LGre
luteus	CBen CMer CRiv CRow CWGN ECha EHon LMay MBal MSta NDea NFai NNor WByw WChe WHal WWin
¶ – 'Variegatus'	GMac
'Magnifique'	CMea WHal
* 'Major Bees'	CDoC GCal NFai
'Malibu'	NFai NNor NRoo
'Malibu Ivory'	NFai NRoo
'Malibu Red'	CBow
'Mandarin'	EBre LBre
moschatus	CRDP CRiv CRow CSam NCat NKay NMen WCla WCru WEas WHal
'Old Rose'	ECha
'Orange Glow'	WHal
'Plymtree'	CNic NKay
¶ 'Popacatapetl'	CBrk GCal LGre SChu
primuloïdes	CRDP ELan EPot GCHN MBar MFos MPit MTho NGre NHar NHol NMen NTow NWCA SBod SFis SHer SIng WAbe WHal WOMN WWin
'Puck'	ECtt GCal
'Quetzalcoatl'	CBrk LGre SMrm
ringens	CBen CDoC CRDP CRiv CRow CWGN EBar EBre EHon EMFW LBre LMay MSta NDea NHol SPer WBon WChe WHal WHol WPer
'Roter Kaiser' ('Red Emperor')	SRms
sp. CW 5233	NTow
sp. Mac&W 5257	See M. 'Andean Nymph'
tilingii	CFee NNrd SHer WOMN
– var. ***caespitosus***	NGre NTow
Verity hybrids	CBrk ERea
'Western Hills'	EFol NRar WCru
'Wisley Red'	ECha ECot ELan LHop SFis SHer SIng

MINA See **IPOMOEA**

MINUARTIA (Caryophyllaceae)

biflora	NHol
§ ***circassica***	ESis GCHN MDHE MHig NTow NWCA WDav WPer
juniperina NS 270	NWCA
laricifolia	NPri WPer
parnassica	See M. ***stellata***
§ ***stellata***	EPot NHed NHol NMen NNrd NTow SIng
§ ***verna***	CLew MCas NHar NHed NHol NMen NNrd NRya SIde
– ssp. ***caespitosa*** 'Aurea'	See SAGINA ***subulata*** 'A.'
– ssp. ***gerardii***	See M. ***verna verna***
– ssp. ***verna***	SIng

MIRABILIS (Nyctaginaceae)

jalapa	CArn ECro ELan LAma MBri NRog SLMG WCru

MISCANTHUS (Gramineae/Poaceae)

floridulus AGM	EFou EHoe SDix SMad WCot
nepalensis	EPla
oligostachyus	CElw

sacchariflorus	CB&S CHEx CRow CWGN EBre ECas ECha ELan EPla ESiP LBre LMay MUlv NHol NJap NVic SCob SHig SPer SPla WBod WWat WWye
sinensis AGM	CHEx EBee EPla
– 'Cabaret' (v)	SRos
– var. ***condensatus***	EFou
– dwarf form	MUlv
– 'Ferne Osten'	ECha EPla MAsh MBri MUlv
¶– 'Flamingo'	EPla MAsh MBri
– 'Goldfeder' (v)	EBre LBre
– 'Goliath'	EFou
– 'Gracillimus'	CB&S CDoC CHEx CRow CWGN EBre ECha EFou ELan ENot EPla ESiP ETPC LBre MBal MBri MRav NBro NHol SAxl SCob SDix SPer WHer
– 'Graziella'	EFou EPla MBri SWas
– 'Grosse Fontäne'	ECha EFou EPla WCot
– 'Hercules'	EFou
– 'Kaskade'	EPla
– 'Kleine Fontäne'	CFee EBre EPla LBre MBri SWas
– 'Kleine Silberspinne'	CRow EFou EHoe EPla ETPC SApp SAxl
– 'Malepartus'	CRow EBre ECha EPla LBre MBri SAxl
– 'Morning Light' (v)	EBre EPla ETPC LBre MBri MUlv SApp
– 'Nippon'	EFou EHoe EPla MAsh MBri SApp
– 'Punktchen' (v)	ECha EPla
– var. ***purpurascens***	EBee EBre ECha ECoo EGol EHoe EPla ESiP ETPC GAri LBre MUlv SCob SMad WHal
¶– 'Roterpfeil'	EPla
– 'Rotsilber' (v)	ECha EFou EHoe EPla MUlv
– 'Silberfeder' ('Silver Feather')	Widely available
– 'Silberpfeil' (v)	EPla ETPC SMad
– 'Silberspinne'	EFou EPla ETPC SApp
¶– 'Sioux'	EPla
– 'Sirene'	EPla SMad
– 'Slavopour'	EPla
– 'Spatgrun'	EPla
– 'Strictus' (v)	ECha EPla MBri MHlr SDix WCot
– 'Undine'	ECha EHoe EPla ETPC MBri MUlv SMad SUsu
– 'Variegatus'	Widely available
¶– 'Yakushima Dwarf'	EPla
– 'Zebrinus' (v)	Widely available
¶sp. CLD 1314	EPla
¶sp. CLD 1325	EPla
sp. ex Yakushima	EPla
****tinctorius*** 'Nanus Variegatus'	CRow EHoe EPla SApp
¶***transmorrisonensis***	NHol
yakushimensis	CLew ECha EPla ETPC SApp

MISOPATES (Scrophulariaceae)

orontium	EWFC WCla

MITCHELLA (Rubiaceae)

repens	CB&S MHig MSal WCru WWat

MITELLA (Saxifragaceae)

breweri	CGle CHan CLew CNic CTom ECha ECro EFol ELan ELun EMar ESis GCal GTou MFir MSte NHol NKay NSti SUsu WByw WCru WEas WOMN WPbr WPer WWat WWin
caulescens	ECha ECro GAbr NBro NCat NHol NSti SFis WPer
diphylla	LGro
¶***formosana*** B&SWJ 125	WCru
stauropetala	MFir NCat

MITRARIA (Gesneriaceae)

coccinea	CAbb CB&S CBot CChu CCla CLan CMac CMer CNic CPle CTrw ELan ERea IBar IOrc ISea MBal MHig MPla SArc SBra SHil SLeo SLon SPer WBod WSHC WThu WWat
– 'Lake Caburgua'	GCal
– Lake Puye form	CB&S CGre CHan ERea GCal LHil LHop WAbe WCru

MITRASACME (Loganiaceae)

¶***pilosa***	ECou

MITRIOSTIGMA (Rubiaceae)

axillare	CNew

MNIUM See PLAGIOMNIUM

MODIOLA (Malvaceae)

¶***caroliniana***	EBee

MODIOLASTRUM (Malvaceae)

See Plant Deletions

MOEHRINGIA (Caryophyllaceae)

glaucovirens	MHig

MOLINIA (Gramineae/Poaceae)

altissima	See M. ***caerulea arundinacea***
caerulea	ECWi
§– ssp. ***arundinacea***	ECha EFou EPla ETPC SPer WPer
– – 'Bergfreund'	EHoe EMon EPla ETPC GCal
– – 'Fontäne'	EPla ETPC GCal
– – 'Karl Foerster'	EFou EHoe EPla GCal
– – 'Strahlenquelle'	EMon EPla ETPC GCal
– – 'Transparent'	EPla ETPC GCal
– – 'Windspiel'	ECha EHoe EPla ETPC GCal NHol WCot
– – 'Zuneigung'	ETPC
– ssp. ***caerulea*** 'Edith Dudszus'	EMon EPla
– – 'Heidebraut' (v)	ECha EHoe EMon EPla ETPC NHol
– – 'Moorhexe'	ECha EHoe EPla GCal
– – 'Variegata' AGM	Widely available
– 'Carmarthen' (v)	CNat
– 'Claerwen'	EPla GBuc GCal
– 'Edith Dudszus'	EHoe ETPC
litoralis	See M. ***caerulea arundinacea***

MOLOPOSPERMUM (Umbelliferae/Apiaceae)

peloponnesiacum ECoo LGre SSvw

MOLTKIA (Boraginaceae)

§ *doerfleri* CPle CSco
graminifolia See M. *suffruticosa*
§ x *intermedia* AGM CNic ELan LHil MWat NKay SIgm WOMN WOld WWin
petraea ECha GAul MWat SIgm SIng
§ *suffruticosa* LBee SIng

MONADENIUM (Euphorbiaceae)

lugardae MBri
ritchiei SGil
'Variegatum' MBri

MONARDA † (Labiatae/Lamiaceae)

'Adam' CDoC CSco ECED EFol EFou GAbr GCal MBri MSte NTow
'Aquarius' CGle CLTr ECha EFou EGle EMon LRHS MNFA SChu SMrm WCHb WMer WRus
'Beauty of Cobham' AGM CBos CBow CCla CGle CHad CHan ECha EFou EHal EOrc MBri MRav MSte MUlv MWat NFai NHol NRoo NSti SChu SHer SMad SMrm SPer WMer WRus WSun WWye
'Blaukranz' EFou
'Blaustrumpf' ('Blue Stocking') CAbb CBow CSco EBre EFou GAbr LBre MArl MSte NHol NOrc SHer SIde SPer WMer WSun
bradburyana CBot CBow CMil EMon SFis
'Cambridge Scarlet' AGM Widely available
'Capricorn' CGle EFou EMon GBuc LRHS SChu WCHb
'Cherokee' EFou EMon
citriodora CArn CBoy EEls EMon GPoy LHol MChe MHew MSal SHer SIde WPer WWye
'Commanche' EFou EMon SMrm
'Croftway Pink' AGM Widely available
'Dark Ponticum' EMon LRHS
didyma CArn CHan CSFH EHer Effi IEde LHol MChe MFir MHew MSal NBee SIde WGwy WHoo WOak WOld WSun
– 'Alba' CBot CBow EOrc GAbr LGan WWat
– 'Duddiscombe' CSam
¶ – 'Red Explode' CBoy
*– 'Variegata' WPer
'Donnerwolke' SChu
'Elsie's Lavender' CLTr ECoo EFou EMon GBuc
'Feuernschopf' ('Firecrown') CGle EBre LBre MSte
'Fishes' ('Pisces') CRDP ECha EFol EFou EHal EMon GCal MNFA MSte SChu SIde SMrm WCHb
fistulosa CArn ECro GPoy LHol MChe MHew MSal SIde WHer WPer WWye
'Hartswood Wine' LBlm
'Kardinal' CGle ECha EFou MNFA SIde SMrm
'Libra' EMon SChu WCHb WRus
'Loddon Crown' CRDP EFou EMon MNFA
'Mahogany' CDoC CMGP CSam EFou EGle EHic EMon LHop MMil MNFA NHol NSti SPer WWye
'Maiden's Pride' EMon
¶ 'Marshall's Delight' WMer
'Meereswogen' SAxl
I 'Melissa' CGle EFou EGle EHal MMil
menthifolia GCal LGre
'Mohawk' EFou EMon SIde SMrm
'Morgenröte' ECha SAxl
'Mrs Perry' EFou WMer
¶ 'Osage' EFou
'Ou Charm' EFou EMon SMrm WCHb
'Pale Ponticum' EMon
'Panorama' CBot ECtt EMil GCra LGan MBal MSal NFai NRoo SGil WPer WTyr
'Pawnee' EFou EMon SMrm
'Pink Tourmalin' MBri SMad
'Poyntzfield Pink' GPoy SChu
'Präriebrand' SUsu
'Prärienacht' ('Prairie Night') CBow CGle CSam CSev EBre ECha EFol ELan Effi LBre MBri MFir MRav MWat NHol NKay NRoo NVic SChu SGil SPer WEas WMer WOld WPer WRus WWin WWye
punctata CArn CBot CGle CHad CRDP ECro ELan EMon LGan LGre MSal NHol SIde WCHb WWye
¶ 'Purple Ann' EFou
'Sagittarius' ('Bowman') EMon LRHS SChu WCHb WRus
§ 'Schneewittchen' ('Snow White') CCla CRDP CSev EBre ECED ECha ECoo ECtt EGol ELan EMon EOrc LBre LHop MRav MWat NFai NHol NOrc NRoo NSti SChu SMrm SPer SUsu WEas WMer WRus WWin WWye
'Scorpion' ('Scorpio') CGle EFou EMon MSte SChu SMrm WCHb WRus
'Sioux' EFou EMon GBuc SMrm
'Snow Maiden' See M. 'Schneewittchen'
'Snow Queen' EFou
'Squaw' CGle CHan ECha EFou EGle EMon MNFA NCat NHol SChu SMrm SUsu WCot
stipitatoglandulosa ECro
'Talud' CGle EMon
'Thundercloud' EMon
'Twins' SAxl WMer
'Vintage Wine' CLTr ECtt EGle ELan EMon

MONARDELLA (Labiatae/Lamiaceae)

macrantha MTho SMrm
odoratissima NHol WPla
villosa LGan
¶ *viridis* EBee

MONOTOCA (Epacridaceae)

glauca GWht

MONSONIA † (Geraniaceae)

emarginata GCHN
speciosa CMon MHul

MONSTERA (Araceae)

deliciosa AGM MBri SRms

– 'Variegata' AGM MBri SRms

MONTBRETIA See CROCOSMIA, TRITONIA

MONTIA (Portulacaceae)

australasica See NEOPAXIA *a.*
♦*californica* See CLAYTONIA *nevadensis*
♦*parvifolia* See NAIOCRENE *p.*
perfoliata See CLAYTONIA *p.*
sibirica See CLAYTONIA *s.*

MORAEA (Iridaceae)

¶ *alticola* SBla
§ *aristata* LBow NRog
§ *bellendenii* LBow
fugax CMon WThi
gawleri CMon WThi
glaucopsis See M. *aristata*
huttonii CHan SBla
iridioïdes See DIETES *i.*
loubseri CMon LBow NRog
natalensis ESma
papilionacea WThi
pavonia var. *lutea* See M. *bellendenii*
polystachya NRog WThi
ramosissima CGre LBow WThi
spathacea See M. *spathulata*
§ *spathulata* CBro CGre CHan CMon GCal MFir MHig SBla WSHC
sp. SH 53 CHan
stricta WThi
tripetala WThi
vegeta WThi
villosa LBow NRog

MORINA (Morinaceae)

alba See ACANTHOCALYX *a.*
longifolia Widely available
persica WPla

MORISIA (Cruciferae/Brassicaceae)

hypogaea See M. *monanthos*
§ *monanthos* CLew CMea EPad LBee MHig NMen NTow NWCA
– 'Fred Hemingway' EBre EPot LBee LBre NHar NMen SBla SHer WAbe

MORUS (Moraceae)

§ *alba* CB&S CBra CChu CCla CGre CHEx CLnd EArb EHal EHar ELan ERea GTwe IOrc SHBN SPer WDin WMou WWat
– 'Black Tabor' LPan
– 'Globosa' See M. *a.* 'Nana'
– 'Laciniata' WMou
– 'Macrophylla' WMou
– var. *multicaulis* ERea
– 'Pendula' CBow CDoC CSco ELan ERea GTwe LHol LNet LPan MBlu MBri MWat NBee SEng SHBN SHil SPer WDin
bombycis See M. *alba*
F *nigra* AGM CArn CB&S CBow CBra CCla CHEx CLnd CMac CSco EBre EHar ELan EWar GRei GTwe LBre LBuc LHol LNet MBri MWat NElm SHBN SHil SKee WDin WHig WMou WNor WWat
F – 'Chelsea' EHar ERea
– 'King James' GTwe SPer
F – 'Wellington' CDoC LPan WDin
platanifolia MBri SEng
rubra CBow
– x *alba* 'Illinois Everbearing' ESim

MUEHLENBECKIA (Polygonaceae)

astonii ECou ELan ISea MUlv
§ *axillaris* CPle ECou EFol EPla ESis GAri IBar MUlv NCat NHol NTow SDry SHil WCru
complexa CB&S CDoC CGre CHEx CHan CPle ECou EFol EPla ESis ESma EWri IBlr ISea LBlm MAll MUlv NFai NRar SArc SBra SDry WCru WSHC WWat WWye
– 'Nana' See M. *axillaris*
– var. *trilobata* EPla GCal IBlr
ephedroïdes ECou MAll
– 'Clarence Pass' ECou
¶ – var. *muriculata* ECou
gunnii ECou
platyclada See HOMALOCLADIUM *platycladum*

MUHLENBERGIA (Gramineae/Poaceae)

japonica 'Cream Delight' (v) EFol EHoe

MUKDENIA (Saxifragaceae)

§ *rossii* CChu CElw CRDP ECro EPla SAxl WBon WCot WOld WSHC

MULBERRY See MORUS *nigra*

MUNDULEA (Leguminosae/Papilionaceae)

See Plant Deletions

MURBECKIELLA (Cruciferae/Brassicaceae)

pinnatifida GPlt

MURRAYA (Rutaceae)

♦*exotica* See M. *paniculata*
§ *paniculata* CNew CTro

MUSA (Musaceae)

F *acuminata* CTro LPal MBri
basjoo CB&S CHEx CTro SArc
§ *campbellii* Raffillii Group 'Dwarf Cavendish' AGM ELan
cavendishii See M. *acuminata* (AAA Group) 'Dwarf Cavendish'
ensete See ENSETE *ventricosum*
nana See M. *acuminata*

MUSCARI † (Liliaceae/Hyacinthaceae)

ambrosiacum	See M. ***muscarimi***
armeniacum AGM	CBro EPar ETub LBow MBri MWBu NRog WPer
– 'Argael Album'	CAvo LAma NEgg
– 'Blue Spike'	CBro EPar LAma LBow MBri MHlr MWBu NEgg NNrd NRog SIng WPer
– 'Early Giant'	LAma SIng
¶ – 'Fantasy Creation'	EPar
– 'Heavenly Blue'	LAma
– 'New Creation'	ETub SGil
– 'Saffier'	ETub LAma
§ *aucheri* AGM	CAvo CBro CNic EPar LAma NRog SIng WThu
§ *azureum* AGM	CAvo CBro CNic ELan LAma MHlr NMen NRog WAbe WHil
– 'Album'	CAvo CBro EPar ETub LAma MHlr NRog WAbe
– 'Amphibolis'	ETub
botryoïdes	LAma NRog
– 'Album'	CAvo CBro ELan ETub LAma LBow MBri MWBu NRog SIng
caucasicum	WChr
chalusicum BSBE	See M. ***pseudomuscari*** BSBE
§ *comosum*	CAvo CBro EPar WPer
– 'Monstrosum'	See M. ***c.*** 'Plumosum'
§ – 'Plumosum'	CAvo CBro ELan EMon EPar ETub LAma LBow MBri MWBu NNrd SIng
grandifolium populeum AB&S 5357	CMon
inconstrictum S&L 19/20	CMon
latifolium	CAvo CBow CBro CMon EPar ETub LAma NRog WHil WPer
§ *macrocarpum*	CAvo CBro EPot LAma LBow SPou WChr WThu
moschatum	See M. ***muscarimi***
§ *muscarimi*	CAvo CBro EPar ETub LAma LBow NHol SIng WChr
– *flavum*	See M. ***macrocarpum***
– 'Major'	LBow
§ *neglectum*	ELan ETub LAma SIng WShi
– B&S 349	CMon
pallens	CMon
paradoxum	See BELLEVALIA ***pycnantha***
§ *pseudomuscari* AGM	CMon WChr
racemosum	See M. ***neglectum***
'Sky Blue'	WChr
spreitzenhoferi MS 712	CMon
tenuiflorum S&L 91	CMon
tubergenianum	See M. ***aucheri***
'White Beauty'	WChr

MUSCARIMIA (Liliaceae/Hyacinthaceae)

ambrosiacum	See MUSCARI ***muscarimi***
macrocarpum	See MUSCARI ***macrocarpum***

MUSSCHIA (Campanulaceae)

wollastonii	CHEx SIgm

MUTISIA (Compositae/Asteraceae)

clematis	CGre
coccinea	EOvi
decurrens	CB&S CHEx IBlr MSto SIgm
ilicifolia	CBow CMac EOvi IBlr MSto SDry WMar WSHC
oligodon	CGre CHEx CHan EOvi IBlr
retusa	See M. ***spinosa pulchella***
spinosa	CGre MSto
¶ – JCA 12451	LGre
§ – *pulchella*	EOvi
¶ *subulata*	MSto
¶ – JJA 12668	CRDP

MYOPORUM (Myoporaceae)

acuminatum	See M. ***tenuifolium***
debile	ECou
¶ *insulare*	CPle
laetum	CHEx CPle ECou
§ *tenuifolium*	CPle

MYOSOTIDIUM (Boraginaceae)

§ *hortensia*	CBos CHEx CPla CRDP CTre CTro IBlr LHop SHer SIgm WCot WCru
nobile	See M. ***hortensia***

MYOSOTIS (Boraginaceae)

alpestris 'Ruth Fischer'	MSto NMen NNrd NTow
arvensis	EWFC
australis	CNic GGar GTou NBro NHol NMen NNrd WEas WHil
colensoi	CElw ECou ELan EMon EPot MHig MRPP MTho NHol NKay NNrd NWCA SCro WAbe
elderi	CBot
explanata	NMen SHer WCot WEas
palustris	See M. ***scorpioïdes***
'Popsy'	ECou
pulvinaris	GCHN
rakiura	EMar GAbr GTou WCla WPer
rehsteineri	MSto SIng
rupicola	See M. ***alpestris***
§ *scorpioïdes*	CBen CBre CRDP CRow CWGN ECWi ECoo EHon ELan EWFC EWav LMay MHew MSta NDea SHig SWat SWyc WChe WEas WHol
– 'Mermaid'	CBen CMGP CNic CRiv CRow EBre ECha EFol GMac ILis LBre LHop MFir MSta NBrk NCat NHol NSti SDix SWat WCru WPer WWin
– 'Pinkie'	CBre CRDP CRow SWat
secunda	CKin
¶ *suavis*	WCot
sylvatica alba	CRow WBon

MYOSURUS (Ranunculaceae)

See Plant Deletions

MYRCEUGENIA (Myrtaceae)

¶ *chrysocarpa*	CGre

MYRICA (Myricaceae)

californica	CFil GAri SLon SSta
gale	CDoC GAri GPoy LHol MGos MUlv SIde SWat WDin WWye
pensylvanica	CCla LHol MAll MBal

MYRICARIA (Tamaricaceae)
See Plant Deletions

MYRIOPHYLLUM (Haloragaceae)

§ ***aquaticum***	CHEx CRiv CRow CWGN EBre EHon ELan EMFW LBre LMay MSta NDea SHig SMad SWat SWyc WChe
brasiliense	See M. ***aquaticum***
proserpinacoïdes	See M. ***aquaticum***
spicatum	CBen EHon EMFW NMir SAWi SWyc WChe
verticillatum	CBen EHon

MYRRHIS (Umbelliferae/Apiaceae)

odorata	CArn CBre CHad CKin CLew CRDP CSFH CSev ECha EHer EJud ELan EWFC GPoy IEde ILis LHol MChe MHew MSal NHol SIde WByw WEas WHal WHer WNdy WOak WWye
– 'Forncett Chevron'	EFou

MYRSINE (Myrsinaceae)

africana	CPle CTre SArc WCru WWat
nummularia	ECou

MYRTEOLA (Myrtaceae)

§ ***nummularia***	CMHG EPot GAbr GArf GAri GDra ITim MBal MHig NHar SIng

MYRTUS (Myrtaceae)

apiculata	See LUMA ***apiculata***
bullata	See LOPHOMYRTUS ***bullata***
chequen	See LUMA ***chequen***
communis **AGM**	Widely available
*– ***citrifolia***	SArc
– 'Flore Pleno'	CDoC CSco LHol MPla
– 'Jenny Reitenbach'	See M. ***c. tarentina***
– 'Microphylla'	See M. ***c. tarentina***
– 'Nana'	See M. ***c. tarentina***
§ – ssp. ***tarentina*** **AGM**	CB&S CHan CLan CMHG CPle CSco CShe ELan ENot ERav EWri ISea LHol LHop MBal MBri NWyt SArc SLMG SLon SPer SReu STre WDin WEas WOak WWat
– – 'Compacta'	WWye
§ – – 'Microphylla Variegata'	CHan CMHG CPle EJud ELan EPla ERav LHol LHop MBal MPla SArc SLMG WOak WSHC WWat
– 'Tricolor'	See M. ***c.*** 'Variegata'
– 'Variegata'	CArn CBot CMCN COtt CWit ECtt ERav EWri LHop SDry SHBN SHer SLMG SLon SPer SPla STre WCru WStI WWat WWye
'Glanleam Gold'	See LUMA ***apiculata*** 'Glanleam Gold'
lechleriana	See AMOMYRTUS ***luma***
luma	See LUMA ***apiculata***
nummularia	See MYRTEOLA ***n.***
obcordata	See LOPHOMYRTUS ***o.***
x ***ralphii***	See LOPHOMYRTUS x ***r.***
'Traversii'	See LOPHOMYRTUS x ***ralphii*** 'Traversii'
ugni	See UGNI ***molinae***

NAIOCRENE (Portulacaceae)

§ ***parvifolia***	CLew CNic

NANDINA (Berberidaceae)

domestica **AGM**	CB&S CBot CBow CDoC CGre CPle CSam ELan GWht IBar IOrc ISea LAbb LHop LPan MBri MUlv NKay NRog SMad SPla SReu SSta WBod WDin WSHC WStI WWat
– 'Firepower'	CB&S CBow CDoC CSco EBre ECtt ELan ENot EPla GAri IBar IOrc LBre LHop LNet MGos MUlv NHol SHBN SHer SPer SSta WAbe WHig WWat
– 'Harbor Dwarf'	EPla WWat
– 'Nana'	See N. ***d.*** 'Pygmaea'
– 'Nana Purpurea'	EPla
§ – 'Pygmaea'	CBra CSam GAri WDin
– 'Richmond'	CB&S CDoC EBre ELan EPla LBre MBlu MGos MMea MUlv SHBN SPer
– 'Wood's Dwarf'	CB&S GAri

NANNORRHOPS (Palmae/Arecaceae)

ritchieana	LPal

NARCISSUS † (Liliaceae/Amaryllidaceae)

'Abalone' (2)	EWal
'Accent' (2)	ICar
'Acclamation' (4)	EWal
'Accolade' (3)	ECop
¶ 'Accord' (2)	ICar
'Achduart' (3)	ECop GEve ICar IDun
'Achentoul' (4)	ICar
'Achnasheen' (3)	GEve ICar
'Acropolis' (4)	ECop EWal ICar LAma
'Actaea' **AGM**	ETub MBri MWBu NRog SIng
'Affable' (4)	ICar
'Aflame' (3)	LAma MBri
¶ 'Ahwahnee' (2)	IDun
'Aircastle' (3)	IBal ICar
¶ 'Akepa' (5)	ICar
'Albus Plenus Odoratus'	See N. ***poeticus*** 'Plenus'
'Algarve' (2)	IDun
'Alliance' (1)	EWal
alpestris	See N. ***pseudonarcissus moschatus***
– MS 571	CMon
'Alpha' (9)	EWal
'Altruist' (3)	EWal IDun
'Amber Light' (2)	EWal
'Ambercastle' (2)	ECop ICar IDun
'Ambergate' (2)	EWal GEve LAma
'Amberglow' (2)	EWal
'Amboseli' (3)	IDun
'Amor' (3)	EWal
'Andalusia' (6)	ECop ICar SIng
'Androcles' (4)	ICar IDun
¶ 'Angel' (3)	ICar
* 'Angel Wings' (5)	ICar
Angel's Tears	See N. ***triandrus triandrus***
'Angkor' (4)	ICar

'Ann Abbott' (2)	EWal
'Annalong' (3)	IBal
'Anniversary' (2)	EWal
'Anthea' (2)	EWal
¶ 'Apostle' (1)	ICar
'Apotheose' (4)	EWal
'Apricot' (1)	CBro
'Apricot Sundae' (4)	ICar
'April Charm' (2)	ICar
'April Love' (1)	ECop IBal ICar IDun
'April Snow' (2)	CBro
'April Tears' (5)	CCla EWal LAma NRog SIng
'Aranjuez' (2)	LAma
'Arbar' (2)	EWal
'Arcady' (2)	EWal
'Arctic Char' (2)	ICar
'Arctic Gold' **AGM**	ECop ICar
'Ardbane' (2)	ICar
'Ardglass' (3)	GEve IBal ICar
'Ardour' (3)	ICar
'Ardress' (2)	IDun
'Arish Mell' (5)	ECop EWal ICar IDun
¶ 'Arizona Sunset' (3)	IDun
'Arkle' (1)	ECop GEve ICar
¶ 'Armley Wood' (2)	ICar
'Armynel' (2)	EWal
'Arndilly' (2)	ECop
'Arpege' (2)	ECop
'Artillery' (3)	EWal
¶ 'Asante' (1)	IDun
'Ashmore' (2)	ICar IDun
¶ 'Ashwell' (3)	ECop
'Aslan' (4)	ICar
'Aspasia' (8)	CBro
§ ***assoanus***	CBro EPar LAma
– MS 582/581/511	CMon
– var. ***praelongus*** MS 656	CMon
§ ***asturiensis***	CBro CRDP ELan EPar EPot IBlr LAma MBal MWBu WChr WHil WPat
– 'Fuente De'	WChr
*– 'Giant'	EPot ETub
'Atholl Palace' (4)	IDun
atlanticus	SPou WChr
'Attrus' (2)	EWal
'Audubon' (3)	EWal
'Avalanche' (8)	EWal GEve
'Avalon' (2)	IDun
¶ 'Ave' (2)	ICar
'Avenger' (2)	ECop ICar
'Ayston' (2)	ECop
'Baby Doll' (6)	EWal ICar
'Baby Moon' (7)	CCla ELan EPar EPot ETub LAma MBri MWBu NRog SIng WPat
'Baccarat' (11)	EWal ICar LAma MBri
'Badbury Rings' (3)	ECop IDun
baeticus	See N. ***assoanus praelongus***
'Bailey' (2)	ICar
¶ 'Baldock' (4)	IDun
'Ballyarnett' (1)	ICar
'Ballycastle' (3)	ICar
'Ballyfrema' (1)	ICar
'Ballygarvey' (1)	EWal
¶ 'Ballylig' (1)	ICar
¶ 'Ballylough' (1)	ICar
'Ballynichol' (3)	IBal

'Ballyrobert' (1)	ECop
'Ballytrim' (2)	ICar
'Baltic Shore' (3)	IBal
'Balvenie' (2)	ECop IDun
'Bambi' (1)	CBro NRog
'Banbridge' (1)	IBal ICar
¶ 'Bandesara' (3)	IDun
'Bandleader' (2)	EWal
'Bantam' **AGM**	CBro EWal
'Barley Sugar' (3)	ICar
'Barleygold' (2)	IBal
'Barleythorpe' (1)	EWal
¶ 'Barnesgold' (1)	IDun
'Barnsdale Wood' (2)	ECop
¶ 'Barnum' (1)	IDun
'Baronscourt' (1)	ICar
'Barrett Browning' (3)	ETub MBri MWBu NRog
'Bartley' (6)	EWal
'Bastion' (1)	EWal
'Beauvallon' (4)	ECop IDun
'Bebop' (7)	CBro
'Beefeater' (2)	EWal
'Beersheba' (1)	MBri
'Beige Beauty' (3)	EWal ICar
'Belisana' (2)	LAma
'Bell Song' (7)	CBro ETub EWal WShi
'Beltrim' (2)	ICar
'Ben Bhraggie' (2)	GEve
'Ben Vorlich' (2)	ICar
'Berkeley Court' (4)	IDun
'Bermuda' (2)	EWal
'Berry Gorse' (3)	ECop
bertolonii	CMon
'Beryl' (6)	CBro EWal ICar LAma LBow
'Best of Luck' (3)	IBal
'Bethany' (2)	EWal
'Big John' (1)	IDun
'Bilbo' (6)	IDun
'Binkie' (2)	CBro EWal LAma MBri
'Birichen' (2)	GEve
'Birma' (3)	EWal LAma MBri MWBu
'Birthday Girl' (2)	IDun
'Birthright' (1)	EWal
'Biscayne' **AGM**	EWal
'Bishopstone' (1)	ICar
'Bithynia' (3)	EWal
'Bittern' (2)	ICar
'Bizerta' (2)	EWal
'Blarney' (3)	EWal
'Blessing' (2)	EWal
'Blue Bird' (2)	EWal
'Bob Minor' (1)	EWal
'Bobbysoxer' (7)	CBro EWal ICar LAma
'Bodilly' (2)	EWal
'Bonamargy' (2)	ICar
¶ 'Border Beauty' (2)	IDun
'Border Chief' (2)	ICar
'Borrobol' (2)	ECop
'Bossa Nova' (3)	IDun
'Boudoir' (1)	ICar
'Bowles' Early Sulphur' (1)	CRow
'Bracken Hill' (2)	ICar
'Braddock' (3)	IBal
'Brandaris' (11)	GEve
'Brave Journey' (2)	ICar

'Bravoure' AGM EWal
'Breakthrough' (2) EWal
'Bridal Crown' (4) EWal LAma
'Bridesmaid' (2) IBal
¶ 'Brierglass' (2) ECop
'Brigton' (1) LAma
¶ 'Brilliant Star' (11) GEve
'Broadland' (2) ECop
'Broadway Star' (11) EWal LAma
¶ 'Brodick' (2) IDun
'Brookdale' (1) IDun
'Broomhill' (2) ECop
¶ ***broussonetii*** CFil
– SF 269 CMon
'Brunswick' (2) EWal LAma WShi
'Bryanston' (2) ECop IDun
'Bryher' (3) ICar
'Buffawn' (7) EWal
'Bulbarrow' (2) IDun
bulbocodium CBro CFil CRiv ETub LBee LBow NHol NWCA SBla WCla WPer
– ssp. ***bulbocodium*** CBro WChr
– – var. ***citrinus*** MS&S
– – var. ***conspicuus*** CAvo CBro CRDP CSam CVer EPar EPot LAma MBal MBri MS&S MWBu NRog NRya SIng WChr WHil WPat WShi
¶ – – var. ***graellsii*** WChr
– – var. ***graellsii*** MS 567/408 CMon
– – var. ***tenuifolius*** CMon CRDP EPot LAma MS&S SIng SPou
– – var. ***tenuifolius*** S &B 189 CMon
*– ***filifolius*** CBro
– ssp. ***genuinus*** SF 177/180 CMon
– ssp. ***mairei*** SF 181 CMon
– var. ***mesatlanticus*** See N. ***romieuxii m.***
– ssp. ***praecox*** var. ***paucinervis*** WChr
– ***tananicus*** See N. ***tananicus***
– ssp. ***viriditubus*** MS 453 CMon
'Bullseye' (3) EWal
'Bunclody' (2) ECop ICar
'Buncrana' (2) ECop
'Bunting' (7) ICar IDun
'Burgemeester Gouverneur' (1) LAma
'Burma Star' (2) ICar
¶ 'Burning Bush' (3) IDun
'Burning Heart' (11) EWal
'Burntollet' (1) IDun
'Bushmills' (3) ICar
'Buster' (2) EWal
'Buttercup' (7) CBro
¶ 'Butterscotch' (2) ICar
'By Jove' (1) EWal
'Cabra' (1) ICar
'Cadence' (3) ICar
'Cairn Toul' (3) ECop
'Cairndhu' (2) ICar
'Cairngorm' (2) ICar
'Calabar' (2) EWal
calcicola B&S 413 CMon
– MS 450 CMon
¶ 'California Rose' (4) IDun
'Callaway' (3) ICar
'Camelot' (2) EWal
'Campion' (9) GEve IDun
canaliculatus See N. ***tazetta lacticolor***
'Canaliculatus' (8) CBro CMon EPar ETub LAma LBow MBri SIng WPer
'Canarybird' (8) CBro
'Candida' (4) EWal
'Canisp' (2) ECop GEve ICar
'Cantabile' (9) CBro ECop IBal SIng
¶ ***cantabricus*** CFil
– ssp. ***cantabricus*** CRiv WChr
– ssp. ***cantabricus*** SF 396 CMon
– – var. ***foliosus*** CAvo EPot SPou WChr
– – var. ***foliosus*** SF 284/2 CMon
– – var. ***petunioïdes*** LAma
¶ – – var. ***petunioïdes*** S&F 365/2 CMon
¶ – ***eualbidus*** S&F 362 CMon
¶ – ***eualbidus*** S&F 385 CMon
¶ – forms SPou
– ssp. ***monophyllus*** var. ***laciniatus*** CMon
'Canticle' (9) IBal
'Cape Cool' (2) ICar
'Capisco' (3) IBal
'Carbineer' (2) LAma
¶ 'Carlingford' (2) IBal
'Carlton' (2) ETub LAma MBri MWBu NRog
'Carnearny' (3) ICar
'Caro Nome' (2) EWal
¶ 'Carson Pass' (2) IDun
'Caruso' (2) LAma
'Cassata' (11) EWal LAma NBir NRog
'Casterbridge' (2) IDun
'Castle Dobbs' (4) ICar
'Castlehill' (3) IBal
¶ 'Cauldron' (2) IDun
¶ 'Cavendish' (4) IDun
'Cavoda' (1) or (2) ICar
'Cedric Morris' (10) CBro ECop SWas
'Celtic Song' (2) ECop
'Cernuus Plenus' (4) ICar
'Ceylon' (2) EWal LAma
'Chablis' (11) GEve
'Chania' (1) ICar
'Chanterelle' (11) EWal ICar LAma NRog
'Charity May' AGM CBro EWal IBal ICar LAma MBri NRog SIng
'Charleston' (2) IDun
'Charter' AGM EWal
'Chat' (7) ICar
'Cheer Leader' (3) GEve IDun
'Cheerfulness' (4) ETub EWal LAma MBri MWBu NRog SIng
¶ 'Chemeketa' (2) IDun
'Chérie' (7) CBro
'Cherrygardens' (2) ECop
'Chesterton' (9) IDun
'Chickerell' (3) IDun
'Chief Inspector' (1) IDun
'Chig' (2) EWal

¶ 'Chilmark' (3) IDun
'Chinchilla' (2) IDun
'Chinese Sacred Lily' (8) ETub MWBu
'Chinese White' (3) ICar
'Chinita' (8) CBro EWal
'Chit Chat' CBro
'Chivalry' (1) EWal
'Churchfield' (2) ICar
'Churchman' (2) IBal ICar
'Clady Cottage' (2) ICar
'Clare' (7) CBro
¶ 'Claridges' (4) IDun
'Clashmore' (2) GEve
'Clockface' (3) EWal
¶ 'Close Encounter' (2) ICar
'Cloud Nine' (2) CBro EWal
¶ 'Cloud's Hill' (4) IDun
'Colblanc' (11) ICar
'Collector's Choice' (3) ICar
'Colloggett' (2) ECop
'Coloratura' (3) ICar
'Colour Sergeant' (2) IBal
'Colston Bassett' (3) IBal
'Columbus' (2) ICar
'Como' (9) GEve
compressus See N. x ***intermedius***
§ ***concolor*** CBro EPot MBal MS&S SIng
'Conestoga' (2) IBal
'Congress' (11) EWal
'Connor' (2) ICar
'Cool Crystal' (3) ECop ICar IDun
'Coolattin' (2) ICar
'Cophetua' (1) ICar
'Copper Nob' (2) IBal
'Cora Ann' (7) CBro
'Coral Fair' (2) IBal
'Coral Light' (2) ICar
'Corbridge' (2) EWal
cordubensis WChr
– MS 434 CMon
'Corinthian' (1) LAma
'Cornerstone' (2) EWal
'Coromandel' (2) IDun
¶ 'Cosmic Dance' (3) IDun
'Country Morning' (3) ICar
'Coverack Perfection' (2) EWal
'Crackington' (4) ECop IDun
'Cragford' (8) EWal LAma
¶ 'Craigarusky' (2) IBal
'Craigdun' (2) ICar
'Craigywarren' (2) EWal
'Creagh Dubh' (2) ICar IDun
'Crenelet' (2) IDun
'Crimson Chalice' (3) IDun
'Crinoline' (2) EWal
'Cristobal' (1) ECop
'Crock of Gold' (2) EWal
'Croila' (2) ECop
'Crown Royalist' (2) IBal
'Cryptic' (2) IDun
'Crystal River' (3) EWal
cuatrecasasii CMon WChr
– MS 429 CMon
– var. ***segimonensis*** MS 559 CMon
¶ 'Cuesta' (2) IDun
¶ 'Cupid's Eye' (2) IDun
'Cushendall' (3) EWal ICar
cyclamineus AGM CBro CFil CNic EPot LAma NRog SBla SIng SWas
'Cyros' (1) IDun
'Dailmanach' (2) ECop IDun
¶ 'Daiquiri' (3) ICar
'Dalliance' (2) ICar
'Dancer' (2) EWal
'Dancing Partner' (2) EWal
'Danes Balk' (2) ICar
* 'Darlow Dale' (2) ECop
'Dateline' (3) IDun
¶ 'Daviot' (2) ICar
'Davlyn' (2) EWal
'Davochfin Lass' (1) GEve
'Dawn' (5) CBro
'Dawn Mist' (2) EWal
¶ 'Dawn Run' (2) IDun
'Daydream' (2) ECop EWal ICar IDun LAma
'Decoy' (2) ICar
'Delia' (6) IDun
'Delibes' (2) LAma
¶ 'Dell Chapel' (3) ICar
'Delnashaugh' (4) ICar
'Delos' (3) IDun
'Delphin Hill' (4) IBal
¶ 'Delta Flight' (6) IDun
'Delta Wings' (6) IDun
¶ 'Demand' (2) ICar
'Derryboy' (3) IBal
'Descanso' (1) ECop EWal
'Desdemona' (2) EWal NRog
'Desert Orchid' (2) IBal
'Desert Rose' (2) ICar
¶ 'Diatone' (4) IDun
'Dick Wilden' (4) ETub EWal LAma MWBu
'Dickcissel' (7) CBro ICar
¶ 'Dimple' (9) IDun
'Dinkie' (3) CBro
¶ 'Discovery' (4) ICar
'Diversion' (3) ICar
'Divertimento' (7) ICar
'Doctor Alexander Fleming' (2) EWal
'Doctor Hugh' (3) EWal IDun
'Dolly Mollinger' (11) EWal ICar LAma
'Don Carlos' (2) ICar IDun
¶ 'Dorchester' (4) IDun
'Double Blush' (4) ICar
'Double Fashion' (4) EWal
'Doubtful' (3) ICar
'Dove of Peace' (6) IBal
'Dove Wings' AGM CBro EWal IBal ICar LAma SIng
'Dovekie' (12) ICar
'Dover Cliffs' (2) ECop
'Downpatrick' (1) ECop ICar
'Dream Castle' (3) EWal ICar
'Drenagh' (2) ICar
'Drumadarragh' (1) ICar
'Drumawillan' (2) ICar
¶ 'Drumboe' (2) ECop
'Drumnabreeze' (2) ICar

'Drumrunie' (2)	ICar
dubius var. ***dubius***	
MS 512	CMon
'Duet' (4)	EWal
¶ 'Dunkery' (4)	IDun
'Dutch Master' (1)	ETub EWal LAma MBri MWBu NRog
'Dynamite' (2)	EWal
¶ 'Earendil' (2)	IDun
'Early Blossom' (1)	IBal ICar
'Early Splendour' (8)	LAma
¶ 'East Wind' (1)	ICar
'Easter Bonnet' (2)	LAma
'Easter Moon' (2)	ICar
'Eaton Park' (3)	IDun
'Eaton Song' (12)	ECop
¶ 'Eclat' (2)	ICar
'Edge Grove' (2)	ICar
'Edwalton' (2)	ECop
'Edward Buxton' (3)	LAma MBri
'Egard' (11)	EWal
'Egg Nog' (4)	ICar
'Eland' (7)	IDun
'Eleanor Rose' (2)	IBal
elegans var. ***elegans***	
SF 316	CMon
– var. ***fallax*** S&L 324	CMon
'Elf' (2)	CBro
'Elfin Gold' (6)	IDun
'Elizabeth Ann' (6)	IDun
'Elka' (1)	IBal ICar
'Elphin' (4)	ICar
'Elrond' (6)	IDun
¶ 'Elven Lady' (2)	IDun
'Elvira' (8)	CBro
'Elwing' (6)	IDun
'Elysian Fields' (2)	EWal
'Embo' (2)	GEve
'Emily' (2)	IBal ICar
'Eminent' (3)	EWal
'Empress of Ireland' **AGM**	ECop EWal IBal IDun
'Englander' (6)	EPot
'Entrancement' (1)	EWal
'Eribol' (2)	GEve
'Eriskay' (4)	GEve
'Eskylane' (2)	ICar
'Estio Pinza' (2)	EWal
'Estrella' (3)	ECop
'Estremadura' (2)	ICar IDun
¶ 'Ethereal Beauty' (2)	IDun
¶ 'Ethos' (1)	IDun
'Evelix' (2)	GEve
'Evendine' (2)	EWal
¶ 'Everglades' (4)	IDun
¶ 'Exalted' (2)	ICar
'Exemplar' (1)	EWal
¶ 'Explosion' (8)	IDun
'Eyecatcher' (3)	ICar
'Eystettensis' (4)	CBro ECha
'Fair Head' (9)	IBal
'Fair Prospect' (2)	ICar IDun
'Fairgreen' (3)	ICar
'Fairlight Glen' (2)	ECop
'Fairmile' (3)	LAma
'Fairsel' (3)	IBal
¶ 'Fairy Chimes' (5)	CBro
'Fairy Footsteps' (3)	IBal ICar
'Fairy Island' (3)	ICar
'Fairy Spell' (3)	IBal
'Falconet' (8)	CBro IDun
'Falstaff' (2)	EWal ICar IDun
'Fanad Head' (9)	IBal
'Far Country' (2)	GEve ICar
'Faraway' (3)	IBal ICar
'Faro' (1)	IBal
'Farranfad' (2)	IBal
'Favor Royal' (3)	IBal
'Favourite' (2)	EWal
'February Gold' **AGM**	CAvo CBro EPar ETub EWal IBal LAma LBow MBri MWBu NRog SIng WPer WShi
'February Silver' (6)	CBro EPar ETub EWal LAma LBow NRog SIng
'Feeling Lucky' **AGM**	EWal
'Felindre' (9)	EWal IBal
'Fellowship' (2)	GEve
'Fergie' (2)	EWal
fernandesii (10)	CBro CMon EHic SPou WChr
'Ferndown' (3)	ECop IDun
'Festivity' (2)	ECop EWal ICar
'Fiji' (4)	ECop ICar
'Filly' (2)	EWal
'Finchcocks' (2)	ECop
'Fionn' (2)	GEve ICar
'Fire Flash' (2)	ICar
'Fire Raiser' (2)	ICar
'Firestorm' (2)	IBal
'Firgrove' (3)	ICar
'First Date' (3)	ICar
'Flaming Meteor' (2)	ICar
'Flirt ' (6)	ICar
'Flomay' (7)	CBro
'Florida Manor' (3)	IBal
'Flower Carpet' (1)	LAma
'Flower Drift' (4)	LAma MWBu
'Flower Record' (2)	ETub LAma
* 'Flowerdream'	LAma
'Flycatcher' (7)	IDun
'Flying Saucer' (2)	EWal
¶ 'Focal Point' (2)	ICar
'Fool's Gold' (4)	ICar
'Foray' (2)	EWal
'Foresight' (1)	ICar LAma WShi
'Forge Mill' (2)	ICar
'Fort Knox' (1)	EWal
'Fortune' (2)	EWal LAma MWBu NRog
'Foundling' (6)	CBro ECop EWal IBal ICar IDun SIng
'Fount' (2)	ICar
'Foxfire' (2)	ICar
'Fragrant Breeze'	EWal
'Fragrant Rose' (2)	EWal ICar IDun
'Frank's Fancy' (9)	IBal
'Frigid' (3)	IBal ICar
'Frolic' (2)	EWal
'Front Royal' (2)	ECop ICar
¶ 'Frostkist' (6)	CBro
'Frou-Frou' (4)	ICar
'Fuego' (2)	ICar
'Fulwell' (4)	IDun
¶ 'Furnace Creek' (2)	IDun
'Gabriël Kleiberg' (11)	ICar
gaditanus (10)	CBro CMon

– MS 526/633	CMon
'Gainsborough' (2)	ICar
'Galway' (2)	EWal
'Ganaway' (3)	IBal
'Garden News' (3)	IDun
'Garden Princess' (6)	CBro LAma
'Gay Kybo' (4)	ECop IDun
'Gay Mood' (2)	EWal
'Gay Song' (4)	ICar
'Gay Time' (4)	EWal
'George's Pink' (2)	ICar
'Georgie Girl' (6)	IDun
'Geranium' (8)	CBro ETub EWal LAma MBri MWBu NRog SIng
'Gettysburg' (2)	IDun
'Gigantic Star' (2)	EWal LAma MBri
'Gilda' (2)	IBal
'Gilford' (3)	ICar
'Gimli' (6)	IDun
'Gin and Lime' (1)	ICar IDun
'Gipsy Moth' (2)	ICar
'Gipsy Queen' (1)	ICar
'Glad Day' (2)	ICar
¶ 'Glasnevin' (2)	ICar
'Glaston' (2)	ICar
'Glenamoy' (1)	ICar
'Glencraig' (2)	ICar
'Glendermott' (2)	ICar
'Glenfarclas' (1/2)	ICar
'Glenganagh' (4)	ICar
'Glorious' (8)	IBal
'Glory of Lisse' (9)	CBro
'Glowing Embers' (2)	ICar
¶ 'Gold Bond' (2)	IDun
'Gold Bullion' (1)	ICar
'Gold Convention' (2)	IDun
'Gold Medal' (1)	EWal LAma
'Gold Medallion' (1)	IBal
'Gold Mine' (2)	IBal
'Gold Phantom' (1)	ICar
'Gold Strike' (1)	ICar
'Golden Amber' (2)	IBal ICar IDun
'Golden Aura' (2)	ECop EWal IBal ICar IDun
¶ 'Golden Bear' (4)	IDun
'Golden Ducat' (4)	EWal ICar LAma MBri NRog
'Golden Halo' (2)	IBal ICar
'Golden Harvest' (1)	ETub LAma MBri MWBu NRog
'Golden Jewel' (2)	ECop GEve ICar IDun
'Golden Joy' (2)	ICar IDun
'Golden Orchid' (11)	LAma
'Golden Perfection' (7)	LAma
'Golden Radiance' (1)	IBal
'Golden Ranger' (2)	IDun
'Golden Riot' (1)	EWal
'Golden Sheen' (2)	IDun
'Golden Showers' (1)	IBal
'Golden Sovereign' (1)	IBal
'Golden Strand' (2)	IBal
'Golden Topaz' (2)	IBal
'Golden Vale' (1)	ECop
'Golden Wings' (6)	IBal
'Goldfinger' (1)	IDun
¶ 'Goldsithney' (2)	CBro
'Golly' (4)	EWal
'Good Measure' (2)	EWal
'Goose Green' (3)	IBal
'Gossamer' (3)	EWal
'Gouache'	EWal
'Gourmet' (1)	LAma
¶ 'Grace Note' (3)	ICar
gracilis	See N. x ***tenuior***
'Gracious Lady' (2)	IDun
'Grand Prospect' (2)	IBal
'Grand Soleil d'Or' (8)	ETub LAma MWBu NRog
'Gransha' (3)	IBal
'Grapillon' (11)	GEve
'Great Expectations' (2)	IBal
'Green Glens' (2)	ICar
'Green Gold' (2)	EWal
'Green Howard' (3)	ECop
¶ 'Green Lodge' (9)	IBal
* 'Green Orchid'	LAma
'Green Rival' (2)	EWal
'Greenfinch' (3)	ICar
'Greenpark' (9)	IBal
'Greenstar' (4)	EWal
'Greenvale' (2)	IDun
'Greeting' (2)	ECop
'Gresham' (4)	IDun
'Grey Lady' (3)	ICar
'Grosvenor' (4)	IDun
'Halley's Comet' (3)	ECop IDun
'Halolight' (2)	EWal
'Halstock' (2)	IDun
'Halvose' (8)	CBro
'Hambledon' (2)	ECop GEve IDun
'Hammoon' (3)	EWal
'Happy Face' (2)	ICar
¶ 'Harmony Bells' (5)	ICar
'Hawaii' (4)	IBal
'Hawera' (5)	CAvo CBro CCla EPar EPot ETub EWal LAma LBow MBri MBro MWBu NRog SIng WHil WPat WPer
'Hazel Rutherford' (2)	GEve
'Hazel Winslow' (2)	IDun
'Heart's Desire' (4)	EWal
'Heat Haze' (2)	ICar
¶ ***hedraeanthus***	EPot
– MS 543/419	CMon
henriquesii	See N. ***jonquilla h.***
'Hero' (1)	EWal IDun
'Hesla' (7)	ICar
'High Note' (7)	EWal
'High Society' (2)	EWal IDun
'Highfield Beauty' (8)	ECop EWal IDun
'Highland Wedding' (2)	ICar
¶ 'Highlite' (2)	ICar
'Highway Song' (2)	ICar
'Hilford' (2)	IBal
'Hill Head' (9)	IBal
'Hilltown' (2)	IBal
'Holbeck' (4)	IDun
'Holiday Fashion' (2)	EWal
'Holland Sensation' (1)	LAma
'Holly Berry' (2)	ICar
'Hollypark' (3)	IBal
'Homage' (2)	EWal
'Home Fires' (2)	ETub
'Honeybird' (1)	ECop EWal ICar
'Hoopoe' (8)	CBro ICar
'Hope' (4)	EWal
'Horace' (9)	ICar

'Hors d'Oeuvre' (8) CBro
'Hot Toddy' (4) ICar
'Hotspur' (2) ICar
'Howard's Way' (3) IBal
**humilis humilis*
AB&S 4301 CMon
*– **mauretanicus** SF 260 CMon
'Ibberton' (3) ECop
'Ibis' (6) CBro
'Ice Follies' AGM ETub EWal LAma MBri MWBu NRog
'Ice King' (4) EWal
'Ice Wings' (5) CBro EWal IDun SIng
¶ 'Immaculate' (2) ICar
'Indian Maid' (7) ICar
'Inglescombe' (4) LAma
'Initiation' (1) ICar
'Innis Beg' (2) ICar
'Innisfree' (3) ICar
'Inniswood' (1) ICar
'Interim' (2) EWal ICar
x ***intermedius*** CBro
'Interval' (2) IBal
'Intrigue' (7) ICar IDun
'Inverpolly' (2) GEve ICar
'Ireland's Eye' (9) IBal
'Irene Copeland' (4) EWal
'Irish Light' (2) ICar
'Irish Linen' (3) ICar
'Irish Luck' (1) EWal LAma
'Irish Mist' (2) ECop ICar
'Irish Nymph' (3) ICar
'Irish Ranger' (3) ICar
'Irish Splendour' (3) ICar
¶ 'Islander' (4) ICar
'Islandhill' (3) IBal
'Itzim' (6) CBro
'It's True' (1) EWal
'Ivy League' (1) ICar
jacetanus MS 580 CMon
'Jack Snipe' (6) CAvo CBro CCla CNic EPot ETub EWal LAma LBow MBri MWBu NRog SIng
'Jambo' (2) IDun
'Jamestown' (3) IBal
¶ 'Jana' (6) ICar
'Jane Frances (1) GEve
'Jane MacLennan' (4) GEve
'Jane van Kralingen' (3) GEve
'Janis Babson' (2) ICar
'Jeannine Hoog' (1) LRHS
'Jenny' AGM CAvo CBro EPar EPot ETub EWal IBal ICar LAma MWBu NRog SIng SUsu
'Jessamy' (12) SPou
'Jetfire' (6) CBro ECop EPot ETub EWal ICar IDun LAma
'Jewel Song' (2) ICar
'Jezebel' (3) CBro GEve
'Johanna' (5) CBro
'John Ballance' (1) IBal
'John of Salisbury' (2) EWal
§ 'Jolity' (2) EWal
'Jolly Roger' (2) ICar
jonquilla CAvo CBro EPar EPot LAma LBow NRog SIng WPer WShi
§ – var. ***henriquesii*** CBro CFil
– var. ***henriquesii***
MS 455 CMon
– var. ***jonquilla*** B&S 420 CMon
– var. ***stellaris*** MS 466 CMon
'Joseph Macleod' (1) EWal
'Joy' See N. 'Jolity'
'Joy Bishop' See N. ***romieuxii*** 'J. B.'
'Jubilation' (2) EWal
'Jules Verne' LAma
'Julia Jane' See N. ***romieuxii*** 'J. J.'
'Jumblie' (12) CAvo CBro CCla CMea EPot EWal LAma MBri MWBu NRog SUsu WPer
'Jumbo Gold' (1) IDun
juncifolius See N. ***assoanus***
¶ 'June Lake' (2) IDun
'Kamau' (9) IDun
'Kanchenjunga' (1) ICar
'Karachi' (2) ICar
'Karamudli' (1) ICar
'Kathleen Munro' (2) GEve
'Kaydee' IDun
'Keats' (9) CBro ICar
¶ 'Kebaya' (2) IDun
'Kehelland' (4) CBro
'Kelanne' (2) IDun
'Kenbane Head' (9) IBal
'Kenellis' (12) CBro
'Kildavin' (2) ICar
'Kildrum' (3) EWal ICar
'Kilkenny' (1) EWal
'Killeen' (2) IBal
'Kilmood' (2) IBal
'Kilmorack' (2) ICar
'Kiltonga' (2) IBal
'Kilworth' (2) EWal LAma
'Kimmeridge' (3) ECop IDun
'Kindled' (2) ICar
'King Alfred' (1) LAma WShi
'King Size' (11) GEve
'Kinglet' (7) ICar
'Kingscourt' AGM ECop ICar
'King's Bridge' (1) IDun
'King's Grove' (1) IDun
'King's Stag' (1) ECop ICar IDun
¶ 'Kirkcubbin' (3) IBal
'Kirkinriola' (3) ICar
'Kirklington' (2) IBal
'Kissproof' (2) LAma
'Kitten' (6) EWal
¶ 'Kitty' (6) CBro
'Klamath' (2) EWal
'Knockstacken' (1) ICar
'Krakatoa' (2) EWal
'La Riante' (3) LAma
¶ 'La Vella' (2) IDun
¶ 'Lady Ann' (2) IDun
'Lady Emily' (2) IBal
¶ 'Lalique' (3) ICar
'L'Amour' See N. 'Madelaine'
'Lanarth' (7) CBro
'Lancaster' (3) IBal ICar
'Landmark' (2) EWal
'Langford Grove' (3) ECop
¶ 'Lapwing' (5) CBro
'Larkelly' (6) CBro ICar
'Larkfield' (2) ICar

¶ 'Larkwhistle' (6)	CBro
'Last Promise' (1)	ICar
'Last Word' (3)	EWal
'Late Call' (3)	IBal
'Lavender Lass' (6)	ECop ICar IDun
'Lemnos' (2)	EWal
'Lemon Beauty' (11)	EWal
'Lemon Candy' (2)	ECop
'Lemon Cloud' (1)	EWal
'Lemon Express' (1)	IDun
'Lemon Heart' (5)	CBro ICar
'Lemon Meringue' (1)	ICar
'Lemon Sherbet' (2)	ICar
'Lemonade' (3)	ECop ICar
'Lennymore' (2)	IDun
'Leonaine' (2)	EWal
'Leslie Hill' (1)	ICar
'Liberty Bells' (5)	CBro EWal LAma MBri NRog SIng
'Lichfield' (3)	EWal
'Lighthouse' (3)	GEve IDun
'Lilac Charm' (6)	IDun
'Lilac Hue' (6)	CBro IDun
'Lillande' (4)	ICar
'Limbo' (2)	EWal IDun
'Limeade' (2)	ICar
'Limelight' (1)	EWal
'Limerick' (3)	EWal ICar
'Lintie' (7)	CBro EWal LAma MBri NRog SIng
'Lionheart' (4)	EWal
'Lisanore' (2)	ICar
'Lisbarnett' (3)	IBal
'Lisnamulligan' (3)	IBal
'Lisrenny' (1)	ICar
'Little Beauty' (1)	CBro EPot ETub LAma
'Little Dancer' (1)	CBro
'Little Gem' (1)	CBro EPot LAma NRog
'Little Princess' (6)	ICar
'Little Sentry' (7)	CBro
'Little Spell' (1)	CBro
'Little Witch' (6)	CAvo CBro CCla EPot EWal LAma LBow MBri MWBu NRog SIng
'Lizard Light' (2)	EWal
lobularis	See N. ***pseudonarcissus*** 'Lobularis'
'Loch Assynt' (3)	ECop GEve ICar
'Loch Brora' (2)	GEve ICar
'Loch Carron' (2)	ICar
¶ 'Loch Coire' (3)	IDun
'Loch Fada' (2)	ICar
'Loch Garvie' (2)	ICar
'Loch Hope' (2)	ECop GEve ICar IDun
'Loch Lundie' (2)	ICar IDun
'Loch Naver' (2)	GEve IDun
'Loch Owskeich' AGM	ECop
'Loch Stac' (2)	ECop ICar
'Loch Tarbert' (2)	GEve
longispathus MS 546	CMon
'Loth Lorien' (3)	IDun
'Lothario' (2)	LAma MBri NRog
'Lough Bawn' (2)	GEve ICar
'Lough Cuan' (1)	IBal
'Lough Ryan' (1)	IBal
'Loughanisland' (1)	IBal
'Loughanmore' (1)	ICar
'Lovable' (3)	EWal
'Lunar Sea' (1)	EWal
'Lurgain' (1)	EWal
¶ 'Lurig' (2)	ICar
'Lusky Mills' (3)	IBal
'Lydwells' (2)	ECop
'Lynwood' (1)	ICar
'Lysander' (2)	IDun
§ 'Madelaine' (2)	EWal
'Madrigal' (2)	EWal
'Magic Flute' (2)	ICar
'Magic Maiden' (2)	IDun
'Magna Carta' (2)	IDun
'Magnet' (1)	LAma MBri
'Magnificence' (1)	LAma
'Mahmoud' (3)	ICar
'Maiden Over' (2)	ECop
'Mairead' (2)	GEve
'Majestic Star' (1)	IDun
'Manchu' (2)	EWal
'Manly' (4)	EWal
'Marabou' (4)	IDun
'Maraval' (1)	EWal ICar
'March Madness' (2)	ICar
'March Sunshine' (6)	CBro EPot EWal ICar LAma
'Marcola' (2)	ICar
'Marie-José' (11)	ETub LAma
'Marshfire' (2)	ICar
'Martha Washington' (8)	CBro
marvieri	See N. ***rupicola m.***
'Mary Bohannon' (2)	EWal
'Mary Copeland' (4)	EWal LAma MBri MWBu
'Mary Kate' (6)	IDun
'Mary Lou' (6)	IDun
'Mary Sumner' (1)	ICar
'Mary's Pink' (2)	ICar
'Masai Mara' (2)	IDun
¶ 'Matador' (8)	IDun
'Mayan Gold' (1)	IBal
'Medalist' (2)	ICar
x ***medioluteus***	CMon
'Megalith' (2)	IDun
'Melbury' (2)	ECop
'Meldrum' (1)	ECop
'Mellon Park' (3)	IDun
'Melody Lane' (2)	EWal
'Mentor' (2)	IDun
'Menucha' (2)	ICar
'Mercato' (2)	LAma
¶ 'Meredith' (3)	ICar
¶ 'Merida' (2)	IBal
'Merlin' AGM	ECop GEve IBal IDun
'Merlin's Castle'	ICar
'Mermaid's Spell' (2)	ICar
'Merry Bells' (5)	ICar
'Merrymaker' (4)	EWal
'Mexico City' (2)	IBal
'Midas Touch' (1)	IDun
'Midget'	CAvo CBro EPot
'Millennium' (1)	CBro
'Millgreen' (1)	EWal
'Minicycla' (6)	CAvo CBro
'Minikin' (3)	ICar
minimus	See N. ***asturiensis***

'Minnow' (8)	CAvo CBro CCla CMea EPot ETub EWal LAma MBri MWBu NRog SIng WHil WPat WPer
§ ***minor***	CBro LAma
– 'Cedric Morris'	ECha
§ – var. ***pumilus***	WPer
– – ***plenus***	See N. 'Rip van Winkle'
'Mint Cup' (3)	ICar
minutiflorus B&S 412	CMon
¶ 'Mission Bells' (5)	ICar
'Missouri' (2)	EWal
'Mistral' (11)	ICar
'Misty Dawn' (3)	IBal
'Misty Glen' (2)	ECop GEve ICar
'Misty Moon' (3)	ICar
'Mockingbird' (7)	IDun
'Modern Art' (2)	ETub
'Moina' (3)	ICar
'Mol's Hobby' (11)	EWal LAma
'Mondaine' (2)	EWal
'Mondragon' (11)	EWal
'Moneymore' (2)	ICar
'Monk Silver' (3)	ECop
'Montalto' (2)	ICar
¶ 'Montclair' (2)	IDun
'Montego' (3)	ECop
'Monument' (2)	ICar
'Monza' (4)	IDun
'Moon Goddess' (1)	IBal
'Moon Jade' (3)	IBal
'Moon Orbit' (2/1)	ETub
'Moon Ranger' (3)	IBal
'Moon Rhythm' (4)	IBal
'Moon Tide' (3)	IBal
'Moon Valley' (2)	GEve IDun
'Moonshine' (5)	CBro
'Moonshot' (1)	EWal
'Moonspell' (2)	IBal ICar
'Moralee' (4)	IDun
'Mother Catherine Grullemans'	LAma
'Mount Angel' (3)	IDun
'Mount Fuji' (2)	IDun
'Mount Hood' (1)	ETub EWal LAma MBri MWBu NBir WShi
'Mount Ida' (2)	IBal
'Mount Oriel' (2)	IBal
'Mount Vernon' (2)	ICar
'Mountjoy' (7)	EWal
'Mountpleasant' (2)	IBal
'Mourneview' (1)	IBal
¶ 'Movie Star' (2)	IDun
¶ 'Moyarget' (3)	ICar
'Moyle' (9)	IBal
'Moyola' (2)	ICar
'Mrs R O Backhouse' (2)	LAma MBri MWBu WShi
'Mrs William Copeland' (4)	EWal
'Muirfield' (1)	IDun
'Mulatto' (1)	EWal
¶ 'Mulroy Bay' (1)	IDun
'Murlough' (9)	IBal
'Murrayfield' (3)	IDun
'My Lady' (2)	EWal
'My My' (2)	EWal
'My Word' (2)	ICar

'Naivasha' (2)	IDun
'Nampa' (1)	EWal
'Namraj' (2)	IDun
'Nancegollan' (7)	CBro
nanus	See N. ***minor***
'Narok' (4)	IDun
¶ 'Neahkahnie' (1)	IDun
'Nether Barr' (2)	IDun
¶ 'New Penny' (3)	ICar
'New Song' (2)	EWal
'New Star' (2)	EWal
'New World' (2)	EWal
'Newcastle' (1)	ECop ICar IDun
'Nirvana' (7)	CBro
'Niveth' (5)	ICar
nobilis var. ***nobilis*** MS 486	CMon
– var. ***primagenius*** MS 593	CMon
¶ 'North Rim' (2)	IDun
'Northern Light' (2)	ICar
'Northern Sceptre' (2)	IBal ICar
'Nor-Nor' (2)	CBro
'Notable' (3)	IBal
¶ 'Notre Dame' (2)	IDun
'Nouvelle' (3)	IBal
'Noweta' (3)	ICar
'Nuage' (2)	EWal
'Nylon' (12)	CBro SPou WChr
'Oadby' (1)	ECop
'Oakwood' (3)	EWal
obesus	WChr
– MS 451	CMon
'Obsession' (2)	IDun
obvallaris	See N. ***pseudonarcissus o.***
– MS 560	CMon
x ***odorus*** 'Campernelli Plenus'	LAma SIng
– 'Rugulosus' (10)	CAvo CBro EPar LAma NRog
'Odyssey' (4)	ICar
Old Pheasant's Eye	See N. ***poeticus recurvus***
'Old Satin' (2)	ICar
'Olympic Gold' (1)	IDun
'Omaha' (3)	IBal
'Oneonta' (2)	ICar
'Orange Beacon' (2)	ICar
'Orange Sherbet' (2)	ICar
'Orangery' (11)	ETub LAma MBri NRog
'Orator' (2)	ECop
'Oratorio' (2)	EWal
'Oryx' (7)	IDun
'Osmington' (3)	ECop IDun
'Ottoman Gold' (2)	IBal
'Owen Roe' (1)	IBal
'Oykel' (3)	GEve ICar
'Pacific Princess' (3)	IBal
'Painted Desert' (3)	ECop ICar
'Pale Sunlight' (2)	ICar
'Palmares' (11)	EWal ICar
'Palmyra' (3)	ICar
'Panache' (1)	ECop EWal GEve ICar
panizzianus	CMon EPot
'Pankot' (2)	ICar
'Paolo Veronese' (2)	EWal
'Paper White'	See N. ***papyraceus***
'Papillon Blanc' (11)	EWal LAma

§ ***papyraceus*** (8)	ETub EWal LAma LBow MBri NRog
– ***papyraceus*** AB&S 4399	CMon
'Parcpat' (7)	CBro
'Parfait' (4)	ICar
'Paricutin' (2)	EWal
'Parisienne' (11)	LAma NRog
¶ 'Park Avenue' (4)	IDun
'Park Springs' (3)	ECop IBal ICar
'Parterre' (2)	IDun
'Parthenon' (4)	ICar
'Passionale' **AGM**	ECop EWal IBal ICar LAma WShi
'Pastorale' (2)	EWal
'Patabundy' (2)	IDun
¶ 'Patois' (9)	IDun
patulus	CMon
'Paula Cottell' (3)	CBro
'Pay Day' (1)	ICar
'Peacock' (2)	ICar
'Pearlax' (11)	EWal
'Peeping Tom' (6)	CBro EPar ETub LAma LBow MBri NRog SIng
'Pencrebar' (7)	CAvo CBro LAma MBri WShi
'Pennine Way' (1)	ECop
'Pennyghael' (2)	GEve
'Penpol' (7)	CBro
'Penvose' (2)	EWal
'Pepper' (2)	CBro
¶ 'Pequenita' (7)	CBro
'Perimeter' (3)	ECop IBal ICar
'Perseus' (1)	GEve ICar
'Pet Finch' (7)	EWal
'Petit Four' (4)	ETub EWal LAma NRog
'Petrel' (5)	CAvo CBro ETub ICar
'Petsamo' (1)	ICar
'Picasso' (3)	ICar
'Pick Up' (11)	ICar
'Pinafore' (2)	EWal
'Pink Angel' (7)	ICar
'Pink Champagne' (4)	ECop
'Pink Charm' (2)	ETub EWal
¶ 'Pink Dawn' (2)	IBal
'Pink Gin' (4)	EWal
'Pink Mink' (2)	IDun
'Pink Monarch' (2)	EWal
'Pink Pageant' (4)	EWal IDun
'Pink Panther' (2)	ICar
'Pink Paradise' (4)	ICar IDun
'Pink Whispers' (2)	IBal
'Pinza' **AGM**	ICar
'Pipe Major' (2)	EWal IBal
'Piper's Barn' (7)	CBro
'Pipit' (7)	CAvo CBro ETub EWal ICar IDun LAma SIng
¶ 'Piquant' (3)	ICar
'Piraeus' (4)	IDun
'Pismo Beach' (2)	ECop ICar IDun
'Pitchroy' (2)	ECop
'Playboy' (2)	ICar
'Playschool' (3)	ICar
poeticus	CAvo LAma
– var. ***hellenicus***	EWal
– Old Pheasant's Eye	See N. ***poeticus recurvus***
§ – 'Plenus'	CBro
– 'Praecox' (9)	CBro
§ – var. ***recurvus*** **AGM**	CBro CGle ETub EWal ICar LAma LBow NBir SIng WShi
'Poet's Way' (9)	ECop IDun
'Polar Circle' (2)	ICar
'Polar Imp' (3)	ICar
'Polglass' (3)	CBro
'Polindra' (2)	EWal
'Polnesk' (7)	CBro
'Pomona' (3)	LAma
'Pontresina' (2)	ICar
'Pops Legacy' (1)	IBal
'Port Patrick' (3)	IBal
'Port William' (3)	IBal
'Portavo' (2)	ICar
'Porthchapel' (7)	ECop
'Portnagolan' (2)	ICar
'Portrush' (3)	EWal
'Portstewart' (3)	IBal
'Post House' (4)	IDun
'Prairie Fire'	IDun
'Preamble' (1)	IBal ICar
'Premiere' (2)	IDun
'President Carter' (1)	LAma
'Pretty Polly' (2)	ICar
'Pride of Cornwall' (8)	CBro
'Primrose Beauty' (4)	CBro
¶ 'Primrose Path' (2)	ICar
'Prince of Brunswick' (2)	IBal
'Printal' (11)	ETub
'Professor Einstein' (2)	ETub LAma NRog
'Prologue' (1)	EWal ICar
'Prophet' (1)	EWal
'Proska' (2)	IDun
¶ 'Prosperity' (1)	ICar
¶ 'Pryda' (2)	ICar
pseudonarcissus	CBro CGle CRow EWFC LAma LBow SIng WChr WShi
– ssp. ***gayi***	CBro
§ – 'Lobularis'	CAvo CBro NLan NRog SIng
§ – ssp. ***moschatus***	CBro CMon
¶ – – 'Plenus'	EBul
– ssp. ***nevadensis***	WOMN
§ – ssp. ***obvallaris*** **AGM**	CAvo CBro EPot ETub LBow NLan NRog SIng WCla WShi
'Pueblo' (7)	ICar
¶ 'Pukawa' (7)	ICar
x ***pulchellus***	SIng
pumilus	See N. ***minor pumilus***
'Puppet' (5)	ICar
'Puppy' (6)	EWal
'Purbeck' (3)	ECop EWal ICar IDun
'Quail' (7)	CAvo CBro EWal ICar LAma NRog
'Quasar' (2)	ICar IDun
'Queen Anne's Double'	See N. 'Eystettensis'
'Queen of Bicolors' (1)	LAma
'Queenscourt' (1)	ECop ICar
'Quetzal' (9)	ICar
'Quick Step' (7)	EWal
'Quiet Day' (2)	ICar IDun
'Quince' (12)	CAvo CBro
'Quirinus' (2)	ETub LAma
'Radiation' (2)	EWal
'Radical' (6)	EWal
'Rainbow' (2)	ECop EWal ICar
'Ramada' (2)	ICar

'Rameses' (2)	ECop
'Rarkmoyle' (2)	ICar
¶ 'Rashee' (1)	ICar
'Rathgar' (2)	ICar
'Ravenhill' (3)	IDun
readinganorum B&S 434	CMon
'Reckless' (3)	ICar
'Red Arrow' (1)	IBal
'Red Bay' (2)	ICar
'Red Cameo' (2)	IDun
'Red Cottage' (2)	ICar
'Red Devil' (2)	ICar
'Red Ember' (3/2)	IDun
'Red Goblet' (2)	LAma
'Red Hall' (3)	ICar
'Red Haze' (2)	IDun
'Red Hugh' (9)	IBal
'Red Mission' (2)	IDun
'Red Spartan' (2)	IDun
'Redlands' (2)	ICar
'Redman' (2)	IBal
'Redstart' (3)	EWal
'Regal Bliss' (2)	IDun
'Reggae' (6)	ICar IDun
'Reliance' (2)	EWal
'Rembrandt' (1)	LAma MBri MWBu
'Replete' (4)	ICar IDun
requienii	See N. ***assoanus***
'Resplendent' (2)	ICar
'Revival' (4)	EWal
¶ 'Ridgecrest' (3)	IDun
'Riding Mill' (3)	EWal
'Rijnveld's Early Sensation' **AGM**	CBro ECop EWal
¶ 'Rim Ride' (3)	ICar
'Rima' (1)	ECop IDun
'Rimmon' (3)	IDun
'Rimski' (2)	IDun
'Ringhaddy' (3)	IBal
'Ringleader' (2)	EWal ICar IDun
'Ringmaster' (2)	ICar
'Ringmer' (3)	ECop
¶ 'Ringwood' (3)	IDun
'Rio Bravo' (2)	IBal
'Rio Gusto' (2)	IBal
¶ 'Rio Rondo' (2)	IBal
'Rio Rouge' (2)	IBal ICar
§ 'Rip van Winkle' (4)	CAvo CBro EPar EPot ETub LAma LBow MBri NRog WShi
'Rippling Waters' (5)	CBro ICar LAma SUsu WHil
'Riptide' (1)	ICar
'Rivendell' (3)	ICar IDun
'Rob Roy' (3)	EWal
'Rockall' (3)	ECop ICar
'Rockport' (2)	ICar
'Rococo' (2)	EWal
'Roger' (6)	CBro ICar
'Roman Tile' (2)	EWal
'Romance' (2)	EWal LAma
'Romany Red' (3)	IDun
romieuxii	CAvo CBro CFil EPot SBla SIng SPou
– AB&S 4384	EPot NHar
– JCA 805	EPot NHar NHol WChr
– SF 370	CMon
– ssp. ***albidus***	WChr
– ssp. ***albidus*** SF 110	CMon
– – var. ***zaianicus***	WChr
– 'Atlas Gold'	EPot
¶ – forms	SPou
– 'Joy Bishop' (10)	EPot NHol SPou WChr
§ – 'Julia Jane' (10)	EPot
§ – ssp. ***romieuxii*** var. ***mesatlanticus***	CAvo CMon CRiv EPot SBla SWas
– 'Treble Chance'	EPot
'Rosapenna' (2)	ICar
'Roscarrick' (6)	ECop
'Rose Gold' (1)	IDun
¶ 'Rose of May' (4)	ICar
'Rose Royale' (2)	IBal ICar
'Roseate Tern' (2)	IDun
'Rosedown' (5)	CBro
'Roseworthy' (2)	LAma
'Rossferry' (2)	IBal
'Rosy Sunrise' (2)	LAma
'Rosy Trumpet' (1)	CBro
'Rosy Wonder' (2)	EWal
'Round Robin' (2)	ICar
'Royal Ballet' (2)	IDun
'Royal Coachman'	ICar
'Royal Command' (2)	See N. 'Royal Decree'
§ 'Royal Decree' (2)	EWal
'Royal Dornoch' (1)	GEve
'Royal Orange' (2)	EWal
'Royal Princess' (3)	ECop IBal IDun
'Royal Regiment' (2)	ICar
'Royal Viking' (3)	IBal
'Royal Wedding' (2)	ICar
'Rubh Mor' (2)	ECop ICar
'Ruby Tail' (2)	EWal
'Rubyat' (6)	IBal
rupicola	CMon CNic CRDP EPot LAma MS&S SIng
– MS 567/455	CMon
§ – ssp. ***marvieri***	WChr
– ssp. ***marvieri*** AB&S 4414	CMon
– ***marvieri*** SF 126	CMon
'Rushlight' (2)	EWal
'Rushmore' (2)	IDun
'Ruth Haller' (5)	ICar
'Ryan Son' (3)	IBal
'Saberwing' (5)	ICar
'Sabine Hay' (3)	EWal ICar IDun
'Sacajawea' (2)	EWal
'Sacramento' (3)	ECop
'Safari' (2)	ICar
'Saint Duthus' (1)	GEve
'Saint Keverne' **AGM**	EWal IBal LAma NRog
'Saint Patrick's Day' (2)	EWal LAma
'Salmon Leap' (2)	ICar
'Salmon Trout' (2)	ECop EWal LAma
'Salomé' (2)	EWal LAma MBri NRog
'Samantha' (4)	ECop ICar
'Samaria' (3)	CBro
'Samite' (1)	EWal
¶ 'Sandy Cove' (2)	IDun
¶ 'Sandymount' (2)	IBal
'Sarah' (2)	EWal
'Sateen' (2)	EWal
'Satellite' (6)	EWal ICar SIng
'Satin Pink' (2)	ETub EWal MBri

'Saturn' (3) ICar
¶ 'Savoir Faire' (2) IDun
scaberulus CBro CRDP LAma SIng WChr WPer
'Scarlet Elegance' (2) LAma
'Scarlet Gem' (8) ETub EWal LAma SIng
'Scarlett O'Hara' (2) LAma
'Scoreline' (1) IDun
'Scotney Castle' (1) ECop
'Sea Dream' (3) IDun
'Sea Gift' (7) CBro
'Sea Green' (9) ECop
'Sealing Wax' (2) EWal
'Segovia' (3) CBro
'Sempre Avanti' (2) LAma MBri MWBu NRog
'Sennocke' (5) CBro
¶ 'Serena Beach' (4) IDun
¶ 'Serena Lodge' (4) IDun
serotinus CMon EPot WThi
– SF 298/285 CMon
'Sextant' (6) EWal IDun
'Shanes Castle' (1) ICar
'She' (2) EWal
¶ 'Sheer Joy' (6) IDun
'Sheerline' (2) IDun
'Sheik' (2) ICar
'Sherborne' (4) IDun
'Sherpa' (1) IDun
'Shining Light' (2) ECop ICar
¶ 'Shorecliffe' (2) IDun
'Shot Silk' (5) LAma
¶ 'Show Band' (2) IDun
'Showboat' (2) ICar
'Shy Face' (2) ICar
'Sidley' (3) IDun
¶ 'Signorina' (2) IDun
'Sigrid Undset' (3) LAma
'Silent Valley' (1) ICar IDun
'Silk Cut' (2) IDun
'Silken Sails' (3) ICar
'Silver Bells' (5) IDun
'Silver Blaze' (2) IDun
'Silver Chimes' (8) CAvo CBro ETub EWal LAma MHlr NRog SIng
'Silver Crystal' (3) IDun
'Silver Princess' (3) EWal
'Silver Standard' (2) EWal
'Silver Surf' (2) IDun
'Silvermere' (2) IDun
'Silversmith' (2) IDun
'Silverwood' (3) IDun
'Sinopel' (3) ETub
'Sir Winston Churchill' (4) EWal LAma NRog
'Skerry' (2) ICar
'Slaney' (3) ICar
¶ 'Sligachan' (1) GEve
'Small Fry' (1) EWal
'Smokey Bear' (4) IDun
'Snoopie' (6) IDun
¶ 'Snow Bunting' (7) CBro
'Snow Dream' (2) EWal ICar
'Snowcrest' (3) IDun
'Snowfire' (4) ICar
'Snowshill' (2) ICar
¶ 'Society Belle' (2) IDun
'Solar Tan' (3) IDun
'Soldier Brave' (2) EWal
'Soledad' (2) ICar
'Soleil d'Or' (8) EWal MBri
'Solferique' (2) IDun
¶ 'Songket' (2) IDun
¶ 'Soprano' (2) IDun
'Sorcerer' (3) ICar
¶ 'South Street' (2) ECop
'Southease' (2) ECop
'Space Age' (2) ICar
'Spanish Moon' (1) EWal
'Sparkling Eye' (8) IBal
'Spellbinder' **AGM** EWal LAma MBri SUsu
¶ 'Sperrin Gold' (1) IDun
'Sportsman' (2) IDun
'Spring Valley' (3) ICar
'Springston Charm' (2) ICar
sp. ABS 4450 SPou
sp. ABS 4656 SPou
sp. C M Stocken (10) CBro
'Stadium' (2) EWal
'Stainless' (2) IBal
'Standard Value' (1) LAma
¶ 'Star Glow' (2) IDun
'Starfire' (7) ICar
'State Express' (2) IDun
'Statue' (2) EWal
'Stint' (6) CBro IDun
'Stoke Charity' (2) ECop ICar
'Stormy Weather' (1) ECop ICar
'Stourbridge' (2) ECop ICar
'Strathkanaird' (1) GEve ICar
'Stratosphere' (7) ECop ICar IDun
¶ 'Stray' (6) ICar
'Strephon' (1) ICar
'Strines' (2) ECop EWal
'Stromboli' (2) EWal
'Suda Bay' (2) ICar
'Sugarbush' (7) CBro LAma MBri NRog SIng
'Suilven' (3) GEve ICar
'Sun Disc' (7) CBro EPot EWal IDun MBri SIng SUsu WPat
'Sunbather' (2) ICar
'Sundial' (7) CAvo CBro EPot ETub EWal ICar LAma
'Sundisc' (7) LAma
'Suntory' (3) IDun
'Super Star' (2) ETub
'Surrey' (2) IDun
'Susan Pearson' (7) ICar
'Suzy' **AGM** CBro EWal ICar LAma MBri NRog SIng
'Swallowcliffe' (6) IDun
'Swallownest' (1) ECop
'Swansdown' (4) EWal ICar
'Sweet Charity' (2) EWal
'Sweet Pepper' (7) CBro ECop GEve ICar
'Sweetness' **AGM** CAvo CBro EWal IBal LAma NRog
'Swing Wing' (6) IDun
'Sydling' (5) IDun
'Sylvan Hill' (1) IBal
'Symphonette' (2) GEve ICar
'Syracuse' (3) ECop ICar
'Taffeta' (12) CBro SPou WChr
'Tahiti' (4) ECop EWal LAma MBri MWBu NRog

¶ 'Tain' (1)	ICar
¶ 'Takoradi' (4)	ICar
'Tamar Fire' (4)	ECop
§ ***tananicus***	WChr
– SF 44	CMon
'Tanera' (2)	ICar
'Tangent' (2)	EWal ICar
'Tardree' (1)	ICar
'Tarlatan' (12)	CBro SPou
tazetta ssp. ***lacticolor*** MS 517	CMon
– ssp. ***lacticolor*** MS 519	CMon
'Tedstone' (1)	EWal
'Tekapo' (2)	ICar
§ 'Telamonius Plenus' (4)	CBro LAma SIng WShi
§ x ***tenuior***	CAvo
¶ 'Terracotta' (2)	IDun
'Testament' (2)	EWal
'Tête-à-Tête' **AGM**	CAvo CBro EPar EPot ETub EWal IBal LAma LBow MBri SIng WHil WPer
'Texas' (4)	ETub LAma MBri
'Thalia' (5)	CAvo CBro ETub EWal ICar LAma LBow MBri MWBu NRog SIng SUsu
'The Little Gentleman' (6)	CBro
'Theano' (2)	ICar
'Thoughtful' (5)	CBro EWal
'Three Trees' (1)	ICar
'Thunderbolt' (1)	EWal
'Tibet' (2)	EWal
'Tiger Moth' (6)	IDun
'Timolin' (3)	ICar
'Tiri Tomba' (11)	EWal
'Tittle Tattle' (7)	CBro EWal IBal ICar LAma
'Toby' (2)	EWal
'Tonga' (4)	ECop ICar
'Top Gallant' (3)	IBal
'Top Notch' (2)	ICar
'Top of the Hill' (3)	IBal ICar
'Topkapi' (2)	IBal
'Topolino' (1)	CAvo CBro ETub LAma NRog SUsu
'Torcross' (3)	IDun
'Torr Head' (9)	IBal
'Torridon' (2)	ECop ICar IDun
'Torrish' (3)	ICar
tortifolius MS 540	CMon
¶ 'Tracey' (6)	CBro
'Tranquil Morn' (3)	EWal
'Trena' (6)	CBro IDun
'Tresamble' (5)	CBro EWal ICar LAma SIng
'Trevithian' (7)	CBro EWal IBal LAma NRog SIng
'Trewirgie' (6)	CBro
triandrus	WChr
– var. ***albus***	See N. ***triandrus triandrus***
– var. ***concolor***	See N. ***concolor***
– var. ***pulchellus***	LAma
¶ – var. ***triandrus***	ECop
¶ 'Triller' (7)	ICar
'Tripartite' (11)	ECop EWal ICar NZep
¶ 'Triple Crown' (3)	IDun
'Tristram' (2)	ICar
'Tropic Isle' (4)	ICar
'Trousseau' (1)	EWal LAma
'Tudor Grove' (2)	IDun
'Tudor Minstrel' (2)	EWal
'Tuesday's Child' (5)	ECop ETub EWal ICar IDun SIng
'Tullycore' (2)	ICar
'Tullygirvan' (2)	ICar
'Tullyglass' (2)	ICar
'Tullynakill' (2)	IBal
'Tullynog' (4)	ICar
'Tullyroyal' (2)	IBal
'Turncoat' (6)	IDun
'Tutankhamun' (2)	ECop
'Twicer' (2)	IDun
'Tynan' (2)	ICar
'Tyneham' (3)	IDun
¶ 'Tyrian Rose' (2)	IDun
'Tyrone Gold' (2)	IDun
'Ufo' (3)	EWal
'Ulster Bank' (3)	IDun
'Ulster Bullion' (2)	IBal
'Ulster Prince' **AGM**	ICar
'Ultimus' (2)	EWal
'Una Bremner' (2)	GEve
'Uncle Ben' (1)	IBal
'Uncle Remus' (1)	EWal
'Unique' (4)	ECop EWal ICar IDun LAma
'Unsurpassable' (1)	LAma
'Upper Broughton' (2)	IDun
'Urchin'	See N. 'Pzaz'
'Vahu' (2)	IDun
'Val d'Incles' (3)	IDun
'Valdrome' (11)	ICar MBri
'Valediction' (3)	IDun
'Valinor' (2)	IDun
¶ 'Value' (2)	IDun
'Van Dyke' (2)	IDun
'Van Sion'	See N. 'Telamonius Plenus'
'Vantage' (2)	ICar
'Verdant' (1)	IDun
'Verdin' (7)	GEve ICar
'Verger' (3)	LAma MBri
'Vernal Prince' (3)	IDun
'Verona' **AGM**	ECop ICar IDun
'Vers Libre' (9)	IDun
'Verwood' (3)	IDun
'Victory' (2)	EWal
'Vigilante' (1)	GEve IDun
'Viking' (1)	ECop GEve
'Vilna' (2)	EWal
¶ 'Vinsky' (3)	ECop
'Violetta' (2)	EWal ICar IDun
'Vireo' (7)	ICar
'Virgil' (9)	EWal
viridiflorus	WThi
– MS 500	CMon
– SF 323	CMon
'Vivarino' (11)	EWal
'Voltage' (2)	IDun
'Vulcan' **AGM**	EWal
'W P Milner' (1)	CAvo CBro LAma MBri MHlr NRog SIng WOMN
'Wahkeena' (2)	ICar
'Waldorf Astoria' (4)	IDun
¶ 'War Dance'	IDun
'Waterperry' (7)	CBro LAma NRog SIng
watieri	CBro CMon EPot SPou WChr
– AB&S 4518	CMon
'Webster' (9)	IDun

'Wee Bee' (1) EWal
'Welvan' (3) ICar
'Wendy Walsh' (2) ICar
¶ 'Westbury' (4) IDun
'Westholme' (2) IDun
'Westward' (4) EWal
'Wetherby' (3) IDun
'Whang-hi' (6) ECop
'Whisper' (5) EWal
'Whitbourne' (3) EWal
'White Butterfly' (2) EWal
'White Cross' (2) IBal
'White Empress' (1) IBal ICar
'White Ermine' (2) IDun
'White Hill' (2) IBal
'White Lion' AGM ETub EWal LAma MWBu NRog
'White Majesty' (1) IBal
'White Marvel' (4) CBro EWal LAma NRog SUsu
¶ 'White Mist' (2) ICar
'White Phantom' (1) ICar
'White Plume' (2) EWal
'White Spray' (2) ICar
'White Star' (1) ICar IDun
'Whiteabbey' (2) IBal
'Widgeon' (2) EWal
willkommii SPou
'Winchester' (2) EWal
'Windjammer' (1) EWal
'Winfrith' (2) EWal
'Witch Doctor' (3) IBal
'Woodcock' (6) CBro
'Woodgreen' (2) EWal
¶ 'Woodland Glade' (3) IBal
'Woodland Prince' (3) ICar
'Woolsthorpe' (2) IBal
'Worcester' (2) EWal
'Xit' (3) SPou WChr
¶ 'Yeats' (9) ICar
'Yellow Cheerfulness' (4) ETub EWal LAma MBri NRog SIng
'Yellow Standard' (2) LAma
'Yellow Sun' (3) LAma
'Yellow Tresamble' (5) CBro
'Yes Please' (2) EWal
¶ 'Yoshiko' (2) IDun
'Young Blood' (2) IDun
'Young Idea' (7) EWal
* ***zaianicus albus*** MS 168 CMon
* – ***lutescens*** SF 374 CMon NHar
'Zeus' (2) ICar
¶ 'Zion Canyon' (2) IDun

NARDOPHYLLUM (Compositae/Asteraceae)

bryoïdes GArf GTou ITim MHig SIng

NARTHECIUM (Liliaceae/Melanthiaceae)

ossifragum CRDP

NASSELLA (Gramineae/Poaceae)

trichotoma EMon EPla ETPC SApp

NASTURTIUM Aiton f. (Cruciferae/Brassicaceae)

officinale CBen SWat WHer WHol

NASTURTIUM hort See TROPAEOLUM

NECTARBERRY See RUBUS

NECTARINE See PRUNUS *persica nectarina*

NECTAROSCORDUM (Liliaceae/Alliaceae)

§ ***siculum*** CAvo CBro CGle CHan CMea CNic ECro ELan EOrc EPar ERav GAul MBal NBir NEgg NSti WDav WHal
§ – ssp. ***bulgaricum*** CBro CHad ECha EFou EPar EPot ETub IBlr LBow SIng
¶ ***tripedale*** SPou

NEILLIA (Rosaceae)

affinis CCla CDec CDoC EFol EHal MBal MUlv WHCG
longiracemosa See N. ***thibetica***
sinensis CMCN CPle LAbb MRav
§ ***thibetica*** CB&S CBow CCla CGre CLan CPle ELan ENot IOrc ISea LAbb MBri MUlv SHil SPer SPla SSta WAbe WBod WEas WPat WTyr WWat WWin
thyrsiflora ERav

NELUMBO (Nelumbonaceae)

'Kermesina' MSta
lutea 'Flavescens' MSta
nucifera MSta
– 'Alba Grandiflora' MSta
– 'Alba Striata' MSta
– 'Pekinensis Rubra' MSta
– 'Rosea' MSta
– 'Rosea Plena' CRDP MSta
'Osiris' MSta
'Pulchra' MSta

NEMASTYLIS (Iridaceae)

tenuis ssp. ***pringlei*** WPer

NEMATANTHUS (Gesneriaceae)

'Black Magic' MBri WDib
'Christmas Holly' WDib
'Freckles' WDib
§ ***glaber*** MBri
§ ***gregarius*** MBri WDib
§ – 'Golden West' (v) MBri WDib
– 'Variegatus' See N. ***g.*** 'Golden West'
radicans See N. ***gregarius***
strigillosus MBri
'Tropicana' AGM MBri WDib

NEMESIA (Scrophulariaceae)

denticulata EOrc MArl NBra NRar
¶ – 'Confetti' MAsh WWeb
¶ 'Elliott's Variety' CBar
foetens See N. ***fruticans***
§ ***fruticans*** CBot CBrk CDoC CSam CTro GMac LHil MArl MTho NNrw NPri NTow SDix SUsu WHoo WKif WOMN WPer WWin

– 'Joan Wilder' misapplied	See N. *f.* lilac/blue
N– lilac/blue	CBrk CElw CGle CMHG CRiv CSam CSpe CTro EBar EOrc GBuc GCal GMac LBlm LHil LHop MBro MFir SAxl SUsu WEas WHer WOMN WPer WRus
'Hermione'	EMon
¶ ***umbonata*** 'Woodcote'	CBrk
umbonata hort.	See N. ***fruticans*** lilac/blue

NEMOPANTHUS (Aquifoliaceae)
See Plant Deletions

NEMOPHILA (Hydrophyllaceae)

¶ ***menziesii***	GAul

NEODYPSIS (Palmae/Arecaceae)

decaryi	CTro LPal

NEOLITSEA (Lauraceae)

glauca	See N. ***sericea***
§ ***sericea***	CHEx SArc

NEOMARICA (Iridaceae)

gracilis	CTro
northiana	SLMG WThi

NEOPANAX See **PSEUDOPANAX**

NEOPAXIA (Portulacaceae)

§ ***australasica***	CMHG ECou ESis MHig NGre NTow WCru WWin
– blue-leaved	See N. ***a.*** 'Koscuisko'
– bronze-leaved	See N. ***a.*** 'Ohau'
§ – 'Great Lake'	ECou
– green-leaved	See N. ***a.*** 'Great Lake'
– grey	See N. ***a.*** 'Kosciusko'
§ – 'Kosciusko '	GAri GDra NBir NGre NHol
– 'Lakeside'	ECou
– 'Lyndon'	ECou
§ – 'Ohau'	ECou GAri GGar

NEOREGELIA (Bromeliaceae)

carolinae	MBri
– f. ***tricolor*** **AGM**	MBri
§ ***carolinae*** Meyendorffii Group 'Flandria'	MBri
– – 'Meyendorffii'	MBri
§ Claret	MBri
¶ 'Fireball'	NTRF

NEPENTHES (Nepenthaceae)

alata	WMEx
× ***coccinea***	MBri WMEx
khasiana	WMEx

NEPETA † (Labiatae/Lamiaceae)

argolica	See N. ***sibthorpii***
'Blue Beauty'	See N. ***sibirica*** 'Souvenir d'André Chaudron'
camphorata	CPou CSam EMon GAbr GPoy LHol SHer SIde SUsu WPer WWye
cataria	CArn CSFH CSev EJud Effi GBar GPoy LHol MChe MHew MSal NBro SHer SIde WHer WOak WPer WWye
– 'Citriodora'	CArn CBot CLTr EFou EHal GBar GCal GPoy LHol MSal SChu SMrm WCHb WHil
clarkei	CHan EBee EFou GCal MSte SUsu SWas
× ***faassenii***	CCla CGle CHad CLew EBre EMon LBre LBuc MNFA MTol NKay NMir NPer NVic SChu SCro SIng SPla WHil WOld
glechoma 'Variegata'	See GLECHOMA ***hederacea*** 'Variegata'
govaniana	Widely available
grandiflora	CLTr CPle EFou LHol NFai SBla SIde
¶ – 'Dawn to Dusk'	EFou
hederacea 'Variegata'	See GLECHOMA ***hederacea*** 'Variegata'
lanceolata	See N. ***nepetalla***
¶ ***latifolia***	EMon
* ***longipes***	CHan EMon SBla SChu SCro
macrantha	See N. ***sibirica***
melissifolia	EBee EHal EMon WCHb WPer
mussinii	See N. ***racemosa***
§ ***nepetella***	CSam EMon LGre LRHS WPer WWye
– ssp. ***amethystina***	EMon
nervosa	CArn CChu CCla CDec CPle CSam ECED ECha EFol EFou ELan EMar EMon LGan LGre LHol MFir MSte NBro NFai NOak NSti NTow SCro SDix SHer SPer WHer WHoo WPer
¶ – 'Forncett Select'	EFou
§ ***nuda***	CSam EBee ECha EFol EHal EMon MNFA NHol WCot WPbr WPer
– ssp. ***albiflora***	EMon LRHS SSvw
¶ – 'Nacre'	EMon
– ssp. ***nuda***	CHan LRHS
pannonica	See N. ***nuda***
parnassica CDB 13073	EMon
§ ***phyllochlamys***	CBot CLTr EMon LHil MSte SBla SSad
– Mac&W 5882	WOMN
'Pool Bank'	ECoo EFou EHal EMon MBel
'Porzellan'	EFou EHal EMon
§ ***prattii***	CSco EHal GCal
§ ***racemosa***	Widely available
– 'Blue Ice'	EMon GBuc
– 'Little Titch'	EFou GCal MSte SChu SMrm SUsu WSun
– 'Snowflake'	Widely available
§ – 'Superba'	CLTr CLew EFou ELan WHoo
– 'Walker's Low'	EFou GCal SMrm WSun
reichenbachiana	See N. ***racemosa***
§ ***sibirica***	CGle CLTr CPle ECha EFou EJud LGre MBri MSal NBro SChu SCro SIgm SUsu WCot WHal WMer WPer WWye
§ – 'Souvenir d'André Chaudron'	CDoC CGle CLew CMHG CRDP CSam CSco ECoo EFou EGol EMon GCal LGan MBri MNFA SCro SMrm SPer WEas WHer WHoo WOld WPer WSun
§ ***sibthorpii***	WPer
sintenisii	EMon

'Six Hills Giant'	Widely available
sp. DS&T 89048T	EMon
sp. DS&T 89054T	EMon MBel
stewartiana CLD 551	EMon
subsessilis	CBot CRDP EBee ECoo EMar GAbr GBuc LGre MSte NCat NNrw NSti SAxl SBla SMrm SWas WOld WPer WWye
– forms	WBon WCot
– var. ***yesoensis***	CHan
teydea	EMon SUsu WPer
'Thornbury'	CShe
tuberosa	CSam EBee ECha LGan SChu WOld
ucranica	NHex

NEPHROLEPIS (Nephrolepidaceae)

cordifolia	MBri NMar
exaltata 'Bostoniensis'	MBri SRms
– 'Rooseveltii'	MBri
– 'Smithii'	MBri
– 'Smithii Linda'	MBri
– 'Teddy Junior'	MBri
– 'Todeoïdes'	NMar

NEPHROPHYLLIDIUM (Menyanthaceae)

¶ ***cristagalli***	IBlr

NERINE † (Liliaceae/Amaryllidaceae)

'Baghdad'	CMon
¶ 'Blanchefleur'	LHop
bowdenii AGM	CAvo CBro CMea CRDP CSco CShe CSut EBre ECha ELan ERav GCal LBre LHop MBal MBri MBro MWBu NHol NRog SDeJ SDix SIng SLMG SPer WCla WEas WHoo WKif
– 'Alba'	ECha
– 'Mark Fenwick'	CB&S ECha EPot ERav LHop WCot
– 'Pink Triumph'	CAvo CB&S CRDP LAma LBow LHop MWBu NHol NRog SDeJ WAbe
– 'Variegata'	SHBN
– 'Wellsii'	CMon WCot
'Brocade'	CMon
¶ 'Camellia'	LHop
¶ 'Canasta'	LHop
¶ 'Catherine'	LHop
¶ 'Catkin'	LHop
¶ 'Christmas'	LHop
corusca major	See N. ***sarniensis corusca***
crispa	See N. ***undulata***
¶ 'Curiosity'	LHop
¶ 'Dover'	LHop
¶ 'Druid'	LHop
¶ 'Enchantress'	LHop
¶ 'Evening'	LHop
¶ 'Fairyland'	LHop
filamentosa	CMon SWas
filifolia	CAvo CBro CRDP EPot GCal
flexuosa	CMon SLMG
– 'Alba'	CAvo CBro CMon EBre LAma LBre LGre SDeJ SGil
– pink	CMon
fothergillii 'Queen Mary'	CMon
'Gaby Deslys'	CMon
¶ 'Gaiety'	LHop
¶ 'Gloaming'	LHop
'Grisle'	CMon LHop
¶ 'Helen Smith'	LHop
'Hera'	ECha LGre
¶ 'Hertha Berg'	SBor
humilis	CMon
– Breachiae Group	CMon
– Tulbaghensis Group	CMon
¶ 'Inchmery Kate'	LHop
¶ 'Janet'	SBor
¶ 'King of the Belgians'	LHop
¶ 'Lady Eleanor Keane'	SBor
¶ 'Lindhurst'	LHop
'Mansellii'	CMon
¶ 'Maria'	SBor
'Marnie Rogerson'	CGle LGre
masoniorum	EHic LGre MTho WCot WOMN WThu
'Miss France Clarke'	LHop
'Mrs Dent Brocklehurst'	LHop
¶ 'Mrs Graham Vivien'	SBor
pudica	LHop SHer
'Rose Camellia'	CMon
'Rushmere Star'	LHop
sarniensis	CMon ECha NRog SLMG WThi
*– 'Alba'	LHop
§ – var. ***corusca***	LAma
– – 'Major'	LBow LHop
– ***fothergillii***	CMon LHop WCot
Smee No. 11	CMon
¶ 'Solent Swan'	LHop
¶ 'Stephanie'	LHop
§ ***undulata***	CAvo CBro CMon ECha EOrc LAma LBow MBri MWBu NHol NRog WCot
'Zeal Giant'	CMon

NERIUM (Apocynaceae)

oleander	CHEx CPle EBak LAbb SEng WOMN
¶ – 'Album'	EEls
¶ – 'Album Plenum'	EEls
– 'Alsace'	ERea LBlm
*– 'Avalanche'	CB&S
– 'Belle Hélène'	LBlm
*– 'Clare'	EEls ERea
– double white	CBot
– 'Emile Sahut'	LBlm
– 'Emilie'	ERea
– forms	CNew CTro EEls SLMG
– 'Géant des Batailles'	EEls ERea LBlm
¶ – 'Hardy Pink'	ERea
– 'Hardy Red'	ERea
– 'Isle of Capri'	ERea
– 'Italia'	ERea
¶ – 'Jannoch'	ERea LBlm
– 'Luteum Plenum'	EEls ERea LBlm
– 'Madame Léon Brun'	LBlm
¶ – 'Madame Planchon' (d)	ERea
– 'Magaly'	ERea LBlm
– 'Margaritha'	EEls ERea
¶ – 'Oportum'	EEls
*– 'Peach Blossom'	EEls ERea LAbb
– 'Petite Salmon'	LBlm
– 'Professeur Granel'	EEls ERea LBlm

– 'Provence' ERea
– 'Rosario' ERea
– 'Rosée du Ventoux' ERea
– 'Roseum' EEls SLMG
– 'Roseum Plenum' CB&S EEls SLMG
¶ – 'Rosita' ERea
– 'Sealy Pink' CB&S
*– 'Snowflake' ERea
– 'Soeur Agnès' ERea
– 'Soleil Levant' ERea
– 'Splendens' ERea
– 'Tito Poggi' ERea LBlm
– 'Variegatum' CBot EEls ERea LAbb LHop NHex SLMG WCot
– 'Ville de Carpentras' ERea
– 'Yellow Queen' CB&S

NERTERA (Rubiaceae)

¶ ***balfouriana*** ECou
depressa ECou
granadensis MBri NTow WOMN

NEVIUSIA (Rosaceae)

alabamensis CHan SPla

NICANDRA (Solanaceae)

physalodes CArn CMea CRiv EJud ELan NBir NHex SIde WHer WWye
– ***alba*** NBir

NICOTIANA (Solanaceae)

¶ ***acuminata*** MSto
glauca CGle CGre CMea CPle CTro LBlm LHil MAll MSte SLMG SMrm WEas WHal
¶ ***knightiana*** MSto
langsdorffii AGM CB&S CBrk CGre CHad CHan CMea ECro EMon GPlt NBro NNrw SLMG SMrm SUsu WEas WHal WRus
noctiflora EBar
rustica ECro
suaveolens WEas WRus
sylvestris AGM CBrk CGre CHEx CHad CHan EBar GCal NNrw SMrm SUsu WEas WHal WRus
tabacum CHEx EJud WWye
¶ ***trigonophylla*** MSal

NIDULARIUM (Bromeliaceae)

flandria See NEOREGELIA ***carolinae*** Meyendorfii Group 'Flandria'

NIEREMBERGIA (Solanaceae)

§ ***caerulea*** AGM ECha WRus WThi
frutescens CGle CHan EMon ESma LGre LHop MAll MTho WPla WRus
hippomanica See N. ***caerulea***
§ ***repens*** CMHG CRiv ELan ELun EPot MCas MPit NMen NNrw NRed SIng WHal WHil WOMN WPer WWin
– 'Violet Queen' CPBP ELan MTho
rivularis See N. ***repens***

NIPHAEA (Gesneriaceae)

oblonga NMos

X NIPHIMENES (Gesneriaceae)

'Lemonade' NMos

NIPPONANTHEMUM (Compositae/Asteraceae)

§ ***nipponicum*** CFee CHan CLew CNic CRiv CSam CSco CSev ECha EMon GCal MTho NFai NRoo NSti WBon WEas

NOCCAEA See THLASPI

NOLANA (Solanaceae)

¶ ***humifusa*** 'Little Bells' NPri
paradoxa CSpe

NOLINA (Dracaenaceae)

beldingii SIgm
¶ ***bigelowii*** CTbh
brevifolia SIgm
¶ ***durangensis*** CTbh
greenii SIgm
humilis CTbh SArc
longifolia CTbh SArc
¶ ***microcarpa*** CTbh
palmeri SIgm
texana CTbh SIgm

NOMOCHARIS (Liliaceae/Liliaceae)

aperta CAvo CBro CNic GBuc GCHN GDra NHol NRog WChr WCru
farreri CAvo CNic GArf NHol WChr
mairei See N. ***pardanthina***
nana See LILIUM ***nanum***
§ ***pardanthina*** CAvo GArf NRog WChr
– f. ***punctulata*** CAvo GDra NRog
saluenensis GDra NHol NRog

NONEA (Boraginaceae)

lutea NGar WAbb WByw

NOTELAEA (Oleaceae)

ligustrina GWht

NOTHOFAGUS † (Fagaceae)

alessandrii CGre GAri ISea
§ ***alpina*** CBra CDoC CGre CLnd CPer GAri GRei IOrc MBal NWea SPer WDin WFro WMou WNor
antarctica CB&S CCla CDoC CGre CLnd CMHG EHar ELan EMil GAbr IOrc ISea LPan MBal MBar MBri MGos NBar NBee NHol SEng SPer STre WBod WCoo WDin WNor WSHC WWat
– 'Prostrata' See N. ***a.*** 'Benmore'
betuloïdes GAri
cunninghamii CB&S CGre GAri ISea WNor
dombeyi CB&S CGre GAri IOrc ISea SArc WBod WMou WNor WWat
fusca WNor

menziesii CB&S CGre CLnd CMHG GAri SArc WCoo WNor WWat
obliqua CDoC CGre CLnd CSam GAbr GAri IOrc ISea MBal NWea WDin WFro WMou WNor
procera See N. ***alpina***
pumilio CGre GAri WNor
solanderi SArc WNor
– var. *cliffortioïdes* CB&S CGre CLnd GAbr GAri ISea MBal STre WCoo WNor WWat
truncata WNor

NOTHOLIRION (Liliaceae/Liliaceae)

bulbuliferum CAvo CRDP GCra NHol WChr
macrophyllum CAvo WChr WCru
thomsonianum EBul ETub

NOTHOPANAX See PSEUDOPANAX, POLYSCIAS

NOTHOSCORDUM (Liliaceae/Alliaceae)

bivalve MSal
inodorum CBro WHil
– *macrostemon* CL 7/76 CMon
neriniflorum See CALOSCORDUM ***n.***

NOTOSPARTIUM (Leguminosae/Papilionaceae)

carmichaeliae CHan ECou
glabrescens ECou
torulosum ECou
¶ – x *glabrescens* ECou

NOTOTRICHE (Malvaceae)

compacta MTho

NUPHAR (Nymphaeaceae)

¶ *japonica* CRDP
– var. *variegata* CRow
lutea CBen CRDP CRow EHon EMFW LMay NDea SWat WChe WHol
– *variegata* See N. ***variegata***
pumila variegata MSta
§ *variegata* WChe

NUT, Cob See CORYLUS *avellana*

NUT, Filbert See CORYLUS *maxima*

NYMPHAEA † (Nymphaeaceae)

'Afterglow' (T/D) MSta
alba (H) CBen CRow CWGN EHon EMFW EWav LMay MSta SAWi SWat SWyc WChe WHol WMAq WStI
§ – ssp. *occidentalis* (H) MSta SWyc
– 'Plenissima' (H) MSta SWyc
'Albatros' (H) EHon EMFW LMay MSta SLon SWat SWyc
'Albatros' missapplied See N. 'Hermine'
'Amabilis' (H) CBen CRiv CRow EMFW LMay MSta SHig SWyc
'American Star' MSta SWyc WMAq
'Andreana' (H) CBen EMFW LMay MSta SWyc
'Anna Epple' EMFW MSta SWyc
♦ 'Apple Blossom Pink' See N. 'Marliacea Carnea'
'Arc-en-ciel' (H) EMFW MSta SWyc
'Arethusa' (H) MSta
'Atropurpurea' (H) CBen EMFW EWav LMay MSta SWyc
'Attraction' (H) CBen CRiv CRow CWGN EHon EMFW EWav LMay MSta SHig SWat SWyc WChe WHol WMAq WStI
'August Koch' (T/D) MSta
'Aurora' (H) CBen EMFW EWav LMay MSta SWyc
¶ 'Ballerina' SWyc
¶ 'Barbara Dobkins' SWyc
¶ 'Baroness Orczy' (H) MSta SWyc
'Bateau' (H) MSta
¶ 'Berit Strawn' SWyc
'Berthold' MSta
¶ 'Betsy Sakata' SWyc
'Blue Beauty' (T/D) CBen
'Bory de Saint-Vincent' (H) MSta
'Brakeleyi Rosea' (H) CBen EMFW LMay MSta SWyc
¶ 'Burgundy Princess' SWyc
candida (H) CBen EMFW LMay MSta SWyc
¶ – var. *biradiata* (H) SWyc
¶ – var. *neglecta* (H) SWyc
'Candidissima' (H) MSta SWyc
'Candidissima Rosea' (H) MSta SWyc
capensis (T/D) MSta
¶ 'Carolina Sunset' SWyc
'Caroliniana' (H) MSta SWyc
'Caroliniana Nivea' (H) CBen CRDP EMFW MSta SWyc
'Caroliniana Perfecta' (H) CBen LMay MSta SWyc
'Caroliniana Rosea' (H) CRiv MSta SWyc
§ 'Charlene Strawn' EMFW MSta SWyc
'Charles de Meurville' (H) CBen CRow EMFW EWav LMay MSta SLon SWyc
¶ 'Charles's Choice' SWyc
¶ 'Cherokee' SWyc
'Chrysantha' (H) EMFW MSta SWyc
¶ 'Chubby' SWyc
'Colonel A J Welch' (H) CBen CRow EHon EMFW EWav LMay MSta SAWi SWat SWyc WChe WMAq
'Colonel Lindbergh' (T/D) MSta
colorata (T/D) CBen MSta
'Colossea' (H) CBen EHon EMFW EWav LMay MSta SWyc WHol WMAq
'Comanche' (H) CBen EMFW MSta SWat SWyc WMAq
'Conqueror' (H) EMFW LMay MSta SAWi SHig SLon SWat SWyc WMAq
¶ 'Dallas' SWyc
'Darwin' (H) MSta
x *daubenyana* (T/D) MSta
'David' MSta
¶ 'Delicata' (H) SWyc
'Director George T Moore' (T/D) MSta
¶ 'Doll House' SWyc
'Ellisiana' (H) CBen CRDP EMFW LMay MSta SWyc
¶ 'Ernst Epple Senior' SWyc

'Escarboucle' **AGM**	CBen CRow CWGN EMFW EWav LMay MSta SAWi SHig SLon SWat SWyc WHol WMAq
¶ 'Esmeralda' (H)	MSta SWyc
'Eucharis' (H)	MSta
'Evelyn Randig' (T/D)	CBen MSta
'Exquisita' (H)	MSta SWyc
'Fabiola' (H)	EMFW LMay MSta SWyc
¶ 'Fantastic Pink'	SWyc
'Firecrest' (H)	CBen EHon EMFW EWav LMay MSta SLon SWyc WMAq
'Formosa' (H)	MSta
'France'	MSta
¶ 'Fritz Junge' (H)	MSta SWyc
'Froebelii' (H)	CBen CRiv CRow CWGN EHon EMFW EWav LMay MSta SHig SLon SWat SWyc WChe WHol WMAq
'Fulva' (H)	MSta
'Galatée' (H)	MSta SWyc
'General Pershing' (T/D)	MSta
'Gladstoneana' **AGM**	CBen CRow CWGN EHon EMFW EWav LMay MSta SAWi SHig SWat SWyc WHol WMAq
'Gloire du Temple-sur-Lot' (H)	CBen EMFW MSta SWyc WMAq
'Gloriosa' (H)	CBen EMFW LMay MSta SWyc
¶ 'Gold Medal'	SWyc
¶ 'Goliath' (H)	SWyc
'Gonnère' **AGM**	CBen CRow CWGN EMFW EWav LMay MSta SHig SWat SWyc WMAq
¶ 'Gracillima Alba' (H)	SWyc
¶ 'Granat'	SWyc
'Graziella' (H)	CBen CWGN EMFW LMay MSta SWyc WMAq
'Green Smoke' (T/D)	MSta
'Guy Maurel'	MSta
'Hal Miller' (H)	EMFW MSta SWyc
'Helen Fowler' (H)	EMFW MSta SWyc WMAq
§ x ***helvola*** **AGM**	CBen CRow CWGN EHon EMFW EWav LMay MSta SWat SWyc WHol WMAq
'Hermine' (H)	CBen EMFW MSta SWat SWyc WMAq
¶ 'Hever White' (H)	MSta SWyc
'Hollandia'	CBen EMFW SWat SWyc WMAq
'Indiana' (H)	CBen CWGN EMFW LMay MSta SLon SWat SWyc WMAq
¶ 'Irene' (H)	SWyc
¶ 'Irene Heritage'	SWyc
'J C N Forestier' (H)	MSta
'James Brydon' **AGM**	CBen CRiv CRow CWGN EHon EMFW EWav LMay MSta SAWi SHig SLon SWat SWyc WHol WMAq
'James Hudson' (H)	MSta
'Jean de la Marsalle' (H)	MSta
'Joanne Pring'	MSta
¶ 'Joey Tomocick'	SWyc
'Julian Decelle'	MSta
'Juliana'	EMFW
¶ 'Kiss of Fire' (H)	SWyc
'Lactea' (H)	MSta
'Laydekeri Fulgens' (H)	CBen EMFW LMay MSta SWyc WMAq
'Laydekeri Lilacea' (H)	CBen CRow EMFW EWav LMay MSta SWat SWyc

'Laydekeri Purpurata' (H)	EMFW LMay MSta SWat SWyc
'Laydekeri Rosea' (H)	CBen EMFW LMay SWyc
'Laydekeri Rosea Prolifera' (H)	MSta
¶ 'Lemon Chiffon'	SWyc
'Leviathan' (H)	MSta
¶ 'Liou'	SWyc
¶ 'Little Sue'	SWyc
¶ 'Livingstone' (H)	MSta SWyc
¶ 'Louise' (H)	SWyc
¶ 'Louise Villemarette'	SWyc
'Luciana' (H)	EMFW MSta SWyc
'Lucida' (H)	CBen EMFW LMay MSta SWyc
'Lusitania' (H)	MSta
'Lustrous' (H)	MSta
'Madame Bory Latour-Marliac' (H)	MSta
'Madame de Bonseigneur' (H)	MSta
'Madame Julien Chifflot' (H)	MSta
¶ 'Madame Maurice Laydeker' (H)	MSta SWyc
'Madame Wilfon Gonnère' (H)	CBen EHon EMFW EWav LMay MSta SWat SWyc WMAq
'Marguerite Laplace' (H)	MSta
'Marliacea Albida' (H)	CBen CRiv CWGN EHon EMFW EWav LMay MSta SWat SWyc WChe WHol
§ 'Marliacea Carnea' (H)	CBen CRiv CRow CWGN EHon EMFW EWav LMay MSta SWat SWyc WHol WMAq
'Marliacea Chromatella' **AGM**	CBen CRDP CRiv CRow CWGN EHon EMFW EWav LMay MSta SAWi SHig SLon SWat SWyc WChe WHol WMAq
'Marliacea Flammea' (H)	MSta SWyc
'Marliacea Ignea' (H)	EMFW MSta SWyc
'Marliacea Rosea' (H)	EMFW EWav MSta SHig SWyc
'Marliacea Rubra Punctata' (H)	MSta
¶ 'Martha'	SWyc
'Martin E Randig'	MSta
¶ 'Mary'	SWyc
'Mary Exquisita' (H)	MSta
'Mary Patricia' (H)	MSta
'Masaniello' (H)	CBen CRow CWGN EHon EMFW EWav LMay MSta SLon SWat SWyc WMAq
'Maurice Laydeker' (H)	EMFW MSta SWyc
¶ 'Mayla'	SWyc
¶ 'Meteor' (H)	MSta SWyc
mexicana (T/D)	MSta
'Moorei' (H)	CBen CWGN EHon EMFW LMay MSta SHig SWyc WHol WMAq
¶ 'Mrs C W Thomas' (H)	SWyc
'Mrs C W Ward' (T/D)	MSta
'Mrs Richmond' (H)	CBen CRow EHon EMFW EWav LMay MSta SAWi SHig SWat SWyc WHol WMAq
¶ 'Murillo' (H)	MSta SWyc
'Neptune' (H)	MSta
'Newton' (H)	EMFW MSta SWyc WMAq

'Nigel' (H)	MSta
'Norma Gedye' (H)	CBen MSta SWat SWyc WMAq
♦'Occidentalis'	See N. ***a. occidentalis***
'Odalisque' (H)	EMFW MSta SWyc
§ ***odorata*** (H)	CBen CRow CWGN LMay MSta SHig SWyc WMAq
¶ – 'Jasmine'	SWyc
¶ – 'Maxima' (H)	SWyc
– 'Pumila' (H)	MSta SWyc
– var. ***rosea*** (H)	EMFW MSta SAWi SWyc
– 'Rubra' (H)	MSta
'Odorata Alba' (H)	See N. ***odorata***
'Odorata Eugène de Land' (H)	MSta
'Odorata Gigantea' (H)	MSta
'Odorata Juliana' (H)	MSta SWyc
'Odorata Minor' (H)	CBen CRow CWGN EMFW LMay MSta SWyc WMAq
'Odorata Sulphurea' (H)	MSta
'Odorata Sulphurea Grandiflora' (H)	CBen CRow CWGN EHon EMFW EWav LMay MSta SWyc
'Odorata Turicensis' (H)	CBen EMFW LMay MSta SWyc
'Odorata William B Shaw' (H)	CBen CWGN EHon EMFW LMay MSta SLon SWat SWyc WMAq
'Pam Bennett'	MSta
'Pamela' (T/D)	CBen MSta
'Paul Hariot'	CBen CWGN EHon EMFW EWav LMay MSta SLon SWat SWyc
¶ 'Peach Blossom'	SWyc
Pearl of the Pool ® (H)	MSta
'Pennsylvania' (T/D)	MSta
¶ 'Perry's Baby Red'	SWyc
¶ 'Perry's Black Opal'	SWyc
¶ 'Perry's Cactus Pink'	SWyc
¶ 'Perry's Crinkled Pink'	SWyc
¶ 'Perry's Darkest Red'	SWyc
¶ 'Perry's Double White'	SWyc
¶ 'Perry's Fire Opal'	SWyc
¶ 'Perry's Magnificent'	SWyc
'Perry's Pink'	MSta SWyc WMAq
¶ 'Perry's Pink Beauty'	SWyc
¶ 'Perry's Pink Bicolor'	SWyc
¶ 'Perry's Pink Delight'	SWyc
¶ 'Perry's Pink Heaven'	SWyc
¶ 'Perry's Red Beauty'	SWyc
¶ 'Perry's Red Bicolor'	SWyc
¶ 'Perry's Red Blaze'	SWyc
¶ 'Perry's Red Dwarf'	SWyc
¶ 'Perry's Red Glow'	SWyc
¶ 'Perry's Red Star'	SWyc
¶ 'Perry's Red Wonder'	SWyc
¶ 'Perry's Rich Rose'	SWyc
¶ 'Perry's Stellar Red'	SWyc
¶ 'Perry's Strawberry Pink'	SWyc
¶ 'Perry's Super Red'	SWyc
¶ 'Perry's Super Rose'	SWyc
¶ 'Perry's Vivid Rose'	SWyc
¶ 'Perry's Viviparous Pink'	SWyc
¶ 'Perry's White Star'	SWyc
¶ 'Perry's White Wonder'	SWyc
¶ 'Perry's Wildfire'	SWyc
'Peter Slocum'	MSta SWyc
'Philippe Laydeker'	MSta
'Phoebus' (H)	MSta SWyc
'Picciola' (H)	EMFW MSta SWyc
¶ 'Pink Cameo'	SWyc
¶ 'Pink Glory' (H)	SWyc
'Pink Opal' (H)	CBen EMFW LMay MSta SWyc
¶ 'Pink Peony'	SWyc
'Pink Platter' (T/D)	CBen
'Pink Sensation' (H)	CBen EMFW MSta SWyc WMAq
¶ 'Pink Shadow'	SWyc
¶ 'Pink Sunrise'	SWyc
¶ 'Pöstlingberg' (H)	MSta SWyc
'Président Viger'	MSta
'Princess Elizabeth' (H)	CBen EMFW LMay MSta SWyc
'Pygmaea Alba' (H)	See N. ***tetragona***
♦'Pygmaea Helvola'	See N. x ***helvola***
'Pygmaea Rubis' (H)	CRow EHon EWav LMay MSta SWat WHol
'Pygmaea Rubra' (H)	CBen EMFW MSta SWyc WMAq
'Queen of the Whites' (H)	SWyc
'Ray Davies'	MSta SWyc
'Red Cup'	MSta
'Red Flare' (T/N)	MSta
¶ 'Red Sensation'	SWyc
¶ 'Red Spider'	SWyc
¶ 'Regann'	SWyc
'Rembrandt' (H)	EMFW SWyc
'René Gérard' (H)	CBen EHon EMFW EWav LMay MSta SAWi SHig SWat SWyc WMAq
¶ 'Rio'	SWyc
'Robinsoniana' (H)	EMFW MSta SWyc
¶ 'Rosa Mundi'	SWyc
¶ 'Rosanna'	SWyc
'Rosanna Supreme' (H)	MSta
'Rose Arey' (H)	CBen CRow CWGN EHon EMFW EWav LMay MSta SLon SWat SWyc WHol WMAq
'Rose Magnolia' (H)	CRiv EMFW MSta SWat SWyc
'Rosennymphe' (H)	CBen LMay MSta SWyc WMAq
¶ 'Rosette'	SWyc
'Rosita' (H)	MSta
'Rosy Morn' (H)	EMFW MSta
'Sanguinea' (H)	EMFW MSta SWyc
'Seignouretti' (H)	EMFW MSta SWyc
'Senegal' (H)	MSta
'Sioux' (H)	CBen CWGN EHon EMFW LMay MSta SHig SWat SWyc WMAq
'Sir Galahad' (T/N)	MSta
'Sirius' (H)	EMFW MSta SWyc
'Solfatare' (H)	EMFW EWav MSta SWyc
'Somptuosa' (H)	EMFW MSta SWyc
'Souvenir de Jules Jacquier' (H)	MSta
'Speciosa' (H)	MSta
'Spectabilis'	MSta
¶ 'Splendida' (H)	MSta SWyc WMAq
¶ 'Stardust'	SWyc
¶ 'Steven Strawn'	SWyc
'Suavissima' (H)	MSta
'Sultan'	EMFW MSta SWyc
'Sunrise' (H)	CRDP EMFW EWav LMay SWat SWyc WMAq
'Superba' (H)	MSta
'Sylphida' (H)	MSta
'Temple Fire'	MSta
§ ***tetragona*** (H)	CBen CRow EMFW LMay MSta SWyc WHol
♦– ***alba***	See N. ***t.***
– 'Johann Pring' (H)	EMFW

'Texas Dawn' EMFW MSta SWyc
tuberosa (H) CBen LMay MSta SWyc
¶ – var. ***maxima*** (H) SWyc
– 'Maxima' (H) MSta
– 'Richardsonii' (H) CWGN EHon EMFW MSta SWyc
– 'Rosea' (H) CBen CWGN EMFW LMay MSta SWyc WHol WMAq
'Tulipiformis' (H) MSta
¶ 'Venus' SWyc
'Venusta' (H) MSta SWyc
'Vera Louise' (H) MSta
'Vésuve' (H) EMFW MSta SWyc
'Virginalis' (H) EMFW MSta SWyc
'Virginia' (H) EMFW MSta SWyc
¶ 'Walter Pagels' SWyc
¶ 'White Cup' SWyc
¶ 'White Sultan' SWyc
'William Doogue' (H) EMFW MSta SWyc WMAq
'William Falconer' (H) CBen CWGN EMFW EWav LMay MSta SAWi SLon SWyc
¶ 'Wow' SWyc
'Yellow Dazzler' (T/D) MSta
¶ 'Yellow Princess' SWyc
¶ 'Yellow Queen' SWyc
¶ 'Yellow Sensation' SWyc
¶ 'Yogi-gi' SWyc
'Yul Ling' EMFW

NYMPHOÏDES (Menyanthaceae)

peltata CRDP CRiv ECoo EMFW NDea SWat SWyc WChe WHol
§ – 'Bennettii' CBen CWGN EBre EHon EWav IBlr LBre LMay MSta

NYSSA (Cornaceae)

aquatica CFil
ogeche CGre
sinensis **AGM** CAbP CB&S CBow CChu CCla CDoC CGre CMCN CPMA CSam EHar ELan MBri MUlv SHil SPer SReu SSta WCoo WWat
sylvatica **AGM** Widely available
– 'Jermyns Flame' SHil

OAKESIELLA See UVULARIA

OCHAGAVIA (Bromeliaceae)

rosea CHEx

OCHNA (Ochnaceae)

serrulata CPle CTro LBlm

OCIMUM (Labiatae/Lamiaceae)

§ ***americanum*** WHer
– 'Meng Luk' WPer
basilicum CArn CSFH CSev EEls EHer EJud GPoy IEde LHol MBri MChe MPit SHer SIde SWat WHer WPer WWye
– 'Anise' CSev MChe WPer
– 'Cinnamon' CSev MChe MSal NPri SHer SWat WHer WPer WWye
– var. ***citriodorum*** CArn MChe MSal NOak SHer SIde SWat WOak WPer
– 'Dark Opal' SWat
– 'Genovese' SHer
*– ***glycyrrhiza*** MSal
– 'Green Ruffles' MChe SWat
– 'Holy' See O. ***tenuiflorum***
– var. ***minimum*** CArn CSFH CSev EEls EHer EJud LHol MBri MChe SHer SIde WHer WOak WPer
*– ***neapolitanum*** MChe NPri SIde SWat WPer
– 'Purple Ruffles' MChe SHer SIde SWat WPer
– var. ***purpurascens*** CArn CSev EEls GPoy LHol MBri MChe SIde WHer WPer WWye
canum See O. ***americanum***
'Horapha' CArn WPer
sanctum See O. ***tenuiflorum***
'Spice' MChe NPri WPer
§ ***tenuiflorum*** CArn CSev GPoy MChe MSal NOak SIde SWat WPer

OEMLERIA (Rosaceae)

§ ***cerasiformis*** CB&S CCla CHan ELan WBod WCot WEas WHCG WWat

OENANTHE (Umbelliferae/Apiaceae)

¶ ***aquatica*** 'Variegata' EMFW
¶ ***crocata*** ECWi
japonica See O. ***javanica***
javanica 'Flamingo' CBre CGle CMil CRow CSpe EBar ECha ECoo EFol EHal ELan EMar EMil EMon EPla GCal LHil LHop MBel MBri NFai NNrw NRar SAxl SUsu WCru WHer WPbr
pimpinelloïdes ECWi WOak

OENOTHERA † (Onagraceae)

§ ***acaulis*** CBot CLew CNic ECha EPad GMac LHop MCas NWyt SAxl SChu SOkh SUsu WThu
– BC&W 4110 MFos
¶ – ***alba*** WDav
§ – 'Aurea' LHop NCat NRed NTow NWCA SOkh WCla WPer WTyr
– ***lutea*** hort. See O. ***a.*** 'Aurea'
* ***alpina*** CPle
¶ ***argillicola*** MSto
berlandieri See O. ***speciosa*** 'Rosea'
§ ***biennis*** CKin CRDP CRow CTom EBre ECWi ECha EHoe EWFC GPoy LBre LHol MChe MHew NBro NHol SHer SIde SIng WEas WHal WHer WOak WPer WWye
¶ ***brachycarpa*** MSto
caespitosa EPad EPot MSto MTho
californica EMon
¶ ***cheiranthifolia*** WPer
¶ ***chicoginensis*** NHol
childsii See O. ***speciosa*** 'Rosea'
cinaeus See O. ***fruticosa glauca***
elata hirsutissima CHan
§ – ssp. ***hookeri*** WCla WPer WTyr
erythrosepala See O. ***glaziouana***
flava CNic MTho NNrd
fruticosa EBre GCal LBre NBro
– cream LGan WHoo
– ssp. ***fruticosa*** CHan

– 'Fyrverkeri' ('Fireworks') AGM	CBow CCla CDoC CGle CKel CRDP CSam CSco CShe EBre ECED ECro EFou ELan ENot EPla GAbr LBre LHop NHol NKay NWyt SPer SUsu WHoo WRus WTyr WWin
§ – ssp. ***glauca*** AGM	CBow CElw CHan CRDP EBar EBre EMon GAbr IDai LBre LGan LHol LWad MTho NBro NCat NHol NNrw NTow SIng WEas WPer
– – 'Erica Robin' (v)	EMon
¶ – – 'Frühlings Gold'	EMon
– 'Lady Brookborough'	LHop MRav MUlv
– var. ***riparia***	ELan EPad IDai LHop NKay WRus
– 'Yellow River'	CB&S CSco ECED EOrc ESma
– 'Youngii'	CBow SFis WPer
glabra hort.	CPBP LHop NSti SChu
glabra Miller	See O. ***biennis***
§ ***glaziouana***	CRDP EHer EMon IBlr IEde NBir NNrw WHaw WPbr WWye
* 'Hollow Meadows'	EPot MUlv NMen
hookeri	See O. ***elata h.***
kunthiana	CTom EPad NWCA WAbe WHil WPer
laciniata	SChu
lamarckiana	See O. ***glaziouana***
¶ ***lavandulifolia***	MSto
linearis	See O. ***fruticosa***
¶ 'Longest Day'	NFai
§ ***macrocarpa*** AGM	Widely available
– ***alba***	CRiv
– 'Greencourt Lemon'	EMon LRHS
mexicana	See O. ***laciniata***
missouriensis	See O. ***macrocarpa***
nuttallii	NHol
odorata 'Sulphurea'	See O. ***stricta*** 'S.'
odorata Jacquin	CArn CDoC CRDP CRiv CSev CSpe EFol ESma GBar GCal IBlr LAbb LHil NOrc SSvw WEas WHil
pallida	CRiv IBlr MWil NFai
– 'Innocence'	CBot WPer
– ssp. ***trichocalyx***	LHol
– 'Wedding Bells'	NPer
'Penelope Hobhouse'	SUsu
§ ***perennis***	CLew CNic CRiv CTom EBre EPla LBre LHop MCas MTho NMen NNrd NPri SFis WCla WEas WPer WThu WWin
¶ ***primiveris***	MSto
pumila	See O. ***perennis***
rosea	CMea MBel NPer SIde SUsu WOMN
¶ ***serrulata***	MSto
¶ – K 92.296	WDav
speciosa	CHan CLew CMGP EMon MBel MTol NCat NPer NWyt SAxl SMad SMrm SPer SUsu WByw WCot WHal WPbr WPer WTyr
¶ – 'Ballerina'	LHop
– var. ***childsii***	See O. ***speciosa*** 'Rosea'
– 'Pink Petticoats'	CB&S ECoo EHal NFai WElm WHil WPla
§ – 'Rosea'	CBot CBoy CGle CLew CMea CNic CRDP EMon NNrw SAxl SFis SUsu WHer WPer WWin
sp. CD&R 1140	CHan
stricta	CKin CMea CSpe EBee EPad EWFC MNFA WHaw WPer WWye
§ – 'Sulphurea'	CHad CHan CMil CSam CTom ECoo ELan EMon EPla GCal IBlr LBlm LGre MBel MNFA NPer SChu SMrm WAbb WCot WPer
¶ ***suaveolens***	EBee
taraxacifolia	See O. ***acaulis***
tetragona	See O. ***fruticosa glauca***
– var. ***fraseri***	See O. ***fruticosa glauca***
tetraptera	NWCA
texensis	WPla
– 'Early Rise'	ELan EMon LHop WEas
¶ ***triloba***	MSto

OLEA (Oleaceae)

europaea AGM	CArn ERea GAri LBlm LHol LPan SArc STre WNor
– var. ***europaea*** 'Cipressino'	ERea
– – 'El Greco'	CB&S ERea GAri
– – 'Picholine'	ERea
– – 'Pyramidalis'	See O. ***e. e.*** 'Cipressino'

OLEARIA † (Compositae/Asteraceae)

albida	CB&S MAll
– x ***paniculata***	CPle
¶ ***algida***	CB&S ECou
arborescens	IBar
argophylla	ECou
avicenniifolia	CMHG CPle ECou EPla MAll WBod WSHC
– 'White Confusion'	WWat
capillaris	CMHG CPle ECou EPla GAbr GGar ISea SDry SIgm SLon WWat
chathamica	GCal IDai
§ ***cheesemanii***	CCla CMHG CPle MAll WSHC
floribunda	CPle
frostii	WSHC
furfuracea	CB&S CHEx
glandulosa	ECou MAll
gunniana	See O. ***phlogopappa***
x ***haastii***	Widely available
– 'McKenzie'	ECou
§ 'Henry Travers' AGM	CAbb CDoC CGre CPle GCal IBar IBlr IDai ISea LAbb MAll MBal SGil WBod
ilicifolia	CBow CCla CPMA CPle CSco MAll SDry
¶ – – ***moschata***	MAll
insignis	WCru
¶ – var. ***minor***	WCru
lacunosa	SDry
lepidophylla	ECou EWes NHol WThi
– green	ECou MAll
– silver	ECou MAll
¶ ***lineata*** 'Dartonii'	ECou MAll
lirata	ECou MAll
x ***macrodonta*** AGM	Widely available
– 'Major'	SHBN
– 'Minor'	CChu ELan
x ***mollis*** hort.	See O. ***ilicifolia***
x ***mollis*** (Kirk) Ckn.	CB&S CBow CPle NNor SLon SPer WSHC WWat
– 'Zennorensis' AGM	CAbb CBow CGre CLan CMHG CPle ELan IBar ISea MAll NNor SDry WSHC
moschata	CPle ECou MAll SLon WSHC

myrsinoïdes CCla CMHG CPle MAll
§ ***nummulariifolia*** CCla CLew CMHG COtt CPle CSco ECou EPla EWri IBar ISea MAll MBal NNor NWyt SArc SBor SDry SIng WBod WSHC WStI
– var. ***cymbifolia*** ECou MAll
– hybrids ECou
odorata CPle ECou MAll SGil WBod WHCG
oleifolia See O. 'Waikariensis'
paniculata CAbb CDoC CGre CMHG CPle CTre GIsl IDai ISea MAll SDry
§ ***phlogopappa*** CHan CMHG ECou GIsl GWht IBar IJoh ISea MAll NPer NTow
– 'Comber's Blue' CB&S CDoC CGre CPMA CTre EBar IBar IBlr ISea MAll NPer
§ – 'Comber's Pink' CB&S CDoC CGre CPMA EBar ELan IBar IBlr ISea SPer SPla
– 'Rosea' See O. ***p.*** 'Comber's Pink'
– Splendens Group CAbb CLew NRar SHil
– var. ***subrepanda*** CGre MAll WBod
****pleniflora*** CLew
§ ***ramulosa*** CGre CPle CTre WCot WWat
¶ – 'Blue Stars' ECou MAll
– ***ramulosa*** ECou
rani hort. See O. ***cheesemanii***
x ***scilloniensis***
Dorrien-Smith 'Master Michael' CBow CCla CPle CTrw NFai SBor SPer WBod WStI
x ***scilloniensis*** hort. See O. ***stellulata***
semidentata See O. 'Henry Travers'
solandri CHan CMHG CMer COtt CPle CSam ECou EMon EPla EWri GAbr GIsl IDai IJoh LAbb MRav NFai SDix SDry SLon SPer
– 'Aurea' CB&S
§ ***stellulata*** AGM CBot CGre CMHG CMer CPle CSco CTre CTrw CWit EBar ECou ELan ENot IBar IHos ISea LAbb MWat NTow SBor SDix SLon SPer SPla SSta WAbe WHCG WStI
stellulata hort. See O. ***phlogopappa***
traversii CAbb CDoC CMHG CPle CTre GIsl IOrc MAll WCru WDin
§ – 'Tweedledum' (v) CPle ECou MAll
– 'Variegata' See O. ***t.*** 'Tweedledum'
virgata CMHG COtt CPle ECou ELan ISea
– 'Laxifolia' CTre
– var. ***lineata*** CMer CPle MAll SArc WDin WSHC
– – 'Dartonii' GIsl SLPl
viscosa CPle
§ 'Waikariensis' CBot CMHG CPle CSam CTre ECou MAll SChu SLon SMrm WBod WDin WSHC WWat

OLSYNIUM (Iridaceae)

§ ***biflorum*** NHol
douglasii AGM CBro CNic CRDP EBur ELan EPot GDra NGar NHar NHol NMen NTow SIng WAbe WGor WThu
– JCA 11132 CNic
– ***album*** EBur EPot GAbr GDra NHar NHol WThu

OLYSNIUM

filifolium NNrw WPer
– ssp. ***junceum***
JCA 12289 CNic CRDP MTho

OMPHALODES (Boraginaceae)

cappadocica AGM Widely available
– 'Alba' EBre LBre SRms WEas
– 'Anthea Bloom' IBlr NTow
– 'Cherry Ingram' CFil CRow ECha GBuc MBri MUlv NBir NCat SAxl SBla SMrm SUsu SWas WCot WCru WDav
– 'Starry Eyes' CElw CGle CMil CRDP ECha EMon EPla IBlr MBri SWas WCru WHal
§ ***linifolia*** AGM CHad CMea CRDP CSpe ECoo EJud MHlr WCru WEas WHil
– ***alba*** See O. ***linifolia***
luciliae WHoo
¶ – var. ***cilicica*** WDav
nitida EMon
verna Widely available
– 'Alba' Widely available

OMPHALOGRAMMA (Primulaceae)

See Plant Deletions

ONCOBA (Flacourtiaceae)

¶ ***spinosa*** CTro

ONIXOTIS (Liliaceae/Colchicaceae)

See Plant Deletions

ONOBRYCHIS (Leguminosae/Papilionaceae)

viciifolia CKin EBee ELan ESis EWFC MHew MSal

ONOCLEA (Dryopteridaceae)

sensibilis AGM CBar CFil CGre CHan CRow CWGN ECha EGol EHon ELan EPar IOrc MBri NBir NDea NHar NHol NKay NMar SAxl SCob SHig SPer SWat WEas WFib WHal WRic
– copper CFil NKay WRic

ONONIS (Leguminosae/Papilionaceae)

cenisia See O. ***cristata***
cristata NTow
natrix EMon
repens CArn CKin ECWi EWFC MHew MSal MWil NMir WGwy
rotundifolia MSal NTow WOMN WPat
spinosa CKin ECWi EWFC GAul MHew MSal WGwy WNdy WPer
– 'Alba' EMon

ONOPORDUM (Compositae/Asteraceae)

acanthium CArn CBow CKin EBre ECha ELan EMil EMon GBar GCra LBre LHol SFis SIde WHer WWye
arabicum See O. ***nervosum***
¶ ***argolicum*** EMon
bracteatum WPer

§ ***nervosum*** AGM — CSpe ECro ERav GAul LHil NBro NSti NVic SFis SMad SMrm WEas
salteri — ECro

ONOSMA (Boraginaceae)

alborosea — CHan CMea CNic ECha EFol ELan EOrc GCal GCra LHop MFir NTow SChu SMrm WCru WEas WOMN WOld WPat WPer
armena — WDav
echioïdes — EPad MHig
montana — NTow
nana — CPBP SIng
– Mac&W 5785 — WOMN
pyramidalis — GCra
stellulata — CLew CNic SMrm SUsu WOld
taurica AGM — CHan EBar NBir NHol WCru WDav WOld WWin
¶ ***tornensis*** — GLil

ONYCHIUM (Adiantaceae)

contiguum — CFil SMrm
japonicum — CFil CRDP NMar SBla WAbe WRic
– L 1649 — SBla

OPHIOPOGON † (Liliaceae/Convallariaceae)

'Black Dragon' — See O. ***planiscapus*** 'Nigrescens'
bodinieri B&L 12505 — EMon EPla
graminifolius — See LIRIOPE ***muscari***
intermedius — EMon EPla MSte SApp WCot
§ – 'Argenteomarginatus' — WChr
– ***parviflorus*** — EBul NSti
♦– 'Variegatus' — See O. ***i.*** 'Argenteomarginatus'
§ ***jaburan*** — CHan CMGP EBul LAma MHFP MSte MUlv NHol WPbr WWat
– 'Variegatus' — See O. ***j.*** 'Vittatus'
§ – 'Vittatus' (v) — EBul NHol SMad WCot
japonicus — CBro CRiv CRow EBul EPla NSti SApp
– 'Albus' — CRDP
– 'Compactus' — CFil WCot
– 'Minor' — EPla
– 'Nippon' — EGol
*– Tamaryu Number Two 'Kigimafukiduma' — EHic NHar SHer WChr WCot
planiscapus — CFee CHan EBul EPad EPar EPla GCal MBel MSte MTho MWat NBro NGar NHar NHol WAbe
– ***leucanthus*** — CRow EPla WCot
§ – 'Nigrescens' AGM — Widely available
sp. DF 617 — EBul
* ***tamaryu*** — WThi
* ***wallichianus*** — CFil SApp WCot WOMN WWat

OPITHANDRA (Gesneriaceae)

See Plant Deletions

OPLISMENUS (Gramineae/Poaceae)

hirtellus — See O. ***africanus***

OPUNTIA (Cactaceae)

lindheimeri — CHEx SArc
linguiformis — See O. ***lindheimeri***
phaeacantha — CHEx SArc

ORANGE, Sour or Seville See CITRUS *aurantium*

ORANGE, Sweet See CITRUS *sinensis*

ORCHIS (Orchidaceae)

elata — See DACTYLORHIZA ***e.***
foliosa — See DACTYLORHIZA ***f.***
fuchsii — See DACTYLORHIZA ***f.***
maculata — See DACTYLORHIZA ***m.***
maderensis — See DACTYLORHIZA ***foliosa***
majalis — See DACTYLORHIZA ***m.***
mascula — CAvo NHar SWes WChe

OREOBOLUS (Cyperaceae)

See Plant Deletions

OREOPANAX (Araliaceae)

epremesnilianus — CHEx

OREOPTERIS (Thelypteridaceae)

§ ***limbosperma*** — NHar

ORIGANUM † (Labiatae/Lamiaceae)

acutidens — WCHb
– JCA 735.000 — EMon
amanum AGM — ECha ELan EPot LHop MBro MFos NTow SBla SChu SHer WOMN WPat WThu
– ***album*** — WOMN
'Barbara Tingey' — CElw CSev ECha ECou EFol ELan ESma LBee LHop MCas MFir MHig MTho SBla SChu SHer SUsu SWas WCru WHoo WPat WThu
* 'Bristol Cross' — ECha NHex SIng
'Buckland' — CGle ESis LGre SBla SUsu WPat
* ***caespitosum*** — NCat
§ ***calcaratum*** — CLew CShe ELan ESma LBee LHop NRar SBla SHer SWas WByw WHer WOld WPat WThu WWye
dictamnus — CMea EEls ELan EPot GPoy LBee NHol NTow SGil SUsu SWas WOMN WRus
'Dingle Fairy' — EFol EWes NBir NHex WPla
'Erntedank' — EFou EMon
heracleoticum hort. — See O. x ***applei***
heracleoticum Linnaeus — See O. ***vulgare hirtum***
§ x ***hybridinum*** — CElw EBee EFol EGol LHop MBro NNrw SBla SChu WDav WPat WWat WWin
'Kent Beauty' — CDec CMHG ECha ELan LBee LGre MBel NGar SBla SChu SGil SHer SUsu SWas WOMN
kopatdaghense — See O. ***vulgare gracile***
laevigatum AGM — Widely available
– 'Herrenhausen' AGM — Widely available
– 'Hopleys' — Widely available
¶ ***libanoticum*** — NTow
¶ – RMRP 93-0311 — LGre

majorana	CArn CSFH CSev EHer ELan Effi GPoy LHol MChe MSal SHer SIde WOak WPer WTyr WWye
microphyllum	CArn CBot CGle CMHG CShe EMon ESis GBar ITim LBee LGre MTho NTow SBla SChu SUsu WCru WHil WHoo WOMN WThu WWye
minutiflorum	ELan
'Norton Gold'	EBee ECha EFol EFou EMon GBuc LRHS NPer WCHb WHoo
'Nymphenburg'	EHic LHop SUsu SWas WCru WPer
onites	CArn CSFH EEls EHer Effi GBar GPoy ILis LHol MChe MSal NRoo SBla SHer SIde WHer WOak WPer WWye
♦***pulchellum***	See O. x ***hybridinum***
'Rosenkuppel'	CGle ECha ELan GCal SUsu SWas WSun
rotundifolium **AGM**	CArn CBos CElw CGle CLew CRDP CSev ECha EFol ELan ESma LGre LHop NBir NHex SBla SChu SUsu SWas WCru WDav WKif WMer WRus WThu
scabrum	CArn
– ssp. ***pulchrum***	LHop
sp. Mac&W 5882	See NEPETA ***phyllochlamys***
tournefortii	See O. ***calcaratum***
* ***villosum***	CBot ESis
vulgare	CArn CKin CSev CTom ECWi ECoo EHer EJud EWFC Effi GBar GPoy LHol MChe MHew NBro NFai NLan NMir NRoo SHer SIde SSvw WByw WEas WHal WHer WOak WPer WWye
– var. ***album***	CElw NHex WHer
– 'Aureum' **AGM**	Widely available
– 'Aureum Album'	EMar WHer
– 'Aureum Crispum'	EOrc GBar ILis NFai NHex NSti SIde WSun WWye
– 'Compactum'	CArn CNic CRDP CSFH CSev EFol GAbr GPoy ILis LGan LHol MHig NHol NRar SBla SIde WCHb WPer WWye
– 'Compactum Album'	MHig SIde
§ – 'Gold Tip' (v)	CArn CElw CMea CMer CSev EFol EHoe EJud EMar EOrc GAbr ILis NFai NHex NRoo NSti SHer WCHb WHal WHer WRus WWye
– 'Golden Shine'	EWes NRoo SIde
§ – ssp. ***gracile***	NHol
§ – ssp. ***hirtum***	EEls GPoy LAbb LHop MSal WPer
– 'Nanum'	CMGP EPla LHop WCla
– 'Polyphant' (v)	CBre NHex
– 'Thumble's Variety'	ECha ECoo EFol EHoe SIde
– 'Variegatum'	See O. ***v.*** 'Gold Tip'
¶ 'Webb's White'	SIde

ORIXA (Rutaceae)

japonica	CBot CCla CMCN GWht WDin

ORLAYA (Umbelliferae/Apiaceae)

¶ ***grandiflora***	WCot

ORNITHOGALUM (Liliaceae/Hyacinthaceae)

arabicum	CAvo CBro CGle LAma LBow MBri NRog SGil WCot
arcuatum	CMon WChr
balansae	See O. ***oligophyllum***
caudatum	See O. ***longibracteatum***
chionophyllum	CMon
concinnum MS 452	CMon
exscapum	CMon
fimbriatum	EPot
lanceolatum	CAvo
§ ***longibracteatum***	CHEx CRDP ELan SLMG WHer
magnum	LRHS
montanum BSBE 2360	CMon
nanum	See O. ***sigmoïdeum***
narbonense	CBro ETub
nutans **AGM**	CAvo CBro CMea CMon CRDP EPar EPot ETub EWFC LAma LBow MBro MTho NHol NLan NMen NRog SIng WHal WPer
§ ***oligophyllum***	CBro EPot ETub WCot
pyramidale	EPot
pyrenaicum	CArn CAvo ECha
– AB&S 4600	CMon
– Flavescens Group	CMon
reverchonii	CMon WChr
saundersiae	LBow
sessiliflorum AB&S 4619	CMon
sibthorpii	See O. ***sigmoideum***
§ ***sigmoïdeum***	EPot
spicatum MS 585	CMon
tenuifolium	CMon EPot
thyrsoïdes	LAma LBow MBri MWBu NRog SRms WCru
umbellatum	CAvo CBro CCla CMea CRiv ELan EPar ETub EWFC GPoy LAma LBow MBri MFir NLan NRog SIng WPer WShi WWye
unifolium MS 435	CMon
woronowii	EPot

ORONTIUM (Araceae)

aquaticum	CBen CHEx CWGN EBre ECtt EHon EMFW EWav LBre LMay MSta NDea SHig SWat WChe WHol

OROSTACHYS (Crassulaceae)

§ ***aggregata***	NGre
chanetii	NBra NMen
¶ ***erubescens***	NGre
iwarenge	ESis NTow
malacophylla	See O. ***aggregata***
§ ***spinosa***	NGre NMen NTow WThu

ORPHIUM (Gentianaceae)

frutescens	CSpe CTro

ORTHROSANTHUS (Iridaceae)

chimboracensis	WPer
laxus	EBee NHol
multiflorus	CHan NTow
polystachyus	CHan EBee

ORYZOPSIS (Gramineae/Poaceae)

miliacea ETPC

OSBECKIA (Melastomataceae)

stellata CGre

OSCULARIA (Aizoaceae)

deltoïdes See LAMPRANTHUS ***d.***

OSMANTHUS (Oleaceae)

armatus CHan CLan NNor SHil SPla WWat
§ x ***burkwoodii*** AGM Widely available
§ ***decorus*** CB&S CDoC CGre EGol ELan ENot MGos MRav MUlv SHil SLon SPer WBod WTyr WWat
– 'Angustifolius' SLon
delavayi AGM Widely available
♦***forrestii*** See O. ***yunnanensis***
x ***fortunei*** CDoC CGre CPle
– 'Variegatus' See O. ***heterophyllus*** 'Latifolius Variegatus'
fragrans CBot CGre SArc
§ ***heterophyllus*** CB&S CBow CGre CLan CPle CSco EHar ELan ENot GCHN LPan MBar MUlv NNor SCob SPer SReu SSta WDin WStI WTyr WWat
§ – all gold EPla
– 'Argenteomarginatus' See O. ***h.*** 'Variegatus'
§ – 'Aureomarginatus' CB&S CDoC CGre CPMA CPle CSco EHoe ELan IOrc MBal MPla SGil SHBN SPer
– 'Aureus' See O. ***h.*** 'Aureomarginatus'
♦– 'Aureus' misapplied See O. ***h.*** all gold
– 'Goshiki' ('Tricolor') (v) CAbP CB&S CBow CDoC CPMA CSco EHar ELan EPla IJoh IOrc LHop MAsh MBal MBar MBlu MBri MGos MPla MUlv NHol SCob SDry SGil SHBN SPer SReu SSta WStI
N– 'Gulftide' AGM EHic ELan EPla LHop MAsh MGos MUlv SCob WWat
§ – 'Latifolius Variegatus' SBla
– 'Myrtifolius' EPla
– 'Purple Shaft' ELan LRHS WWat
– 'Purpureus' CAbP CB&S CBow CMHG EGol EHar ELan EWri IBar MBal MBri MRav SDry SSta WStI WTyr
– 'Rotundifolius' CB&S MBri
§ – 'Variegatus' AGM Widely available
ilicifolius See O. ***heterophyllus***
serrulatus CBot EPla GWht SHil
§ ***yunnanensis*** CHan CLan CMHG MBlu SArc WWat

X OSMAREA (Oleaceae)

burkwoodii See OSMANTHUS x ***burkwoodii***

OSMARONIA See OEMLERIA

OSMORHIZA (Umbelliferae/Apiaceae)

claytonii MSal

OSMUNDA † (Osmundaceae)

cinnamomea CFil NHar NKay SPer
claytoniana CFil NKay
regalis AGM Widely available
– 'Crispa' NMar
– Cristata Group CFil CRDP ELan MBri NHol WFib WRic
– ***purpurascens*** CFil CRDP CRow EBre ELan IOrc LBre MBri NBro NHar NHol NMar NOrc SCob SMad SWat WFib WRic
¶ – var. ***spectabilis*** WRic
– ***undulata*** ELan NHol
– Undulata Group WRic

OSTEOMELES (Rosaceae)

schweriniae B&L 12360 EMon
subrotunda CPle

OSTEOSPERMUM † (Compositae/Asteraceae)

'African Queen' See O. 'Tresco Purple'
¶ 'Anglia Yellow' LHop
'Ballyrogan Pink' CRDP IBlr
barberae hort. See O. ***jucundum***
¶ 'Basutoland' CMer
'Blackthorn Seedling' See O. ***jucundum*** 'B.S.'
'Bloemhoff Belle' CMHG GBuc GCal GMac MBri MSte SBor WEas
'Blue Streak' CB&S CBrk CCan CGre CHol CMHG CSpe CTre EBar ECtt ELan EMar ERav GAbr LAbb SAxl SMrm WHal WHil WMar WRus
'Bodegas Pink' CBrk CElw EFol ELan EOrc ERav GCal LHop MBri SChu SMrm
'Brickell's Hybrid' CBrk CCan CLTr CMHG CSam CSev CTre EBar EMar EOrc ESma GCal LHop MArl MSte NRoo SAxl SSvw WAbe WHal WHil WPer WTyr
¶ 'Brodget's Pink' WCot
'Buttermilk' AGM Widely available
'Cannington John' CB&S CCan CMHG ECtt EOrc LAbb LHop MArl WHil
'Cannington Joyce' CCan ECtt EDon SAxl WAbe
'Cannington Katrina' CCan ECtt
'Cannington Roy' CB&S CBar CCan CGle CGre CLTr CMHG CSam CSpe CTre CTrw EBar EBre ECtt EDon ELan EMar GAbr GCal GMac LBre LHop MBri NBrk NFai NHar NPer WAbe WEas WRus
'Catriona' GCal
caulescens See O. ***ecklonii prostratum***
'Coconut Ice' CElw NBrk
'Croftway Coconut Ice' WRus
'Croftway Snow' WRus
'Dennis Weston' ECtt
ecklonii CCla CGle CHEx CHad CMHG CRiv CSam CShe CTre ERom IDai ISea LAbb MTho NBro NHol SBla SBor SCro SHer SMrm WPer WTyr WWin
*– deep pink MBri
– 'Giant' CCan CHan

§– *prostratum* AGM — CBrk CCan CHan CLTr CMHG CTre EFol ELan ERom EWri GAbr GCal IBlr LHop MBri NFai NHol NPer NSti SAxl SChu SCro SDix SLMG SMad SPla SUsu SWas WRus
– 'Starshine' — EOrc NBro
'Edna Bond' — WEas
¶ 'Giant' — CSpe
¶ 'Giles Gilbey' — CB&S EBee EOrc NPri WRus
¶ 'Glistener' — CB&S
'Gold Sparkler' (v) — EOrc NPri NRoo
'Gweek Variegated' — CBot CBrk CSpe CTre EOrc ERav ERom LHil LHop WRus
'Hampton Court Purple' — LHop SAxl
'Hopleys' — CCan CTre EBar EOrc LHop WCru
'James Elliman' — CB&S CCan CMHG ECtt EOrc MSte NFai NHar WRus
§*jucundum* AGM — CBrk CCan CCla CGle CMHG CMea CShe CTre ECha ELan ENot EOrc GAbr MWat NBrk NFai NHol NPer NSti SBla SBor SChu SDix SFis SIng SPer SUsu WHil WMar WTyr
– 'Blackthorn Seedling' — CMer ECha MBri SBla SFai WCru WKif WRus
– var. *compactum* — CB&S CLTr ECha ELan GCal LBlm LHop MHig MSte SBla SMrm WAbe WDav WMar WRus
'Killerton Pink' — CCan CGle CMHG EOrc SCro WPer WRus
'Kriti' — EOrc
'La Mortola' — CHad CLTr CMer LAbb
§ 'Lady Leitrim' — CCan CHEx CLTr CSam CTre EBar ECha EFol EOrc LBlm LHop LLWP MArl MBri NBrk NSti SAxl SBla SChu SSvw SUsu WAbe WRus
'Langtrees' — CCan ECtt EDon EFol GAbr GMac LHop NBrk SMrm
'Molly's Choice' — EOrc SMrm SUsu
¶ 'Mrs Reside's Purple' — GCal
'Nairobi' — See O. 'Tresco Purple'
'Pale Face' — See O. 'Lady Leitrim'
'Peggyi' — See O. 'Tresco Purple'
'Penny Pink' — CCan CSpe ECtt EMar EOrc LHop MArl NFai NSti
'Perhill Purple' — WPer
'Perhill White' — WPer
'Pink Whirls' AGM — Widely available
'Port Wine' — CGre ECtt SFis
prostratum — See O. ***ecklonis prostratum***
'Silver Sparkler' AGM — Widely available
'Sparkler' — CB&S CCla CHEx EBre EOrc LAbb LBre LHil MSte
'Stardust' — COtt EBee LAbb NPer
'Starshine' — See O. ***ecklonii*** 'S.'
'Sunny Boy' — CB&S EBar LHil
'Sunny Girl' — EBee ECtt LHil SUsu
'Tauranga' — See O. 'Whirligig'
'Tresco Pink' — CB&S IBlr
§ 'Tresco Purple' — Widely available
'Tresco Sally' — CRDP WEas
'Weetwood' — CBrk CGle CMHG EBar ECtt EDon GCal LHop MBri MSte NBrk NRar SChu SIng SMrm SWas WAbe WCru WPer WRus
§ 'Whirligig' AGM — Widely available
*'White Pim' — LHil
'Wine Purple' — See O. 'Tresco Purple'

Wisley hybrids — LAbb WEas WElm WRus

OSTROWSKIA (Campanulaceae)
See Plant Deletions

OSTRYA (Corylaceae)
carpinifolia — CB&S CDoC CGre CLnd CMCN CPle EArb EHar ELan IOrc MBar SHil WMou WNor
virginiana — CDoC CMCN EArb EHar WNor

OTANTHUS (Compositae/Asteraceae)
See Plant Deletions

OTHONNA (Compositae/Asteraceae)
cheirifolia — CBot CHan CLew CPle CSam CTbh EBar ECha ELan EOrc GCal MAll MBel NBir NNor NRar NTow SDry SIgm SLon SPer SUsu WCru WEas WHal WPer WRus

OTHONNOPSIS See OTHONNA

OURISIA † (Scrophulariaceae)
caespitosa — ELan EPot GGar NMen NWCA
– var. *gracilis* — GArf GGar GTou IBlr
coccinea — CBot CGle GArf GCra GDra GGar IBar MTho NRya WCru WDav WWat
crosbyi — IBlr
elegans — NBir
'Loch Ewe' — CChu CLew GAbr GCal GDra GGar IBlr MUlv NHar NKay WCru WWin
macrophylla — GAbr GDra GGar IBlr NHar NRoo WBon
microphylla — EPot WAbe WThu
'Snowflake' AGM — EPot GAbr GArf GDra GGar IBlr MTho NBir NHar NMen NSla NTow NWCA SBla WAbe
vulcanica — WCru

OXALIS † (Oxalidaceae)
acetosella — CKin CRow EWFC MHew MSal NGre NMir SIde WBon WHer WNdy
– *subpurpurascens* — EMon
adenophylla AGM — Widely available
– dark form — GDra MHig
§ *articulata* — CRiv CTom LGro MTho MTol NEgg NPer WCot WWin
'Beatrice Anderson' — GAbr GDra MDHE MTho NHar NHol NNrd SBla WAbe
bowiei — EPot NGre
'Bowles' White' — MTho WHil WThu
brasiliensis — CNic EPot MTho WDav
chrysantha — CRDP CRow ELan GAbr GAri SHer SIng WAbe
corniculata
var. *atropurpurea* — MTho
deppei — See O. ***tetraphylla***
§ *depressa* — CNic CRow ELan EPot GAbr GPlt LBee MCas MTho NBir NGre NHol NMen NRya SHer SIng
§ *drummondii* — GCal

enneaphylla AGM	ECou EPar EPot GArf IDai MCas MTho NMen WThu
– 'Alba'	EPot GArf MDHE MHig NHol NNrd WAbe
– 'Minutifolia'	CNic EPot GArf MHig MTho NGre NHol NKay NNrd NRya SSmi WAbe WDav
– 'Rosea'	CBro EPot GAbr GDra MBal MTho NGre NHol SBla
– 'Rubra'	GAbr GDra NHar NKay WAbe
– x ***adenophylla***	See O. 'Matthew Forrest'
floribunda	See O. ***articulata***
glabra	CMon
hedysaroïdes	GCra
hirta	CAvo CBro CMon CRiv LBow LHil MCas MTho NGre NHol WAbe WChr
– 'Gothenburg'	EPot MTho
inops	See O. ***depressa***
'Ione Hecker' AGM	CLew CRiv EPot GAbr GArf LBee LHop MHig MRPP MTho NGre NHar NHol NMen NNrd NTow WAbe WChr WDav WThu
japonica 'Picta'	WThu
§ ***laciniata***	EPot GArf GCLN GDra GTou MCas MSto MTho NHar NHol NSla SBla WAbe WChr WOMN
lactea double form	See O. ***magellanica*** 'Nelson'
lasiandra	CAvo
lobata	CAvo CBro CLew CRow ELan EPot LBow MFos MTho NHol NTow SHer SUsu SWas WOMN
magellanica	CFee CMHG CNic CRiv CSam CTom ELan ESis GAbr GCHN LRHS MTho NHol NMen SHer SIng WCru WDav WHil WPer
– 'Flore Pleno'	See O. ***m.*** 'Nelson'
§ – 'Nelson' (d)	CElw CGle CLew CMil CRDP CRiv CRow CSpe ESis GCHN MTho NBir NHar NHol NNrd NRar NRya SHer WCru WHil WPer
– 'Old Man Range'	ECou
'Matthew Forrest'	WAbe
melanosticta	LBow
obtusa	CMon CRiv ECha ELan EPot ESis MCas MHig MTho NCat NTow SHer SSad SWas WOMN
oregana	CAvo CGle CNic CRDP CRiv CRow ECha SFis WBon WCru
¶ – ***smalliana***	WCru
ortgiesii	SLMG
palmifrons	CMon EPot MTho NHol
patagonica	MCas MDHE MHig MSto NHol NKay WChr WHil
§ ***purpurea***	GPlt LBee LHop NGre NHol WAbe
– 'Ken Aslet'	CAvo CBro CMon CRow EPot MCas MFos MTho NGar NGre NHol NNrd NTow SBla WAbe WOMN WThu
regnellii	See O. ***triangularis papilionacea***
rosea 'Aureoreticulata'	MTho
'Royal Velvet'	NBir
speciosa	See O. ***purpurea***
♦ ***squamosoradicosa***	See O. ***laciniata***
stipularis	CMon WChr WThu
§ ***tetraphylla***	CRiv CRow CSam EPar LAma MBri MTho NCat NOrc NPer NRog SDeJ SIng SLMG WByw
– 'Iron Cross'	CAvo CRow ELan LAma NBir SAxl WCot WEas WHal WHil
triangularis	GAri LAma NPer SMad WChr WPat
– 'Cupido'	CB&S CRDP EBee EHoe EOrc GAbr LHop NWyt
§ – ssp. ***papilionacea***	CMon CRow NRog SDeJ WChr WHal
– – ***rosea***	CMon
– – 'Atropurpurea'	SDeJ WCot WPbr
tuberosa	GPoy WHer
versicolor	CRiv EPot MCas MTho NNrd SBla SSad WChr WThu
vespertilionis Torey & A Gray	See O. ***drummondii***
vespertilionis Zuccarini	See O. ***latifolia***
vulcanicola	CFee WCru

OXYCOCCUS See VACCINIUM

OXYDENDRUM (Ericaceae)

arboreum	CB&S CCla CWSG EHar MBal MBri MGos SHil SPer SReu SSta WDin WFro WWat

OXYLOBIUM (Leguminosae/Papilionaceae)

lancelolatum	CHan

OXYPETALUM (Asclepiadaceae)

caeruleum	See TWEEDIA ***caerulea***

OXYRIA (Polygonaceae)

digyna	GCHN GGar WGwy WHer

OXYTROPIS (Leguminosae/Papilionaceae)

campestris	GTou
halleri	GTou
¶ ***persica***	SIgm
podocarpa	MFos NWCA
williamsii	GTou NWCA

OZOTHAMNUS (Compositae/Asteraceae)

§ ***ledifolius*** AGM	CCla CElw CMHG CPle CSam ECha ELan GTou IBar IJoh LHop MAll MBri MBrk MPla NNor SBla SChu SIgm SLon SPer WHCG WKif WMar WPat WSHC WWat
microphyllus	ITim
¶ 'Rose Dazzler'	MAll
§ ***rosmarinifolius***	CB&S CCla CDoC CMHG CPle CSco CWit ELan ERea GWht IBar IDai IOrc LAbb MAll MBlu NNor SChu SHer SLon SPer SSta WBod WHCG WSHC WStI WWat
– 'Purpureus'	CMHG ESma
– 'Silver Jubilee' AGM	CB&S CCla CDoC CHan CMHG CSam CTre ELan EPla IBar IJoh LBlm MAll NNor NSti NTow SBla SHBN SLon SMad SPer WAbe WHCG WSHC WStI
scutellifolius	ECou
§ ***selago***	ESis GTou ITim LBee NTow SBla
¶ – 'Minor'	MHig NWCA
¶ 'Sussex Silver'	CPle
'Threave Seedling'	SPer
§ ***thyrsoïdeus***	CB&S MAll WWat

PACHYLAENA (Compositae/Asteraceae)

atriplicifolia JCA 12522 CNic

PACHYPHRAGMA (Cruciferae/Brassicaceae)

§ *macrophyllum* EBee ECha EFol ELan EMon IBlr MNFA NSti WCru WEas

PACHYPODIUM (Apocynaceae)

lamerei MBri

PACHYSANDRA (Buxaceae)

¶ *procumbens* NWyt
stylosa EPla
terminalis AGM CB&S CMer CRow CSam CSco CWGN EBre ECED ECha ELan ENot GRei IHos IJoh LBre LBuc MBar MGos NHol NNor NWea SHBN SLon SPer SReu WDin WStI WWat WWin
– 'Green Carpet' CCla CDoC ECot EFou EGol EPla GAri MAsh MBar MBri MGos SPla WRus WWat
– 'Variegata' AGM CB&S CBot CBra CCla CRiv CRow CSam CSco EBre ECha EGol EHoe ELan ENot EPar IJoh LBre MBal MBar MBri MGos NHol SHBN SMad SPer SPla WDin WRus WWat WWin

PACHYSTACHYS (Acanthaceae)

lutea AGM MBri

PACHYSTEGIA See OLEARIA

PACHYSTEMA See PAXISTIMA

PACKERA (Compositae/Asteraceae)

§ *werneriifolius* NHol

PAEDERIA (Rubiaceae)

scandens WCru WSHC
¶ – *velutina* WCru

PAEDEROTA (Scrophulariaceae)

§ *bonarota* CLew

PAEONIA † (Paeoniaceae)

albiflora See P. ***lactiflora***
anomala EPot MPhe NHol SCou
arietina See P. ***mascula a.***
'Avant Garde' WKif
bakeri MAus
'Ballerina' CKel
banatica See P. ***officinalis b.***
beresovskii CKel MPhe
broteroi CMon LGre SBla SCou
¶ – JCA 12740 MPhe
'Buckeye Belle' MAus
* 'Byzantine' CKel
cambessedesii AGM CMon EPot LGre MPhe SBla SCou WAbe WOMN
'Carol' MAus
caucasica See P. ***mascula mascula***
'Chocolate Soldier' MUlv
clusii CMon
'Coral Fay' MAus
corallina See P. ***mascula mascula***
daurica See P. ***mascula triternata***
'Daystar' CKel
decora See P. ***peregrina***
delavayi AGM CAbb CB&S CCMG CCla CGre CKel COtt CSam EOrc GAbr GCal IBlr MBal MBri NBro NSti SCou SMad SMrm SPer STre WBod WEas WHal WWat
§ – var. *ludlowii* AGM CB&S CCMG CCla CGle CGre CKel CLan COtt CSco EHar ELan ISea MBal NBrk NHol SBla SMad SPer WEas WHoo WOMN WWat
§ – var. *lutea* (S) CCla CHad CRiv ELan LGan MPhe NPal SHBN STre WEas WWat
– 'Mrs Sarson' CCla EBee
§ – Potaninii Group (S) MPhe WWat
– Trollioïdes Group (S) MPhe
– 'Yellow Queen' NBar
'Ellen Cowley' MAus
emodi SCou
'Horizon' MAus
humilis See P. ***officinalis microcarpa***
'Illini Belle' MAus
'Illini Warrior' MAus
japonica See P. ***lactiflora***
kevachensis See P. ***mascula mascula***
'Kinkaku' See P. x ***lemoinei*** 'Souvenir de Maxime Cornu'
'Kinko' See P. x ***lemoinei*** 'Alice Harding'
'Kinshi' (S) See P. x ***lemoinei*** 'Chromatella'
'Kintei' See P. x ***lemoinei*** 'L'Esperance'
§ *lactiflora* ECha SCou WCot
¶ – 'A F W Hayward' CKel
– 'Adolphe Rousseau' CB&S CKel LRHS MAus MBri
*– 'Afterglow' CKel
– 'Agida' COtt EBre ECtt ELan GCHN LBre MRav
¶ – 'Albâtre' CKel
– 'Albert Crousse' CB&S CKel CMGP IDai MAus
– 'Alexander Fleming' CKel CMGP CSco EBee ECot LWad MUlv NBar SMrm
¶ – 'Alice Graemes' CKel
– 'Alice Harding' CKel MAus
¶ – 'Anna Pavlova' CKel
¶ – 'Antwerpen' CKel
– 'Arabian Prince' CKel
– 'Argentine' CB&S CKel
¶ – 'Armance Dessert' CKel
¶ – 'Artist' CKel
¶ – 'Asa Gray' CKel
– 'Auguste Dessert' CB&S CKel
– 'Augustin d'Hour' LWad
¶ – 'Augustus John' CKel
¶ – 'Aureole' CKel
¶ – 'Bahram' CKel
¶ – 'Ballerina' CKel
– 'Balliol' COtt
¶ – 'Banner of Purity' CKel
– 'Baroness Schröder' CKel ELan MPhe
– 'Barrymore' CKel
¶ – 'Beacon' CKel

¶ – 'Beatrice Kelway' CKel
¶ – 'Beau Geste' CKel
¶ – 'Beauty Spot' CKel
– 'Beersheba' CKel
– 'Belle Center' MAus
¶ – 'Belle of Somerset' CKel
¶ – 'Bethcar' CKel
¶ – 'Birtha Gorst' CKel
¶ – 'Blaze of Beauty' CKel
¶ – 'Blaze of Glory' CKel
¶ – 'Blenheim' CKel
¶ – 'Blithe Spirit' CKel
¶ – 'Bloodshot' CKel
¶ – 'Bloodstone' CKel
– 'Blush Queen' CKel ELan MAus
¶ – 'Blush White' CKel
– 'Border Gem' COtt EBre ELan GCHN LBre MRav
¶ – 'Bouchela' CKel
¶ – 'Boulanger' CKel
¶ – 'Bower of Roses' CKel
– 'Bowl of Beauty' **AGM** CB&S CBow CCMG CCla CKel CSco EBre ECtt ELan EOrc LBre MAus MBri MUlv NBar NKay NRoo NVic SMad SPer SPla WEas WKif
– 'Bowl of Cream' MAus
¶ – 'Boy Kelway' CKel
– 'Bridal Gown' MAus
– 'Bridal Veil' CKel
¶ – 'Bridesmaid' CKel
¶ – 'Bright Era' CKel
– 'Bright Knight' MAus
– 'British Beauty' CKel
¶ – 'British Empire' CKel
– 'Bunker Hill' CB&S CDoC CKel CShe MAus MPhe NHol
– 'Butch' MAus
– 'Butter Ball' MAus
– 'Calypso' CKel
¶ – 'Canari' CKel
¶ – 'Candeur' CKel
¶ – 'Captain Alcock' CKel
– 'Captivation' CKel
– 'Carmen' CKel
– 'Carnival' CKel
¶ – 'Cascade' CKel
¶ – 'Catherine Fontijn' CKel
¶ – 'Cecilia Kelway' CKel
– 'Charm' MAus
– 'Cherry Hill' CKel MAus
– 'Chestine Gowdy' CKel
– 'Chocolate Soldier' MPhe
¶ – 'Christine Kelway' CKel
– 'Claire Dubois' CKel EBre LBre
– 'Colonel Heneage' CKel
– 'Cornelia Shaylor' CKel EBre ELan LBre
¶ – 'Coronation' CKel
– 'Countess of Altamont' CKel
– 'Country Girl' CKel
¶ – 'Crimson Banner' CKel
– 'Crimson Glory' CKel MPhe
¶ – 'Crimson Velvet' CKel
¶ – 'Dark Lantern' CKel
¶ – 'Dark Song' CKel
¶ – 'Dark Vintage' CKel
¶ – 'David Kelway' CKel
¶ – 'Dawn Crest' CKel
– 'Dayspring' CKel
¶ – 'Daystar' CKel
¶ – 'Denise' CKel
¶ – 'Desire' CKel
¶ – 'Diana Drinkwater' CKel
– 'Dinner Plate' MAus
¶ – 'Display' CKel
– 'Docteur H Barnsby' CKel
– 'Dominion' CKel
– 'Doreen' MAus
¶ – 'Dorothy Welsh' CKel
¶ – 'Dragon' CKel
– 'Dresden' CKel
¶ – 'Duc de Wellington' CKel
¶ – 'Duchess of Bedford' CKel
– 'Duchess of Marlborough' CBow CCMG SPla
¶ – 'Duchess of Somerset' CKel
– 'Duchesse de Nemours' **AGM** CCla CKel CMGP COtt CSco EBre ECtt EFou ELan LBre MAus MBri MUlv NBar NBro NRoo SPer
– 'Duke of Devonshire' CKel
– 'Edith Cavell' CKel MAus
¶ – 'Edmund Spencer' CKel
¶ – 'Edouard Doriat' CKel
– 'Edulis Superba' CKel COtt EBre ELan LBre MAus SPer
¶ – 'Elegant Lass' CKel
¶ – 'Ella Christine Kelway' CKel
– 'Elsa Sass' MAus
– 'Emperor of India' CKel
¶ – 'Enchantment' CKel
¶ – 'English Elegance' CKel
¶ – 'English Princess' CKel
¶ – 'Ethelreda' CKel
– 'Eugénie Verdier' MUlv
– 'Eva' SHig
¶ – 'Evening Glow' CKel
– 'Evening World' CKel MPhe MUlv
¶ – 'Fantin-Latour' CKel
– 'Félix Crousse' **AGM** CBow CKel CMGP COtt CShe EBre ECtt ELan LBre MBri NHol NRoo NVic SMrm SPer
– 'Festiva Maxima' **AGM** CBow CCla CKel COtt EBre ECot ECtt ELan LBre MBri NKay SFis SPer SRms WTyr
¶ – 'Fire Flower' CKel
¶ – 'Flag of War' CKel
¶ – 'Flamboyant' CKel
– 'Flamingo' CKel
– 'France' CKel
¶ – 'Full Moon' CKel
¶ – 'Gainsborough' CKel
¶ – 'Ganymede' CKel
¶ – 'Garden Beauty' CKel
– 'Gay Paree' MAus
¶ – 'Gay Sister' CKel
– 'Gayborder June' CKel EBre LBre
¶ – 'Gazelle' CKel
¶ – 'Général Joffre' CKel
– 'Général MacMahon' See P. *l.* 'Augustin d'Hour'
¶ – 'General Wolfe' CKel
¶ – 'Germaine Bigot' CKel
¶ – 'Gertrude' CKel
– 'Gilbert Barthelot' MAus

- 'Gleam of Light' CKel
¶ – 'Glory of June' CKel
- 'Glory of Somerset' CKel
¶ – 'Gold Mine' CKel
¶ – 'Grace Loomis' CKel
¶ – 'Great Lady' CKel
- 'Great Sport' CKel
¶ – 'Grover Cleveland' CKel
¶ – 'Gypsy Girl' CKel
¶ – 'Heartbeat' CKel
- 'Heirloom' CKel
- 'Helen Hayes' MAus
¶ – 'Henri Potin' CKel
¶ – 'Her Grace' CKel
- 'Her Majesty' CKel
¶ – 'Herbert Oliver' CKel
- 'Hiawatha' MAus
¶ – 'His Majesty' CKel
¶ – 'Huge Delight' CKel
- 'Hyperion' CKel
¶ – 'Immaculée' CKel
¶ – 'Indian Pink' CKel
¶ – 'Ingenieur Doriat' CKel
- 'Inspecteur Lavergne' CDoC CKel COtt CSco EFou LWad MRav MUlv NBar NBee SPer
- 'Instituteur Doriat' CKel MPhe
¶ – 'Jacques Doriat' CKel
¶ – 'James Kelway' CKel
¶ – 'James R Mann' CKel
- 'Jan van Leeuwen' CKel LRHS MBri
- 'Jeanne d'Arc' CKel
¶ – 'Joan Kelway' CKel
- 'John Howard Wigell' MAus
¶ – 'Joseph Plagne' CKel
¶ – 'Joy of Life' CKel
¶ – 'June Morning' CKel
- 'June Rose' MAus
- 'Kansas' CKel EBee ELan
- 'Karl Rosenfield' CCla CKel CMGP COtt CSco EBee ECot IDai LWad MBri NBar NBee SMrm SPla WAbe
¶ – 'Katherine Havermeyer' CKel
¶ – 'Kathleen Mavoureen' CKel
- 'Kelway's Brilliant' CKel
¶ – 'Kelway's Fairy Queen' CKel
¶ – 'Kelway's Glorious' CKel LWad
¶ – 'Kelway's Lovely' CKel
- 'Kelway's Majestic' CKel MPhe
¶ – 'Kelway's Malmaison' CKel
¶ – 'Kelway's Queen' CKel
¶ – 'Kelway's Rosemary' CKel
¶ – 'Kelway's Scented Rose' CKel
- 'Kelway's Supreme' CKel MPhe MUlv
- 'Kelway's Unique' CKel
¶ – 'Kestrel' CKel
- 'King Arthur' CKel
- 'King of England' CKel
¶ – 'Knight of the Thistle' CKel
- 'Knighthood' CKel
- 'Krinkled White' MAus
- 'Lady Alexandra Duff' **AGM** CB&S CDoC CKel MAus NBar
¶ – 'Lady Ley' CKel
¶ – 'Lady Mary Dashwood' CKel
¶ – 'Lady Mayoress' CKel
- 'Lady Orchid' MAus
¶ – 'Langport Triumph' CKel
- 'Laura Dessert' **AGM** CKel MPhe SPer
¶ – 'Legion of Honor' CKel
¶ – 'Lemon Ice' CKel
¶ – 'Letitia' CKel
¶ – 'Limosel' CKel
- 'Lois Kelsey' MAus
- 'Lora Dexheimer' MAus
¶ – 'Lord Avebury' CKel
¶ – 'Lord Cavan' CKel
- 'Lord Kitchener' CKel SPer
¶ – 'Lord Rosebery' CKel
¶ – 'Lorna Doone' CKel
¶ – 'Lottie Dawson Rea' CKel
- 'Lotus Queen' MAus
¶ – 'Louis Barthelot' CKel
¶ – 'Louis van Houtte' CKel
¶ – 'Love Mist' CKel
¶ – 'Lyric' CKel
- 'L'Eclatante' CKel
- 'Madame Calot' CKel EBee LWad MRav SRms
- 'Madame Claude Tain' LRHS MHlr WCot
- 'Madame Ducel' CKel
- 'Madame Emile Debatène' CKel MAus
- 'Madelon' CKel
¶ – 'Magic Melody' CKel
- 'Magic Orb' CKel
¶ – 'Major Loder' CKel
¶ – 'Margaret Truman' CKel
- 'Marie Lemoine' CKel MAus
¶ – 'Marquisite' CKel
¶ – 'Mary Brand' CKel
¶ – 'Meteor Flight' CKel
- 'Mischief' MAus
- 'Miss America' MAus
- 'Miss Eckhart' CKel CSco
- 'Mister Ed' MAus
- 'Mistral' LRHS
- 'Monsieur Jules Elie' **AGM** CKel EFou LWad MBri MPhe SPer SPla
¶ – 'Monsieur Martin Cahuzac' CKel
- 'Mr G F Hemerik CKel ECtt LRHS MBri
- 'Mrs Franklin D Roosevelt' CKel ELan
¶ – 'Myrtle Gentry' CKel
¶ – 'Nectar' CKel
¶ – 'Newfoundland' CKel
¶ – 'Nobility' CKel
¶ – 'Noonday' CKel
- 'Ornament' CKel
- 'Orpen' CKel
¶ – 'Othello' CKel
¶ – 'Pageant' CKel
¶ – 'Paper White' CKel
- 'Paul M Wild' MAus
¶ – 'Pauline Maunder' CKel
- 'Peregrine' CKel
- 'Persier' EBee
- 'Peter Brand' CKel LRHS

¶ – 'Peter Pan'	CKel
¶ – 'Phedar White'	MPhe
– 'Philomèle'	MAus
– 'Pink Dawn'	CKel MAus
¶ – 'Pink Delight'	CKel
– 'Pink Giant'	LRHS MAus MBri
– 'Pink Parfait'	MAus
– 'Poetic'	CKel
– 'President Franklin D Roosevelt'	EBre ECtt ELan GCHN LBre MRav NRoo SPer
– 'Président Poincaré'	CCla CKel COtt EBre EHic LBre SPer
– 'President Taft'	See P. *l.* 'Reine Hortense'
¶ – 'President Wilson'	CKel
¶ – 'Pride of Huish'	CKel
¶ – 'Pride of Somerset'	CKel
– 'Primevere'	CKel LRHS MBri
¶ – 'Princess Beatrice'	CKel
¶ – 'Pure Delight'	CKel
¶ – 'Queen Alexandra'	MPhe
¶ – 'Queen Elizabeth'	CKel
¶ – 'Queen of Hearts'	CKel
– 'Queen of Sheba'	MAus
¶ – 'Queen of the Belgians'	CKel
¶ – 'Queen's Grace'	CKel
¶ – 'R W Marsh'	CKel
– 'Raspberry Sundae'	MAus MRav
¶ – 'Red Champion'	CKel
¶ – 'Red Dwarf'	CKel
– 'Red Flag'	CKel
¶ – 'Red King'	CKel
¶ – 'Red Warrior'	CKel
§ – 'Reine Hortense'	CKel MAus
¶ – 'Rembrandt'	CKel
¶ – 'Rhododendron'	CKel
– 'Richard Carvel'	MAus
– 'Rose of Delight'	CKel MPhe MUlv
¶ – 'Rose of Silver'	CKel
¶ – 'Ruby Light'	CKel
¶ – 'Ruigegno'	CKel
¶ – 'Sainfoin'	CKel
– 'Sarah Bernhardt' AGM	CB&S CBow CCMG CCla CHad CKel CMGP CShe EBre ELan GCHN IDai IHos LBre MAus MBri MPhe MRav MUlv NBar NBee NBro NHol NRoo NVic SPer SPla WAbe WEas
– 'Shimmering Velvet'	CKel
– 'Shirley Temple'	CKel EFou ELan LWad MBri MMil WCot
– 'Silver Flare'	CKel
– 'Sir Edward Elgar'	CKel
¶ – 'Smiling Morn'	CKel
– 'Snow Cloud'	IDai
– 'Solange'	CKel
¶ – 'Souvenir de Louis Bigot'	CKel
¶ – 'Spearmint'	CKel
¶ – 'Starlight'	CKel
– 'Strephon'	CKel
– 'Surugu'	ELan MBri
¶ – 'Suzette'	CKel
– 'Sweet Sixteen'	MAus
¶ – 'The Nymph'	CKel
¶ – 'Thérèse'	CKel
– 'Thura Hires'	MAus
– 'Top Brass'	MAus
– 'Torpilleur'	CKel
¶ – 'Tourangelle'	CKel
¶ – 'Translucent'	CKel
¶ – 'Utopia'	CKel
– 'Victoire de la Marne'	CKel COtt NBar
– 'Vogue'	CKel MAus
– 'Westerner'	MAus
– 'White Wings'	CB&S CKel COtt EBre ELan LBre MAus MBri MPhe NSti SPer
– 'Whitleyi Major' AGM	CKel MBri
– 'Wiesbaden'	CKel MAus
¶ – 'Wilbur Wright'	CKel
¶ – 'Windsor Lad'	CKel
¶ – 'Wings of Love'	CKel
¶ – 'Winston Churchill'	CKel
'Late Windflower'	ECha
§ x ***lemoinei*** 'Chromatella' (S)	LAma
§ – 'L'Espérance'	LAma
§ – 'Souvenir de Maxime Cornu' (S)	LAma
lobata 'Fire King'	See P. ***perigrina***
lutea	See P. ***delavayi lutea***
– var. ***ludlowii***	See P. ***delavayi ludlowii***
'Mai Fleuri'	SHig
§ ***mascula***	CKel MPhe WHaw
§ – ssp. ***arietina***	ESma MPhe SCou WKif
– ssp. ***arietina*** JCA 746.800	SBla
– – 'Northern Glory'	MAus MBri SHig SPer WCot
– 'Immaculata'	EBee EFou
§ – ssp. ***mascula***	EPot NHol NTow SCou
§ – ssp. ***russoi***	LGre SCou
§ – ssp. ***triternata***	SCou WHoo
mlokosewitschii AGM	CCla CFil CHad EBre ECha EPot LBre LGre LHop MBal MPhe NEgg NTow SApp SChu WAbb WDav WEas WHoo WThu
mollis	CKel ELan GAbr
'Montezuma'	MAus
obovata AGM	SCou
– var. ***alba*** AGM	CAvo WAbb WAbe WEas
– 'Grandiflora'	ELan SPer
officinalis	EBre LBre NBrk WEas
– 'Alba Plena'	CCMG CKel CPou CSco MAus MBri SPer
– 'Anemoniflora Rosea' AGM	MAus MBri
– ssp. ***banatica***	MAus MPhe
– 'China Rose'	ELan
♦ – ssp. ***humilis***	See P. ***o. microcarpa***
– 'James Crawford Weguelin'	CSco
– 'Lize van Veen'	ELan NRoo SPer
§ – ssp. ***microcarpa***	CKel ESma SCou
– 'Mutabilis Plena'	IBlr
¶ – ssp. ***officinalis***	MPhe
– 'Rosea Plena' AGM	CCMG CCla CKel GAbr LRHS MPhe NBar SPer
– 'Rosea Superba Plena'	CKel COtt CSco EBre LBre MAus NKay NRoo
– 'Rubra Plena' AGM	CAvo CCMG CCla CKel CPou CSco EBre ECtt LBre MAus MBri NKay NRoo SPer WHoo
¶ – ssp. ***villosa***	MPhe
'Paladin'	CKel
§ ***paradoxa***	See P. ***officinalis microcarpa***
'Paula Fay'	MAus

§ ***peregrina*** MAus MPhe NHar SCou
– 'Fire King' NBar
§ – 'Otto Froebel' AGM COtt EBee EHic ELan MBri NKay NRoo SHig SMad SPer
– 'Sunshine' See P. ***p.*** 'Otto Froebel'
'Polindra' CKel
'Postilion' MAus
potaninii See P. ***delavayi*** Potaninii Group
¶ ***rhodia*** MPhe
romanica See P. ***peregrina***
'Roselette' MAus
russoi See P. ***mascula r.***
'Scarlett O'Hara' MAus
sinensis See P. ***lactiflora***
'Smouthii' MBri
suffruticosa (S) CSco ELan MGos MPhe WStI
– 'Cardinal Vaughan' (S) CKel
– 'Duchess of Kent' (S) CKel
– 'Gessekai' ('Moon World') (S) MAus
– 'Godaishu' (S) LAma
– 'Hakuojisi' ('King of White Lions') (S) MAus
– 'Hana-daigin' ('Magnificent Flower') (S) LAma MAus SPer
– 'Hana-kisoi' ('Floral Rivalry') (S) LAma MAus
– 'Higurashi' ('Twilight') (S) LAma
– 'Howki' ('Charming Age') (S) MAus
– 'Kamada-fuji' ('Wisteria at Kamada') (S) LAma
– 'Kamada-nishiki' ('Kamada Brocade') (S) MAus
– 'Kaow' ('King of Flowers') (S) MAus
– 'Kokuryu-nishiki' ('Black Dragon Brocade') (S) LAma
– 'Lord Selbourne' (S) CKel
– 'Mrs William Kelway' (S) CKel NEgg
– 'Naniwa-nishiki' ('Brocade of the Naniwa') (S) MAus
– 'Raphael' (S) CKel
– 'Renkaku' ('Flight of Cranes') (S) MAus
– 'Rimpo' ('Bird of Rimpo') (S) LAma
¶ – ssp. ***rockii*** EHar
– 'Shugyo-kuden' ('Palace of Gems') (S) MAus
– 'Sitifukujin' ('Seven Gods of Fortune') (S) MAus
– 'Superb' (S) CKel
– 'Taisho-no-hokori' ('Pride of Taisho') (S) MAus
– 'Taiyo' ('The Sun') (S) LAma SPer
– 'Tama-fuyo' ('Jewel in the Lotus') (S) LAma
– 'Tama-sudare' ('Jewelled Screen') (S) MAus
– 'Yachiyo-tsubaki' ('Eternal Camellias') (S) LAma MAus
– 'Yae-zakura' ('Double Cherry') (S) LAma MAus
'Sunshine' See P. ***peregrina*** 'Otto Froebel'
tenuifolia EPot NHol
veitchii LGre MBal MPhe SCou WAbb
– 'Alba' MAus
– var. ***woodwardii*** CAvo GDra LGre NHar NHol SCou WCot WHoo
'Walter Mains' MAus
wittmanniana MPhe NTow

PAESIA (Dennstaedtiaceae)

scaberula CFil EFer GCal NMar WAbe WCot

PALISOTA (Commelinaceae)

barteri CTro

PALIURUS (Rhamnaceae)

spina-christi SMad

PALLENSIS (Compositae/Asteraceae)

spinosus See ASTERISCUS ***s.***

PANAX (Araliaceae)

¶ ***ginseng*** GPoy
¶ ***japonicus*** GPoy
quinquefolius GPoy

PANCRATIUM (Liliaceae/Amaryllidaceae)

¶ ***canariense*** WChr
foetidum S&L 354 CMon
maritimum CAvo

PANDANUS (Pandanaceae)

See Plant Deletions

PANDOREA (Bignoniaceae)

jasminoïdes CAbb CNew CSpe EBak ECot ELan IBlr SLMG
– 'Alba' CTro EMil ERea SFai
§ – 'Charisma' (v) CB&S CNew CTro EMil SFai
– 'Lady Di' CB&S CNew
– 'Rosea Superba' AGM CB&S CNew CRHN CTro EMil ERea SFai SPer
♦ – 'Variegata' See P. ***j.*** 'Charisma'
lindleyana See CLYTOSTOMA ***callistegioïdes***
pandorana CB&S CSam ERea LHop LRHS SLMG
¶ – 'Golden Showers' ERea

PANICUM (Gramineae/Poaceae)

bulbosum CHan EPla ETPC
clandestinum EMon EPla ETPC
coloratum 'Bambatsi' ETPC
miliaceum EFou EGle EPla ETPC
– 'Violaceum' WPer

virgatum	ECha EMon EPla MSte NHol WPer WWat
– 'Hänse Herms'	EFou EHoe EPla ETPC
– 'Pathfinder'	ETPC
– 'Rehbraun'	CDec EFou ETPC NEgg WCot
– 'Rotstrahlbusch'	SPla
– 'Rubrum'	CCla CGle CMGP EBre ECha EHoe ELan EPla LBre MSte MTol NFai NHol NSti SApp SDix SMad SPer WHow
– 'Strictum'	EHoe ETPC

PAPAVER † (Papaveraceae)

alboroseum	GCHN GTou
§ ***alpinum*** Linnaeus	EMNN ESis GCHN GDra GTou MBal MRPP MWat NGre NKay NOak SHer SIng SPla WByw WEas WPer WWin
– ***album***	ECro WHil
– 'Flore Pleno'	NBir
¶ ***argemone***	EWFC
§ ***atlanticum***	CNic ECoo EMar GBuc GCHN NBro NOak SWas WCru WPer
– ***flore-pleno***	MRav NBro NFai NSti WCot WCra WOld
bracteatum	See P. ***orientale b.***
§ ***commutatum*** AGM	ELan EMon LHol SMrm SUsu WEas
– 'Ladybird'	See P. ***commutatum***
degenii	GCHN
dubium	ECWi
§ 'Fireball'	CBos CMHG CRow CVer EBre ECha ELan GCal LBre LGre LHop MWat NCat WAbb WCru
heldreichii	See P. ***spicatum***
x ***hybridum*** 'Flore Pleno'	EMon
kerneri	WCru
kluanense	MSto
lateritium	MSto
– 'Flore Pleno'	NSti
§ ***miyabeanum***	CGle CMea CNic ECro ELan EPot GCHN GCra GDra GTou LGan LHop MSto NBro NGar NKay NMen NTow NWCA SHer WEas WHal WOMN WPer WWin
– ***album***	ELan SHer WPla
– ***tatewakii***	See P. ***miyabeanum***
nanum 'Flore Pleno'	See P. 'Fireball'
nudicaule	ELan GBur MHlr WOMN WPer
– Champagne Bubbles Group	CBow CHol NFai SRms
– 'Constance Finnis'	EMon GBuc LHop LRHS
– Gartenzwerg Group (Garden Gnome)	CDoC MBri MPit NPri WPbr
§ – Oregon Rainbow Group	ECro
– 'Pacino'	MPit WPer
– Wonderland hybrids	NRoo
orientale	CB&S CHol LHil NBee WBod WPer
– 'Allegro'	CBow CMGP CMil CSam CSco CShe EBar EBre ECro ECtt EFou GAbr LAbb LBre MBri MPit NBrk NFai NRoo SHer SPer SSvw WByw WCra WPbr
– 'Avebury Crimson'	MWat
– 'Beauty Queen'	CMGP EBre ECot EOrc LBre MBri NBar NBrk NCat NRoo SMrm WPbr
– 'Black and White' AGM	CCla CGle CHad CMGP CSco CSev CShe EBre ECha EFou ELan GAbr GCHN GMac LAbb LBre MRav MUlv NBrk NRoo NWyt SChu WPbr WRus WTyr
– 'Blue Moon'	CHad CMGP EBee EBre GGar LBre NBir NSti SMrm WPbr
– 'Bonfire Red'	ELan
§ – var. ***bracteatum*** AGM	ECha EMon GCHN GDra NBir SIng SMad
– 'Brilliant'	NFai
– ***carneum***	ECro
– 'Cedar Hill'	EFou WMer
– 'Cedric Morris' AGM	CHad EGle GCra GMac NBrk NFai WEas
– 'Cedric's Pink'	CHad ECha EGle GCra GMac MUlv NBrk NFai SWas WEas
– 'Charming'	LGre MHlr
– 'Curlilocks'	CMGP EBre EFou ELan GAbr LBre MUlv NBrk NKay NRoo SGil SMrm SPer WPbr
– 'Doubloon'	CDoC EBre GMac LBre NBrk NRoo WCot WCra
– 'Dwarf Allegro'	MFir NNor NOak
– 'Elam Pink'	ECha LGre
*– 'Flore Pleno'	EFou EMon GLil SSvw
– 'Garden Gnome'	CBow NOak
– 'Glowing Embers'	COtt EBre LBre WCot
*– 'Goldie'	ELan WPbr
– Goliath Group	CBow CGle CHan CRDP EFou ELan GMac LWad MUlv NBrk NBro NOak NVic SDix SSte SSvw SUsu WHoo
– Goliath Group 'Beauty of Livermere' AGM	CHad WEas
– 'Graue Witwe'	ECha NFai
– 'Harvest Moon'	CShe EBre ECro LBre MBri MRav NBar WCot
– 'Helen Elisabeth'	COtt EBre ECtt EFou GMac LBre MHlr MRav MUlv NBrk NFai NRoo WCot WCra WMer WRus
– 'Indian Chief'	WCra WMer
– 'Juliane'	ECha LGre NFai
– 'Karine'	CRDP EBee ECha LBuc LGre NBrk NFai SMrm
– 'King George'	MWat WEas
¶ – 'Kleine Tänzerin'	EFou LGre
– 'Lady Frederick Moore'	WMer
– 'Ladybird'	COtt EBre ELan LBre MUlv NBrk NRoo WCot WPbr
– 'Lilac Girl'	ECha
– 'Marcus Perry'	CBow CDoC CMGP COtt CSco GGar LWad SMrm WMer WPbr WTyr
– 'Midnight'	EBre LBre NBar WCot
♦– 'Mrs Marrow's Plum'	See P. ***o.*** 'Patty's Plum'
– 'Mrs Perry' AGM	Widely available
– 'Nanum Flore Pleno'	See P. 'Fireball'
– 'Orange Glow'	WMer
– 'Oriana'	MMil NCat
§ – 'Patty's Plum'	CBos CHad CRDP LGre SMrm SWas
– 'Perry's White'	Widely available
– 'Picotée'	CMGP CSco CShe EBre ECro EFou ELan EMon EOrc GMac LBre LHop MRav MUlv MWat NBro NOak SGil SMrm SPer SSte WByw WCot WPbr WTyr
– 'Pink Chiffon'	CGle

– 'Pinnacle'	GLil NFai NPri
– 'Prinzessin Victoria Louise'	CDoC EFou LRHS LWad MMil SMrm SSvw WCot WMer WPer
– 'Raspberry Queen'	ELan GLil WCot WMer WPbr
– 'Redizelle'	EBre LBre
– 'Rembrandt'	ECot MMil NPri WMer WPer
– 'Salmon Glow'	CBow CSco GLil NFai WMer WPbr
– 'Scarlet King'	EWll MMil NPri SMrm WTyr
– 'Showgirl'	CBow
– 'Sindbad'	EFou
– 'Sultana'	ECha GMac LGre
N– 'Türkenlouis' AGM	CCla CMGP CSco EBre EFol EFou ELan EMon EOrc GCHN GMac LBre LWad MMil MRav NBar NBir NBro NCat SChu SMrm SPer WByw WPbr WTyr
– 'Turkish Delight'	See P. *o.* 'Türkenlouis'
¶– 'Watermelon'	WMer
pilosum	CLew CVer GBuc MSto NCat SRms
radicatum	MSto
rhaeticum	ELan EPot GTou SHer
– JCA 752.500	CNic
rhoeas	CArn CSFH ECWi EWFC GPoy LHol
– 'Mother of Pearl'	ECro
– 'Valerie Finnis'	ELan
rupifragum	CDec CGle ECha ESis GAbr GCHN GCra MFir MSto NNrw SUsu WEas WHer WPer WPla WWin
– 'Flore Pleno'	SSte SSvw WCot WCru WHer
sendtneri	MSto
somniferum AGM	CArn CSFH GPoy ILis LHol SIde
– 'Pink Chiffon'	WEas
§ ***spicatum***	CNic CSam ECha ECro LGre LHop MHlr NBir SUsu WCot WEas
suaveolens	NNrw
triniifolium	EMar LGan SMrm

PARABENZOIN See LINDERA

PARADISEA † (Liliaceae/Asphodelaceae)

liliastrum AGM	LBee MNFA MPhe NCat WDav WPla
– 'Major'	WPer
lusitanica	CGle CMHG

PARAHEBE † (Scrophulariaceae)

x ***bidwillii***	CLew CMHG CRiv ECou EMNN GAri GGar GPlt MHig NMen SBod WWat
– 'Gillian'	CNic ECou ECtt GAri GGar GIsl GPlt MCas MMil NMen SFis
– 'Kea'	CMea CNic EBur ECou ECtt ELan EMNN ESis GCHN GCal GPlt LBee MHig NHar NMen SBla SHer SUsu WPer
canescens	ECou
§ ***catarractae*** AGM	CCla CHan CMHG CMer CShe ECou ELan EMNN EMar GPlt GWht MCas MFir MPla NBee NMen NNor NNrw NTow SAxl SBod SPer SPla SUsu WHil WPer WWin
– blue	GIsl GMac SPer WSun WWat
§ – 'Delight' AGM	CGre ECou ESis ESma EWes GCHN GCal GGar LHop MAll NBrk NPer SDix SFis SLon WEas WHen WHoo
– ssp. ***diffusa***	CMHG ECou EMNN GPlt IOrc MCas MMil NHar NMen NPer NVic
– – 'Annie'	ECou
– – 'Pinkie'	ECou
– garden form	ECha LLWP SBla WAbe
– ssp. ***martinii***	ECou EWes
– 'Miss Willmott'	CNic CShe GIsl LGan MAll NVic SPer WBod WPer WPla
– 'Porlock Purple '	See P. *c.* 'Delight'
– 'Rosea'	CMea CNic ESma LGan MAll NHol NNor NRed SBla SIng SMrm WWat
– 'Tinycat'	ESma MAll
– white	CBot CCla CHan ECha ELan EMNN ESis GCHN GIsl GMac GPlt IBlr LHop MBro MFir NCat NMen SAxl SPla SUsu WEas WPer WSun
decora	ECou EMNN GAbr GAri GCHN GPlt NHol NTow SGil WHil
derwentiana	ECou EMon
formosa	CPle ECou MAll
– erect form	ECou
– lax form	ECou
– white	ECou
'Greencourt'	See P. ***catarractae*** 'Delight'
§ ***hookeriana***	CNic CShe ESma GAbr GGar LGre MAll NMen NTow SMrm WHoo WStI WWat
'Joy'	ECou ESma EWes
linifolia	CLew EMNN MCas MHig NMen NNrd SGil
– 'Blue Skies'	CNic ECou GIsl LHop NHed
§ ***lyallii***	CBot CMer ECou ELan EMNN EMon ESis GIsl GPlt LHop MAll MCas MPit MPla MRav NHol NMen NNor NOrc NWCA SBor SIng SSmi WAbe WWin
– 'Clarence'	ECou GIsl
– 'Engel's Blue'	LGan
– 'Glacier'	ECou EWes
– 'Julie-Anne'	CMHG ECou GCal GIsl
– 'Rosea'	GGar MBal WHoo WPer
'Mervyn'	CNic ECou ECtt GCHN GGar GIsl GPlt LGre LHop MAll MCas NHol NMen NRed SFis WAbe WHen WPer
olsenii	ECou GGar NHol
peltata	NHol
perfoliata AGM	Widely available
– dark blue	EMar EMon GBuc GCal GWht NCat SMad
¶ 'Snowcap'	WCot
spathulata	MHig

PARAJUBAEA (Palmae/Arecaceae)

cocoïdes	LPal

PARAQUILEGIA (Ranunculaceae)

adoxoïdes	See SEMIAQUILEGIA ***adoxoïdes***
§ ***anemonoïdes***	MFos
¶ – Gothenbury Strain	CPBP
grandiflora	See P. ***anemonoïdes***

PARASERIANTHES (Leguminosae/Mimosaceae)

♦*distachya*	See P. ***lophantha***
§ *lophantha*	CGre CHEx CPle CTre CTro ISea SArc WNor

PARASYRINGA See LIGUSTRUM

X PARDANCANDA (Iridaceae)

norrisii	CArn EBee WPer

PARDANTHOPSIS (Iridaceae)

dichotoma	ECro WThi

PARIETARIA (Urticaceae)

§ *judaica*	GPoy MHew MSal WHer
– 'Corinne Tremaine'	WHer
officinalis	See P. ***judaica***

PARIS (Liliaceae/Trilliaceae)

incompleta	EPot SPou
§ *polyphylla*	CRDP NRog SMad WChr WCru
quadrifolia	GPoy SPou WCru WHer

PARNASSIA (Parnassiaceae)

cabulica	GDra
nubicola	GDra LGan MBal
palustris	MTol

PAROCHETUS (Leguminosae/Papilionaceae)

communis AGM	CB&S CFee CGle CGre CLew CMer CNic CRDP CRiv ELan GDra GMac LAbb LBlm LHil LHop NBro NKay NPer NWCA SIng WAbe WCru WEas WHal WOMN WPer WThu WWat
– *africanus*	GCal WCru
– dark form	GCal
– Himalayan form	IBlr WCru
¶ – 'summer-flowering	CRDP

PARONYCHIA (Illechebraceae)

argentea	EPot MBro WPer
§ *capitata*	CLew CMHG CNic CRiv ELan NHol NKay NMen NNrd WPat WPer WWin
§ *kapela*	MCas NHol NTow SSmi WPer
nivea	See P. ***capitata***
serpyllifolia	See P. ***kapela***

PARROTIA (Hamamelidaceae)

persica AGM	CB&S CBow CBra CCla CPMA CSco EHar ELan EMil ENot IDai IJoh LPan MBal MBri MGos NBar NBee NHol SHBN SPer SSta WBod WDin WHCG WWat
– 'Pendula'	CBow CCla CPMA EHar ELan IOrc MBal SHBN SPer WWes
– 'Vanessa'	CPMA LRHS WMou

PARROTIOPSIS (Hamamelidaceae)

jacquemontiana	CB&S MBri

PARRYA (Cruciferae/Brassicaceae)

menziesii	See PHOENICAULIS ***cheiranthoïdes***

PARSONSIA (Apocynaceae)

capsularis	ECou
heterophylla	ERea

PARTHENIUM (Compositae/Asteraceae)

integrifolium	MSal

PARTHENOCISSUS † (Vitaceae)

§ *henryana* AGM	Widely available
himalayana	ECtt
– var. *rubrifolia*	EHic WCru WWat
§ *quinquefolia* AGM	Widely available
– var. *engelmannii*	CDoC MGos SPer WAbe WStI
striata	See CISSUS ***s.***
thomsonii	See CAYRATIA ***t.***
tricuspidata AGM	CBow CHEx CShe ECtt MBal MGos NNor SPer SReu WBod WDin
– 'Beverley Brook'	CDoC CMac CSco CShe EBre LBre MBri SBra SPer SPla WAbe WBod
– 'Green Spring'	CDoC CSco EHal IHos IJoh MBri MGos NBrk SBra
– 'Lowii'	CDoC CMac EBre ECot EPla LBre MGos SMad
§ – 'Veitchii'	CBow CBra CMac EBre ECtt EHar ELan ENot IDai IHos IJoh LBre MBar MGos MRav MWat NKay NWea SBra SHBN SLon SPer SSta WDin WPat WWat

PASITHEA (Liliaceae/Asphodelaceae)

¶ *caerulea*	EMon

PASSIFLORA † (Passifloraceae)

actinia	CPas
adenopoda	CPas
adulterina	CPas
alata AGM	CPas CTro ERea SFai
x *alatocaerulea*	See P. x ***belotii***
allantophylla	CPas
allardii	CGre CPas CTro SHil
ambigua	CPas
'Amethyst'	CPas CSPN EOrc
amethystina AGM	CAbb CB&S CDoC CPas CRHN CTro ERea SLMG WWeb
ampullacea	CPas
anfracta	CPas
antioquiensis AGM	CB&S CBot CGre CHEx CNew CPas CTro ELan ERea IBlr ISea LBlm LHop LPri SFai SLMG WRus
¶ *apetala*	CPas
atomaria	CPas
§ *aurantia*	CPas ERea
auriculata	CPas
banksii	See P. ***aurantia***
§ x *belotii*	CNew CPas CSPN CTro ERea LPri WDin
– 'Impératrice Eugénie'	See P. x ***b.***
biflora	CPas CTro
* *boenderii*	CPas
brevipes	CPas

§ ***caerulea*** AGM	Widely available
– 'Constance Elliott' AGM	CB&S CBot CBow CCla CGre CMac CPas CRHN CSPN CSco EBre ELan EMil GCal LBre LHop LPri SBra SHer SLMG SPer SPla SReu SSta WBod WCru WHen WWeb
– forms	SLMG
– ***rubra***	ECtt
x ***caeruleoracemosa*** AGM	CB&S CCla CKni CPas CRHN ERea ISea SPla
– 'Eynsford Gem'	CPas IOrc
– 'Lilac Lady'	SFai
¶ – 'Victoria'	LPri
x ***caponii***	ERea
capsularis	CPas CTro SLMG
– ***quinquadrangularis***	CPas
chinensis	See P. ***caerulea***
cinnabarina	CTro
* ***cissifolia***	CPas
citrina	CPas CTro ERea
coccinea	CB&S CPas CTro
x ***colvillei***	CPas
coriacea	CPas
costaricensis	CPas
¶ ***cumbalensis*** var. ***cumbalensis*** JJA 13988	MSto
¶ ***discophora***	CPas
edulis	CPas CTro EBak LAbb SHil SLMG
– 'Crackerjack'	CAbb CB&S COtt ERea
F – f. ***edulis***	CB&S
F – f. ***flavicarpa***	CPas
– 'Supreme'	CB&S
eichleriana	CPas
'Empress Eugenie'	See P. x ***belotii***
x ***exoniensis*** AGM	CBot CGre CPas CTro ESim LAbb LPri SHil
foetida	CPas CTro
¶ – var. ***hirsutissima***	CPas
¶ ***gibertii***	CPas
¶ ***gigantifolia***	CPas
¶ ***gilbertiana***	CPas
glandulosa	CPas
¶ 'Golden Glow'	CPas
gracilis	CPas
guatemalensis	CPas
¶ ***hahnii***	CPas
helleri	CPas
herbertiana	CPas
holosericea	CPas
incana	See P. ***seemannii***
incarnata	CArn CPBP CPas ESim MSal
'Incense' AGM	CNew CPas
x ***innesii***	See P. x ***decaisneana*** 'Innesii'
* ***iralda***	CPas
jorullensis	CPas
x ***kewensis***	CPas CTro
laurifolia	CPas
'Lavender Lady'	CPas ELan EMil IOrc LPri SFai SPla
ligularis	CPas CTro
lowei	CPas
'Lucia'	CPas
lutea	CNew CPas
maliformis	CPas
manicata	CPas
'Mavis Mastics'	CPas
mayana	See P. ***caerulea***
menispermifolia	See P. ***pilosa***
* ***microstipula***	CPas
misera	CPas
mixta	ERea
– x ***antioquiensis***	CPas
mollissima AGM	CAbb CB&S CBot CGre CPas CTro ELan ERea LBlm LHop SFai SHil SLMG
morifolia	CPas CTro
naviculata	CPas
nelsonii	CPas
nitida	CPas
oerstedii	CPas
onychina	See P. ***amethystina***
¶ ***organensis***	CPas
¶ ***ornitheura***	CPas
pallens	CPas
perfoliata	CPas CTro
§ ***pilosa***	CPas
pinnatistipula	CPas
platyloba	CPas
punctata	CPas
'Purple Passion'	See P. ***edulis edulis***
quadrangularis AGM	CB&S CBot CNew CPas CTro ERea SHil
¶ – ***macrocarpa***	CPas
¶ ***quadriflora***	CPas
¶ ***quadriglandulosa***	CPas
racemosa AGM	CAbb CPas CSPN CTro ELan ERea ERom IBlr SHil WGor
¶ ***reticulata***	CPas
¶ ***rovirosae***	CPas
rubra	CPas ELan LPri NPal WStI WWeb
'Saint Rule'	CPas
sanguinolenta	CNew CPas CRHN CTro ERea
§ ***serrata***	CPas
serratifolia	CPas
♦ ***serratodigitata***	See P. ***serrata***
sexflora	CPas
'Star of Bristol' AGM	CPas
'Star of Clevedon'	CPas
'Star of Kingston'	CPas
suberosa	CPas
subpeltata	CPas
'Sunburst'	CPas CTro
§ ***tetrandra***	CGre CPas ECou
trifasciata	CPas
¶ ***tripartita*** JJA 13982	MSto
tuberosa	CPas
umbilicata	CBot CPas SHil
urbaniana	CPas
vespertilio	CPas
violacea	CPas CTro ERea MBri
viridiflora	CPas
vitifolia	CB&S CNew CPas ERea
yucatanensis	CPas
zamorana	CPas

PASSION FRUIT, Purple See **PASSIFLORA** ***edulis edulis***

PASSION FRUIT, Yellow See **PASSIFLORA** ***edulis flavicarpa***

PASTINACA (Umbelliferae/Apiaceae)

sativa	CKin

PATRINIA (Valerianaceae)

gibbosa	ECha ECro GCHN LGan MHig NHol
scabiosifolia	CLew ECha ECro GBuc SMad SSvw WByw WWin
triloba	CRDP ECha NGre NHol NMen
– var. *palmata*	CShe NBro NKay SHer
– var. *triloba*	CGle CLew GCal MCas MHig NNrd NTow WWin

PAULOWNIA (Scrophulariaceae)

coreana	CGre
fargesii Franchet	CB&S CBow CChu CGre CHEx CLnd CWSG EHar SMad
fargesii Osborn	See P. *tomentosa* 'Lilacina'
fortunei	CChu CWSG
tomentosa AGM	CB&S CBot CBow CBra CGre CHEx CLnd CPle EArb EHar ELan EMil ENot IOrc LPan MBri MUlv NPal SEng SHBN SHil SMad SPer SSta WAbe WHCG WNor
§ – 'Lilacina'	CGre GWht WCoo

PAVONIA (Malvaceae)

§ x *gledhillii*	CNew CTro
x *intermedia*	See P. x *gledhillii*
¶ *multiflora* Jussieu	ERea
♦ *multiflora* misapplied	See P. x *gledhillii*
praemorsa	CBot

PAW PAW See **CARICA** ***papaya***

PAXISTIMA (Celastraceae)

canbyi	CPle EPla MUlv WThu WWin
myrsinites	See P. *myrtifolia*
myrtifolia	CPle WWat

PEACH See **PRUNUS** ***persica***

PEAR See **PYRUS** ***communis***

PEAR, Asian See **PYRUS** ***pyrifolia***

PECAN See **CARYA** ***illinoinensis***

PECTEILIS (Orchidaceae)

§ *radiata*	EFEx

PEDICULARIS (Scrophulariaceae)

canadensis	MSal
verticillata	NWCA

PEGANUM (Zygophyllaceae)

harmala	MSal

PELARGONIUM † (Geraniaceae)

'A Happy Thought'	See P. 'Happy Thought'
'A M Mayne' (Z/d)	SDen WFib
'Abel Carrière' (I/d)	SDen SKen WFib
abrotanifolium (Sc)	CNat MHul NWyt SKen WEas WFib
– broad-leaved	SDen
¶ 'Acapulco'	NPri
acerifolium hort.	See P. *vitifolium*
acerifolium L'Héritier	See P. *cucullatum strigifolium*
acetosum	GCHN GCal LGre LHil MHul MSte SMrm SSad SUsu
acraeum	MHul WFib
Action ® (Z/d)	WFib
'Ada Sutterby' (Dw/d)	SBro SKen WFib
'Adagio' (Dw)	ESul NKin SBro
'Adam's Quilt' (Z/C)	SDen SKen SOld WEas
'Adele' (Min/d)	ESul LVer SBro WFib
¶ 'Ade's Elf' (Z/St)	SBro
¶ 'Admiral Bouvant' (I)	EBSP
'Aerosol' (Min)	ESul
'Aerosol Improved' (Min)	CSpe SBro
'Ailsa' (Min/d)	ESul MBri NKin SBro
'Ainsdale Angel' (A)	ESul LDea SBro SDen
'Ainsdale Beauty' (Z)	EBSP
'Ainsdale Claret' (Z)	EBSP SDen WFib
'Ainsdale Eyeful' (Z)	EBSP
¶ 'Ainsdale Glasnost' (Z)	EBSP
'Ainsdale Happiness' (Z/d)	EBSP
'Ainsdale Sixty' (Z)	EBSP
'Akela' (Min)	ESul SBro
'Alan West' (Z/St)	SDen
'Albert Sheppard' (Z/C/d)	WFib
'Alberta' (Z)	NWyt SKen WFib
'Albert's Choice' (R)	EBSP WFib
album	MHul
alchemilloïdes	CNat MHul WFib
'Alcyone' (Dw/d)	ESul IHos LVer NKin SBro SDen SKen
'Alde' (Min)	ESul MWhe NKin SBro SDen SKen WEas
'Aldham' (Min)	ESul LVer SBro
'Aldwyck' (R)	LDea
'Alex' (Z)	SKen
'Alex Kitson' (Z)	EBSP
¶ 'Alfred Wolfe'	SDen
'Algenon' (Min/d)	ESul NKin SBro WFib
'Alice Crousse' AGM	SKen WFib
¶ 'Alice Greenfield' (Z)	EBSP LVer
'Alison' (Dw)	ESul SBro
'Alison Wheeler' (Min/d)	MWhe
'All My Love' (R)	LDea WFib
'Alma' (Min/C)	ESul SBro
'Alpine Glow' (Z/d)	EBSP MSmi MWhe NWyt SDen SKen SOld
'Alpine Orange' (Z/d)	SDen
'Alta Bell' (R)	WFib
'Altair' (Min/d)	ESul MWhe SBro
alternans	MHul

'Always' (Z/d) LVer
¶ 'Amari' (R) LDea
'Ambrose' (Dw/d) ESul NKin SBro WFib
'Amelia' (Min) SBro
'Amethyst' AGM EBSP ECtt IHos LDea LVer MWhe NPri WFib
– (R) EBSP LDea MBri MSmi MWhe SDen SKen WFib
'Ami' (R) WFib
¶ 'Amy Parmer' (Min) SBro
'Anabell Stephenson' (Dw/d) SBro WFib
'Andersonii' (Sc) EWoo WFib
'Andrew Salvidge' (R) LDea WFib
I 'Andromeda' (Min) NKin SBro WFib
'Ange Davey' (Z/d) WFib
'Angela' (Min) SBro
'Angela Mitchell' (Z/C/d) SBro
'Angela Read' (Dw) ESul SBro
'Angelique' (Dw/d) ESul LVer SBro
'Anglia' (Dw) ESul NKin SBro
'Ann Hoysted' (R) WFib
'Ann Redington' (R) LDea SDen WFib
'Anna' (Dw) ESul LVer SBro
¶ 'Annabelle' (Dw) NKin
¶ 'Anne Mitchell' (Min) SBro
antidysentericum MHul
'Antigua' (R) LDea WFib
'Antoinette' (Min) ESul LVer SBro
'Apache' AGM WFib
'Aphrodite' (Z) EBSP ECtt SHer WFib
¶ 'Apollo' (R) SDen
appendiculatum GCHN
'Apple Blossom Rosebud' AGM EBSP ECtt MBri MWhe NKin NWyt SDen SHer SKen SMrm SOld SUsu WEas WFib
'Apricot' (Z/St/d) ESul NKin SDen SKen
'Apricot Queen' (I/d) EBSP LDea LVer
'Apuldram' (R) EBSP LDea
¶ 'Arctic Frost' SDen
§ 'Arctic Star' (Z/St) CSpe ESul LVer SBro SOld WEas
'Arcturus' (Min) LVer NKin SBro
x ***ardens*** LGre LHil MHul SDen SSad
¶ 'Ardwick Cinnamon' ESul
aridum MHul
'Aries' (Min/C) ESul MWhe SBro
'Arizona' (Min/d) ESul NKin NWyt SBro SDen SKen WFib
'Arthings Slam' (R) LDea LVer SKen
'Arthur Biggin' (Z) MWhe SKen
¶ 'Arthur Mitchell' (Min) SBro
articulatum MHul
'Ashdown Forest' (Dw) SBro
* 'Ashey' SDen
'Ashfield Blaze' (Z/d) EBSP SDen WFib
'Ashfield Jubilee' (Z/C) LVer SKen
'Ashfield Monarch' AGM LVer MWhe WFib
'Ashfield Serenade' AGM EBSP LVer SDen SKen WFib
'Ashley Stephenson' (R) WFib
'Askham Fringed Aztec' (R) EBSP LDea LVer
'Askham Slam' (R) LDea
asperum Ehr. ex Willd. See P. 'Graveolens'
'Astrakan' (Z/d) SDen
'Athabasca' (Min) ESul LVer SBro
'Atomic Snowflake' (Sc/v) CArn ESul LBlm LHil LVer NWyt SDen SIde WCHb WEas WFib WWye
'Attar of Roses' AGM CArn CLTr CNat ESul GBar IHos LBlm LHil LVer MWhe NHHG NKin NSty NWyt SDen SHer SIde SKen WCHb WEas WElm WFib WWye
'Attraction' (Z/St/d) LVer WFib
'Aubusson' (R) WFib
'Audrey' (Z/d) SDen WFib
'Audrey Clifton' (I/d) ECtt SDen WEas WFib
'Augusta' LHop SMrm
Auralia ® (Z/d) WFib
auritum MHul
'Aurora' (Z/d) MWhe SDen
'Aurore' (U) See P. 'Unique Aurore'
australe CNat EPad GCHN IHos MHul MSte WFib WHer
'Autumn' (Z/d) IHos LVer MWhe
'Autumn Colours' (Min) ESul SBro
'Autumn Festival' (R) WFib
'Autumn Haze' (R) EBSP
'Autumn Mist' (R) WFib
¶ 'Avril' ESul
'Aztec' AGM EBSP LDea LVer SKen WFib
'Baby Birds Egg' (Min) CSpe ESul SBro SDen
'Baby Brocade' (Min/d) ESul NKin NWyt SBro
'Baby Clare' (Min) LVer NKin SBro
'Baby Doll' (Min/d) SBro
'Baby Helen' (Min) ESul LVer NKin SBro
'Baby James' (Min) ESul LVer SBro SKen
'Babylon' (R) WFib
'Badley' (Dw) ESul SBro
Balcon Imperial ® See P. 'Roi des Balcons Impérial'
♦ 'Balcon Lilas' (I) See P. 'Roi des Balcons Lilas'
♦ 'Balcon Rose' (I) See P. 'Hederinum'
'Ballerina' (Dw/d) MWhe WFib
– (R) LDea
'Ballet Dancer' (Min/d) SBro
¶ 'Bandit' (Min) ESul LVer SDen
'Bantam' (Min/d) ESul LVer SBro WFib
§ 'Barbe Bleu' (I/d) EBSP ECtt LDea MWhe SDen SKen WFib
'Barcelona' (R) EBSP
'Barham' (Min/d) SBro SDen
'Barking' (Min) ESul LVer SBro
barklyi MHul WFib
Barock ® (I) EBSP NPri
'Baron de Layres' (Z/d) WFib
'Baronne A. de Rothschild' (Z/d) WFib
'Bashful' (Min) ESul SBro
'Bath Beauty' (Dw) LVer NKin SBro SDen SKen WEas
'Baylham' (Min) ESul SBro SDen
'Beacon Hill' (Min) ESul LVer NKin SBro
'Beatrice Cottington' (I/d) SKen
'Beatrix' (Z/d) ESul LVer SBro SKen
'Beatrix Little' (Dw) NWyt
'Beau Geste' (R) EBSP
'Beauty of Bath' (R) WFib
'Beauty of Calderdale' (Z/C) WFib

'Beauty of Coldwell' (Z/C) MWhe
N 'Beauty of Eastbourne' See P. 'Lachskönigin'
'Beauty of El Segundo' (Z/d) SKen WFib
'Beauty of Jersey' (I/d) EBSP WFib
'Beckwith's Pink' (Z) SDen SKen
'Belinda Adams' AGM ESul LVer MWhe NKin SBro
'Belladonna' (I/d) ECtt IHos NPri NWyt
'Belstead' (Min) SBro
'Bembridge' SDen
'Ben Franklin' AGM EBSP IHos LVer MWhe SDen
'Ben Nevis' (Dw/d) ESul NKin SBro SDen
'Benedict' (Min) NKin SBro
'Bengal Fire' (Z/C) LVer
'Bentley' (Dw) ESul SBro
Bergpalais ® (Z/d) WFib
'Berliner Balkon' (I) SDen SKen
'Bernado' NPri SHer
'Beronmunster' (Dec) ESul EWoo LDea LHil LVer NKin SOld WFib
'Bert Pearce' (R) EBSP LDea
'Beryl Gibbons' (Z/d) EBSP LVer MWhe
'Beryl Read' (Dw) ERea ESul NKin SBro
'Beryl Reid' (R) LDea
'Berylette' (Min/d) ESul LVer NKin SBro
'Bess' (Z/d) ESul LVer SBro SDen SKen
'Beta' (Min/C) ESul LVer SBro
'Betsy Trotwood' (Dw) NKin SBro
'Bette Shellard' (Z/d) EBSP MWhe SBro
'Betty Dollery' (Z/d) SDen
'Betty Hulsman' (A) ESul SBro
'Betty Read' (Dw) ESul SBro
'Betty West' (Min/d) SBro SDen
betulinum GCHN MHul WFib
¶ 'Betwixt ' (Z/v) SBro
'Bewerley Park' (Z/C/d) LVer SKen WFib
'Bianca' (Min/d) ESul SBro
¶ 'Bicester Gem' SDen
bijugum MHul
'Bildeston' (Z/C) ESul LVer NKin SBro SDen
'Bill West' (I) SDen
'Billie Read' (Dw/d) ERea ESul LVer SBro
'Bingo' (Min) ESul SBro
'Bird Dancer' AGM CSpe ERav ESul GBur LHil LVer MWhe NKin NWyt SBro SDen SKen SOld WEas WFib WPer
'Birthday Girl' (R) WFib
'Bi-Coloured Startel' (Z/St/d) CBot MWhe
'Black Butterfly' (R) See F. 'Brown's Butterfly'
'Black Knight' (R) CSpe MSte
'Black Magic' (R) WFib
'Black Pearl' (Z/d) LVer NWyt SDen
¶ 'Black Prince' (R) WEas
¶ 'Black Top' (R) NKin SOld
'Black Velvet' (R) LDea LVer
'Black Vesuvius' See P. 'Red Black Vesuvius'
'Blackcurrant Sundae' LVer
'Blakesdorf' (Dw) CSpe ESul MWhe NKin SBro
'Blanchland Cerise' (Dw) SBro
'Blanchland Dazzler' (Min) SBro
§ 'Blandfordianum' (Sc) EWoo MHul WHer
§ 'Blauer Frühling' (I/d) IHos SDen SKen WFib
'Blaze Away' SDen
'Blazonry' (Z/v) CBrk EBSP MWhe SBro SDen
'Blisworth Mrs Mappin' (Z/v) MWhe
¶ 'Blizzard Cascade' NPri
'Blooming Gem' (Min/I/d) LDea SBro
'Blue Beard' (I) See P. 'Barbe Bleu'
¶ 'Blue Fox' (Z) SDen
¶ 'Blue Orchid' (R) LDea
'Blue Peter' (I/d) SKen
'Blue Spring' See P. 'Blauer Frühling'
§ 'Blues' (Z/d) IHos NWyt SHer
'Blush Mariquita' (R) WFib
'Blush Petit Pierre' (Min) ESul SBro
¶ 'Blushing Belle (Dw) SBro
'Blushing Bride' (I/d) IHos LDea SKen
'Blushing Emma' (Z) ESul
'Bob Legge' (Z/d) WFib
'Bold Romance' (Z) EBSP
'Bold Sunset' (Z/d) EBSP NKin
'Bolero' (U) EWoo IHos
'Bosham' (R) EBSP LDea
'Botley Beauty' (R) EBSP LDea
'Boudoir' (Z/C/d) SBro
¶ 'Bouldner' SDen
bowkeri MHul
'Brackenwood' AGM ESul LVer SBro
'Bramford' (Dw) ESul SBro
'Braque' (R) LDea WFib
'Bravo' (Z/d) MWhe SHer
'Break o' Day' (R) LDea SDen SKen WEas
'Bredon' AGM WFib
'Brenda' (Min/d) ESul SBro
'Brenda Hyatt' (Dw/d) ESul NKin SBro
'Brenda Kitson' (Z/d) LVer MWhe WFib
'Brett' (Min) SBro
'Brettenham' (Min) LVer SBro
¶ 'Brialyn Beauty' (A) LDea NKin SBro
¶ 'Brialyn Moonlight' (A) NKin SBro
¶ 'Brialyn Star' (A) SBro
'Bridal Veil' AGM SBro
'Bridesmaid' (Dw/C/d) ESul LVer NKin SBro SDen SOld WFib
¶ 'Brightstone' SDen
'Brightwell' (Min/d) ESul LVer SBro WFib
'Brilliant' (Dec) EWoo
¶ 'Bristol' (Z/v) SBro SDen
¶ 'Bristol Dandy' (Z/C/d) SBro
'Britannia' (R) LDea
'Brixworth Boquet' (Min/C/d) MWhe SBro
'Brixworth Charmer' (Z/v) MWhe SBro
'Brixworth Gold' (Min/C/d) MWhe SBro
'Brixworth Melody' (Z/v) MWhe
'Brixworth Pearl' (Z) MWhe
'Brixworth Rhapsody' (Z/v) MWhe
'Brixworth Serenade' (Min/C/d) MWhe
'Brixworth Starlight' (I/v) MWhe
'Brocade' (Z/d) IHos LVer NWyt WFib

'Bronze Corinne' (Z/C/d)	EBSP SDen SKen
¶ 'Bronze Nuhulanby' (R)	EBSP
'Bronze Queen' (Z/C)	MWhe NWyt
'Bronze Velvet' (R)	WFib
¶ 'Brook'	SDen
¶ 'Brookside Abigail'	LVer
¶ 'Brookside Arundel'	LVer
¶ 'Brookside Astra'	LVer
'Brookside Betty' (Dw/C/d)	ESul SBro SDen
'Brookside Bolero' (Z)	ESul SBro
¶ 'Brookside Candy' (Dw/d)	ESul SBro
¶ 'Brookside Champagne' (Min/d)	SBro
¶ 'Brookside Cinderella' (Z/C/d)	ESul SBro
'Brookside Flamenco' (Min/d)	ESul LVer MWhe SBro
'Brookside Jupiter' (Z)	EBSP
'Brookside Primrose' (Min/C/d)	ESul LVer MWhe SBro
¶ 'Brookside Rosita' (Min)	ESul SBro
'Brookside Serenade' (Z)	ESul SBro
¶ 'Brookside Spitfire' (Dw/d)	ESul SBro
'Brook's Purple'	See P. 'Royal Purple'
'Brownie' (Min)	SBro
§ 'Brown's Butterfly' (R)	EBSP LBlm LDea LHop SMrm SUsu WFib
'Bruni' (Z/d)	IHos MWhe WFib
'Brunswick' (Sc)	EWoo NWyt SDen WWye
'Brutus' (Z)	SDen
'Bucklesham' (Dw)	ESul SBro
'Bumblebee' (Dw)	ESul SBro
'Burgenlandmädel' (Z/d)	LVer SKen WFib
'Burgundy' (R)	LDea LVer WFib
'Burstall' (Min/d)	NKin SBro SDen
'Butley' (Min)	ESul SBro
¶ 'Buttercup Don' (Z/d)	EBSP
'Butterfly' (Min/v)	ECtt NPri
Butterfly ® (I)	IHos
Cabaret ® (Z/d)	MBri
caffrum	MHul
'Cal' (Z/d)	See P. 'Salmon Irene'
'Caledonia' (Z)	LVer NWyt SDen SKen
'Caligula' (Min/d)	NKin SBro WFib
'Cally' (Min/d)	SBro
'Cameo' (Dw/d)	LVer MWhe NWyt SBro WFib
'Camilla' (Dw)	SBro SDen
'Camphor Rose' (Sc)	CLTr ESul
candicans	GCHN MHul WFib
'Candy' (Min/d)	ESul LVer SBro
'Candy Kisses' (D)	ESul SBro
canescens	See P. 'Blandfordianum'
'Can-Can' (I/d)	WFib
'Capel' (Dw/d)	ESul NKin SBro
'Capella' (Min)	SBro
Capen ® (Z/d)	WFib
capitatum (Sc)	CNat EWoo GCHN MHul SDen WCHb WEas WFib
'Caprice' (R)	EWoo SKen WFib
'Capricorn' (Min/d)	ESul NKin SBro
'Captain Starlight' (A)	ESul EWoo LDea LVer SBro
'Cardinal' (Z/d)	See P. 'Kardinal'
'Carefree' (U)	EWoo
'Cariboo Gold' AGM	ESul SKen
'Carisbrooke' (R)	SDen SKen WEas WFib
'Carnival' (R)	See P. 'Marie Vogel'
– (Z)	WFib
carnosum	MHul
'Carol Gibbons' (Z/d)	EBSP LVer MWhe
'Carol Munroe' (Z/d)	LVer SDen
'Carol Plumridge' (Dw/C)	WFib
¶ 'Carol West' (Z/v)	EBSP SBro SDen
'Carole' (R)	EBSP SOld
'Caroline Schmidt' AGM	CBrk EBSP LVer MBri MWhe NKin NWyt SDen SKen WFib
'Carolyn' (Min)	NKin SBro
'Carousel' (Z/d)	LVer
Casino ® (Z/d)	IHos NWyt
'Cassio' (Min/d)	SBro
'Catford Belle' (A)	CSpe ESul LDea LHil LVer MWhe SBro SDen SKen SOld WEas WFib
caucalifolium ssp. ***caucalifolium***	MHul
– ssp. ***convolvulifolium***	MHul WFib
caylae	MHul
'Cayucas' (I/d)	SKen
'Celebration' (Z/d)	ESul LVer SBro
'Celia' (Min)	NKin SBro SDen
ceratophyllum	MHul
'Cerise' (I/d)	MWhe
'Cézanne' (I/d)	SHer
– (R)	IHos LDea LVer NKin SDen SKen SMrm SUsu WFib
¶ 'Chantilly Claret' (R)	EBSP LDea
'Chantilly Lace' (R)	EBSP LDea
§ 'Charles Gounod' (Z/d)	SDen
Charleston ® (Z)	IHos
'Charlie Boy' (R)	LDea SDen WFib
¶ 'Charlotte Bidwell'	ESul
'Charlotte Read' (Dw)	ERea ESul SBro
'Charm' (Min)	ESul NKin
'Charmer' (R)	LDea
'Chattisham' (Min)	LVer SBro
'Chelmondiston' (Min/d)	ESul MWhe NKin SBro
§ 'Chelsea Gem' AGM	CBrk EBSP LVer NKin SDen SKen SOld WFib
'Chelsworth' (Min/d)	ESul NKin NWyt SBro SDen
'Chelvey' (R)	WFib
'Cherie' (Min)	NKin SBro WFib
– (R)	EBSP LDea WFib
¶ 'Cherie Bidwell'	ESul
'Cherie Maid' (Z/v)	EBSP
'Cherie Mitchell' (Min)	SBro
'Cherry' (Min)	LVer SBro WFib
– (Z/d)	SHer WFib
'Cherry Blossom' (Z/d)	SKen
'Cherry Cocktail' (Z/v)	MWhe SBro SDen
'Cherry Galilee' (I/d)	LVer SKen
'Cherry Hazel Ruffles' (R)	LDea
'Cherry Orchard' (R)	LDea LVer SKen SMrm WFib
'Cherry Sundae' (Z/d/v)	ESul LVer SDen
'Cherryade' (Dw)	SDen
¶ 'Chessington' (Z/C)	SDen
'Chew Magna' (R)	WFib

'Chieko' (Min/d) ESul LVer MWhe NKin NWyt SBro SDen WFib
'Chiltern Beacon' (Min/d) SBro
'Chime' (Min/d) ESul LVer NKin SBro
'China Doll' (Dw/d) SBro WFib
¶ 'Chinese Red' (Z/d) LVer
¶ 'Chintz' (R) LDea
'Chiquita' (R) LDea WFib
'Chi-Chi' (Min) ESul SBro
'Chocolate Blotch' (Z/C) CNat SBro
§ 'Chocolate Peppermint' AGM CLTr CMer CSev ERav ERom ESul IHos LBlm MWhe NHHG NWyt SDen SHer SKen WCHb WEas WElm WFib WHer WPer
'Chocolate Tomentosum' See P. 'Chocolate Peppermint'
'Choice Cerise' (R) LDea
'Chorus Girl' (R) LVer SDen WEas
'Christopher Ley' (Z) LVer SDen SKen
'Christopher Mitchell' (Min) SBro
'Cindy' (Dw/d) ESul NWyt SBro
'Circus Day' (R) LDea WFib
'Citriodorum' (Sc) CArn LVer NHHG NWyt SIde WCHb WFib WPer
'Citronella' (Sc) NHHG SHer WCHb WFib
citronellum (Sc) LHil MHul NSty SDen SKen WFib WHer WPer
'Clair' (Min) WFib
'Clara Read' (Dw) ESul LVer SBro
'Clare' (Min) SBro
'Claret Rock Unique' (U) CLTr EWoo LVer NWyt SDen SKen WFib
'Clarissa' (Min) ESul
¶ 'Clatterbridge' (Dw) ESul SBro
'Claude Read' (Dw) ERea ESul NKin SBro
'Claudette' (Min) ESul SBro
'Claudius' (Min) ESul SBro SDen WFib
'Claydon' (Dw/d) CSpe ESul LVer NKin SBro
¶ 'Clevedon Joy' (Z/c) SDen
'Clorinda' (U/Sc) CSev ESul EWoo GBar LBlm LHil LVer NWyt SDen SHer SIde SKen WCHb WFib WHer
'Clorinda Variegated' See P. 'Variegated Clorinda'
Coco-Rico ® (I) NWyt
'Coddenham' (Dw/d) ESul SBro WFib
§ 'Colonel Baden-Powell' (I/d) LDea WFib
'Colour Sergeant' (Min) SBro
Columbia ® (Z/Sc) IHos SBro
columbinum MHul
'Concolor Lace' (Sc) ESul LVer SKen
¶ 'Congestum' MHul
'Contrast' (Z/d/C/v) EBSP LVer MWhe NKin NWyt SBro SDen SKen WFib
'Copdock' (Min/d) ESul NKin SBro
'Copthorne' AGM CSpe WFib WHer
'Coral Frills' (Dw) ESul SBro
'Coral Island' (Z/d) EBSP SBro SDen
'Coral Reef' (Z/d) NKin NWyt
'Coralglow' (Z/d) IHos
cordifolium EWoo MHul WFib
coriandrifolium See P. ***myrrhifolium***
'Cornell' (I/d) ECtt IHos MBri MWhe SDen
'Coronia' (Z/Ca) LVer
¶ ***coronopifolium*** MHul
'Corsair' AGM MWhe WFib
cortusifolium MHul
'Cotswold Queen' (Z/d) WFib
'Cotton Candy' (Dw/d) ESul SBro
'Cottontail' (Min/d) ESul LVer NKin SBro
cotyledonis GCHN MHul WFib
'Countess Mariza' See P. 'Gräfin Mariza'
'Countess of Scarborough' See P. 'Lady Scarborough'
'Country Girl' (R) IHos LDea NKin
'Cover Girl' (Z/d) WFib
'Cramdon Red' (Dw) SKen SOld
'Crampel's Master' (Z) LVer SKen
¶ 'Cranbrook Black' EWoo
'Cransley Blends' (R) EBSP LDea
'Cransley Star' (A) LDea
crassicaule MHul
crassipes GCHN
'Creamery' (Z/d) SDen WFib
§ 'Creamy Nutmeg' CArn CLTr ESul GBar LVer MWhe NKin
'Creed's Seedling' (Z/C) EBSP LVer
'Creeting St Mary' (Min) ESul SBro
'Creeting St Peter ' (Min) ESul SBro
'Crescendo' (I/d) ECtt
'Crestfield Pink' (Min) SBro
'Crimson Fire' (Z/d) MBri MWhe SKen
'Crimson Glow' (Dw/d) SBro
'Crimson Unique' AGM EWoo LHil LVer SKen WFib
crispum (Sc) CSFH NHHG SDen SHer SIde WCHb WEas WFib
– 'Major' (Sc) ESul GPoy NSty SDen SKen WFib WHer WPer
– 'Peach Cream' (Sc/v) MWhe SDen SIde
– 'Variegatum' AGM CSev CSpe GBar GCHN IHos LDea LHil LVer MWhe NKin NRoo NSty NWyt SBro SDen SHer SKen SOld WCHb WEas WFib WHer WPer WWye
crithmifolium GCHN MHul
'Crocketta' (I/d) EBSP LVer
'Crocodile' See P. 'The Crocodile'
'Crowfield' (Min/d) ESul NKin SBro
'Crystal Palace Gem' (Z/v) EBSP LBlm LVer MWhe NKin SDen SKen
cucullatum EWoo MHul WFib
– ssp. ***strigifolium*** GCHN WHer
¶ 'Culm' (A) LDea
'Culpho' (Min/C/d) ESul NKin SBro
'Cupid' (Min/Dw/d) ESul LVer NKin SBro WFib
'Cynthia' (Min) ESul SBro
'Cyril Read' (Dw) ERea ESul NKin SBro
'Czar' (Z/C) WFib
'Dainty Lassie' (Dw/v) ESul SBro
¶ 'Dainty Maid' ESul
'Dale Queen' (Z) EBSP WFib
'Dame Anna Neagle' AGM LVer NKin
'Dancer' (Dw) ESul SBro
'Danny West' SDen
I 'Dark Pink Sugar Baby' (I) LVer
'Dark Red Irene' (Z/d) LVer MWhe WFib

'Dark Secret' (R) CSpe EBSP LDea SDen SKen WFib
'Dark Venus' (R) LDea
'Darmsden' (A) ESul LDea LVer SBro
¶ 'Dart' (A) LDea
dasyphyllum MHul
'David John' (Dw/d) ESul LVer NKin NWyt SBro SDen
'David Mitchell' (Min/Ca/C/d) SBro
'Davina' (Min/d) ESul MWhe SBro WFib
¶ 'Dawn Star' (Z/St) SBro
'Daydream' (Z/C/d) EBSP LVer NWyt
'Deacon Arlon' (Dw/d) ESul MWhe NKin SKen
'Deacon Avalon' (Dw/d) WFib
'Deacon Barbecue' (Z/d) ESul LVer MWhe NKin NWyt SBro SDen
'Deacon Birthday' (Z/d) ESul LVer MWhe NKin SBro SDen
'Deacon Bonanza' (Z/d) ESul LVer MWhe NKin SBro SDen SKen WFib
'Deacon Clarion' (Z/d) ESul LVer NKin SBro SKen
'Deacon Constancy' (Z/d) ESul LVer MWhe NKin NWyt SBro SDen
'Deacon Coral Reef' (Z/d) ESul LVer MWhe SBro SKen SOld
'Deacon Finale' (Z/d) ESul LVer NKin SBro SDen
'Deacon Fireball' (Z/d) ESul LVer MWhe NKin NWyt SBro SDen SKen SOld
'Deacon Flamingo' (Z/d) ESul LVer MWhe SDen
'Deacon Gala' (Z/d) ESul LVer MWhe NKin SBro SDen
'Deacon Golden Bonanza' (Z/C/d) ESul NKin SBro SDen
'Deacon Golden Gala' (Z/C/d) ESul NKin SBro SDen
I 'Deacon Golden Lilac Mist' (Z/C/d) ESul NKin NWyt SBro SDen
'Deacon Jubilant' (Z/d) ESul LVer MWhe NKin NWyt SBro SDen SKen
'Deacon Lilac Mist' (Z/d) ESul LVer MWhe NKin NWyt SBro SDen SKen SOld
'Deacon Mandarin' (Z/d) ESul LVer MWhe SBro SKen
'Deacon Minuet' (Z/C/d) ESul LVer MWhe NKin NWyt SBro SDen SKen
'Deacon Moonlight' (Z/d) ESul LVer MWhe SBro
'Deacon Peacock' (Z/C/d) ESul LVer MWhe NKin SBro SDen SKen
'Deacon Picotee' (Z/d) ESul IHos LVer MBri SBro SDen
'Deacon Regalia' (Z/d) ESul LVer MWhe NKin SDen SKen
'Deacon Romance' (Z/d) ESul LVer MWhe NKin SBro SDen SKen
'Deacon Summertime' (Z/d) ESul LVer MWhe SBro
'Deacon Sunburst' (Z/d) ESul LVer MWhe NKin NWyt SBro SDen SKen SOld
'Deacon Suntan' (Z/d) ESul LVer MWhe NKin SBro SDen SKen
'Deacon Trousseau' (Z/d) ESul LVer NKin SBro SDen
'Decora Impérial' (I) LDea LVer SKen
*'Decora Lavender' (I) LVer
§ 'Decora Lilas' (I) ECtt LDea NPri SKen WFib
'Decora Mauve' (I) See P. 'Decora Lilas'
§ 'Decora Rose' (I) ECtt IHos LDea LVer SKen
'Decora Rouge' (I) ECtt LDea LVer NPri NWyt SKen WFib
'Degas' (R) WFib
'Delilah' (R) LDea SDen
'Della' (Min/d) LVer SBro
¶ 'Delli' (R) EBSP
'Delta' (Min/d) NKin SBro
'Denebola' (Min/d) ESul LVer NKin SBro WFib
Denticulatum Group (Sc) MHul NHHG NWyt SDen SHer SIde SKen WCHb WFib
§ – 'Filicifolium' (Sc) CLTr CSev CSpe EWoo GCHN IHos LHil NHHG NWyt SDen SKen WFib WHer WPer WWye
desertorum MHul
'Destiny' (R) WFib
'Dewit's' (Dw) NWyt SBro
'Di' (Min/d) SBro
'Diadem' (R) SKen WFib
'Diana Palmer' (Z/d) EBSP LVer
'Diane' (Min/d) ESul LVer SBro SDen WFib
'Dibbinsdale' (Z) ESul SBro
dichondrifolium EWoo MHul SSad WFib
'Dick's White' (Dw/d) SBro
'Didden's Improved Picardy' (Z/d) MWhe
'Diddi-Di' (Min/d) ESul SBro
'Didi' (Min) SBro
'Dinky' (Min/d) ESul NKin SBro
dipetalum MHul
§ Disco ® (Z/d) IHos NWyt
'Distinction' (Z) CBrk EBSP IHos MWhe NKin NWyt SDen SKen WFib WPer
'Doctor A Chipault' (I/d) LDea LVer WFib
'Dodd's Super Double' (Z/d) IHos
'Dollar Bute' (R) LDea LVer
'Dollar Princess' (Z/C) SDen SKen
'Dolly Daydream' (C) SDen
'Dolly Moon' (C) SDen
'Dolly Read' (Dw) ERea ESul SBro WFib
'Dolly Varden' AGM EBSP IHos LHop LVer MBri MWhe NKin NWyt SBro SDen SKen WFib
dolomiticum GCHN MHul WFib
'Dolphin' (Min) NKin NWyt SBro WFib
'Don Quixote' (A) EWoo LDea
'Dondo' (Dw/d) SBro
¶ 'Don's Agnes Brown' (Min) SBro
¶ 'Don's Carosel' (Z/v) SBro
¶ 'Don's Diamond Jubilee' (Z/C/v) SBro
¶ 'Don's Mona Noble' (Z/C/v) SBro
¶ 'Don's Seagold' SBro
¶ 'Don's Silva Perle' (Dw/v) SBro
¶ 'Don's Sunkissed' (Dw/v) SBro
¶ 'Don's Swanland Girl' (Min) NKin
'Dopey' (Min) ESul SBro
'Doreen Featherby' (R) SDen
'Doris Brook' (Z/d) WFib
'Doris Frith' (R) LDea WFib
'Doris Hancock' (R) WFib

¶ 'Doris Moore' (Z)	LVer
'Doris Shaw' (R)	WFib
'Double Bird's Egg' (Z/d)	NWyt
'Double Grace Wells' (Min/d)	ESul SBro
♦ 'Double Henry Jacoby' (Z/d)	See P. 'Double Jacoby'
§ 'Double Jacoby' (Z/d)	SDen WFib
'Double Lilac White' (I/d)	IHos MWhe NPri
'Double New Life' (Z/d)	SBro
'Double Orange' (Z/d)	SKen
'Double Pink Bird's Egg' (Z/d)	SKen
'Dove' (Z)	NWyt WFib
'Dovedale' (Dw/C)	ESul LVer NKin NWyt SBro
'Downlands' (Z/d)	LVer SDen
'Dream' (Z)	WFib
'Dresden China' (R)	LDea
'Dresden Pink' (Dw)	LVer SBro SDen WFib
'Dresden White' (Dw)	CSpe LVer SBro
'Drummer Boy' (Z)	SDen SKen
drummondii	GCHN
'Dryden' (Z)	LVer NWyt SDen SKen
'Dubonnet' (R)	LDea NKin WFib
'Duchess' (I)	CSpe
'Duchess of Devonshire' (Z)	SKen
'Duke of Buckingham' (Z/d)	LVer NWyt SDen
'Duke of Devonshire' (Z/d)	LVer SDen
'Duke of Edinburgh'	See P. 'Hederinum Variegatum'
'Dulcie' (Min)	ESul NKin SBro
'Dunkery Beacon' (R)	LDea WFib
'Dusty Rose' (Min)	ESul SBro
'Dutch Vermillion' (Min)	SBro
§ 'Dwarf Miriam Baisey' (Min)	LVer NKin SBro SDen WFib
'Dwarf Miriam Read'	See P. 'Dwarf Miriam Baisey'
'E Dabner' (Z/d)	SKen WFib
'Earl of Chester' **AGM**	SBro
'Earleana' (Dec)	CSpe ESul LDea SBro SKen
'Earth Magic' (Z/v)	SBro SDen
'Eastbourne Beauty' (I/d)	WFib
'Easter Greeting'	See P. 'Ostergruss'
¶ 'Easter Morn' (Z/St)	NWyt SBro
echinatum	GCHN MHul SSad
– 'Album'	SDen SSad
♦– 'Miss Stapleton'	See P. 'M. S.'
'Eclipse' (Min/d)	ESul LVer MWhe NKin NWyt SBro SDen SKen
'Eden Gem' (Min/d)	ESul LVer NKin SBro SDen
'Edith Steane' (Dw/d)	LVer SBro
'Edmond Lachenal' (Z/d)	WFib
'Edward Humphris' (Z)	SDen SKen
'Edwin Clarke' (Dw/Min)	SBro
¶ 'Eileen' (Min)	LVer SDen
'Eileen Postle' (R)	WFib
¶ 'Eldorado'	SHer
'Eleanor' (Z/d)	SDen
'Electra' (Z/d)	LVer SDen WFib
elegans	MHul
'Elfin Rapture' (R)	NKin WFib
'Elgar' (R)	WFib
'Elizabeth Angus' (Z)	SDen SKen WFib
'Elizabeth Cartwright' (Z)	WFib
'Elizabeth Read' (Dw)	ERea ESul NWyt SBro
'Elmscfi' (Dw)	NWyt
'Elmsett' (Z/C/d)	ESul LVer NKin SBro
'Elna' (Min)	ESul SBro
elongatum	GCHN MHul
'Els' (Min/St)	ESul LHil LVer NKin SBro SKen
'Elsi' (I/d/v)	EBSP SDen WFib
'Elsie' (Z/C/d)	SBro
'Elsie Hickman' (R)	LDea SDen SKen WFib
'Elsie Portas' (Z/C/d)	ESul LVer SKen
'Embassy' (Dw)	ESul LVer SBro WFib
'Emerald' (I)	MSmi SDen SKen
¶ 'Emilia Joy' (A)	SBro
'Emma' (Min/C/d)	SBro
'Emma Hössle'	See P. 'Frau Emma Hössle'
'Emma Jane Read' (Dw/d)	ERea ESul MWhe SBro WFib
'Emma Louise' (Z)	LVer SKen
'Emperor Nicholas' (Z/d)	NWyt
'Empress' (Z)	SKen
'Ena' (Min)	ESul LVer SBro
'Enchantress' (I)	EBSP LVer MBri MWhe SDen
endlicherianum	CMon EPot GCHN MHul SApp SAxl SPou
'Endora' (Min)	SBro SDen
'Endsleigh' (Sc)	SDen
'Enid Blackaby' (R)	WFib
'Enid Read' (Dw)	ERea SBro
'Eric Ellis' (Dw/d)	WFib
¶ 'Eric Hoskins' (Z/d)	EBSP
'Erwarton' (Min/d)	ESul LVer NKin SBro SDen
'Escapade' (Dw/d)	ESul SBro
'Etna' (Min)	SBro
¶ 'Evelyn'	ESul
'Evesham Wonder' (Z/d)	SDen WFib
exhibens	MHul
¶ 'Expo' (I/d)	EBSP
exstipulatum	MHul WFib
'Fair Dinkum' (Z/v)	MWhe SBro
§ 'Fair Ellen' (Sc)	CLTr EWoo SIde SKen WFib WPer
'Fairlee' (DwI)	SDen
'Fairy Orchid' (A)	ESul LDea LVer NKin SBro SDen
'Fairy Princess' (Min)	SBro
– (R)	LDea
¶ 'Fairy Queen'	EWoo WEas
¶ 'Fairy Storey' (Min/v)	SBro
'Fairy Tales' (Dw)	ESul SBro
'Falkenham' (Min)	SBro
¶ 'Falklands Brother' (Z/C/v)	EBSP SBro
'Falklands Hero' (Z/v)	EBSP LVer MWhe SBro SDen SKen WFib
'Fanny Eden' (R)	WFib
'Fantasie' **AGM**	ESul LVer MWhe SBro WFib
¶ 'Fantasy' (R)	LDea
'Fareham' (R)	EBSP LDea
'Fascination' (Z/Ca)	SDen WFib

'Feneela' (Dw/d) ESul SBro
'Fenton Farm' (Z/C) SDen
'Festal' (Min/d) ESul SBro
'Feu d'Amour' (I/d) WEas
'Feuerriese' (Z) LVer
'Fiat' (Z/d) SKen
'Fiat Queen' (Z/d) SKen WFib
'Fiat Supreme' (Z/d) SKen WFib
§ 'Fidelio' (Z/d) IHos NWyt
'Fiery Sunrise' (R) EBSP LDea
'Fiesta' (Z) LDea LVer
'Fifth Avenue' (R) CSpe SDen
'Filicifolium' See P. Denticulatum Group 'Filicifolium'
'Filigree' (Dw/v) IHos SBro
'Finger' SBro
'Finito' (Dw/d) ERea SBro
'Fire Cascade' (I) LVer
'Fire Dragon' (Z/St/d) LVer MWhe SDen SKen WFib
'Firebrand' (Z/d) LVer
'Firefly' (Min/d) ESul SBro WFib
'Fireglow' (Z/d) ESul
¶ 'Firestone' (Dw) ESul SBro
¶ 'Fireworks' (Dw) SBro
'First Blush' (R) WFib
¶ 'First Ladies' SDen
'First Love' (Z) EBSP
fissifolium MHul
'Flakey' **AGM** CSpe ESul LDea MWhe NWyt SBro SDen SKen
'Flame' (Z) WFib
¶ 'Flamenco' (R) LDea NKin
'Flamingo Dancer' (Z/Ca) SBro
¶ 'Flarepath' (Z/C/v) SBro SDen
'Flash' (Min) SBro
'Fleur d'Amour' (R) WFib
'Fleurette' (Dw/d) ESul MWhe NKin NWyt SBro SDen SKen SOld WFib
§ Flirt ® (Min) ESul LVer MBri NKin NWyt SDen
'Floral Cascade' (Fr/d) NWyt WFib
¶ 'Florence Mitchell' (Dw) SBro
'Florence Storey' (Z/C/d) WFib
'Flower of Spring' **AGM** CSpe EWoo LVer MWhe NWyt SDen SKen WFib
'Flowerfield' (Z) SDen
'Flowton' (Dw/d) ESul SBro
'Fox' (Z/d) WFib
'Foxhall' (Dw) ESul SBro
Fragrans Group (Sc) CLTr CMil CSev ERav ESul EWoo GCHN GCra GPoy MWhe NHHG NKin NSty NWyt SDen SHer SKen WFib WHer WPer WWye
– 'Creamy Nutmeg' (Sc/v) See P. 'C.N.'
§ – 'Fragrans Variegatum' (Sc/v) CMil CSev CSpe ERav LBlm LHil LHop MHul MWhe NSty NWyt SDen SHer SKen WCHb WFib WPer
– 'Snowy Nutmeg' See P. Fragrans Group 'Fragrans Variegatum'
'Francis James' (Z) NWyt SDen
¶ 'Francis Parmenter' (MinI/v) SBro
'Francis Parrett' **AGM** ESul LVer MWhe NKin NWyt SBro SDen WFib
'Francis Read' (Dw/d) ERea ESul LVer SBro
'Frank Headley' **AGM** CBrk CSpe ESul IHos LHil LVer MSte MWhe NKin NWyt SBro SDen SKen SMrm SOld WEas WFib WSun
'Frank Parrett' (Min/d) ESul SBro
§ 'Frau Emma Hössle' (Dw/d) MWhe NKin NWyt WFib
'Frau Käthe Neubronner' (Z/d) SDen
'Freak of Nature' (Z/v) EBSP IHos MWhe NKin SDen SKen WEas WFib
'Frensham' (Sc) ESul IHos
'Freston' (Dw) ESul
'Freya' (Min) ESul SBro
'Friary Wood' (Z/C/d) ESul LVer NKin NWyt SBro SDen SKen WFib
'Friesdorf' (Dw) ERav ESul LHil LVer MWhe NWyt SBro SDen SKen WEas WFib
'Frills' (Min/d) ESul LVer MWhe NKin NWyt SBro SKen WFib
'Fringed Aztec' (R) EBSP LDea LVer NKin SDen SKen SOld
'Fringed Rouletta' (I) LDea
♦ 'Frosty' (Min/v) See P. 'Variegated Kleine Liebling'
♦ 'Frosty Petit Pierre' See P. 'Variegated Kleine Liebling'
¶ 'Frühlingszauber Lilac' (R) EBSP
fruticosum MHul WFib WHer
fulgidum GCHN MHul WFib
'Fynn' (Dw) ESul SBro
'Galilee' **AGM** IHos LDea LVer SDen SKen WFib
'Galway Star' **AGM** CSpe LVer MWhe NWyt SDen SIde WFib
'Gama' (Min) SBro
'Garda' (I/d) ECtt
'Garibaldi' (Z/d) NWyt WFib
'Garland' (Dw/d) NKin SBro
– (R) ESul LVer SKen
'Garnet' (Z/d) LVer NKin WFib
'Garnet Rosebud' (Min/d) ESul LVer SBro
'Garnet Wings' (R) WFib
¶ 'Garten Direktor' EWoo
'Gary Salvidge' (R) LDea
'Gauguin' (I/d) IHos
'Gay Baby' (DwI) ESul LDea MWhe NWyt SBro SDen
'Gay Baby Supreme' (DwI) ESul SDen SKen
'Gazelle' (Z) SDen SKen
'Gemini' (Z/St/d) SBro SKen
'Gemma' (Min/C) SBro SKen
– (R) EBSP LDea
'Gemma Jewel' (R) EBSP
'Gemstone' (Sc) ESul SBro
'Genetrix' (Z/d) WFib
'Genie' (Z/d) LVer MWhe SDen WFib
'Geoff May' (Dw) ESul NKin SBro SDen WFib
'Geoffrey Horsman' (R) WFib
'Georgia Peach' (R) SDen WFib
'Geo's Pink' (Z/v) MWhe
'Gerald Portas' (Dw/C) ESul LVer SBro SDen
'Gerald Wells' (Min) SBro

'Geraldine' (Min) ESul NKin SBro
'Geratus' (Min/Ca/d) SBro
'Gess Portas' (Z/v) ESul LVer SBro SKen
'Giant Butterfly' (R) LDea
gibbosum CTro GCHN MHul SDen SSad WFib
'Gilbert West' (Z) SDen SKen
'Gilda' (R) LDea SKen
'Gill' (Min/Ca) ESul NKin SBro
'Gillian Clifford' (Z/d) SDen
'Gina' (Min) SBro
'Glacier Claret' (Z) IHos
Glacis ® (Z/d) WFib
'Gladys Evelyn' (Z/d) WFib
'Gladys Stevens' (Min/d) ESul LVer NKin SBro SDen
¶ x ***glaucifolium*** MHul
glaucum See P. ***lanceolatum***
'Gleam' (Z/d) LVer
'Glenn Barker' (Z/d) WFib
'Glenshree' (R) LDea SKen
Gloria ® (Z/d) NWyt
'Gloria Pearce' (R) LDea WFib
'Glory' (Z/d) WFib
'Glowing Embers' (R) LDea WFib
§ ***glutinosum*** CSev MHul WWye
'Goblin' (Min/d) ESul IHos LVer NKin NWyt SBro SDen SKen WFib
¶ 'Gold Star' (Z/St/C) ESul SBro
'Golden Baby' (DwI/C) MWhe
'Golden Brilliantissimum' (Z/C) EBSP LVer MWhe NWyt SBro SDen SKen WFib
'Golden Butterfly' (Z/C) ESul LVer SBro
'Golden Chalice' (Min/v) LVer MWhe NKin SBro SDen SKen
¶ 'Golden Chance' (Min/C/v) SBro
'Golden Clorinda' (U/Sc/C) EWoo SDen WEas
'Golden Crest' (Z/C) NWyt SDen SKen SMrm
'Golden Ears' (Dw/St/C) ESul LVer MWhe NWyt SBro SDen SKen SOld WFib
'Golden Everaarts' (Dw/C) ESul SBro
¶ 'Golden Fireball' (Z/C) SBro
'Golden Fleece' (Min/C/d) ESul SDen SKen
¶ 'Golden Flora' SDen
'Golden Gates' (Z/C) ESul SBro SDen SKen
'Golden Gleam' (Z/C) SDen
'Golden Harry Hieover' (Z/C) CBrk ESul LVer SDen SKen WEas
'Golden Lilac Mist' NKin NWyt SBro
'Golden Mirage' (Z/v) SBro
'Golden Mist' (Dw/C/d) LVer
'Golden Orange' (Dw/C) ESul SBro
'Golden Orfe' (Dw/C) SBro WFib
'Golden Petit Pierre' (Min/C) ESul NKin SBro SDen
'Golden Princess' (Min/C) ESul SBro SDen WFib
– (R) LDea
'Golden Roc' (Min/C) ESul SBro
'Golden Staphs' (St/C) ESul LVer NWyt SBro SDen
'Golden Tears' (MinI/C/d) ESul SDen
'Goldie' (R) WFib
'Goldilocks' (A) ESul LDea
♦ 'Gooseberry Leaf' See P. ***grossularioïdes***
'Gordano Midnight' (R) WFib
'Gordino Pixie' (R) LDea
'Gosbeck' (A) ESul LDea MWhe SBro SDen
'Gosport Girl' (R) EBSP LDea
'Grace Read' (Min) ESul SBro
'Grace Wells' (Min) ESul SDen WFib
§ 'Gräfin Mariza' (Z/d) IHos NKin NWyt SDen SKen WFib
'Granada' (R) IHos
'Grand Slam' (R) IHos LDea LVer NKin SKen SOld WFib
grandiflorum GCHN MHul WFib
'Grandma Fischer' See P. 'Grossmutter Fischer'
'Grandma Ross' (R) EBSP LDea
'Granny Hewitt' (Min/d) ESul MWhe NKin SBro
§ 'Graveolens' (Sc) CLTr CNat CSFH CSev GCHN GPoy LBlm LHil LVer MHul MWhe NKin NSty NWyt SDen SHer SKen WElm WFib
'Great Blakenham' (Min) ESul LVer SBro
'Great Bricett' (Min/d) ESul LVer NKin SBro SDen
¶ 'Green Ears' ESul
'Green Eyes' (I/d) LDea SDen
'Green Goddess' (I/d) EBSP SKen
¶ 'Green Gold Petit Pierre' (MiN) ESul SDen
'Green Woodpecker' (R) LDea LVer SDen
§ 'Greengold Kleine Liebling' (Min/C/v) ESul NKin NWyt SBro SDen SKen
'Greengold Petit Pierre' See P. 'Greengold Kleine Liebling'
'Greetings' (Min/v) SBro
Gregor ® (Z/d) WFib
'Grenada' (R) SKen
§ 'Grenadier' AGM LVer NWyt SBro SDen
'Grenche Belle' (I/d) LVer
'Grey Lady Plymouth' (Sc/v) EWoo GBar LBlm SDen SIde WElm WFib
¶ 'Grey Monk' (Z) EBSP
'Grey Sprite' (Min/v) SBro WFib
¶ ***greytonense*** MHul
griseum MHul WFib
§ 'Grossmutter Fischer' (R) LDea NKin WEas WFib
§ ***grossularioïdes*** ESul MHul NSty
'Grozser Garten' (Dw) ESul
'Grozser Garten Weiss' (Dw) ESul
¶ 'Gurnard' SDen
'Gustav Emich' (Z/d) LVer SDen SKen WFib
'Gwen' (Min/v) LVer SBro
'H Guinier' See P. 'Charles Gounod'
¶ 'H Rigler' (Z) SDen
'Hadleigh' (Dw) ESul SBro
'Haidee' (Min) SBro
'Hamble Lass' (R) EBSP LDea
¶ 'Hanchen Anders' (Z) SDen
§ 'Hannaford Star' (Z/St) ESul SBro SDen
§ 'Happy Thought' AGM CLTr EBSP IHos MBri MWhe NKin NWyt SBro SDen SKen

'Happy Valley' (R) EBSP LVer WFib
'Harbour Lights' (R) EBSP LDea
'Harewood Slam' (R) LDea NKin SMrm WFib
'Harkstead' (Min) ESul NWyt SBro
¶ 'Harlequin' (Dw) SBro
'Harlequin Alpine Glow' (I) LDea LVer MWhe SDen WFib
'Harlequin Hilda Day' (I) LVer
'Harlequin Mahogany' (I/d) LDea LVer MBri MWhe SDen SKen SOld WFib
§ 'Harlequin Miss Liver Bird' (I) LDea SDen SKen SOld
'Harlequin My Love' (I) SKen
'Harlequin Picotee' (I/d) LDea LVer MWhe SDen
'Harlequin Pretty Girl' (I) LVer MWhe SDen SKen WFib
'Harlequin Rosie O'Day' (I) LDea LVer MWhe SDen SKen WFib
'Harlequin Ted Day' (I) LDea LVer
'Harold Headley' (Z/v) LVer WFib
'Harriet Le Hair' (Z) SKen
'Harvard' (I) SDen
'Harvey' (Z) MWhe
'Hayley Charlotte' (Z/v) MWhe
'Hazel' (R) SDen SKen WFib
'Hazel Anson' (R) LDea
'Hazel Birkby' (R) EBSP LDea
'Hazel Blake' (R) EBSP
'Hazel Burgundy' (R) EBSP LDea
'Hazel Burtoff' (R) EBSP LDea
'Hazel Carey' (R) LDea
'Hazel Cherry' (R) LDea WFib
'Hazel Chick' (R) LDea
'Hazel Choice' (R) EBSP LDea
'Hazel Frances' (R) LDea
'Hazel Frills' (R) LDea
'Hazel Gipsy' (R) LDea
'Hazel Glory' (R) LDea
'Hazel Harmony' (R) LDea
'Hazel Heather' (R) LDea
'Hazel Henderson' (R) LDea LVer
'Hazel Herald' (R) LDea SDen
'Hazel Mistique' (R) LDea
'Hazel Peach' (R) LDea
¶ 'Hazel Rosei' (R) LDea
'Hazel Saga' (R) EBSP LDea
'Hazel Satin' (R) LDea
'Hazel Star' (R) EBSP LDea
¶ 'Hazel Stardust' (R) EBSP LDea
'Hazel Wright' (R) LDea
§ 'Hederinum' (I) IHos LDea MWhe SDen SKen WEas WFib
§ 'Hederinum Variegatum' (I/v) CSpe GBur LDea MWhe SKen WFib
'Heidi' (Min/d) ESul SBro SDen SKen WFib
'Helena' (I/d) EBSP LDea MWhe SDen SKen
¶ 'Helena Hall' (R) LDea
¶ 'Helter Skelter' (Z/v) SDen
'Hemingstone' (A) ESul LDea SBro SDen
'Henhurst Gleam' (Dw/C/d) WFib
'Henri Joignot' (Z/C/d) EBSP
'Hermione' (Z/d) MWhe NWyt WFib
'High Tor' (Dw/C/d) ESul LVer NWyt SKen
'Highfields Always' (Z/d) IHos LVer WFib
'Highfields Appleblossom' (Z/d) IHos LVer SKen
'Highfields Attracta' (Z/d) LVer SDen SKen
'Highfields Ballerina' (Z/d) LVer
'Highfields Cameo (Z/d) LVer
'Highfields Candy Floss' (Z/d) LVer SDen
'Highfields Charisma' (Z/d) LVer
'Highfields Choice' (Z) LVer SDen SKen
'Highfields Comet' (Z) SKen
'Highfields Concerto' (Z) LVer
'Highfields Contessa' (Z/d) LVer SDen SKen
'Highfields Dazzler' (Z) LVer
'Highfields Delight' (Z) LVer
'Highfields Fancy' (Z/d) IHos LVer SKen
'Highfields Fantasy' (Z) SKen
'Highfields Fashion' (Z) LVer
'Highfields Festival' (Z/d) EBSP LVer MWhe SDen
'Highfields Flair' (Z/d) LVer SDen
'Highfields Flash' (Z/d) LVer
'Highfields Glow' (Z/d) LVer
'Highfields Joy' (Z/d) SDen WFib
'Highfields Melody' (Z/d) LVer SDen
'Highfields Orange' (Z) LVer
'Highfields Paramount' (Z) MWhe SDen SKen
'Highfields Pearl' (Z) LVer SDen
'Highfields Pink' (Z) LVer
'Highfields Prestige' (Z) LVer SKen
'Highfields Pride' (Z) LVer SKen
'Highfields Prima Donna' (Z/d) EBSP LVer MWhe SDen SKen
'Highfields Promise' (Z) SDen SKen
'Highfields Salmon' (Z/d) LVer
'Highfields Serenade' (Z) LVer
'Highfields Snowdrift' (Z) LVer SKen
'Highfields Sonata' (Z/d) LVer SDen
'Highfields Sugar Candy' (Z/d) EBSP ECtt IHos LVer NWyt SDen SKen
'Highfields Supreme' (Z) LVer
'Highfields Symphony' (Z) LVer
'Highfields Vogue' (Z) LVer
¶ 'Highland Princess' (Dw) SBro
'Hildegard' (Z/d) SKen WFib
'Hills of Snow' (Z/v) EBSP LVer SDen SKen
'Hillscheider Amethyst' (I/d) See P. 'Amethyst'
'Hindoo' (R) WFib
'Hintlesham' (Min) ESul SBro

hirtum GCHN MHul
hispidum MHul
'Hitcham' (Min/d) ESul SBro
'Holbrook' (Min/C/d) ESul LVer SBro
¶ 'Holly West' SDen
'Hollywood Star' **AGM** MWhe
¶ 'Holmes Miller' (Z/d) SBro
'Honeywood Hannah' (R) EBSP
'Honeywood Jonathan' (R) LDea
'Honeywood Lindy' (R) EBSP LDea LVer SDen
'Honeywood Matthew' (Dw) NKin SBro
'Honeywood Suzanne' (Min/Fr) ESul LVer NKin SBro
'Honne Früling' (Z) SKen WFib
'Honneas' (Min) ESul
'Honnestolz' (Min) ESul SBro SKen
'Hope' (Z) WFib
'Hope Valley' **AGM** ESul LVer MWhe NKin SBro SDen SKen
'Horace Parsons' (R) LDea WFib
'Horace Read' (Dw) ERea ESul LVer SBro
'House and Garden' (R) LVer WFib
'Howard Stanton' (R) WFib
'Howard's Orange' (R) LDea SKen
'Hugo de Vries' (Z/d) WFib
'Hula' (U) EWoo
'Hunter's Moon' (Z/C) ESul SBro SKen
'Hurdy-Gurdy' (Z/d/v) SBro SDen WFib
HWD Corelli ® IHos
HWD Gabrieli ® IHos
HWD Monteverdi ® IHos
HWD Onyx ® IHos
HWD Romanze ® IHos
HWD Vivaldi ® IHos
'Ian Read' (Min/d) ERea ESul SBro WFib
'Ice Cap' (Min) SBro
'Icing Sugar' (I/d) ESul LDea LVer MWhe NWyt
'Immaculatum' (Z) SDen WFib
'Imperial Butterfly' (A) LDea SBro
'Improved Petit Pierre' (Min) ESul SDen
'Improved Ricard' (Z/d) WFib
'Improved Rubin' (Z/d) LVer
Ina ® (Z/d) WFib
'Inca' (R) EBSP LDea SDen
incrassatum GCHN MHul
'Ingres' **AGM** ECtt IHos SHer
¶ 'Inka' SDen
inquinans GCHN MHul WFib
iocastum MHul
'Ione' (Z/d) LVer
ionidiflorum CSpe MHul
'Ipswich Town' (Dw/d) ESul
'Irene' **AGM** LVer NWyt WFib
'Irene Cal' **AGM** SKen
'Irene Corsair' (Z/d) SKen
'Irene Hardy' (Z/d) LVer SDen
'Irene La Jolle' (Z/d) SKen
'Irene Lollipop' (Z/d) SKen
'Irene Toyon' **AGM** NWyt
'Isaac Middleton' (Z) LVer
'Isaac Read' (Dw) SBro
'Isidel' **AGM** MSmi SKen WFib
'Isobel Gamble' (Z/d) LVer SKen
'Isobell' (Z/d) WFib
'Italian Gem' (I) SKen
'Ivalo' (Z/d) IHos LVer MWhe SDen SKen WFib
'Ivory Snow' (Z/d/v) EBSP NWyt SBro SDen SKen
'Jacey' (Z/d) LVer SDen SKen
'Jack Cox' (Dw/d) SBro
'Jack of Hearts' (I) LVer
'Jack Read' (Dw) ERea SBro
'Jack Wood' (Z/d) ESul
'Jackie's Gem' (I/d) MWhe
'Jacky Gall' (I/d) IHos LVer MBri MWhe SKen
'Jacqueline' (Z/d) SDen SKen
'Jan Portas' (Min/C) MWhe
'Jana' (Z/d) WFib
'Jane Biggin' (Dw/C/d) ESul LVer MWhe NKin SBro SKen
'Jane Shoulder' (Min) SBro SDen
'Janet Hofman' (Z/d) LVer
'Janet Kerrigan' (Min/d) MWhe NKin SBro WEas WFib
'Janna Whelan' (Dw/d) SDen
'Jasmine' (R) EBSP LDea NKin
'Jaunty' (Min/d) ESul NWyt SBro SDen
'Jay' (Dw) SBro
'Jayne' (Min/d) CAbP SBro
'Jayne Eyre' (Min/d) ESul LVer MWhe NKin NWyt SBro SDen WFib
'Jazz' IHos SHer
¶ 'Jean Bart' (I) MWhe
'Jean Beatty' (Dw/d) LVer SBro
'Jean Oberle' (Z/d) SDen SKen
§ 'Jeanne d'Arc' (I/d) SKen WFib
'Jenifer Read' (Dw) ERea ESul SBro
'Jennifer' (Min) ESul SBro
'Jessel's Unique' (U) LVer SDen
'Jessika' (Z/d) WFib
¶ 'Jewel' (R) EBSP
– (Z/d) NWyt SDen
'Jeweltone' (Z/d) WFib
'Jill Portas' (Z/C) ESul SKen
¶ 'Jilly Mitchell' (Dw/d) SBro
'Jim Field' (R) WFib
'Jimmy Read' (Min) ERea SBro
'Jim's Delight' (Z/C) EBSP LVer
'Jinny Reeves' (R) EBSP LDea
'Joan Cashmore' (Z/d) SDen
'Joan Fairman' (R) WFib
'Joan Hayward' (Min) ESul SBro
'Joan Morf' (R) LDea LHop SDen SKen WFib
'Joan of Arc' (I/d) See P. 'Jeanne d'Arc'
'Joan Sharman' (Min) SBro
'Joanna Pearce' (R) EBSP LDea SKen
'John West' SBro SDen
¶ 'John's Angela' LVer
¶ 'John's Chameleon' LVer
'John's Dilys' NKin
'John's Pride' SBro
¶ 'John's Valerie' LVer
¶ 'John's Wishy-Washy' LVer
'Joseph Haydn' (R) EBSP NKin
'Joseph Haydon' (R) LDea
'Joseph Paul' (R) SDen
'Joseph Warren' (I/d) LDea
'Joy' (R) EBSP NPri SHer WFib
'Joy Lucille' (Sc) CSev ESul LVer SDen WCHb WFib

'Joyce Delamere' (Z/C/d) NWyt WFib
'Joyce Headley' (Dw/C) LVer SBro
'Joyden' LVer
'Joyful' (Min) SBro
'Jubel Parr' (Z/d) SDen
'Judith Thorp' (R) EBSP LVer
'Judy Read' (Dw) ESul SBro
'Julia' (R) EBSP LDea
'Julie' (A) ESul LDea SBro SKen
'Julie Smith' (R) LDea WFib
¶ 'Jungle Night' (R) EBSP
'Jupiter' (Min/d) LVer SBro WFib
– (R) EBSP LDea NKin
'Just William' (Min/C/d) ESul SBro
'Kamahl' (R) WFib
'Kardinal' (Z/d) IHos
'Karen' (Dw/C) SBro
¶ 'Kari Anne' SDen
'Karl Hagele' (Z/d) SKen WFib
¶ 'Karmin Ball' SDen
karooicum MHul
karrooense 'Graham Rice' See P. 'Grollie's Cream'
¶ ***karrooense*** Knuth EWoo
¶ 'Kath Parmer' (Dw/C) SBro
'Kathleen Gamble' (Z) SKen
'Kathleen Mott' (Z/C) WFib
'Kathryn' (Min) ESul SBro
'Kathryn Portas' (Z/v) ESul SBro SKen
'Kayleigh West' (Min) SBro SDen
'Keepsake' (Dw/d) ESul NKin SBro WFib
'Keith Vernon' (Fr/d) LVer SDen
¶ 'Kelly' (I) EBSP
'Kelvedon Beauty' (Min) SBro WEas
'Ken Salmon' (Dw/d) SBro
¶ 'Kenny's Double' (Z) EBSP SDen
'Kerensa' (Min/d) ESul SBro SKen
'Kershy' (Min) ESul SBro
'Kesgrave' (Min/d) ESul SBro
'Kettle Baston' (A) ESul LDea LVer MWhe SBro
'Kewense' (Z) NWyt
'Kimono' (R) EBSP LDea
'King Edmund' (R) LDea SDen
'King of Balcon' See P. 'Hederinum'
'King of Denmark' (Z/d) SKen WFib
'Kingsmill' (R) LDea
'Kingswood' (Z) SDen
'Kirton' (Min/d) ESul SBro
§ 'Kleine Liebling' (Min) CSev EWoo LHop MWhe NWyt SBro SKen
'Koora' (Min/d) SBro
'Kosset' (Min/d) LVer NKin SBro
'Krista' (Min/d) ESul NKin NWyt SBro SDen WFib
'Kyra' (Min/d) ESul SBro WFib
'L E Wharton' (Z) SDen SKen
'La France' AGM EBSP LDea LVer MBri MSmi MWhe SDen SKen SOld WEas WFib
'La Jolla' (Z/d) SDen
'La Paloma' (R) LDea NKin SKen WEas
'Laced Belle Notte' (I) NWyt
¶ 'Laced Mini Cascade' ESul
'Laced Red Mini Cascade' (I) LVer SDen
'Laced Sugar Baby' (DwI) NWyt SDen
Lachsball ® (Z/d) EBSP WFib
§ 'Lachskönigin' (I/d) IHos LDea MWhe NPri SKen WEas WFib
'Lady Churchill' (Z/v) WFib
'Lady Cullum' (Z/C/v) MWhe SBro
'Lady Ilchester' (Z/d) NWyt SDen SKen WFib
'Lady Lexington' (I) SKen
'Lady Mary' (Sc) EWoo LVer SDen WFib
'Lady Plymouth' AGM CLTr CMil CSpe ESul IHos LBlm LHop LVer MSte MWhe NHHG NKin NRoo NSty NWyt SDen SHer SKen SOld WEas WFib WHer WPer WWye
§ 'Lady Scarborough' (Sc) CArn SKen WFib WWye
laevigatum MHul
'Lakeland' (I) EBSP LVer SBro
'Lakis' (R) LDea
'Lamorna' (R) LDea NKin SDen SKen
lanceolatum MHul WFib
'Langley' (R) LDea LVer SDen
'Lanham Lane' (I) EBSP LDea MWhe SBro
'Lanham Royal' (Min/d) ESul NKin SBro
'Lara Jester' (Sc) EWoo
'Lara Nomad' (Sc) EWoo
'Lara Starshine' (Sc) EWoo
'Lark' (Min/d) ESul NKin SBro
N 'Lass o'Gowrie' (Z/v) EBSP LVer MWhe NWyt SBro SDen SKen WFib
'Lass o'Gowrie' (American) (Z/v) WFib
'Laura' (Z/d) WFib
'Lauripen' (Z/d) WFib
'Lavender Frills' (R) LDea
'Lavender Grand Slam' (R) EBSP IHos LDea LVer NKin SDen SKen SOld WFib
'Lavender Harewood Slam' (R) LDea
'Lavender Mini Cascade' See P. 'Lila Mini Cascade
'Lavender Sensation' (R) WFib
laxum MHul
'Layham' (Dw/d) ESul SBro
'Layton's White' (Z/d) SKen
'Le Lutin' (Z/d) WFib
'Lee Gamble' (Z) LVer
'L'Elégante' AGM CSpe EBSP ERav IHos LBlm LDea LVer MBri MSmi MWhe NPri SDen SHer SKen SOld WEas WFib
'Lemon Fancy' (Sc) IHos LVer MWhe NWyt SDen WFib
¶ 'Lemonii' EWoo
'Lemore' (Min/d) SBro
'Len Chandler' (Min) ESul SBro SDen
'LEnfer' (Min/C) See P. 'Mephistopheles'
'Lenore' (Min) ESul
'Leo' (Min) ESul SBro
'Leonie Holbrow' (Min) NKin SBro
'Leopard' (I/d) SKen
'Lerchenmuller' (Z/d) LVer
'Lesando' (Z) EBSP
'Leslie Judd' (R) WFib
'Leslie Salmon' (Min/C) ESul MWhe SBro
'Lethas' (R) LDea
'Letitia' (A) ESul LHil SBro

Leucht-Cascade ® WFib
'Levington' (Min/d) SBro
Lila Compakt-Cascade ® See P. 'Decora Lilas'
§ 'Lila Mini Cascade' (I) ESul MWhe
'Lilac Cascade' See P. 'Roi des Balcons Lilas'
'Lilac Domino' See P. 'Telston's Prima'
'Lilac Gem' (Min/I/d) EBSP IHos LDea LVer MWhe NWyt SDen SKen SOld WFib
¶ 'Lilac Jewel' (R) EBSP
'Lilac Mini Cascade' (I) LDea SBro SDen
'Lilac Ricard' (Z/d) WFib
'Lili Marlene' (I) LVer NWyt SKen
'Lilian' (Dw) LVer SBro
¶ 'Lilian Lilett' NPri
'Lilian Pottinger' (Sc) CArn LVer SDen SIde SKen WEas WFib WHer
'Limoneum' (Sc) NWyt SDen SKen WEas WFib
'Lin Davis' (Z/C) WFib
'Linda' (R) EBSP LDea
– (Z/d) WFib
'Lindsey' (Min) ESul SBro
'Lindy Portas' (I/d) SKen
'Lisa' (Min/C) ESul SBro
'Little Alice' AGM ESul LVer MWhe NKin SBro SDen WFib
'Little Blakenham' (A) ESul LDea SBro
¶ 'Little Dazzler' (Min) SBro
'Little Fe Fine' (Min) ESul SBro
'Little Gem' (Sc) EWoo LVer SDen
'Little John' (Min/d) SBro
'Little Love' (A) LDea SBro
'Little Margaret' (Min/v) ESul LVer SBro SDen
'Little Primular' (Min) ESul SBro
'Little Trot' (Z/v) SBro WFib
'Little Vectis' (D) SDen
¶ 'Little Witch' (Z/St) SBro
'Lively Lady' (Dw/C) ESul NKin SBro SDen
'Liverbird' (I) See P. 'Harlequin Miss Liver Bird'
lobatum GCHN MHul
'Lolette' (Min) ESul
'Lollipop' (Z/d) SDen WFib
'Lord Baden-Powell' (I/d) See P. 'Colonel Baden-Powell'
'Lord Bute' AGM EBSP ERav EWoo LBlm LCot LDea LVer MSte SIde SKen SMrm SUsu WEas
'Lord de Ramsey' See P. 'Tip Top Duet'
'Lorelei' (Z/d) WFib
'Loretta' (Dw) ESul
'Lorna' (Dw/d) ESul
'Lorraine' (Dw) SBro
'Louise' (Min) ESul SBro
'Love Song' (R) EBSP EWoo LDea SOld
'Love Story' (Z/v) ESul SBro
*'Loverly' (Min/d) ESul SBro
Lovesong ® (Z/d) WFib
'Lowood' (R) WFib
'Lucilla' (Min) ESul SDen
'Lucinda' (Min) ESul SBro
'Lucy' (Min) ESul SBro
'Lucy Gunnet' (Z/d/v) EBSP MWhe SBro SDen
'Lucy Jane' (R) LDea
¶ 'Lulu' (I) NPri
luridum MHul
'Lustre' (R) WFib
luteolum MHul
'Luz del Dio' (R) WFib
'Lyewood Bonanza' (R) EBSP LDea
¶ 'Lyn West' SDen
'Lyric' (Min/d) ESul LVer SBro WFib
I 'M A F F' (Min) SBro
'M J Cole' (I/d) LDea WFib
'Mabel Grey' AGM CSev CSpe ERav ESul EWoo IHos LBlm LHil LVer MWhe NHHG NWyt SDen SKen SMrm WEas WFib WHer WWye
¶ 'Mac's Red' (Z/C) SBro
madagascariense NWyt SDen
§ 'Madame Auguste Nonin' (Sc) LHil LVer SDen SMrm WFib
'Madame Butterfly' (Z/C/d) ESul MWhe SBro SDen SKen SOld
'Madame Crousse' AGM NWyt SDen WEas WFib
'Madame Dubarry' (Z) WFib
'Madame Fournier' (Min/C) ESul SBro
'Madame Guinier' See P. 'Charles Gounod'
'Madame Hibbault' (Z) SDen SKen
'Madame Kingsbury' (U) EBSP SDen
'Madame Layal' (A) CSpe ESul EWoo LDea LVer SBro SDen SKen WFib
'Madame Margot' See P. 'Hederinum Variegatum'
'Madame Recamier' (Z/d) WFib
'Madame Salleron' AGM LBlm LDea LHil LVer NWyt SDen SKen
'Madame Thibaut' (Z/d) CSpe LDea WFib
'Madge Hill' (Min) ESul LVer SBro SDen WFib
'Magaluf' (I/C/d) LDea SDen WFib
'Magda' (Z/d) ESul LVer NWyt SBro SDen
magenteum MHul
'Magic Lantern' (Z/C) IHos MWhe SDen SKen
'Magic Moments' (R) WFib
'Magnum' (R) WFib
'Mahogany' (I/d) EBSP ECtt MSmi
'Maid of Honour' (Min) ESul SBro SDen
'Mairi' (A) ESul LDea LVer SBro SKen
'Maloja' (Z) NWyt SDen SKen
'Mamie' (Z/d) SDen SKen
'Mandarin' (Z) NKin SDen
'Mangles' Variegated' (Z/v) SDen
'Manta' (Min) NKin SBro
'Mantilla' (Min) SBro SKen
'Manx Maid' (A) ESul LDea SBro SDen SKen WFib
'Marble Sunset' See P. 'Wood's Surprise'
¶ 'Marchioness of Bute' (R) LDea
'Maréchal MacMahon' (Z/C) CBrk EBSP LVer SDen SKen WFib
'Margaret Bryan' (Z/C) SBro SDen
'Margaret Pearce' (R) LDea SDen WFib
'Margaret Salvidge' (R) LDea WFib
'Margaret Soley' (R) LDea
'Margery Stimpson' (Min/d) ESul LDea SBro SDen WFib
'Maria Wilkes' (Z/d) WFib
'Marie Rober' (R) SKen WFib
§ 'Marie Vogel' (R) WFib

'Marion' (Min) ESul SBro
'Mariquita' (R) WFib
'Market Day' (R) SDen
'Marktbeherrscher' (Z/d) WFib
'Marmalade' (Dw/d) ESul LVer MWhe NKin SBro SDen WFib
'Mars' (Z/d) NWyt
'Martin Parrett' (Min/d) ESul SBro
¶ 'Martina' (I) EBSP
'Martin's Splendour' (Min) ESul SBro
¶ 'Martlesham' ESul
'Mary Ellen Tanner' (Min/d) ESul SBro
'Mary Godwin' (Z) WFib
¶ 'Mary Lee' (Min) SBro
'Mary Read' (Min) ERea ESul SBro
'Mary Webster' (Min) ESul SBro
'Masquerade' (R) ESul LDea SBro
¶ 'Master Paul' (Z/v) EBSP
'Masterpiece' (Z/C/d) EBSP ESul SDen SKen
'Mataranka' (Min/d/C/v) MWhe SBro
¶ 'Matthew Salvidge' (R) EBSP LDea
'Maureen' (Min) SBro
¶ 'Maureen Mew' SDen
'Mauve Beauty' (I/d) EBSP IHos SKen WFib
'Mauve Duet' (A) ESul SBro
'Maxime Kovalevski' (Z) SDen WFib
'May Day' (R) LDea
'May Magic' (R) WFib
'May Rushbrook' (Z) LVer
I 'Meadowside Dark and Dainty' SBro
¶ 'Meadowside Midnight' SBro
'Medallion' (Z/C) SKen WFib
'Meditation' (Dw) ESul SBro
'Medley' (Min/d) ESul MWhe SBro WFib
'Melanie' (Min/d) ESul LDea SBro
I 'Melissa' (Min) CSpe ESul NKin SBro
Melody ® (Z/d) WFib
'Memento' (Min/d) ESul SBro SKen
'Memories' (Z/d) LVer
'Mendip' (R) SKen WFib
'Meon Maid' (R) EBSP LDea
§ 'Mephistopheles' (Min/C) ESul IHos SBro
¶ 'Mercia' (R) LVer
'Mercia Glory' (R) LDea
Mercutio ® (Z/d) WFib
'Mere Casino' (Z) LVer
'Mere Greeting' (Z/d) MWhe
'Mere Ripon' (R) LDea
¶ 'Mere Sunglow' (R) LDea
'Merry-Go-Round' (Z/C/v) LVer SBro SDen WFib
'Meshed Pink Gay Baby' (DwI) See P. 'Laced Sugar Baby'
'Mexican Beauty' (I) MWhe NWyt SDen SKen WEas WFib
'Mexicanerin' See P. 'Rouletta'
'Mia' (Min/d) SBro
'Michelle' (Min/C) SBro WFib
'Michelle West' (Min) SBro SDen
'Milden' (Z/C) ESul LVer SBro SDen
'Milkmaid' (Min) SBro SDen WFib
'Mill Purple' (I) MWhe
'Millbern Clover' (Min/d) MWhe SBro
'Millbern Engagement' (Min/d) MWhe SBro
'Millbern Sharna' (Min/d) MWhe SBro
¶ 'Miller's Valentine' LVer SBro
'Millfield Gem' (I/d) LBlm LDea LVer NWyt SDen SKen WFib
¶ 'Millfield Rival' (Z) SDen
'Millfield Rose' (I/d) IHos LVer MWhe NWyt SDen SKen
'Millie' (Z/d) WFib
'Mimi' (Min/C/d) ESul LVer SBro
minimum MHul
Minipel Karminrot ® (Dw) SBro
Minipel Orange ® (Dw) SBro
* Minipel Red ® (Dw) SBro
Minipel Rosa ® (Dw) SBro
Minipel Scharlach ® (Dw) SBro
'Mini-Czech' (Min/St) ESul LVer SBro WEas
¶ 'Minnie Clifton' SDen
¶ 'Minstrel' ESul
'Minstrel Boy' (R) EBSP LDea SDen WFib
'Minx' (Min/d) LVer SBro SDen WFib
'Miranda' (Dw) ESul SBro
'Miriam Basey' See P. 'Dwarf Miriam Baisey'
'Miss Australia' (R/v) EWoo LDea SKen WFib
'Miss Burdett Coutts' (Z/v) ESul IHos LVer MWhe SBro SDen
¶ 'Miss Farren' (Z/v) SDen
¶ 'Miss Flora' (I) MWhe
'Miss Liverbird' (I/d) ECtt
'Miss Muffett' (Min/d) ESul SBro
'Miss Prim' (Min) SBro
§ 'Miss Stapleton' MHul SDen SSad
'Miss Wackles' (Min/d) ESul NKin NWyt SBro SDen WFib
'Mission Dubonnet' (R) LDea
'Misty' (Z) ESul NKin SBro
'Mitzi' (Min) SBro
'Mixed Blessings' (Min/C) SBro
'Modesty' (Z/d) LVer NWyt SDen WFib
'Modigliani' (R) SDen SKen
¶ 'Mole' (A) LDea
mollicomum MHul
'Mollie' (R) LDea WFib
'Momo' NPri
'Monarch' (Dw/v) ESul LVer SBro
'Monica Bennett' (Dw) ESul NKin SBro SDen SKen SOld WEas
¶ 'Monks Eleigh' ESul
'Monkwood Charm' (R) LDea
'Monkwood Delight' (R) SDen
'Monkwood Dream' (R) LDea
'Monkwood Rhapsody' (R) NKin SDen SOld
'Monkwood Sprite' (R) LDea NKin SOld
'Monsal Dale' (Dw/C/d) ESul SKen
'Monsieur Ninon' (U) CLTr EWoo NWyt

'Monsieur Ninon' misapplied	See P. 'Madame Auguste Nonin', P. *scabrum*
'Mont Blanc' (Z/v)	EBSP EWoo LVer MWhe SBro WFib
'Monty' (I/d)	WFib
'Moon Maiden' (A)	ESul LDea LVer SBro WFib
¶ 'Moonlight'	NKin SDen
'Moor' (Min/d)	ESul LVer SBro
'Moppet' (Min/d)	SBro
'Morello' (R)	SDen WFib
'Morning Cloud' (Min/d)	NKin SBro SDen
'Morning Sunrise' (Min/v)	ESul NKin SBro
'Morval' AGM	ESul LVer MWhe NKin NWyt SBro SKen SOld WFib
'Morwenna' (R)	LDea NKin SMrm WFib
¶ 'Mosaic Bella Notte' (I)	EBSP
'Mountie' (Dw)	ESul SBro
'Mozart' (R)	LDea
'Mr Everaarts' (Dw/d)	ESul LVer MWhe NKin NWyt WFib
¶ 'Mr Henry Apps' (Dw/C/d)	MWhe
'Mr Henry Cox' AGM	CBrk EBSP IHos MWhe NWyt SBro SOld WFib
'Mr Pickwick' (Dw)	SBro
'Mr Ritson' (Min)	ESul SBro
'Mr Wren' (Z)	IHos LHop LVer MWhe SDen SKen WFib
'Mrs Cannell' (Z)	SDen SKen
'Mrs Dumbrill' (A)	ESul LDea LVer SDen
'Mrs Farren' (Z/v)	SKen WFib
'Mrs G H Smith' (A)	CSpe ESul EWoo LDea LVer MSte MWhe SBro SDen SKen SOld
'Mrs G More' (R)	WFib
'Mrs J C Mappin' AGM	EBSP EWoo NWyt SDen SKen
'Mrs Kingsbury' (U)	EWoo LHil SKen WEas
'Mrs Kingsley' (Z/v)	WPer
'Mrs Langtry' (R)	LDea
'Mrs Lawrence' (Z/d)	SDen SKen WFib
'Mrs Martin' (I)	NWyt WFib
¶ 'Mrs Mavis Colley' (Z/v)	SBro
'Mrs Morf' (R)	LDea
'Mrs Parker' (Z/v)	EBSP IHos LVer MWhe NWyt SDen SKen WFib
'Mrs Pat' (Min/St/C)	ESul LVer MWhe SBro SDen
'Mrs Pollock' (Z/v)	CBrk LVer MWhe NRoo NWyt SBro SDen SKen WFib
'Mrs Quilter' (Z/C)	LVer MWhe NWyt SDen SKen SMrm WFib WPer
¶ 'Mrs Reid's Pink'	EWoo
'Mrs Salter Bevis' (Z/Ca/d)	ESul LVer NWyt SDen WFib
'Mrs Strang' (Z/d/v)	SBro SDen SKen SOld WEas
'Mrs Tarrant' (Z/d)	NWyt WFib
'Mrs W A R Clifton' (I/d)	LDea SKen WFib
multibracteatum	MHul
multicaule	MHul
– ssp. ***multicaule***	GCHN
¶ 'Muriel'	SDen
'Music Man' (R)	WFib
'Mustang'	IHos
mutans	MHul
'Mutzel' (I/v)	LDea
'My Choice' (R)	LDea
'My Love' (I/d)	EBSP LDea SDen
¶ ***myrrhifolium***	CNat SDen
– var. ***coriandrifolium***	GCHN WHer
'Nacton' (Min)	ESul SBro
'Nadine' (Dw/C/d)	ESul NKin SBro WFib
Nadja ® (Z/d)	WFib
'Nan Greeves' (Z/v)	SDen
'Nancy Grey' (Min)	ESul NKin SBro WFib
'Nancy Hiden' (R)	WFib
'Nanette' (Z)	SDen
¶ ***nanum***	MHul
'Naomi' (R)	LDea
'Naughton' (Min)	ESul SBro
'Naunton Velvet' (R)	WFib
'Naunton Windmill' (R)	WFib
'Nedging Tye' (A)	ESul LDea SBro
'Needham Market' (A)	CSpe ESul EWoo LDea SBro SDen
'Neene' (Dw)	ESul MWhe SBro
¶ 'Neil Jameson' (Z/v)	SBro
'Nella' (Min)	SBro
'Nellie' (R)	LDea LVer
'Neon Fiat' (Z/d)	WFib
'Nervosum' (Sc)	ESul
¶ 'Nervous Mabel'	ESul
'Nettlestead' (Dw)	SBro
¶ – (I)	ESul SDen
'Neville West' (Z)	EBSP SBro SDen
I 'New Dawn Rose Form' (I)	EBSP
'New Life' (Z)	ESul MWhe NWyt SDen SKen
'Nicholas Purple' (R)	LDea
¶ 'Nicola Gainford'	SDen
'Nicor Star' (Min)	ESul SBro SDen
'Night and Day' (Dw)	SBro
'Nimrod' (R)	LDea
'Nina West' (Z)	SDen
'Noche' (R)	LDea LVer SKen SMrm WFib
'Noel' (Z/Ca/d)	WFib
'Noele Gordon' (Z/d)	LVer WFib
'Noir' (R)	LDea
'Nono' (I)	LDea WFib
'North Star' (Dw)	ESul LVer SBro
'Northern Lights' (R)	LDea
'Notting Hill Beauty' (Z)	SKen
'Nuhulunbuy' (R)	EBSP WFib
¶ 'Oakfield'	SDen
'Obergarten' (Z/d)	WFib
oblongatum	MHul
'Occold Embers' (Dw/C/d)	ESul LVer NKin NWyt SBro SDen SOld
'Occold Lagoon' (Dw/d)	ESul LVer SBro SDen SKen
'Occold Orange Tip' (Min/d)	ESul LVer NKin SBro SDen
'Occold Profusion' (Min/d)	ESul NKin SBro
'Occold Ruby' (Dw/C)	SBro
'Occold Shield' (Dw/C/d)	ESul SBro SDen
'Occold Surprise' (Min/d)	ESul SBro
'Occold Tangerine' (Dw)	SBro

'Occold Volcano' (Dw/d) ESul SBro
ochroleucum MHul
odoratissimum (Sc) ESul GPoy IHos LVer MHul NHHG NSty SDen SHer SIde SKen WCHb WEas WFib WWye
– 'Variegatum' (Sc) WEas
oenothera MHul
'Offton' (Dw) ESul SBro
'Old Spice' (Sc/v) ESul LVer WFib
'Olga' (R) IHos LDea
'Olive West' SDen
'Olympia' (Z/d) WFib
'Onnalee' (Dw) ESul SBro
¶ 'Orange Embers' (Dw) SBro
'Orange Fizz' (Z/d) SDen
'Orange Glow' (Dw/d) SBro
'Orange Imp' (Dw/d) ESul NKin SBro
'Orange Ricard' (Z/d) MWhe SDen SKen SOld WFib
'Orange River' (Dw/d) ESul SBro SKen
¶ 'Orange Ruffy' (Min) SBro
¶ 'Orange Sal' (R) LDea
'Orangeade' (Dw/d) ESul LVer SBro SKen
'Orangesonne' (Z/d) LVer SDen WFib
'Orchid Paloma' (Dw/d) ESul LVer NKin SBro SDen
oreophilum MHul
'Orion' (Min/d) ESul LVer MWhe NKin NWyt SBro SDen SKen WFib
'Orwell' (Min) SBro
'Otley' (Min) SBro
ovale ssp. *hyalinum* MHul
– ssp. *ovale* MHul WFib
¶ – ssp. *veronicifolium* MHul
¶ 'Oyster' (Dw) ESul SBro
'Oyster Maid' (Min) SBro
PAC cvs See under ***name***
'Paddie' (Min) ESul NWyt SBro
'Pagoda' (Z/St/d) ESul LVer NKin NWyt SBro SDen SKen
'Paisley Red' (Z/d) LVer
'Palais' (Z/d) SKen WFib
'Pamela Underwood' (R) WFib
panduriforme GCHN MHul WFib
papilionaceum CHEx CTro EWoo MHul
'Paradise Moon' (Min/d) SBro
'Parasol' (R) WFib
'Parisienne' (R) EBSP LDea SDen
¶ 'Parmenter Pink' (Min) ESul SBro
'Party Dress' (Z/d) MWhe NWyt SDen WFib
'Pascal' (Z) SKen
'Patience' (Z/d) IHos SKen WFib
'Paton's Unique' AGM EWoo IHos LBlm LHop LVer NWyt SDen SKen SOld WEas WFib
'Patricia Andrea' (T) EBSP LVer NWyt SDen SOld
'Patricia Read' (Min) ERea ESul SBro
'Patsy 'Q'' (Z/C) EBSP IHos LVer SKen
patulum GCHN
'Paul Crampel' (Z) CBrk EBSP LVer NWyt WFib
'Paul Gotz' (Z) SKen
'Paul Gunnett' (Min) MWhe SBro
'Paul Humphries' (Z/d) NWyt SDen WFib
'Paul West' (Min/d) SBro SDen
'Pauline' (Min/d) ESul MWhe NKin SBro
'Pavilion' AGM ESul SBro
'Pax' (R) LDea
'Peace' (Min/C) SBro WFib
'Peace Palace' (Dw) ESul SBro
'Pearl Brocade' (R) WFib
'Pearl Eclipse' (I) SDen SKen
'Pearl Necklace' (Z/d) SDen
'Pearly Queen' (Min/d) ESul LVer SBro
'Pegasus' (Min) LVer NKin SBro
'Peggy Franklin' (Min) SBro
'Peggy Sue' (R) EBSP LDea LVer
'Peggy West' (Min/C/d) SBro SDen
See under ***name***
peltatum MHul NWyt SDen WFib
– 'Lateripes' MHul
'Penny' (Z/d) LVer MWhe SDen WFib
¶ 'Penny Lane' (Z) EBSP LVer SDen
'Penny Serenade' (Dw/C) ESul LVer SKen
'Penve' (Z/d) WFib
'Percival' (Dw/d) LVer SBro SDen SOld
'Perfect' (Z) SDen SKen
Perlenkette Orange ® (Z/d) WFib
Perlenkette Weiss ® (Z/d) WFib
'Persian King' (R) LDea
'Persian Queen' (R) WFib
'Petals' (Z/v) EBSP SKen
'Peter Godwin' (R) EBSP LDea
'Peter Read' (Dw/d) ERea ESul SBro
'Peter's Choice' (R) EBSP LDea
'Petit Pierre' (Dw) See P. 'Kleine Liebling'
'Petite Blanche' (Dw/d) LVer SBro SDen WFib
'Petronella' (Z/d) ESul
¶ 'Phil Rose' (I) MWhe
'Philomel' (I/d) SDen SKen WFib
'Philomel Rose' (I/d) LDea
'Phlox New Life' (Z) ESul SBro
¶ 'Phyllis' (U/v) EWoo
'Phyllis Mary' (R) WFib
'Phyllis Read' (Min) ERea ESul MWhe SBro WFib
'Phyllis Richardson' (R/d) LDea LVer NKin SDen WFib
'Phyllis Variegated' ERom LHop
'Picardy' (Z/d) LVer
Picasso ® IHos
'Pickaninny' (Min) ESul LVer SBro
¶ 'Picotee' NKin
'Pier Head' (Z) EBSP
'Pin Mill' (Min/d) ESul SBro
¶ 'Pink Aura' ESul
'Pink Aurore' (U) LVer
'Pink Bonanza' (R) LDea SOld WFib
'Pink Bouquet' (R) EBSP WFib
– (Z/d) IHos LVer
¶ 'Pink Bridal Veil' (Z/C) SBro
♦ 'Pink Capitatum' See P. 'Pink Capricorn'
'Pink Carnation' (I/d) EBSP IHos LDea SDen SKen
'Pink Cascade' (I) See P. 'Hederinum'
'Pink Champagne' (Sc) ESul SDen WFib WHer
'Pink Countess Mariza' (Z) SDen SKen
¶ 'Pink Eggshell' (Dw) LVer NKin SBro
¶ 'Pink Elizabeth Read' (Dw) SBro
'Pink Flamingo' (R) LDea

'Pink Floral Cascade' (Fr/d)	SBro
'Pink Fondant' (Min/d)	ESul LVer SBro SDen
'Pink Fringed Aztec' (R)	LDea
'Pink Gay Baby' (I)	See P. 'Sugar Baby'
'Pink Golden Ears' (Dw/St/C)	SBro
'Pink Golden Harry Hieover' (Z/C)	ESul LVer SBro SDen
'Pink Grace Wells' (Min)	ESul NKin SBro
¶ 'Pink Grozser Garten' (Dw)	SDen
'Pink Happy Thought' (Z/v)	EBSP LVer SBro SKen WFib
'Pink Ice' (Min/d)	ESul LVer NKin NWyt SBro
'Pink Kewense' (Min)	ESul SBro
'Pink Lively Lady' (Dw/C)	ESul SBro
'Pink Margaret Pearce' (R)	SDen
'Pink Mini Cascade'	See P. 'Rose Mini Cascade'
'Pink Nosegay'	NWyt
¶ 'Pink Parfait' (Z)	EBSP EWoo
¶ 'Pink Profusion' (Min)	SBro
'Pink Rambler' (Z/d)	MWhe SKen SOld WFib
'Pink Raspail' (Z/d)	WFib
'Pink Rosebud' (Z/d)	IHos NWyt SDen SKen WFib
'Pink Satisfaction' (Z)	IHos
'Pink Slam' (R)	WFib
'Pink Snow' (Min/d)	SBro
'Pink Splash' (Min/d)	SBro SDen
'Pink Splendour' (Min/d)	SBro
¶ 'Pink Startel' (Z/St)	SBro
pinnatum	MHul
'Pixie' (Dw)	ESul NKin SBro
¶ 'Pixie Glow' (Z/St)	SBro
¶ 'Pixie Prince' (Z/St)	SBro
¶ 'Pixie Rose' (Z/St)	SBro
'Platinum' (Z/v)	EBSP EWoo LBlm SBro SDen
'Playboy Blush' (Dw)	SBro
'Playboy Candy' (Dw)	SBro
'Playboy Cerise' (Dw)	SBro
'Playboy Coral' (Dw)	SBro
'Playboy Coral Orange' (Dw)	SBro
'Playboy Mauve' (Dw)	SBro
'Playboy Powder Pink' (Dw)	SBro
'Playboy Salmon' (Dw)	SBro
'Playboy Salmon Eyed' (Dw)	SBro
'Playboy Scarlet' (Dw)	SBro
'Playboy White' (Dw)	SBro
'Playford' (Dw)	SBro
'Playmate' (Min/St)	ESul LVer NKin SBro SKen
'Plenty' (Z/d)	WFib
'Plum Rambler' (Z/d)	EWoo LVer SDen SKen WFib
'Poetesse' (A)	EWoo LDea
'Polaris' (Min)	SBro
'Polka' (U)	EWoo
'Pompeii' (R)	LDea NKin WFib
'Posey' (Min/d)	NWyt
'Potpourri' (Min)	SBro SKen
¶ 'Powder Puff' (Dw/d)	ESul SBro
praemorsum	MHul
'Presto' (Min)	ESul SBro SDen
'Preston Park' (Z/C)	CBrk LBlm SDen SKen SMrm WFib
'Pretty Girl' (I)	EBSP LDea
'Pride of the West' (Z)	SKen
'Prim' (Min/d)	ESul LVer
'Primavera' (R)	EBSP LDea
'Prince Harry' (I)	SKen
'Prince of Orange' (Sc)	CArn CLTr CNat CSFH CSev ESul EWoo GBar GPoy IHos LVer NHHG NSty NWyt SDen SKen WCHb WEas WFib WHer WPer WWye
'Prince of Wales' (Z)	NWyt WFib
¶ 'Prince Regent' (R)	LVer
¶ 'Princeanum' (Sc)	EWoo
'Princess Alexandra' (R)	LVer NWyt WFib
– (Z/d/v)	EBSP MWhe SDen WFib
'Princess Anne' (Z)	CSpe
'Princess Josephine' (R)	WFib
'Princess Margaretha' (Z)	MWhe
'Princess of Balcon' (I)	See P. 'Roi des Balcons Lilas'
'Princess of Wales' (R)	LDea SDen SKen
'Princess Pink' (Z)	SKen
'Princess Virginia' (R/v)	CSpe EBSP LDea
'Professor Eckman' (R)	WFib
'Promenade' (Z/d)	WFib
'Prospect' (Z/d)	MWhe
'Prudence' (Min)	NKin SBro SKen
pseudoglutinosum	WFib
pulchellum	MHul
pulverulentum	GCHN MHul
punctatum	GCHN
♦ 'Purple Ball'	See P. Purpurball ®
'Purple Emperor' (R)	LDea WFib
'Purple Gem' (Min)	NKin
¶ 'Purple Heart' (Dw/St)	ESul SBro
'Purple Light'	See P. 'Purple Gem'
'Purple Orchid' (R)	LDea
'Purple Pat' (Min/d)	SBro
'Purple Rambler' (Z/d)	EBSP MWhe SDen
'Purple Unique' (U/Sc)	EWoo IHos LVer SDen SKen WCHb WFib
Purple Wonder ® (Z/d)	WFib
Purpurball ® (Z/d)	EBSP SDen SKen SOld
'Pygmalion' (Z/d/v)	SDen WFib
'Quakeress (R)	LDea
'Quakermaid' (Min)	ESul SBro
'Quantock' (R)	WFib
'Queen Ingrid' (Z)	IHos
'Queen of Denmark' (Z/d)	NWyt SDen SKen WFib
'Queen of Hearts' (I/d)	LVer NWyt WFib
I 'Queen of the Lemons'	EWoo
N ***quercifolium*** (Sc)	CNat CSev EWoo GPoy MHul NHHG NSty NWyt SHer SKen WCHb WEas WFib WWye
– 'Fair Ellen'	See P. 'Fair Ellen'
quinquelobatum	GCHN MHul
'Rachel' (Min)	ESul SBro
'Rachel Fisher' (Z)	NWyt WFib
radens (Sc)	MHul NHHG SIde WFib
'Radiance' (Z/d)	WFib
'Radiant' (Z/d)	WFib
'Rads Star' (Z/St)	ESul SBro

Radula Group (Sc) CLTr ERav ESul GBar GCHN LHil LVer MWhe NKin NWyt SDen SKen WCHb WFib WPer
'Radula Roseum' LHil
radulifolium MHul
'Ragamuffin' (Min/d) ESul MWhe SBro
'Rager's Pink' (Dw/d) ESul LVer NKin SBro
'Rager's Star' (Min) ESul LVer SBro
'Ragtime' (St) LVer NWyt SBro
ranunculophyllum MHul
rapaceum GCHN MHul
'Rapture' (R) LDea WEas WFib
'Raspberry Parfait' (R) LDea SDen
'Raspberry Ripple' (A) ESul LDea LVer SBro
'Raspberry Sundae' (R) CLTr LDea LVer
¶ 'Ravensbeck' SDen
'Raviro' (I) MSmi WFib
¶ 'Ray Bidwell' ESul
'Ray Coughlin' (Z/C/d) WFib
'Raydon' (Min) ESul LVer SBro
'Rebecca' (Min/d) ESul SBro
– (R) LVer
'Red Admiral' (Min/d/v) ESul NKin SBro SKen
§ 'Red Black Vesuvius' (Min/C) ESul LVer MWhe NKin NWyt SDen SKen WEas WFib
'Red Brooks Barnes' (Dw/C) SBro SDen
'Red Cascade' AGM MWhe SKen
'Red Comet' (Min) SBro
¶ 'Red Devil' (Z/St) SBro
'Red Dollar' (Z/C) LVer
'Red Dwarf' (Min/d) SBro
¶ 'Red Elmsett' (Z/C/d) SBro
'Red Fox' (Min) SBro SDen
'Red Galilee' (I/d) MWhe SKen
'Red Gem' (Min) ESul
'Red Glow' (Min) ESul SBro
¶ 'Red Grace Wells' (Min) SBro
'Red Ice' (Min/d) LVer MWhe NKin NWyt SBro
*'Red Kewense' ESul
'Red Light' (Z/d) WFib
'Red Magic Lantern' (Z/C) EBSP SKen
'Red Mini Cascade' (I) See P. 'Rote Mini-Cascade'
'Red Pandora' (T) NWyt
'Red Pearl' (Min) SBro
'Red Rambler' (Z/d) EBSP LVer MWhe NWyt SDen SKen WFib
'Red Satisfaction' (Z) IHos
¶ 'Red Silver Cascade' LVer
'Red Spider' (Min/Ca/d) CSpe ESul SBro
'Red Star' (Z) LVer
'Red Startel' (Z/d) LVer MWhe
'Red Streak' (Min/Ca) SBro SDen
'Red Susan Pearce' (R) EBSP LDea
'Red Tiny Tim' (Min) SBro
'Red Velvet' (R) WFib
'Red Witch' (Dw/St) CSpe ESul LVer NKin SBro SDen
'Redondo' (Min/d) CSpe ESul MWhe NWyt SBro SDen WEas WFib
'Reg 'Q'' (Z/C) LVer SBro
'Regal Perchance' SDen
'Regina' (Z/d) LVer NWyt SDen SKen SOld WEas WFib
¶ 'Reifi Vanderlea' EWoo
'Rembrandt' (R) LDea LVer SDen SKen WEas WFib
'Remo' (Z/d) WFib
'Renee Ross' AGM WFib
reniforme CNat GBar MHul SSad WEas WFib
¶ 'Retah's Crystal' (Z/v) EBSP SDen
'Rhineland' (I) SKen
'Rhodamant' AGM MWhe NPri WFib
'Rhodamine' (R) EBSP LDea SKen
'Rhodo' (R) WFib
Rica ® (Z/d) WFib
¶ 'Richard Gibbs' EWoo
'Richard Key' (Z/d/v) NWyt SBro WFib
'Richard West' (I/d) SDen
'Rietje van der Lee' (A) ESul SBro
'Rigel' (Min/d) ESul LVer MWhe NKin SBro SDen SKen WFib
'Rigi' (I) ECtt IHos LDea LVer MBri MSmi NPri NWyt SDen SKen
'Rigoletta' (I) EBSP LDea MWhe NWyt
'Rimfire' (R) WFib
'Ringo Rose' (Z) SKen
'Rio' (Z) NWyt SHer
'Rio Grande' (I/d) CSpe EBSP LDea LVer MWhe NWyt SDen SKen SOld WEas WFib
'Rita Brook' (Z/d) WFib
'Rita Coughlin' (R) WFib
'Rita Scheen' (A) ESul LDea LVer MWhe SBro WFib
'Robbie Hare' (R) WFib
'Robe' (Z/d) WFib
'Robert Fish' (Z/C) ESul SBro SDen
'Rober's Lavender' (Dw) ESul LVer SBro
'Rober's Lemon Rose' (Sc) CNat CSFH ESul EWoo GBar LHil LVer NHHG NKin SDen SHer SIde WCHb WFib WHer WWye
'Rober's Salmon Coral' (Dw/d) ESul SBro
'Robin' (R) EWoo LDea
'Robinson Crusoe' (Dw/C) WFib
¶ ***rodneyanum*** MHul
rogersianum See P. ***worcesterae***
'Rogue' (R) EBSP LDea WFib
'Roi des Balcons' (I) See P. 'Hederinum'
§ 'Roi des Balcons Impérial' (I) IHos LDea MWhe
§ 'Roi des Balcons Lilas' (I) IHos LDea MWhe SKen WFib
'Roi des Balcons Rose' See P. 'Hederinum'
Rokoko ® (Z) IHos
'Roller's David' (I) SDen
'Roller's Echo' (A) ESul LDea LVer SBro
'Roller's Pathfinder' (I/v) EBSP LVer
¶ 'Roller's Pearly Lachs' (I) EBSP
'Roller's Pioneer' (I/v) EBSP LVer NWyt SKen
'Rollisson's Unique' (U) ERav LVer NWyt SDen SKen WFib
Romy ® (I) LDea
¶ 'Ron's Elmsett' (Dw/C/d) SBro
¶ 'Ron's Semer' (Min) SBro
¶ 'Ron's Shelley' (Dw) SBro

Rosais ® (I/d) EBSP
'Rosaleen' (Min) SBro
'Rosalie' (Min) ESul SBro
'Rosamunda' (Z/d) WFib
'Roscobie' (Z/d) SDen SKen
'Rose Bengal' (A) CMil ESul LDea LVer NSty SDen SKen WEas WFib WPer
'Rose Crousse' (I/d) MWhe
'Rose Irene' (Z/d) MWhe NWyt SDen WFib
'Rose Mini Cascade' (I) ESul LVer MWhe SBro SDen SOld
'Rose of Amsterdam' (Min/d) SBro
'Rose Silver Cascade' (I) LDea LVer SBro SDen
'Rose Slam' (R) LDea
'Rose Startel' (Z/St) LVer
¶ 'Rosebud Supreme' (Z/d) EBSP
'Rosee Normande' (Z/d) WFib
'Rosemarie' (Z/d) MWhe
'Rosette' (Dw) SBro SKen WFib
¶ 'Rose's Orange' EWoo
'Rosina Read' (Dw) ERea ESul LVer SBro
'Rosita' **AGM** NKin SBro SDen
* 'Rosmaroy' (R) EBSP LDea
'Rospen' (Z/d) LVer WFib
* 'Rosseau' (Min) SBro
'Rosy Dawn' (Min/d) SBro
§ 'Rote Mini-Cascade' (I) IHos LDea MWhe NPri NWyt SBro SDen SKen WFib
Rote Mini-Cascade ® See P. 'Rote Mini-Cascade'
'Rotherfield' (I/d) LDea
'Rotlieb' (Z/d) WFib
§ 'Rouletta' (I) EBSP ECtt IHos LDea LVer MSmi MWhe NPri NWyt SDen SKen SOld WEas WFib
'Rousillon' (R) WFib
'Royal Ascot' (R) EWoo LDea LVer NKin
'Royal Blaze' (Z/v) SDen SKen
'Royal Carpet' (Min/d) ESul NKin SBro
'Royal Fiat' (Z/d) WFib
'Royal Norfolk' (Min/d) ESul LVer MWhe NKin SBro SDen SKen SOld WFib
'Royal Oak' (Sc) CSFH CSev GBar LBlm LHil LVer MWhe NWyt WFib WHer WPer
¶ 'Royal Parade' (R) LVer
§ 'Royal Purple' (Z/d) WFib
'Royal Sovereign' (Z/d/v) LVer
¶ 'Royal Star' (R) LVer
'Royal Surprise' (R) LDea
'Royal Wedding' (R) LDea
'Rubella' (Z/d) WFib
'Ruben' (I/d) EBSP
'Ruby' (Min/d) ESul SBro WFib
'Ruffled Velvet' (R) SDen
'Rushmere' (Dw/d) ESul NKin SBro
'Rusty' (Dw/C/d) ESul LVer SBro SDen
'Ruth Bessley' LVer SBro
'Ruth Karmen' (I/d) LDea
'Ryan Dollery' (Z) SDen
'Ryecroft Pride' (Z/d) WFib
¶ 'Saint Catherine' SDen
'Sally Anne' (R) LDea WEas
'Sally Munroe' (R) LDea
'Sally Read' (Dw/d) ERea ESul LVer NKin SBro
'Salmon Beauty' (Min/d) SBro WFib
'Salmon Black Vesuvius' (Min/C) ESul SBro
'Salmon Comet' (Min) ESul SBro
'Salmon Grozser Garten' (Dw) SDen
§ 'Salmon Irene' (Z/d) EBSP MWhe WFib
'Salmon Queen' See P. 'Lachskönigin'
'Salmon Slam' (R) LVer SDen WFib
'Salmon Startel' (Z/St/d) LVer MWhe
x *salmoneum* SDen
'Saltford' (R) WFib
'Samantha' (R) EBSP LDea
'Sancho Panza' (Dec) CSpe ESul LDea LHil MSte SBro SDen SKen SOld WEas WFib
§ x *sanguineum* MHul
'Santa Maria' (Z/d) LVer NWyt SDen SKen WFib
'Santa Marie' (R) LDea
'Santa Paula' (I/d) ECtt LDea LVer MWhe NPri SDen SKen
'Sante Fe' (Z/C) LVer SDen
'Sarah Mitchell' (Min) SBro
'Sarkie' (Z/d) EBSP
'Sasha' (Min) SBro WFib
Sassa ® (Z/d) WFib
Satellite ® (Z/St) IHos SBro
¶ 'Satsuki' (R) EBSP LDea
¶ 'Saturn' (Z) EBSP SDen
'Saxifragoïdes' GCHN SBro
scabrum WFib
'Scarlet Breakway' (Z) MWhe
'Scarlet Crousse' (I/C) WFib
'Scarlet Gem' (St) NWyt SBro
* 'Scarlet Kewense' ESul
'Scarlet Pet' (U) CLTr ESul EWoo MWhe
'Scarlet Pimpernel' (Z/C/d) ESul SBro SDen WFib
'Scarlet Rambler' (Z/d) LVer NKin NWyt SKen SOld WEas WFib
¶ 'Scarlet Shelley' (Dw) SBro
'Scarlet Unique' (U) EWoo LVer NWyt SDen SKen WCHb WFib
'Scarlett O'Hara' (Min) SBro
schizopetalum MHul
§ 'Schneekönigin' ('Snow Queen') (I/d) CSpe ECtt IHos LDea MSte NPri SHer WEas
§ Schöne Helena ® (Z/d) SHer
x *schottii* See P. x ***sanguineum***
'Seaview Star' (Z/St) SBro SDen
'Seeley's Pansy' (A) CSpe ESul LDea SBro
'Sefton' (R) EBSP LDea SKen
'Selby' (Z/C/d) NWyt WFib
'Selina' ESul SBro
'Semer' (Min) ESul LVer NKin SBro SDen SKen
senecioïdes GCHN MHul
'Senorita' (R) LDea LVer
'Sensation' (Z) SKen
'Serena' (Min) ESul SBro
sericifolium MHul
'Shalimar' (St) CSpe SBro SDen
'Shanks' (Z) EBSP SDen
'Sharon' (Min/d) ESul SBro
'Sharon Louise' (Min) SDen
'Sharon West' (Dw) SBro SDen
'Shaun Jacobs' (Min/d) SBro SDen
'Shaunough' (Min) ESul SBro

'Sheila' (Dw)	ESul NKin SBro SDen
'Sheila Thorp' (Dw/d)	SBro
'Shelley' (Dw)	ESul LVer NKin NWyt SBro SDen
'Shenandoah' (Min)	WFib
'Sheraton' (Min/d)	ESul MWhe SBro
'Shimmer' (Z/d)	IHos LVer MWhe SDen SKen SOld WFib
'Shiraz' (R)	SKen
'Shirley Anne' (Dw/d)	SBro SDen
'Shirley Ash' (A)	ESul SBro
'Shirley Maureen' (R)	LDea
¶ 'Shiva'	NPri
'Shocking' (Z/d)	LVer NWyt
'Shotley' (Min)	ESul SBro
'Shottesham Pet' (Sc)	EWoo SIde
'Shrubland Pet' (U/Sc)	LVer NWyt SDen SKen
sidoïdes	MHul
'Sienna' (R)	LDea
'Silas Marner' (Dw)	SBro
'Silberlachs' (Z/d)	SDen WFib
'Silepen' (Z/d)	EBSP WFib
¶ 'Silky'	ESul LVer
'Silver Kewense' (Dw/v)	ESul IHos LVer SBro SDen SKen SOld WFib
'Silver Wings' (Z/v)	EBSP MWhe SBro SDen
'Simon Read' (Dw)	ERea ESul SBro
'Simplicity' (Z)	LVer
'Single New Life' (Z)	LVer NKin SBro
'Sir Arthur Hort' (I)	WFib
'Sister Teresa' (Z/d)	EBSP IHos SDen SKen
'Skelly's Pride' (Z)	LVer NWyt SDen SKen WEas
'Skies of Italy' (Z/C/d)	EBSP SBro SDen
'Sleuring's Robin' (Min/d)	LVer SBro SDen
'Small Fortune' (Dw)	LVer SBro SKen
'Smuggler' (R)	LDea
¶ 'Snape'	ESul
'Sneezy' (Min)	ESul SBro
'Snow Queen' (I)	See P. 'Schneekönigin'
'Snow White' (Min)	ESul SBro
¶ 'Snow Witch' (Z/St)	SBro
'Snowbaby' (Min/d)	ESul NWyt
'Snowball' (Z/d)	SDen
'Snowdon' (Min)	SBro
'Snowdrift' (I/d)	LVer NWyt WFib
'Snowflake' (Min)	ESul LVer NKin SBro SDen SIde WPer
'Snowmass' (Z/d)	LVer MWhe SDen SKen
¶ 'Snowmite'	SDen
'Snowstorm' (Z)	SKen WFib
'Snowy Baby' (Min/d)	LVer SBro SDen WFib
'Sofie'	See P. 'Deacora Rose'
¶ 'Sofie Cascade' (I)	NPri
'Solano' (R)	WFib
'Solent Star'	SDen
'Solent Sunrise' (Z/C)	SDen
'Solent Waves' (R)	EBSP LDea
'Solferino' (A)	ESul LDea SBro SKen
Solidor ® **AGM**	EBSP NWyt
'Somersham' (Min)	ESul SBro
'Something Special' (Z/d)	LVer MWhe SDen
'Sonata' (Dw/d)	ESul LVer SBro
'Sophie Dumaresque' (Z/v)	LVer MWhe SBro SDen SKen SOld
'Sophie Koniger' (Z/d)	WFib
'Sorcery' (Dw/C)	ESul IHos MWhe NWyt SBro SKen
'South American Bronze' **AGM**	LDea LVer SDen SKen SMrm WFib
¶ 'South American Delight' (R)	LVer
'Southampton' (Z)	EBSP
¶ 'Southern Belle' (Z/d)	SDen WFib
¶ 'Southern Charm'	SDen
'Souvenir' (R)	LDea LVer SDen
'Spanish Angel' (A)	ESul LDea
'Sparkle' (Dw)	SBro
'Speckled Egg' (Dw)	SBro
'Speckled Hen' (Dw)	SBro
'Speckled Orange' (Dw)	SBro
'Speckles' (Z)	MWhe SBro
'Spellbound' (R)	WFib
¶ 'Spital Dam'	ESul
'Spitfire' (Z/Ca/v)	ESul LVer NWyt SBro WFib
'Spithead Cherry' (R)	EBSP LDea
¶ 'Splash Down'	SDen
§ 'Splendide'	CRDP CSpe LGre LHop SSad WEas
¶ 'Splendour' (R)	LDea
'Sporwen' (Min)	SBro
'Spot-on-Bonanza' (R)	LDea SOld
'Spring Bride' (R)	LDea
'Spring Park' (A)	ESul LVer SBro SDen
'Springfield Black' (R)	EBSP LDea LVer
'Springfield Lilac' (R)	LDea
'Springfield Pearl' (R)	LDea
'Springfield Rose' (R)	LDea
'Springfield Unique' (R)	LDea
'Springtime' (Z/d)	EBSP LVer MWhe SDen WFib
'Sprite' (Min/v)	SBro
'Sproughton' (Dw)	ESul
'St Helen's Favourite' (Min)	ESul SBro
'Stacey' (R)	LDea
'Stadt Bern' (Z/C)	IHos LVer MBri MWhe SDen SKen WEas WFib
'Stanton Drew' (Z/d)	WFib
¶ ***staphysagrioïdes***	EWoo
'Staplegrove Fancy' (Z)	NWyt SDen SKen
x ***stapletonae***	See P. 'Miss Stapleton'
¶ 'Star Flecks'	SDen
¶ 'Star Glitter'	SDen
'Star of Persia' (Z/Ca)	LVer
¶ 'Starbust'	SDen
¶ 'Starlight Magic' (R)	ESul LDea
'Starry Eyed' (Dw)	ESul SBro
¶ 'Stella May' (Dw)	SBro
'Stella Read' (Dw/d)	ERea ESul LVer NKin SBro
¶ 'Stellar Apricot' (Z/St)	LHil LVer
'Stellar Arctic Star' (Z/St/d)	See P. 'Arctic Star'
'Stellar Cathay' (Z/St/d)	ERav LVer WFib
'Stellar Dawn Star' (Z/St)	LVer SOld WEas WFib
'Stellar Grenadier' (Z/St/d)	See P. 'Grenadier'
'Stellar Hannaford Star' (Z/St/d)	See P. 'Hannaford Star'
¶ 'Stellar Orange' (Z/St)	SDen

'Stellar Ragtime' (Z/St/d) SDen
stenopetalum GCHN MHul
'Stephen Read' (Min) ERea ESul SBro
'Stewart Read' (Dw) ERea ESul SBro
stipulaceum MHul
¶ 'Stirling Stent' (Z) LVer
'Strawberry Sundae' (R) LDea LVer SDen WFib
¶ 'Stringer's Delight' ESul LVer
¶ 'Stringer's Souvenir' ESul LVer
'Stutton' (Min) ESul SBro
sublignosum GCHN MHul
suburbanum
ssp. ***bipinnatifidum*** MHul
'Suffolk Gold' (Min/C) EBSP SDen
§ 'Sugar Baby' (DwI) ECtt ESul IHos LDea LVer MBri MSmi MWhe NWyt SBro SDen SKen SOld WEas WFib
'Summer Cloud' (Z/d) NWyt SKen WFib
'Summertime' (R) NKin SDen
'Sun Rocket' (Dw) ESul LVer MWhe SBro WFib
'Sunbeam' (Dw/d) SBro
'Sundridge Moonlight' (Z/C) SBro
'Sunrise' (R) EBSP LDea LVer SKen SOld WEas WFib
¶ 'Sunset Marble' (I) EBSP
'Sunset Snow' (R) WFib
'Sunspot Petit Pierre' (Min/v) ESul SBro SDen SKen
'Sunstar' (Min/d) ESul LVer SBro WFib
'Suntrap' (Z/C) EBSP
'Super Rose' (I) EBSP LVer MBri MSmi MWhe NWyt SDen SKen
'Supernova' (Min/d) LVer
– (Z/St/d) ESul NKin NWyt SBro
'Surcouf' (I) LDea WFib
'Susan' (Dw) SBro WFib
'Susan Baldwin' See P. 'Salmon Kovalevski'
'Susan Payne' (Dw/d) ESul LVer NKin SBro
'Susan Pearce' (R) LDea LVer SKen
'Susan Read' (Dw) ERea ESul SBro
'Susie 'Q'' (Z/C) ESul LVer MWhe SBro SDen SKen
'Sussex Beauty' (Dw/C/d) ESul SBro
'Sussex Delight' (Min) ESul SBro SKen
'Sussex Gem' (Min) LVer SBro SKen
'Sussex Jewel' (Min) SBro SKen
'Sussex Lace' See P. 'White Mesh'
'Sussex Surprise' (Dw/v) SBro
¶ 'Swanland Lace' (I) LVer
'Swedish Angel' (A) ESul LDea LVer SBro SDen SKen
'Sweet Mimosa' (Sc) CLTr EWoo LHil LVer NWyt SDen SKen WEas WFib
'Sweet Sue' (Min) ESul SBro SDen
'Swilland' (A) ESul LDea LVer MWhe SBro SDen
'Swing' (Z) SHer
'Sybil Bradshaw' (R) LDea WFib
'Sybil Holmes' (I/d) EBSP ECtt IHos LVer MBri MSmi MWhe NWyt SDen SKen WFib
'Sylvia' (R) LDea
'Sylvia Gale' (R) WFib
'Sylvia Marie' (Dw/d) LVer MWhe SKen
'Sylvia Mariza' IHos
'Tami' (Min) ESul SBro
'Tamie' (Dw/d) ESul LVer MWhe SBro
'Tamie D' (Min) SKen
'Tammy' (Dw/d) ESul LVer MWhe NWyt SBro WFib
'Tangerine' (Min/Ca/d) ESul SDen WFib
'Tango' (Z/d) IHos
'Tanya' (Min) SBro
'Tanzy' (Min) ESul SBro
'Tapestry' (Min/v) LDea SDen WEas
'Tashmal' (R) LDea
'Tattingstone' (Min) ESul LVer SBro
'Tattoo' (Min) SBro
'Tavira' (I/d) EBSP IHos LDea LVer MSmi SDen SKen SOld WFib
'Ted Brooke' (Z/d) WFib
'Ted Dutton' (R) SDen WFib
'Telstar' (Min/d) ESul NKin SBro WFib
§ 'Telston's Prima' (R) LDea WFib
'Ten of Hearts' (I) NWyt SDen
'Tenderly' (Dw/d) NKin SBro
'Tenerife Magic' (MinI/d) ESul SBro
tenuicaule WFib
'Terence Read' (Min) ERea ESul SBro
ternatum MHul
¶ 'Terry' (I) EBSP
tetragonum EPad GCHN MHul NWyt SSad WFib
'The Barle' (A) LDea
'The Boar' (Fr) CSpe EWoo LBlm LVer WEas WPer
§ 'The Crocodile' (I/C/d) ECtt GBur IHos MWhe SDen SKen WEas WFib
I 'The Culm' See P. 'Culm'
'The Czar' See P. 'Czar'
I 'The Dart' See P. 'Dart'
'The Lynn' (A) LDea
I 'The Mole' See P. 'Mole'
'The Prince' (Min) ESul SBro
'The Speaker' (Z/d) SDen SKen WFib
'The Tone' (A) LDea
¶ 'Thea' (R) LVer
'Thomas Gerald' (Min/C) ESul LVer SBro SKen
¶ 'Thorley' SDen
'Tiberias' (I/d) WFib
¶ 'Tiffany' (Min/d) SHer
'Tilly' (Min) NKin SBro
'Tim' (Min) ESul SBro
'Timmy Griffin' (Min) SBro
'Timothy Clifford' (Min/d) ESul MWhe NKin NWyt SBro SDen WFib
¶ 'Tina Vernon' (Dw/C) SBro
'Tiny Tim' SBro
§ 'Tip Top Duet' (A) ESul EWoo LDea LHil LVer MWhe SBro SDen SKen WEas WFib WPer
¶ 'Titan' (Z) EBSP SDen
'Token' (Z) IHos
'Tom Portas' (Dw/d) ESul
'Tom Tit' (Dw) SBro
'Tomcat' (Z/d) NPri WFib
tomentosum **AGM** CHEx CSev CSpe ERav EWoo GCHN GPoy LBlm LHil LHop LVer MHul MWhe NHHG NSty NWyt SDen SKen WEas WFib WWye
– 'Chocolate' See P. 'Chocolate Peppermint'

'Tommays Delight' (R) EBSP LDea
tongaense GCHN MHul WEas WFib
'Toni' (Min) SBro
'Tony' (Min) ESul NKin SBro SDen
'Topscore' (Z/d) WFib
'Torento' (Sc) CNat ESul EWoo LVer SDen
'Tornado' (R) EBSP LDea
'Tortoise Shell' (R) WFib
'Toyon' (Z/d) LVer SDen WFib
¶ 'Tracery' (Dw/St) SBro
'Tracy' (Min/d) NKin SBro
tragacanthoïdes MHul
transvaalense MHul WFib
'Trautlieb' (Z/d) WFib
¶ 'Travira' (I) MWhe
'Treasure' (Z/d) LVer
'Treasure Chest' (Z/d) EBSP LVer SDen
'Treasure Trove' (Z/v) EBSP SBro SDen
tricolor MHul SDen
tricolor hort. See P. 'Splendide'
trifidum GCHN MHul WFib
'Trimley' (Dw/d) ESul SBro
'Trinket' (Min/d) IHos SBro SDen SKen
'Triomphe de Nancy' (Z/d) NWyt WFib
triste CBre CTro GCHN MHul SDen SSad WFib
'Trudie' (Dw) CSpe ESul SBro SKen WFib
'Trulls Hatch' (Z/d) LVer MWhe NWyt SDen SKen
'Trumps' (Min) SBro
'Tu Tone' (Dw/d) ESul
'Tuddenham' (Min/d) LVer NKin SBro
'Tuesday's Child' (Dw/C) LVer SKen
'Tunias Perfecta' (R) WFib
¶ 'Turkish Coffee' (R) EBSP
'Turkish Delight' (Dw/v) ESul LVer MWhe NKin SBro SDen SOld
'Turtle's Surprise' (Z/d/v) NWyt SDen SKen
'Turtle's White' (R) LDea LVer SKen
'Tweedle-Dum' (Dw) MWhe
'Twinkle' (Min/d) ESul NKin SBro SDen WFib
'Twist' (Z) SDen
'Tyabb Princess' (R) WFib
§ 'Unique Aurore' (U) LVer SKen WEas WFib
¶ 'Unique Mons Ninon' EWoo
¶ 'Unity' LVer
'Urchin' (Min) CSpe ESul LVer NKin SBro SDen
'Ursula Key' (Z/v) SKen WFib
'Vagabond' (R) WFib
'Valanza' (A) ESul LDea SBro
'Valcandia' (Dw) ESul SBro
'Valencia' (R) EBSP LDea WEas
'Valenciana' (R) LDea WFib
'Valentin' (R) LDea
'Valentina' (Dw/d) ESul SBro
'Valerie' (Z/d) SDen
'Valley Court' (I) LDea
'Vancouver Centennial' **AGM** ERav ESul LVer MWhe NWyt SBro SDen SOld
§ 'Variegated Clorinda' (Sc/v) EWoo WCHb WHer
'Variegated Fragrans' See P. 'Fragrans Variegatum'
§ 'Variegated Kleine Liebling' (Min/v) CSpe ESul LVer NKin SBro SDen SKen
¶ 'Variegated Lorelei' (Z/d/v) SDen
'Variegated Madame Layal' (A/v) ESul LDea SBro
'Variegated Petit Pierre' See P. 'Variegated Kleine Liebling'
'Vasco da Gama' (Dw/d) ESul NKin SBro
'Vectis Cascade' SDen
¶ 'Vectis Glitter' SDen
¶ 'Vectis Gold' (Z/St/C) SBro SDen
¶ 'Vectis Star' SDen
'Velvet' (Z) IHos
'Velvet Duet' (A) ESul EWoo LDea LVer SBro SDen SKen
'Venus' (Dw/d) LVer SBro
'Vera Dillon' (Z) NWyt SKen WFib
'Vera Vernon' (Z/v) EBSP
'Verona' (Z/C) EBSP LVer SDen SKen
'Veronica' (Z) MWhe SDen SKen
'Vesuvius' (Z) SBro WPer
¶ 'Vibrant' SDen
'Vicky Claire' (R) EBSP LDea SDen SKen
'Vicky Town' (R) LDea SOld WFib
'Victoria Regina' (R) LDea WFib
'Vida' (Min) SBro
'Video Blush' (Min) CSpe SBro
'Video Red' (Min) SBro
'Video Rose' (Min) SBro
'Video Salmon' (Min) SBro
'Viking' (Min/d) LVer SBro SKen
'Viking Red' (Z) MWhe
'Village Hill Oak' (Sc) ESul LVer
'Ville de Paris' (I) See P. 'Hederinum'
'Vina' (Dw/C/d) EBSP ESul LVer MWhe SDen SKen WFib
'Vincent Gerris' (A) LDea SDen
¶ 'Vinco' NPri
violareum hort. See P. 'Splendide'
'Violet Lambton' (Z/v) NWyt WFib
'Violetta' (R) LDea
– (Z/d) WFib
'Virginia' (R) IHos LDea WEas
'Virginia Ley' (Z) SKen
'Viscossisimum' NWyt WCHb
viscosum See P. ***glutinosum***
§ ***vitifolium*** GCHN
'Vivat Regina' (Z/d) WFib
'Voodoo' (U) CSpe EWoo LCot SSad
Vulcan ® (Z/d) IHos
¶ 'Vulcano Fire' (Dw) SBro
'W H Heytman' (R) WFib
'Wallace Fairman' (R) LDea LVer
'Wallis Friesdorf' (Dw/C/d) MWhe NKin SBro SOld
'Waltz' (Z) IHos
'Wantirna' (Z/v) EBSP ECtt LVer SDen
'Warrior' (Z/d) WFib
'Washbrook' (Min/d) ESul SBro
'Watersmeet' (R) LDea
'Wattisham' (Dec) ESul LDea LVer
'Waveney' (Min) ESul NKin SBro
'Wayward Angel' (A) ESul EWoo LDea SBro SKen
'Wedding Gown' (R) LDea

'Wedding Royale' (Dw/d)	ESul LVer SBro SDen
Weisse Perle ® (Z/d)	WFib
'Wellington' (R)	LDea WFib
'Wendy' (Min)	SBro SDen
'Wendy Hawley' (R)	LDea
'Wendy Read' (Dw/d)	ERea ESul MWhe NKin SBro
'Wensum' (Min/d)	ESul NKin SBro SDen WFib
¶ 'West Priory'	SDen
'Westerfield' (Min)	SBro
¶ 'Weston Triumph' (Z/C/v)	EBSP SBro
'Wherstead' (Min)	SBro
'Whisper' (R)	CSpe
'White Bird's Egg' (Z)	WFib
'White Boar' (Fr)	CBrk EWoo LBlm NWyt SDen
'White Bonanza' (R)	EBSP LDea SOld
'White Charm' (R)	EBSP LDea
'White Chiffon' (R)	CSpe EBSP LDea
'White Eggshell' (Min)	ESul LVer NKin SBro
'White Gem' (Min)	ESul SBro
'White Glory' (R)	LDea WFib
'White Lively Lady' (Dw/C)	ESul LVer SBro
§ 'White Mesh' (I/v)	EBSP ECtt MBri MWhe NWyt SDen SKen WEas WFib
'White Nosegay'	NWyt SDen
'White Pearl Necklace' (Z/d)	WFib
'White Roc' (Min/d)	SBro
¶ 'White Swaine' (Min)	SBro
'White Unique' (U)	EWoo LVer NSty NWyt SDen SKen WFib
'White Wooded Ivy'	NWyt
¶ ***whytei***	MHul
'Wico'	NPri SHer
'Wilf Vernon' (Min/d)	SBro
'William Sutton' (R)	WFib
¶ 'Wine Red'	SBro
'Winford Festival'	LVer
¶ 'Winford Winnie'	LVer
'Winnie Read' (Dw/d)	ERea ESul LVer SBro
'Winston Churchill' (R)	LDea
¶ 'Wirral Moonglow'	SDen
* 'Wirral Supreme' (Z)	EBSP
'Wirral Target' (Z/d)	EBSP SBro
¶ 'Wishing Star'	ESul
'Witnesham' (Min/d)	ESul SBro
§ 'Wood's Surprise' (MinI/d)	ESul LDea LVer MWhe SBro SDen SKen WFib
'Wookey' (R)	WFib
worcesterae	GCHN MHul
'Wrington' (R)	WFib
'Wyck Beacon' (I/d)	SKen
'Wycombe Maid' (Min/d)	LVer NKin SBro SDen WFib
'Xenia Field' (Z)	NWyt SDen SKen
xerophyton	MHul WFib
'Yale' AGM	CSpe EBSP IHos LDea LVer MBri MSte MWhe NWyt SDen SKen SOld WFib
¶ 'Yellow Snowball' (Z/C/d)	SBro
'Yhu' (R)	LDea LVer
'Yolanda' (Min/C)	ESul SBro
'York Minster' (Dw/v)	SBro SDen SKen
'Yours Truly' (Z)	MWhe SKen
'Yvonne' (Z)	SKen
'Zinc' (Z/d)	NWyt SBro WFib
'Zoe' (D)	SDen
zonale	MHul WFib

PELLAEA (Adiantaceae)

¶ ***calomelanos***	SBla
falcata	MBri
rotundifolia AGM	MBri NMar
sagittata	NMar

PELLIONIA See ELATOSTEMA

PELTANDRA (Araceae)

♦ ***alba***	See P. ***saggitifolia***
§ ***saggitifolia***	SWyc
§ ***undulata***	CBen CRDP CRow CWGN EHon LMay MSta NDea SRms SWat SWyc
¶ ***virginica*** Rafinesque	SWyc
virginica Schott	See P. ***undulata***

PELTARIA (Cruciferae/Brassicaceae)

¶ ***alliacea***	ECha

PELTIPHYLLUM See DARMERA

PELTOBOYKINIA (Saxifragaceae)

§ ***tellimoïdes***	EBre ECro LBre NHol
¶ ***watanabei***	CBow GCal GTou SHer SIng

PENNANTIA (Icacinaceae)

corymbosa	ECou

PENNISETUM (Gramineae/Poaceae)

§ ***alopecuroïdes***	CKel COtt EGol EPla ETPC GCal MHlr NHol SApp SCob SPer WWat
– 'Hameln'	ECha EFou EPla ETPC LHop MBri MSte SGil SPla WPer
– f. ***viridescens***	EBee ELan ETPC GAbr NSti WCot WWat
– 'Woodside'	EBre EGol EHoe EPla LBre NRoo WHal
compressum	See P. ***alopecuroïdes***
imcomptum purple	ETPC
longistylum	See P. ***villosum***
macrourum	CHan EHoe ETPC
orientale AGM	EBre ECha EPla ETPC LBre MMil NBir NHol SAxl SIgm SUsu WCot WHoo WOMN
ruppelii	See P. ***setaceum***
§ ***setaceum***	EOrc ETPC
– 'Rubrum'	ECha
§ ***villosum***	EBar ECha EHoe EMon EPla ERav ETPC GCal LHop MHlr NBro NSti SApp SAxl SMad SPla SUsu WBon WCot

PENSTEMON † (Scrophulariaceae)

* 'Abberley'	WPer
albertinus K 92.315	WDav
'Alice Hindley' AGM	Widely available
'Alice Howarth'	NHol

alpinus	GTou MSto NOak NTow WAbe WHil WSpr WThi
– ***brandegeei***	See P. ***b.***
§ 'Andenken an Friedrich Hahn' **AGM**	Widely available
§ ***angustifolius***	ECro MHew MSal WPer WSpr
¶ – K 92.3128	WDav
* ***anquinensis***	WHil
antirrhinoïdes	See KECKIELLA ***a.***
N 'Apple Blossom' **AGM**	Widely available
♦ 'Apple Blossom' misapplied	See P. 'Thorn'
arizonicus	See P. ***whippleanus***
arkansanus	EBee GTou
¶ 'Astley'	WPer
attenuatus	MSto SCou WPer
azureus	SCou WPer
baccharifolius	LGre
'Barbara Barker'	See P. 'Beech Park'
§ ***barbatus***	CBot CBow CGle CSco ECha ECro EFol EGol ELan EMar ERav GAbr GCHN IBar LGre MBel MWat NMir SBor SCou SPer SSvw SUsu WAbe WEas WHCG WHil WPbr WSpr
¶ – K 92.319	NHar WDav
– 'Coccineus'	CHol EHic GBuc MBri NBro NOak SCou SCro WPer WSpr WTyr
¶ – 'Jingle Bells'	EHic
– Limoges form	GCal
– 'Praecox'	WPer
– 'Praecox Nanus'	CBot GCHN GCal MHlr MSte SRms WRus WSpr
¶ – 'Rose Elf'	SMrm
* 'Barbelles'	NBro
barrettiae	CNic GCHN NRoo WHil WSpr
§ 'Beech Park' **AGM**	CChu CRos ELan EMar ESma LHil LHop MBel SAga SAxl SCou SMrm SPer WRus WSpr
* 'Beverley'	GCal
'Bisham Seedling'	See P. 'White Bedder'
'Blackbird'	Widely available
'Blue Eye'	WEas
'Blue King'	SCro
'Blue Spring'	CBot CBow ERom EWri MBri NBrk SFis SHer SUsu
'Bodnant'	WPer WSpr
brandegeei	CNic
'Breitenbrush Blue'	LHop SAga
bridgesii	SCou
'Bridget's White'	CSam
Broken Tops Mountain Form	WPer
'Burford Seedling'	See P. 'Burgundy'
'Burford White'	See P. 'White Bedder'
§ 'Burgundy'	Widely available
caeruleus	See P. ***angustifolius***
caespitosus	SCou
§ ***campanulatus***	CHan CMHG CMea CRiv CSam EFol EMNN EPot LGre LHil LHop MBro MPit MSto MTho NBrk NHar NHol NMen NRar NTow SAga SCou SFis SSmi WAbe WPat WPer WRus WSpr
– ***chihuahuensis***	SAga
– ***pulchellus***	See P. ***campanulatus***
– ***roseus***	WEas
'Candy Pink'	WEas
¶ ***cardinalis***	GTou
cardwellii	CNic ECha ECtt ESma LBee LGan LGre NHar SAga WDav WPer
¶ – K 92.321	WDav
'Castle Forbes'	CGle GMac WEas WPer WSpr
'Catherine de la Mare' **AGM**	CBrk CGle CLTr COtt EBar ECtt EDon EFou ELan ERav GCHN GMac LGre LHil MHFP NBir NBro NRar NVic SAga SAxl SChu SCro SMrm SPer WPer WSpr WSun
¶ ***centranthifolius*** JJA 13106	LGre SIgm
'Charles Rudd'	See P. 'Countess of Dalkeith'
¶ 'Cherry'	SMrm
'Cherry Ripe'	CChu EBar EPla ERom GMac LHil NNrw SCou WHCG WHal WHoo WKif WPer WPla WRus WSpr WSun
§ 'Chester Scarlet' **AGM**	CElw CGle CHan EOrc EPla ERom GBri GCHN GCal GGar GMac LBlm LHop MBel MBri NBrk NFai NHol NRar SAga WEas WHCG WPer WRus WSpr
clutei	SUsu
comarrhenus	LGre WDav
confertus	CMHG CNic EBar ECtt ELan EMNN GPlt MCas MFir MHig MSto NGre NMen NNrd NRed NRoo NSti NTow WAbe WHal WHil WPbr WPer
* 'Coral Pink'	GMac SRos
cordifolius	See KECKIELLA ***cordifolia***
§ 'Cottage Garden Red'	CMer EHic ESma LHil MHFP NTow WCot WSpr
§ 'Countess of Dalkeith'	CElw CGle CHan CLTr CRos EBee EOrc ERom GCal LGre LHop LLWP MNes NFai NRar NVic SAga SAxl SBor SChu SCou SMrm WHCG WPer
crandallii ssp. ***glabrescens***	LGre NHar SAga SMrm SUsu WDav
§ – – var. ***taosensis***	CLTr EOrc ESma LGre LHop SChu SGil SMrm WAbe WCot WRus
cristatus	See P. ***eriantherus***
¶ ***cyaneus***	SMrm
davidsonii	CMHG LGre MHig WAbe WHil WPat
§ – var. ***menziesii*** **AGM**	CSam EPot GTou MFir NHar SBla SMrm WEas WPer
– – 'Microphyllus'	CMea MBro MSto NHar NMen SChu SMrm SWas WDav WMar
– ***praeteritus***	LGre WDav
'Dazzler'	CGre NRoo WPer
deustus	MBel
'Devonshire Cream'	WHCG WPer
'Diane'	WMer
diffusus	See P. ***serrulatus***
digitalis	CGle CHan CMil CNic ECha EPad ERav GCra LGan LGre LHop MBel MNFA MRav NHol SCro SSvw WAbb WKif WPer WTyr
§ – 'Huskers Red'	CB&S CBow CRDP EBre ECro EFol EFou EMar EMon LBre MHlr NBir NHol NNrw SAga SBla SCro SFis SPla SUsu WCot WDav WEas WHer

¶ – pink	SUsu
– ***purpureus***	See P. ***d.*** 'Husker's Red'
discolor	CVer LGre
§ 'Drinkstone'	CGle CLTr CMGP CRiv CSam ECha EFou EPla ESma LGre LHop MBel SAga SAxl SDix SGil SHer SMrm WDav WPer WSpr
'Drinkwater Red'	See P. 'Drinkstone'
¶ ***duchesnensis***	MSto
eatonii	CHan LGre SBla
¶ – K 93.325	WDav
'Edithiae'	EFol EOrc GPlt MBal NRoo SChu WAbb WDav WEas WMar WPer
§ ***eriantherus***	EBar MFos WDav WPer
§ 'Evelyn' AGM	Widely available
fendleri	See P. ***nitidus***
'Firebird'	See P. 'Schoenholzeri'
'Flame'	CGle EMar ESma LHop NHol WPer WSpr
'Flamingo'	WHoo WOld WPer
frutescens	GTou
fruticosus	CVer NHar NNrw NWCA WDav WHil WSpr
§ – var. ***scouleri*** AGM	CNic EHic MAsh MBel NRed NSti SCou WHil WPat WPer
– – ***albus*** AGM	CBot CHan EFol ELan EMon GArf GDra LGre LHop SAga SBla SChu WAbe WEas WMar WOMN WPer
– – f. ***roseus***	NRar
– – f. ***ruber***	WOMN
– – 'Amethyst'	WAbe
– – 'Hopleys'	LHop WPer
¶ – ssp. ***serratus***	WHil
¶ – – 'Holly'	LGre
* 'Gaff's Pink'	EOrc NRar SChu
♦ 'Garden Red'	See P. 'Cottage Garden Red'
'Garnet'	See P. 'Andenken an Friedrich Hahn'
¶ 'Garnet Variegated'	WThi
gentianoïdes	NBro NNrw WCot WRus
§ 'George Home' AGM	CGle CLTr ECtt EHic ERom GAbr LHil SCou WByw WSpr
glaber	CElw CMHG CRiv CSev EDon EGol ESma GMac LGan LGre LHil LHop LLWP MRav NBro NSti SAga SCou SMrm SSvw WEas WHCG WKif WPer WRus WSpr
'Gletsjer'	CBow
gracilis	CNic GCHN GTou WPer
¶ ***grahamii***	MSto
hallii	CNic GTou LBlm LGre NTow WDav
hartwegii AGM	CGre CShe EOrc GMac LHil LHop NCat NRar SAga SChu WAbe WCru WKif WPer WRus WSpr
– ***albus***	CGle CRiv EOrc LGan LGre LHil LHop LRHS MMil MSte NNor SChu SPer WRus
§ ***heterophyllus***	CGle CMer ECro EFol IHos LGre LGro LHop MBro MWat NBir NHol NRar NRoo SAga SAxl SChu SCou SUsu WAbe WEas WHCG WHil WHoo WMar WPat WPer WRus WSpr WWin
– ***australis***	See P. ***australis***
– 'Blue Gem'	EBre EOrc IDai LBre NRoo SIng SMrm WHoo WPer WSpr
– 'Blue Springs'	CGle CSam EBar EOrc MSte NHol SAga SBla SChu SMrm SPla SUsu WAbe WEas WRus
– 'Heavenly Blue'	ECtt EHal LHop NRar SFis SLon WRus
– 'Perhill Purple'	WPer
– ssp. ***purdyi***	SMrm WHCG
– 'True Blue'	See P. ***heterophyllus***
– 'Züriblau'	CBow CChu CHan WWat
'Hewell Pink Bedder' AGM	CGle CLTr CMGP EBar EBee EBre ECro EFou EGol GBri LBre LHil NRar NRoo SChu SCou SCro WHCG WHal WPer WRus WSpr
'Heythrop Park'	WSpr
§ 'Hidcote Pink' AGM	Widely available
'Hidcote Purple'	CElw CHan LHil MArl NBrk SChu
* 'Hidcote White'	CBot EBar EOrc MBel WAbe WPer WPla WRus WWin
¶ 'Hillview Pink'	WHil
¶ 'Hillview Red'	WHil
§ ***hirsutus***	CGle EBar ESma GPlt LBlm MNFA SCou WOMN WPer WThi
– bronze-leaved	WThi
– 'Minimus'	WHil WThi
– 'Pygmaeus'	Widely available
¶ – 'Pygmaeus Albus'	SMrm WPer
'Hopleys Variegated'	CRDP EBee ECtt EFol EHal EMon EOrc EPla LHop MBel NBir NNrw NRar NSti SMrm WHil
humilis 'Pulchellus'	LGre
'Hyacinth'	ELan
isophyllus AGM	CBrk CGle CVer EBee GMac MMil MNes SChu SCou WCot WEas WHCG WOld WPer WSpr
jamesii	CGle CHan CNic EOrc GTou SWas WPer
¶ ***janishiae***	MSto
'Jeannie'	NHol
'John Booth'	WEas
'John Nash'	CElw CHan CMil CRiv EBar ERom LHil LHop LLWP SIgm SMrm
'Joy'	CChu MSte WHoo WPer WSpr
'June'	See P. 'Hidcote Pink'
'King George'	Widely available
'Knightwick'	WPer
¶ 'Kummel'	EBee ELan
kunthii	See P. ***campanulatus***
laetus ssp. ***roezlii***	EFol ESma GDra LBee MBro MPla MSto NHar NHol NMen SIng SMrm WAbe WDav WHil WPer WSHC WWin
¶ ***laevis***	LGre WDav
laricifolius	CPBP
¶ ***leonensis***	EBee
¶ ***linarioïdes***	WPat
– JCA 9694	SIgm WDav
– ssp. ***taosensis***	See P. ***crandallii glabrescens t.***
'Little Witley'	WPer
* 'Logan Pink'	GMac
'Lord Home'	See P. 'George Home'
lyallii	EBee ELan EMar EMon ERav LHil MNFA
* 'Lynette'	WHil WMar WOld WPer
'Macpenny's Pink'	EBar SAxl

'Madame Golding'	CGle LGre LHil MMil SAga SMrm
'Margery Fish' AGM	EBar ESis MMil NFai NNrw WOld WPer WSpr WSun
menziesii	See P. ***davidsonii m.***
¶ 'Merlin'	CLTr
'Midnight'	Widely available
'Modesty'	CChu CHan LGre LRHS WSpr
montanus	GCHN GTou
'Mother of Pearl'	Widely available
* 'Mountain Wine'	LRHS SChu WThi
'Mrs Golding'	WPer
'Mrs Morse'	See P. 'Chester Scarlet'
'Myddelton Gem'	CGle EMon MWat NFai NPer SAxl SCou WHCG WRus WSpr
¶ 'Myddelton Red'	CRos
newberryi AGM	CGle CLew CMHG CVer ELan LBee LGre MBro MFos NBir NMen NRar NRoo SChu WHil WKif WMar WPat WPer WWin
– f. *humilior*	EPad MBel MSto
'Oaklea Red'	ECtt EDon LHil NRar
* old candy pink	EOrc LLWP MBel WPer WRus WSpr
oliganthus	WDav
'Osprey' AGM	CElw CGle CHan CMil EBar EOrc EPla GMac LGre LHil MHlr NBrk NNrw SUsu WCot WEas WHal WOld WPer WRus
ovatus	CBow CHan CHol EBee ELan ESma GCHN GCal GCra LGan MNFA MTol NCat SAga SFis WAbe WHCG WKif WPer WSun WWat
palmeri	GCra LGre MSto WDav
'Papal Purple'	CChu CMHG EBar EDon GMac LHil LLWP MMil NBrk NCat NRar SAga SChu SMrm SUsu SWas WByw WEas WHCG WHoo WOld WPer WRus WSpr
¶ 'Papal Purple' x 'Evelyn'	LHil
'Park Garden'	WPer
'Peace'	CLTr CRos LHop LRHS SCou WSun
peckii	WPer
'Pennington Gem' AGM	CChu CGle CSam CWit ECtt ELan EOrc ERom ESma GBri GMac LGre LHil LHop MSte NBrk NNrw NRar SAga SCou SMrm SPer WEas WHCG WMar WMer WOld WPer WRus
'Phare'	WPer
'Phyllis'	See P. 'Evelyn'
pinifolius AGM	Widely available
– 'Mersea Yellow'	Widely available
– 'Wisley Flame'	ESis SIgm
pink and cream	CHan
'Pink Dragon'	EOrc GCHN GDra LGre MBal MHig MPla NHar SAga SChu SMrm WPat WRus
§ 'Pink Endurance'	CMea ELan EMar EOrc ESis LGan LHop MMil NCat NRar NRoo SChu SCou WEas WHCG WHal WHoo WPat WPer WSpr
'Pink Ice'	WHil
'Pink Profusion'	SIgm SMrm SUsu
'Plum Beauty'	EDon
'Port Wine' AGM	CChu CGle CLTr CSam EMar ESma GAbr GCHN LHil NCat NHol SCou SHer SPla WHCG WPer WSpr
'Powis Castle'	WPer
'Prairie Fire'	GCal
'Primrose Thomas'	MBel
'Priory Purple'	WHCG WPer
procerus	GCra SCou WPer WSpr
– *formosus*	CNic
– ssp. *tolmiei*	CSev EPot GCHN GCal LGre NRoo NTow NWCA SSvw WCla WDav
pubescens	See P. ***hirsutus***
pulchellus	See P. ***campanulatus***
¶ *pulcherrimus*	NBro
¶ *pumilus*	MSto
♦ 'Purple and White'	See P. 'Countess of Dalkeith'
'Purple Bedder'	CChu CGle CGre CVer EHic LHop MWat SFis
'Purple Dragon'	MPla SBla
'Purple Gem'	GDra WMar
♦ 'Purpureus Albus'	See P. 'Countess of Dalkeith'
purpusii	LGre WAbe WCru
'Rajah'	EBee LHop
rameleyi	WDav
'Raven'	CChu EOrc GBri GMac LHil MArl MBel MSte NBrk NBro SChu SUsu WCot WEas WHCG WHal WHoo WMer WPer WPla WRus WSpr WSun
'Razzle Dazzle'	WPer
¶ 'Red Ace'	NNrw
'Red Emperor'	CMHG ECtt EDon NFai SFis WMer WPer WSpr WTyr
'Red Knight'	NNrw
'Rich Ruby'	CBrk CChu CElw CGle CHan CMGP EDon ELan LAbb LGre LHil LHop LLWP NBrk SAga SAxl SChu SMrm SUsu WCot WHCG WPer WRus WSpr
richardsonii	CNic EBee LHop MBel SIgm SOkh WOMN WPer
roezlii	See P. ***lactus r.***
* *roseocampanulatus*	LGre NRar SIgm SMrm WAbe WMar
rostriflorus	ESma SMrm WPer
– JJA 9548	SBla
* 'Roy Davidson'	CElw WPer
'Royal White'	See P. 'White Bedder'
'Rubicundus' AGM	CBot CChu CGle CRiv EBar EBee ECtt EDon ESma GMac LHil LHop NRar NSti SAga SCou SMrm SPla WAbe WCot WHCG WHoo WMer WPer WRus
'Ruby'	See P. 'Schoenholzeri'
'Ruby Field'	GAbr WHCG WOld
rupicola AGM	GDra GTou MBro MPla NWCA SBla SIgm WAbe WOMN WPer
– 'Albus'	LGre
– 'Diamond Lake'	CNic NHar WDav WPat
– mauve hybrid	GDra LGre
'Russian River'	CKel EDon EFou LHil SChu SMrm SOkh SUsu WSpr
rydbergii	WDav WPer
'Scarlet Queen'	ERom LRHS WSpr
'Scarlet 'n' White'	WAbe
§ 'Schoenholzeri' AGM	Widely available
scouleri	See P. ***fruticosus s.***
¶ *secundiflorus*	CMea
§ *serrulatus*	ECha GTou LRHS MBel MSte SCou WEas
– 'Albus'	LHil MSte WAbe
'Shell Pink'	WPer

*'Sherbourne Blue'	WPer
*'Shrawley'	WPer
'Sissinghurst Pink'	See P. 'Evelyn'
'Six Hills'	CLew CRiv CVer GMac MBro MCas MHig MPla NHar NRoo SAga WDav WHCG WMar WPat WPer WSHC
*'Skyline'	CBow EBar ECtt WHil
smallii	EPot GCal SIgm WPer
'Snow Storm'	See P. 'White Bedder'
'Snowflake'	See P. 'White Bedder'
****sonomensis***	LGre
'Sour Grapes'	CBot CCla CMil CRos ECot EHic ELan GBuc GMac LHil MBel NRar SMrm SSvw SUsu SWas WEas WWat
'Sour Grapes' misapplied	See P. 'Stapleford Gem'
'Southgate Gem'	MWat SCro
'Souvenir d'Adrian Regnier'	EHic GCHN WOld
'Souvenir d'André Torres'	See P. 'Chester Scarlet'
spectabilis	WPer
§ 'Stapleford Gem' AGM	Widely available
strictus	EBar ECro EHal GCHN GTou LBlm LGre LHop NBro SSvw WAbe WPer WSpr
– 'Bandera'	GCal
taosensis	See P. ***crandallii glabrescens t.***
*'Tapestry'	WCot
ternatus	See KECKIELLA ***ternata***
teucrioïdes	EPot NMen WThi
'Thorn'	CGle CSam EFou LHop LRHS MBel NBrk NNrw SCou SMrm WHCG WPer WRus WSpr
'Threave Pink'	See P. 'Pink Endurance'
*'Threave White'	CHan CMil LBlm
'Torquay Gem'	CElw GBuc LHop WHCG WOld WPer WRus
utahensis	CBot CVer EBre GBri LBre MHlr WCot WPer WTyr
venustus	CSam EBar GBuc GCal GTou WHil WPer
virens	CElw EFol EMar MHig NRoo SAxl WSpr
– R/Mr 7890	WPer
– *albus*	GCHN NHol SFis WDav WWin
virgatus ssp. *arizonicus*	CPBP EBee
¶ – ssp. *virgatus*	WDav
watsonii	LHop SAga SCou WCot WPbr WPer WTyr
§ *whippleanus*	CBot CElw CGle ECro GCal GCra GMac LGan LGre MBel MSte SAga WAbb WCla WPer WRus
– JCA 9504	LBlm
¶ – K 92.353	WDav
§ 'White Bedder' AGM	Widely available
'Whitethroat'	CGre MHlr WCot WHCG WMer WPer WSpr
♦ 'Windsor Red'	See P. 'Cottage Garden Red'
wislizenii	LGre WDav

PENTAGLOTTIS (Boraginaceae)

§ *sempervirens*	CArn CKin ECWi EJud Effi MHew MSal WHen WOak WWye

PENTAPTERYGIUM See AGAPETES

PENTAS (Rubiaceae)

lanceolata	ERea LAbb MBri

PENTASCHISTIS (Gramineae/Poaceae)

See Plant Deletions

PEPEROMIA (Piperaceae)

§ *argyreia* AGM	MBri
caperata	MBri
¶ *incana*	CTro
magnoliifolia	See P. ***obtusifolia*** Magnoliifolia Group
obtusifolia 'Jamaica'	MBri
– 'Tricolor'	MBri
obtusifolia Magnoliifolia Group 'Golden Gate'	MBri
– – 'Greengold'	MBri
– – 'USA'	MBri
orba 'Pixie'	MBri
I – 'Pixie Variegata'	MBri
pulchella	See P. ***verticillata***
resediflora	See P. ***fraseri***
sandersii	See P. ***argyreia***
scandens AGM	MBri
– 'Variegata'	MBri

PERESKIA (Cactaceae)

¶ *aculeata*	CTro

PEREZIA (Compositae/Asteraceae)

linearis	GBuc SIgm
recurvata	EPot GTou MCas NNrd NTow NWCA WAbe

PERICALLIS (Compositae/Asteraceae)

appendiculata	NGar
§ *lanata*	CBrk CHan CPle CSev CTro ELan EOrc ERav ERom LBlm LGre LHop MTol SMad SMrm
¶ *multiflora*	LGre

PERILLA (Labiatae/Lamiaceae)

§ *frutescens* var. *crispa* AGM	CArn MChe
♦ – *nankinensis*	See P. ***f. crispa***
– *rubra*	CArn MChe

PERIPLOCA (Asclepiadaceae)

graeca	CB&S CMac CPle SBra SPer WCru

PERISTROPHE (Acanthaceae)

speciosa	ERea SLMG

PERNETTYA See GAULTHERIA

PEROVSKIA (Labiatae/Lamiaceae)

atriplicifolia AGM	CArn CBot CHan CPle CShe GPoy LGre LHol MBri NNor SIde SPer WBod WHCG WOld WPer WSHC WWye

¶ 'Blue Haze'	GCal
'Blue Spire' **AGM**	Widely available
'Superba'	WWeb

PERROTTETIA (Celastraceae)

racemosa	CMCN

PERSEA (Lauraceae)

ichangensis	CTre SArc
lingue	CGre

PERSICARIA (Polygonaceae)

§ ***affinis***	CB&S CTom CWGN ECha EFol MBar MTho NBro NKay NSti SAxl WCru WEas WHal WOld WWat WWin
– 'Darjeeling Red' **AGM**	CB&S CCla CGle CRDP CRow CSco ECED ELan ENot EPla GCal IDai LGro LWad MBal MBri NBar NBir NFai NMir SChu WAbe WHen
– 'Dimity'	See P. ***a.*** 'Superba'
– 'Donald Lowndes' **AGM**	CGle CRow CSco CShe ECha EFol EGol ELan EMar ENot EOrc EPla LHop MBal MSta MTho MWat NDea NKay NMir NNor NRoo SChu SPer SPla WAbe WOld WTyr
– 'Hartswood'	EMon
¶ – Kew form	SBla
– 'Ron McBeath'	ECha EFou SBla
§ – 'Superba' **AGM**	CCla CLew CRow EBre EFou EGol EMon EPla ERav LBre MBri MFir NBar NBro NHol NRoo SFis SIng SMrm WHoo WPer WRus
alata	CRow EPla NHol SMad
alpina	CRow
amphibia	CRDP CRow
§ ***amplexicaulis***	CBre CRow CShe EBre ELan ELun EMar ERav LBre LGro MBal NDea NNor NOrc SChu SUsu WBon WHoo WMar
– 'Alba'	CRow ECha EPla SLga
– 'Arun Gem'	See P. ***a. pendula***
– 'Atrosanguinea'	CKel CNic CRow CSco EBre ECED ECha EPla LBre MFir NBir NDea NFai NHol NKay NTow NVic SFis SHig SPer WOld WWin
¶ – 'Clent Rose	WMar
¶ – 'Eggins Pink'	WMar
– 'Firetail' **AGM**	CCla CDec CHan CLew CRow CTom EBre ECED ECha ECtt EFou EPla LBre LLWP NHol NRoo NSti SMrm WHal WOld WRus
– 'Inverleith'	CBre CHan CRow EBre ECha ECtt EGol EPla LBre NCat NRoo WWye
§ – var. ***pendula***	CHan COtt CRow CShe EBre ECha EGol GAri LBre NBir NRoo NSti
– 'Rosea'	CRow ECha ELan
§ ***bistorta***	CArn CKin CRow CSFH CShe Effi GPoy LHol MChe MHew MSal SIde WBon WNdy WWye
– ssp. ***carnea***	CRow ECha EFol ELan EMon NBir
– 'Superba' **AGM**	Widely available
¶ ***bistortoïdes***	MSal
campanulata	COtt CRow CSco ECha ECoo EFol ELan EMar EOrc EPar ISea LHop NBro NKay NNor NRoo SCro SPla WPer WThu WWat WWin WWye
– Alba Group	CGle CRow CTom ELan EMar EMon EOrc GCal NBro NCat NSti SChu WWat
– pale pink	GBuc GCal
– 'Rosenrot'	CBre CRow CSFH EBee EGol ELan EMon EOrc GCal IBlr NHol SCro SFis WOld
– 'Southcombe White'	CRow
capitata	CGle CLTr CNic CRiv CRow CWGN EFol ELan MMil SCro SIng SUsu WEas WPer
elata	EMon GBuc GGar
emodi	CRow WWat
filiformis	See P. ***virginiana***
§ ***macrophylla***	CRow EBre LBre WCot WPer
microcephala	CRow WCot
milletii	CGle CRDP CRiv CRow ECha GAri GDra LGan MBri MFir MTho NOak NSti WCru WMer WRus
mollis	EHal
runcinata	CRow EHal LHop MTol NBro NFai SChu SLga WCru WEas WFox WHer WOld WPer
scoparia	See POLYGONUM ***scoparium***
sphaerostachya Meissner	See P. ***macrophylla***
tenuicaulis	CGle CLew CRiv CRow CTom EBre EMon EPar EPla GGar LBre MBal NDea NHol NKay SIng WOMN
vacciniifolia **AGM**	Widely available
¶ – 'Ron McBeath'	EMon
§ ***virginiana***	EPla
§ – 'Painter's Palette' (v)	CArn CB&S CBot CChu CDec CGle CHad CRow CSco EBre ECha ECtt EFol EFou ELan EPla ERav GCal LBre LHop NVic SLon SMad SMrm SPer WCru WEas WMer WOld WPer
§ – Variegata Group	CBot CHan CRow ECha EFol EPla GCal LHop WOld
vivipara	CRow
§ ***wallichii***	CRow IBlr NSti
weyrichii	GCal NBir WCot

PETAMENES See GLADIOLUS

PETASITES (Compositae/Asteraceae)

albus	CRow EBee EMon GPoy LRHS MSal NSti
fragrans	CHEx CNat ELan EMon EPar MSta MUlv SHer SWat WHal
hybridus	CKin EMFW WHer
japonicus var. ***giganteus***	CHEx CRow CWGN ECha EGol ELan EMon EPar MBri MTol MUlv NDea NVic WCra WCru
– – 'Variegatus'	CRDP CRow ECoo EMon EPla IBlr LHil MUlv WCot
kablikianus	
AL&JS 90170YU	EMon
palmatus	CRDP
– JLS 86317CLOR	EMon WCot
paradoxus	CRDP EMon

PETREA (Verbenaceae)
volubilis CNew CTro

PETROCALLIS (Cruciferae/Brassicaceae)
lagascae See P. ***pyrenaica***
§ *pyrenaica* MHig NTow NWCA WDav WPer

PETROCOPTIS (Caryophyllaceae)
§ *glaucifolia* CMea CNic EBar ESis MCas MPla NBir NCat NGre NMen NRed NWCA WPer WWin
¶ *grandiflora* SUsu
pyrenaica SRms WOMN
¶ – *rosea* GTou

PETROCOSMEA (Gesneriaceae)
See Plant Deletions

PETROMARULA (Campanulaceae)
See Plant Deletions

PETROPHYTUM (Rosaceae)
caespitosum GArf NHar NWCA WDav
cinerascens SIng
§ *hendersonii* EPot GArf NHol NKay WAbe WDav WOMN

PETRORHAGIA (Caryophyllaceae)
nanteuilii CNat
§ *saxifraga* AGM CNic EBur MHew MNFA MPit NCat NKay NMen NNrw NPri NVic SSvw WPer WThu WTyr
§ – 'Rosette' ECha GCal MTho WAbe WWin
¶ *velutina* WPer

PETROSELINUM (Umbelliferae/Apiaceae)
§ *crispum* AGM CArn CSFH CSev EHer EJud Effi GPoy IEde ILis LHol MChe NPri SIde WPer WWye

PETTERIA (Leguminosae/Papilionaceae)
ramentacea CB&S EHal EMon MPla SMad

PEUCEDANUM (Umbelliferae/Apiaceae)
¶ *officinale* ECWi
¶ *palustre* ECWi
¶ *verticillare* LGre

PEUMUS (Monimiaceae)
boldus CGre

PHACELIA (Hydrophyllaceae)
sericea ssp. *ciliosa* SIgm
tanacetifolia WWye

PHAEDRANASSA (Liliaceae/Amaryllidaceae)
dubia CMon
¶ *tunguraguae* WChr
¶ *viridiflora* WChr

PHAEDRANTHUS See **DISTICTIS**

PHAENOSPERMA (Gramineae/Poaceae)
globosa EBee EMon EPla SPla

PHAGNALON (Compositae/Asteraceae)
See Plant Deletions

PHAIOPHLEPS (Iridaceae)
biflora See OLSYNIUM ***biflorum***
nigricans See SISYRINCHIUM ***striatum***

PHALARIS (Gramineae/Poaceae)
aquatica ETPC
arundinacea CKin CWGN EHal ETPC MHew SWat
– 'Elegantissima' See P. ***a. picta*** 'Picta'
¶ – 'Luteovariegata' EMon
– var. *picta* 'Aureovariegata' CB&S CRow ECas EFer SWat WHol
– – 'Feesey' (v) CElw CRDP CRow ECha ECtt EHoe EMon EPla ETPC GAbr GAri GBuc IBlr LLWP NHol NSti SMad WWat
– – 'Luteopicta' EHoe WCot
§ – – 'Picta' AGM CBow CRDP CRow CSco EBre EHoe EHon ELan EMar EPla EPot ETPC GCHN IBlr LBre LGro MBal MBar NHol NNor NSti SCob SPer SWat SWyc WChe WEas WWin WWye
– – 'Tricolor' (v) EHoe EMon EPla ETPC LRHS SMad
– 'Streamlined' (v) EMon EPla ETPC WCot
canariensis EHoe GAul
tuberosa stenoptera See P. ***aquatica***

PHANEROPHLEBIA (Dryopteridaceae)
♦ *caryotidea* See CYRTONIUM ***caryotideum***
♦ *falcata* See CYRTONIUM ***falcatum***
♦ *fortunei* See CYRTONIUM ***f.***
macrosora WRic

PHARBITIS See **IPOMOEA**

PHASEOLUS (Leguminosae/Papilionaceae)
caracalla See VIGNA ***c.***

PHEGOPTERIS (Thelypteridaceae)
§ *connectilis* EBul EFer MBal NKay NMar SRms WRic
decursive-pinnata NMar WRic

PHELLODENDRON (Rutaceae)
amurense CB&S CCla EArb EHar ELan SEng SHil WDin WFro
– var. *sachalinense* WCoo
japonicum EArb

PHILADELPHUS † (Hydrangeacae)

'Avalanche' CMHG EBre ELan ISea LBre NWyt SPer SPla WDin WHCG WWat
'Beauclerk' AGM CB&S CBow CDoC CLan CMHG CSco CShe EBre ENot IDai LBre MBri MGos NBee NHol NKay NWyt SHer SLon SPer SPla SReu WBod WHCG WWat WWin
'Belle Etoile' AGM Widely available
'Boule d'Argent' CMHG WEas
'Bouquet Blanc' IDai MBri SPer SRms WKif
brachybotrys IOrc
'Buckley's Quill' MUlv
'Burfordensis' MAsh SLon SPer WWat WWeb
coronarius CDec CSco EHar LAbb LBuc MWat NNor SHBN SPer WDin
– 'Aureus' AGM Widely available
– 'Bowles' Variety' (v) See P. ***c.*** 'Variegatus'
– 'Gold Mound' MGos
§ – 'Variegatus' AGM Widely available
'Coupe d'Argent' MRav
delavayi var. ***calvescens*** See P. ***purpurascens***
'Enchantment' EWri SDix
'Erectus' CSco EFol ENot ISea MBal MRav NWea SPer
'Frosty Morn' CB&S CCla CDoC EHal IJoh MBri NHol SPer
'Galahad' LRHS
incanus CMCN
§ 'Innocence' (v) CBot CCla CDec CDoC CPMA CPle CSco ECtt EFol EHoe ELan EPla EWri IJoh LHop MBri MBrk MPla MUlv NHol NWyt SDry SGil SPer SPla SReu SSta WHCG WPat WRus
'Innocence Variegatus' See P. 'Innocence'
§ ***insignis*** WBod
¶ ***intectus*** WWes
x ***lemoinei*** CMer EBee IDai IJoh MGos NNor NWyt SHBN SLon WStI
lewisii EHal WWat
'Manteau d'Hermine' AGM Widely available
'Marjorie' CHan GCal
microphyllus CBot CCla CHan CMHG CSco CShe EHar ELan EPla ERav ESis IDai LGre MPla NHol SDry SLon SPer SReu WHCG WKif WPat WSHC WWat
'Minnesota Snowflake' ECtt EHic EWri
'Mrs E L Robinson' ECtt EPla
'Natchez' ECtt
'Perryhill' SPer
'Silberregen' ('Silver Showers') CBow CCla CPle CSco ECtt IJoh IOrc ISea MBal MBar MGos MUlv NHol NWyt SHBN WAbe WDin WPat WWat
'Snowflake' MBal NHol
'Souvenir de Billiard' See P. ***insignis***
subcanus CMCN
'Sybille' AGM CBow CCla CMHG COtt CSco ENot IDai ISea MBri MBrk MRav SSta WAbe WHCG WWat
tomentosus WHCG
'Virginal' AGM Widely available
– LA '82 MBal MUlv
'White Rock' COtt MBal SPer

PHILESIA (Liliaceae/Philesiaceae)

buxifolia See P. ***magellanica***
§ ***magellanica*** CB&S CBow CCla GGGa IBar IDai MBal SArc SPer WBod

PHILLYREA (Oleaceae)

angustifolia CCla CHan COtt WWat
decora See OSMANTHUS ***decorus***
§ ***latifolia*** CBot CHan SArc SHBN SHil WCoo WWat
media See P. ***latifolia***

PHILODENDRON (Araceae)

§ ***angustisectum*** AGM MBri
elegans See P. ***angustisectum***
'Emerald Queen' MBri
epipremnum See EPIPREMNUM ***pinnatum***
erubescens AGM MBri
– 'Burgundy' AGM MBri SGil
– 'Imperial Red' MBri
– 'Red Emerald' EBak MBri
– 'Valeria' MBri
melanochrysum MBri
'New Red' MBri
§ ***ornatum*** CTro
panduriforme See P. ***bipennifolium***
pedatum MBri
'Purple Queen' MBri
radiatum MBri
sodiroi See P. ***ornatum***
tuxtlanum 'Royal Queen' MBri
– 'Tuxtla' MBri

PHLEBODIUM See **POLYPODIUM**

PHLEUM (Gramineae/Poaceae)

hirsutum ETPC
montanum ETPC
pratense CKin EHoe MWil

PHLOMIS † (Labiatae/Lamiaceae)

* ***anatolica*** CHan CKni ELan SPla WCru
* – 'Lloyd's Variety' CAbP CChu CKni ELan EMon EPla GCal LHop MSte SGil SPla WCru WSHC WWat
¶ ***armeniaca*** SIgm
¶ ***atropurpurea*** EMon WPhl
¶ ***betonicoïdes*** WPhl
– B&L 12600 EMon
bovei ssp. ***maroccana*** CBot CChu CHan CRDP GCal NWyt SFis WCot WCru WPhl WWat
¶ ***breviflora*** WPhl
cashmeriana CAbb CBot CDec CGle CHan CPle CPou ECha WPhl WSHC
chrysophylla AGM CBot CBow CChu CGre CHan CMil CPle CSam ELan EPla GCal NTow SDix SDry SLon SMrm SPer WCru WPhl WWat
§ 'Edward Bowles' CDoC CSco GCal LHop NRar SDry WCot WCru WPhl
fruticosa AGM Widely available
grandiflora CBot CChu ELan WPhl
herba-venti ssp. ***pungens*** WCru

italica	CB&S CBot CCla CGre CHan CMer CSco ELan GCal LHop NBir NSti SChu SLon SPer SUsu WCru WEas WHer WPbr WPhl WSHC WWat WWin WWye
lanata	CChu CHan CMHG CMer CPou ELan EMon EPla LHop SBla SDry SMrm SPer SUsu WCru WDav WEas WHer WPhl WSHC WWat
leucophracta	CKni SPla
¶ – 'Golden Janissary'	WPhl
longifolia	CBot CHan ECoo SPer WCru WPhl
– var. ***bailanica***	CChu CKni CPle EMon EPla GCal WWat
¶ ***lunariifolia***	WPhl
¶ ***lychnitis***	WPhl
lycia	CCla CHan CKni WPhl
¶ ***monocephala***	WPhl
¶ ***nissolii***	WPhl
* 'Nova'	CBot
purpurea	CBow CHan ELan NBir WCru WPhl WSHC
– ***alba***	CBot CHan LHop WCru WPhl
¶ – ssp. ***almeriensis***	WPhl
– dark form	WCru
rigida	WCru
§ ***russeliana*** AGM	CArn CChu CHan CSev ECha EFol EFou ELan EPla GMac GTou LHol MBri MFir NBro NHol NSti SHBN SPer WAbb WAbe WCru WDav WEas WHal WOak WPhl WSHC WWat
samia Boissier	See P. ***russeliana***
tuberosa	CBot CHan CPou EMon GCal WPhl
– 'Amazone'	ECha WCot
¶ ***viscosa***	WPhl
viscosa hort.	See P. ***russeliana***
¶ 'Whirling Dervish'	WPhl

PHLOX † (Polemoniaceae)

adsurgens AGM	ITim MHig SBla
– 'Alba'	CMea NHar SBla
– 'Red Buttes'	CGle CRDP ELan EPot EWes LGre LHop NHar NHol SBla SCro SMrm
– 'Wagon Wheel'	CRDP CRiv EBre ECha ELan EPad EPot ESis EWes LBre LHop MCas MHig NGre NHar NHol NMen SIng SUsu WEas WHal WHil WPat WThu WWin
amoena hort.	See P. x ***procumbens***
x ***arendsii*** 'Anja'	WCot
– 'Hilda'	EMon WCot
– 'Lisbeth'	WCot
austromontana	EPot
bifida	ITim MBro MHig WHil WThi WThu WWin
– 'Alba'	CNic
– blue	ELan LBee LHop LRHS SHer SUsu SWas WDav
– 'Colvin's White'	EPot LBee LHop MCas WPer
– 'Minima Colvin'	ECtt
– 'Petticoat'	NCat SBla SWas
¶ – 'Ralph Haywood'	NHar
– 'Starbrite'	EPot ITim LBee MBro NMen WHoo WThi
– 'Starcleft'	CNic
* – 'The Fi'	WPer
'Black Buttes'	CPBP EPot WDav WThi
borealis	CShe ELan GDra ITim NRed NTow WThi
caespitosa	EPot EWes GCHN ITim LBee NHed NMen NTow SGil
canadensis laphamii	See P. ***divaricata laphamii***
carolina 'Bill Baker'	CBot CChu CGle CHan CRDP CSam CSco ECha ECoo EMar EMon GMac LGan LHop MBel MMil MSte NBrk NCat NNrw SCro SLga SMrm SUsu SWas WAbe WOMN WOld
¶ – 'Magnificence'	EMon
– 'Miss Lingard' AGM	CSam EBee EFou EMon GBuc GCal LRHS MBel MMil SBla SDix WCot
'Charles Ricardo'	CRDP ERav GBuc NTow SMrm WHoo WMar
'Chattahoochee' AGM	Widely available
¶ 'Chattahoochee Variegated'	LHop
* ***chonela*** 'Nana'	NHol
* ***colvillea***	CNic
condensata	NWCA
'Daniel's Cushion'	See P. ***subulata*** 'McDaniel's Cushion'
diffusa	LHop
divaricata AGM	MRav MSte NKay WMar WPer WWin
– ***alba***	ELan SWas
– 'Blue Dreams'	EBee GBuc SMrm SUsu SWas
¶ – 'Clouds of Perfume'	EMon SMrm
– 'Dirigo Ice'	CHad CRDP ERav LBee LGre LHop SBla SFar SSvw
¶ – 'Fuller's White'	EMon
§ – ssp. ***laphamii***	CNic NVic SBla WCru WKif WPer WRus WThi
– 'May Breeze'	CRDP EBee ECha LHop SMrm SWas
douglasii	EBar NHol NWCA SRms SUsu
– 'Apollo'	ELan EMNN GAbr GDra LBee MBro MHig NGre NHol NMen SHer WAbe WWin
– 'Blue Mist'	NHol
– 'Boothman's Variety' AGM	CGle CShe ECha ELan EMNN EPar EPot ESma MHig MPit MPla MWat NHol NKay NMen NRoo SBod SGil SHer SIng WEas WHil WPer WWin
– 'Concorde'	GDra NHar
– 'Crackerjack' AGM	CSam CShe CTom ELan EMNN EPot ESis GAbr GDra ITim LBee MHig MPla MWat NGre NHar NKay NMen NRed NRoo SBod SIng WAbe WDav
– 'Eva'	CNic EBre ELan EMNN EPot GAbr GTou LAbb LBee LBre MHig MRav NBir NGre NHar NHol NKay NRoo SBod SGil SHer SIng WAbe WPer WThi WTyr WWin
– 'Galaxy'	ESis GDra NHar NHol
– 'Holden Variety'	NHol
– 'Ice Mountain'	CNic ELan IHos SHer
– 'Iceberg' AGM	EPot ESis GDra ITim MBro NHar NHol NMen NRed SGil WDav WWin
– 'J A Hibberson'	EPot ESis LRHS MHig WThi
– 'Lilac Cloud'	NHol

– 'Lilakönigin' ('Lilac Queen') WHil
– 'Millstream Laura' CNic
– 'Pink Chintz CNic
– 'Red Admiral' AGM CMHG CShe EBre EMNN EPot GCHN GDra IHos LBre MHig NHar NHol NMen NNrd NRoo SBod SChu SGil SHer
– 'Rose Cushion' CNic ESis GDra LRHS MPla NHol NPri SGil SHer
– 'Rose Queen' CMHG ESis GDra NHol
– 'Rosea' EBre ELan EMNN EPad EPar ESis LBee LBre MBal MCas MRav NGre NKay NRed NRoo SBod SHer SIng SSmi SSte WAbe
– 'Sprite' SRms
– 'Tycoon' ESis GDra GTou NMen WAbe
– 'Violet Queen' ELan EMNN EPot EWes GDra NHar NHol SGil SHer
– 'Waterloo' CTom EBre EPot EWes GAri ITim LBre LHop MRav NHar NHol NMen NPri SChu SIng SUsu WAbe WWin
– 'White Drift' WThu
– x *nana depressa* EPot MBro NHol WDav
hoodii CPBP EPot LBee SIde
'Kelly's Eye' AGM CMHG CSam ECha ECtt ELan EMNN EPot GAbr ITim LBee LHop MHig MMil NMen NRoo SBod SIng SMrm SWas WPer
kelseyi MFos
– 'Rosette' ESis LBee MCas MHig NGre NMen WAbe WOMN WPer
maculata NOrc WPer
– 'Alpha' AGM CGle CHan CRDP CSco EBre ECha EFou GCHN GCal GMac LBre LGan MBri MRav MUlv NHol NOrc NRoo NVic SBla SChu SCro SLga SMrm SPer SSvw WByw WOld WRus
– 'Delta' EBre LBre NSti SPla WRus
– 'Good White' SMrm
– 'Omega' AGM CChu CDec CHad CHan CSco EFou EOrc GCHN GCal GMac LGan MBri MBro MRav MTho MUlv NHol NRoo NSti SChu SLga SMrm SPer WByw WOld WPer WRus WSHC
– 'Rosalinde' EFou MBel SAxl SChu SUsu
mesoleuca See P. ***nana ensifolia***
Mexican hybrids See P. ***nana***
'Millstream' See P. x ***procumbens*** 'M.'
'Minima Colvin' SHer
missoulensis SIng
'Mrs Campbell' See P. ***paniculata*** 'Elizabeth Campbell'
§ ***nana*** EPad
– 'Arroya' SBla
§ – ssp. ***ensifolia*** EPad EPot WThu
– 'Manjana' NHol SBla WThu
– 'Mary Maslin' SBla WThu
– 'Paul Maslin' NHol
– 'Vanilla Cream' NHol SBla WThu
nivalis GAbr NMen
– 'Camla' ELan EPot ITim LBee LHop WAbe WDav WThi
– 'Jill Alexander' NHol
– 'Nivea' ITim NGre NTow SIng
ovata CRDP
paniculata CHad CShe NNor SChu SDix SMrm WEas WOld
– 'A E Amos' CBow EFou ERou
– 'Aida' CB&S CKel ERou MWat NPri
– ***alba*** CBos GCal SDix WCot
– 'Alba Grandiflora' AGM WEas
– 'Albert Leo Schlageter' AGM CShe ERou SRms WMer
– 'Amethyst' AGM CCla CDoC CKel CSam EBre ERou LBre MArl MBel NBee NBir SChu WCra WHoo WPer
– 'Annie Laurie' SRms
– 'Anthony Six' WPer
– 'Balmoral' CBow CDoC CGle CMGP ECas ECtt MSte NCat NMir
– 'Barnwell' ELan NBar WMer
– 'Betty Symons-Jeune' ERou
– 'Bill Green' CMGP EBre LBre LBuc
– 'Blue Boy' CMGP EFou ERou LWad WMer
– 'Blue Ice' AGM CMGP EBre ECas EFou ELan LBre MBro NCat NRoo SMrm WCra
¶ – 'Blue Paradise' EMon
– 'Blushing Bride' SRms
– 'Bonny Maid' CBla
– 'Border Gem' CB&S CBow CDoC EBre ECas EFou EMon ENot LBre MHlr MSte NRoo WCot
– 'Boy Blue' NFai
– 'Branklyn' CKel EBre LBre MArl SBla
– 'Brigadier' AGM CDoC CSam CSco ELan ENot LWad MFir MWat NBar NCat NKay NVic SApp SMrm SPer WCra
– 'Bright Eyes' AGM CBla MArl
– 'Caroline van den Berg' ERou NPri SRms
– 'Cecil Hanbury' CDoC ERou NFai NPri SRms WHoo
– 'Charmaine' CBla
– 'Chintz' SRms
– 'Cinderella' CDoC ERou WMer
– 'Cool of the Evening' CBla WCot
– 'Dodo Hanbury Forbes' AGM CBla CKel
– 'Dresden China' ERou MUlv
– 'Düsterlohe' NBar
– 'Elizabeth Arden' EFou ERou NBar NBee WMer
§ – 'Elizabeth Campbell' ECtt
– 'Endurance' ERou
– 'Europe' CB&S CGle CMGP EBee EFou ELan ERou LBuc MFir NFai SMrm SPer SSte WHil WHoo WMer
– 'Eva Cullum' EBre EFou LBre MArl NRoo WCot
– 'Eventide' AGM CBow CDoC CMGP CSco EBre ECED ECas ECtt EFou EHal ENot ERou LBre LWad MArl NMir SChu SMrm SPer WCra
– 'Excelsior' CDoC MRav
– 'Fairy's Petticoat' MWat
– 'Firefly' ENot SFis
– 'Flamingo' NBar
– 'Franz Schubert' CRDP EBre EFou LBre MHlr NRoo SApp WCot WCra
§ – 'Frau A von Mauthner' NKay NPri

§ – 'Fujiyama' AGM CBos CCla CHad CKel CSam EBre ECas ECha EFou EMon EOrc GCra LBre LHop LLWP MSte NBir NSti SApp SChu SMrm WAbb WCot WCra WEas WThi
– 'Gaiety' CSco
– 'Glamis' MWat
– 'Graf Zeppelin' CBla ELan MWat NPri SRms
– 'Hampton Court' NBrk
– 'Harewood' ERou
– 'Harlequin' (v) CChu EBre GBuc LBre NVic SPla WCot
– 'Iceberg' MFir
– 'Iris' SRms SWas
– 'Juliglut' ('July Glow') EBre ELan LBre MWat WCot
– 'Kirmesländler' CB&S CKel ERou
– 'Lady Clare' SRms
– 'Latest Red' See P. *p.* 'Spätrot'
¶ – 'Lavendelwolke' ('Lavender Cloud') ELan
– 'Le Mahdi' AGM ELan MWat SRms
– 'Lilac Time' CSco MWat NCat NPri
– 'Look Again' ERou
– 'Mary Fox' CSam ERou NRoo
– 'Mia Ruys' EFou ERou LWad MArl NVic WMer
– 'Mies Copijn' CDoC CSco CShe NBar WCra WMer
– 'Mother of Pearl' AGM CGle CHad CMGP CSco EFou ELan MWat NVic SPer
– 'Mount Fujiyama' See P. *p.* 'Fujiyama'
– 'Mrs A E Jeans' SRms
– 'Mrs Fincham' SFis
– 'Newbird' ERou SRms
– 'Norah Leigh' (v) Widely available
– 'Orange Perfection' CB&S EFou NPri WHil
– 'Othello' CBla
– 'Otley Choice' ECas EFou MSte MWat NCat NVic SMrm
– 'Pastorale' MWat WCot
– 'Pike' WCot
– 'Prince of Orange' AGM CBla CCla CGle CMGP CSam EBre ECas EFou ELan ERou GGar LBre MRav MUlv MWat NKay NRoo SApp SPer WCot
– 'Prospero' AGM CRiv EOrc MArl NRoo SChu SFis SPer WOld
– 'Rapture' MWat
– 'Red Indian' ERou MWat
– 'Rembrandt' CSco CShe ERou MUlv WCot
– 'Rheinländer' WPer
– 'Rijnstroom' CB&S CMGP EBee ECas ECot EFou ERou LAbb MBel NCat NFai SMrm WCot WCra WHil WHoo WTyr
¶ – 'Rosa Spier' WMer
– 'Rougham Supreme' ERou
– 'Russian Violet' CSco MWat
– 'San Antonio' CMGP CSco SChu SMrm WCot
– 'Sandringham' CBow CCla CSam EBre ECas ELan ENot LBre LHop MArl MSte MUlv NBar NBir NCat NKay NMir NRoo NVic SChu SMrm SPer
– 'Shenstone' MWat
– 'Sir John Falstaff' CSco SFis WMer
– 'Sir Malcolm Campbell' ERou
– 'Skylight' CShe EBee LBuc NKay SFis SMrm SPer
– 'Snowdrift' ERou
§ – 'Spätrot' EFou WMer
– 'Spitfire' See P. *p.* 'Frau A von Mauthner'
– 'Starfire' CB&S CBla CBow CGle CSam CSco EBre EFou ELan ENot ERou LBre LHop MArl MFir NBar NBee NKay NRoo NSti SChu SFis SPer WCot WHoo WMer
– 'Sternhimmel' ERou
– 'Tenor' CBow EBee ECas EFou LWad MSte NMir NPri SMrm WHil WTyr
– 'Toits de Paris' MWat
– 'Vintage Wine' WMer
– 'White Admiral' AGM CB&S CBla CBow CCla CGle CHad CKel EBre ECas ELan ENot EOrc GMac LBre LHop LWad MBel MRav MUlv MWat NBee NKay NRoo SPer WEas WHil WMer WTyr
– 'William Ramsay' ELan
– 'Windsor' AGM CBla CMGP ECas EFou ERou LWad MBel NBar NBee NMir SFis SMrm
pilosa CMGP ECha NSti SMrm SUsu
§ x ***procumbens*** 'Millstream' AGM ECha ELan EPad LBee LHop SBla SIng SMrm WOMN WThi WWin
– 'Variegata' CBot CRDP ECha ELan EMNN ESis LGro MHig MPla MTho NEgg NGre NHol NNor NRoo NSti SBla WAbe WDav WPat WThi WThu WWin
x ***rugellii*** CNic ECha NHol SRms WWin
stolonifera CCla CHan EPar LBee MTho WMer WPbr WPer
– 'Ariane' CMGP CNic CRDP CRiv ECha EPar LGre LHop MFir NVic SBla SWas WAbe WPbr WPer WThu WWin
– 'Blue Ridge' AGM CRDP ECha EGle EPar GBuc LHop NVic SBla SIng SMrm SWas WWin
¶ – 'Compact Pink' WCru
¶ – 'Fran's Purple' SWas
– 'Mary Belle Frey' CNic CRDP ECha LGre LHop MFir SBla SMrm SWas WMar WPer WTyr WWin
– 'Pink Ridge' SIng
– 'Violet Vere' CRDP EGle EMon LGre MFir SBla SChu SMrm SUsu SWas WHoo WKif
subulata NWCA
– 'Alexander's Surprise' CGle CMea CNic CRiv CSam CShe EBre ECtt EPot GAbr GCHN LBee LBre LHop MBal MCas MFir MPit NBir NCat NGre NHol NKay NMen NRoo
– 'Amazing Grace' ELan EPad EPot ESis GAbr ITim LHop NHol NMen NPri NRoo SHer WAbe WEas WPer WThi WWin
– 'Apple Blossom' GAbr GDra NHol SChu
– 'Atropurpurea' EBre GCHN LBre NKay NNor WWin
– 'Beauty of Ronsdorf' See P. *s.* 'Ronsdorfer Schöne'

– 'Betty'	ECtt EMNN MDHE NMen NNrd NRoo WPer
– 'Blue Eyes'	See P. *s.* 'Oakington Blue Eyes'
– 'Blue Saucer'	EPot NHol
– 'Bonita'	EMNN GAri LBee MRav NMen NRoo SChu SMrm SWas
– 'Bressingham Blue Eyes'	See P. *s.* 'Oakington Blue Eyes'
– 'Brightness'	CNic CRiv GCHN GTou LRHS MCas MRav NKay SChu
– ssp. ***brittonii*** 'Rosea'	EBar EPot NHol WOMN WPer
– 'Daisy Hill'	NHol
– 'Drumm'	EPot LBee LHop LRHS
– 'Emerald Cushion Blue'	CNic CRiv EBre ELan EPad GTou LBee LBre MBal MCas MRav NHol NRoo SBod SHer SIng SUsu WAbe WPer WSun WThi
– 'Fairy'	WPer WSun WTyr
– 'G F Wilson'	CMea CShe CTom ECha ECtt ELan EPad GTou IDai LBee LGro MBal MCas MFir MHig MWat NGre NHol NKay NMen NNor NNrd NRoo SChu SSmi WAbe WDav WPer WWin
– 'Greencourt Purple'	NCat NHol
– 'Jupiter'	SChu SUsu
– 'Kimono'	MCas MFos WHal
– 'Lavinia'	NHol
§ – 'Maischnee' ('May Snow')	EBre ECtt ELan EMNN EPot GAbr LBee LBre LGro LHop MBal MFos MHig MPla MWat NGre NHol NNor NRoo SIng WEas WWin
– 'Marjorie'	ECtt ELan EMNN LBee MBal MCas NKay NMen SChu SHer WDav WEas WTyr
§ – 'McDaniel's Cushion' AGM	CMHG CShe EBre ECha ELan EMNN EPad EPot ESis GAbr GTou ITim LBee LBre MCas MFos MHig MMil NGre NHol NNor NRoo SBla SHer SUsu WPer WWin
¶ – 'Mikado'	LBuc
¶ – 'Millstream Jupiter Blue'	NHol
– 'Model'	LGro MWat
– 'Moonlight'	CNic ECtt WPer
– 'Nelsonii'	CShe
§ – 'Oakington Blue Eyes'	CMHG EBre EPar ESma GAbr GCHN GDra LBee LBre NGre NHol NRoo WPer
¶ – 'Pink Pearl'	EWes
– 'Red Wings' AGM	EBre ECtt GCHN LBre MBal MCas MPit MRav NHol NKay NMen NNor NRoo WHil
§ – 'Ronsdorfer Schöne'	EPad EPot NNrd
– 'Rose Mabel'	NVic
– 'Samson'	CNic ELan GAbr GTou IDai LBee NHol NKay SBod SHer WPer WThi WWin
– 'Scarlet Flame'	CNic CTom EBre ECha ECtt ELan EMNN EPot GDra LBre LGro MBal MCas MPit MRav MWat NHol NKay SBod SUsu WPer WWin
– 'Schneewitchen'	LBuc NHol
– 'Sensation'	SRms
– 'Snow Queen'	See P. *s.* 'Maischnee'
– 'Starglow'	GTou LRHS NHol NPri WPer
– 'Tamaongalei'	CMea CNic EWes NCat NHar SBla SChu SMrm SUsu SWas WDav
– 'Temiskaming'	CMHG CNic EBre ECha EMNN GCHN GDra IDai LAbb LBre LGro MCas MFir NGre NHol NKay NMen NRoo SChu WAbe WEas
– violet seedling	NHol NKay
– 'White Delight'	CRiv EBre ECha ECtt ELan EMNN EPad GCHN GTou LBre MCas MFir MHig NHol NKay NMen NRoo SBod SChu SHer WPer
– 'White Swan'	WThi
– 'Winifred'	LMer
'Vivid'	EPad

PHOEBE (Lauraceae)

sheareri	CMCN

PHOENICAULIS (Cruciferae/Brassicaceae)

§ ***cheiranthoïdes***	GTou NTow WOMN

PHOENIX (Palmae/Arecaceae)

canariensis AGM	CGre CHEx CTbh CTro LPal MBri NPal SMad WNor
F ***dactylifera***	LPal
paludosa	LPal
reclinata	CTro
roebelenii AGM	CTro LPal MBri NPal
sylvestris	LPal
theophrasti	LPal

PHORMIUM † (Agavaceae/Phormiaceae)

'Apricot Queen' (v)	CAbb CB&S COtt IBlr IJoh MBal
'Bronze Baby'	CAbb CB&S CBar CBow CLTr CSam CSco EB&P ECtt EHoe ELan EWri ISea MBal MSte MWat SApp SHBN SHer SPer SPla WStI
colensoi	See P. ***cookianum***
§ ***cookianum*** AGM	CB&S CHEx CHan CTrw GIsl IBlr MBal MBrk MGos NTow SArc WWat
– 'Alpinum Purpureum'	See P. ***tenax*** 'Nanum Purpureum'
– ssp. ***hookeri*** 'Cream Delight' AGM	CAbb CB&S CSco EBre ELan ENot ERav IJoh IOrc LBre MBal MGos SHBN SLon SPer WAbe WCot
– – 'Tricolor' AGM	CB&S CBra CHEx CMGP EBre ELan ENot IBar IBlr IJoh LBre MBal NFai SArc SHBN SPla WCot WDin WWye
'Dark Delight'	CB&S CDoC
'Dazzler' (v)	ENot IOrc MBal
'Duet' AGM	CB&S COtt
'Dusky Chief'	COtt
'Gold Spike'	CB&S
'Jack Spratt' (v)	CB&S CDec COtt ECou IBlr
'Jester'	CB&S COtt EWll NFai
§ 'Maori Chief' (v)	CB&S EBee EGol IJoh SHBN
¶ 'Maori Eclipse'	EB&P SPla
'Maori Maiden' (v)	CB&S CDoC MBal NBrk
'Maori Queen' (v)	CB&S

'Maori Sunrise' (v)	CB&S EWri GWht IJoh MSte SHer SLon WWye
'Pink Panther' (v)	CAbb CB&S CDoC EWll MGos NFai
¶ 'Purple Queen'	EWll
'Rainbow Chief'	See P. 'Maori Chief'
Rainbow Hybrids	CSpe EWll IJoh MBal NFai SHer
'Smiling Morn' (v)	WDin
'Sundowner' AGM	CB&S CBar CBow CSco CTro EBre EGol ELan ENot IBar IBlr IJoh IOrc LBre LHop MBal MGos SHBN SPer WAbe WStI
'Surfer' (v)	COtt
tenax AGM	CB&S CBra CHEx CSco CTro ELan ENot EWri IBar ISea MBal MWat NBro NNor SArc SBla SLon SMad SPer SPla SReu WBod WCot WDin WOld
§ – 'Nanum Purpureum' AGM	CRDP SWas
– Purpureum Group AGM	CAbb CB&S CBot CBow CBra CElw CGre CHEx CHad CSco EBre EGol EHoe ELan ENot ERav EWri IBar IJoh IOrc ISea LBre MBal SLon SMad SPer WDin
– 'Radiance' (v)	MBal SBla
– 'Variegatum' AGM	CBow CHEx IBlr MBal SArc SEng SRms
'Thumbelina'	CB&S MSte
'Tom Thumb'	CB&S WDin
'Yellow Wave' AGM	CAbb CB&S CBar CDoC CHEx CSco EBre EHoe ELan EWri IBar IBlr IJoh IOrc LBre LHop MBal NNrw SHer SPer SPla WAbe WCot WDin

PHOTINIA † (Rosaceae)

§ *arbutifolia*	CPle
beauverdiana AGM	CB&S CChu CDoC CGre CPle EHar MBrk SHil WWat
§ *davidiana*	CCla CMCN CPle CSco CShe CTrw ELan EMil GRei GWht IDai LHop MBal MBar MBri MGos MRav MWat SPer SReu WBod WNor WTyr WWat
– 'Palette' (v)	CB&S CBow CChe CCla CPle CSco CTrw EFol EGol EHar EHoe ELan EMil IJoh LHop MBal MBar MBri MGos MPla MRav NHol NSti SPer SReu SSta WPat WSHC WStI
– var. *undulata*	CMCN MRav
– – 'Fructu Luteo'	CBow CMHG CTrw EHar EPla MBri MRav WWat
– – 'Prostrata'	CCla EHar ELan LHil MBar MBri NHol SPer WSHC WWat
x *fraseri*	IDai ISea WDin
– 'Birmingham'	CChu CLan CMHG EHar LAbb LHop MBal SHBN WDin WSHC WWeb
– 'Red Robin' AGM	Widely available
– 'Robusta' AGM	CMHG MBal WWat
– 'Rubens'	CChu CDoC CPMA EHar ELan MBri SDry SPer SPla SSta WPat WWat
§ *glabra* 'Parfait' (v)	CPle CSco ELan EWll LHop MBal MUlv NWyt SDry SHBN SPer WAbe WPat
– 'Pink Lady' (v)	See P. *g.* 'Parfait'
– 'Rubens'	See P. x *fraseri* 'R.'
– 'Variegata'	See P. *g.* 'Parfait'
glomerata	CHEx CMHG
lasiogyna	CMCN MNes
§ 'Redstart' AGM	EHar MGos MUlv SHil SLon SPer SSta WWat
§ *serratifolia*	CBot CBow CChu CDoC CHEx CPle EHar MBal SArc SDry SHil SPer WBod WPat WWat
serrulata	See P. *serratifolia*
villosa AGM	CAbP CChu CCla CDoC EHar GAri IDai IOrc MBal MBar SPer WBod WDin
– var. *laevis*	CB&S
– f. *maximowicziana*	CCla

PHRAGMITES (Gramineae/Poaceae)

§ *australis*	CBen LMay NDea SWat WHol
– *giganteus*	See P. *a. altissimus*
– *pseudodonax*	GCal
– 'Variegatus'	CBen CRDP EHoe EMFW EMon GCal MUlv SWyc WChe WCot WHal
communis	See P. *australis*
karka 'Variegatus'	WChe

PHUOPSIS (Rubiaceae)

§ *stylosa*	CBre CElw CGle CLTr CLew CMea CMer CRiv ECha EFol EFou ELan ESis GMac LGan MFir NBar NBro NRoo NSti NWCA SChu SSvw SUsu WAbb WHal WPbr WPer WWin WWye
– 'Purpurea'	CBos CMea ECha EFol ELan ESis NBrk NCat SChu WByw WHal

PHYGELIUS (Scrophulariaceae)

aequalis	CBot CBow CCla CFee CGle CMHG CMer CSev CTre ELan EOrc MFir MPla NNor SBor SChu SDix SLon SUsu WPer WSHC WWat
– *albus*	See P. *a.* 'Yellow Trumpet'
– 'Aureus'	See P. *a.* 'Yellow Trumpet'
– 'Cream Trumpet'	See P. *a.* 'Yellow Trumpet'
– 'Indian Chief'	See P. x *rectus* 'African Queen'
*– 'Pink Trumpet'	CLTr EFou ERav NNor SLga SMrm
§ – 'Yellow Trumpet'	Widely available
capensis AGM	CBot CGle CHan CLTr CMea CPle CShe EBar ELan ENot EOrc MBel NBro NNor NRoo SBor SLon SPer WAbe WEas WHil WOld WPer WWye
¶ – S&SH 50	CHan
– *coccineus*	CAbb CBow CSco CTrw EOrc IDai IJoh LAbb LWad MBal MPla SMad WBod WTyr
– orange	EPla
– *roseus*	CTrw
– x *aequalis*	See P. x *rectus*
* 'Golden Gate'	MAll
§ x *rectus*	EPla
§ – 'African Queen'	CBow CFee CGle EBre ECtt EFou EGol ELan EOrc EPla ESis GMac LBre LHop MBri MBro MPla MRav NBir NHol NKay NTow SUsu WMer WOld WPer WRus WTyr WWin

– 'Devil's Tears'	CAbb CBow CCla CFee CMHG CTre EBar EOrc EPla GGar MArl NFai SHil SLon WHoo WMer WPer WRus WWat
*– 'Logan's Pink'	GMac
– 'Moonraker'	CAbb CLTr CMHG EBar ECtt EFol ELan EOrc EPla ERav ESis ESma GGar GMac MAll MBri SHil SMad WHoo WMer WSun WWat
– 'Pink Elf'	CTre ELan EOrc ERav ESis
– 'Salmon Leap'	CAbb CBow CMHG EBar EOrc ESma GGar MAll MAsh MBel NBro NTow SHil WPer
§ – 'Winchester Fanfare'	CAbb CMHG EBre EOrc EPla ESis LAbb LBre MBel MBro SChu SCro SFis SHil SLon SPer WEas WHal WHoo WMer WOld WPer WRus WSHC WSun WWat
– 'Winton Fanfare'	See P. x ***r.*** 'Winchester Fanfare'
'Trewidden Pink'	LHop MBel

PHYLA (Verbenaceae)

§ ***canescens***	CLew NHol WCru WHal
§ ***nodiflora***	CMer CRow ECha SMrm WHil WPer WTyr

PHYLICA (Rhamnaceae)

¶ ***arborea*** 'Superba'	CB&S
ericoïdes	CB&S

X PHYLLIOPSIS (Ericaceae)

'Coppelia'	CMHG CNic GArf GGGa MAsh MBal SSta WAbe WPat
hillieri	GArf
– 'Pinocchio'	EPot GDra GGGa MAsh MBal MBri SHil SSta WAbe WPat WThu
'Hobgoblin'	GArf MBal SSta
'Mermaid'	SSta
'Puck'	SSta WAbe
'Sprite'	SSta WAbe WPat

PHYLLITIS See ASPLENIUM

PHYLLOCLADUS (Phyllocladaceae)

aspleniifolius var. ***alpinus***	CKen

PHYLLODOCE † (Ericaceae)

aleutica	CRiv EPot GAbr GArf GGGa MBal MBar MHig NHar SSta WPat WThu
§ – ssp. ***glanduliflora***	GArf GDra GWht MBal NHol WThu
§ – – 'Flora Slack'	GGGa MBal MHig WThu
– – white	See P. ***a. g.*** 'Flora Slack'
x ***alpina***	GDra
breweri	GArf GDra GGGa GWht WThu
caerulea AGM	GAbr GArf GDra GGGa GWht MBal MHig NHar WAbe
– ***japonica***	See P. ***nipponica***
empetriformis	CNic CRiv GArf GDra GGGa GWht MBal MBar MBri MGos MHig NHar NHol SSta WAbe WPat WThu
glanduliflora	See P. ***aleutica g.***
x ***intermedia***	GArf GDra MBal
– 'Drummondii'	GArf GGGa GWht
– 'Fred Stoker'	GArf GGGa GWht MHig NHol
§ ***nipponica*** AGM	GDra GWht MBal NHar SSta

PHYLLOSTACHYS † (Gramineae/Poaceae-Bambusoideae)

angusta	SBam SDry WJun
arcana	EPla SBam SDry WJun
– 'Luteosulcata'	SDry
§ ***atrovaginata***	SBam SDry
aurea AGM	CHEx EFul EPla GAri ISta LBam LNet LPan SArc SBam SCob SDry SHil WJun WWat
– 'Albovariegata'	WJun
– 'Flavescens Inversa'	EPla ISta SBam SDry WJun
– ***formosana***	WJun
– 'Holochrysa'	EFul EPla ISta SBam SDry WJun
– 'Koi'	SBam SDry WJun
– 'Variegata'	EFul EPla SBam SDry
aureosulcata	EFul EPla NJap SBam SDry WJun
– f. ***alata***	EPla SDry
– 'Aureocaulis'	SBam SDry WJun
– 'Harbin'	SDry
– 'Spectabilis'	EFul EPla LNet SBam SDry WJun
bambusoïdes	CB&S EPla ISta LBam NJap SBam SDix SDry SHil WJun
§ – 'Allgold' ('Holochrysa')	SBam SDry
– 'Castilloni' AGM	EFul EPla ISta LNet SArc SBam SDry WJun
– 'Castilloni Inversa'	SBam SDry WJun
– 'Katashibo'	WJun
– 'Kawadana'	SDry WJun
– 'Slender Crookstem'	WJun
– f. ***subvariegata***	EPla SBam SDry
– 'Sulphurea'	See P. ***b.*** 'Allgold'
– 'Tanakae'	SDry
bissetii	EPla ISta LBam SBam SDry WJun
congesta hort.	See P. ***atrovaginata***
decora	SBam SDry WJun
dulcis	SBam WJun
§ ***edulis***	CGre EPla GAri ISta MBal NJap SArc SBam SDry WJun
– 'Bicolor'	SBam SDry WJun
– var. ***heterocycla***	EBee SBam SDry SMad
– f. ***pubescens***	See P. ***e.***
flexuosa	EFul EPla ISta LBam LNet SBam SCob SDry SHil WJun
fulva	WJun
glauca	EPla
– 'Yunzhu'	EPla SDry WJun
§ ***heteroclada***	SBam SDry WJun
♦– 'Solid Stem' misapplied	See P. ***h.*** 'Straight Tem'
– 'Straight Stem'	EPla SBam SDry WJun
heterocycla	See P. ***edulis h.***
humilis	EPla SBam SDry WJun
iridescens	SDry
lithophila	WJun
makinoi	WJun
mannii	SBam SDry WJun
meyeri	EPla SBam SDry WJun
nidularia	EPla ISta SBam SDry WJun
– Smooth Sheath	WJun
nigra AGM	CHEx EFul EPla LBam LNet LPan SBam SCob SDix SDry WJun
– 'Boryana'	EPla ISta LBam MUlv SBam SDix SDry WJun

– 'Han-chiku'	WJun
– var. ***henonis*** AGM	EPla ISta LBam SBam SDry WJun
– 'Megurochiku'	EPla SBam SDry WJun
– f. ***punctata***	EPla ISta SBam SDry WJun
nuda	EPla SBam SDry
– ***localis***	SBam SDry
propinqua	SBam WJun
purpurata	See P. ***heteroclada***
rubicunda	WJun
rubromarginata	EPla SBam SDry
stimulosa	WJun
sulphurea 'Houzeau'	EPla SBam SDry
– 'Robert Young'	EPla ISta SBam SDry WJun
– 'Sulphurea'	See P. ***bambusoïdes*** 'Allgold'
§ – var. ***viridis***	EFul EPla ISta SBam SCob SDry
♦– – 'Mitis'	See P. ***s. v.***
violascens	EPla ISta SBam SDry WJun
viridiglaucescens AGM	CBar CGre CHEx EFul EPla ISta LBam SArc SBam SCob SDry WCot WJun
vivax	EPla SBam SDry WJun
– 'Aureocaulis'	SDry

X PHYLLOTHAMNUS (Ericaceae)

erectus	EPot GDra GGGa MHig NHar WAbe WPat WThu

PHYMOSIA (Malvaceae)

§ ***umbellata***	CBot CGre

PHYODINA See CALLISIA

PHYSALIS (Solanaceae)

alkekengi AGM	WOak
– var. ***franchetii***	CArn CB&S CBow CSco ECED ELan ENot EPla GLil LAbb LWad MBri MFir MSto NBar NBir NBro NFai NMir NRoo SHer SPer WHal WPer WTyr WWin WWye
– – 'Gigantea'	GBuc NNor
– – 'Variegata'	CDec IBlr MUlv
F ***peruviana***	CRDP

PHYSARIA (Cruciferae/Brassicaceae)

alpestris	MFos
floribunda	WDav

PHYSOCARPUS (Rosaceae)

¶ ***bracteatus***	CPle
capitatus	CPle EMon
opulifolius	EBre EGol EMil LBre MSal
– 'Dart's Gold' AGM	CCla CSco EBre EFol EGol EHoe EMil ENot IJoh IOrc LBre MBar MBri MWat NBar NNor NSti SPer SPla SSta WAbe WDin WSHC WWin
§ – 'Luteus'	CB&S CBot CPle CSam ELan ENot ESis ISea MBar MGos MRav NHol NNor NRoo SLon SPer WBod WDin WSHC
ribesifolius 'Aureus'	See P. ***opulifolius*** 'Luteus'

PHYSOCHLAINA (Solanaceae)

orientalis	CRDP MSal

PHYSOPLEXIS (Campanulaceae)

§ ***comosa*** AGM	EPad GArf MCas NHol NSla SIng SPou WHoo

PHYSOSTEGIA (Labiatae/Lamiaceae)

angustifolia	CHan EBee ECro
§ ***virginiana***	CHol CTom EBar ECoo ECro EOrc GCHN LGan MSal NRoo SSvw WByw WHaw
– 'Alba'	CBot CChu CGle CRiv CSam EBre ECro GBri LBre LHop MSte NOrc NRoo SSvw WEas WHil
*– 'Crown of Snow' ('Schneekrone')	CBot CBow CHol EBar ECoo ECro ECtt ESma LWad NHol NMir SPla WCot WHil WPer
– dwarf form	ECha
– 'Galadriel'	EMon LRHS
– pale pink	ECoo EFou LGan
– 'Red Beauty'	CBow WRus
– 'Rosea'	CB&S CBot CBow MBel WHil WPer
*– 'Snow Queen'	MWat NVic
– ssp. ***speciosa***	EMon
– – 'Bouquet Rose' ('Rose Bouquet')	CBow CHan EBre ECED ECha EMar LBre LLWP MBri MFir MRav MSte NCat NKay NMir NPri SChu SFis WHal WHoo WRus WTyr
§ – – 'Variegata'	Widely available
– 'Summer Snow' AGM	CB&S CCla CKel CSco ECha EFou EGol ELan ENot EOrc LHop MBel MBri MFir NHol SHer SPer WHal WHoo WOld WRus WWin
– 'Summer Spire'	ECha ECro ELan EPla MSte NHol NKay SPer
– 'Vivid' AGM	CChu CGle CMGP CRDP CSam CSco EBre ECED ECha ECro EFou ELan LBre MBro MRav MWat NHol NOak SDix SHer SPer SUsu WEas WHoo WWin

PHYTEUMA (Campanulaceae)

balbisii	See P. ***cordatum***
betonicifolium	ESma WPer
charmelii	NBro WHaw WPer WThi
comosum	See PHYSOPLEXIS ***comosa***
§ ***cordatum***	EBar NBir
halleri	See P. ***ovatum***
hemisphaericum	MTho WPer
humile	NNrd NWCA SHer
nigrum	CLew CRiv SHer WHoo WPer WThi
orbiculare	WCru WHoo
scheuchzeri	CNic CRDP CRiv ECha EFol ELan ESis LGan MBro NCat NHol NKay NRoo SBla SFis SHer WCru WPer WThi
sieberi	ELan GDra NBir NCat
spicatum	NBro NHol WPer WWye
– ***caeruleum***	WPer
tenerum	CKin

PHYTOLACCA (Phytolaccaceae)

acinosa	EBar ELan IBlr MHew MSal SFis

§ ***americana***	CArn CCla CHEx CRDP CSev EBar ECha ELan EMar GPoy IBlr LHol MChe MSal NWyt SIde WByw WEas WPer WWye
clavigera	See P. ***polyandra***
decandra	See P. ***americana***
¶ ***heteropetala***	CGre
§ ***polyandra***	ECha GBuc GCHN GWht LHol NBro NHex SAxl WWye

PICEA † (Pinaceae)

§ ***abies***	CPer EHar EHul ENot GRei IDai LBuc LCon MBar MBri MGos NBee NRoo NWea WDin WMou WThu
– 'Acrocona'	CDoC EBre EHar EHul LBre LCon LPan MBar MBri MGos MPla NHol SHil SLim SSta
– 'Argenteospica' (v)	LCon MAsh NHol
– 'Aurea'	LLin LPan SLim
– 'Aurea Magnifica'	LCon
– 'Capitata'	CKen GAri LCon MBar NHol
*– 'Cinderella'	MAsh MBri
– 'Clanbrassiliana'	CKen LCon MBar
– 'Columnaris'	EBre GAri LBre LCon
– 'Compacta'	LBee
I – 'Congesta'	CKen
– 'Crippsii'	CKen
I – 'Cruenta'	CKen
– 'Cupressina'	CKen
– 'Diffusa'	CKen LCon MBar WAbe
– 'Dumosa'	WAbe
– 'Elegans'	LCon MBar
– 'Ellwangeriana'	LCon
– 'Excelsa'	See P. ***abies***
– 'Finedonensis'	LCon NHol
– 'Formanek'	CKen LCon LLin
– 'Four Winds'	CAbP
– 'Frohburg'	CDoC ENHC GAri LCon MBar MBri MGos NHol SLim
I – 'Frohburg Prostrata'	LCon
– 'Globosa'	LCon MBar WStI
– 'Globosa Nana'	MGos
– 'Gregoryana'	CDoC CKen ELan LCon MBar MBri MPla MWat NHar NHol WAbe
– 'Gregoryana Veitchii'	LCon
– 'Inversa'	CDoC EHul ENHC GAri IJoh IOrc LCon LPan MBar SHil SLim
– 'Little Gem' **AGM**	CDoC CKen CMac EHul ENHC LBee LCon LLin MAsh MBar MBri MGos MPla MRPP MWat NHar NHol NRoo SLim WAbe WThu
– 'Maxwellii'	CMHG EHul LCon MBar MGos NHar
– 'Merkii'	GAri WAbe
– 'Nana'	LCon MBar
– 'Nana Compacta'	CKen EHul ESis LCon MBar SLim WAbe
– 'Nidiformis' **AGM**	CDoC CKen CMac EBre EHul ENHC ENot GRei IJoh IOrc LBre LCon LLin MAsh MBal MBar MBri MGos MPla MWat NBee NHar NRoo NWea SHBN SLim SLon SPer WDin WStI
– 'Norrkoping'	CKen
– 'Ohlendorffii'	CKen EHul ENHC LCon MBar MBri MPla MWat NHar NHol NRoo SHBN SLim WDin WStI
– 'Pachyphylla'	CKen
– 'Pendula Major'	SHBN
– 'Procumbens'	LCon MBar
– 'Pseudomaxwellii'	LCon NHol
– 'Pumila'	IDai NHed
– 'Pumila Nigra'	CMac EHul LCon LLin MBar MGos MPla NHar SLim WAbe
– 'Pygmaea'	CKen GDra LCon MBar MGos MPla NHol SLim WAbe
– 'Pyramidata'	MBar
– 'Reflexa'	EHul LCon LLin WThu
– 'Remontii'	LPan
– 'Repens'	MBar MBlu MGos
– 'Rydal'	LCon
– 'Saint James'	CKen NHol
– 'Saint Mary's Broom'	CKen
– 'Tabuliformis'	MBar
– 'Veitchii'	See P. ***a.*** 'Gregoryana Veitchii'
– 'Waugh'	LCon MBar
– 'Wills Zwerg' ('Will's Dwarf')	LCon MBri
§ ***alcockiana***	LCon MAsh MBri
– 'Prostrata'	LCon MBal MBar NHol
asperata	LCon
*– 'Blue Sky'	LCon
balfouriana	MBri NHol
bicolor	See P. ***alcockiana***
brachytyla	LCon
breweriana **AGM**	Widely available
engelmannii	EBre LBre LCon MBar
– f. ***glauca***	EHar EHul LCon SSta
glauca	GAul NWea
– var. ***albertiana*** 'Alberta Globe'	CDoC CSco EBar EBre EHul ENHC EPot GRei IJoh LBee LBre LCon LLin MAsh MBar MBri MGos MPla NBee NHar NHed NHol NRoo SLim WAbe WDin
– – 'Conica' **AGM**	Widely available
– – 'Gnome'	CKen LCon
– – 'Laurin'	CDoC CKen EBre LBee LBre LCon LLin MAsh MBri MRPP NHar SSta WAbe
– 'Coerulea'	LCon MBar
– 'Echiniformis' **AGM**	CKen EHul EPot GAri IJoh LBee LCon LLin MBal MBar MBri NHar WDin
– 'Lilliput'	EPot LCon MBar MBri SIng WAbe
– 'Nana'	CKen LCon
– 'Piccolo'	CDoC CKen LCon LLin SLim
– 'Sander's Blue'	CKen
– 'Tiny'	CKen EHul LCon LLin MBar NHol WAbe
– 'Zucherhut'	LCon
glehnii 'Sasanosei'	CKen
– 'Shimezusei'	CKen
– 'Yatsubusa'	LCon
jezoensis	GAri MGos
– ssp. ***hondoensis***	EHar WNor
kosteri 'Glauca'	See P. ***pungens*** 'Koster'
§ ***koyamae***	CGre CLnd LCon STre WHCr WThu
likiangensis	CGre LCon MBal WWat
– var. ***balfouriana***	See P. ***b.***
– var. ***purpurea***	See P. ***p.***
mariana	LCon NWea
– 'Aureovariegata'	LCon

– 'Doumetii' LCon
– 'Ericoides' GAri LCon MPla NHol
– 'Fastigiata' CKen
– 'Nana' AGM Widely available
x *mariorika* MBar
– 'Machala' CDoC
meyeri EArb
omorika AGM CB&S CDoC CMCN CSco EHar ENHC ENot GRei IDai IJoh LBuc LCon LNet MBal MBar MGos NWea SMad SPer SReu WCoo WDin WMou
– 'Nana' CMac EHar ENHC GAri LCon LNet MBar MBri NHol SEng SHil SLim
– 'Pendula' AGM EHar EHul IOrc LCon MBar MBri SHBN SHil SSta
– 'Pimoko' CKen LCon MBri
– 'Treblitsch' CKen
orientalis AGM CMCN LCon MBal NWea SHil STre WCoo WMou
§ – 'Aurea' AGM CBra CDoC CMac EHar EHul ELan ENHC IJoh IOrc LCon LLin LPan MBar MBri NHol SHBN SLim WThu
– 'Bergman's Gem' CKen
– 'Early Gold' EBre LBre NHol SSta
– 'Gowdy' MBar NHol
– 'Gracilis' LCon
– 'Kenwith' CKen
– 'Pendula' MGos
– 'Reynolds' CKen
– 'Skylands' CKen LCon MGos SLim
– 'Wittboldt' LCon MAsh
pungens LCon MBar NWea WDin WNor
¶ – 'Blue Trinket' LCon
– 'Endtz' CKen EBre LBre LCon LLin
– 'Erich Frahm' CDoC EBre EHar ENHC GAri LBee LBre LCon MAsh MBri SLim WStI
– *glauca* CBra CDoC CSam EHul GRei IBar LBee LPan MBal MBar NBee NWea SReu WDin WMou WStI
– 'Glauca Globosa' See P. *p.* 'Globosa'
– 'Glauca Procumbens' EHar LNet NHol
§ – 'Glauca Prostrata' CKen CMac EBre EHul LBre LCon MBal SLim SSta
– 'Globe' CKen LCon NHol
§ – 'Globosa' AGM CDoC CKen CSam CSco EBre EHar EHul ELan ENHC GRei IJoh IOrc LBee LBre LCon LLin MBar MBri MGos MWat NBee NHar NHol SHBN SHil SLim SPer SSta WAbe WStI
I – 'Globosa Viridis' EHul
– 'Gloria' CKen LCon
– 'Hoopsii' AGM Widely available
– 'Hoto' CMac EBre EHul ENHC IOrc LBee LBre LCon MBar SSta
– 'Hunnewelliana' LLin
– 'Iseli Fastigiate' LCon MAsh
§ – 'Koster' AGM CBra CDoC CMac EBre EHar EHul ENHC ENot GRei IJoh IOrc LBre LCon LLin LNet LPan MAsh MBar MGos NWea SLim SMad SPer SReu SSta WDin WStI
– 'Koster Prostrate' MBal NHol
– 'Lucky Strike' CKen EBre LBre LCon MAsh MGos MRPP
– 'Moerheimii' CBra CMac EBre EHul LBre LCon LNet MBar MGos
– 'Montgomery' CKen LCon LLin MBar NHol
¶ – 'Oldenburg' LCon
– 'Procumbens' AGM EBre LBre LCon SHil
– 'Prostrata' See P. *p.* 'Glauca Prostrata'
¶ – 'Prostrate Blue Mist' LCon
– 'Saint Mary's Broom' CKen
– 'Thomsen' CKen LCon MAsh MBal MBri SLim
– 'Thuem' LCon LLin
purpurea AGM CMCN MBri
¶ *retroflexa* LCon
rubens CGre GAri LCon
schrenkiana CMCN LCon
sitchensis CPer GRei IDai LBuc LCon MGos NWea WMou
¶ – 'Nana' NHol
– 'Papoose' See P. *s.* 'Tenas'
¶ – 'Silberzwerg' CKen
– 'Strypemonde' CKen
§ – 'Tenas' LCon MAsh NHol
smithiana AGM EHar GAri IBar ISea LCon MBal MBar MBri SLim WCoo

PICRASMA (Simaroubaceae)

§ *ailanthoïdes* CMCN SHil
quassioïdes See P. *ailanthoïdes*

PICRIS (Compositae/Asteraceae)

echioïdes CKin EWFC

PIERIS † (Ericaceae)

'Bert Chandler' CTrh ELan SPer
'Flaming Silver' AGM CB&S CBra CHig CKni CLan COtt CSam EBre EHoe ELan IHos IJoh IOrc LBre MBar MBri MGos NHol SEng SHBN SMad SReu WAbe WPat WWeb
'Flamingo' CB&S CBra CCla CHig CTrw MBal MBar MGos NHol SHil SPer SReu SSta WAbe WPat
floribunda IDai IOrc MBal SPer
'Forest Flame' AGM Widely available
formosa CHig CTrh
– var. *forrestii* CDoC CSco CTre CTrw ENot GPlt GRei IBar IJoh ISea NWea SExb WAbe WWeb
– – 'Charles Michael' CB&S CLan
– – 'Fota Pink' WSHC
– – 'Jermyns' AGM CB&S GWht IOrc MBal SHBN
– – 'Wakehurst' AGM CB&S CBra CCla CHig CLan CSco CTrh EBre ERav IBar IOrc LBre LHyd MBal MRav NKay SArc SLon SPer SReu WAbe WBod WPat WThu WWeb
'Havila' IOrc LRHS MBal MBri MGos NHed NHol SGil SHer
japonica CB&S CHig CLan CTrh CTrw GGGa MBal MBar MGos NHol NWea SArc SExb SReu WDin WWeb
– 'Bisbee Dwarf' CTrh MAsh NHol SIng WAbe WPat WThu
– 'Blush' AGM CCla NHol SBod SHBN SPer WSHC
– 'Cavatine' CMHG GWht SBod

§ – 'Christmas Cheer' CCla CDoC CHig CLan CTrh IOrc MBal MGos NHed NHol NKay NWyt SHer SPer WDin
– 'Coleman' CMHG
– 'Compact Crimson' MBal
– 'Compacta' NHol
– 'Crispa' CHig
– 'Cupido' LRHS MBar MGos NHol
– 'Daisen' CLan CTrw NHol SPer
– 'Daisy Hill' IDai
§ – 'Debutante' AGM CHig ELan MAsh MPla NHol SPer WStI WWat
♦– 'Don' See P. *j.* 'Pygmaea'
– 'Dorothy Wyckoff' CB&S CDoC CLan CMHG CTrw EBre IDai LBre NHed NHol SHBN SHer SPer SSta
– 'Firecrest' AGM CB&S CBra CCla CMHG CTrh EGol GPlt IDai IOrc LAbb MBal MBri NHol NRoo SGil SHer WAbe WWeb
– 'Flaming Star' ECot IBar SBod SPer
– 'Glenroy Pink Plenty' MBal
– 'Grayswood' AGM CGre CHig CMHG CSam EBre GAul GPlt IBar IOrc LBre MBri SPla
– 'Hino Crimson' CB&S
– 'Little Heath' AGM CBra CCla CDoC CHig CMHG CRiv CTrh EBar EBre EHoe EPla GCHN IOrc LBre MBar MBri MGos MHig NHed NHol SPer SReu SSta WAbe WBod WPat WWeb
– 'Little Heath Green' AGM CDoC CGre CHig CMHG CTrh EBre EPla GAri LBre LHyd MBar MBri NHar NHol SEng SMrm SPer SSta
– 'Minor' EPla MAsh NHol WPat WThu
– 'Mountain Fire' AGM CB&S CBra CDoC CMHG CSco CTrh EBre GCHN GRei IBar IDai IOrc LBre MBal MBar MBri MGos NHol NJap SBod SHBN SPer SReu SSta WPat WWeb
– pink NHol
– 'Pink Delight' AGM CAbP CB&S CBra CHig MBal MBar MGos MPla MRav NHol NKay SHBN SHer SPer WPat WThu
– 'Prelude' GCHN MAsh MBri MRav MUlv NHol WPat WThu
– 'Purity' AGM CB&S CDoC CHig CMHG CTrh GPlt GWht IBar IDai IOrc MBal MBar MGos NHol NJap SExb SPer SReu SSta WDin WPat WStI
§ – 'Pygmaea' CNic CTrh EPla GDra IDai MAsh MBal NHol SIng WPat WThu
– 'Red Mill' CAbP CDoC CHig CMHG CSco MAsh NHol SBod SPer
– 'Robinswood' SSta
– 'Rosalinda' CSco
– 'Rosamund' IDai
– 'Rosea' LHyd
– 'Sarabande' MAsh MBri MGos NHol SHer SPer WPat
– 'Scarlett O'Hara' CB&S IBar MGos SSta
– 'Select' IDai MGos
– 'Silver Sword' CSco
– 'Snowdrift' CGre GCHN MAsh MSta SPer SSta
– 'Spring Candy' CB&S MGos
– Taiwanensis Group CCla CDoC CGre CHig CMHG CSco CTre ENot GCHN GPlt GRei IDai IOrc LHyd MBal MBar MRav NHol NWea SLon SPer SSta WAbe WPat WWat WWeb
– 'Tickled Pink' CB&S
– 'Tilford' CCla CHig MBal MBri NHar NHol SHer SSta WWeb
– 'Valley Rose' CBra CChe CDoC CSam CTrh ENot GCHN IBar IDai MAsh MBal MGos NHol WStI
– 'Valley Valentine' AGM CLan CMHG COtt EHic LRHS MAsh MBal MBri MGos SHer SPer SReu SSta WStI
§ – 'Variegata' AGM Widely available
♦– 'Variegata' misapplied See P. *j.* 'White Rim'
– 'Wada's Pink' See P. *j.* 'Christmas Cheer'
– 'White Caps' CTrh MBal
– 'White Cascade' CTrh WWat
– 'White Pearl' CAbP CDoC CLan IDai IJoh MBal MBri MGos SHer SSta
– 'White Rim' (v) CB&S MPla
– 'William Buchanan' MAsh MHig MUlv NHol WPat WThu
nana GArf GAri MBal MBar WThu
– 'Redshank' MBal
ryukuensis 'Temple Bells' CB&S IBar
yakushimensis CLan CMHG

PILEA (Urticaceae)

* 'Anette' MBri
cadierei AGM MBri SLMG
– 'Minima' AGM SLMG
nummulariifolia MBri
peperomioïdes CSev EPad
repens MBri

PILEOSTEGIA (Hydrangeaceae)

viburnoïdes AGM CAbb CB&S CChu CCla CGre CHEx CLan CMac CSPN CTrw EHar EMil IDai LHop SArc SBra SDix SHBN SHil SLon SPer SSta WBod WPat WSHC WWat

PILOSELLA (Compositae/Asteraceae)

§ ***aurantiaca*** CNic CRiv CRow CTom CWGN EBar ECWi EFol ELan EWFC MFir MHew NMir NOrc NSti SIng SSmi WCla WEas WHer WNdy WPer
§ – ssp. ***carpathicola*** MWil
§ ***officinarum*** CKin CRow ECWi EWFC MWil WGwy WNdy WPer
§ ***stoloniflora*** CRow

PILULARIA (Marsileaceae)

globulifera CNat

PIMELEA (Thymelaeaceae)

arenaria ECou WCru
argentea LGre
coarctata See P. ***prostrata***
filiformis ECou MAll WCru
§ ***prostrata*** ECou GArf LBee MAll MBar MFir MHig NHar NHol SHer SIng WAbe WCru WHil WPat WPer WThu

– f. ***parvifolia***	ECou WCru
¶ ***sericeovillosa***	ECou
suteri	ECou WCru

PIMENTA (Myrtaceae)

¶ ***dioica***	CTro

PIMPINELLA (Umbelliferae/Apiaceae)

anisum	CArn EHer GPoy IEde LHol MChe MSal SHer SIde
flahaultii	CBos CRDP
major 'Rosea'	CHan CRDP ECha ECoo EFol EMon LHop SAxl SUsu WCot WEas
saxifraga	EWFC LHol

PINELLIA (Araceae)

cordata	EPot SPou
pedatisecta	CRDP MRav SAxl
§ ***pinnatisecta***	CMon
ternata	CMon CRDP EPar EPot SIng WCru WOld WThu WWye
tripartita	See P. ***pinnatisecta***

PINGUICULA † (Lentibulariaceae)

agnata	MHel WMEx
alpina	EFEx
caerulea	WMEx
cyclosecta	MSte WMEx
ehlersiae	EFEx MHel MSte
esseriana	EFEx MHel WMEx
¶ 'Fraser Beaut'	EFEx
¶ 'George Sargent'	EFEx
grandiflora	CRDP CRiv EFEx EPot MHel MSto NHar NKay NMen NRya NWCA WAbe WMEx WThu
gypsicola	WMEx
¶ 'Hamburg'	EFEx
¶ 'Hameln'	EFEx
ionantha	WMEx
'Kewensis'	EFEx MHel WMEx
laueana	EFEx WMEx
lusitanica	WMEx
lutea	WMEx
macrophylla	EFEx WMEx
moranensis alba	EFEx MHel WMEx
– var. ***caudata***	EFEx MHel MSte WMEx
– ***flos-mulionis***	MHel WMEx
¶ – 'Kirkbright'	MHel
– var. ***mexicana***	EFEx WMEx
– ***moreana***	EFEx
– ***morelia***	EFEx WMEx
– ***superba***	EFEx
oblongiloba	EFEx
orchidioïdes	EFEx
¶ 'Pachuca'	EFEx
planifolia	WMEx
* ***rayonensis***	EFEx
rosea	WMEx
'Sargent'	WMEx
'Sethos'	EFEx MHel WMEx
¶ 'Tina'	EFEx
¶ 'Vera Cruz'	EFEx
vulgaris	EFEx WMEx
'Weser'	EFEx MHel WMEx
zecheri	MHel

PINUS † (Pinaceae)

¶ ***albicaulis*** 'Flinck'	CKen
– 'Nana'	See P. ***a.*** 'Noble's Dwarf'
§ – 'Noble's Dwarf'	CKen
N ***aristata***	CAbP CDoC CKen CMCN EBre EHar EHul IBar LBre LCon LLin MAsh MBal MBar MBri MGos MRPP NBee NHol SEng SHil SReu SSta STre WCoo WThu
– 'Cecilia'	CKen
– 'Sherwood Compact'	CKen LCon
armandii	CChu CGre LCon STre
attenuata	STre
austriaca	See P. ***nigra nigra***
N ***ayacahuite***	SLim
banksiana	EHul LCon MBal
– 'Chippewa'	CKen
I – 'Compacta'	CKen
¶ – 'H J Welch'	CKen
– 'Manomet'	CKen
– 'Neponset'	CKen LCon
– 'Wisconsin'	CKen
♦ ***brutia***	See P. ***halepensis b.***
bungeana	CChu CGre CKen CLnd CMCN EHar EHul LCon LLin MBal MBlu SHil STre WFro
canariensis	CTro EHul ISea
cembra AGM	CDoC EHar EHul ENHC LBee LCon MBal MBar NWea STre
– 'Aurea'	See P. ***c.*** 'Aureovariegata'
§ – 'Aureovariegata'	CKen EHar LCon
– 'Barnhourie'	CKen
– 'Blue Mound'	CKen
– 'Chalet'	CKen
– 'Compacta Glauca'	LCon
– 'Glauca'	NHol
* – 'Griffithii'	WDin
– 'Inverleith'	CBra CKen MBri
– 'Jermyns'	CKen
– 'King's Dwarf'	CKen
– ***nana***	See P. ***pumila*** 'Nana'
– 'Roughills'	CKen
– 'Stricta'	CKen
– Witches' broom	CKen
cembroïdes	EHar
contorta	CB&S CDoC CPer EBre GRei LBre LCon MBal MBar MGos NWea SEng STre WDin WMou
– 'Asher'	CKen
– 'Frisian Gold'	CKen
– var. ***latifolia***	CLnd MBal
– 'Spaan's Dwarf'	CKen LCon LLin MBar MBri MGos NHol SLim
corsicana	See P. ***nigra maritima***
coulteri AGM	CAbb CMCN EHar LCon MBal SHil SMad WCoo WNor
densiflora	CDoC CMCN EHul ENHC GAri LCon MBal WNor
– 'Alice Verkade'	LCon LLin MBri SLim
– 'Aurea'	LCon MBar MGos SLim
– 'Jane Kluis'	CKen MBri
– 'Oculus Draconis'	CDoC LCon MBar SHil SLim
– 'Pendula'	CKen LLin MBal SLim
– 'Pygmy'	CKen
– 'Umbraculifera'	CDoC EHul IOrc LCon LLin MBar MBri MGos NHar NHol SLim SSta
edulis	LCon

¶ ***engelmannii***	SArc
flexilis	LCon MBal
– 'Firmament'	LCon LLin MBri
– 'Glenmore Dwarf'	CKen
– 'Nana'	CKen
– 'Pendula'	MAsh
– WB No. 2	CKen
gerardiana	EHar LCon MBal
griffithii	See P. ***wallichiana***
§ ***halepensis*** ssp. ***brutia***	LCon WCoo
hartwegii	CChu LCon MUlv
§ ***heldreichii*** var. ***leucodermis*** AGM	CMac COtt EHar LCon LNet LPan MBal MBar STre WDin
– – 'Aureospicata'	LCon MBar
– – 'Compact Gem'	CDoC CKen EBre IOrc LBre LCon LLin MBar MBri MGos NHar SLim SSta
– – 'Groen'	CKen
– – 'Malink'	CKen
– – 'Pygmy'	CKen
– – 'Satellit'	CDoC CSco ENHC IOrc LBee LCon LLin MBri SEng SLim
– 'Schmidtii' AGM	CDoC CKen LCon LLin MAsh MBar MBri SHil SLim
jeffreyi AGM	CBot CLnd EHar ISea LCon MBal MBar WFro
– 'Joppi'	CKen
koraiensis	CMCN LCon MBal WNor
– 'Bergman'	CKen
– 'Compacta Glauca'	SHil
– 'Dragon Eye'	CKen
– 'Jack Corbit'	CKen
– 'Shibamichi'	CKen
– 'Silver Lining'	LCon MAsh
– 'Silvergrey'	CKen
– 'Winton'	CKen
lambertiana	LCon
¶ ***lawsonii***	CGre
leucodermis	See P. ***heldreichii leucodermis***
magnifica	See P. ***montezumae***
¶ ***massoniana***	LCon
monophylla	CKen EHar MBal SEng
N ***montezumae***	CB&S CChu CGre CHEx CMCN ESma IOrc ISea LCon LLin MUlv NWyt SArc SHil SLim WBod WCoo
monticola	CLnd LCon
– 'Pendula'	MBar
– 'Pygmy'	See P. ***m.*** 'Raraflora'
§ – 'Raraflora'	CKen
– 'Skyline'	MBar
– 'Windsor Dwarf'	CKen
mugo	CB&S CBra EHul ENot GRei MAsh MBal MBar MGos WDin WStI
– 'Brownie'	CKen
¶ – 'Carsten'	CKen
– 'Carsten's Wintergold'	See P. ***m.*** 'Winter Gold'
– 'Corley's Mat'	CKen EBre LBre LCon LLin MAsh SLim SSta
– 'Gnom'	CKen CMac EHul IJoh LCon LLin MBar MBri NBar NBee SLim WDin WWat
– 'Humpy'	CKen EBre ENHC GAri LBee LBre LCon LLin MAsh MBri NHar SLim
– 'Jacobsen'	CKen

– 'Kissen'	CKen LCon NHol
– 'Knapenburg'	LCon
– 'Kobold'	LCon NHol
– 'Krauskopf'	CKen
– 'Laarheide'	LCon MAsh
– 'March'	CKen LCon NHol
¶ – 'Mini Mops'	CKen
– 'Minikin'	CKen
– 'Mops' AGM	CDoC CMac CSco EBre EHar EHul ENHC IDai IHos LBee LBre LCon LLin LPan MAsh MBar MBri MGos NBee NHar NHol SLim SPer SSta
¶ – 'Mops Midget'	LCon MAsh
♦ – var. ***mughus***	See P. ***m. mugo***
§ – var. ***mugo***	GRei LPan MBar
– 'Mumpitz'	CKen
– 'Ophir'	CKen CSco EBre EHar EHul ENHC IOrc LBee LBre LCon LLin LNet MAsh MBar MBri MGos NHar NHol SEng SLim SPer SPla SSta WDin
– 'Pal Maleter'	LCon MBri
– var. ***pumilio*** AGM	CDoC CMac EHul ENot GRei IOrc LCon LLin MBar MBro MGos NWea SHBN SPer STre WNor
– var. ***rostrata***	See P. ***m. uncinata***
– 'Spaan'	CKen
§ – ssp. ***uncinata***	CLnd GRei LCon NWea
– 'White Tip'	CKen
§ – 'Winter Gold'	CKen EBre EHul IOrc LBee LBre LCon MAsh NHar SSta
¶ – 'Winzig'	CKen
– 'Zundert'	CKen LCon MBar MBri MGos NHar
muricata AGM	CAbP CDoC CLnd LCon MBal MGos WCoo
nigra AGM	CB&S CDoC CSco ENHC ENot GRei IJoh LBuc LCon LNet MBar MGos NWea SHBN SPer WMou
– var. ***austriaca***	See P. ***nigra nigra***
– 'Black Prince'	CKen LLin SLim
N – 'Cebennensis Nana'	CKen
♦ – ***corsicana***	See P. ***n. laricio***
– 'Hornibrookiana'	CKen LCon MAsh NHol SHil SSta
§ – ssp. ***laricio*** AGM	CDoC CKen CPer CSco ENot GRei IHos LBuc LCon NWea SMad WMou
– – 'Bobby McGregor'	CKen LLin
– – 'Globosa Viridis'	GAri LLin NHol
– – 'Goldfingers'	CKen LLin
§ – – 'Moseri' AGM	CKen GAri LCon LLin MAsh MBri SHil SLim SSta
– – 'Pygmaea'	CKen SLim
– – 'Spingarn'	CKen
– – 'Talland Bay'	CKen
– – 'Wurstle'	CKen
♦ – ssp. ***maritima***	See P. ***n. laricio***
– 'Nana'	MBri
§ – ssp. ***nigra***	LPan NWea WStI
– – 'Bright Eyes'	CKen EHul LCon LLin
– – 'Helga'	CKen
– – 'Schovenhorst'	CKen
– – 'Strypemonde'	CKen
– – 'Yaffle Hill'	CKen
¶ – 'Obelisk'	CKen
I – 'Semeriana'	LCon
palustris	LCon LLin WCoo

parviflora **AGM**	CChu GAri LCon NWea SPer STre WCoo WDin WNor
– 'Adcock's Dwarf' **AGM**	CDoC CKen GAri LCon MAsh NHol SLim
– 'Al Fordham'	CKen
– 'Aoi'	CKen
– 'Azuma-goyo'	CKen
I – 'Baasch's Form'	CKen
– 'Bergman'	CDoC LCon MAsh MBar
– 'Bonnie Bergman'	CKen
– 'Brevifolia'	GAri
– 'Daisetsusan'	CKen
– 'Dai-ho'	CKen
– 'Fukai Seedling'	CKen
– 'Fukiju'	CKen
– 'Fukushima-goyo'	CKen
– 'Gimborn's Pyramid'	NHol
– 'Glauca'	CDoC CMac EHul ENHC GAri IHos IOrc LCon LLin MBar MBri NHol WDin
I – 'Glauca Nana'	CKen
– 'Goyokusui'	CKen
– 'Go-ko-haku'	CKen
– 'Gyokkesen'	CKen
– 'Gyokuei'	CKen
– 'Gyokukan'	CKen
– 'Gyokusen Seedling'	CKen
– 'Hagaromo Seedling'	CKen
– 'Hakko'	CKen NHol
¶ – 'Hatsumi'	LCon NHol
– 'Ibo-can'	CKen
– 'Ichi-no-se'	CKen
– 'Iri-fune'	CKen
– 'Janome'	CKen
– 'Kanzan'	CKen
– 'Ka-Ho'	CKen
– 'Kiyomatsu'	CKen
– 'Kobe'	CKen
– 'Kokonde'	CKen
– 'Kokonoe'	CKen LCon NHol
– 'Kokuho'	CKen NHol
– 'Koraku'	CKen
– 'Meiko'	CKen
– 'Michi-noku'	CKen
– 'Nasu-goyo'	CKen
– 'Negishi'	CKen GAri LCon MAsh MBal MBlu MBri
– 'Ogonjanome'	CKen
– 'Ryokuho'	CKen
– 'Ryuju'	CKen
– 'Sanbo'	CKen NHol
§ – 'Saphir'	CKen EBre LBre LCon MBri
– 'Setsugekka'	CKen
– 'Shikashima'	CKen
¶ – 'Shiobara'	CKen
– 'Shizukagoten'	CKen
– 'Shure'	CKen
– 'Tempelhof'	ENHC GAri LNet MBar MBri SLim
patula **AGM**	CAbb CChu CGre CSam CTre GAri ISea LCon MBal MBlu SArc SHil SIgm WCoo WWat
peuce	LCon MBar NWea STre WFro
– 'Arnold Dwarf'	CKen
pinaster **AGM**	CB&S CDoC CLnd EHul LCon MBal
– ssp. ***hamiltonii***	SIng
pinea **AGM**	CHEx CKen CMac EHar IOrc LCon LPan MGos SArc WNor
– 'Queensway'	CKen
ponderosa **AGM**	EHar LCon LPan NWea SIgm WCoo
pseudostrobus	CGre MBal
pumila 'Buchanan'	CKen
– 'Draijer's Dwarf'	LLin SLim
– 'Dwarf Blue'	See P. ***p.*** 'Glauca'
§ – 'Glauca' **AGM**	CKen IDai LCon LLin LNet MBri NHar NHol
– 'Globe'	LCon MAsh MBar MBri
¶ – 'Jeddeloh'	CKen
– 'Knightshayes'	CKen
– 'Säntis'	CDoC CKen EBre LBre LCon
♦ – 'Saphir'	See P. ***parviflora*** 'S.'
* ***pungens*** 'Glauca'	SPer
radiata **AGM**	CB&S CDoC CGre CHEx CPer CSco CTre CTrw EBre ENot IHos IOrc LBre MBal SArc SHBN SLim SPer STre WDin WHCr
– 'Aurea'	CKen EBre LBre LCon LLin MAsh SLim
– 'Marshwood'	CKen
¶ ***resinosa*** 'Don Smith'	CKen
– 'Joel's Broom'	CKen
– 'Nobska'	CKen
– 'Quinobequin'	CKen
– 'Watnong'	CKen
rigida	EHul LCon
roxburghii	CDoC CMCN ISea
sabineana	LCon
x ***schwerinii***	CDoC LCon
sibirica	See P. ***cembra s.***
strobiformis	LCon
strobus	CDoC CSco EHul GAri GRei IOrc ISea LCon MBar NWea STre
§ – 'Alba'	LCon NHol SHil
– 'Amelia's Dwarf'	CKen
– 'Anna Fiele'	CKen
– 'Bergman's Mini'	CKen
I – 'Bergman's Sport of Prostrata '	CKen
– 'Blue Shag'	CKen COtt LLin MGos SLim
– 'Contorta'	LCon
– 'Densa'	CKen EBre LBre LCon MAsh
– 'Dove's Dwarf'	CKen
– 'Fastigiata'	CKen LLin
– 'Hillside Gem'	CKen
– 'Horsford'	CKen
– 'Jericho'	CKen EBre LBre
– 'Krügers Liliput'	CKen EBre LBre LCon MBri MRPP SLim
– 'Merrimack'	CKen
– 'Minima'	CDoC CKen LCon MBar MBlu MBri NHar NHol SLim
– 'Minuta'	CKen
– 'Nana'	See P. ***s.*** 'Radiata'
– 'Nivea'	See P. ***s.*** 'Alba'
– 'Northway Broom'	CKen LLin
§ – 'Radiata' **AGM**	CSco EHul ENHC IHos IOrc LBee LLin LNet MBri NBee NHar NHol SLim
– 'Reinshaus'	CKen LCon NHol
¶ – 'Sayville'	CKen
– 'Sea Urchin'	CKen
– 'Uncatena'	CKen
– 'Verkade's Broom'	CKen

sylvestris AGM	CB&S CBra CDoC CGre CKin CPer CSam CSco EHar EHul ENot GRei IHos LBuc LCon LLin MAsh MBal MBar MGos NBee NWea SHBN SPer SReu STre WDin WMou WNor WStI
– 'Andorra'	CKen
§ – 'Argentea'	EHar LNet SHil
– 'Aurea' AGM	CKen CMac EBre EHar EHul IOrc LBre LCon LLin LNet MAsh MBal MBar NHol SHBN SHil SLim SSta
¶ – 'Avondene'	CKen
– 'Beuvronensis' AGM	CKen CMac EHar GAri LCon LLin LNet MAsh MBlu MGos NHol SLim SSta
– 'Bonna'	LCon
– 'Brevifolia'	LCon MBar NHol
– 'Buchanan's Gold'	CKen
– 'Burghfield'	CKen LCon NHol
– 'Chantry Blue'	LCon LLin MAsh MBar NHol SLim
– 'Compressa'	GAri
– 'Dereham'	CKen
– 'Doone Valley'	CKen
– 'Edwin Hillier'	See P. ***s.*** 'Argentea'
– 'Fastigiata'	CDoC CKen EHar LCon LLin MAsh MBar MBri NHar SLim SSta
– 'Frensham'	CKen LCon LLin NHol
– 'Gold Coin'	CBra CDoC CKen LCon LLin MBar MBri MGos SLim
– 'Gold Medal '	CKen LCon
– 'Grand Rapids'	CKen
– 'Green Flare'	CKen
– 'Hibernia'	ENHC LCon
– 'Hillside Creeper'	CKen SLim
– 'Inverleith' (v)	GAri LCon LLin MAsh MBar MGos NHol SLim
– 'Jade'	See P. ***s.*** 'Iceni'
– 'Jeremy'	CKen LCon LLin
– 'Kelpie'	CKen
– 'Kenwith'	CKen NHol
– 'Little Brolly'	CKen
– 'Lodge Hill'	CKen LCon LLin MAsh MBar MRPP NHol SLim
– 'Longmoor'	CKen
– 'Martham'	CKen
– 'Moseri'	See P. ***nigra maritima*** 'M.'
– 'Nana'	See P. ***s.*** 'Watereri'
– 'Pixie'	CKen LCon NHol
– 'Repens'	CKen
– 'Sandringham'	LCon NHol
– 'Saxatilis'	LCon NHol
¶ – 'Scrubby'	LCon
– 'Sentinel'	CKen
I – 'Skjak I'	CKen
I – 'Skjak II'	CKen
– 'Spaan's Slow Column'	CKen
– 'Tabuliformis'	CMCN
– 'Tage'	CKen
– 'Treasure'	CKen LCon
– 'Variegata'	NHol
§ – 'Watereri'	CDoC CMac EHul ENHC ENot IDai IHos IOrc LBee LCon LLin LNet LPan MAsh MBar MBri MGos NBar NHar NHol SLim SPer SSta WDin
tabuliformis	CLnd EHul LCon
taeda	LCon WCoo
thunbergii	CDoC CGre EArb EHar EHul LCon LLin MBal MBar MGos STre WCoo WFro WNor
– 'Akame'	CKen
– 'Banshosho'	CKen
– 'Dainagon'	CKen
– 'Iwai'	CKen
– 'Kotobuki'	CKen
– 'Ko-yo-sho'	CKen
– 'Kujaku'	CKen
– 'Nishiki-nee	CKen
§ – 'Sayonara'	CKen EBre GAri LBre LCon NHol
– 'Senryu'	CKen
– 'Shio-guro'	CKen
– 'Sunsho'	CKen
– 'Taihei'	CKen
– 'Yatsubusa'	See P. ***t.*** 'Sayonara'
uncinata	See P. ***mugo u.***
– 'Paradekissen'	CKen
virginiana	MBal
– 'Wate's Golden'	CKen
§ ***wallichiana***	CAbP CChu CDoC CKen CMCN CSco EHar EHul ENHC GRei IBar IOrc LCon LLin MBal MBar MGos NBee NHol NWyt SEng SLim STre WCoo WMou WWat
– 'Nana'	CKen MBar SHil
– 'Umbraculifera'	MBal
– 'Zebrina' (v)	LCon MBar
yunnanensis	LCon

PIPER (Piperaceae)
See Plant Deletions

PIPTANTHUS (Leguminosae/Papilionaceae)

forrestii	See P. ***nepalensis***
laburnifolius	See P. ***nepalensis***
§ ***nepalensis***	CB&S CBot CBra CCla CHEx CHan CMCN CMac CPle CSco ECha EHar ELan EPla IBar LHop MBri MFir MGos MWat SDix SHBN SHil SLon SMad SPer WBod WCru WDin
tomentosus	SDry

PISONIA (Nyctaginaceae)

brunoniana	See P. ***umbellifera***
§ ***umbellifera***	CHEx
– 'Variegata'	CHEx

PISTACIA (Anacardiaceae)

chinensis	CB&S EHar ELan
¶ ***terabinthus***	CFil

PISTIA (Araceae)

stratiotes	CBen MSta

PITTOSPORUM † (Pittosporaceae)

anomalum	ECou SDry
¶ 'Arundel Green'	ECou LRHS SDry
bicolor	ECou SArc
colensoi	ECou
¶ – 'Wanaka'	ECou
crassifolium	CB&S ECou SHil
¶ – 'Havering Dwarf'	ECou

¶ – 'Napier' ECou
– 'Variegatum' CGre LHop SHil
– x *tenuifolium* ECou
dallii CHEx SArc SHil
divaricatum ECou
¶ 'Essex' (v) ECou
eugenioïdes CB&S CGre
¶ – 'Platinum' CB&S
– 'Variegatum' AGM CB&S CGre EBre IOrc LBre SHil
'Garnettii' AGM CB&S CBot CBra CChe CCla CDec CLan CMHG CPle CSco CShe CTrw EBre EHoe ELan ENot IBlr IJoh IOrc ISea LBre LHop MAll MBal SLon SPer WAbe WDin WSHC WTyr
heterophyllum ECou
'Limelight' (v) CB&S CGre WWes
¶ *lineare* ECou
§ 'Margaret Turnbull' (v) CB&S COtt ECou IReg LHop
michiei ECou
obcordatum
var. *kaitaiaense* ECou
pimeleoïdes
var. *reflexum* ECou
ralphii ECou IBlr
– 'Green Globe' ECou
– 'Variegatum' SLon
'Saundersii' (v) CGre CKni CMHG ENot MBal
tenuifolium AGM CB&S CBra CSco CShe EBre ECou ELan ENot IDai ISea LBre LHop MAll MBal MBri MUlv NTow SDix SLon SReu STre WAbe WDin WOMN WStI WWat
– 'Abbotsbury Gold' (v) CAbb CBot CChe CCla CDoC CSam EBre ECou ELan LBre MAll SDry SHBN SHer SPer WSHC WStI WWeb
– 'Atropurpureum' CB&S CSco
¶ – 'Churchills' CChu
– 'County Park Dwarf' ECou WCru
– 'Deborah' (v) CB&S CBra EBre ECou LBre LHop
– 'Dixie' CMHG ECou
§ – 'Eila Keightley' (v) CDoC CMHG EHic IOrc MBal
– 'Gold Star' CB&S
– 'Golden King' CB&S CDoC CMHG IJoh MBal MRav MUlv
– 'Irene Paterson' AGM CAbb CB&S CChe CCla CGre CMHG CPle CSam CSco EBre ECou ELan ERav IJoh IOrc LBre LHop MAll MBal MGos MRav MUlv SDry SHer SLon SPer SPla SSta WAbe
– 'James Stirling' CDoC ECou IOrc SLon
– 'John Flanagan' See P. 'Margaret Turnbull'
¶ – 'Katie' CB&S
– 'Marjory Channon' (v) CB&S MUlv
– 'Nigricans' CB&S CLan CMHG GWht
– 'Nutty's Leprechaun' IMal
– 'Purpureum' CBot CBra CChe CMHG CPle CSam CTrw ELan IJoh IOrc MBal MRav SDry SHBN SHer SPer SPla WDin
*– 'Silver Dollar' MBri
– 'Silver Magic' CB&S
– 'Silver Queen' AGM CB&S CBow CBra CCla CGre CLan CMHG CSam CSco EBre ECou GWht IBar IDai IJoh IOrc ISea LAbb LBre MAll MBal MRav NKay SHBN SPer SPla WKif WSHC WStI
– 'Stirling Gold' (v) CB&S EWll
– 'Sunburst' See P. *t.* 'Eila Keightley'
– 'Tiki' CB&S
– 'Tom Thumb' AGM CB&S CBow CCla CMHG CTrw EBre ECou ECtt EHoe IBar IJoh IOrc IReg ISea LBre LHop MAll MBal MPla MUlv NRoo SDry SHBN SPer SPla SSta WAbe WSHC WStI WWat
– 'Tresederi' (m/f) CDoC CSco CTrw MBal
– 'Variegata' CB&S
– 'Warnham Gold' AGM CB&S CDoC CMHG COtt CSco CTrw EBre ECou ELan EPla IOrc ISea LBre MUlv SDry WAbe WDin WWat
– 'Wendle Channon' (v) CB&S CBow CBra CDoC CMHG CSam EBre ECot ECou IJoh LBre MAll MBal MUlv SHer SPer SPla WStI WWeb
– 'Winter Sunshine' SSta
tobira AGM CB&S CBot CCla CHEx CHan CLTr CMCN CMHG CNew CPle CTro ELan IJoh MAll MGos SArc SHBN SHil SPer SSta WEas
– 'Nanum' CB&S CCla ERea MUlv
– 'Variegatum' AGM CB&S CBot CDoC CGre CHEx CPle ERea LHop MBri SHil SPer SSta WSHC
undulatum CAbb CB&S CHEx CPle
– 'Variegatum' CGre

PITYROGRAMMA (Adiantaceae)

triangularis SBla

PLAGIANTHUS (Malvaceae)

betulinus See P. ***regius***
lyallii See HOHERIA *lyallii*
§ *regius* CGre ECou ISea SHil
– var. *chathamicus* IReg

PLAGIOMNIUM (moss)

affine LFle

PLANERA (Ulmaceae)

See Plant Deletions

PLANTAGO (Plantaginaceae)

asiatica 'Variegata' EHoe ELan EMon NSti WByw WHer
coronopus CKin EWFC
cynops EMon LRHS MTho WCot
¶ *lanceolata* ECWi EWFC
– 'Streaker' (v) CRDP CRow WCot
major EWFC
– B&L 12649 EMon GPoy WPla
– 'Atropurpurea' See P. *m.* 'Rubrifolia'
§ – 'Rosularis' CArn CGle CRDP CRiv CRow CTom CWGN ECha ECro ELan EMon GMac LHol MFir MTho NBro NFai NMir WBon WHal WHer WHil WRus WWye

§ – 'Rubrifolia' CBos CGle CRiv CRow CSFH CTom EBar ECha ECoo EHoe ELan EMar EMon LHol MFir NBro NFai NHar NMir NRed NSti SFis WHer
– 'Variegata' CRDP CRiv CRow ECro EFol LHol
maritima CKin
media CKin ECWi WNdy WPla
nivalis CLew ECro MFir NTow WDav WHer WThu
psyllium MSal
raoulii NHol
rosea See P. ***major*** 'Rosularis'
sempervirens ECro WHer

PLATANUS † (Platanaceae)

x *acerifolia* See P. x ***hispanica***
§ x ***hispanica*** AGM CB&S CDoC CGre CKin CLnd CSco CTho EHar EMil ENot IDai IJoh LBuc LPan MGos NWea SHBN SPer WDin WMou
– 'Bloodgood' WMou
– 'Liberty' WMou
– 'Suttneri' (v) CDoC SHil SMad WMou
occidentalis CSto
orientalis AGM CBow CLnd CMCN CSto EBre EHar IOrc LBre WCoo WMou
– 'Autumn Glory' WMou
§ – f. *digitata* CLnd CTho SHil SMad WMou
– var. *insularis* EHar
– 'Laciniata' See P. ***o. digitata***
– 'Mirkovec' CDoC IJoh MBri SMad SPer WMou

PLATYCARYA (Juglandaceae)

strobilacea CB&S CGre CMCN EArb

PLATYCERIUM (Polypodiaceae)

alcicorne hort. See P. ***bifurcatum***
§ *bifurcatum* AGM MBri
grande hort. See P. ***superbum***

PLATYCLADUS (Cupressaceae)

orientalis See THUJA ***o.***

PLATYCODON † (Campanulaceae)

grandiflorus AGM CGle CNic CSco CWGN ECha ECoo EPad GLil LHop MFir MHFP MHew MSal NBro NFai NKay NNor NOrc NWyt SAxl SFis SUsu WCla WCru WDav WHoo WOld WWye
– *albus* CBow CCla CSco ECro EFou ELan EPad LAbb LHop LWad MBri MBro NBro NFai NOak NTow SPer SSvw WHoo WPer WWin
– *apoyama* AGM CNic EPad EPot ESma GMac MBel MBro MCas MHig NKay SWas WAbe WHil WHoo WPer WWin
– – *albus* CNic ECro LGre SAxl SIde SWas WCru WEas
¶ – *apoyana* 'Fairy Snow' NHol
– 'Baby Blue' ECro
– blue CBow
– 'Blue Pearl' WHoo
– 'Blue Surf' SFis SSvw WPer
– 'Florist Rose' ECro EPad MWil NOak
– 'Florist Snow' ECro LGan NOak NPri
– 'Fuji Pink' CRDP NHol NPri NSti SPer WDav WHil
– 'Fuji White' CMil NHol WHil
– 'Hakone' CRDP EBee ECro LHop NCat SSte WHil WHoo
– 'Mammoth Blue' ECro NMir
– 'Mammoth White' ECro NMir
– *mariesii* AGM CBow CCla CGle CKel CNic EBre ECtt EFou ELan ENot EPad LBre MBal MBro MFir MHig NHol NPri SDix SFis SGil SIng SPer SSvw WEas WHoo WOMN WPer WTyr WWin
– – *albus* CNic MBro WHoo WOMN
– 'Misato Purple' NHol WHil
– 'Park's Double Blue' LGan MHFP NOak WHer WHoo
– 'Perlmutterschale' ('Mother of Pearl') CGle CMil EBre ECro ELan EPad LBre MBri WHoo
– *pumilus* GArf GMac NWCA WHoo
– *roseus* ECro EFou WHoo
¶ – 'Sentimental Blue' EPad
– 'Zwerg' LGre

PLECOSTACHYS (Compositae/Asteraceae)

§ *serpyllifolia* CCla CLTr ERom IHos LAbb LBlm SDix

PLECTOCOLEA (liverwort)

hyalina LFle

PLECTRANTHUS (Labiatae/Lamiaceae)

australis SLMG
behrii See P. ***fruticosus***
¶ *ciliatus* LHil
coleoïdes 'Marginatus' See P. ***forsteri*** 'M.'
– 'Variegatus' See P. ***madagascariensis*** 'Variegated Mintleaf'
§ *forsteri* 'Marginatus' CBar CLTr ERea ESma LHil MRav NFai SIde SLMG WHal
§ *fruticosus* LHil SLMG
§ *madagascariensis* 'Variegated Mintleaf' LHil
oertendahlii AGM EBak SLMG

PLEIOBLASTUS † (Gramineae/Poaceae-Bambusoideae)

akebono SBam SDry
§ *auricomus* AGM Widely available
– 'Bracken Hill' EPla ISta SBam SDry WJun
– f. *chrysophyllus* EPla SBam SDry WJun
§ *chino* EPla IJoh ISta LBam SBam SDry WJun
§ – f. *angustifolius* EPla ISta LBam LHil SBam SDry
– 'Aureostriatus' (v) EPla ISta SBam SDry
– *chrysanthus* See SASA ***chrysantha***
– f. *elegantissimus* EPla SBam SDry WJun
– 'Kimmei' SDry
– 'Murakamianus' SBam SDry
fortunei See P. ***variegatus***
'Gauntlettii' See P. ***humilis pumilus***
glaber 'Albostriata' (v) See SASAELLA ***masamuneana*** 'Albostriata'
gramineus EPla ISta SBam SDry WJun

§ ***hindsii*** hort.	EPla ISta SArc SBam SDry SHil WJun
§ ***humilis***	ELan SBam SHil
§ – var. ***pumilus***	CPMA CRow CSco CTom EHoe EPar EPla ISea ISta LBam MBlu MBri NHol SArc SBam SCob SDry SHil SPla WJun WNor WPat
kongosanensis 'Aureostriatus' (v)	EPla SBam SDry
linearis	EPla ISta SBam SDry WJun
oleosus	SDry WJun
§ ***pygmaeus***	CBar CCla CLew CPMA CRow CWit EFul EHoe ELan EPla IOrc ISea ISta MBar MBri MGos SBam SCob SDry SHil SIng SPer WJun
§ – var. ***distichus***	EFul EPla ISta LBam SArc SBam SCob SDry WJun
§ – 'Mirrezuzume'	EPla SBam WWat
shibuyanus 'Tsuboi'	COtt EPla SDry
§ ***simonii***	CHEx EFul ISta LBam SBam SCob SDry SHil
– var. ***heterophyllus***	See P. ***s. variegatus***
§ – ***variegatus***	EPla ISta LBam MBlu SBam SDry SPer WJun
§ ***variegatus*** **AGM**	Widely available
– var. ***viridis***	SDry
viridistriatus	See P. ***auricomus***

PLEIONE † (Orchidaceae)

§ ***albiflora***	WChr
Alishan	CNic SWes
'Asama'	SWes
aurita	WChr
'Berapi'	SWes
§ ***bulbocodioïdes***	EPot IBlr NHol NNrd
– 'Yunnan'	EPot
bulbocodioïdes Limprichtii Group **AGM**	CRiv EFEx EPot NNrd NTow SWes
– – 'Primrose Peach'	EPot SWes
– Pricei Group	See P. ***formosana***
x ***confusa***	EPot WChr
Danan	SWes
Eiger	EPot WChr
¶ Eiger cream form	EPot
El Pico	SWes
Erebus	SWes
Etna	SWes
§ ***formosana*** **AGM**	CAvo CNic CRiv EFEx ELan IBlr LAma MBri NHar NHol NTow SDeJ SHer SIng WChr
I – 'Alba'	CAvo CNic EPot IBlr NWCA
– 'Avalanche'	WChr
– 'Cairngorm'	WChr
– 'Clare'	CAvo EPot
I – 'Iris'	EPot NNrd
– 'Lilac Beauty'	EPot SWes
– 'Oriental Grace'	EFEx EPot NHol SWes
– 'Oriental Jewel'	SWes
– 'Oriental Splendour'	EPot NNrd SIng SWes
– Pricei Group	CNic EPot MCas NHol NTow
– 'Ruby Throat'	CNic
– 'Snow Cap'	EFEx NHol SWes
forrestii	CRDP EFEx EPot LAma NHol SWes WChr
Fuego	SWes
Hekla	EPot SWes
hookeriana	WChr
humilis	SDeJ WChr
Jorullo	SWes
Katla	SWes
maculata	SWes
'Myosin'	SWes
pinkepankii	See P. ***albiflora***
pogonioïdes hort.	See P. ***speciosa***
pogonioïdes Rolfe	See P. ***bulbocodioïdes***
praecox	SWes WChr
Shantung 'Muriel Harberd' **AGM**	EPot
– 'Piton'	LAma
¶ – 'Pixie'	EPot
– 'Ridgeway'	CAvo EPot
¶ – 'Silver Wedding'	EPot
¶ 'Soufrière'	EPot
§ ***speciosa***	CAvo EPot SWes WChr
¶ Stromboli	EPot
Tarawera	SWes
Tolima	EPot SWes
Tongariro	EPot
Versailles	EFEx LAma SWes
– 'Bucklebury' **AGM**	CNic EPot SWes
– 'Muriel Turner'	EPot LAma SWes
Vesuvius	EPot
yunnanensis hort.	See P. ***bulbocodioïdes*** 'Yunnan'
yunnanensis Rolfe	LAma NHol SWes

PLEOMELE See DRACAENA

PLEUROCHAETE (moss)

luteoalba	LFle

PLEUROSPERMUM (Umbelliferae/Apiaceae)

brunonis	CBos CLTr CRDP GTou WHal

PLUM See PRUNUS *domestica*

PLUMBAGO (Plumbaginaceae)

§ ***auriculata*** **AGM**	CB&S CLTr CNew CPle CRHN CTre CTro EBak EEls ELan ERav ERea ERom LAbb LBlm LHol LHop MBri MRav NEgg NPal NRog SIde SLMG SLon SPer WBod WEas
– var. ***alba***	CB&S CBot CBow CBrk CNew CRHN CTro EBak ELan EMil ERav ERea ERom IBlr LAbb LBlm LHol SHer SLMG SPer
capensis	See P. ***auriculata***
indica	CPle SLMG
– ***rosea***	CNew CTro
larpentiae	See CERATOSTIGMA ***plumbaginoïdes***
zeylanica	CPle

PLUMERIA (Apocynaceae)

forms	CNew
§ ***obtusa***	CNew
rubra	CNew CTro
'Singapore'	See P. ***obtusa***

PNEUMATOPTERIS See **CYCLOSORUS**

POA (Gramineae/Poaceae)
acicularifolia NHol
araratica ETPC
badensis 'Ingelkissen' ETPC
bulbosa ETPC
chaixii CElw EHoe EMon ETPC NHol
colensoi EHoe ETPC WDav
glauca ETPC
imbecilla ETPC
x ***jemtlandica*** NHol
nemoralis ETPC

PODALYRIA (Leguminosae/Papilionaceae)
calyptrata CTro

PODANTHUS (Compositae/Asteraceae)
ovatifolius G&K 4386 CGre

PODOCARPUS (Podocarpaceae)
acutifolius ECou GWht STre
andinus See PRUMNOPITYS ***andina***
chilinus See P. ***salignus***
cunninghamii See P. ***hallii***
dacrydioïdes See DACRYCARPUS ***d.***
ferrugineus See PRUMNOPITYS ***ferruginea***
'Golden Dwarf' See PRUMNOPITYS ***ferruginea*** 'G.D.'
§ ***hallii*** (m) ECou WBod WThu
– 'Roro' (m) ECou
– x ***nivalis*** (f) ECou
¶ ***henkelii*** CTro
lawrencei (f) ECou MBar MGos MPla SSmi WWat
– 'Alpine Lass' (f) ECou
– – ***acutifolius*** 'Autumn Shades' (m) ECou
lawrencei alpinus EHul GAri IBar IOrc MBar SBor
– – 'Blue Gem' (f) MAsh MBri MGos WWat
– – 'Bluey' CDoC LLin SLim WWat
– x ***nivalis*** 'Blaze' (f) ECou
– – 'Spring Sunshine' (f) ECou
– – 'Young Rusty' (f) ECou
macrophyllus CGre CMCN SArc SMad STre WWat
– 'Angustifolius' CHEx
nivalis (f) CMHG CMac CSco ECou EHar EPla GWht LLin MBar MHig MPla SBor SLon SPer SPla SSmi WThu WWat
– bronze EPla MBri
– 'Clarence' (m) ECou
– 'Green Queen' (f) ECou
– 'Jack's Pass' (m) ECou
– 'Little Lady' (f) ECou
– 'Livingstone' (f) ECou
– 'Lodestone' (m) ECou
– 'Moffatt' (f) ECou
– 'Otari' (m) ECou
– 'Park Cover' ECou
– 'Princess' (f) ECou
– 'Ruapehu' ECou
§ ***salignus*** AGM CB&S CChu CDoC CGre CHEx CLan CMer CPle IOrc ISea SArc WWat
spicatus See PRUMNOPITYS ***taxifolia***
totara CHEx CHan ECou STre
– 'Aureus' CB&S CDoC ECou EPla MBal MBar MUlv SHBN
– 'Pendulus' ECou

PODOLEPIS (Compositae/Asteraceae)
jaceoïdes MHig

PODOPHYLLUM (Berberidaceae)
emodi See P. ***hexandrum***
– var. ***chinense*** See P. ***hexandrum c***
§ ***hexandrum*** CBro CChu CCla CHEx CRDP CRow ECha EFou GAbr GCal GCra GDra GPoy MBal MBri MHig MSal MTol NHar NSti WDav
§ – var. ***chinense*** CPou LGre WCru WWat
– 'Majus' NHol SHig WCru
peltatum CArn CBro EBre EBul ECro GPoy LAma LBre MBri MSal NSti WChr WWat
versipelle ECro

PODRANEA (Bignoniaceae)
§ ***ricasoliana*** CNew CSpe CTro EMil ERea LHil LHop SLMG

POGONATHERUM (Gramineae/Poaceae)
paniceum See P. ***saccharoideum***
saccharoïdeum MBri

POGOSTEMON (Labiatae/Lamiaceae)
See Plant Deletions

POINSETTIA hort. See **EUPHORBIA *pulcherrima***

POLEMONIUM † (Polemoniaceae)
♦ ***acutifolium nipponicum*** See P. ***caeruleum n.***
♦ 'Apricot Beauty' See P. ***carneum*** 'Apricot Delight'
N ***archibaldiae*** WCot
boreale ECro GGar GTou LCot NHol
brandegeei ECro ESma MHig NBro NRed SMrm SUsu WByw WDav WPer
– JCA 9501 CNic
– ssp. ***mellitum*** CArn GCHN LCot MSto NTow
caeruleum Widely available
– ***album*** Widely available
– ssp. ***amygdalinum*** 'Album' NHol
– 'Blue Bell' CGle NMir NNrd
¶ – ***dissectum album*** CBre
– dwarf form CNic
♦ – Himalayan misapplied See P. ***cashmerianum***
– ssp. ***himalayanum*** CRDP GCra WCot WPer
– 'Hopleys' CBre CHan CSco ECha GCal LHop NBrk WByw WCot
♦ – 'Humile' See P. x ***richardsonii***
¶ – 'Lewdon Farm' CLew
§ – var. ***nipponicum*** NNrw WPer

carneum	CChu CGle EBre ECha EMon EOrc LBre LWad MNFA MTho NHar NMir NNrw SHer SUsu WOMN WPer WWin
§ – 'Apricot Delight'	CBre CElw CHan CMil ECoo ECro ELan ESis ESma GAbr GBri GMac MHFP NBir NNrw NOak NRar WCot WHil WSun WThi
cashmerianum	CBre CChu CHan ECro EMon ESma GAbr GCHN NOak SFis SHer WEas WHen WHoo WSun
'Churchills'	CBre CChu
confertum	See P. ***viscosum***
delicatum	CNic MTho NHar NWCA
¶ *eximium*	EBee
flavum	See P. ***foliosissimum flavum***
N *foliosissimum* A Gray	CBot CCla CGle CHan CSco EBre ECha EJud GMac LBre SCro WHen WPer
– 'Album'	See P. ***f. alpinum***
§ – var. *alpinum*	CMea ECro NBir SCro
– *flavum*	CBre CHan GAbr LCot MHig NSti WHil
♦ *foliosissimum* hort.	See P. ***archibaldiae***
'Glebe Cottage Lilac'	CGle CMil
¶ 'Hannah Billcliffe'	LCot
x *jacobaea*	WCot
§ 'Lambrook Mauve' AGM	CChu CElw CGle CHan CLew EBre ECha EFol EOrc GAbr GCal LBre MBro MHFP MNFA MSte MTho MUlv NBrk NTow SUsu SWas WAbb WHoo WRus WSun
pauciflorum	CBre CGle CMea ECro ELan EMon EOrc ESis ESma LHop LWad MTho NBir NMir NNrw NOak SMrm SSvw SUsu WAbe WCla WEas WHal WHer WHil WOMN WPer WRus WWin WWye
¶ – silver-leaved	MHFP
pulchellum Salisbury	See P. ***reptans***
pulchellum Turczaninow	See P. ***caeruleum***
¶ *pulchellum* Willdenow	CBre NHol NRed WCot
pulcherrimum	CBre CTom EBre ECro ELan EPla ESma GAbr GCal GTou LBre LHil LHop NBro NHar WHen WPer
– *calycinum*	LCot
– ssp. *pulcherrimum*	NHol SPer
– 'Tricolor'	NFai NNrw SFis WDav
reptans	CArn CLew GBar GCra GPoy LHol MHew MSal MTho NBro NHar WDav WEas WPer WWye
– 'Blue Pearl'	CBow CBre CGle CLew CMGP CMea CSco ECro EFol GAri NCat NHol NNrw NRoo SPer SUsu WByw WHen
– 'Dawn Flight'	EBre LBre NCat
– 'Firmament'	NHol
– 'Lambrook Manor'	See P. 'Lambrook Mauve'
– 'Pink Beauty'	CMGP EFou ELan EMon LRHS MTol NCat NFai SPer
§ x *richardsonii*	ELan EMon LRHS NKay WEas
'Sapphire'	CBre CSco ELan EMon MBel NNor
scopulinum	NHol WPer
'Sonia's Bluebell'	CGle
§ *viscosum*	EBee ESma GBuc GCHN LCot LGre LHil MSto WByw WDav WHen
yezoense	NNrw WCot WGwy WPer

POLIANTHES (Agavaceae)

geminiflora	LAma LBow WChr
tuberosa AGM	CAvo CB&S NRog
– 'The Pearl' (d)	LAma SHer SLMG

POLIOTHYRSIS (Flacourtiaceae)

sinensis	CAbP CB&S CChu CGre CMCN CPle LBuc SMad WWat WWes

POLYGALA (Polygalaceae)

calcarea	MHig NHar NKay SIng WOMN WPat
– Bulley's form	CLew LBee SIng
– 'Lillet' AGM	CFee ELan EPot LHop LMer MHig MSto MTho SIng SWas WPat WWin
chamaebuxus AGM	CFee EBre GDra GGGa LBre MBal MBro MHig MPla NHar NHol NKay SHer WHil WThu WWin
– *alba*	LBee WAbe
§ – var. *grandiflora* AGM	Widely available
– 'Kamniski'	CMHG EPot GGGa
– 'Loibl'	EPot GGGa GPlt MAsh SBla
– 'Purpurea'	See P. ***c. grandiflora***
– 'Rhodoptera'	See P. ***c. grandiflora***
§ x *dalmaisiana* AGM	CAbb CB&S CBar CDoC CLTr CSPN EMil ERea LBlm LHil LHop SBla WBod
'Dolomite'	GGGa
myrtifolia	CBrk CFee CPle CTre CTro IBlr SChu SMrm SUsu
– 'Grandiflora'	See P. x ***dalmaisiana***
virgata	CArn ERea
vulgaris	EWFC IOrc

POLYGONATUM (Liliaceae/Convallariaceae)

§ *biflorum*	CBro CCla CPou CSpe EBre ELan GCHN LBre LWad MSal NRoo SMad WCru WHer
– dwarf form	WChr WCot
canaliculatum	See P. ***biflorum***
cirrhifolium	WCru
commutatum	See P. ***biflorum***
curvistylum	CRDP SWas
cyrtonema misapplied	See DISPOROPSIS ***pernyi***
§ *falcatum*	CHan CRiv CRow EBre EBul ELan EMon ERav LBre MBal MSto NOak SIng WAbe WChr WThu WWin
– 'Variegatum'	CBos CChu CDoC CMil CSpe ECha EFou ELan EPar LGre MBri NDea NHol NSti SBla SCro
'Falcon'	See P. ***humile***
geminiflorum	SWas
giganteum	See P. ***biflorum***
graminifolium	EPot LGre
§ *hirtum*	EBul EMon EPla SPou
hookeri	Widely available
§ *humile*	CGle CRDP EPot MBel SWas WCot WHal WRus
§ x *hybridum* AGM	Widely available
– 'Flore Pleno'	WHer

§ – 'Striatum' (v)	CAvo CBos CBot CPou CRow EBre ECha EFol EPla IDai LBre MBal MBel MBri MHig MRav MUlv NBar NDea NHar NOak NOrc NRoo SBla SGil SHer WHal WHil
– 'Variegatum'	See P. x *h.* 'Striatum'
latifolium	See P. ***hirtum***
multiflorum hort.	See P. x ***hybridum***
– ***giganteum***	See P. ***biflorum***
multiflorum Linnaeus	EBul NHol WHil
§ ***odoratum***	CBro CRow EBul EPar EPla EPot MSal NRya SPou WHil
– 'Flore Pleno' **AGM**	ECha MCas SPou WChr
– 'Grace Barker'	See P. x ***hybridum*** 'Striatum'
– Kew form	EPot
– 'Silver Wings'	ECha SPou
N– 'Variegatum'	CBro CChu CCla CRDP EBul EFol EGol ELun EOrc EPla LGan LGre MBal MCas NRoo NRya SPer SPla WCru WRus WWat WWin
officinale	See P. ***odoratum***
pumilum	See P. ***falcatum***
racemosum	SIng
roseum	CRDP SPou WThu
sp. Ewlat	SPou
sp. Himalaya	WCru
sp. SS&W	CRDP
verticillatum	CTom ECha EPla EPot LBuc MBal NHol WWat
– ***rubrum***	CArn ECha MSte MUlv SPou SWas

POLYGONUM † (Polygonaceae)

	See also PERSICARIA
affine	See PERSICARIA ***affinis***
amplexicaule	See PERSICARIA ***amplexicaulis***
aubertii	See FALLOPIA ***baldschuanica***
baldschuanicum	See FALLOPIA ***baldschuanica***
bistorta	See PERSICARIA ***bistorta***
cuspidatum	See FALLOPIA ***japonica***
equisetiforme hort.	See P. ***scoparium***
♦***molle***	See PERSICARIA ***mollis***
polystachyum	See PERSICARIA ***wallichii***
reynoutria	See FALLOPIA ***japonica compacta***
§ ***scoparium***	CRow EPla LHil MUlv NFai NSti SDry

POLYMNIA (Compositae/Asteraceae)

See Plant Deletions

POLYPODIUM † (Polypodiaceae)

aureum **AGM**	CTro
– ruffled form	NMar
australe	See P. ***cambricum***
§ ***cambricum***	NHar NKay NMar WCot WFib WRic
§ – 'Barrowii'	NKay NMar WRic
– 'Cristatum'	WRic
– 'Oakley'	WAbe
– 'Prestonii'	WRic
– 'Wilharris'	CFil NKay WRic
x ***font-queri***	WRic
¶ ***glycyrrhiza***	WRic
– 'Longicaudatum'	NMar WRic
interjectum	EFer NMar WAbe WFib WRic WWat
¶ – 'Bifidograndiceps'	WRic
– 'Cornubiense'	CBos CFil CRDP CWGN ECha EFer EMon EPla GCal NBir NBro NHar NHol NKay NMar NVic SDix SPer SWas WAbe WFib WRic
¶ – 'Glomeratum Mullins'	WRic
¶ – 'Ramosum Millman'	WRic
malhattense (fertile form)	WRic
¶ ***mallhatense*** (sterile form)	WRic
x ***mantoniae***	NKay
scouleri	NBro
x ***shivasiae***	NKay
vulgare	CBar CKin CWGN ECWi GPoy MBal NBro NEgg NHol NKay NMar NOrc SCob SPer WFib WRic
– 'Acutum'	NMar
– 'Bifidocristatum'	NHar NHol NKay WFib WWat
– 'Bifidograndiceps'	NMar
§ – 'Congestum Cristatum'	NKay WRic
¶ – 'Cornubiense Grandiceps'	WRic
– 'Cornubiense Multifidum'	NHar NKay
– 'Crispum Cristatum'	See P. *v.* 'Congestum Cristatum'
– 'Elegantissimum'	WRic
– 'Jean Taylor'	See P. *v.* 'Congestum Cristatum'
– 'Longicaudatum'	WFib
¶ – 'Macrostachyon'	WRic
– 'Omnilacerum Oxford'	WRic
vulgare Cristatum Group 'Forster'	NKay SWas
– Pulcherrimum Group	EGol NHar NKay SWas
– – 'Pulcherrimum Addison'	WRic
– – 'Pulcherrimum May'	WRic
– – 'Pulchritudine'	WRic
– Ramosum Group	NMar
– Semilacerum Group	NMar WRic
– – 'Falcatum O'Kelly'	WRic
– – 'Jubilee'	NMar WRic
– – 'Robustum'	WRic

POLYPOGON (Gramineae/Poaceae)

viridis	ETPC

POLYSCIAS (Araliaceae)

'Elegans'	MBri
fruticosa	MBri
scutellaria 'Pennockii' (v)	MBri

POLYSTICHUM † (Dryopteridaceae)

acrostichoïdes	IOrc NHar NMar
aculeatum **AGM**	CBar EBre EBul ECha EHon ELan IOrc LBre LWad MBri NHar NHol NKay SRms WFib WRic

aculeatum Grandiceps Group	NMar WFib
andersonii	NHar NHol
braunii	CB&S EGol WRic
¶ ***californicum***	CFil
♦ ***caryotideum***	See CYRTOMIUM ***c.***
¶ ***discretum***	SWas
♦ ***falcatum***	See CYRTOMIUM ***f.***
falcinellum	CFil NKay
fallax	WRic
♦ ***fortunei***	See CYRTOMIUM ***f.***
imbricans	NHar
¶ ***interjectum***	SPla
lonchitis	NKay
makinoi	NHol WCot
¶ ***mohrioïdes***	CFil
munitum	CFil IOrc NHar NHol NOrc SWas WFib WRic
polyblepharum	CBar CFil EBre ELan EPla IOrc LBre MBri NHar NHol NMar SBla SPla SRms WAbe WCot WFib WHal WRic
proliferum hort.	See P. ***setiferum*** Acutilobum Group
proliferum (R.Br.) C. Presl.	SApp
rigens	NHar NHol NMar SMad WRic
§ ***setiferum*** AGM	CBar CFil CKin CSam CSpe CWGN EBre EFer EFou EGol ELan IOrc LBre LWad MBri NBee NEgg NHol NOrc SApp SArc SBla SCob SIng SPer WEas WFib WHow WStI
– ***angulare***	See P. ***setiferum***
– ***cristatogracile***	See P. ***s.*** Percristatum Group
¶ – 'Cristatopinnulum'	CFil
– 'Foliosum'	NKay
– 'Imbricatum'	NKay
– ***proliferum***	See P. ***s.*** Acutilobum Group
– 'Pulcherrimum Bevis'	NKay SDix SWas WRic
*– ***ramopinnatum***	NMar
*– ***ramulosum***	NMar
N– 'Wollaston'	NBar
¶ ***setiferum*** 'Plumosomultilobum'	WRic
¶ – 'Vivien Green'	WRic
§ – Acutilobum Group	CB&S CFil CRDP EBul ECha EPot GAri LWad MBal NHar NKay SCob SDix SMad WAbe WCot
¶ – Congestum Cristatum Group	WRic
– Congestum Group	CRDP IOrc MBri NHar NHol NKay NMar SApp SMad SPla SRms WFib WRic
– Cristatum Group	SApp
– Dahlem Group	ECha ELan SCob SMad WRic
– Divisilobum Group	CDec CFil CWGN EBre EFer ELan EPar LBre MBri MBro MNFA NHol NKay NMar SMad SPer SPla SRms WBon WEas WFib WHoo WRic
– – 'Divisilobum Densum'	MBal NMar NOrc
– – 'Divisilobum Grandiceps'	WRic
– – 'Divisilobum Iveryanum'	NHol NMar SRms WFib WRic
– – 'Herrenhausen'	EBre ECha ELan LBre MBri NMar NOrc SPer WRic
– – 'Mrs Goffy'	NMar
– Lineare Group	CFil NKay SApp
– Multilobum Group	WRic
§ – Percristatum Group	NHar NMar
– Perserratum Group	NKay
– Plumosodivisilobum Group	CMil EGol NHar SApp SDix SPla WAbe WCru
– – 'Baldwinii'	NMar
– Plumosum Group	CBar CNic CSam CSpe CWGN NOrc WFib WHow WStI
– Rotundatum Group	CRDP NMar WRic
stenophyllum	CFil WRic
tsussimense	CBar CRDP EFou MBri NHol NMar SMad SMrm SRms WFib WRic
yunnanense	WRic

POLYXENA (Liliaceae/Hyacinthaceae)

ensifolia	See P. ***pygmaea***
odorata	LBow
§ ***pygmaea***	LBow

POMADERRIS (Rhamnaceae)

See Plant Deletions

POMEGRANATE See PUNICA *granatum*

PONCIRUS (Rutaceae)

§ ***trifoliata***	CB&S CBra CChu CCla CDoC CGre CLan CMCN CPle CTro ECtt EHar ELan EMil ENot ERea MBlu SArc SHil SMad SPer STre WCru WDin WNor WWat

PONTEDERIA (Pontederiaceae)

cordata AGM	CBen CRDP CRiv CRow CWGN EBre ECha ECtt EHon ELan EMFW EWav LBre LMay MSta NDea SHig SWat SWyc WChe WHol
– ***alba***	CRow NDea SWyc
§ – var. ***lancifolia***	CRiv CRow EMFW MSta SRms SWat SWyc
dilatata	CRDP SRms
lanceolata	See P. ***cordata lancifolia***

POPULUS † (Salicaceae)

alba	CDoC CKin CLnd CPer EBre ENot GRei IDai LBre LBuc MBar MRav NBee NWea SHBN SPer WDin WMou WStI WWin
– 'Bolleana'	See P. ***a. pyramidalis***
§ – f. ***pyramidalis***	CB&S WMou
– 'Raket' ('Rocket')	CLnd CTho EHar ELan ENot MGos SPer
– 'Richardii'	CBot CCla CGre CSco CTho CWit EBre ECtt EFol EHar EPla LBre MBar MUlv SHil SMad SMrm SPer WMou
§ 'Balsam Spire' AGM	CDoC CLnd ENot GRei LBuc NWea WMou
§ ***balsamifera***	CDoC ELan EMil ENot MGos NWea SHBN SPer WDin
x ***berolinensis***	CDoC

x ***canadensis***	
'Aurea' **AGM**	CDoC CLnd CSco EMil ENot MRav SPer WDin WMou
– 'Eugenei' (m)	ENot WMou
– 'Robusta' (m)	CDoC CKin CLnd EMil ENot LBuc NWea WDin WMou
– 'Serotina' (m)	CDoC CTho EHar GRei NWea WDin WMou
x ***candicans***	WDin
– 'Aurora'	CB&S CCla CKin CPle CSco CTrw EBre EHar EHoe ELan ENot GRei IDai IJoh ISea LBre LBuc MBar MBri NBar NBee NRar NWea SHBN SMad SPer SReu SSta WDin
x ***canescens***	CDoC ELan WDin WMou
– 'De Moffart' (m)	ENot
x ***euroamericana***	See P. x ***canadensis***
lasiocarpa **AGM**	EHar ELan ENot SHil SMad SPer WMou
§ – var. ***tibetica***	CBot EHar WMou
nigra	EHar ELan ENot WDin WMou
¶ – (f)	EHar
¶ – (m)	EHar
– ssp. ***betulifolia*** **AGM**	CKin CTho LBuc MGos WMou
¶ – ssp. ***betulifolia*** (f)	EHar
¶ – ssp. ***betulifolia*** (m)	EHar
N – var. ***italica*** **AGM**	CB&S CDoC CLnd CMHG CTho EBre ELan ENot LBre LBuc MBri MGos NWea SHBN SPer WDin
– 'Italica Aurea'	See P. 'Lombardy Gold'
§ – 'Lombardy Gold' (m)	EHar ELan GRei LMer SMad WMou
– 'Pyramidalis'	See P. ***n. italica***
simonii	CTho
– 'Fastigiata'	WMou
tacamahaca	See P. ***balsamifera***
'Tacatricho 32'	See P. 'Balsam Spire'
tremula **AGM**	CKin CLnd CPer EBre EHar ELan ENot GRei LBre LBuc MBar NBee NWea SHBN SPer WDin WMou
§ – 'Erecta'	CLnd EHar EMil SMad WMou
– 'Fastigiata'	See P. ***t.*** 'Erecta'
– 'Pendula' (m)	CLnd EHar SHil WDin WMou
trichocarpa	EHar GRei
– 'Fritzi Pauley' (f)	WMou
violascens	See P. ***lasiocarpa tibetica***
wilsonii	WMou
yunnanensis	WMou

PORTULACA (Portulacaceae)

grandiflora	MBri
oleracea	CArn EHer GPoy MChe SIde WHer WOMN WWye
– ***aurea***	EHer MChe

POTAMOGETON (Potamogetonaceae)

crispus	CBen EHon EMFW SAWi SRms SWyc
pectinatus	EHon

POTATO See SEED Supplier's Index

POTENTILLA † (Rosaceae)

alba	CGle CMil CNic CShe EBar ECha EFou ELan EMar GCHN ISea LGro MCas MNFA MRav MTho NHol NRoo NSti SAxl SCro SPer SUsu WByw WCra WPer WTyr
alchimilloïdes	CLew CTom MHig SOkh WPer
alpicola	WPer
ambigua	See P. ***cuneata***
anserina	CArn CKin ECWi GBar WHer
– 'Ortie' (v)	CNat
I – 'Variegata'	WHer
anserinoïdes	GCal WCot
arbuscula D Don	See P. ***fruticosa a.***
arbuscula hort.	See P. ***fruticosa*** 'Elizabeth'
argentea	CMGP EBar ELan GAul MBel NFai WCla WCru WPer
– 'Calabre'	EFol GAbr
– ***glabra***	SIgm WWin
argyrophylla	See P. ***atrosanguinea a.***
atrosanguinea	CBre CGle CHad CHan CMea CRDP CSco CShe ECas ECha ELun EOrc GCal GTou LGan LGre MBal MBri MRav NFai NHol NKay NNor NSti SUsu WCru WEas WHoo WSHC WTyr
§ – var. ***argyrophylla***	CGle CHan CMHG ECro ELan GCHN GCal GTou LGan LHop MBel NBir NBro NFai NMir NOak NRed SCro SUsu WAbe WByw WHal WHil WPer WTyr WWin
– var. ***argyrophylla*** SS&W 7768	GAbr GDra MPla MSte NGre
– var. ***leucochroa***	See P. ***a. argyrophylla***
aurea	CBow CLew ECtt ELan EMNN MBri MTho NMen NMir NOrc NWCA SHer SIng SSmi
– 'Aurantiaca'	GCHN MRav NNrd NRoo SBod SHer SUsu
§ – ssp. ***chrysocraspeda***	EGle MSto NHol NKay NMen NNrd NRoo
§ – 'Goldklumpen'	EFou EPla GAbr NBar SCro
– 'Plena'	CNic GCHN GDra GTou MRav NHar NNrd SBod SHer WWin
'Blazeaway'	CB&S CBow CMil MBel MBri NCat
calabra	ECha EMar MSto WByw WPer
§ ***cinerea***	CLew CRiv CShe CSpe CTom ELan MCas NHar NMen NNrd SIgm SSmi WAbe
§ ***crantzii***	CMea CTom EWFC GCHN GTou LBlm MBar MCas MHig MSte NMen NNrd NTow SIng WCla WHil WPer WThu
– ***nana***	WPer
– 'Pygmaea'	ECtt GPlt
§ ***cuneata*** **AGM**	CLew CNic CRiv CTom ELan ESis GDra GTou MHig MPla MTho NHar NKay NMen NWCA SIng SSmi WPer WWin
*– ***aurea***	ECro
delavayi	MBro NHol
detommasii	WPer
dickinsii	NTow
dombeyi	GCHN NHol
*'Emilie'	GCal

§ ***erecta***	CArn CKin ECWi GBar GPoy MChe MHew MSal
eriocarpa	CNic EMNN GArf GCHN GDra MBro MFir MHig MNFA MPla MWat NGre NHar NKay NMen NNrd NRed NRoo SBod SHer SSmi WAbe WCla
*– 'Aurea'	NGre
'Etna'	CElw CHad CSco ECtt EJud ELan EMon GAbr GCal GCra GTou LGre MFir NBrk NCat NFai NNor NRoo SMad WByw WCru WDav WHen WMer WPer
'Everest'	See P. ***fruticosa*** 'Mount Everest'
'Fireflame'	ECha
fissa	LBlm MBri MSte
'Flambeau'	WRus
'Flamenco'	CB&S CSam CSco ELan MBri MRav NCat NFai NRoo WAbb WByw WHoo WOld WTyr
fragiformis	See P. ***megalantha***
fruticosa	LAbb LBuc NHar NMen
– 'Abbotswood' AGM	CB&S CBot CMHG CMer CSco EGol EHar ELan ENot GRei IDai IJoh LHop MBal MBar MBri MGos NNor NRoo NSti SPer WBod WDin WHCG WSHC WWat WWeb
– 'Abbotswood Silver'	CB&S CBow CDoC CMHG CPle CSco ECtt EFol ELan MRav NHol NMen SHer SPla WHCG WWat WWeb
– 'Annette'	CDoC CSco WHCG
– var. ***arbuscula*** KW 5774	WWeb
– 'Argentea Nana'	See P. *f.* 'Beesii'
– 'Barnbarroch'	SIng
– 'Beanii'	NHol SPer WWeb
§ – 'Beesii' AGM	CBot CBow CDoC CSco CShe EHar ELan EPla ESis IDai MBar MBlu MBri MPla NHol NKay NRoo SIng SPer WAbe WDin WHCG WSHC WWat WWeb WWin
– 'Beverley Surprise'	SPer WWeb
– 'Buttercup'	WHCG WWeb
– 'Cascade'	LHop WHCG
*– 'Chelsea Star'	WHCG
– 'Clotted Cream'	MBar
– 'Dart's Cream'	MBri
– 'Dart's Golddigger'	CB&S ECtt MBal NHol NRoo NSti SLPl WHCG WWeb
– 'Dart's Nugget'	WHCG WWeb
– var. ***davurica***	WHCG
– – 'Hersii'	See P. *f.* 'Snowflake'
– – 'Rhodocalyx'	CPle EPla MGos WHCG WPat WWat
– 'Daydawn' AGM	Widely available
*– 'Donard Orange'	NNor
– 'Eastleigh Cream'	CCla SPer
§ – 'Elizabeth' AGM	Widely available
– 'Farreri'	See P. *f.* 'Goldkugel'
♦– 'Farreri Prostrata'	See P. *f.* 'Pyrenaica'
– 'Floppy Disc'	CDoC ECtt ELan EPla MGos SHBN SPer SPla
– 'Frances Lady Daresbury'	ISea MPla WWeb
– 'Friedrichsenii'	WWeb
– 'Glenroy Pinkie'	EBee EPla MBal WAbe WHCG
– 'Glenroy Seashell'	MBal
– 'Goldcharm'	NKay
– 'Goldfinger ' AGM	CChe CDoC CMer EBre ELan ENot GRei IOrc LBre LHop MBri MGos MRav MWat SPla WAbe WDin WHCG WStI WWeb
§ – 'Goldkugel' ('Gold Drop')	ENot NHol NNor SPla WHCG WStI WWeb
– 'Goldrush'	CSco
– 'Goldstar'	CBot CDoC CMHG EBre EPla GAri GCHN IOrc LBre MBri MGos SIng SSta WHCG WPat WWeb
– 'Goldteppich'	MBar NBar SHBN
– 'Goscote'	MGos
– 'Hachmann's Gigant'	WWeb
– 'Hopleys Little Joker'	WPat WWin
– 'Hopleys Orange'	CB&S CBow CDoC CMHG CSco EPla GAri GCHN LHop MBri SHer WGor WHCG WPat WWin
– 'Hurstbourne'	WWeb
– 'Jackman's Variety'	CChe CDoC CSam CSco ECtt ENot SPer WBod WDin WWeb
– 'Judith'	WWeb
– 'Katherine Dykes' AGM	CBow CChe CDoC CPle CSco ELan ENot GDra IDai MBal MBar NHol SLon SPer SReu WBod WDin WHCG WStI WWeb
– 'Klondike' AGM	CB&S CDoC CLan CSco ELan IDai MAsh NNor NRoo NWea WAbe WDin WWeb
– 'Knap Hill'	ENot WWeb
*– 'Knap Hill Buttercup'	EPar GDra GRei MPit NNor SHer WWeb
– 'Kobold'	MBar WWeb
– 'Logan'	WWeb
– 'London Town'	CMHG SLon
– 'Longacre Variety' AGM	CSco GDra GRei MBar NWea SLPl SLon WBod WWat WWeb
– 'Maanelys' ('Moonlight') AGM	CPle CSco CTrw ECtt ELan MBal MWat NRoo NWea SPer WDin WHCG WWeb
§ – var. ***mandshurica*** 'Manchu'	CCla CLew CMHG CSco ENot EPar GDra IDai MBar MBri MPla MRav NHol NNor SChu SHBN SIng SLon SPer SPla SSta WEas WSHC WWat WWeb WWin
*– 'Medicine Wheel Mountain'	EHal ELan NTow SPer WHCG WWeb
– 'Milkmaid'	WWeb
§ – 'Mount Everest'	CChe CDoC ELan MBar MPla MWat NHol NWea WBod WHCG WWeb
– 'Nana Argentea'	See P. ***fruticosa*** 'Beesii'
– 'Northman'	WWeb
– 'Nugget'	See P. *f.* 'Dart's Nugget'
– 'Ochroleuca'	WWeb
– 'Orange Star'	MPla NHol WWeb
– 'Orange Stripe'	WWeb
– 'Orangeade'	MAsh SPla
– var. ***parvifolia***	EPla
– 'Pastel Pink'	LHop
– 'Peaches and Cream'	EBee EPla WWeb
– 'Perryhill'	SPer
– 'Pink Glow'	GDra
– 'Pink Pearl'	EBre LBre NSti WWin
– 'Pink Queen'	MBro NHar WDav

– 'Pretty Polly' CDoC CMHG COtt CSco EBre ELan EPla IOrc LBre LHop MBar MBlu MBri MGos MPla MRav NHol NRoo SHBN SLon SPer SPla SSta WDin WHCG WStI WWeb
– 'Primrose Beauty' AGM CBow CLan CPle CSco CShe CTre ELan ENot ISea MBal MBar MBri MGos MPla NNor NRoo SLon WBod WDin WHCG WStI WWat WWeb
§ – 'Princess' ('Blink') CCla CSco EBre EHar ELan GRei IJoh LBre MBal MBar MBri MGos MWat NHar NHol NRoo SMad SPer SReu WDin WHCG WRus WStI WWat WWeb
– 'Prostrate Copper' GAbr NHol
¶ – 'Pumila' WPat
– 'Pumila' CC 312 GTou
§ – 'Pyrenaica' SIng
– 'Red Ace' CBra CMer CPle CSco EBre EHar ELan ENot GRei IJoh LBre LHop MBar MBri MGos MWat NHol NRoo SMad SPer SReu WBod WDin WHCG WWeb
– 'Red Robin' EBre GCHN GRei LBre MAsh MBri MGos NBar NRoo SPer WDin
– 'Royal Flush' CBra CCla CPle GAri LHop MAsh MBar MBri WHCG WStI
– 'Ruth' SHil WWeb
– 'Sandved' IDai WWeb
– 'Silver Schilling' LHop
– 'Snowbird' MAsh
§ – 'Snowflake' CB&S NHar WHCG WWeb
– 'Sophie's Blush' CBow CLTr IBar MBal NHol NRoo NSti WSHC WWeb
– 'Sunset' CB&S CBow CChe CDoC CSam CSco ELan ENot GDra GPlt MBal MBar MBri MGos MPla NKay NNor NWea SPer SReu SSta WStI WWeb
– 'Tangerine' AGM CB&S CBow CBra CLan CPle CTre CTrw ELan ENot GRei IDai IJoh ISea MBal MBar MWat NHol NKay NRoo NWea SIng SLon SPer WAbe WBod WDin WHCG WWat WWeb WWin
– 'Tilford Cream' AGM CBow CChe CMHG CSco EBre ELan ENot GDra IJoh LBre MBar MBri MPla MRav MWat NHol NRoo SHBN SHer SPer SReu WDin WHCG WStI WWat WWeb
– 'Tom Conway' MUlv WHCG
§ – 'Veitchii' CBow CCla CDoC CPle CSco NHol SHBN SPer WHCG WStI WWeb
– 'Vilmoriniana' CBot CBow CSco EFol ELan IDai NNor SHil SIng SLon SMad SPer WAbe WHCG WSHC WWat WWeb
– 'Walton Park' MBal WWeb
– 'Wessex Silver' CDoC WHCG
– 'Whirlygig' CPle WHCG
– 'White Rain' CLTr CMer GDra NNor WWeb
– 'William Purdom' WHCG WWeb
– 'Yellow Carpet' WHCG
– 'Yellow Giant' WWeb
– 'Yellow Star' LHop
– var. ***arbuscula*** hort. See P. ***f.*** 'Elizabeth'
♦***fulgens*** See P. ***lineata***
gelida See P. ***crantzii ternata***

'Gibson's Scarlet' AGM Widely available
glandulosa EBee MFir WPer
'Gloire de Nancy' CBos ELan MRav NBir SPer
'Gold Clogs' See P. ***aurea*** 'Goldklumpen'
'Grace Darling' CWit
gracilis NNrd
§ – var. ***glabrata*** EBee
♦– ***nuttallii*** See P. ***g. glabrata***
– var. ***pulcherrima*** NHol
'Helen Jane' CBre CDoC CGle EFou ESma LHop NBir NBro NCat NFai NHol SChu SMrm WAbb WMer WPer WPla WTyr
x ***hopwoodiana*** CBos CGle CHad MUlv NBir SWas WAbb WByw
hyparctica nana LBee NHol WPat
* 'Limelight' CKni ELan EPla MAsh SPla
§ ***lineata*** EMon
'Mandshurica' See P. ***fruticosa mandshurica*** 'Manchu'
'Master Floris' GCal
§ ***megalantha*** AGM Widely available
'Melton' CSco EFou NBir NBrk NOak WElm WHen
'Monsieur Rouillard' CGle CRDP EBar GAbr MBel MUlv MWat NBrk NBro NHol NNor NNrw NRoo SUsu WByw WCru WHoo
montana CTom GCHN NHol WHer WPer
nepalensis CHan CNic CRDP ECha ECro GAbr LAbb MFir NBro NNor NSti SAxl SSvw SWas WCru WHoo WWat
– 'Kirsten' MHig WHil
§ – 'Miss Willmott' AGM Widely available
– 'Roxana' CGle CSco CShe EBar ELan EOrc MBel MFir MRav NBro NFai SUsu WAbb WByw WCra WHil WOld
§ ***neumanniana*** EWFC WAbe WHil
– 'Goldrausch' ECha MBri SHer WHil
§ – 'Nana' CLew CNic CSam ECro EMNN ESis LBee LHop MCas MHig MPla MRPP MWat NHar NHol NKay NMen NNrd NRed NRoo SBla SIng WDav WEas WWin
nevadensis ESis NHol SHer WPer WThu
nitida NHar NHol NKay NMen SHer SIng
– 'Alba' EPot GArf
– 'Lissadell' CPBP
– 'Rubra' CShe EFol EPot GTou MRPP NBir NRoo NTow NWCA SBla SSmi WAbe WWin
nivea GTou NHol
* 'Olympic Mountains' WPer
¶ ***ovina*** WPer
palustris CRDP ECWi MSta WCla WGwy
peduncularis EMon SUsu
– C&Mc 532 ECro GCHN
'Pink Panther' See P. ***fruticosa*** 'Princess'
'Pyrenaica' See P. ***fruticosa*** 'Farreri Prostrata'
recta CHad CHan ELan EWFC GTou MHew MRav SIgm WDav WHil
– 'Alba' NPri WPer
– 'Citrina' See P. ***recta pallida***
– 'Macrantha' See P. ***r.*** 'Warrenii'

§ – ***pallida*** AGM	CGle CMil CSam EBar ECoo EPad ERav GCal LHop MBel MFir MUlv NCat NFai NRoo NSti SIgm SIng SSvw SUsu WBon WCra WHal WHoo WPer
– var. ***sulphurea***	See P. ***r. pallida***
§ – 'Warrenii'	CBow CHol CSam EBar ECro EPad GAbr LGan MFir MRav MWat NFai NMir NOrc NRoo SIng SPer SSvw WCru WHal WHoo WPer WTyr
reptans	CKin ECWi EWFC
– 'Pleniflora'	EMon
rupestris	CGle ECha EMon EWFC GCra MFir MNFA NHol NRed NRoo NSti SSvw WByw WCla WHal WPer WSHC WWin
salesoviana	MFos
¶ ***schillingii***	CBot
¶ 'Songbird'	LRHS
speciosa	EPad LGre WDav WOMN
– var. ***speciosa***	MFir NRed NWCA
¶ sp. CLD 286	EMon
sterilis	ECWi ELan EWFC
– 'Turncoat' (v)	EMon
'Sungold'	ESis WThi
tabernaemontani	See P. ***neumanniana***
ternata	See P. ***aurea chrysocraspeda***
thurberi	EPad LGre SAxl WCot WDav WKif WPer
tommasiniana	See P. ***cinerea***
x ***tonguei*** AGM	Widely available
tormentilla	See P. ***erecta***
tridentata	See SIBBALDIOPSIS ***tridentata***
verna	See P. ***neumanniana***
– ***pygmaea***	See P. ***neumanniana nana***
'Versicolor Plena'	GCal WCru
villosa	See P. ***crantzii***
* 'White Beauty'	CKni
¶ 'White Queen'	CMea
'Wickwar Trailer'	CShe EPot MPla WHCG WSHC
'William Rollison' AGM	CB&S CBow CKel CRDP CSam EBar ECas ECro EFou ELan GAbr LHop MBel MBri MRav NFai NHol NOrc SChu SCro SPer SRms WCru WPer WRus WSHC WTyr
willmottiae	See P. ***nepalensis*** 'Miss Willmott'
'Yellow Queen'	CB&S CKel CSco ELan MRav NHol NRoo SChu SCro SPer WMer WSun WTyr

POTERIUM See SANGUISORBA

PRATIA (Campanulaceae)

angulata	CMea MTho NGre NHar NHol NMen SSmi WAbe
– 'Jack's Pass'	GAri MTho NHar
– 'Messenger'	ECou
– 'Ohau'	ECou EPla ESis
– 'Tim Rees'	ELan MTho SBla SIde SIng SMrm WCru
– 'Woodside'	ECou
pedunculata	CHan CHol CMHG CMea CRow CWGN ECha ECou EFol ELan EPot ESis GCHN LAbb LBee LHop MBar NBro NGre NKay NRya SIng SSmi WAbe WHen WHil WHoo WPer WWin
– 'Blue Stars'	ECou WCru WThi
– 'Clear Skies'	ECou
– 'County Park'	CLew CMea CRDP CRiv CSpe ECha ECou ELan ELun EPot ESis LAbb LBee LRHS NGre NHar NHol NRya NWCA SIng SSmi WHal WHen WHoo WPat WPer WRus WThi
– 'Kinsey'	ECou
– 'Klandra'	ECou
– 'Tom Stone'	CLTr EBar ECou EPot NHar
perpusilla	ECou
– 'Fragrant Carpet'	ECou SIng
– 'Summer Meadows'	CLew ECou WPer
repens	ECou
treadwellii	ECha ESis LBee MHig MTho NMen SUsu WAbe WHal WHen WWin

PRESLIA See MENTHA

PRIMULA † (Primulaceae)

acaulis	See P. ***vulgaris***
¶ 'Aire Mist' (2)	EMNN MCas NHar
'Alan Robb' (D.Prim)	EBre ECtt EFol ELan LBre MBri SPer WHal WHil WPbr
algida (11)	CNic CPla GCra NGre WAbe
allionii (2)	EMNN EPot ITim LFox MBro MCas MHig MRPP NCra NHar NHol NNrd NRya NSti SHer SIng WAbe WDav WHil WWin
– JCA 4161.21/2/3 (2)	EPot
– W 1971 (2)	WDav
– 'A K Wells' (2)	EPot
– 'Adrian Jones' (2)	EMNN NNrd WAbe
– var. ***alba*** (2)	MCas MHig WHil
– 'Anna Griffith' (2)	CHoc CNic EPot GCHN ITim MCas MHig MRPP NNrd WAbe WDav WThu
– 'Anne' (2)	WDav
– 'Apple Blossom' (2)	NNrd WDav WThu
– 'Austen' (2)	EPot LFox MHig NHol NMen WAbe
– 'Avalanche' (2)	EPot ITim LFox MHig NHar NHol NSla WAbe WDav WHil
– 'Bill Martin' (2)	EPot
– Burnley form (2)	EPot
– 'Crowsley Variety' (2)	EPot MCas MHig NHed NHol NMen NNrd NRya NSla WAbe WDav WThu
¶ – 'Crusader'	NGar
– 'E K Balls' (2)	WDav
§ – 'Edinburgh' (2)	CNic EPot ITim MHig
– 'Edrom' (2)	ITim
¶ – 'Elizabeth Baker'	EMNN
– 'Elizabeth Earle' (2)	EPot
– 'Elliott's Variety'	See P. ***a.*** 'Edinburgh'
– 'Fanfare' (2)	WDav
– 'Frank Barker' (2)	EPot NHol
¶ – 'Gavin Brown'	EPot
¶ – 'Giuseppi's Form'	WOMN
– 'Hartside' (2)	EPot NHol NNrd
¶ – 'Hemswell Blush'	CBre

– 'Hemswell Ember' (2) EMNN NHar NHed
– Ingwersen's form (2) NHol SIng
– 'Joan Hughes' (2) NGar SIng
– 'K R W' (2) See P. *a.* 'Ken's Seedling'
§– 'Ken's Seedling' (2) EPot NHar NHol NNrd NSla WAbe WDav WHil WThu
¶– 'Lea Gardens' NHar
¶– 'Lee Myers' NHar NHed NNrd
– 'Lindisfarne' (2) WDav
– 'Lismore Treasure' (2) WDav
– 'Margaret Earle' (2) NHol
– 'Marion' (2) EMNN EPot ITim LFox NHed
¶– 'Marjorie Wooster' MRPP
¶– 'Mars' NHar
– 'Martin' (2) EPot MCas MHig MYat NHol NNrd WDav
– 'Mary Berry' (2) EPot MHig NHar WDav
– 'Mrs Dyas' (2) CNic EMNN NHar NHol WAbe WDav
¶– 'Nymph' MCas
– 'Peggy Wilson' (2) EPot EWes
– 'Pennine Pink' (2) EPot MRPP NHol NNrd WDav
¶– 'Phobos' MFie
– 'Picton's Variety' (2) EPot NHed
– 'Pinkie' (2) WDav WHil
– 'Praecox' (2) EPot MCas NHol NNrd NSla
– R C E form (2) WAbe
– 'Raymond Wooster' (2) EMNN EPot
– 'Scimitar' (2) NGar NHar
– 'Snowflake' (2) EPot MCas NGar NHar NNrd NRya WDav WThu
– Stanton's form (2) NHed NHol WAbe
– 'Stradbrook Charmer' (2) EPot
– 'Stradbrook Dream' (2) WDav
¶– 'Stradbrook Gem' WAbe
¶– 'Superba' MCas
– 'Tranquillity' (2) NHar NHol NNrd WDav
– 'Travellers' (2) EPot
– 'Viscountess Byng' (2) WDav
– 'Wharfedale Ling' (2) EPot MRPP NHar
– 'William Earle' (2) EMNN EPot NHar NHed NHol WAbe WDav WHil WThu

allionii* x *auricula See P. x ***loiseleurii***
¶– x 'Harlow Car' NHar
– x ***hirsuta*** (2) See P. x ***pubescens***
¶– x 'Lee Myers' CNic
– x ***marginata*** (2) EBre LBre NHar NNrd
¶– x 'Old Red Dusty Miller' NHar
– x ***pubescens*** (2) MYat
¶– x ***rubra*** NHol
¶– x 'White Linda Pope' NHar

alpicola (26) CBot CBre CCla CHoc COtt CRow CWGN EBre ELun GAbr GDra LBre LMay MBal MBro MFie NCra NHol NKay NLin SPer WAbe WDav WRus WWat
– var. ***alba*** (26) CNic CPla CRow ESma GCra MBal NGre NRoo
– hybrids (26) NHol
– ***luna*** (26) CNic GBuc
– var. ***violacea*** (26) CPla CRow ELun GAbr GDra MBal MBri MFie NHar NHol

altaica grandiflora See P. ***elatior meyeri***
'Altaica' See P. ***elatior meyeri***
amoena See P. ***elatior meyeri***
angustifolia (20) WDav
anisodora (4) CNic CPla ELan GCra MBal MFie NHol NKay SHig
'April Rose' (D.Prim) CGle EBre ECtt ESis GAbr LBre NEgg NHar NHol SHer SIng SPer WCla WHil WPbr
x ***arctotis*** (2) See P. x ***pubescens***
aurantiaca (4) CPla EHon MSta NGre SRms WChe
aureata (21) GArf NCra
auricula 'A H Spring' (A) MFie
– 'Adrian' (A) CHoc EDon MCas MFie NBra NCra NJap NNrd SHya
– 'Alan Ravenscroft' (A) MFie
– 'Albury' (D) EDon MFie
– 'Alfred Niblett' (S) MFie
– 'Alice' (D) MFie
– 'Alice Haysom' (S) MFie NBra NNrd SHya WHil
¶– 'Alicia' CHoc
– 'Alien' (S) MFie
– 'Alison Jane' (A) EDon MFie NCra SHya
– 'Almondbury' (S) SHya
– ***alpina*** See P. *a.* hort.
– Alpine mixed (A) CNic GCra GDra NCra SRms
– 'Andrea Julie' (A) CHoc EDon MCas MFie NBra NCra NHar NHol NJap NNrd NRed SHya WHil WSun
– 'Ann Taylor' (A) MFie NCra
– 'Antoc' (S) MFie NCra
– 'Anwar Sadat' (A) MFie SHya
– 'Applecross' (A) EMNN ESis GAbr LFox MCas MFie NBra NCra NHar NJap NNrd NRed NRya SHya
– 'Argus' (A) CHoc CNic EDon ELan ESis LFox MCas MFie NBra NCra NHar NJap NMen NNrd NRed NRya SHya WHil WRus
– 'Arundel Stripe' (S) SHya
¶– 'Ashcliffe Gem' (A) SHya
– 'Astolat' (S) EMNN MFie NBra NCra SHya
– 'Athur Delbridge' (A) MFie
– 'Aurora' (A) MCas MFie SHya
– 'Aviemore' (A) MFie
– 'Avocet' (S) MFie
– 'Avril Hunter' (A) CHoc MFie SHya
– 'Bacchus' (A) MFie SHya
– 'Balbithan' (B) MFie
– 'Ballet' (S) MFie SHya
– 'Banana Split' CGle MRob
– 'Barbarella' (S) MFie
– 'Basuto' (A) EMNN MFie SHya
– 'Baupaume' (S) NCra
– 'Beatrice' (A) GAbr LFox MCas MFie NBra NCra NNrd
– 'Beckjay' (S) MFie
¶– 'Bedford Lad' (A) SHya
– 'Beechen Green' (S) SHya
¶– 'Bendigo' (S) SHya
– 'Bilton' (S) EDon MFie NCra
– 'Blackfield' (S) MFie
– 'Blackhill' (S) EMNN MFie
– 'Blairside Yellow' (B) EWes LFox MCas NHar NMen SSmi WAbe WDav WHil WThu WWin
– 'Blossom' (A) EDon LFox MFie NCra NJap SHya WHil
– 'Blue Garden' MCas

- 'Blue Jean' (S) CGle EDon LFox MFie NCra NJap NRed
- 'Blue Mist' (B) MFie
- 'Blue Nile' (S) EDon EMNN MFie NBra NCra SHya
- 'Blue Steel' (S) SHya
- 'Blue Velvet' (B) CHoc EMNN MCas MFie NNrd SHya WHil
- 'Blue Wave' (D) NNrd
- 'Bob Lancashire' (S) EMNN MFie NHar
¶ – 'Bolero' CHoc SHya
- 'Bookham Firefly' (A) ESis GAbr LFox MCas MFie NBra NCra NHar NJap
- 'Border Stripe' (B) CHoc MFie
- 'Bramshill' (S) SHya
- 'Brazil' (S) EDon EMNN ESis LFox MCas MFie NBra NCra NHol NRed WHil
- 'Brenda's Choice' (A) MFie SHya
- 'Bright Eyes' (A) CHoc MFie
¶ – 'Bright Ginger' (S) SHya
- 'Broadwell Gold' (B) LFox MCas MFie SHya WHil
- 'Brookfield' (S) EDon MFie NMen
- 'Broughton' (S) MFie SHya
- 'Brown Bess' (A) EMNN MCas MFie NBra NCra NNrd
- 'Bunty' (A) MFie
- 'Butterwick' (A) EDon MFie SHya
- 'C G Haysom' (S) CNic EDon ELan EMNN LFox MCas MFie NBra NCra NJap NNrd NRed SHya
- 'C W Needham' (A) CHoc CNic EDon EMNN MFie NCra NJap NNrd NRed SHya WHil
- 'Café au Lait' (A) MFie
- 'Camelot' (D) CRDP EDon ELan EMNN MCas MFie MRob NCra NHar NHol NJap NNrd NRed SHya WAbe WHil
- 'Camilla' (A) MFie
- 'Carole' (A) MFie NBra NNrd SHya
¶ – 'Carreras' CHoc
- 'Catherine' (D) EDon MFie MRob NCra NJap NRed
- 'Chaffinch' (S) LFox MFie SHya
- 'Chamois' (B) NMen
¶ – 'Chantilly Cream' (D) SHya
- 'Cherry' (S) EMNN LFox MFie NCra SHya
- 'Cheyenne' (S) EMNN MFie
- 'Chloe' (S) NBra NJap SHya
- 'Chorister' (S) EDon EMNN EPot ESis GAbr LFox MBro MCas MFie NBra NCra NHed NRed NRya SHya WDav
¶ – 'Cicero' (A) SHya
- 'Cindy' (A) MFie
¶ – 'Cinnamon' (S) SHya
- 'Claudia Taylor' SHya
- 'Clunie' (S) EDon
- 'Coffee' (S) MFie
- 'Colbury' (S) LFox MFie NCra
- 'Coll' (A) SHya
- 'Colonel Champney' (S) MFie SHya
- 'Comet' (S) MCas MFie
- 'Commander' (A) SHya
- 'Connie' (S) MFie
- 'Conservative' (S) MFie SHya
- 'Consett' (S) EMNN MFie NCra SHya
- 'Coppernob' (S) SHya
- 'Coral' (S) MCas MFie NCra NHed SHya
- 'Cortina' (S) EDon EMNN LFox MCas NBra NCra NHar NJap NNrd
- 'County Park Red' (B) ECou
- 'Craig Vaughan' (A) MFie NCra NNrd NRya
- 'Creenagh Stripe' (A) MFie
- 'Crimson Cavalier' CGle
¶ – 'D S J' (S) SHya
- 'Dakota' (S) EMNN MFie NCra
- 'Daphnis' (S) LFox
- 'Delilah' (D) EDon MFie
- 'Devon Cream' (D) CGle CHoc ECha EDon ESis MCas MFie MRob NCra NHol NJap NRed SHer WRus
- 'Diane' MFie NCra NRed WDav
- 'Doctor Duthie' (S) MFie
- 'Doctor Lennon's White' (B) MFie NBra
¶ – 'Doctor S Shama' (S) SHya
¶ – 'Dogan' (S) SHya
- 'Donhead' (A) EDon MCas MFie SHya WHil
- 'Donna Claney' (S) MFie SHya
¶ – 'Doris Jean' (A) SHya
- 'Doublet' (D) EDon EMNN MCas MFie MRob NCra NNrd SHya WDav WHil WPbr
- 'Douglas Black' (S) SHya
- 'Douglas Green' (S) MFie SHya
- 'Douglas Rose' (S) SHya
- 'Douglas Salmon' (S) SHya
- 'Douglas White' (S) MFie
- 'Dowager' (A) MFie SHya
¶ – 'Dusky Maiden' (A) CHoc MCas
- 'Dusky Yellow' CNic MCas WDav
- 'E' NNrd
- E82 (S) MFie
¶ – 'Eileen K' (S) SHya
- 'Elegance' (S) MFie SHya
- 'Elizabeth Ann' (A) GAbr MFie NCra SHya
- 'Ellen Thompson' (A) MFie NBra NNrd SHya
¶ – 'Elmor Véte' (S) SHya
- 'Elsie' (A) MFie SHya
- 'Elsie May' (A) CHoc CNic EDon MFie NBra NCra NRed SHya
- 'Elsinore' (S) SHya
- 'Embley' (S) NCra
- 'Emerald' (S) SHya
- 'Emery Down' (S) MFie NNrd
- 'Erica' (A) MFie
- 'Ettrick' (S) SHya
- 'Eventide' (S) MFie
- 'Everest Blue' (S) EDon SHya
¶ – 'Everest Green' (S) SHya
- 'Fairy' (A) SHya
- 'Falcon' (S) SHya
- 'Fanciful' (S) EDon MFie SHya WHil
- 'Fanny Meerbeck' (S) CGle CRiv EDon EMNN LFox MCas MFie NBra NCra NJap NNrd NRed WHil
- 'Faro' (S) MFie
¶ – 'Favorite' EMNN SHya
- 'Fawsley's Favourite' (S) SHya
- 'Finchfield' (A) MFie SHya
- 'Flamingo' (S) MFie
- 'Fleminghouse' (S) CGle EDon ELan NJap NRed SHya

¶– 'Foreign Affairs' (S) SHya
¶– 'Frank Bailey' (d) SHya
– 'Frank Crosland' (A) MFie NCra NNrd NRya SHya WHil
¶– 'Frank Edger' (d) SHya
¶– 'Frank Taylor' (S) SHya
– 'Freda' (S) SHya
– 'Frittenden Yellow' (B) LFox
– 'Fuller's Red' (S) MCas MFie
– 'G Douglas' (A) NCra
– 'G Swinford' (B) SHya
– 'Galen' (A) EDon MFie NCra SHya WDav
– 'Gay Crusader' (A) EMNN MFie
– 'Gee Cross' (A) MFie
¶– 'Geldersome Green' See P. *a.* 'Gildersome Green'
– 'Gem' (A) SHya
– 'George Swinnerton's Leathercoat' CGle CHoc
– 'Geronimo' (S) MFie SHya
§– 'Gildersome Green' (S) EMNN LFox MCas MFie NBra NHar SHya
– 'Gizabroon' LFox MCas MFie NCra NRed
– 'Gleam' (S) EMNN MFie NBra NHar NNrd SHya
– 'Glencoe' (S) SHya
– 'Gleneagles' (S) SHya
– 'Glenelg' (S) MFie SHya
– 'Glenluce' (S) SHya
– 'Gold Blaze' (S) SHya
– 'Goldcrest' (S) MFie SHya
– 'Golden Chartreuse' (S) WHil WPbr
¶– 'Golden Fleece' (S) SHya
– 'Golden Gleam' (A) WHil
¶– 'Golden Hill' (S) SHya
¶– 'Golden Meadow' (S) SHya
¶– 'Goldilocks' (S) SHya
¶– 'Goldthorn' (A) SHya
– 'Gooseberries and Cream' CGle MRob
– 'Gordon Douglas' (A) EDon MFie SHya
– 'Grace Ellen' (S) SHya
¶– 'Gracie' (A) SHya
– 'Green Isle' (S) EMNN MFie NBra SHya
– 'Green Mouse' (S) MFie
– 'Green Parrot' (S) EMNN LFox MFie NBra NHar WHil
– 'Green Shank' (S) MFie NBra SHya
– 'Greenfinger' (S) SHya
– 'Greenheart' (S) EDon SHya
¶– 'Greenough Stripe' NBra
– 'Greensleeves' (S) SHya
– 'Greta' (S) EDon EMNN NHar NMen NNrd SHya
– 'Gretna Green' MFie SHya
– 'Grey Bonnet' (S) LFox SHya
¶– 'Grey Hawk' (S) SHya
– 'Grey Lag' EMNN MFie
– 'Grey Monarch' (S) MFie SHya
¶– 'Grey Seal' (S) SHya
– 'Grizedale' (S) MFie
§– 'Guildersome Green' (S) See P. *a.* 'Gildersome Green'
– 'Guinea' (S) CHoc EDon EMNN LFox MCas MFie NCra NNrd NRya SHya
– 'Gwen Baker' (D) EDon
– 'Harmony' (B) MFie SHya
– 'Harrison Weir' (S) SHya
– 'Harry 'O'' (S) MFie SHya
– 'Harvest Moon' (S) MFie
– 'Haughmond' (A) MFie
– 'Hawkwood' (S) EMNN LFox NBra NCra NHar NNrd
– 'Hawkwood Fancy' (S) MCas MFie SHya
– 'Hazel' (A) ESis MFie NCra SHya
– 'Headdress' (S) LFox MFie
– 'Helen' (S) NBra SHya
– 'Helen Barter' (S) SHya
¶– 'Helen Brown' (S) SHya
– 'Helena' (S) EMNN LFox MFie NHar NMen SHya
¶– 'Hermia' CHoc
– 'Hinton Fields' (S) MFie
– 'Holyrood' (S) MFie SHya
– 'Hopley's Double Mauve' (D) MFie
¶– 'Humphrey' (S) SHya
– 'Hurstwood Majesty' (S) NNrd
– 'Hyacinth' (S) NJap NWCA WDav
– 'Ibis' (S) MFie
– 'Idmiston' (S) SHya
¶– 'Impassioned' (A) MCas
– 'Jack Dean' (A) MFie SHya
¶– 'Jack Stant' (S) SHya
– 'James Arnot' (S) LFox MFie NCra NHar SHya
– 'Jane Myers' (D) MFie
¶– 'Janet' NBra
– 'Jeannie Telford' (A) CHoc NCra SHya
– 'Jenny' (A) EMNN GArf MFie MRob MYat NHar SHya WHil
– 'Jezebel' (B) SHya
– 'Joan Elliott' (A) GAbr MFie MYat NBra WHil
¶– 'Joan Goalby' (d) SHya
– 'Joanne' (A) SHya
– 'Johann Bach' (B) MFie
– 'John' (S) SHya
– 'John Gledhill' (A) CNic SHya
– 'John Stewart' (A) MFie
– 'John Wayne' (A) MFie
– 'Joy' (A) EDon MCas MFie MRob NBra NCra NNrd NRed SHer SHya
– 'Joyce' GAbr MFie NRya
– 'Jungfrau' (D) EDon
– 'Jupiter' (S) MFie SHya
– 'K H B' (S) NNrd
– 'Kath Dryden' WHil
– 'Kathy' (A) SHya
– 'Kelso' (A) MFie
– 'Kercup' (A) MFie NCra NNrd SHya
– 'Kim' (A) EMNN MFie NCra NNrd SHya
– 'Kincraig' (S) SHya
– 'Kingcup' (A) MFie NCra SHya
– 'Kinloch' (A) SHya
– 'Kiowa' (S) MFie
– 'Kirklands' (D) EDon MFie MRob
– 'Lady Croft' (S) SHya
– 'Lady Daresbury' (A) MFie NCra SHya
– 'Lady Emma Monson' (S) SHya
– 'Lady Joyful' (S) EDon SHya

– 'Lady Zoë' (S)	MCas MFie NBra NCra
– 'Lamplugh'	MFie NNrd
¶– 'Landy' (A)	CHoc MCas
– 'Langley Park' (A)	MCas MFie
– 'Laverock Fancy' (S)	MFie
¶– 'Leather Jacket'	NHed
– 'Lechistan' (S)	EMNN MCas MFie MRob NBra NHar NHol NJap NNrd NRed
– 'Lee Paul' (A)	CHoc EDon EMNN MFie NCra SHya
– 'Lemon Drop' (S)	SHya
– 'Lemon Sherbert' (B)	MFie
– 'Lemon White Eye' (B)	MFie
¶– 'Light Hearted'	CHoc
– 'Lilac Domino' (S)	MFie NGar SHya
– 'Lime 'n' Lemon'	CGle MRob
– 'Lindley' (S)	EMNN NCra
– 'Lindsey Moreno' (S)	SHya
– 'Ling' (A)	CHoc EMNN MFie NCra SHya
– 'Lisa' (A)	CNic EDon GAbr MBal MCas MFie NBra NCra NNrd NRed SHya
– 'Lisa's Red' (S)	EMNN NBra
– 'Lisa's Smile' (S)	LFox MFie NCra NMen SHya
– 'Little Rosetta' (D)	EDon WHil
– 'Lochlands' (S)	SHya
– 'Lockyer's Gem' (B)	MFie
– 'Louisa' (D)	MFie
– 'Lovebird' (S)	EDon EMNN GAbr LFox MCas MFie MRob NBra NCra NHar NJap NRed SHya SUsu
– 'Madame Gina' (S)	MFie
– 'Magnolia' (B)	MFie
– 'Magpie' (S)	EMNN MFie
– 'Maid Marion' (D)	EDon SHya
– 'Mandan' (S)	SHya
– 'Manka' (S)	EDon MFie NCra SHya
– 'Mansell's Green'	MFie
¶– 'Margaret' (S)	SHya
– 'Margaret Faulkner' (A)	LFox MCas MFie NCra SHya
– 'Marigold' (D)	EDon MFie MRob NCra NJap NRed
– 'Mark' (A)	CHoc MFie MRob NCra NHol NJap SHya WHil
– 'Marmion' (S)	SHya
– 'Marsco' (S)	LFox
– 'Martin Luther King' (S)	MFie
– 'Mary' (D)	EDon MFie MRob NBra SHya
– 'Matley' (S)	MFie NBra
– 'Matthew Yates' (D)	EDon MFie MRob NCra
– 'Maureen Millward'	MCas MFie
¶– 'May Tiger' (S)	SHya
¶– 'Mellifluous'	CHoc
– 'Mermaid'	CHoc EDon MFie MRob NCra NNrd NRed WHil
– 'Merridale' (A)	EDon EMNN MCas MFie NCra SHya
¶– 'Mersey Tiger' (S)	SHya
¶– 'Metha'	CHoc
– 'Midnight' (S)	CBot CGle MRob NCra NHar NHol
– 'Mikado' (S)	EDon MFie NBra SHya
¶– 'Milkmaid' (A)	SHya
– 'Millicent' (A)	MFie
– 'Mink' (A)	MFie SHya WHil
– 'Minley' (S)	EDon EMNN LFox MFie NHar SHya
– 'Minsmere' (S)	SHya
¶– 'Minstrel' (S)	SHya
– 'Mipsie Miranda' (D)	MFie
¶– 'Mish Mish' (d)	WHil
– 'Mojave' (S)	CHoc EMNN LFox MBro MFie NBra NCra NHar NMen SHya WDav
– 'Moneymoon' (S)	MFie SHya
– 'Monica' (A)	MFie
– 'Monk' (A)	MFie
– 'Moonbeam' (S)	MFie
– 'Moonglow' (S)	CGle EDon ELan EMNN MFie NCra NJap SHya
– 'Moonrise' (S)	MFie
– 'Moonstone' (D)	EDon MFie
– 'Moscow' (S)	MFie
– 'Mr 'A'' (S)	NBra WHil
¶– 'Mrs A Harrison'	CHoc
¶– 'Mrs Dargan'	CHoc
¶– 'Mrs Harris' (B)	MCas
– 'Mrs L Hearne' (A)	EDon EMNN MFie NBra NCra NNrd NRed SHya WHil
– 'Mrs R Bolton' (A)	SHya
– 'Nathan Silver' (A)	MFie
– 'Neat and Tidy' (S)	EDon EMNN ESis LFox MCas MFie MHig NBra NCra NHar NJap NRed SHya WHil
– 'Neville Telford' (S)	EMNN MFie
– 'New Baby' (A)	SHya
– 'Nigel' (D)	EDon
– 'Night and Day' (S)	EMNN MFie NCra
– 'Night Heron' (S)	SHya
– 'Nocturne' (S)	CGle ELan EMNN GAbr LFox MCas MFie MRob NCra NHol NRed SHya
– 'Norah' (A)	SHya
– 'Norma' (A)	MFie NBra NNrd
– 'Nubian' (S)	MFie
– 'Oake's Blue' (S)	MFie NCra
– 'Oban' (S)	SHya
– 'Old Double Green' (D)	MFie SHya
– 'Old England' (S)	SHya
– 'Old Gold' (S)	LFox SHya
– 'Old Gold Dusty Miller' (B)	MFie SHer
– 'Old Irish Blue' (B)	CNic MCas MFie NHol SHya WHil
¶– 'Old Irish Scented'	CHoc
– 'Old Lilac' (B)	MFie
– 'Old Pink Lace'	CGle
– 'Old Red Dusty Miller' (B)	CRiv ECha GAbr LFox MCas MFie MHig MRob NBir SHer SHya WDav
– 'Old Suffolk Bronze' (B)	LFox MFie SHya
– 'Old Tawny' (B)	CHoc MFie
– 'Old Wine' (A)	MCas MFie
– 'Old Yellow Dusty Miller' (B)	CHoc EMNN EWes GAbr LFox MBro MCas MFie MHig MRob NHol SHya WAbe WDav WHil WWin
– 'Olton' (A)	MFie SHya
– 'Orb' (S)	EDon LFox MCas MFie NJap NMen NRed SHya WHil

– 'Osbourne Green' (B) MFie
– 'Paradise Yellow' (B) EMNN EPar GAbr LFox MFie NBra NMen SHya
– 'Paris' (S) MFie
– 'Party Dress' (S) SHya
– 'Pastiche' (A) MFie
– 'Pat' (S) EDon LFox MFie NCra SHya
– 'Patience' (S) MFie
– 'Pauline' (A) MFie SHya
– 'Peggy' (A) EDon EPot MCas MFie NNrd NWCA
– 'Phyllis Douglas' (A) CHoc LFox MFie NCra SHya
– 'Pierot' (A) MFie
¶– 'Piers Telford' CHoc
– 'Pink Lady' (A) MFie SHya
– 'Pioneer Stripe' (S) EDon MFie
– 'Pippin' (A) MFie NBra SHya
– 'Plush Royal' (S) MFie
– 'Portree' (S) SHya
– 'Pot of Gold' (S) EDon EMNN LFox MFie MRob NCra NHar SHya
– 'Prague' (S) EDon MFie MRob NBir NBra NMen SHya
– 'Prince Charming' (S) CHoc EDon MFie
– 'Prince John' (A) CHoc EDon LFox MCas MFie NBra NCra NJap NNrd NRya SHya
– 'Purple Emperor' (A) SHya
– 'Purple Frills' CGle MRob
– 'Purple Mermaid' (D) EDon MFie
– 'Purple Sage' (S) EMNN MFie
– 'Purple Velvet' (S) MFie NHol
– 'Queen Bee' (S) MFie
¶– 'Queen's Bower' (S) SHya
– 'Rabley Heath' (A) EDon EMNN LFox MFie SHya
– 'Radiant' (A) MFie
– 'Rajah' (S) CGle EDon ELan MCas MFie MRob NCra NHar NJap NRed SHya WHil
¶– 'Ray Brown' (v) CRDP
¶– 'Ray's Grey' (S) SHya
– 'Red Beret' (S) EMNN LFox MFie NCra NJap WHil
– 'Red Gauntlet' (S) EDon EMNN LFox MCas MFie NCra NHar NJap NMen NNrd NRed SHya
– 'Red Mark' (A) MFie SHya
– 'Red Rum' (S) MFie NCra SHya
– 'Redstart' (B) NBra
– 'Remus' (S) CHoc EDon LFox MCas MFie MRob NBra NCra NHar NNrd NRed NWCA SHya WHil
– 'Renata' (S) MFie SHya
– 'Riatty' (D) MFie
– 'Richard Shaw' (A) MFie NNrd
¶– 'Rishworth' (S) SHya
– 'Roberto' (S) SHya
– 'Rock Sand' (S) EMNN MFie NHar
– 'Rodeo' (A) EDon MFie NCra SHya
– 'Rolts' (S) CRDP EDon EMNN LFox MCas MFie MRob NBra NCra NHar NNrd NRya SHya WHil
– 'Rosalie Edwards' (S) EMNN LFox MFie NCra SHya WHil
– 'Rosamund' (D) SHya
– 'Rosanna' (S) MFie SHya
– 'Rose Kaye' (A) SHya
– 'Rosebud' (S) CDec MFie
– 'Rosemary' (S) EMNN MFie
– 'Rossiter's Grey' (S) SHya
– 'Rover Stripe' (S) EDon
– 'Rowena' (A) CHoc EDon EMNN MCas MFie NCra NHar NHol NJap NNrd NRya SHya
– 'Royal Purple' (S) NHed NNrd
– 'Royalty' (S) MFie
– 'Ruby Hyde' (B) MCas MFie
¶– 'Rusty Dusty' GAbr
– 'Ruth Steed' (S) SHya
– 'Sailor Boy' (S) LFox MFie SHya
– 'Saint Boswells' (S) MFie SHya
– 'Saint Elmo' (D) MFie
– 'Saint Gerrans' White' (B) CHoc MFie
¶– 'Saint Quentin' (S) SHya
– 'Salad' (S) MFie
– 'Salome' (A) SHya
– 'Sandhills' (A) SHya
– 'Sandmartin' (S) MFie SHya
– 'Sandra' (A) CHoc EMNN ESis GAbr LFox MFie NBra NNrd SHya
– 'Sandwood Bay' (A) CNic EDon EMNN GAbr LFox MCas MFie NBra NCra NHar NMen NNrd NRed SHya WHil WRus WSun
– 'Sarah Lodge' (D) EMNN MFie SHya
¶– 'Satchmo' EMNN SHya
– 'Serenity' (S) LFox MFie SHya
– 'Shalford' (D) EDon MFie MRob
– 'Sheila' (S) EDon GAbr LFox MFie MRob NBra NHar NNrd NRed SBla SHya
– 'Shere' (S) EDon LFox MFie NCra SHya
¶– 'Shergold' (A) SHya
– 'Sherwood' EMNN MCas MFie NBra NHar
– 'Shotley' (A) MFie
¶– 'Silverway' (S) SHya
¶– 'Sir Hardy Amies' (A) SHya
– 'Sir Robert Ewbank' (D) MCas
– 'Sirius' (A) CHoc CRDP EDon LFox MFie NBra NCra NHar NHol SHya
– 'Slioch' (S) EMNN MFie MRob NBra NHar NNrd SHya
– 'Snooty Fox' CGle EMNN MFie NNrd
¶– 'Snooty Fox II' NBra
– 'Snowy Owl' MFie
– 'Sonya' (A) NHol NNrd
– 'South Barrow' (D) MFie WHil
– 'Sphinx' (A) SHya
¶– 'Splendour' (S) SHya
– 'Spring Meadows' (S) EDon MFie NCra SHya
– SS TY 72 (S) MFie
– 'Standish' (D) EDon MCas MFie MRob NBra NCra NHol NJap
– 'Stant's Blue' (S) EDon EMNN LFox MCas MFie NHol NJap NNrd SHya
¶– 'Stan's Grey' (S) SHya
– 'Starry' (S) MFie
– 'Stella' (S) EDon LFox MFie
¶– 'Stoney Cross' (S) SHya
– 'Stonnal' (A) MFie SHya
¶– 'Stratton' (A) SHya
¶– 'Streamlet' (S) SHya
– 'Stubb's Tartan' (S) MCas SHya
– 'Sue' (A) MFie NRya
¶– 'Sue Douglas' (A) SHya
¶– 'Sugar Plum Fairy' EMNN

– 'Summer Sky' (A)	SHya
– 'Sunflower' (S)	LFox MFie
– 'Sunsal' (S)	MFie
– 'Sunstar' (S)	EMNN MFie
– 'Super Para' (S)	EMNN MFie SHya
– 'Superb' (S)	SHya
– 'Susan' (A)	LFox MFie SHya
– 'Susannah' (D)	EDon MFie SHya
– 'Swale' (A)	SHya
– 'Sweet Pastures' (S)	EDon EMNN MCas MFie NCra NHol NJap SHya
– 'Swift' (S)	MFie
¶– 'Swinley' (S)	SHya
– 'Symphony' (A)	SHya
– 'Tall Purple Dusty Miller' (B)	MFie
– 'Tarantella' (A)	CHoc MCas MFie NCra NJap NNrd SHya
– 'Tavistock' (S)	SHya
– 'Ted Roberts' (A)	EDon EMNN MCas MFie NBra NCra SHya
– 'Teem' (S)	EMNN MFie NBra NCra NJap NMen SHya WHil
– 'Tenby Grey' (S)	MFie SHya
– 'The Baron' (S)	CGle LFox MCas MFie NBra NJap NRed
– 'The Bishop' (S)	MFie NCra
– 'The Bride' (S)	EDon MCas NCra NJap SHya
– 'The Cardinal' (D)	EDon SAsh SHya
– 'The Czar' (A)	SHya
– 'The Maverick' (S)	SHya
– 'The Raven' (S)	EMNN MFie
¶– 'The Sheep'	CHoc
– 'The Snods' (S)	MFie NCra
– 'Thetis' (A)	MFie NCra SHya
– 'Thirlmere' (D)	MFie
– 'Tinkerbell' (S)	MFie NJap
– 'Tomboy' (S)	MFie
– 'Tomdown' (S)	SHya
– 'Tosca' (S)	EMNN SHya
– 'Trojan' (S)	NBra SHya
– 'Trouble' (D)	EDon MFie MRob NCra NHar NHol SHya
– 'Trudy' (S)	EMNN MCas MFie NCra NHar
– 'True Briton' (S)	MFie SHya
– 'Trumpet Blue' (S)	MFie
– 'Tumbledown' (A)	MFie
– 'Tye Lea' (S)	EDon MFie
– 'Typhoon' (A)	MFie SHya
¶– 'V de Wemyss' (A)	SHya
¶– 'V I Hinney'	EMNN
– 'Valerie' (A)	EDon MCas MFie NBra NCra NNrd SHya WHil
– 'Vee Too' (A)	CHoc MFie SHya
– 'Vera' (A)	MFie
– 'Verdi' (A)	MFie NCra NJap SHya
– 'Victoria' (S)	MFie
– 'Victoria de Wemyss'	MFie
– 'Vulcan' (A)	EDon MCas MFie NCra NNrd SHya
– 'Waincliffe Red' (S)	MFie
¶– 'Waincliffe Yellow' (S)	SHya
– 'Walhampton' (S)	EMNN MFie SHya
– 'Walton' (A)	MFie SHya
– 'Walton Heath' (D)	EDon MFie MRob NBra SHya WHil
– 'Warwick' (S)	EDon NMen
– 'Watt's Purple' (D)	EDon MCas MFie MRob
– 'Wedding Day' (S)	MFie
– 'Westcott Pride' (D)	EDon
– 'White Ensign' (S)	EMNN MFie SHya
– 'White Wings' (S)	MFie NBra NCra NHar SHya
– 'Wide Awake' (A)	CHoc MFie
– 'Wincha' (S)	MFie SHya
– 'Windways Mystery' (B)	MFie
– 'Winifrid' (A)	EDon MCas MFie NCra NHar NHol SHya WHil
– 'Wor Jackie' (S)	EMNN MFie NHar
¶– 'Wye Lemon' (S)	SHya
¶– 'Wye Orange' (S)	SHya
– 'Y I Hinney' (A)	MFie
– 'Yorkshire Grey' (S)	EDon MFie
¶– 'Young Rajah' (S)	SHya
– 'Zambia' (D)	EDon MFie MRob SHya WHil
§ ***auricula*** **AGM**	CArn ELan EPar ESis GDra GTou MBal MRav MTho NBro NCra NHar NHol NRoo NWCA SPer SSmi WCla WDav WThu
– ssp. ***auricula*** Linnaeus	GTou NHol
– ssp. ***bauhinii*** (2)	MBro NHol
auriculata (11)	MFie WDav
¶– JCA 785.600 (11)	MFie
'Barbara Barker' (2)	WAbe
¶ 'Barbara Midwinter' (30 x *6*)	SBla
* 'Barnard's Crimson' (Prim)	CCot
Barnhaven Blues Group (Prim)	CDec GAbr
Barnhaven doubles (D.Poly)	EGol MFie WPbr
¶ Barnhaven Gold Laced Group (Poly)	GAbr MFie
Barnhaven Reds (Prim)	See P. Tartan Reds Group
Barnhaven Traditional Group (Poly)	MFie
'Beatrice Wooster' (2)	CHoc CNic EPot EWes LFox MBro MCas MFie MYat NGre NHar NHed NMen NNrd NRed NRya SGil SIng SSmi WAbe WDav WHil WThu
¶ 'Beeches' Pink'	GAbr
beesiana (4)	CArn CHoc CHol CMea CRow EBar EHon ELan GCHN LMay MBri MFie MSta MSte NHar NHol NKay NOak NRoo NSti NWCA SHer SHig SMrm SPer WChe WWat
'Belle Watling' (D.Prim)	GAbr NHar NHol
bellidifolia (17)	CPla NGre
beluensis	See P. x ***pubescens*** 'Freedom'
¶ Bergfrühling Julianas Group (Prim)	MFie
§ x ***berninae*** 'Windrush' (2)	NHar NNrd WAbe WDav
'Betty Green' (Prim)	MBri NHol
'Bewerley White'	See P. ***pubescens*** 'Bewerley White'
bhutanica	See P. ***whitei*** 'Sherriff's Variety'
¶ x ***biflora*** (2)	GArf
'Big Red Giant' (D.Prim)	NHar NHol SIng
bileckii	See P. x ***forsteri*** 'Bileckii'
'Blue Riband' (Prim)	CCot CGle COtt EPot GAbr GGar LFox MHig NCat NHol SPer

Plant	Suppliers
'Blue Sapphire' (30)	CBot EDon GAbr NEgg SIng SPer
Blue Striped Victorians Group (Poly)	GAbr
'Blutenkissen' (Prim)	ELun EPot LFox NNrd
'Bon Accord Elegance' (D.Poly)	CGle
'Bon Accord Gem' (D.Poly)	CCot CGle
'Bon Accord Purple' (D.Poly)	CCot CGle EJud
'Bonfire' (4)	GDra NHar
– (Poly)	ELun
¶ 'Bootheosa' (21)	NHol
boothii (21)	GArf
¶ 'Boudicca' (Prim)	NRar
¶ ***boveana*** (12)	MFie
bracteosa (21)	ITim NHar NHol
'Brimstone' (Poly)	CGle
¶ 'Broxbourne'	NHar
'Buckland Enchantress'	CRow
'Buckland Wine' (Prim)	CCot CRow
x ***bulleesiana*** (4)	NBro NHol NKay NRoo WPer
– Asthore hybrids (4)	EHon
bulleyana **AGM**	Widely available
– CLD 920 (4)	MFie NHol
burmanica (4)	CBow CPla CWGN ELun GDra GGar LBee MBal MFie MSta NCra NDea NHar NHol NKay SIng WDav
'Butterscotch' (Prim)	CGle GAbr
'Caerulea Plena' (D.Prim)	GCal
calderiana (21)	GDra NHar
Candelabra hybrids (4)	CBro CMil EMNN LFox MTho NCra NLin SHer
Candy Pinks Group (Prim)	GAbr NHol
capitata (5)	CArn CBot CGle CMea CNic CPla GAbr GDra GTou MBal MBri MFie MSte NCra NGre NHar NLin NSti SIng WCla WHal WPer
– CLD 497/274 (5)	MFie
¶ – KEKE 274 (5)	MFie
¶ – KEKE 497 (5)	MFie
– ssp. ***capitata*** (5)	EPot
– ssp. ***crispata*** AGS/ES 407 (5)	GCra
– dark forms (5)	MFie
– ssp. ***mooreana*** (5)	CWGN LMay NVic WCla WDav WHoo
– ssp. ***sphaerocephala***	GCra NWCA
'Captain Blood' (D.Prim)	CBos CBot CDec CGle CVer ECtt ELan EOrc ESis GAbr NEgg NHar NHol SIng SMrm SPer WHil WPbr
'Carmen' (Prim)	LFox NNrd
– (x ***pubescens***) (2)	See P. x ***p.*** 'Boothman's Variety'
'Carnation' (Poly)	EWoo GAbr MFie NJap
'Casquet'	GAbr
cernua (17)	GArf GDra MFie NGre NHar WDav
'Charlene (D.Prim)	GAbr NHar SRms
Chartreuse Group (Poly)	CGle EDon GAbr MFie NJap WSun
'Cherry' (Prim)	CCot CVer LSur
'Chevithorne Pink' (Poly)	CGle
chionantha **AGM**	Widely available
§ – Sinopurpurea Group (18)	CGle CHoc CPla ELun EMNN GCra GDra MBal MBro NCra NKay NLin
'Chocolate Soldier' (D.Prim)	CBot CGle ECtt ELan GGar MBal NHol NJap SIng WHil WPbr
chungensis (4)	CCla CGle CHoc CMea GCal GCra GTou MBri MSta NHar NKay NLin WDav WHal
§ – x ***pulverulenta*** (4)	EBre LBre NHol
x ***chunglenta***	See P. ***chungensis*** x ***pulverulenta***
¶ 'Clarence Elliott' (2)	MCas
clarkei (11)	EPot GArf GTou MFir MHig NHar NWCA SGil SHer
'Cluny'	GArf
clusiana (2)	GDra MBal NGre NHol WDav
cockburniana (4)	CHoc CRow CVer GDra GGar GTou MBal MBri MFie NCra NGre NHar NHol NLin WDav
¶ – hybrids (4)	WDav
concholoba (17)	CPla EBar ELan GAbr GArf GCra GGar GTou MFie NGre NHar NLin NMen WDav
'Corporal Baxter' (D.Prim)	CGle EDon ELan EOrc GAbr MCas NEgg NHol SHer SIng WElm WHil WPbr WSun
cortusoïdes (7)	CPla GCra MBro NCra NWCA SRms
Cottage Mixed (Prim)	NCat
Cowichan (Poly)	CCot CDec CWGN GAbr LFox MBri MBro NCra NJap
Cowichan Amethyst Group (Poly)	EDon GAbr
Cowichan Blue Group (Poly)	EDon EWoo GAbr LHop WSun
Cowichan Garnet Group (Poly)	CMil EDon EWoo GAbr MFie SMrm WSun
Cowichan Venetian Group (Poly)	EDon GAbr
Cowichan Yellow Group (Poly)	EDon GAbr WCot
'Craven Gem' (Poly)	LSur MHig NKay NRoo
'Crescendo' (Poly)	GAbr MPit NRoo
'Crimson Cushion'	NNrd
'Crimson Queen' (Prim)	LSur
'Crimson Velvet' (2)	GAbr WDav
crispa	See P. ***glomerata***
¶ x ***crucis*** (2)	NGar
* ***cuneata***	GTou
¶ 'Dales Red'	NHed
daonensis (2)	MFie NMen
darialica (11)	CGle CPla ELan GDra MYat NCra NHol NMen
'David Green' (Prim)	CVer
'Dawn Ansell' (D.Prim)	CBot CBre CGle CRow EBre ECas ECtt EDon EFol ELan EOrc ESis GGar LBre LHop MBal MBri MRav NEgg NHar NSti SAxl SIng SPer WHil WRus WSun
Daybreak Group (Poly)	EWoo GAbr MFie
denticulata **AGM**	Widely available
– ***alba*** (9)	Widely available

– 'Bressingham Beauty' (9)	EBre LBre MUlv
– ***cashmeriana*** (9)	CNic ELan MUlv WCla WPbr
– 'Glenroy Crimson' (9)	CRDP MBal
– 'Inshriach Carmine' (9)	GDra
– lilac (9)	CBow EHon GTou MFie NJap NPri
– purple (9)	GAbr IBlr NRoo
– red (9)	CRow EMNN EPar NOrc NPri
– 'Robinson's Red' (9)	EPot
– rose (9)	MFie NHar
– 'Rubinball' (9)	EBre GAri LBre NHol NRoo
– ruby (9)	CSco EHon GAbr GTou MBri MFie NBro NJap NOak WHen WHoo WPbr
– 'Snowball' (9)	MBro MFir NOak WHen WHoo
x ***deschmannii***	See P. x ***vochinensis***
'Desert Sunset' (Poly)	EDon EWoo GAbr MFie
'Dianne'	See P. x ***forsteri*** 'D.'
'Dorothy' (Poly)	CBre CBro LSur NNrd
'Double Lilac' (D.Prim)	See P. ***vulgaris*** 'Lilacina Plena'
'Duckyls Red' (Prim)	ELan GAbr SRms
'Dusky Lady'	MBri WPbr
'E R Janes' (Prim)	LSur
'Early Irish Yellow' (Prim)	LSur
'Easter Bonnet'	NHar
edelbergii (12)	EPot MFie WDav
edgeworthii (21)	GArf NHol WAbe
elatior AGM	CGle CKin CNic CPla CRow CSev CShe ELun ESis GDra GLil LFox MHew MSal NCra NHol NJap NMir NOrc NRoo NSla NSti SIng SPer SUsu WCla WEas WHil
– JCA 785.150 (30)	WDav
– ssp. ***intricata*** (30)	CNic MFie
– ssp. ***leucophylla*** (30)	ELun EPad MHig
§ – ssp. ***meyeri*** (30)	CShe MFos NHol
¶ – ssp. ***pallasii*** (30)	LGre
– ssp. ***pallasii*** JCA 786.500 (30)	MFie
¶ – ssp. ***pallasii*** JJH 9192145 (30)	MFie
ellisiae (21)	MFie WDav
'Erin's Gem' (Poly)	CGle
erythra (26)	NGre NHol
'Ethel Barker' (2)	EPot ITim LFox MCas MHig NGre NHar NHed NMen SIng SSmi WAbe WDav WThu
'Ethel M Dell' (D.Prim)	ELan EOrc NHar NHol SIng SRms WCla WHal
'Eugénie' (D.Prim)	CBot CGle EFol ELan GAbr MYat NHar SIng SPer WHil WPbr
farinosa (11)	CArn CNic CPla ELun GAbr LGan MBal MBri MBro MHew MSal NCra NGre NHar NKay NMen WCla WDav WPer
¶ – JCA 786.500 (11)	MFie
'Fire Dance' (Poly)	EDon EWoo GAbr MFie
Firefly Group (Poly)	GAbr LFox NCat
firmipes (26)	EPot NHol
§ ***flaccida*** AGM	ELan GCLN GCra GDra MBal MFie NCra NGre NHar NHol NMen WAbe
x ***flagellicaulis***	See P. x ***polyantha***
Flamingo Group (Poly)	EDon MFie NJap
§ x ***floerkeana*** (2)	NHar WAbe
florindae AGM	Widely available
– hybrids (26)	CBre LFox MFie NHol WDav WHal
– orange (26)	CSam IBlr WCru
– red (26)	CBre MSta NHol NKay NOak
Footlight Parade Group (Prim)	CMil EWoo GAbr NCat
forrestii (3)	CNic EPot MFie NGre NHar NSla SGil
– CLD 1242 (3)	MFie
– CLD 738 (3)	MFie
§ x ***forsteri*** (2)	CShe EMNN ITim MHig NHar NHed NHol NKay NMen WAbe
§ – 'Bileckii' (2)	CHoc ELun LBee MBal MBro MHig MYat NGre NHar NHed NHol NKay NNrd NWCA SGil SIng SSmi WAbe WDav WHil
§ – 'Dianne' (2)	CHoc CNic EPot GAbr MBro MCas MHig MYat NHar NHol NNrd NRed NRya SGil SIng WAbe WThu
'Freckles' (D.Prim)	ELan GGar NHar NHol SIng SPer WCla WHil WPbr
'Freedom'	See P. x ***pubescens*** 'F.'
frondosa AGM	CGle CHoc CMea CPla CShe EMNN ESis GAbr GCra LFox MBal MBri MBro MFie MPit NCra NHar NHol NJap NKay NMen NWCA SMrm WAbe WEas WHil WHoo WOMN WThu
'Frühlingszauber' (Prim)	NHol
Fuchsia Victorians Group (Poly)	EWoo GAbr MFie NJap
Galligaskins Group (Poly)	CCot NGar
'Garryard Guinevere'	See P. 'Guinevere'
'Gartenmeister Bartens' (Prim)	LSur
gaubaeana (12)	MFie WDav
¶ ***gemmifera*** var. ***zambalensis*** (11)	WAbe
geraniifolia (7)	MFie NRoo
§ 'Ghia'	EDon EWoo GAbr
'Gigha' (Prim)	NHol
glaucescens (2)	CNic MFie NHar NHol NSla SIng WDav
– JCA 786.900 (2)	MFie NHol
'Glebe Grey' (Prim)	CGle
§ ***glomerata*** (5)	NKay WDav
'Gloriosa' (Prim)	CCot LSur
'Glowing Embers' (4)	ELun MArl NBir NLin
glutinosa (2)	ITim WDav
Gold Laced Group (Poly)	Widely available
'Gordon'	NGar
gracilipes (21)	CGle GArf NHar NKay SRms
– L&S 1 (21)	NHar NHol
– L&S 1166 (21)	NHar NHol
– early form (21)	NHar NHol
– 'Heathpool' (21)	NHar NHol
– late form (21)	NHar NHol
♦ – 'Major' (21)	See P. ***bracteosa***
¶ – 'Masterton' (21)	NHar NHol
– mid form (21)	NHol
– 'Minor'	See P. ***petiolaris***
– 'Winter Jewel' (21)	NHar NHol
'Graham'	NGar
Grand Canyon Group (Poly)	EWoo GAbr MFie NJap

'Granny Graham' (Prim) CBot ELan NHar SRms WCla WHil WPbr
griffithii (21) NHol
'Groeneken's Glory' (Prim) CGle CNic CRiv ELan ELun MBri NCra NHol SPer WPbr
§ 'Guinevere' AGM Widely available
§ *halleri* (11) CNic CPla GAbr GCHN GCra MBal MFie NCra NHar NNor NNrw NRed NWCA WCla WOMN WPat
– 'Longiflora' See P. *h.*
Harbinger Group (Prim) CDec CGle GAbr LSur NHol NNrd
'Harbour Lights' EWoo GAbr MFie
Harlow Carr hybrids (4) NDea NHol NRoo WDav WHil
Harvest Yellows Group (Poly) EDon EWoo GAbr MFie
¶ *hazarica* JCA (11) CNic
x *heeri* (2) EPot
helodoxa See P. *prolifera*
¶ 'Hemswell Blush' MFie
¶ 'Hemswell Embers' MFie
'Herbert Beresford' NMen
heucherifolia (7) CBot CCla CPla GAbr LFox NLin WHil
hirsuta (2) CNic GTou LBee MFie NWCA
¶ – 'Lismore Snow' (2) WDav
Hose in Hose (Poly) CCot CGle LFox NCra NGar NNrd
¶ 'Hurstwood Midnight' MFie
* 'Husky' AGM MPit NPri NRoo
hyacinthina (17) GArf NGre WThu
ianthina (4) GGar
Indian Reds Group (Poly) EDon EWoo GAbr MFie NJap
'Ingram's Blue' (Prim) CRow
Inshriach hybrids (4) CMHG CNic GAbr GDra GGar LHop MBri MFie MSte NHol WDav WHal
x *intermedia* (2) MHig WHil
'Inverewe' AGM CBro CRiv GAbr GDra GGar LHop NHar NRoo SMrm
involucrata (11) CBot CRiv NHar NKay NMen NTow WPat
– ssp. *yargongensis* (11) CBre CGle CHoc CPla GGar MBal MBri MFie NGre NWCA SIng WHil
ioessa (26) CPla EBre GCra LBre MBal MBri NHol NJap NTow WOMN
– hybrids MFie
'Iris Mainwaring' (Prim) EPot LSur NCra SIng WHil WPbr
'Ivy Agnee' NGar
Jack in the Green Group (Poly) CCla CCot CDec CGle CNic ECas GAbr LFox NBar NCra NGar NNrd NRya SHer WHer WRus
¶ Jackanapes Group (Poly) NGar
¶ Jackanapes on Horseback Group (Poly) NGar
japonica AGM CBow CCla CGle CMHG CMea CRDP CRow CWGN ECha ELun EPot GMac GPlt GTou LMay MFir NBro NCra NHar NMen NNor NRoo SBla SUsu WChe WCla
– 'Alba' (4) GAul
– 'Apple Blossom' (4) NHed
– 'Fuji' (4) ELun GCra GDra LHop MBal MBri MSta NJap SIng WHal
– 'Glowing Embers' (4) CGle ELan MBri MFie NJap
– 'Miller's Crimson' (4) Widely available
– 'Oriental Sunrise' (4) NJap SPer
– 'Postford White' (4) Widely available
– red shades (4) NJap NSti WAbe
– 'Valley Red' (4) GCra GGar
jesoana (7) NTow
'Jill' GAbr LSur
¶ 'Joan Hughes' SIng
'Johanna' (11) EBre EPot GAbr GArf GGar LBre NGar NHar
'Jo-Jo' (2) MCas
juliae (30) CGle CPla CRDP CRiv MHlr NGre NHol NKay NNrd WEas
– white (30) CGle
x *juribella* (2) NHar
'Ken Dearman' (D.Prim) CBot CGle CSpe ECtt EDon EFol ELan ESis GAbr GGar MBal MHlr MRav NEgg NSti SIng SPer WCot WHal WHil WPbr
kewensis AGM MFie NWCA
'Kinlough Beauty' (Poly) CCot CDec CElw CRow CShe ELun EMNN EPar EPla GAbr LFox LSur NCra NHol NRoo NSti SIng WCru WDav WEas WHil
kisoana (7) CNic CPla WCru
– *alba* (7) CBre CPla CRDP WCru
'Lady Greer' AGM CBro CCot CElw CGle CPla CRow ELan EMNN GAbr LFox LSur MBri MCas MFir MHig NBir NCra NGre NHar NHol NNrd NSti NWCA SIng SSmi WEas WPbr WWat
'Lambrook Lilac' (Poly) CRow CVer
'Lambrook Yellow' (Poly) CGle
§ *latifolia* (2) CShe NCra NHar WDav
– cream (2) NGre NHed
– 'Crimson Velvet' (2) EPot MHig SRms WThu
laurentiana See P. *mistassinica macropoda*
'Lee Myers' (2) WDav
¶ 'Lilac Fairy' MCas
'Lilian Harvey' (D.Prim) CBot CGle EBre ECtt ELan LBre MCas MRav NBir NEgg NHol NRed SPer WHal WHil WPbr
Limelight Group (Poly) EWoo GAbr MFie
'Lingwood Beauty' (Prim) CVer LSur NKay
'Linnet' (21) ITim NHol
¶ 'Lismore Snow' NHar
'Lismore Yellow' (2) CNic MHig NGre NHar NHol WAbe WDav
Lissadel hybrids (4) MFie NHol
'Little Egypt' (Poly) EDon EWoo GAbr
littoniana See P. *vialii*
'Lizzie Green' (Prim) NCra NHol
§ x *loiseleurii* (2) EBre LBre
luteola (11) MFie
macrophylla (18) GCLN GLil GTou MBal
– H 78 (18) GDra MSte NGre
¶ – var. *moorcroftiana* (18) GCLN
magellanica (11) WAbe
malacoïdes (3) MBri

marginata **AGM**	CGle CRiv ELun EMNN EPar EPot GAbr GDra LFox LHop MRPP MYat NCra NGre NHar NHed NHol NNrd NRed NRya SSmi WAbe
– ***alba*** (2)	EPot EWes GAbr MBro MCas MHig MYat NCra NGar NHar NHed NKay NNrd SIng SSmi WAbe WDav WHil WThu
– 'Amethyst'	EPot
– 'Arthur Branch' (2)	EPot WAbe
– 'Baldock's Mauve'	NGar
– 'Barbara Clough'	NGar WAbe
– 'Beamish' (2)	EPot NGar NRya
– 'Beatrice Lascaris' (2)	CRiv EPot ITim MBro MCas MFie MHig MYat NGar NHar NHol NMen NNrd NRya WAbe WDav WHil WThu
¶ – 'Boothman's Variety'	NGar
– 'Caerulea' (2)	EPot GArf MHig MYat NGar NHol WAbe WThu
– 'Clear's Variety' (2)	CHoc EMNN EPot MCas MHig MYat NHar NMen WDav
– 'Correvon's Variety' (2)	NCra NGar
– cut-leaved (2)	WDav
– 'Doctor Jenkins' (2)	NHar WDav
– 'Drake's Form' (2)	EPot ITim MCas MHig NHol NNrd
– 'Earl L Bolton' (2)	EPot NGar NHol NNrd WAbe WDav
– 'Elizabeth Fry' (2)	LFox MCas NNrd
– 'F W Millard' (2)	NHar WDav
– 'Grandiflora' (2)	NGar NHar NHol NNrd WDav
– 'Highland Twilight' (2)	CNic MRPP NNrd
– 'Holden Variety' (2)	CNic MBal MBro MCas MHig NGar NHar NHed NHol NMen NNrd WAbe WDav
¶ – 'Hurstwood' (2)	CNic
– 'Hyacinthia' (2)	CShe EPot MCas NHol NNrd WAbe
– 'Ivy Agea' (2)	EPot
– 'Janet' (2)	MHig WDav
– 'Jenkins Variety' (2)	EPot
– 'Kesselring's Variety' (2)	ELan EPot MBro MCas MHig MRPP MYat NGar NHar NHed NHol NRed SSmi WAbe WDav WHil WWin
¶ – KND seedling (2)	CNic
– 'Laciniata'	NGar
– 'Lilac' (2)	GCLN GDra LFox NGar NHar NNrd
– 'Linda Pope' **AGM**	CGle CNic CShe EPot ITim LBee NCra NHar NHed NHol NRed WAbe WDav
– 'Marven' (2)	EPot MBro MCas NCra NGar NNrd WDav
¶ – 'Messingham' (2)	EPot
– 'Millard's Variety' (2)	CHoc NGar NMen
– 'Miss Savory' (2)	MCas
– 'Mrs Carter Walmsley' (2)	NGar
¶ – 'Nancy Lucy' (2)	WAbe
– 'Prichard's Variety' (2)	Widely available
– 'Rheniana' (2)	EPot NGar WDav
– 'Rosea' (2)	EPot
– 'Sheila Denby' (2)	EMNN NGar
– 'Shipton' (2)	NGar

– small flowered form (2)	NGar
– 'Violet Form' (2)	MBro NHar WDav
– 'Waithman's Variety' (2)	EPot WDav
'Marianne Davey' (D.Prim)	CGle EDon EFol ELan EOrc GAbr MBri MRav MYat NEgg NHar NHol NRed NSti SHer SPer WHil WPbr
'Marie Crousse' (D.Prim)	CGle CVer EBre EDon EFol GTou LBre LHop MBal MBro MFie MYat NHar NHol NNrd NRed SHer WHal
Marine Blues Group (Poly)	EWoo GAbr MFie NCat WSun
'Mary Anne'	CTom
Mauve Victorian Group (Poly)	EDon EWoo MFie
'McWatt's Claret' (Poly)	CBre CCot EPot GAbr LSur NCra
'McWatt's Cream' (Poly)	CRiv GAbr GGar LSur NCra NMen NRya SIng
melanops (18)	CGle CPla ELan GAbr NGre NHar NWCA WDav
'Mexico'	EWoo MFie
Midnight Group (Poly)	EWoo GAbr MFie
'Miniera' (2)	EPot MCas
minima (2)	GArf GCLN GTou MCas MHig NGre NHar NHol NRed NWCA SGil
¶ – JCA 788.900 (2)	WDav
– ***alba*** (2)	EPot NHol NRya NSla
minima x ***glutinosa*** (2)	See P. x ***floerkeana***
– x ***hirsuta*** (2)	See P. x ***forsteri***
– x ***villosa*** (2)	See P. x ***truncata***
– x ***wulfeniana*** (2)	See P. x ***vochinensis***
'Miss Indigo' (D.Prim)	CGle CSam CWGN EBre ECtt EDon EFol ELan ELun EOrc LBre MBri MRav MYat NEgg NHar NHol NRed SPer WCla WHal WHil WPbr
¶ ***mistassinica alba*** (11)	MFie
§ – var. ***macropoda*** (11)	CNic GAbr MSte NWCA
¶ ***miyabeana*** B&SWJ 153	WCru
modesta (11)	CNic
– ***alba*** (11)	GCLN
*– ***arsimanimontana***	MFie
– var. ***faurieae*** (11)	MBro MFie WHoo
*– ***saximontana*** (11)	NGre
'Morton'	NGre
'Mrs McGillivray' (Prim)	NNrd
¶ Munstead Strain (Poly)	LSur
muscarioïdes (17)	CGle CPla GCra GTou MFie NHar NLin
Muted Victorian Group (Poly)	EWoo GAbr MFie
nepalensis	See P. ***tanneri n.***
New Pinks Group (Poly)	EDon EWoo GAbr MFie NCat
nivalis (18)	CPla
nutans Delavay	See P. ***flaccida***
nutans Georgi (25)	GCra GDra NHar
obconica (19)	MBri
'Old Port' (Poly)	WPat
'Old Rose' (Poly)	EWoo MFie

'Olive Wyatt' (D.Prim) CGle ELan EOrc MPit MYat NHol WHal WHil
'Oriental Sunrise' (4) LAbb MBri MFie NHol
Osiered Amber Group (Prim) CRow GAbr NHol
'Our Pat' (D.Poly) CHoc GAbr GCal IBlr NCat WCot
Pagoda hybrids (4) ELan MBri MFie NHol NJap
palinuri (2) MFie SIng
¶ Pantaloons Group (Poly) NGar
'Paris '90' (Poly) EDon EWoo MFie
parryi (20) CNic NCra NGre NHar NHol NMen NSla WDav
pedemontana (2) GCLN MSte NGre NHar NHol SIng WDav
¶ 'Peggy Fell' NSla
¶ 'Peggy Wilson' NHol
'Perle von Bottrop' (Prim) LSur MHig
'Peter Klein' (11) CRiv GDra ITim MBal MBro NHar SGil WCru WHoo WOMN
'Peter's Red' GAbr
'Peter's Violet' CHol
§ ***petiolaris*** (21) EMNN EPar GArf GCHN ITim MPit NCra NHar NHol
– LS&H 19856 (21) EPot GArf NHar
'Petticoat' NHar SIng
'Pink Gem' (D.Prim) LHop
¶ 'Pink Ice' EPot
pinnatifida (17) CNic GDra
poissonii (4) CBot CGle CPla CRDP CVer CWGN EMon GCal GCra GGar IBlr LGan LMay MBal NGre NHol NJap NKay NLin WBon
¶ – CLD 1404 (4) MFie
– CLD 485 (4) MFie
§ x ***polyantha*** (30) NHol
Polyanthus (30) GDra NCra NKay
polyneura (7) CBot CNic CPla GCra MBal MBro MFie MHig MNes NDea NHol NMen NWCA WDav WEas WWat
praenitens See P. ***sinensis***
'Prince Silverwings' (D.Poly) WEas
§ ***prolifera*** AGM CMHG CTrw ECha GAbr GCra GGar LGan LMay MArl MFir NHol NLin NSti SBla SHig SPer SPla SUsu WHal WHil WWat
x ***pruhonicensis*** See under ***cultivar name***
pseudosikkimensis See P. ***sikkimensis***
§ x ***pubescens*** AGM EPot GDra LFox MBro MFie MYat NHol NRed SGil SHer SSmi WDav WOMN
¶ – 'Alba' (2) NGar WAbe
– 'Apple Blossom' (2) EMNN EPot MFie NHol SGil SIng WDav
– 'Balfouriana' (2) CNic LFox MBro WDav
§ – 'Bewerley White' (2) CNic CRiv ELun EPot ESis MBal MBro MCas MFie MRPP NCra NHed NMen NNrd NRed NRya WEas WRus WThu WWin
– 'Blue Wave' (2) MFie
§ – 'Boothman's Variety' (2) Widely available
♦ – 'Carmen' (2) See P. x ***p.*** 'Boothman's Variety'
– 'Chamois' (2) MFie
– 'Christine' (2) CNic EMNN EPot GArf MBro MFie MHig MYat NCra NHar NHed NNrd NRed SBod WDav WHil WOMN WThu
– 'Cream Viscosa' (2) CRiv EMNN GPlt MCas MFie NHed NMen NNrd SGil WHil
– 'Crimson Velvet' (2) EMNN MFie
– 'Deep Mrs Wilson' (2) MFie
– 'Ellen Page' (2) MFie
– 'Elphenor' (2) CRiv
– 'Faldonside' (2) CNic CRiv EMNN EPot ESis GCHN MBro MCas MFie MHig MYat NCra NHed NKay NMen NNrd NRed NRya SHer WAbe WHil WThu WWin
§ – 'Freedom' (2) CHoc CNic ELan EMNN EPot GArf GPlt GTou ITim MBro MCas MFie MHig MYat NCra NHar NHed NNrd NRya SBod SHer SIng SSmi WDav WHil WPat WThu WWin
– 'George Harrison' (2) MFie
– 'Gnome' (2) WThu
– 'Harlow Car' (2) EMNN EPot ESis GCLN ITim LFox MCas MFie MHig MYat NGre NHar NHed NMen NNrd NRya SBla WAbe WDav WHil WThu
– 'Henry Hall' (2) ELun MCas MFie SGil SHer WDav
¶ – 'Hurstwood Red Admiral' (2) EMNN
– 'Joan Danger' (2) CNic EMNN MFie
– 'Joan Gibbs' (2) EPot MFie MHig NCra NHar NHed NNrd SGil WDav
– 'Kath Dryden' (2) MCas MFie
¶ – 'Lilac Fairy' (2) NHed
¶ – 'Moonlight' MCas
– 'Mrs J H Wilson' (2) CRiv ITim MBal MCas MFie MHig NCra NHed NKay NMen NNrd NRed SSmi WHil WRus
– 'Pat Barwick' (2) EPot LFox MFie NHed NMen NRed WDav WHil
– 'Peggy Fell' (2) MFie
– 'Pink Freedom' (2) NHed WDav
¶ – 'Pink Ice' (2) CBre
– 'Rufus' (2) CHoc CRiv ITim MBal MCas MFie MHig NCra NHed SBla SGil WDav WHil WThu
– 'S E Matthews' (2) NNrd
¶ – 'Sid Skelton' (2) EMNN
– 'Sonya' (2) MFie
– 'The General' (2) CHoc MCas MFie MHig NCra NNrd SGil WDav WHil WWin
¶ – 'Wedgwood' (2) EMNN
– 'Wharfedale Gem' (2) NHar NNrd
x ***pubescens*** x ***allionii*** (2) NNrd
pulchra (21) NHar
pulverulenta AGM Widely available
– Bartley hybrids AGM CBot CGle ELun NCat NKay SUsu WHal
– 'Bartley Pink' (4) CPla NHol
¶ 'Purple Splendour' LSur
'Purpurkissen' (Prim) NHol NNrd
'Quaker's Bonnet' See P. ***vulgaris*** 'Lilacina Plena'
'Ramona' (Poly) EDon EWoo MFie
'Raven' NMen
'Ravenglass Vermilion' (4) See P. 'Inverewe'

Plant	Suppliers
'Red Paddy' (D.Prim/Poly)	MPit
'Red Sunset' (4)	GDra
'Red Velvet' (D.Prim)	LHop NHar NHol
¶ 'Redpoll'	NHar
reidii (28)	MBri MFie NCra NHar
– var. ***williamsii*** (28)	CPla EBre GCLN GDra GTou LBre MBal MBri NGre NHar NRya NSla WAbe WDav
– – ***alba*** (28)	GCLN GDra MBal MBri NGre NHar WDav
'Reverie' (Poly)	EDon EWoo GAbr MFie NCat
'Rhubarb and Custard' (Poly)	CGle
'Romeo' (Prim)	CVer NCra
'Rose O'Day' (D.Prim)	ELan EOrc MBal NEgg NHol NSti WElm WHil
rosea AGM	CBot CPla CRDP CRow CTom ELun GDra GTou LHop MBal MFie MHig NCra NDea NGre NHar NJap NKay NSti NVic SBla SIng WChe WEas WRus
– C&Mc 367 (11)	GCHN
– 'Delight'	See P. ***r.*** 'Micia Visser-de Geer'
– 'Gigas' (11)	MSta
– 'Grandiflora' (11)	CBow CGle CHoc CNic CWGN EHon ELan EMNN EPar GPlt LAbb LMay MBri MCas MPit NHed NHol NLin NMen NRed NRoo NTow SCro WHil WOMN WPer
§ – 'Micia Visser-de Geer' (11)	NKay SPer
*– ***splendens*** (11)	IDai SChu
rotundifolia	See P. ***roxburghii***
'Rowallane Rose' (4)	CBro
roxburghii (25)	GArf
'Roy Cope' (D.Prim)	CSpe EBre EDon GGar LBre MBal MPit NBir NNrd SIng
rubra	See P. ***erythra***
rusbyi (20)	MFie NHar NMen WDav
Rustic Reds Group (Poly)	EWoo MFie NJap
'Sandy's Form' (21)	EPot NHol
saxatilis (7)	CHoc GGar MCas MFie SIng WHil
scandinavica (11)	MFie
x ***scapeosa*** (21)	GArf MBal NHar
scapigera (21)	NHol
– DF 614 (21)	EBul
§ 'Schneekissen' (Prim)	CCot CElw CTom CVer EBre ELun EOrc EPla GAbr LBre LSur WHer WRus
scotica (11)	CHoc CNic GArf GTou LFox MBal MFie NCra NRed NTow NWCA WAbe WCla WThu
'Sea Way' (Prim)	LGre MRav
secundiflora (26)	CBow CCla CGle CHoc CNic CPla CWGN ELan GAbr GCra GDra GTou MBal NCra NKay NMen NRed SPer SUsu WAbe WDav
– CLD 363/488 (26)	MFie
x ***serrata*** (2)	See P. x ***vochinensis***
serratifolia (4)	SBla
sibirica	See P. ***nutans*** Georgi
sibthorpii	See P. ***vulgaris sibthorpii***

Plant	Suppliers
sieboldii AGM	CBre CGle CHan CRDP CRiv CRow CShe EGol ELun EMNN LAbb LFox MBal MBri NCra NHar NRya NVic NWCA SAxl SIng WEas WHal WHil
– ***alba*** (7)	SWas WCru
– 'Carefree' (7)	GMac NHol NNrd
– 'Cherubim' (7)	CHoc EBre ECtt GCHN LBre NNrd
– 'Colin' (7)	EDon
– 'Dancing Ladies' (7)	CGle CNic ELan GAbr MFie NHol NJap NRed WSun
– 'Galaxy' (7)	CMil GAbr NHol NRed
– 'Geisha Girl' (7)	CTom EBre ECtt GCHN LBre MRav NHed
– 'Joan Jervis' (7)	EDon
– 'Lilac Sunbonnet' (7)	CGle NHol NNrd
– 'Manankoora' (7)	CDec CGle ELan MFie NHol NJap NRed
– 'Mikado' (7)	EBre ECtt GCHN LBre MFie MRav NNrd
– 'Pago-Pago' (7)	CGle CNic ELun MFie NHol NJap NRed
*– 'Seraphim' (7)	EBre LBre
– 'Snowflake' (7)	CGle EBre EDon GCHN LBre NHol NNrd NRed
– 'Tah-ni' (7)	CNic ELan NHol NJap NNrd NRed
– 'Winter Dreams' (7)	CGle CNic ELun MFie NJap
– 'Wrangle Blush' (7)	EDon
– 'Wrangle Snowflake' (7)	EDon
– 'Wrangle White' (7)	EDon
§ ***sikkimensis*** (26)	Widely available
– BM&W 40 (26)	NHol
¶ – C&Mc 1022 (26)	GTou
– crimson and gold (26)	MFie NHol WDav
*– 'Phokphey' (26)	NHar
– var. ***pudibunda*** (26)	GPlt
– 'Tilman Number 2' (26)	ELun GDra MFie NHol
Silver-laced Group (Poly)	CDec CGle CRDP ELan EPar WEas WHer
§ ***sinensis*** (27)	MBri
sinoplantaginea (18)	CPla GAbr
sinopurpurea	See P. ***chionantha*** Sinopurpurea Group
smithiana	See P. ***prolifera***
* 'Snow Carpet' (Prim)	CB&S
'Snow Cushion' (Prim)	See P. 'Schneekissen'
sonchifolia (21)	GArf GDra NHar
¶ ***sorachiana*** (11)	GArf
'Soup Plate' (21)	NHol
spectabilis (2)	CArn CNic NHar NHol NMen WAbe WHoo
¶ – JCA 789.400	MFie WDav
¶ – JCA 789.401	MFie
¶ ***specuicola***	WDav
– JCA 8926 (11)	CNic
Spice Shades Group (Poly)	CDec EDon EWoo GAbr MFie NHol
Springtime Group (Prim)	NCat
sp. CLD 1173	MFie
¶ sp. CLD 1217 (4)	MFie
sp. CLD 183	EMon
sp. CLD 222 (26)	NHol
sp. CLD 351 (7)	NHol

sp. CLD 487 (4)	MFie
sp. CLD 586 (26)	NHol
sp. CLD 708 (7)	NHol
x ***steinii***	See P. x ***forsteri***
'Stradbrook Gem'	NGar
'Strawberries and Cream'	CRow
stricta (11)	CNic MFie
Striped Victorian Group	CMil EWoo GAbr MFie NHol
'Sue Jervis' (D.Prim)	CVer EBre EDon ELun GCal LBre MBri NHar WEas WHer WHil WPbr WRus
suffrutescens (8)	NMen NSla WDav WThu
Sunset Group	CNat MFie WFro
'Sunshine Susie' (D.Prim)	CGle CHoc EBre ECtt EDon ELan GAbr LBre MBri MRav MYat NCat NEgg NHol NSti SHer SIng WHal WHil WPbr
'Sylvia' (Prim)	NHol
takedana (24)	NHar
tanneri (21)	NHol
– ssp. ***nepalensis*** (21)	ITim NHol
'Tantallon' (21)	EPot GArf
'Tawny Port' (Poly)	CBrd CBro CCot CGle CHoc CRiv CRow CVer EPot GAbr LSur NCra NNrd WRus
'Techley Red' (Prim)	EPot GAbr
'The Grail' (Prim)	LSur NKay
'Tipperary Purple' (Prim)	GAbr LSur
'Tomato Red' (Prim)	CRow CVer GAbr NCra NKay
'Torchlight' (Prim)	LHop
tosaensis (24)	NMen
¶ 'Tournaig Pink' (4)	GGar
x ***truncata*** (2)	NHal
uralensis	See P. ***veris macrocalyx***
'Val Horncastle' (D.Prim)	CSpe ECtt EFol EOrc GAbr MRav MYat NEgg NHar NHol NSti SHer SPer SPla WCla WElm WHal WHil WPbr
Valentine Victorians (Poly)	EWoo GAbr MFie
x ***variabilis***	See P. x ***polyantha***
veris **AGM**	Widely available
¶ – ssp. ***canescens*** JCA 789.600 (30)	MFie
– ssp. ***columnae*** (30)	NHol
– hybrids (30)	NHol WDav
– red (30)	CRDP
vernalis	See P. ***vulgaris***
verticillata (12)	MFie
§ ***vialii*** **AGM**	Widely available
Victorian shades (Poly)	NCat
§ ***villosa*** (2)	GTou NHol
– var. ***cottica*** (2)	See P. ***villosa***
Violet Victorians (Poly)	MFie WSun
viscosa Allioni	See P. ***latifolia***
§ x ***vochinensis*** (2)	CRiv EPot MBro MHig MSte MYat NHar NHol NKay NNrd NWCA SIng WAbe
§ ***vulgaris*** (30)	CArn CBre CBro CGle CKin CPla CRow CSFH EBre ECha ELun ENot EPar LBre LFox LHol MBri MHig NCra NHol NJap NLan NMir NOrc SIng SPer WChe WCla WOak WRus
– ***alba*** (30)	CGle CRow ECha MHig NSla WDav
– 'Alba Plena' (30)	CBro CGle CRow GAbr GGar IBlr NSla SHer SRms WEas
– Ballyrogan cream edge (30)	CRow IBlr
– 'Brendon Hills' (30)	CRow
– Cornish pink (30)	GAbr
* – double red	NHar
– 'Double Sulphur' (30)	CRow ELan
– green flowered (30)	See P. *v.* 'Viridis'
§ – 'Lilacina Plena' (30)	CBot CDec CGle CRow CSam EFol GAbr IBlr MYat NSti SHer SIng SSvw WCla WEas WHal WHer WHil
§ – ssp. ***sibthorpii*** **AGM**	CBro CElw CGle CHoc CNic COtt EJud ELun EPla GAbr GTou LFox LHop LSur NBro NCra NHol NNrd NWCA SBla SChu WCra WDav
¶ – ssp. ***sibthorpii*** JCA 790.401 (30)	MFie
– 'Viridis' (30)	CRow IBlr WCot
waltonii (26)	CBot CNic CPla CWGN GCra MBal MHig WCru WHal
¶ – hybrids (26)	GGar
'Wanda' **AGM**	CB&S CBro CCot CGle CRow CShe CWGN EFou ELan ELun EPar GAbr LHop LSur MPit NGre NHol NSti SBla SIng SPer WEas WHoo WPbr
'Wanda Hose in Hose' (Prim)	CBro CGle CTom GAbr NHol NRya SRms WHer WHil
'Wanda Jack in the Green' (Prim)	CRow
wardii	See P. ***involucrata***
warshenewskiana (11)	CBre CNic CPla EMNN EPot GAbr GCHN MBal MCas MHig MRPP NCra NGre NHar NMen NNrd NRed NTow NWCA SBod WEas WThu
¶ 'Wharfedale Bluebell'	NGar NHar NHol
¶ 'Wharfedale Butterfly'	NGar
'Wharfedale Ling' (2)	NGar NHol NSla WAbe
'Wharfedale Superb' (2)	NGar NHar NHol WAbe
'Wharfedale Village' (2)	NGar NHar
'White Wanda' (Prim)	CRow LGre LSur SHer WCru
whitei (21)	CBrd MBal NHar SHer
§ – 'Sherriff's Variety' (21)	GArf IBlr
'William Genders' (Poly)	CBro CTom GAbr LSur
wilsonii (4)	CPla GAbr GArf GBuc GCra MNes NHol
'Windrush'	See P. x ***berninae*** 'W.'
¶ 'Winifred'	NHed
'Winter White' (Poly)	See P. 'Ghia'
'Wisley Red' (Prim)	CTom CVer LSur
wulfeniana (2)	CNic CRiv MFie NMen
yargongensis	See P. ***involucrata yargongensis***
yuparensis (11)	GAbr GTou MFie NMen WDav
'Zenobia'	NGar

PRINSEPIA (Rosaceae)

¶ ***sinensis***	MBlu

PRITCHARDIA (Palmae/Arecaceae)

See Plant Deletions

PROSOPIS (Leguminosae/Mimosaceae)

chilensis	See P. ***glandulosa***
pubescens	CGre

PROSTANTHERA (Labiatae/Lamiaceae)

¶ *aspalathoïdes*	LGre
cuneata AGM	Widely available
– 'Alpine Gold'	CDec CMHG GCal
– 'Fastigiata'	CPle GCal
lasianthos	CAbb CB&S CHan CPle CTro ECou LGre WPer WWye
– *coriacea*	CPle
melissifolia	LBlm
– var. *parvifolia*	CB&S CTrw GCHN WBod WHer WSHC
nivea	CPle CTre CTro
ovalifolia	ECou LHop
'Poorinda Ballerina'	LGre LHop
'Poorinda Pixie'	CBot WBod
rotundifolia AGM	CArn CB&S CBow CGre CHan CNew CPle CTre CTro ERea ISea LAbb LBlm MAll SHil SLMG WBod WWye
– *alba*	CBot
– 'Chelsea Girl'	See P. ***r. rosea***
§ – *rosea*	CB&S CGre CPle CSev CTre ERea GCal LHop SLMG WWye
¶ *saxicola* var. *montana*	LGre
sieberi	CBow CNew CTre CTrw
walteri	CMHG CPle ECou LGre SAxl SChu SUsu

PROTEA (Proteaceae)

compacta	SIgm
cynaroïdes	CHEx CTro SIgm

PRUMNOPITYS (Podocarpaceae)

§ *andina*	CGre SLon WWat
elegans	See P. ***andina***
§ *ferruginea*	ECou SBor
§ – 'Golden Dwarf'	CMer
§ *taxifolia*	ECou

PRUNELLA (Labiatae/Lamiaceae)

§ *grandiflora*	CBow CHol CLew CRow CSco GBar MWat NBee NGre NKay SRms WCHb WHoo WWye
– *alba*	CBow CDoC CPle NKay SChu WCHb WHil
– 'Blue Loveliness'	CBoy CNic ELan GAbr GDra SPla WCHb
– 'Little Red Riding Hood'	See P. ***g.*** 'Rotkäppchen'
– 'Loveliness' AGM	CBow CDoC CSco CTom EBre ECha ECtt ELan EOrc EPar LBre MRav NBro NMir SBod SPer WHal WHil WWin
– 'Pagoda'	EHal LAbb NBrk NOak NPri WCHb WElm
– 'Pink Loveliness'	CBos CBow CBoy CNic CRow CSco EBre ECha EGol EOrc EPar GCHN GDra GMac LBre MBal NMir SPer WByw WEas WPer WWin
– *rosea*	CPle WByw
§ – 'Rotkäppchen'	CRDP CTom EBre ECtt GCHN LBre MRav SPer WCHb
– 'White Loveliness'	CRow CTom EBre ECha EGol EOrc EPar GAbr GCHN GDra GGar GMac LBre NBrk NMir SPer SPla WByw WEas WPer WRus WTyr WWin
incisa	See P. ***vulgaris***
* 'Inshriach Ruby'	NBir SPla WCHb
laciniata	CRDP WCHb WHer WHil
§ *vulgaris*	CArn CKin CSFH ECWi EJud ELan EWFC Effi GAbr GBar GPoy IEde LHol MChe MHew MSal NLan NMir NSti SIde WCHb WCla WHer WOak WWye
– *alba*	WHer WNdy
– *lilacina*	LBlm
x *webbiana*	See P. ***grandiflora***

PRUNUS † (Rosaceae)

'Accolade' AGM	CAbP CDoC CLnd COtt CSam CSco CTho EBre ECtt ENot GRei IOrc LBre MBri NWea SHBN SIgm SPer SSta WDin WJas WStI
§ 'Amanogawa' AGM	CB&S CBra CLnd CSam CSco EBre EHar ELan ENot GRei IDai IJoh LBre LBuc LNet MBal MBar MBri MGos NBar NWea SChu SHBN SIgm SKee SPer SPla SReu WJas WTyn
* – 'Baggesen's Variety '	CLnd
x *amygdalopersica* 'Pollardii'	ENot NWea SIgm WJas
– 'Spring Glow'	CDoC MBri WJas WTyr
amygdalus	See P. ***dulcis***
F *armeniaca* 'Alfred'	CSco ECas EHar GTwe MBri SDea SFru SIgm SKee SPer WJas
F – 'Bredase'	SDea
– 'De Nancy'	See P. ***a.*** 'Gros Pêche'
F – 'Early Moor Park'	CDoC ECas EWar GBon GRei GTwe MBea NElm SDea SFam SFru SIgm WWeb
F – 'Farmingdale'	SDea SFru SKee
F – 'Goldcot'	SDea
F – 'Gros Pêche'	CMac
F – 'Hongaarse'	SDea
F – 'Moor Park'	CSco EHar ERea GTwe IJoh LBuc MGos NRog SDea SFru SKee WHig WStI
F – 'New Large Early'	CSco ECas GTwe SDea SFru SIgm SKee
F – 'Royal'	CMac
F – 'Tross Orange'	SDea
'Asano'	See P. 'Geraldinae'
avium AGM	CB&S CBra CKin CLnd CPer EHar ENot GRei ISea LBuc MBar MBri MGos MRav NBee NRoo NWea SHBN SKee SPer WDin WMou
F – 'Amber Heart'	SDea SKee
F – 'August Heart'	SKee
F – 'Bigarreau Gaucher'	CSco SDea SFru SKee
F – 'Bigarreau Napoléon'	CSco GTwe MGos NElm SDea SFru SKee
F – 'Black Eagle'	SKee
F – 'Black Elton'	SKee
F – 'Black Glory'	SKee
F – 'Black Heart'	SKee
F – 'Black Tartarian'	SKee

F – 'Bradbourne Black' CSco SFru SKee
F – 'Caroon' SKee
– 'Cherokee' See P. *a.* 'Lapins'
F – 'Circassian Black' SKee
F – 'Colney' GTwe SFru
F – 'Early Rivers' CSco ECas EWar GTwe IJoh SDea SFru SKee
F – 'Elton Heart' SKee
F – 'Emperor Francis' SKee
F – 'Florence' CSco SKee
F – 'Frogmore Early' CSco
F – 'Governor Wood' CSco GTwe NElm SKee
F – 'Hertford' SFru
F – 'Inga' MBea
F – 'Ironsides' SKee
F – 'Kassins Frühe Herz' SKee
F – 'Kent Bigarreau' CSco
F – 'Kentish Red' CSco
F – 'Lapins' CSco GTwe SDea SFru SKee WHig WJas
– 'May Duke' See P. x *gondouinii* 'M.D.'
F – 'Merchant' CDoC GTwe SFru SKee
F – 'Mermat' GTwe
F – 'Merpet' GTwe
F – 'Merton Bigarreau' CMac CSco SDea SFru SKee
F – 'Merton Bounty' CMac CSco
F – 'Merton Crane' CSco
F – 'Merton Favourite' CSco SFru SKee
F – 'Merton Glory' CDoC CSco ECas EHar EWar GChr GTwe MGos SDea SFru SKee
F – 'Merton Heart' CMac CSco SDea SKee
F – 'Merton Late' CSco SKee
F – 'Merton Marvel' CSco SKee
F – 'Merton Premier' CSco SKee
F – 'Merton Reward' CSco SKee
F – 'Nabella' CSco
– 'Napoléon' See P. *a.* 'Bigarreau Napoléon'
F – 'Newstar' SFru
F – 'Noble' SKee
F – 'Noir de Guben' GChr GTwe SFru SKee
F – 'Nutberry Black' SKee
– 'Plena' **AGM** CB&S CLnd CTho ELan ENot GRei IOrc LBuc LPan MBal MGos NBee NWea SKee SPer WDin WJas
F – 'Ronald's Heart' SKee
F – 'Roundel' CSco SDea SFru SKee
F – 'Sasha' GTwe
F – 'Smoky Dun' SKee
F – 'Stark Hardy Giant' SKee
F – 'Starkrimson' GTwe
F – 'Stella' **AGM** CMac CSam CSco ECas EHar EWar GBon GChr GRei GTwe IJoh LBuc MBea MBri MGos NBar NBee NElm NRog SDea SFru SIgm SKee SPer WHig WJas WWeb
F – 'Stella Compact' CSco ECas GTwe LBuc MBri SKee WHig
F – 'Strawberry Heart' SKee
F – 'Summit' SFru
F – 'Sunburst' CSco ECas GTwe LBuc MBri SDea SFru SKee WHig WJas
F – 'Turkish Black' SKee
F – 'Van' CDoC CSco ECas EHar GTwe SFru SIgm SKee
F – 'Vega' ECas
F – 'Waterloo' SFru SKee
F – 'White Heart' NElm SKee
besseyi EPla
* 'Birch Bark' GRei
x ***blireana*** **AGM** CDoC CLnd CSco CTho ECtt IDai MBar MBri MRav MWat NBee SPer SReu WTyn
'Blushing Bride' See P. 'Shôgetsu'
¶ ***campanulata*** SKee
capuli See P. ***salicifolia***
cerasifera CSco GAri LBuc NWea SKee WDin WMou
F – 'Cherry Plum' SKee
– 'Crimson Dwarf' CDoC SPer
– 'Hessei' (v) CDoC MRav WPat
F – 'Kentish Red' SKee
F – Myrobalan Group CKin CSco SDea SFru SKee
N – 'Nigra' **AGM** CDoC CLnd CSco EHar ELan IDai IOrc LBuc LNet LPan MBri MGos NBar NBee SDea SHBN SPer SPla WAbe WDin WStI WTyn
– 'Pendula' WMou
§ – 'Pissardii' CBra CSco EBre GRei LBre LBuc MBar MRav NNor NWea SIgm SPer WJas
– 'Rosea' SHil
¶ – 'Vesuvius' SKee
F ***cerasus*** 'Montmorency' SDea SFru SKee
F – 'Morello' **AGM** CMac CSam CSco EBre ECas EHar EWar GBon GChr GRei GTwe IJoh LBre LBuc MBea MBri NBar NBee NElm NRog SDea SFru SIgm SKee SPer WHig WJas WWeb
F – 'Nabella' EWar
– 'Rhexii' EHar MGos SHil SPer WAbe
F – 'Wye Morello' SKee
'Cheal's Weeping' See P. 'Kiku-shidare'
§ 'Chôshû-hizakura' **AGM** CDoC CLnd EBar ECtt GRei IOrc LNet SDea SHil SPer
§ x ***cistena*** **AGM** CB&S CBot CPle CSco CShe EBre EFol ELan ENot IJoh IOrc LBre MBar MBri MGos MPla MWat NBee NKay NRoo SHBN SPer SPla WAbe WDin WPat WStI
– 'Crimson Dwarf' See P. x ***c.***
'Collingwood Ingram' SHil
conradinae See P. ***hirtipes***
F ***domestica*** 'Angelina Burdett' (D) CSco GTwe NRog SKee
F – 'Anna Späth' (C/D) SKee
F – 'Ariel' (C/D) SDea SKee
F – 'Autumn Compote' (C) SKee
F – 'Avalon' ECas GTwe SFru SIgm SKee WHig
F – 'Belgian Purple' (C) SKee
F – 'Belle de Louvain' (C) CSco GTwe NRog SDea SFru SKee
F – 'Black Prince' (C) CSco
F – 'Blaisdon Red' (C) CSco
F – 'Blue Imperatrice' (C/D) SKee
F – 'Blue Tit' (C/D) SKee
F – 'Bonne de Bry' (D) CSco SKee
F – 'Bountiful' (C) CSco
F – 'Brandy Gage' (C/D) CSco SKee
F – 'Bryanston Gage' (D) CSco SKee
F – 'Burbank' (C/D) SDea

F – 'Bush' (C) SKee
F – 'Cambridge Gage' (D) CDoC CSam CSco EBre ECas EHar ERea GBon GTwe LBre LBuc MBri MGos MWat NRog SDea SFam SFru SIgm SKee SPer WHig WStI WWeb
F – 'Coe's Golden Drop' (D) CSco GTwe MBri MGos SDea SFam SFru SIgm SKee
F – 'Count Althann's Gage' (D) EHar GTwe NRog SDea SFru SIgm SKee
F – 'Cox's Emperor' (C) CSco SKee
F – 'Crimson Drop' (D) SKee
– 'Cropper' See P. *d.* 'Laxton's Cropper'
F – 'Curlew' (C) SDea
F – 'Czar' **AGM** CDoC CSam CSco EBre ECas EHar EWar GChr GTwe IJoh IOrc LBre LBuc MBea MGos NBar NElm NRog SDea SFru SIgm SKee SPer WWeb
– 'Delicious ' See P. *d.* 'Laxton's Delicious'
– 'Denniston's Superb' See P. *d.* 'Imperial Gage'
F – 'Diamond' (C) SKee
F – 'Dittisham Ploughman' (C) CSam SKee
F – 'Early Laxton' **AGM** CSco GTwe SDea SFam SKee
– 'Early Orleans' See P. *d.* 'Monsieur Hâtif'
– 'Early Prolific' See P. *d.* 'Rivers's Early Prolific'
– 'Early Rivers' See P. *d.* 'Rivers's Early Prolific'
F – 'Early Transparent Gage' (C/D) CSco ECas GTwe SDea SFam SFru SIgm
F – 'Edwards' (C/D) CSco ECas EWar GTwe MBri NBee SDea SFam SFru SIgm SKee WHig
F – 'Excalibur' ECas GTwe SFru SIgm
F – German Prune Group (C) SKee
F – 'Giant Prune' (C) CSco GTwe NRog SKee
F – 'Godshill Blue' (C) SDea
F – 'Golden Transparent' (D) CSco GTwe NRog SFam SFru SPer
F – 'Goldfinch' (D) CSco GTwe NRog SKee
F – Green Gage Group (C/D) EHar GTwe MBea NElm NRog SDea SFam SKee SPer
F – Green Gage Group 'Old Green Gage' (D/C) SFru SIgm
F – 'Grove's Late Victoria' (C/D) CSco SKee
F – 'Guthrie's Late Green' (D) SKee
F – 'Herman' (C/D) CSam GTwe SIgm
F – 'Heron' GTwe
F – 'Imperial Epineuse' (D) SKee
F – 'Imperial Gage' **AGM** CMac ECas GRei GTwe LBuc MBri SDea SFru SIgm SKee WHig
– ssp. *institia* See P. *institia*
F – 'Jefferson' (D) CSco ECas GTwe NRog SDea SFam SFru SIgm SKee
F – 'Kea' (C) SKee
F – 'Kirke's' (D) CSco CWSG ECas GTwe MBri SDea SFam SFru SIgm SKee
F – 'Late Muscatelle' (D) SKee
F – 'Late Transparent Gage' (D) CSco
– 'Laxton's Bountiful' See P. *d.* 'Bountiful'
F – 'Laxton's Cropper' (C) CSco GTwe NRog SKee
F – 'Laxton's Delicious' (D) CSco GTwe SKee
F – 'Laxton's Delight' (D) CSco GTwe
F – 'Laxton's Gage' (D) CSco SDea SKee
F – 'Laxton's Supreme' (C/D) CSco
F – 'Marjorie's Seedling' **AGM** CDoC CSco EBre ECas EHar GBon GTwe LBre LBuc MGos MWat NElm SDea SFam SFru SIgm SKee SPer WHig WJas
F – 'McLaughlin' (D) SKee
F – 'Merton Gem' (C/D) CSco GTwe SFam SFru SKee
F – 'Monarch' (C) CSco GTwe SKee
F – 'Monsieur Hâtif' (C) SKee
F – 'Olympia' (C/D) SKee
F – 'Ontario' (C/D) CSco GTwe SKee
F – 'Opal' (D) CDoC CSco ECas EWar GTwe IJoh IOrc MGos MWat NElm SDea SIgm SKee WHig
F – 'Orleans' (C) SKee
F – 'Ouillins Gage' **AGM** CMac CSam CSco ECas EHar ERea EWar GBon GChr GTwe IJoh LBuc MBri MWat NElm NRog SDea SFam SIgm SKee SPer WJas
F – 'Peach Plum' (D) SKee
F – 'Pershore' **AGM** CSco
F – 'Pond's Seedling' (C) SDea SKee
F – 'President' (C/D) GTwe SDea SKee
F – 'Prince Englebert' (C) SKee
F – 'Priory Plum' (D) SDea
F – 'Purple Pershore' (C) CSco CWSG GTwe NRog SDea SKee
– 'Quetsche d'Alsace' See P. *d.* German Prune Group
F – 'Reeves' (C) CSco GTwe SFru SIgm SKee
F – 'Reine Claude de Bavais' (D) CSco GTwe NRog SFam SKee
– 'Reine Claude Dorée' See P. *d.* Green Gage Group
F – 'Reine Claude Violette' (D) SKee
F – 'Rivers's Early Prolific' (C) CSco ECas GTwe MBri MWat NRog SDea SFru SIgm SKee
F – 'Royale de Vilvoorde' (D) SKee
F – 'Ruth Gerstetter' (C) SKee
F – 'Sanctus Hubertus' **AGM** CSco EWar GTwe LBuc SDea SIgm SKee
F – 'Severn Cross' (D) GTwe SKee
F – 'Stint' (C/D) SKee
F – 'Swan' (C) GTwe SIgm
F – 'Thames Cross' (D) CSco
F – 'Transparent Gage' (D) CSco SFru SKee
F – 'Utility' (D) SKee
F – 'Victoria' **AGM** Widely available
F – 'Warwickshire Drooper' (C) CSam CSco EWar GBon GTwe SDea SFru SKee SPer
F – 'Washington' (D) CSco SKee
F – 'White Magnum Bonum' (C) SDea

F– 'Wyedale' (C)	CSco GTwe
F– 'Yellow Egg' (C)	GTwe SDea SFam
F– 'Yellow Pershore' (C)	MBea NRog SKee
§ ***dulcis***	CLnd CSco ENot MBar NWea SDea SKee WDin WTyn
F– 'Macrocarpa'	EHar ESim SFam SHil
¶– 'Praecox'	SKee
fruticosa 'Globosa'	CDoC MBri
'Fudan-zakura'	SHil
§ 'Geraldinae'	CLnd EBar SHil
glandulosa 'Alba Plena' **AGM**	CB&S CBot CCla CPMA CSco CTre ECtt EGol EHar ELan ESis MBal MBar MGos MPla MWat NHol SHBN SHil SPer SPla STre WBod WDin WHCG WPat WSHC
– 'Rosea Plena'	See P. *g.* 'Sinensis'
§– 'Sinensis' **AGM**	CBot CCla CPMA CTre EGol EHar ELan EPla ESis EWri GPlt LHop MBal MGos MPla NHol SHBN SHil SPer SPla SSta WHCG WPat WSHC
F x ***gondouinii*** 'May Duke'	SKee
'Hally Jolivette'	COtt ELan MBri WAbe
'Hillieri'	EBre LBre MBar MGos
'Hillieri Spire'	See P. 'Spire'
hirtipes 'Semiplena'	SKee
'Hisakura'	See P. 'Chôshû-hizakura'
Hollywood ®	See P. 'Trailblazer'
'Ichiyo'	See P. 'Chôshû-hizakura'
'Imose'	EBar
incisa	GAri IOrc SPer WWes
– 'February Pink'	MBri MPla
– 'Fujima'	NHol WPat WWat
– 'Kojo-no-mai'	EBre ECtt EPla ESis GAri LBre MAsh MBri
– 'Oshidori'	MBri NHol WPat
– 'Pendula'	MBri
– 'Praecox' **AGM**	LRHS MBri SHil
F ***institia***	EHar SFru
F– 'Blue Violet Damson'	SKee
F– 'Bradley's King Damson'	CSco SKee
F– 'Farleigh Damson' (C)	CSco GTwe NBee SDea SFru SIgm SKee SPer WJas
F– 'Godshill Damson' (C)	SDea
– 'Golden Bullace'	See P. *i.* 'White Bullace'
– 'King of Damsons'	See P. *i.* 'Bradley's King Damson'
F– 'Langley Bullace'	CSco SKee
F– 'Merryweather Damson' (C)	CDoC CMac CSco EBre ECas EHar ERea GBon GChr GRei GTwe LBre LBuc MBea MBri NBar NBee NRog SDea SFam SFru SKee SPer WJas WStI
– 'Mirabelle de Metz' (C)	CSco SFru
F– Mirabelle de Nancy (C)	GTwe SDea SKee
F– 'Mirabelle de Nancy (Red)' (C)	SDea
– 'Mirabelle Petite'	See P. *i.* 'Mirabelle de Metz'
F– 'Prune Damson'	CSam CSco ECas EHar EWar GBon GTwe LBuc MBri MGos MWat NRog SDea SFam SFru SIgm SKee WHig WJas
F– 'Shepherd's Bullace'	SKee
– 'Shropshire Damson'	See P. *i.* 'Prune Damson'
F– 'Small Bullace'	SKee
F– 'White Bullace'	CSco SKee
F– 'Yellow Apricot'	SKee
§ ***jamasakura***	GAri SHil
'Jô-nioi'	CLnd SHil
'Kanzan' **AGM**	CB&S CBra CLnd CSco EBre EHar ELan GRei IDai IJoh LBre LBuc LPan MBal MBar MBri MGos NWea SDea SHBN SPer SReu SSta WJas
§ 'Kiku-shidare-zakura' **AGM**	Widely available
Korean Hill Cherry	See P. x ***verecunda***
kurilensis	See P. ***nipponica k.***
'Kursar' **AGM**	CBar COtt EHar IOrc LNet LRHS MBri SEng SHil WTyn
laurocerasus **AGM**	CB&S CBow CBra CChe CKin CSco ELan GRei IDai LNet MRav MWat NNor NWea SArc SPer SReu WAbe WMou WStI WWin
– 'Aureovariegata'	See P. *l.* 'Taff's Golden Gleam'
– 'Camelliifolia'	CChu EPla EWri ISea SMad WHCG
N– 'Castlewellan' (v)	CBot CChu COtt CPle CTrw EFol EGol ELan EMon EPla EWri IBar IJoh IOrc ISea MBar MBri MGos NHol SLon SPer SPla SSta WDin WPat
– 'Caucasica'	EMon IDai WWeb
– 'Cherry Brandy'	ENot SFai SGil SPer
– 'Dart's Low Green'	ENot
– 'Golden Splash'	EMon
– 'Green Marble' (v)	CBow EMon MUlv SFai WSHC
– 'Grünerteppich' ('Green Carpet')	COtt EMil
– 'Herbergii'	CDoC
§– 'Latifolia'	CHEx EMon EPla SArc
– 'Magnoliifolia'	See P. *l.* 'Latifolia'
– 'Marbled White'	See P. *l.* 'Castlewellan'
– 'Mischeana'	ENot MBri MUlv SKee
– 'Mount Vernon'	MBar MBri MGos NBee SFai WDin
– 'Otto Luyken' **AGM**	Widely available
– 'Reynvaanii'	MBri MGos
– 'Rotundifolia'	CDoC EBar ELan ENot EWri LBuc MBar MBri WDin
– 'Rudolf Billeter'	EPla
– 'Schipkaensis'	CSco GAul NNor SPer
§– 'Taff's Golden Gleam' (v)	CCla CPMA SMad
– 'Van Nes'	EMil IOrc MUlv WStI WWeb
N– 'Variegata'	EMon EWri MGos
– 'Zabeliana'	CDoC CLan CMHG CSco ENot LHop MBar NRoo SHBN SLon SPer WCru WDin WPat WWin
lusitanica **AGM**	CB&S CChe CKin CLan CMHG CSco EBre EHar ELan ENot GRei IDai ISea LBre LNet MBal MBar MBri MGos NNor NWea SLon SPer SSta WDin WHCG WMou WWat
– ssp. ***azorica*** **AGM**	CSco EPla SHil SLon SPer WMou WWat
– 'Myrtifolia'	EHar EPla MUlv SMad
– 'Variegata'	CB&S CBot CBra CCla CMHG CSco EBre EFol EHar EHoe ELan ENot IJoh IOrc ISea LBre MBal MBri MWat SDix SHBN SLon SPer SSta WDin WPat WWat

maackii	CTho EHar LPan WTyn WWat
– 'Amber Beauty'	CBow CPMA EHar
mahaleb	CTho
'Mount Fuji'	See P. 'Shirotae'
mume	CDoC WNor
– 'Alboplena'	CChe GAri SHil
– 'Alphandii'	GAri SHil
– 'Beni-chidori'	CB&S CPMA EBre EHic ELan GAri LBre LPan LRHS MBri SHil SIgm
– 'Beni-shidori'	See P. ***m.*** 'Beni-chidori'
§ – 'Omoi-no-mama'	CPMA EHic GAri LRHS MBri
– 'Omoi-no-wac'	See P. ***mume*** 'Omoi-no-mama'
– 'Pendula'	CLnd MBri
myrobalana	See P. ***cerasifera*** Myrobalan Group
nipponica var. ***kurilensis***	CB&S WPat
– – 'Ruby'	COtt LRHS MGos SKee
'Okame' **AGM**	CLnd CSam CTho EBee EBre EHar LBre MBri MGos NWea SHil SPer WHCG
§ 'Okumiyako'	CB&S
'Opal'	LBuc
padus	CDoC CKin CLnd CPer EHar IDai IOrc LBuc LNet MBri MGos NBee NRoo NWea SKee WDin WMou WStI
– 'Albertii'	CTho SEng SHil WJas
– 'Colorata' **AGM**	CDoC CMHG CTho ELan IOrc LNet MBri MWat SHBN SPer WDin WJas
– 'Dropmore'	SPer
– 'Grandiflora'	See P. ***p.*** 'Watereri'
– 'Purple Queen'	CTho ENot MGos
§ – 'Watereri' **AGM**	CB&S CDoC CLnd CTho EHar ELan ENot IDai IOrc MBri SHBN SIgm SPer SPla SReu SSta WDin WJas
'Pandora' **AGM**	CBar CDoC CLnd EBre ECtt ENot LBre MBal NWea SHBN SPer WAbe
§ ***pendula*** var. ***ascendens*** 'Rosea'	CLnd SReu
§ – 'Pendula Rosea' **AGM**	CB&S CDoC ECtt ENot MBar MBri SIgm SPer WJas
§ – 'Pendula Rubra' **AGM**	CDoC COtt EBee ENot LNet MBri MGos SFam SHBN SKee SPer
§ – 'Stellata'	SHil
F ***persica*** 'Amsden June'	ELan ERea GTwe SDea SFam
F – 'Bellegarde'	ERea GTwe SDea SFam SFru SKee
F – 'Bonanza'	ELan ERea
F – 'Doctor Hogg'	SDea
F – 'Duke of York'	ECas ERea EWar GTwe SDea SFam SFru SKee WWeb
F – 'Dymond'	GTwe
F – 'Early Alexander'	GTwe
F – 'Early Rivers'	CDoC CMac EHar GTwe NRog SDea
F – 'Francis'	SKee
F – 'Garden Anny'	ELan ERea MBri
F – 'Garden Lady'	ERea GTwe WHig
F – 'Hale's Early'	ECas ERea GTwe MBri SDea SFam SKee SPer
F – 'Kestrel'	GTwe
– 'Klara Mayer' (d)	SIgm WJas
F – 'Miriam'	SKee

F – nectarina Crimson Gold®'	SDea
F – var. ***nectarina*** 'Early Gem'	SDea
F – – 'Elruge'	ERea GTwe SFam SFru
F – – 'Fantasia'	SDea
F – – 'Fire Gold'	SDea
F – – 'Fuzalode'	SDea
F – – 'Humboldt'	GTwe SFru
F – – 'John Rivers'	ERea GTwe SFam SFru
F – – 'Lord Napier'	CDoC CWSG ECas EHar ERea IJoh LBuc MBea MGos SDea SFam SFru SIgm SKee SPer WHig WJas WStI
F – – 'Nectared'	GTwe SKee
F – – 'Nectarella'	ERea GTwe WHig
F – – 'Pineapple'	CDoC ECas EHar ERea GTwe NElm SDea SFam SFru SIgm SKee WHig
F – – 'Red Haven'	CDoC ECas GTwe SIgm SKee
F – – 'Rivers Prolific'	SDea
F – – 'Ruby Gold'	SDea
F – 'Nemarquard'	CDoC
F – 'Peregrine'	CMac CWSG ECas EHar ERea EWar GBon GRei GTwe IJoh LBuc MBea MBri MGos NBee NElm NRog SDea SFam SFru SIgm SKee SPer WHig WJas WWeb
– 'Red Peachy'	NBar
F – 'Reliance'	SDea
F – 'Robin Redbreast'	SDea
F – 'Rochester'	CWSG ECas EHar ERea EWar GBon GTwe MBea MBri NElm SDea SFam SIgm SKee WHig WJas WStI
F – 'Royal George'	GTwe NRog SFam SFru SKee
– 'Rubira'	EPla
F – 'Springtime'	SDea
– 'White Peachy'	NBar
'Pink Perfection' **AGM**	CB&S CLnd CSco EBre GRei LBre LPan MBri SFam SHBN SKee SPer SPla SReu WTyr
'Pink Shell' **AGM**	CLnd CTho MBri SFam SHil WStI WTyn
pissardii	See P. ***cerasifera*** 'Pissardii'
'Pissardii Nigra'	See P. ***cerasifera*** 'Nigra'
prostrata	CLew WThu WWat
¶ ***pseudocerasus*** 'Cantabrigiensis'	SIgm
pumila var. ***depressa***	CLew CPMA CPle EGol GAri LHop MBar MPla MRav SHil SPla
'Red Cascade'	SDea
'Rhexlicer'	CDoC
rufa FK 40	WHCr
sargentii **AGM**	CBra CDoC CLnd CTho EBar EHar ELan ENot IDai IHos IJoh IOrc LBuc LPan MBri MGos NBee NWea SFam SHBN SPer SPla SReu SSta STre WDin WMou WTyn
– Rancho ®	CLnd ENot MBri SKee SPer
x ***schmittii***	CLnd CTho SHil SPer
'Sekiyama'	See P. 'Kanzan'
serotina	NWea WMou
§ ***serrula*** **AGM**	Widely available
– var. ***tibetica***	See P. ***serrula***
serrulata	WNor
– 'Erecta'	See P. 'Amanogawa'
– 'Grandiflora'	See P. 'Ukon'

– 'Longipes'	See P. 'Okumiyako'
– 'Miyako'	See P. 'Okumiyako'
N– *pubescens*	See P. x ***verecunda***
– 'Rosea'	See P. 'Kiku-shidare-zakura'
– var. *spontanea*	See P. ***jamasakura***
'Shidare-zakura'	See P. 'Kiku-shidare-zakura'
'Shimizu-zakura'	See P. 'Okumiyako'
'Shirofugen' AGM	CB&S CBra CDoC CLnd ECtt EHar IDai IOrc LPan MBri SDea SFam SPer WDin
§ 'Shirotae' AGM	CDoC CLnd CSam CTho ELan ENot IDai IOrc MBal MGos MRav NWea SKee SPer SPla SReu WTyn
§ 'Shôgetsu' AGM	CLnd CSco EBar ELan ENot GRei IOrc MBal MBri SFam SHBN SHil SPer
'Shosar'	CLnd CSco MBri SEng SPer
'Snow Goose'	MBri
spinosa	CDoC CKin CPer LBuc MBri NBee NNor NWea SKee SPer STre WDin WMou WNor
¶ – 'Plena'	WMou
– 'Purpurea'	CSco SHil WHCG WPat
§ 'Spire' AGM	CBra CDoC CLnd CSam CSco CTho EHar ENot GRei IOrc LPan SPer WJas
x *subhirtella*	WNor
x *subhirtella ascendens*	See P. ***pendula a.***
x *subhirtella* 'Autumnalis' AGM	CB&S CBra CLnd CSco CTho EBre EGol EHar ELan ENot IDai IHos IJoh ISea LBre MBal MBar MBri NWea SDea SFam SHBN SIgm SKee SPer SReu SSta WDin WWat
– 'Autumnalis Rosea' AGM	CB&S CPMA CSam CTho EHar ELan ENot GRei IJoh LBuc LNet MBar MBri MGos NBar NBee NWea SChu SHBN SIgm SKee SPer SPla SReu WAbe WDin WHCG WHen WWat
– 'Fukubana' AGM	CLnd CTho ELan MBri SHil WDin
– 'Pendula' (hort.)	See P. ***pendula*** 'Pendula Rosea'
– 'Pendula Rubra'	See P. ***pendula*** 'Pendula Rubra'
N– 'Rosea'	CLnd
– 'Stellata'	See P. ***pendula*** 'Stellata'
'Taihaku' AGM	CB&S CDoC CLnd CSam CSco CTho EBre EHar ELan ENot IOrc LBre LNet LPan MBri MGos NWea SFam SHBN SPer SReu WDin WJas WStI WTyn
'Taoyame'	CLnd
tenella	CB&S CBra CCla CSco ECtt ELan MBri NBee SEng SHer SIng WHCG WStI WWat
– 'Fire Hill' AGM	CCla CDoC CPMA CSco CShe EBre EHar ELan IJoh LBre LNet MBar MGos MPla SHBN SHil SPer SWas WDin WPat
tibetica	See P. ***serrula***
tomentosa	EPla ESim WAbe
F 'Trailblazer' (C/D)	CLnd CSco IOrc LPan MGos NWea SKee
triloba	CB&S CBow CBra CLnd CSco ECtt IJoh LAbb LBuc LPan MBar MBri MGos MPla NBee SHBN SIgm SPer WDin WTyn
– 'Multiplex' AGM	EBre EGol ENot IHos LBre SRms
– 'Rosenmund'	MBri
§ 'Ukon' AGM	CB&S CCla CDoC CLnd CSco CTho EBar EHar ENot IOrc LNet MBal MBri NWea SChu SFam SPer SReu WDin WStI WTyn
'Umineko'	CDoC CLnd ENot IOrc LBuc MGos SPer
§ x *verecunda*	CDoC CLnd EBar LBuc NWea SPer WJas
– 'Autumn Glory'	EBre LBre SHil SPer
virginiana 'Shubert'	CDoC CLnd CTho EBee EHar ELan ENot EPla IOrc MBri SEng SIgm SSta WBod WJas
'Wood's Variety'	See P. ***cerasifera*** 'Woodii'
x *yedoensis* AGM	CBra CLnd CTho ENot SFam SPer WDin WJas WWat
– 'Ivensii'	CB&S CDoC ECtt SHBN WStI
x *yedoensis pendula*	See P. x ***y.*** 'Shidare-yoshino'
x *yedoensis* 'Perpendens'	See P. x ***y.*** 'Shidare-yoshino'
§ – 'Shidare-yoshino'	CDoC CLnd CSco EBar ECtt LNet MBar MBri MRav MWat SPer WWat
– 'Tsubame'	MBri

PSEUDOCYDONIA (Rosaceae)

§ *sinensis*	LNet

PSEUDOFUMARIA (Papaveraceae)

§ *alba*	CAvo CMil CRow EMar EPot ESis GCra MTho
§ *lutea*	CHad ECro EHal EMar IBlr LGro MPit MTol MUlv NFai NPer NRar WBon WCot WPer

PSEUDOLARIX (Pinaceae)

§ *amabilis* AGM	CAbP CDoC CGre CMCN CMHG EBre EHar EHul ISea LBre LCon LNet MBal MBar MBri NHol SHil SMad STre WCoo WNor WWat
kaempferi	See P. ***amabilis***

PSEUDOMERTENSIA (Boraginaceae)

See Plant Deletions

PSEUDOMUSCARI See MUSCARI

PSEUDOPANAX † (Araliaceae)

Adiantifolius Group 'Adiantifolius'	CB&S CHEx
– 'Cyril Watson' AGM	CB&S
arboreus	CAbb CHEx
chathamicus	CHEx
crassifolius	CBot CHEx ECou SArc
ferox	CHEx SArc
laetus	CHEx
lessonii	CB&S CHEx ECou
– 'Gold Splash' AGM	CB&S CTro
– hybrids	CHEx
'Sabre'	SMad

PSEUDOPHEGOPTERIS (Thelypteridaceae)

levingei	CRDP EMon

PSEUDOPHOENIX (Palmae/Arecaceae)
**nativo* MBri

PSEUDOSASA (Gramineae/Poaceae-Bambusoideae)
§ ***amabilis*** ISta SBam SCob SDry
amabilis hort. See ARUNDINARIA ***tecta***
§ ***japonica*** AGM CB&S CHEx EFul ELan EPla ERav IDai ISta LBam MBal NJap SBam SCob SDry SHil SMad SPer WDin WJun
§ – 'Akebonosuji' (v) EFul EPla SBam SDry
– 'Tsutsumiana' EPla LBam SBam SDry WJun
♦– 'Variegata' See P. *j.* 'Akebonosuji'
owatarii SDry
pleioblastoïdes EPla SBam SDry
usawai WJun

PSEUDOTSUGA (Pinaceae)
§ ***menziesii*** AGM CB&S CDoC CPer EHar IDai IOrc LBuc LCon MBar NWea SPer WMou
¶ – 'Bhiela Lhota' CKen
– 'Blue Wonder' CKen LCon MAsh
– 'Densa' CKen
– 'Fastigiata' CKen
– 'Fletcheri' CKen LCon MAsh MBar MBri SLim
– var. ***glauca*** EHar LCon MBar STre
– 'Glauca Pendula' AGM CDoC EHar MBar MGos
I – 'Gotelli's Pendula' CKen
– 'Graceful Grace' CKen
– 'Julie' CKen
– 'Little Jamie' CKen
– 'Little Jon' LCon MBar NHol SLim
¶ – 'Lohbrunner' CKen
– 'Nana' CKen
– Pendula Group LCon MAsh MBri
– 'Stairii' CKen
– 'Tempelhof Compact' SLim
– f. ***viridis*** GRei
taxifolia See P. ***menziesii***

PSEUDOWINTERA (Winteraceae)
§ ***colorata*** CB&S CDec CDoC CLan CPle CTrw IBar IDai IJoh IOrc ISea MAll NHol SDry SHil WBod WPat

PSIDIUM (Myrtaceae)
cattleianum See P. ***littorale longipes***
F ***littorale*** ERea
§ – var. ***longipes*** CTro
– var. ***lucidum*** See P. ***l. littorale***

PSILOSTROPHE (Compositae/Asteraceae)
See Plant Deletions

PSORALEA (Leguminosae/Papilionaceae)
affinis CHEx
¶ ***corylifolia*** MSal
pinnata CTro

PSYCHOTRIA (Rubiaceae)
capensis SLMG

PTELEA (Rutaceae)
trifoliata AGM CB&S CBow CBra CChu CLnd CMHG CSco EHar GWht LHol SHil SPer WBod WCoo WHCG WNor WOMN
– 'Aurea' AGM CAbP CBot CBow CCla CPMA CSco EHar ELan GWht MBri MGos MUlv SHBN SHil SPer WHCG WHig WPat

PTERACANTHUS See **STROBILANTHES**

PTERIDIUM (Dennstaedtiaceae)
aquilinum Percristatum Group IOrc NKay

PTERIDOPHYLLUM (Papaveraceae)
racemosum EPot

PTERIS (Adiantaceae)
argyraea MBri NMar
cretica AGM MBri SArc
– ***albolineata*** AGM MBri NMar SRms
– ***cristata*** MBri
– 'Gautheri' MBri
– 'Parkeri' MBri
– 'Rivertoniana' MBri
– 'Rowei' MBri
– 'Wimsettii' MBri
ensiformis MBri NMar
– 'Arguta' MBri
– 'Victoriae' MBri
tremula MBri NMar
umbrosa MBri

PTEROCARYA (Juglandaceae)
fraxinifolia AGM CAbb CB&S CDoC CLnd CMCN CSam EArb EHar ENot IBar IOrc MBlu SHil SPer WDin WMou
– var. ***dumosa*** WMou
x ***rehderiana*** WMou
rhoifolia CMCN EHar WCoo WMou
stenoptera CB&S CLnd CMCN EArb EHar WMou
– 'Fern Leaf' WMou

PTEROCELTIS (Ulmaceae)
See Plant Deletions

PTEROCEPHALUS (Dipsacaceae)
parnassi See P. ***perennis perennis***
§ ***perennis*** CShe EFol ESis MPit NBir NHar NKay NRar WAbe WHil WPat WPer
§ – ssp. ***perennis*** CLew CNic ELan EPot GCHN LBee MBro MCas MFos MHig NTow SBla SIng SPla WEas WHoo WOMN WOld WWin

PTEROSTYLIS (Orchidaceae)
curta CRDP

PTEROSTYRAX (Styracaceae)
corymbosa CChu CMCN GWht LRHS WWat

hispida AGM	CB&S CChu CCla CGre CMCN CPle ELan MRav SHer SHil SReu SSta WBod WCoo WWat

PTILOSTEMON (Compositae/Asteraceae)

See Plant Deletions

PTILOTRICHUM See ALYSSUM

PTYCHOSPERMA (Palmae/Arecaceae)

¶ ***elegans***	CTro
macarthurii	CTro

PUERARIA (Leguminosae/Papilionaceae)

See Plant Deletions

PULICARIA (Compositae/Asteraceae)

§ ***dysenterica***	CArn CKin ECWi EWFC IEde MChe MSal NMir SIde WCHb WGwy WHaw WNdy WOak WWye

PULMONARIA † (Boraginaceae)

affinis	CRDP EMon
angustifolia AGM	CBow CHad CRow CSam GDra GPlt MFir MNFA MSal MWat NBrk NHol NNrw NOrc SChu WEas WPer WRus WWin
– ssp. ***azurea***	CBow CBro CElw CLew CMil CRow CWGN EBre EFou EGol ELan ELun EPla ERav IDai LBre MBri NBro NKay NRoo NSti NTow SPer SPla SSte SSvw WCru WHil WTyr
– 'Blaues Meer'	SWas WThi
– 'Munstead Blue'	CBre CChu CElw CGle CRDP CShe ECha EGol EHal ENot EPar EPla MBel MTho NBrk NCat NRya SCro WCru
♦– 'Rubra'	See P. ***rubra***
'Barfield Regalia'	EMon SPer
'Beth's Blue'	ECha EOrc MBri MUlv WSun
'Beth's Pink'	ECha NCat NSti
¶ 'Blue Crown'	SWas
'Blue Ensign'	CRDP EBee ECha EPla LRHS MArl MBel SUsu
'Botanic Hybrid'	NCat
'Cleeton Red'	NCat
'Glacier'	CGle CRDP ECha EMon EPla LRHS MBel NCat SAxl
'Highdown'	See P. 'Lewis Palmer'
§ 'Lewis Palmer' AGM	Widely available
longifolia	Widely available
¶ – 'Ankum'	SWas
– 'Bertram Anderson'	CGle CHad CRDP CSpe CWGN EBee GAbr MUlv SBla SMrm SUsu SWas WCHb WCot
– ssp. ***cevennensis***	EMon
– 'Dordogne'	CGle CRDP EGle SBla SUsu SWas
¶ – forms	ECha
'Mary Mottram'	CCot MBel MMil MUlv NBir NSti WCru
'Mawson's Blue'	CRDP CTom ECha EMon EPla MArl MBel MBri MWat NCat WCru WElm WPbr WSun WWat
'Merlin'	EMon EPla
mollis	CBot CHan CMHG EOrc EPla GCal NBrk NCat NSti SFar
– 'Royal Blue'	EFou EGol GCHN MRav NRoo WRus
'Mournful Purple'	CGle CRDP CRow EPla ERav MUlv NBrk NCat WCru
'Mrs Kittle'	CMil NSti WMer
'Nürnberg'	CRDP EMon EPla LRHS MBel
obscura	EMon
officinalis	CArn CBro CGle CRow CSFH ECWi EOrc EPar EWFC Effi GPoy LHol LLWP MBel MChe MFir MHew NBar NBrk NKay SIde WCru WEas WHal WOak
– 'Alba'	EHal NCat WByw
– 'Blue Mist'	NCat NSti SWas WCru
– 'Bowles' Blue	CChu CGle CRow EBre ECha LBre LGre SAxl WAbb WFox WPbr WRus WThi
– Cambridge Blue Group	CBre CBro CElw CHan CLew CMea CRDP EFol EFou EGol EMon EOrc EPla ERav MWat NHol NSti SAxl WBon WByw WEas WHal
*– ***rubra***	EOrc EPla MWat NBir WByw WCHb
– 'Sissinghurst White' AGM	Widely available
– 'White Wings'	CElw CHan CRDP CSco EPla NHol SChu WBon WCHb WCra WEas WSun
'Oxford Blue'	CCot
'Patrick Bates'	NSti
¶ 'Red Freckles'	WSun
'Roy Davidson'	CBos CGle CHad CMHG CMil CRDP EBre LBre SWas WCru
§ ***rubra*** AGM	CElw CGle CHan CLew CRDP CSam CShe ECha ECoo ELan ELun EMar EPar LWad MFir NHol NNrw NOak NOrc NRar NSti SChu SFis SHer SIng SRms SUsu WBon WCru WElm
– ***albocorollata***	CBre CElw CRDP ECha EFol EMon EPla LRHS MNFA MUlv NCat NSti SAxl WCru
¶ – 'Ann'	EMon
– 'Barfield Pink'	CBre CElw CMil CRow ECtt EFol ELan EMar EMon EPla GCal MBel MBri MBro MHFP MMil MNFA MUlv NSti SAxl SChu SMrm SUsu SWas WCru WPbr WRus
– 'Barfield Ruby'	CRDP EMon EPla GBuc LRHS
– 'Bowles' Red'	CBot CBow CBre CBro CCla CMea CSco EBre ECtt EFol EJud ENot ERav GAbr LBre LHop MNFA NHol NRoo NSti SCro SMrm SPer WCra WHal WRus WTyr
– 'David Ward' (v)	CFee CRow ECha ECtt EFol EMon EOrc EPla LGre MBel MUlv NBir NCat NSti SMad WCot WCru WEas WHoo WPbr
– 'Prestbury Pink'	CElw EMon WEas
– 'Redstart'	Widely available
§ ***saccharata***	CBow CHEx CMea CRDP CRow CShe ECha ELan EPad LAbb LGro MFir NBee NHol SChu SCro SIng SSvw WBon WCHb WCru WEas WHoo WPbr WPer WWat WWin
– 'Alba'	CBro CRow ECha EFol LBlm MBel NOak SIng SRms WCru

– Argentea Group AGM	CBow CBro CChu CGle CRow CWGN ECha ECoo EFol EFou EGol ELan EMar EOrc EPla ERav ESma GAbr LBlm MPit MTho NBro NHol NSti SPer SUsu WCru
– 'Blauhimmel'	CCot NSti
– 'Brentor'	CRow
– 'Dora Bielefeld'	CBos CMil CRDP ECha EFou EPla MBel NCat NSti SAxl WHal WRus
– 'Frühlingshimmel'	CElw CGle ECha EOrc EPla LGre MUlv NCat NSti SAxl SBla SMrm SUsu SWas WBon WCHb WHal
¶ – 'Jill Richardson'	EBee
– 'Lady Lou's Pink'	CElw NCat WCru
– 'Leopard'	CGle EBee EBre ECtt ELun EPla LBre MUlv NCat NSti SBla SMrm WMer WRus
– 'Mrs Moon'	CBow CDoC EBee ECoo ECtt EFou ELun ENot LWad MHFP NBrk NBro NFai NHol NMir NOrc NSti SChu SFis SPer SSvw WCHb WCru WFox WHen WSun
– 'Picta'	See P. *s.*
– 'Pink Dawn'	CDoC CSco EOrc EPla MBri MUlv SPer WPbr
– 'Reginald Kaye'	CRow ECha NSti
– 'Snow Queen'	NHol
¶ 'Saint Ann's	NSti
* 'Salmon Glow'	MTho
¶ 'Smoky Blue'	GBri WCot WMer
'Tim's Silver'	ECha EPla
vallarsae 'Margery Fish' AGM	CBro CChu CGle CKel COtt CRDP EGol EOrc MBri MUlv NBro NRoo NSti SAxl SMad SPer WByw WCru WEas WMer WPbr WRus WSun
'Weetwood Blue'	CChu MMil MSte
¶ 'Wendy Perry'	CRDP

PULSATILLA (Ranunculaceae)

alba	CBro MSto
albana	CBro MSto SPou
¶ – var. ***albana***	WDav
– 'Lutea'	SPou
– white	MSto SWas
alpina	CBot CRDP MRPP NRoo SRms
§ – ssp. ***apiifolia*** AGM	CBot ELan GAbr GArf GDra GTou LGre NHar NHol NRoo WAbe WOMN
– ssp. ***sulphurea***	See P. ***a. apiifolia***
ambigua	MSto NHol
¶ ***bungeana***	MSto
¶ ***chinensis***	MSto
dahurica	MFos
halleri AGM	MMil MSto NHol NRoo
– ssp. ***grandis***	NHol SPou
– ssp. ***slavica*** AGM	CBro SPou SWas WWin
– ssp. ***styriaca***	SPou
– ssp. ***taurica***	SPou
koreana	CBro MSto
¶ ***lutea***	WDav
montana	LGre MSto NRoo
occidentalis	NMen WOMN
patens	WDav
pratensis	GTou MTho NRoo
– ssp. ***nigricans***	CBro CRDP LRHS
sp. JH 908145	NHol WDav
turczaninovii	MSto
§ ***vernalis*** AGM	EPot GArf GDra GTou MSto NHar NHol NSla NWCA SIng WAbe WDav WHoo
§ ***vulgaris*** AGM	Widely available
– ***alba*** AGM	CAvo CB&S CBow CCla CGle CMea CNic EFou ELan EPar GAbr LGan LGre LHop MBri MBro NHar NHol NOak NRoo SBla SIng SPer WAbe WHal WPat WPer WRus WThu
– 'Eva Constance'	CBro EBre LBre LHop LRHS SWas
– 'Flore Pleno'	CNic CRDP
– 'Gotlandica'	GAbr GDra
¶ – pale pink	CNic
¶ – 'Papageno'	CBot LGre
– 'Röde Klokke' ('Rote Glocke')	CBot ERav LGan LGre MBro MUlv NHol SPou WDav WHil
– ***rubra***	Widely available
– 'Weisse Schwan' ('White Swan')	MBro WHil

PUMMELO See CITRUS *grandis*

PUNICA (Lythraceae)

granatum	CTro ERea GAri STre WSHC
– 'Flore Pleno Luteo'	GAri
– 'Flore Pleno Rubro'	GAri
– ***nana*** var.	CArn CPle ERea GAri LAbb LHop MPla SHil SMad WPat WWat
– f. ***plena***	CB&S

PURSHIA (Rosaceae)

tridentata	CPle

PUSCHKINIA (Liliaceae/Hyacinthaceae)

scilloïdes Polunin 5238	CMon
§ – var. ***libanotica***	CAvo CBro CCla ELan EPar EPot ETub LAma MBal NEgg NRog SIng SUsu WPer
¶ – var. ***libanotica*** S&L 113	CMon
– – 'Alba'	CAvo EPar EPot LAma NRog SIng WCot

PUTORIA (Rubiaceae)

calabrica	NWCA

PUYA (Bromeliaceae)

alpestris	CBow CHEx NWyt SArc SMad
berteroniana	CHEx LHil
chilensis	CAbb CB&S CBow CHEx CPle CTbh ESma MUlv NWyt SArc WCot
coerulea	CHEx SIgm
– var. ***violacea***	CGre
conquimbensis	CTbh CTro
laxa	CHEx
mirabilis	CHEx CTbh CTro GCra
¶ ***mitis***	CTbh
raimondii	CHEx
sp. G&P 5036	CGre
venusta	CGre CHEx

weberbaueri	CHEx

PYCNANTHEMUM (Labiatae/Lamiaceae)

¶ ***muticum***	EBee
pilosum	CArn CSev GBar GPoy MSal NPri SIde WGwy WPer WWye

PYCNOSTACHYS (Labiatae/Lamiaceae)

* ***virginiana***	ECha

PYGMAEA See CHIONOHEBE

PYRACANTHA † (Rosaceae)

'Alexander'	CPMA CSco EHal ENot EPla GAri LHop MGos MRav SLon WStI WWat
'Alexander Pendula'	See P. 'Alexander'
angustifolia	CB&S CSco ELan WWat
§ ***atalantioïdes***	CB&S CBra CChe CDoC CMac CSam CSco CShe IDai MRav SLon SPer SPla WBod WDin WPat WWat
§ – 'Aurea'	CSco SLon WWin
– 'Nana'	MRav
'Brilliant'	CB&S CBra
'Buttercup'	EPla GAri
coccinea	CTrw
§ – 'Kasan'	MWat
§ – 'Lalandei'	CBra CMac CSam MGos NNor SPer WBod WDin
– 'Red Column'	CChe CMac EBre ECtt ELan GRei IJoh LBre LBuc MBar MGos MRav MWat NBee WDin WPat
– 'Red Cushion'	EBre ENot IHos LBre LBuc LRHS SRms
– 'Telstar'	CB&S SPer
crenulata	CMer
fortunei B&L 12398	EPla
gibbsii	See P. ***atalantioïdes***
– 'Flava'	See P. ***atalantioïdes*** 'Aurea'
'Golden Charmer'	CBow CDoC CSco EBre ECtt ELan IJoh LBre MBal MGos NKay NTow NWyt SHBN SPer WAbe WBod WDin WTyr
'Golden Dome'	CBra
'Golden Sun'	See P. 'Soleil d'Or'
'Harlequin' (v)	CB&S CBot CBow CMac CPMA EBre ECtt EFol ELan EPla IJoh LBre MBal MBar MRav NSti SHBN SReu WSHC
'John Steadman'	MAsh
'Mohave'	CB&S CChe CMac CMer CSco EBre ELan ENot EPla GRei IJoh LBre MBal MBar MGos MRav MWat NKay NNor NRoo SHBN SLon SPer SReu WBod WDin WStI
'Mohave Silver' (v)	CBow CMHG CPMA CSam ELan EPla LRHS MBar MWat NHol NNor SPer SPla WDin WPat WStI
'Monrovia'	See P. ***coccinea*** 'Lalandei'
*'Mozart'	MBri WWeb
'Navajo'	CBow CDoC EBre LBre MPla MRav NWyt SDry SReu WAbe WBod
'Orange Cadence'	IJoh
N 'Orange Charmer'	CBow CDoC CSco CShe ELan ENot IJoh MBal MBar MBri MGos MWat SHBN SPer WAbe WStI
'Orange Giant'	See P. ***coccinea*** 'Kasan'
'Orange Glow' **AGM**	CChe CMac CSco CShe EBre ECtt ENot GRei IDai IHos IJoh LBre LBuc MBar MBri MGos MRav NBee NKay NNor NRoo NWea SLon SPer WBod WDin WPat WStI
'Red Delight'	MPla
'Red Pillar'	CDoC CSco MBri
'Renault d'Or'	SLPl
rogersiana **AGM**	CBra ENot IJoh MPla NNor
– f. ***flava*** **AGM**	CBra CLTr EBee ENot IDai LHop MAsh MBal MBar MGos NNor SPla WBod
¶ Saphyr Orange ®	COtt MBri
¶ Saphyr Rouge ®	COtt MBri
'Shawnee'	CB&S CMac ECot MAsh MBri MRav MWat WBod WDin WWeb
§ 'Soleil d'Or'	CBow CDoC CMac CSam CSco CShe EBre ECtt ELan ENot EPla IHos LAbb LBre MBar MBri MPla MRav MWat NBee NNor NRoo SPer SReu WDin WPat WStI WTyr
'Sparkler' (v)	CBra CMac CPMA CSco EBar EBre EFol EHoe ELan LBre LHop NHol NNor SDry SEng SMad SPer SPla WStI
'Teton'	CBow CBra CChe CDec CMHG CMac CSco ELan ENot EPla ESis LHop MBar MBri MGos MRav NHol NRoo SLon SPer SPla WAbe WBod WDin WPat WStI
'Watereri' **AGM**	NWea SPer
'Yellow Sun'	See P. 'Soleil d'Or'

X PYRACOMELES (Rosaceae)

See Plant Deletions

PYRETHROPSIS See RHODANTHEMUM

PYRETHRUM See TANACETUM

PYROLA (Ericaceae)

¶ ***rotundifolia***	WHer

PYROSTEGIA (Bignoniaceae)

venusta	CNew CTro

PYRROSIA (Polypodiaceae)

serpens	EBul

PYRUS † (Rosaceae)

betulifolia	CMCN SHil WJas
calleryana 'Bradford'	CLnd CTho
– 'Chanticleer' **AGM**	CDoC CLnd CTho ECtt EHar ENot IOrc NBee SHBN SPer WDin WJas WWat
F ***communis***	CKin MBlu SKee SPer STre WMou
F – 'Abbé Fétel' (D)	SKee
F – 'Admiral Gervais'	SFru SKee
F – 'Alexandrina Bivort' (D)	CSco

F– 'Autumn Bergamot' (D) SKee
F– 'Barland' (Perry) CSco WMou
F– 'Baronne de Mello' (D) CSco SFam SKee
F– 'Beech Hill' CLnd CSco CTho EHar ENot
F– 'Belle Guérendais' SKee
F– 'Belle Julie' (D) SFru SKee
F– 'Bellissime d'Hiver' (C) SFru
F– 'Bergamotte d'Automne' (D) CSco SKee
F– 'Bergamotte Esperen' (D) SKee
F– 'Beth' **AGM** CDoC CSco CWSG EBre ECas EWar GBon GChr GTwe LBre LBuc MBea MBri MGos NBar NBee NElm NRog SDea SFam SFru SIgm SKee SPer WWeb
F– 'Beurré Alexandre Lucas' (D) CSco SKee
F– 'Beurré Bachelier' (D) CSco
F– 'Beurré Bedford' (D) CSco NRog SIgm SKee
F– 'Beurré Bosc' (D) CSco SKee
F– 'Beurré Clairgeau' (C/D) GTwe SKee
F– 'Beurré de Jonghe' (D) SKee
F– 'Beurré de Naghin' (C/D) SKee
F– 'Beurré Diel' (D) CSco
F– 'Beurré Dumont' (D) CSco SFam SFru
F– 'Beurré d'Amanlis' (D) CSco SKee
F– 'Beurré Giffard' (D) SFru
F– 'Beurré Hardy' **AGM** CDoC CSco ECas ERea GTwe IJoh LBuc MBri MWat NRog SDea SFam SFru SIgm SKee
F– 'Beurré Jean van Geert' (D) SKee
F– 'Beurré Mortillet' (D) SKee
F– 'Beurré Six' (D) CSco SKee
F– 'Beurré Superfin' (D) CSco GTwe SFam SFru SIgm SKee
F– 'Bianchettone' SKee
F– 'Black Worcester' (C) CSco GTwe SKee WJas WMou
F– 'Blakeney Red' (Perry) CSco SDea WMou
F– 'Blickling' SKee
F– 'Bonne de Beugny' SKee
F– 'Brandy' (Perry) CSco SDea WMou
F– 'Bristol Cross' (D) CSco GTwe SIgm SKee
F– 'Buckland' CSco
F– 'Butt' (Perry) CSco
F– 'Catillac' **AGM** CSco GTwe NRog SFam SFru SKee
F– 'Chalk' See P. *c.* 'Crawford'
F– 'Charles Ernest' CSco
F– 'Chaumontel' (D) SKee
F– 'Clapp's Favourite' (D) CSco GTwe IOrc SIgm SKee
F– 'Comte de Lamy' (D) SFru SKee
F– 'Concorde' **AGM** CDoC CSam CSco CWSG ECas EHar EWar GTwe LBuc MBri MGos NBee NElm SDea SFru SIgm SKee WHig WJas
F– 'Conference' **AGM** Widely available
F– 'Craig's Favourite' (D) GTwe
F– 'Crawford' (D) SKee
F– 'Deacon's Pear' (D) SDea
F– 'Docteur Jules Guyot' (D) CSco SKee
F– 'Double de Guerre' (C) SFru SKee
F– 'Doyenné Boussoch' (D) SKee
F– 'Doyenné du Comice' **AGM** CDoC CMac CSam CSco CWSG EBre ECas EHar ERea EWar GBon IOrc LBre MBea MBri MWat NBar NRog SDea SFam SFru SIgm SKee SPer WHig WWeb
F– 'Doyenné d'Eté' (D) CSco SFam SKee
F– 'Doyenné Georges Boucher' SKee
F– 'Duchesse de Bordeaux' (D) SFru SKee
F– 'Duchesse d'Angoulême' (D) CSco SKee
F– 'Durondeau' (D) CSco GTwe NRog SFru SIgm SKee
F– 'Easter Beurré' (D) CSco SFru
F– 'Emile d'Heyst' (D) CSco GTwe SIgm SKee
F– 'Eva Baltet' SKee
F– 'Fertility' (D) CSco
F– 'Fertility Improved' See P. *c.* 'Improved Fertility'
F– 'Fondant d'Automne' (D) CSco SFru SKee
F– 'Forelle' (D) SKee
F– 'Gin' (Perry) CSco WMou
F– 'Glou Morceau' (D) CSco GBon GTwe MWat NRog SDea SFam SFru SIgm SKee
F– 'Glow Red Williams' (D) SFam
F– 'Gorham' (D) CSco GTwe NBee SFam SKee
F– 'Green Horse' (Perry) CSco
F– 'Green Pear of Yair' (D) SKee
F– 'Hacon's Imcomparable' (D) SKee
F– 'Hellens Early' (Perry) CSco
F– 'Hendre Huffcap' (Perry) CSco WMou
F– 'Hessle' (D) CSco GTwe NRog SDea SFam SKee
F– 'Highland' SKee
F– 'Improved Fertility' (D) CDoC GBon GTwe SDea SKee
F– 'Jargonelle' (D) CSco GTwe NRog SDea SFam SFru SKee
F– 'Joséphine de Malines' **AGM** CSco GTwe SDea SFam SFru SIgm SKee
F– 'Judge Amphlett' (Perry) CSco WMou
F– 'Laxton's Early Market' (D) CSco
F– 'Laxton's Foremost' (D) CSco SKee
F– 'Laxton's Satisfaction' CSco SFam SKee
F– 'Longueville' (D) GTwe
F– 'Louise Bonne of Jersey' (D) CDoC CSco ECas EWar GTwe MBri NRog SDea SFam SFru SIgm SKee
F– 'Louise Marillat' CSco
F– 'Madame Treyve' (D) SFru

F– 'Maggie Duncan' GTwe
F– 'Marguérite Marillat' GTwe SKee
F– 'Marie Louise d'Uccle' (D) SKee
F– 'Marie-Louise' (D) CSco SKee
F– 'Martin Sec' (C/D) SKee
F– 'Merton Pride' (D) CSco GTwe MWat SDea SFam SFru SIgm SKee
F– 'Moorcroft' (Perry) CSco WMou
F– 'Muirfield Egg' (D) SKee
F– 'Nouveau Poiteau' (C) CSco GTwe SFru SKee
F– 'Nouvelle Fulvie' (D) CSco SKee
F– 'Oldfield' (Perry) CSco WMou
F– 'Olivier de Serres' (D) CSco SFam SFru SKee
F– 'Onward' **AGM** CSco GChr GTwe MGos NBee NRog SDea SFam SFru SIgm SKee
F– 'Ovid' CSco
F– 'Packham's Triumph' (D) CDoC CSco ECas GBon GTwe NRog SFru SKee
F– 'Parsonage' (Perry) CSco
F– 'Passe Crassane' (D) CSco SKee
F– 'Pear Apple' (D) SDea
F– 'Pitmaston Duchess' **AGM** CSco CWSG GTwe SDea SFru SIgm SKee
F– 'Red Comice' (C) GTwe SIgm SKee
F– 'Red Pear' (Perry) CSco
F– 'Robin' (C/D) CSco ERea SDea SKee
F– 'Roosevelt' SKee
F– 'Santa Claus' CSco SDea SFam SFru SKee
F– 'Seckle' (D) CSco GTwe SFam SFru SIgm SKee
F– 'Souvenir du Congrès' (D) CSco NRog
F– 'Starkrimson' (D) SFru
F– 'Sweet Huffcap' See P. ***c.*** 'Hellens Early'
F– 'Taynton Squash' (Perry) CSco
F– 'Thompson's' (D) CSco GTwe SFam SFru SIgm SKee
F– 'Thorn' (Perry) CSco WMou
F– 'Triomphe de Vienne' (D) CSco SFam SKee
F– 'Triumph' See P. ***c.*** 'Packham's Triumph'
F– 'Uvedale's St Germain' (C) SKee
F– 'Vicar of Winkfield' (D) CSco GTwe SDea SKee
F– 'Williams Red' (D) CSam GTwe SKee WHig
F– 'Williams' Bon Chrétien' **AGM** CMac CSco CWSG EBre ECas EHar ERea EWar GBon GChr GRei IOrc LBre LBuc MBea MBri MGos MWat NBar NElm NRog SDea SFam SFru SIgm SKee SPer WJas WWeb
F– 'Winnal's Longdon' (Perry) CSco
F– 'Winter Christie' GTwe
F– 'Winter Nelis' (D) CSco ECas EHar GTwe SDea SFam SFru SKee
F– 'Yellow Huffcap' (Perry) CSco WMou
cordata CNat SKee
nivalis CLnd CSco CTho EHar ENot SHBN SHil SPer
pashia CLD 114 EPla
¶– C&Mc 369 WHCr
pyraster CPer EHar
pyrifolia WHig
– '20th Century' See P. ***p.*** 'Nijusseiki'
F– 'Chojura' IOrc WHig
F– 'Kumoi' ESim LBuc MGos NBar SDea WHig
F– 'Nijisseiki' IOrc SKee
F– 'Shinko' IOrc
F– 'Shinseiki' CWSG SDea WHig
F– 'Shinsui' SDea SKee WHig
salicifolia 'Pendula' **AGM** Widely available

QUERCUS † (Fagaceae)

acuta CB&S CBow CHEx CMCN SArc
acutissima CMCN EArb WCoo WHCr WNor
– ssp. ***chenii*** CMCN
aegilops See Q. ***macrolepis***
agrifolia CB&S CMCN EArb WCoo
alba CMCN EArb WCoo
aliena WCoo
alnifolia CMCN
arkansana CMCN
bicolor CMCN IOrc WCoo
borealis See Q. ***rubra***
¶× ***bushii*** MBlu
canariensis **AGM** CMCN SHil WMou
castaneifolia CMCN WMou
– 'Greenspire' **AGM** CDoC CMCN COtt EHar LBuc MBri SHil SMad WMou
cerris **AGM** CB&S CDoC CKin CLnd CMCN CSco EHar EMil ENot IOrc NWea SPer SSta STre WCoo WDin WFro WMou
§– 'Argentoariegata' CMCN CTho EHar MBlu SHil WMou
– 'Variegata' See Q. ***c.*** 'Argenteovariegata'
– 'Wodan' WMou
chrysolepis CMCN WCoo
coccifera CFil CMCN WCoo
coccinea CAbP CB&S CBow CBra CChu CMCN CWSG EArb EHar ELan IBar IOrc SEng SPer STre WCoo WNor
– 'Splendens' **AGM** CDoC CMCN COtt CSco EHar ELan IOrc MBlu SHBN SHil SPer WDin
dentata CMCN WCoo
– 'Pinnatifida' CMCN MBlu
douglasii CMCN EArb WCoo
dumosa CMCN EArb WCoo
durifolia CMCN
ellipsoidalis CAbP CDoC CGre CMCN WCoo WWat
¶– Hemelrijk Form MBlu
engelmannii CMCN
¶***faginea*** MNes
falcata CLnd CMCN EArb
– var. ***pagodifolia*** CMCN EArb
frainetto CDoC CLnd CMCN CTho EHar EMil IOrc MBri SMad SPer WDin WMou WWat
– 'Trump' SMad
♦***fruticosa*** See Q. ***lusitanica*** Lamarck
gambelii CMCN
garryana CMCN

georgiana	CMCN
glabra	See LITHOCARPUS ***glaber***
¶ ***glabrescens***	CB&S
glandulifera	CMCN WCoo
glauca	CMCN
graciliformis	WCoo
hemisphaerica	CMCN
♦x ***hispanica***	See Q. x ***lucombeana***
♦– 'Leucombeana'	See Q. x ***lucombeana*** 'William Lucombe'
ilex AGM	Widely available
ilicifolia	CMCN WWat
imbricaria	CMCN EArb WWes
incana Bartram	CMCN EArb
incana Roxburgh	See Q. ***leucotrichophora***
kelloggii	CMCN EArb
x ***kewensis***	SHil WMou
laurifolia	CMCN EArb
leucotrichophora	CMCN
x ***libanerris*** 'Rotterdam'	CMCN
libani	CMCN WCoo WMou
lobata	CMCN EArb
x ***lucombeana*** 'Diversifolia'	WMou
– 'Suberosa'	CTho
– 'Wageningen'	WMou
§ – 'William Lucombe' AGM	CMCN CTho EHar MBri SHil SPer WDin WMou
x ***ludoviciana***	SArc SHil WMou
lusitanica Brotero	See Q. ***fruticosa***
lusitanica Lamarck	CMCN
lyrata	CMCN
macranthera	CMCN
macrocarpa	CMCN EArb WCoo WNor
§ ***macrolepis***	CMCN WCoo
marilandica	CMCN SHil
mexicana	CMCN
michauxii	CMCN
mongolica	WCoo
– var. ***grosseserrata***	CMCN
muehlenbergii	CMCN WCoo
myrsinifolia	CB&S CBow CMCN SArc WCoo
nigra	CMCN CMHG EArb SHil WCoo
nuttallii	CMCN EArb WWes
¶ ***oxyodon***	CB&S
palustris AGM	CBow CDoC CGre CLnd CMCN CSam EArb EHar IJoh IOrc LPan MBal SMad SPer WDin WNor WWat
– 'Pendula'	CMCN EHar
pedunculata	See Q. ***robur***
§ ***petraea*** AGM	CDoC CKin CLnd CPer EHar EMil GRei IOrc LBuc MBal NWea SPer WDin WFro WMou
§ – 'Insecata'	CMCN WMou
– 'Laciniata'	See Q. ***p.*** 'Insecata '
– 'Mespilifolia'	WMou
– 'Purpurea'	CMCN SHil WMou
§ ***phellos*** AGM	CLnd CMCN EArb ISea SHil WDin WNor
– ***latifolia***	IOrc MBlu
phillyreoïdes	CB&S CMCN EArb WCoo WWat
§ ***prinus***	CMCN WCoo
pubescens	WCoo
pumila Michaux	See Q. ***prinus***
pumila Walt.	See Q. ***phellos***
pyrenaica	CMCN CTho
*– 'Argenteomarginata'	CMCN
– 'Pendula'	CMCN EHar
§ ***robur*** AGM	CB&S CBow CBra CDoC CKin CLnd CMCN CPer CSco EBre ENot GRei IJoh IOrc LBre LBuc LPan MBar MBri MGos NBee NWea SHBN SPer SPla WCoo WDin WMou WStI
– 'Atropurpurea'	SHil SPer WMou
– 'Aureobicolor' (v)	WMou
– 'Concordia'	CB&S CMCN COtt EHar ELan MBlu MBri NEgg SHil SMad WMou
– 'Cristata'	CMCN
– 'Cucullata'	CMCN
– f. ***fastigiata***	CDoC CLnd CSco CTho EHar EMil ENot IOrc LBuc LPan MBar MBri NBee NWea SPer WMou
– 'Fastigiata Koster' AGM	CMCN COtt
– 'Fastigiata Purpurea'	CMCN IOrc
¶ – 'Fennessii'	MBlu
– 'Hungaria'	MBlu MBri
¶ – 'Pectinata'	MBlu
– f. ***pendula***	CMCN CTho WMou
¶ – 'Purpurascens'	MBlu
– 'Strypemonde'	CMCN
x ***rosacea*** 'Filicifolia'	WMou
§ ***rubra*** AGM	Widely available
– 'Aurea'	CMCN MBlu WMou
rugosa	CMCN
sadleriana	CMCN
x ***saulii***	CMCN
x ***schochiana***	SHil
serrata	See Q. ***acutissima***
sessiliflora	See Q. ***petraea***
shumardii	CMCN EArb SHil
stellata	EArb
suber	CB&S CBow CDoC CMCN EArb EHar GAri ISea SArc SHil WDin WMou
trojana	CMCN
x ***turneri***	CDoC CLnd CMCN CTho EHar MBri SHil WMou
– 'Pseudoturneri'	CB&S ELan
vacciniifolia	MBal
variabilis	CMCN WCoo
velutina	CBow CGre CLnd CMCN EArb WWat
– 'Rubrifolia'	CMCN SHil
virginiana	CMCN EArb ISea
wislizenii	CMCN IOrc

QUESNELIA (Bromeliaceae)

See Plant Deletions

QUILLAJA (Rosaceae)

saponaria	CGre CPle

QUINCE See CYDONIA *oblonga*

QUIONGZHUEA (Gramineae/Poaceae-Bambusoideae)

tumidinoda	See CHIMONOBAMBUSA ***tumidissinoda***

RACOPILUM (moss)

robustum	LFle

RACOSPERMA See ACACIA

RAMONDA (Gesneriaceae)

§ ***myconi*** AGM — CMHG CRDP CRiv CShe EPot GDra MBro MCas NHar NKay NMen NSla NTow NWCA SBla SIgm SIng SPou WCru WThu
– 'Rosea' — NKay SPou
nathaliae AGM — NHar SIgm WCru
– 'Alba' — SBla SWas
pyrenaica — See R. ***myconi***
serbica — GDra NSla NTow SIgm
¶ – 'Alba' — SPou

RANUNCULUS † (Ranunculaceae)

abnormis — SWas WOMN WThi
¶ – JCA 809.500 — WDav
aconitifolius — CElw CGle CLew CRDP CTom EBre ECha LBre NSti
– 'Flore Pleno' AGM — CRDP CRow EBre ECha IBlr LBre LGre MUlv NBir NRya NTow SBla WByw
¶ ***acris*** — ECWi EWFC MWil
– 'Farrer's Yellow' — CRow
– 'Flore Pleno' — CAvo CElw CFee CGle CRDP CRow CSco ECha EMon EPar GAbr MNFA NBro NFai NHol NRya WByw WHal WHow
¶ – 'Stevenii' — CFee
– 'Sulphureus' — CBre CElw CGle CLew EMon NRed SMrm WBon WCot
alpestris — NKay NMen SRms
amplexicaulis — CMon EPot GDra GTou NHar SBla SWas
aquatilis — CBen EHon EMFW NDea SWat SWyc WChe
arendsii — GArf
asiaticus — CAvo CMon
– Accolade — NNrd WStI
– red — SPou WChr
*– Tecolote hybrids — LAma
– white — SPou
¶ – yellow — SBla
auricomus — CKin
bulbosus — CKin EWFC MWil
§ – 'F M Burton' — CBos CRDP EMon MTho SBla SWas WCot WHal
♦– ***farreri*** — See R. ***b.*** 'F M Burton'
– 'Speciosus Plenus' — See R. ***constantinopolitanus*** 'Plenus'
calandrinioïdes AGM — CAvo CMon NGar SPou WAbe WDav WOMN
– SF 37 — CMon
¶ ***caucasicus*** ssp. ***caucasicus*** — GLil
§ ***constantinopolitanus*** 'Plenus' — CBos CDec CGle CRDP CRow ECha GCal GGar MBri NBro NRya NTow SUsu WBon WCot WEas
¶ ***cortusifolius*** — CRDP WCot
crenatus — ELan GArf ITim MBal MHig NHar NHol NMen NNrd NRya NTow SBla WAbe WHal
ficaria — CArn CKin CNat CRow CSFH ECWi EWFC GBar GCal MChe MHew MSal SIde WHer WOak WShi WWye
I – 'Aglow in the Dark' — CNat
– ***albus*** — CBre CGle CLew CMon CRow NGar NGre NHol NRya SIng WByw
– anemone centred — See R. *f.* 'Collarette'
– ***aurantiacus*** — See R. *f.* 'Cupreus'
¶ – 'Brambling' — EMon
¶ – 'Brazen Daughter' — CRow
– 'Brazen Hussy' — Widely available
– 'Button Eye' — CMon
¶ – 'Champernowne Giant' — CRow
§ – 'Collarette' (d) — CBre CGle CMil CRDP CRow ECha EMon EPar EPot GAbr GGar MTho NGar NNrd NRya NSla SAxl SIng WCot WHil
– 'Coppernob' — CBos CRow CVer
§ – 'Cupreus' — CBos CBre CLew CMil CMon CNic CRDP CRow ECha EMon EPar EPot GDra MBro NGar NGre NMen NNrd NRya NSla SAxl SBla SIng WCru WHil
¶ – 'Damerham' — EMon
– 'Double Bronze' — EMon NGre NRya
– double cream — CBos CBre NGar SBla SIng WCot WHal
– double green eye — CRow
– 'Double Mud' — EMon SWas
♦– double yellow — See R. *f.* ***flore-pleno***
– 'E A Bowles' (d) — GBar GCal NGar NGre NRya SBla SIng WAbe WCla WCot
§ – ***flore-pleno*** — CBro CFee CGle CMil CMon CNic CRDP CRow ECha ELan EMar EMon EPar GAbr GDra NDea NGre NHol NNrd NRya NSla SAxl SIng WCot WHil WThu
– 'Green Petal' — CMil CRDP CRow EMon MTho NGar NGre NHol NNrd NRya NSla SIng
– 'Lemon Queen' — NHol SIng WCot
¶ – 'Little Southey' — CRow
– 'Major' — CBre CRDP CRow ECha EPot NGre NRya SIng WCot WCru
– 'Mobled Jade' — CNat
– 'Picton's Double' — CGle CRDP CRow GBar GCal
– 'Primrose' — CBre CRow EMon GGar MTho NCat NGre NHol NRya
– 'Randall's White' — CGle CMea CRow MTho NRya NTow WCot WCru
– 'Rowden Magna' — CRow NGre
– 'Salmon's White' — CAvo CBos CFee CRow EPot NGre NNrd NRya SBla SFar WCru WHal WHil
– 'Single Cream' — EMon
¶ – 'Tortoishell' — CBos CRow
– 'Wisley Double Yellow' — CLew
– 'Yaffle' — CBos CBre CRow
x ***flahautii*** — GArf
flammula — CArn CBen CKin CRDP CRow ECWi EHon EMFW GBar LMay MSta NDea SWat SWyc WChe WHol
glacialis — GTou WPer
gouanii — CRDP EPot MFir NBro NGre NHol NKay
gramineus AGM — CDec CLew CMea CRDP ELan EMar EPad EPot LBee LGan MBro MTho MWat NGre NHol NNrd NRya SAxl SChu SHer SIgm SIng SUsu WByw WCot WDav WHoo WPer WThu
– 'Pardal' — SPou

¶ ***hederaceus***	SWyc
illyricus	CElw CRDP EMon
insignis	GCal
kochii	EPot
lanuginosus	WCot
¶ – AL&JS 89066YU	EMon
lingua	CKin CRDP ECWi ECoo EMFW MHew WChe WHaw WNdy
– 'Grandiflorus'	CBen CRiv CRow CWGN EHon LMay MSta NDea SWat SWyc WHol WWye
lyallii	CPla GCLN GCal GTou SBla
millefoliatus	NNrd NRya SIng WHil
montanus	MBal
– 'Molten Gold' AGM	CMea ELan EPad EPot MHig MRav MTho NHar NHol NKay NMen NNrd NRya NTow SIng SMrm
muelleri brevicaulis	NTow
ophioglossifolius	CNat
parnassiifolius	GTou NGre NHar NTow SBla WAbe
platanifolius	LGre
pyrenaeus	MBal
repens	CKin ECWi EWFC
– 'Joe's Golden'	CRDP EFol EHoe EMon
– var. ***pleniflorus***	CBre CDec CGle CRow ECha ELan EMon GCal NSti WEas
rupestris	See R. ***spicatus***
speciosus 'Flore Pleno'	See R. ***constantinopolitanus*** 'Plenus'
§ ***spicatus***	CRDP WOMN
¶ sp. ex Morocco	WHil

RANZANIA (Berberidaceae)

japonica	CRDP

RAOULIA (Compositae/Asteraceae)

australis Hooker	CLTr ECou EHoe ELan EMNN EPot GAbr GCHN GDra ITim MBal MBar MCas MHig MRPP MWat NGre NHol NKay NNrd NRoo NSti NWCA SGil SIng WAbe WDav WHoo WOMN WThu
– 'Calf'	ITim NHol SHer
§ – Lutescens Group	ECha EPot GAri ITim MHig MSto NHol NTow SGil WAbe
– 'Saxon Pass'	ESma GCHN NHol SGil
australis hort.	See R. ***hookeri***
glabra	ECou EPot GAbr NHol NKay NTow
haastii	ECou GArf GDra NHol
§ ***hookeri***	CLew EBre ECha ECou ELan EPot GCHN ITim LBee LBre MBro MCas NHol NMen NTow NWCA SBla SBod SGil SIng WAbe WDav WOMN WPat WPer WThu
– var. ***apice-nigra***	GArf NHol
– var. ***hookeri***	NHol
x ***loganii***	See X LEUCORAOULIA ***loganii***
lutescens	See R. ***australis*** Lutescens Group
monroi	ECou ELan EPot GCHN ITim NHol NTow
* ***nova***	EPot GDra NKay
x ***petrimia*** 'Margaret Pringle'	MHig NHar WAbe
subsericea	ECou MHig NGre NHol NMen WHil
tenuicaulis	ECha ECou GAbr GAri NHol WHil

RAOULIA X LEUCOGENES See X LEUCORAOULIA

RASPBERRY See RUBUS *idaeus*

RATIBIDA (Compositae/Asteraceae)

columnifera	CRDP GBuc
¶ – K 92.377	WDav

RAVENALA (Strelitziaceae)

madagascariensis	LPal

RAVENEA (Palmae/Arecaceae)

rivularis	LPal

RECHSTEINERIA See SINNINGIA

REEVESIA (Sterculiaceae)

See Plant Deletions

REGELIA (Myrtaceae)

See Plant Deletions

REHDERODENDRON (Stryracaceae)

macrocarpum	CB&S

REHMANNIA (Scrophulariaceae)

angulata	See R. ***elata***
§ ***elata***	CBot CBoy CCla CGre CHad CHol CMGP CSev ECro EGol GMac MSto NPer NPri NRar SFis SMrm WCot WCra WCru WHil WPer WRus WWin WWye
glutinosa AGM	WOMN

REINECKEA (Liliaceae/Convallariaceae)

§ ***carnea***	CElw CHan CNic CRDP EBul ECha ELan EMar EPar EPla GCal LGan MFir MTho MUlv NNrd NSti SFis WBon WCru WHal

REINWARDTIA (Linaceae)

§ ***indica***	CPle CTro
¶ – S&SH 106	CHan
trigyna	See R. ***indica***

RELHANIA (Compositae/Asteraceae)

¶ ***acerosa***	NHed

RESEDA (Resedaceae)

lutea	CKin ECWi EWFC MChe MSal SHer SIde
luteola	CKin CSFH ECWi EWFC GBar GPoy LHol MChe MHew MSal SIde WCHb WHer WWye

RESTIO (Restionaceae)

subverticillatus	See ISCHYROLEPIS ***subverticillata***
tetraphyllus	CFee ECou

RETAMA (Leguminosae/Papilionaceae)

§ ***monosperma***	CPle

REYNOUTRIA See **FALLOPIA**

RHABDOTHAMNUS (Gesneriaceae)

solandri	ECou WCru

RHAGODIA (Chenopodiaceae)

triandra	ECou

RHAMNUS (Rhamnaceae)

§ ***alaternus*** 'Argenteovariegatus' AGM	Widely available
– ***variegatus***	See R. ***a.*** 'Argenteovariegatus'
catharticus	CKin EBre LBre LBuc WDin WMou
frangula	CArn CDoC CKin CPer CSam EBre ENot GPoy LBre LBuc STre WDin WMou
x ***hybridus*** 'Billardii'	ESis
imeretinus	SHil
¶ ***japonicus***	SPer

RHAPHIOLEPIS (Rosaceae)

x ***delacourii***	CChu EPla IJoh SPer WBod
– 'Coates' Crimson'	CBow CCla CSPN MUlv SHBN SPer WSHC
– 'Enchantress'	CB&S CGre EBre IBlr LBre
– 'Spring Song'	EBee SHil
indica	CBow CGre CPle
ovata	See R. ***umbellata***
§ ***umbellata*** AGM	CAbb CB&S CBot CBow CChu CCla CDoC CHEx CMCN CNew CPle CSam LHop MAll MUlv NTow SHil WAbe WCru WHCG WSHC

RHAPHITHAMNUS (Verbenaceae)

cyanocarpus	See R. ***spinosus***
§ ***spinosus***	CGre CHan CPle EPla ERea IBar SArc WBod

RHAPIDOPHYLLUM (Palmae/Arecaceae)

hystrix	LPal

RHAPIS (Palmae/Arecaceae)

§ ***excelsa*** AGM	CTro LPal
humilis AGM	CTro LPal

RHAZYA (Apocynaceae)

orientalis	See AMSONIA ***o.***

RHEKTOPHYLLUM See **CERCESTIS**

RHEUM † (Polygonaceae)

§ 'Ace of Hearts'	CBot CCla CHad CMGP CRow CWit ECha ECtt EFol EFou EGol ELan EOrc EPar EPla MBri MUlv NDea NSti SMrm WCot
'Ace of Spades'	See R. 'Ace of Hearts'
acuminatum	CRow SAxl
alexandrae	EBre GAri LBre MUlv NNor SPer WCot
§ ***australe***	CArn CChu CCla CRow LWad NHol WCot WHer WHoo
compactum	CRow
x ***cultorum***	See R. x ***hybridum***
delavayi	EMon
emodi	See R. ***australe***
N x ***hybridum*** 'Cawood Delight'	GTwe
– 'Champagne'	GTwe
– 'Early Champagne'	GTwe
– 'Fenton's Special'	GTwe WHig
– 'Hammond's Early'	GTwe
– 'Harbinger'	GTwe
– 'Hawke's Champagne'	GTwe
– 'Mac Red'	GTwe
– 'Prince Albert'	GTwe
¶ – 'Red Prolific'	GTwe
– 'Reed's Early Superb'	GTwe
¶ – 'Stein's Champagne'	GTwe
– 'Stockbridge Arrow'	GTwe
– 'Strawberry'	GTwe
– 'The Sutton'	GTwe LBuc
– 'Timperley Early'	CDoC CMac CSam ECas ECtt GChr GTwe LBuc MBea MMor NElm NFai SDea WHig
– 'Victoria'	GTwe
kialense	ECha WCot
¶ ***moorcroftianum*** C&Mc 813	GTou
officinale	CHEx MBri
palmatum AGM	CB&S CBow CCMG CCla CHEx CHol ECha EHal LHop MRav NDea NNor SHig SPer WHal WHoo WPbr WPer WStI
– 'Atropurpureum'	See R. ***p.*** 'Atrosanguineum'
§ – 'Atrosanguineum'	CBot CHEx CRow CSco CShe CWes EBre ECha ECtt EGol ELan EPar LBre NBro NNor WCru WWin
– 'Bowles' Crimson'	CHad LRHS MBri
– 'Hadspen Crimson'	CHad
– ***rubrum***	CCla CDoC COtt CWGN EFou EHic GCHN MHlr SMad SPer WCot
– var. ***tanguticum***	CRow CWit ECha ELun EOrc LWad MNFA MSta MUlv NCat NSti SMrm WCot WWat
I – – 'Rosa Auslese'	NHol
¶ ***reticulatum*** JJH 9209375	WDav
spiciforme	GTou SAxl WCot
undulatum	CRow

RHEXIA (Melastomataceae)
See Plant Deletions

RHINANTHUS (Scrophulariaceae)
See Plant Deletions

RHINEPHYLLUM (Aizoaceae)

broomii	NGre NTow

RHIPSALIS (Cactaceae)

baccifera	CTro
cassytha	See R. ***baccifera***

RHODANTHEMUM (Compositae/Asteraceae)

atlanticum	NHol NTow
catananche	ELan EOrc EPad EPot LBee LHop MHig NTow SHer SMrm WAbe
§ *gayanum*	CCan CMHG CMer CSam CSpe EBar EDon ELan IHos LBee LHil NSty NTow SChu SIng WHil WKif WOMN WPer WRus WSun
♦– 'Flamingo'	See R. ***g.***
– 'Tizi-n-Test'	SBla SWas
– 'Tizi-n-Tichka'	CRiv ELan LBee LRHS NBir SBla
§ *hosmariense* AGM	CCan CGle CLew CMHG CSam CSco CSev ECha ELan EPot GCal LBee LGre LHop MBal MCas MTho NHol NSti SBla SHer SIng SPer SUsu WEas WHil WOMN WRus WWin

RHODIOLA (Crassulaceae)

¶ *arctica*	NGre
crassipes	See R. ***wallichiana***
§ *fastigiata*	EMon GCal NGre
– x *kirilovii*	NGre
§ *heterodonta*	ECha EGle ELan NGre
himalensis	CNic NGre SSmi
kirilovii	GTou
– var. *rubra*	NGre SSmi
pachyclados	See SEDUM ***p.***
pamiroalaica	NGre
primuloïdes	See SEDUM ***p.***
rhodantha	NGre
§ *rosea*	CSco ECha ECro EFou EGol ELan EPla GGar LGre MBal MFir NGre NNor NRoo SCro SIng SSmi STre WEas
§ – ssp. *integrifolia*	NGre
sp. CLD 1196	EMon NHol
¶ sp. CLD 1329	EMon
sp. C&Mc 158	GCHN
¶ sp. EMAK 0516	NHol
sp. JJH 392	CNic WDav
trollii	NGre
§ *wallichiana*	LHil NGre NTow WCot
yunnanense	EMon

RHODOCHITON (Scrophulariaceae)

§ *atrosanguineus* AGM	CArn CDoC CGle CHEx CMac CRHN CTro ECtt ELan ERea LAbb LHop MNes NEgg NFai NNrw NSti NTow SFis SMad SUsu WAbe WCru WEas WHal WHer WHil WOld
volubilis	See R. ***atrosanguineus***

RHODODENDRON † (Ericaceae)

aberconwayi	CWal GWht IOrc ISea LMil MBal NMun SLeo SReu
¶ – McLaren U35A	NMun
– dwarf form	GGGa
– 'His Lordship'	GGGa LHyd
¶ – pink	NMun
adenogynum	CWal GGGa NMun SLeo
– CLD 795	LMil
¶ – white	NMun
§ *adenogynum* Adenophorum Group	CWal NMun SLeo
– – F 20444	NMun SLeo
¶ – – R 11471	NMun
¶ – – 'Kirsty'	NMun
adenophorum	See R. ***adenogynum*** Adenophorum Group
adenopodum	CWal GGGa NMun SLeo
adenosum	LMil NMun
– R 18228	GGGa
– Kuluense Group	NMun SLeo
adroserum R/USDA 59201	See R. ***lukiangense*** R 11275
aeruginosum	See R. ***campanulatum a.***
aganniphum	GGGa NMun SLeo
¶ – var. *aganniphum* F 16472	NMun
§ – – Doshongense Group	CWal GGGa NMun SLeo
¶ – – Doshongense Group KW 5863	NMun
– – Glaucopeplum Group	GGGa
– – Schizopeplum Group	GGGa
– var. *flavorufum*	GGGa NMun SLeo
¶ – 'Rusty'	NMun
agapetum	See R. ***kyawii*** Agapetum Group
agastum	NMun SLeo
albertsenianum	NMun SLeo
¶ – F 14195	NMun
¶ *albiflorum* (A)	GGGa
albrechtii AGM	GGGa LHyd SReu WAbe
alutaceum	NMun
– var. *alutaceum*	GGGa
§ – – Globigerum Group	LMil
– – Globigerum Group R 11100	GGGa NMun SLeo
– var. *iodes*	GGGa LMil NMun
§ – var. *russotinctum*	GGGa NMun SLeo
§ – – Triplonaevium Group	NMun
– – Triplonaevium Group R/USDA 59442/R10923	GGGa
§ – – Tritifolium Group	GGGa NMun
¶ – – Tritifolium Group R 158*	NMun
amagianum (A)	LMil
– x *reticulatum* (A)	SSta
ambiguum	CDoC CHig CWal LMil NMun SLeo SReu
– dwarf form	GGGa
– 'Jane Banks'	LMil
– 'Keillour Castle'	GGGa
amesiae	CWal NMun SLeo
annae	GGGa LMil NMun SLeo
§ – Hardingii Group	CWal NMun
anthopogon	GWht LMil NMun SLeo
– 'Annapurna'	CSam GGGa

– 'Betty Graham'	LMil NMun
§ – ssp. ***hypenanthum***	CWal LMil
anthosphaerum	GGGa NMun
¶ – F 17943	NMun
– F 26432	NMun SLeo
¶ – KW 5684	NMun
– Eritimum Group	CWal
¶ ***anthosphaerum*** Gymnogynum Group	NMun
§ – Heptamerum Group	NMun
anwheiense	See R. ***maculiferum a.***
aperantum	GGGa NMun
– F 26933	NMun SLeo
¶ – F 27020	NMun
araiophyllum	NMun SLeo
§ ***arborescens*** (A)	GGGa LKna LMil NMun SLeo
arboreum	CB&S CWal GGGa GWht IOrc ISea LMil NMun SLeo SReu
– B 708	MBal
– BM&W 172	MBal
¶ – C&S 1651	NMun
¶ – C&S 1695	NMun
¶ – KR 966	NMun
– Sch 1111	CWal
¶ – TSS 26	NMun
– 'Blood Red'	CWal GWht NMun
– ssp. ***cinnamomeum***	CBow CWal NMun SLeo SReu
– – var. ***roseum***	CWal NMun
¶ – – var. ***roseum*** BB 151	NMun
¶ – – var. ***roseum crispum***	NMun
– – Campbelliae Group	NMun SLeo
– ssp. ***delavayi***	GGGa NMun SLeo
¶ – ssp. ***delavayi*** C&S 1515	NMun
¶ – ssp. ***delavayi*** KW 21796	NMun
§ – – var. ***peramoenum***	NMun
– 'Goat Fell'	CWal
* – ***nigrescens***	NMun SLeo
¶ – ssp. ***nilagiricum***	GGGa
§ – ssp. ***nilagiricum***	NMun
§ – 'Sir Charles Lemon' **AGM**	CWal MLea NMun SLeo SPer SReu SSta
– 'Tony Schilling' **AGM**	CWal LHyd NMun SLeo
§ – ssp. ***zeylanicum***	NMun SLeo
x ***arbutifolium***	See R. Hybrid Arbutifolium
§ ***argipeplum***	CWal NMun SLeo
¶ – KR 1231	NMun
– Bhutan form	GGGa
– Eastern form	GGGa
argyrophyllum	CWal NMun SLeo
– KR 184	GGGa
¶ – W 1210	NMun
– 'Chinese Silver' **AGM**	CWal LHyd LMil NMun SLeo
§ – ssp. ***hypoglaucum***	GGGa NMun SLeo
– – 'Heane Wood'	GGGa
– ssp. ***nankingense***	GGGa IOrc LMil NMun
– 'Sichuan'	GGGa
arizelum	See R. ***rex arizelum***
atlanticum (A)	CCla CWal GAri GGGa NMun SLeo
– 'Seaboard' (A)	LMil
augustinii	CB&S CSam CTrw EBre GGGa IOrc ISea LBre LHyd LMil MBal MLea NMun SCog SLeo SPer SSta WBod
¶ – W A 1207	NMun
– ssp. ***augustinii*** Vilmorinianum Group	CWal
– ssp. ***chasmanthum***	CWal GGGa LMil
– Dartington Form	CWal
§ – Electra **AGM**	CBow CWal GGGa LHyd LMil NMun SCog SLeo
– Exbury best form	SReu
§ – ssp. ***hardyi***	CWal GGGa LHyd NMun SLeo
– Reuthe's dark form	SReu
§ – ssp. ***rubrum***	GGGa LMil
¶ – ssp. ***rubrum*** F 25914	NMun
– – 'Papillon'	CWal NMun
– 'Werrington'	MUlv
aureum	GGGa LMil NMun SLeo WDav
auriculatum	CGre CWal GGGa LHyd LMil MBal NMun SLeo SReu SSta
¶ – compact form	NMun
– Reuthe's form	SReu
auritum	CWal GGGa NMun
§ ***austrinum*** **AGM**	LMil
Azalea 'Abbot' (E)	CTrh
– 'Addy Wery' **AGM**	CBow CMac CSco CTrh CWal IDai IOrc LHyd LKna MBal MBar MGos NMun SBod SCog SLeo SPer SReu WBod WStI
– 'Adonis' (E/d)	CMac IOrc SCog SPer SReu SSta
– 'Adorable' (E)	CTrh IOrc
– 'Advance' (O)	CTrh GPlt NMun SGil SLeo WAbe WPat
– 'Ageeth' (E)	LRHS
– 'Aida' (R/d)	GGGa SReu
– 'Aladdin' (E)	IJoh IOrc MAsh
– 'Alexander' (E)	CB&S CTrh EHic GPlt IOrc LMil MBri MGos SBod SCog SSta
– 'Alice' (E)	CBow CMac IHos LHyd LKna WBod
– 'Ambrosia' (E)	CTrh
§ – 'Amethystinum' (E)	LKna
– 'Amoenum' (E/d)	CB&S CChe CMHG CMac CTrw GWht IOrc LHyd LKna MBar MGos NHol NMun SCog SExb SLeo WBod
– 'Amoenum Coccineum' (E/d)	CBow GWht SCog
– 'Anchorite' (E)	CTrh LMil
– 'Andrew Elphinstone' (E)	CBow LMil
– 'Annabella' **AGM**	CWal LHyd MBri MMor NBar SExb SReu
– 'Anne Frank' (E)	MGos NBar WBod
– 'Anne Rothwell'	LHyd
– 'Anneke' (K)	GGGa MBar MBri MMor NBar SSta
– 'Anny' (E)	CMac IOrc LKna
§ – 'Antilope' (Vs)	LMil MMor SPer SSta
– 'Aphrodite' (E)	LMil
N – 'Appleblossom' (E)	See R. A. 'Ho-o'
– 'Apricot Surprise'	CDoC
– 'Arabesque'	MBri MMor
– 'Arborescens'	See R. ***arborescens***
– 'Arcadia' (E)	CSco LKna
§ – 'Arpege' (Vs)	CDoC LMil MBal SPer SReu WWat
– 'Asa-gasumi' (E)	LHyd
– 'Audrey Wynniatt' (E)	MAsh SExb
– 'Azuma-kagami' **AGM**	CB&S LHyd LKna SCog WBod
– 'Baby Scarlet'	SSta
– 'Ballerina' (K)	CWal MBal

Azalea 'Balzac' (K) CSam CWal IJoh IOrc MBri MGos SReu
– 'Banzai' (E) CWal NMun SLeo
– 'Barbara Coates' LHyd
– 'Barbecue' (K) LMil
– 'Basilisk' (K) CWal SExb
– 'Beaulieu' (K) LMil SPer
¶– 'Beaver' (E) GGGa
– 'Beethoven' **AGM** LHyd LKna MBal NMun SBod SLeo SReu WBod WGor
– 'Bengal Beauty' (E) LMil
– 'Bengal Fire' (E) CMac SExb
§– 'Benifude' (E) WBod
– 'Benigasa' (E) CTrh SReu WPat
– 'Beni-giri' (E) CMac
– 'Berryrose' **AGM** CSco CWal EBre GWht IDai IJoh IOrc LBre LHyd LKna LMil MAsh MBal MBar MBri MMor MRav NBar NMun SExb SPer SReu WAbe
– 'Betty' **AGM** LHyd SReu SRms
– 'Betty Anne Voss' (E) LHyd LRHS MAsh
– 'Bijou de Ledeberg' (E) SSta
– 'Blaauw's Pink' **AGM** CBow CHig CMac CSco CWal GWht IDai IJoh IOrc ISea LHyd LKna LMil MAsh MBar MBri MGos NKay NMun SBod SCog SLeo SPer SReu WBod
– 'Black Hawk' (E) CB&S
– 'Blazecheck' LRHS NBar NHol
– 'Blizzard' (E) CTrh
– 'Blue Danube' ('Blaue Donau') **AGM** Widely available
– 'Blue Monday' MBri WBod
¶– 'Blue Moon' MBar
– 'Bouquet de Flore' **AGM** CDoC CSco LMil MAsh MBar MBri SPer SReu
– 'Bravo' (E) CTrh
– 'Brazier' (E) LHyd NMun SLeo
– 'Brazil' (K) CWal LKna SExb SReu
– 'Breslau' (E) SSta
– 'Bridesmaid' (O) GWht
– 'Bridesmaid White' NKay
– 'Bride's Bouquet' (E/d) LRHS
– 'Bright Forecast' (K) LMil MBri SExb
– 'Brilliant' (E) NBar
¶– 'Brilliant Blue' MAsh
*– 'Brilliant Crimson' SSta
*– 'Brilliant Pink' MAsh SSta
– 'Buccaneer' (E) CSco CTrh CWal IOrc LHyd MBal SBod SCog SExb SPer SReu
– 'Bungo-nishiki' (E/d) CMac CWal SReu SRms WPat WThu
¶– 'Buttons and Bows' (K) GGGa
– 'Buzzard' (K) LKna LMil
– 'Caerhays Lavender' CB&S IOrc
§– 'Campfire' (E) MBri NKay
– 'Canby' (K) LMil
– 'Cannon's Double' (K) GGGa LMil
– 'Canzonetta' (E) NBar
– 'Carat' CDoC MBri SReu
– 'Carnival' (E) CTrh
– 'Cassley' (Vs) LMil
– 'Cayenne' (E) SExb
– 'Cecile' **AGM** CB&S CSam CSco CWal GGGa GWht IJoh ISea LHyd LKna LMil MAsh MBal MBar MBri MGos MMor NBar NMun SExb SPer SReu
– 'Celestial' (E) CMac CTrh
– 'Centennial' See R. A. 'Washington State Centennial'
– 'Chaffinch' (K) LKna
– 'Chameleon' (E) IOrc
– 'Chanel' (Vs) MMor SSta
– 'Chanticleer' (E) LRHS SPer
– 'Cheerful Giant' (K) GGGa ISea
– 'Chelsea Reach' (K) LKna
– 'Chenille' (K) LKna
– 'Chetco' (K) GGGa LMil
– 'Chicago' (M) LKna
¶– 'Chinchilla' (E) GGGa
– 'Chippewa' (E) CDoC GGGa LMil MBri NKay SReu
– 'Chocolate Ice' (K) LKna
– 'Chopin' (E) WBod
– 'Chorister' (K) LKna
– 'Christina' (E/d) CMac MBri MMor NKay SPer WBod
– 'Christmas Cheer' (E) See R. A. 'Ima-shojo'
§– 'Christopher Wren' (K) CSco ELan MBal NBar
¶– 'Clarissa' (E/d) IOrc
– 'Coccineum Speciosum' **AGM** CBow CSco CWal GGGa IDai IOrc LHyd LMil MBar MGos SExb SPer SReu SSta
– 'Cockade' (E) LKna
– 'Cockatoo' (K) LKna
– 'Colin Kenrick' (K) LKna
– 'Colyer' (E) LHyd
– 'Commodore' (E) WAbe
– 'Congo' See R. A. 'Robin Hill Congo'
– 'Cora Grant' (E) SExb
– 'Coral Redwing' (E) CTrh
– 'Coral Wing' (E) CTrh
– 'Corneille' **AGM** LKna SReu
– 'Coronation Lady' (K) LKna MBri MMor
– 'Corringe' **AGM** GWht
– 'Crimson Glory' See R. A. 'Natalie Coe Vitetti'
– 'Crinoline' (K) SPer SSta WWeb
¶– 'Crown Jewel' (E/d) WThu
– 'Cumberlandense' See R. ***calendulaceum***
– 'Daimio' (E) CMHG LHyd SPer
– 'Daisetsuzan' CTrh
– 'Darkness' (E) CTrh
– 'Daviesii' **AGM** CB&S CSam GGGa IDai LHyd LKna LMil MAsh MBal MBri MLea MMor MRav SExb SPer SReu WWat WWeb
N– 'Daybreak' (K) See R. A. 'Kirin'
N– 'Debutante' GRei GWht IHos ISea MMor NBar
– 'Delectable' (K) LMil
– 'Delicatissimum' **AGM** GGGa LMil LRHS MAsh MBri SExb
– 'Desert Pink' (K) LKna
– 'Diabolo' (K) LKna
– 'Diamant' CDoC GAri GGGa
– Diamant Group (lilac) (E) GGGa MBri

Azalea Diamant Group (pink) (E) GGGa MGos
– Diamant Group (rosy-red) (E) COtt GAri GGGa MBri
– 'Diamant Purpur' ('Purple Diamond') (E) CTrh MGos
– 'Diamant Rot' ('Red Diamond') (E) CTrh
– 'Diorama' (Vs) CDoC MBri MMor SReu SSta
– 'Doctor M Oosthoek' **AGM** CSco LHyd MMor NBar SReu
– 'Dorothy Corston' (K) LKna
– 'Dorothy Hayden' (E) LHyd
– 'Double Beauty' (E/d) CTrh IOrc LKna MMor SBod SCog SPer SReu SSta
– 'Double Damask' **AGM** LHyd LKna
– 'Double Delight' (K/d) CBow GGGa
– 'Driven Snow' (E) SBod SExb
– 'Early Beni' (E) LHyd
– 'Eastern Fire' (E) CTrh
– 'Eddisbury' (K) MMor
– 'Eddy' (E) LKna NMun SLeo
– 'Edna Bee' (E) LMil
N– 'Elizabeth' (E) CBow CTrh ESis GPlt IOrc ISea MGos SCog SGil WAbe
– 'Elizabeth Gable' (E) NKay
– 'Elsie Lee' (E) CGre GGGa SBod SCog SReu SSta
– 'Elsie Pratt' (K) MBri MMor NBar SSta
N– 'Esmeralda' CMac SBod
– 'Eunice Updike' (E) LHyd
– 'Eva Goude' (K) LKna
– 'Evensong' (E) LKna
– 'Everbloom' (E) NMun
– 'Everest' (E) CBow CWal LHyd MAsh MBar MBri WAbe WBod
– 'Everest White' NKay
– 'Exbury White' (K) GWht SExb
– 'Exquisitum' **AGM** GGGa LMil MAsh MBri SExb SReu
¶– F H 8 LMil
– 'Fanny' See R. A. 'Pucella'
– 'Favorite' (E) CMac CTrw IOrc LKna MBri MMor NMun SExb SLeo SPer SSta
– 'Fedora' **AGM** CB&S CTre CTrh LHyd LKna MRav SPer SReu
– 'Fénelon' (G) GGGa
¶– 'Fidelio' (E) SCog
– 'Fireball' (K) CB&S CBow CMHG CSco GGGa GRei GWht IJoh ISea LHyd LMil MBri MLea NKay SExb SPer WWeb
– 'Firefly' (E) See R. A. 'Hexe'
– 'Firefly' (K) LMil SExb WBod
– 'Fireglow' MBri
– 'Flaming June' (K) LKna
– 'Floradora' (M) SReu
– 'Florida' **AGM** CChe CMac CTrh GWht LKna MRav SBod SCog SPer SSta WAbe WBod
– 'Frans van der Bom' (M) IDai
– 'Fraseri' (M) CBow GGGa
– 'Fridoline' (E) NBar
– 'Frills' (K/d) CWal LHyd
– 'Frilly Lemon' (K/d) LMil
– 'Frome' (K) LKna
– 'Fudetsukasi' NMun SLeo
– 'Fuko-hiko' (E) CWal NMun SLeo
¶– 'Gabrielle Hill' (E) SCog
– 'Gaiety' (E) GGGa GWht IOrc LMil MAsh SCog
– 'Galathea' (E) GGGa
– 'Gallipoli' (K) SPer
– 'Garden State Glow' (E/d) SBod SCog
*– 'Geisha Lilac' (E) MBri
*– 'Geisha Orange' (E) CBow GGGa MBar MBri MGos NHed
*– 'Geisha Purple' (E) MBar
*– 'Geisha Red' (E) MBar MBri
– 'Gekkeikan' (E) CB&S
– 'General Wavell' (E) CMac CTrh CWal GAri LKna
– 'Georg Arends' CDoC IJoh NBar
– 'George Reynolds' (K) CWal SExb
– 'Getsutoku' (E) CTrh
– 'Gibraltar' **AGM** CB&S CMHG CSam CSco EBre GGGa GRei GWht IDai IJoh IOrc LBre LHyd LKna LMil MAsh MBal MBar MBri MGos MLea MMor MRav NBar SExb SPer SReu SSta WAbe
– 'Gilbert Mullier' MBri
– 'Ginger' (K) CWal GWht LMil MBal NMun SExb
§– 'Girard's Hot Shot' (E) GGGa SBod SGil SReu SSta
– 'Girard's Pink' (E) SReu
– 'Girard's Scarlet' (E) SReu
– 'Glencora' (E) LHyd
♦– 'Glenn Dale Adorable' See R. A. 'Adorable'
– 'Glockenspiel' (K) LKna
– 'Gloria Mundi' (G) SReu WAbe
– 'Glowing Embers' (K) CMHG CSam GAri GRei GWht ISea MAsh MBal MBri MLea MMor NBar NKay SExb SPer SReu WWeb
– 'Gog' (K) CSam CWal LHyd LKna MAsh MBal SPer
– 'Gold Crest' (K) LKna
– 'Goldball' See R. A. 'Christopher Wren'
– 'Golden Eagle' (K) CB&S CDoC COtt LKna MAsh MBri MGos
– 'Golden Eye' (K) LKna
– 'Golden Flare' (K) CB&S CMHG ISea MAsh MBri WWeb
– 'Golden Horn' (K) CWal SExb WGor
– 'Golden Lights' LMil
– 'Golden Oriole' (K) LKna SReu
– 'Golden Sunlight' (M) See R. A. 'Directeur Moerlands'
– 'Golden Sunset' (K) CSco IJoh LKna LMil MAsh MBri MGos MMor NBar WStI
– 'Goldfinch' (K) LKna
– 'Goldtopas' (K) GGGa
– 'Gorbella' NHol
– 'Graciosum' (O) LKna
– 'Greenway' (E) CB&S CGre CTre IOrc SPer
– 'Greta' (E) LHyd
§– 'Gumpo' (E) CMac CTrh EPot SCog SPer WAbe WThu
– 'Gumpo Pink' (E) SReu SSta WBod
– 'Gumpo White' (E) SBod SSta WAbe WBod
– 'Gumpo' x ***nakaharae*** SSta
– 'Gwenda' (E) LHyd SCog
– 'Gyokushin' (E) MBal

	Azalea 'H H Hume' (E)	MBal SGil
	– 'H O Carre' (E)	CMac SExb
	– 'Hachmann's Rokoko' (E)	GGGa
	– 'Hamlet' (M)	LMil
	– 'Hana-asobi' (E)	CB&S LHyd SExb WBod
	– 'Harbinger' (E)	NMun SBod SCog SLeo
¶	– 'Hardijzer Beauty' (E)	IOrc
	– 'Hardy Gardenia' (E/d)	SCog SSta
	– 'Harkwood Red'	LMil LRHS
	– 'Harumiji' (E)	CWal NMun SLeo
	– 'Haru-no-hikari' (E)	CTrh
	– 'Haru-no-sono' (E)	CTrh
	– 'Harvest Moon' (K)	IHos MBri NBar SExb SReu
	– 'Hatsugiri' **AGM**	CHig CMac IJoh IOrc LHyd LKna MBar MBri MMor SBod SCog SReu SSta WBod WPat
	– 'Heather Macleod' (E)	LHyd
	– 'Heiwa-no-kagami' (E)	CTrh GAri
	– 'Helen Close' (E)	LHyd LRHS
	– 'Helen Curtis' (E)	SReu
	– 'Herbert' (E)	CMac
	– 'Hexe' (E/d)	WBod
	– 'Higasa' (E)	CTrh GAri
	– 'Hinode-giri' (E)	CB&S CHig CMac CTrw CWal IDai LHyd LKna NMun SBod SExb SLeo SReu WBod
	– 'Hinode-no-kumo' (E)	CWal NMun SLeo
	– 'Hino-crimson' **AGM**	CBow CGre CMac CSco CWal GWht IDai IJoh IOrc LKna LMil MBar MBri MGos MMor NHol NJap NKay SPer SReu SSta WPat WStI
	– 'Hino-mayo' **AGM**	CB&S CCla CMHG CMac CSco CTre CWal EBre GRei IOrc LBre LHyd LKna LMil MBri MRav NKay NMun SCog SExb SLeo SPer SReu SSta WBod WStI
	– 'Hino-Scarlet'	See R. A. 'Campfire'
	– 'Hino-tsukasa' (E)	CWal NMun SLeo
	– 'Homebush' **AGM**	CB&S CCla CMHG CWal GGGa GWht IJoh IOrc ISea LHyd LKna LMil MAsh MBal MBri SExb SPer SReu SSta WWeb
	– 'Honeysuckle' (K)	IOrc MBar MMor NBar SExb
	– 'Hortulanus H Witte' (M)	MMor SReu
	– 'Hot Shot'	See R. A. 'Girard's Hot Shot'
	– Hotspur Group **AGM**	ELan GGGa SExb SPer WWeb
	– 'Hotspur Red' **AGM**	CWal LKna LMil MBri SCog SReu
	– 'Hotspur Yellow' (K)	CWal LHyd SReu
§	– 'Ho-o' (E)	CB&S CGre CMac SCog SExb
	– 'Hyde Park' (K)	LMil
	– 'Ightham Pink'	SReu
	– 'Il Tasso' (R/d)	LKna SRms
§	– 'Ilam Melford Lemon'	LMil
§	– 'Ilam Ming'	LMil
	– 'Imago' (K)	LKna
§	– 'Ima-shojo' **AGM**	CMac GAri IHos LHyd MAsh SPer WBod
	– 'Impala' (K)	LKna
	– 'Indicum'	See R. ***indicum***
	– 'Irene Koster' **AGM**	CMHG CWal ELan GGGa GWht ISea LHyd LKna LMil MAsh MBri SExb SPer SReu WWeb
	– 'Irohayama' **AGM**	CBow CHig CMac CTrw LHyd LKna LMil SCog SReu SSta WBod
	– 'Ishiyama' (E)	SCog
	– 'Issho-no-haru' (E)	CTrh
	– 'Ivette' (E)	CMac LHyd LKna
	– 'Iwato-kagami' (E)	CWal NMun SLeo
	– 'Izayoi' (E)	WBod
	– 'J Jennings' (K)	WAbe
	– 'James Gable' (E)	MAsh
¶	– 'Jan Wellen' (E)	IOrc
	– 'Jean Read'	LHyd
	– 'Jeanette' (E)	LKna
¶	– 'Jo Madden'	LHyd
	– 'Jock Brydon' (0)	GGGa
	– 'Jock Coutts'	LKna
	– 'Johann Sebastian Bach' (E)	WBod WWeb
	– 'Johann Strauss' (E)	WBod
	– 'Johanna' (E)	CDoC CMac GGGa LMil MAsh MBar MBri MMor MRav NHol SExb SPer WBod
	– 'John Cairns' **AGM**	CMac CWal LHyd LKna LMil MBal SCog SPer SReu WBod
	– 'Jolie Madame' (Vs)	CDoC MBri SReu
	– 'Joseph Haydn' (E)	WBod
	– 'Joseph Hill' (E)	LMil
	– 'June Fire'	GGGa
	– 'Kaho-no-hikari' (E)	GAri
	– 'Kakiemon' (E)	LHyd SPer
N	– 'Kathleen'	CWal GWht IOrc LHyd LKna MMor SCog SExb
	– 'Katinka' (E)	MBal MGos
	– 'Katisha' (E)	LHyd
	– 'Katsura-no-hana ' (E)	WBod
*	– 'Keija'	SCog
	– 'Keinohana' (E)	CWal NMun SLeo
	– 'Kermesinum' (E)	CDoC COtt GGGa GPlt MBar MBri NBar SReu WPat
	– 'Kermesinum Album' (E)	GGGa MBar MBri NBar WThu
	– 'Keston Rose'	SReu SSta
	– 'Kijei'	CB&S
	– 'Killarney' (E)	CTrh
	– 'Kimigayo' (E)	LHyd SExb
§	– 'Kirin' **AGM**	CGre CMac CTrh CTrw CWal IOrc LHyd LKna MBri SBod SCog SExb WBod WPat
	– 'Kirishima' (E)	LKna SReu SRms
	– 'Kiritsubo' (E)	GAri IOrc LHyd WBod
	– 'Kiusianum'	See R. ***kiusianum***
	– 'Klondyke' **AGM**	CB&S CSam CSco EBre ELan GGGa IOrc LBre LMil MBri MGos NBar SExb SPer SReu
	– 'Knap Hill Apricot' (K)	LKna LMil
	– 'Knap Hill Red' (K)	LKna LMil
	– 'Kobold' (E)	NMun SLeo SSta
	– 'Komurasaki' (E)	CWal NMun SLeo
	– 'Koningin Emma' ('Queen Emma') (M)	LMil MBri
§	– 'Koningin Wilhelmina' (M)	IOrc SCog WBod
	– 'Koster's Brilliant Red' (M)	CSco MBal MBar SReu

Azalea 'Kozan' (E)	MBal
§ – 'Kumo-no-ito' (E)	SExb
§ – 'Kure-no-yuki' **AGM**	CBow CMac CWal LHyd LKna SBod SCog SExb SReu SSta WBod
– 'Kusudama' (E)	CTrh GAri
– 'Lady Elphinstone' (E)	LHyd
– 'Lady Rosebery' (K)	LKna MBri SReu
– 'Langmans'	LKna
– 'Lapwing' (K)	CBow GAri GGGa LKna MBri
– 'Late Love' (E)	IJoh MGos
– late pink Inverewe	WBod
– 'Laura Morland' (E)	LHyd
* – 'Lavender Brilliant'	CTrh
– 'Ledifolium'	See R. ***mucronatum***
– 'Ledifolium Album'	See R. ***mucronatum***
– 'Leibnitz' (G/d)	GGGa
– 'Lemonora' (M)	ELan MAsh MBri
– 'Lemur' (E)	EPot GGGa MAsh MBri MGos NHar WPat WThu
– 'Leo' (E)	CBow CWal LHyd LKna LMil NMun SBod SCog SLeo SPer SReu WAbe WWeb
– 'Lilac Time' (E)	MBar WBod
– 'Lilacinum'	SCog
– 'Lillie Maude' (E)	CTrh
– 'Lilliput' (E)	MAsh SBod SPer
– 'Lily Marleen' (E)	CDoC CWal MMor SReu
– 'Linearifolium'	See R. ***macrosepalum*** 'L.'
– 'Linnet'	LKna
– 'Lobster Pot' (K)	LMil
– 'Lorna' (E)	CSco LMil
– 'Lotte' (E)	SReu
– 'Louis B Williams'	GGGa
– 'Louisa' (E)	SExb
– 'Louise Dowdle' (E)	CDoC CTrh LMil MMor SGil SPer
– 'Lullaby' (E)	LKna
I – 'Mac Ovata'	CMac
– 'Macranthum'	See R. ***indicum***
– 'Macranthum Roseum' (E)	MAsh SBod SExb
– 'Macrosepalum'	See R. ***macrosepalum***
– 'Macrostemon'	See R. ***obtusum*** 'Macrostemon'
¶ – 'Madame Knutz'	SCog
– 'Madame van Hecke' (E)	COtt MAsh MBri NBar SReu
N – 'Magnificum'	CBow LMil MBri SCog
– 'Malvaticum' (E)	WBod
– 'Margaret George' (E)	LHyd
– 'Marie' (E)	CMac SCog
– 'Marilee' (E)	MGos
– 'Marion Merriman' (K)	LKna
– 'Marionette'	CTrh
¶ – 'Marmot' (E)	GGGa
– 'Martha Hitchcock' (E)	GPlt LKna SCog SGil SRms
– 'Martine'	See R. Azaleodendron 'M.'
– 'Mary Helen' (E)	CDoC LHyd LRHS SExb SReu WBod
– 'Mary Meredith' (E)	LHyd
* – 'Mary Poppins'	CDoC GRei
– 'Master of Elphinstone' (E)	SCog
– 'Mauna Loa' (K)	LKna
– 'Maxwellii' (E)	CMac SCog SExb WBod
– 'Mazurka' (K)	LKna
– 'Megan' (E)	GGGa GWht IOrc MAsh
– 'Meicho' (E)	CTrh GAri
– 'Melford Lemon'	See R. A. 'Ilam Melford Lemon'
– 'Mephistopheles' (K)	LKna
N – 'Merlin' (E)	LMil MBal WWeb
– 'Michael Hill' (E)	CB&S CBow CTrh EHic GPlt MAsh SCog SPer WWeb
– 'Mikado' (E)	CMHG CWal SBod SCog SPer SReu SSta
– 'Mimi' (E)	CMac LHyd MBri
– 'Ming'	See R. A. 'Ilam Ming'
– 'Misomogiri'	CHig
– 'Miss Muffet' (E)	SExb
– 'Mizu-no-yamabuki' (E)	CWal NMun SLeo
– 'Moidart' (Vs)	LMil
– 'Moira Salmon' (E)	LHyd
– Mollis orange	SRms
– Mollis pink	GGGa SRms
– Mollis red	SRms
– Mollis salmon (M)	GGGa
– Mollis yellow	SRms
– 'Moon Maiden' (E)	MMor
– 'Motet'	LKna
– 'Mother's Day' **AGM**	Widely available
– 'Mount Rainier' (K)	LMil
– 'Mount Saint Helens'	CBow GGGa LHyd LMil
– 'Mozart' (E)	SBod WBod
– 'Mrs Anthony Waterer' (O)	LKna
– 'Mrs Doorenbos'	CMac
– 'Mrs Emil Hager' (E)	LHyd
– 'Mrs Peter Koster' (M)	IJoh
– 'Mucronatum' (E)	See R. ***mucronatum***
– 'Mucronatum Amethystinum'	See R. A. 'Amethystinum'
– 'Multiflorum'	NBar
– 'Nakahari Orange'	See R. ***nakaharae*** Orange
– 'Nakahari-mariko'	See R. ***nakaharae*** 'Mariko'
– 'Nancy Buchanan' (K)	SExb
– 'Nancy of Robinhill' (E)	LHyd
– 'Nancy Waterer' **AGM**	CSco GGGa MBri NBar SReu
– 'Nanki Poo' (E)	LHyd SPer
– 'Naomi' (E)	GWht IOrc LHyd LKna LMil SCog SPer SReu
– 'Narcissiflorum' **AGM**	CDoC CSco CWal IOrc LHyd LKna LMil MBri SExb SReu
– 'Nettie' (E)	SCog
– 'Niagara' **AGM**	CTrh LHyd LMil MBal SCog WBod
– 'Nichola' (E)	MAsh SBod SCog
– 'Nico'	CDoC CMac MAsh MBri MRav SPer WBod WPat
– 'Nihon-no-hana' (E)	CTrh
– 'Nishiki' (E)	CMac
N – 'Norma' **AGM**	LMil SReu
– 'Northlight'	MBri
– 'Nuccio's Bit o' Sunshine' (E)	CTrh
– 'Oi-no-mezame' (E)	LHyd
– 'Old Gold' (K)	SReu
N – 'Ophelia'	CBow
– 'Optima' (E)	SCog

Azalea 'Orange Beauty' AGM	CMac CSco CTrh CWal GGGa IDai IJoh LHyd LKna LMil MBal MBar MGos MMor NMun SBod SCog SExb SLeo SPer SReu SSta WAbe WBod
– 'Orange King' (E)	MBar WStI
¶ – 'Orange Scout'	WGor
– 'Orangeade' (K)	GGGa
– 'Oryx' (O)	LKna
– 'Ouchiyama'	LKna
– 'Oxydol' AGM	CWal GGGa LHyd
– 'Palestrina' AGM	CB&S CChe CMac CSco CWal EPot GWht IDai IOrc LHyd LKna MBal MBar MMor NMun SBod SCog SLeo SPer SReu SSta WBod WPat WStI
– 'Pallas' (G)	CSco MBri SReu
– 'Pamela Miles'	LHyd
– 'Pancake'	CMac
– 'Panda' (E)	CDoC CMac EBre GGGa LBre LHyd LMil MBri NHar NHed SCog SReu
– 'Paramount' (K)	LKna
– 'Pavane' (K)	LKna
– 'Peach Blossom' (E)	See R. A. 'Saotome'
– 'Pearl Bradford' (E)	LMil
– 'Peep-Bo' (E)	LHyd LMil SPer
– 'Perfect'	MBal SPer
– 'Persil' AGM	CB&S CSco CWal ELan GGGa GRei IDai IJoh LHyd LKna MBar MBri MGos MMor NBar SExb SPer SReu WBod
– 'Peter Berg'	NBar
– 'Petrouchka' (K)	LKna MAsh MBri
– 'Pettychaps' (E)	SReu
– 'Phoebe'	SReu
– 'Piccolo' (K)	LKna
N – 'Pink Delight'	LHyd LKna SExb WBod
– 'Pink Pancake' (E)	CB&S CTrh IJoh LMil MAsh MGos SCog SGil WWeb
N – 'Pink Ruffles'	WBod
– 'Pippa' AGM	CMac SRms
– 'Polar Bear' (E)	IJoh MBal MGos
– 'Polar Haven' (E)	LKna
– 'Polar Sea' (E)	CTrh SBod SExb
– ***ponticum***	See R. ***luteum***
– 'Pooh-Bah' (E)	LHyd
– 'Port Knap' (E)	LKna
– 'Port Wine' (E)	LKna
¶ – 'Princess Elizabeth' (M)	SExb
– 'Princess Ida' (E)	LHyd
– 'Prins Bernhard' (E)	IOrc LKna MAsh SExb
– 'Prinses Juliana' (E)	CDoC MMor SExb SGil SHer SReu WAbe WBod
§ – 'Pucella' AGM	LHyd NBar
– purple Glenn Dale (E)	SExb
– 'Purple Queen' (E/d)	MAsh
– 'Purple Splendor' (E)	CMac CWal EBre IOrc LBre LKna MGos NHol
– 'Purple Triumph' (E)	CB&S CWal EBre IJoh IOrc LBre LKna LMil NMun SLeo SReu SSta WBod
♦ – 'Queen Wilhelmina'	See R. A. 'Koningin Wilhelmina'
¶ – 'Racoon' (E)	GGGa
– 'Raphael de Smet' (G/d)	SReu
– 'Rashomon' (E)	LHyd LKna NMun SLeo WBod
– 'Raspberry Delight' (K/d)	LMil
– 'Red Bird' (E)	CMac
– 'Red Fountain' (E)	COtt SCog
– 'Red Red'	GGGa
– 'Red Sunset' (E/d)	LMil
– 'Redmond' (E)	LHyd
¶ – 'Redshank' (K)	MBri
– 'Redwing' (E)	LMil LRHS MAsh SPer
– 'Rennie' (E)	SExb
– 'Rêve d'Amour' (Vs)	MMor SSta
– 'Rex' (E)	CWal SPer
– 'Robin Hill Frosty' (E)	LHyd SExb
– 'Robin Hill Gillie' (E)	LHyd
– 'Rosalinda' (E)	GGGa
– 'Rosata' (Vs)	CDoC GGGa MBri MMor SReu SSta
– 'Rose Glow'	MMor
– 'Rose Greeley' (E)	CDoC CHig CSco CTrh IOrc SBod SExb SHer SReu
– 'Rose Haze'	MMor
– 'Rose Plenum' (G)	GGGa
– 'Rose Ruffles' (K)	GGGa LMil
– 'Rose Torch'	MMor
– 'Rosebud' AGM	CB&S CHig CMac CSco CTrh CTrw CWal GGGa GWht IOrc ISea LHyd LKna MBar MGos MMor NKay NMun SBod SCog SExb SLeo SPer SReu WBod
– 'Rosiflorum'	See R. ***indicum*** 'Balsaminiflorum'
– 'Rosy Lights'	LMil
– 'Royal Command' (K)	CSco GAri GRei MBar MMor NBar SExb
– 'Royal Lodge' AGM	CWal GGGa GWht LHyd
– 'Royal Ruby' (K)	LMil MBri MMor
– 'Rozanne Waterer'	LKna
– 'Rubinetta' (E)	CDoC
– 'Rumba' (K)	LKna
– 'Sabina'	NBar
– 'Sahara' (K)	LKna
– 'Sakata Red' (E)	CGre CMac IOrc SExb WBod
– 'Sakon' (E)	CWal NMun SLeo
– 'Salmon Sander' (E)	LKna SExb
¶ – 'Salmon's Leap'	SHil
– 'Samuel Taylor Coleridge' (M)	MMor
– 'Sang de Gentbrugge' (G)	SReu
– 'Santa Maria'	COtt EBre IDai LBre NHol SGil SHer SReu SSta
§ – 'Saotome' (E)	CMac LHyd
– 'Saroi' (E)	CWal NMun SLeo
– 'Saskia' (K)	LKna
– 'Satan' AGM	CWal ELan GAri GGGa GWht LKna MBri MMor NBar SReu
– 'Satsuki' (E)	CGre IJoh LNet MAsh SExb SSta WWeb
– 'Saturnus' (M)	ELan
– 'Scarlatti' (K)	LKna
– 'Scarlet Pimpernel' (K)	CWal GWht NKay
– 'Schubert' (E)	MBar MGos WAbe WBod
– 'Shanty' (K)	LKna
– 'Shiho' (E)	CTrh
– 'Shiko' (E)	CTrh SReu
– 'Shin Seikai' (E/d)	CB&S

Azalea
'Shinimiagagnoo' (E) CWal NMun SLeo
– 'Shinnyo-no-hikari' GAri
– 'Shinsei' (E) GAri
– 'Shintoki-no-hagasane' (E) LHyd WBod
– 'Shintsune' (E) CWal NMun SLeo
– 'Shi-no-noe' (E) NMun SBod SLeo
– 'Shukishima' (E) CWal NMun SLeo
– 'Shuku-fuku' (E) GAri
– 'Silver Glow' (E) CMac
– 'Silver Moon' (E) CTrh IOrc NMun SBod SCog SExb SLeo SPer
– 'Silver Slipper' **AGM** CWal GAri GWht LHyd LKna LMil MBal MBar MBri MLea MMor NBar SReu SSta
– 'Silverwood' (K) LMil
– 'Silvester' (E) COtt MBri MMor WAbe WPat
– 'Sir William Lawrence' (E) LKna SExb SReu
– 'Snow' (E) CMac COtt IJoh MAsh
– 'Snow Hill' (E) LHyd LMil
– 'Snowbird' GGGa
– 'Snowflake' See R. A. 'Kure-no-yuki'
– 'Soft Lips' (K) GWht
– 'Soho' (E) CTrh GAri LNet
– 'Soir de Paris' (Vs) MBar MBri MMor SExb SSta
– 'Solway' (Vs) LMil
– 'Sophie Hedges' LKna
– 'Souvenir du Président Carnot' (G) LKna
– 'Spek's Orange' **AGM** CWal LHyd MBri MGos SExb SReu
– 'Spicy Lights' LMil
– 'Spoonbill' LKna
– 'Spring Beauty' (E) CBow CMac SExb
– 'Squirrel' (E) CDoC CMac EBre GGGa GRei LBre LHyd LMil MAsh MBal MBri MGos NHar NHed SCog SGil SReu SSta WBod WPat
– 'Star of Zaffelare' NHol
– 'Stewartstonian' **AGM** CMac CTrh CWal IJoh IOrc LHyd LMil MBal MBar MBri MMor SBod SSta
¶– 'Stoat' (E) GGGa
– 'Stour' (K) GGGa
– 'Stranraer' MAsh MBri
– 'Strawberry Ice' **AGM** CBow CMHG CSco CWal GGGa GWht IJoh IOrc ISea LHyd LKna LMil MBri MGos SExb SPer SReu
– 'Sugared Almond' **AGM** CWal MBal
– 'Sugi-no-ito' See R. A. 'Kumo-no-ito'
– 'Summer Fragrance' **AGM** NBar SReu SSta
– 'Sun Chariot' **AGM** CB&S CSam CWal GRei ISea LHyd LKna LMil MBri SPer SReu
– 'Sun Charm' NHol
– 'Sunbeam' See R. Azalea 'Benifude'
– 'Sunset Pink' (K) CDoC ISea LHyd LMil MAsh SExb WWeb
– 'Sunte Nectarine' **AGM** GWht LHyd LMil MAsh MBri SExb
– 'Surprise' (E) CDoC CTrh EBre ISea LBre MAsh NMun SCog SExb SLeo SPer SReu SSta WWeb
– 'Susannah Hill' (E) CB&S CTrh LMil MBri SBod SGil SPer
– 'Swansong' (E) CMac SCog
– 'Sword of State' (K) LMil
– 'Sylphides' (K) GAri LKna MBri
– 'Sylvester' CDoC MGos SReu
– 'Takasago' (E/d) LHyd LMil SCog
– 'Tanager' (E) CTrh LKna
– 'Tangiers' (K) SExb
– 'Tender Heart' (K) LMil
– 'Terra-cotta Beauty' (E) WPat WThu
– 'Tinsmith' (K) LMil
– 'Tit Willow' (E) CWal GRei LHyd SPer
– 'Titipu' (E) CWal LHyd
– 'Tonkonatsu' (E) CWal NMun SLeo
*– 'Top of the Rockery' MAsh
– 'Toreador' (E) CMac SExb
– 'Torridon' (Vs) LMil
– 'Totally Awesome' (K) CBow GGGa
– 'Tower Beauty' (C) LHyd
– 'Tower Dainty' (C) LHyd
– 'Tower Daring' (C) LHyd
– 'Tower Dexter' (C) LHyd
– 'Tower Dragon' (C) LHyd
– 'Trent' (K) SReu
– 'Troll' (E) SReu
– 'Troupial' (K) LKna
– 'Tsuta-momiji' (E) LHyd SExb
– 'Tunis' (K) CWal MBri MLea
N– 'Twilight' MBri
– 'Twilight Sky' MAsh
– 'Ukamuse' (E/d) LHyd
– 'Umpqua Queen' (K) GGGa
– 'Unique' (G) LKna SReu
– 'Van Heka' CDoC NHol
– 'Velvet Gown' (E) IOrc LRHS MBri
– 'Venetia' (K) MBri MMor
– 'Vespers' (E) CTrh MAsh
– 'Vida Brown' (E/d) CMac GWht LKna MAsh MBri SBod SCog SExb SPer SReu SSta WPat WThu
– 'Viking' (E) LHyd
– 'Violet Longhurst' LHyd
– 'Violetta' (E) GGGa ISea NBar
– 'Vuyk's Rosyred' **AGM** CB&S CBow CHig CMac CSco CTrh CWal GRei GWht IJoh IOrc ISea LHyd LKna LMil MBar MBri MGos MMor MRav NHol NKay SBod SExb SPer SReu WAbe WBod WStI
– 'Vuyk's Scarlet' **AGM** Widely available
– 'W E Gumbleton' (M) SReu
– 'Wallowa Red' (K) LMil
– 'Ward's Ruby' (E) CTrh CTrw SReu
– 'Washington State Centennial' GGGa
– 'Waxwing' LKna
– 'Westminster' (O) LKna LMil
– 'White Frills' (E) LMil MBal SExb
– 'White Jade' (E) SExb
– 'White Lady' (E) IJoh LKna SRms
– 'White Lights' CBow GGGa LMil LRHS
– 'White Swan' (K) SExb
– 'Whitethroat' **AGM** IOrc LKna MBri SReu
– 'Willy' (E) CBow GGGa LHyd LKna MBri SReu
– 'Windsor Apple Blossom' (K) LMil
– 'Windsor Peach Glow' (K) LMil

Azalea 'Windsor Sunbeam' (K)	LMil
– 'Winston Churchill' (M)	MBar MMor NBar
– 'Wintergreen' (E)	CB&S CTrh SSta WWeb
– 'Wombat' (E)	CDoC EPot GGGa GRei LHyd LMil MAsh MBal MBar MBri MGos NHar NHed NHol SCog SReu SSta WPat
– 'Wryneck' AGM	LHyd LMil MBri SReu
– 'Yamato-no-hikari'	CTrh
– 'Yoga' (K)	LKna
– 'Yo-zakura' (E)	CWal NMun SLeo
Azaleodendron 'Cameronian'	LKna
– 'Govenianum'	CLan LKna
– 'Hammondii'	LKna
§ – 'Hardijzer Beauty' AGM	LKna MBal MBri
– 'Joy's Delight'	LKna
– 'Martha Isaacson'	MBal MGos
– 'Martine'	LHyd LKna MBri MGos NMun SLeo WBod
– 'Ria Hardijzer'	LKna MBri SSta
– 'Wilsonii'	LKna
baileyi	CWal GGGa LHyd LMil NMun
¶ – LS&H 17359	NMun
bainbridgeanum R/USDA 59184/R 11190	CWal NMun SLeo
bakeri (A)	See R. ***calendulaceum***
balfourianum	GGGa NMun
¶ – F 16811	NMun
¶ – F 29256*	NMun
– Aganniphoïdes Group	CWal LMil NMun
barbatum	CBow CWal GGGa GWht LHyd LMil NMun SLeo SReu
¶ – B 235*	NMun
– BB 152	MBal
¶ – BL&M 325	NMun
¶ – Cave 6714	NMun
– DF 525	MBal
¶ – KW 5659*	NMun
¶ – LS&H 17512	NMun
¶ – TSS 30	NMun
§ ***basilicum***	CWal GGGa LHyd LMil NMun SLeo
bathyphyllum	NMun SLeo
♦ ***bauhiniiflorum***	See R. ***triflorum b.***
beanianum	CWal GGGa LMil NMun SLeo
¶ – KW 6805	NMun
– compact form	See R. ***piercei***
beesianum	GGGa NMun SLeo
¶ – F 10195	NMun
¶ – R 176	NMun
bergii	See R. ***augustinii rubrum***
¶ ***bhutanense*** AC 119	NMun
¶ – AC 124	NMun
– EGM 077	GGGa LMil
– KR 1753	LMil
bodinieri	LMil
¶ – R/USDA 59585/ R11281	NMun
brachyanthum	CWal GGGa NMun SExb SLeo
§ – L&S 2764	LMil
– ssp. ***hypolepidotum***	CWal GGGa LMil MBal NMun SLeo
brachycarpum	CWal GGGa MBal NMun SLeo
– ssp. ***fauriei***	CWal NMun SLeo
– pink	NMun SLeo
– 'Roseum Dwarf'	GGGa NMun
brachysiphon	See R. ***maddenii maddenii***
bracteatum CH&M 2586	GGGa
bullatum	See R. ***edgeworthii***
bureaui AGM	CAbP CBow CWal GGGa GWht IOrc LHyd MBal MBlu NMun SExb SLeo SReu SSta
– EGM 141	LMil
¶ – F 15609	NMun
¶ – R 25439	NMun
– 'Ardrishaig'	GGGa
¶ ***bureauoïdes***	NMun
¶ – C 5039, 5066, 5076	GGGa
¶ – EGM 141	LMil
burmanicum AGM	CWal GGGa LMil NMun SBor SExb SLeo
caesium	GGGa
¶ – F 26798	NMun
§ ***calendulaceum*** (A)	GGGa LHyd LMil MBal NMun SLeo
– yellow	LMil
callimorphum	CWal GGGa LMil NMun
– var. ***myiagrum***	CWal
– var. ***myiagrum*** F 21821A	NMun SLeo
¶ – var. ***myiagrum*** KW 6962	NMun
calophytum AGM	CHEx CWal GGGa LHyd LMil NMun SLeo
¶ – W A 4279	NMun
¶ – W V 1523	NMun
¶ – Grieg's form	NMun
calostrotum	CWal GPlt LMil MBlu SExb SIng WAbe
– R/USDA 03954/R18453	GGGa
– 'Gigha' AGM	CSam CWal GGGa LHyd LMil MBri NHar NHol
§ – ssp. ***keleticum*** AGM	GAri GDra GWht LHyd MBal MBar MGos NKay SBod SIng SReu WAbe WBod WThu
– ssp. ***keleticum*** F 19915	NHol NMun
– ssp. ***keleticum*** F 21756	CWal NMun SLeo
– ssp. ***keleticum*** R 58	NHol
§ – – Radicans Group	CWal GAbr GPlt GWht IDai LHyd LMil MBar MLea NHol WAbe WBod WPat WThu
– – Radicans Group mound form	NHol
– – Radicans Group R 59182	MLea
– ssp. ***riparioïdes***	LMil
– ssp. ***riparium***	CWal GAbr MBal
– – Calciphilum Group	GGGa MBar WAbe WBod
– – Calciphilum Group Yu 19754	GGGa
§ – – Nitens Group	GGGa LMil
– – Rock's form R 178	GGGa GWht NHol
caloxanthum	See R. ***campylocarpum caloxanthum***
¶ ***calvescens*** var. ***duseimatum***	NMun
camelliiflorum	CWal GGGa
¶ – Rump 5696A	NMun
campanulatum	GWht IOrc LHyd LKna LMil NMun SLeo SReu
– B 643	MBal
¶ – BL&M 283	NMun
– DF 563	MBal
– SS&W 9107	CWal GGGa NMun SLeo

¶– SS&W 9108	NMun
– TSS 11	NMun SLeo
¶– TSS 44	NMun
– TSS 7	NMun SLeo
§ – ssp. ***aeruginosum***	CWal GGGa LMil NMun SReu
– ssp. ***aeruginosum*** EGM 068	LMil
– ***album***	CWal NMun SLeo
¶– ***album*** SS&W	NMun
– 'Knap Hill' AGM	CWal LHyd NMun SExb SReu
¶– 'Roland Cooper'	NMun
– 'Waxen Bell'	LHyd NMun SLeo
campylocarpum	CHig CWal GGGa GWht LHyd LMil NMun SCog SLeo SReu
– BM&W 150	MBal
– DF 558	MBal
¶– LS&H 16495	NMun
¶– TSS 12	NMun
¶– TSS 43	NMun
§ – ssp. ***caloxanthum***	CWal GGGa IOrc
– – forms	NMun SLeo
¶– – Telopeum Group	NMun
§ – – Telopeum Group KW 5718B	NMun SLeo
– ssp. ***campylocarpum*** Elatum Group	CWal NMun
campylogynum	CB&S CMHG CTrw CWal GGGa GWht IOrc LMil NHar NKay NMun SLeo SReu
– KW 21481	NHol
– 'Album'	See R. ***c. leucanthum***
– apricot	LMil
– 'Beryl Taylor'	GGGa LMil NMun WBod
– 'Bodnant Red'	CHig GAbr GGGa LHyd LMil MAsh NMun SLeo WBod
– Castle Hill form	LMil
– claret	GCLN GGGa LMil MBal WAbe
– copper	SReu
§ – var. ***leucanthum***	CHig GGGa LMil
¶– Myrtilloïdes Group	NMun SIng
¶– 'New Pink'	NHol
– pink	MBar
– plum	GGGa
¶– 'Plum Brandy'	NHar NHol
– salmon pink	CWal GGGa MBal NBar NHar NHol WAbe WBod
campylogynum Celsum Group	LMil NMun
– Charopoeum Group	CWal GCLN GGGa GPlt LMil MBal MGos NHar NHol WAbe WBod
– – 'Patricia'	GGGa MBal WAbe WBod WThu
§ – Cremastum Group	CWal GGGa LHyd LMil NHol NMun SLeo
¶– – 'Thimble'	WThu
– Myrtilloïdes Group	CHig CWal EPot GAri GGGa GWht LHyd LMil MBal MBri NHar NHol NMun SExb SLeo WAbe WBod
– – Farrer 1046	GGGa NHar NHol
camtschaticum	GArf GAri GDra GGGa MBal MLea SReu
– ***album***	GGGa
– red	GGGa
canadense (A)	GGGa MBal NHol NMun NSla SLeo
– f. ***albiflorum*** (A)	GGGa
§ x ***candelabrum***	NMun SLeo
canescens (A)	CWal
capitatum	GGGa
♦***cardiobasis***	See R. ***orbiculare c.***
carneum	GGGa LMil
carolinianum	See R. ***minus minus*** Carolinianum Group
catacosmum	GGGa NMun SLeo
¶– F 21727	NMun
– R 11185	NMun SLeo
catawbiense	CHig GGGa LHyd NMun SLeo
– 'Powell Glass'	CWal NMun
caucasicum	CWal LHyd MBal
– ex AC&H	GGGa NMun SLeo
cephalanthum	EPot GGGa
– SBEC 0751	GGGa
– ssp. ***cephalanthum***	MBal
– – Crebreflorum Group	GAri GGGa
¶– – Crebreflorum Group KW 8337	NMun
– – Crebreflorum Group Week's form	GDra
cerasinum	GGGa LMil NMun SLeo
¶– KW 11011	NMun
– KW 5830	NMun SLeo
– KW 6923	CWal NMun
¶– KW 8258	NMun
– 'Cherry Brandy'	CWal LHyd NMun
– 'Coals of Fire'	CWal NMun SLeo
– deep pink	NMun SLeo
– x ***forrestii forrestii***	MBal
♦***chaetomallum***	See R. ***haematodes c.***
chamaethomsonii	CSam CWal GGGa GWht LMil MBal NHar NMun SExb SLeo
– var. ***chamaethauma*** F 21768	LMil
– var. ***chamaethauma*** KW 5847	LMil
– var. ***chamaethomsonii*** Exbury form L&S	GGGa
– – pink forms L&S	GGGa
– – Rock form	GGGa
chameunum	See R. ***saluenense c.***
championiae	GGGa
charitopes	CWal GGGa LMil MBal MBri NMun SLeo
§ – ssp. ***tsangpoense***	CWal GGGa LMil NHol SExb
– ssp. ***tsangpoense*** KW 5844	NHol
chasmanthum	See R. ***augustinii c.***
chlorops	NMun SLeo
♦***chryseum***	See R. ***rupicola c.***
chrysodoron	CWal GGGa LMil NMun
chrysomanicum	See R. Hydrid 'Chrysomanicum'
ciliatum AGM	CB&S CHig CNic CSam CWal EPot GGGa GWht IDai IOrc LHyd MBal NMun SBor
– BL&M 324	NHol
– 'Multiflorum'	See R. Hybrid 'Multiflorum'
ciliicalyx	CWal
– ***lyi***	See R. ***lyi***
cinnabarinum	CBow CWal LMil MBal NMun SLeo SReu
– B 652	MBal
– BL&M 234	GWht LMil
¶– LS&H 21283	NMun
¶– SHE 638	NMun
– Caerhays John	CWal

– 'Caerhays Lawrence'	CWal MBal NMun SLeo
– 'Caerhays Philip'	CWal MBal
– ssp. ***cinnabarinum*** 'Aestivale'	LMil
– – Blandfordiiflorum Group	GGGa LMil MBal NMun SLeo
§ – – 'Mount Everest'	CWal LMil NMun SLeo SReu SSta
– – 'Nepal'	CWal LHyd LMil NMun SLeo
– – Roylei Group	CWal GGGa LHyd LMil MBal MBlu MLea NMun SExb SLeo SReu
¶ – – Roylei Group KW 8239	NMun
– – 'Vin Rosé'	CWal LMil
§ – 'Conroy' AGM	GGGa LHyd LMil MBal WAbe
§ – ssp. ***tamaense***	GGGa LMil NMun SLeo
¶ – ssp. ***tamaense*** KW 21003	NMun
¶ – ssp. ***tamaense*** KW 21021	NMun
§ – ssp. ***xanthocodon*** AGM	CWal GWht LMil MBal NMun SCog SExb SLeo SReu
– ssp. ***xanthocodon*** EGM 088	GGGa LMil
– ssp. ***xanthocodon*** KW 6026	WThu
– – Concatenans Group	CB&S CSam CWal GGGa NMun SCog SLeo SSta WBod
– – Concatenans Group mustard form	NMun SLeo
– – Concatenans Group KW 5874	LMil LRHS
– – Concatenans Group LS&T 6560	NMun SLeo
– – 'Daffodilly'	CWal NMun SLeo
– – forms	CWal NMun SLeo
– – Purpurellum Group	CWal GGGa LMil NMun SLeo
citriniflorum	CWal NMun SReu
– R 108	GGGa
¶ – var. ***horaeum***	NMun
– var. ***horaeum*** F 21850	GGGa LMil
– var. ***horaeum*** F 25901	GGGa LMil NMun
clementinae	GGGa LHyd NMun SLeo
– F 25705	NMun SLeo
– F 25917	LMil
coelicum	CWal NMun
– F 21830	NMun SLeo
¶ – F 25625	NMun
coeloneuron	GGGa
– EGM 108	LMil
¶ ***collettianum***	NMun
– H&W 8975	GGGa
complexum F 15392	GGGa NMun
concatenans	See R. ***cinnabarinum xanthocodon*** Concatenans Group
concinnum	CHig CTrw CWal LHyd LMil MBal NMun SLeo
¶ – C 5011, 5085	GGGa
¶ – Benthamianum Group	NMun
– Pseudoyanthinum Group AGM	CWal GGGa LMil NMun SLeo
cookeanum	NMun
coriaceum	CBow CWal GGGa LMil NMun SLeo
¶ – F 16364	NMun
¶ – F 21843	NMun
¶ – R 120	NMun
coryanum	CWal GGGa NMun SLeo
– 'Chelsea Chimes' ex KW 6311	LMil
cowanianum	GGGa GTou
coxianum C&H 475B	GGGa
crassum	See R. ***maddenii crassum***
cremastum	See R. ***campylogynum*** Cremastum Group
crinigerum	CWal GGGa LMil NMun SLeo
¶ – KW 7123	NMun
¶ – KW 8164	NMun
¶ – bicolored form	NMun
¶ – var. ***crinigerum*** R 100	NMun
¶ – ***crinigerum*** R 38	NMun
¶ – var. ***euadenium***	NMun
crutwellii	GGGa
cubittii	See R. ***veitchianum*** Cubittii Group
♦ ***cucullatum***	See R. ***roxieanum c.***
cumberlandense (A)	LMil
cuneatum	CWal GGGa NMun
– F 27119*	NMun SLeo
¶ – R 11392	NMun
cyanocarpum	CWal GGGa LMil NMun SLeo
dalhousieae	CWal GGGa NMun SLeo
§ – var. ***rhabdotum*** AGM	GGGa NMun SLeo
♦ ***dasycladum***	See R. ***selense d.***
dasypetalum	GGGa MBal MBar MLea NBar
dauricum	EPot GPlt LMil MBal MBlu NMun SExb SLeo WBod WThu
– ***album***	See R. ***d.*** 'Hokkaido'
– 'Arctic Pearl'	GGGa
¶ – 'Dark St Andrews'	GGGa
– dwarf	GAri
§ – 'Hokkaido'	GAri GGGa LHyd NMun
– 'Midwinter' AGM	CWal GGGa LHyd LMil MBri NMun SLeo
– 'Nanum'	MBal
– 'Suzuki'	NMun SLeo
davidsonianum AGM	CB&S CBow CTrw CWal GGGa GWht IOrc ISea LHyd LMil MBal MBlu MMor NMun SCog SExb SLeo SPer SSta WBod
¶ – C 5007, 5091	GGGa
– Bodnant Form	LMil
– 'Caerhays Pink'	GGGa
– 'Ruth Lyons'	LMil SPer
– 'Serenade'	LMil
decorum	CWal IOrc LHyd LMil NMun SLeo SReu
¶ – R 54021*	NMun
¶ – SBEC 1060	NMun
¶ – SBEC 181	NMun
¶ – SBEC 439	NMun
– 'Cox's Uranium Green'	SReu
– forms	GGGa NMun
degronianum	GGGa NMun
§ – ssp. ***degronianum***	CWal NMun SLeo
– – 'Gerald Loder'	CWal GGGa LHyd
§ – ssp. ***heptamerum***	CWal GGGa ISea NMun SLeo
¶ – – ***micranthum***	LMil
– – 'Ho Emma'	LMil
– 'Metternianum'	See R. ***d.*** Kyomaruense Group
delavayi peramoenum	See R. ***arboreum d. p.***
dendricola KW 20981	GGGa
– Taronense Group	CWal
dendrocharis	GGGa

Name	Suppliers
denudatum Cox 5090	GGGa
desquamatum	See R. ***rubiginosum*** Desquamatum Group
x ***detonsum***	CWal NMun SLeo
diaprepes	IOrc NMun
– Farrer 979	NMun SLeo
– 'Gargantua'	CWal NMun SLeo SReu
dichroanthum	CWal GGGa IOrc MBal NMun SCog SLeo SReu
¶– F 27137	NMun
¶– F 6781	NMun
– SBEC 0545	GGGa
– SBEC 0601	GGGa
– ssp. ***apodectum***	CWal GGGa LMil NMun SLeo
¶– forms	NMun
– ssp. ***scyphocalyx***	CWal GGGa GWht LMil MBal NMun SCog SLeo
– ssp. ***septentrionale***	GGGa
♦***dictyotum***	See R. ***traillianum d.***
didymum	See R. ***sanguineum didymum***
dilatatum leucanthum (A)	GGGa
diphrocalyx	CWal NMun
♦***discolor***	See R. ***fortunei d.***
♦***doshongense***	See R. ***aganniphum*** D. Group
drumonium	See R. ***telmateium***
dryophyllum	See R. ***phaeochrysum levistratum***
dryophyllum Balfour & Forrest	See R. ***phaeochrysum phaeochrysum***
eclecteum	CWal LMil NMun SLeo
¶– R 23512	NMun
– var. ***bellatulum***	CWal NMun
¶– var. ***bellatulum*** R 110*	NMun
¶– 'Kingdon Come'	NMun
¶– 'Rowallane Yellow'	NMun
edgarianum	CWal LMil
§ ***edgeworthii*** AGM	CTrw CWal GGGa LHyd MBal NMun SLeo WBod
– Yu 17431*	LMil
– forms	GGGa WBod
elegantulum	CWal GGGa LHyd LMil NMun SLeo
elliottii	GGGa NMun SLeo
¶– KW 7725	NMun
♦***eriogynum***	See R. ***facetum***
♦***eritimum heptamerum***	See R. ***anthosphaerum*** Heptamerum Group
erosum	NMun SLeo
erubescens	See R. ***oreodoxa fargesii*** Erubescens Group
§ x ***erythrocalyx*** Panteumorphum Group	NMun SLeo
euchaïtes	See R. ***neriiflorum neriiflorum*** Euch. Group
¶ ***euchroum***	NMun
eudoxum	GGGa LMil NMun
¶– KW 5879	NMun
¶– var. ***eudoxum*** R 10950	NMun
¶– var. ***eudoxum*** R 6C	NMun
eurysiphon	CWal NMun
¶– KW 21557*	NMun
exasperatum	CWal NMun SLeo
– KW 8250	GGGa NMun
¶ ***excellens*** AC 146	GGGa
eximium	See R. ***falconeri e.***
§ ***faberi***	CBow CWal GGGa NMun SLeo
– EGM 111	LMil
– ssp. ***prattii***	CWal GGGa LMil NMun SLeo
– ssp. ***prattii*** EGM 147	LMil
§ ***facetum***	GGGa NMun SLeo
¶– F 1022	NMun
falconeri AGM	CBow CHEx CWal GGGa IOrc LHyd LMil NMun SArc SLeo SReu
– BM&W 66	MBal
– DF 526	MBal
– EGM 055	LMil
§ – ssp. ***eximium***	GGGa LMil
fargesii	See R. ***oreodoxa f.***
fastigiatum	CWal EPot GAbr GDra LMil MBal MBar MLea NMun SLeo WBod
– SBEC 0804/4869	GGGa NHol WThu
– 'Blue Steel'	GGGa LMil NHol
– 'Harry White'	LMil
– pink	GGGa
faucium	GGGa NMun SLeo
¶– KW 5732	NMun
§– KW 6401	NMun
fauriei	See R. ***hyperythrum f.***
ferrugineum	COtt CSco CWal GGGa GPlt IDai LKna LMil MBal MBar MGos NBar NMun SLeo SReu WAbe
– f. ***album***	CWal
– 'Ascreavie'	NHol
– Atrococcineum Group	GWht
– 'Glenarn'	NHol
¶– 'Hill of Tarvit'	NHol
fictolacteum	See R. ***rex fictolacteum***
fimbriatum	See R. ***hippophaëoïdes hipp.*** Fimbriatum Group
flavidum	CWal GGGa MBal SExb SSta
– 'Album'	CWal LMil SBod SExb
fletcherianum	MBal NMun
– R 22302	CWal NMun SLeo
– 'Yellow Bunting'	GGGa NMun
§ ***flinckii***	GGGa LMil NMun
floccigerum	CWal GGGa LMil NMun SLeo
– F 20305	NMun SLeo
¶– R 10	NMun
¶– R/USDA 03966/R18465	NMun
¶– bicolored	NMun
floribundum	LMil NMun SLeo
– Cox 5090	GGGa
¶– 'Swinhoe'	SExb
¶ ***formosanum***	GGGa
formosum AGM	CB&S CGre CWal ERea GGGa LMil NMun
¶– Chamberlain 109	NMun
§ – formosum Iteaphyllum Group	CWal GGGa NMun SLeo WBod
– var. ***inaequale*** C&H 301	GGGa GWht
– 'Khasia'	GGGa
forrestii	GAbr GGGa NMun SExb
¶– ssp. ***forrestii*** F 21723	NMun
¶– ssp. ***forrestii*** LS&T 5582	NMun
– – Repens Group	CWal GAbr GGGa LMil MBal NHar NMun SLeo WAbe WBod

– – Tumescens Group	CWal GGGa NHar NMun SLeo
fortunei	GGGa IOrc LHyd LMil NMun SLeo
– McLaren S146	CWal
§ – ssp. ***discolor*** AGM	CWal GGGa LHyd LMil NMun SLeo
§ – – Houlstonii Group	CWal LMil NMun SLeo
– 'Foxy'	NMun SLeo
– 'Mrs Butler'	See R. *f.* 'Sir Charles Butler'
§ – 'Sir Charles Butler'	CWal LMil
¶ ***fragariiflorum*** LS&E 15828	NMun
fulgens	CWal GGGa LHyd LMil NMun SLeo
– DF 543	MBal
fulvum AGM	CWal GGGa IOrc LHyd LMil NMun SExb SLeo SReu SSta
¶ – F 17636	NMun
– F 24110	NMun SLeo
¶ – R 143	NMun
¶ – R 180	NMun
¶ ***fulvum*** Fulvoïdes Group	NMun
galactinum	CWal GGGa LMil NMun SLeo
– CC&H 4023	GGGa
¶ – W A 4254	NMun
genestierianum	CWal NMun
§ x ***geraldii***	NMun SLeo
♦ ***giganteum***	See R. ***protistum g.***
glaucophyllum	CWal GGGa LHyd LMil NMun SExb SLeo SPer SReu
– L&S 2764	See R. ***brachyanthum*** L&S 2764
– BH form	LMil
– 'Branklyn'	GGGa
– 'Glenarn'	GGGa
§ – var. ***tubiforme***	CWal GWht NMun SCog SLeo
– white	GGGa
glischrum	GGGa NMun SExb SLeo
– ssp. ***glischroïdes***	LMil NMun SLeo
– ssp. ***glischrum***	GGGa
§ – ssp. ***rude***	GGGa NMun SLeo
♦ ***globigerum***	See R. ***alutaceum*** G. Group
glomerulatum	See R. ***yungningense*** Glomerulatum Group
grande	CGre CWal GGGa IOrc NMun
– DF 524	MBal
– EGM 058	LMil
¶ – TSS 37	NMun
¶ – pink	NMun
griersonianum	CWal GGGa IOrc ISea MBal NMun SCog SExb SLeo
¶ – F 24116	NMun
griffithianum	CWal GGGa NMun SLeo
– EGM 101	LMil
¶ ***vernicosum*** Euanthum Group F 5880	NMun
§ ***yunnanense*** Suberosum Group	NMun
gymnocarpum	See R. ***microgynum*** Gymnocarpum Group
habrotrichum	CWal GGGa LMil NMun SLeo
¶ – F 15778	NMun
haematodes	CWal GGGa LHyd MBal MBri NMun SLeo
– CLD 1282	LMil
– F 6773	NMun SLeo
– McLaren S124A	NMun SLeo
– ssp. ***chaetomallum***	GGGa NMun
¶ – ssp. ***chaetomallum*** F 25601	NMun
– ssp. ***chaetomallum*** KW 21077	NMun SLeo
– ssp. ***chaetomallum*** KW 5431	CWal
– ssp. ***chaetomallum*** R 18359	NMun SLeo
¶ – ssp. ***chaetomallum*** R 41	NMun
hanceanum	CHig NKay NMun SLeo
– 'Canton Consul'	EPot GGGa LHyd SSta
– Nanum Group	CB&S CWal EPot GAbr GGGa IDai LMil MBal NMun WAbe WBod WThu
♦ ***hardingii***	See R. ***annae*** H. Group
hardyi	See R. ***augustinii h.***
headfortianum	See R. ***taggianum*** Headfortianum Group
¶ ***heftii***	NMun
heliolepis	CWal GGGa IOrc LMil MBal NMun SLeo
¶ – Yu 7933*	NMun
– var. ***brevistylum***	CWal
§ – – Pholidotum Group F 6762	NMun SLeo
♦ ***hemidartum***	See R. ***pocophorum h.***
x ***hemigynum***	NMun SLeo
hemitrichotum	LMil NMun
¶ – KW 4050	NMun
hemsleyanum	CWal GGGa IOrc NMun SLeo
♦ ***heptamerum***	See R. ***degronianum h.***
hippophaëoïdes AGM	CHig CSco CWal LKna LMil MBri NMun SExb SLeo SSta
– F 22197A	NMun SLeo
– Yu 13845	GGGa
– 'Bei-ma-shan'	GGGa MBri
– 'Habashan'	WThu
§ – ***hippophaëoïdes*** Fimbriatum Group	CWal
hirsutum	CWal GGGa GWht MBal SReu WThu
– f. ***albiflorum***	GGGa
– 'Flore Pleno'	EPot GGGa IDai MBal MBar NKay WAbe
hirtipes	GGGa NMun
– KW 5659	GGGa NMun SLeo
– KW 6223	NMun SLeo
¶ – LS&T 3624	NMun
¶ x ***hodconeri***	NMun
¶ – LS&H 21296	NMun
¶ – TSS 9	NMun
¶ – 'pink'	NMun
hodgsonii	CBow GGGa IOrc LMil NMun SLeo
– B 653	MBal
¶ – BL&M 232	NMun
– DF 532	MBal
– EGM 081	LMil
¶ – TSS 42A	NMun
¶ – 'Poet's Lawn'	NMun
hongkongense	GGGa NMun SLeo
hookeri	NMun SLeo
¶ – KW 13859	NMun
¶ – KW 8238	NMun
¶ – 'Golden Gate'	NMun
– Tigh-na-Rudha form	GGGa
horlickianum	CBow GGGa LMil NMun SLeo

¶– KW 9403 NMun
houlstonii See R. ***fortunei discolor*** Houlstonii Group
hunnewellianum CWal GGGa SExb
Hybrid 'A Bedford' GGGa LHyd LKna
– 'A J Ivens' See R. H. 'Arthur J Ivens'
– 'Abegail' MGos NMun SLeo
– 'Abendrot' MBri SSta
– 'Achilles' CWal NMun SLeo
– 'Actress' CWal IOrc ISea LHyd NMun SLeo
– 'Adamant' CWal
– Adelaide (g.&cl.) CWal SExb
– 'Admiral Piet Hein' SReu
– 'Adriaan Koster' CWal IOrc LHyd
*– 'Ahren's Favourite' SSta
– 'Airy Fairy' GGGa LHyd
– 'Aksel Olsen' CDoC GPlt MBal MBar NHol WBod
– Albatross (g.&cl.) LHyd LKna LMil MBlu NMun SLeo SReu SSta
– 'Albatross Townhill Pink' LMil
– 'Albert Schweitzer' CWal IJoh LMil MBal MBar NMun SLeo SReu SSta WStI
– 'Alice' **AGM** CBow CWal IOrc LHyd LKna MMor NMun SCog SLeo SPer SReu
*– 'Alice Gilbert' CWal
– 'Alice Street' NMun SLeo
– Alison Johnstone (g.&cl.) CB&S CBow COtt CSam CTrw CWal GGGa LHyd MBal MLea NHol NMun SCog SExb SLeo SPer SSta WBod WThu
¶– 'Allen's Surprise' CB&S
– 'Aloha' CAbP CBow LMil MAsh MBar MBri MLea MMor NHed SCog SHBN WWeb
– 'Alpine Dew' GGGa
– Alpine Gem GGGa NHol
– 'Alpine Glow' **AGM** CWal NMun SLeo
– Amalfi (g.&cl.) CWal
– Amaura WBod
– 'America' CB&S IJoh IOrc MAsh MBal MBar MGos NMun SExb SLeo
– 'Amethyst' CWal LHyd
– Amor (g.&cl.) LHyd NMun SLeo SReu
– 'Anah Kruschke' SExb
– 'Analin' See R. H. 'Anuschka '
– 'Anchorage' SExb
– 'Andre' MBri NMun SLeo SReu SSta
– Angelo LHyd LMil MMor SCog SReu
– 'Angelo Solent Queen' SExb
– Anita CWal NMun SLeo
– 'Anita Dunstan' GAul LMil
– 'Anna Baldsiefen' **AGM** CSam GGGa IDai LMil MAsh MBri NHol SPer SSta
– 'Anna H Hall' GGGa IOrc MAsh MBri SCog WWeb
– 'Anna Rose Whitney' **AGM** CB&S GGGa GRei IOrc LHyd LKna LMil MBar MBri MGos MLea NMun SExb SHBN SLeo SPer SReu SSta
– 'Annapurna' SReu
– 'Anne George' LHyd
– 'Anne's Delight' GGGa
– 'Antje' LRHS MAsh SCog
– Antonio (g.&cl.) CWal SCog
– 'Antoon van Welie' SSta
§– 'Anuschka' GGGa LRHS MAsh
– 'Apotrophia' CWal
– 'Apple Blossom' CSco CWal LKna
– 'Apricot Fantasy' LMil
– 'April Chimes' WThu
¶– 'April Dawn' GGGa
– 'April Gem' GGGa
§– 'April Glow' LHyd NKay NMun SLeo
– 'April Showers' See R. H. 'April Glow'
¶– 'April Snow' (d) GGGa
– 'April White' GGGa
– Arbcalo NMun SLeo
– Arblact CWal
– 'Arborfield' NMun SLeo
– Arbsutch NMun SLeo
§– Arbutifolium NHol
N– 'Arctic Tern' See X LEDODENDRON 'A.T.'
– Argosy **AGM** CWal LMil SReu
– Ariel NMun SLeo
– 'Arkle' LHyd
– 'Armantine' LKna
– Armia CWal
– 'Arthur Bedford' LRHS MBri NMun SExb SLeo SReu
– 'Arthur J Ivens' CWal LHyd
– 'Arthur Osborn' CHig CWal NMun SLeo
– 'Arthur Stevens' **AGM** CWal NMun SLeo
– 'Arthur Warren' LKna
– 'Ascot Brilliant' NMun SLeo
– Atroflo GGGa
– Augfast CB&S CTrw CWal EPot IJoh IOrc ISea MBal SBod SReu WBod
– Aurora (g.&cl.) NMun SLeo
– 'Autumn Gold' CDoC GGGa LMil MBal NHol SExb
– Avalanche **AGM** CWal SReu
– Avocet CWal
– 'Award' GGGa LMil
– Azor (g.&cl.) CHig CWal GGGa LHyd NMun SLeo SReu SSta
*– 'Azorazie' NMun SLeo
– 'Azurika' GGGa LMil
– 'Azurro' GGGa LMil
– 'Azurwolke' GGGa
– 'Bad Eilsen' SSta
– 'Baden-Baden' CSco CWal EBre ELan EPot GCHN GGGa GRei GWht IJoh ISea LBre LHyd LKna MBal MBar MBri MGos MMor NBar NHol NKay SBod SCog SExb SHBN SPer SSta WAbe WBod
– 'Bagshot Ruby' **AGM** LKna SBod SReu
– 'Balsaminiflorum' See R. ***indicum*** 'Balsaminiflorum'
– 'Bambi' CWal LHyd MBri NMun SCog SLeo SReu
– 'Bambino' CAbP CBow GAul LMil LNet MLea NMun SExb SLeo
– 'Bandoola' SReu
– 'Barbara Reuthe' SReu
¶– Barclayi LHyd
– 'Barclayi Helen Fox' CWal
– 'Barclayi Robert Fox' CWal NMun SLeo
– 'Barmstedt' GAul SExb
*– 'Barnaby Sunset' CSam GAri GGGa MAsh NHol

Hybrid 'Bashful' AGM	CWal ELan GGGa GRei GWht IOrc ISea LHyd MBal MBlu MBri MGos MMor NMun SCog SExb SLeo SReu
– 'Bastion'	SExb
– 'Beatrice Keir' AGM	CWal LHyd NMun SLeo SReu
– Beau Brummel AGM	LMil
– 'Beautiful Day'	GGGa
– 'Beauty of Littleworth' AGM	CWal LHyd LKna LMil NMun SLeo SReu
– 'Belle Heller'	CSam GGGa LRHS MBal MBri SExb
– 'Belle of Tremeer'	CWal
– 'Ben Moseley'	GGGa SSta
– 'Bengal'	CDoC GGGa GPlt ISea MAsh MBal MBar MBri NBar NHol SCog SExb SReu
– 'Bernard Shaw'	SReu
– 'Bernstein'	GGGa
– Berryrose (g.&cl.)	CWal SExb
– 'Bert's Own'	CWal
– 'Betty Arrington'	GGGa
*– 'Betty Robertson'	NKay
– 'Betty Stewart'	NMun SLeo
– 'Betty Wormald' AGM	CBow CHig CWal GGGa IHos LHyd LKna LMil MGos NBar NMun SCog SExb SHBN SLeo SPer SReu SSta
– Bibiani (g.&cl.)	LHyd SExb
– 'Billy Budd'	LHyd SCog SExb SPer
– 'Binfield'	NMun SLeo
¶– 'Birthday Girl'	SExb
– 'Birthday Greeting'	SExb
– 'Biscuit Box'	NMun SLeo
– Biskra (g.&cl.)	CWal GGGa SExb
– 'Black Magic'	LMil
– 'Black Satin'	GGGa
– 'Blanc-mange' (g.&cl.)	SExb
– 'Blewbury' AGM	CWal LHyd LMil SCog SPer SSta
– 'Blitz'	LRHS MBri NMun SLeo
– 'Blue Bell'	LKna
– 'Blue Boy'	LMil MBlu
– 'Blue Chip'	LHyd NMun SLeo
– 'Blue Danube'	CB&S CWal LKna
– Blue Diamond (g.&cl.)	CB&S CChe CMHG CSco CTrw CWal GAbr GGGa GRei GWht IDai IJoh LHyd LKna MBal MBar MGos NHol NMun SBod SCog SExb SHBN SLeo SPer SReu WBod WThu
– 'Blue Ensign'	CWal GAul LRHS SExb
*– 'Blue Gown'	LKna
– 'Blue Haze'	LHyd
– 'Blue Jay'	MBlu NKay SReu
– 'Blue Mountain'	GDra MBal WThu
– 'Blue Pacific'	SBod
– 'Blue Peter' AGM	CB&S CHig CSco CWal GGGa GWht IHos IOrc LKna MBar MBri MGos MMor NMun SCog SExb SHBN SLeo SPer SReu SSta WStI
– 'Blue Pool'	LMil LRHS MBal MBar WBod
– Blue Ribbon	CMHG CTrw ISea
– 'Blue Silver'	GGGa NHol
– 'Blue Star'	CMHG CWal LHyd MBri SExb SPer
– 'Blue Steel'	See R. ***impeditum*** 'Blue Steel'
– Blue Tit	CB&S CSam CSco CTre CWal ELan GDra GGGa IDai IJoh ITim LHyd LKna MBal MBar MMor NHol NKay NMun SExb SHBN SLeo SReu SSta STre WBod
– Bluebird (g.&cl.)	CBow CWal IOrc LKna MBal MBar MGos MMor NBar SExb SPer WBod
¶– 'Blueshine Girl'	LHyd
– Bluestone	MMor SExb WBod
– 'Bluette'	GWht ISea MBal NMun SLeo
– Boadicea	CWal
– 'Bob's Blue'	GAul ISea SReu
– 'Boddaertianum' AGM	CWal LHyd SExb
– 'Bodnant Yellow'	CSam CWal
– 'Bonfire'	CWal SReu
– Bonito (g.&cl.)	SCog
– 'Borderer'	NMun SCog SLeo
– 'Boule de Neige'	NMun SBod SLeo
– 'Bounty'	GGGa
– Bow Bells AGM	CBow CSam CSco CWal EBre ELan GWht IOrc ISea LBre LHyd LKna LMil MBal MBar MBri MGos MLea MMor NKay SBod SCog SExb SHBN SPer SReu WBod
– 'Bow Street'	LHyd
– Bo-peep AGM	CB&S CBow CHig CSam CWal LHyd LMil MBal MLea NKay NMun SExb SLeo SReu
– Break of Day (g.&cl.)	CWal NMun SLeo
– 'Bremen'	SExb
– 'Brentor'	NMun SLeo
– 'Brets Own'	NMun SLeo
– Bric-a-Brac AGM	CB&S CSam CTrw CWal LHyd MBal NHol NMun SExb SLeo SReu WThu
– 'Brigitte'	GGGa LHyd
– 'Brilliant'	GGGa MAsh NHol
– 'Britannia' AGM	CB&S CSam CSco EBre GGGa IJoh IOrc LBre LHyd LKna LNet MBal MBar MBlu MBri MGos MMor NMun NWea SBod SCog SExb SHBN SLeo SPer SReu SSta
– Brocade AGM	CSam CWal GWht LHyd LKna LMil MAsh MBri NMun SCog SExb SLeo SPer
– 'Brookside'	CWal
– 'Broughtonii'	NMun SExb SLeo
– 'Bruce Brechtbill'	GGGa LMil LRHS MAsh MBal MLea NHol SExb SSta
– 'Bud Flanagan'	MBlu SExb
– 'Buketta'	GGGa MBri
¶– 'Bulbul' (g.&cl.)	SExb
– Burning Bush	CWal
– Bustard	NMun SLeo
– 'Butter Yellow'	NMun SLeo
*– 'Buttered Popcorn'	LMil
– 'Butterfly'	LKna LRHS NMun SLeo
– 'Buttermint'	CSam GAri GGGa LMil MBal MBri MLea NBar NMun SCog SHBN SLeo SPer SReu SSta
– 'Buttersteep'	NMun SLeo
– 'C B van Nes' AGM	CWal
– 'C I S'	MBlu NMun SLeo
– 'Caerhays'	See R. ***cinnabarinum*** 'C.'
– Calfort (g.&cl.)	CWal
– Calstocker	NMun SLeo
– Calsutch	NMun SLeo
– 'Canadian Beauty'	SExb

Hybrid 'Canary' GGGa LKna MBal NMun SLeo SReu
*– 'Candida' SExb
– 'Captain Jack' GGGa
– 'Caractacus' IOrc MBar NMun SLeo
– Cardinal (g.&cl.) CWal
– Carex (g.&cl.) SCog
– Carita CWal LKna SExb SReu
– 'Carita Golden Dream' AGM CWal LKna LMil NMun SLeo
– 'Carita Inchmery' AGM CWal LHyd LKna NMun SCog SExb SLeo
– Carmen AGM CSam CWal GDra GGGa GRei GWht IDai ISea LHyd LKna LMil MBal MBri MLea MMor NHar NHol NMun NWea SBod SExb SHBN SLeo SReu WBod
– 'Caroline Allbrook' AGM CBow CHig CSam CWal GGGa ISea LHyd LMil MBri NHed NHol NMun SCog SExb SLeo SReu SSta WWeb
– 'Caroline de Zoete' LHyd
– 'Cary Ann' CDoC CSam GCHN GRei ISea LMil MBal MLea NMun SExb SLeo SSta
– 'Castle of Mey' SExb
§– 'Catalode' SPer
¶– 'Catawbiense Album' IOrc
¶– 'Catawbiense Boursault' IOrc
– 'Catawbiense Grandiflorum' IJoh IOrc LRHS
– 'Catherine Hopwood' NMun SLeo
– Cauapo CWal
– 'Caucasicum Pictum' GGGa LMil MAsh MBri
– 'Cavalcade' CWal
– Cavalier GWht
– 'Centennial Celebration' GGGa IOrc
– 'Cetewayo' NMun SLeo SReu
§– 'Champagne' AGM CWal IOrc LHyd LMil MGos NMun SCog SExb SLeo
– 'Charlotte Currie' NMun SLeo
– 'Charlotte de Rothschild' AGM CWal LMil
– Charmaine (g.&cl.) CSam GGGa IDai LMil MBal MBri NHol WBod
¶– 'Cheapside' LHyd
– 'Cheer' GGGa IJoh IOrc LMil MAsh MBal MBar MBri SSta WGor
– 'Chelsea Seventy' CWal ELan IHos ISea MAsh MBal NHol NMun SCog SLeo SReu
– 'Chevalier Felix de Sauvage' AGM CWal LMil MGos NMun SBod SExb SLeo SReu SSta
– 'Cheyenne' CWal NMun SLeo
– 'Chiffchaff' GCLN LHyd NMun SLeo SPer WAbe
– 'Chikor' CMHG CSam CWal EPot GDra GGGa GWht IDai LKna MBal MBar MBlu MBri MGos MLea MMor NHar NHol NKay NMun NRoo SExb SLeo SReu SSta WBod WSHC WThu
– China (g.&cl.) CDoC CWal LKna SReu
– 'China A' LKna
– 'Chink' AGM CB&S CSam CWal GPlt LHyd MBal MBar NBar NMun SCog SExb SLeo SPer WBod WThu
– 'Chionoïdes' CWal GAul GGGa GWht IOrc ISea LKna
– 'Choremia' CTrw GWht SCog SExb WBod
– 'Christmas Cheer' AGM CBow CDoC CHig CWal ELan GGGa GWht IOrc ISea LHyd LKna LMil MBlu MBri NKay NMun SCog SExb SLeo SPer SReu
– 'Christobel Maude' LHyd
§– Chrysomanicum AGM CWal NMun SLeo
– Cilpinense AGM CB&S CBow CCla CSam CWal ELan GGGa GWht IDai IJoh IOrc LHyd LKna LMil MBal MBar NHol NMun SCog SExb SLeo SPer SReu SSta WAbe WBod WThu
– Cinnkeys (g.&cl.) CWal GGGa LMil SReu
– Cinzan LHyd LMil SReu
– 'Circus' GGGa
– 'Cliff Garland' LMil
– Clio CWal NMun SLeo
– 'Colonel Coen' LMil MBal SHBN
– Colonel Rogers CWal LHyd NMun SLeo SReu
– Comely CWal LHyd NMun SLeo
– 'Comte de Gomer' CB&S
– 'Concorde' LHyd MMor NBar SCog
– 'Conroy' See R. ***cinnabarinum*** 'C.'
– 'Constable' CWal LHyd NMun SLeo
– 'Constant Nymph' LKna
– 'Contina' GGGa
– Conyan LHyd
– 'Coral Reef' NMun SLeo SReu
¶– 'Coral Velvet' COtt
– 'Cornish Cracker' NMun SLeo
– Cornish Cross CWal LHyd NMun SCog SLeo SReu
– Cornish Early Red See R. H. Smithii Group
– 'Cornish Red' See R. H. Smithii Group
– Cornsutch CWal
– Cornubia CWal NMun SLeo
– 'Corona' AGM CWal LKna SCog SReu
– 'Coronation Day' SReu
– Coronet SExb
– 'Corry Koster' LKna
– 'Cosmopolitan' CDoC GGGa IJoh IOrc MBar MGos NBar SExb SSta
– 'Costa del Sol' NMun SLeo
– 'Cotton Candy' LHyd LMil
– 'Countess of Athlone' CWal IOrc LKna
– 'Countess of Derby' IOrc ISea SPer SReu
– 'Countess of Haddington' AGM CB&S CTre ERea ISea LMil NMun SLeo
– 'County of York' See R. H. 'Catalode'
– Cowslip CSam ELan IDai IJoh LHyd LKna LMil MBal MBar MBri MGos NHol NMun SCog SExb SHBN SLeo SReu WBod
– 'Cranbourne' SExb SReu
¶– 'Crane' GGGa
– 'Crater Lake' GWht
– 'Cream Crest' ISea NMun SHBN SLeo SPer
– 'Cream Glory' GAul LHyd SCog SReu WWeb
– 'Creamy Chiffon' CSam GCHN GGGa ISea LHyd LMil MAsh MBal MLea NMun SLeo SReu SSta

§ Hybrid 'Creeping Jenny' AGM	CBow CWal GGGa IDai LHyd MBal MBar MLea NBar NHol SCog SExb SPer WBod
§ – 'Crest' AGM	CBow CSam CSco CWal GGGa GWht IOrc LHyd LKna LMil MBal MBlu MGos MLea NMun SCog SHBN SLeo SPer SReu SSta WThu WWeb
– 'Crete'	COtt GAul GGGa LMil MAsh MBri MGos SReu
– 'Crimson Pippin'	GGGa LMil
– Crossbill	CB&S GGGa MBal NKay NMun SExb SLeo
– 'Crowthorne'	SCog
– 'Crushed Strawberry'	WBod
– 'Cunningham's Blush'	GAri GGGa GWht MAsh SHBN
– 'Cunningham's Sulphur'	See R. ***caucasicum*** 'C.S.'
– 'Cunningham's White' AGM	CB&S CHig CSam CWal ELan GGGa GRei IJoh IOrc LKna LMil MBar MBri MGos MMor NMun SLeo SPer SReu WStI
*– 'Cupcake'	GGGa
– 'Curlew' AGM	Widely available
– 'Cutie'	NMun SLeo SSta
– 'Cynthia' AGM	CB&S CHig CSam CSco CWal GGGa IJoh IOrc ISea LHyd LKna LMil MBal MBar MBri MGos MMor NBar NMun NWea SBod SExb SHBN SLeo SPer SReu SSta
*– 'Dagmar'	GGGa
– 'Dairymaid'	CWal ISea LHyd LKna NMun SLeo SReu
– Damaris	CWal NMun SLeo
– 'Damaris Logan'	See R. H. 'Logan Damaris'
– Damozel (g.&cl.)	CWal LRHS SCog SExb SPer WThu
– 'Dandy'	LKna
– Dante	CWal NMun SLeo
– 'Daphne'	NMun SLeo
– 'Daphne Jewiss'	SReu
– 'Daphne Magor'	NMun SLeo
– 'Daphnoïdes'	GGGa MLea
– 'Dartmoor Dawn'	MBal
– 'David' AGM	CWal GGGa LHyd LKna NMun SLeo SReu
– 'David Grant'	GDra
– 'David Rockefeller'	SExb
*– 'Davidson'	ISea
– 'Dawn's Delight' AGM	ISea
– Day Dream AGM	CWal IOrc LHyd LKna SCog SReu WBod
– 'Dayan'	SExb
– 'Desert Orchid'	LHyd
– 'Dexter's Spice'	GGGa
– 'Diana Colville'	CWal
– 'Diana Pearson'	NMun SLeo
– 'Diane'	LKna NMun SLeo SReu
– Dicharb	CWal
– 'Dido'	LHyd
– 'Dietrich'	SSta
– 'Diny Dee'	CAbP COtt MBal MGos SSta
– Diva (g.&cl.)	SExb
– 'Doc' AGM	CB&S CWal ELan GRei IOrc LMil MBal MBar MGos MMor NBar NKay NMun SCog SLeo SReu WStI
– 'Doctor Arnold W Endtz' AGM	IOrc MAsh MMor NBar NMun SLeo
– 'Doctor Ernst Schäle'	GGGa MAsh MBri
– 'Doctor H C Dresselhuys'	IOrc SHBN
– 'Doctor Stocker'	CWal NMun SLeo
– 'Doctor Tjebbes'	ISea
– 'Doctor V H Rutgers'	IOrc MGos
– 'Doncaster'	CWal GRei IOrc LKna MGos NHol NMun NWea SBod SCog SExb SHBN SLeo
– 'Dopey' AGM	CBow CCla CDoC CSam CSco CWal GGGa GRei GWht IHos IJoh IOrc ISea LHyd LMil MBal MBar MBri MLea MMor NBar NHed NHol NMun SCog SExb SHBN SLeo SPer SReu
– 'Dora Amateis' AGM	COtt CSam CWal EBre GGGa IDai LBre LHyd LMil MBal MBar MBri MGos MLea MMor NHar NHol NKay NMun NRoo SCog SExb SLeo SPer SReu
– Dormouse	LMil SExb
– 'Dorothea'	CWal NMun SLeo
– 'Dorothy Amateis'	SSta
¶ – 'Dorothy Swift'	GGGa
– 'Double Date'	GGGa
– 'Douglas McEwan'	MBri
– Dragonfly	CWal NMun SLeo SReu
– 'Drake's Mountain'	GPlt MBar MRav
– 'Dreamland'	GGGa ISea LHyd LMil MAsh MBri SReu
– 'Duchess of Portland'	CWal
– 'Dusky Dawn'	CWal
– 'Dusty Miller'	CAbP CDoC COtt CWal GAul IHos ISea LMil MBal MBri MGos NHed NMun SCog SExb SHBN SLeo SPer SReu WAbe
– 'Earl of Athlone'	LHyd SReu
– 'Earl of Donoughmore' AGM	CWal IDai LHyd LKna MMor SPer SReu SSta
– Early Brilliant	LKna
– 'Early Gem'	ISea MBri
– ***edgeworthii*** x ***leucaspis***	CB&S
– ***edgeworthii*** x ***moupinense***	CB&S
– 'Edith Bosley'	LMil LRHS
– 'Edith Mackworth Praed'	CWal
– 'Egret' AGM	CDoC CSam EPot GAri GGGa GWht ITim MBal MBri MGos NHar NHol NMun SExb SLeo SPer SSta WAbe
*– 'Ehrengold'	GGGa
– 'Eider'	CSam GCHN GCLN GGGa MAsh MBal NMun SCog SLeo SReu
– 'Eileen'	LMil SReu
– 'El Alamein'	CWal NMun SLeo
– 'El Camino'	GGGa MBal MBlu MLea NMun SExb SHBN SLeo
– 'El Greco'	NMun SLeo
– Eldorado	SExb
– Eleanore (g.&cl.)	IOrc ISea SExb
– Electra (g.&cl.)	See R. ***augustinii*** E.
¶ – 'Elfenbein'	SCog
– 'Elisabeth Hobbie' AGM	GDra GGGa GWht LKna LMil MBal MBar MGos SCog SExb WBod

Hybrid Elizabeth — Widely available
– 'Elizabeth de Rothschild' — LMil SExb
– 'Elizabeth Jenny' — See R. H. 'Creeping Jenny'
– 'Elizabeth Lockhart' — CBow CWal GGGa IDai MBal MGos MLea
– 'Elizabeth of Glamis' — GGGa
– Elizabeth red foliage — GGGa
– Elsae (g.&cl.) — CWal NMun SLeo
– 'Else Frye' — GGGa
– 'Elsie Straver' — CDoC GWht MBal NHol SExb SHBN SPer SReu WStI
– 'Elspeth' — CWal LHyd LKna
– 'Emanuela' — SExb
– 'Emasculum' **AGM** — CGre CSam CWal GWht LKna SPer SReu WThu
¶ – 'Emma Williams' — SExb
– 'Empire Day' — LKna
– 'Enborne' — LHyd NMun SLeo
– 'Endre Ostbo' — CWal NMun SLeo
– 'English Roseum' — IOrc
– 'Ernest Inman' — CWal LHyd NMun SLeo
– Ethel (g.&cl.) — CHig CWal GWht WBod
– 'Etta Burrows' — GGGa LMil MBal MLea
– 'Euan Cox' — GGGa MBal MBri NHar NHol SCog
– 'Europa' — SReu
– 'Evening Glow' — CDoC NHol
– 'Everestianum' — IOrc LKna MBar NMun SLeo SSta
– 'Exbury Albatross' — LKna
– 'Exbury Fabia' — SReu
§ – 'Exbury Lady Chamberlain' — SReu
– 'Exbury May Day' — SReu
– F C Puddle (g.&cl.) — NMun SLeo
– Fabia **AGM** — CBow CWal GCHN GGGa IJoh IOrc LHyd LKna LMil NMun SCog SExb SLeo
– 'Fabia Tangerine' — MBal SExb SReu SRms WBod
– 'Faggetter's Favourite' **AGM** — CWal LKna LMil MMor NMun SLeo SReu SSta
– Fairy Light — CWal LMil SExb SRms
– 'Faltho' — NMun SLeo
– Fandango — CWal
– 'Fantastica' — GGGa LHyd LMil
¶ – 'Fashion' — CChe
– 'Fastuosum Flore Pleno' **AGM** — CSco CWal GGGa IDai IOrc LHyd LKna LMil MAsh MBal MBar MBlu MBri MGos MMor NBar NMun NWea SCog SLeo SPer SReu SSta
¶ – 'Festive' — LHyd
– Fine Feathers — WBod
– Fire Bird — LHyd NMun SCog SExb SLeo SReu
– 'Fireball' — CWal
– Firedrake — SReu
– 'Fireman Jeff' — GGGa MBal SPer
– 'First Love' — GGGa
– 'Flamenco Dancer' (V) — ERea
– Flamingo — CWal
– 'Flare' — CWal
– Flashlight — CWal NMun SExb SLeo
– 'Flautando' — GGGa
§ – Flava (g.&cl.) — CWal GGGa LMil MBar MGos SSta
I – 'Flava Glendoick' — GGGa
§ – 'Flavour' — LKna
– 'Flirt' — COtt GGGa
– 'Florence Archer' — SSta
– 'Floriade' — LHyd LKna
– Fortorb — NMun SLeo
– Fortune (g.&cl.) — CWal GWht NMun SLeo
¶ – Fortune Seedling — LKna
– 'Fox Hunter' — LKna
– 'Fragrantissimum' **AGM** — CB&S CGre CTre CTrw CWal ELan ERea GGGa IOrc ISea LBlm LHyd LMil MBal MRav SReu WBod
¶ – 'Francis B Hayes' — IOrc
– Francis Hanger (Reuthe's) — CWal GWht NMun SLeo SReu
– 'Frank Baum' — MBal MBri NMun SLeo SSta
– 'Frank Galsworthy' **AGM** — GAul GGGa LKna LMil NMun SLeo SReu SSta
– 'Fred Peste' — CAbP GGGa IOrc LMil MAsh MBri MLea MMor SCog
– 'Fred Rose' — NMun SLeo
– Fred Wynniatt **AGM** — LMil
– 'Frill' — CTrw
– 'Frilled Petticoats' — MLea NMun SLeo
– 'Frontier' — GGGa LMil
§ – 'Frühlingstraum' — LHyd
– 'Frühlingszauber' — CWal SExb
– 'Fuju-kaku-no-matsu' — MGos
– 'Fulbrook' — CWal LHyd
– 'Fulgarb' — CWal NMun SLeo
– Full House — LHyd
– 'Furnivall's Daughter' **AGM** — CSam GGGa IOrc LHyd LKna LMil MBal MBlu MBri MGos MMor NMun SExb SLeo SPer SReu SSta WWeb
– Fusilier **AGM** — CWal LHyd SReu
– 'Galactic' — NMun SLeo
– Garnet — CWal
– 'Gartendirektor Glocker' — CSam GGGa SExb SSta WAbe
– 'Gartendirektor Rieger' — GGGa LMil MAsh MBri NHol
– 'General Eisenhower' — SReu
– 'General Eric Harrison' — CWal LHyd NMun SCog SLeo
¶ – 'General Practitioner' — SPer
– 'General Sir John du Cane' — SExb
– 'Gene's Favourite' — SReu
– 'Genghis Khan' — MLea
– 'Geoffroy Millais' — LMil
– 'George Hardy' **AGM** — CWal SExb
– 'George Johnstone' **AGM** — MBal
– 'Georgette' — CWal LHyd NMun SCog SLeo
– 'George's Delight' — GGGa LRHS
– Gertrud Schale — CWal GPlt MBal MBar MLea NHol SReu
– 'Gigi' — GAul GGGa
– 'Ginny Gee' **AGM** — CDoC CHig COtt CSam EPot GAul GGGa GPlt GWht LHyd LMil MBal MBri MGos MLea NBar NHar NHol NRoo SExb SReu SSta WAbe WBod WThu
– Gipsy King — SExb WThu
– 'Gipsy King Memory' — SExb

Hybrid 'Glad Tidings'	NMun SLeo
– Gladys (g.&cl.)	SCog
– 'Gleam'	CWal
– 'Glen's Orange'	SExb
– 'Gletschernacht'	GGGa
– 'Gloriana'	SReu
– 'Glory of Leonardslee'	NMun SLeo
– 'Glory of Penjerrick'	CWal NMun SLeo
– 'Gold Mohur'	NMun SLeo SReu
– 'Golden Bee'	GGGa
– 'Golden Belle'	LMil MBal MBri MLea NMun SLeo SPer
– 'Golden Coach'	ISea LMil SExb
– 'Golden Fleece'	CWal LKna NMun SCog SLeo SReu
– 'Golden Gate'	CDoC GGGa NMun SExb SLeo
– Golden Horn (g.&cl.)	IOrc MBal NMun SCog SLeo
– 'Golden Horn Persimmon'	See R. H. 'Persimmon'
– 'Golden Orfe' AGM	CWal LHyd NKay SCog
– Golden Oriole	CB&S NHol NMun SLeo SPer
– 'Golden Oriole Talavera'	CB&S CWal MBal SCog
*– 'Golden Princess'	GGGa LMil NHol
§– 'Golden Queen'	CWal
– 'Golden Star'	GGGa LHyd LMil
– 'Golden Torch' AGM	CAbP CCla COtt CSam CSco CWal GGGa GWht IOrc ISea LHyd LMil LNet MBal MBlu MBri MGos MLea MMor NMun SCog SExb SHBN SLeo SPer SReu SSta WBod WWeb
– 'Golden Wedding'	CBow GGGa LMil MAsh MBal MBri MLea SCog
– 'Golden Wit'	MBal MBri MLea SBod SCog
– 'Goldfee'	LHyd
– Goldfinger	MBal
– 'Goldflimmer'	GGGa LMil MAsh MGos NHol
– 'Goldfort'	LKna NMun SLeo SReu
– 'Goldika'	GGGa LMil
– 'Goldilocks'	CSam GGGa
– 'Goldkrone'	GGGa LHyd LMil SCog
– 'Goldstrike'	GGGa LMil
¶– 'Goldsworth Crimson'	LHyd
– 'Goldsworth Orange'	CWal GGGa LHyd LKna MBal MBar MBlu MGos MMor NMun SLeo SPer SReu SSta
– 'Goldsworth Orange' x *insigne*	GGGa
– 'Goldsworth Pink'	LKna SReu
– 'Goldsworth Yellow'	CSam LKna MGos NMun SLeo SReu
– 'Gomer Waterer' AGM	CHig CSam CSco CWal GGGa IJoh IOrc LHyd LKna LMil MBal MBar MBri MGos MMor NBar NMun NWea SBod SCog SExb SLeo SPer SReu SSta
– 'Goosander'	SExb
– 'Grace Seabrook'	COtt GGGa ISea LHyd LMil MBlu MBri MLea NMun SExb SLeo SPer SReu
– 'Graf Lennart'	GGGa
– 'Graf Zeppelin'	GGGa
*– 'Grafton'	SExb
– 'Grand Pré'	GGGa
– 'Grayswood Pink'	CSam SPer
– 'Green Eye'	CWal
– 'Greensleeves'	LKna LMil
– Grenadier (g.&cl.)	CWal GWht
– 'Gretzel'	NMun SLeo
¶– 'Grierdal'	GGGa
– Grierocaster	SCog
– 'Grisette'	NMun SLeo
– 'Gristede'	GGGa LMil MBri NHol SExb SReu SSta WBod
– Grosclaude AGM	CWal NMun SCog SLeo
– 'Grouse'	GGGa MBal
– 'Grumpy'	CDoC CWal EBre ELan GGGa GRei GWht IHos IOrc ISea LBre LHyd LMil LNet MBal MBar MBri MLea MMor NHed NHol NMun SCog SExb SHBN SLeo SPer SReu
– Guardsman	NMun SLeo
– 'Gwillt-King'	CWal NMun SLeo
– 'H Whitner'	NMun SLeo
¶– 'Hachmann's Bananaflip'	LHyd
– 'Hachmann's Diadem'	GGGa
– 'Hachmann's Marlis'	LHyd
– 'Hachmann's Porzellan'	GGGa LHyd
– 'Hachmann's Rosita'	GGGa
– 'Hachmann's Violetta'	GGGa
– 'Haida Gold'	GGGa LMil MBal MBri MGos MLea NKay SExb SSta WWeb
– Halcyone	CWal NMun SLeo
– 'Halfdan Lem'	CAbP CSam GGGa LHyd LMil MBal MGos MLea MMor NMun SCog SExb SHBN SLeo SPer SSta WWeb
– 'Hallelujah'	GGGa MBal
– 'Handsworth Scarlet'	NMun SLeo
– Happy	CCla CWal ELan IJoh IOrc ISea SHBN
– 'Hardijzer's Beauty'	See R. Azaleodendron 'Hardijzer's Beauty'
– 'Harkwood Moonlight'	LMil LRHS MAsh
– 'Harkwood Premiere'	LMil LRHS MAsh
– 'Harry Tagg'	GGGa LHyd
– 'Harvest Moon'	CSam CWal GGGa LHyd MBal MBar MBlu MGos NKay NMun SLeo SReu SSta
– Hawk 'Crest'	See R. H. 'Crest'
*– Hawk 'Falcon'	SReu
– 'Hawk 'Jervis Bay'	See R. H. 'Jervis Bay'
– 'Haze'	NMun SLeo
– 'Hazel Fisher'	LMil
– Hebe	CWal SExb
– 'Helene Schiffner' AGM	GGGa NMun SLeo SReu
*– 'Henry Street'	NMun SLeo
– Hermes	SExb
– Hesperides	CWal SExb
– 'High Gold'	LMil
– 'High Summer'	LMil
– 'Hilda Margaret'	SReu
– 'Hill Ayah'	CWal
– 'Hollandia'	IOrc MMor NBar SHBN
– 'Honey'	CWal LKna NMun SLeo
– 'Honey Bee'	MAsh SSta
– 'Honeymoon'	SExb
– 'Hope Findlay'	LHyd
– 'Hoppy'	CBow CWal EBre GWht LBre LMil MBal MBlu MBri MLea MMor NMun SCog SExb SLeo SReu WWeb
– 'Horizon'	LMil
– 'Horizon Snowbird'	LMil

Hybrid 'Hotei' **AGM**	CAbP CBow CWal GCHN GGGa GWht IJoh ISea LHyd LMil MBal MBar MBri MGos MLea MMor NKay NMun SCog SExb SHBN SLeo SPer SReu SSta
– 'Hugh Koster'	CB&S CSam CWal IOrc LHyd LKna MAsh MGos NMun SExb SLeo SPer
– Humming Bird	CB&S CMHG CSam CWal EPot GPlt GWht IDai ISea LHyd LKna MBal MBar MBri MGos MMor NHol NMun SCog SExb SHBN SLeo SPer WBod WThu
– 'Hurricane'	COtt LMil MBlu MBri
– 'Hydon Ball'	CWal LHyd SReu
– 'Hydon Ben'	LHyd
– 'Hydon Dawn' **AGM**	COtt CWal GGGa ISea LHyd LMil MAsh MGos NHed NMun SCog SLeo SReu SSta WAbe
– 'Hydon Glow'	CWal LHyd NMun SLeo
– 'Hydon Gold'	LHyd
– 'Hydon Hunter' **AGM**	COtt CWal GGGa IOrc LHyd LMil LNet NHed NMun SCog SLeo SPla SReu SSta
– 'Hydon Mist'	LHyd
– 'Hydon Pearl'	LHyd
– 'Hydon Pink'	LHyd
– 'Hydon Rodney'	LHyd
– 'Hydon Salmon'	LHyd NMun SLeo
– 'Hydon Snowflake'	CWal GGGa
– 'Hydon Velvet'	LHyd
– Hyperion	LKna SReu SSta
– Ibex (g.&cl.)	CWal
– Icarus	CWal
– 'Ice Cream'	SCog
– 'Iceberg'	See R. H. 'Lodauric Iceberg'
– 'Icecream Flavour'	See R. H. 'Flavour'
– 'Icecream Vanilla'	See R. H. 'Vanilla'
– Idealist **AGM**	CWal LHyd MBri NMun SExb SLeo SPer SReu
– 'Ightham Gold'	SReu
*– 'Ightham Peach'	SReu
*– 'Ightham Purple'	SReu
– 'Ightham Yellow'	CWal MMor NMun SLeo SReu SSta
– 'Ilam Violet'	GGGa LKna LMil
– Impi **AGM**	CWal LKna MBri NMun SExb SLeo WThu
¶ – 'Ina Hair'	CB&S
– Intermedium	MBal
– Intrifast	CWal GAri GGGa GWht LHyd MBal MBri NHar NHol NKay
¶ – Iola	SExb
– 'Isabel Pierce' **AGM**	CSam LMil MBal NBar NMun SLeo SSta WWeb
– 'Isabella Mangles'	LHyd
– Italia	NMun SLeo
– Ivanhoe (g.&cl.)	CWal
– 'Ivery's Scarlet' **AGM**	CWal IOrc SExb
– Iviza	SReu
¶ – 'Ivory Coast'	SExb
*– 'J C Williams'	CB&S
– 'J G Millais'	LHyd
– 'J M de Montague'	See R. H. 'The Hon. Jean Marie de Montague'
– 'Jabberwocky'	LHyd
*– 'Jack'	CTrw
*– 'Jack Skelton'	CWal LHyd
– 'Jacksonii' **AGM**	CWal IOrc ISea LKna MBal MBar NMun SLeo SReu
– Jacques	NMun SCog SLeo SReu
– Jacquetta	WBod
– 'Jade'	NMun SLeo
– Jaipur	CWal
– Jalisco (g.&cl.)	CWal NMun SExb SLeo
– 'Jalisco Eclipse' **AGM**	CWal LKna SExb
– 'Jalisco Elect' **AGM**	LKna LMil SExb
– 'Jalisco Goshawk' **AGM**	NMun SLeo
– 'Jalisco Janet'	CWal SExb
– 'Jalisco Jubilant'	LHyd SExb
– 'James Barto'	CWal IOrc LHyd LMil NMun SLeo SPer SSta
– 'James Burchett' **AGM**	GGGa LKna LMil NMun SLeo SPer
– 'Jan Bee'	GGGa MBal
– 'Jan Dekens'	SReu
– 'Jancio'	SExb
– 'Janet Ward'	LHyd LKna
– 'Janine Alexandre Debray'	NMun SCog SLeo
– Jean	SCog
– 'Jean Mary Montague'	See R. H. 'The Hon. Jean Marie de Montague'
– 'Jennie Dosser'	LMil
– 'Jenny'	See R. H. 'Creeping Jenny'
§ – 'Jervis Bay' **AGM**	LMil
– 'Jingle Bells'	GGGa
– 'Joan Scobie'	CWal NMun SLeo
– Jock	CB&S CMHG LHyd
*– 'Jock's White'	MBal SPer
¶ – 'Joe Paterno'	SExb
– 'John Barr Stevenson'	LHyd NMun SLeo
– 'John Keats'	CWal
¶ – 'John Marchand'	IDai
– 'John Tremayne'	NMun SLeo
– 'John Walter'	GRei MGos SSta
– 'John Waterer'	IOrc LKna SPer
– Johnnie Johnston (g.&cl.)	CWal NMun SLeo
– 'Johnny Bender'	GAul ISea MLea SExb
– 'Johnson's Impeditum'	SExb
– 'Joseph Whitworth'	CWal
– 'Jubilee'	LKna
– Jubilee Queen (g.&cl.)	NMun SLeo
– 'Julischka'	MGos
– 'Jungfrau'	SExb
– 'Juwel'	MGos
– 'Kalinko'	GGGa LHyd MGos NHol
¶ – 'Karen Triplett'	LMil
– 'Karin'	GGGa IJoh MBal SBod SExb SHBN
– 'Kate Waterer' **AGM**	CWal IOrc LKna MBar MGos NMun SLeo SSta
– Keiskrac	CWal
– 'Ken Janeck'	See R. ***yakushimanum y.*** 'Ken Janeck'
N – Kewense	See R. H. Loderi
– Kilimanjaro **AGM**	NMun SCog SLeo SReu SSta
– 'Kimberly'	GGGa
– 'Kimbeth'	GGGa
– 'Kingston'	GAul LHyd LMil LRHS MAsh
– 'Kluis Sensation' **AGM**	CB&S CSam GGGa IOrc LHyd LKna MGos MMor NMun SExb SHBN SLeo SReu
– 'Kluis Triumph'	CSco LKna SReu
– 'Koichiro Wada'	See R. ***yakushimanum*** 'Koichiro Wada'
– 'Kokardia'	GGGa LMil

Hybrid 'Lacs'	NMun SLeo
– 'Lady Adam Gordon'	CWal NMun SLeo
– 'Lady Alice Fitzwilliam' **AGM**	CB&S CBow CGre CMHG CWal ERea GGGa GWht IDai ISea LMil MBal NMun SLeo
– 'Lady Annette de Trafford'	LKna
– Lady Berry (g.&cl.)	SExb
– Lady Bessborough (g.&cl.)	LHyd NMun SLeo
– 'Lady Bessborough Roberte'	See R. H. 'Roberte'
– 'Lady Bowes Lyon'	CWal LHyd NMun SCog SLeo SPer SReu
– Lady Chamberlain (g.&cl.)	CBow CWal LMil MBal MBlu MGos NMun SLeo SReu
– 'Lady Chamberlain Exbury'	See R. H. 'Exbury Lady Chamberlain'
– 'Lady Chamberlain Golden Queen'	See R. H. 'Golden Queen'
– 'Lady Chamberlain Salmon Trout'	See R. H. 'Salmon Trout'
– 'Lady Clementine Mitford' **AGM**	CSam CWal GGGa IHos LHyd LKna LMil MBri MGos NMun SExb SHBN SLeo SPer SReu SSta
– 'Lady Eleanor Cathcart' **AGM**	CHig CWal GGGa IOrc LKna NMun SLeo
– 'Lady Grey Egerton' **AGM**	CWal LKna MMor
– Lady Jean	CWal
– Lady Linlithgow	LMil NMun SCog SLeo
– 'Lady Longman'	CWal LHyd SSta
– Lady Montagu (g.&cl.)	SExb
– 'Lady of Spain'	LMil
– 'Lady Primrose'	SReu
– 'Lady Romsey'	LMil
– Lady Rosebery (g.&cl.)	CWal GGGa MLea NMun SLeo SReu
– 'Lady Rosebery Pink Delight'	See R. H. 'Pink Lady Rosebery'
– Ladybird (g.&cl.)	SExb SReu
– Lamellen	CWal LHyd NMun SLeo
– 'Lampion'	GGGa
– 'Lamplighter' **AGM**	LMil NMun SLeo SReu
– 'Langworth'	LKna SReu
– 'Lascaux'	SReu
– Laura Aberconway (g.&cl.)	NMun SLeo
– 'Lava Flow'	CWal LHyd NHol SCog
– 'Lavender Girl' **AGM**	GRei IJoh LHyd LKna LMil MBal MGos NMun SLeo SPer SReu SSta
– 'Lavender Princess'	LMil
– 'Lavender Queen'	MBlu
– 'Lavendula'	CSam GGGa LMil
– 'Lea Rainbow'	MLea
– 'Lee's Dark Purple'	IJoh ISea MBlu SExb SPer
– 'Lee's Scarlet'	LKna LMil
– 'Lemon Ice'	SCog
¶ – 'Lemon Lodge'	CB&S
– 'Lem's 121'	LMil SExb
– 'Lem's Cameo' **AGM**	GGGa LMil SReu SSta
– 'Lem's Monarch' **AGM**	GGGa LMil MGos SReu SSta
– 'Lem's Stormcloud'	LMil MLea SReu SSta
– 'Leny'	NHol SSta
– Leo (g.&cl.)	CWal NMun SLeo
– 'Leonardslee Brilliant'	NMun SLeo
– 'Leonardslee Giles'	NMun SLeo
– 'Leonardslee Pink Bride'	NMun SLeo
– 'Leonardslee Primrose'	NMun SLeo
– Leonore (g.&cl.)	SReu
– Letty Edwards (g.&cl.)	CWal LKna NMun SCog SLeo SReu
¶ – 'Leverett Richards'	LHyd
– 'Lila Pedigo'	GGGa LMil MBal MLea SExb SReu
– 'Lillian Peste'	MBri
– 'Lincill'	CWal
– 'Linda'	CSam GGGa LMil MBal MBar MBri MGos MLea NHol SBod SCog SExb SReu
– Lionel's Triumph (g.&cl.)	CWal LHyd LMil NMun SLeo
*– 'Lissabon Rosa'	SExb
– 'Little Ben'	GPlt MBal MBar NBar SCog WAbe
– 'Little Bert'	NMun SLeo SReu
*– 'Little Jock'	MBal
– 'Llenroc'	ISea
– 'Loch Rannoch'	GGGa
– 'Loch Tay'	GGGa
– 'Loch Tummel'	GGGa
§ – 'Lodauric Iceberg' **AGM**	CWal LKna LMil SReu
*– 'Lodbrit'	SReu
N– Loderi	LMil SExb
– 'Loderi Fairy Queen'	NMun SLeo
– 'Loderi Fairyland'	CWal LHyd NMun SLeo
§ – 'Loderi Game Chick'	GGGa LHyd LMil MBal NMun SLeo SPer SReu SSta
– 'Loderi Georgette'	NMun SLeo
– 'Loderi Helen'	NMun SLeo
§ – 'Loderi Julie'	NMun SLeo SReu
– 'Loderi King George' **AGM**	CAbP CB&S CSam CSco GGGa ISea LHyd LKna LMil MBlu MBri MLea NMun SCog SExb SHBN SLeo SPer SReu SSta
– 'Loderi Patience'	LHyd NMun SLeo
– 'Loderi Pink Diamond' **AGM**	LMil SExb
– 'Loderi Pink Topaz'	LMil NMun SExb SLeo
– 'Loderi Pretty Polly'	NMun SLeo
– 'Loderi Princess Marina'	NMun SLeo
– 'Loderi Sir Edmund'	NMun SLeo
– 'Loderi Sir Joseph Hooker'	NMun SLeo
– 'Loderi Titan'	SReu
§ – 'Loderi Venus' **AGM**	CAbP CWal GGGa IOrc LHyd LKna LMil MBal MLea NMun SCog SHBN SLeo SPer SReu SSta
– 'Loderi White Diamond'	CWal NMun SExb SLeo
– 'Loder's White' **AGM**	CBow CWal GGGa IHos LHyd LKna LMil MBal MBlu MLea NMun SCog SLeo SPer SReu SSta
§ – 'Logan Damaris'	CWal LHyd NMun SLeo SReu
– 'Loki'	NMun SLeo
– 'Looking Glass'	CAbP MAsh MBri SHBN

Hybrid 'Lord Roberts'	CB&S CBow CHig CSam CWal EBre ELan GGGa GRei GWht IOrc LBre LKna LMil MBal MBar MBri MGos MMor NMun SExb SHBN SLeo SPer SSta
– 'Lord Swaythling'	LHyd NMun SLeo
– 'Lori Eichelser'	CSam MAsh MBal
– 'Louis Pasteur'	SReu SSta
– 'Lovely William'	CSam MBal SExb SPer
– ***lowndesii*** x Yaku Fairy	SSta
– 'Lucy Lou'	CSam GGGa NHol SExb
– ***ludlowii*** x ***mekongense*** Viridescens Group	NHol
– 'Lunar Queen'	CWal LHyd
– Luscombei	LHyd
– 'Madame Albert Moser'	LKna
– 'Madame de Bruin'	CWal LKna MBal NMun SExb SLeo SReu
– 'Madame Masson'	CDoC CHig LMil MGos NHol NMun SCog SHBN SLeo SReu SSta
– 'Maestro'	CWal
– 'Maharani'	GGGa
– Mai	CWal
– 'Manda Sue'	GGGa LMil MBal MLea SPer
– Mandalay	CDoC CWal LHyd MBri NMun SExb SLeo
– 'Mannheim'	LMil
– 'Marchioness of Lansdowne'	MGos
– 'Marcia'	LHyd NMun SExb SLeo
¶ – 'Mardi Gras'	GGGa
– Margaret Dunn (g.&cl.)	CWal NMun SLeo
– Marie Antoinette	CWal LMil
– Mariloo	CWal NMun SLeo
– 'Marinus Koster' **AGM**	CWal LKna MMor NBar
– 'Marion'	LMil
– 'Marion Street'	CWal LHyd LMil NMun SCog SLeo
– 'Markeeta's Prize' **AGM**	GAri GGGa LMil MBri
– 'Marlene Peste'	CAbP NHol
– 'Mars'	SReu
– Marshall	CWal
– 'Martha Isaacson'	GGGa
– 'Mary Belle'	GGGa
– 'Mary Drennen'	LMil
– 'Mary Fleming'	GAbr LHyd MBlu SBod SCog SExb SSta
– 'Mary Forte'	NMun SLeo
*– 'Master Mariner'	LHyd
– Matador **AGM**	CWal LHyd NKay SCog SExb WBod
¶ – 'Maurice Skipworth'	CB&S
– May Day **AGM**	CB&S CBow CCla CSam CTrw CWal GWht ISea LHyd LKna MBal MBri MGos NKay NMun SCog SExb SHBN SLeo SReu SSta WAbe WBod
*– 'May Glow'	MGos
*– 'Mayor Johnstone'	CDoC
– Medea	CWal
– Medusa	CWal GGGa SReu
– 'Merganser' **AGM**	CDoC GGGa LMil MAsh MBal NHol SReu WAbe WBod
– Merops	CWal
¶ – Metis	WBod
– 'Michael Waterer' **AGM**	CWal NMun SBod SExb SLeo
– 'Michael's Pride' **AGM**	CB&S CGre CWal ISea MBal
– 'Midsummer'	GGGa NMun SLeo
– 'Minterne Cinnkeys'	MBal
§ – 'Moerheim' **AGM**	CSam CSco CWal EBre GAbr GWht IDai IJoh LBre MBal MBar MMor MRav NHol NKay SReu SSta WAbe WStI
§ – 'Moerheim's Pink'	ELan GGGa LHyd LKna LMil NHol SPer WThu
– 'Moerheim's Scarlet'	LKna
– Mohamet (g.&cl.)	CWal MLea
– 'Molly Ann'	CDoC GGGa LMil MAsh MLea SExb SReu
– 'Molly Buckley'	SExb
¶ – 'Molly Fordham'	SExb
– 'Monaco'	LMil
– 'Monica'	SCog SReu
– 'Monica Wellington'	LHyd
– Moonbeam	LKna
– Moonshine (g.&cl.)	SReu
– 'Moonshine Bright'	GGGa LHyd SReu
– 'Moonshine Crescent'	GGGa SReu
– 'Moonshine Supreme'	LKna SReu
– Moonstone	CHig CWal EPot GAri GPlt MBal MBar MLea NMun SCog SExb SLeo WAbe
– 'Moonstone Pink'	CWal SExb
*– Moonstone pink-tipped	GGGa NHol
– 'Moonstone Yellow'	GGGa SExb
– 'Moonwax'	CSam ISea LMil MBal
– 'Morgenrot' ('Morning Red') **AGM**	GGGa LMil MBri MGos SReu
– 'Morning Cloud' **AGM**	CAbP CBow CWal GGGa IOrc LHyd LMil MAsh MBar NHed NMun SCog SLeo SPer SReu WWeb
– 'Morning Magic'	CWal ISea LHyd NMun SCog SLeo
– 'Morvah'	NMun SLeo
– 'Mosaique'	SExb
– 'Moser's Maroon'	LHyd LKna MGos NMun SLeo
– 'Moser's Strawberry'	LKna
– 'Moth'	GGGa NHol
– 'Mother Greer'	GGGa
– 'Mother of Pearl'	CWal GGGa LKna SCog SReu
– 'Mother Theresa'	LKna
– 'Mount Everest'	See R. ***cinnabarinum c.*** 'M. E.'
– 'Mountain Dew'	SReu
– 'Mountain Star'	NMun SLeo
– 'Mrs A T de la Mare' **AGM**	GGGa IDai IOrc LHyd LKna LMil MBri MMor NMun SLeo SPer SReu SSta
– 'Mrs Anthony Waterer'	LKna SSta
– 'Mrs Ashley Slocock'	SReu
– 'Mrs Betty Robertson'	CHig MBri MLea SExb SReu
– 'Mrs C B van Nes'	SPer SReu
– Mrs C Whitner	NMun SLeo
– 'Mrs Charles E Pearson' **AGM**	CB&S CBow CWal LHyd LKna LMil MLea NMun SCog SExb SHBN SLeo SPer SReu
*– 'Mrs Chitton'	SExb
– 'Mrs Davies Evans' **AGM**	LHyd LKna MBar MMor SReu SSta

Hybrid 'Mrs Donald Graham' SReu
– 'Mrs E C Stirling' LKna SExb SRms
– 'Mrs Furnival' **AGM** CB&S LHyd LKna LMil MAsh MBri MGos SExb SReu
– 'Mrs G W Leak' CSam CWal GGGa LHyd LKna LMil MBri MLea MMor NMun SCog SExb SHBN SLeo SPer SReu SSta
– 'Mrs Helen Koster' LKna
– 'Mrs Henry Agnew' NMun SLeo
– 'Mrs J C Williams' LKna LMil NMun SLeo
– 'Mrs J G Millais' GGGa LKna LMil NMun SLeo
– 'Mrs James Horlick' CWal LHyd NMun SLeo
– 'Mrs John Kelk' CWal
– 'Mrs Kingsmill' CWal NMun SLeo
– 'Mrs Lindsay Smith' LKna
– Mrs Lionel de Rothschild **AGM** CWal LKna SReu
– 'Mrs P D Williams' **AGM** LKna SExb SReu
– 'Mrs Philip Martineau' LKna
– 'Mrs R S Holford' **AGM** CWal LKna NMun SExb SLeo
– 'Mrs T H Lowinsky' MBri
– 'Mrs Tom H Lowinsky' **AGM** GCHN GGGa LKna LMil MAsh MGos NMun SExb SLeo SReu SSta WWeb
– 'Mrs W C Slocock' CWal LHyd LKna MAsh NMun SLeo SPer SReu SSta
– 'Mrs William Agnew' LKna NMun SLeo
– 'Muncaster Mist' LHyd
– 'Muriel' NMun SLeo
– 'My Lady' GGGa
– 'Mystic' CWal
– 'Nancy Evans' COtt CSam GGGa GWht ISea LMil MAsh MBal MLea MMor SCog SPla
– Naomi (g.&cl.) CSam LKna LMil SExb SReu
– 'Naomi Astarte' LKna NMun SExb SLeo
– 'Naomi Exbury' CWal LKna LMil NMun SExb SLeo SReu
– 'Naomi Glow' CWal LMil
– 'Naomi Hope' SExb
– 'Naomi Nautilus' LMil
– 'Naomi Pink Beauty' MBlu
– 'Naomi Stella Maris' CWal LMil SExb
– Naomi 'Paris See R. H. 'Paris'
– Neda WBod
– Neriihaem NMun SLeo
– 'New Comet' LHyd LMil SReu
– 'New Moon' CWal NMun SLeo SReu
– 'Newcomb's Sweetheart' GGGa LMil
– 'Night Sky' GGGa LMil NMun SLeo
– 'Nightingale' LMil SReu
– 'Nimbus' LKna LMil NMun SLeo
– Nimrod NMun SExb SLeo
¶ – 'Noble Fountain' GGGa
– 'Noble Mountain' LMil
§ – Nobleanum GGGa ISea LHyd LKna LMil NMun SCog SLeo SSta WThu
– 'Nobleanum Album' **AGM** LHyd LKna LMil MBal NMun SLeo SReu SSta
– 'Nobleanum Coccineum' ISea NMun SLeo SReu
– 'Nobleanum Lamellen' CWal NMun SLeo
– 'Nobleanum Venustum' **AGM** ISea LHyd LKna LMil SReu SSta WBod
– 'Nofretete' GGGa
– Norman Shaw (g.&cl.) LHyd
– 'Northern Star' CWal NMun SLeo
* – 'Nosutchianum' GGGa
– 'Nova Zembla' CSam GGGa IJoh MBar MBlu MGos NMun SExb SHBN SLeo SReu SSta WStI
– 'Noyo Brave' GGGa
– 'Odee Wright' **AGM** GGGa LMil MAsh MBlu MLea NMun SExb SLeo SPer SSta WBod
– 'Old Copper' CDoC GGGa LNet MBri MLea NHol
– 'Old Port' CWal SHBN SReu SSta
– Oldenburgh CWal NMun SLeo
– 'Olga' LHyd LKna LMil SPer SReu SSta
– 'Olga Mezitt' GGGa LHyd LMil NHol
– 'Olin O Dobbs' LMil MAsh MBri
– 'Olive' **AGM** LHyd LKna LMil NMun SLeo SPer SReu
– 'Olive Judson' NMun SLeo
– 'Oliver Cromwell' SReu
– Olympic Lady CWal LHyd MLea NMun SLeo
– Omar MBar NKay
§ – 'One Thousand Butterflies' COtt CSam GGGa ISea
– 'Orangengold' GGGa
– ***orbiculare*** x ***decorum*** CWal
– Oregonia SExb
– Oreocinn MBal
– 'Osmar' CDoC GGGa MGos
¶ – 'Ostara' CB&S COtt
– 'Ostfriesland' SRms
– 'Oudijk's Favorite' MBal MGos SExb
– 'Oudijk's Sensation' CSco CWal GCHN GWht IDai LKna MGos MMor SExb
* – 'Ovation' GGGa
– Oxlip NMun SExb SLeo
– P J M CSam ISea MAsh MBal MBri MLea SExb SSta
– 'P J M Elite' GGGa
– 'P J Mezitt' See R. H. 'Peter John Mezitt'
– 'Palma' See R. ***parmulatum*** 'Palma'
– 'Pamela-Louise' LHyd
– Pandora WBod
– 'Papaya Punch' LMil
– 'Paprika Spiced' GGGa LMil LRHS MAsh MBal MBlu MLea SExb
– 'Paris' LHyd
– 'Parisienne' SCog SExb
– 'Party Pink' GGGa
– 'Patty Bee' **AGM** CSam EPot GGGa GWht LHyd LMil LRHS MBlu MBri MGos MLea NBar NHar NHol SBod SReu SSta WAbe
– 'Peace' CWal GGGa LHyd MBal NMun SLeo WAbe
– 'Pearl Diver' LHyd
– 'Peekaboo' SExb
– 'Peeping Tom' LMil LRHS MAsh NMun SHBN SLeo
¶ – 'Peking' SExb
– 'Pematit Cambridge' SBod
– 'Pematit Oxford' SReu
– Penelope SReu

Hybrid 'Penheale Blue' AGM	CTre CWal GGGa ISea LMil NHol NMun SGil SLeo WWeb
– Penjerrick (g.&cl.)	GGGa SCog
– 'Penjerrick Cream'	CWal NMun SLeo
– 'Penjerrick Pink'	CWal NMun SLeo
– 'Penrose'	CB&S
– 'Percy Wiseman'	Widely available
– 'Perfect Lady'	LRHS
§ – 'Persimmon'	CWal LKna NMun SExb SLeo
– 'Peter Alan'	LMil
§ – 'Peter John Mezitt' AGM	GGGa LHyd LMil NMun SLeo SReu WThu
– 'Peter Koster' AGM	IJoh NMun SExb SHBN SLeo WStI
– 'Phalarope'	CSam CWal GAbr GGGa LHyd MBal MBar MBlu MBri MGos NHol NKay SReu WBod
– 'Pheasant Tail'	NMun SCog SLeo
– 'Philomene'	SReu
– 'Phyllis Korn'	CAbP LHyd LMil SPer
– Pilgrim (g.&cl.)	LKna SExb
– 'Pink Bountiful'	LKna WAbe
– 'Pink Cherub' AGM	CMHG CWal EBre ELan GWht IHos LBre MBal MBar MBri MMor NBar NMun SCog SLeo SReu WWeb
– 'Pink Drift'	Widely available
– 'Pink Frills'	CB&S
– 'Pink Ghost'	CWal NMun SLeo
– 'Pink Gin'	LMil
– 'Pink Glory'	NMun SLeo
– 'Pink Leopard'	LMil SExb
– 'Pink Pearl'	Widely available
– 'Pink Pebble' AGM	CTrw CWal LHyd NMun SExb SLeo SReu WBod
– 'Pink Perfection'	MGos NMun SLeo SReu
– 'Pink Petticoats'	MBlu
– 'Pink Rosette'	LKna
– 'Pink Sensation'	MBri
– 'Pinkerton'	LKna
¶ – 'Pioneer Silvery Pink'	SExb
– 'Pipaluk'	CWal LHyd
– 'Pipit'	GGGa MBal NHol WAbe
– 'Piquante'	CWal
– 'Point Defiance'	MLea
– Polar Bear AGM	CBow COtt CSam CWal GAri GGGa LHyd LMil NMun SLeo SPer SReu
– 'Polaris'	LHyd MGos
*– 'Polgrain'	CB&S
*– 'Polycinn'	SCog
– 'Ponticum'	See R. ***ponticum***
– 'Pook'	CWal LHyd
– 'Popacatapetl'	SReu
– 'Powder Puff'	LMil
§ – 'Praecox' AGM	Widely available
– 'Prawn'	LKna SReu
– Prelude (g.&cl.)	CWal
– 'President Roosevelt' (v)	CBow CWal GGGa IHos IJoh IOrc LKna LNet MBal MBri MGos MMor NMun SCog SDry SHBN SLeo SPer SReu SSta
– 'Pretty Girl'	LKna
– 'Prima Donna'	LMil SReu
– 'Prince Camille de Rohan'	LMil
– 'Princess Alice' AGM	CB&S CGre CHig COtt ERea GGGa ISea LHyd MBal SCog WBod
– 'Princess Anne' AGM	CHig CMHG CSam CSco CTrw CWal GDra GGGa GRei GWht LHyd LMil MBal MBar MBri MGos MLea NHol NKay NMun SBod SCog SExb SHBN SLeo SPer SReu SSta WBod WThu
– 'Professor Hugo de Vries' AGM	LKna MGos SReu
– 'Professor J H Zaayer'	CWal IDai MGos NMun SLeo
§ – 'Prostigiatum'	CWal GDra GGGa GWht MGos NMun
– Psyche	See R. H. Wega
– 'Ptarmigan' AGM	CB&S CMHG CTrw CWal EPot GGGa GPlt GWht IDai LHyd LMil MBal MBar MBri MGos MMor NHar NHol NMun SBod SCog SExb SLeo SPer SReu SSta WAbe WBod WThu
– 'Puget Sound'	NMun SLeo
– 'Puncta'	NHol
*– 'Purple Carpeter'	SReu SSta
– 'Purple Emperor'	LKna
– 'Purple Gem'	GGGa GWht ISea NHar NHol SReu
– 'Purple Splendour' AGM	CB&S CHig CSam CSco CWal EBre GGGa ISea LBre LHyd LKna LMil MBal MBar MBlu MBri MGos MMor NBar NMun NWea SCog SExb SHBN SLeo SPer SReu SSta
*– 'Purple Split'	ISea
– Quaver	SExb SRms
– 'Queen Alice'	SPer
– 'Queen Anne's'	GGGa LMil LRHS MBal SSta
– 'Queen Elizabeth II' AGM	CWal LHyd LMil SPer SReu SSta
– 'Queen Mary'	MBar MMor NBar
– 'Queen Mother'	See R. H. 'The Queen Mother'
– Queen of Hearts AGM	CWal LHyd NMun SExb SLeo
– 'Queen Souriya'	SReu
¶ – 'Queen's Wood'	LHyd
– 'Racil'	GPlt LHyd LKna MBal MBar MGos MLea MMor NBar SExb WAbe
– 'Radistrotum'	GGGa
– 'Raeburn'	GPlt
– 'Rainbow'	GGGa LKna
– 'Ramapo' AGM	EBre GGGa GPlt LBre LMil MBal MBri MGos MLea NHar NHol SExb SPer SReu SSta WAbe WBod
– 'Raspberry Ripple'	LKna
– 'Rasputin'	GGGa
– 'Razorbill' AGM	CSam GGGa LHyd LMil MBri MGos NHar NHol SReu
– Red Admiral AGM	CWal NMun SLeo
– Red Argenteum	NMun SLeo
– Red Cap	CWal SExb
– 'Red Carpet' AGM	LMil LRHS
– 'Red Delicious'	LMil
– 'Red Dragon'	NMun SLeo
¶ – 'Red Elf'	IDai
– 'Red Glow'	LHyd NMun SLeo
– 'Red Poll'	LHyd
– 'Red Riding Hood'	CWal LKna

Hybrid 'Red Rum'	LHyd
– 'Red Velour'	CAbP
– 'Red Walloper'	MBlu
*– 'Red Wood'	GGGa LHyd
– Remo	CWal MBal NMun SCog SLeo SReu
– Remus	CWal
– 'Renoir' AGM	LHyd NMun SCog SLeo
– Repose (g.&cl.)	GGGa LKna
– 'Reuthe's Purple'	See R. ***lepidotum*** 'Reuthe's Purple'
– Rêve Rose (g.&cl.)	SCog
– Review Order	CWal
– 'Revlon'	LHyd LMil SReu
– ***rex*** x 'Sincerity'	NMun SLeo
– Rickshaw	NMun SLeo
– 'Ring of Fire'	LMil
– 'Rio'	GGGa
– 'Ripe Corn'	LKna NMun SLeo SReu
– Riplet AGM	EPot GAri GGGa NHar NMun SLeo
¶– 'Rivulet'	SExb
– 'Robert Keir' AGM	CWal LHyd NMun SLeo
– 'Robert Seleger'	GGGa LMil NHar
§– 'Roberte'	CWal NKay SCog
– 'Robin Redbreast'	LHyd NMun SLeo
*– 'Robinette'	GGGa
– 'Rocket'	CAbP GWht LMil MLea SExb WWeb
– Romany Chai AGM	CWal LHyd LMil NKay SExb
– Romany Chal	CWal LHyd MBal SCog SExb SPer
– 'Romy'	NMun SLeo
– 'Rose Bud' AGM	WThu
– 'Rose Elf'	CDoC MBal NHol WAbe
– 'Roseum Elegans'	IJoh LMil MBar NMun SExb SLeo
– 'Rosevallon'	CWal
– 'Rosy Bell'	IDai LKna
*– 'Rosy Cream'	SPer
– 'Rosy Dream'	CAbP LMil
*– 'Rosy Lea'	MLea
– 'Rothenburg'	LHyd LMil SExb SReu WThu
– 'Royal Blood'	LHyd
– Royal Flush	CB&S CWal MBlu
– Royal Flush pink form	CWal
– Royal Flush yellow	CWal
– 'Royal Pink'	SBod
– Royalty	WBod
– 'Roza Stevenson' AGM	CWal LHyd NMun SLeo SPer
– Rubicon	CB&S GGGa WWeb
– Rubina	CWal NMun SExb SLeo
– 'Ruby F Bowman'	CSam MGos MLea NMun SExb SLeo SReu
– 'Ruby Hart'	GGGa NHol SReu
– Russautinii	LMil
– 'Russellianum'	SExb
– 'Sacko'	GGGa NHol
– 'Saffron Queen'	CB&S CGre CTrw GGGa ISea MBal SExb
– 'Saint Breward'	CB&S CWal GGGa IDai LHyd MBal MBri MLea NHol SBod SCog SExb SPer SReu WBod
– 'Saint Keverne'	CWal
– 'Saint Kew'	CWal
– 'Saint Merryn' AGM	CWal GAri GGGa LHyd MAsh MBri NHol NMun SExb SLeo
– 'Saint Michael'	SReu
– 'Saint Minver' AGM	CWal LHyd LRHS MBri
– 'Saint Tudy' AGM	CB&S CWal GPlt IDai LHyd LKna MBal MBri MMor NMun SExb SLeo SPer WAbe WBod
– 'Saint Wenn'	CWal
§– 'Salmon Trout'	CWal
– 'Sandling'	LHyd
– 'Santa Claus'	CWal
– 'Sapphire' AGM	CBow CWal GAbr GPlt LKna MBal MBar NKay NMun NRya SBod SExb SLeo SPer WAbe WBod WThu
– 'Sappho' AGM	CB&S CSco CWal ELan GGGa GWht IDai IHos IOrc ISea LHyd LKna LMil MBal MBar MGos MMor NMun SCog SExb SHBN SLeo SPer SReu SSta WBod
– Sarita Loder (g.&cl.)	NMun SLeo
– Sarled AGM	CMHG CSam CWal EPot GDra GGGa LHyd LMil MBal MBri NHar NMun SLeo SReu WThu WWat
– 'Scarlet Wonder' AGM	CSco CWal EBre ELan GGGa GRei GWht IDai IJoh ISea LBre LKna LMil MBal MBar MBri MGos MLea MMor NBar NHol NMun SBod SCog SExb SLeo SPer SReu SSta WBod
¶– Scarlett O'Hara	LHyd
– 'Schneekrone'	GGGa NHol
– 'Scintillation'	CDoC CSam CSco EBee GGGa LMil MBal MBri NMun SHBN SLeo
– Seagull (g.&cl.)	NMun SLeo
– 'Sea-Tac'	MLea
– 'Second Honyemoon'	LRHS MAsh MLea SExb SHBN SSta
– 'Senator Henry Jackson'	LMil
– 'Sennocke' AGM	LHyd SReu SSta
*– 'September Song'	CBow CDoC GGGa LHyd LMil MAsh MBal NBar SPer
– 'Sesterianum'	CMHG CWal
– Seta (g.&cl.)	CB&S CHig CWal GPlt LHyd MBal MLea NMun SCog SExb SLeo SReu WThu
– 'Seven Stars' AGM	CWal GGGa LHyd LMil NMun SCog SExb SLeo SReu
– 'Seville'	CWal
– 'Shamrock'	CAbP CDoC CSam EPot GAbr GGGa GWht ISea MAsh MBal MBar MBri NHar SExb SPer SSta WBod
– 'Sham's Candy'	CWal
– Sheperd's Delight	CWal
– Shilsonii	CWal LHyd NMun SLeo
– 'Shrimp Girl'	CDoC CWal ELan IHos LHyd MBal MBri MGos MLea NMun SCog SLeo SPer SReu
– 'Silberwolke' ('Silver Cloud')	CBow SExb SReu
– 'Silkcap'	WThu
*– 'Silky'	MBal
– 'Silver Jubilee'	GGGa ISea LHyd LMil
– 'Silver Sixpence' AGM	CBow CDoC CMHG CSam CSco CWal IHos IOrc ISea LMil MBal MBar MBlu MLea NMun SCog SExb SHBN SLeo SReu WAbe WBod WWeb
¶– 'Silvetta'	LHyd
*– 'Simmon's Classic'	GGGa LMil
– 'Simona'	GGGa LHyd

Hybrid 'Sinbad' NMun SLeo
– 'Sir Charles Lemon' See R. **arboreum** 'Sir Charles Lemon'
– Sir Frederick Moore (g.&cl.) SCog
*– 'Sir G E Simpson' NMun SLeo
– 'Sir George Sansom' CWal
*– 'Sir John Tremayne' CWal
– Siren (g.&cl.) CWal MBal WBod
– 'Sirius' LHyd SReu
– 'Skookum' LMil MGos SPer
– 'Sleepy' CWal ELan GWht IHos IOrc NHed NMun SCog SExb SLeo SPer SReu
§ – Smithii Group CWal
– 'Sneezy' CB&S CDoC CWal ELan GGGa GRei IHos ISea LHyd MBal MBar MBlu MGos NMun SCog SLeo SReu SSta
– 'Snipe' AGM CSam EBre EPot LBre LHyd LMil MAsh MBal MBar MBri MGos NHar NHol SExb SSta WAbe
– 'Snow Crown' ISea
– 'Snow Lady' AGM GGGa GPlt IDai MBal MBar MGos NBar NHar NHol NKay SCog SExb SIng WAbe WThu
– Snow Queen AGM GGGa LKna SReu
– 'Soldier Sam' SReu SSta
– 'Solidarity' MBal WWeb
– 'Sonata' CWal GAri GGGa GWht MBal MBri NKay SReu
– 'Songbird' CBow CSam CWal GAbr GCHN GDra GGGa GPlt LHyd LKna LMil MBal MBar MBri MLea NHol NKay SExb SReu WBod
– 'Songster' NMun SLeo
– Souldis CWal LMil
– 'Southern Cross' LHyd LMil
– 'Souvenir de Doctor S Endtz' CWal LKna MBal MBar MMor SReu
– 'Souvenir of Anthony Waterer' LHyd LKna MMor SReu SSta
– 'Souvenir of W C Slocock' CSam LKna NMun SHBN SLeo SReu SSta
– 'Sparkler' CCla COtt ISea MBlu MGos MLea SExb SReu WWeb
– 'Spinulosum' LHyd
– 'Spitfire' MGos MMor NBar NMun SLeo SReu
♦– 'Spring Dream' See R. H. 'Frühlingstraum'
– 'Spring Magic' LMil MAsh WThu
– 'Spring Parade' LRHS SExb
– 'Spring Pearl' See R. H. 'Moerheim's Pink'
– 'Spring Song' ESis
– 'Springbok' LHyd
*– 'Springday' CWal
– Stadt Essen (g.&cl.) GGGa LMil
– 'Stanley Rivlin' CWal LHyd NMun SCog SLeo
– 'Stanway' LMil SExb
– 'Starcross' LHyd
– 'Starfish' SReu
– 'Stella' NMun SLeo
– 'Stephanie' MBlu
– 'Strategist' CWal
– 'Strawberry Cream' GGGa NHol
– 'Streatley' AGM CWal NMun SCog SLeo
*– 'Striped Beauty' MBal
– 'Suave' SCog WBod
– 'Suede' SReu
– 'Sugar Pink' LMil
– 'Sumatra' GWht
– 'Sunbeam' LKna SReu
– 'Sunny Splendour' (V) ERea
– 'Sunset over Harkwood' LRHS
– 'Surrey Heath' AGM CB&S CCla COtt CWal GGGa GRei GWht ISea LHyd LMil LNet MBal MBar MBri MGos MLea MMor NBar NHed NHol NMun SCog SExb SLeo SReu SSta WAbe WBod
– 'Susan' AGM CSam CWal GGGa LHyd LKna LMil MBri MMor NMun SCog SExb SLeo SReu
– 'Sussex Bonfire' NMun SLeo
– 'Swamp Beauty' GGGa
– 'Swansdown' SPer
– 'Sweet Simplicity' AGM LKna MBal
– 'Sweet Sixteen' NMun SLeo
– 'Sweet Sue' CWal MAsh MBal NMun SCog SLeo SPer SReu
– 'Swift' GGGa
– Tally Ho (g.&cl.) CWal NMun SLeo SReu
– 'Tan Crossing' SReu
– 'Tangerine' See R. H. 'Fabia Tangerine'
– 'Tara' NMun SLeo
– Tasco SExb
– 'Taurus' AGM COtt GGGa LMil MBri MLea MMor SExb WWeb
– 'Teal' CDoC CSam GGGa GPlt MBal MBar NHol NMun SCog SExb SLeo SPer SReu WAbe
– 'Teddy Bear' GGGa LMil
– Temple Belle AGM CSam CWal ISea LHyd LKna LRHS MBal MBri MLea NMun SCog SLeo
– 'Tequila Sunrise' GAul LMil MBal NMun SLeo
*– 'Terra-Cotta' LKna LMil
– Tessa (g.&cl.) LKna LMil MGos SBod SExb
– 'Tessa Bianca' LMil
– 'Tessa Roza' AGM EPot GGGa LHyd MAsh MBri
¶ – Thais WBod
§ – 'The Hon Jean Marie de Montague AGM CAbP CSam CWal GAul IDai IOrc LKna MBal MBri MLea MMor NBar NMun SLeo WWeb
– 'The Master' AGM CWal LHyd LKna NMun SLeo SReu
§ – 'The Queen Mother' CWal LHyd
– 'The Warrior' SExb
¶ – 'Theme Song' SExb
– Thomdeton CWal
– Thomwilliams CWal MBal SExb
– Thor (g.&cl.) GGGa MMor NMun SLeo
– 'Thousand Butterflies' See R. H. 'One Thousand Butterflies'
– 'Thunderstorm' AGM CDoC LHyd LKna SReu
– 'Tibet' MBal MBar NBar NHar SExb SHBN
– 'Tidbit' GGGa LHyd LKna LMil MAsh MBal MBri MGos MLea NMun SLeo
*– 'Tilford Seedling' LKna
– 'Timothy James' SReu

Hybrid 'Titian Beauty' AGM	CB&S COtt CSco CWal EBre ELan GGGa IHos IOrc LBre LHyd LMil LNet MBal MBri MGos MLea MMor NBar NHed NKay NMun SCog SExb SLeo SReu
– 'Tolkien'	SSta
– 'Too Bee'	GGGa
– 'Top Banana'	GGGa LMil LRHS MBal MLea
– 'Top Brass'	CAbP
– 'Top Hat'	MLea
– 'Topaz'	CDoC
– 'Topsvoort Pearl'	SReu
– 'Torch'	LKna SReu
– 'Tortoiseshell Biscuit'	CWal LMil
– 'Tortoiseshell Champagne'	See R. H. 'Champagne'
– 'Tortoiseshell Orange' AGM	CWal LHyd LKna LMil MBri SCog SHBN SReu SSta
– 'Tortoiseshell Pale Orange'	LKna
– 'Tortoiseshell Salome'	LKna SSta
– 'Tortoiseshell Scarlet'	LKna SReu
– 'Tortoiseshell Wonder' AGM	CWal LHyd LKna LMil MBal MGos NMun SExb SLeo SReu SSta
– 'Tottenham'	MBal
– 'Travis L'	SPer
– Treasure	CWal GAri GDra IOrc LHyd MAsh MBal
– 'Trebah Gem'	CWal NMun SLeo
– 'Tregedna'	NMun SLeo
– 'Tretawn'	CWal NMun SLeo
– 'Trewithen Orange'	CBow CSam CTrw CWal GGGa MBal MBlu NHol NMun SCog SHBN SLeo SPer WAbe
*– 'Trewithen Purple'	CTrw CWal
– 'Trianon'	LMil
– 'Trilby'	GGGa NMun SLeo SReu
– 'Trude Webster'	CSam GGGa MLea SExb SSta
– 'Tulyar'	LKna
– 'Turkish Delight'	MLea
– 'Twilight Pink'	MBlu MLea
– 'Tyermannii' AGM	CWal NMun SLeo
– Ungerio	NMun SLeo
– 'Unique' AGM	CB&S CSam CSco CWal GAul GGGa LHyd LKna LMil LNet MBal MBri MMor NKay NMun SExb SHBN SLeo SPer SReu SSta WThu
– 'Unknown Warrior'	CWal MMor SReu
*– 'V M H'	CWal
– Valaspis (g.&cl.)	SExb
– 'Valley Sunrise'	GGGa
¶– 'Valpinense' (g.&cl.)	WBod
– 'Van Nes Sensation'	LMil
– Vanessa AGM	CWal LHyd LMil SCog SReu WBod
– 'Vanessa Pastel' AGM	CHig CWal GGGa LHyd LMil MBal NMun SCog SLeo SReu WBod
– Vanguard	ISea
§– 'Vanilla'	LKna
– Varna	WBod
– 'Veldtstar'	LHyd
– 'Venetian Chimes'	CWal ELan IHos IOrc ISea MBal MLea NMun SCog SExb SLeo SPer SReu WWeb
– 'Veryan Bay'	CB&S LMil
– 'Vincent van Gogh'	MBlu
¶– 'Vinecrest'	LMil
– 'Vinestar'	LHyd LMil
– 'Vintage Rose' AGM	CWal ELan LMil MBal MBri MLea NMun SCog SLeo SReu
– Virginia Richards (g.&cl.)	CDoC CHig GAri GGGa LHyd MBal MBri MGos MLea NMun SCog SExb SLeo SPer SSta WBod
– 'Viscy'	GGGa LHyd LMil
– Volker	See R. H. Flava
– 'Voodoo'	MBlu
– 'Vulcan' AGM	CB&S CSco GGGa LMil MBal MLea SExb SHBN SSta
– 'Vulcan's Flame'	GGGa MBlu
– W F H AGM	LMil NMun SCog SLeo
– 'Wagtail'	GGGa LRHS NHar NHol
– Walloper	NMun SLeo SReu
– 'Wally Miller'	SSta
– 'Waterfall'	MBal
– 'Wee Bee'	EPot GGGa LMil MAsh NHar NHed NHol WAbe
– Wega	CWal
– 'Wellesleyanum'	NMun SLeo
– 'Werei'	NMun SLeo
– 'Weston's Pink Diamond'	GGGa
– 'Weybridge'	NMun SLeo
– 'Whisperingrose'	CSam GGGa LMil MAsh MBal MBri NHol WAbe
– White Glory (g.&cl.)	NMun SLeo
– 'White Gold'	GGGa
– 'White Olympic Lady'	LKna
– 'White Swan' AGM	LKna LMil MBal MBlu SReu
– 'White Wings' AGM	NMun SLeo
*– 'Whitney's Best Yellow'	GGGa
– 'Whitney's Dwarf Red'	NMun SLeo
– 'Wigeon'	GGGa LMil LRHS NHol SPer
– 'Wilbrit Rose'	SBod
– 'Wild Affair'	LRHS
– 'Wilgen's Ruby' AGM	CSam CWal GGGa IJoh LKna LMil MBri MGos MMor NBar SBod SExb SHBN SPer SSta WStI
– 'Willbrit'	GPlt LHyd MBri SCog SExb
– Wilsonii	CWal
– Windbeam	SBod
– 'Windlesham Scarlet' AGM	EBee LHyd LMil SPer
– 'Windsor Lad'	LKna SReu
– Winsome AGM	CB&S CHig CSam CTrw CWal GCHN GGGa GWht IOrc ISea LHyd LKna MBal MBar MMor NHol NMun SCog SExb SLeo SSta WBod WThu
– 'Wishmoor' AGM	CWal LHyd LMil NMun SCog SLeo SReu
– 'Witch Doctor'	GWht MBlu MBri SBod
– 'Witchery'	GGGa
– 'Wonderland'	LKna
– 'Woodchat'	GGGa
– 'Woodcock'	LHyd SPer
– 'Woodside'	CWal NMun SLeo

Name	Suppliers
Hybrid 'Wren'	CSam EPot GGGa MAsh MBal MBar MBri NHar NHol SReu WWeb
– 'Xenophile'	CWal
– 'Yaku Angel'	NBar
§ – 'Yaku Fairy' **AGM**	CWal GAri LMil LRHS MBal NHar NHol SIng WThu
– 'Yaku Prince'	CAbP IOrc MBri NBar SPer
– 'Yaku Princess'	CAbP IOrc MAsh MBri MLea NBar NMun SLeo SPer WWeb
– 'Yaku Queen'	GAul LHyd MAsh MBri NMun SLeo
– ***yakushimanum*** x ***bureaui***	MBal MLea SCog
– x ***decorum***	MMor SReu
– x ***lanatum***	GGGa
– x ***pachysanthum***	GGGa
– x ***recurvoïdes***	GGGa
– x ***rex***	GGGa
– x ***tsariense***	GGGa
* – 'Yellow By Trailer'	MLea
– Yellow Hammer **AGM**	CB&S CCla CMHG CSam CSco CWal ELan GGGa GWht IDai IJoh ISea LKna LMil MBal MBar MBri MGos MMor NHol NMun SBod SExb SHBN SLeo SPer SReu SSta WBod
– 'Yellow Petticoats'	CSam IJoh ISea LMil MAsh MBri NMun SExb SLeo
– 'Youthful Sin'	CWal MBal WBod
– Yuncinn	CWal
– Yvonne	CWal
– 'Yvonne Dawn'	NMun SLeo
– Zelia Plumecocq (g.&cl.)	SExb
– Zuiderzee	NMun SLeo SReu
hylaeum	NMun SExb
♦ – KW 6401	See R. ***faucium*** KW6401
– KW 6833	NMun SLeo
hypenanthum	See R. ***anthopogon hypenanthum***
hyperythrum	CWal GGGa LHyd LMil NMun SExb SLeo
¶ – ***album***	NMun
– ssp. ***fauriei***	NMun SLeo
¶ – pink	NMun
hypoglaucum	See R. ***argyrophyllum hypoglaucum***
– 'Heane Wood'	See R. ***argyrophyllum h.*** 'H.W.'
impeditum **AGM**	CB&S CHig CRiv CSam CWal ELan GGGa GPlt GRei ISea LHyd LKna MBal MBar MGos MLea MPla NBar NBir NHar NKay NMun NWea SCog SExb SLon SPer SReu SSta WPat
– F 20454	LMil
§ – 'Blue Steel'	CB&S COtt ELan LMil MBal MBri NHar NMun SLeo SReu WAbe WPat
– dark compact form	LKna
– 'Harry White's Purple'	ESis WThu
– 'Indigo'	CMHG GWht LMil MAsh MBri NHar SCog WThu
– 'Johnston's Impeditum'	LKna
– 'Moerheim'	See R. Hybrid 'M.'
– 'Pygmaeum'	WAbe
– Reuthe's form	SReu
– 'Russell's Blue'	SReu
imperator	See R. ***uniflorum imperator***

Name	Suppliers
§ ***indicum*** (EA)	CWal MBal
§ – 'Balsaminiflorum' (d)	CMac SReu WAbe WBod
– 'Crispiflorum'	GWht
– var. ***eriocarpum*** 'Gumpo'	See R. Azalea 'Gumpo'
inopinum	GGGa NMun
insigne **AGM**	CWal GGGa IOrc LMil MGos NMun SExb SLeo
– Reuthe's form	SReu
x ***intermedium*** white	GGGa
intricatum	GGGa WAbe
– KW 4184	NMun SLeo
♦ ***iodes***	See R. ***alutaceum i.***
irroratum	CWal LMil NMun SLeo
¶ – KW 5002A	NMun
¶ – R 72	NMun
¶ – pale pink	NMun
§ – ssp. ***pogonostylum***	NMun SLeo
– 'Polka Dot'	GGGa NMun SExb SLeo
– white	GGGa
iteaphyllum	See R. ***formosum formosum*** Iteaphyllum Group
japonicum var. ***japonicum*** Schneider	See R. ***degronianum heptamerum***
– var. ***pentamerum***	See R. ***degronianum degronianum***
japonicum Suringar (A)	GGGa LHyd
– JR 871 (A)	GGGa
jasminiflorum (V)	ERea GGGa
javanicum Sands 74 (V)	GGGa
johnstoneanum **AGM**	CB&S CSam CWal GGGa ISea LMil MBal NMun SExb SLeo WBod
– 'Double Diamond' (d)	CGre CWal LHyd
– 'Rubrotinctum' KW 7723	NMun SLeo
kaempferi **AGM**	CHig GGGa LHyd LMil
– 'Damio'	See R. ***k.*** 'Mikado'
¶ – dark form	SCog
– 'Eastern Fire'	LMil
– 'Firefly'	See R. Azalea 'Hexe'
– ***latisepalum***	GGGa
¶ – light form	SCog
§ – 'Mikado'	LMil
¶ – orange	IOrc
¶ – pink	IOrc
keiskei	CHig CWal LMil MBal NMun SExb
– 'Cordifolium'	NMun SLeo
– 'Ebino'	GGGa NHol WAbe
keleticum	See R. ***calostrotum keleticum***
§ ***kendrickii***	CWal GGGa NMun SLeo
¶ ***kesangiae*** KR 1640	GGGa NMun
¶ – CH&M 3058, 3099	GGGa
– EGM 061	GGGa LMil
¶ – KR 1136	NMun
keysii	CWal GGGa LMil MBal NMun SLeo
¶ – KR 974	NMun
¶ – KW 8101*	NMun
– 'Unicolor'	NMun SLeo
♦ ***kingianum***	See R. ***arboreum zeylanicum***
§ ***kiusianum*** **AGM**	CWal GGGa LHyd NHol SReu WAbe
– 'Album'	GWht LHyd LMil SReu WAbe

Plant	Suppliers
§ ***kiusianum*** **AGM**	CWal GGGa LHyd NHol SReu WAbe
– 'Album'	GWht LHyd LMil SReu WAbe
– 'Benichidori'	LMil
– 'Hillier's Pink'	LMil
– 'Mountain Gem'	SReu SSta
– 'Mountain Pride'	LMil SReu
kongboense	GGGa
¶ ***konorii*** M Black (V)	GGGa
kotschyi	See R. ***myrtifolium***
kyawii	NMun SLeo
§ – Agapetum Group	NMun SLeo
lacteum	CWal LMil NMun SLeo
– SBEC 0345	GGGa
¶ – bright yellow	NMun
– forms	NMun SLeo
laetum (V)	GGGa
¶ ***lanatoïdes***	NMun
¶ – KW 5971	NMun
lanatum	CWal LHyd LMil NMun SLeo
¶ – 716652	NMun
¶ – BB 185B	NMun
¶ – C 2148	NMun
– Cooper 2148	NMun SLeo
– DF 538	MBal
– KR 873	GGGa
– dwarf cream	GGGa
– Flinckii Group	See R. ***flinckii***
lanigerum	CWal NMun SLeo
¶ – KW 6258	NMun
– KW 8251	GGGa
– 'Chapel Wood'	CWal NMun
– pink	NMun SLeo
¶ – red	NMun
– 'Round Wood'	LHyd
lapponicum Japanese	GGGa
§ ***latoucheae*** (EA)	MBal NMun SLeo
laudandum	
var. ***temoense***	CWal GGGa LMil
ledifolium 'Bulstrode'	See R. Azalea 'Bulstrode'
– 'Magnificum'	See R. Azalea 'Magnificum'
– 'Ripense'	See R. ***ripense***
lepidostylum **AGM**	CB&S CHig CWal EPot GAbr GGGa GWht LHyd LMil MBar MBri NHar NMun SCog SExb SIng SLeo SReu SSta WAbe WBod WThu
lepidotum	CGre CWal GArf GGGa GWht LHyd NMun SLeo
– FMB 279	MBal
– Elaeagnoïdes Group	GWht
§ – 'Reuthe's Purple' **AGM**	GGGa MBal NHol NMun SLeo SReu SSta WThu
– white	GGGa
§ ***leptocarpum*** C&H 420	NMun SLeo
leptothrium	CWal GGGa NMun SLeo
leucaspis	CHig CWal EPot ERea GGGa IOrc LHyd MBal NMun SCog SReu
– KW 7171	NMun SLeo
¶ ***levinei***	GGGa
liliiflorum Guiz 163	GGGa
lindleyi **AGM**	CBow CWal LMil NMun SExb SLeo
– L&S	GGGa MBal
¶ – 'Dame Edith Sitwell'	GGGa
– 'Geordie Sherriff'	GGGa
litiense	See R. ***wardii wardii*** Litiense Group
lochiae (V)	GGGa
loderi	See R. Hybrid Loderi
longesquamatum	CWal GGGa LMil NMun SLeo
¶ ***longistylum***	NMun
lopsangianum	See R. ***thomsonii l.***
lowndesii	GGGa
– x ***keiskei*** 'Yaku Fairy'	See R. Hybrid 'Yaku Fairy'
ludlowii	LMil MBal
¶ ***ludwigianum***	NMun
lukiangense	GGGa NMun SLeo
§ – R 11275*	NMun SLeo
luteiflorum	CWal LMil
– KW 21040	GGGa NMun
lutescens	CB&S CBow CGre CHig CTre CWal GWht IBlr IDai IOrc ISea LMil MBal MBri NMun SCog SExb SReu SSta WAbe WBod WWat
¶ – C 5092, 5100	GGGa NHol
– 'Bagshot Sands' **AGM**	CWal GGGa LHyd LMil NMun SPer SReu
– 'Exbury'	CWal
– pink	CWal NMun
§ ***luteum*** **AGM**	CB&S CCla CTre CWal GDra GGGa GWht ISea LKna LMil MBal MBar MBri MGos MUlv NMun SLeo SReu SSta WBod WWat
§ ***lyi***	CWal NMun SLeo
lysolepis KW 4456	GGGa
macabeanum **AGM**	CB&S CBow CHEx CWal GGGa GWht LHyd LMil MBal NMun SLeo SReu SSta
– KW 7724	NMun SLeo
– Reuthe's form	SReu
macgregoriae (V)	ERea
– P Woods 2646 (V)	GGGa
– yellow (V)	GGGa
macranthum	See R. ***indicum***
macrophyllum	GGGa LMil
§ ***macrosepalum*** (A)	SExb
§ – 'Linearifolium' (A)	CMac CTre CWal ISea LMil NMun SLeo
§ ***macrosmithii***	CWal NMun SLeo
¶ ***maculiferum***	NMun
– Guiz 120,121,148	GGGa
§ – ssp. ***anwheiense*** **AGM**	CWal GGGa LHyd LMil NMun SLeo
maddenii **AGM**	CGre CWal LHyd LMil NMun SLeo
§ – ssp. ***crassum*** **AGM**	CTrw CWal GGGa LMil MBal
§ – – Obtusifolium Group	CWal NMun SLeo
§ – ssp. ***maddenii***	CWal NMun SLeo
§ – – Polyandrum Group	CWal ISea MBal NMun SLeo
– pink	CWal
magnificum	NMun SLeo
maius Herklots	GGGa
makinoi	See R. ***yakushimanum m.***
mallotum	CWal GGGa LHyd LMil NMun SLeo
¶ – F 17853	NMun
¶ – Farrer 815	NMun
manipurense	See R. ***maddenii crassum*** Obtusifolium Group
martinianum	NMun SLeo
– KW 21557	GGGa
maximum	GGGa NMun SLeo

Plant	Suppliers
– var. ***atrokermesinum*** F 26476	NMun SLeo
– var. ***atrokermesinum*** KW 21006A	GGGa
megacalyx	CWal GGGa GWht LMil NMun SExb SLeo
megaphyllum	See R. ***basilicum***
megeratum	CWal GGGa NMun SLeo SReu
– 'Bodnant'	WAbe WBod
mekongense	GGGa NMun
§ – var. ***mekongense*** Rubroluteum Group	GGGa LMil
§ – – Viridescens Group	GGGa LMil MBal
– – Viridescens Group KW 5829	CWal NMun SLeo
– – Viridescens Group 'Doshang La'	LMil
– – 'Yellow Fellow'	LMil
§ – var. ***melinanthum***	CWal NMun SLeo
– – Semilunatum Group	LMil
– var. ***rubrolineatum***	LMil NMun SLeo
melinanthum	See R. ***mekongense melinanthum***
metternichii	See R. ***degronianum heptamerum***
micranthum	CWal GGGa LMil NMun
microgynum	NMun SLeo
– F 14242	GGGa NMun SLeo
§ – Gymnocarpum Group	CWal LMil
microleucum	See R. ***orthocladum m.***
micromeres	See R. ***leptocarpum***
¶ ***microphyton***	NMun
mimetes	LMil NMun SLeo
minus	CWal
§ – var. ***minus*** Carolinianum Group	CWal GGGa LHyd LMil
§ – – Punctatum Group	GRei MBar
mollicomum	NMun
¶ – F 10347	NMun
– F 30940	NMun SLeo
monosematum	See R. ***pachytrichum*** Monosematum Group
montroseanum	LHyd LMil NMun SLeo
* – 'Baravalla'	GGGa
– 'Benmore'	GGGa NMun
morii AGM	CWal GGGa LHyd LMil NMun SLeo
– W A 10955	NMun SLeo
§ ***moulmainense***	CWal NMun SLeo
moupinense AGM	CB&S CHig CWal ERea GGGa LHyd LMil NMun SCog SLeo SReu WBod
– pink	GGGa NMun WBod
§ ***mucronatum*** (EA)	CMCN CTre GGGa NMun SLeo SPer WBod
– var. ***ripense*** (EA)	GWht
mucronulatum	CSto GGGa LHyd LMil NMun SLeo
¶ – var. ***chejuense***	GGGa
– – 'Dwarf Cheju'	CWal
¶ – 'Cornell Pink'	NMun
– 'Crater's Edge'	LMil
– 'Winter Brightness' AGM	CWal
♦ ***myiagrum***	See R. ***callimorphum m.***
§ x ***myrtifolium***	COtt CSco GGGa LHyd NMun SLeo SPla SReu
* – 'Kotscaki'	NMun

Plant	Suppliers
nakaharae (EA)	CWal MBal NMun SCog SLeo SReu WAbe
§ – 'Mariko'	CWal EPot GGGa LHyd LMil MAsh MBal MBar MGos NHol SCog WAbe WPat WThu
– 'Mount Seven Stars'	CHig GGGa LHyd LMil NHol SCog SSta WPat
§ – orange	LMil MAsh SCog SPer SReu SSta
– pink	CHig LHyd MAsh SCog SPer SSta
– Starborough form	SSta
neriiflorum	CWal GGGa GWht ISea LMil NMun SCog SExb SLeo
– L&S 1352	GGGa
§ – ssp. ***neriiflorum*** Euchaites Group	NMun SLeo
– – Euchaites Group KW 6854	CWal
– – 'Lamellen'	CWal
¶ – – Phoenicodum Group	NMun
– – Phoenicodum Group Farrer 877	GGGa NMun
¶ – ssp. ***phaedropum***	NMun
– ssp. ***phaedropum*** C&H 422	NMun SLeo
¶ – ssp. ***phaedropum*** KR 1778	LMil
– ssp. ***phaedropum*** KW 6845*	NMun SLeo
– ssp. ***phaedropum*** KW 8521	NMun SLeo
nigroglandulosum	GGGa
nigropunctatum	See R. ***nivale boreale*** Nigropunctatum Group
♦ ***nilagiricum***	See R. ***arboreum n.***
nitens	See R. ***calostrotum riparium*** Nitens Group
¶ ***nitidulum***	NMun
– var. ***omeiense*** KR 185	GGGa LMil NHol
nivale	GArf
¶ – ssp. ***boreale***	NMun
§ – – Stictophyllum Group	GGGa LMil
¶ – ssp. ***nivale*** Sch 2269	NMun
niveum AGM	CWal GGGa LMil MBal NMun SExb SLeo SSta
– 'Nepal'	LHyd
nobleanum	See R. Hybrid Nobleanum
nudiflorum	See R. ***periclymenoïdes***
nuttallii AGM	GGGa LMil MBal
x ***obtusum*** (EA)	CHig CWal LHyd
§ – 'Macrostemon'	IDai WBod
occidentale AGM	CGre GGGa LMil MBal
– forms (A)	GGGa
oldhamii (EA)	CTre CWal NMun SLeo
oleifolium 'Penheale Pink'	See R. ***virgatum o.*** 'P.P.'
orbiculare	CWal GGGa LHyd LMil NMun SCog SLeo SSta
¶ – C&K 230	GGGa
– W V 1519	NMun SLeo
§ – ssp. ***cardiobasis***	NMun
– Sandling Park form	SReu
oreodoxa	CWal LMil NMun SExb SLeo
¶ – W A 4245	NMun
§ – var. ***fargesii*** AGM	CWal GGGa IOrc LHyd LMil NMun SLeo
§ – – Erubescens Group	CWal NMun SLeo
oreotrephes	CWal IOrc LHyd LMil MBal NMun SExb SLeo SReu

§ – – Erubescens Group	CWal NMun SLeo
oreotrephes	CWal IOrc LHyd LMil MBal NMun SExb SLeo SReu
¶ – F 20489	NMun
¶ – F 20629	NMun
¶ – KW 9509	NMun
¶ – R 96	NMun
¶ – R/USDA 59593/R11300	NMun
– 'Davidian's Favourite'	GGGa
– Exquisitum Group	SReu
– Timeteum Group	SReu
orthocladum	CWal LHyd LMil
– F 20488	GGGa NMun SLeo
§ – var. ***microleucum***	CWal GGGa LMil MBal NHar NMun SLeo WAbe
ovatum (A)	CB&S CWal NMun SExb SLeo WBod
– W A 1391	GGGa NMun SLeo
§ ***pachypodum***	GGGa LMil
pachysanthum AGM	NMun
– RV 72/001	CWal GGGa LMil NMun SLeo
– x ***morii***	GGGa
pachytrichum	GGGa NMun SLeo
¶ – W A 1203	NMun
– Monosematum Group W V 1522	CWal NMun SLeo
– Monosematum Group 'Blackhills'	GGGa
– 'Sesame'	LMil
panteumorphum	See R. x ***erythrocalyx*** Panteumorphum Group
¶ ***papillatum***	NMun
paradoxum	NMun
parmulatum	CWal LMil NMun SLeo
– KW 5875	NHol NMun
– mauve	CWal NMun
– 'Ocelot'	CWal GGGa LHyd
– pink	GGGa NHol NMun
patulum	See R. ***pemakoense*** Patulum Group
pemakoense	CMHG CSam CWal EPot GGGa GWht IDai LHyd LMil MBal MBar MGos NKay NMun SExb SIng SLeo SReu WAbe WBod WThu
§ – Patulum Group	GGGa GPlt MBar NHol NMun SLeo WPat
pendulum	GGGa LMil
¶ – LS&T 6660	NMun
pennivenium	See R. ***tanastylum p.***
pentaphyllum (A)	CWal
♦***peramoenum***	See R. ***arboreum delavayi p.***
peregrinum	NMun SLeo
– 'Wilson'	CWal
§ ***periclymenoïdes*** (A)	GGGa LMil
♦***phaedropum***	See R. ***neriiflorum p.***
phaeochrysum	CWal GGGa NMun SLeo
¶ – R/USDA 59929/R11325	NMun
¶ – var. ***agglutinatum***	GGGa NMun
– var. ***agglutinatum*** EGM 134	LMil
– Glendoick form	GGGa
§ – var. ***levistratum***	CWal NMun
– var. ***levistratum*** EGM 143	LMil
– McLaren cup winner	NMun SLeo
¶ – var. ***phaeochrysum***	GGGa
– var. ***phaeochrysum*** EGM 129	LMil
¶ – – 'Greenmantle'	NMun
♦***phoenicodum***	See R. ***neriiflorum*** P. Group
pholidotum	See R. ***heliolepis brevistylum*** Pholidotum Group
§ ***piercei***	GGGa LMil NMun SLeo
– KW 11040	NMun SLeo
pingianum	NMun
¶ – KR 150	NMun
planetum	NMun SLeo
¶ ***pleistanthum***	NMun
¶ – R 11288*	NMun
pocophorum	CWal GGGa LHyd NMun SLeo
¶ – KW 21075	NMun
¶ – R/USDA 59190/R11201	NMun
– forms	NMun SLeo
§ – var. ***hemidartum***	GGGa NMun SExb SLeo
¶ – var. ***hemidartum*** R/USDA 59190/R11201	NMun
pogonostylum	See R. ***irroratum p.***
polyandrum	See R. ***maddenii maddenii*** Polyandrum Group
§ ***polycladum***	CSam EPot GGGa GWht LHyd LMil MBal MLea
– Scintillans Group AGM	GDra MBar MBri MLea NHol NMun SLeo WAbe WThu
polylepis	GGGa NMun SLeo
ponticum	CKin CWal GGGa IDai ISea LHyd MBar MGos MMor SExb SPer
– (Azalea)	See R. ***luteum***
– AC&H 205	GGGa
– 'Cheiranthifolium'	CAbb CWal NMun SLeo
¶ – 'Silver Edge'	LMil
– 'Variegatum'	CAbb CB&S CHig CWal EBre GGGa IOrc ISea LBre MBal MBar MBri MGos MMor MUlv NMun SPer SReu SSta WThu
poukhanense	See R. ***yedoense p.***
♦***praecox***	See R. Hybrid 'Praecox'
praestans	CWal GGGa LMil NMun SLeo
¶ – KW 13369	NMun
praeteritium	NMun SLeo
praevernum	CWal GGGa GWht NMun SReu
prattii	See R. ***faberi p.***
preptum	CWal GGGa NMun SLeo
primuliflorum	CWal GGGa LMil
¶ – KW 4160	NMun
– Cephalanthoïdes Group	GGGa
¶ – 'Doker-La'	LMil
principis	GGGa LMil NMun
¶ – LS&E 15831	NMun
– Vellereum Group	CWal NMun SLeo
prinophyllum	See R. ***austrinum***
pronum	GGGa NMun
¶ – R 151*	NMun
♦***prostigiatum***	See R. Hybrid 'Prostigiatum'
prostratum	See R. ***saluenense chameunum*** Prostratum Group
proteoïdes	GGGa
¶ – R 151	NMun
protistum	NMun SLeo
¶ – KR 1986	GGGa
¶ – KW 8069	NMun
§ – var. ***giganteum***	CWal NMun SLeo

przewalskii	GGGa NMun SLeo
– CH&M 2545	LMil
– Cox 2545	NHol
pseudochrysanthum AGM	CBow CSam CWal GGGa LHyd LMil MBal NMun SCog SExb SLeo SSta
– AM 1956 Form	CWal
pubescens	CWal LMil NMun SLeo
– 'Fine Bristles'	SReu
¶ ***pudorosum***	NMun
– L&S 2752	GGGa
pumilum	GDra GGGa MBal WAbe
punctatum	See R. ***minus minus*** Punctatum Group
purdomii	NMun SLeo
quinquefolium AGM	CWal NMun SLeo SReu
racemosum	CB&S CGre CSam CWal GWht LMil MBar NMun SLeo SSta
– 'Glendoick'	GGGa
– 'Rock Rose' AGM	GGGa LHyd LMil NMun SExb
– 'White Lace'	LHyd
– x ***tephropeplum***	MBal MBar MLea
– – ***trichocladum*** SBEC	NHol
radicans	See R. ***calostrotum keleticum*** Radicans Group
ramsdenianum	CWal NMun SLeo
ravum	See R. ***cuneatum*** Ravum Group
recurvoïdes	GGGa LHyd LMil NMun SReu SSta
– KW 7184	CWal NMun SLeo
– Keillour form	GGGa
♦ ***recurvum***	See R. ***roxieanum roxieanum***
reticulatum AGM	CWal NMun SLeo SReu SSta
– ***dilatatum***	See R. ***d.***
– 'Sea King'	LHyd
rex	CBow CWal GGGa IOrc LHyd LMil MBal NMun SLeo
§ – ssp. ***arizelum***	GGGa LMil NMun SLeo
– ssp. ***arizelum*** F 21861	CWal
– ssp. ***arizelum*** KW 20922	CWal
– – 'Brodick'	CWal
– – Rubicosum Group	NMun SLeo
§ – ssp. ***fictolacteum***	CWal GGGa LHyd LMil MBal NMun SLeo SReu
– ssp. ***fictolacteum*** R/USDA 59104/R11043	NMun SLeo
– – 'Cherry Tip' R 11395	NMun SLeo
rhabdotum	See R. ***dalhousieae rhabdotum***
rigidum	CWal LHyd LMil NMun SCog SLeo
– ***album***	CHig NMun
ripiense	See R. ***mucronatum r.***
ririei	CWal GGGa LHyd NMun
– Guiz 75	GGGa
¶ – W 5139	NMun
– W 5254A	CWal
¶ – W V 1808	NMun
♦ ***roseotinctum***	See R. ***sanguineum didymoides*** R. Group
roseum	See R. ***austrinum***
rothschildii	GGGa LMil NMun SLeo
roxieanum	CWal LMil NMun SLeo SReu
– R 25422	NMun SLeo
– R/USDA 59159/R11141	NMun SLeo
§ – var. ***cucullatum***	NMun
¶ – var. ***cucullatum*** R 10920	NMun
– var. ***cucullatum*** SBEC 0345	NMun SLeo
§ – var. ***roxieanum***	NMun
¶ – var. ***roxieanum*** F 16508	NMun
– – Oreonastes Group AGM	CWal GGGa LHyd LMil NMun SLeo SSta
– – Oreonastes Group R/USDA 59222/ R11312	GGGa NMun
– – Oreonastes Group Nymans form	SReu
rubiginosum	CBow CWal GGGa GWht IOrc ISea LHyd LMil MBal NMun SCog SLeo SReu
§ – Desquamatum Group	CWal LHyd NMun SExb SLeo
– white	LMil
rubroluteum	See R. ***mekongense m.*** Rubroluteum Group
rude	See R. ***glischrum rude***
rufum	CWal GGGa NMun SLeo
¶ – Hummel 31	NMun
– W V 1808*	NMun SLeo
rupicola	CWal GDra LMil MBal NMun
§ – var. ***chryseum***	GGGa LMil NMun SLeo
– var. ***muliense***	LMil NMun
russatum AGM	CSam CWal ESis GDra GGGa GPlt LHyd LMil MBri NMun SLeo
– blue-black	LMil
– 'Collingwood Ingram'	SCog
– 'Purple Pillow'	NHar SExb
¶ – 'Tower Court'	NMun
– Waterer form	LMil
♦ ***russotinctum***	See R. ***alutaceum r.***
saluenense	CWal GGGa LHyd LMil MBal NMun SExb
¶ – F 19479	NMun
– ssp. ***chameunum*** AGM	CWal GGGa LMil MBal NMun SLeo
– ssp. ***chameunum*** F 25560	NHol
– – Exbury form R 11005	LMil
§ – – Prostratum Group	GGGa MBal WAbe
– hairy form	NHol
sanctum (A)	GGGa NMun SLeo
sanguineum	CWal GGGa LMil NMun SLeo
§ – ssp. ***didymum***	GGGa NMun SLeo
– ssp. ***sanguineum*** var. ***cloiophorum*** F 25521	LMil
– – var. ***cloiophorum*** R 10899	NMun SLeo
– – var. ***cloiophorum*** R/USDA 59096/R 11029	NMun SLeo
– – var. ***cloiophorum*** R/USDA 59553/R 11212	NMun SLeo
– – var. ***didymoïdes*** R 10903	GGGa LMil NMun SLeo
– – var. ***didymoïdes*** Consanguineum Group	NMun SLeo
– – var. ***didymoïdes*** Consanguineum Group KW 6831	LMil

– – var. ***didymoïdes*** R10903	GGGa LMil NMun SLeo
– – var. ***didymoïdes*** Consanguineum Group	NMun SLeo
– – var. ***didymoïdes*** Consanguineum Group KW 6831	LMil
§ – – var. ***didymoïdes*** Roseotinctum Group	LMil
¶ – – var. ***didymoides*** Roseotinctum Group R/USDA 59038/R10903	NMun
– – var. ***haemaleum***	GGGa LMil NMun SLeo
– – var. ***haemaleum*** F 21732	NMun SLeo
– – var. ***haemaleum*** F 21735	NMun SLeo
– – var. ***haemaleum*** R 10893	NMun SLeo
– – var. ***haemaleum*** R/USDA 59303/R 10895	NMun SLeo
– – var. ***haemaleum*** R/USDA 59453/R 10938	NMun SLeo
– – var. ***himertum*** R 10906	LMil
santapaui (V)	GGGa
sargentianum **AGM**	CWal MLea NMun SLeo WAbe
– 'Maricee'	GGGa MBri
– 'Whitebait'	GGGa NMun
scabrifolium	NMun SLeo
– SBEC K 160	GGGa
§ – var. ***spiciferum***	CWal GGGa LMil MBal NMun SLeo WAbe
¶ ***schistocalyx*** F 17637	NMun
schlippenbachii **AGM**	CGre CMCN CWal GGGa LHyd LMil MBal MBri NMun SLeo SPer SReu SSta WAbe WWat
– 'Sid's Royal Pink' (A)	GGGa
scintillans	See R. ***polycladum***
scopulorum	LHyd LMil NMun SLeo
– KW 6354	GGGa NMun
– Magor's hardy form	CWal
scottianum	See R. ***pachypodum***
scyphocalyx	See R. ***dichroanthum s.***
searsiae	CWal GGGa LMil NMun SExb SLeo
¶ – W A 1343	NMun
seinghkuense KW 9254	GGGa
selense	CWal NMun
– ssp. ***dasycladum***	LMil NMun SLeo
¶ – ssp. ***dasycladum*** F 11312	NMun
¶ – ssp. ***dasycladum*** KW 7189	NMun
¶ – ssp. ***dasycladum*** R 11269	NMun
– ssp. ***jucundum***	GGGa LMil NMun
– ssp. ***selense*** Probum Group	CWal
§ – ssp. ***setiferum***	CWal NMun
– ssp. ***setiferum*** F 14458	NMun SLeo
semnoïdes	CWal GGGa GWht LMil NMun SLeo

¶ – F 21870	NMun
¶ – F 25639	NMun
¶ – R 25388	NMun
serotinum	CWal NMun SLeo SReu
serpyllifolium (A)	CB&S CWal NMun SLeo
– ***albiflorum***	GAri
♦ ***setiferum***	See R. ***selense setiferum***
setosum	GGGa GWht LMil MBal NMun SLeo
shepherdii	See R. ***kendrickii***
sherriffii	CWal GGGa LHyd NMun SLeo
– AM 1966 Form	CWal
¶ – L&S 2751	NMun
shweliense	GGGa LMil SReu
sidereum	CWal GGGa NMun SLeo
– KW 13649	NMun SLeo
¶ – KW 6792	NMun
siderophyllum	GGGa NMun
¶ ***sikangense***	NMun
– EGM 108	GGGa LMil
¶ – R 18142	NMun
simiarum	CWal GGGa
simsii (EA)	CMac CWal
¶ ***simulans***	NMun
¶ – F 20428	NMun
¶ ***sinofalconeri*** KR 1992	GGGa
sinogrande **AGM**	CB&S CHEx CWal GGGa IOrc LMil MBal NMun SArc SLeo
– KW 21111	NMun SLeo
smirnowii	CWal GGGa LHyd LMil MBal NMun SLeo SSta
smithii	See R. ***macrosmithii***
– Argipeplum Group	See R. ***argipeplum***
souliei	CWal GGGa IOrc LHyd LMil NMun SLeo
– white	GGGa NMun
sperabile	CWal LMil NMun SExb
– F 26446	NMun SLeo
– F 26453	NMun SLeo
– var. ***weihsiense***	GGGa NMun SLeo
sperabiloïdes	GGGa NMun
¶ – R 125	NMun
sphaeranthum	See R. ***trichostomum***
sphaeroblastum	CWal GGGa LMil NMun SLeo
¶ – F 17110	NMun
– F 20416	NMun SLeo
♦ ***spiciferum***	See R. ***scabrifolium spiciferum***
spilotum	GGGa NMun SLeo
spinuliferum	CWal GGGa GWht LHyd NMun SLeo
– 'Jack Hext'	CWal
¶ ***stamineum***	NMun
– W V 887	NMun SLeo
stenaulum	See R. ***moulmainense***
stewartianum	CWal GGGa NMun SLeo
¶ – CLD 1300	LMil
¶ – F 26921	NMun
stictophyllum	See R. ***nivale boreale*** Stictophyllum Group
strigillosum	CWal GGGa NMun SLeo
– Reuthe's form	SReu
subansiriense C&H 418	CWal GGGa NMun SLeo
♦ ***suberosum***	See R. ***yunnanense*** S. Group
succothii	CWal GGGa LHyd NMun SLeo
¶ – BB 185A	NMun
– EGM 086	LMil
¶ – KW 13666	NMun

¶ ***superbum*** (V)	GGGa NMun
sutchuenense	CB&S CWal GGGa LMil NMun SLeo
§ – var. ***geraldii***	See R. x ***geraldii***
taggianum	CWal
– 'Cliff Hanger'	LMil
– Headfortianum Group	LMil
* ***taiwanense***	GGGa
taliense	CWal GGGa LHyd LMil NMun SLeo
– F 6772	NMun SLeo
– SBEC 0350	GGGa
♦ ***tamaense***	See R. ***cinnabarinum t.***
tapetiforme	NMun
tashiroi (EA)	CWal NMun
tatsienense	GGGa LMil
¶ ***telmateium***	NMun
telopeum	See R. ***campylocarpum caloxanthum*** Telopeum Group
¶ ***temenium*** F 21809	NMun
¶ – R 101	NMun
– R 10909	NMun SLeo
¶ – var. ***dealbatum***	LMil
– – Glaphyrum Group F 21902	NMun SLeo
¶ – var. ***gilvum*** R 22271	NMun
– – 'Cruachan' R 22272	GGGa LMil NMun SLeo
– var. ***temenium*** F 21734	NMun SLeo
– x ***eclecteum***	GGGa
tephropeplum AGM	CB&S CWal NMun SLeo
– KW 6303	NMun SLeo
– R/USDA 03914	GGGa
thayerianum	CWal GGGa LMil NMun
thomsonii	CWal GGGa LHyd LMil NMun SLeo SPer
– BL&M 153	MBal
– DF 540	MBal
¶ – LS&H 1949*	NMun
– L&S 2847	GGGa NMun
– 'Balbirnie'	GGGa
♦ – var. ***candelabrum***	See R. x ***candelabrum***
§ – ssp. ***lopsangianum*** LS&T 6561	CWal NMun SLeo
¶ – ssp. ***thomsonii*** BL&M 228	NMun
thymifolium	GGGa
tosaense 'Ralph Clarke' (EA)	NMun SLeo
traillianum	CBow CWal GGGa LMil NMun SLeo
– F 5881*	NMun SLeo
§ – var. ***dictyotum***	NMun
¶ – – Katmandu	NMun
trichanthum	CHig CWal GGGa IOrc LMil NMun SLeo
– W 1342	GGGa
– 'Honey Wood'	LHyd
trichocladum	CWal LMil NMun SLeo
– KW 21079	GGGa
§ ***trichostomum*** AGM	GGGa MLea NMun WAbe
¶ – KW 4465	NMun
– Radinum Group	CWal SSta
trichostomum Ledoïdes Group	CWal LMil NMun SLeo SReu
– – 'Collingwood Ingram'	LMil
triflorum	CWal GGGa GWht IOrc LMil MBal NMun SLeo WThu
– var. ***bauhiniiflorum***	CWal LMil NMun SLeo
– var. ***triflorum*** Mahogani Group	NMun SLeo
♦ ***triplonaevium***	See R. ***alutaceum russotinctum*** T. Group
♦ ***tritifolium***	See R. ***alutaceum russotinctum*** T. Group
tsangpoense	See R. ***charitopes t.***
tsariense	GGGa NMun
¶ – L&S 2766	NMun
– forms	NMun SLeo
¶ – ***magnum***	NMun
– var. ***trimoense***	GGGa NMun
– 'Yum Yum'	CWal NMun SLeo
tubiforme	See R. ***glaucophyllum t.***
ungernii	GGGa NMun
uniflorum	CWal GGGa LMil NMun WThu
– KW 5876	NMun SLeo
§ – var. ***imperator***	GGGa LMil
uvariifolium	CWal GGGa NMun SLeo
¶ – R/USDA 59623/R11391	NMun
– Griseum Group LS&E 15817	GGGa
– 'Reginald Childs'	CWal LMil
– 'Yangtze Bend'	CWal GGGa NMun
valentinianum	CB&S CSam CWal GGGa MBal NMun SLeo
– F 24347	NMun SLeo SReu
vaseyi AGM	GGGa LHyd LMil MBal
veitchianum AGM	GGGa
§ – Cubitii Group AGM	CWal GGGa NMun SLeo
– Cubitii Group Ashcombe	CWal LHyd
vellereum	See R. ***principis*** Vellereum Group
venator	CWal GGGa NMun SLeo
vernicosum	CWal GGGa GWht LMil NMun SLeo
– F 5881	NMun SLeo
¶ – McLaren T 71	NMun
¶ – Yu 13961	NMun
¶ – Yu 14694	NMun
verruculosum	SLeo
vesiculiferum	NMun SLeo
vialii (A)	GGGa
virgatum	CWal NMun
– ssp. ***oleifolium*** KW 6279	NMun SLeo
viridescens	See R. ***mekongense mekongense*** Viridescens Group
viscidifolium	GGGa NMun
viscosum AGM	CWal GGGa LHyd LKna LMil
– ***aemulans*** (A)	LMil SReu
– 'Antilope'	See R. Azalea 'Antilope'
– 'Arpege'	See R. Azalea 'A.'
¶ – var. ***montanum*** (A)	IBlr
– f. ***rhodanthum*** (A)	LMil
wallichii	CGre GGGa GWht LHyd
¶ – KR 813	NMun
¶ – KR 882	NMun
– LS&H 17527	CWal NMun SLeo
¶ ***walongense***	NMun
– C&H 373	GGGa
wardii	CWal IOrc LHyd LMil MBal MLea NMun SLeo SPer

¶ ***walongense*** NMun
– C&H 373 GGGa
wardii CWal IOrc LHyd LMil MBal MLea NMun SLeo SPer
¶ – LS&T 6591 NMun
¶ – SHEG 5672 NMun
– L&S form * CWal GGGa NMun SLeo SReu
– var. ***puralbum*** CWal GGGa NMun
¶ – var. ***puralbum*** F 10616 NMun
¶ – var. ***puralbum*** Yu 14757 NMun
¶ – var. ***wardii*** F 21551 NMun
– var. ***wardii*** KW 4170 GGGa
¶ – var. ***wardii*** KW 5736 NMun
¶ – var. ***wardii*** LS&E 15764 NMun
¶ – var. ***wardii*** LS&T 5679 NMun
¶ – var. ***wardii*** LS&T 5686 NMun
¶ – var. ***wardii*** R 18333 NMun
¶ – var. ***wardii*** R 25391 NMun
§ – – Litiense Group CWal NMun SLeo
– yellow GGGa
wasonii CWal GGGa LHyd NMun
¶ – McLaren AD 106 NMun
– f. ***rhododactylum*** GGGa NMun SLeo
– white NMun SLeo
watsonii GGGa NMun SLeo
¶ – CC&H 3939 GGGa
– EGM 109 LMil
websterianum EGM 146 LMil
weyrichii (A) CWal
wightii CWal GArf GGGa NMun SLeo
– BM&W 153 MBal
– DF 542 MBal
– KR 877 LMil
williamsianum AGM CB&S CHig CSam CWal EPot GGGa IDai ISea LHyd LMil MBal MBar MGos MLea NHol NKay NMun SCog SExb SLeo SPer SReu WAbe WBod WThu
– Caerhays form CWal MPla
¶ – pink WWat
– 'Special' GGGa
– white CWal GGGa MBal NMun SLeo WWat
wilsoniae See R. ***latoucheae***
wiltonii CWal GGGa LMil NMun SExb
wongii CSam CWal GGGa LMil NMun
xanthocodon See R. ***cinnabarium x.***
xanthostephanum CWal NMun
yakushimanum CB&S CBow CCla CSam GGGa IOrc LKna LMil MBar MBri MGos NBar NMun SCog SPer SReu SSta WAbe
I – 'Angel' SCog SPer
I – 'Beefeater' SCog
– 'Edelweiss' GGGa
– Exbury form SReu
– FCC form MUlv SReu
§ – 'Koichiro Wada' AGM CWal GGGa LHyd MBal MGos NHol NMun SLeo WThu
§ – ssp. ***makinoi*** AGM CHig CWal GGGa LHyd LMil NHol NMun SExb SLeo SReu SSta
– 'Snow Mountain' SReu
I – 'Torch' SCog
– Tremeer tall form CWal
– ssp. ***yakushimanum*** 'Ken Janeck' GGGa LMil
yungningense CWal LMil NMun
¶ – F 29268 NMun
yunnanense CBow CWal EHar GGGa GWht IDai IOrc ISea LHyd LMil NMun SCog SLeo
– 'Diana Colville' CWal NMun
– Hormophorum Group CWal
– 'Openwood' AGM LMil
– pink GGGa
– selected form SReu
– 'Tower Court' CWal
– white CBow GGGa SCog
zaleucum GWht
– F 15688 GGGa
– F 27603 NMun SLeo
– Flaviflorum Group KW 20837 NMun SLeo
♦***zeylanicum*** See R. ***arboreum z.***

RHODOHYPOXIS (Hypoxidaceae)

'Albrighton' CAvo CBro CRiv ELan EPot LAma NHar NHol NKay SBla SGil SHer WAbe WChr WThu
'Appleblossom' CAvo EWes NHar NMen SIng WAbe
baurii AGM CAvo CCla CElw CMHG CNic CRDP CRiv CWGN ELan EPad EPot IDai MFos MHig MTho NHar NKay NNrd NTow SGil SHer WCru WThu WWin
– 'Alba' CBro CCla CRDP WCru
– var. ***baurii*** EPot NHar
– var. ***confecta*** EPot
– 'Dulcie' EPot NHar NTow SWas WAbe
– forms WHil
– 'Pinkeen' EPot WAbe
– 'Susan Garnett-Botfield' CRiv EPot NHar NMen WAbe WChr
baurii var. ***platypetala*** CRDP CRiv EPot NHar NHol NMen WAbe
¶ – var. ***platypetala*** x ***milloïdes*** Burtt 6981 NHar
*– x ***parousia*** EWes
'Betsy Carmine' NHar WChr
'Dawn' CAvo CRiv EPot EWes LAma NHar NHol SBla SGil SHer WAbe WChr
¶ ***deflexa*** WChr
'Douglas' CRDP CRiv EPot LAma NHar NHol SGil SHer WPat
'Dusky' EPot
'E A Bowles' WAbe
'Emily Peel' EPot WAbe WChr
'Eva-Kate' CAvo EPot LAma NHar NHol SBla SGil WAbe WChr
'Fred Broome' CBro CCla CRiv ELan EPot EWes LAma NHar NHol NTow SBla SGil SHer WAbe WChr WPat
'Garnett' EPot NHol NKay NMen SBla
'Great Scott' EPot EWes NHar WChr
'Harlequin' CBro ELan EPot EWes LAma NHar NHol SBla SGil SHer WChr
'Helen' EPot NHar NHol SBla SHer WAbe WChr
hybrids ELan LBow
'Knockdolian Red' NHol
'Margaret Rose' NHar SWas WAbe WChr

milloïdes	CRDP EPot EWes NHar NMen SBla WAbe WChr
¶ – pink	WChr
I – 'Super Milloïdes'	WChr
'Monty'	EPot WAbe WChr
¶ 'New Look'	NHar WChr
'Perle'	EPot NHar NMen WAbe WChr
'Picta'	CAvo CRiv CSam EPot LAma NHar NHol SBla SGil WAbe WChr
'Pink Pearl'	EPot EWes NHol
¶ 'Pinkeen'	EWes NHar WChr
'Ruth'	EPot EWes LAma NHar NHol SBla SGil WAbe WChr
'Shell Pink'	NKay SBla
'Stella'	CAvo CRiv EPot EWes NHol SBla WAbe
'Tetra Pink'	SHer WAbe WChr
'Tetra Red'	EPot NHar NHol SHer WAbe WChr
'Tetra White'	See R. 'Helen'
thodiana	CAvo EPot

RHODOHYPOXIS X HYPOXIS (Hypoxidaceae)

–	See also HYPOXIS X RHODOHYPOXIS
¶ *baurii* x *parvula*	
Burtt 7376	NHar
¶ – – JJ's pink	NHar

RHODOPHIALA (Liliaceae/Amaryllidaceae)

¶ *advena*	WChr
§ *bifida*	CMon LBow WChr
*– *spathacea*	CMon

RHODORA See **RHODODENDRON**

RHODOTHAMNUS (Ericaceae)

chamacistus	WCru

RHODOTYPOS (Rosaceae)

kerrioïdes	See R. ***scandens***
§ *scandens*	CB&S CBot CChu CMHG CPle EWri MPla NHol NTow SPla WBod WCru WWin

RHOEO See **TRADESCANTIA**

RHOICISSUS (Vitaceae)

See Plant Deletions

RHOPALOBLASTE (Palmae/Arecaceae)

See Plant Deletions

RHOPALOSTYLIS (Palmae/Arecaceae)

baueri	CTbh LPal NPal
sapida	CHEx ECou LPal NPal

RHUBARB See **RHEUM** x ***hybridum***

RHUS † (Anacardiaceae)

aromatica	LRHS MBel NHol WCoo
copallina	CMHG ELan SHil WPat
cotinus	See COTINUS ***coggygria***
glabra	CArn CB&S CDoC IJoh MBlu SPer SSta
– 'Laciniata' AGM	CBow CCla CDoC CSco MAsh MBlu MBri MGos SHBN SMad SPer WPat
N *hirta* AGM	CB&S CLnd EBre ECtt ELan ENot GPoy IDai IJoh IOrc ISea LBre MBar MBri MGos MWat NNor SHBN SPer SReu SSta WAbe WDin WStI WTyr WWin
– 'Laciniata' AGM	CB&S CBra CLnd CSco ELan ENot GRei IJoh IOrc MBar MBri MWat NBee NKay NWyt SPer WAbe WDin WPat WTyr
integrifolia	CArn
pendulina	CGre
potaninii	WWat
punjabensis	CB&S
§ *radicans*	GPoy
succedanea	LRHS
toxicodendron	See R. ***radicans***
trichocarpa	CAbP CMHG CPle ELan SHil
trilobata	CFil EMon
typhina	See R. ***hirta***
verniciflua	CLnd

RHYNCHELYTRUM See **MELINIS**

RIBES † (Grossulariaceae)

alpinum	CBow ELan ENot ESis GRei IOrc NSti NWea SPer SPla WDin
– 'Aureum'	CCla CMHG EBre EFol ELan ISea LBre MHig MPla NNor WDin WSHC
¶ *americanum*	EPla
– 'Variegatum'	EFol ELan EPla EWri LHop NHol SDry SFai SMad WPat
atrosanguineum	See R. ***sanguineum*** 'Atrorubens'
aureum hort.	See R. ***odoratum***
F x *culverwellii* Jostaberry	GTwe LBuc WHig
F *divaricatum*	
Worcesterberry	CMac CWSG GChr IJoh MBri MGos MMor NBar NRog SDea SPer WHig WStI
fasciculatum	
var. *chinense*	EMon EPla
gayanum	CGre CPle LHop SPla WCru WHCG WSHC WThu
glutinosum 'Albidum'	CSco LHop SChu WWat
x *gordonianum*	CB&S CBrd CChu CGre CHan CMHG CPle CSco EHal EHar ERav LHop MBal MRav SLon WHCG WWat WWeb
grossularia	See R. ***uva-crispa***
laurifolium	CB&S CBot CChu CCla CGre CPle CSam EFol ELan EPla ERav GCal IOrc LAbb MBal SChu SHil SPer WDin WHCG WSHC WWat WWin
– 'Mrs Amy Doncaster'	EPla
magellanicum	CGre
F *nigrum* 'Amos Black'	GTwe
F – 'Baldwin'	CDoC CMac ECas EWar GBon IJoh MBea SDea SKee SPer WStI WWeb
F – 'Ben Alder'	SDea
F – 'Ben Connan'	GTwe

F – 'Ben Lomond' **AGM** CSam EBre ECas EHar EWar GBon GRei GTwe IJoh LBre LBuc MBea MBri MGos NBar NBee NElm NRog SDea SKee SPer WHig WStI WWeb
F – 'Ben Loyal' GTwe
F – 'Ben More' ECas GChr GRei GTwe LBuc MBri MGos NBar NBee SDea SKee SPer WStI
F – 'Ben Nevis' ECas GRei GTwe MBea NElm NRog SDea SKee
F – 'Ben Sarek' **AGM** CSam EBre ECas ERea GChr GTwe LBre LBuc MBri MGos NBar SDea SKee SPer WHig WWeb
F – 'Ben Tirran' CSut ECas WHig
F – 'Black Reward' MGos
F – 'Blackdown' SDea
F – 'Boşkoop Giant' CMac EWar GTwe NEgg NElm NRog SPer
F – 'Daniel's September' GTwe
F – 'Green's Black' SKee
F – 'Jet' ECas GTwe SDea SKee WHig
F – 'Laxton's Giant' GTwe SDea
F – 'Loch Ness' **AGM** NBar
F – 'Malling Jet' EHar NElm NRog
F – 'Mendip Cross' GTwe NRog
F – 'Seabrook's' EWar WHig
F – 'Wellington XXX' ECas EHar ERea ESha EWar GTwe IJoh LBuc MBea MBri NBar NBee NEgg NRog SDea SKee SPer WStI WTyr WWeb
F – 'Westwick Choice' GTwe
§ ***odoratum*** CB&S CBow CMHG CPMA CPle CSam CSco ECoo ELan ENot EPla ERav GRei LAbb MBar MGos MPla NHol NWea SHBN SLon SPer WHCG WStI WWat WWin
praecox CB&S
F ***rubrum*** Pink Currant Group 'Hollande Rose' GTwe
F – – 'October Currant' GTwe
F – Red Currant Group 'Fay's New Prolific' GTwe
F – – 'Jonkheer van Tets' **AGM** ECas GRei IJoh MGos SDea SKee
F – – 'Junifer' ECas
F – – 'Laxton Number One' CMac CSam EBre ECas EHar ESha GBon GChr LBre MBea MBri NBar NElm NRog SDea SKee SPer WHig
F – – 'Raby Castle' GTwe
F – – 'Red Lake' **AGM** CB&S CMac EBre ERea GBon GRei LBre LBuc MBea MBri MGos NBee NEgg NElm NRog SDea SKee SPer WStI
F – – 'Redstart' ECas LBuc MBri NBar SDea SKee WHig
F – – 'Rondom' SDea
F – – 'Rovada' ECas
F – – 'Stanza' **AGM** CSut SDea
F – – 'Wilson's Long Bunch' GTwe
F – White Currant Group 'Versailles Blanche' ('White Versailles') CDoC CMac CSam ECas GTwe LBuc MBea MBri MGos NBar NBee SDea SKee SPer WHig WWeb
F – – 'White Grape' **AGM** GTwe NElm NRog
F – – 'White Pearl' CB&S GRei IJoh
F – – 'White Transparent' GTwe
sanguineum CLTr CPle CSam ISea LBuc MBal MBar NNor WStI WWin
– 'Albescens' EHar SPer
– 'Brocklebankii' **AGM** CAbP CCla CSco ECtt EHar ENot EPar EPla EWri LHop MBar MGos MPla NHol SHBN SLon SPer SPla WAbe WSHC WWat
– double MBlu MUlv
– 'Giant White' EPla
– 'King Edward VII' CBow CDoC CSco ECtt IJoh MBar MBri MGos MWat NBee NNor NRoo NWea SHBN SHer SMad SPer SPla SReu WDin WStI WWeb
¶ – 'Koja' LRHS
– 'Lombartsii' CShe SLon
– 'Pulborough Scarlet' **AGM** CB&S CBow CChe CDoC CLTr CSco CShe EFol ELan ENot MBri MGos MPla MRav MWat NKay SPla WAbe WBod WWeb
– 'Pulborough Scarlet Variegated' CPMA EPla LHop MUlv SDry SFai
– 'Red Pimpernel' MAsh
– ***roseum*** See R. *s.* 'Carneum'
– 'Splendens' GRei IDai
– 'Tydeman's White' **AGM** CChe CCla EBre ECtt LBre MBar WDin
– 'White Icicle' CCla MAsh
speciosum **AGM** Widely available
tenue EPla
F ***uva-crispa*** var. ***reclinatum*** 'Achilles' (C/D) GTwe
F – – 'Admiral Beattie' GTwe NRog
F – – 'Alma' (D) NRog
F – – 'Annelii' SDea
– – 'Aston Red' See R. *u-c. r.* 'Warrington'
F – – 'Australia' NRog
F – – 'Bedford Red' (D) GTwe NRog
F – – 'Bedford Yellow' (D) GTwe
F – – 'Beech Tree Nestling' GTwe
F – – 'Bellona' (C) NRog
F – – 'Black Velvet' CMac MBea MBri NBar SPer
F – – 'Blucher' NRog
F – – 'Bright Venus' (D) GTwe
F – – 'Broom Girl' (D) GTwe NRog
F – – 'Captivator' CSam GTwe SDea
F – – 'Careless' **AGM** CDoC CMac CSam ECas EHar ERea ESha EWar GBon GTwe IOrc MBea MBri MGos NBee NElm NRog SDea SKee SPer WTyr WWeb
F – – 'Catherina' SDea
F – – 'Champagne Red' GTwe
F – – 'Clayton' NRog
F – – 'Cook's Eagle' (C) GTwe
F – – 'Cousen's Seedling' GTwe

F-- 'Criterion' (C) GTwe NRog
F-- 'Crown Bob' (C/D) GTwe NRog
F-- 'Dan's Mistake' (D) GTwe NRog
F-- 'Drill' GTwe
F-- 'Early Sulphur' (D) GRei GTwe IJoh NRog SDea SKee WStI
F-- 'Edith Cavell' GTwe
F-- 'Firbob' (D) GTwe NRog
F-- 'Forester' (D) GTwe
F-- 'Freedom' (C) GTwe NRog
F-- 'Gipsey Queen' GTwe
F-- 'Glenton Green' GTwe
F-- 'Golden Ball' (D) SDea
F-- 'Golden Drop' (D) GTwe
-- 'Green Gascoigne' (D) See R. ***u-c. r.*** 'Early Green Hairy'
F-- 'Green Gem' (C/D) GTwe NRog
F-- 'Green Ocean' GTwe NRog
F-- 'Greenfinch' GTwe
F-- 'Greengage' (D) NRog
F-- 'Gretna Green' GTwe
F-- 'Guido' GTwe NRog
F-- 'Gunner' (D) GTwe NRog
F-- 'Heart of Oak' GTwe NRog
F-- 'Hebburn Prolific' (D) GTwe
F-- 'Hedgehog' (D) GTwe
F-- 'Hero of the Nile' (C) GTwe NRog
F-- 'High Sheriff' (D) GTwe
F-- 'Hinnonmäki Röd' SDea
F-- 'Howard's Lancer' (C/D) GTwe NRog SDea SKee
F-- 'Invicta' **AGM** CDoC CMac CWSG EBre ECas EWar GBon GChr GRei IJoh LBre LBuc MBea MBri MGos SDea SKee SPer WHig WStI WWeb
F-- 'Ironmonger' GTwe
F-- 'Jubilee' LBuc MBri MGos NBar NRog SKee
F-- 'Keen's Seedling' (D) GTwe
F-- 'Keepsake' (C/D) GTwe NRog
F-- 'King of Trumps' GTwe NRog
F-- 'Lancashire Lad' (C/D) GTwe NRog
F-- 'Langley Gage' (D) GTwe NRog
F-- 'Laxton's Amber' (D) GTwe
F-- 'Leveller' **AGM** CDoC CMac CSut EBre ECas EHar EWar GBon GTwe LBre LBuc MBea MBri MGos NBar NElm NRog SDea SKee SPer WStI WWeb
F-- 'London' (C/D) GTwe NRog
F-- 'Lord Derby' (C/D) GTwe MBri NRog
F-- 'Lord Kitchener' NRog
F-- 'Macherauch's Seedling' NRog
F-- 'Marigold' NRog
F-- 'Matchless' (D) NRog
F-- 'May Duke' (C/D) IJoh NRog SDea
F-- 'Mitre' (C) GTwe
F-- 'Pitmaston Green Gage' (D) GTwe
F-- 'Plunder' NRog
F-- 'Prince Charles' GTwe
F-- 'Queen of Hearts' NRog
F-- 'Queen of Trumps' (C) GTwe NRog
F-- 'Red Rough' (D) GTwe
F-- 'Rifleman' (D) GTwe
F-- 'Roseberry' (D) GTwe
F-- 'Scottish Chieftan' (D) GTwe
F-- 'Sir George Brown' (D) NRog
F-- 'Snowdrop' (C) GTwe
F-- 'Speedwell' NRog
F-- 'Spinefree' GTwe
F-- 'Sultan Juror' NRog
F-- 'Surprise' (C) GTwe NRog
F-- 'Suter Johnny' NRog
F-- 'Telegraph' GTwe
F-- 'The Leader' NRog
F-- 'Tom Joiner' GTwe
F-- 'Trumpeter' (C) NRog
F-- 'Victoria' GTwe NRog
F-- 'Warrington' (D) GTwe NRog
F-- 'Whinham's Industry' **AGM** CDoC CMac CSam CSut ECas EHar ERea EWar GBon GRei GTwe IJoh IOrc LBuc MBri MGos NBee NEgg NElm NRog SDea SKee SPer WHig WStI
F-- 'White Eagle' (C) NRog
F-- 'White Lion' (C/D) GTwe NRog
F-- 'White Transparent' (C) GTwe
F-- 'Whitesmith' (C/D) ECas GTwe IJoh LBuc NEgg NRog SDea SKee WHig
F-- 'Woodpecker' GTwe NRog
F-- 'Yellow Champagne' GTwe NRog
viburnifolium CGre CHan CMHG CPle NTow

RICHEA (Epacridaceae)

dracophylla SArc
scoparia SArc

RICINUS (Euphorbiaceae)

See Plant Deletions

RIGIDELLA (Iridaceae)

See Plant Deletions

RIVINA (Phytolaccaceae)

¶ ***humilis*** CTro

ROBINIA † (Leguminosae/Papilionaceae)

x ***ambigua*** 'Bella Rosea' MUlv
fertilis 'Monument' WDin
hispida **AGM** CBot CBow CCla CSco ELan ENot LNet MBlu MUlv SHBN WDin WSHC
- 'Macrophylla' SHil
N- 'Rosea' CB&S CBot SPer WRus
kelseyi CSco IOrc MUlv SPer
luxurians CB&S

x *margaretta* 'Pink Cascade' ('Casque Rouge')	CBow CCla CDoC CSPN CSco EHar EMil LNet LPan MBri MGos MMea SChu SHBN SHer SPer WDin
neomexicana	CLnd
pseudoacacia AGM	CB&S CHEx CLnd CPer ELan ENot GAri LPan WDin WFox WNor
– 'Bessoniana'	CBow CLnd CTho EMil ENot SPer
– 'Fastigiata'	See R. *p.* 'Pyramidalis'
– 'Frisia' AGM	CB&S CBra CCla CHEx CLnd CSam CSco CTho EBre EHar ELan EMil ENot IOrc LBre LNet MBal MBri MGos NBar SHBN SHer SPer SPla SReu SSta WDin WMou WWat
¶ – 'Lace Lady'	ELan
§ – 'Pyramidalis'	CBow EHar ENot
– 'Rozynskiana'	CTho
– 'Tortuosa'	CBow CBra CTho EHar ELan EMil MBri MMea SHer SMad SPer
§ – 'Umbraculifera'	EMil IJoh LPan MGos
– 'Unifoliola'	CLnd
pseudoacacia hort. 'Inermis'	See R. *p.* 'Umbraculifera'
x *slavinii* 'Hillieri' AGM	CBow CCla CLnd CPMA CSco CTho ELan IOrc SHil SPer WWat

ROCHEA See CRASSULA

RODGERSIA † (Saxifragaceae)

aesculifolia AGM	Widely available
– 'Irish Bronze'	CHad EBre IBlr LBre
¶ ***henrici***	GLil
– hybrid	LRHS MUlv NHol WCru
'Parasol'	CHad ELan NHol
pinnata	CBow CDoC CGle CHEx CHad CMGP CRow CSco CWGN EBre EFol EGol EHon ERav LBre LHil MBal MBri MSta NDea NHol NVic SBla SChu SHig SLon SPer WHoo WWat
– CLD 432	NHol
– 'Alba'	NHol
– 'Elegans'	CBow CChu CCla CHad EBre EFou ELan ELun EPar GAbr GCal GGar LBre LHop MNFA NHol NOrc SMrm SPer WWat WWin
¶ – 'Maurice Mason'	SDix
– 'Superba' AGM	CCla CHEx CHad CShe EBar EBre ECha ECtt GAbr GCal IDai LBlm LBre LGro MBal MBri MBro MUlv NBee NHar NPer NSti SBla SFis SPer WCru WHoo WKif
podophylla AGM	CB&S CChu CCla CHEx CHad CHan CHol CRDP CWGN CWit EBre ECha EFol EGol ELun GAbr LBre MNFA NBir NDea NHol SAxl SBla SDix SHig SPer WCru WEas WHer
– Donard form	IBlr WCot
– 'Rotlaub'	LRHS MBri MUlv
– 'Smaragd'	CRow EBre LBre MUlv
purdomii	CRow
sambucifolia	CB&S CChu CCla CDoC CHEx CHad CRow CShe EBre GAbr LBre MBri MFir MUlv NDea NHar NHol SFis SMrm SPer WCru WMer WPer WWat
sp. CLD 1329	EMon NHol
sp. CLD 1432	NHol
tabularis	See ASTILBOIDES ***tabularis***

ROHDEA † (Liliaceae/Convallariaceae)

japonica	SApp
– 'Talbot Manor'	CRDP SApp

ROMANZOFFIA (Hydrophyllaceae)

californica	See R. ***suksdorfii***
sitchensis	CLew CRDP EBar NRed WHoo
tracyi	WEas WThi
unalaschkensis	CNic CRiv ECro ELan GArf GTou MHig NGre NMen NTow NWCA SHer WAbe WPer

ROMNEYA (Papaveraceae)

coulteri AGM	Widely available
– var. ***trichocalyx***	CDoC CGre GMac IBlr LGre
§ – 'White Cloud'	CBow CChu CCla EHar ERea SMad SPer SReu SSta
x ***hybrida***	See R. ***coulteri*** 'White Cloud'

ROMULEA (Iridaceae)

battandieri AB&S 4659	CMon
bifrons AB&S 4359/4360	CMon
bulbocodium	CBro CMon CNic CRiv EBul EHic MHig
– var. ***clusiana***	LAma
– ***clusiana*** SF 237	CMon
– – Serotina Group	EPot
– white	EBul
campanuloïdes	CMon
columnae AB&S 4659	CMon
engleri SF 3	CMon
hirta	CMon
ligustica var. ***rouyana*** SF 360	CMon
linaresii	EPot LAma
¶ – var. ***graeca***	CNic
– var. ***graeca*** CE&H 620	CMon
longituba	See R. ***macowanii***
macowanii	MHig WAbe
– var. ***alticola***	GCLN
minutiflora	NRog
monticola	CMon
nivalis	LAma WChr WThi
pratensis	CNic WThi
ramiflora	CMon
– SF 63	CMon
¶ ***requienii***	WOMN
rosea	NRog
sabulosa	CBro
sp. SF 367	CMon
tempskyana	CMon
'Zahnii'	CMon CSam EHic LAma

ROSA † (Rosaceae)

¶ Aalsmeer Gold ® (HT)	MJon

'Abbandonata'	See R. 'Laure Davoust'
Abbeyfield Rose ® AGM	GCoc LStr SApu SJus SPer
§ 'Abbotswood' (*canina* x)	EBls
Abigaile ® (F)	MJon NBat
Abraham Darby ® (S)	CCMG CDoC CSam EBre EWar LBre LGod LStr MAus MFry MHay MJon MRui SChu SPer WAct WStI
Ace of Hearts ® (HT)	CSan MBur
¶ Acey Duecy ® (Min)	MHay
acicularis	WWat
– var. ***engelmannii***	CCor
– var. ***nipponensis***	EBls EWar
'Adam' (T/Cl)	EBls
'Adam Messerich' (Bb)	CCMG EBls ETWh MAus WHCG
'Adélaïde d'Orléans' AGM	CCMG EBls MAus SPer SRum WAct WHCG
'Admiral Rodney' (HT)	EWar MGan MHay MJon NBat NRog
Adolf Horstmann ® (HT)	MAus MGan
'Agatha' (G)	EBls
'Agatha Christie' (F/Cl)	CGre MBri MJon MMat SApu SJus
'Agathe Incarnata' (GxD)	EWar
'Agnes' (Ru)	CCMG CSan EBls EBro ENot ETWh GCoc IHos MAus MGan MMat NSty SJus SPer SPla WAct WHCG
'Aimée Vibert' (Ra)	CCMG EBls ETWh MAus SPer WAct WHCG WSHC
Air France ® (Min)	EWar
'Akebono' (HT)	MHay
'Alain Blanchard' (G)	CCor EBls MAus WHCG
N Alba Meidiland ® (GC)	EWar
x ***alba***	CBow EBls NRog WWeb
§ – 'Alba Maxima' AGM	CCMG CCla CCor CHad CSan EBls ENot ETWh EWar GCoc MAus MMat NSty SFam SPer WAct WHCG
– 'Alba Semiplena' AGM	CBow CCMG EBls EMFP ETWh EWar MAus NSty SJus SPer WAct WHCG
'Albéric Barbier' AGM	Widely available
'Albertine' AGM	Widely available
'Alchymist' (S/Cl)	CCMG CCor CHad CNat EBls EBro ETWh MAus MBri MMat SPer SPla WAct WHCG WSHC
Alec's Red ® (HT)	CB&S CCMG CDoC CGro CSan EBls ESha EWar GCoc IHos IJoh LPlm LStr MAus MBri MGan MHay MJon MMat MMor NBar NElm NRog SApu SPer WWeb
Alec's Red, Climbing ® (HT/Cl)	SPer
'Alexander Von Humbolt' (Cl)	MGan
Alexander ® AGM	CDoC CGro CSan EBls ESha EWar GCoc IHos IJoh LGod LPlm LStr MAus MFry MGan MHay MJon MMat MMor NBar NElm NRog SApu SPer WWar
Alexandra Rose ® (S)	MRui
'Alexandre Girault' (Ra)	CCMG CCor EBls EBro EMFP ETWh MAus SPer WHCG WHow
'Alfred Colomb' (HP)	EBls
'Alfred de Dalmas' misapplied	See R. 'Mousseline'
'Alida Lovett' (Ra)	EBls MAus
§ 'Alister Stella Gray' (N)	CCMG EBls EMFP ETWh MAus MGan SFam SPer WAct WHCG WSHC
All in One ®	See R. 'Exploit'
'Allen Chandler' (HT/Cl)	EBls MAus NSty
Allgold ® (F)	CB&S CGro EBls LStr MAus MGan MJon MMor NBar SApu SRum WStI WWeb
'Allgold, Climbing' (F/Cl)	CBow CCMG EBls ETWh EWar GCoc GGre IHos IJoh MGan MHay SRum WWeb
'Aloha' (HT/Cl)	CB&S CCMG CCor CDoC CGro CSan EBls EBre ETWh IHos IOrc LBre MAus MBur MFry MGan MHay MJon MMat MRui NBat NRog NSty SApu SFis SJus SPer SRum WAct WHCG
alpina	See R. ***pendulina***
Alpine Sunset ® (HT)	CCMG EBls ESha EWar GCoc LStr MAus MGan NBar NElm SPer SRum
altaica hort.	See R. ***pimpinellifolia*** 'Grandiflora'
Altissimo ® AGM	CCMG CHad EBls ETWh LPln LStr MAus MBri MGan MHay MJon MMat SPer
'Amadis' (Bs)	EBls MAus WHCG
Amanda ® (F)	LStr MBri MJon SApu
'Amatsu-otome' (HT)	MHay
'Amazing Grace' (HT)	GGre
Amber Queen ® AGM	CDoC CGro CSan EBls ELan ESha EWar GCoc GGre IHos LGod LPlm LStr MAus MBri MBur MFry MGan MHay MJon MMat MMor NBar NRog SApu SJus SPer SRum WWar
'Amberlight' (F)	MAus
Ambridge Rose ® (S)	MAus MBri WWeb
'Amélia' (D)	See R. 'Celsiana'
¶ 'Amelia Louise' (Min)	MHay
'American Pillar' (Ra)	CB&S CCMG CDoC CGro CSan EBls EBre EOrc ESha ETWh EWar ISea LBre LGod LStr MAus MGan MHay MMat MMor NBar NBat NRog NSty SApu SJus SPer SRum WHCG
'Amy Robsart' (HSwb)	EBls ETWh MAus SJus
Anabell ® (F)	WWar
'Anaïs Ségalas' (G)	MAus
§ 'Andersonii' (*canina* x)	EBls ISea MAus WAct
'Andrea' (Min)	MHay
§ 'Andrewsii' (pimpinellifolia)	MAus WAct
§ 'Anemone' (Cl)	CCor EBls MAus SPer
anemoniflora	See R. x ***beanii***
anemonoïdes	See R. 'Anemone'
– 'Ramona'	See R. 'Ramona'
Angela Rippon ® (Min)	EBee EBre EWar IHos LBre MFry MGan MJon MMat MRui WStI
'Angela's Choice' (F)	MGan
'Angèle Pernet' (HT)	EBls MAus
'Angelina' (S)	EBls EWar MMat
Anisley Dickson ® AGM	EBee GCoc IDic LGod LStr MGan MHay MJon NBat SApu SPer
'Ann Aberconway' (F)	CDoC MJon MMat
'Anna de Diesbach' (HP)	EBls

Anna Ford ® **AGM**	CDoC CGro CSan EWar GGre IHos LGod LPlm LStr MAus MGan MJon NBat SApu SPer SRum WWar WWeb
Anna Livia ® (F)	EBee IHos MJon MMat SApu SJus
'Anna Olivier' (T)	EBls
'Anna Pavlova' (HT)	EBls
Anne Cocker ® (F)	CDoC EBls GCoc MGan MHay
¶ 'Anne Dakin'	MAus
Anne Harkness ® (F)	CCMG CDoC EWar LStr MAus MGan MHay MJon NBat NRog SPer WWar
Anne Moore ® (Min)	MHay
'Anne of Geierstein' (HSwB)	EBls MAus MGan
'Anne Watkins' (HT)	EBls
Antique '89 ® (F/Cl)	EBee MJon MMat SJus
'Antoine Rivoire' (HT)	EBls MAus
'Antonia d'Ormois' (G)	EBls
¶ Anusheh ® (F)	MHay
Anvil Sparks ® (HT)	MGan
Apothecary's Rose	See R. ***gallica officinalis***
'Apple Blossom' (Ra)	EBls EWar NSty WHCG
♦ 'Apricot Garnet' (Ga)	See R. 'Garnette Apricot'
'Apricot Nectar' (F)	LStr MAus MGan SPer
'Apricot Silk' (HT)	CB&S CCMG CGro EBls EWar IHos IJoh MAus MGan MHay NBar NRog SPer SRum WWeb
Apricot Sunblaze ® (Min)	CSan EBls EWar IHos MJon NElm SApu WWeb
Arcadian ® (F)	MJon MMat WWar
'Archiduc Joseph' (T)	See R. 'Général Schablikine'
'Archiduchesse Elisabeth d'Autriche' (HP)	EBls
Arctic Sunrise ® (Min/GC)	MJon MRui WWar
'Ardoisée de Lyon' (HP)	EBls
Ards Beauty ® (F)	IDic MGan MJon SApu SJus
'Ards Rover' (HP/Cl)	EBls
'Arethusa' (Ch)	CCMG EBls ETWh
'Arizona Sunset' (Min)	MHay
arkansana	CCor
§ – var. ***suffulta***	EBls WHCG
– x ***moyesii***	CCor
Armada ® (S)	GCoc MAus SApu SPer
Arnold Greensitt ® (HT)	MHay
'Arthur Bell' **AGM**	CCMG CCla CSan EBls EBre ESha EWar GGre IHos IJoh LBre LPlm LStr MAus MBur MGan MHay MMat NBar NBat NElm NRog SApu SPer SRum WWeb
'Arthur Bell, Climbing' (F/Cl)	NRog SApu SPer SRum
'Arthur de Sansal' (D/Po)	EBls MAus
'Arthur Hillier' (S)	CCor
'Arthur Scargill' (Min)	MHay
arvensis	CCor CKin EBls ETWh MAus
'Ash Wednesday' (Cl)	EBls
'Assemblage des Beautés' (G)	EBls MAus
'Astrid Späth Striped' (F)	EBls
¶ Atco Royale ® (F)	MFry
Audrey Gardner ® (Min/Patio)	SRum
Audrey Wilcox ® (HT)	MFry
'August Seebauer' (F)	EBls MAus
'Auguste Gervais' (Ra)	EBls MAus SPer SRum WHCG
'Augustine Guinoisseau' (HT)	EBls MAus
'Augustine Halem' (HT)	EBls
'Aunty Dora' (F)	EWar
Austrian Copper	See R. ***foetida*** 'Bicolor'
Austrian Yellow	See R. ***foetida***
'Autumn' (HT)	NRog
'Autumn Bouquet' (S)	EBls
'Autumn Delight' (HM)	EBls MAus WHCG
'Autumn Fire'	See R. 'Herbstfeuer'
'Autumn Sunlight' (HT/Cl)	EWar MBur MGan MHay SPer
'Autumn Sunset' (S)	EBls
'Autumnalis' (Ra)	See R. 'Princesse de Nassau'
'Aviateur Blériot' (Ra)	EBls MAus
Avocet ® (F)	MBri SApu
Avon ® (GC)	CCla EWar GCoc LGod LStr MBur MFry MJon SRum
'Awakening' (Cl)	CCMG EBls WHCG
'Ayrshire Splendens'	See R. 'Splendens'
'Baby Bio' (F)	CB&S MBri MGan NElm NRog SJus SRum
'Baby Darling' (Min)	MAus MGan MRui
'Baby Faurax' (Poly)	MAus
'Baby Gold' (Min)	LPlm
'Baby Gold Star' (Min)	MAus MGan SPer
¶ 'Baby Katie' (Min)	MHay
¶ 'Baby Love' (Patio)	MHay
Baby Masquerade ® (Min)	CGro CSan EBre ELan EWar GCoc GGre IHos LBre LGod LPlm MAus MBur MGan MJon MMat MMor MRui NBar NElm NRog SJus WStI WWeb
'Baby Princess' (Min)	MRui
Baby Sunrise ® (Min)	MJon MMat
'Bad Neuenahr' (Cl)	MGan
'Bakewell Scots Briar' (pimpinellifolia)	NSty
'Ballerina' **AGM**	Widely available
'Baltimore Belle' (Ra)	EBls EWar MAus NBrk
banksiae (Ra)	CGre SPer
– ***alba***	See R. ***b. banksiae***
§ – var. ***banksiae*** (Ra/d)	CBot CPMA EMFP ERea MAus SHil
– 'Lutea' **AGM**	CB&S CCMG CCla CFee CGre CPMA CSam EBls ELan EMFP ERea ETWh ISea LGre MAus MMat NSty SBra SHil SMad SPer SUsu WAct WBod WHCG WSHC WWat
– 'Lutescens' (Ra)	SHil
– var. ***normalis*** (Ra)	CBot MAus NSti SHil
¶ – 'Purezza'	CCor
Bantry Bay ® (HT/Cl)	CCMG CSan EBls EBro EWar LStr MGan MMat SJus SPla SRum WWeb
'Barbara Richards' (HT)	MAus
Barkarole ® (HT)	EWar LStr MJon SApu SJus WWar WWeb
'Baron de Bonstetten' (HP)	EBls
'Baron de Wassenaer' (Ce/Mo)	EBls MGan

'Baron Girod de l'Ain' (HP)	CCMG EBls EBro EMFP ETWh IHos MAus NSty SPer SPla WAct WHCG
Baron Sunblaze ®	See R. Baron Meillandina ®
'Baroness Rothschild' (HP)	See R. 'Baronne Adolph de Rothschild'
– (HT)	See R. Baronne Edmond de Rothschild ®
§ 'Baronne Adolph de Rothschild' (HP)	CCMG EMFP ETWh IHos IOrc MGan
'Baronne de Rothschild' (HP)	See R. 'Baronne Adolph de Rothschild'
Baronne Edmond de Rothchild ® (HT)	CSan EWar
'Baronne Henriette de Snoy' (T)	EBls
'Baronne Prévost' **AGM**	EBls MAus SFam WAct WHCG
'Bashful' (Poly)	MGan
Basildon Bond ® (HT)	MJon
'Beauté' (HT)	EBls MAus MGan NElm
Beautiful Britain ® (F)	CSan EBls GCoc GGre IDic IHos LGod LStr MAus MBri MGan MJon NBar NRog SJus SRum WWar
'Beauty of Rosemawr' (T/Cl)	EBls
Belfast Belle ® (HT)	IDic WWar
'Belle Amour' (D x A)	EBls MAus NSty WHCG
'Belle Blonde' (HT)	MGan NElm SPer
'Belle de Crécy' **AGM**	CBow CBoy CCMG CCla CDoC EBls ETWh EWar GCoc IOrc MAus MMat NSty SFam SJus SPer SPla WAct WHCG
'Belle des Jardins'	See R. 'Centifolia Variegata'
¶ Belle Epoque ® (HT)	MFry
'Belle Isis' (G)	CCMG EBls MAus SPer
'Belle Lyonnaise' (T/Cl)	EBls
'Belle Poitevine' **AGM**	EBls MAus NSty
'Belle Portugaise' (Cl)	EBls MAus
Belle Story ® (S)	MAus SPer
Belle Sunblaze ® (Min)	NElm
¶ Bellevue ® (HT)	MJon
'Belvedere' (Ra)	MAus WHCG
'Bengal Beauty'	ELan WWat
'Bennett's Seedling' (Ra)	MAus
Benson and Hedges Gold ® (HT)	EWar MGan
Benson and Hedges Special ® (Min)	ELan MJon MMat
¶ 'Berkshire' (GC)	LStr MMat MRui
Bettina ® (HT)	MAus MGan NRog
Bettina, Climbing ® (HT/Cl)	EBls MAus SRum
Betty Driver ® (F)	MBri MGan SPer
'Betty Prior' (F)	GCoc MGan
'Betty Uprichard' (HT)	EBls MAus NSty
'Beyreuth' (S)	MGan
'Bharami' (Min)	MGan
Bianco ® (Patio/Min)	CSan GCoc MAus SJus
Bibi Mezoon ® (S)	CCMG CDoC EWar IHos MAus MRui NBar SJus
Biddulph Grange ® (S)	MFry
¶ 'Bidy' (Min)	MHay
§ ***biebersteinii***	EBls
'Big Chief' (HT)	LGod MJon NRog
Big Purple ® (HT)	EBee MJon SApu SRum WWar
¶ 'Birthday Girl' (F)	GCoc
'Bishop Darlington' (HM)	EBls
¶ 'Bishop Elphinstone' (F)	GCoc
'Bit o'Sunshine' (Min)	MGan MMor
'Black Beauty' (HT)	IJoh MAus MJon NBar
'Black Ice' (F)	MGan SRum
'Black Jack' (Ce)	See R. 'Tour de Malakoff'
Black Jack ® (Min)	MHay
¶ Black Jade ® (Patio)	MBur MHay
'Black Prince' (HP)	EBls
'Blairii Number One' (Bb)	EBls NSty
'Blairii Number Two' **AGM**	EBls ETWh MAus NSty SPer WAct WHCG WHow WSHC
'Blanche de Vibert' (DPo)	EBls MAus
'Blanche Double de Coubert' **AGM**	Widely available
'Blanche Moreau' (CeMo)	CCMG CSan EBls EBro IHos MAus MGan NElm NSty SPer WAct
'Blanchefleur' (Ce)	CCor EBls IHos MAus NSty
blanda	EBls
Blessings ® **AGM**	Widely available
Blessings, Climbing ® (HT/Cl)	EBls
'Bleu Magenta' (Ra)	CCMG EBls EWar MAus WHCG
'Bloomfield Abundance' (Poly)	CCMG CCor CSan EBls MAus MMat NSty SPer SRum WHCG WWat
'Blossomtime' (Cl)	NRog
'Blue Diamond' (HT)	MGan
Blue Moon ® (HT)	CGro CSan EBls EBre EBro ELan ESha EWar GGre IHos IJoh LBre LGod LPlm MAus MBur MFry MGan MHay MJon MMor NBar NElm NRog SApu SPer SRum WWeb
'Blue Moon, Climbing' (HT/Cl)	MBur MGan
Blue Parfum ® (HT)	MAus MJon
Blue Peter ® (Min)	IHos MFry MJon MRui SApu
'Blush Boursault' (Bs)	EBls MAus
'Blush Damask' (D)	CCMG CCor EBls
'Blush Noisette'	See R. 'Noisette Carnée'
'Blush Rambler' (Ra)	CCMG EBls ETWh EWar MAus SPer WHCG
'Blushing Lucy' (Cl)	MAus WSHC
'Bob Collard' (F)	SRum
¶ 'Bob Greaves'	MFry
'Bob Woolley' (HT)	MHay NBat
'Bobbie James' **AGM**	CBow CCMG CHad CSan EBls EBre ETWh EWar IHos LBre LStr MAus MGan MHay MMat NBat NSty SJus SPer SRum WAct WHCG
'Bobby Charlton' (HT)	MFry MGan MHay NRog SApu
'Bobolink' (Min)	GGre MGan
'Bon Silène' (T)	EBls
Bonfire Night ® (F)	CGro MBur MGan MMat

Name	Suppliers
Bonica ® **AGM**	CCMG CCor CDoC EBls EBre ELan ENot GCoc IHos LBre LGod LStr MAus MBur MGan MJon MMat SApu SJus SPer SRum
'Bonn' (HM)	CB&S MAus MGan NRog
'Bonnie Scotland' (HT)	MBur MGan
Bonsoir ® (HT)	MAus MGan MHay
'Border Coral' (F)	NRog
'Born Free' (Min)	MBur
'Botzaris' (D)	CCMG EBls SFam WHCG
'Boule de Nanteuil' (G)	CCor EBls GCoc
'Boule de Neige' (Bb)	CCMG CCla CSan EBls EMFP ENot ETWh LHol LStr MAus MBur MMat MRav NSty SApu SFam SJus SPer SPla WAct WHCG WHow WWeb
'Bouquet d'Or' (N)	EBls MAus
'Bourbon Queen' (Bb)	CCMG EBls ETWh MAus NBrk NSty WHCG
Bow Bells ® (S)	MAus
Boys' Brigade ® (Patio)	CDoC CGro EWar GCoc MAus MGan NBat SApu WWeb
§ ***bracteata***	ESha MAus WWat
Breath of Life ® (HT/Cl)	CCMG CGro CSan ELan ESha EWar GGre LGod LStr MAus MBri MFry MGan MHay MJon NBar NBat SApu SJus SPer SPla SRum
Bredon ® (S)	MAus MBri
'Breeze Hill' (Ra)	EBls MAus
§ 'Brenda Colvin' (Ra)	CBot MAus
'Brennus' (Ch x)	EBls
'Briarcliff' (HT)	EBls
¶ Bridal Pink ® (F)	MJon
Bright Smile ® (F/Patio)	CDoC GCoc IDic LStr MAus MFry MGan MMat NBar SPer
Bright Spark ® (Min)	MFry MRui
'Brindis' (F/Cl)	MGan
'Bristol Post' (HT)	CSan
Brother Cadfael ® (S)	EWar MAus MRui NBar SPer
Brown Velvet ® (F)	MJon MMat SApu
'Brownie' (F)	MAus
'Browsholme Rose' (Ra)	NSty
§ ***brunonii*** (Ra)	CHan EBls EWes MAus
§ – 'La Mortola' (Ra)	MAus SPer
Buck's Fizz ® (F)	EWar MBur MFry MGan MMat NBar SApu SJus
'Buff Beauty' **AGM**	Widely available
'Bullata'	See R. x ***centifolia*** 'Bullata'
§ 'Burgundiaca' (G)	CCor EBls ETWh MAus WAct WHCG
Burgundian Rose	See R. 'Burgundiaca'
'Burma Star' (F)	ESha EWar GCoc
Burnet, Double Pink	See R. ***pimpinellifolia*** 'Double Pink'
Burnet, Double White	See R. ***pimpinellifolia*** 'Double White'
Bush Baby ® (Min)	LGod LStr MJon MRui NBat SApu WStI
Buttons ® (Min/Patio)	IDic IHos LStr MBur MFry SApu
By Appointment ® (F)	CCMG GCoc MJon SJus
'C F Meyer'	See R. 'Conrad Ferdinand Meyer'
'Café' (F)	MAus
'Cairngorm' (F)	ESha GCoc
'Caledonian' (HT)	NBat

Name	Suppliers
californica	MAus
– 'Plena'	See R. ***nutkana*** 'Plena'
'Callisto' (HM)	CCMG EBro ETWh EWar MAus WHCG
'Camaïeux' (G)	CCMG CCor CSan EBls EBro ETWh MAus MMat SPer WHCG
¶ 'Cambridgeshire' (GC)	MMat
'Camélia Rose' (Cl)	EBls WHCG
'Cameo' (Poly)	EBls ETWh MAus MGan
¶ Canadian White Star ® (HT)	MBri MJon
'Canary Bird'	See R. ***xanthina*** 'C.B'
Candy Rose ® (S)	EWar NBar NElm
canina	CB&S CKin CPer ECWi LBuc MAus MHew NWea WMou
– 'Abbotswood'	See R. 'Abbotswood'
– 'Andersonii'	See R. 'Andersonii'
'Cantabrigiensis' (S)	CCMG CSam EBee EBls ENot GCoc MAus NRog SPer WAct WWat WWeb
'Canterbury' (S)	MAus
Can-Can ® (HT)	CDoC EWar MJon NBar SJus SRum
'Capitaine Basroger' (Mo)	EBls MAus
'Capitaine John Ingram' **AGM**	CSan EBls ETWh EWar MAus NSty SFam SPer SPla
'Captain Christy, Climbing' (HT/Cl)	EBls MAus
Captain Cook ® (F)	MJon NBat
'Captain Hayward' (HP)	EBls
¶ 'Cardiff Bay' (HT)	MHay
'Cardinal de Richelieu' **AGM**	CBoy CCMG CDoC CHad EBls EBro EMFP ETWh EWar GCoc IOrc MAus MFry MMat NSty SApu SFam SPer WAct WHCG
Cardinal Hume ® (S)	EBls LStr MAus MGan SApu SPer WHCG
Carefree Beauty ® (S)	EWar
'Carmen' (Ra)	EBls MAus
§ 'Carmenetta' (S)	EBls EWar
'Carol'	See R. 'Carol Amling'
§ 'Carol Amling' (Gn)	MJon SRum
carolina	CGre LHop WHCG
Caroline Davison ® (F)	MAus
¶ Caroline de Monaco ® (HT)	MJon
'Caroline Testout'	See R. 'Madame Caroline Testout'
§ Casino ® (HT/Cl)	CCMG CGro CSan EBls EBre ESha EWar IJoh LBre LPlm MAus MBur MFry MGan MHay MJon MMor MRui NElm SRum WStI WWeb
¶ Castle of Mey ® (F)	MJon
Catherine Cookson ® (HT)	NBat
'Catherine Mermet' (T)	EBls MAus
'Catherine Seyton' (HSwB)	EBls
caudata	CCor
§ 'Cécile Brünner' (Poly)	CBow CCMG EBls EBro ELan EMFP ENot ETWh EWar GCoc LHol LStr MAus MGan MMat NRog NSty SApu SJus SPer SPla SRum WHCG WHow WWat

'Cécile Brünner, Climbing' **AGM**	CBow CCMG CHad CHan CSan EBls EFol ETWh LStr MAus NSty SApu SJus SPer WAct WHCG WSHC WWat
§ 'Cécile Brünner, White' (Poly)	CCMG EBls MAus WHCG
¶ Cecily Gibson ® (F)	MJon
§ 'Céleste' **AGM**	CB&S CCMG CCla CSan EBls EBro ELan EMFP ENot ETWh GCoc IHos MAus MFry MHay MMat MRui NSty SApu SFam SJus SPer SRum WAct WHCG WWeb
'Celestial'	See R. 'Céleste'
'Célina' (Mo)	CCor EBls MGan
'Céline Forestier' (N)	CBoy CCMG EBls ETWh MAus SFam SPer WAct WHCG WHow
§ 'Celsiana' (D)	CCMG CCor EBls EWar MAus NBar SFam SPer WAct WHCG
Centenaire de Lourdes ® (F)	EBls
§ 'Centifolia Variegata' (Ce)	EBls MGan
§ x ***centifolia***	CBow CBoy CCMG EBls ETWh GCoc IOrc LHol NRog SJus WAct WHCG
§ – 'Bullata'	EBls MAus SFam
§ – 'Cristata' **AGM**	CCla CSan EBls EMFP ENot ETWh EWar IHos MMat NBar NRog SFam SJus SPer SPla WAct
§ – 'Muscosa' **AGM**	CDoC EBls EMFP ENot ETWh EWar GCoc IHos IOrc MGan MMat NRog NSty SFam SJus WWeb
– 'Parvifolia' (G)	See R. 'Burgundiaca'
cerasocarpa (Ra)	CCor ETWh
'Cerise Bouquet' **AGM**	CCMG EBls EMFP ETWh MAus MMat NSty SJus SPer WAct WWeb
Cha Cha ® (Patio/Min)	MBur SApu
'Chami' (HM)	EBro
Champagne Cocktail ® (F)	EHar EWar GCoc MJon NBat SApu WWar WWeb
¶ Champagne ® (F)	MJon
'Champion' (HT)	MAus MFry MHay MJon NElm
'Champneys' Pink Cluster' (Ch x)	EBls WKif
Champs Elysées ® (HT)	MGan
'Chanelle' (F)	CCMG CSan EBls GCoc MAus MGan NRog SPer
Chapeau de Napoléon	See R. x ***centifolia*** 'Cristata'
'Chaplin's Pink Climber' (Cl)	CBow EBls EBro ETWh EWar MGan MHay
Chardonnay ® (HT)	MBri MJon
¶ Charisma ® (F)	MBri MJon
Charles Austin ® (S)	MAus MBri NSty SJus SPer WHCG
Charles Aznavour ® (F)	EWar
'Charles de Mills' **AGM**	CCMG CCla CCor CHad CSan EBls EBro EMFP ENot ETWh GCoc MAus MFry MHay MJon MMat NBar NSty SFam SJus SPer SPla SRum WAct WHCG WWeb
'Charles Gater' (HP)	EBls
'Charles Lefèbvre' (HP)	EBls
'Charles Mallerin' (HT)	EBls
Charles Rennie Mackintosh ® (S)	CCla EWar MAus
Charleston ® (F)	MGan
Charleston '88 ® (HT)	EWar
'Charley's Aunt' (HT)	MHay
¶ 'Charlotte'	MAus
Charmian ® (S)	MAus
'Charter 700' (F)	MFry
'Château de Clos-Vougeot' (HT)	MGan
'Château de Clos-Vougeot, Climbing' (HT/Cl)	EBls EBro MAus
Chaucer ® (S)	MAus MBri
Chelsea Pensioner ® (Min)	LPlm MMat SApu
Cherry Brandy ® (HT)	MBur MFry MGan MJon SRum
'Cherry Pie' (HT)	MGan
'Cherryade' (S)	MGan
'Cherryade, Climbing' (HT/Cl)	MGan
'Cheshire Life' (HT)	CSan ESha GGre MAus MBur MFry MGan MJon MMor NBar SRum WStI WWeb
¶ Chester Cathedral ® (HT)	MJon
'Chianti' (S)	CCla EBls MAus MBri NSty
Chicago Peace ® (HT)	CB&S CCMG EBls ESha EWar GCoc GGre IHos IJoh LGod LPlm LStr MAus MBur MGan MJon MMor NElm NRog SRum WStI WWeb
Chinatown ® **AGM**	Widely available
chinensis 'Mutabilis'	See R. x ***odorata*** 'Mutabilis'
– 'Old Blush'	See R. x ***odorata*** 'Pallida'
'Chloris' (A)	EBls
'Chorus Girl' (F)	MGan
Chorus ® (F)	CSan
Christian Dior ® (HT)	EBls MGan
'Christine Gandy' (HT)	MGan
'Christine, Climbing' (HT/Cl)	MAus
'Christopher' (HT)	GCoc
¶ Christopher Columbus ® (HT)	MBri MJon MMat SApu
'Chrysler Imperial' (HT)	EBls MAus MGan NElm
Cider Cup ® (Min/Patio)	CDoC EBee ESha EWar GGre IDic MAus MBur MFry MHay MJon NBat SApu SJus SPer WWar
'Cinderella' (Min)	GAri MGan
cinnamomea	See R. ***majalis***
'Circus' (F)	MAus MGan
'City Lights' (Patio)	LGod MMat
'City of Bath' (HT)	MHay
City of Belfast ® (F)	EBls IHos MAus NElm
City of Birmingham ® (S/HT)	MJon MMat
¶ 'City of Cardiff' (HT)	MHay
'City of Glasgow' (HT)	MHay
'City of Gloucester' (HT)	MGan MHay
'City of Leeds' (F)	EBls ESha EWar GGre MAus MGan MHay MMat NBar NRog SApu SPer WStI WWeb
City of London ® **AGM**	CCMG ESha EWar LStr MBur MHay MJon SApu
'City of Portsmouth' (F)	CB&S MBur MGan

Name	Suppliers
'City of Worcester' (HT)	MHay
'City of York' (Ra)	EBls
Clair Matin ® (S/Cl)	CCMG CCor CHad EBls ETWh MAus MJon SPer SPla
'Claire Jacquier' (N)	CCMG EBls MAus SPer WAct WHCG
Claire Rayner ® (F/Patio)	LPlm MJon MRui
Claire Rose ® (S)	CSam EWar IHos MAus MJon NBar SChu SPer
Claire Scotland ® (Patio)	GCoc
Clarissa ® (Min)	IHos MAus SApu
'Clementina Carbonieri' (T)	EBls
¶ 'Cleopatra' (HT)	MMat
'Clio' (HP)	MJon
¶ Clive Lloyd ® (HT)	MJon
'Cloth of Gold' (N)	EBls MAus
Clydebank Centenary ® (F/Min)	GCoc
'Clytemnestra' (HM)	EBro
Cocktail ® (S)	EBls MGan WAct
Colibre ® (Min)	LGod MFry MGan SJus
§ Colibre '79 ® (Min)	CSan ELan EWar GGre LStr MRui WStI WWar
Colibre '80 ®	See R. Colibre '79 ®
'Colonel Fabvier'	EBls
'Colonial White'	See R. 'Sombreuil, Climbing'
Colorama ® (HT)	MBri
'Columbian' (Cl)	WHCG
colvillei	CCor
§ Colwyn Bay ® (F)	MJon
'Commandant Beaurepaire' (Bb)	CCor EBls MAus NSty SPer
Common Moss	See R. x ***centifolia*** 'Muscosa'
'Compassion' **AGM**	Widely available
§ 'Complicata' **AGM**	CBow CCMG CSam CSan EBls EBro ETWh EWar MAus MBri MGan MMat MRav NRog NSty SApu SJus SPer WAct WHCG WSHC WWat
'Comte de Chambord'	See R. 'Madame Knorr'
'Comtesse Cécile de Chabrillant' (HP)	EBls MAus
'Comtesse de Lacépède'	See R. 'Du Maître d'Ecole'
'Comtesse de Murinais' (D/M)	CCMG CCor EBls MAus SFam
'Comtesse du Cayla' (Ch)	MAus
'Comtesse Vandal' (HT)	MAus
'Comtesse Vandal, Climbing' (HT/Cl)	EBls MAus
'Conchita' (Poly)	ETWh
§ 'Conditorum' (G)	EBls SFam
Congratulations ® (HT)	CSan EWar GCoc GGre IHos LGod LPlm LStr MFry MGan MJon MMat NElm SApu SChu SJus SPer WWar
§ 'Conrad Ferdinand Meyer' (Ru)	CCMG EBls IHos MAus MGan NSty SPer SRum WAct
Conservation ® (Min/Patio)	ESha GCoc LStr MJon NBat SApu
'Constance Fettes' (F)	GCoc
Constance Spry ® **AGM**	CCMG CCla CGro CHad CSan EBls EBre ENot ETWh EWar GCoc IOrc LBre LStr MAus MBri MGan MJon MMat MMor MRui NSty SApu SChu SJus SPer SRum WHCG WWeb
'Cooper's Burmese'	See R. ***laevigata*** 'Cooperi'
'Copenhagen' (S)	EBls MAus MBri
'Copper Delight' (F)	NRog
Copper Pot ® (F)	MBur MGan SPer
'Coral Cluster' (Poly)	EBls MAus MGan
Coral Dawn ® (HT/Cl)	EBls MAus MFry MJon MRui
Coral Reef ® (Patio)	GCoc GGre LStr
'Coral Satin' (Cl)	MGan
'Coralie' (D)	EBls
'Coralin' (Min)	LGod MGan MRui
¶ Cordon Bleu ® (HT)	MBur
'Cornelia' **AGM**	Widely available
'Coronation Gold' (F)	ESha GCoc
'Corso' (HT)	GCoc
'Coryana'	EBls
I 'Corylus' (Ru)	See R. 'Hazel Le Rougetel'
corymbifera	EBls
corymbulosa	EBls
'Cosimo Ridolfi' (G)	EBls
'Cottage Maid'	See R. 'Centifolia Variegata'
Cottage Rose ® (S)	CBow CDoC MAus MJon MRui SChu SJus
Country Lady ® (HT)	MBur SApu SJus
Country Living ® (S)	CBow CBoy CCMG EWar IHos MAus MRui NBar WHow
'Country Maid' (F)	EWar
'Coupe d'Hébé' (Bb)	EBls ETWh MAus
'Cramoisi Picotée' (G)	CCor EBls MAus
'Cramoisi Supérieur' (Ch)	CCMG CCor EBls EBro EMFP ETWh MAus WHCG WHow
'Cramoisi Supérieur Grimpant' (Ch/Cl)	EBls MAus
Crathes Castle ® (F)	GCoc
'Crépuscule' (N)	EBls NSty WHCG
'Cressida' (S)	CCMG MAus
Crested Moss	See R. x ***centifolia*** 'Cristata'
Cricri ® (Min)	MAus MGan
Crimson Cascade ® (Cl)	EWar MBri MFry SApu SJus
'Crimson Conquest' (HT/Cl)	EBls
'Crimson Damask'	See R. ***gallica officinalis***
Crimson Gem ® (Min)	MGan NBat
'Crimson Globe' (Mo)	MGan
'Crimson Glory' (HT)	EBls MAus MBur MGan
'Crimson Glory, Climbing' (HT/Cl)	EBls ETWh GCoc MAus MGan MHay NRog SRum WStI
'Crimson Rambler' (Ra)	MAus
'Crimson Shower' **AGM**	EMFP ETWh EWar GGre IHos LGod LPlm MAus MGan MJon MMat NBar NRog SPer WStI
'Cristata'	See R. ***centifolia*** 'Cristata'
'Cuisse de Nymphe'	See R. 'Great Maiden's Blush'
'Cupid' (HT/Cl)	CCMG EBls ETWh EWar MAus SPer
Curiosity ® (HT/v)	MJon
Cymbeline ® (S)	MAus SPer SRum
'Cynthia Brooke' (HT)	EBls
'DAguesseau' (G)	EBls EBro MAus SPer
Daily Express ® (HT)	MFry

Name	Suppliers
'Daily Mail'	See R. 'Madame Edouard Herriot'
Daily Post ® (F)	MFry
Daily Sketch ® (F)	MGan SRum
'Dainty Bess' (HT)	EBls EBro MAus MRav NSty
Dainty Dinah ® (Min/Patio)	GCoc LStr MAus SApu
'Dainty Maid' (F)	MAus
'Dairy Maid' (F)	MAus
'Daisy Hill' (*macrantha* x)	CCMG EBls
¶ Dalli Dalli ® (F)	MJon
x *damascena bifera*	See R. x *d. semperflorens*
§ x *damascena semperflorens*	CCMG CSan EBls EBro ETWh IHos
§ x *damascena versicolor*	CGro CSan EBls ENot ETWh IHos LHol MGan NSty WAct WWeb
N x *damascena* hort. 'Trigintipetala'	See R. 'Professeur Emile Perrot'
'Dame Edith Helen' (HT)	EBls
Dame of Sark ® (F)	ESha
Dame Wendy ® (F)	EBee EWar LGod MAus MBri MFry MGan MJon MMat SApu WWar
'Danaë' (HM)	CBoy CCMG EBls EBro ETWh MAus WHCG
'Danny Boy' (HT/Cl)	SRum
Danse des Sylphes ® (Cl)	EBls MHay NBat
'Danse du Feu' (Cl)	Widely available
'Daphne Gandy' (F)	MGan
'Dapple Dawn' (S)	MAus MBri NBar SPer
Darling Flame ® (Min)	CGro CSan EBre ELan EWar GCoc GGre LBre MFry MGan MHay MJon MMat MRui NElm SApu SPer WStI WWar
'Dart's Defender'	SLPl
David Whitfield ® (R)	MGan
davidii	EBls MAus
davurica	CCor
– DF 90010	EBul
'Dawn Chorus' (HT)	CGro EWar GCoc LGod LPlm LStr MBri MBur MFry MGan MHay MJon MMat SApu SJus SPer SRum
'Daybreak' (HM)	EBls EBro MAus NRog WAct WHCG
Daylight ® (F)	IDic MBur MJon
§ 'De Meaux' (Ce)	CBow CBoy CCMG CSan EBls EMFP ENot ETWh MAus MMat NSty SPer SPla
§ 'De Meaux, White' (Ce)	CCMG EBls MAus
§ 'De Rescht' AGM	CCMG CCla CCor CSan EBls EBro ETWh LHol MAus MBri MGan MHay MJon MMat NSty SPer SPla WAct
'Dearest' (F)	CB&S CCMG CCla CDoC EWar GGre IJoh LStr MAus MBri MGan MHay MJon MMor NElm NRog SPer SRum WStI WWeb
¶ 'Debbie Thomas' (HT)	MHay
'Debutante' (Ra)	CCMG EBls MAus
Deb's Delight ® (F)	ELan EWar GCoc MFry MJon WWeb
'Deep Secret' (HT)	CCMG CDoC CGro CSan EBre ESha EWar GCoc GGre LBre LPlm MBur MFry MGan MJon MMor NRog SJus SPer SRum WWeb
'Delambre' (DPo)	EBls MAus WHCG
'Dembrowski' (HP)	EBls
Denman ® (HT)	MJon SApu
'Dentelle de Malines' (S)	MAus MBri WAct
'Deschamps' (N)	EBls
'Desprez à Fleurs Jaunes' (N)	CBow CCMG EBls ETWh MAus NSty SPer WHCG WHow WSHC
'Deuil de Paul Fontaine' (Mo)	EBls
'Devon Maid' (Cl)	WWar
'Devoniensis, Climbing' (T/Cl)	CCMG EBls MAus
Diadem ® (F)	MFry MJon
'Diamond Jubilee' (HT)	EBls MAus MHay
'Dicbar'	See R. Memento ®
'Dickson's Flame' (F)	MGan
Die Welt ® (HT)	MHay NBat
'Dimples' (F)	NSty
'Diorama' (HT)	IJoh MAus MGan NElm NRog SRum
'Directeur Alphand' (HP)	EBls
Disco Dancer ® (F)	IDic IHos WWar
'Doc' (Poly)	MGan
'Docteur Andry' (HP)	EBls
'Docteur Grill' (T)	EBls MAus
'Doctor A J Verhage' (HT)	MGan
¶ 'Doctor Abrahams' (HT)	MJon
Doctor Dick ® (HT)	GCoc MHay NBat
'Doctor Eckener' (Ru)	EBls MAus MGan
'Doctor Edward Deacon' (HT)	EBls
Doctor Goldberg ® (HT)	MGan
Doctor Jackson ® (S)	MAus
'Doctor John Snow' (HT)	MGan
Doctor McAlpine ® (F/Patio)	GCoc LStr MBri MJon SRum
'Doctor W Van Fleet' (Ra/Cl)	CCMG EBls MAus WSHC
Dollie B ® (Min)	MJon MRui
'Don Charlton' (HT)	MHay NBat
'Don Juan' (Cl)	MGan
¶ Donald Davis ® (F)	MJon
'Doncasteri'	EBls MAus
'Dopey' (Poly)	MGan
'Doreen' (HT)	NRog
Doris Tysterman ® (HT)	CDoC CGro CSan EBls EBre EBro ESha EWar GGre IHos IJoh LBre LGod LPlm LStr MAus MBur MFry MGan MHay MJon MMor NBar NBat NElm NRog SRum WWar WWeb
'Dorothy Perkins' (Ra)	CB&S CCMG CDoC CGro CSan EBls ETWh EWar GGre IJoh LPlm LStr MAus MGan MJon MMat MMor MRui NBar NElm NPer NRog NSty SApu SPer SRum WAct WHCG WWeb

'Dorothy Wheatcroft' (F)	ESha IHos MGan MHay SRum WWeb
Dortmund ® (HScB/Cl)	CCMG EBls ETWh LPlm MAus MGan MHay MMat MMor SPer WAct WHCG
Double Delight ® (HT)	CGro CSan ELan ESha GCoc GGre IJoh LStr MBri MGan MHay MJon NElm NRog SApu SPer SRum WWar
'Double Joy' (Min)	MBur
Dove ® (S)	MAus MBri NBar
Dream Girl ® **AGM**	CCMG MAus MBri NSty
'Dream Time' (HT)	MHay NBat
'Dream Waltz' (F)	MHay
'Dreamglo' (Min)	MHay NBat
'Dreaming Spires' (Cl)	IHos MBri MJon MMat SApu SJus SPer
Dreamland ® (F)	MFry MGan NElm
'Dresden Doll' (Min/Mo)	EBls MAus MRui SApu SPer
Drummer Boy ® (F/Patio)	CSan ESha GCoc GGre LStr NElm SApu WWar
§ 'Du Maître d'Ecole' **AGM**	CCMG CCor EBls ETWh MAus
Dublin Bay ® **AGM**	CDoC CSan EBls ESha EWar IHos IJoh LGod LPlm LStr MBri MBur MFry MGan MHay MJon MMat NBar NRog SApu SPer WWar
'Duc de Fitzjames' (G)	EBls
'Duc de Guiche' **AGM**	CCMG CCor CSan EBls ETWh MAus SFam SPer WHCG WHow
'Duchess of Portland'	See R. 'Portlandica'
♦Duchess of York ®	See R. Sunseeker ®
'Duchesse de Buccleugh' (G)	CCor EBls MAus
§ 'Duchesse de Montebello' **AGM**	CCMG CCor EBls ETWh MAus SPer SRms WHCG WHow
'Duchesse de Rohan' (CexHP)	EBls
'Duchesse de Verneuil' (Mo)	EBls MAus SFam
'Duchesse d'Albe' (T)	EBls
'Duchesse d'Angoulême' (G)	CBoy CCMG CCor EBls ETWh MAus NSty WHCG
'Duchesse d'Auerstädt' (N)	EBls
'Dukat' (Cl)	EWar
Duke Meillandina ® (Min)	MRui SApu
'Duke of Edinburgh' (HP)	EBls MAus
'Duke of Wellington' (HP)	EBls WHCG
'Duke of Windsor' (HT)	CDoC GGre IHos IJoh MGan MJon NElm NRog SPer SRum
'Duke of York' (Ch)	EBls
Duke Sunblaze	See R. Duke Meillandina ®
'Dundee Rambler' (Ra)	EBls MAus
§ 'Dunwich Rose' (pimpinellifolia)	CCMG CCor EBee EBls ENot MAus MBri MMat SPer
'Dupontii' (S)	EBls MAus SFam SPer WWat
'Dupuy Jamain' (HP)	EBls WHCG
'Durham Prince Bishop' (HT)	NBat
'Dusky Maiden' (F)	CHad EBls MAus WHCG
'Dusterlohe' (R)	CCor EBls
Dutch Gold ® (HT)	CDoC CGro EWar LStr MAus MGan MJon NElm NRog SJus SPer
'Dwarf King'	See R. 'Zwergkönig'
Dwarf Queen '82 ® / Zwerkönigin '82 (Min)	MGan SJus
'E H Morse'	See R. 'Ernest H Morse'
'Easlea's Golden Rambler' (Ra)	EBls EBre EMFP ETWh LBre MAus NSty WHCG
'Easter Morning' (Min)	CSan ELan GGre LGod MAus MBur MGan MJon MRui NBar NElm SApu SJus SPer WWeb
'Eblouissant' (Poly)	MGan
ecae	EBls MAus
– 'Helen Knight'	See R. 'Helen Knight'
'Eclair' (HP)	EBls
'Eddie's Jewel' (moyesii x)	EBls MAus MGan NSty
Eden Rose ® (HT)	EBls IHos MGan SRum
Eden Rose '88 ® (HT/Cl)	EWar MJon SApu SJus SPer
'Edith Bellenden' (HSwB)	EBls
Edith Holden ® (F)	LGod MAus MBri MJon SApu SJus WWar WWeb
eglanteria **AGM**	CB&S CCMG CCor CKin CPer CSan EBls ENot ETWh GPoy ILis LBuc LHol MAus MHew MMat SHer SPer WAct WMou WWye
'Egyptian Treasure' (F)	MGan
'Elegance' (HT/Cl)	EBls MAus MGan
§ ***elegantula***	CCor GAbr
§ – 'Persetosa'	CCMG EBls ENot MAus SPer WAct WHCG
¶ Elfin ® (Min)	MJon
§ Elina ® **AGM**	CCMG CSan ESha EWar IDic IHos LGod LStr MAus MBur MFry MGan MHay MJon MMat NElm NRog SApu SJus SPer WWar
Elizabeth Harkness ® (HT)	EBls EWar MAus MBur MGan SPer
Elizabeth Heather Grierson ® (HT/Cl)	MMat
Elizabeth of Glamis ® (F)	CCMG CDoC CGro EBls EBro ELan ESha EWar GCoc GGre IHos IJoh LStr MAus MBri MGan MMat MMor NElm NRog SRum WWeb
'Elizabeth Philp' (F)	LPlm
'Ellen Poulsen' (Poly)	MGan
'Ellen Willmott' (HT)	EBls ETWh MAus
Ellen ® (S)	MAus MBri SPer
'Elmshorn' (S)	CB&S CCMG CDoC CSan ENot MGan WHCG
'Elsa' (HT)	SRum
Elsie Warren ® (F)	NBat
Emanuel ® (S)	MAus SPer
'Embassy' (HT)	MHay
'Emily Gray' (Ra)	CCMG CGro CSan EBls EBre EBro ETWh EWar IHos LBre LStr MAus MBur MGan MHay MJon MMat MMor NBar NElm NRog NSty SPer SPla SRum WHCG WSHC

¶ Emily ® (S) MAus
¶ Emma Mitchell ® (Patio) NBat
'Emma Wright' (HT) MAus
'Emmerdale' (F) ESha WStI
'Empereur du Maroc' (HP) CCMG EBls MAus MMat NSty WHCG
'Empress Josephine' See R. x ***francofurtana***
'Empress Michiko' (HT) EWar IDic MJon SApu
Ena Baxter ® (HT) GCoc
'Ena Harkness' (HT) CGro CSan EBls EBro ELan EWar GGre LStr MBur MGan NElm NRog SRum WStI WWeb
'Ena Harkness, Climbing' (HT/Cl) CB&S CGro EBls GCoc GGre IHos MAus MBri MBur MGan NRog SPer SPla SRum WStI WWeb
§ 'Enfant de France' (HP) EBls
English Elegance ® (S) MAus
'English Estates' (HT) NBat
English Garden ® (S) CAbP CBow CBoy CCla CSan EBre EMFP ENot ETWh EWar LBre LStr MAus MBri MMat MRui NBar SApu SPer WWeb
'English Miss' (F) CBow CCMG CDoC CSan EBls EWar IHos LPlm LStr MAus MFry MGan MJon SApu SJus SPer SRum WStI WWeb
'Eos' (***moyesii*** x) EBls MAus
'Erfurt' (HM) CCMG EBls ETWh MAus NSty SPer SPla SRms WHCG
'Ernest H Morse' (HT) EBls ESha EWar GCoc GGre IHos IJoh LStr MAus MBur MFry MGan MHay MJon MMor NElm NRog SApu SPer SRum WWeb
'Ernest H Morse, Climbing' (HT/Cl) MGan NElm
Eroica ® (HT) EBro NRog WWeb
Escapade ® (F) EBls MAus MGan
Essex ® (GC) CCor EBee EBre ENot EWar IHos LBre MAus MGan MMat SApu SPer WHCG WWar
Esther Ofarim ® (F) EWar
Esther's Baby ® (Patio) MAus
Estima ® (Min) MFry MRui
Ethel Austin ® (F) MFry
'Etoile de Hollande, Climbing' **AGM** CBow CCMG CSam CSan EBls EBre ETWh GCoc LBre LHol LStr MAus MJon MRav NRog NSty SApu SJus SPer SRum WHCG
'Etoile de Lyon' (T) EBls
'Etude' (Cl) CSan
'Eugène Fürst' (HP) EBls WHCG
'Eugénie Guinoisseau' (Mo) EBls EWar WHCG
Euphrates ® (persica x) MAus MGan
Europeana ® (F) CGro MAus MGan MHay SRum
'Eva' (HM) EBls
'Evangeline' (Ra) EBls MAus NSty SPer
Evelyn ® (S) CAbP CBoy CDoC EMFP EWar MAus MJon MMat MRui SApu SPer SPla WHow
Evelyn Fison ® (Irish Wonder ®) (F) CB&S CDoC ELan EWar GCoc GGre IHos IJoh LGod LStr MAus MBur MGan MHay MJon MMor NElm NRog SApu SPer SRum WWeb
¶ 'Evelyn Taylor' (F) NBat
'Evening Star' (HT) IDic MAus
'Evening Telegraph' (HT) MHay
'Everest Double Fragrance' (F) EBls
'Excelsa' (Ra) CCMG CDoC CSan EBls EMFP EWar GGre IJoh LGod LStr MAus MGan MHay MJon MMor MRui NBar NElm NRog NSty SRum WAct WStI
§ Exploit ® (Cl) EWar
Eye Paint ® (F) CSan EWar LStr MAus MGan MJon NRog
Eyeopener ® (S/GC) CGro EWar IDic MGan MJon SRum WWar
'F E Lester' See R. 'Francis E Lester'
§ 'F J Grootendorst' (Ru) CCMG EBls EWar IHos IOrc LGod LStr MAus MGan MJon MMor NRog NSty SMad WAct
'Fabvier' See R. 'Colonel Fabvier'
Fair Bianca ® (S) IJoh IOrc MAus MBri
Fairy Changeling ® (Poly) MAus
Fairy Damsel ® (Poly/GC) CDoC EBls MAus
Fairygold ® (Patio) MRui
Fairyland ® (Poly) EBls ESha EWar MAus SApu
Fairysnow ® (S) MFry
'Falkland' (pimpinellifolia) EBls MAus
¶ Fancy Pants ® (Min) MHay
Fantan ® (HT) MAus
'Fantin-Latour' **AGM** CBoy CCMG CCla CCor CHad CSan EBls EBro ELan ENot ETWh EWar GCoc IHos LStr MAus MBri MGan MHay MMat NRog NSty SApu SChu SJus SPer WAct WHCG WHow WSHC
fargesii hort. See R. ***moyesii*** 'Fargesii'
farreri See R. ***elegantula***
– var. ***persetosa*** See R. ***elegantula*** 'Persetosa'
'Fashion Flame' (Min) MGan NBar
'Fashion, Climbing' (F/Cl) EBls
Father's Day ® (Min) MAus MJon NElm
Favorite Rosamini ® (Min) MFry MRui
fedtschenkoana CCor EBls MAus MGan NSty WHCG
'Felicia' **AGM** CCMG CDoC CSam EBls EBro ENot ETWh EWar GCoc IHos LHol LStr MAus MBri MFry MHay MJon MMat MMor MRui NBar NRog NSty SApu SJus SPer SRum WAct WHCG WHow
'Félicité Parmentier' **AGM** CCMG EBls EBre LBre MAus NBar NSty SJus SPer WAct WHCG WHow

§ 'Félicité Perpétue' **AGM** CBow CCMG CCla CCor CSan EBls ETWh EWar GCoc IHos LHol MAus MBri MGan MMat MRui NSty SApu SJus SPer SRum WAct WHCG
Felicity Kendal ® (HT) LStr MBri MHay MJon NBat SApu
'Fellenberg' (Ch) EBls MAus WHCG
Fellowship ® (F) GCoc LGod LStr MBri MBur MFry MJon MMat SRum WWar
'Femina' (HT) MGan
'Ferdinand de Lesseps' (HP) EBls
'Ferdinand Pichard' **AGM** CBow CBoy CCMG EBls EBro EMFP ENot ETWh EWar MAus MJon MMat NBar NSty SJus SPer WAct WHCG WHow
Ferdy ® (GC) CCMG CDoC EBls EBre ELan ENot ETWh EWar LBre MAus MGan MMat SApu SPer
Fergie ® (F/Patio) MGan SApu
¶ 'Festival' (Patio) ESha GCoc LPlm LStr MBur MFry MMat NBat
¶ Figurine ® (Min) MHay
filipes 'Brenda Colvin' See R. 'Brenda Colvin'
§ – 'Kiftsgate' **AGM** Widely available
'Fimbriata' (Ru) CCMG CCor CSan EBls EBro EMFP ETWh MAus MBri SPer WAct WHCG WHow
Financial Times Centenary ® (S) EWar IHos MAus
Fine Gold ® (HT) EWar
Fiona ® (S/GC) EBee EBls EWar IHos MBur MGan SApu SPer WHCG
'Fire Princess' (Min) GCoc MHay MRui NBar NElm WWeb
'Firecracker' (F) EBls
Firefly ® (Min) MJon MRui
'First Love' (HT) EBls MGan
'Fisher and Holmes' (HP) EBls MAus WAct WHCG
Fisherman's Friend ® (S) CBoy CDoC EMFP ETWh EWar IHos MAus MHay SApu SPer SRum
¶ 'Flair' (HT) IDic LStr MJon SJus
Flaming Rosamini ® (Min) MFry
'Fleet Street' (HT) MHay
'Fleur Cowles' (F) MBur
'Flora' (Ra) EBls MAus
'Flora McIvor' (HSwB) EBls MAus MGan
Florence Nightingale ® (F) MBri MBur MGan SApu WWeb
Flower Carpet ® **AGM** MAus MBur MFry MJon MMat MRui NBat SJus SPer
§ *foetida* EBls MAus NSty
§ – 'Bicolor' CCMG CCla EBls ENot ETWh MAus MMat NRog NSty SMad SPer WAct
§ – 'Persiana' EBls MAus MGan SPer
foliolosa EBls WHCG
Fontainebleau ® (HT) MHay
'Forgotten Dreams' (HT) MJon
forrestiana CCor EBls MAus MMat
x *fortuneana* EBls
Fortune's Double Yellow See R. x *odorata* 'Pseudindica'
'Fountain' (S) CSam EBls EWar LStr MAus MFry MGan NElm SPer SRum
Fragrant Cloud ® (HT) CDoC CGro CSan EBls EBre ESha EWar GCoc GGre IHos IJoh LBre LGod LStr MAus MBri MBur MFry MHay MJon MMat MMor NBar NBat NRog SApu SPer WWeb
Fragrant Cloud, Climbing ® (HT/Cl) CB&S ELan MGan NElm SRum
Fragrant Delight ® (F) CCMG CCla CSan ESha EWar GCoc IHos LPlm LStr MFry MGan MJon NBar NBat NElm SApu SPer WWar WWeb
Fragrant Dream ® (HT) EWar IDic LStr MBri MBur SApu
Fragrant Gold ® (HT) GCoc LStr SRum
'Fragrant Hour' (HT) MGan MMat
'Francesca' (HM) CCMG CCor EBls EBro ETWh MAus MGan NSty SPer WAct WHCG
Francine Austin ® (S/GC) IHos MAus MRui SPer WAct
'Francis Dubreuil' (T) EBls
§ 'Francis E Lester' (HM/Ra) CCMG CSam EBls EBro ETWh MAus MBri MHay NBar NSty SApu SPer WAct WHCG WHow
¶ 'Franck MacMillan' (HT) MHay
§ x *francofurtana* **AGM** CCMG EBls EBro ETWh IHos SFam WAct
'François Juranville' **AGM** CCMG CSam CSan EBls ETWh EWar LHol LStr MAus MBri MGan MMat NElm NRog SApu SPer
'Frank Naylor' (S) EWar MAus
'Frau Astrid Späth' (F) NElm NRog
'Frau Karl Druschki' (HP) CSan EBls ETWh MAus MGan MHay NSty
§ 'Frau Karl Druschki, Climbing' (HP/Cl) EBls MGan NRog
'Fraulein Octavia Hesse' (Ra) CCMG EBls
'Fred Gibson' (HT) MHay
'Fred Loads' **AGM** CSam EBls ENot ESha EWar MAus MFry MGan MHay MMat SApu
Freddy ® (F) MJon
¶ Free Spirit ® (Min) MHay
Freedom ® **AGM** CSan EWar GCoc IDic LGod LPlm LStr MBur MFry MGan NBat NRog SJus WWar WWeb
'Freiherr von Marschall' (T) EBls
'Frensham' (F) CB&S CCMG CGro EBls LStr MGan MMat SRum WStI
Fresh Pink ® (Min) MGan
¶ 'Friend for Life' (F) GCoc
'Fringette' (Min) MGan MMor
'Fritz Nobis' **AGM** CCMG CHad CSan EBls EMFP ENot ETWh EWar GCoc IHos LStr MAus MGan MHay MMat MRav NSty SApu SJus SPer WHCG
'Frosty' (Min) MRui
¶ Frothy ® (Min) MJon
'Fru Dagmar Hastrup' **AGM** Widely available

'Frühlingsanfang' (HScB) — EBls MAus MBri
'Frühlingsduft' (HScB) — CCMG EBls ETWh NRog NSty SPer
Frühlingsgold ® AGM — Widely available
'Frühlingsmorgen' (HScB) — CCMG EBls ENot ETWh EWar GCoc IHos LStr MAus MBri MGan MMat MMor NBar NElm NRog NSty SApu SJus SMad SPer WAct WHCG WWeb
'Frühlingsschnee' (HScB) — EBls EWar
'Frühlingszauber' (HScB) — EBls
'Fulgens' — See R. 'Malton'
Fulton Mackay ® (HT) — GCoc MFry SApu WWar
¶ 'Fyfield Princess' (F) — MHay
Fyvie Castle ® (HT) — GCoc MGan
'Gail Borden' (HT) — ESha MAus MGan SRum
§ ***gallica*** — EBls MHay
– 'Beckett's Single' — CCor
– 'Complicata' — See R. 'Complicata'
– 'Conditorum' — See R. 'Conditorum'
§ – var. ***officinalis*** AGM — CCMG CCor CDoC CSan EBls EBro ENot ETWh GCoc GPoy LHol MAus MBri MMat NRog NSty SApu SJus SPer WAct WHCG
– 'Velutiniflora' — EBls
§ – 'Versicolor' AGM — CBoy CCla CCor CHad CSan EBls EBro EHar ELan ENot ETWh EWar GCoc LHol LStr MBri MFry MGan MJon NRog NSty SApu SJus SPer SPla WHCG WWeb
Galway Bay ® (HT/Cl) — CSan GCoc IJoh LStr MAus MFry MGan MMat MRui SPer
'Gardener's Delight' (Ra) — NWyt
'Gardenia' (Ra) — SPer
§ 'Garnette' (Ga) — SRum
§ 'Garnette Apricot' (Gn) — SPla SRum
'Garnette Carol' — See R. 'Carol Amling'
'Garnette Pink' — See R. 'Carol Amling'
'Garnette Red' (Gn) — See R. 'Garnette'
Gary Lineker ® (F) — MJon
'Gary Player' (HT) — MHay
'Gateshead Festival' (HT) — NBat
'Gaujard' — See R. 'Rose Gaujard'
'Gavotte' (HT) — MHay
¶ Gee Gee ® (Min) — MHay
'Général Galliéni' (T) — EBls
'Général Jacqueminot' (HP) — EBls WAct WHCG
'Général Kléber' (Mo) — CCor EBls IHos MAus NSty SFam SPer WAct WHCG
'General MacArthur, Climbing' (HT/Cl) — EBls MAus
§ 'Général Schablikine' (T) — EBls EBro ETWh MAus WSHC
N ***gentiliana*** (Ra) — CCor EBls WHCG
Gentle Touch ® AGM — CCla CDoC CGro CSan EBls EBre ESha EWar GCoc GGre IDic LBre LGod LStr MBri MFry MGan MHay MJon MMat MRui NBar NBat SApu SJus SPer SRum WWeb
'Geoff Boycott' (F) — ESha
Geordie Lad ® (HT) — NBat
'Georg Arends' (HP) — CCMG EBls MAus SFam SPer WHCG
'George Dickson' (HT) — MAus SRms
'George R Hill' (HT) — NBat
'Georges Vibert' (G) — EBls MAus WHCG
Geraldine ® (F) — ESha GCoc LStr MBri MGan MJon SRum
§ 'Geranium' (***moyesii*** x) AGM — CB&S CBoy CCMG CCla CGro CSan EBre EBro EHar ELan ENot ETWh EWar GCoc IOrc LBre MAus MBri MGan NBar NElm NSty SApu SPer SRum WAct WHCG WSHC WWeb
'Geranium Red' (F) — MAus
Gerbe d'Or ® — See R. 'Casino'
'Gerbe Rose' (Ra) — EBls MAus NSty
Gertrude Jekyll ® (S) — CCMG CDoC CHad CSam CSan EBre EMFP ENot EWar IJoh IOrc LBre LGod LPlm LStr MAus MBri MFry MJon MMat MRui NBar SApu SChu SJus SPer WAct WHCG WHow WStI
¶ 'Geschwind's Orden' — CCor
'Ghislaine de Féligonde' (S/Ra) — CCor EBls
gigantea — EBls
– ***cooperi*** — See R. ***laevigata*** 'Cooperi'
Gilda ® (F) — CSan
Gingernut ® (F/Patio) — EBee ESha GCoc LStr NBat SApu
Ginny-Lou ® (Min) — MJon MRui
'Gipsy Boy' — See R. 'Zigeunerknabe'
Glad Tidings ® (F) — CGro ESha EWar GGre LPlm LStr MBri MBur MGan MHay MJon MMat NBar NBat SApu SJus SPer SRum WWar WWeb
Glamis Castle ® (S) — MAus MBri MJon MRui NBar SJus SPer WHCG
§ ***glauca*** AGM — Widely available
'Glenfiddich' (F) — CCMG CGro CSan ESha EWar GCoc GGre IHos LGod LPlm LStr MAus MBri MFry MGan MHay MJon NBar NBat NElm NRog SRum WStI WWeb
'Glenn Dale' (Cl) — ETWh
'Gloire de Bruxelles' (HP) — EBls
'Gloire de Dijon' AGM — Widely available
'Gloire de Ducher' (HP) — CCMG ETWh MAus MGan WAct WHCG
'Gloire de France' (G) — CBow CCMG CCor EBls ETWh MAus
'Gloire de Guilan' (D) — EBls MAus NSty WAct
'Gloire des Mousseuses' (Mo) — CCMG CCor CSan EBls EBro ETWh IHos MAus SFam WHCG
'Gloire du Midi' (Poly) — MAus
'Gloire Lyonnaise' (HP) — CCMG EBls EBro ETWh SPla WHow
'Gloria Mundi' (Poly) — CBoy CCMG EBls MGan
§ 'Glory of Edzell' (pimpinellifolia) — EBls MAus WSHC
glutinosa — See R. ***pulverulenta***
'Godfrey Winn' (HT) — WWeb
'Goethe' (Mo) — EBls
Gold Bunny ® (F) — EWar MGan MJon
¶ Gold Bunny, Climbing ® (F/Cl) — MJon

'Gold Pin' (Min) MMat
'Goldbusch' (S) EBls MAus MGan SRms
Golden Celebrations ® (S) MAus MBri MJon MRui NBar SApu SJus SPer
Golden Chersonese ® (S) EBls MAus NRog NSty
'Golden Dawn' (HT/Cl) MAus
Golden Days ® (HT) EWar LGod MBri MFry
¶ 'Golden Garnette' (Ga) SRum
'Golden Glow' (Cl) EBls MGan
Golden Jubilee ® (HT) ELan EWar GCoc GGre LPlm LStr MAus MBur NBat
'Golden Melody' (HT) EBls
Golden Moments ® (HT) EWar MBur MFry MJon NBat SApu
'Golden Moss' (Mo) EBls
'Golden Ophelia' (HT) EBls MAus
'Golden Penny' (Min) MBur
'Golden Rambler' See R. 'Alister Stella Gray'
Golden Rosamini ® (Min) MFry MRui
'Golden Salmon' (Poly) MGan
'Golden Salmon Supérieur' (Poly) EBls
'Golden Shot' (F) ESha MGan
Golden Showers ® **AGM** Widely available
'Golden Slippers' (F) CB&S MAus MGan
'Golden Sunblaze' See R. 'Rise 'n' Shine'
'Golden Times' (HT) WWeb
'Golden Treasure' (F) SRum
Golden Wedding ® (F/HT) CCMG CSan EWar GCoc GGre LGod LPlm LStr MBri MBur MFry MGan MHay MJon MMat NBat SApu SJus SPer WStI
'Golden Wings' **AGM** CCMG CHad EBls ENot ETWh GCoc IHos LStr MAus MBri MFry MGan MHay MJon MMat NSty SApu SJus SPer SRum WHCG WHow
Golden Years ® (F) EWar GCoc GGre MAus MJon NBat
'Goldfinch' (Ra) CBow CCMG CCor CHad CSan EBls EBre EMFP ETWh EWar GCoc LBre MAus MBri NSty SApu SPer WAct WHCG WHow
'Goldfinger' (F) ESha LPlm MBri MJon
'Goldilocks' (F) NElm NRog
'Goldkrone' ('Gold Crown') (HT) MGan SRum
Goldstar ® (HT) EWar MFry MGan SApu
'Goliath' (HT) MHay
'Good News' EWar
'Gordon's College' (F) GCoc SApu
'Grace Abounding' (F) EWar MHay NBat
'Grace Darling' (T) EBls
Grace de Monaco ® (HT) EBls MAus MGan
¶ Graceland ® (Patio) MJon
Graham Thomas ® **AGM** Widely available
Grand Hotel ® (HT/Cl) EWar IHos LStr MBri MJon MMat SPer
§ 'Grandiflora' (pimpinellifolia) CCor EBls ETWh MAus SJus
'Grandpa Dickson' (HT) CCMG EBls ESha EWar GGre IHos IJoh LGod LPlm MAus MBur MFry MGan MHay MJon MMat MMor NBar NBat NElm NRog SApu SPer SRum WWeb
'Grand-mère Jenny' (HT) EBls MGan
'Grand-mère Jenny, Climbing' (HT/Cl) EBls
§ 'Great Maiden's Blush' (A) CBow CSan EBls GCoc MBur MFry MMat NElm NSty WAct WWeb
'Great News' (HT) MAus
'Great Ormond Street' (F) EBls
'Great Western' (Bb) EBls
'Green Diamond' (Min) MAus MFry MJon MMat MRui
Green Snake ® (S/GC) ELan
Greenall's Glory ® (F/Patio) MJon WWeb
'Greenmantle' (HSwB) EBls MAus MGan
Greensleeves ® (F) EBls LStr MAus SApu
'Greer Garson' (HT) GCoc
'Grootendorst Supreme' (Ru) MAus SPer
N 'Gros Choux de Hollande' (Bb) EBls WHCG
Grouse ® (S/GC) CCMG CCor EBls ENot ETWh GCoc IHos MAus MGan MJon MMat SApu SJus SPer WWeb
'Grumpy' (Poly) MGan
'Gruss an Aachen' (Poly) CCMG CCor CHad EBls ETWh LStr MAus MBri MGan NSty SPer WAct WHCG
'Gruss an Teplitz' (Ch x) CSan EBls EBro MAus SFam SPer WHCG
Guernsey Love ® (Min) MJon MRui
Guiding Spirit ® (Min/Patio) MBur MRui WWeb
'Guinée' (HT/Cl) CBow CCMG CHad CSan EBls EBro ELan ETWh IHos LStr MAus MBur MGan MHay MMat NSty SChu SPla
Guletta ® See R. 'Rugul'
'Gustav Grünerwald' (HT) EBls MAus
Gwent ® (GC) LGod LStr MBur MFry MGan MRui
'Gypsy Boy' See R. 'Zigeunerknabe'
'Gypsy Jewel' (Min) CGro NBar NElm
'Gypsy Moth' (F) SRum
'Hakuun' (F/Patio) GCoc MAus MGan MRui SPer
'Hamburger Phönix' (Ra) CGro EBls LStr MGan NElm SPer
Hampshire ® (GC) CCor ENot EWar IHos MAus MFry MGan MMat SApu
Handel ® **AGM** Widely available
Hannah Gordon ® (F) CDoC EWar LStr MBur MGan MHay MJon MMat NBar NBat SRum
'Hannah Hauwxell' (Patio) NBat SRum
'Hannes' (HT) NRog
'Hansa' (Ru) CCor EBls ENot IHos LBuc MAus MGan MMat SPla
§ 'Hansestadt Lübeck' (F) MGan
'Happy' (Poly) MGan

Name	Suppliers
¶ Happy Anniversary ® (F)	MJon
¶ 'Happy Child'	MAus
'Happy Thought' (Min)	MAus MJon
Happy Wanderer ® (F)	EWar
§ x ***harisonii*** 'Harison's Yellow' (HScB)	EBls MAus SPer
§ – 'Lutea Maxima' (HScB)	EBls MAus
§ – 'Williams' Double Yellow' (HScB)	CCMG CCla CCor EBls ETWh MAus
Harkness Marigold ® (F)	SApu
Harold Macmillan ® (F)	NBat WWar
'Harry Maasz' (GC/Cl)	EBls
Harry Wheatcroft ® (HT)	CB&S CGro EBls ESha GGre IHos MAus MBri MBur MGan MJon NElm NRog
Harvest Fayre ® (F)	CGro GCoc GGre IDic LGod LStr MAus MBri MBur MFry MGan MMat NBar NBat SApu SPer SRum WWeb
Harvest Home ® (Ru)	EWar
'Headleyensis'	CCor EBls ETWh MAus
'Heart of England' (F)	MBur
§ 'Heather Muir' (***sericea*** x)	EBls MAus NSty WKif
'Heaven Scent' (F)	MJon NBat
§ 'Hebe's Lip' (D x SwB)	EBls MAus
'Hector Deane' (HT)	EBls MBur MGan NSty
'Heidi Jayne' (HT)	MBur SRum
'Heinrich Schultheis' (HP)	EBls
§ 'Helen Knight' (***ecae*** x)	CSan EBls EHar MAus MBri MMat NSty SPer WHCG
'Helen Traubel' (HT)	EBls MGan
helenae	CCor EBls MAus SPer WHCG
Hello ® (Min/Patio)	GCoc MJon NBat
hemisphaerica	EBls ETWh MAus WAct
'Henri Fouquier' (G)	EBls
§ 'Henri Martin' AGM	CCMG CCor EBls IOrc MAus NRog SPer WAct WHCG
'Henry Nevard' (HP)	EBls MAus
'Her Majesty' (HP)	EBls
§ 'Herbstfeuer' (HSwB)	CCor EBls NSty
Heritage ® (S)	CCMG CDoC CSam CSan EBls ELan EMFP ENot ETWh IHos LGod LHol LPlm LStr MAus MBri MFry MJon MMat MRui NBar NBat SApu SChu SJus SPer SRum WAct WHCG WHow
'Hermosa' (Ch)	CCMG EBls EBro ETWh MAus NSty WAct WHCG WHow
Hero ® (S)	MAus
Hertfordshire ® (GC)	ENot EWar MMat MRui
'Hiawatha' (Ra)	EBls ETWh MAus WHCG
'Hibernica' (***canina*** x)	MAus
'Hidcote Gold'	EBls MAus
High Hopes ® (Cl)	GCoc LStr MBri MBur MFry MJon SApu SJus SRum
¶ High Spirits ® (Min)	MHay
§ 'Highdownensis' (***moyesii*** x)	CCla EBls ELan MAus MMat SPer
Highfield ® (Cl)	CDoC ESha EWar LGod MAus MBri MJon SApu SJus SPer
Highland Laddie ® (Min)	GCoc
Hilda Murrell ® (S)	MAus
§ 'Hillieri' (***moyesii*** x)	EBls MAus SRms
¶ 'Himmelsauge' (Ra)	CCor
'Hippolyte' (G)	EBls MAus WSHC
Hollie Roffey ® (Min)	MJon SPer
holodonta	See R. ***moyesii rosea***
Holy Rose	See R. ***richardii***
'Home Sweet Home' (HT)	EBls MAus
'Home Sweet Home, Climbing' (HT/Cl)	MAus
'Homère' (T)	EBls MAus
'Honey Bunch' (F/Patio)	CDoC CSan GCoc LGod MBri MJon NBat SApu
'Honey Favorite' (HT)	MAus
'Honeymoon' (F)	CB&S GCoc MAus MMor NElm SRum WWeb
'Honeysweet' (F)	MFry
'Honorine de Brabant' (Bb)	CBow CCMG CCor CSan EBls ETWh EWar MAus MMat SFam SPer SPla WAct WHCG
'Horace Vernet' (HP)	EBls
horrida	See R. ***biebersteinii***
'Horstmanns Rosenresli' (F)	EBls
'Hot Pewter' (HT)	MHay
Hotline ® (Min/Mo)	MRui
'Hugh Dickson' (HP)	CCMG EBls EBro ETWh MAus NSty SJus
hugonis	See R. ***xanthina h.***
'Hula Girl' (Min)	CSan LGod MBur MFry MJon MRui
Hume's Blush	See R. x ***odorata*** 'Odorata'
'Hunslet Moss' (Mo)	EBls
'Hunter' (Ru)	WAct
'Hutton Village' (HT)	EWar
hypoleuca	CCor
Iceberg ® (Schneewittchen ®) AGM	Widely available
'Iceberg, Climbing ' AGM	CCMG CGro EBls EBre EBro ELan ETWh EWar GGre LBre LPlm LStr MAus MBri MGan MHay MJon MMor NElm NRog SPer SRum WHCG WHow WSHC WWeb
¶ 'Icecream' (HT)	LStr MMat NBat SJus
'Iced Ginger' (F)	CCMG CSan EWar MAus MFry MGan NBar SApu SPer
'Ideal' (Poly)	ETWh
'Ideal Home' (HT)	MMor
'Illusion' (Cl)	MGan
Ilse Krohn Superior ® (Cl)	EBls
Indian Summer ® (HT)	CCMG EWar GCoc LGod MBri MJon
'Indian Sunblaze' (Min/Patio)	IHos WWeb
Ingrid Bergman ® AGM	CDoC EWar GCoc LGod LStr MBri MBur MGan MJon MMat NBar SApu WWar WWeb
Inner Wheel ® (F)	MFry
'Inspiration' (Cl)	EWar
'Intermezzo' (HT)	MBur MGan
International Herald Tribune ® (F/Patio)	ESha LStr MAus
Intrigue ® (F)	MMat WWar
Invincible ® (F)	EBee EWar MFry MGan

'Invitation' (HT) MBur MGan
'Ipsilanté' (G) CCor EBls MAus WAct WHCG
'Irene of Denmark' (F) EBls
'Irène Watts' **AGM** EBls ETWh MAus SPla WHCG
Irene's Delight ® (HT) MHay NBat
'Irish Brightness' (HT) MAus
'Irish Elegance' (HT) EBls MAus
'Irish Fireflame' (HT) EBls MAus
'Irish Fireflame, Climbing' (HT/Cl) MAus
Irish Mist ® (F) MGan
'Irish Wonder' See R. Evelyn Fison ®
¶ Irresistible ® (Min/Patio) MBur MHay
'Isis' (F) MBri
'Isobel' (HT) MAus
¶ Isobel Derby ® (HT) MBur MJon
'Ispahan' **AGM** CCMG CCla CCor CHad EBls EBro EMFP ETWh EWar MAus NSty SApu SFam SJus SPla WAct WHCG WHow WSHC
'Ivory Fashion' (F) EBls MAus
'Ivory Tip Top' (F) MHay
§ x ***jacksonii*** 'Max Graf' CCMG CSan EBls ELan ENot ETWh IHos MAus MBur MGan MJon MMat MMor NRog NSty SPer SRum WAct WSHC WWeb
– Red Max Graf ® (GC) See R. Rote Max Graf
– 'White Max Graf' ENot IHos MMat
Jacobite Rose See R. ***alba*** 'Alba Maxima'
Jacqueline du Pré ® (S) CCMG EWar GCoc MAus MJon SApu SJus SPer WWar
'Jacquenetta' (S) MAus SRms
'Jacques Cartier' See R. 'Marquise Boccella'
'James Bourgault' (HP) EBls
'James Mason' (G) EBls MAus
'James Mitchell' (Mo) EBls MAus MBur WHCG
'James Veitch' (DP/Mo) EBls MAus WHCG
'Jan Guest' (HT) MHay NBat
Jane Asher ® (Min/Patio) CDoC MJon SApu SJus
'Janet's Pride' (HSwB) EBls MAus
¶ Janina ® (HT) MJon
'Japonica' (Mo) MAus
Jardins de Bagatelle ® (HT) SApu
¶ 'Jason' (HT) MHay
'Jayne Austin' MAus MJon MRui SApu WHCG
¶ Jean Kenneally ® (Min) MHay
'Jean Mermoz' (Poly) MAus NElm NRog NSty SPer SRum
'Jean Rosenkrantz' (HP) EBls
'Jean Sisley' (HT) EBls
'Jeanne de Montfort' (Mo) EBls MAus
'Jeannie Deans' (HSwB) MAus
Jennie Robinson ® (Min/Patio) MJon SApu
¶ Jennifer ® (Min) MHay
'Jenny Charlton' (HT) MHay NBat
'Jenny Duval' (G) See R. 'Président de Sèze'
'Jenny Wren' (F) EBls MAus
'Jenny's Dream' (HT) MHay
¶ 'Jens Munk' (Ru) WAct
'Jersey Beauty' (Ra) EBls MAus
¶ Jim Dandy ® (Min) MHay
'Jiminy Cricket' (F) EBls
'Jimmy Greaves' (HT) MGan
Joan Ball ® (Min) MJon MRui
'Joan Bell' (HT) MHay
'Joanna Hill' (HT) EBls
'Joanne' (HT) EWar MHay MJon
'Jocelyn' (F) EBls MAus
'John Cabot' (S) WWar
'John Hopper' (HP) CCMG EBls ETWh MAus NSty
John Hughes ® (F) CSan
'John Waterer' (HT) MAus
Johnnie Walker ® (HT) MFry MGan SApu
'Josephine Bruce' (HT) CB&S CCMG CGro EBls EWar LGod MAus MBur MGan MHay NRog SRum WStI
'Josephine Bruce, Climbing' (HT/Cl) MAus MGan
'Josephine Wheatcroft' See R. 'Rosina'
Joseph's Coat ® (S/Cl) CSan EBls IHos LGod LStr MFry MGan MHay MMor MRui SRum WWeb
'Journey's End' (HT) MGan
'Joybells' (F) MAus
Joyfulness ® (F) NElm WWeb
¶ 'Jubilee Celebration' (F) MJon
'Judy Fischer' (Min) EWar LGod MAus MRui NElm WWeb
Judy Garland ® (F) SJus
'Julia Mannering' (HSwB) MAus
Julia's Rose ® (HT) CCMG CGro EWar LStr MAus MBur MFry MGan MJon NElm SApu SPer
Julie Andrews ® (F) MFry
Julie Cussons ® (F) MFry
'Juliet' (HP) EBls
¶ June Laver ® (Min) MHay
'June Time' (Min) MMor MRui NElm
'Juno' (Ce) EBls EWar MAus WHCG
¶ 'Just Jenny' (Min) MHay
Just Joey ® **AGM** Widely available
¶ Just Magic ® (Min) MJon
'Karl Foerster' (HScB) EBls MAus
'Kassel' (S/Cl) EBls MAus MMat SPer SRms WAct
'Katharina Zeimet' (Poly) EBls MAus MGan NRog NSty WAct WHCG
'Kathleen' (HM) EBls EBro
'Kathleen Ferrier' (F) EBls MGan MHay MMat MMor
'Kathleen Harrop' (Bb) CCMG CHad EBls ENot LStr MAus MBur MMat NSty SFam SPer SPla WAct WHCG WSHC WWat WWeb
'Kathleen O'Rourke' (HT) EWar
¶ Kathleen's Rose ® (F) MJon
Kathryn Morley ® (F) EWar MAus MJon MRui
'Katie' (F/Cl) MGan
'Kazanlik' misapplied See R. 'Professeur Emile Perrot'
Keepsake ® (HT) LPlm MGan MHay MMat NBat NElm NRog
Kent ® (S/GC) CCor CSan EBee EWar IHos LGod LStr MAus MJon MMat MRui SPer SPla SRum WWar
'Kerrygold' (F) IJoh MFry MGan
'Kerryman' (F) EWar MGan
'Kew Rambler' (Ra) CBow CCMG EBls ETWh EWar MAus SPer WHCG
'Kiese' (canina x) CCor MJon
'Kiftsgate' See R. ***filipes*** 'Kiftsgate'
'Kilworth Gold' (HT) MGan SRum

Name	Suppliers
'Kim' (Patio)	MAus NRog
¶ 'Kingig' (Min)	MHay
King's Ransom ® (HT)	CB&S CDoC CGro EBls ESha EWar GGre IHos IJoh LStr MAus MBur MGan MHay MJon MMor NBar NElm SApu SPer SRum WWeb
'Kitchener of Khartoum'	See R. 'K of K'
¶ 'Kitty Hawk' (Min)	MHay
x ***kochiana***	EBls
'Köln am Rhein' (Cl)	MGan
§ 'Königin von Dänemark' **AGM**	CCMG CCla CHad EBls EBro EMFP EOrc EPla ETWh GCoc MAus MBri MMat NSty SApu SChu SJus SPer WAct WHCG
'Korbell' (F)	MGan
¶ Kordes Golden Times ® (F)	MJon
'Kordes Robusta'	See R. Robusta ®
¶ 'Kordialo' (F/Patio)	MGan
Korona ® (F)	MGan NRog
'Korresia' (F)	CCMG CSan EHar ESha EWar GCoc GGre IHos IJoh LGod LStr MAus MBri MFry MGan MHay MJon MMat MMor NBat NRog SJus SPer SRum WWar
Kronenbourg ® (HT)	EBls LPlm MAus MJon SRum
'Kronprinzessin Viktoria' (Bb)	CCMG CCor EBls ETWh MAus
L D Braithwaite ® (S)	CCMG CDoC CSam EBre EWar LBre LGod LPlm LStr MAus MBri MGan MJon MMat MRui SJus SPer WHCG WWeb
'La Belle Distinguée' (HSwB)	EBls MAus WHCG
'La Belle Sultane'	See R. 'Violacea'
'La Follette' (Cl)	EBls
'La France' (HT)	EBls EBro MAus
'La France, Climbing' (HT/Cl)	MAus
'La Mortola'	See R. ***brunonii*** 'La M.'
'La Noblesse' (Ce)	EBls
'La Perle' (Ra)	MAus
'La Plus Belle des Ponctuées' (G)	CCor
'La Reine' (HP)	EBls NSty
'La Reine Victoria'	See R. 'Reine Victoria'
'La Rubanée'	See R. 'Centifolia Variegata'
La Sevillana ® (F/GC)	EBls EWar NBar SApu SPer SRum
'La Ville de Bruxelles' **AGM**	CCMG CCor EBls EBro ETWh IHos MAus MRav NSty SFam SPer WAct WHCG WHow
'Lady Alice Stanley' (HT)	EBls MAus
'Lady Barnby' (HT)	EBls
'Lady Belper' (HT)	EBls MAus MBur
'Lady Curzon' (Ru)	EBls IHos MAus NSty
'Lady Elgin'	See R. Thaïs ®
'Lady Forteviot' (HT)	EBls
'Lady Gay' (Ra)	MAus WHCG
'Lady Godiva' (Ra)	CDoC MAus
'Lady Helen' (HT)	CGro
'Lady Hillingdon' **AGM**	CCMG ETWh MAus NSty WHow

Name	Suppliers
'Lady Hillingdon, Climbing' (T/Cl)	CBow CBoy CCMG CSan EBls EBre EBro EMFP EWar LBre MAus MGan NSty SApu SPer WHCG WSHC
'Lady Iliffe' (HT)	MGan
¶ 'Lady Jane' (HT)	MHay
'Lady MacRobert' (F)	GCoc
'Lady Mary Fitzwilliam' (HT)	EBls
Lady Mavis Pilkington ® (HT)	MFry MMat
'Lady of Stifford' (F)	EWar
§ 'Lady Penzance' (HSwB)	CB&S CCMG CSam EBls EWar MAus MFry MGan NSty SPer WAct WStI
'Lady Romsey' (F)	EBls
¶ Lady Rose ® (HT)	MJon
'Lady Seton' (HT)	MGan SPer
'Lady Sylvia' (HT)	CCMG EBls MAus MGan NRog NSty SPer WStI
'Lady Sylvia, Climbing' (HT/Cl)	CCMG EBls EMFP ETWh MAus MGan NElm NRog SMad SPer WStI
Lady Taylor ® (F/Patio)	MBur
'Lady Waterlow' (HT/Cl)	CCMG EBls EBro ETWh MAus SPer WHCG
laevigata	CBot EBls ETWh MAus
– 'Anemonoides'	See R. 'Anemone'
§ – 'Cooperi'	CAbP CCMG EBls ETWh MAus SPer WSHC
'Lafter' (S)	EBls
'Lagoon' (F)	EBls
'Lakeland' (HT)	MAus NRog
'Lamarque' (N)	MAus
¶ Laminuette ® (F)	MJon
Lancashire Life ® (F)	MBri MFry MJon
'Lanei' (Mo)	EBls
'Langdale Chase' (F)	MFry MJon
Langford Light ® (Min/GC)	MBri MBur
Laughter Lines ® (F)	IDic MBri MGan WWar
Laura ® (HT)	EWar
Laura Ashley ® (Min/Cl)	EBee EWar LStr MAus MBur NBat WWar
Laura Ford ® **AGM**	CDoC EWar LGod LStr MAus MBri MBur MFry MJon MMat MRui NBat SApu SJus SMad SRum WWar WWeb
'Laura Jane' (HT)	MGan
Laurence Olivier ® (F)	MJon SApu
'Lavender Jewel' (Min)	CSan MAus MBur MHay MMat MRui
'Lavender Lace' (Min)	EBre LBre MAus
'Lavender Lassie' **AGM**	CCMG IOrc MAus MBur MFry MGan MHay MMat MRui SPer SRum WHCG
'Lavender Pinocchio' (F)	MAus
Lavinia ® (Cl)	EBee EBre EWar LBre LGod LStr MBri NElm SApu SJus SPer
'Lawrence Johnston' (Cl)	CCla EBls MAus MRav NSty SPer
'Le Havre' (HP)	EBls
'Le Rêve' (Cl)	CCMG EBls ETWh MAus

'Le Vésuve' (Ch) EBls MAus
Leander ® (S) CCMG MAus MBri
Leaping Salmon ® (HT/Cl) CCMG CGro CSan ELan EWar GCoc IHos IJoh IOrc LGod LStr MBri NBat SApu SPer SRum WStI
'Leda' (D) CCMG EBls EBro ETWh EWar MAus SFam SPer WAct
'Lemon Pillar' See R. 'Paul's Lemon Pillar'
Len Turner ® (F) CDoC IDic IHos MBri SApu
'Léonie Lamesch' (Poly) EBls ETWh SGil
'Léontine Gervais' (Ra) CAbP EBre LBre MAus NBar WAct WHCG
¶ 'Leslie's Dream' (HT) IDic
'Leuchtstern' (Ra) EBls
'Leverkusen' (Cl) CCMG CDoC CHad CSan EBls EBre EMFP ETWh LBre MAus MGan NElm NSty SPer SPla SRum WAct WHow WSHC
'Leveson-Gower' (Bb) EBls
'Ley's Perpetual' (T/Cl) CCMG CCor EBls ETWh MAus WHCG
Lichtkönigin Lucia ® (S) WWar
'Lilac Charm' (F) CHad EBls MAus
Lilac Rose ® (S) MAus NBar
Lilian Austin ® (S) EWar IHos MAus MBri SPer
Lilli Marlene ® (F) CB&S CCMG CCla CDoC CHad EBls ESha GCoc GGre IHos IJoh LStr MAus MBur MGan MMat MMor NElm NRog SPer SRum WWeb
¶ 'Lily the Pink' (HT) MHay
Lincoln Cathedral ® (HT) MGan MHay MJon SApu SPer
Lincolnshire Poacher ® (HT) NBat
¶ 'Linda Guest' (HT) MHay
Little Artist ® (Min) MJon MRui WWeb
Little Bo-Peep ® (Min/Patio) EBee MBur MFry MJon MMat MRui WWar
'Little Buckaroo' (Min) CGro CSan ELan EWar GCoc GGre LGod MGan NBar NElm SPer WStI
'Little Dorrit' (Poly) CDoC NElm NRog
'Little Flirt' (Min) CGro EBee EWar GCoc GGre MAus MGan MRui WWeb
'Little Gem' (DPMo) EBls EBro MAus MGan
¶ 'Little Girl' (Min/Cl) MHay
¶ Little Jackie ® (Min) MHay
Little Jewel ® (Patio) GCoc MAus
¶ 'Little Len' (Min/Patio) MJon
Little Marvel ® (Min) MBri MFry
Little Prince ® (F/Patio) GCoc MAus WWar
Little Russell ® (Min) MJon
'Little Stephen' (HT) CSan
'Little White Pet' See R. 'White Pet'
'Little White Pet, Climbing' See R. 'Félicité Perpétue'
Little Woman ® (Patio) CDoC IDic IHos LStr SApu
'Liverpool Echo' (F) LPlm MHay MJon NBat
Liverpool Remembers ® (HT) EWar LGod MBri MFry WWeb
'Living Fire' (F) EBls MBur MGan
Lloyds of London ® (F) LGod
'Lollipop' (Min) MGan
'Long John Silver' (Cl) CCor EBls

longicuspis hort. (Ra) CBow CCMG CCla ELan ETWh ISea SJus SPer SPla WWat
§ – ***sinowilsonii*** (Ra) EBls GCal MAus WHCG
longicuspis Bertoloni EBls
– B&L 12386 EMon
Longleat ® (Min) MMat
'Lord Penzance' (HSwB) CBoy CCMG EBls ETWh MAus MGan NSty SPer WAct
LOréal Trophy ® (HT) CSan MAus MGan MJon NBar WWar
'Lorraine Lee' (T) EBls
'Los Angeles' (HT) EBls
'LOuche' See R. 'Louise Odier'
'Louis Gimard' (Mo) EBls IHos MAus SPer WAct WHCG
'Louis Philippe' (Ch) EBls
'Louis XIV' (Ch) CHad EBls LGre WHCG
'Louise Odier' (Bb) CBoy CCMG CCla CSam EBls EBro EMFP ETWh LStr MAus MBri MMat NSty SApu SFam SJus SPer SRum WAct WHCG WHow
'Love Token' (F) MBur
¶ 'Lovely Fairy' (Poly) IDic
Lovely Lady ® **AGM** CDoC EBee IDic LGod LStr MGan MJon SApu SJus
'Lovers' Meeting' (HT) CSan ESha GGre IJoh LPlm LStr MBri MBur MGan MHay MJon MMat NBar NBat SApu SPer WStI WWar WWeb
Loving Memory ® (HT) CSan EWar GCoc LPlm LStr MFry MGan MHay MMat SRum WWar
Loving Touch ® (Min) MHay
Lucetta ® (S) CCMG MAus SPer
luciae CMHG EBls
¶ – var. ***onoei*** EPot
'Lucilla' (Patio) NBat
'Lucy Ashton' (HSwB) MAus
'Lübeck' See R. 'Hansestadt Lübeck'
'Luis Brinas' (HT) NSty
¶ Luis Desamero ® (Min) MHay
'Lutea Maxima' See R. x ***harisonii*** 'L.M.'
'Lykkefund' (Ra) CCor EBls MAus
'Lyon Rose' (HT) EBls
'Ma Perkins' (F) EBls MAus
'Ma Ponctuée' (DPMo) EBls
'Mabel Morrison' (HP) EBls MAus
Macartney Rose See R. ***bracteata***
'Macrantha' (G x) CCor EBls MAus WAct
'Macrantha Raubritter' See R. 'Raubritter'
'Macrexy' See R. Sexy Rexy ®
macrophylla CCor MAus MMat
– SF 16/131 ISea
– 'Doncasteri' See R. 'Doncasteri'
§ – 'Master Hugh' **AGM** EBls MAus NSty
'Madame Abel Chatenay' (HT) EBls MAus
'Madame Abel Chatenay, Climbing' (HT/Cl) CCMG EBls MAus NElm SPer WWeb
'Madame Alfred Carrière' **AGM** CBow CCor CHad CSam CSan EBls EMFP ETWh EWar LHol LPlm LStr MAus MFry MGan MJon MMat NRog NSty SApu SFam SJus SPer SPla SRum WAct WHCG WHow WSHC WStI

'Madame Alice Garnier' (Ra)	CBoy CCMG CSan EBls ETWh
'Madame Antoine Mari' (T)	EBls
¶ 'Madame Bérard' (T/Cl)	CCor
'Madame Berkeley' (T)	EBls
'Madame Bravy' (T)	EBls MAus
'Madame Butterfly' (HT)	EBls MAus MBur MGan NSty SApu SRum
'Madame Butterfly, Climbing' (HT/Cl)	EBls MAus MGan SJus SPer
§ 'Madame Caroline Testout, Climbing' (HT/Cl)	CBow EBls LHol MAus NRog NSty SPer WSHC
'Madame de Sancy de Parabère' (Bs)	EBls ETWh MAus WHow
'Madame de Watteville' (T)	EBls
'Madame Delaroche-Lambert' AGM	EBls MAus SPer WAct WHCG
'Madame Driout' (T/Cl)	EBls
'Madame d'Arblay' (Ra)	EBls
§ 'Madame Edouard Herriot, Climbing' (HT/Cl)	CCMG EBls ETWh MAus MGan SPer
'Madame Eliza de Vilmorin' (HT)	EBls
'Madame Ernest Calvat' (Bb)	CCMG CSan EBls MAus NSty
'Madame Eugène Résal' misapplied	See R. 'Contesse du Cayla'
'Madame Gabriel Luizet' (HP)	EBls
'Madame Georges Bruant' (Ru)	EBls MAus
§ 'Madame Grégoire Staechelin' AGM	CCMG CSam CSan EBls EBro ETWh EWar MAus MBri MGan MHay MJon MMat MRui NBar NRog NSty SApu SJus SPer SRum WAct WHCG WWeb
'Madame Hardy' AGM	CBoy CCMG CCla CSan EBls EBro ENot ETWh EWar GCoc LStr MAus MBri MBur MGan MHay MJon MMat NBar NSty SApu SFam SJus SPer WAct WHCG WHow
'Madame Henri Guillot, Climbing' (HT/Cl)	EBls MAus
'Madame Isaac Pereire' (Bb/Cl)	Widely available
'Madame Jules Gravereaux' (T/Cl)	EBls MAus
'Madame Jules Thibaud' (Poly)	MAus
N 'Madame Knorr' ('Comte de Chambord') (D/P)	CBow CBoy CCMG CSan EBls EBre EMFP ETWh IHos LBre MAus NSty SJus SPer WAct
'Madame Laurette Messimy ' (Ch)	CCMG EBls MAus WHCG WSHC
'Madame Lauriol de Barny' (Bb)	CCMG EBls ETWh MAus MGan NSty WHCG WHow
'Madame Legras de Saint Germain' (A/N)	CCMG CCor EBls EMFP ETWh IHos MAus NSty SFam SJus SPer WAct WHCG
'Madame Lombard' (T)	EBls
'Madame Louis Laperrière' (HT)	EBls MAus MGan NSty SPer WWeb
'Madame Louis Lévêque' (DPMo)	EBls WHCG
'Madame Pierre Oger' (Bb)	CCMG CSan EBls EBro ENot ETWh EWar GCoc IHos LHol LStr MAus MMat NSty SApu SFam SPer SRum WAct WHCG WWeb
'Madame Plantier' (A/N)	CBow CCMG CCla CCor CHad EBls ETWh LHol MAus MMat SPer WHCG
'Madame Scipion Cochet' (T)	EBls WHCG
'Madame Victor Verdier' (HP)	EBls
'Madame Wagram, Comtese de Turenne' (T)	EBls
'Madame William Paul' (PMo)	EBls
'Madame Zöetmans' (D)	CCMG EBls MAus NSty
'Madeleine Selzer' (Ra)	EBls MAus MGan MHay
Maestro ® (HT)	EHar MAus NBar
'Magenta' (S/HT)	EBls MAus MHay WAct WHCG
Magic Carrousel ® (Min)	CGro CSan GCoc LPlm MAus MBur MFry MHay MRui NBat WStI WWar WWeb
'Magna Charta' (HP)	EBls
'Magnifica' (HSwB)	EBls MAus MGan
N 'Maiden's Blush' (A)	CBow CCMG CCla CDoC CHad CSam EBls EBre ELan EMFP ENot ETWh LBre LHol MAus MGan NBar SApu SFam SJus SMad SPer SPla SRum WHCG WHow
'Maiden's Blush, Great'	See R. 'Great Maiden's Blush'
'Maigold' AGM	Widely available
§ *majalis*	CCor
'Malaga' (HT/Cl)	MMat
Malcolm Sargent ® (HT)	NBar SApu SPer SRum
'Maltese Rose'	See R. 'Cécile Brunner'
§ 'Malton' (Chx)	EBls
'Maman Cochet, Climbing' (T/Cl)	EBls MAus
Mandarin ® (Min)	MBur MJon MMat
'Manettii' (N)	EBls
'Manning's Blush' (HSwB)	CCor EBls MAus NSty WAct WHCG
Manou Meilland ® (HT)	EWar MGan
Manuela ® (HT)	MGan
'Manx Queen' (F)	MGan MJon

Many Happy Returns ® **AGM** CDoC CGro CSan ESha EWar LPlm LStr MAus MBri MBur MGan MJon MMat NBat SApu SJus SPer SRum WWar WWeb
'Marbled Pink' (pimpinellifolia) MAus
'Marbrée' (D/P) EBls MAus
'Marcel Bourgouin' (G) CCor EBls
'Marchenland' (S) EBls MAus
N 'Marchesa Boccella' ('Jacques Cartier') **AGM** CCMG CCla CCor CSam EBls EBro ETWh MAus MGan NBar SJus SPer SPla WAct
'Marcie Gandy' (HT) MGan
'Maréchal Davoust' (Mo) EBls MAus NSty SFam
'Maréchal Niel' (N) CCMG EBls ERea ETWh MAus MGan NSty SPer
'Margaret' (HT) MBur MGan
Margaret Merril ® **AGM** CCMG CDoC CSan EBls ESha EWar GCoc GGre IHos LGod LPlm LStr MAus MBri MBur MFry MGan MHay MJon MMat NBat NElm NRog SApu SChu SJus SPer SRum WWar WWeb
Margaret Thatcher ® (HT) MJon MMat SRum
'Margo Koster' (Poly) MAus NRog SPer SRum
'Marguerite Guillard' (HP) EBls
'Marguerite Hilling' **AGM** CBow CCMG EBls EBro ENot ETWh EWar GCoc MAus MBri MGan MJon MMat MMor NElm NRog NSty SApu SPer SRum WAct WHCG WWeb
¶ Maria Therese ® (HT/S) MHay
x *mariae-graebnerae* SLPl WBod WHCG
Marianne Tudor ® (HT) MFry
'Marie de Blois' (Mo) EBls
'Marie Louise' (D) CCMG CCor EBls EBro ETWh IHos MAus SFam WAct WHCG WHow
'Marie Pavié' (Poly) EBls MAus WHCG
'Marie van Houtte' (T) EBls MAus
'Marie-Jeanne' (Poly) EBls MAus
'Marijke Koopman' (HT) MFry
Marjorie Fair ® (S/GC) CSam CSan EBls EWar LPlm LStr MAus MFry MGan MHay MMat SApu SPer SRum WAct
'Marlena' (F/Patio) CSan GCoc MAus MBri MFry MGan
'Marshall P Wilder' (HP) NSty
'Martha' (Bb) EBls MAus
'Martian Glow' (F/S) MGan
'Martin Frobisher' (Ru) CCor EBls MAus
'Mary' (Poly) LStr
Mary Campbell ® (F) NBat
Mary Donaldson ® (HT) EWar MGan
Mary Gamon ® (Patio) MFry
Mary Hayley Bell ® (S) GCoc MJon WWar WWeb
'Mary Manners' (Ru) EBls SPer
'Mary Pope' (HT) MMat
'Mary Queen of Scots' (pimpinellifolia) EBls MAus NSty SRms WAct
Mary Rose ® (S) Widely available
'Mary Wallace' (Cl) EBls MAus SPer
Mary Webb ® (S) MAus MBri
'Masquerade' (F) CB&S CGro CSan EBls EBro ESha GGre IJoh LGod LStr MAus MGan MHay MJon MMat MMor NBar NElm NRog SRum WStI WWeb
'Masquerade, Climbing' (F/Cl) CBow CSan EBls EBre EBro GGre LBre LPlm MAus MGan MHay MJon NRog SRum WStI WWeb
'Master Hugh' See R. ***macrophylla*** 'M. H. '
Matangi ® (F) EWar LGod LStr MGan MHay MMat WWar
Matthias Meilland ® (F) EWar
'Max Graf' See R. x ***jacksonii*** 'Max Graf'
'Maxima' See R. ***alba*** 'Alba Maxima'
May Lyon ® (HT) LGod
'May Queen' (Ra) CCMG EBls ETWh MAus NBrk SPer WAct WHCG WHow
'May Woolley' (F) NBat
'McGredy's Sunset' (HT) NRog
'McGredy's Yellow' (HT) EBls MBur MGan
'McGredy's Yellow, Climbing' (HT/Cl) MGan
'Meg' (HT/Cl) CCMG CCla CHad CSan EBls ETWh MAus MBur MGan NSty SPer SRum WHCG
'Meg Merilees' (HSwB) EBls LHol MAus MGan
'Megiddo' (F) MGan WWeb
Meirov ® (Min) MGan
¶ 'Meitosier' (Cl) MBri MJon
melina EBls
Melina ® (HT) See R. Sir Harry Pilkington
Melody Maker ® (F) CDoC EWar GCoc GGre IDic LStr MBri MBur MGan MJon MMat NBar NBat SApu SJus SRum WWeb
§ Memento ® (F) CDoC EBee EWar GCoc IDic MBri MGan MMat WWar
'Memoriam' (HT) MGan MHay
¶ Mercedes ® (F) MJon
'Mermaid' **AGM** Widely available
'Merveille de Lyon' (HP) EBls
Message ® (HT) MAus MGan NBar NElm
Meteor ® (F/Patio) GCoc MGan WWeb
§ 'Mevrouw G A van Rossem, Climbing' (HT/Cl) EBls MAus
§ 'Mevrouw Nathalie Nypels' **AGM** CCla CHad EBls ETWh LStr MAus SPer WAct
'Mexico' (Min) LPlm
¶ Michael Crawford ® (HT) GCoc LGod
'Michèle Meilland' (HT) EBls MAus MGan NSty SRum
x ***micrugosa*** EBls MAus
– 'Alba' EBls MAus
Middlesex County ® (F) NBat
¶ Millie Walters ® (Min) MHay
Mimi ® (Min) MGan SJus
Mini Metro ® (Min) MFry MRui

Minijet ® (Min)	EWar IHos MGan NBat
Minilights ® (Patio)	CDoC EWar IDic MRui SApu SPer
'Minnehaha' (Ra)	CSan EBls EBro EMFP LGod MAus
Minnie Pearl ® (Min)	MHay WWar
'Miranda Jane' (F)	GCoc
mirifica stellata	See R. ***stellata mirifica***
Mischief ® (HT)	CSan EBls EWar GCoc GGre IJoh LStr MAus MBur MGan NElm NRog SApu SPer SRum WWeb
'Miss Edith Cavell' (Poly)	EBls
Miss Harp ® (HT)	MGan NElm NRog
Miss Ireland ® (HT)	MGan NRog
'Miss Lowe' (Ch)	CCor EBls LGre
Miss Pam Ayres ® (S)	MMat WWar
§ Mister Lincoln ® (HT)	EBls EBro IHos LGod LStr MAus MBri MBur MGan NElm SPer
Modern Art ® (HT)	WWeb
'Modern Times' (HT)	MBur MGan
'Mojave' (HT)	MAus MGan
Moje Hammarberg ® (Ru)	CCor ENot IHos MJon MMat WAct
Molly McGredy ® (F)	MGan
'Mona Ruth' (Min)	MGan
'Monique' (HT)	EBls MGan NSty
'Monsieur Tillier' (T)	EBls
'Moon Maiden' (F)	MMat
'Moonbeam' (S)	MAus
'Moonlight' (HM)	CCMG EBls EBro ETWh EWar IHos MAus MGan MHay MMat NElm NRog NSty SJus SPer SPla SRum WAct WHCG
'Morgengruss' (Cl)	MGan SPer
Moriah ® (HT)	MGan
'Morlettii' (Bs)	EBls
Morning Jewel ® **AGM**	CB&S EWar GCoc LPlm MFry MJon NElm NRog SPer SRum
moschata (Ra)	CCMG CSan EBls ETWh MAus WAct
– ***autumnalis***	See R. 'Princesse de Nassau'
– var. ***nastarana***	See R. 'Nastarana'
– var. ***nepalensis*** (Ra)	See R. ***brunonii***
Mother and Baby ® (HT)	CSan
'Mothers Day' (F)	EBee ELan MAus MJon NElm
¶ 'Mother's Love' (Min)	MHay
Mountain Snow ® (Ra)	MAus MBri
Mountbatten ® **AGM**	Widely available
§ 'Mousseline' (D/PMo)	CBoy CCMG CSan EBls EBro ETWh MAus NSty SPla WAct WHCG
moyesii	CBow CCMG CSam EBls ELan ENot ETWh IHos IOrc ISea MAus MFry MGan MJon MMat MMor NRog NSty NWea SPer WAct WStI WWeb
– 'Evesbatch'	WAct
§ – var. ***fargesii***	EBls SMad
– 'Geranium'	See R. 'Geranium'
– 'Highdownensis'	See R. 'Highdownensis'
– 'Hillieri'	See R. 'Hillieri'
– ***holodonta***	See R. ***m. rosea***
§ – f. ***rosea***	EBls ENot
– 'Sealing Wax'	See R. 'Sealing Wax'
¶ 'Mozart' (HM)	MJon
'Mr Bluebird' (Min/Ch)	EWar LGod MAus MGan MMor SJus WStI
'Mr Chips' (HT)	MBur
'Mr J C B' (S)	IDic WWar
'Mr Lincoln'	See R. Mister Lincoln ®
'Mrs Aaron Ward, Climbing' (HT/Cl)	EBls MAus
'Mrs Anthony Waterer' (Ru)	EBee EBls EMFP ENot IHos MAus MMat NSty SPer WAct
'Mrs Arthur Curtiss James' (HT/Cl)	CCor ETWh
'Mrs Colville' (pimpinellifolia)	EBls MAus
¶ 'Mrs Doreen Pike'	MAus
'Mrs Eveline Gandy' (HT)	MGan
'Mrs G A van Rossem, Climbing'	See R. 'Mevrouw G A van Rossem, Climbing'
'Mrs Herbert Stevens, Climbing' (HT/Cl)	CBow CCMG EBls EMFP ETWh MAus NRog NSty SMad WHCG
'Mrs John Laing' (HP)	CCMG EBls EBro ETWh EWar MAus NSty SJus SPer WHCG
'Mrs Oakley Fisher' **AGM**	CHad EBls MAus NSty WAct
'Mrs Paul' (Bb)	EBls MAus
'Mrs Pierre S du Pont' (HT)	EBls
'Mrs Sam McGredy' (HT)	MAus MBur MGan
'Mrs Sam McGredy, Climbing' **AGM**	CGro EBls ETWh LPlm MAus MBri MGan MHay MJon MMor NBar NElm NRog SPla SRum
'Mrs Walter Burns' (F/Patio)	MGan
'München' (HM)	MAus
'Mullard Jubilee' (HT)	EWar MAus MGan
mulliganii **AGM**	EBls MAus WHCG
multibracteata	CCor EBls MAus WHCG WWeb
multiflora	CCMG CCor EBls MAus
– 'Carnea'	EBls
– var. ***cathayensis***	EBls
§ – 'Grevillei'	EBls ETWh NSty SPer SPla
– 'Platyphylla'	See R. ***m.*** 'Grevillei'
– var. ***watsoniana***	See R. ***watsoniana***
– 'Wilsonii'	CSan
mundi	See R. ***gallica*** 'Versicolor'
– ***versicolor***	See R. ***gallica*** 'Versicolor'
muriculata	CCor
'Mutabilis'	See R. x ***odorata*** 'Mutabilis'
'My Choice' (HT)	MGan
'My Joy' (HT)	EWar MHay
'My Little Boy' (Min)	MBur
'My Love' (HT)	GGre MBur MGan MHay MJon WWeb
'My Love, Climbing' (HT/Cl)	MGan
My Valentine ® (Min)	EBre LBre MHay
Myra ® (HT)	NBat
Myriam ® (HT)	GCoc MJon SApu
nanothamnus	See R. ***webbiana microphylla***
'Narrow Water' (Ra)	EBls WAct WHCG
§ 'Nastarana' (N)	CCMG EBls
'Nathalie Nypels'	See R. 'Mevrouw Nathalie Nypels'

'National Trust' (HT) EBls ESha EWar GGre IHos LGod LStr MAus MGan MHay MJon MMat MMor NBar NElm NRog SPer WStI WWeb
'Nestor' (G) EBls MAus
'Nevada' **AGM** Widely available
§ 'New Dawn' **AGM** Widely available
¶ 'New Fashion' (S) MMat
New Horizon ® (F) CDoC IDic
'New Look' (F) MGan
'New Penny' (Min) CGro EWar GGre MAus MBur MGan MJon MMor MRui WWeb
New Zealand ® (HT) MHay MJon NBat SApu
News ® (F) IHos LGod MAus MGan
¶ Nice Day ® (Min/Cl) LStr MBur MFry MRui NBat WWar
'Nicola' (F) EWar MGan MHay
Night Light ® (Cl) CDoC EBee EWar LPlm MBri MBur MGan NBat SApu SJus WWar
Nina Weibull ® (F) MGan
'Niphetos' (T/Cl) EBls MAus
nitida CBow CCor EBls EBro ELan ENot GCal IHos MAus NSty NWea SPer WHCG
§ 'Noisette Carnée' (N) CCMG CCor CHad EBls EMFP ETWh NBrk NSty SPer WAct WSHC
¶ 'Non Plus Ultra' (Ra) CCor
'Norah Cruickshank' (HT) GCoc
Norfolk ® (GC) CCMG CCla CCor CSan EBre ENot EWar GCoc IHos LBre LGod LPlm LStr MAus MFry MHay MMat SApu SPer
¶ 'Norma Major' (HT) MHay
Northamptonshire ® (GC) ENot EWar LGod MHay MMat
Northern Lights ® (HT) GCoc
'Northumberland WI' (HT) NBat
'Norwich Castle' (F) EBls
'Norwich Pink' (Cl) MAus
'Norwich Salmon' (Cl) MAus
'Norwich Union' (F) EBls
'Nova Zembla' (Ru) CCMG EBls MAus NSty
'Nozomi' **AGM** CCMG CGro CSan EBls EFol ELan ENot ESha EWar GCoc GGre IHos LPlm LStr MAus MBur MFry MGan MJon MMat MMor NBar NElm SApu SJus SPer SRum WAct WHCG WWeb
'Nuits de Young' (Mo) CBoy CCMG CCor CHad EBls ETWh GCoc MAus MMat NSty SFam WHCG
'Nur Mahal' (HM) EBls EBro MAus WHCG
nutkana EBls MAus SRms
§ – var. ***hispida*** EBls
§ – 'Plena' **AGM** CCMG CCla CCor EBls ENot NSty SPer WAct WHCG
'Nymphenburg' (HM) CBoy CCMG EBls ETWh IHos MAus SPer
'Nypels' Perfection' (Poly) MAus
'Nyveldt's White' (Ru) CCor EBls IHos MAus
'Oakington Ruby' (Min/Ch) CCor GAri
'Octet' (S) CCor
x ***odorata*** 'Bengal Crimson' EMon
– 'Fortune's Double Yellow' (Cl) See R. x ***o.*** 'Pseudindica'
§ – 'Mutabilis' **AGM** CCMG CCor CGre CSco EBls EBro EMFP ENot ETWh IDai LGre MAus MMat NSty SJus SMad SPer WKif WWat
§ – 'Ochroleuca' (Ch) EBls
§ – 'Odorata' (Ch) EBls
§ – 'Pallida' (Ch) CCMG CCla CCor CHad EBls EMFP ETWh IHos MMat NSty SPer SPla
§ – 'Pseudindica' EBls MAus SHil WSHC
§ – Sanguinea Group (Ch) CHad EBls
§ – 'Viridiflora' CCMG CSan EBls IHos MAus MBur MMat SMad SRum
'Oeillet Flamand' See R. 'Oeillet Parfait'
'Oeillet Parfait' (G) EBls MAus
officinalis See R. ***gallica o.***
'Oh La La' (F) WWeb
'Ohl' (G) EBls
Ohshima Rose ® (HT) GCoc MBri
'Oklahoma' (HT) MGan
'Old Blush China' See R. x ***odorata*** 'Pallida'
Old Cabbage See R. x ***centifolia***
¶ Old Glory ® (Min) MHay
Old Master ® (F) MAus MBur MGan
Old Pink Moss See R. x ***centifolia*** 'Muscosa'
¶ Old Port ® (F) MBri MJon SApu
Old Velvet Moss See R. 'William Lobb'
Old Yellow Scotch See R. x ***harisonii*** 'Williams' Double Yellow'
Olympiad ® (HT) MBri
'Omar Khayyám' (D) EBls ENot IHos MAus SPer
§ 'Ombrée Parfaite ' (G) EBls
omeiensis f. ***pteracantha*** See R. ***sericea o. p.***
'Ophelia' (HT) CCMG EBls MAus MBur MGan NSty WHow
'Ophelia, Climbing' (HT/Cl) CBow EBls EBro ETWh MAus
'Orange Honey' (Min) MBur MFry MHay SJus WWeb
§ Orange Sensation ® (F) EBls ESha EWar GGre IJoh MAus MGan MHay MJon MMor NElm NRog SRum WWeb
¶ Orange Star ® (Min) MHay
Orange Sunblaze ® (Min) CGro EBls EWar GCoc GGre IHos IJoh LGod MGan MJon MRui NElm SApu SJus SPer WWeb
Orange Sunblaze, Climbing ® (Min/Cl) EWar LStr MBri MJon MRui SApu WStI
Orange Triumph ® (Poly) CCla EBls
'Orangeade' (F) CDoC EBro MGan
'Oranges and Lemons' (F) GCoc LGod LStr MBri MBur MFry MGan MJon SApu SJus
'Oriana' (HT) CGro
'Orient Express' (HT) MJon NBat
'Ormiston Roy' (pimpinellifolia) MAus NSty
'Orpheline de Juillet' See R. 'Ombrée Parfaite'
Othello ® (S) CBoy CDoC CSan EWar MAus SApu SPer WAct WHCG
Our Love ® (HT) GGre
¶ 'Our Molly' (S) IDic

'Over the Rainbow' (Min)	CSan MBur MHay
¶ Owen's Pride ® (F)	MJon
'Oxfam' (HT)	MHay
¶ Pacesetter ® (Min)	MHay
Paddy McGredy ® (F)	CGro EWar GGre MAus MGan MHay MJon NElm NRog SRum
Painted Moon ® (HT)	CDoC IDic MFry
Paint-Pot ® (Min)	MJon MRui
'Pam Ayers' (S)	See R. Miss Pam Ayers ®
Pandora ® (Min)	MJon MRui
'Panorama Holiday' (F)	MBur
'Papa Gontier' (T)	EBls MAus
'Papa Hémeray' (Ch)	EBls
Papa Meilland ® (HT)	CB&S CGro EBls EBro MAus MGan MHay MJon NElm NRog SApu SPer SRum WWeb
'Papillon' (T)	EBls
Paprika ® (F)	MAus MMor
'Pâquerette' (Poly)	EBls
§ 'Para Ti' (Min)	EBee EWar MBur MGan MJon MMat SJus SPer
'Parade' **AGM**	MAus MFry MGan MHay MMat MRui SJus
Paradise ® (HT)	MGan MMat
Parkdirektor Riggers ® (Cl)	CCMG CCla CDoC CHad CSam CSan EBls EBre EBro EWar LBre LStr MAus MBri MBur MGan MMat MMor NElm SPer SRum WHCG WSHC WWar
Parks' Yellow China	See R. x ***odorata*** 'Ochroleuca'
'Parkzierde' (Bb)	EBls
'Parsons' Pink China'	See R. x ***odorata*** 'Pallida'
Partridge ® (GC)	CCMG EBls ENot IHos MAus MGan MJon MMat SApu SJus SPer WAct WHCG WWeb
'Party Girl' (Min)	MHay
¶ 'Party Trick'	IDic WWar
parvifolia	See R. 'Burgundiaca'
Pascali ® (HT)	CCMG CGro CSan EBls EBre EBro ELan ESha EWar GCoc GGre IHos IJoh LBre LPlm LStr MAus MBur MGan MJon MMat MMor NBar NElm NRog SApu SPer SRum WWeb
'Pascali, Climbing' (HT/Cl)	CB&S MGan
Patricia ® (F)	SRum
'Paul Crampel' (Poly)	EBls MAus MGan NElm NRog NSty SPer
'Paul Lédé, Climbing' (T/Cl)	CBow CCMG EBls EMFP ETWh MAus WHow
Paul McCartney ®	See R. The McCartney Rose ®
'Paul Neyron' (HP)	CBoy CCMG EBls EBro ETWh MAus MMat NSty SPer WAct WHCG
'Paul Ricault' (CexHP)	CCor EBls MAus
Paul Shirville ® **AGM**	CCMG CDoC EWar GCoc GGre IHos LPlm LStr MAus MFry MGan MHay MMat NBar NBat NRog SApu SJus SPer WWar WWeb
'Paul Transon' **AGM**	CBoy CCMG CCor CSan EBls EMFP EMon ETWh MAus MBri SPer WHow
'Paul Verdier' (Bb)	EBls
§ 'Paulii' (Ru)	CCor CSan EBls EHar ELan ENot ETWh IHos MAus MBur MMor SPer WAct WHCG WWeb
'Paulii Alba'	See R. 'Paulii'
'Paulii Rosea' (Ru/Cl)	EBls MAus MBri WAct WHCG
'Paul's Early Blush' (HP)	EBls
'Paul's Himalayan Musk' **AGM**	CBoy CCMG CCla CCor CHad CSam CSan EBls EBre EBro EHar EMFP EOrc ETWh EWar LBre MAus MBri MJon MRui NBar NSty SApu SJus SPer WAct WHCG WHow WKif
§ 'Paul's Lemon Pillar' (HT/Cl)	CCMG EBls EBro ETWh MAus NRog NSty SPer SRum
'Paul's Perpetual White' (Ra)	EBls ETWh WHCG
'Paul's Scarlet Climber' (Ra/Cl)	CCMG CGro CSan EBls EBro ELan EOrc ETWh EWar GCoc GGre IHos IJoh LGod LStr MAus MBur MGan MHay MJon MMat MMor NElm NSty SApu SPer SRum WWeb
'Pax' (HM)	CCMG EBls EBro MAus NSty SPer WHCG
Peace ® **AGM**	Widely available
Peace Sunblaze ® (Min)	EWar SApu
Peach Blossom ® (S)	EWar MAus MRui
Peach Sunblaze ® (Min)	MJon MRui
'Peachy' (HT)	MRui
'Peachy White' (Min)	MAus
Pearl Drift ® (GC)	EBls EWar LStr MAus MJon SPer WHCG
Peaudouce ® (HT)	See R. 'Elina'
Peek A Boo ® (Min/Patio)	CDoC EBre ELan EWar GGre IDic IHos LBre LGod LStr MAus MFry MGan MMat MRui SApu SPer WStI WWar
Peer Gynt ® (HT)	EBre ESha IHos LBre LPlm MAus MGan MMat
'Pélisson' (Mo)	EBls WHCG
§ ***pendulina***	EBls MAus WHCG
'Penelope' **AGM**	Widely available
Penelope Keith ® (Min/Patio)	MJon MMat SApu
Penelope Plummer ® (F)	EBls
Pensioner's Voice ® (F)	MFry WWar WWeb
Penthouse ® (HT)	EWar MJon
x ***penzanceana***	See R. 'Lady Penzance'
Peppermint Ice ® (F)	CCMG MBur MJon SApu
Perdita ® (S)	CCMG EWar IHos IOrc MAus MBri SPer WAct WHCG
Perestroika ® (F/Min)	EBee LStr MBur MJon MMat MRui SApu SJus WWar
Perfecta ® (HT)	EBls MGan MHay SRum
'Perla de Montserrat' (Min)	EWar
'Perla d'Alcañada' (Min)	EWar IHos MAus MMat
'Perle des Jardins' (T)	EBls MAus
'Perle des Panachées' (G)	EBls

'Perle d'Or' (Poly)	CBoy CCMG CCor CHad CSan EMFP ENot ETWh GCoc MAus MMat NRog NSty SPer SPla WHCG WHow WWat
'Perle von Hohenstein' (Poly)	EBls
Pernille Poulsen ® (F)	EBls MGan
'Persian Yellow'	See R. ***foetida*** 'Persiana'
Peter Frankenfeld ® (HT)	MHay
Petit Four ® (Min/Patio)	IDic MAus MJon SApu
'Petite de Hollande' (Ce)	CCMG EBls ETWh MAus NSty SPer WAct WHCG
Petite Folie ® (Min)	GGre MGan
'Petite Lisette' (Ce/D)	EBls MAus SPer WHCG
'Petite Orléannaise' (Ce)	EBls
¶ Phantom ® (S/GC)	MBur MJon
'Pharisäer' (HT)	EBls
Pheasant ® (GC)	CCor ENot GCoc IHos MAus MGan MJon MMat SJus SPer WAct WStI WWeb
'Phoebe' (S)	MRui
'Phyllis Bide' **AGM**	CBow CBoy CCMG CSan EBls EMFP ETWh EWar MAus MGan NSty SJus SPer WHCG WHow
Picasso ® (F)	EBls MAus MGan
Piccadilly ® (HT)	CB&S CGro CSan EBls ESha EWar GCoc GGre IJoh LPlm LStr MAus MBur MGan MHay MJon MMat MMor NBat NElm NRog SApu SPer SRum WWeb
Piccolo ® (F/Patio)	CGro EWar GGre LStr MBri MFry MGan MHay MJon MMor SApu SJus WWar WWeb
'Picture' (HT)	EBls MAus MGan NRog NSty SPer
'Picture, Climbing' (HT/Cl)	EBls MAus MGan
'Pierre Notting' (HP)	EBls
¶ Pierrine ® (Min)	MHay
Pigalle '84 ® (F)	SRum
Pillar Box ® (F)	LGod MGan WWar
§ ***pimpinellifolia***	CCMG CKin EBls ENot ETWh LBuc LGre MAus MGan MMat NWea SPer WHCG
– cultivars	See under cultivar names
§ – double pink	CCor EBls
§ – double white	CCMG CNat EBls GCoc MAus WAct
– double yellow	See R. x ***harisonii*** 'Williams' Double Yellow'
– 'Harisonii'	See R. x ***harisonii*** 'Harison's Yellow'
– ***lutea***	See R. x ***harisonii*** 'Lutea Maxima'
– x ***pendulina***	See R. x ***reversa***
– ***altaica*** hort.	See R. 'Grandiflora'
Pink Bells ® (GC)	CCMG CCla CDoC CGro CSan EBls ENot EWar GCoc IHos LStr MAus MGan MMat SApu SPer WAct WHCG WWeb
'Pink Bouquet' (Ra)	MAus
Pink Chimo ® (S/GC)	IDic MJon
Pink Drift ® (Min/GC)	EBee ENot IHos MMat
'Pink Elizabeth Arden' (F)	EWar WWeb
'Pink Favorite' (HT)	IHos IJoh MAus MGan MHay MMor NBat NElm NRog SRum WWeb
¶ 'Pink Garnette' (Ga)	SRum
'Pink Grootendorst' **AGM**	CB&S CCMG CSan EBls ENot EWar IHos IOrc LStr MAus MGan MJon MMat MMor NRog NSty SMad SPer SPla SRum WAct WHCG
¶ 'Pink Hedgrose' (F)	MMat
Pink La Sevillana ® (F/GC)	EWar NBar SRum
Pink Meidiland ® (GC)	MGan
Pink Moss	See R. ***centifolia*** 'Muscosa'
Pink Nevada ® (S)	CSan
Pink Panther ® (HT)	EWar
'Pink Parfait' (F)	CSan EBls GCoc GGre IHos IJoh LPlm LStr MAus MBur MGan MMor NBar NBat NElm NRog SPer SRum WWeb
Pink Peace ® (HT)	CB&S ESha GGre MAus MMor NElm SRum WWeb
'Pink Pearl' (HT)	MBri MJon MMat SApu WWar
'Pink Perpétué' (Cl)	Widely available
'Pink Petticoat' (Min)	MHay WWar
Pink Posy ® (Min/Patio)	GCoc MAus
'Pink Prosperity' (HM)	CCMG EBls MAus
Pink Sunblaze ® (Min/Patio)	CSan EWar GCoc MRui NBar NElm SApu WWeb
Pink Surprise ® (Ru)	MAus
Pink Wave ® (GC)	ENot IHos MMat
'Pinocchio' (F)	EBls
'Pinta' (HT)	EBls
¶ 'Piroschka' (HT)	MJon
pisocarpa	CCor
'Pixie Rose' (Min)	IHos
Playgroup Rose ® (F)	NBat
Pleine de Grâce ® (S)	MAus SPer
'Plentiful' (F)	EBls MAus
Polar Star ® (HT)	EBls EHar ESha EWar GCoc IHos LGod LPlm LStr MAus MFry MGan MHay MJon MMat NBar NBat NElm NRog SApu SJus SPer SRum WWar WWeb
'Polly' (HT)	EBls MAus MGan NElm NRog
polyantha grandiflora	See R. ***gentiliana***
pomifera	See R. ***villosa***
– 'Duplex'	See R. 'Wolley-Dod'
¶ Pomona ® (F)	MFry
'Pompon Blanc Parfait' (A)	CCMG EBls MAus SFam
'Pompon de Bourgogne'	See R. 'Burgundiaca'
'Pompon de Paris, Climbing' (Ch/Cl)	CBot CCor CDec EBls LHop MAus MRav NSty SIng SPer WHCG WSHC WThu
'Pompon Panaché' (G)	CCMG EBls MAus
Portland Rose	See R. 'Portlandica'
§ 'Portlandica'	CCMG EBls ETWh SJus SPer WAct
Pot o' Gold ® (HT)	CDoC ESha IDic IHos LStr MAus MFry MGan MJon SApu SPer WWar
Potter and Moore ® (S)	IHos MAus
¶ 'Poulgold' (Min/Patio)	MJon
'Poulmouti'	MGan MRui
'Pour Toi'	See R. 'Para Ti'
Prairie Rose	See R. ***setigera***
prattii	CCor

'Precious Platinum' (HT)	IDic IHos LGod LStr MAus MBri MGan MHay MJon SApu SJus SPer
§ 'Président de Sèze' **AGM**	CBoy CCMG CCor EBls EMFP ETWh MAus NSty SFam SPer WHCG WHow
'Prestige' (S)	NRog
Pretty Jessica ® (S)	IHos MAus SPer
Pretty Polly ® (Min)	CGro EBee EWar GGre LStr MFry MGan MJon MMat MRui SApu WWar WWeb
Pride of Park ® (F)	MFry
Prima Ballerina ® (HT)	CB&S CCMG CGro CSan EBls GCoc GGre IHos IJoh LPlm LStr MAus MBur MFry MGan MJon MMat MMor NBat NElm NRog SPer SRum WWeb
primula **AGM**	CCMG CHad CSan EBls EBro EHar EMFP ENot ETWh IHos MAus MJon MMat NSty WAct WHCG WKif
'Prince Camille de Rohan' (HP)	EBls MAus WHCG
'Prince Charles' (Bb)	CCMG CCor EBls ETWh MAus NSty SPla WHCG
Prince Sunblaze ® (Min)	MRui
Princess Alice ® (F)	CDoC EWar LGod MGan MHay SApu
Princess Margaret of England ® (HT)	EWar
Princess Michael of Kent ® (F)	MGan WWar
'Princess Michiko' (F)	EWar
Princess Royal ® (HT)	GCoc GGre IDic MBri MFry SApu
§ 'Princesse de Nassau' (Ra)	EBls MAus WHCG
'Princesse Louise' (Ra)	MAus
'Princesse Marie' (Ra)	CCMG EBro MBri
Priscilla Burton ® (F)	EWar MAus
Pristine ® (HT)	EWar IDic IHos LPlm LStr MAus MGan MJon NBar WWar
N 'Professeur Emile Perrot' (D)	CCMG CCor EBls ETWh IHos NSty SPla
'Prolifera de Redouté' misapplied	See R. 'Duchesse de Montebello'
'Prosperity' (HM)	CBow CCor CSan EBls EBre EBro ENot ETWh EWar GCoc IOrc LBre MAus MBur MFry MGan MHay MJon MMat MRui NElm NRog SJus SPer SPla WAct WHCG WWeb
Prospero ® (S)	CCMG ETWh MAus MBri SPer WAct
x ***pruhoniciana*** 'Hillieri'	See R. 'Hillieri'
Pucker Up ® (Min)	MHay
§ ***pulverulenta***	EBls
'Purity' (Ra)	CCor CSan
'Purple Beauty' (HT)	MGan
'Purple Splendour' (F)	MAus
Purple Tiger ® (F)	IDic MBri MBur MJon SApu
Quaker Star ® (F)	IDic
Quatre Saisons	See R. x ***damascena semperflorens***
'Quatre Saisons Blanche Mousseuse' (D/Mo)	EBls ETWh
Queen Charlotte ® (HT)	GCoc MBri MBur
Queen Elizabeth ® (F)	See R. 'The Queen Elizabeth'
Queen Mother ® (Patio)	EBee ELan GCoc IHos LStr MAus MBur MFry MGan MJon MMat SPer WWeb
Queen Nefertiti ® (S)	IHos MAus SApu
'Queen of Bedders' (Bb)	EBls
'Queen of Denmark'	See R. 'Königin von Dänemark'
'Queen of Hearts'	See R. 'Dame de Coeur'
¶ Radiant ® (Min)	MHay
Radox Bouquet ® (F)	EWar GCoc MBur
'Radway Sunrise' (S)	EBls
'Rainbow' (S)	MMat
¶ Rainbow's End ® (Min)	MHay
'Rambling Rector' **AGM**	Widely available
§ 'Ramona' (Cl)	CCMG EBls ETWh MAus WHCG WSHC
§ 'Raubritter' (***macrantha*** x)	CCMG CCor CHad EBls ETWh IHos MAus MBri MMat NSty SApu SPer WAct WHCG
Ray of Sunshine ® (Patio)	ESha GCoc GGre LPlm LStr MBri MFry
'Raymond Chenault' (Cl)	MGan
'Rebecca Claire' (HT)	GCoc MJon SApu
Red Ace ® (Min)	LGod LPlm MFry MHay MJon MRui
'Red Beauty' (Min)	MHay
Red Bells ® (Min/GC)	CCla CDoC CGro CSan EBls ENot EWar IHos LStr MAus MGan MMat SApu SPer WHCG WWeb
Red Blanket ® **AGM**	CGro CSan EBls ENot EWar GCoc IDic IHos LGod MAus MGan MMat SPer SRum WAct WWeb
'Red Coat' (F)	IHos MAus
'Red Dandy' (F)	MGan
Red Devil ® (HT)	CSan ESha EWar GGre LPlm LStr MAus MGan MHay MJon NBar NBat NElm NRog SRum
Red Dot ® (S/GC)	IDic MMat
'Red Elf' (Min)	GAri
'Red Empress' (Cl)	LStr
♦ 'Red Garnette' (Ga)	See R. 'Garnette'
'Red Grootendorst'	See R. 'F J Grootendorst'
'Red Lion' (HT)	MGan MHay
'Red Max Graf'	See R. 'Rote Max Graf'
Red Minimo ® (Min)	IHos MFry MRui
Red Moss	See R. 'Henri Martin'
Red Rascal ® (Patio)	CSan EWar GCoc IDic MBri MBur MFry MJon SApu
Red Rose of Lancaster	See R. ***gallica officinalis***
Red Splendour ® (F)	MHay
Red Sunblaze ® (Min)	EWar GCoc IHos IJoh MJon NBar SJus WWar WWeb
Red Trail ® (S/GC)	EWar IDic MJon SApu
§ 'Red Wing' (***hugonis*** x)	EBls MAus WHCG
Redgold ® (F)	GGre MGan NBar
Redouté ®	MAus MRui SJus SPer
Regensberg ® (F/Patio)	ESha EWar GCoc IHos LPlm LStr MAus MBri MFry MGan MHay MJon MMat NBar NRog SApu
'Reine des Centifeuilles' (Ce)	EBls SFam

'Reine des Violettes' (HP) — CCMG CCor CHad CSan EBls EBro ETWh EWar LStr MAus NSty SApu SFam SJus SPer WAct WHCG WHow
'Reine Marie Henriette' (HT/Cl) — EBls
§ 'Reine Victoria' (Bb) — CCMG CCor CSan EBls EBro EMFP ETWh IHos LStr MAus MGan MHay NSty SApu SJus SPer SPla WAct
Remember Me ® **AGM** — CDoC CSan ESha EWar GCoc GGre LGod LPlm LStr MBri MFry MGan MHay MJon MMat NBar NBat NRog SApu SJus WWar
¶ Remembrance ® (F) — GCoc SRum
Rémy Martin ® (HT) — LStr MBri
¶ Renaissance ® (HT) — GCoc MBur MFry
'René André' (Ra) — CCMG EBls ETWh MAus
'René d'Anjou' (Mo) — EBls MAus
Repens Meidiland ® (S) — EWar
'Rescht' — See R. 'De Rescht'
'Rêve d'Or' (N) — CCMG EBls ETWh MAus WHow WSHC
'Réveil Dijonnais' (HT/Cl) — EBls MAus
'Reverend F Page-Roberts' (HT) — EBls
'Rhodes Rose' (S) — NSty
'Richard Buckley' (F) — MBur
§ x *richardii* — EBls MAus MBri
'Richmond, Climbing' (HT/Cl) — EBls MAus
§ 'Rise 'n' Shine' (Min) — CSan EBee EWar LGod MGan MRui NBat NElm SJus
'Ritter von Barmstede' (Cl) — MGan MMor
'Rival de Paestum' (T) — EBls MAus
¶ 'River Gardens' — NPer
Rob Roy ® (F) — CCMG GCoc MBur MGan SPer
§ Robbie Burns ® (pimpinellifolia) — MAus WAct
'Robert le Diable' (Ce) — CCor EBls MAus NSty SPer WAct WHCG
'Robert Léopold' (DPMo) — EBls
'Robin Hood' (HM) — EBls EBro
Robin Redbreast ® (Min/GC) — CCla CGro EBee EBls IDic IHos MAus MJon SApu SPer WWeb
§ Robusta ® (Ru) — EBls MAus MJon MMat
'Roger Lambelin' (HP) — EBls ENot MAus MMat NSty
Romance ® (S) — MJon WWeb
Rosabell ® (F/Patio) — GCoc LPlm MFry SApu
'Rosalie Coral' (Cl) — MBri MJon MRui NBat SApu SJus WWar
¶ Rosarium Uetersen ® (Cl) — MJon
'Rose à Parfum de l'Hay' (Ru) — EBls
'Rose de Meaux' — See R. 'De Meaux'
'Rose de Meaux White' — See R. 'De Meaux White'
'Rose de Rescht' — See R. 'De Rescht'
'Rose des Maures' — See R. 'Sissinghurst Castle'
'Rose du Maître d'Ecole' — See R. 'Du Maître d'Ecole'
'Rose du Roi' (HP/D) — EBls MAus NSty WAct WHCG
'Rose du Roi à Fleurs Pourpres' (HP) — EBls MAus
§ 'Rose d'Amour' **AGM** — EBls ETWh EWar ISea MAus SJus WHCG
'Rose d'Hivers' (D) — EBls
'Rose d'Orsay' (S) — EBls
'Rose Edouard' (Bb) — EBls
§ Rose Gaujard ® (HT) — EBls ESha EWar GGre IJoh LGod LPlm LStr MAus MBur MGan MHay NElm SRum WWeb
¶ 'Rosecanpe' (HT) — NBat
'Rosemary Gandy' (F) — MGan
Rosemary Harkness ® (HT) — CDoC EWar IHos LStr MBur MJon MMat SApu SPer WWeb
'Rosemary Rose' (F) — EBls MAus MBri NRog SPer
'Rosenelfe' (F) — EBls
'Roseraie de l'Haÿ' **AGM** — Widely available
'Rosette Delizy' (T) — EBls MAus
§ 'Rose-Marie Viaud' (Ra) — MAus NSty SPer WHCG
'Rosie Larkin' (S) — LPlm MFry
¶ Rosie ® (Min) — MHay
§ 'Rosina' (Min) — EWar GCoc MGan MMat
'Rosy Cheeks' (HT) — GGre LPlm MBur MFry MGan WWeb
Rosy Cushion ® **AGM** — CGro ENot EWar GCoc IDic IHos IJoh LGod MAus MGan MJon MMat SApu SPer SRum WAct WHCG WWeb
Rosy Future ® (F/Patio) — GCoc MJon SApu
Rosy Gem ® (Min) — GGre
'Rosy Mantle' (Cl) — CB&S EWar GCoc LPlm MGan SPer
§ Rote Max Graf ® (GC) — EBls ENot EWar IHos LStr MJon MMat WAct
'Roundelay' (S) — EBls MAus
Roxburghe Rose ® (HT) — GCoc
roxburghii — CB&S CCla CCor CMCN EMon MMat NSty WAct WHCG
– f. ***normalis*** — CFee EBls MAus
– 'Plena' — See R. ***r. roxburghii***
§ – f. ***roxburghii*** — CCor MAus
'Royal Albert Hall' (HT) — EBls GCoc
Royal Baby ® (F/Min) — MBur MHay
§ Royal Brompton Rose ® (HT) — EWar MJon
¶ Royal Flush ® (Patio) — MJon
'Royal Gold' (Cl) — CCMG EBls EWar IHos IJoh LPlm LStr MAus MBri MFry MGan MHay MMor MRui NElm NRog SRum WStI WWeb
'Royal Highness' (HT) — CGro EBls MGan MHay SRum WWeb
Royal Meillandina ® (Min/Patio) — EWar
'Royal Occasion' (F) — SPer
Royal Romance ® (HT) — MFry SJus
Royal Salute ® (Min) — EWar MMat NElm NRog SPer
'Royal Smile' (HT) — EBls
Royal Sunblaze ® (Min) — EWar
Royal Volunteer ® (HT) — GCoc
Royal William ® **AGM** — CDoC CGro CSan EHar ELan ESha EWar GCoc LGod LPlm LStr MAus MBur MGan MHay MJon MMat MMor NBar NElm SApu SJus SPer SRum WWar WWeb
¶ Royal Worcester ® (S) — MJon
'Rubens' (HP) — EBls
rubiginosa — See R. ***eglanteria***

rubra	See R. ***gallica***
rubrifolia	See R. ***glauca***
– 'Carmenetta'	See R. 'Carmenetta'
'Rubrotincta'	See R. 'Hebe's Lip'
rubus (Ra)	MAus
¶ 'Ruby Pendant' (Min)	MHay
'Ruby Wedding' (HT)	CB&S CCMG CSan EBre ELan EWar GCoc GGre LBre LGod LPlm LStr MAus MBri MFry MGan MHay MJon MMat MMor NBat NElm NRog SApu SJus SPer SRum WWeb
'Ruga' (Ra)	EBls MAus
rugosa	CCor CPer CSam CSan EPla IHos ISea LBuc LHol MAus MBri WStI
– 'Alba' **AGM**	CB&S CCMG CCor CDoC CSan EBls ELan ETWh EWar IHos IJoh LBuc LStr MAus MBri MMat NRoo NSty SJus SPer SPla SRum WAct
– var. ***kamtschatica***	See R. ***r. ventenatiana***
– ***rubra*** **AGM**	CB&S CCor CDoC ETWh EWar IJoh LBuc MMat NRoo NSty SPer SRum WAct
– 'Scabrosa'	See R. 'Scabrosa'
§ – var. ***ventenatiana***	CCor
'Rugosa Atropurpurea' (Ru)	NRog
§ 'Rugul' (Min)	IHos MFry MGan MJon MRui
'Ruhm von Steinfurth' (HP)	EBls MGan
Rumba ® (F)	MGan
Running Maid ® (S/GC)	MAus WAct
'Ruskin' (Ru x HP)	EBls MAus SPer WAct
'Russelliana' (Ra)	CCMG CCor EBls EMFP ETWh MAus WHCG WHow
Rutland ® (Min/GC)	ENot EWar IHos MMat
'Sadler's Wells' (S)	EBls
'Safrano' (T)	EBls
Saint Boniface ® (F/Patio)	ESha MHay MMat
Saint Cecilia ® (S)	CCMG ELan ETWh EWar IHos MAus MRui NBar SChu SJus
Saint Dunstan's Rose ® (S)	MAus MBri MJon NBat SApu
Saint John's Rose	See R. x ***richardii***
Saint Mark's Rose	See R. 'Rose d'Amour'
'Saint Nicholas' (D)	CCor EBls MAus WHCG
'Saint Prist de Breuze' (Ch)	EBls
¶ 'Saint Swithin'	MAus
'Salet' (DPMo)	CCMG EBls EBro ETWh MAus WHCG
salictorum	CCor
Salita ® (Cl)	NBat WWar
Sally Holmes ® **AGM**	CHad EBls GCoc MAus MBri MFry MGan MHay MJon MMat NBat SApu WAct
Samaritan ® (HT)	SApu SJus
sancta	See R. x ***richardii***
'Sanders' White Rambler' **AGM**	CBow CCMG CCla CCor CDoC CSan EBls EBre EBro EMFP ETWh GGre IHos LBre LGre MAus MBri MGan MHay MJon MMor NRog NSty SPer SRum WAct WHCG WHow
'Sandringham Centenary' (HT)	EBls
'Sanguinea'	See R. x ***odorata*** Sanguinea Group
Sarabande ® (F)	MGan
Sarah ® (HT)	CCMG EWar MBur MJon
¶ Sarah Robinson ® (Min)	MJon
'Sarah van Fleet' (Ru)	CCMG CGro EBls EBre EMFP ENot ETWh GCoc LBre LStr MAus MFry MGan MMat MMor MRui NElm NRog NSty SApu SPer SRum WAct
♦ Sarah, Duchess of York ® (F/Patio)	See R. Sunseeker ®
Satchmo ® (F)	ESha EWar IHos
Savoy Hotel ® **AGM**	CCMG CSan EWar GCoc GGre LGod LStr MAus MBri MBur MFry MGan MHay MJon MMat NBar SApu SJus SPer WWeb
§ 'Scabrosa' **AGM**	CBow CCMG CCla CSan EBls EBro ETWh GCoc IHos MAus MGan MJon MMat WAct WHCG WHow
'Scarlet Fire'	See R. 'Scharlachglut'
§ Scarlet Gem ® (Min)	ELan EWar GGre MGan MMor
'Scarlet Glow'	See R. 'Scharlachglut'
Scarlet Meidiland ® (S/GC)	EWar IHos MGan MMat
'Scarlet Patio' (Patio)	MMat
'Scarlet Pimpernel'	See R. Scarlet Gem ®
Scarlet Queen Elizabeth ® (F)	CB&S CGro EBls GGre IJoh MBur MJon MMor NElm SRum WStI WWeb
'Scarlet Showers' (Cl)	MGan
Scarletta ® (Min)	GGre IHos MJon
'Scented Air' (F)	MGan MMat SPer
§ 'Scharlachglut' **AGM**	CCMG CCla EBls ELan ENot ETWh LStr MAus MGan MMat NSty SPer WAct WHCG WSHC
Scherzo ® (F)	EWar
'Schneelicht' (Ru)	EBls MAus
'Schneewittchen'	See R. 'Iceberg'
§ 'Schneezwerg' **AGM**	CCMG EBls ELan ENot ETWh GCoc IHos IOrc MAus MGan MJon MMat MMor NSty SApu SPer SPla WAct WHCG WWeb
'Schoolgirl' (Cl)	Widely available
'Scintillation' (S/GC)	CCMG MAus
Scotch	See R. ***pimpinellifolia***
¶ 'Scotch Yellow' (HT)	MJon
Scottish Special ® (Min/Patio)	GCoc MJon NBat
Sea Foam ® (S)	CDoC MJon
'Sea Pearl' (F)	MGan MMat
'Seagull' **AGM**	CCMG CSan EBls EBre EBro ELan EMFP ESha ETWh EWar LBre LGod LStr MAus MGan MJon NElm NRog NSty SPer WAct WHCG
§ 'Sealing Wax' (***moyesii*** x)	EBls MAus WAct
Seaspray ® (F)	SApu
Selfridges ® (HT)	MMat NBat
'Semiplena'	See R. x ***alba*** 'Alba Semiplena'
sempervirens (Ra)	CCor
'Sénateur Amic' (Cl)	EBls
sericea	CCor CFee MAus MBal WHCG
– 'Heather Muir'	See R. 'Heather Muir'

§ – ssp. ***omeiensis***
f. ***pteracantha*** CBow CCMG CHad CPMA CSan EBls EHar ELan EMFP ENot EPla ETWh EWar MAus MGan MJon MMat NRog NSty SApu SJus SMad SPer WAct WWeb
– 'Red Wing' See R. 'Red Wing'
'Serratipetala' (Ch) CCor
§ ***setigera*** EBls MAus
setipoda EBls MAus WAct WHCG WWat
'Seven Seas' (F) MBur
Seven Sisters Rose See R. ***multiflora*** 'Grevillei'
§ Sexy Rexy ® **AGM** CGro CSan EBre ELan EWar GGre IHos IJoh LBre LStr MBri MFry MHay MJon NBar NBat SJus SPer SRum WWeb
§ 'Shailer's White Moss' **AGM** CBow CCMG CDoC EBls EBro ETWh EWar MAus MGan MMat NRog NSty SFam SJus WHCG WHow
Sharifa Asma ® (S) CAbP CBow CCMG EWar MAus MJon MMat MRui WWeb
Sheila's Perfume ® (HT/F) CDoC EWar GCoc GGre LPlm LStr MGan MHay MJon NRog SApu SJus WWar
¶ 'Sheldon' CNat
¶ Shell Beach ® (Min) MJon
'Shepherd's Delight' (F) MGan
Sheri Anne ® (Min) MAus MFry MHay MRui
¶ 'Shine On' GCoc IDic MFry WWar
Shocking Blue ® (F) LPlm MGan MJon MMat SPer WWar
Shona ® (F) IDic SApu
'Shot Silk' (HT) EBls GCoc MAus MBur MGan
'Shot Silk, Climbing' **AGM** CCMG CSan EBls ETWh MAus MGan MHay SJus SRum
Shrewsbury Show ® (HT) MFry
'Shropshire Lass' (S) MAus MBri SPer
Silver Jubilee ® **AGM** Widely available
'Silver Lining' (HT) EBls LPlm MAus MBur SRum
'Silver Moon' (Cl) CCMG EBls ETWh MAus
'Silver Tips' (Min) MAus MGan
'Silver Wedding' (HT) CCMG CSan EBls EBre ELan GCoc GGre LBre LPlm MBur MFry MGan MHay MJon MMat MMor NBar NElm NRog SPer SRum WStI WWeb
Simba ® (HT) CSan LStr MBri MGan MHay MMat SJus
Simon Robinson ® (Min/GC) EBls MJon
'Single Cherry' (pimpinellifolia) EBls MAus
sinowilsonii See R. ***longicuspis s.***
'Sir Cedric Morris' (Ra) EBls ELan
'Sir Clough' (S) MAus
'Sir Edward Elgar' (Cl) MAus
'Sir Frederick Ashton' (HT) EBls
Sir Harry Pilkington ® (HT) NElm
'Sir Lancelot' (F) MGan
Sir Walter Raleigh ® (S) EWar MAus MBri
Sir William Leech ® (HT) NBat
§ 'Sissinghurst Castle' (G) EBls
'Sleepy' (Poly) MGan
Smarty ® (S/GC) EBls ENot IDic IHos MAus MGan MJon SPer WAct
¶ Smooth Lady ® (HT) LStr MHay
¶ Smooth Prince ® (HT) LStr MHay
'Sneezy' (Poly) MGan
'Snow Bride' (Min) MHay
Snow Carpet ® **AGM** CCla CSan EBls ENot GCoc IHos LStr MAus MFry MGan MJon MMat SApu WAct
'Snow Dwarf' See R. 'Schneezwerg'
'Snow Queen' See R. 'Frau Karl Druschki'
Snow Sunblaze ® (Min) LStr MRui
Snow White ® (HT) CDoC LStr MBri MJon SApu
Snowball ® (Min/GC) MJon MRui
'Snowdon' (Ru) MAus
Snowdrop ® (Min/Patio) MFry MRui
'Snowflake' (Ra) WHCG
'Snowline' (F) EWar MGan
'Soldier Boy' (Cl) EBro WHCG
'Soleil d'Or' (HT) MAus
Solitaire ® (HT) EWar MBri MJon SApu WWar WWeb
§ 'Sombreuil, Climbing' (T/Cl) CCMG CHad CSan EBls ETWh MAus MRav SJus SPer WAct WHCG
'Sophie's Perpetual' (Ch/Cl) EBee EBls ENot MAus MGan MMat SJus SPer WWeb
Soraya, Climbing ® (HT/Cl) MAus
soulieana **AGM** EBls ETWh GWht MAus MMat WKif
'Soupert et Notting' (PMo) EBls MAus SPer WHCG
'Southampton' **AGM** CSan EBls EWar LStr MAus MBri MGan MHay MMat NElm NRog SApu SPer
'Souvenir de Claudius Denoyel' **AGM** CCMG EBls ETWh MAus MMat NRog SPer
'Souvenir de François Gaulain' (T) EBls
'Souvenir de Jeanne Balandreau' (HP) EBls
'Souvenir de la Malmaison' (Bb) CBow CCMG CCla CCor EBls EBro EMFP ENot EOrc ETWh GCoc IHos IOrc MAus MGan MMat NSty SPer WAct WHCG WWeb
'Souvenir de la Malmaison, Climbing' (Bb/Cl) CBow CBoy CCMG CSan EBls ETWh MAus WAct WHCG
'Souvenir de Madame Léonie Viennot' (T/Cl) EBls MAus
'Souvenir de Philémon Cochet ' (Ru) EBls ETWh MAus
'Souvenir de Pierre Vibert' (DPMo) EBls
'Souvenir de Saint Anne's' **AGM** CBoy CCMG CHad EBls EBro ETWh MAus WAct WHCG WHow

'Souvenir du Docteur Jamain' (HP/Cl) — CBow CCMG CHad EBls EBro EMFP ETWh LGre LStr MAus MMat NSty SFam SJus SPer WAct WHCG WHow
'Souvenir du Président Carnot' (HT) — EBls MAus
'Souvenir d'Alphonse Lavallée' (HP/Cl) — CSan EBls WHCG
'Souvenir d'Elise Vardon' (T) — EBls
'Souvenir d'un Ami' (T) — EBls
spaldingii — See R. ***nutkana hispida***
'Spanish Beauty' (HT/Cl) — See R. 'Madame Grégoire Staechelin'
Sparkling Scarlet ® (Ra) — EBre ELan EWar LBre LPlm MGan
'Sparrieshoop' (S/Cl) — EWar
'Spartan, Climbing' (F/Cl) — EWar
¶ 'Special Guest' (HT) — MHay
'Spectabilis' (Ra) — EBls MAus WHCG
¶ Spek's Centennial ® (F) — MJon
'Spek's Yellow' (HT) — CB&S EBls MGan
'Spek's Yellow, Climbing' (HT/Cl) — MAus MGan
'Spencer' — See R. 'Enfant de France'
spinosissima — See R. ***pimpinellifolia***
§ Spirit of Youth ® (HT) — MJon SApu
§ 'Splendens' (Ra) — CCMG CCor EBls ELan ETWh MAus
'Spong' (G) — CCMG EBls ETWh MAus
Spot Minijet ® (Min) — MRui
'Stacey Sue' AGM — MAus
§ 'Stanwell Perpetual' (pimpinellifolia) — CBow CBoy CCMG CCor EBls EMFP ENot EOrc ETWh EWar GCoc IHos LStr MAus MMat NSty SApu SPer WAct WHCG WWeb
Star Child ® (F) — EWar IDic
Starina ® (Min) — CSan EWar MFry MGan MHay MRui SJus WWeb
'Stars 'n' Stripes' (Min) — CSan LGod LPlm MAus MFry MRui NElm
Stella ® (HT) — EBls MGan SRum
§ ***stellata*** var. ***mirifica*** — EBls MAus MGan MMat
'Stephanie Diane' (HT) — LPlm MHay
'Sterling Silver' (HT) — EBls LStr MAus MGan
Strawberry Fayre ® (Min/Patio) — GCoc LStr MJon NBat
'Strawberry Ice' (F) — IJoh MJon
'String of Pearls' (Poly) — SPer
Sue Lawley ® (F) — MBri MGan MJon NRog
Sue Ryder ® (F) — EWar MHay
Suffolk ® (S/GC) — CCMG CCor CSan EBee EBre ENot EWar IHos LBre LGod MAus MMat SApu SJus SPer SRum WBod
suffulta — See R. ***arkansana suffulta***
Suma ® AGM — CSan EWar GCoc GGre LGod LPlm LStr MFry MJon MRui SApu SJus WWeb
Summer Dream ® (HT) — CCMG LStr MAus MFry SApu SJus
Summer Fragrance ® (HT) — CCMG EWar GCoc MGan MJon
Summer Holiday ® (HT) — MBur MGan SPer WWeb
Summer Love ® (F) — MJon
Summer Sérénade ® (F) — MJon
'Summer Sunshine, Climbing' (HT/Cl) — MBri NElm
Summer Wine ® AGM — EBee EWar IHos MBri MGan MJon MMat NBat SApu SJus SPer WWar
¶ 'Sun Hit' (Patio) — MMat
'Sunblaze' — See R. Orange Sunblaze ®
'Sunblest ® (HT) — CSan ESha GGre IHos IJoh LGod LPlm MAus MBri MBur MFry MGan MMor NRog SJus WWeb
Sunderland Supreme ® (HT) — MHay NBat
Sunmaid ® (Min) — MJon MMor MRui
Sunny Sunblaze ® (Min) — MJon MRui
¶ 'Sunrise' (Cl) — MMat
§ Sunseeker ® (F/Patio) — CDoC IDic LGod MBri MBur MJon WWar
Sunset Song ® (HT) — ESha GCoc
'Sunshine' (Poly) — MGan
'Sunsilk' (F) — MBri MFry MGan
¶ Super Dorothy ® (Ra) — CCor
¶ Super Excelsa ® (Ra) — CCor
Super Star ® (HT) — CB&S CGro EBls EBro ESha EWar GCoc IJoh LPlm LStr MAus MBur MGan MHay MJon MMat MMor NBar NRog SRum WWeb
Super Star, Climbing ® (HT/Cl) — MAus MHay MMor NElm SRum
'Super Sun' (HT) — ESha MBur NElm SRum
'Surf Rider' (S) — MMor
'Surpasse Tout' (G) — EBls MAus WHCG
§ 'Surpassing Beauty of Woolverstone' (HP/Cl) — EBls WHCG
Surrey ® AGM — CCMG CCor EBre ENot EWar GCoc IHos LBre LPlm LStr MAus MFry MGan MHay MJon MMat MRui SApu SJus SPla SRum WStI
Susan Hampshire ® (HT) — EBls EWar MGan SRum
Sussex ® (GC) — CCMG CCla CCor ENot EWar LStr MAus MBur MFry MJon MMat MRui SApu SJus SPer SPla SRum
'Sutter's Gold' (HT) — EBls MAus MBur MGan NElm NRog
'Sutter's Gold, Climbing' (HT/Cl) — MAus MGan
'Swan Lake' (Cl) — CCMG CSan EBls EBre ELan ESha ETWh EWar IHos IJoh LBre LGod LStr MAus MBri MBur MFry MGan MHay MMat MMor NBar SPer SRum WWeb
Swan ® (S) — EWar IHos MAus MBri MJon
Swany ® (Min/GC) — CCMG CCla EBls EHar ELan EWar IHos LStr MAus MGan MHay MMat SApu SPer SRum WAct WHCG WWeb
'Swedish Doll' (Min) — MBur
Sweet Dream ® AGM — Widely available
'Sweet Fairy' (Min) — LPlm MMat MRui
'Sweet Honesty' (Min — EBee MBur
Sweet Juliet ® (S) — CAbP CCMG EWar LGod LPlm MAus MBri MJon MRui NBat SApu WAct WWeb

Sweet Magic ® **AGM**	CDoC CGro CSan EBre ESha EWar GGre IDic IHos LBre LGod LPlm LStr MBri MBur MFry MGan MJon MMat MRui NBat NElm SApu SJus SPer SRum WWar WWeb
Sweet Nell ® (F)	LGod
Sweet Promise ® (GC)	MGan NElm
'Sweet Repose' (F)	MAus MGan
¶ Sweet Symphony ® (Min)	MFry
'Sweet Velvet' (F)	MGan
N Sweetheart ® (HT)	GCoc MGan NBat SJus
sweginzowii	CCor GCal MAus MMat
– 'Macrocarpa'	EBls
'Sydonie' (HP)	EBls
Sympathie ® (HT/Cl)	IHos IJoh LPlm MAus MFry MGan MMat MMor MRui SJus SPer SRum
Symphony ® (S)	EBee EWar MAus MJon
'Talisman' (HT)	EBls
'Talisman, Climbing' (HT/Cl)	EBls
Tall Story ® **AGM**	EWar IDic MJon SApu SPer SRms SRum
'Tallyho' (HT)	EBls
'Tamora' (S)	MAus MBri
Tango ® **AGM**	EWar LPlm MJon MMat NBat WWar WWeb
¶ Tatjana ® (HT)	MJon
§ 'Tausendschön' (Ra)	CSan EBls
'Tea Rambler' (Ra)	CCor EBls NSty
Tear Drop ® (Min/Patio)	CCla GCoc IDic LStr MBur MGan MJon NBat SApu SPer
Ted Gore ® (F)	NBat
Teeny Weeny ® (Min)	MJon MRui
Telford's Promise ® (GC/S)	MRui NBat WWar
'Telstar' (F)	MGan
'Temple Bells' (Min/GC)	EBls MAus NRog
¶ Temptation ® (F/Patio)	MJon
'Tenerife' (HT)	ESha NElm SRum WStI WWeb
Tequila Sunrise ® **AGM**	CDoC ESha EWar GCoc IDic LPlm LStr MBri MBur MFry MGan MJon MMat NBat SApu SJus WWar
'Texas Centennial' (HT)	EBls
§ Thaïs ® (HT)	EBls
'Thalia'	MAus
'The Bishop' (Ce/G)	EBls MAus
'The Bride' (T)	EBls NSty
The Children's Rose ® (F)	SApu
♦ 'The Colwyn Rose' (F)	See R. Colwyn Bay ®
The Countryman ® (S)	CAbP CCMG CCla CSam EBee EWar MAus MFry MRui SApu SJus
The Coxswain ® (HT)	GCoc
The Dark Lady ® (S)	CBoy IHos MAus MBri NBar SChu
'The Doctor' (HT)	EBls MAus MGan
'The Doctor, Climbing' (HT/Cl)	MGan
'The Ednaston Rose' (Cl)	CCla WHCG
'The Fairy' **AGM**	Widely available
The Flower Arranger ® (F)	MFry MJon
'The Garland' **AGM**	CCMG EBls ETWh MAus MMat NSty SPer SPla WHCG
'The Havering Rambler'	EBro
The Herbalist ® (S)	MAus
'The Honorable Lady Lindsay' (S)	NSty
'The Knight' (S)	NSty
The Lady ® **AGM**	CCMG EBee GCoc MAus MBur MFry MHay MJon NBat SApu
'The Maid Marion'	EBro
§ The McCartney Rose ® (HT)	ESha EWar GGre LPlm LStr MBri MJon MMat SApu SJus WWeb
'The Miller' (S)	MAus
'The New Dawn'	See R. 'New Dawn'
The Nun ® (S)	IHos MAus
The Observer ® (HT)	MFry MJon
The Pilgrim ® (S)	CAbP MAus MBri MJon MRui NBar SJus SPer
The Prince ® (S)	CAbP CBoy EWar IHos MAus MJon MRui NBar SPer WHow
'The Prioress' (S)	MAus WHCG
§ 'The Queen Elizabeth' **AGM**	Widely available
'The Queen Elizabeth, Climbing' (F/Cl)	CCla EBls MGan SRum
The Reeve ® (S)	MAus
'The Royal Brompton Rose'	See R. Yves Piaget ®
The Seckford Rose ® (S)	ENot MJon MMat
The Squire ® (S)	MAus WAct
The Times Rose ® **AGM**	CDoC CSan EWar GCoc IHos LGod LStr MGan MHay MJon MMat SJus SPer
The Valois Rose ® (R)	MJon MMat
'The Wife of Bath' (S)	MAus MBri NBar SPer
'Thelma' (Ra)	EBls MAus
'Thérèse Bugnet' (Ru)	EBls
'Thisbe' (HM)	CCMG EBls EBro MAus SPer WAct WHCG
Thomas Barton ® (HT)	LStr
Thora Hird ® (F)	MAus WWeb
'Thousand Beauties'	See R. 'Tausendschön'
Threepenny Bit Rose	See R. ***elegantula*** 'Persetosa'
'Tiara' (HSwB)	SRum
Tigris ® (***persica*** x) (S)	MAus
'Till Uhlenspiegel' (HSwB)	EBls
'Tina Turner' (HT)	MBur MJon NBat
¶ Tiny Tot ® (Min)	MHay
Tip Top ® (F/Patio)	CB&S CGro EBls ELan EWar GCoc GGre IHos LStr MBri MFry MGan MHay MMor NElm NRog SPer SRum WStI WWeb
'Tipo Ideale'	See R. x ***odorata*** 'Mutabilis'
'Tipsy Imperial Concubine' (T)	EBls
'Toby Tristam' (Ra)	WWat
'Tom Tom' (F)	IJoh
'Top Marks' (Min/Patio)	CDoC CSan ESha EWar LGod LPlm LStr MBri MBur MFry MGan MJon MMat MRui NBat SApu SJus SRum WStI WWar
'Topeka' (F)	SRum
Toprose ® (F)	GCoc SJus

Name	Suppliers
Topsi ® (F/Patio)	EWar GGre IHos IJoh LGod MAus MFry MJon MMor NElm SPer SRum WWeb
¶ Torch of Liberty ® (Min)	MHay
Torville and Dean ® (HT)	CDoC NRog
§ 'Tour de Malakoff' (Ce)	CBoy EBls ETWh MAus SApu SFam SPer SPla WHCG
Tournament of Roses ® (HT)	IDic MJon
'Toy Clown' (Min)	MAus
Toynbee Hall ® (F)	MMat
'Trade Winds' (HT)	MGan
Tranquillity ® (HT)	MBur MJon SApu
'Treasure Trove' (Ra)	CCMG CCor EBls MAus MBur
'Tricolore de Flandre' (G)	EBls GCoc MAus
Trier ® (Ra)	CCMG CCor EBls ETWh MAus MMat WHCG
'Trigintipetala' misapplied	See R. 'Professeur Emile Perrot'
'Triomphe de l'Exposition' (HP)	MAus
'Triomphe du Luxembourg' (T)	EBls MAus
triphylla	See R. x ***beanii***
Troika ® **AGM**	CSan ESha IJoh LPlm LStr MAus MBur MFry MGan MHay MJon MMat SPer
Troilus ® (S)	CCMG MAus NBar
'Truly Yours' (HT)	MGan
Trumpeter ® **AGM**	CSan ESha EWar GCoc IHos IJoh LGod LPlm MAus MBri MFry MGan MHay MJon MMat NBar NBat SApu SPer WWar
* 'Turkestan'	WSHC
'Tuscany' (G)	CHad CSan GCoc MAus SJus SPer WHCG
'Tuscany Superb' **AGM**	CCMG CSan EBls EBro EMFP ENot ETWh EWar IHos LHol MAus MMat NSty SPer WAct WHCG WHow WKif WSHC WWeb
¶ 'Twenty One Again' (HT)	MBur
Tynwald ® (HT)	EWar LStr MJon MMat
'Typhoon' (HT)	MBur MJon WWar
'Ulrich Brunner Fils' (HP)	EBls MAus
ultramontana	CCor
'Uncle Bill' (HT)	EBls
Uncle Walter ® (HT)	EBls ESha MMor NElm NRog SRum WStI
'UNICEF' (F)	GCoc
§ 'Unique Blanche' (Ce)	CBoy CCMG EBls ETWh MAus
'Vagabonde' (F)	MGan
Valencia ® (HT)	EWar MBur MJon MMat NBat
Valentine Heart ® (F)	CDoC EBre IDic LBre MJon SApu SJus
'Vanguard' (Ru)	EBls MAus SPer
'Vanity' (HM)	EBls EBro IHos MAus SPer SRms
'Variegata' (pimpinellifolia)	CArn
'Variegata di Bologna' (Bb)	CBow CCMG CCla EBls EBro ETWh EWar MAus MMat NSty WAct

Name	Suppliers
'Veilchenblau' **AGM**	CBow CCMG CCla CHad CSan EBls EBro ELan ETWh EWar MAus MBri MBur MGan MHay NSty SJus SPer SRum WAct WHCG WHow WKif WSHC
Velvet Fragrance ® (HT)	GCoc MAus MBur MFry MJon SApu
'Venusta Pendula' (Ra)	EBls MAus
versicolor	See R. ***gallica*** 'Versicolor'
'Vesuvius' (HT)	MAus
'Vick's Caprice' (HP)	EBls MAus NSty
'Vicomtesse Pierre du Fou' (HT/Cl)	EBls MAus NSty
Victor Hugo ®	See R. Spirit of Youth ®
'Victoriana' (F)	MAus
¶ Vidal Sassoon ® (HT)	GCoc MBur
'Village Maid'	See R. 'Centifolia Variegata'
§ ***villosa***	EBls MAus MMat NSty
– 'Duplex'	See R. 'Wolley-Dod'
§ 'Violacea' (G)	CCor EBls
Violet Carson ® (F)	ESha MAus MGan
'Violette' (Ra)	CCMG EBls ETWh MAus NSty SPer WAct WHCG
'Violinista Costa' (HT)	EBls MAus
virginiana **AGM**	CCor EBls ETWh MAus MGan MSte WHCG WHen
– 'Plena'	See R. 'Rose d'Amour'
'Virgo' (HT)	EBls IJoh MAus SRum
'Viridiflora' (Ch)	See R. x ***odorata*** 'V.'
Vital Spark ® (F)	MGan
'Vivid' (Bb x)	EBls
'W E Lippiat' (HT)	EBls
Wandering Minstrel ® (F)	MGan SApu
wardii var. ***culta***	MAus
'Warley Jubilee' (F)	EWar
Warm Welcome ® **AGM**	CDoC EWar GCoc LStr MAus MBri MBur MFry MJon MMat MRui NBat SJus SMad WWar
¶ Warm Wishes ® (HT)	GCoc LPlm LStr MBur MFry MGan NBat
'Warrior' (F)	EWar MGan SPer WWeb
Warwick Castle ® (S)	MAus
Warwickshire ® (GC)	ENot EWar MMat MRui
§ ***watsoniana***	EBls
webbiana	CCor EBls ETWh MAus WHCG
'Wedding Day' (Ra)	CCMG CDoC CSan EBls EBre EBro ELan ETWh EWar LBre LPlm LStr MAus MBri MBur MGan MJon MMat NSty SApu SJus SPer SRum WAct WHCG WWeb
Wee Barbie ® (Min)	MRui NElm SApu WWar
Wee Jock ® (F/Patio)	CDoC GCoc MAus
'Wee Man' (Min)	WWeb
'Weetwood' (Ra)	CCMG MAus SPer
'Weisse aus Sparrieshoop' (S)	MGan
'Welcome Guest' (HT)	MHay
'Wembley Stadium' (HT)	MGan
'Wendy Cussons' (HT)	CB&S CCMG CDoC CGro EBls EBro EWar GCoc GGre IHos IJoh LPlm LStr MAus MBur MGan MHay MJon MMor NBar NElm NRog SApu SPer SRum WWeb
Wenlock ® (S)	CSam EWar MAus SPer

Westerland ® **AGM** — LPlm MGan MHay MJon MMat WWar
'Westfield Star' (HT) — MAus
'Whisky Gill' (HT) — MGan
Whisky Mac ® (HT) — Widely available
'White Bath' (CeMo) — See R. 'Shailer's White Moss'
White Bells ® (Min/GC) — CCMG CCla CCor CDoC EBls ENot EWar IHos LStr MAus MGan MMat SApu SPer WAct WHCG WWeb
'White Cécile Brunner' — See R. Cécile Brunner, White'
'White Christmas' (HT) — ELan MBur MGan SRum
¶ White Cloud ® (Min) — MMat
'White Cockade' **AGM** — CB&S CCMG CDoC EBls GCoc LPlm MAus MFry MGan NElm SApu SJus SPer
'White Flower Carpet' (GC) — MFry MMat
'White Grootendorst' (Ru) — EBls MAus WAct
White Meidiland ® (S/GC) — CCMG EBre EWar LBre MGan
White Moss — See R. 'Shailer's White Moss'
§ 'White Pet' **AGM** — CBow CCMG CCor CHad EMFP ETWh GCoc IHos LStr MBri MBur MGan MJon MRui SApu SJus SPer SPla WAct
White Provence — See R. 'Unique Blanche'
'White Queen Elizabeth' (F) — EBls SRum
White Rose of York — See R. 'Alba Semiplena'
'White Spray' (F) — EBls
'White Wings' (HT) — CBow CCMG EBls MAus MGan NSty SApu SPer WAct
Whitley Bay ® (F) — NBat
wichuraiana (Ra) — CBow CCor EBls LHol MAus SRum WHCG
*– 'Variegata' (Ra) — CB&S CBow CCor CLew CPMA EBar EBro EFol EHoe ELan EPla EPot ETWh MAus MPla NHol SDry SMad WPat
*– 'Variegata Nana' (Ra) — LHop MCas
¶ 'Wickham Highway' (F) — NBat
'Wickwar' (Ra) — CCor EBls EFol ELan EPla GCal MHlr WAct WCot WHCG
'Wild Flower' (S) — MBri
'Wilhelm' **AGM** — CCor EBls EBro IHos MAus NSty WHCG
'Will Scarlet' (HM) — IHos LStr MAus
'Willhire Country' (F) — EBls
'William Allen Richardson' (N) — CBoy EBls ETWh MAus WHCG
'William and Mary' (S) — EBls
'William III' (pimpinellifolia) — EBls LHop MAus SChu
§ 'William Lobb' **AGM** — CCMG CCla CCor CHad CNat CSan EBls EBro ENot EOrc ETWh EWar GCoc IDai IHos IOrc MAus MGan MMat NSty SApu SJus SPer SRum WAct WHCG WKif WWeb
'William R Smith' (T) — EBls
William Shakespeare ® (S) — CBoy CCMG ELan ETWh EWar IHos LStr MAus MBri SPer SPla SRum WStI WWeb
'Williams' Double Yellow' (HScB) — See R. x ***harisonii*** 'W. D. Y'
willmottiae — EBls MAus MGan MMat NSty SPer WAct WBod WHCG
Wiltshire ® (S/GC) — CCMG MFry MJon MMat MRui SJus
Wimi ® (HT) — EWar MGan MHay NBat SApu
Winchester Cathedral ® (S) — CBoy CCMG CDoC EBre ETWh EWar LBre LGod LStr MAus MBri MJon MRui NBar SApu SChu SPer SPla SRum WHow WWeb
Windrush ® (S) — CCMG MAus MBri NBar SPer WAct WHCG
¶ Winsome ® (Min) — MHay
¶ Winter Magic ® (Min) — MHay
x ***wintoniensis*** — EHic WAct WHCG
Wise Portia ® (S) — CCMG MAus
Wishing ® (F/Patio) — CCMG CDoC GCoc IDic MFry MJon SApu WWeb
With Love ® (HT) — MJon SApu
'Woburn Abbey' (F) — CGro EBls GGre MJon NElm NRog
§ 'Wolley-Dod' (S) — EBls WAct
¶ Woodland Sunbeam ® (Min/Patio) — MJon
¶ Woodlands Lady ® (Min/Patio) — MJon MRui
'Woodrow's Seedling' (Cl) — MMor
Woods of Windsor ® (HT) — MMat SJus
§ ***woodsii*** — CCor CMCN EBls MAus MMat SPer WHCG
– var. ***fendleri*** — See R. ***woodsii***
'Woolverstone Church Rose' — See R. 'Surpassing Beauty of Woolverstone'
¶ 'Wor Jackie' (HT) — NBat
xanthina — EBls ETWh MGan MMat
§ – 'Canary Bird' **AGM** — CCMG CCla CDoC CGro CSam CSan EBls EBre ELan ENot EWar GCoc IJoh IOrc LBre LGod LPlm LStr MAus MBri MBur MMat SApu SBod SJus SMad SPer SRum WAct WHCG
§ – f. ***hugonis*** **AGM** — CCMG CCor EBls EFol ELan ETWh MAus MGan MMat NRog SPer WAct WHCG
'Xavier Olibo' (HP) — EBls
yainacensis — CCor
'Yellow Beauty' (Min) — NBar
'Yellow Button' (S) — CCMG MAus MBri SPer
Yellow Charles Austin ® (S) — MAus MBri SJus WHCG
'Yellow Cushion' (F) — EWar MAus
Yellow Dagmar Hastrup ® (Ru) — CBow CCla CCor EBee EMFP MAus MBri MGan MJon MMat MRui SApu SJus SPla WAct WHCG
'Yellow Doll' (Min) — CGro ELan EWar GGre IJoh MAus MGan MRui
'Yellow Pages' (HT) — MAus
'Yellow Patio' (Min/Patio) — LStr
'Yellow Petals' (HT) — MBur
'Yellow Ribbon' (F) — ESha

Yellow Scotch	See R. x ***harisonii*** 'Williams' Double Yellow'
Yellow Sunblaze ® (Min)	CSan EWar IHos NBar NElm SApu WWeb
Yesterday ® AGM	CCMG EBls ESha ETWh EWar LGod MAus MGan MMat SPer SRum WHCG
'Yolande d'Aragon' (HP)	EBls
York and Lancaster	See R. x ***damascena versicolor***
Yorkshire Bank ® (HT)	MFry
¶ 'Yorkshire Lady' (HT)	NBat
Yorkshire Sunblaze ® (Min)	EWar SApu
Young Quinn ® (HT)	MBur
Yves Piaget ® (HT)	See R. Royal Brompton Rose®
'Yvonne Rabier' AGM	CBow CCMG EBls LStr MAus MMat MRui SPer WAct WHCG
Zambra ® (F)	CB&S
'Zéphirine Drouhin' AGM	Widely available
§ 'Zigeunerknabe' AGM	CCMG CCla CCor EBls EMFP ENot ETWh EWar MAus MMat NSty SChu SPer WAct WHCG
Zitronenfalter ® (S)	MGan
'Zola' (S)	CSan
'Zweibrücken' (Cl)	MGan
§ 'Zwergkönig' (Min)	EWar MGan SJus

ROSCOEA † (Zingiberaceae)

alpina	CBos CBro CRDP GDra MTho NHol NKay NWCA SBla SWas WChr
¶ – pink	WChr
auriculata	CAvo CBro NHar NHol SBla WChr WThi
'Beesiana'	CRDP ECha LAma LBow MNFA MTho NHar NHol NRya WChr WCot
¶ – white	NHol
capitata	See R. ***scillifolia***
cautleoïdes AGM	CAvo CBro CGle CRDP GArf GDra LAma LBow LGre MNFA MTho NHar NHol NKay NRog NSla SAxl SBla SUsu WChr WCru WThi
– 'Grandiflora'	EPot
– 'Kew Beauty'	MUlv SBla
humeana AGM	CBro CSpe GLil NHar NPri SAxl SMrm
§ ***purpurea***	CBro CChu CCla CGle CRDP EGol ELan ELun EPar GCHN GCal LAma MFir MUlv NBir NHar NHol SAxl SPer SWas WChr WCot WOMN WThi WWin
– ***procera***	See R. ***purpurea***
§ ***scillifolia***	CBro CRDP GCal LAma LBow NBir NHar NHol NRog WChr WCru WThi WThu
tibetica	SAxl WHer

ROSMARINUS † (Labiatae/Lamiaceae)

angustifolius	See R. ***officinalis angustissimus***
* ***calabriensis***	WCHb WHer
* ***capicanalli***	CHan
corsicus 'Prostratus'	See R. ***officinalis*** Prostratus Group
lavandulaceus Noë	See R. ***eriocalyx***
x ***lavandulaceus*** hort.	See R. ***officinalis*** Prostratus Group
officinalis	Widely available
– var. ***albiflorus***	CArn CCla CPMA CSFH CSev EBre ESis GAbr GPoy IBar LBre LHop MBar MChe MPla NHHG NSti NWyt SBla SChu SLon WEas WHer WHil WOMN WSHC WWye
§ – ***angustissimus*** 'Corsican Blue'	CArn CBow CDec SCro SPer
– 'Aureovariegatus'	See R. ***o. aureus***
§ – 'Aureus' (v)	CDec CLan CMer CMil EFol ELan GAbr IBlr NHHG NRar SDry SMad WByw WCHb WEas WHer WOMN WWye
§ – 'Benenden Blue'	Widely available
– 'Collingwood Ingram'	See R. ***o.*** 'Benenden Blue'
– 'Corsicus Prostratus'	CB&S
– 'Eden'	IEde
– 'Fastigiatus'	See R. ***o.*** 'Miss Jessopp's Upright'
– 'Fota Blue'	CDoC CMGP MChe NHHG NSti SCro SIde
– 'Frimley Blue'	See R. ***o.*** 'Primley Blue'
– 'Guilded'	See R. ***o.*** 'Aureus'
– 'Jackman's Prostrate'	CB&S ECtt NHar NWyt WSHC
– 'Lady in White'	CLan ELan NBar SPer SPla WWat
– ***lavandulaceus***	See R. ***o.*** Prostratus Group
– 'Lockwood Variety'	NHHG
– 'Majorca Pink'	CB&S CDec CLan CPMA CSam GAbr GBar MPla NWyt SIde SPer WCHb WMar WOMN WWat WWye
– 'McConnell's Blue'	CDoC CLTr CLan EBre EFou ELan GAbr LBre MAsh MGos NHHG NWyt SDry SPla WCHb WOld WSun WWye
§ – 'Miss Jessopp's Upright' AGM	Widely available
§ – 'Primley Blue'	CArn CSam CSev MChe NHHG NHar NSti SChu WCHb WHer WOak WPer WWeb WWye
§ – Prostratus Group AGM	CArn CB&S CHad CLan CMea CRiv CSFH CSco CSev CShe CTre CTrw EFol IJoh LHop MChe NHHG NSti SArc SBla SLon SPer SUsu SWas WHil WOMN WOak WPer WRus WWat
– ***pyramidalis***	See R. ***o.*** 'Miss Jessopp's Upright'
– ***repens***	See R. ***o.*** Prostratus Group
– 'Roseus'	CArn CHan CMer CWit EBre ELan GPoy LBre LHop MChe NHHG NHar NSti SBla SChu SLon SMad SPla SUsu WAbe WHer WSHC WWat WWye
– 'Russell's Blue'	NOak WHer
– 'Severn Sea' AGM	Widely available
– 'Sissinghurst Blue' AGM	CArn CMGP CMer CSev CShe ECha ELan ERav ESma MAsh MSta SPla WWat WWye
– 'Sudbury Blue'	GBar MChe NHHG NRoo NSti WEas
– 'Trusty'	ECtt ELan LHop LRHS SPla WPer
– 'Tuscan Blue'	CShe ECot NHex SDry SIde SLon WCHb WHer WWat WWye
– 'Variegatus'	See R. ***o.*** 'Aureus'
– 'Vicomte de Noailles'	ERea

repens	See R. *officinalis* Prostratus Group

ROSTRINUCULA (Labiatae/Lamiaceae)

dependens Guiz 18	CBot

ROSULARIA (Crassulaceae)

acuminata	See R. *alpestris alpestris*
adenotricha	
ssp. *adenotricha*	NGre
§ *aïzoön*	ESis MFos
alba	See R. *sedoïdes*
alpestris	CWil MSte WOMN
– CC 327	NHol
§ – ssp. *alpestris*	WThu
§ *chrysantha*	CRiv EBur NGre NHol NMen NNrd WPer
– Number 1	CWil SMit WThu
– Number 2	CWil WThu
crassipes	See RHODIOLA *c.*
globulariifolia	NHar WDav
haussknechtii	NGre
¶ *hissarica* K 92.380	WDav
muratdaghensis	EBur LBee MBro NGre NMen
pallida A. Berger	See R. *chrysantha*
pallida Stapf	See R. *aïzoön*
platyphylla hort.	See R. *muratdaghensis*
rechingeri	CWil
§ *sedoïdes*	CLew CMHG CWil ELan EPot GCHN MBar MCas SChu SMit SSmi WPer WThu WWin
§ – var. *alba*	CLew CMHG CWil ELan EPot GCHN MBar MCas MHig NGre SChu SIng WHoo WOMN WThu WWin
sempervivum	CWil NGre NHol NMen NNrd WThu
– ssp. *amanensis*	NGre
§ – ssp. *glaucophylla*	CWil NTow WThu
serpentinica	CWil
serrata	NGre
– from Crete	SMit
spatulata hort.	See R. *sempervivum glaucophylla*

ROTHMANNIA (Rubiaceae)

capensis	CTro
globosa	CTro

RUBIA (Rubiaceae)

peregrina	CKin EHic GPoy MHew MSal
tinctoria	CArn GBar GPoy LHol MChe MHew MSal NHex SIde SWat WHer WWye

RUBUS † (Rosaceae)

arcticus	CGle ESim ESis MBal MHig NCat SReu SSta WCru WPat WSun WThu
– ssp. *stellarcticus*	ESim
– – 'Anna'	ESim
– – 'Beata'	ESim
– – 'Linda'	ESim
– – 'Sofia'	ESim
x *barkeri*	ECou
§ 'Benenden' AGM	CB&S CBot CCla CGle CMHG CSam CSco EBar EHar ELan ENot IDai ISea LHop MBal MBri MGos MWat NKay NNor SHBN SLon SPer WBod WDin WHCG WHal WWat WWeb WWin
'Betty Ashburner'	CDoC CHan CWit EGol EPla GCal IBar IJoh MGos SAxl WHCG WWat
biflorus	EHar ELan EMon EPla ERav
F 'Boysenberry, Thornless'	ECas GTwe LBuc SDea SPer WHig
¶ *caesius* 'Sidings'	CNat
calycinoïdes Hayata	See R. *pentalobus*
chamaemorus	GPoy
cockburnianus AGM	CB&S CGle EBre EHar ELan ENot EPar EPla IOrc LBre MBal MRav MWat NHol SPer WCru WDin WEas WWat
– Golden Vale ®	CB&S CPMA EBre EPla IJoh LBre MBlu MPla SMad SPer
crataegifolius	EPla WWat
deliciosus	WDin
'Emerald Spreader'	MBri SBod
flagelliflorus	MBar WHCG
fockeanus hort.	See R. *pentalobus*
x *fraseri*	EPla
fruticosus	CKin
F – 'Ashton Cross'	GRei GTwe LBuc SDea WHig
F – 'Bedford Giant'	EHar GTwe MBea MGos NBar SDea SKee WWeb
F – 'Black Satin'	CSam GRei GTwe MBea MBri MGos SDea SPer WWeb
– 'Dart's Robertville'	SLPl
F – 'Denver Thornless'	EWar
F – 'Fantasia Blackberry' AGM	CSam GTwe MGos
F – 'Godshill Goliath'	SDea
F – 'Himalayan Giant'	CDoC CSam EWar GTwe MBea NRog SDea SKee SPer
F – 'John Innes'	NElm NRog
¶ – 'Kotata'	ECas
F – 'Loch Ness' AGM	CSam ECas GChr GTwe LBuc MBri MGos NBar SDea SPer WHig
F – 'Merton Thornless'	EHar GTwe MBea MGos NBee NEgg NElm NRog SDea SKee
F – 'No Thorn'	SDea
F – 'Oregon Thornless'	ECas EWar GTwe IJoh LBuc MBea MBri SDea SKee SPer WHig WWeb
F – 'Parsley Leaved'	SDea
F – 'Thornfree'	CDoC SDea
– 'Variegatus'	CBot CRDP EFol EPla LHop WCot
– 'Waldo'	CSut ECas WHig
henryi	CBot EPla MRav WHCG WWat
– var. *bambusarum*	CDec CHan CMCN CPle EBar ELan EPar EPla SHil SMad WWat
F 'Hildaberry'	WHig
hupehensis	SLPl
ichangensis	CAbb CBot CHan CMCN EPla GCal GWht ISea MBal
idaeus	CKin
F – 'Augusta'	SKee
F – 'Aureus'	CBos ECha EFol EHal ELan EPla GCal LHop NRoo NSti SDry WRus

F – Autumn Bliss ® **AGM** CSam CSut CWSG ECas GTwe IJoh LBuc MBri MGos MMor NBar NBee SDea SKee SPer WHig WWeb
F – 'Fallgold' GTwe SDea SPer
F – 'Glen Clova' ECas EHar EWar GRei GTwe IJoh LBuc NBar NBee NRog SDea SKee SPer WWeb
F – 'Glen Coe' ECas GTwe
F – 'Glen Garry' WHig
F – 'Glen Lyon' GTwe LBuc SKee
F – 'Glen Moy' **AGM** CSut CWSG ECas GChr GRei GTwe IJoh LBuc MGos MMor NBee NEgg NRog SPer WHig
F – 'Glen Prosen' **AGM** CSam CWSG ECas GChr GTwe IJoh LBuc MBri MMor NBar NEgg NRog SKee SPer WHig
F – 'Golden Everest' EWar GTwe SDea SPer
F – 'Heritage' EHar IJoh SDea SPer
F – 'Leo' **AGM** CDoC CSut ECas GTwe MGos SDea SKee SPer WHig
F – 'Malling Admiral' **AGM** EHar ESha GTwe MBri MMor NBar NRog SKee SPer
F – 'Malling Augusta' ECas
F – 'Malling Delight' ECas GRei GTwe MMor NRog SDea SKee SPer WHig WWeb
F – 'Malling Jewel' **AGM** ECas EWar GTwe IJoh LBuc NBar NBee SDea SKee SPer WHig
F – 'Malling Joy' GTwe
F – 'Malling Orion' ESha MGos MMor
F – 'Malling Promise' EWar GTwe NBar SDea SPer
F – 'September' EWar SPer
F – 'Summer Gold' GTwe
F – 'Zefa Herbsternte' EWar GTwe SDea SPer WWeb
F ***illecebrosus*** ESim WCot WPat
irenaeus CHan
'Kenneth Ashburner' EMon EPla MBri WWat
laciniatus EPla
lambertianus CMCN
lineatus CAbb CBot CBrd CPle CRDP EPla GCal IBar LHop MBal SDix SDry SMad WCru WPat
F Loganberry 'LY 59' **AGM** CDoC EHar GTwe MMor NBar NElm NRog SDea SPer
F – 'LY 654' **AGM** CSam ECas GRei GTwe LBuc MBea MBri MGos MMor NElm SDea SKee SPer WHig WWeb
F – 'New Zealand Black' SDea
F 'Loganberry Thornless ECot GTwe IJoh NRog SDea
'Margaret Gordon' CPMA IBar IJoh
microphyllus 'Variegatus' EPla EWri IJoh SHil WAbb WPat WWeb
§ ***nepalensis*** CDoC CGle EPla ESis GWht WWat
nutans See R. ***nepalensis***
odoratus CDoC CHEx CSco CWit ELan MHlr SAxl SPer WCot WHCG
parviflorus CArn GAul
– 'Sunshine Spreader' EPla LHop MHlr
parvus ECou
§ ***pentalobus*** CGle CLew CSco CWit EGol ELan ENot EPla ESis LHop MBal MBar NNor SBor SIng SPer WAbe WCru WDin WEas WWat WWin
– 'Emerald Carpet' ESim SBod
¶ – 'Green Jade' WWat

F ***phoenicolasius*** Japanese Wineberry CB&S CCla CHan ELan EPla ESim GTwe GWht MBri NBar NRog SDea SPer WAbb WCru WHCG WHig WPat WWat WWye
rosifolius 'Coronarius' (d) ELan EOrc EPla WCot
setchuenensis CMCN SBra
F 'Silvanberry' ECas GTwe
spectabilis CChu CMHG CWit EBee EFol ELan LHop MBal MRav NHol SFis WHal
– 'Flore Pleno' See R. *s.* 'Olympic Double'
¶ – 'Gun Hildi' WCru
– 'Olympic Double' CChu CCla CMHG CPMA EFol ELan EMon GCal LBuc MBri SMrm SPer WCot WPat WSHC WWeb
squarrosus ECou EPla SDry
F 'Sunberry' GTwe SKee WHig
¶ ***taiwanicola*** B&SWJ 317 WCru
F Tayberry CSam ECas EHar EWar GChr GRei GTwe IJoh MBea MBri MGos MMor NBar NElm NRog SPer WHig WWeb
F – 'Medana Tayberry' CSut LBuc SDea
§ ***thibetanus*** **AGM** Widely available
– 'Silver Fern' See R. *t.*
treutleri WCot
tricolor Widely available
– 'Dart's Evergreen' SLPl
– 'Ness' SLPl
Tridel 'Benenden' See R. 'Benenden'
trilobus CCla SLon
F 'Tummelberry' ECas GTwe
ulmifolius 'Bellidiflorus' CBot CCla CSev ELan EMon ENot EPla MBal NNor SChu SDix SHil SPer WAbb
F 'Veitchberry' GTwe NRog WHig
F 'Youngberry' SDea

RUDBECKIA (Compositae/Asteraceae)

californica WPer
echinacea purpurea See ECHINACEA ***purpurea***
fulgida var. ***deamii*** **AGM** CBow CGle CKel EBre ECED ECha ECtt ELan ELun GMac LBre MRav MWat NBar NBrk NKay NOak NRoo NSti SChu SCro SPer WByw WCra WEas WHoo
§ – var. ***speciosa*** CGle CSco CShe ECha ELan EPla IDai LWad MPit NBar NRoo SFis WOld WPer WRus
– var. ***sullivantii*** 'Goldsturm' **AGM** Widely available
gloriosa See R. ***hirta***
'Goldquelle' **AGM** CBow CGle CSco ECED EFou ELan LHop NOrc NPri SCro SHer SMad SMrm SPer WWin
¶ ***grandiflora*** var. ***alismifolia*** EBee
'Herbstsonne' ('Autumn Sun') CSco ECha IDai MBel MWat NOrc NPri NVic SFis SHer SMad SPer SPla SSvw WEas WTyr
§ ***hirta*** LHil WCra
'Juligold' ('July Gold') EFou MNFA NCat SMrm
laciniata CSam EBee ELan GCal LGre LHil MArl NHol NOrc SFis WByw

– 'Golden Glow' — See R. *l.* 'Hortensia'
§ – 'Hortensia' — CSco EMon MFir NFai
maxima — CGle ECha EMon EPla MBri WCot
newmannii — See R. ***fulgida speciosa***
occidentalis — CHan LGre WHil WPer
– 'Green Wizard' — CHan ESma NBro NRar SMad
purpurea — See ECHINACEA ***purpurea***
subtomentosa — CPou EFou EMon GCal MNFA NNrw WCot WOld

RUELLIA (Acanthaceae)

amoena — See R. ***graecizans***
¶ *colorata* — CTro
devosiana — MBri SLMG
§ *graecizans* — CTro ERea
makoyana AGM — IBlr MBri SLMG

RUMEX (Polygonaceae)

§ *acetosa* — CArn CKin CSev ECWi ECha EHer EJud Effi GAbr GBar GPoy IEde LHol MChe MHew NBir NPri SIde WWye
♦– 'Redleaf' — See R. ***a. vineatus***
§ – ssp. *vineatus* — WCot
acetosella — ECWi MWil
alpinus — WCot
flexuosus — CElw CHan EFol EHoe EMon GCal MHlr WCot
hydrolapathum — ECWi EMFW MSta MWil NDea
montanus 'Ruber' — See R. ***alpestris*** 'R.'
¶ *rubrifolius* — SIde
rugosus — MBar
¶ *sanguineus* — GGar
– var. *sanguineus* — CArn CElw CMGP CRow EFol EHoe ELan EMon EPla LHil LHol MTho NBro NHol NSti WFox WHer WOak WWye
scutatus — CArn CSFH CSev EJud Effi GAbr GBar GPoy IEde LHol MChe MHew MTho SIde WWye
– 'Silver Shield' — CRDP EFol EMar EMon EPla IBlr LHil NSti SUsu WCHb WCot WCru WDav WHer WOak WWye

RUMOHRA (Dryopteridaceae)

adiantiformis AGM — CFil CTro

RUPICAPNOS (Papaveraceae)

africana — EPot NMen NWCA SBla SIng WAbe WOMN

RUSCHIA (Aizoaceae)

§ *putterillii* — EPot
¶ – S&SH 64 — CHan

RUSCUS † (Liliaceae/Ruscaceae)

aculeatus — CSco ECro ENot GPoy IJoh MBri MFir MRav MUlv MWat SArc SSta WCru WDin WStI WWye
¶ – (f) — WWat
¶ – (m) — WWat
¶ – var. *angustifolius* (f) — EPla
– hermaphrodite — CSco EPla
*– 'Wheeler's Variety' (f/m) — CPMA SPer WWes
hypoglossum — EPla MUlv SArc SHil SRms
¶ *ponticus* — EPla
racemosus — See DANAË ***racemosa***

RUSSELIA (Scrophulariaceae)

§ *equisetiformis* AGM — CB&S ERea SIgm
juncea — See R. ***equisetiformis***

RUTA (Rutaceae)

chalepensis — CArn ELan LHol WCHb WHil WWye
§ – 'Dimension Two' — EMon LHol WHer
– prostrate form — See R. ***c.*** 'Dimension Two'
corsica — NTow
graveolens — CArn CBow CGle CMer CSFH EHer EJud IEde LGan LHol MChe MHew NMir NOak SIde WEas WHal WHer WOak WPer WStI WTyr
– 'Jackman's Blue' AGM — Widely available
– 'Variegata' — CBot CBow CSFH ECha EFol EFou ELan EOrc EPla ERav EWri GPoy MChe NNor NOak NPer NSti WHer WHoo WPer WSHC WWye
montana — CBot WHer
prostrata — See R. ***chalepensis*** 'Dimension Two'

RUTTYA (Acanthaceae)

See Plant Deletions

SABAL (Palmae/Arecaceae)

§ *mexicana* — CTbh NPal
minor — CTbh LPal NPal
palmetto — CArn CTro LPal NPal WNor
texana — See S. ***mexicana***

SACCHARUM (Gramineae/Poaceae)

ravennae — CElw EHoe EMon EPla ETPC MSte NHol NSti

SAGERETIA (Rhamnaceae)

§ *thea* — STre
theezans — See S. ***thea***

SAGINA (Caryophyllaceae)

boydii — CLew EMNN EPot GArf ITim MRPP NTow WThu
glabra 'Aurea' — See S. ***subulata*** 'Aurea'
§ *subulata* 'Aurea' — CLew CMea CRiv EBar ECha EFol ELan LGro LHop MCas NPri NVic SIng WEas WHal WPer WWin

SAGITTARIA (Alismataceae)

japonica — See S. ***sagittifolia***
latifolia — CHEx CRDP EMFW NDea WChe WHol
§ *sagittifolia* — CBen CRDP CRow CWGN ECWi EHon EMFW LMay MHew MSta SHig SWat SWyc WChe WHol
– 'Flore Pleno' — CBen CRDP CRow CWGN EHon EMFW LMay MBal MSta NDea SHig SWat SWyc WChe
subulata — CRow

SAINTPAULIA (Gesneriaceae)

¶ ***confusa*** GUzu
¶ ***velutina*** GUzu

SALIX † (Salicaceae)

acutifolia ELan ENot EPla IOrc SPla
– 'Blue Streak' **AGM** CMHG CSco EHar IOrc MBal NBir SHil SPer
– 'Pendulifolia' (m) IOrc SMad
adenophylla Hooker See S. ***cordata***
aegyptiaca CDoC CLnd ENot NWea WMou
alba CBow CKin CLnd CPer LBuc SPer WDin WMou
– f. ***argentea*** See S. ***a. sericea***
– 'Aurea' CTho EHar WMou
– ssp. ***caerulea*** ENot NWea WMou
– 'Cardinalis' (f) ISea
– 'Dart's Snake' ELan LRHS
– 'Hutchinson's Yellow' EHar MBri
– 'Liempde' (m) ENot
– 'Orange Spire' LMer
– 'Richmond' SPer
§ – var. ***sericea*** **AGM** CB&S CLnd EBre EFol EGol EHar ENot EPla IOrc LBre MBal MBri MNFA MRav NNor SHBN SHil SPer WDin WMou WWat
– 'Splendens' See S. ***a. sericea***
N– 'Tristis' CLnd ELan IJoh MBri MRav NWea SPer WDin WMou
– ssp. ***vitellina*** **AGM** CKin CPer EBar EGol EHar ELan LBuc NHol NWea WDin WMou
§ – ***vitellina*** 'Britzensis' **AGM** CBow CDoC CKin CLnd CMHG EHar ELan ENot GRei IOrc LBuc LHop MBal MBar MGos MRav NNor NWea SHBN SPer SPla SSta WDin WMou WWat
– 'Vitellina Pendula' See S. ***a.*** 'Tristis'
– 'Vitellina Tristis' See S. ***a.*** 'Tristis'
alba hort. 'Chermesina' See S. ***a. vitellina*** 'Britzensis'
§ ***alpina*** CShe EPot ESis GAri GPlt MBal MCas MMil MPla NHol NRoo NRya SGil SIng
apoda ESis MBal NHol WHal WPat WPer
§ ***arbuscula*** CLew CNic CShe EBar EPad ESis MBal MPla SSta
arctica var. ***petraea*** WPat
aurita WDin
babylonica NBee SHBN WDin WMou
– 'Annularis' See S. ***b.*** 'Crispa'
§ – 'Crispa' CGre CTho EHar EHic ELan EPla LHop SHBN SMad SPla
– var. ***pekinensis*** 'Pendula' EHar SHil
– – 'Tortuosa' **AGM** CArn CDec CLnd CSco CTho EGol EHar ELan ENot ERav IDai IJoh IOrc LHop LPan MBal MBar MGos MWat NNor NPer NWea SHil SPer SReu WWat
x ***balfourii*** GWht SPla
bicolor Willdenow SSta
bockii CBra CDoC EPla MBar WPer
§ 'Bowles' Hybrid' CDoC EHar LBuc MRav WMou
'Boydii' **AGM** CChu CFee CSam ECtt EHar ELan EPot ESis GArf GDra GTou LGre MBal MBri MBro NHar NHol NNor NNrd NRoo SIng STre WAbe WCru WPat WThu
§ 'Boyd's Pendulous' (m) CFee EHar EPla GAri MBal MBar WDav
breviserrata GDra
candida MNFA
caprea CB&S CKin CLnd CPer ENot GRei LBuc NRoo NWea WDin WMou
– 'Kilmarnock' **AGM** CBra CLnd CMHG CSco EHar ELan ENot GRei IDai IJoh LBuc MBar MGos MWat NBar NBee NWea SHBN SMad SPer SPla WAbe WDin WMou WWat
– ***pendula*** (f) See S. ***c.*** 'Weeping Sally'
– ***pendula*** (m) See S. ***c.*** 'Kilmarnock'
*– ***variegata*** CBrd SPer
capusii LMer
cascadensis MBal
cashmiriana WPat WThu
'Chrysocoma' See S. x ***sepulcralis chrysocoma***
cinerea CB&S CDoC CKin CPer GRei NWea WDin
– 'Tricolor' CArn EFol
– 'Variegata' EGol EWri
x ***cottetii*** CBra CDoC
daphnoïdes CDoC CLnd CSam EFol EHar ELan ENot GRei IHos IOrc MWat NWea SHBN SPer STre WDin WMar WMou WWat
– 'Aglaia' **AGM** CB&S MBal
'E A Bowles' See S. 'Bowles' Hybrid'
§ ***elaeagnos*** **AGM** CBrd CCla CDoC CTho EBar EPla MNFA WDin WMou
§ – ssp. ***angustifolia*** CLnd EGol EHar ELan ENot EPar ERav IOrc LHop MBal MUlv NNor NWea SMad STre WAbe WWat WWin
'Elegantissima' See S. x ***pendulina*** 'E.'
§ 'Erythroflexuosa' CB&S CDoC CShe CTho EGol EHar ELan EPla SLon SPer WDin WOak
exigua CB&S CCla CDoC CTho EBar EBre EFol EGol EHar ELan ENot EPla IJoh IOrc LBre MBar MBri MGos MNFA NBar SDry SMad SPer WMou WPat WWat
fargesii CBot CChu CFil EBre EGol EHar ELan EPla LBre LHop MBal MGos MRav MUlv NHar NHol SDix SHil SMad SPla WCru WPat WWat
§ x ***finnmarchica*** GPlt
formosa See S. ***arbuscula***
fragilis CKin CLnd NWea WDin WMou
§ ***fruticulosa*** CGle CLew GDra GGar GTou MBal MBar NKay WPer WThu
'Fuiri-koriyanagi' See S. ***integra*** 'Hakuro-nishiki'
furcata See S. ***fruticulosa***
glauca CNat
glaucosericea EHic
'Golden Curls' See S. 'Erythroflexuosa'
gracilistyla CSco EHar WMou WWat
§ – 'Melanostachys' **AGM** CAbb CB&S CBot CBra CHan CMHG EBar ECtt EGol EHar ELan EPot ERav GDra IDai ISea LHop MBal MBar NHol NNor SPla STre WMou WWat WWin
x ***grahamii*** (f) CLew MBal
– 'Moorei' (f) ESis MBal NNrd
x ***greyi*** CSam EPla

'Hagensis'	See S. 'The Hague'
hastata	
'Wehrhahnii' AGM	Widely available
helvetica AGM	CB&S CLew CPMA CSco EBre EFol ELan ENot ESis GDra GRei IJoh IOrc LBre LHop MBal MBar MBri MGos NBee NHar NHol NNor NRoo SHBN SPer WDin WPat WWat WWin
herbacea	GAri LRHS MBal MCas NMen
hibernica	See S. ***phylicifolia***
x ***hirtei*** 'Reifenweide' (f)	CDoC
hookeriana	EHar ELan WMar WMou WWat
hylematica	See S. ***fruticulosa***
incana	See S. ***elaeagnos***
integra 'Albomaculata'	See S. ***i.*** 'Hakuro-nishiki'
§ – 'Hakuro-nishiki' (v)	Widely available
irrorata	CBot CBow CMHG EHar IOrc ISea MNFA WMou
'Jacquinii'	See S. ***alpina***
japonica hort.	See S. ***babylonica*** 'Lavallei'
japonica Thunberg	EGol
kinuyanagi (m)	ELan LHop
'Kuro-me'	See S. ***gracilistyla*** 'Melanostachys'
lanata AGM	Widely available
– hybrid	NHol
– 'Stuartii'	See S. 'Stuartii'
lapponum	GAri SLon SRms
x ***laurina*** (f)	CMHG SPer
§ ***lindleyana***	CHan CNic CRiv EPot MPla NKay NMen NOak NRoo SGil STre WWat
magnifica AGM	CBot CChu CFil CPle EHar ELan EPar MBal MSte SDry SHil SMad WMou
'Mark Postill' (f)	CDoC EBar EHic WWat
matsudana	See S. ***babylonica pekinensis***
– 'Tortuosa'	See S. ***babylonica pekinensis*** 'Tortuosa'
– 'Tortuosa Aureopendula'	See S. 'Erythroflexuosa'
'Melanostachys'	See S. ***gracilistyla*** 'M.'.
moupinensis	IOrc MBri SHil WMou
x ***myricoïdes***	See S. x ***bebbii***
§ ***myrsinifolia***	EHar EPla MNFA SPer
myrsinites var. ***jacquiniana***	See S. ***alpina***
myrtilloïdes 'Pink Tassels' (m)	ELan ESis GAri MBal MGos SHer
– x ***repens***	See S. x ***finmarchica***
nakamurana var. ***yezoalpina***	CBrd CChu CFee EPla GAri LHop MBal NHol WPat
nepalensis	See S. ***lindleyana***
nigricans	See S. ***myrsinifolia***
nivalis	EPot GPlt
occidentalis	See S. ***humilis***
* 'Onoga'	CB&S
'Onusta' (m)	CDoC NBar
x ***ovata***	EHal GPlt NRoo
pentandra	CBot CKin IOrc NWea WDin WMou WWat
§ ***phylicifolia***	CNat EGol SPer WMou
polaris	ESis GPlt MBal
procumbens	See S. ***myrsinites***
prunifolia	See S. ***arbuscula***
§ ***purpurea***	CB&S EHal EPad IOrc WDin WMou
– f. ***gracilis***	See S. ***p.*** 'Nana'
– 'Helix'	See S. ***p.***
– 'Howki'	WMou
§ – 'Nana'	CLTr CPle ELan EPla MBal NHol SChu SPer SPla STre WBod WStI WWat
– 'Nancy Saunders' (f)	EFol EPla ERav GBuc MNFA MSte SMrm SWas
– 'Pendula' AGM	CBra CMer EHar ENot IJoh MBal MBar MBri NBar NBee NHol NNor NWea SPer WDin WStI WWat
pyrenaica	EWes
pyrifolia	WMou
reinii	MNFA
repens	CNic CRiv ERav GAri LHil NCat SEng STre WDin
– var. ***argentea*** AGM	CGle CMer CSco CShe EGol ENot GDra IOrc MBal MBar MRav NNrd NWea SPer SSta WBod WDin WWin
– 'Iona' (m)	EWes
– ***pendula***	See S. 'Boyd's Pendulous'
– 'Voorthuizen' (f)	EBee ELan ESis MBri MWat NNrd NRya WDin
reticulata AGM	EPot GAri GDra MAsh MBal NHar NTow WPat WThu
retusa	GAri GDra MHig MPla NHar NHol NMen NNrd WPat
rosmarinifolia hort.	See S. ***elaeagnos angustifolia***
x ***rubens*** 'Basfordiana' AGM	CDoC CLnd EBar EGol EHar EPla WMou
x ***rubra*** 'Eugenei' (m)	EHar MNFA WMou WWat WWin
sachalinensis	See S. ***udensis***
x ***sadleri***	LHil
♦ ***schraderiana*** Willdenow	See S. ***bicolor***
x ***sepulcralis***	EHar NWea
§ x ***sepulcralis chrysocoma*** AGM	CDoC CSco EHar ELan ENot GAri IDai LBuc MBal MGos MWat SHBN SPer
x ***sepulcralis*** 'Salamonii'	NWea
serpillifolia	CLew CNic GPlt LHop MBal MBro MCas MHig NMen SGil WPat WPer
serpyllum	See S. ***fruticulosa***
'Setsuka'	See S. ***udensis*** 'Sekka'
x ***simulatrix***	GAri WWat
♦ x ***smithiana***	See S. x ***stipularis***
§ x ***stipularis*** (f)	CDoC CLnd CMHG WDin
§ 'Stuartii'	CSam MBar NNrd SRms
subopposita	CBow CDoC CPMA CSco EHic ELan EPla MBar MPla SHil SIng
syrticola	See S. ***cordata***
x ***tetrapla*** 'Hutchinson's Nigricans'	CNat
triandra	WMou
– 'Rouge d'Orléans'	WMou
– 'Semperflorens'	CNat
tristis	See S. ***humilis***
x ***tsugaluensis*** 'Ginme' (f)	CMHG WWat
§ ***udensis***	WWat

§ – 'Sekka' (m)	CDec CLnd CMer ECtt EGol EHar ELan EPar ESma IOrc LHop MBal NHol NRoo NWea SPla SSta STre WMou
uva-ursi	GAri MBal WMou
viminalis	CKin CPer ENot GRei NWea WDin WMou
– 'Bowles' Hybrid'	See S. 'Bowles' Hybrid'
* *violescens*	CBot
vitellina 'Pendula'	See S. ***alba*** 'Tristis'
x *wimmeriana*	EGol NBee SRms
'Yelverton'	MBri SPer

SALVIA † (Labiatae/Lamiaceae)

acetabulosa	See S. ***multicaulis***
aethiopis	CPle ELan EMon MNFA MSte NSti WPer
afghanica	WEas
§ *africana-caerulea*	CBrd CPle SUsu
– 'Kirstenbosch'	CPle WPer
§ *africana-lutea*	CBrk CPle CSco CTre ELan LHil LHop MMil WHal WPer
algeriensis	CPle
amarissima	CPle
ambigens	See S. ***guaranitica*** 'Blue Enigma'
* *amgiana*	CPle
§ *amplexicaulis*	CPle WPer
angustifolia Cavanilles	See S. ***reptans***
angustifolia Michaux	See S. ***azurea***
apiana	CPle
argentea AGM	Widely available
arizonica	CPle WPer
atrocyanea	CPle SBla
aucheri	GBuc GCal
aurea	See S. ***africana-lutea***
austriaca	CPle MBel WByw WPer
azurea	CBrd CHan CPle ERav LHol LHop MSte SMrm WPer
– ssp. *pitcheri*	EMon GCal MSto
bacheriana	See S. ***buchananii***
barrelieri	CHan CPle
¶ 'Belhaven'	GCal
♦ *bertolonii*	See S. ***pratensis*** Bertolonii Group
bicolor Desfontaines	See SALVIA ***barrelieri***
blancoana	CBot CBrk CHan CPle CSpe ECha EFol EMon ERav GCal LGre LHop MSte NSti SSvw WHer WPer WRus
blepharophylla	CAbb CB&S CBrk CCan CHan CPle LHop WCot WPer
¶ *brachyantha*	CPle
¶ *brandegeei*	CPle
§ *brevilabra*	CPle WPer
broussonetii	CPle LHil
§ *buchananii* AGM	CAbb CBow CCan CPle ELan ERea ERom LGre LHop NOak SAga SCro SMad SMrm WOMN WOld
bulleyana	CChu CGle CHan CPle CRDP CSev EBre ECoo ECro EFou ELan GCal LBre LHol NBrk NSti SIde SUsu WCra WCru WEas WHow WOld WPer
cacaliifolia AGM	CCan CGre CHan CLTr CMer CPle CSpe EOrc ERav ERom GCal LBlm LHil LHol LHop MSte NOak SBor SUsu WCHb WEas WHer WPer WWye
cadmica	CPle
caerulea hort.	See S. ***guaranitica*** 'Black and Blue'
caerulea Linnaeus	See S. ***africana-caerulea***
caespitosa	CPle NNrd NTow NWCA WAbe
* – *anatolica*	WDav
campanulata	CPle
canariensis	CPle LHil MSte
candelabrum AGM	CHan CPle CSev LGre SAxl WCHb WCru WHer WKif WSHC
candidissima	CPle
cardinalis	See S. ***fulgens***
¶ *carduacea*	CPle
castanea	CPle CRDP SBla
chamaedryoïdes	CCan CPle CSpe
chapalensis	CPle
chinensis	See S. ***japonica***
cinnabarina	CPle
clevelandii	CPle
coccinea	CBot CPle EBar ELan LBlm LHil MSte WCHb WOMN WPer WWye
– 'Indigo'	ELan
– 'Lactea'	CBot CPle
– pink	CPle
columbariae	CPle
¶ *compacta*	CPle
concolor hort.	See S. ***guaranitica***
concolor Lamb.	CPle
confertiflora	CAbb CCan CPle CWit ELan EMon GCal LHil LHop MSte NRar SBor SMrm WCHb WEas WPer WWye
¶ *cyanescens*	CPle
¶ *darcyi*	LGre
deserta	See S. x ***sylvestris***
discolor AGM	CBot CBrk CDec CMea CPle CSam CSev ELan ERav ERea LBlm LHil LHol LHop MTho SUsu WCHb WHal WPer
¶ *dolichantha*	CPle
dombeyi	CPle
dominica	CPle
dorisiana	CHan CPle CSev ELan LBlm MSte WPer
dorrii	CPle
¶ – K 92.390	WDav
§ *elegans*	CCan CCla CGre CPle CSev EBar GCal LBlm LHol LHop MSte SAga SBor SCro SIde WOld
§ – 'Scarlet Pineapple'	Widely available
fallax	CPle
farinacea 'Alba'	LBlm LGre
– 'Silver'	CPle
– 'Victoria' AGM	CPle LBlm
forsskaolii	CGle CHan CLTr CPle CSev ECro ELan EMon EPad GLil LHil LLWP MBro MFir NHol SChu SCro SSvw SUsu WByw WEas WHil WHoo WPer WWye
frigida	CPle
§ *fruticosa*	CArn CPle EEls LHol SIde
§ *fulgens* AGM	CGle CPle CSam CSev ERav GMac LBlm LHil NBro NHex SIde SMad SUsu WCHb WCru WEas WHal WPer WWye
gesneriiflora	CAbb CCan CHan CPle CSev GCal LBlm LHil LHol LHop MSte NBrk SIde WPer WWye

glutinosa	CChu CHad CHan CPle ECha ELan EMon GCal LGan LHol LHop MNFA NBro NNrw NSti SAga SSvw WByw WPer WWye
grahamii Bentham	See S. *microphylla microphylla*
grahamii hort.	See S. *microphylla neurepia*
greggii	CBrk CPle EPad ERav LHil MSte NOak SAga SPer SUsu WHil WPer WTyr WWin WWye
– 'Alba'	CBrk CPle CSev LHil LHop WPer WRus WWye
♦– 'Blush Pink'	See S. *microphylla* 'Pink Blush'
– 'Keter's Red'	CPle EMon
– 'Peach'	CB&S CBrk CHan CPle CSev CSpe EHic EOrc GCal LHop NOak SAga SUsu
♦– 'Peach' misapplied	See S. x *jamensis* 'Pat Vlasto'
– 'Raspberry Royal'	CHan CPle EBee ELan EOrc ESma EWoo LHil LHop MBel SAga WRus
– x *lycioïdes*	CPle EBee LHil LHop SAga WPer
§ *guaranitica* AGM	CAbb CBot CCan CChu CGle CHan CMer CPle EBre ECha ELan GCal LAbb LBre LHil LHol MRav NRar SAga SMrm SUsu WCHb WPer
§ – 'Black and Blue'	CBrd CCan CGle CLTr CPle GCal LGre MSte SBor WCot WHal WPer WWye
*– 'Black Knight'	GCal
§ – 'Blue Enigma'	CArn CB&S CBot CBrd CCan CHad CSev EFou GCal LHil LHop WEas
¶ – 'Purple Majesty'	SMrm
haematodes	See S. *pratensis* Haematodes Group
hians	CGle CPle EBar ECro EMar EPad GCal GCra NNrw SAga SBla WEas WHaw WHoo WPer WWye
hierosolymitana	CPle
hispanica hort.	See S. *lavandulifolia*
horminoïdes	CKin NMir SHer WCla WWye
horminum	See S. *viridis*
¶ *hydrangea*	WDav
hypargeia	CPle
'Indigo Spires'	CBrd CPle SAga SMrm
interrupta	EBee EHal EOrc ERom LGre LHil LHop SAga SChu SDix SPer WCHb WEas
involucrata AGM	CBow CHan CPle CSev ERom GCal LHil LHol NBro SMrm SSte WCot WEas
– 'Bethellii'	CBot CBow CBrk CCan CCla CGle CMil CPle CSev EBar ECha ELan EMon GCal LBlm LHop SAga SBor SHil SLon WCru WEas WOMN WOld WPer WSHC WWye
– 'Boutin'	CCan CCla CPle LBlm WPer
– dark form	GCal MSte SMrm
§ – 'Hadspen'	CBot CCan CHad CSam ECro SMrm
– 'Mrs Pope'	See S. *i.* 'Hadspen'
iodantha	CPle LHop
¶ x *jamensis* 'Devantville'	CPle LGre
¶ – 'El Duranzo'	CPle LGre
¶ – 'Fuego'	LGre
– 'James Compton'	LBlm LGre MSte SAxl SIgm SMrm
¶ – 'La Luna'	CBrk CPle LGre
¶ – 'La Siesta'	CPle LGre
¶ – 'La Tarde'	CBrk CPle LGre
– 'Pat Vlasto'	CPle LGre LHil MSte SAga SMrm
§ *japonica*	CPle
¶ *judaica*	CPle
jurisicii	CPle EBee EWll MBro SUsu WHoo WPer
– 'Alba'	CPle
¶ *keerlii*	CPle
¶ *koyamae*	CPle
¶ *lanigera*	CPle
§ *lavandulifolia*	CArn CBow CCla CMHG CPle CSFH ECha EFou ELan EMon LHil NSti SAxl SBor SCro SHer SLon SPer SPla SUsu WAbe WCHb WDav WEas WHer WOak WPer WSun WWat WWye
lemmonii	See S. *microphylla wislizenii*
leptophylla	See S. *reptans*
leucantha AGM	Widely available
leucophylla	CPle
longispicata	CPle
♦ *lycioïdes* misapplied	See S. *greggii* x *l.*
lyrata	CPle EBee MHew MSal
macellaria	CPle
macrosiphon	CPle
madrensis	CPle
mellifera	CArn CPle LHop
¶ *mexicana*	CPle LBlm
– var. *minor*	CCan CPle LHop WPer
microphylla	CBow CCan CCla CGle CHol CLTr CMHG CMer CPle ESma GBar MChe MFir MHew NFai SAga SChu SLMG SLon WCru WHCG WPer
– *alba*	SFis
¶ – 'La Foux'	LGre
§ – var. *microphylla*	CCan CGle CHol CPle CSev ELan EOrc ESma LGre LHol MBel MTho SBor SChu SLon SMrm WEas WOld WSHC WWat
§ – var. *neurepia*	CB&S CFee CGle CPle CSam ECro EMon ERav GCHN IMal LAbb LBlm LHol LHop NNrw NRar NSti NTow SAga SDry SHil SMrm SPer WCHb WCru WPer WSHC WSun WWye
– – 'Newby Hall'	CBrd CBrk CPle LHil MBel WPer
§ – 'Pink Blush'	CBot CCan CPle EBee ELan LHil LHop LWad MSte SWas
§ – 'Ruth Stungo' (v)	CPle
♦– 'Variegata' (margined)	See S. *m.* 'Roy Cheek'
♦– 'Variegata' (splashed)	See S. *m.* 'Ruth Stungo'
§ – var. *wislizenii*	CBrd CPle LHop WPer
¶ *microstegia*	CPle
moorcroftiana	CPle GCal WCot WEas WPer
§ *multicaulis*	CHan CPle CSev ECha EFou EMon NTow SAxl SChu SMrm SUsu SWas WAbb WByw WCHb WOMN WOld WPer WSHC
¶ *munzii*	CPle
nemorosa	GLil NBrk
– 'Amethyst'	CPle EFou SWas
– 'Lubecca'	CHad CPle CSco CSev CShe EBre EFou LBre SMrm SPer WRus
¶ – 'Mariosa'	ECha

– 'Ostfriesland' ('East Friesland') CCla CKel CPle CSco EBre ECha ECtt EFou ELan EPla GCHN LBre MRav MSte MWat NBar NFai NKay SCro SDix SMad SPer SPla WCHb WHoo WPer WRus WWin
¶ – 'Plumosa' EMon
¶ – 'Rose Queen' ECtt WCot
– 'Rosenwein' SWas
– ssp. ***tesquicola*** CHan CPle ECha GCal
– 'Wesuwe' ECha
nilotica CPle WHer
nipponica CPle
nubicola CM 813 GTou
¶ ***nutans*** CPle
officinalis CArn CChe CSFH CShe EHer ENot Effi GBar GPoy IEde MBal MBar MBri MChe MGos MHew NNor NPri SHBN SLon WByw WDin WEas WOak WPer WTyr WWat WWye
– 'Alba' See S. ***o.*** 'Albiflora'
§ – 'Albiflora' CBot CMea CMil CPle ECha EFou LHil SBla SIde WHer WPer
N – 'Aurea' CPle GPoy MBar MFir NPri SHer SMad SUsu WWin
– 'Berggarten' CPle ECro EFou EMon GBar GCal LGre SMad SWas WHer
§ – broad-leaved CBot EJud NSti SIde WWye
¶ – 'Grandiflora' CPle
– 'Herrenhausen' CPle MSte
§ – 'Icterina' AGM Widely available
– 'Kew Gold' ECha EMon LHop MRav SMad
– ***latifolia*** See S. ***o.*** broad-leaved variety
– 'Minor' WHer
– narrow-leaved See S. ***lavandulifolia***
* – 'Purple Rain' EPar
– Purpurascens Group AGM Widely available
– 'Purpurascens Variegata' CPle EFol GBar NPri NSti SFar WEas
– 'Robin Hill' GBar LRHS NHol WSun
– 'Rosea' CPle SUsu WHer
– Tomentosa Group CArn
– 'Tricolor' (v) Widely available
– 'Variegata' See S. ***o.*** 'Icterina'
oppositiflora AGM CPle EOrc LHop SAga
¶ ***pachyphylla*** CPle
patens AGM Widely available
♦ – 'Alba' misapplied See S. ***p.*** 'White Trophy'
– 'Cambridge Blue' CBot CBow CHad CPle CRDP CSam CSev ECha EFou ELan GCal LGre LHil LHol LHop MFir MRav NPer SAga SBla SBor SLon WAbe WEas WOMN WOld WPer
– 'Chilcombe' CPle CRDP EBar LHil LHop SAga SChu SUsu WPer
– 'Guanajuato' CPle LGre LHil LHop
– 'Oxford Blue' EOrc WRus
– 'Royal Blue' ECha EGle ERav
¶ – 'White Trophy' CBot CPle CRDP ELan LHop WRus
penstemonoïdes CPle GTou
polystachya CPle
¶ ***pomifera*** CPle
¶ ***potentillifolia*** CPle
* 'Powis Castle' CTro
pratensis CArn CKin CPle ECWi EJud ELan EMon GBar LWad MHew MPit MSal NFai SIde WHil WPer WWye
§ – Bertolonii Group GCal
§ – Haematodes Group AGM CHad CPle EBre ECha ELan EMon LBre MBel MFir MRav NBro NKay NNrw SCro SDix SPer SUsu WHil WHoo WOld WPer
– 'Lapis Lazuli' CPle EMon
¶ – 'Rosea' CPle
– 'Tenorei' WPer
przewalskii CBow CHol CPle ECro GCal NNrw SAga SFis SUsu WPer
– CLD 247 CPle NHol
puberula CHan CPle
– 'El Butano' CPle
purpurea CPle LHop
recognita CBot CPle GCal LGre SUsu
reflexa CPle
regeliana EBee EMon GCal NBir WPer
¶ ***regla*** CPle
repens CPle LHil
§ ***reptans*** CCan CPle CSam CSpe LHop SAga SUsu WPer
ringens CPle EBee GCHN SBor
riparia CPle
roemeriana CPle WCru WHil WOMN WPer
rutilans See S. ***elegans*** 'Scarlet Pineapple'
* ***sariczelek tienschen*** WPer
sclarea CArn CGle CPle EHer EJud Effi GPoy LHol LWad MChe MHew NFai NNrw SFis SIde WCHb WHer WHoo WOak WPbr WPer WWye
N – var. ***turkestanica*** hort. Widely available
semiatrata LGre
sinaloensis CPle LGre LHil LHop SAga SUsu
¶ ***somalensis*** CPle
sonomensis CPle
♦ ***souliei*** See S. ***brevilabra***
spathacea CPle
spinosa CPle
¶ sp. C&Mc 77 GTou
sp. T&K 550 CBot
§ ***staminea*** CPle GCal NBrk SIde
stenophylla CPle WPer
x ***superba*** AGM CBot CCla CGle CHad CKel CPle CShe EBre EFol ELan LBre LHil MBri MBro MWat NRoo SAxl SCro SDix SFis SMrm SSvw WEas WHoo WWye
¶ – 'Forncett Dawn' EFou
– 'Rubin' EFou SRos
– 'Superba' CSco CSev ECha EFou SPer
x ***sylvestris*** 'Blauhügel' CCla CMGP CPle CRDP CSev ECha EFou ELan GCal LGre MArl MBri MSte MWat NHol NVic SChu SMrm WPer
– 'Blaukönigin' ('Blue Queen') CBow CGle CHol EBre ECro EFou GBri GCHN LBre LWad MNFA MWat NCat NMir NOak NRoo SFis WHoo WPer
– 'Indigo' EBre EFou EWll LBre

– 'Lye End'	EBre ECtt GCal LBre MRav NBar WRus
– 'Mainacht' ('May Night')	CHad CMGP CRDP CSco EBre ECro EFou LBre LHop MArl MBri MSte NBar NCat NHol NSti SMrm SPer SPla WEas WRus
– 'Rose Queen'	CBow CLTr CMGP CPle EBre ECha EFou ELan EMon ESis GCHN LBre MNFA MSte NCat NOak NOrc NRoo SFis SSvw SUsu WByw WHoo WPer WWin
– 'Rügen'	MArl MBri
– 'Tänzerin'	EFou SMrm
– 'Viola Klose'	EFou SUsu
¶ – 'Wissalink'	SMad
¶ ***tachiei***	SMrm
taraxacifolia	CPle LHop
¶ ***tarayensis***	CPle
tesquicola	See S. ***nemorosa t.***
tiliifolia	CPle
tingitana	CPle
tomentosa	CGre CPle
transcaucasica	See S. ***staminea***
transsylvanica	CArn CMil CPle EMon EWll WCot WOld WPer
trijuga	CPle
triloba	See S. ***fruticosa***
uliginosa AGM	Widely available
*– 'African Skies'	GCal
urica	CPle
verbenaca	CPle EWFC GCHN MHew MSal MWil NHol NNrw WPer
– pink	CPle
verticillata	CArn CBow CLTr CPle EBar ECha ELan EMon GLil LHil LHol MHew MSal NHol NNor NSti NWyt SSvw WBon WPbr WPer WPla WWye
– 'Alba'	CBrd CLTr CPle ECha EMon LHol MBel NHol SIde SUsu WBon WHer WPer
– ssp. ***amasiaca***	CPle
– 'Purple Rain'	CPle EBre ECha EFou GCal LBre LHil MArl MBel NSti SMrm SUsu SWas WCot
♦ ***villicaulis***	See S. ***amplexicaulis***
virgata	CPle WCot WPer
§ ***viridis***	CArn CPle LHol MChe SIde SUsu WHil
– var. ***alba***	CPle
viscosa Jacquin	CPle
♦ ***viscosa*** Sesse & Moc.	See S. ***riparia***
wagneriana	CPle

SALVINIA (Salviniaceae)

braziliensis	MSta

SAMBUCUS † (Caprifoliaceae)

adnata L 864	EPla
caerulea	EPla
– var. ***neomexicana***	EMon
canadensis	ESim
F – 'Adams'	ESim
– 'Aurea'	CDoC ELan IOrc NWea NWyt WAbe
– 'Maxima'	CHEx ERav GCal SMad
F – 'York'	ESim
♦ ***coraensis***	See S. ***sieboldiana coreana***
ebulus	CKin CRow
§ ***javanica***	EHal
nigra	CKin CPer EHar ENot GPoy GRei LBuc LHol MBri NNor NWea SIde WMou
– 'Albomarginata'	See S. ***n.*** 'Marginata'
N – 'Aurea' AGM	CB&S CCla CLnd CMHG CRow CSco EHar ELan ENot EPla ERav GRei LHol MBar NRoo SPer WDin
– 'Aureomarginata'	CSam ELan EPla ERav GAri LAbb MBal NNor NSti SHBN SLon
– 'Bimble' (v)	EMon
– 'Cae Rhos Lligwy'	WHer
– 'Castledean'	EHal SMad
– 'Din Dryfol' (v)	CNat
¶ – 'Golden Locks'	EFol SMrm
¶ – 'Greener Later' (v)	CNat
§ – 'Guincho Purple' AGM	Widely available
– 'Heterophylla'	See S. ***n.*** 'Linearis'
– f. ***laciniata*** AGM	Widely available
§ – 'Linearis'	CChu CPle EBre EHal ELan EPla ERav GCal LBre LHop SMad SUsu WAbe
– 'Madonna' (v)	CBow CChu CDoC COtt CPMA EFol EHal EPla IBar MPla NBar NBee SMad SPer
§ – 'Marginata'	CBra CCla CMHG CRow CSco EFol EHar ELan GRei IBar IOrc MBar MBri MGos NRoo SDix SMad SPer SSta SUsu WAbe WDin WSHC WWat WWin
¶ – mosaic virus	CNat
– 'Nana'	EMon SLon
¶ – 'Pendula'	EPla
– 'Plena'	EMon EPla
– 'Pulverulenta' (v)	CChu CDoC CRow CSco EBre EFol EHar ELan EPar EPla ERav EWri GCal IBar LBre LHol LHop MBri NSti SApp SDry SHil SPer WSHC
– 'Purpurea'	See S. ***n.*** 'Guincho Purple'
– 'Pygmy'	EHal EPla ESis MPla NHol WPat
– 'Pyramidalis'	EHar EMon EPla SMad WCot
*– 'Tenuifolia'	CKni LHol
– 'Variegata'	See S. ***n.*** 'Marginata'
¶ – 'Viridis'	EMon
– 'Witches Broom'	EMon EPla
racemosa	GRei
– 'Aurea'	CSco EBre GRei LBre NKay
– 'Goldenlocks'	EHal LHop NHol SPer WPat
¶ – 'Moerheimii'	EPla
– 'Plumosa Aurea'	CB&S CBot CMHG CRow CTrw EBre EFol EHar ELan ENot IDai IJoh LBre LHop MBal MBri NBee NNor NRoo SDix SHBN SLon SMad SPer SReu SSta WDin WHCG WWin
– 'Sutherland Gold' AGM	Widely available
– 'Tenuifolia' AGM	CPMA CSco EHal ELan MGos MPla MUlv NHol NSti SMad SPer WCru WHCG WPat WWat
¶ ***sieboldiana***	EMon
§ – var. ***coreana***	CMCN
wightiana	See S. ***javanica***

SAMOLUS (Primulaceae)

repens	ECou

SANCHEZIA (Acanthaceae)

nobilis hort. — See S. *speciosa*

SANDERSONIA (Liliaceae/Colchicaceae)

aurantiaca — LAma LBow NRog WChr WCru

SANGUINARIA (Papaveraceae)

canadensis — CArn CAvo CBro CChu CCla CGle CRDP CSpe ECha ELan EPar EPot GCal GPoy LAma LHop NNor NRog NRya NSti SDeJ SHig WAbe WChr WCru WMar WWat
¶– 'Multiplex' — WChr
– pink — SWas WThi
– 'Plena' AGM — CAvo CBrd CBro CChu CCla CMea EBre EPar EPot LBre MBri MFos MHig MRPP MTho NGar NHar NHol NRya SBla SHer SIng SPer SPou SWas WAbe WDav WEas

SANGUISORBA (Rosaceae)

albiflora — ELan
benthamiana — CHEx
canadensis — CHan CRow ECha GAbr GCal GPoy MFir SPer WOld WWye
hakusanensis — NBir
**magnifica alba* — CCla CRow EBre ECro EFou EPla GAri LBre NRoo WWin
§ *minor* — CArn CKin EEls EHer EWFC GPoy IEde LHol MBar MChe MHew NBro NMir SIde WCHb WCla WEas WHer WNdy WOak WPer WWye
obtusa — CCla CHan CRow CSco CShe ECha ECro EFol EFou ELan GAbr GCal LHil MRav MUlv NBro NHol NSti SFis SLga SMad SMrm SPer WEas
officinalis — CArn CLew CSev ECWi EGol EWFC Effi GBar NLan NMir WCla WNdy WWin WWye
¶– 'Tanna' — EMon
pimpinella — See S. *minor*
sitchensis — See S. *stipulata*
§ *stipulata* — GCal MUlv
tenuifolia — MUlv
– 'Alba' — ECha

SANICULA (Umbelliferae/Apiaceae)

europaea — CKin CNat EWFC GBar GPoy LHol MHew WHer

SANIELLA (Liliaceae/Hypoxidaceae)

verna — MHig

SANSEVIERIA (Dracaenaceae)

trifasciata 'Gigantea' (v) — MBri
– 'Golden Hahnii' AGM — CDoC MBri
– 'Laurentii' AGM — MBri

SANTOLINA † (Compositae/Asteraceae)

§ *chamaecyparissus* AGM — Widely available
– var. *corsica* — See S. *c. nana*
– 'Lambrook Silver' — EBee ECtt ESis ESma GAbr MAsh NH&H NHol SGil SPla WHer WWat
– 'Lemon Queen' — CArn CDoC ESis GBar MBal MBel MGos NBir NH&H NSti NWyt SHer SIde SPla WCHb WOak WPer WWat
§ – var. *nana* AGM — CB&S CBow CSFH CSco EBre ECha ENot EPla LBre LHop MBar NFai NH&H NNor SAxl SLon SPer WAbe WPer WWat WWye
– – 'Weston' — CLew CShe EFol EWes MBri MCas MGos NH&H NHol NTow
– 'Pretty Carol' — CAbP CDoC CKni CSco ELan EMil ESis LHop MAsh NFai NH&H NHol SHer SIde SPla WWat WWeb
– 'Small-Ness' — EMon LHop MAsh MSte NHol SIng WPat
– ssp. *squarrosa* — NH&H
elegans — NHar WDav
incana — See S. *chamaecyparissus*
'Oldfield Hybrid' — NH&H
pectinata — See S. *rosmarinifolia canescens*
§ *pinnata* — CBow CSev EMon ESma LHol NH&H WPbr WPer
– ssp. *neapolitana* AGM — CArn CHan CMHG CSFH CSev CShe ECha ELan ENot ISea LHol LHop MBri NH&H NNor NSti SDix WBod WEas WHCG WOak WTyr WWat WWye
– – cream — See S. *p. n.* 'Edward Bowles'
§ – – 'Edward Bowles' — CCla CGle CMil EBar EFol EFou EJud ELan EMil EOrc EPad ESis GCal LHop NBir NH&H NHol NPer NSti SAxl SChu SLon SPla SSvw WAbe WHen WHer WSHC
– – 'Sulphurea' — CBow CDoC CMer EPla LGre MBel NCat NH&H SPer SUsu WKif WPer
rosmarinifolia — ESis
§ – ssp. *canescens* — NH&H
§ – ssp. *rosmarinifolia* — CB&S CCla CHan CMHG CSFH CSco CSev ECha ELan ENot GCHN LHol MBri NH&H NHol NKay NSti SDix WBod WDav WEas WSHC WWat WWin WWye
– – 'Primrose Gem' AGM — CB&S CLew CSam ECha EFol EMil EPad ESis IJoh LAbb LHop MBal MPla NCat NH&H NHol NSti SAxl SBod SHer SPla WPer
**serratifolia* — CSco EBee LHol NH&H WPer WWye
tomentosa — See S. *pinnata neapolitana*
virens — See S. *rosmarinifolia rosmarinifolia*
viridis — See S. *rosmarinifolia rosmarinifolia*

SAPINDUS (Sapindaceae)

drummondii — WCoo

SAPIUM (Euphorbiaceae)

See Plant Deletions

SAPONARIA (Caryophyllaceae)

'Bressingham' AGM — EBre ECha ELan EMNN LBee LBre NHar NHol SBla SHer SIng WPat WPer WThu WWin

caespitosa	EPot EWes GTou MHig NTow WOMN
x ***lempergii*** 'Max Frei'	ECoo ECro GAbr
lutea	CNic
ocymoïdes AGM	CB&S CLTr ECha ECtt EFol EFou EHon ELan EMNN ESis GAbr GCHN IDai LAbb LGro MCas MPla NKay NNrw NRoo WPbr WPer WStI WWin
– 'Alba'	ECha
– 'Rubra Compacta' AGM	LBee WAbe WPat WPer
officinalis	CArn CBre CKin CRow CSFH ECWi EJud EWFC Effi GAbr GPoy IEde LHol MChe MHew MSal SIde WHal WHer WNdy WOak WPer WWye
– 'Alba Plena'	CGle CHad CMea CMil CSFH CSam ECha ECoo ECro EMon GBar NBrk NHol NSti SChu WCHb WHer WPer WWin
§ – 'Dazzler' (v)	EBar ECoo EFol EHoe ELan EMon ESma GBri LHol LHop MTho NBir NBrk NRoo NSti SIde WCHb WCot WHal WPbr
– 'Rosea Plena'	Widely available
– 'Rubra Plena'	CGle CHad CMHG CMea CMil CRDP ECha ELan EMon SChu WCHb WCot WPbr WThi
– 'Variegata'	See S. *o.* 'Dazzler'
x ***olivana*** AGM	CNic ECha EMNN EPot LBee MHig MPla NKay NMen SBod SFis WOMN WPat WThu WWin
pulvinaris	See S. ***pumilio***
§ ***pumilio***	GCHN GTou MHig NHol NWCA
'Rosenteppich'	NTow SWas WDav WPat
sicula	WOld WPer WTyr
zawadskii	See SILENE *z.*

SARCOCAPNOS (Papaveraceae)

¶ ***baetica***	NWCA
enneaphylla	EPot WAbe

SARCOCOCCA † (Buxaceae)

confusa AGM	Widely available
hookeriana AGM	CBow ECot IOrc SHer SReu WOMN
– Sch 2396	EPla
– var. ***digyna*** AGM	Widely available
– – 'Purple Stem'	CCla EPla MGos SHil WDin
– var. ***humilis***	CBow CDoC CPle CSco ELan ENot EPar EPla ERav IJoh LHop MBal MBar MBri MCas MGos MPla MWat NNor SHBN SPer SPla WBod WDin WSHC WWat
orientalis	CFil CMCN SHil
♦ 'Roy Lancaster'	See S. ***ruscifolia*** 'Dragon Gate'
ruscifolia	CB&S CBow CCla CDoC CMCN CPMA CPle CSam CSco EGol ELan ENot EPla ERav IHos IOrc MBri MBrk MGos MPla SGil SLon SPer SPla WWat
– var. ***chinensis*** AGM	CBot EPla
¶ – var. ***chinensis*** L 713	EPla
§ – 'Dragon Gate'	CFil EPla
saligna	CB&S CCla CMCN EPla WBod

SARCOPOTERIUM (Rosaceae)

See Plant Deletions

SARMIENTA (Gesneriaceae)

¶ ***repens*** AGM	WAbe WCru

SARRACENIA † (Sarraceniaceae)

'Ahlsii'	WMEx
alata	EPot WHal WMEx
– 'Red Lid'	WMEx
alata x ***oreophila***	WMEx
x ***areolata***	WMEx
'Brook's Hybrid'	EPot
x ***catesbyi*** AGM	EPot MHel WMEx
– red	WMEx
x ***catesbyi*** x ***excellens***	WMEx
x ***catesbyi*** x ***flava***	WMEx
x ***catesbyi*** x ***popei***	WMEx
x ***catesbyi*** x ***rubra***	WMEx
x ***chelsonii*** AGM	WMEx
x ***comptonensis***	WMEx
x ***courtii***	MHel WHal
'Evendine'	WMEx
x ***excellens*** AGM	MHel
x ***excellens*** x ***wrigleyana***	WMEx
x ***exornata***	WMEx
x ***farnhamii***	See S. x ***readii***
flava AGM	EPot MHel MSte WHal WMEx
– 'Maxima'	EPot WHal WMEx
¶ ***flava*** 'Maxima' x ***purpurea venosa***	MHel
¶ ***flava*** 'Maxima' x ***rubra jonesii***	MHel
x ***formosa***	MHel
x ***formosa*** x ***excellens***	WMEx
'Gulf Rubra'	WMEx
x ***harperi***	WMEx
'Judy'	WMEx
leucophylla AGM	EPot MHel MSte WHal WMEx
leucophylla x ***catesbyi***	WMEx
¶ – x ***excellens***	MHel
– x ***oreophila***	WMEx
– x ***popei***	WMEx
x ***melanorhoda***	MHel WMEx
x ***miniata***	WMEx
minor	EPot MHel WHal WMEx
– 'Okefenokee Giant'	MSte WMEx
minor x ***wrigleyana***	WMEx
x ***mitchelliana*** AGM	EPot MHel WHal WMEx
x ***moorei***	MHel WMEx
– 'Marston Select'	WMEx
x ***moorei*** x ***catesbyi***	WMEx
– ***readii***	WMEx
oreophila	EPot
¶ ***oreophila*** x ***leucophylla***	MHel
– x ***minor***	EPot WMEx
¶ – x ***purpurea***	MHel
x ***popei*** x ***flava***	WMEx
x ***popei*** x ***purpurea venosa***	WMEx
psittacina	EPot MSte WHal WMEx
purpurea	EPot WMEx
– 'Louis Burke'	WMEx
– ssp. ***purpurea***	WMEx
– ssp. ***venosa***	CRDP WHal WMEx

§ x ***readii***	WMEx
x ***readii*** x ***excellens***	WMEx
'Red Burgundy'	WMEx
x ***rehderi***	MHel WMEx
rubra	EPot WHal WMEx
– ssp. ***gulfensis***	EPot WHal
– ssp. ***jonesii***	MHel MSte WMEx
rubra x ***alata*** 'Red Lid'	WMEx
– x ***excellens***	WMEx
x ***swaniana***	MHel WMEx
willisii x ***flava***	WMEx
– x ***minor*** 'Giant'	WMEx

SASA † (Gramineae/Poaceae-Bambusoideae)

borealis	See SASAMORPHA ***borealis***
chrysantha	EPla
chrysantha hort.	See PLEIOBLASTUS ***chino***
disticha 'Mirrezuzume'	See PLEIOBLASTUS ***pygmaeus*** 'M.'.
glabra f. ***albostriata***	See SASAELLA ***masamuneana a.***
kurilensis	EPla ISta LBam SBam SDry WJun
– 'Shimofuri'	EPla SBam SDry WJun
– short form	EPla
megalophylla 'Nobilis'	SBam SDry
nana	See S. ***veitchii minor***
nipponica	COtt EPla SBam SDry WJun
– 'Aureostriata'	SBam SDry
oshidensis	EPla
§ ***palmata*** AGM	CHad CHan ENot GAri ISta LBam SBam
– f. ***nebulosa***	CB&S CHEx EPla MUlv SArc SBam SDry WJun
– 'Warley Place' (v)	SBam SDry
quelpaertensis	EPla GAri ISta LBam SBam SDry
senanensis	EPla SBam SDry
tessellata	See INDOCALAMUS ***tessellatus***
tsuboiana	CB&S EPla ISta LBam MUlv SBam SDry
§ ***veitchii***	CB&S CBow CGre CHEx CTro CWit ECha EPar EPla ERav IOrc ISea ISta LBam LNet MBri MUlv NJap SBam SCob SDry SPer WJun WPat WWye
§ – ***minor***	SBam

SASAELLA (Gramineae/Poaceae-Bambusoideae)

bitchuensis hort.	SBam SDry
glabra	See S. ***masamuneana***
¶ ***masamuneana***	EPla
§ – f. ***albostriata*** (v)	COtt EPla SBam SDry WJun
– f. ***aureostriata*** (v)	EPla ISta SBam SDry
§ ***ramosa***	EHoe EPla GAri ISta LBam MBal NRya SBam SCob SDry SHil WJun
*– 'Tsuyu-zasa'	EPla

SASAMORPHA (Gramineae/Poaceae-Bambusoideae)

§ ***borealis***	GAri LBam SBam

SASSAFRAS (Lauraceae)

albidum	CArn CBot CHEx CMCN EHar SHil

SATSUMA See CITRUS *reticulata* Satsuma Group

SATUREJA (Labiatae/Lamiaceae)

coerulea AGM	EWes SFis SIde
cuneifolia	MCas
hortensis	EHer GPoy IEde ILis LHol LHop MChe MHew WHer
montana	CArn CRiv EEls EHer ELan EWFC Effi GPoy IEde ILis LHol MBri MChe MHew MPla NMen NRoo NSti SDix SIde WCHb WHer WOak WPer WWye
§ – ssp. ***illyrica***	WThi
– prostrate white	CRDP LGan
¶ – 'Purple Mountain'	GPoy
– ***subspicata***	See S. ***m. illyrica***
parnassica	WPer WWye
repanda	See S. ***spicigera***
seleriana	GCal MHig NTow WPer
¶ ***spicata***	WHow
§ ***spicigera***	CArn CLew CRiv CSFH EPot LHol MHig NKay NMen NTow SFis SIde WCHb WHil WPer WWin WWye

SATYRIUM (Orchidaceae)

See Plant Deletions

SAURAUIA (Actinidiaceae)

subspinosa	CHEx

SAUROMATUM (Araceae)

guttatum	See S. ***venosum***
§ ***venosum***	ELan LAma MBri SMad WCot WCru

SAURURUS (Saururaceae)

cernuus	CBen CRDP CWGN EBre EHon ELan EMFW LBre LMay MSta NDea SRms SWat WChe WHol
¶ ***chinensis***	SPou

SAUSSUREA (Compositae/Asteraceae)

alpina	SIng
chinophylla	WPer
¶ ***discolor***	SIng
¶ ***hypoleuca***	GAul

SAXEGOTHAEA (Podocarpaceae)

conspicua	CGre CMCN EHar EPla IBar LCon SBor SLon SMad WThu

SAXIFRAGA † (Saxifragaceae)

'Aemula' (x ***borisii***) (8)	WAbe
aïzoïdes var. ***atrorubens*** (6)	MBal MBro NGre WGor
*– ***aurantiana*** (6)	NGre
aïzoön	See S. ***paniculata***
'Alba' (x ***apiculata***) (8)	CLew CShe ELan EMNN ESis GPlt GTou LFox MBal MBro MHig NHed NHol NMen NRed SBla SIng SSmi WAbe WCla WHoo WPat WThu WWin
– (x ***arco-valleyi***)	See S. 'Ophelia'

– ***(oppositifolia)*** (9)	CRiv ELan EMNN GTou MYat NGre NHar NNrd NRya SHer SIng SSmi WAbe WThu WWin
– ***(sempervivum)***	See S. 'Zita'
'Albert Einstein' (x ***apiculata***) (8)	NHol WAbe
'Albertii' ***(callosa)*** (7)	CShe GTou MHig NNrd SGil SSmi WWin
'Aldebaran' (x ***borisii***) (8)	EMNN EPot GCLN NHar
'Alfons Mucha' (8)	EPot MWat NGre NRed WAbe
'Alpenglow' (8)	MWat
'Amitie' (x ***gloriana***) (8)	MYat NHol
*'Anagales Sunset'	WThu
andersonii (8)	EMNN EPot GCLN ITim MBal MYat NGre NMen NNrd NRya NTow WAbe WDav
x ***andrewsii*** (3x7)	LBee MDHE MFir MHig MTho NHol SSmi
§ ***androsacea*** (12)	NTow
'Anne Beddall' ***(cinerea)*** (8)	MWat NGre
x ***apiculata***	See S. 'Gregor Mendel'
'Apple Blossom' (12)	LBuc LHop WGor
'Archfield White' ***(callosa)*** (7)	CLew CNic NNrd
§ 'Arco' (x ***arco-valleyi***) (8)	EPot MWat NNrd WAbe
x ***arco-valleyi***	See S. 'Arco'
x ***arendsii*** (12)	MFos MPit WEas
§ 'Aretiastrum' (x ***boydii***) (8)	EMNN EPot LFox MYat NGre NHed NMen NNrd SIng WAbe WThu
aretioïdes (8)	GCHN WAbe WThu
'Ariel' (x ***hornibrookii***) (8)	LFox
* ***armstrongii***	NRed
'Assimilis' (x ***petraschii***) (8)	MBro MWat MYat WAbe
'August Hayek' (x ***leyboldii***) (8)	MWat NNrd NRed
§ 'Aureopunctata' (x ***urbium***) (3/v)	CArn CGle CMil CShe CTom ECha EFol ELan EMar EPla GBuc GCal GCra LHop MBal MBro MFir NGre NHol NRoo SHer SMrm WBon WFox WHen WHil
'Balcana'	See S. ***paniculata orientalis***
'Baldensis'	See S. ***paniculata baldensis***
'Ballawley Guardsman' (12)	EPar IDai LFox MBal NKay NRoo SHer SIng
§ 'Beatrix Stanley' (x ***anglica***) (8)	EMNN EPot LFox MBal MBro MCas MYat NGre NHar NHol NMen WAbe
'Becky Foster' (x ***borisii***) (8)	MWat
'Beechcroft White'	LBee
'Berenika' (x ***bertolonii***) (8)	MWat
'Bettina' (x ***paulinae***) (8)	GCHN LBee WAbe
♦x ***biasolettoi***	See S. 'Phoenix'
'Biegleri' (8)	EPot
'Birch Baby' (12)	SIng
'Birch Yellow'	See S. 'Pseudoborisii'
'Black Beauty' (12)	LBee SGil SHer
*'Blackhouse White'	NGre NNrd
'Blanka' (x ***borisii***)	MWat
'Bob Hawkins' (12/v)	CLew CMHG CMer ELan EPad EPar GCHN GDra LBee LFox NMen NNrd NRed NVic WWin
§ 'Bodensee' (x ***hofmannii***) (8)	WAbe WPat
x ***borisii***	See S. 'Sofia'
'Boston Spa' (x ***elisabethae***) (8)	EMNN ESis GCHN GPlt MBro MCas MHig MPit MYat NGre NHed NKay NMen NNrd NRed NRoo NTow SGil SHer SIng WAbe WPat WThu WTyr
'Bridget' (x ***edithiae***) (8)	CNic CShe ELan ESis ITim LFox MBal MCas NGre NHed NMen NNrd NRed NTow SGil SHer SIng WAbe WThu
'Brookside' ***(burseriana)*** (8)	EPot SGil SIng WAbe
brunoniana	See S. ***brunonis***
§ ***brunonis*** (2)	EPot LFox NWCA WCru
¶– EMAK 0406 (2)	NHol
bryoïdes (5)	GTou MHig
x ***burnatii*** (7)	EPot LFox MBro MCas MHig NHed NKay NNrd NRed SIng WGor WTyr
burseriana (8)	GCHN NRed NRya WAbe
'Buttercup' (x ***kayei***) (8)	EPot GTou MBro MWat MYat NGre NHed NNrd NWCA WAbe WHoo WPat
caesia (7)	NHol SRms
§ ***callosa*** AGM	GCHN GTou MBro MPla MWat NGre NHar NKay SBla WAbe WPat
§ – var. ***australis*** (7)	CNic CRiv ESis MBro MCas MHig NNrd SIng
– var. ***bellardii***	See S. ***callosa***
§ – ssp. ***catalaunica*** (7)	MBro NHol
– var. ***lantoscana***	See S. ***c. australis***
– ***lingulata***	See S. ***callosa.***
'Cambria Jewel' (12)	NNrd
'Cambridge Seedling' (8)	MWat MYat
§ ***camposii*** (12)	GAbr SIng
'Camyra' (8)	MWat MYat NGre NHed WAbe
x ***canis-dalmatica*** (7)	CMHG ECtt EMNN ESis GGar GTou LBee LBuc MBro MHig NHar NHed NMen NNrd SIng
§ 'Carmen' (x ***elisabethae***) (8)	CShe ELan EMNN IDai ITim LFox MBro MCas MHig MRPP MYat NHed NKay NNrd NPri NRya SHer SIng WAbe WThu
* ***carolinica***	LFox NWCA
'Castor' (x ***bilekii***) (8)	MWat NHed WAbe WThu
catalaunica (7)	See S. ***callosa catalaunica***
'Caterhamensis' ***(cotyledon)*** (7)	WEas
§ ***caucasica*** (8)	NKay
cebennensis AGM	EPad EPot LFox MRPP NHed NMen NRed NRya NTow SIgm SIng
– dwarf form (12)	WAbe
cespitosa (12)	NWCA
– var. ***emarginata*** (12)	MFos NHol WDav
'Chambers' Pink Pride'	See S. 'Miss Chambers'
§ ***cherlerioïdes*** (5)	EBar ELan NRed NRya SHer WCla WEas WWin

'Cherrytrees' (x ***boydii***) (8) — MCas NMen NNrd NRed NRya WAbe
'Chetwynd' (***marginata***) (8) — MWat WAbe
'Chez Nous' (x ***gloriana***) (8/v) — NGre
'Christine' (x ***anglica***) (8) — LFox MWat SIng
♦***chrysopleniifolia*** — See S. ***rotundifolia c.***
x ***churchillii*** (7) — NKay
'Clare Island' (12) — SIng
§ 'Clarence Elliott' (***umbrosa primuloïdes***) AGM — CNic CShe ELan GCal GDra MBro MCas MHig NCat NGre NHol NKay NNrd NRar NRya NVic SHer STre WCla WOMN WPat WThu
¶ 'Cleo' (x ***boydii***) (8) — MCas
§ 'Cloth of Gold' (***moschata***) (12) — CLew CMea CShe ECha ELan EPar EPot GDra GTou LBee MBal MBar MBro MCas MPla NKay NRoo NRya NWCA SBla SBod SIng SSmi SUsu WAbe WPat WThu WWin
cochlearis (7) — CMea CShe ESis LBee MBal NHed NNor NWCA SGil SIng SSmi WWin
– ***probynii*** (7) — MWat
'Cockscomb' — MDHE MWat
'Compacta' (***moschata***) (12) — SHer SIng
♦***corbariensis*** — See S. ***fragilis***
'Cordata' (***burseriana***) (8) — MWat
'Corona' (x ***boydii***) (8) — LFox MWat NGre
*x ***correvensis*** — ECtt GCHN MFir
'Correvoniana' (***paniculata***) (7) — CNic EBre EPad ESis LBre MBar MBro NHed NKay WAbe WWin
corsica ssp. ***cossoniana*** (11) — WOMN
§ ***cortusifolia*** (4) — CChu CHEx MBal NHar NKay SAxl
– dwarf form — EPot LGre
– var. ***fortunei*** — See S. ***fortunei***
§ ***corymbosa*** (8) — EPad NGre NKay
cotyledon (7) — GDra LBee MPla NKay NNor SHer SIng WAbe WCla WEas WTyr
§ 'Cranbourne' (x ***anglica***) AGM — CRiv CShe EBre EMNN EPot LBre LFox MBro MCas MYat NGre NHar NHol NMen NRed NRya SBla SGil SHer SIng WAbe WPat WThu
'Cream Seedling' (8) — EBre ESis LBre MBro MDHE MWat NGre NHed NRed
'Crenata' (***burseriana***) (8) — EPot GCHN GCLN LFox MBro MFos MWat MYat NGre NHar NHed NHol NKay NMen SSmi WAbe WHoo
'Crimson Rose' — NNrd
crispa (4) — SIng
crustata (7) — GCHN MDHE MPla SIng WThu
'Crystalie' (x ***biasolettoi***) (8) — EPot MBro NGre WAbe WPat WThu
'Cultrata' (***paniculata***) (7) — NKay
cuneata (12) — NHol
cuneifolia (3) — CHEx CRiv GDra GGar LBee MBal MCas MFir MWat NGre NHed NRoo NSti NWCA SSmi
– var. ***capillipes*** — See S. ***c. cuneifolia***
§ – ssp. ***cuneifolia*** (3) — NKay
cuscutiformis (4) — EPla GCal LRHS NCat NRar WCru
'Cwm Idwal' (***rosacea***) (12) — CNat
cymbalaria (13) — CRDP EBur WCla
– var. ***huetiana*** (13) — CNic
'Dainty Dame' (x ***arco-valleyi***) (8) — LFox NGre NHed NMen SIng WAbe
'Dana' (x ***megaseiflora***) (8) — EMNN LBee MWat NRed
'Dartington Double' (12) — EBre GCHN GDra GTou LBee LBre MBal MCas NHar NKay NMen NNrd NRed SGil
§ 'Denisa' (x ***pseudokotschyi***) (8) — MBal WAbe
densa — See S. ***cherlerioïdes***
'Dentata' (x ***geum***) (3) — CBos CLTr ECha ECro EPla GAbr GGar NVic
desoulavyi (8) — MHig NNrd
diapensioïdes (8) — NGre
Dixter form (x ***geum***) (3) — CRDP ECha EPla
'Doctor Clay' — WAbe
'Doctor Ramsay' (7) — ELan ESis ITim LBee MCas MPla MRPP NHed NKay NNrd NRed SIng
'Dorothy Milne' (8) — WThu
'Drakula' (***ferdinandi-coburgii***) (8) — MWat NHed NRya WAbe
'Dubarry' (12) — EWes NKay SHer SIng
'Duncan Lowe' (***stolitzkae***) (8) — NGre
¶ 'Dwight Ripley' (8) — LFox MWat
'Edgar Irmscher' (8) — LFox NRya WAbe
'Edie Campbell' (12) — NGre
'Edith' (x ***edithiae***) — LRHS NNrd
'Edward Elgar' (x ***megaseiflora***) (8) — MWat NHol NRed
¶ 'Eleanora Francini Corti' — MWat
'Elf' (12) — CRiv ELan EMNN LBee NKay NMen NRoo SGil SHer SIng WCla
'Eliot Hodgkin' (x ***millstreamiana***) (8) — LFox WAbe
x ***elisabethiae*** — See S. 'Carmen'
'Ellie Brinckerhoff' (x ***hornibrookii***) (8) — NGre
'Elliott's Variety' (***urbium primuloïdes***) (3) — See S. 'Clarence Elliott'
'Esther' (x ***burnatii***) (7) — CRiv EBre ELan ESis LBee LBre MHig MPit MPla NKay NNrd NRed NTow SBla SIng SSmi WAbe WThu WTyr

§ 'Eulenspiegel'	
(x *geuderi*) (8)	EPot LBuc MCas NKay NNrd SIng
exarata (12)	ITim LFox WAbe
– ssp. ***moschata*** (12)	NGre NWCA
– ***pyrenaica***	See S. ***androsacea***
Fair Maids of France	See S. ***granulata*** 'Flore Pleno'
'Fairy' (12)	CRiv ELan MCas NPri WHil
'Faldonside'	
(x ***boydii***) **AGM**	CRiv EPot LFox MBro MWat NGre NHed NMen NRed SBla WAbe WHoo WPat
'Falstaff' (***burseriana***)	
(8)	EPot LFox MDHE MYat SBla SIng
x ***farreri*** (7)	NHed NNrd
§ 'Faust' (x ***borisii***) (8)	EMNN MBro NGre NKay NMen SBla SIng
federici-augusti	See S. ***frederici-augusti***
'Ferdinand'	
(x ***hofmannii***) (8)	WAbe
ferdinandi-coburgi **AGM**	LFox NGre NHed NRed NTow NWCA WAbe WDav
– var. ***pravislavia***	See S. ***f.-c. rhodopea***
– var. ***radoslavoffii***	See S. ***f.-c rhodopea***
§ – var. ***rhodopea*** (8)	EPot LRHS MCas NHed SIng WThu
ferruginea (1)	NTow WCru
'Findling' (12)	CMHG CMea GCHN GPlt NGre NHol NKay NNrd NRoo SBod SIng WAbe WEas WPat WWin
flagellaris (2)	WCla WHil
– ***crassiflagellata***	
CC 298 (2)	NTow
x ***fleischeri*** (8)	NMen
'Florissa'	
(***oppositifolia***) (9)	CRiv EBre GCHN LBre LRHS WAbe
'Flowers of Sulphur'	See S. 'Schwefelblüte'
§ ***fortunei*** **AGM**	CBos EPla NBir NHol SIng SPer WCru WHal
'Four Winds' (12)	EGle GAbr LBee MFos NMen NNrd SBla SHer SIng
§ ***fragilis*** (12)	NHed
'Francis Cade' (7)	ELan ITim MDHE NGre
'Franzii' (x ***paulinae***) (8)	MWat MYat NHed
frederici-augusti (8)	SBla
– ssp. ***grisebachii*** **AGM**	GPlt GTou MFos MYat NGre WCla
¶ 'Friar Tuck' (x ***boydii***)	
(8)	MWat
§ 'Tvuj Přítel' ('Your Friend')	
(x ***poluanglica***) (8)	MWat NHed
'Friesei' (x ***salmonica***)	
(8)	CShe EMNN EPot MBro MYat NHar NHed NMen WDav
§ x ***fritschiana*** (7)	MDHE NKay NNrd SIng WAbe WTyr
'Funkii' (x ***petraschii***)	
(8)	MWat WAbe
'Gaiety' (12)	CRiv ELan GDra NEgg NRoo SHer SIng
'Galaxie'	
(x ***megaseiflora***) (8)	EPot LFox MCas NGre WAbe
'Ganymede'	
(***burseriana***) (8)	SIng
x ***gaudinii*** (7)	NKay
¶ 'Gelber Findling' (8)	WAbe
'Gem' (x ***irvingii***) (8)	EMNN EPot NHar NMen NRya
'Geoïdes'	See S. ***hirsuta paucicrenata***
georgei (8)	WAbe
¶ ***geranioïdes*** (11)	GCHN
x ***geuderi***	See S. 'Eulenspiegel'
x ***geum*** (3)	ECha ELan EPar MCas
'Gladys'	ELan
§ 'Glauca' (***paniculata brevifolia***) (7)	MDHE NGre SIng
¶ 'Glenborg'	EWes
'Gloria'	
(***burseriana***) **AGM**	CLew CNic CRiv CShe LFox MBal MBro MCas MRPP MYat NGre NMen NNrd NRya SBla WAbe WPat WThu
x ***gloriana*** (8)	EMNN EPot
'Godiva' (x ***gloriana***)	
(8)	EPot NHol WAbe
'Goeblii' (8)	MDHE NGre SIng WAbe WThu
'Gold Dust'	
(x ***eudoxiana***) (8)	CRiv EMNN GCLN GTou LFox MBro MHig MYat NHar NKay NMen SBod SIng WAbe WTyr WWin
'Golden Falls' (12/v)	CLew CMea EMNN EPot GTou LBee LHop NGre NMen NRoo SIng
'Golden Prague'	
(x ***pragensis***) (8)	EMNN NGre NNrd SIng WAbe
'Grace Farwell'	
(x ***anglica***) (8)	CRiv EMNN EPot GCHN ITim MBar MBro MCas MYat NGre NHed NMen NRya SGil SHer SIng WAbe WHoo
'Gracilis' (x ***geum***) (3)	CNic
granulata (11)	CCla CElw CHan CNic ECWi EWFC MCas MHew NMen NRed WBon WCla WGwy WHil WOak
§ – 'Flore Pleno' (11)	CElw CMil CRDP GAbr GArf LFox NBir NRya NSla SUsu WAbe
'Gratoïdes' (x ***grata***) (8)	MWat MYat NGre WAbe
¶ Greenslacks forms	
(***oppositifolia***) (9)	NGre
§ 'Gregor Mendel'	
(x ***apiculata***) **AGM**	CMea CNic ELan EMNN ESis GDra GTou IDai MBal MBro MHig MPla MYat NGre NHed NKay NRed SBla SBod SHer SIng SPla SSmi WAbe WCla WHoo WThu
grisebachii	See S. ***frederici-augusti g.***
'Gustav Hegi'	
(x ***anormalis***) (8)	WAbe
'Haagii' (x ***eudoxiana***)	
(8)	CRiv ELan EMNN EPot ESis GCHN MBal MBro MCas NGre NHed NKay NNrd NRed NTow SBla SIng SSmi WAbe WHoo WWin
hallii	GCHN WWin
'Harlow Car' (8)	LFox
¶ 'Hartside Pink'	
(***umbrosa***) (3)	CNic
'Hartswood White' (12)	LBuc SIng
x ***hausmannii*** (7x6)	NKay
¶ 'Hedwig' (x ***malbyana***)	
(8)	MWat
'Herbert Cuerdon'	
(x ***elisabethae***) (8)	NGre NHed NNrd
'Highdownensis' (7)	NHol

'Hindhead Seedling'
(x *boydii*) (8) EMNN LRHS MDHE MWat NHar NHed NMen NNrd SHer WAbe
hirsuta (3) NRya WBon WHil
'Hirsuta' (x *geum*) See S. x ***geum***
'Hirtella' (*paniculata*)
(7) MDHE SIng
'His Majesty'
(x *irvingii*) (8) EMNN LFox NHar NMen SIng WAbe WThu
'Hi-Ace' (12/v) CRDP ELan EMNN LBee LFox MBro MCas MPit NGre NRoo NTow SBla SBod SHer SIng SSmi WAbe WHal WHil WPat WThu WWin
'Hocker Edge'
(x *arco-valleyi*) (8) ITim LFox MHig MWat MYat NHed NHol NNrd WAbe WThu
'Holden Seedling' (12) EMNN EPot
x *hornibrookii* (8) NKay
hostii (7) ESis GTou ITim LBee MCas MHig NHol NKay SIng WAbe
– var. *altissima* See S. ***h. hostii***
§ – ssp. *hostii* (7) EPad MDHE NTow STre
– ssp. *rhaetica* (7) MDHE NMen
hypnoïdes (12) GAbr GTou MPla SSmi
§ – var. *egemmulosa* (12) MBal
¶ 'Icicle' (x *elisabathae*)
(8) MWat
'Ingeborg' (12) ECha LBee SChu SIng
iranica (8) EMNN GCHN GTou MWat MYat NGre NHar SIng WAbe
¶ 'Irene Bacci' MWat
'Iris Prichard'
(x *hardingii*) (8) CShe EMNN EPot MBro MCas MYat NGre NHol NNrd SIng WAbe WHoo WThu
irrigua (11) EWes
x *irvingii* See S. 'Walter Irving'
jacquemontii C&Mc 414 GTou
'James Bremner' (12) EWes GGar LBee MCas NRya SBod SIng
'Jason' (x *elisabethae*)
(8) NHol
'Jenkinsiae'
(x *irvingii*) AGM Widely available
§ 'Johann Kellerer'
(x *kellereri*) (8) EPot LFox MCas MHig MYat NGre NHed NNrd SIng WAbe
'John Tomlinson'
(*burseriana*) (8) MCas
'Josef Capek'
(x *megaseiflora*) (8) EPot NGre
'Joy' See S. 'Kaspar Maria Sternberg'
'Judith Shackleton' (8) CNic MWat WAbe
'Juliet' See S. 'Riverslea'
§ *juniperifolia* (8) CLew ELan EMNN GCHN GPlt ITim MBro MCas NGre NHar NHed NHol NKay NMen NRed NRoo NWCA SChu SGil SHer SIng SSmi
– var. *macedonica* See S. ***juniperifolia***
'Jupiter'
(x *megaseiflora*) (8) EMNN LBee MCas MWat NGre NHar WAbe
'Karel Capek'
(x *megaseiflora*) (8) EPot LBee MWat NGre NHed NRed WAbe
'Karel Stivin' (*edithiae*) EMNN NGre NRed

'Karlstejn' (x *borisii*) (8) WAbe
§ 'Kaspar Maria Sternberg'
(x *petraschii*) (8) EMNN GCHN ITim LFox MBro NGre NHar NHol NKay NMen NNrd NRya SIng WPat
'Kath Dryden'
(x *anglica*) (8) NNrd SIng WAbe
'Kathleen Pinsent' AGM CShe EPad EPot MBro NHar NNrd NVic SGil SHer SSmi WAbe
x *kellereri* See S. 'Johann Kellerer'
'Kestoniensis'
(x *salmonica*) (8) MWat NNrd
'Kewensis' (x *kellereri*)
(8) SIng WAbe
'King Lear'
(x *bursiculata*) (8) LFox LRHS MWat NRya SIng
'Kingii' See S. ***hypnoïdes egemmulosa***
'Kingscote White' SIng
§ 'Tvuj Polibek' ('Your Kiss')
(x *poluanglica*) (8) MWat NHed
'Klondike' (x *boydii*) (8) MDHE WAbe
'Knapton Pink' (12) CMHG MCas NRya SIng SSmi
'Knapton White' (12) EWes LBuc SIng WCla
§ 'Kolbiana' (x *paulinae*)
(8) MWat MYat
'Koprvnik'
(*paniculata*) (7) MDHE NNrd SIng
kotschyi (8) NGre WAbe WDav
¶ 'Krakatit'
(x *megaseiflora*) (8) NHol
'Krasava'
(x *megaseiflora*) (8) EMNN EPot GCLN LBee NGre NHar NHol NRya
'Kyrillii' (x *borisii*) (8) EMNN NNrd NRed
'Labe' (x *arco-valleyi*)
(8) CNic EPot NMen WAbe
'Lady Beatrix Stanley' See S. 'Beatrix Stanley'
'Lagraveana'
(*paniculata*) (7) ELan LBee NGre NHed WWin
x *landaueri* See S. 'Leonore'
'Lenka'
(*byam-groundsii*) (8) EMNN ITim NGre NHar
'Leo Gordon Godseff'
(x *elisabethae*) (8) MBro MHig MYat NKay NRed SBla SIng
§ 'Leonore' (x *landaueri*)
(8) MWat
'Letchworth Gem'
(x *urbium*) (3) CRiv EPla WBon
x *leyboldii* (8) GTou
'Lidice' (8) EMNN GCLN LBee NGre NHar NMen NRya WAbe
lilacina (8) CLew EMNN MWat NGre NHar WAbe WPat
lingulata See S. ***callosa***
'Lismore Carmine' (8) MWat WAbe
'Lismore Pink' (8) MWat
'Lohengrin'
(x *hoerhammeri*) (8) MWat
longifolia (7) EBar EPad NHol NSla WAbe
– JJA 861600 (7) SBla
'Love Me' See S. 'Miluj Mne'
'Lowndes' (*andersonii*)
(8) WAbe
¶ *lowndesii* NHol

¶ 'Ludmila Šubrova' (x *bertolonii*) (8) — NGre
'Luna' (x *millstreamiana*) (8) — WAbe
'Lusanna' (x *irvingii*) (8) — NGre
'Lutea' (*paniculata*) AGM — CNic EPot ESis GDra GTou LBee MBal MCas MRPP NGre NHed NHol NMen NNrd NRoo SBla SChu SHer SIng SSmi
§ 'Luteola' (x *boydii*) AGM — EPot WAbe
luteoviridis — See S. *corymbosa*
¶ 'Luznice' (x *poluluteo*) (8) — MWat NHed
x ***macnabiana*** (7) — NKay
'Magna' (*burseriana*) (8) — MWat
major lutea — See S. 'Luteola'
'Major' (*cochlearis*) AGM — NNrd WAbe WGor
mandschuriensis (1) — GDra NKay
'Margarete' (x *borisii*) (8) — NHed NNrd WAbe
marginata (8) — LFox MYat NGre WAbe WThu
– var. ***balcanica*** — See S. *m. rocheliana*
– var. ***boryi*** (8) — EPot MYat NGre
– var. ***coriophylla*** (8) — MDHE MYat NWCA WAbe
– var. ***karadzicensis*** (8) — EMNN LRHS NNrd WAbe
– 'Lutea' — See S. 'Faust'
§ – var. ***rocheliana*** (8) — CMHG ELan EPot GCLN MCas NGre NKay NMen NNrd SIng WAbe
'Maria Luisa' (x *salmonica*) (8) — CRiv EMNN EPot LFox MBro MCas NHed NHol NKay NNrd SIng WAbe
'Marianna' (x *borisii*) (8) — CNic MWat MYat NHed NMen NNrd
'Mars' (x *elisabethae*) (8) — MWat
'Marshall Joffre' (12) — LBuc WHil
§ 'Martha' (x *semmleri*) (8) — EMNN GCLN NHol NMen NRed
'May Queen' — MWat SIng
media (8) — NGre
x ***megaseiflora*** — See S. 'Robin Hood'
mertensiana (1) — GTou NBir
– var. ***bulbifera*** (1) — CNic CRDP
'Meteor' (8) — NRya WAbe
'Millstream Cream' (x *elisabethae*) (8) — EPot MDHE MWat NNrd WAbe
¶ 'Miluj Mne' ('Love Me') (x *poluanglica*) (8) — LFox MWat NHed
'Minehaha' (x *elisabethae*) (8) — WAbe
'Minor' (*cochlearis*) AGM — EFol EMNN EPad GDra GTou LBee LFox MBal MBro MCas MHig MRPP NHol NKay NVic NWCA SIng SSmi WCla WHil WHoo WPat WThu
– (*paniculata*) — See S. *p. brevifolia*
'Minor Glauca' (*paniculata*) — See S. 'Glauca' (*paniculata brevifolia*)
'Minutifolia' (*paniculata*) (7) — CLew CNic EPad ESis LBee LFox MBal MDHE NHed NWCA SIng
'Miss Chambers' (x *urbium*) (3) — CBos EMon SWas
'Mona Lisa' (x *borisii*) (8) — MDHE MYat NRya SIng WAbe
§ 'Mondscheinsonate' (x *boydii*) (8) — WAbe
'Moonlight' — See S. 'Sulphurea'
'Moonlight Sonata' (x *boydii*) — See S. 'Mondscheinsonate'
moschata — See S. *exarata m.*
'Mother of Pearl' (x *irvingii*) (8) — EMNN NHar NHol WAbe
'Mother Queen' (x *irvingii*) (8) — MBro MDHE WHoo WPat
'Mount Nachi' (*fortunei*) (4) — ECha GArf NHar SWas
'Mrs E Piper' (12) — LBuc NKay SRms WCla
'Mrs Gertie Prichard' (x *megaseiflora*) (8) — LFox WAbe
'Mrs Helen Terry' (x *salmonica*) (8) — EPot GCLN LRHS MCas MDHE MWat MYat NHed NMen NNrd
'Mrs Leng' (x *elisabethae*) (8) — EMNN NHol NMen
mutata (7) — WCru
'Myra' (x *anglica*) (8) — CRiv EMNN EPot LFox MBro MWat MYat NHol WAbe WHoo WPat WThu
'Myra Cambria' (x *anglica*) (8) — GCHN MFir MWat MYat NGre WAbe
'Nancye' (8) — WAbe
§ ***nelsoniana*** (1) — NHol
¶ 'Nepal' (*andersonii*) (8) — WAbe
'Norvegica' (*cotyledon*) (7) — GTou MDHE NGre WWin
'Notata' (*paniculata*) (7) — NKay NNrd
'Nottingham Gold' (x *boydii*) (8) — MWat NGre WAbe
'Nugget' (8) — SIng
'Obristii' (x *salmonica*) (8) — EMNN ITim NMen NNrd WAbe
§ ***obtusa*** (8) — NHol NKay WAbe
'Obtusocuneata' (*fortunei*) (4) — WCru
'Ochroleuca' (x *elisabethae*) (8) — CRiv EMNN GPlt ITim NHol NRed WAbe WThu
'Opalescent' (8) — LFox MWat NGre WAbe
§ 'Ophelia' (x *arco-valleyi*) (8) — MWat NGre SIng
oppositifolia (9) — CRiv EBre GTou ITim LBre MHig MYat NHol NKay WWin
¶ – ***florissa*** — GCHN
– ssp. ***latina*** (9) — ELan EMNN GDra GGar GTou NHar NHol SGil WWin
* – ***pyrenaica*** (9) — EMNN EPad GCLN NHar
– Skye form (9) — WAbe
– x ***biflora*** (9) — NHar NHol
'Oriole' (x *boydii*) (8) — NMen
'Orjen' (*paniculata orientalis*) (7) — MDHE NHol NNrd
§ ***paniculata*** (7) — CShe ELan ESis GTou LBee MBal MBro MCas MWat NHed NKay NRoo SHer WCla WHoo
– ***backhouseana*** (7) — WAbe
§ – var. ***baldensis*** (7) — ELan GDra GTou ITim MBar MBro MCas MWat NGre NHed NKay NNrd SBla SHer SIgm SSmi WAbe WCla WWin

Plant	Suppliers
§ – var. ***brevifolia*** (7)	CNic CTom NHol NKay NNrd SIng SSmi
*– ***carniolica*** (7)	EFol LBee MCas MHig NRed SBla
§ – ssp. ***cartilaginea*** (7)	NNrd SBla
*– ***eriophylla*** (7)	NKay
– ssp. ***kolenatiana***	See S. ***p. cartilaginea***
– ***labradorica***	See S. ***p. neogaea***
§ – ***neogaea*** (7)	MDHE NKay
§ – var. ***orientalis*** (7)	MBro MDHE SHer SSmi WAbe WCla
paradoxa (14)	MCas NBra SBla SIng WGor
'Parcevalis' (x ***finnisiae***) (8x6)	WAbe
'Parsee' (x ***margoxiana***) (8)	WAbe
'Paula' (x ***paulinae***) (8)	NGre NKay
'Peach Blossom' (8)	CNic MWat MYat NGre NHol NRya SIng WAbe
'Pearly Gates' (x ***irvingii***) (8)	MWat NGre NMen
*'Pearly Gold' (12)	CMea EBar GPlt MCas NRoo SHer WThu
'Pearly King' (12)	CMea ELan GPlt LBee MBal NKay NMen NVic SChu SHer WAbe
x ***pectinata***	See S. x ***fritschiana***
pedemontana (12)	EPot
– ssp. ***cymosa*** (12)	NWCA WDav
¶ – ssp. ***cymosa*** NS 674 (12)	NWCA
'Penelope' (x ***boydilacina***) (8)	CNic EMNN EPot ITim LBee MBro MCas MFos MYat NGre NHed NRya WAbe WHoo WPat WThu
'Perle Rose' (x ***anglica***) (8)	LFox NGre
'Peter Burrow' (x ***poluanglica***) (8)	MWat WAbe
'Peter Pan' (12)	ELan EMNN EPot GDra LBee LFox MCas NGre NHol NKay NMen NRoo SBod SSmi WHil WPat
'Petra' (8)	NHol NKay NNrd WAbe
petraea (14)	ESis
x ***petraschii*** (8)	ITim NRed
'Phoenix' (x ***biasolettoi***) (8)	GCLN
'Pilatus' (x ***boydii***) (8)	MWat SIng
'Pixie' (12)	EBre EMNN EPar LBee LBre MBal MBar MPla MWat NGre NKay NMen NNrd NRoo NRya SChu SIng SSmi
'Pixie Alba'	See S. 'White Pixie'
¶ 'Planegg' (8)	MWat
'Plena' (***granulata***) (12)	ELan MCas MTho NHar NKay SIng
poluniniana (8)	EMNN GCLN ITim LFox NGre NHar NMen NRed NWCA WAbe WThu
'Pompadour'	NNrd
'Popelka' (***marginata***) (8)	NRed
porophylla (8)	GDra NGre NNrd NWCA WAbe WThu
– ***thessalica***	See S. ***sempervivum stenophylla***
– x ***sempervivum*** (8)	WThu
aff. ***porophylla*** (8)	NWCA

Plant	Suppliers
'Portae' (***paniculata***) (7)	NKay NNrd
'Primrose Bee' (x ***apiculata***) (8)	EPot MBro NKay WAbe
'Primrose Dame' (x ***elisabethae***) (8)	CNic CRiv CShe EMNN ESis ITim MBal MBro MCas MWat MYat NRya SIng WAbe
x ***primulaize*** (6x3)	MBro NGre NKay NMen SHer WOMN
'Primulina' (x ***malbyana***) (8)	LFox NHed WAbe
♦***primuloïdes***	See S. ***umbrosa p.***
'Prince Hal' (***burseriana***) (8)	EMNN EPot ESis GCLN ITim MCas MDHE NHar NHed NMen NNrd
'Princess' (***burseriana***) (8)	LBee NMen NNrd
'Prometheus' (x ***prossenii***) (8)	NGre
'Prospero' (x ***petraschii***) (8)	MWat NGre NNrd
x ***prossenii***	See S. 'Regina'
§ 'Pseudoborisii' (x ***borisii***) (8)	EPot ITim
x ***pseudokotschyi***	See S. 'Denisa'
'Pseudosalomonii' (x ***salmonica***) (8)	EPot
pubescens ssp. ***iratiana*** (12)	EPot WThu
punctata	See S. ***nelsoniana***
'Pungens' (x ***apiculata***) (8)	MWat NHed NKay WAbe
'Purpurea' (***fortunei***)	See S. 'Rubrifolia'
§ 'Pygmalion' (x ***webrii***) (8)	CNic CRiv ESis GPlt MYat NGre NHol NMen NRed WPat WThu
'Pyramidalis' (***cotyledon***) (7)	SRms
'Rainsley Seedling' (7)	MDHE
'Red Poll' (8)	MWat NGre WAbe
¶ 'Redsox' (***marginata***) (8)	NHol
§ 'Regina' (x ***prossenii***) (8)	GCHN ITim NNrd SIng WAbe
retusa (9)	EMNN EPot NGre NWCA WAbe
'Rex' (***paniculata***) (7)	LBuc MDHE NMen NNrd SIng
§ 'Riverslea' (x ***hornibrookii***) **AGM**	CGle EMNN EPot LFox MWat NGre NHar NMen SIng WAbe WPat
§ 'Robin Hood' (x ***megaseiflora***) (8)	CRiv EMNN EPot ITim LFox LRHS MYat NGre NHar NKay NMen SBla SIng
'Rokujo' (***fortunei***) (4)	LGre WEas WHal
rosacea ssp. ***hartii*** (12)	SIng
'Rosamunda' (8)	WAbe
'Rosea' (***cortusifolia fortunei***) (8)	SHer
– (x ***stuartii***) (8)	NHed WAbe
– (***paniculata***) (7)	CTom GDra LBee MBal MBro MCas NGre NHed NKay NRed NRoo SBla SIng SSmi STre WAbe WCla WHoo WWin
'Rosemarie' (x ***anglica***) (8)	ITim MHig MYat WAbe
'Rosenzwerg' (12)	LBee

'Rosina Sündermann' (x *rosinae*) (8) EPot LRHS NHed WAbe
rotundifolia (10) CTom LHop WBon WCot WCru
§ – ssp. *chrysopleniifolia* (10) WCot WCru WPer
'Roy Clutterbuck' MWat
'Rubella' (x *irvingii*) (8) EPot MCas MWat
§ 'Rubrifolia' (*fortunei*) (8) ECha EPar NHar NRoo SWas WCru
'Ruth Draper' (*oppositifolia*) (9) CRiv CShe EMNN EPot GCHN NGre NHar NKay NTow SBla SHer WAbe WThu
'Ruth McConnell' (12) CMea LBuc MBro MCas
¶ 'Sabrina' (x *fallsvillagensis*) (8) MWat
'Saint John' (*caesia*) (7) CRiv EBur MDHE NNrd WWin
'Salmon' (x *primulaize*) (6x3) CLew EPot ESis GArf LBuc MCas MHig NHed
x *salmonica* (8) SIng
'Salomonii' (x *salmonica*) (8) EPot ITim MHig NHed NHol NMen NNrd NRed SIng WAbe WThu
sancta (8) CRiv EPot GCHN LFox MBal MBro MHig NHol NNrd SSmi WAbe WThu WTyr
– var. *macedonica* See S. *juniperifolia*
'Sanguinea Superba' (x *arendsii*) AGM GDra IDai MBro NKay SIng
'Sara Sinclair' (x *arco-valleyi*) (8) MYat NNrd
sarmentosa See S. *stolonifera*
'Sartorii' See S. 'Pygmalion'
'Saturn' (x *megaseiflora*) (8) MWat NGre
¶ 'Sazava' (x *poluluteo*) (8) MWat NHed
scardica (8) EMNN MDHE NRed WAbe
– *dalmatica* (8) See S. *obtusa*
– var. *obtusa* (8) See S. *obtusa*
§ 'Schelleri' (x *petraschii*) (8) WAbe
'Schleicheri' (x *kellereri*) (8) EMNN NKay SHer
§ 'Schwefelblüte' (12) CNic LBee MBal NRoo SHer SIng SSmi WAbe WPat
x *semmleri* See S. 'Martha'
sempervivum (8) EPot LFox MBro NSla NWCA SPou WDav WThu
– JCA 864.003 (8) MBro
– f. *sempervivum* (8) WAbe
§ – f. *stenophylla* (8) GCHN GTou NHed WAbe
sibirica (11) EPot GTou
* 'Silver Cushion' (v) CMea EBre ELan EWes GTou LBee LBre MCas MFir NPri NRoo SIgm SIng
¶ 'Silver Edge' (x *arco-valleyi*) (8) WAbe
'Silver Mound' (12) NHol
'Sir Douglas Haig' (12) NKay NNrd SIng
* 'Snowcap' (*pubescens*) (12) EPot NHed
'Snowdon' (*burseriana*) (8) MWat
'Snowflake' (7) MCas MHig NHed
§ 'Sofia' (x *borisii*) (8) LFox NGre NKay WAbe
§ 'Southside Seedling' AGM CLew CNic CRiv CShe ELan ESis GPlt LHop MBar MBro MCas MFos MTho NGre NHar NHol NKay NMen NNrd NRed NRoo SIng SSmi SUsu WAbe WCla WEas WHoo WPat WWin
'Spartakus' (x *apiculata*) (8) NRya WAbe
spathularis (3) MHlr NCat WCot WEas WWin
'Speciosa' (*burseriana*) (8) MDHE NHed
'Splendens' (*oppositifolia*) AGM CRiv ELan EMNN EPar EPot ITim LFox MBal NHed NHol NMen NPri NRed SGil SHer SIng SRms WAbe WGor WHil
'Sprite' (12) GCHN LBee
spruneri (8) MYat NNrd NWCA WThu
– var. *deorum* (8) NGre
sp. BM&W 118 GDra
sp. CLD 1350 NHol
sp. McB 1377 MWat
sp. SEP 549 MWat
'Stansfieldii' (12) CRiv EBre EMNN LBre NGre NMen NNrd SBod SSmi WWin
§ 'Stella' (x *stormonthii*) (8) NHol NKay SBla WThu
stellaris (1) GTou
stolitzkae (8) CNic EMNN EPot NGre NMen NRed WThu
§ *stolonifera* AGM CArn ELan EPla SPer
'Stormont's Variety' See S. 'Stella'
stribrnyi (8) EBur EPot NKay NMen NSla
'Sturmiana' (*paniculata*) (7) MBro NHol NKay SIng SRms
'Suendermannii' (x *kellereri*) (8) MWat NHed NRya NWCA SIng
¶ 'Suendermannii Purpurea' (x *kellereri*) (8) GCHN
§ 'Sulphurea' (x *boydii*) (8) CNic CRiv CShe EMNN EPot GCLN LBee LFox MBro MCas MYat NBra NGre NHar NHed NMen NNrd NWCA WAbe WHoo WPat WThu
'Superba' (*callosa australis*) (7) GCra GDra GTou NNrd SSmi
'Sylva' (x *elisabethae*) (8) NGre
taygetea (10) NMen
x *tazetta* (10x3) MCas NRed
tenella (12) NNrd
'Theoden' (*oppositifolia*) AGM CNic EMNN GCLN MBro NHar NHol NWCA WAbe WDav
'Thorpei' (8) ITim
'Timballii' (7) SIng
'Timmy Foster' (x *irvingii*) (8) NGre SIng WAbe
¶ x *tiroliensis* (7) NHed
'Tom Thumb' (12) NMen
tombeanensis (8) NGre
'Tricolor' (*stolonifera*) AGM EBak ELan
trifurcata (12) SIng

'Triumph' (x *arendsii*) (12) — CShe ECtt EMNN GCHN GDra LBee MFir NEgg NKay NMen NRoo NVic SBod WHil
'Tulley' (x *elisabethae*) (8) — MBro NHol WPat
'Tumbling Waters' AGM — CGle GAbr MCas MTho NKay NMen NSla NTow SHer SIng SSmi WAbe WThu WWin
¶ 'Tvuj Den' (x *poluanglica*) (8) — MWat NHed
¶ 'Tvuj Píseň' ('Your Song') (x *poluanglica*) (8) — MWat NHed
¶ 'Tvuj Přítel' ('Your Friend') (x *poluanglica*) (8) — MWat NHed
¶ 'Tvuj Úsměv' ('Your Smile') (x *poluanglica*) (8) — MWat NHed
¶ 'Tvuj Úspěch' ('Your Success') (x *poluanglica*) (8) — MWat NHed
¶ 'Tycho Brahe' (x *doerfleri*) (8) — WAbe
umbrosa (3) — CBow CHol EBre EMon EPar IDai LBre LWad NGre NNor SPer WHen WOak WWin
§ – var. ***primuloïdes*** AGM — CGle CShe GCHN LFox MYat WBon WEas WFox
– ***variegata*** — See S. 'Aureopunctata'
'Unique' — See S. 'Bodensee'
x ***urbium*** AGM — CTom EJud ELan GAri GDra MBal NNrd NSti NVic WAbe WBon
'Vaccarina' (***oppositifolia***) (9) — EBre EWes LBre MRPP NVic SGil SHer WAbe
'Vaclav Hollar' (x *gusmusii*) (8) — MWat NGre
'Vahlii' (x *smithii*) (8) — WAbe
'Valborg' — See S. 'Cranbourne'
'Valentine' — See S. 'Cranbourne'
'Valerie Finnis' — See S. 'Aretiastrum'
'Variegata' (x *urbium*) (3) — CBos CMer ELan EPar GDra GGar LBee LGro MBal MCas NCat NHol NNor NSti SPer SSmi WAbe WCla WEas WWin
– (***cuneifolia***) (3) — CNic ECtt ELan ESis GCHN GPlt MBar MCas NKay NPri NRoo NTow NVic SIde SSmi WPer WThu
vayredana (12) — SIng
veitchiana (4) — EMon EPla MHig NCat NKay NNrd WCru WHil
'Venetia' (***paniculata***) (7) — MDHE NKay NNrd SSmi
'Vesna' (x *borisii*) (8) — EMNN GCHN GCLN MCas MFir MHig NGre NKay NMen NNrd NTow WAbe WThu WWin
'Vincent van Gogh' (x *borisii*) (8) — ITim LBuc NKay NNrd
'Vladana' (x *megaseiflora*) (8) — CRiv EMNN GCLN NGre NHar NRed NRya WAbe
'Vlasta' (8) — WAbe
'Vltava' (8) — NGre
'Volgeri' (x *hofmannii*) (8) — EPot
'W A Clark' (***oppositifolia***) (9) — MBal WAbe
'Wada' (***fortunei***) (8) — CChu CGle CHan CWit EPar EPot GAbr GArf GCHN MBal NBir NHar NHol NRoo SCro SPer SWas WWin
'Waithman's Variety' (7) — NNrd
wallacei — See S. ***camposii***
'Walpole's Variety' (***longifolia***) (7) — MCas NHar NHed NNrd WTyr
'Walter Ingwersen' (***umbrosa primuloïdes***) (3) — SIng
§ 'Walter Irving' (x *irvingii*) (8) — EMNN MYat NHar WAbe
'Welsh Dragon' (12) — WAbe WHen
'Welsh Red' (12) — WAbe
'Welsh Rose' (12) — WAbe
wendelboi (8) — EMNN EPot LFox MYat NGre SIng WAbe WThu
'Wendrush' (x *wendelacina*) (8) — WAbe
'Wendy' (x *wendelacina*) (8) — NGre WAbe
'Wetterhorn' (***oppositifolia***) (9) — MBal NNrd SIng WAbe
¶ 'Wheatley Gem' (8) — MWat
'Wheatley Rose' (8) — LRHS
§ 'White Pixie' (12) — CMea EMNN EPar GGar LBee LFox MCas NGre NNrd SBla SChu SHer SIng SSmi WCla
'White Spire' (12) — NNrd
'White Star' (x *salmonica*) — See S. 'Schelleri'
'Whitehill' (7) — CShe EBre ELan ESis GCHN LBee LBre LFox MBal MBro MCas MHig MPla NEgg NGre NKay NMen NNrd SIng SSmi WAbe WHil WHoo WPat WThu WWin
'Whitlavei Compacta' (***hypnoïdes***) (12) — CRiv MCas NKay
'William Boyd' (x *boydii*) (8) — MWat WAbe
'Winifred' (x *anglica*) (8) — EPot LFox MWat NGre NNrd SIng WAbe
'Winifred Bevington' (7x3) — EBre ELan EMNN ESis GDra GTou LBee LBre LHop MBro NHar NHed NHol NMen NNrd NRed NRoo SChu SHer SIng SPla WCla WHoo
'Winston Churchill' (12) — LBuc NNrd SIng
'Winter Fire' (7) — See S. 'Winterfeuer'
§ 'Winterfeuer' (***callosa***) (7) — CShe
'Wisley' (***frederici-augusti grisebachii***) AGM — CNic GCHN MBal MCas NHar NKay SIng WHoo WPat
'Wisley Primrose' — See S. 'Kolbiana'
'Yellow Rock' (8) — MWat NHol WAbe
♦ 'Your Day' — See S. 'Tvuj Den'
♦ 'Your Friend' — See S. 'Tvuj Přítel'
♦ 'Your Good Fortune' — See S. 'Tvuj Úspěch'

♦'Your Kiss' See S. 'Tvuj Polibek'
♦'Your Smile' See S. 'Tvuj Úsměv'
♦'Your Song' See S. 'Tvuj Píseň'
♦'Your Success' See S. 'Tvuj Úspěch'
x *zimmeteri* (7x3) NNrd NRed NTow SSmi
**zohlenschaferi* NBra

SCABIOSA † (Dipsaceae)

alpina See CEPHALARIA ***alpina***
anthemifolia CHan
atropurpurea 'Sunburst' SMrm
'Butterfly Blue' EBar EFol GMac MBri MPit NCat SHer
caucasica CRDP CSam ECha LAbb LGan NCat SBla WHil WHoo WOld WWin
– *alba* CBot ECro MBri NNor NRoo NTow WHil WHoo
– 'Bressingham White' SAsh
– 'Clive Greaves' AGM CB&S CBow CCla CDoC CMea CSco CShe ECha EFol EFou EGol ELan EOrc GCal IDai LHop MBri MBro MWat NBar NMir NNor SHer SPer SPla SUsu WDav WEas WRus WTyr
– 'Fama' CHol CMGP CSam EBar EBee ECro LBuc MArl MBel MPit MRav NBir NRoo SBla SMrm SRms WHoo WPla WTyr
– 'Floral Queen' ECha
– 'Goldingensis' EBar NPri NRoo SFis
¶ – House's Hybrids CBot
¶ – 'Isaac House' WHil
– 'Kompliment' EFou MUlv NBro
– 'Miss Willmott' AGM CBow CCla CDoC CGle CHad CMGP CRDP CSco CSev ECas ECha EFou EGol ELan GCal LHop MBel MBri MNFA MUlv MWat NBar NSti SHer SPer SUsu WDav WRus WTyr
– 'Moerheim Blue' ECha MBri MUlv
– 'Mount Cook' SAsh
– 'Penelope Harrison' CShe
¶ – 'Perfecta' CBow NPri
– 'Perfecta Alba' CBow CSco NOrc NPri
– 'Stäfa' CDoC LHop MBri MUlv SMrm SPer WCot WTyr
cinerea WWin
columbaria CKin ECWi EWFC GMac MChe MHew NLan NMir NTow NWCA SHer SUsu WCla WHal WHoo
– 'Nana' NBir NMen SSmi WHoo
§ – var. *ochroleuca* CBot CGle CHan CMea CRDP CSam EBar ECha EPla LGan MBro MSto NBir NSti SMrm SUsu SWas WOld WWin
– var. *webbiana* WRus
– var. *webbiana* JCA 862.850 CLew
cretica EBee SUsu
farinosa CBot EMon MFir WAbe WPer
gigantea See CEPHALARIA ***gigantea***
graminifolia CLew CNic EFol ELan ESis LGan NBir NRoo NTow WOld
– *rosea* EWes SCro
japonica WPer
– var. *alpina* EFou GDra LBlm MBel NHol
lucida CGle CMea CNic CSev ELan GDra GMac LGan LHop MBro MCas MHig MNFA MPit NKay NMen NRoo SBla SIng SMrm SSmi WAbe WEas WPat WPer WTyr
minoana EMon LGre
ochroleuca See S. ***columbaria o.***
¶ *olgae* EBee
parnassi See PTEROCEPHALUS ***perennis***
* 'Pink Mist' CGle EBee MBri MPit NBir SRms
pterocephala See PTEROCEPHALUS ***perennis***
rumelica See KNAUTIA ***macedonica***
succisa See SUCCISA ***pratensis***
tatarica See CEPHALARIA ***gigantea***

SCABIOSA X CEPHALARIA (Dipsaceae)

¶ *cinerea* x *alpina* WDav

SCADOXUS (Liliaceae/Amaryllidaceae)

multiflorus LAma LBow MBri NRog WChr
§ – ssp. *katherinae* 'King Albert' SLMG
§ *puniceus* NRog SLMG
rigidus SLMG

SCAEVOLA (Goodeniaceae)

¶ *aemula* 'Alba' LGre
– 'Blue Fan' CBrk CSpe NWyt SChu WRus
– 'Blue Wonder' LHop NPri SHer SUsu
– 'Petite' CBrk LHop WRus
amoena CTro
hookeri ECou
suaveolens See S. ***calendulacea***

SCANDIX (Umbelliferae/Apiaceae)

¶ *pecten-veneris* EWFC

SCHEFFLERA (Araliaceae)

actinophylla AGM EBak MBri
arboricola AGM MBri
– 'Compacta' MBri
– 'Gold Capella' AGM MBri
– 'Jacqueline' MBri
– 'Trinetta' MBri
digitata CHEx SArc

SCHIMA (Theaceae)

argentea See S. ***wallichii noronhae superba***
§ *wallichii* ssp. *noronhae* var. *superba* CHEx CPle WBod
– ssp. *wallichii* var. *khasiana* ISea

SCHINUS (Anacardiaceae)

polygamus CGre

SCHISANDRA (Schisandraceae)

chinensis CChu CHan EHal WSHC
grandiflora EBee EBre ECot EOvi LBre SPer
– var. *cathayensis* See S. ***sphaerandra***
propinqua var. *chinensis* CBot SHil

rubriflora SHil
– (f) CB&S CBow CCla EHar ELan EOvi LGre MBlu MGos SBla SBra SDix SHil SLon SPer SSta WSHC WWat WWeb
– (m) CChu EMil MPla SBla SDix
sphenanthera CCla EHic ELan EMil EOvi IJoh WSHC WWeb

SCHISTOSTEGA (moss)

pennata LFle

SCHIVERECKIA (Cruciferae/Brassicaceae)

doerfleri CNic
podolica MCas WWin

SCHIZACHYRIUM (Gramineae/Poaceae)

§ *scoparium* CRow EHoe GCal WPer

SCHIZANTHUS (Solanaceae)

¶ *gilliesii* MSto
hookeri JCA 12492 CNic

SCHIZOCENTRON See HETEROCENTRON

SCHIZOCODON See SHORTIA

SCHIZOLOBIUM (Leguminosae/Papilionaceae)

¶ *excelsum* CTro

SCHIZOPHRAGMA (Hydrangeaceae)

hydrangeoïdes CB&S CBow CChu CCla CHEx CSco EBre EHar EMil LBre MBal MBri MGos MMea SBra SPer SSta WCru WDin WSHC WWeb
– 'Roseum' CChu SBla SHil
integrifolium AGM CB&S CBow CChu CCla CHEx CMac CSco EHar ELan EMil LAbb MBal MBri SDix SHBN SHil SPer SSta WSHC WWat

Var. climbing hydrangea.

SCHIZOSTACHYUM (Gramineae/Poaceae-Bambusoideae)

§ *funghomii* EPla SDry WJun

SCHIZOSTYLIS † (Iridaceae)

coccinea CArn CAvo CB&S CBro CHan CKel CNic CRDP CRow CSco CWGN EFol ELan LAma MBal MFir NBro NHol NKay NNor NRoo NSti SIng WEas WHal WHil WHoo WOld WWye
– *alba* Widely available
– 'Ballyrogan Giant' IBlr
– 'Cardinal' CHan CKel CRow
– 'Fenland Daybreak' EBre LBre MBel
– 'Gigantea' See S. *c.* 'Major'
– 'Grandiflora' See S. *c.* 'Major'
– 'Hilary Gould' MUlv SWas
– 'Jennifer' AGM CAvo CB&S CBro CElw CGle CMHG COtt CRDP GAbr GAri MUlv SAxl SBla SCro SHer SRms SUsu SWas WCot WRus WWat
– 'Maiden's Blush' EBee EBre ELun LBre MUlv SPer
§ – 'Major' AGM Widely available
¶ – 'Mary Barnard' EPot
– 'Mrs Hegarty' Widely available
– 'November Cheer' CCla CDec CMHG CRiv CRow EBre ECot IBlr LBre MHFP MSte NFai NRar NRoo SHer WOld WPer
– 'Pallida' CRow CSam ECha ELan GMac SHer SIng
¶ – 'Pink Ice' WCot
– 'Professor Barnard' CB&S CChu CFee CGle CMHG CRow GCal IBlr MArl MSte SApp SBla WHoo WOld WWat
– 'Salmon Charm' CRiv CRow WStI
– 'Snow Maiden' ELun SPer
§ – 'Sunrise' AGM Widely available
– 'Sunset' See S. *c.* 'Sunrise'
– 'Tambara' CHan CHol CMHG LGan LGre NCat SAxl WOld WWat
– 'Viscountess Byng' CB&S CBro CChu CCla CGle CHol CMil CRow CShe GAbr GCal MBri MRav NFai NRog SAxl SChu SDix WHal WPer WTyr WWat
– 'Zeal Salmon' CBro CRiv CRow GAbr GAri LGre SApp SCro

SCHOENOPLECTUS (Cyperaceae)

lacustris ECWi EMFW SWyc WChe
– ssp. *tabernaemontani* 'Albescens' CBen CWGN EBre EHon EMFW LBre LMay MSta SRms SWat SWyc WChe WHol
– – 'Zebrinus' (v) CBen CRDP CRiv CWGN EBre EHon ELan EMFW EWav LBre LMay MSta MUlv NDea SHig SWat SWyc WChe WHol

SCHOENUS (Cyperaceae)

pauciflorus ECou EHoe EPar EPla LGan SFar

SCHOTIA (Leguminosae/Caesalpiniaceae)

See Plant Deletions

SCIADOPITYS (Sciadopityaceae)

verticillata AGM CB&S CChu CDoC CKen IOrc LCon LLin LNet LPan MBar MBri NBee SEng SLim WDin WNor
¶ – 'Gold Star' CKen
¶ – 'Picola' CKen

SCILLA (Liliaceae/Hyacinthaceae)

adlamii See LEDEBOURIA *cooperi*
x *allenii* See X CHIONOSCILLA *a.*
amethystina See S. *litardierei*
amoena CMon LAma NHol
autumnalis CAvo CMon EPot LAma NHol WChr WCru WOMN WShi WThu
– *fallax* AB&S 4345 CMon
bifolia AGM CAvo CBro CMea EPar ETub LAma LBow NHol NNrd NRog
– 'Rosea' CAvo CMea EPar EPot LAma LBow NHol NRog SIng WPer
bithynica LBow WWat
campanulata See HYACINTHOIDES *hispanica*

cilicica	CBro CMon LAma
greilhuberi	CAvo NHol
¶ ***haemorrhoïdalis***	WChr
– MS 923	CMon
hohenackeri	LAma
– BSBE 811	CMon
hyacinthoïdes	CMon
italica	See HYACINTHOÏDES ***i.***
japonica	See S. ***scilloïdes***
liliohyacinthus	CBro CRDP CRow
– 'Alba'	WChr
lingulata MS 320	CMon
– SF 288/281	CMon
– S&L 253	CMon
– ***ciliolata***	CBro
§ ***litardierei***	CAvo CMon EPot ETub LAma NEgg NHol
mauretanica SF 65	CMon
– ***alba***	CMon
messeniaca	MBro
§ ***mischtschenkoana***	CAvo CBro CMon EPot ETub LAma LBow MBri MHlr NNrd NRog SIng
monophyllos	CFil LAma
morrisii M 4015	CMon
non-scripta	See HYACINTHOIDES ***n-s.***
nutans	See HYACINTHOIDES ***non-scripta***
obtusifolia AB&S 4410	CMon
ovalifolia	See LEDEBOURIA ***ovalifolia***
paucifolia	SLMG
persica BSBE 1054	CMon
peruviana	CAvo CB&S CBrd CBro CFee CHEx EBre EBul EPar EPot ETub LAma LBre MTho NRog
– 'Alba'	CAvo CMon EBul LAma NRog
– ***elegans***	CMon
– ***venusta***	CMon
pratensis	See S. ***litardierei***
puschkinioïdes	CAvo EPot LAma
ramburei	EPot LAma
– B&S 406	CMon
– MS 417	CMon
reverchonii MS 418	CMon
rosenii	EPot WChr
§ ***scilloïdes***	CBro EPot GArf WOMN
siberica **AGM**	CAvo CCla ETub LAma LBow MWBu NEgg NRog SIng WPer
– 'Alba'	CAvo CBro CCla EPar ETub LAma LBow NEgg NNrd NRog SIng WPer
– 'Spring Beauty'	CAvo CBro CMea EPar LAma MBri MHlr MWBu NNrd NRog SIng
– ***taurica*** M&T 4148	CMon
tubergeniana	See S. ***mischtschenkoana***
verna	CMon WAbe WShi
– MS 483	CMon
vicentina	See HYACINTHOIDES ***italica vicentina***
violacea	See LEDEBOURIA ***socialis***

SCINDAPSUS (Araceae)

aureus	See EPIPREMNUM ***aureum***
pictus (v)	MBri

SCIRPOÏDES (Gramineae/Poaceae)

holoschoenus	ETPC

SCIRPUS (Cyperaceae)

cernuus	See ISOLEPIS ***cernua***
cespitosus	MBal
§ ***fauriei*** var. ***vaginatus*** 'Golden Spear'	CRow SRms
holoschoenus	See SCIRPOÏDES ***h.***
lacustris	See SCHOENOPLECTUS ***l.***
– ***spiralis***	See JUNCUS ***effusus*** 'Spiralis'
mucronatus	MSta
¶ ***sylvaticus***	SWyc
♦ ***tabernaemontani***	See SCHOENOPLECTUS ***lacustris t.***
variegatus	CBot

SCLERANTHUS (Illecebraceae)

biflorus	CLew ECou EGle ELan ESis EWes MBro NTow WPer
¶ ***perennis***	CNat
singuliflorus	ECou MTho WPat
uniflorus	CLew GAbr GAri NHed NHol NWCA

SCOLIOPUS (Liliaceae/Trilliaceae)

bigelowii	SWas

SCOLOPENDRIUM See ASPLENIUM

SCOLYMUS See CYNARA

SCOPOLIA (Solanaceae)

anomala	CArn
carniolica	EBee EGle GCal GDra GPoy MSal NSti WCru WSun
– forms	ECha IBlr
– ssp. ***hladnikiana***	ECro
– ***podolica***	CMea WPer
¶ – Slovenia	MPhe
lurida	CArn ECro EMon MSal
physaloïdes	MSal
sinensis	See ATROPANTHE ***s.***

SCORZONERA (Compositae/Asteraceae)

humilis	GPoy

SCROPHULARIA (Scrophulariaceae)

aquatica	See S. ***auriculata***
§ ***auriculata***	ECWi EWFC LHol MSal NDea NOrc WHer WWye
– 'Burdung' (v)	EFol EMon
§ – 'Variegata'	Widely available
¶ ***canina*** ssp. ***bicolor***	WHer
coccinea	EMon
macrantha	WDav
nodosa	CArn CKin CSFH LHol MChe MHew MSal NLan NMir SIde WCla WHer WNdy
– ***variegata***	See S. ***auriculata*** 'V.'
umbrosa	MSal
vernalis	NSti

SCUTELLARIA (Labiatae/Lamiaceae)

§ *alpina* CRiv GCHN LBee MHig MSal NHol SBla SHer SIng WPer WWin
altissima CGle EBee EMon GBuc MSal NBro NWCA SFis SUsu WPer
baicalensis CHan ESis IBlr LHop NHol NPri WPer
canescens See S. ***incana***
diffusa ESis NHol WPer
¶ *formosana* WCot
galericulata CKin CTom EWFC Effi GPoy MHew MSal WNdy
hastata See S. ***hastifolia***
§ *hastifolia* CNic ECot ECtt EMNN NMir SHer SIng WOMN WPer WTyr
§ *incana* EFou ELan EMon LGre SBor SFis SWas WCot
indica var. *japonica* See S. ***indica parvifolia***
§ – var. *parvifolia* CLew CRiv EBur ELan LBee MHig MTho NTow SFis SUsu WCru WPer
– – 'Alba' LBee
integrifolia MSal SIng
lateriflora CArn CSFH ESis GBar GPoy IEde LHol MChe MHew MSal SIde WPer WWye
minor CKin MSal WPer
¶ *nana* var. *sapphirina* CPBP
novae-zelandiae ECou WThi
orientalis ESis LBee NGre SBla WCru WOMN WPer WWin
– ssp. *carica* WOMN
¶ – ssp. *pinnatifida* NHol WHil
pontica WPer WThi
prostrata CNic ESis NRed SUsu WOMN WPer WThi
repens WPer
scordiifolia CLew CMea CMil CRiv CSam ECha EFou ELan EPot ESis MCas NKay NMen NNrd SBla SFis WCla WHil WHoo WPer WRus WWin
serrata CArn
supina See S. ***alpina***

SEAKALE See CRAMBE *maritima*

SECURIGERA See CORONILLA

SEDASTRUM See SEDUM

SEDUM † (Crassulaceae)

acre ECWi ECot ELan GPoy LHol MBar NGre NNrd SIde
– (tetraploid) MPit
– var. *aureum* CHad CNic CRiv EFol ELan EPot MBar MCas MWat NHol NKay NNrd NRed NVic SHer SIng WHoo WPat
– var. *elegans* ECtt GDra GTou MBal NGre NMen
§ – var. *majus* NGre NHol SIde SSmi
– 'Minus' NGre NHol SIde SSmi
aggregatum See OROSTACHYS ***aggregata***
§ *aïzoön* NGre NKay NVic SChu SIde WEas
– 'Aurantiacum' See S. ***a.*** 'Euphorbioïdes'
§ – 'Euphorbioïdes' EBre ECha ECro ECtt ELan EMon EOrc GGar LBre MBel MRav SChu SPer WCot
– *maximowiczii* See S. ***aizoon***
albescens See S. ***forsterianum purpureum***
§ *alboroseum* MTho NGre WTyr
§ – 'Mediovariegatum' CBot ECro EFol EGol EHoe ELan EMon EPla LGan LHop MBri NGre NOrc NRoo WEas WPer
§ *album* EBar GGar SIde WPer
§ – 'Chloroticum' CRiv GGar NGre SIde SSmi
– *clusianum* See S. ***gypsicola glanduliferum***
– 'Coral Carpet' CNic ELan EPot GDra MBar MCas MWat NGre NHol NKay NMen NNrd SChu SHer SIng SSmi STre
– var. *micranthum* See S. ***a.*** 'Chloroticum'
§ – ssp. *teretifolium* var. *murale* CRiv LBuc MBar NGre NKay SIng
altissimum See S. ***sediforme***
amplexicaule See S. ***tenuifolium***
§ *anacampseros* CHEx CLew CNic CRiv CTom EPad GCHN NGre NHol NKay SCro SIde SIng SSmi WCla WEas WPer
anglicum ECWi GGar NGre SIng WCla
anopetalum See S. ***ochroleucum***
– alpine form See S. ***ochroleucum montanum***
athoum See S. ***album***
atlanticum See S. ***dasyphyllum mesatlanticum***
'Autumn Joy' See S. 'Herbstfreude'
batesii See S. ***hemsleyanum***
§ 'Bertram Anderson' EBre ECha ECro EPot GAri LBre LHop MBel MBri MCas MNFA MSte NGre NNrw NRoo NSti SMrm WMer WPer WTyr
beyrichianum hort. See S. ***glaucophyllum***
beyrichianum Masters NGre
brevifolium MDHE MFir SChu
§ – var. *quinquefarum* NGre SSmi
§ *caucasicum* NGre
– DS&T 89001T EMon
cauticola AGM CLew CMHG CShe GCal ITim LHop MBro MCas MHig MRav NGre NKay NNor NRoo SBod SIng SSmi WAbe WWin
§ – 'Lidakense' CLew CRiv CSam CTom EBar EBre ELan EMon LBre MBar MBri NGre NHar NHol NVic SBla SSmi
clusianum See S. ***gypsicola glanduliferum***
cockerellii K 92.401 WDav
crassipes See RHODIOLA ***wallichiana***
crassularia See CRASSULA ***milfordiae***
§ *cyaneum* GCHN MDHE NGre NWCA
dasyphyllum CLew CMer CNic CRiv CTom ELan EPot ESis GTou MBal MBar MCas MFir MRPP MWat NGre SSmi WCla WTyr
– ssp. *dasyphyllum* var. *glanduliferum* CHEx SIng
– – var. *macrophyllum* NGre
§ – – var. *mesatlanticum* CNic CRiv NGre SSmi WThu
– *mucronatis* NBir
debile NGre

divergens	NGre SIng
¶ – large form	NGre
douglasii	MFir NNrd SRms
'Dudley Field'	GCHN NGre
♦ 'Eleanor Fisher'	See S. ***telephium ruprechtii***
ellacombeanum	See S. ***kamschaticum e.***
erythrostichum	See S. ***alboroseum***
§ ***ewersii***	CLew CMHG CNic CRiv EBre ELan EMNN ESis GCHN GTou LBre MCas NGre NMen SSmi WEas
§ – var. ***homophyllum***	MHig NGre NKay SSmi
§ ***fabaria***	NGre WEas
* 'Fabianum'	NHol
farinosum	MHig
♦ ***fastigiatum***	See RHODIOLA ***fastigiata***
floriferum	See S. ***kamtschaticum***
§ ***forsterianum***	CMGP EMar MBar NGre NHol SIng SSmi WCla WEas
– ssp. ***elegans***	LGro
gracile	NGre SSmi
gypsicola	CHEx MDHE NGre WPer
§ 'Herbstfreude' AGM	CCla CHol CKel CSco CShe EBre ECha EFou ELan IDai LBre LGro LHop MBal MWat NBar NGre NHol NRoo NSti SDix SHig SIng SMad SPer WBod WEas WOld WPer
heterodontum	See RHODIOLA ***heterodonta***
¶ ***hidakanum***	GTou
hillebrandtii	See S. ***urvillei*** Hillebrandtii Group
himalensis	See RHODIOLA ***h.***
hirsutum	See RHODIOLA ***hirsuta***
§ ***hispanicum***	EPar EPla MFir NKay SHer
– 'Albescens	CNic NGre
– var. ***bithynicum***	NGre SIng
– ***glaucum***	See S. ***h. minus***
§ – var. ***minus***	CNic ECtt GAri GGar GTou MBar NGre NNrd NPri NRar SIde SIng SSmi STre
§ – – 'Aureum'	CB&S CRiv CTom ECha EPot MCas MHig MRPP NGre NHol NKay NMen SBod SIng SSmi
humifusum	EBur EPot MHig NMen NTow SIng SSmi WAbe WOMN WThu
hybridum	CShe NGre SIng
hyperaïzoön	NGre
integrifolium	See RHODIOLA ***rosea integrifolia***
jaeschkei	See S. ***oreades***
'Joyce Henderson'	SAxl SUsu WEas WOld
§ ***kamtschaticum*** AGM	MBar MCas NGre
– ***ellacombeanum*** AGM	CNic CRiv ELan EMNN EMon ESis GPlt IDai NGre NKay NMen NNrd SCro SIng
§ – var. ***floriferum*** 'Weihenstephaner Gold' AGM	CLew CMea CNic EBre EMNN ESis LBre MBal MBar MCas MHig MPit MWat NGre NHol NKay NMen NNor NNrd NRoo SChu SIng SSmi WAbe WCla WDav WEas WHil WPat
– var. ***kamtschaticum*** 'Variegatum' AGM	CHEx ECro ELan EPar GCHN LBee LHop MBar MCas MHig NGre NKay NRoo SBla SBod SIng SSmi WEas WHil WHoo
lanceolatum	NGre
laxum ssp. ***heckneri***	NGre
– ssp. ***laxum***	NHol
– ***retusum*** JCA 11601	CNic
lineare	ELan SLMG
– 'Variegatum'	CNic MBri SIde
litorale	NGre
lydium	CLew CNic CRiv CTom EMNN GTou MBal MBar MCas MFir MHig MRPP MWat NGre NKay NNrd NRoo SIng SSmi STre
– ***aureum***	See S. ***hispanicum minus*** 'Aureum'
– 'Bronze Queen'	NMen
makinoi makinoi	SSmi
– 'Variegatum'	EBre LBre
maweanum	See S. ***acre majus***
mexicanum	MBri
middendorfianum	CTom ELan EMon GTou LHop MCas MDHE MHig MWat NGre NHol NKay NNrd SBod SHer SSmi WHoo WWin
– var. ***diffusum***	NGre SSmi
monregalense	NGre
* 'Moonglow'	NGre SSmi
moranense	CNic CRiv NGre NHol SIde SSmi WHil
¶ 'Morchen'	SUsu
morganianum AGM	EBak MBri
multiceps	NGre SSmi
murale	See S. ***album teretifolium murale***
N ***nevii***	CLew CShe EGle NKay
nicaeënse	See S. ***sediforme***
obtusatum	EGle MBro WHil WTyr
– ssp. ***boreale***	See S. ***oreganum b.***
– ssp. ***retusum***	See S. ***retusum***
§ ***ochroleucum***	SIng SSmi
– 'Green Spreader'	SSmi
§ – ssp. ***ochroleucum glaucum***	NGre
§ ***oppositifolium***	CLew ELan ESis NCat NGre SIde SIng
§ ***oreganum***	CLew CMHG CTom ECha EMNN ESis GTou LHop MBar MCas MHig MWat NGre NKay NMen NNrd NRoo SBod SChu SIng WAbe WHil WHoo WWin
– 'Procumbens'	CNic NHol
oregonense	GTou NGre NMen
oryzifolium minor	EBur
§ ***pachyclados***	EBur ELan ESis GAbr GPlt GTou LBee MDHE NBir NGre SIde SSmi WCla WPat WPer
pallidum	NGre
palmeri	NBir NTow SIng SMrm SSmi
¶ 'Philip Houlbrook'	NHol
pilosum	CLew CRiv EBur NGre NWCA SBla SIng WAbe WOMN WThu
§ ***pluricaule***	CMea CNic ECha EHoe EPot GCHN GDra MBar MCas NGre NHol NKay NMen SBod SChu SFar WCla WPat
polytrichoïdes	See RHODIOLA ***komarovii***
populifolium	CLew CMHG ECha EMon GCHN GCal MCas NGre NHol SDry SSmi STre WEas WHil WPer
praealtum	EMon
§ ***primuloïdes***	NGre NMen SSmi WHil
pruinatum	NGre NKay

pruinosum See S. ***spathulifolium p.***
pulchellum CShe NGre SIde
purdyi NGre NHol
quinquefarium See S. ***brevifolium q.***
ramosissima See VILLADIA ***r.***
reflexum CNic CRiv EBar ELan EMon GGar NGre NHol NKay NPri SIde SIng SSmi WHil
– 'Minus' CNic NGre
– 'Monstrosum Cristatum' CLew GGar MBal NBir SMad
retusum NGre
rhodiola See RHODIOLA ***rosea***
rosea See RHODIOLA ***rosea***
rubroglaucum CRiv MHig NNrd
rubromucronatum See S. sp. RBGE 736791
x ***rubrotinctum*** SLMG
§ 'Ruby Glow' **AGM** CCla CKel CMea CSco EBre ECha EFou ELan EMar LBre LGro MBal MBri MWat NGre NHol NKay NNrd NSti SCro SDix SIng SPer SPla SUsu WAbe WEas WPer
rupestre See S. ***forsterianum***
♦***ruprechtii*** See S. ***telephium r.***
sarcocaule See CRASSULA ***sarcocaulis***
sarmentosum NGre SIng SSmi
§ ***sediforme*** CTom LHop MBro NGre NKay SIde SSmi
– ***nicaeense*** See S. ***sediforme***
selskianum CLew GAul GDra GTou NPri
sempervivoïdes EBur NGre WThi
sexangulare CLew CRiv EMNN ESis GDra GGar GPlt MBar MCas NGre NHol NKay NMen SIng SSmi
sichotense NGre SIng
§ ***sieboldii*** CSam LGro MBri NGre SSmi
– 'Mediovariegatum' **AGM** ELan LHop NGre SCro SSmi WEas WPer
'Silvermoon' MDHE NGre NHol SIng
spathulifolium CLew ECha ELan ESis GPlt GTou MRPP NKay SChu WEas
– 'Aureum' CRiv ECtt EMNN GTou MBar MHig MWat NGre NHol NNor SBod
N– 'Cape Blanco' **AGM** Widely available
– 'Major' NMir SIng
§ – ssp. ***pruinosum*** NGre NHol
– 'Purpureum' **AGM** Widely available
– 'Roseum' CTom SSmi
§ ***spectabile*** **AGM** CArn CBow CDoC CRiv EJud ELan NBar NSti SPer WHil WTyr WWin
– 'Album' EOrc
– 'Brilliant' **AGM** CBow CDoC CSco CShe EBre ECED ECha EFou ELan EMon EPla LBre LWad MBri NGre NOrc SDix SMad SPer SPla WEas
– 'Iceberg' CRDP ECha EFou EMon EPla LGre SMad
– 'Indian Chief' See S. 'Herbstfreude'
– 'Meteor' EBar ECha MWat SCro SPer WAbe WCot
*– 'Mini' ELan
– 'Rosenteller' EFou
– 'Septemberglut' ('September Glow') EMon
– 'Stardust' CLew EBar SIde
– 'Variegatum' See S. ***alboroseum*** 'Mediovariegatum'
spinosum See OROSTACHYS ***spinosa***
spurium CRiv CTom EJud ELan GBur LGro NGre NNor SBod SIng STre WEas WHil
– ***album*** misapplied See S. ***oppositifolium***
¶ – 'Album' ESis
*– 'Atropurpureum' ECha NNor NRoo SHig SPla WPat
– 'Coccineum' CRiv EMar GAul MBar NPri WOMN WTyr
– 'Erdblut' EBre GGar LBre MHig NGre NMen NNrd NRoo
– 'Fool's Gold' (v) EMon
– 'Fuldaglut' EBre EHoe LBre MNFA NGre NHar NMir NRed SChu SIng WDav WPer WWin
– 'Glow' STre
– 'Green Mantle' ECha MPit NHol
– 'Purpureum' CHan ELan GDra
– 'Purpurteppich' ('Purple Carpet') CShe CTom EBre EMil EPot ESis LBre LGro MHig MRav NEgg NGre NHol NKay SAxl SHer SUsu WCla WThu
– 'Roseum' NHol
– 'Ruby Mantle' CRiv GGar SIng WCot
– 'Schorbuser Blut' ('Dragon's Blood') **AGM** CMea CNic CRiv EBar ELan LHop MBal MCas MFir MWat NGre NHol NKay NRar NVic WAbe WEas WHil WHoo
– 'Tricolor' ELan SPla WPat WThu
§ – 'Variegatum' CHan CLew CMHG CMer CNic CSam CShe ECha EHoe ELan ESis LHop MCas MHig NGre NHol NKay NRoo SBod SIng SSmi STre WCla WEas WHil WWin
stenopetalum 'Douglasii' CNic NHol
stephanii See RHODIOLA ***crassipes s.***
stoloniferum NGre SSmi
stribrnyi See S. ***urvillei*** Stribrnyi Group
'Sunset Cloud' CMHG CSam NGre SPer WOld WPer
takesimense NGre
§ ***tatarinowii*** EWes NGre WPer
§ ***telephioïdes*** MHlr WCot
§ ***telephium*** EBar EPla EWFC MHlr NSti SRms WCla WCot
– 'Arthur Branch' CElw EHal EMon EPla GBuc MTho WCot WDav
– ssp. ***fabaria*** See S. ***fabaria***
§ – ssp. ***maximum*** CMGP ECha EMon MBel SChu
– – 'Atropurpureum' **AGM** CBot CGle CHad CLew CSev CWGN ECha ECoo ELan EMon EPla MBri MFir MNFA SChu SMrm SPer WEas WHal WPer WTyr WWin
– 'Munstead Dark Red' CMGP CRiv CSco EBee EJud EMon MNFA MUlv NGre SFis SHig WCot
¶ – 'Roseovariegatum' EMon
– 'Roseum' EFol LHop
§ – ***ruprechtii*** CMHG ECha EMon MBri NGre SUsu WCot WDav WEas WPer
– 'Variegatum' CMHG COtt CSco GPlt MBel NRoo SFis SPla WHal WWin
tenuifolium EBur GGar SSmi

§ – ssp. ***ibericum***	NGre NHol
– var. ***tenuifolium***	EBur
ternatum	NGre NKay
* ***trollii***	MHig NGre
§ 'Vera Jameson' AGM	CMHG CSam CSco CShe EBre ECha ECro EHoe LBre MBri MCas MFir NGre NHol NKay NSti SBla SChu SPer SUsu WDav WEas WHil WPer WWat
verticillatum	NGre
'Weihenstephaner Gold'	See S. ***kamtschaticum floriferum*** 'W.G.'
weinbergii	See GRAPTOPETALUM ***paraguayense***
yunnenense	See RHODIOLA ***yunnanensis***

SEEMANNIA See GLOXINIA

SELAGINELLA (Selaginellaceae)

apoda	MBri
braunii	NMar
douglasii	NMar
emmeliana	See S. ***pallescens***
helvetica	NHol
kraussiana AGM	GArf MBal MBri NMar WRic
– 'Aurea'	GGar MBri NMar
– 'Brownii' AGM	MBri NMar
– 'Variegata' AGM	MBri
martensii 'Variegata'	MBri
– 'Watsoniana'	MBri NMar
§ ***pallescens***	NMar
– 'Aurea'	NMar
vogelii	NMar

SELAGO (Scrophulariaceae)

See Plant Deletions

SELINUM (Umbelliferae/Apiaceae)

tenuifolium	See S. ***wallichianum***
§ ***wallichianum***	CBos CDec CGle CHad CMil EFou LGre NSti SIgm SMrm WEas WHer

SELLIERA (Goodeniaceae)

radicans forms	ECou

SEMELE (Liliaceae/Ruscaceae)

androgyna	CHEx

SEMIAQUILEGIA † (Ranunculaceae)

§ ***adoxoïdes***	CHad EDra ESma NCat NRya SFis SIng WAbe WHil WPer
§ ***ecalcarata***	CBot CGle CMil CRiv ECro EDra GAbr GCal GPlt GTou LGan LHop MBro NHar NOak SFis SMrm SUsu WCru WDav WPer WThu WWin
– 'Flore Pleno'	CNic LBlm LGan WEas
simulatrix	See S. ***ecalcarata***

SEMIARUNDINARIA †

(Gramineae/Poaceae-Bambusoideae)

§ ***fastuosa*** AGM	CHEx EFul EPla ISta LBam NJap SArc SBam SCob SDry WJun
– var. ***viridis***	EPla ISta SBam SDry WJun
kagamiana	EPla LBam SDry WJun
makinoi	WJun
nitida	See SINARUNDINARIA ***nitida***
okuboi	WJun
villosa	See S. ***okuboi***
yamadorii	EPla ISta SBam SDry WJun
– 'Brimscombe'	SDry
yashadake	EPla SBam SDry WJun
– ***kimmei***	SDry WJun

SEMPERVIVELLA See ROSULARIA

SEMPERVIVUM † (Crassulaceae)

'Abba'	CWil
acuminatum	See S. ***tectorum glaucum***
'Aglow'	CWil
'Alcithoë'	CWil
'Aldo Moro'	CWil EBar NNrd SMit SSmi
allionii	See JOVIBARBA ***allionii***
'Alluring'	CWil MCas SMit
'Alpha'	CRiv CWil ESis LBee MCas NGre NHol NKay SIng SSmi STre
altum	CWil MCas SSmi
'Amanda'	CWil MDHE NMen SIng
'Ambergreen'	CWil NBra SSmi
'Amtmann Fischer'	NBra
andreanum	CWil GAri MCas NGre NHol SIng SMit SSmi
'Apache'	CWil NNrd SSmi
'Apple Blossom'	CWil MCas SIng SMit SSmi
arachnoïdeum AGM	CMea CSam CShe CWil EBar ELan EPot ESis GAbr LBee MBar MCas MSto MWat NHed NHol NNrd NNrw NRoo NWCA SBla SHer SIng SLMG SSmi WEas WHil WHoo WWin
– var. ***bryoïdes***	CWil GCHN NMen
– 'Clairchen'	CWil NBra
– ***cristatum***	NHol
– ssp. ***doellianum***	See S. ***a. glabrescens***
– 'Form No 1'	LBee LRHS SSmi
§ – var. ***glabrescens***	MCas NMen SSmi
– – 'Album'	CRiv WThu
– 'Laggeri'	See S. ***a. tomentosum***
– 'Mole Harbord'	WThu
– 'Rubrum'	NBra
– 'Sultan'	SSmi
N– ssp. ***tomentosum*** AGM	CRiv CWil EBre ECro EMNN EPad EPar GCHN GPlt LBee LBre MCas MRPP MSto NGre NHed NHol NKay NMen NWCA SChu SIng SSmi WHil WPer WWin
– – 'Minor'	NHol SIng
§ – – 'Stansfieldii'	CRiv GAbr MCas NGre NHol NKay NMen STre
– x ***calcareum***	CWil NGre NMen SMit SSmi
– – ***grandiflorum***	SIng
– – ***montanum***	SIng
– – ***nevadense***	CRiv CWil SMit SSmi
– – ***pittonii***	CWil NGre NHol NMen SMit SSmi
arenarium	See JOVIBARBA ***arenaria***
'Arlet'	SMit
armenum	CWil
– var. ***insigne*** from Akyarma Gecidi	SMit

'Aross'	CWil NBra NMen SSmi
'Arrowheads Red'	MCas SSmi
arvernense	See S. ***tectorum***
'Ashes of Roses'	CWil NMen NTow SSmi WAbe
'Asteroid'	CWil SSmi
atlanticum	CWil EBar NMen NNrd SIng SSmi
– 'Edward Balls'	SIng
– from Oukaimaden	CWil NHol
'Atlantis'	NHol
'Atropurpureum'	CWil NBra
'Aureum'	See GREENOVIA ***aurea***
§ 'Aymon Correvon'	NBra
ballsii	CWil GAri GCHN NHed WHil
– from Kambeecho	SIng
– from Smólikas	NMen SSmi
– from Tschumba Petzi	SIng SSmi
'Banderi'	CWil
'Banyan'	SSmi
x ***barbulatum***	SSmi
§ x ***barbulatum barbulatum***	GCHN MCas NKay NMen SIng WAbe WHoo WThu
§ x ***barbulatum*** 'Hookeri'	CWil EPad ESis GAri MCas NHol NRoo SIng SMit SSmi WAbe
'Bascour Zilver'	CWil
'Bedivere'	CWil NGre SSmi
'Bella Meade'	CWil NGre SMit SSmi
'Belladonna'	CWil MCas NHol NMen NTow SSmi
'Bellotts Pourpre'	SMit
'Bennerbroek'	SSmi
'Bernstein'	CWil MCas NHed NMen SIng
'Beta'	MCas NHol NKay NMen NRoo SIng SSmi
'Bethany'	CWil
¶ 'Bicolor'	GCal
'Birchmaier'	CWil NMen
'Black Mini'	CWil MCas NHed
'Black Mountain'	CWil
'Black Prince'	CWil NBra SWas
'Black Velvet'	CWil MCas
'Blari'	NBra SSmi
'Blood Tip'	CRiv ESis GAbr GAri GCHN LBee MDHE NHar SChu SHer WGor WHal
'Blue Boy'	CWil MCas
'Blush'	NBra SSmi
'Boissieri'	See S. ***tectorum tectorum*** 'B.'
¶ 'Bold Chick'	SIng
'Booth's Red'	SSmi
borisii	See S. ***ciliosum b.***
borissovae	CWil GAri SIng SSmi
'Boromir'	CWil NBra SMit SSmi
'Brock'	CWil MRPP NHol
'Bronco'	CWil ELan EPad NMen SMit SSmi
'Bronze Pastel'	CWil MCas NGre NMen SMit SSmi WHil
'Bronze Tower'	SMit
'Brown Owl'	CWil
'Brownii'	GAbr NBra NMen
'Burgundy'	NBra
'Burnatii'	CWil
'Butterbur'	CWil
'Café'	CWil NNrd SIng SSmi
x ***calcaratum***	SIng
calcareum	CWil EPar MBro NGre NKay SIng SSmi WThu
– from Benz	CWil
– from Ceuze	CWil
– from Colle St. Michael	CWil
– from Gleize	CWil
– from Gorges du Cains	CWil SSmi
– 'Greenii'	CWil MRPP NBra NGre NHed NMen SMit SSmi
§ – 'Grigg's Surprise'	CWil NBra NMen SMit
– from Guillaumes, Mont Ventoux	CWil GAbr NMen
– from La Mata de la Riba	SMit
– 'Limelight'	CWil EWes LBuc SMit SSmi
– 'Monstrosum'	See S. ***c.*** 'Grigg's Surprise'
– from Mont Ventoux	SSmi
– 'Mrs Giuseppi'	CMGP CRiv EPar ESis GAbr GCHN LBee MCas NOak NRoo SChu SSmi STre WThu
– 'Nigricans'	NKay
– 'Pink Pearl'	CWil SSmi
– from Queyras	CWil SSmi
– from Route d'Annôt	CWil SSmi
– 'Sir William Lawrence'	CWil ESis NRoo SSmi WHal WThu
– 'Spinulifolium'	SMit
– from Triora	CWil
¶ ***californicum***	NHed
'Canada Kate'	CWil SMit SSmi
'Cancer'	SSmi
'Candy Floss'	CWil SSmi
cantabricum	CWil SSmi
– ssp. ***cantabricum*** from Leitariegos	CWil NMen SMit
– – from Someido No 1	SMit
– ssp. ***guadarramense*** from Lobo No 1	CWil SMit SSmi
– – from Lobo No 2	SMit SSmi
– – from Morcuera No 1	SMit
– – from Morcuera No 3	SMit
– – from Navafria No 1	SMit
– – from Valvanera No 1	SMit SSmi
– from Lago de Enol	CWil
– from Navafria	CWil
– from Peña Prieta	SSmi
– from Piedrafita	CWil SMit SSmi
– from Riaño	CWil
– from San Glorio	CWil GAri SSmi
– from Santander	SSmi
– from Ticeros	CWil
– ssp. ***urbionense*** from Picos de Urbión	CWil SMit
– from Valvernera	CWil
– x ***montanum stiriacum***	CWil NGre SMit SSmi WEas
'Canth'	CWil NBra
'Caramel'	CWil
'Carluke'	CWil NBra
'Carmen'	CWil EPar GAbr MCas SSmi
'Carneus'	NBra
'Carnival'	MCas SSmi
caucasicum	CWil NKay SSmi
'Cavo Doro'	CWil NBra NGre SSmi
'Celon'	CWil
charadzeae	SMit
'Cherry Frost'	NGre NNrd SSmi WHil
'Cherry Tart'	CWil
'Chocolate'	CWil NBra SSmi WAbe
x ***christii***	CWil NHol SSmi WThu

chrysanthum	NBra NMen
ciliosum from Ali Butús	MCas WThu
– var. ***borisii***	CNic ESis GCal GTou MRPP MSto NGre NHed NHol NMen NNrd NRoo NTow
¶ – var. ***borisii*** K 92.408	WDav
– var. ***galicicum*** 'Mali Hat'	CWil GAbr NHol NMen
ciliosum AGM	CWil NGre NKay
ciliosum x ***ciliosum borisii***	CWil
– x ***marmoreum***	CWil SSmi
– – from Sveta Peta	SMit
'Circlet'	NBra SSmi
* ***cistaceum***	WEas
'Clara Noyes'	SSmi
'Clare'	NGre SSmi
'Cleveland Morgan'	CWil ECro GAbr GAri NBra NHar SSmi
'Climax'	NBra
'Cobweb Capers'	NBra
'Collage'	CWil
'Collecteur Anchisi'	NBra NGre SMit SSmi
'Commander Hay' AGM	CRiv EPar GCal LHop MCas MRPP NGre NHol NPer NTow SChu STre WEas WHal WThu
'Compte de Congae'	NBra SPla
'Congo'	CWil SMit SSmi
'Cornstone'	CWil
'Corona'	MCas NBra
'Coronet'	SSmi
'Correvons'	See S. 'Aymon Correvoa'
'Corsair'	CWil NMen NNrd SIng
'Crimson Velvet'	CWil NGre SSmi
§ 'Crispyn'	CWil MBro MCas MRPP NHol NMen SSmi WEas
'Cupream'	CWil NBra NGre NHed
'Dakota'	CWil
'Dallas'	CWil
'Damask'	CWil GAbr NGre SSmi
'Dame Arsac'	SMit
'Dark Beauty'	CWil SMit WHal
'Dark Cloud'	CWil NBra SMit SSmi
'Dark Point'	CWil MCas NMen SMit SSmi
'Darkie'	CWil
'Deep Fire'	CWil SSmi
x ***degenianum***	CWil NBra
'Delta'	MCas
densum	See S. ***tectorum***
'Director Jacobs'	CRiv CWil GAbr GCHN MCas NGre SMit SSmi WEas
dolomiticum x ***montanum***	CWil NBra NHed NMen SMit SSmi
'Downland Queen'	CWil SMit
'Dragoness'	SMit
'Duke of Windsor'	CWil MRPP NGre SSmi
'Dusky'	CWil NBra SSmi
'Dyke'	CWii MBro MCas
dzhavachischilii	SMit
'Edge of Night'	CWil
'Educator Wollaert'	NBra
'El Greco'	CWil
'El Toro'	CWil
'Elgar'	CWil MCas SIng
'Elvis'	CWil MBro NMen SSmi
'Emerald Giant'	CWil
'Emerson's Giant'	CWil
'Engle's 13-2'	CWil NHar NHol
'Engle's Rubrum'	CLew GTou NHol NMen NRar SHer
erythraeum	CWil NGre NHol SIng
– from Pirin	NGre
– from Rila	MCas
'Excalibur'	CWil SSmi
* ***excelsum***	NKay
'Exhibita'	CWil SSmi
'Exorna'	CWil NMen SHer SIng SSmi WEas
'Fair Lady'	NBra NMen
'Fame'	CWil MDHE SSmi
'Fat Jack'	MCas
x ***fauconnettii***	CWil NBra NHol SIng SSmi WThu
x ***fauconnettii thompsonii***	NGre NHol SSmi
'Festival'	CWil NMen
'Fiesta'	CWil
fimbriatum	See S. x ***barbulatum barbulatum***
'Finerpointe'	CWil SSmi
'Fire Glint'	CWil NBra
'Firebird'	CWil
'First Try'	NBra
'Flaming Heart'	CWil SSmi
'Flander's Passion'	LBee
'Flasher'	CWil MCas WEas
'Forden'	NBra
'Ford's Amability'	CWil NBra NGre SSmi
'Ford's Giant'	CWil
'Ford's Spring'	CWil NBra SSmi
¶ 'Frigidum'	NHed
'Frosty'	CWil NBra
'Fuego'	CWil MCas SIng
x ***funckii***	CRiv CWil NBra NGre NHol NMen SIng
'Fusilier'	NBra
'Fuzzy Wuzzy'	NBra SSmi
'Gamma'	LBee NHol NMen SChu
'Garnet'	CWil NBra
'Gay Jester'	CWil NGre SSmi WHoo
'Gazelle'	CRiv NBra
'Ginnie's Delight'	CWil SSmi
'Gipsy'	CWil
giuseppii	CRiv CShe CWil MRPP NGre NHol NMen SIng SRms SSmi WThu
– from Peña Espigüete	CWil NHol
– from Peña Prieta	CWil SMit
'Gizmo'	CWil
'Gleam'	NBra
'Gloriosum'	NGre NRoo SSmi
'Glowing Embers'	CWil SSmi
'Godaert'	CWil
'Gollum'	SMit SSmi
'Granada'	CWil NGre
'Granat'	CWil GCal LBuc MCas
'Granby'	NMen
grandiflorum	CWil EBar GAri GCHN MRPP NBra NGre NHed NMen NRed SSmi WThu
– ***fasciatum***	CWil GAri SMit SSmi
– 'Keston'	EWes NGre SSmi
– x ***montanum***	SIng
– – ***tectorum***	NKay
'Grape Idol'	CWil
'Grapetone'	CWil NGre SSmi

'Green Apple'	CWil NBra NGre SSmi
'Green Gables'	CWil SSmi
'Greenwich Time'	CWil MCas NMen SSmi
**greigii*	NNrd
'Grey Dawn'	SSmi
'Grey Ghost'	CWil
'Grey Green'	CWil
'Grey Lady'	CWil NBra SSmi
'Greyfriars'	CPBP CWil NHol NMen
'Greyolla'	CWil MCas SSmi
'Gruaud Larose'	SMit
'Hall's Hybrid'	MCas NHar NKay SIng
'Happy'	CWil MCas
*'Hart'	CWil
'Havana'	CWil
'Hayling'	CWil EWes NHol SSmi
'Hayter's Red'	NBra
'Heigham Red'	CWil NGre NHol SMit SSmi
'Hekla'	NBra
helveticum	See S. *montanum*
'Hester'	CWil GAbr MDHE NHar SIng SSmi
'Hey-Hey'	CRiv EPot LBee NKay
'Hidde'	CWil SSmi
'Hiddes Roosje'	SSmi
'Highland Mist'	SMit
hirtum	See JOVIBARBA *hirta*
'Hookeri'	See S. x *barbulatum* 'H.'
'Hortulanus Smit'	SSmi
'Hot Peppermint'	CWil
'Hot Shot'	MCas
'Hullabaloo'	CWil SSmi
'Hurricane'	NBra
'Hyacintha'	NBra
'Icicle'	CWil MCas NGre NHol NMen SSmi
imbricatum	See S. x *barbulatum barbulatum*
'Imperial'	CWil SSmi
ingwersenii	CWil GAri NBra NGre SSmi
– *marmoreum* from Sveta Peta	SMit
'Interlace'	SSmi
'Iophon'	NBra SSmi
'Irazu'	CWil
italicum	CWil
'Itchen'	NMen SSmi
'IWO'	CWil GAbr
'Jack Frost'	CWil NGre SIng SSmi
'Jane'	NBra
'Jasper'	CWil
'Jelly Bean'	CWil
'Jet Stream'	CWil NMen SSmi
'Jewel Case'	CWil SIng SSmi
'Jolly Green Giant'	CWil SSmi
'Jo's Spark'	CWil
'Jubilee'	CNic EBar ELan GAbr GPlt MCas NHol NMen NRed NRoo SSmi WEas WPer WWin
'Jubilee Tricolor'	NPri
'Jungle Fires'	MCas NBra
'Justine's Choice'	CWil
'Kalinda'	NGre SSmi
'Kappa'	CWil NHol SSmi
'Katmai'	CWil
'Kelly Jo'	CWil NGre NHar NMen SIng SSmi
'Kermit'	CWil SSmi
'Kerneri'	CWil
'Kimono'	CWil
kindingeri	CWil MCas NMen NWCA SMit SSmi WDav
'King George'	CRiv CWil ESis LBee NGre NMen NPer SSmi WHoo
'Kip'	CWil NMen SIng SMit SSmi
'Kismet'	NGre SSmi
'Kolibri'	GAbr MDHE
kosaninii	CWil NGre NKay NMen SSmi
– from Koprivnik	CWil SMit SSmi WAbe WCru
'Kramers Spinrad'	CWil NGre NMen SIng SMit SSmi WEas
**lacktugum* 'Metaoicum'	GPlt
'Lady Kelly'	CWil ESis SWas
'Lavender and Old Lace'	CWil GAbr GAri MCas MRPP NGre SMit
'Laysan'	CWil
'Leneca'	NBra NGre SSmi
'Lennik's Glory'	See S. 'Crispyn'
'Lennik's Time'	SSmi
'Lentezon'	CWil SSmi
'Leocadia's Nephew'	CWil
'Lilac Time'	CWil NGre SSmi
'Liliane'	SMit
'Lipari'	CWil
'Lipstick'	CWil GAbr NGre SMit
'Lively Bug'	CWil MBro MCas NNrd SSmi
'Lloyd Praeger'	See S. *montanum stiriacum*
'Lou Bastidou'	SSmi
'Lowe's Rubicundum'	ESis
'Lynne's Choice'	CWil
macedonicum	CWil NGre SSmi
– from Ljuboten	SSmi
'Magic Spell'	SSmi
'Magical'	CWil NBra SSmi
'Magnificum'	CWil
'Mahogany'	CRiv GPlt LBee MBro MCas NHol NMen NRoo SPla WCru WGor WHal
'Maigret'	CWil
'Majestic'	NGre SSmi
'Malabron'	CWil SSmi
*'Malby's Hybrid'	CShe MDHE NBra
'Marella'	CWil
'Marijntje'	SSmi
'Marjorie Newton'	CWil
'Marmalade'	MCas SSmi
§ *marmoreum*	CMea CWil LBee NMen SHer SIng SPla STre WEas
– var. *angustissimum*	SMit
– var. *blandum*	NKay
– 'Brunneifolium'	CWil ESis GAri MCas NGre NHol SChu SIng SMit SSmi
– from Kanzas Gorge	NBra NGre NHol SIng SSmi
– ssp. *marmoreum* var. *dinaricum*	CWil
§ – – 'Rubrifolium'	CShe CWil GCal MRPP
– from Monte Tirone	CWil SSmi
– from Okol	CWil SSmi
§ – 'Ornatum'	NGre NHed SRms SSmi WAbe
– from Sveta Peta	NGre SSmi
'Mary Ente'	NBra
'Mate'	NMen SSmi
'Mauna Kea'	SSmi
'Mauvine'	NBra
'Mavbi'	NNrd

'Medallion'	CWil
'Meisse'	SSmi
'Melanie'	CWil MCas
'Mercury'	CWil MDHE NHol SIng SMit SSmi
'Merkur'	NBra
'Merlin'	CWil SSmi
'Midas'	CWil
'Mila'	CWil
'Mini Frost'	CWil MCas
'Missouri Rose'	CWil
'Moerkerk's Merit'	CWil SSmi
'Mondstein'	CWil
§ ***montanum***	CRiv CWil ESis MCas NNrd SCro SIng
– from Anchisis	CWil
– from Arbizion	CWil
– ssp. ***burnatii***	NGre SSmi WThu
– ssp. ***montanum*** var. ***braunii***	MRPP
– 'Rubrum'	See S. 'Red Mountain'
§ – ssp. ***stiriacum***	CWil EPar GAri NBra SIng
– – from Mauterndorf	SSmi
– – 'Lloyd Praeger'	CWil NGre SSmi
– from Windachtal	CWil
'More Honey'	CWil
'Mount Hood'	CWil
* 'Moyin'	SMit
'Mulberry Wine'	CWil MCas
'Myrrhine'	CWil
'Mystic'	CWil NMen NNrd SIng
nevadense	CWil MRPP NGre NHol NKay NMen SRms SSmi
– ***hirtellum***	CWil SIng SSmi
– from Puerto de San Francisco	SMit
'Nico'	CWil
'Night Raven'	CWil MCas NMen SMit SSmi
'Nigrum'	See S. ***tectorum*** 'N.'
'Niobe'	CWil
'Nixes 27'	NBra
'Noir'	CRiv CWil GAbr NBra NGre NKay NMen SIng SSmi
'Norbert'	CWil
'Nouveau Pastel'	CWil SMit
'Octet'	NBra
octopodes	ESis MDHE NBir NHed
– var. ***apetalum***	CWil GAri MCas MSto NBra NMen SIng SSmi
'Oddity'	CPBP CWil SMit
'Ohio Burgundy'	CWil MDHE SSmi WAbe
'Olivette'	CWil SSmi
'Omega'	SIng SSmi
'Opitz'	CWil MCas
'Ornatum'	NGre SSmi WAbe WEas
ossetiense	CWil SSmi
'Othello'	EBre LBre MCas MRPP NBir NVic WAbe
'Packardian'	CWil SMit SSmi
'Painted Lady'	SSmi
'Palissander'	CWil NGre SMit SSmi
'Pam Wain'	NBra
'Pastel'	CWil MCas
patens	See JOVIBARBA ***heuffelii***
'Patrician'	CWil EBre ESis GAri LBre SSmi
'Peach Blossom'	CWil
'Pekinese'	CWil EPar EWes LBuc NNrd SIng SSmi WEas WWin
'Peterson's Ornatum'	NGre SSmi
'Pilatus'	CWil
'Pilosella'	NBra
'Pink Cloud'	CWil MCas SSmi
'Pink Dawn'	CWil
'Pink Lemonade'	CWil
'Pink Puff'	CWil SSmi
'Pippin'	CWil NBra SIng SMit
'Piran'	CWil
pittonii	CMea CWil ESis GAbr NMen SIng SSmi
'Pixie'	CNic CWil NHed
'Plumb Rose'	CWil MCas SIng
'Pluto'	CWil SSmi
'Poke Eat'	NBra SSmi
'Polaris'	CWil MCas SSmi
'Poldark'	CWil
¶ 'Pompeon'	SSmi
'Pottsii'	CWil GAbr NHed
x ***praegeri***	CWil
'Precious'	CWil NBra SSmi
'President Arsac'	LBuc SSmi
'Proud Zelda'	CWil SSmi
'Pseudoörnatum'	LBee SChu
'Pumaros'	CWil NMen SSmi
pumilum	CWil MCas NBra NGre NMen
– from Adyl Su No 1	MCas SSmi
– from Adyl Su No 2	SSmi
– from Armchi	MRPP SSmi
– from Armchi x ***ingwersenii***	NMen SMit
– from El'brus No 1	MRPP NMen SSmi
– from El'brus No 2	SSmi
'Purdy'	WAbe
'Purdy's 50-6'	CWil
'Purple Beauty'	CWil NBra
'Purple King'	CWil
'Purple Passion'	NBra
'Purpurriese'	CWil
'Queen Amalia'	See S. ***reginae-amaliae***
'Query'	NBra
'Quintessence'	CWil
'R H I'	NBra
'Racy'	CWil
'Radiant'	CWil
* 'Ramis'	MCas NBra
'Raspberry Ice'	MCas NHol WAbe
'Red Ace'	CWil EBar NMen SIng SSmi
'Red Beam'	MDHE NGre SSmi
'Red Cap'	NBra
'Red Delta'	CWil SSmi
'Red Devil'	CWil MBro NMen SSmi
'Red Giant'	NBra
§ 'Red Mountain'	MCas MWat NKay SSmi
'Red Prince'	CWil
'Red Shadows'	CWil MCas
'Red Skin'	CWil
'Red Wings'	GAbr NGre SRms
'Regal'	NBra
'Regina'	NBra SSmi
reginae	See S. ***reginae-amaliae***
§ ***reginae-amaliae***	ELan NHol SSmi STre
– from Kambeecho No 1	CWil SSmi
– from Kambeecho No 2	CWil MCas NMen
– from Mavri Petri	CWil SIng SMit SSmi
– from Peristéri	SMit SSmi

– from Sarpun	CWil SSmi
'Reginald Malby'	CWil MCas NGre SSmi
'Reinhard'	CWil LBuc NMen NNrd SIng
'Remus'	CWil SIng
'Rex'	NBra NMen
'Rhone'	CWil
* ***richardii***	MBar
'Risque'	CWil MCas
'Rita Jane'	CWil EBar MCas SSmi
'Robin'	CWil MCas NHol NNrd
'Ronny'	CWil
x ***roseum fimbriatum***	CWil NHed NHol SSmi WEas
'Rosie'	CMea CRiv CWil GAbr NGre NMen NRoo SIng SMit SSmi WHoo
'Rotkopf'	CWil NBra SMit
'Rotmantel'	MCas SSmi
'Rotsand'	NBra
'Rouge'	CWil SRms
'Royal Flush'	CWil SSmi
'Royal Mail'	NBra SSmi
'Royal Opera'	CWil MCas NGre SSmi
'Royal Ruby'	CWil GCHN LBee NRoo SChu SIng SSmi
'Rubellum'	NBra
'Rubikon Improved'	NBra SChu SSmi
'Rubin'	CRiv EBar EFol EPad EPar ESis MCas MRPP NGre NMen SCro WAbe WEas WHoo WThu
'Rubrifolium'	See S. ***marmoreum marmoreum*** 'R.'
'Rubrum Ornatum'	MCas SIng
'Rubrum Ray'	NBra SSmi
'Ruby Heart'	NGre SSmi
'Rule Britannia'	SMit
'Rusty'	CWil
'Ruth'	NBra
ruthenicum	NGre
'Saffron'	CWil
'Saga'	CWil
'Sanford's Hybrid'	NBra
'Saturn'	CWil SSmi
schlehanii	See S. ***marmoreum***
'Seminole'	CWil
'Shawnee'	CWil
'Sheila'	GAbr
'Shirley's Joy'	CWil GAbr SSmi WEas
'Sigma'	NBra
¶ 'Silberkarneol'	GCal
'Silberspitz'	CWil NMen SIng
'Silver Jubilee'	CWil MDHE NGre NHed SSmi
'Silver Spitz'	NBra
'Silver Spring'	NBra
'Silver Thaw'	CWil NNrd SSmi
'Simonkaianum'	See JOVIBARBA ***hirta***
'Sioux'	CWil GAbr NGre SIng SSmi
'Skrocki's Bronze'	CWil NBra SMit
'Slabber's Seedling'	CWil
¶ 'Smaragd'	LBuc
'Smokey Jet'	CWil SSmi
'Snowberger'	CWil ESis GAbr NHar SIng
soboliferum	See JOVIBARBA ***sobolifera***
'Sopa'	CWil
sosnowskyi	CWil
'Soul'	CWil
'Spanish Dancer'	CWil SSmi
'Sparkle'	CWil
'Spherette'	CWil SIng SSmi
'Spice'	NBra
'Spinnelli'	NHed WThu
'Spode'	SSmi
'Spring Mist'	CWil GCHN LBuc NHar SIng
'Sprite'	CWil GAbr SMit SSmi
sp. from Mont Cenis	NBra
sp. Sierra del Cadi'	NHol
¶ sp. Sierra Nova	NHed
stansfieldii	See S. ***arachnoideum tomentosum*** 'Stansfieldii'
'Starshine'	CWil SIng SSmi
'State Fair'	CWil MCas NGre SIng SSmi
'Strawberry Sundae'	NBra
'Strider'	MCas SMit
'Stuffed Olive'	SSmi
'Sun Waves'	NBra SSmi
'Sunkist'	SSmi
'Superama'	CWil SSmi
'Supernova'	CWil
'Tamberlane'	CWil SIng
'Tarn Hows'	CWil
'Teck'	MCas NBra
§ ***tectorum*** AGM	CArn CNic CRiv CSFH CWil EJud ELan EPar EWFC GAbr GPoy GTou IEde MBar MDHE SHer SIde SIng SMad STre WAbe WHoo WOak WWye
– ssp. ***alpinum***	CWil MCas NKay SIng SSmi
– from Andorra	CWil
¶ – 'Atropurpureum'	GCal
– 'Atrorubens'	NBra
– 'Atroviolaceum'	CWil ESis GCal NHol SIng SMit
§ – var. ***glaucum***	CWil ESis NHed NKay SSmi
– from Mont Ventoux	CWil
– from Neuvéglise	SMit
– 'Nigrum'	CWil ESis NBra NGre NHol NMen SIng SSmi
– 'Red Flush'	CWil NHar NMen SIng SMit SSmi
– 'Robustum'	NKay
– 'Royanum'	WEas
– from Sierra del Cadi	CWil SSmi
– 'Sunset'	CWil EWes MCas NMen SIng SMit SSmi WAbe WEas
– ssp. ***tectorum***	NGre
§ – – 'Atropurpureum'	CWil MCas NBra SIng SSmi
§ – – 'Boissieri'	CWil NGre NKay SSmi
– – 'Triste'	CWil LBee MCas SSmi
– 'Violaceum'	SIng WAbe
'Thayne'	NBra NMen
'Theo'	SMit
thompsonianum	CWil ESis MRPP NGre NHed NHol NMen SIng SSmi WThu
'Tiffany'	NBra NHol
'Tina'	SSmi
'Titania'	CWil NBra NHar SIng SSmi
'Tombago'	MCas
'Topaz'	CWil GAbr LBee LRHS SChu
'Tordeur's Memory'	CWil NBra NGre NMen SMit SSmi
'Traci Sue'	CWil SMit SSmi
transcaucasicum	CWil SSmi
'Tristesse'	CWil GCal NMen SMit
'Tristram'	SSmi
'Truva'	CWil MCas
'Twilight Blues'	CWil
'Unicorn'	CWil
x ***vaccarii***	NBra NGre SSmi

'Vanbaelen'	CWil SSmi
'Vaughelen'	CWil NBra
'Verdo'	MCas
x ***versicolor***	NHol
vicentei	CWil NHed
'Victorian'	NBra
'Video'	CWil SSmi
'Violet Queen'	CWil
'Virgil'	CWil SIng SSmi
'Virginus'	CWil
'Vulcano'	CWil
webbianum	See S. ***arachnoideum tomentosum***
'Webby Flame'	CWil
'Webby Ola'	NBra SSmi
'Weirdo'	CWil NBra
'Wendy'	CWil MCas NBra SSmi
'Westerlin'	CWil GAbr NGre SIng SSmi
'Whitening'	CWil NGre NMen SSmi
x ***widderi***	NHed SSmi
¶ 'Wolcott's Variety'	MRPP
'Wollcott's Variety'	GAbr NBir NHar SIng
wulfenii	CNic CWil NMen SIng
'Zackenrone'	CWil
zeleborii	MDHE NHed
'Zenith'	MCas
'Zenocrate'	CWil
'Zeppelin'	CWil MBro
'Zinaler Rothorn'	LRHS
'Zircon'	NMen
'Zone'	CWil SSmi
'Zulu'	CWil MCas NHed SSmi

SENECIO (Compositae/Asteraceae)

§ ***abrotanifolius***	GAri LHil NTow
– ***tiroliensis***	See S. ***abrotanifolius***
aquaticus	CKin
¶ ***argyreus*** JJA 12431	SIgm
§ ***articulatus***	GBur
bicolor cineraria	See S. ***cineraria***
bidwillii	See BRACHYGLOTTIS ***bidwillii***
buchananii	See BRACHYGLOTTIS ***b.***
♦ ***candicans***	See S. ***cineraria***
chilensis	CGre
chrysanthemoïdes	See EURYOPS ***c.***
§ ***cineraria***	CHEx IBlr LHil MBri
– 'Alice'	EFou
– 'Ramparts'	LHop
– 'Silver Filigree'	ENot
– 'Sleights Hardy'	NPer
– 'White Diamond' **AGM**	CLTr ECha LGro WBod WEas WWin
compactus	See BRACHYGLOTTIS ***compacta***
crassulifolius	CBot
doria	SAxl WCru
elaeagnifolius	See BRACHYGLOTTIS ***elaeagnifolia***
formosus	CBot
¶ ***gilliesii*** JJA 12379	SIgm
glastifolius	CSam CTbh WCot
'Gregynog Gold'	See LIGULARIA 'G.G.'
greyi Hooker	See BRACHYGLOTTIS ***greyi***
greyi hort.	See BRACHYGLOTTIS Dunedin Hybrid Group 'Sunshine'
¶ ***harbourii*** K 92.410	WDav
heritieri	See PERICALLIS ***lanata***
herreianus	MBri SLMG
* ***huteri***	WEas
kirkii	See BRACHYGLOTTIS ***k.***
laciniata	CHEx
laxifolius Buchanan	See BRACHYGLOTTIS ***laxifolia***
laxifolius hort.	See BRACHYGLOTTIS Dunedin Hybrids Group 'Sunshine'
'Leonard Cockayne'	See BRACHYGLOTTIS 'L.C.'
leucostachys	See S. ***viravira***
macroglossus	
'Variegatus' **AGM**	CAbb CB&S EBee ERea SLMG
maritimus	See S. ***cineraria***
mikanioïdes	See DELAIREA ***odorata***
monroi	See BRACHYGLOTTIS ***monroi***
petasitis	CHEx
polyodon S&SH 29	CHan CRDP EBee SFis WCot
populifolius	See PERICALLIS ***appendiculata***
* ***populnea***	CBot
przewalskii	See LIGULARIA ***przewalskii***
pulcher	CBos CChu CGle CHan CRDP CSam LGre SFis SUsu WCot
reinholdii	See BRACHYGLOTTIS ***rotundifolia***
rowleyanus	EBak
scandens	CB&S CGre CMac CPle ELan EMon ERav ERea ISea MSto MTho NTow SHil WCru WSHC
serpens	MBri
§ ***smithii***	CChu CHan CRDP CRow ECha ELan ERav MSta WCru
¶ ***solandella***	NWCA
speciosus	SUsu WCru
♦ ***spedenii***	See BRACHYGLOTTIS ***s.***
'Sunshine'	See BRACHYGLOTTIS Dunedin Hybrids Group 'Sunshine'
takedanus	See TEPHROSERUS ***t.***
tamoïdes 'Variegatus'	ERea
tanguticus	See SINACALIA ***tangutica***
§ ***viravira*** **AGM**	CDec CGle CGre CHan CMea CPle CSpe ECha ELan ERea LHop MBel MRav SChu SHil SPer SUsu WAbe WByw WCru WHal WOld WRus WSHC WWat
werneriifolius	See PACKERA ***werneriifolia***

SENNA (Leguminosae/Caesalpiniaceae)

artemisioïdes **AGM**	CPle
candolleana	WHaw
corymbosa	CAbb CB&S CBot CHEx CPle CTro ERea LAbb LHil SLMG
didymobotrya	CPle CTro
hebecarpa	MSal
marilandica	CB&S CHol CPle MSal WCru WSHC
§ ***multiglandulosa***	CTro
obtusa Clos	See S. ***candolleana***
obtusa (Roxb.) Wight	CGre CNew CWit SHil
§ ***obtusifolia***	MSal

polyantha	CGre
procumbens	CPle
splendida	CGre
sturtii	CPle
♦*tomentosa*	See S. *multiglandulosa*
♦*tora*	See S. *obtusifolia*

SEQUOIA (Taxodiaceae)

sempervirens	CB&S CDoC CGre EHar EHul IJoh IOrc ISea LCon LPan WCoo WDin WMou WNor
– 'Adpressa'	CBra CDoC CMHG CMac CSco EBre EHar EHul EPla LBre LCon LLin MBal MBar MBri MGos MPla NHol SLim
– 'Prostrata'	CGre CMac EBre EHar GAri GWht LBre LCon LLin MAsh MBar MBri MGos

SEQUOIADENDRON (Taxodiaceae)

giganteum AGM	CB&S CDoC CMac CSco EHar EHul ELan ENot GRei IBar IJoh IOrc ISea LCon LNet MBar MBri NBee NPal NWea SEng SHil SMad SPer WCoo WFro WMou WNor
– 'Barabits' Requiem'	SMad WMou
– 'Glaucum'	EHar MBri SMad WMou
¶ – 'Hazel Smith'	WMou
– 'Pendulum'	CDoC EHar LCon MBar SEng SHil SMad WMou
¶ – 'Variegatum'	EHar

SERAPIAS (Orchidaceae)

lingua	NHar SBla

SERENOA (Palmae/Arecaceae)
See Plant Deletions

SERIPHIDIUM (Compositae/Asteraceae)

caerulescens ssp. *gallicum*	EEls
§ *canum nanum*	WBon
§ *ferganense*	EEls
maritimum AGM	EMon GBar GGar GPoy ILis WHer
– *maritimum*	EEls
§ *nutans*	EBre EEls LBre MWat NSti WAbe
tridentatum	CArn
– ssp. *tridentatum*	EEls
– ssp. *wyomingense*	EEls
vallesiacum AGM	CSFH EEls EMon LBlm WHer
vaseyanaum	EEls

SERISSA (Rubiaceae)

foetida	See S. *japonica*
§ *japonica*	STre
– 'Variegata'	CGre CPle

SERRATULA (Compositae/Asteraceae)

§ *seoanei*	CLew CNic CRDP ECha ECoo EMon MCas MHig MUlv MWat NNrd SDix SIng SUsu WByw
shawii	See S. *seoanei*
tinctoria	CArn CKin ECWi GBar MHew MSal SIde WNdy
– ssp. *macrocephala*	CLew

SESAMUM (Pedaliaceae)

indicum	CArn

SESBANIA (Leguminosae/Papilionaceae)
See Plant Deletions

SESELI (Umbelliferae/Apiaceae)

dichotomum	SIgm
gummiferum	SIng
¶ *libanotis*	SIgm

SESLERIA (Gramineae/Poaceae)

§ *albicans*	ETPC
§ *argentea*	ETPC
autumnalis	ETPC
caerulea	CElw EHic EHoe ELan EPla ETPC GCal MUlv SFar
– ssp. *calcarea*	See S. *albicans*
cylindrica	See S. *argentea*
glauca	EHoe WPer
heufleriana	EMon EPla ETPC LRHS
insularis	EMon EPla ETPC LRHS
nitida	CElw EHoe EMon ETPC LRHS
¶ *sadleriana*	GCal

SETARIA (Gramineae/Poaceae)

chevarlaria	CTro

SETCREASEA See **TRADESCANTIA**

SHADDOCK See **CITRUS** ***grandis***

SHEPHERDIA (Elaeagnaceae)

argentea	CB&S CBot

SHERARDIA (Rubiaceae)

arvensis	MHew MSal

SHIBATAEA †
(Gramineae/Poaceae-Bambusoideae)

kumasasa	CB&S CBar CBra CCla CPMA EPla ESiP IOrc ISta LBam LNet MBal MGos MUlv NHol NJap SBam SCob SDry SHil WJun
– *aureastriatus*	EPla ISta SDry
lancifolia	EPla SDry WJun

SHORTIA (Diapensiaceae)

soldanelloïdes var. *ilicifolia*	IBlr
uniflora 'Grandiflora'	IBlr

SIBBALDIA (Rosaceae)

cuneata	CNic
¶ *parviflora* NS 668	NWCA
procumbens	NWCA

SIBBALDIOPSIS (Rosaceae)

tridentata 'Lemon Mac'	SIng

SIBIRAEA (Rosaceae)

altaiensis CLD 781	EMon
laevigata	See S. ***altaiensis***

SIDA (Malvaceae)

hermaphrodita	EMon

SIDALCEA † (Malvaceae)

'Brilliant'	CMGP LBuc MBel NBar SGil WMer WTyr
candida	CElw CGle CHad CHan CMGP CRDP CSco CSpe EFou ELan EPar EPla GAbr GCal GGar MFir MSte NRoo NSti SCro SGil SMrm SPer SUsu WBon WDav WRus WTyr
– 'Bianca'	CBot SFis
'Crimson King'	WTyr
'Croftway Red'	CB&S EBee EBre ECED ELan LBre MFir NRoo NVic SChu SCro SPer WTyr
'Elsie Heugh'	CBot CDoC CHad CHan EBre EFol EFou ELan GBri GCal LBre MArl MBri MUlv NBar NBro NSti SChu SGil SLga WBod WRus WTyr
'Interlaken'	NMir NOrc WTyr
'Loveliness'	CGle CRDP CSco EBee ECED ELan MBel NCat SGil SHer SMrm SPer WHal WRus WTyr
malviflora	CBos CBre CLew MFir NNor NSti SChu WByw WEas WHoo
¶ – dark form	GMac
¶ 'Mr Lindbergh'	SPer
'Mrs Borrodaile'	CTom MUlv NKay
'Mrs Cadman'	SFis
'Mrs Galloway'	WTyr
'Mrs T Alderson'	GAbr
neomexicana	GCal
'Oberon'	CHan GBuc NHol NTow SPer WEas
¶ 'Paramount'	CBot
'Party Girl'	CBot CBow CDoC CHol CLew CSam EBre ECot ECtt EHal GGar LBre MNFA NHol NPri NRoo SGil SMad WPbr WPer WTyr
¶ 'Puck'	WTyr
'Reverend Page Roberts'	CShe NVic SFis WTyr
¶ 'Rosaly'	CBot
'Rose Queen'	CBow CGle CMGP CSco CTom EBre ECha LBre LGan LWad MBel NHol NKay NRoo SHer SPer WTyr
Stark's hybrids	MPit SRms
'Sussex Beauty'	CBos CMGP CRDP ECha EFou SChu SLga WCot
'The Duchess'	CSco CShe WTyr
'Twixt'	SFis
'William Smith' AGM	CMGP COtt CSam CSco EBre ECED ECha GAbr LBre LHop NCat NHol NKay NMir NOrc SGil SPer WEas WTyr

SIDERITIS (Labiatae/Lamiaceae)

hyssopifolia	EBee WPer
syriaca	CBot ECha SIgm
– NS 551	NWCA

SIEVERSIA (Rosaceae)

§ ***reptans***	CNic GAbr GTou MFir NHol SIng WPer WThu

SILAUM (Umbelliferae/Apiaceae)

silaus	CKin EWFC

SILENE (Caryophyllaceae)

acaulis	CLew EMNN EPad EPot GCHN GTou ITim LBee MBro MCas MPla MTho NMen NRoo NWCA SFis SIng WAbe WPat WThu WWin
– 'Alba'	CLew EPot GDra LBee MBro NHar NHol NMen NNrd NRed WDav WHil
§ – ssp. ***elongata***	NCat NHol SGil SHer SRms WPer
– ssp. ***exscapa***	WPer
– 'Flore Pleno'	NBrk SGil
– 'Frances'	CNic EPot GAbr GArf GCHN GDra GTou ITim MHig NHar NHol NRya NWCA SGil WAbe
– ssp. ***longiscapa***	CMHG GAbr GDra MCas NRed
*– ***minima***	CLew
– 'Mount Snowdon'	EBre ELan EMNN EPad GArf LBee LBre MTho NHar NHol NMen NRed NRya NWCA SGil SHer WPat
– 'Pedunculata'	See S. ***a. elongata***
– from Pfiezujoch	NHol
alba	See S. ***latifolia***
alpestris	CLew CNic ELan ESis GLil MBro MCas MHig MPla MTho NGre NKay NNrd NNrw NWCA WAbe WCla WPer
– 'Flore Pleno' AGM	CGle CMil CShe EOrc ESis EWes LBee LBlm MHig NKay WWin
argaea	NGre
x ***arkwrightii***	See LYCHNIS x ***a.***
armeria	WHer
asterias	CHan CLew EBar EJud ESma LGan LHil MBel NBrk NBro NNrw NSti WCla WPer WWin
§ ***compacta***	ECro WCot WEas WKif
¶ ***conica***	EWFC
delavayi	NHol
dioica	CArn CKin CNat CSFH ECWi ELan EWFC MChe MHew NHol NLan SWat WCla WHen WHer WNdy WWye
¶ – 'Clifford Moor'	WByw
– ***compacta***	See S. ***d.*** 'Minikin'
§ – 'Flore Pleno'	CBot CHan CRDP CSFH ECha ECoo GMac LGan MTho NBro NNrw WByw WCot WEas WHoo WPer WWin
§ – 'Graham's Delight' (v)	CRDP EFol EMon GBri WByw
§ – 'Minikin'	ELan EMon GBri LRHS WBon WCot
– 'Richmond' (d)	ECha EMon GBuc NNrw
§ – 'Rosea Plena'	CBre CChu CGle CLew CMil CSam ELan EMon EOrc MTho NKay SChu SMrm WBon WByw WHer WPer
– 'Rosea Plena Variegata'	WHer
– 'Rubra Plena'	See S. ***d.*** 'Flore Pleno'
¶ – 'Thelma Kay' (v)	WCot
♦ – 'Variegata'	See S. ***d.*** 'Graham's Delight'
elisabethae	LBee LRHS NWCA SHer
– JCA 917.100	WDav

– 'Alba'	WCla
§ *fimbriata*	CHad CHan ELan EMon MFir MNFA NCat SAxl SWas
¶ – 'Marianne'	EMon
foliosa	CLew
¶ *fortunei*	EBee
¶ – B&SWJ 296	WCru
frivaldskyana	GCHN LGan NHol
¶ *gallica*	EWFC
hifacensis	EMon
hookeri	CLew MTho WPat WPer
¶ – Ingramii Group	GArf NHar WAbe WDav
italica	CKin
keiskei	ECha ELan NKay NNrd NTow SBla WPer
– *akaisialpina*	MRPP
– var. *minor*	CNic EWes GArf MCas MTho NWCA WAbe WOMN WWin
laciniata	WDav
§ *latifolia*	CArn CKin ECWi EWFC MWil NMir WCla WHaw WHen WHer
lerchenfeldiana	CNic
maritima	See S. ***uniflora***
moorcroftiana	WOMN WPer
multifida	See S. ***fimbriata***
nigrescens	WPer
noctiflora	CKin EBee WCla WNdy
nutans	CArn CKin CNat EJud EWFC NMir WHer WNdy WPer
orientalis	See S. ***compacta***
¶ *parnassica*	NGar
pendula 'Compacta'	CNic
– *rosea*	LHil
petersonii petersonii	NHol
pusilla	LGan NWCA WPer
¶ *pygmaea*	SIng
rubra 'Flore Pleno'	See S. ***dioica*** 'F.P.'
saxatilis	NHol NKay
schafta **AGM**	CHol CMea CNic ECha EFol ELan EMNN GAbr GCHN LBee LGan MBro MCas MFir MPla MWat NGre NKay NNrd NRoo NWCA SIng SSvw WCla WHoo WPer WTyr WWin
– 'Abbotswood'	See LYCHNIS x ***walkeri*** 'Abbotswood Rose'
¶ – 'Brilliant'	NNrw
– 'Ralph Haywood'	CGle EPot EWes NHol
– 'Shell Pink'	EFol LHop MHig WHoo WOMN WThi
sieboldii	See LYCHNIS ***coronata sieboldii***
sp. CDB 13013	EMon
sp. L 887	NHol
suksdorfii	CLew NHol WHoo
* *surortii*	WPer
tatarica	WPer
§ *uniflora*	CGle CHan CKin ELan EMNN EMar EWFC GAbr GTou MFir NBro NGre NKay NNor NOak NSti NWCA SBod WCla WHen WHer WHil WWin
– 'Alba Plena'	See S. ***u.*** 'Robin Whitebreast'
§ – 'Druett's Variegated'	CElw CLew CMHG ECha EFol EHal EWes LBee SGil SIde SIng WCot WPat
– 'Flore Pleno'	See S. ***u.*** 'Robin Whitebreast'
§ – 'Robin Whitebrest' ('Weisskehlchen')	CGle CLew CMHG CMea CMil CRiv CSam EBar ECha ECro ECtt EFol ELan EOrc GAbr GCal MFir MTho MTol MWat NBro NHol NOak NVic SIng SUsu WEas WHoo WPer WWin
– 'Rosea'	CGle CNic CTom ECha ECtt EMNN GTou NHol NWCA SAxl SIng SMrm WPer
– 'Silver Lining' (v)	ELan EMon EPla GBuc
– 'Variegata'	See S. ***u.*** 'Druett's Variegated'
– 'White Bells'	CMea CVer EBee EPad EPla NNrd WHoo WSHC
vallesia	WPer
§ *vulgaris*	CKin CNic ECWi EWFC MChe MHew MWil NLan NMir WNdy
– *alpina*	See S. ***v. prostrata***
– ssp. *maritima*	See S. ***uniflora***
wallichiana	See S. ***vulgaris***
wrightii	NGre
§ *zawadskii*	EBar NGre NHol NTow WHil WPer

SILPHIUM (Compositae/Asteraceae)

laciniatum	EMon MSal NPri
perfoliatum	ECro GPoy NSti
trifoliatum	MSal

SILYBUM (Compositae/Asteraceae)

marianum	CArn CGle ECoo ECro EJud ELan EMar EMil GPoy LGan LHil LHol MFir MSal SIde WEas WOak WWye

SIMMONDSIA (Simmondsiaceae)

chinensis	MSal

SINACALIA (Compositae/Asteraceae)

§ *tanguticus*	CBre CGle CHEx CHan CRDP CRow CWGN ELan EPla GGar MBal NBro NDea NSti SDix WAbb WCru

SINARUNDINARIA † (Gramineae/Poaceae-Bambusoideae)

anceps	See YUSHANIA ***a.***
jaunsarensis	See YUSHANIA ***anceps***
maling	See YUSHANIA ***m.***
♦ *murieliae*	See FARGESIA ***m.***
nitida	See FARGESIA ***n.***

SINNINGIA (Gesneriaceae)

'Arion'	NMos
'Blanche de Méru'	NMos SDeJ
'Blue Wonder'	MBri
'Boonwood Yellow Bird'	NMos
§ *cardinalis*	EBak WDib
§ x *cardosa*	MBri
'Cherry Belle'	NMos
'Diego Rose'	MBri
'Duchess of York'	CSut
'Duke of York'	CSut
'Etoile de Feu'	LAma MBri MWBu NMos
'Hollywood'	LAma NMos SDeJ
'Island Sunset'	NMos

'Kaiser Friedrich' LAma MBri NMos NRog
'Kaiser Wilhelm' LAma MBri MWBu NMos NRog
'Medusa' NMos
'Mont Blanc' CSut LAma MBri NMos SDeJ
'Pegasus' NMos
'Princess Elizabeth' SDeJ
'Red Tiger' CSut
'Reine Wilhelmine' SDeJ
'Royal Crimson' CSut
Royal Pink Group CSut
'Royal Tiger' CSut
Tigrina Group NMos SDeJ
'Violacea' MBri NMos NRog
'Waterloo' NMos NRog

SINOBAMBUSA (Gramineae/Poaceae-Bambusoideae)

tootsik SBam SDry WJun
– f. ***albostriata*** SDry
– 'Variegata' See S. ***t. albostriata***

SINOFRANCHETIA (Lardizabalaceae)

chinensis WWat

SINOJACKIA (Styracaceae)

rehderiana CMCN

SINOWILSONIA (Hamamelidaceae)

See Plant Deletions

SISYMBRIUM (Cruciferae/Brassicaceae)

§ ***luteum*** CLew EMon

SISYRINCHIUM † (Iridaceae)

* ***album*** CGle
x ***anceps*** See S. ***angustifolium*** Miller
¶ ***angustifolium album*** MSto
§ ***angustifolium*** Miller Widely available
§ ***arenarium*** CRow EBur NHol SBla
atlanticum CMea EBur MDHE SSvw WAbe WPer
bellum hort. See S. ***idahoense***
bermudianum 'Album' See S. ***graminoïdes*** 'A.'
bermudianum Linnaeus See S. ***angustifolium***
'Biscutella' CGle CLew CMea CRiv CTom EBur ECtt ELan ESis LHop MFir MTho NDea NNrd SAxl SChu SMrm SPer SSmi SSvw SUsu WCla WHal WOMN WPer
* 'Blue Ice' CLew CMea CNic CRDP CRiv CSpe CTom EBur MDHE NCat WHal WHoo WPat WPer
boreale See S. ***californicum***
brachypus See S. ***californicum*** Brachypus Group
'Californian Skies' CBro CElw CGle CLew CMil EBur ECha GAbr LBee LGre MDHE MSto NBro SAsh SMrm SSmi SSvw SUsu SWas WKif
§ ***californicum*** CBen CBro CHan CRow CShe CWGN EBur EFol EHon EPot ESis LMay MBar MCas MFir MSta MWat NBro NGre NHol NKay NMen NNrd SSmi SWyc WCla WPer WRus WWin
§ – Brachypus Group CBro CMea EBar ECtt GCHN GCra MPit NDea NGre NMen NNrw NRed NSti SHer SWat WEas WOMN WOak
§ ***chilense*** MSto SIng
coeleste EBur ESis MDHE
coeruleum See GELASINE ***coerulea***
cuspidatum See S. ***arenarium***
demissum CNic EBur
depauperatum EBur EMar ESis ESma MSte NWCA WAbe WHer WPer
douglasii See OLSYNIUM ***d.***
'E K Balls' CLew EBur ELan EPla EPot LBee MBro MTho NBro NKay NRya SHer SSmi SSvw SUsu WAbe WCla WHen WPat WSun WThu WWin
filifolium See OLYSNIUM ***f.***
§ ***graminoïdes*** NBro WPer
§ – 'Album' EBur GAri MTol NBro WCla WPer
grandiflorum See OLSYNIUM ***douglasii***
'Hemswell Sky' EBur GAbr MDHE MMil MSto
§ ***idahoense*** Widely available
§ – 'Album' Widely available
– blue ELan SWas
iridifolium See S. ***micranthum***
junceum EBur NHol NSla
littorale EBur MSto WCla WHil
macounii See S. ***idahoense***
macrocarpon AGM CBro CLew CMea CNic EBur EMNN EPot ESis ESma GPlt LBee LHop NGre NHol NMen NWCA SIng SMrm WAbe WCla WDav WEas WHal WHil WOMN WPat WPer
'Marie' EBur ECha
'May Snow' See S. ***idahoense*** 'Album'
§ ***micranthum*** CBro EBur NCat
montanum CCla EBur NHol WThi
¶ – ***cebrum*** NHol
¶ – ***montanum*** NHol
'Mrs Spivey' CNic CRiv CRow EBar EBur ECtt EMNN EPla ESis MBal MBar NGre NHol NOak WAbe WCla WHil
narcissiflorum GArf
'North Star' See S. 'Pole Star'
nudicaule NHol
– x ***montanum*** CFee CSam EBur EMNN ESis GCal ITim MCas MDHE NHar NHol NNrd NRya WAbe WPer
patagonicum EBur EPla MSto NCat NNrd NWCA WCla WHil
§ 'Pole Star' CFee CNic CSpe CTom EBur GTou IBlr MFir NHar NHol NMen NRed SHer WHal WPer
'Quaint and Queer' CAvo CMil CRow EBur ECha EMar EOrc EPla GCra GMac LGan MTho MTol NBro SSmi WAbe WCra WDav WPer WRus WTyr WWin
'Raspberry' EBur NHol
scabrum See S. ***chilense***
¶ 'Sisland Blue' EBur
§ ***striatum*** Widely available
§ – 'Aunt May' (v) Widely available
¶ – 'Rushfields' WRus
– ***variegatum*** See S. ***s.*** 'Aunt May'
* 'Tierra del Fuego' CRow

***yucciflium** NHol

SIUM (Umbelliferae/Apiaceae)

sisarum GPoy LHol MSal SIde WGwy WHer WOak

SKIMMIA † (Rutaceae)

anquetilia ISea WBod WWat
x ***confusa*** EGol SRms
– 'Kew Green' AGM CB&S EBre ELan EPla IOrc LBre LRHS MBal MBri NHol SBla SHil SPer SPla SReu WWat
§***japonica*** CBow CBra CHEx CLan CMHG CPle CSco CShe CTrw EBre ENot IDai IJoh LBre MBri MGos NBee NKay SDix SLon SReu SSta STre WBod WHCG WStI
– 'Alba ' See S. *j.* 'Fructu Albo'
– 'Bowles' Dwarf Female' (f) CChu EPla MBar MBri MGos MPla MRav NHol SHer SPer WWat
– 'Bowles' Dwarf Male' (m) CChu MBar MBri MPla SMad SPer WWat
*– 'Bronze Beauty' SReu
– 'Bronze Knight' (m) CDoC EHic EPla IHos MAsh NHol
– 'Cecilia Brown' (f) MUlv WWat
– 'Emerald King' MBar MBri SPla
N– 'Foremanii' See S. *j.* 'Veitchii'
– 'Fragrans' AGM CBra CDoC CHig CSam CSco CTrw EPla IOrc MBal MBar MBri MGos MUlv NHol SHBN SHer SPer SPla SReu WBod WThu WWat
– 'Fragrantissima' (m) LRHS MBri
§– 'Fructu Albo' (f) CB&S CDoC CPle CTrw EGol EPla GWht IBar MBar MBri MUlv SLon SMad SPer SPla SSta WWat
– 'Highgrove Redbud' (f) MBar MBri MGos
– 'Keessen' LRHS MBri
– 'Kew White' (f) CSam EBre LBre MAll MBal NHol
– 'Nymans' AGM CBot CDoC EBre EGol IOrc ISea LBre MAll MBal MBar MBri MRav MUlv NHol SArc SBla SHBN SHil SPer SPla SReu SSta WStI WWat
– 'Oblata' MBar SCob
– 'Obovata' (f) EPla
– 'Pigmy' (f) CB&S
– 'Red Princess' (f) LRHS MBar MBri
*– 'Red Riding Hood' SHil SLon
– 'Redruth' (f) CB&S CDoC CLan IOrc MBal MBar MGos MUlv NHol SMad
§ – ssp. ***reevesiana*** CBra CChu CCla CDec EBre EHar EPla IJoh IOrc ISea LBre MBal MBar MBri MGos NBee NHol NKay NRoo NTow SHBN SPer SReu SSta WBod WDin WStI WThu
¶– – 'Chilean Choice' SBla
– – 'Robert Fortune' AGM MBar WWat
– 'Rubella' AGM Widely available
¶– 'Rubinetta' (m) MBar
– 'Ruby Dome' (m) MBar MBri NHol WWat
– 'Ruby King' CSam EPla MBal MBar MBri MGos NHol WStI
– 'Scarlet Dwarf' (f) MBar MBri
– 'Stoneham Red' LRHS
– 'Tansley Gem' (f) MBar
– 'Thelma King' LRHS MBar MBri
§– 'Veitchii' (f) CChe EBre EPla ERav LBre MAll MAsh MBar NHol SHBN SPer WBod WDin WStI
– ***viridis*** NBar
– 'Winifred Crook' (f) MBri WWat
– 'Winnie's Dwarf' CHig MBar MGos
– 'Wisley Female' (f) ECtt EGol EHic EPla NHol NWyt WWat
§***japonica*** Rogersii Group ENot GRei IDai IHos IOrc MBal MBar MGos MPla MWat SBla SChu SLon SPla
– – 'Dunwood' MBar
– – 'George Gardner' MBar
– – 'Helen Goodall' (f) MBar
§– – 'Nana Femina' (f) CSam IHos NHol SBla
§– – 'Nana Mascula' (m) MGos MUlv NKay SBla
– – 'Rockyfield Green' MBar
– – 'Snow Dwarf' (m) MBar MBri
laureola CCla CDoC CMHG ECot ENot IBar LAbb MAsh MBal MGos NGar NHol SArc SLon SReu WSHC
– T 132 WWat
– 'Fragrant Cloud' MBar
****mica*** ISea
reevesiana See S. ***japonica r.***
rogersii See S. ***japonica*** Rogersii Group

SMELOWSKIA (Cruciferae/Brassicaceae)

calycina WPer

SMILACINA (Liliaceae)

racemosa AGM Widely available
stellata CAvo CBos CBre CBro CRDP CRow CVer EBee EBul EPar EPla EPot NHol NKay WDav

SMILAX (Smilacaceae)

asparagoïdes nanus See ASPARAGUS ***a.*** 'Myrtifolius'
aspera CGre
discotis CB&S
sieboldii MRav

SMITHIANTHA (Gesneriaceae)

'Calder Girl' NMos
'Carmel' NMos
'Carmello' NMos
'Castle Croft' NMos
'Cinna Barino' NMos
'Corney Fell' NMos
'Dent View' NMos
'Ehenside Lady' NMos
'Harecroft' NMos
'Little One' NMos
'Matins' NMos
'Meadowcroft' NMos
'Multiflora' NMos
'New Yellow Hybrid' NMos
'Orange King' NMos

'Orangeade' NMos
'Pink Lady' NMos
'Sandybank' NMos
'Santa Clara' NMos
'Starling Castle' NMos
'Summer Sunshine' NMos
'Vespers' NMos
'Zebrina Hybrid' NMos

X SMITHICODONIA (Gesneriaceae)

§ 'Cerulean Mink' NMos

SMYRNIUM (Umbelliferae/Apiaceae)

olusatrum CArn CKin CSev ECWi GBar LHol MChe MHew MSal SIde SWat WCot WHer WOak WWye
perfoliatum CRDP EFou ELan EMar MFir

SOLANDRA (Solanaceae)

grandiflora CTro
hartwegii See S. ***maxima***
§ *maxima* CNew ERea

SOLANUM (Solanaceae)

aviculare ERea
crispum CCla CHan CSco ELan ISea NEgg WDin WPer WStI WWat
– 'Autumnale' See S. ***c.*** 'Glasnevin'
§ – 'Glasnevin' AGM Widely available
– 'Variegatum' NTow
dulcamara CArn CMer EWFC GPoy MHew
– var. *album* EMon
– 'Variegatum' CB&S CChe CHan CMHG CMac CRow EBar EFol ELan EMon IBlr IOrc ISea MBal MBri MRav NNor NSti SBra SFis SLon SPer WEas WStI
jasminoïdes CB&S CDoC EBee EOrc IBar SLon SPer WDin WSHC
– 'Album' AGM CB&S CBot CChu CCla CGle CMac CMer CPle CSco ECha EFou ELan ERav IHos IJoh IReg LAbb LHop MBri SBra SDix SHBN SLon SPer SReu SSta SUsu WBod WHil WSHC
¶ – 'Album Variegatum' WCot
laciniatum CAbb CGle CPle CTro ERea GCal IBlr LHil LHop LRHS NHex SArc SMad
mauritianum SLMG
F *muricatum* 'Lima' ESim
F – 'Otavalo' ESim
F – 'Quito' ESim
pseudocapsicum MBri
– 'Ballon' MBri
– 'Thurino' MBri
rantonnetii See LYCIANTHES ***r.***
'Royal Robe' CB&S CPle
sisymbriifolium GCal WKif
wendlandii CB&S CTro ERea SLMG

SOLDANELLA (Primulaceae)

alpina CNic CShe ELan GArf GDra GTou MBal MTho NHar NHol NMen NRya NVic SBla SGil SHer SIng WCru WHal
austriaca NHar NHol NTow
carpatica AGM CRiv GTou MBal NCat NHol NRed NRya NSla NTow SGil WAbe
– 'Alba' CRiv SWas WDav
cyanaster GArf MBal NBir NHol NNrd NRya NSla
dimoniei EPot ITim NHar WDav
hungarica CNic GArf MBal MHig MTho NWCA WDav
minima GArf MHig NHar NNrd NRed NSla WAbe
– 'Alba' ITim
montana CRDP CRiv EPot GArf GTou MTho NHol NKay NMen NRed SHer WAbe
pindicola CElw ELan EPot ESma EWes MBal MBro MCas NHar NHol NMen NRed NRya SGil SHer WAbe WCru
pusilla GDra ITim NHar NHol
¶ 'Tinkerbell' WDav
villosa CBos MBal MCas MHig MTho NHar NRed NRya NSla NTow SAxl WDav WOMN

SOLEIROLIA (Urticaceae)

soleirolii CHEx CMer EPot LMay MBri SIng WEas WOak
– 'Argentea' See S. ***s.*** 'Variegata'
§ – 'Aurea' WOak
– 'Golden Queen' See S. ***s.*** 'Aurea'
– 'Silver Queen' See S. ***s.*** 'Variegata'
§ – 'Variegata' WOak

SOLENOMELUS (Iridaceae)

chilensis See S. ***pedunculatus***
lechlek NHol
pedunculatus CFee WPer WThi
sisyrinchium NHol WThi

SOLENOPSIS (Campanulaceae)

axillaris CBar CRDP CSpe ECou EOrc GBur LHil LHop SChu SSad SUsu WWin
¶ – *alba* SUsu
fluviatilis CLTr ECou WCru
laurentia CTro

SOLENOSTEMON (Labiatae/Lamiaceae)

aromaticus CHal SIde
'Autumn' CBrk CHal
'Beauty' CBrk CHal
'Beauty of Lyons' CBrk
'Beckwith's Gem' CHal
'Bizarre Croton' CBrk
'Black Prince' CBrk CHal
'Blackheart' CBrk
¶ 'Brilliant' CBrk
'Bronze Gloriosa' CBrk
¶ 'Bronze Queen' CBrk
'Buttermilk' CBrk CHal
'Carnival' (v) CBrk CHal
'Chamaeleon' CBrk
'Cream Pennant' CBrk
'Crimson Ruffles' (v) CBrk CHal
¶ 'Crimson Velvet' CHal
¶ 'Dairy Maid' CBrk

'Dazzler'	CBrk
¶ 'Display'	CBrk
¶ 'Etna'	CHal
'Firebrand'	CBrk
¶ 'Firedance'	CBrk
'Freckles' (v)	CBrk CHal
'Funfair'	CBrk CHal
'Gloriosa'	CBrk
'Glory of Luxembourg'	CBrk
'Goldie'	CBrk
'Holly'	CBrk
'Inky Fingers'	CBrk
'Jean'	CBrk
'Joseph's Coat'	CBrk
'Juliet Quartermain'	CBrk
¶ 'Jupiter'	CHal
'Kentish Fire'	CBrk CHal
'Kiwi Fern'	CBrk CHal
'Klondike'	CBrk
'Laing's Croton'	CBrk
'Lemon Dash'	CBrk
'Lemondrop'	CHal
¶ 'Leopold'	CBrk
¶ 'Lord Falmouth'	CBrk CHal
'Luminous'	CBrk
¶ 'Melody'	CBrk
'Mission Gem'	CBrk
'Mrs Pilkington'	CBrk
'Nettle'	CBrk
'Paisley Shawl' (v)	CHal
pentheri	CHal
¶ 'Percy Roots'	CBrk
¶ 'Petunia Gem'	CHal
'Picturatum' (v)	CBrk CHal
'Pineapple Beauty' (v)	CBrk CHal
'Pineapplette'	CBrk CHal
¶ 'Pink Shawl'	CBrk
'Primrose Cloud'	CBrk
'Primrose Spire'	CBrk
'Red Croton'	CBrk
'Red Heart'	CBrk
'Red Mars'	CBrk
¶ 'Red Nettie'	CBrk
'Red Paisley Shawl'	CBrk
'Red Velvet'	CBrk
'Rosie'	CBrk
'Royal Scot'	CBrk CHal
'Salmon Plumes'	CBrk
'Scarlet Ribbons'	CBrk
scutellarioïdes	MBri
'Spire'	CBrk
¶ 'Surprise'	CBrk
thyrsoideus	See PLECTRANTHUS ***t.***
¶ 'Treales'	CBrk
'Vesuvius'	CBrk
'Walter Turner' (v)	CBrk CHal
'White Gem'	CBrk
'White Pheasant'	CBrk
¶ 'Winsome'	CBrk CHal
'Winter Sun'	CBrk CHal
¶ 'Wisley Flame'	CBrk
'Yellow Croton'	CBrk

SOLIDAGO (Compositae/Asteraceae)

altissima	See S. ***canadensis scabra***
bicolor	CGre
brachystachys	See S. ***cutleri***
caesia	CChu ECha EGol EMon LRHS NKay WCot
canadensis	ELan WByw WOld
§ – var. ***scabra***	WOak
'Cloth of Gold'	CB&S CKel CLew COtt EBre ECro IDai LBre MBri NBar SHer WCot WOld
'Crown of Rays' ('Strahlenkrone')	CTom EBre ECtt EFou LBre MRav NBar NHol WWin
§ ***cutleri***	CLew CNic ELan EMon IDai LGan MBar MPit MTho MWat NGre NKay NMen NMir NNrd NRoo NVic SIng WHoo WPat WPer WThu WWin
¶ – ***nana***	EWes
§ ***flexicaulis*** 'Variegata'	CRDP ECoo EJud ELan EMar EMon GCal LHop NSti SFar SUsu WCot
¶ ***gigantea***	EMon
glomerata	EMon WPer
'Golden Baby' ('Goldkind')	CBow CLTr ECoo ECtt GAbr GLil LHil LWad MBri MFir NFai NOak NOrc SFis SGil SPla SSvw WByw WPer
'Golden Dwarf' ('Goldzwerg')	CDoC CSco EBre EFou GLil LBre
'Golden Falls'	WOld
'Golden Rays'	See S. 'Goldstrahl'
'Golden Shower'	MWat
'Golden Thumb'	See S. 'Queenie'
'Golden Wings'	GLil LHil MWat
'Goldenmosa' AGM	CDec CSco CShe EHal EMon MBel MWat NKay SChu SGil SPer WBon
'Goldilocks'	NMir NPri
§ 'Goldstrahl'	LHil SGil
graminifolia	EMon
hybrida	See X SOLIDASTER ***luteus***
latifolia	See S. ***flexicaulis***
'Laurin'	NFai NHol SFis WHoo
'Leda'	SFis
'Ledsham'	CMGP MMil SGil
'Lemore'	See X SOLIDASTER ***luteus*** 'Lemore'
'Lesden'	CSco
'Loddon'	CSco
microcephala	EMon
'Mimosa'	NHol NKay NVic
multiradiata	CLew WPer
– var. ***scopulorum***	NHol WDav
odora	CLew MSal
§ 'Queenie'	CLew CMGP ECha ECro ELan ESis GCHN LHil MBri MTho MWat NKay NNor NVic SPer WHal WPer
randii	EMon
rigida JLS 88002WI	EMon
¶ ***rugosa***	EMon
sempervirens	EMon
'Spätgold'	EFou
spathulata	LHop
– ***nana***	CMHG WPer
– var. ***nana*** JCA 9627	CLew
'Tom Thumb'	EGle MRav SRms WEas
virgaurea	CArn CKin CRiv ECWi GPoy LHol SIde WNdy WPer

– ssp. ***alpestris*** var. ***minutissima*** CLew ITim MTho WAbe
– ***cambrica*** WCla
¶ – pale yellow EMon
– 'Praecox' WOld
§ – 'Variegata' EFol EHoe EPla WOld
vulgaris 'Variegata' See S. ***virgaurea*** 'V.'

X SOLIDASTER (Compositae/Asteraceae)

hybridus See X S. ***luteus***
§ ***luteus*** CAll CB&S EFou GBri MBri SPla WEas WHal WOld
§ – 'Lemore' **AGM** CBre CChu CDec CLew CMHG CSco CShe EBre ECha EFou ELan EMon LBre MUlv MWat NBar NSti SFis SPer
'Super' EFou EMon LHil

SOLLYA (Pittosporaceae)

fusiformis See S. ***heterophylla***
§ ***heterophylla*** **AGM** Widely available
¶ – 'Alba' CB&S LGre
– mauve ECou
parviflora ECou

SONCHUS (Compositae/Asteraceae)

¶ ***oleraceus*** WHaw
palustris EMon
platylepsis CHEx

SOPHORA (Leguminosae/Papilionaceae)

¶ ***alopecuroïdes*** EBee
§ ***davidii*** CChu CPle SLMG
japonica **AGM** CAbP CB&S CBra CGre CLnd EHar ELan EMil ENot GAri ISea NBee SHBN SPer WDin WFro WNor
– 'Pendula' COtt ELan LNet LPan SEng SHil SMad WFro
'Little Baby' CDoC ERea IJoh MBlu NBar WStI
macrocarpa CHan MUlv WBod
microphylla CGre CHan CPle ECou GAri LHop MBrk SArc SLMG WBod WCru
– 'Dragon's Gold' ECou
– 'Early Gold' CB&S ERea
– var. ***fulvida*** ECou
– 'Goldilocks' CB&S
– var. ***longicarinata*** ECou
mollis ESma
N ***prostrata*** CBot CChu ECou GAri MUlv
– Pukaki form ECou
tetraptera **AGM** CAbP CB&S CBot CBow CBra CCla CDoC CGre CHEx CHan CMac CPle CWit EBul ECou IOrc ISea LHil LHop NRar SHer SIgm
– 'Gnome' CB&S IMal
viciifolia See S. ***davidii***

SORBARIA † (Rosaceae)

aitchisonii See S. ***tomentosa angustifolia***
arborea See S. ***kirilowii***
§ ***kirilowii*** CSco CShe IOrc MRav NNor SPer
lindleyana See S. ***tomentosa***
sorbifolia CAbP CChu CCla CDoC CSco EMil EPla GBel MGos SLPl SPer STre WDin
– var. ***stellipila*** SLPl
§ ***tomentosa*** **AGM** CAbP CBow CPle EBre EHal LBre MRav SHBN SLon WCru WEas WHCG
– var. ***angustifolia*** **AGM** CCla CSco EFol ELan EMar EMil ENot MBal MBar SHil SPer WBod WWat

SORBUS † (Rosaceae)

§ ***alnifolia*** CLnd CMCN EArb WNor WWat
americana CLnd CMCN GBel NWea
– 'Belmonte' MBri
– ***erecta*** See S. ***decora***
anglica CSam
'Apricot Lady' CLnd SPer WJas
aria CBow CBra CKin CLnd CPer EBre EHar GRei LBre LBuc MBar NBee NRoo NWea SPer WDin WMou
– 'Chrysophylla' CBar CWSG IJoh MBri SHil SMad SPer WAbe WTyn
– 'Decaisneana' See S. ***a.*** 'Majestica'
– 'Lutescens' **AGM** CB&S CBra CLnd CSam CTho EBre EHar ELan ENot GBel GRei IDai IJoh LBre LBuc MBar MBri MGos NBar NBee NWea SHBN SPer SReu WAbe WDin WJas WTyn WWat
– 'Magnifica' CDoC CTho ENot GBel WDin
§ – 'Majestica' **AGM** CDoC CLnd CTho ELan GBel MGos SPer WJas
– 'Mitchellii' See S. ***thibetica*** 'John Mitchell'
¶ x ***arnoldiana*** 'Brilliant Yellow' MBlu
– 'Chamois Glow' CAbP
¶ – 'Schouten' MBlu
¶ ***aronioïdes*** CFil
aucuparia CB&S CBow CBra CKin CLnd CPer EHar ELan ENot GBel GRei IDai IJoh ISea LBuc MBal MBar MBri MGos NBar NBee NRoo NWea SHBN SKee SReu STre WAbe WDin WMou
– 'Aspleniifolia' CB&S CBra CLnd CTho EBre ENot GBel GRei LBre MBar MGos MRav NWea SPer WAbe WDin WJas WTyn
§ – 'Beissneri' CBow CLnd CTho EHar GBel MBri MGos SHil WWat
– 'Cardinal Royal' MBri SHil WJas
– 'Dirkenii' CBar CLnd COtt IJoh WJas
– 'Edulis' CTho ESim IOrc LBuc WDin
§ – 'Fastigiata' CAbP CDoC CSam CTho EBre GBel IOrc LBre MBri MGos SHBN WDin WStI
§ – 'Fructu Luteo' **AGM** ENot EPla GBel MGos WDin
– 'Harvest Moon' CAbP
– ***pluripinnata*** See S. ***scalaris***
– 'Rossica Major' CDoC CTho
– 'Rowancroft Coral Pink' CTho
– 'Sheerwater Seedling' **AGM** CB&S CBra CDoC CLnd COtt CTho EBre ELan ENot GBel IOrc LBre MGos NBee SPer WAbe WDin
– 'Winterdown' CNat

– 'Xanthocarpa'	See S. ***a.*** 'Fructu Luteo'
bristoliensis	CNat
'Carpet of Gold'	CLnd CTho IOrc
¶ ***cascadensis***	MNes
cashmiriana **AGM**	Widely available
¶ – pink	MBri
chamaemespilus	GDra
'Chinese Lace'	CLnd CTho EBee EBre ECot EHar IJoh LBre MBri MGos MUlv SHBN SMad WJas
§ ***commixta***	CB&S CBra CLnd CMCN CSam CTho ENot GBel GRei IJoh IOrc MBar MGos MUlv SPer WAbe WDin WJas
– 'Embley' **AGM**	CB&S CLnd CSam CTho ENot GBel IHos MBar MBri MGos NBee WHCr
– var. ***rufoferruginea***	GBel WAbe
conradinae hort.	See S. ***pohuashanensis*** Hedlund
conradinae Koehne	See S. ***esserteauana***
'Coral Beauty'	CLnd
croceocarpa	CNat
cuspidata	See S. ***vestita***
decora	CLnd CTho MNes NBee SPer
* – 'Grootendorst'	MBri
devoniensis	CTho WMou
discolor Hedlund	CBra CLnd CMCN CSam EBar ECtt ELan GRei IDai MBar MGos MUlv NWea SReu WJas WTyn
discolor hort.	See S. ***commixta***
domestica	EHar NWea WMou WThu
– 'Maliformis'	See S. ***d. pomifera***
§ – var. ***pomifera***	EHar WMou
§ – var. ***pyrifera***	EHar WMou
– 'Pyriformis'	See S. ***d. pyrifera***
'Eastern Promise'	LRHS MBri SHil
esserteauana	CDoC CSam CTho ENot GBel WAbe
– 'Flava'	MBri WWat
folgneri	CPMA
– 'Lemon Drop'	CPMA LRHS SHil SMad
forrestii	CSam CTho EHar MBri SHer WHCr WWat
fruticosa	CChu NSti WHCr
'Ghose'	IOrc MBri SPer
glabrescens	See S. ***hupehensis***
'Golden Wonder'	CB&S CDoC CTho EBee GBel LBuc MGos NWea WAbe WJas
gracilis	CTho
hedlundii	IBlr
hemsleyi	CChu
x ***hostii***	ENot SPer
§ ***hupehensis*** **AGM**	CB&S CBra CChu CLnd CMCN CSam CTho EFol EHar GBel GRei IDai IJoh ISea MBal MBar NBee NWea SHBN SSta WAbe WDin WJas WNor WTyn WWat WWin
§ – var. ***obtusa*** **AGM**	CChu CDoC CSam GAri MBlu MUlv NTow SHer SSta WWat
– 'Pink Pagoda'	CLnd EHar MBri MGos MSta SPer
– 'Rosea'	See S. ***h. obtusa***
x ***hybrida*** 'Gibbsii' **AGM**	CDoC ELan MBri SHil
x ***hybrida*** hort.	See S. x ***thuringiaca***
x ***hybrida*** Linnaeus	NWea
insignis	EBar
intermedia	CB&S CKin CLnd CPer CSam EHar ENot GRei ISea MBal MGos NBee NWea SPer WDin WStI
– 'Brouwers' **AGM**	ELan GBel SEng
'Joseph Rock' **AGM**	Widely available
§ x ***kewensis*** **AGM**	CBow CLnd CSam ECtt SPer
'Kirsten Pink'	CDoC CLnd MBlu MGos
koehneana **AGM**	CDoC COtt EBar EHar EPla MBlu MBri MMea NHol NTow NWea SReu
¶ ***kurzii*** KR 1501	MNes
lanata hort.	See S. ***vestita***
lancastriensis	CNat
latifolia	CLnd ENot NWea WDin WThu
'Leonard Springer'	ENot SPer
'Lowndes'	CSam CTho
matsumurana	ENot IHos
megalocarpa	CFil CPMA CSam WCru
meliosmifolia	CSam EPla
microphylla BM&W 98	NHar
minima	CNat
moravica 'Laciniata'	See S. ***aucuparia*** 'Beissneri'
'November Pink'	COtt IOrc WJas
'Pearly King'	CB&S CSam CTho NBee WHCr
pohuashanensis hort.	See S. x ***kewensis***
pohuashanensis (Hance) Hedlund	CCla CSam CTho EArb EHar IBar MBlu WNor
¶ ***porrigentiformis***	CNat
poteriifolia	GArf
§ ***prattii***	GAri
– var. ***tatsienensis***	See S. ***p.***
randaiensis	MNes
'Red Tip'	CDoC CLnd CTho NBar
reducta **AGM**	Widely available
¶ – B&L 12091	MNes
– CLD 297	NHol
reflexipetala	See S. ***commixta***
rehderiana	MBal MBri WNor
– 'Pink Pearl'	WAbe
¶ ***rupicola***	CNat
'Salmon Queen'	CLnd ECtt
sargentiana **AGM**	CBot CLnd CSam CTho EBre EHar ENot IHos LBre LBuc MBlu MBri NHol NWea SHil SPer WJas WTyn WWat
§ ***scalaris*** **AGM**	CSam CTho ECtt IJoh IOrc MBri SHil SPer SReu WJas WWat
'Schouten'	ENot GBel MBlu MBri
scopulina hort.	See S. ***aucuparia*** 'Fastigiata'
setchuenensis	GAri
* ***sinensis***	WWat
sp. Harry Smith 12799	CChu MBri
¶ sp. McLaren D 84	WBod
¶ sp. SEP 492	MNes
'Sunshine'	CDoC MBri SHil WJas
thibetica	CGre CMCN
§ – 'John Mitchell' **AGM**	CB&S CCla CLnd CSam CTho EBar EHar ENot MBri MGos MUlv SHil SPer WJas
§ x ***thuringiaca*** 'Fastigiata'	CB&S CBra CDoC CLnd ENot MGos SPer WDin WJas
torminalis	CKin CLnd CSam CTho EHar MBri NWea SHil SKee SPer SSta STre WCoo WDin WMou WThu
umbellata var. ***cretica***	See S. ***graeca***
ursina	CAbP CChu CGre CLnd IOrc SMad

§ ***vestita***	CLnd CMCN CTho WWat
vilmorinii **AGM**	Widely available
wardii	SHil
'White Wax'	CBow ECtt EPla MGos SHil
'Wilfrid Fox'	SHBN
willmottiana	CNat
'Winter Cheer'	SHil
zahlbruckneri hort.	See S. ***alnifolia***

SORGHASTRUM (Gramineae/Poaceae)

avenaceum	ECha EHoe EPla ETPC
nutans	See S. ***avenaceum***

SORGHUM (Gramineae/Poaceae)

halepense	ETPC MSte

SPARAXIS (Iridaceae)

bulbifera	NRog
elegans	NRog
– 'Coccinea'	LBow
fragrans acutiloba	NRog
hybrids	LAma
tricolor	EPar MBri NRog
§ ***variegata***	NRog

SPARGANIUM (Typhaceae)

§ ***erectum***	CRow CWGN ECoo EHon EMFW LMay MHew MSta NDea NMir SWat SWyc WHer WWye
ramosum	See S. ***erectum***

SPARRMANNIA (Tiliaceae)

africana **AGM**	CAbb CB&S CGre CHEx CPle CTre CTro ERea LBlm LHil MBri SArc WOak
¶ – 'Variegata'	ERea

SPARTINA (Gramineae/Poaceae)

pectinata	
'Aureomarginata'	CElw EBre ECha EFol EGol EHoe ELan EMon ETPC GCHN GCal LBre LHil MSta MSte NDea NHol NSti SCob SHig SPer WRus WWye

SPARTIUM (Leguminosae/Papilionaceae)

junceum **AGM**	CB&S CBow CBra CPle CSco CShe EHar ELan ENot EPla IBar IDai MBal MBri MGos MWat NKay SArc SDix SHBN SPer SPla SReu SSta WBod WCru WStI

SPARTOCYTISUS See **CYTISUS**

SPATHICARPA (Araceae)
See Plant Deletions

SPATHIPHYLLUM (Araceae)

'Adagio'	MBri
'Viscount'	MBri
wallisii	MBri

SPEIRANTHA (Liliaceae/Convallariaceae)

§ ***convallarioïdes***	CRDP EBul EMon SAxl WChr WCot WCru
gardenii	See S. ***convallarioïdes***

SPERGULARIA (Caryophyllaceae)

marina	MHig
¶ ***purpurea***	WPer
rupicola	CKin CNic CRiv EWFC

SPHACELE See **LEPECHINIA**

SPHAERALCEA (Malvaceae)

ambigua	ELan
fendleri	CB&S CBot CBrk CHan CLTr CMHG CMer CNic CSam EBar EOrc ESma SMrm SUsu WAbe WMar WOMN WPer
– ***venusta***	ECro
¶ 'Hyde Hall'	LHop
malviflora	WPer
miniata	CMHG ELan LGre LHil SMrm WMar
munroana	CBot CHan CMHG CSev EOrc ERom GMac LAbb LGre LHil LHop MFir MUlv NTow SMad SMrm SUsu WByw WEas WMar WOMN WSHC
¶ – 'Dixieland Pink'	WEas
– pale pink	CBrk CSpe ECtt LBlm LGre LHop SMrm SUsu WCot
parvifolia	EBee LHop
rivularis	NRar
umbellata	See PHYMOSIA ***u.***

SPHAEROMERIA (Compositae/Asteraceae)

§ ***capitata***	NWCA WDav
¶ ***compacta***	CPBP WDav

SPHAGNUM (moss)

fuscum	LFle
magellanicum	LFle
pulchrum	LFle

SPHENOTOMA (Epacridaceae)
See Plant Deletions

SPIGELIA (Loganiaceae)
See Plant Deletions

SPILANTHES (Compositae/Asteraceae)

acmella	MSal
¶ ***oleracea***	MSal

SPIRAEA † (Rosaceae)

albiflora	See S. ***japonica albiflora***
arborea	See SORBARIA ***kirilowii***
arcuata	MBri
§ 'Arguta'	Widely available
x ***arguta*** 'Bridal Wreath'	See S. 'Arguta'
– 'Compacta'	See S. x ***cinerea***
x ***arguta nana***	See S. x ***cinerea***
bella	CPle MBar WHCG
betulifolia	CDoC EBee EFol MBri MRav SCob WHCG WPer WWeb

– var. ***aemiliana***	CBot CCla CMHG CPle EBre ECtt EHal ESis IJoh LBre MPla SLPl WWat
x ***billiardii*** 'Macrothyrsa'	CB&S
– 'Triumphans'	ENot NNor WWin
x ***bumalda***	See S. ***japonica***
x ***bumalda wulfenii***	See S. ***japonica*** 'Walluf'
calcicola	NHol
callosa 'Alba'	See S. ***japonica albiflora***
canescens	CNic EHal GAul
cantoniensis	CPle
– 'Flore Pleno'	CPle EMon
§ x ***cinerea***	SSta
– 'Grefsheim' AGM	CB&S CDoC CMer COtt CShe ECtt MBel MBri SPer SPla SSta WStI
– 'Variegata'	MPla
¶ 'County Park'	CBot
crispifolia	See S. ***japonica*** 'Bullata'
decumbens	WDin
¶ 'Dingle Apricot'	EFol
'Dingle Gold'	EFol
douglasii	NRoo SRms
¶ – ssp. ***menziesii***	CPle
fritschiana	CPle SHil SLPl WHCG
hendersonii	See PETROPHYTUM ***h.***
¶ ***henryi***	CPle
§ ***japonica***	CPle NHol SBod
– 'Alba'	See S. ***j. albiflora***
§ – var. ***albiflora***	CB&S CPle ESis MBal MBar MPla MWat NRoo SChu SPer WHCG
– 'Allgold'	CDoC NBee
– 'Alpina'	See S. ***j.*** 'Nana'
– 'Anthony Waterer' AGM	Widely available
– 'Blenheim'	SGil
§ – 'Bullata'	CFee CMHG ELan ESis MBal MBar MBri MHig MPla NKay NRoo SHil SIng SLon SPla WAbe WBod WHCG WPat WSHC WThu
– 'Candle Light'	MAsh SHil SPla
– 'Coccinea'	IDai
§ – 'Crispa'	CDoC CMHG EPla MBar MBri WBod
– 'Dart's Red'	CDoC IOrc MBri NBar SGil SHer SLPl SSta
– 'Fire Light'	ELan MAsh MWat SHil SPer SPla SSta
– var. ***fortunei*** 'Atrosanguinea'	WHCG
– – 'Ruberrima'	NKay
– 'Froebelii'	ISea LBuc WFox
– 'Glenroy Gold'	MBal WAbe WHen
– 'Gold Mound' AGM	CMHG CShe EHar ELan EPla ESis IJoh LHop MBal MBar MBel MBri MGos MRav MWat NNor NRoo SChu SHBN SHer SIng SPer SPla WSHC WWat
– 'Gold Rush '	CMHG EBar MPla WHCG WRus
– 'Golden Dome'	WHCG
– 'Golden Princess'	CCla CSco EBre ELan GRei IDai IJoh IOrc LBre MBal MBar MPla MUlv NHol NRoo SPer SReu SSta
– 'Goldflame' AGM	Widely available
– 'Little Maid'	CBot
– 'Little Princess'	CB&S CBra CCla CMer CPle CSco CShe ELan ENot IJoh ISea LAbb LHop MBal MBar MBel MBri MWat NBee NHol NRoo NWCA SMad SPer SPla SSta WDin WHCG WThu WWat
– 'Magnifica'	WHCG
§ – 'Nana' AGM	CMHG CSco ELan ENot ESis LHop MBal MBar MBri MHig MPla MTho NHar NHol NKay NNor SReu WDav WEas WHCG WPat WPer WWeb
– 'Nyewoods'	See S. ***j.*** 'Nana'
– 'Pamela Harper'	SPla
N– 'Shirobana' AGM	Widely available
§ – 'Walluf'	CPle NNor SLon WHCG
'Margaritae'	NKay SHBN SLPl SPer
nipponica	CB&S ESma MBar MGos WHCG
– 'Halward's Silver'	ESma MGos SLPl
– 'June Bride'	WHCG
§ – 'Snowmound' AGM	Widely available
– var. ***tosaensis*** hort.	See S. ***n.*** 'Snowmound'
– var. ***tosaensis*** (Yatabe) Makino	LHop MWat SPer SReu WBod WWat
palmata elegans	See FILIPENDULA ***palmata*** 'Elegantissima'
'Pink Ice' (v)	CAbP CBow CDoC COtt CPMA CWit EBre EFol EHoe ELan ESma IJoh LBre LHop MAsh MBal MBel MGos MPla NHol SHBN SLon SPer SPla WDin
prunifolia (d)	CCla CPle CSco EBre EHar ELan ENot EPla LAbb LBre LHop MPla SPer SPla WHCG WWin
salicifolia	CPle SHBN
¶ sp. CLD 1389	CPle
stevenii	GAri SPla
'Summersnow'	SLPl
thunbergii AGM	CPle CSco EHar ELan ENot EPla IOrc LHop MPla MRav NNor NWea SGil SLon SPer SReu WDin WHCG
– 'Mount Fuji'	CPMA
trichocarpa	CMCN
trilobata	CPle
ulmaria	See FILIPENDULA ***ulmaria***
x ***vanhouttei*** AGM	CB&S ELan ENot IDai IJoh IOrc LAbb MBal MBar MRav MWat NKay NNor SHBN SLon SPer SPla WDin WStI WWin
veitchii	MBal MRav
venusta 'Magnifica'	See FILIPENDULA ***rubra*** 'Venusta'
wilsonii	CHan
'Wynbrook Gold'	NHol WPat

SPIRANTHES (Orchidaceae)

See Plant Deletions

SPIRODELA (Lemnaceae)

See Plant Deletions

SPODIOPOGON (Gramineae/Poaceae)

sibiricus	EPla ETPC NHol SApp WCot

SPOROBOLUS (Gramineae/Poaceae)

fertilis	ETPC

SPRAGUEA (Portulacaceae)

umbellata	WAbe
¶ – JCA 12950	CNic
§ – *glandulifera*	NGre

SPREKELIA (Liliaceae/Amaryllidaceae)

formosissima AGM	CAvo CMon GCra LAma LBow LHop NRog WChr

STACHYS (Labiatae/Lamiaceae)

§ *affinis*	GPoy
¶ *alopecuros*	WWin
¶ *balansae*	EMon
betonica	See S. *officinalis*
§ *byzantina*	CBow CCla CGle CHad CSco CShe EBre ELan EOrc EPla GCal IDai LBre LHop MBri MFir NBro NNor NOrc NPer SApp SCro WEas WPer WTyr WWin
§ – 'Big Ears'	ECha EMon MNFA SAxl SMrm
§ – 'Cotton Boll'	CBre CMGP CMil CSam ECha EFou EMon GCal MTho NSti NVic SApp SPer WDav WWat
– gold-leaved	See S. *b.* 'Primrose Heron'
– large-leaved	See S. *b.* 'Big Ears'
§ – 'Primrose Heron'	COtt EBee ECot EMil EPla GCra GGar LBuc NSti SLga SMrm SPer WHow
– 'Sheila McQueen'	See S. *b.* 'Cotton Boll'
– 'Silver Carpet'	CB&S CGle CKel CSam CSco CShe CTom ECha EFou EGol EHoe ELan EOrc GCra LGro MBel MBri MFir NBro NRoo SApp SHer SPer SPla WWat
§ – 'Striped Phantom' (v)	CHan EFol ELan EMon MBel WPbr
– 'Variegata'	See S. *b.* 'Striped Phantom'
candida	WOMN WThi
chrysantha	LGre WHer
citrina	ECha EMon GCal MSto SAxl WHal WHil
coccinea	CBos CElw CGle CHan CMil CPle EBar EFou GCra LBlm LGre LHop MFir NBir SAxl SMrm SUsu WEas WHer WHil WPer
– 'El Salto'	CBos CRDP SUsu
¶ *cretica*	WHer
densiflora	See S. *monieri*
§ *discolor*	EBee EGol EPla GCal MBri MCas WCru WHil WPer WPla
germanica	CNat EBee MFir
grandiflora	See S. *macrantha*
iva	ESis NTow
lanata	See S. *byzantina*
lavandulifolia	NHol
§ *macrantha*	CArn CBos CCla CLew CShe EBre ECha ECoo EPot LBre MFir NOak NOrc NSti SAxl WDav WEas WHal WHoo WOld WTyr WWin
– 'Nivea'	EFol EFou EGol ELan EPla GCal MNFA NTow WPat
§ – 'Robusta' AGM	CGle CHan ECoo ELan EMon MBri NBro SApp SPer SUsu SWas WCot
– 'Rosea'	CKel CMGP CRiv CSco EFol EFou ELan SCro SPer WCra WEas WHoo WOld WPer
– 'Rosea Compacta'	WOld
– 'Superba'	CGle CHan CRDP EBar EPla MBri SMrm WByw WCot
¶ – 'Violacea'	EMon
§ *monieri*	CLew SIgm SMrm SOkh WDav WPer
nivea	See S. *discolor*
§ *officinalis*	CArn CKin CSFH CSev ECWi EWFC Effi GPoy LGan LHil MChe MHew MHig MSal NLan NMir SIde SIng WCla WGwy WHal WHer WNdy WWye
– 'Alba'	CBos CBre CGle CSFH MHig NBro NHol SIng WDav WNdy
– 'Rosea Superba'	CBos CGle CMil EBee ECha EGol ELan EPla WCot
olympica	See S. *byzantina*
palustris	CKin ECWi MHew MSta WChe
¶ *saxicola villosissima*	CPBP
spicata	See S. *macrantha*
sylvatica	CArn CKin ECWi EWFC GPoy MHew NLan WCla WHer
¶ *tmolea*	EMon
tuberifera	See S. *affinis*

STACHYTARPHETA (Verbenaceae)

See Plant Deletions

STACHYURUS (Stachyuraceae)

chinensis	CB&S CBow CMCN CRos EBre LBre MBri SHil WAbe
– 'Magpie' (v)	CCla CPMA CSco EBre ELan ESma LBre SHil WWat
himalaicus	CBot
praecox AGM	CB&S CBot CBow CCla CDoC CPMA CPle CSco EHar ELan EMil ENot IOrc MBar MBlu MBri SHBN SPer SReu SSta WCoo WDin WSHC WWat
salicifolius	CMCN

STAEHELINA (Compositae/Asteraceae)

See Plant Deletions

STANLEYA (Cruciferae/Brassicaceae)

See Plant Deletions

STAPHYLEA (Staphyleaceae)

bumalda	CMCN
colchica AGM	CB&S CCla CDoC CHan CMHG CSco IOrc SHil SPer WWat WWye
holocarpa	WWat
N– var. *rosea*	EBee EHar ENot MUlv WNor
N– 'Rosea'	MBlu SHil
pinnata	EHal ELan EPla WNor
trifolia	CMCN

STATICE See LIMONIUM

STAUNTONIA (Lardizabalaceae)

hexaphylla	CBow CChu CCla CDoC CHEx CSam EMil SBra SHil SLon SPer SSta WSHC

STEIRODISCUS (Compositae/Asteraceae)

* *euryopoïdes*	CKni NSty SHer

STELLARIA (Caryophyllaceae)
graminea CKin
holostea CKin ECWi EWFC MChe MWil NMir WHaw WNdy
ruscifolia ITim MHig

STENANTHIUM (Liliaceae/Melanthiaceae)
occidentale CRDP

STENOCHLAENA (Blechnaceae)
palustris MBri

STENOGLOTTIS (Orchidaceae)
¶ *longifolia* GUzu
* *plicata* EPot

STENOMESSON (Liliaceae/Amaryllidaceae)
§ *miniatum* EPot

STENOTAPHRUM (Gramineae/Poaceae)
secundatum
'Variegatum' AGM CMer CTro IBlr

STENOTUS (Compositae/Asteraceae)
§ *acaulis* NWCA
¶ – K 91.5054 WDav

STEPHANANDRA (Rosaceae)
incisa CB&S CBow CGle CLan CPle CShe EMil IOrc SChu SPla WHCG
§ – 'Crispa' CBow CGle CMHG CPMA CPle CSco EGol ELan EMil ENot GRei LHop MBar MBlu MRav MWat NKay NNor NRoo SHBN SLon SPer WDin WHCG WPat WWat
– 'Dart's Horizon' SLPl
– 'Prostrata' See S. *i.* 'Crispa'
tanakae CBow CCla CDoC CGle CPMA CPle CSco EGol ELan IOrc MBar MBlu MUlv MWat NNor SChu SHBN SHil SLPl SLon SPer SPla STre SUsu WBod WDin WHCG

STEPHANOTIS (Asclepiadaceae)
floribunda AGM CB&S CBow CTro EBak MBri SLMG

STERNBERGIA (Amaryllidaceae)
candida CBro CMon LAma WChr
§ *clusiana* CMon ELan EPot LAma SIng WChr
colchiciflora EPot WChr
fischeriana CBro CMon EPot LAma
¶ *greuteriana* WChr
lutea CBro CHan CMHG CRDP ECha ELan EPot LAma MBri NRog SDix SIng SPou WChr WThu
– Angustifolia Group CMea CMon EMon SPou WChr
– *lutea* MS 971 CMon
macrantha See S. *clusiana*
sicula CBro EPot SPou
– MS 796 CMon
– Dodona form WChr
– var. *graeca* CMon
– 'John Marr' ex JRM 3186/75 WThu

STEWARTIA † (Theaceae)
koreana See S. *pteropetiolata k.*
malacodendron ELan MBri SReu SSta WWat
monadelpha CB&S WCoo WNor
ovata CCla CGre WWat
N– var. *grandiflora* LRHS
pseudocamellia AGM CB&S CBow CCla CDoC CGre COtt CPMA EHar ELan IJoh IOrc LHyd MBri SEng SHBN SHil SReu SSta WNor WWat
§ *pteropetiolata*
var. *koreana* AGM CDoC CMCN LBuc MBri SHil SReu SSta WDin WNor WWat
serrata CB&S CCla CGre SHil WCoo WWat
sinensis AGM CCla EHar SHil SPer WNor

STICTOCARDIA (Convolvulaceae)
See Plant Deletions

STIPA (Gramineae/Poaceae)
arundinacea CElw CFee CHan CRow CTom CVer EBar ECha EFer EFol EFou EHoe EMar EPla ESiP ETPC GCal IBar IBlr LGan MFir NSti SChu SDix SWas WPer
– 'Autumn Tints' ECou
– 'Gold Hue' ECou
barbata ETPC NHol SMrm
* *brachytricha* ECha EGle EPla ETPC SGil
§ *calamagrostis* CElw CHan CWGN ECha EHoe EMon EPla ESiP ETPC GAbr GCal MBri NCat NSti SApp
capillata ETPC NHol SGil
elegantissima CElw ETPC SGil
extremiorientalis EGle ETPC
gigantea AGM Widely available
krylovii ETPC
lasiagrostis See S. *calamagrostis*
papposa ETPC NRar
patens EMon
pennata CB&S CHan EHoe EPla ETPC MFir NHol WHoo
¶ *pulcherrima* 'Windfeder' ECha
spartea ETPC
§ *splendens* EFou EPla ESiP ETPC NHol NKay SDix WHer
tenacissima CRDP EFou EHoe EPla
tenuifolia EBee MBri NHol WHal
tenuissima EBre ECha EFol EHoe EMon ESiP ESis ETPC GAri LBre NRar SGil SUsu WCot
tirsa EMon EPla
turkestanica EPla
zalesskyi ETPC

STOEBE (Compositae/Asteraceae)
¶ *plumosa* CTro

STOKESIA (Compositae/Asteraceae)
laevis CBre CChu CDoC CHol ECha EHal GAbr LAbb MBro NBro NNor SAxl SFis SLga WPer

- 'Alba' — CChu CHan CHol CMGP CRDP EBre ECha ECro EMar EMon EOrc GAbr LBre LGan LGre MBri NBrk NHol NRoo NWyt SLga SMrm SUsu WDav
- 'Blue Star' — Widely available
- 'Träumerei' — ECro EFou EMar NHol SFis WTyr
- 'Wyoming' — EBre LBre NOak

STRANSVAESIA See **PHOTINIA**

STRATIOTES (Hydrocharitaceae)

aloïdes — CBen CHEx CRow CWGN EBre ECoo EHon EMFW EWav LBre LMay MSta NDea SAWi SWat SWyc WChe WHol

X STRAVINIA See **PHOTINIA**

STRAWBERRY See **FRAGARIA** x *ananassa*

STRAWBERRY, Alpine See **FRAGARIA** *vesca*

STRELITZIA (Strelitziaceae)

nicolaii — CTro LPal
reginae AGM — CB&S CCla CHEx CNew CTro ELan ERea IBlr LPal NPal SArc

STREPTOCARPELLA See **STEPTOCARPUS**

STREPTOCARPUS (Gesneriaceae)

'Albatross' AGM — WDib
'Amanda' — WDib
'Anne' — WDib
'Athena' — WDib
¶ *baudertii* — GUzu
'Beryl' — WDib
'Blue Gem' — WDib
buchananii — GUzu
candidus — GUzu WDib
'Carol' — MBri WDib
caulescens — GUzu WDib
- var. *pallescens* — WDib
¶ 'Chorus Line' — WDib
'Cobalt Nymph' — MBri
compressus — GUzu
'Concord Blue' AGM — MBri WDib
confusus — GUzu
'Constant Nymph' seedling — MPit WEas
cooksonii — GUzu
cooperi — GUzu
cyanandrus — GUzu
cyaneus — GUzu WDib
'Cynthia' AGM — MBri WDib
¶ *daviesii* — GUzu
dunnii — GUzu
'Elsi' — LBlm WDib
eylesii — GUzu
- ssp. *silvicola* — GUzu
'Falling Stars' AGM — MBri WDib
fanniniae — GUzu
fasciatus — GUzu
'Festival Wales' — WDib
'Fiona' — WDib
galpinii — GUzu
gardenii — GUzu WDib
glandulosissimus — GUzu WDib
'Gloria' AGM — WDib
¶ *goetzei* — GUzu
grandis — CNew GUzu
haygarthii — GUzu
'Heidi' AGM — MBri WDib
'Helen' AGM — WDib
¶ 'Jennifer' — WDib
'Joanna' — MBri WDib
johannis AGM — GUzu
'Julie' — WDib
¶ *kentaniensis* — GUzu
'Kim' AGM — WDib
kungwensis — GUzu
latens — GUzu
'Lisa' AGM — CSpe MBri WDib
'Lynne' — WDib
¶ 'Megan' — WDib
meyeri — GUzu
'Mini Nymph' — WDib
molweniensis — GUzu
'Myba' — MBri
'Neptune' — MBri
'Nicola' — MBri WDib
parviflorus — GUzu
'Paula' AGM — MBri WDib
polyanthus — GUzu
¶ *porphyrostachys* — GUzu
primulifolius — GUzu
- ssp. *formosus* — WDib
¶ *prolixus* — GUzu
rexii — GUzu WDib
'Rosebud' — MPit WDib
'Ruby' AGM — MBri WDib
'Sally' — WDib
'Sandra' — MBri WDib
'Sarah' AGM — WDib
¶ *saundersii* — GUzu
saxorum AGM — CBrk CNew CTro GUzu LHil MBri NTow WDib
- compact form — GUzu WDib
'Snow White' AGM — CSpe WDib
solenanthus — GUzu
'Stella' AGM — WDib
'Susan' AGM — WDib
'Tina' AGM — MBri WDib
'Tracey' — WDib
'Wiesmoor Red' — MBri
'Winifred' — WDib

STREPTOPUS (Liliaceae/Convallariaceae)

roseus — LAma

STREPTOSOLEN (Solanaceae)

jamesonii AGM — CDoC CLTr CNew CPle CSev EBak ELan ERea IBlr LAbb NRog SLMG WBod
- yellow — CBrk ERea

STROBILANTHES (Acanthaceae)

atropurpureus	CBot CGle CGre CHan CLew CPle CRDP ECha ECoo EFou EHal ELan EPla GCal NBrk NSti SAxl SBor SMrm WCru WOMN WOld WPer WWye
attenuatus	CCla
dyerianus AGM	MBri
sp. from Nepal TSS	CGle CRDP EBee SWas WCru
violaceus	ERea LHop WPer

STROMANTHE (Marantaceae)

amabilis	See CTENANTHE ***a.***
'Freddy'	MBri
sanguinea	MBri
'Stripestar	MBri

STROPHANTHUS (Apocyanaceae)

kombe	CTro SLMG
speciosus	CTro

STUARTIA See STEWARTIA

STYLIDIUM (Stylidiaceae)

¶ ***caespitosum***	SIng

STYLOMECON (Papaveraceae)

See Plant Deletions

STYLOPHORUM (Papaveraceae)

diphyllum	CHan CPou EBre ECha EMar EMon LAma LBre MSal SSvw SWas WCru WDav
lasiocarpum	EMon MBel NCat SAxl SFar SWas WBon WCot WCru WHal

STYPHELIA (Epacridaceae)

colensoi	See CYATHODES ***colensoi***

STYRAX (Styracaceae)

americana	CB&S
dasyanthus var. ***cinerascens***	CBow CPMA
hemsleyanus AGM	CCla LHyd MAsh MBri SSta WWat
japonicus AGM	CB&S CBow CBra CCla CGre CMCN CPMA EArb EHar ELan IJoh IOrc LHop LHyd MBal MBri MGos MUlv NPal SEng SHBN SPer SReu SSta WBod WCoo WDin WNor WWat
– 'Carillon'	ELan LRHS
– 'Fargesii'	CPMA
– 'Pendulus'	SSta
– 'Roseus'	See S. ***j.*** Benibana Group
§ ***japonicus*** Benibana Group	CBow CCla CDoC CPMA CSco SPer SReu SSta
– – 'Pink Chimes'	LRHS MAsh SHil
obassia AGM	CBow CChu CCla CGre CMCN MBri SHil SReu SSta WNor WWat
¶ ***serrulatus***	CPMA

SUCCISA (Dipsacaceae)

§ ***pratensis***	CArn CKin ECWi ECoo EWFC MChe MFir MHew MHig NLan WGwy WHer WNdy WOak WPer
– dwarf form	GDra MTho NGre NTow WHil

SUNBERRY See RUBUS Sunberry

SUTERA (Scrophulariaceae)

¶ ***cordata***	LHop
¶ – mauve	CSpe
¶ ***diffusa***	LHil

SUTHERLANDIA (Leguminosae/Papilionaceae)

frutescens	CPle LHop SMrm WHer WPer WWye
– 'Prostrata'	SIgm
microphylla S&SH 56/61	CHan
montana	LHil SIgm

SWAINSONA (Leguminosae/Papilionaceae)

galegifolia 'Albiflora'	LGre

SWERTIA (Gentianaceae)

¶ ***kingii***	WThi
sp. EMAK 0412	NHol
sp. EMAK 0941	NHol

SYAGRUS (Palmae/Arecaceae)

§ ***romanzoffiana***	LPal

X SYCOPARROTIA (Hamamelidaceae)

semidecidua	CKni CPMA SSta

SYCOPSIS (Hamamelidaceae)

sinensis	EHar SBor SHil WBod WSHC
tutcheri	See DISTYLIUM ***racemosum t.***

SYMPHORICARPOS (Caprifoliaceae)

albus	CKin CMer CPer ENot GPlt NWea WDin WStI
– 'Constance Spry'	MUlv SRms
§ – var. ***laevigatus***	CB&S ENot GRei LBuc MBar NKay WDin
– 'Taff's White' (v)	CMer
– 'Turesson'	CDoC
– 'Variegatus'	See S. ***a.*** 'Taff's White'
x ***chenaultii*** 'Hancock'	CB&S CChe CDoC CSco ELan ENot GRei LHop MBar MGos MRav MWat SHBN SPer WDin
x ***doorenbosii*** 'Magic Berry'	CDoC CSco ENot LBuc MBar
– 'Mother of Pearl'	CDoC CSco EBee ECha ELan ENot LBuc LHop MBar MBel MGos NWea SPer WDin
– 'White Hedge'	CDoC CSco ELan ENot LBuc MWat NWea SPer WDin
orbiculatus	NBee WThi
– 'Albovariegatus'	See S. ***o.*** 'Taff's Silver Edge'
– 'Argenteovariegatus'	See S. ***o.*** 'Taff's Silver Edge'
– 'Bowles' Golden Variegated'	See S. ***o.*** 'Foliis Variegatis'

§ – 'Foliis Variegatis' CB&S EHal EHar EHoe ELan EPla LHop MBal MBel MGos MRav NRoo SHBN SPer WAbe WDin WEas WHCG WWat WWin
§ – 'Taff's Silver Edge' (v) CHan CSco ELan ENot EPla IOrc ISea MBar MGos MPla NKay NNor SGil WWat
– 'Variegatus' See S. *o.* 'Foliis Variegatis'
rivularis See S. ***albus laevigatus***

SYMPHYANDRA † (Campanulaceae)

armena EBur ECro ELan GBuc GDra LGan MSto NHol WPer
****campanulata*** SUsu
¶ ***cretica*** EPad
– ***alba*** NTow
hofmannii CCla CGle CRiv CTom CWGN EBur ELan EPad EPot ITim LHop MTho NBrk NHol NRoo NWCA SIng SSvw WHer WOMN WPer WWin
ossettica CElw CGle EPad MBel WPer WThi
pendula CTom ECro EPad EPot GBuc GCra LGre NBrk NBro NRoo SFis WPer WThi
– ***alba*** CCla GBri
wanneri CMea CNic EBur ECro EPad GCra LGan NBrk NMen SIng WOMN WPer WWin
zanzegura CElw ECro EPad LCot SUsu

SYMPHYTUM † (Boraginaceae)

asperum ECha ELan EMon LRHS MHew MSal WCHb
****azureum*** MBri MSte MSto
'Boking' GAbr
caucasicum CCla CElw CHad CHan CSam CSco ECha EPad EPar ERav GPoy MBri NFai NKay NRar NSti SSvw WCHb WCru WHer WOak WSun WWye
– 'Eminence' CGle CRDP EMon LRHS WCot
– 'Norwich Sky' EJud NMir
§ 'Goldsmith' (v) Widely available
grandiflorum See S. ***ibericum***
'Hidcote Blue' CBre ECha ELan EMon EPla ILis MBri MSte NHol NSti SChu SPer SUsu WCru WElm WHal
§ 'Hidcote Pink' CCla CGle EBre ECha EMil ENot EPla LBre LHol LHop MBel MSte NSti SChu SPer
'Hidcote Variegated' CGle WCHb WWye
§ ***ibericum*** CArn CCla CGle CHan CLew CNic CSFH ECha ELun EMil Effi GPoy LGro LHol MFir NRar NSti SIde SSvw WCHb WCru WHal WOak WWat
– 'All Gold' ECha EFol WCru
– 'Blaueglocken' ECha
– 'Gold in Spring' EMon WCHb
– 'Jubilee' See S. 'Goldsmith'
– 'Lilacinum' CCla EMar WHer WWat
– 'Pink Robins' EMon WCHb
– variegated form CRow
– 'Variegatum' See S. 'Goldsmith'
– 'Wisley Blue' CCla CDoC ELan
'Langthorns Pink' ELan EMon GBar GBuc GCal WCHb WSun
'Mereworth' (v) CRDP EMon WCHb
officinale CArn CKin CSev CShe ECWi EHer EJud EPla Effi GPoy IEde LHol MChe MHew MSal NFai NMir NPer SIde WHaw WHer WOak WWye
*– blue WWat
– ***ochroleucum*** CLew WCHb WHaw WHer
orientale CGle EMon WCHb WCru
peregrinum See S. x ***uplandicum***
'Roseum' See S. 'Hidcote Pink'
'Rubrum' CCla CRDP CSco ECha ECoo ECot ELan EOrc EPla MSte NRoo NSti SChu SMrm SPer WCru WSun
tuberosum CBre CSFH GPoy MFir NCat NHol NSti WCHb WHer WWat
§ x ***uplandicum*** CGle CLew CRow CSco CSev ELan Effi MHew MSal NFai WCHb WOak WWin WWye
¶ – 'Jenny Swales' EMon
– 'Variegatum' **AGM** CBot CChu CCla CGle CHan CRDP CSam CSco CSev CWGN ECha EFol EGol ELan EMil EOrc GCal GPoy MTho MUlv NRar NRoo SPer SUsu WCHb WEas WHil WRus WWat WWin

SYMPLOCARPUS (Araceae)

foetidus MSal

SYMPLOCOS (Symplocaceae)

paniculata CB&S EHic WWat

SYNADENIUM (Euphorbiaceae)

¶ ***grantii*** CTro
¶ – 'Rubrum' CTro

SYNEILESIS (Compositae/Asteraceae)

See Plant Deletions

SYNGONIUM (Araceae)

'Jenny' MBri
'Maya Red' MBri
podophyllum 'Silver Knight' MBri
– 'Variegatum' MBri
'White Butterfly' MBri

SYNNOTIA See SPARAXIS

SYNTHYRIS (Scrophulariaceae)

missurica NGre
pinnatifida NWCA
¶ – var. ***lanuginosa*** NTow
reniformis IBlr
stellata GCal GGar SWas WCru WOMN

SYRINGA † (Oleaceae)

afghanica See S. ***protolaciniata***
amurensis See S. ***reticulata a.***
x ***chinensis*** 'Saugeana' CDoC
x ***correlata*** IOrc
x ***diversifolia*** 'William H Judd' EMon
emodi CBot CChu WHCG

– 'Aurea'	EPla
– 'Aureovariegata'	MMor
'Fountain'	CBrd SHil
x *hyacinthiflora*	WStI
– 'Esther Staley' AGM	CDoC CSco ENot SFam SHil WAbe
x *josiflexa*	
'Bellicent' AGM	CSco ELan ENot ISea MBal MBar MGos MRav MUlv NSti SChu SHBN SHer SHil SPer SPla WHCG WStI
– 'Lynette'	EPla
– 'Royalty'	CDoC
josikaea	CBow CCla SPer WHCG
§ x *laciniata* Miller	CBot CCla CGre CHan CPle IJoh SChu SHil SPer WWat
§ *meyeri* 'Palibin' AGM	Widely available
microphylla	CBow CSco EPot
– 'Superba' AGM	CBow CCla CShe ELan ENot ERav IDai IOrc MBel MBri MGos NBar NBee NRoo SHBN SLon SPer SPla SSta WBod WHCG WPat WSHC WWat
palibiniana	See S. ***meyeri*** 'Palibin'
patula hort.	See S. ***meyeri*** 'Palibin'
§ *patula* (Palibin) Nakai	ELan IHos IOrc LNet MBal MWat NBee NRoo SHer SPla STre WStI
– 'Miss Kim' AGM	MGos SHBN SHil
pekinensis	CBot CMCN
x *persica* AGM	CCla CSco EHal ERav ISea MGos MWat SHer SHil SPer SPla WWat WWin
– 'Alba' AGM	CBot CCla SPer SPla WSHC
x *persica laciniata*	See S. ***laciniata***
pinnatifolia	CBot CBrd CHan CPle EPla
x *prestoniae* 'Audrey'	MGos
– 'Desdemona'	CB&S
– 'Elinor' AGM	CDoC CMHG CPMA CSco EBee ENot SHil SPer
– 'Isabella'	MGos SHil
§ *protolaciniata*	CChu CGre CMHG CSco EPla ESis MAsh MBlu MPla SHer WWeb
reflexa AGM	CCla CDoC CMCN EBee EFol MBar MGos MRav NKay SHil WWat
reticulata	CCla CMCN CPle WWat
§ – *amurensis*	MBal
– var. *mandschurica*	See S. ***r. amurensis***
sweginzowii	MBal NHol WRus
– 'Superba'	SHil
velutina	See S. ***patula*** (Palibin) Nakai
vulgaris	GRei LBuc MBar NNor NWea
– 'Adelaide Dunbar' (d)	GCHN
– var. *alba*	MBar
§ – 'Andenken an Ludwig Späth' AGM	CB&S CBot COtt CSco ECtt ENot IJoh IOrc MBar MBri MGos NWea SDix SHBN SPer WDin
¶ – 'Aucubifolia'	EMon
– 'Aurea'	EMon EPla MRav
– 'Belle de Nancy' (d)	CBow ECtt ELan MAsh MBri NBee SHBN WDin
– 'Charles Joly' AGM	CB&S CBra CSco ELan ENot GCHN GRei IDai IHos IJoh IOrc LHol LNet MBal MBar MBri MGos MRav NBee NWea SHBN SPer WDin WStI
– 'Charm'	GCHN NRoo
– 'Condorcet' (d)	LNet
– 'Congo'	ENot GCHN NRoo SPer
– 'Edward J Gardner' (d)	SPer
– 'Firmament' AGM	CSco ELan ENot SHBN SPer SRms
– 'Glory of Horstenstein'	See S. ***v.*** 'Ruhm von Horstenstein'
– 'Katherine Havemeyer' AGM	CB&S CBot CBow CDoC CSam CSco EBre ELan ENot GRei IDai IJoh LBre MBri MGos MRav NBee SFam SHBN SPer SReu WDin WStI
– 'Madame Antoine Buchner' AGM	CSco ENot SFam SPer
– 'Madame Florent Stepman'	CDoC
– 'Madame Lemoine' AGM	CB&S CBot CBra CSco EBre ELan ENot GCHN GRei IDai IJoh LBre LBuc LHol LNet MBal MBar MBri MGos NBee NRoo NWea SDix SFam SHBN SPer SReu WAbe WDin WStI
– 'Masséna'	ENot SFam SPer
– 'Maud Notcutt'	CSco ENot SFam SPer
– 'Michel Buchner' (d)	CB&S CBow ECtt ENot GRei IHos IJoh IOrc LHol MBar MBri NBar NBee WStI
– 'Mrs Edward Harding' AGM	EBre ECtt ENot LBre LBuc LNet MBal MBri MGos SFam SPer WStI
– 'Paul Deschanel' (d)	NBee
– 'Président Grévy' (d)	IJoh NTow
– 'Primrose'	CBot CBow CBra CCla CSco EBre EFol ELan ENot LBre MBal NRoo SFam SPer WDin
– 'Sensation'	CBow CSco ENot SHBN SMad SPer
– 'Souvenir de Louis Spaeth'	See S. ***v.*** 'Andenken an Ludwig Späth'
– variegated double	EFol MBal
– 'Vestale' AGM	ENot MAsh SDix SRms
yunnanensis	ELan WBod
– 'Rosea'	ISea

SYZYGIUM (Myrtaceae)

¶ *paniculatum*	CTro

TABERNAEMONTANA (Apocynaceae)

♦ *coronaria*	See T. ***divaricata***
§ *divaricata*	CNew

TACITUS See GRAPTOPETALUM

TAGETES (Compositae/Asteraceae)

lucida	MSal

TAIWANIA (Taxodiaceae)

See Plant Deletions

TALINUM (Portulacaceae)

calycinum	NGre NHol
okanoganense	ITim MFos NGre NHol NNrd NTow NWCA SIng

spinescens	NGre
teretifolium	NWCA WThi
'Zoe'	SHer SIng WThi

TAMARIX (Tamaricaceae)

africana	WTyr WWin
gallica	CDoC ENot GCHN SArc
germanica	See MYRICARIA ***germanica***
§ ***parviflora***	CB&S IOrc WTyr
pentandra	See T. ***ramosissima***
§ ***ramosissima***	CBow CDoC CSco CShe EBre ELan ISea LAbb LBre MBri MUlv NBee SPla SSta WDin WHil WWeb
– 'Pink Cascade'	CBow EBee ELan ENot EPla MBri SPer WDin WStI
– 'Rubra' AGM	CChe CDoC CSco ENot ESma IOrc MBlu MGos SLon SPer SReu
tetrandra AGM	CBow CBra CMHG CSco EBre ELan ENot LBre LNet LPan MWat NNor SHBN SHer SLon SPer SReu SSta WAbe WBod WHCG WStI WWeb
– var. ***purpurea***	See T. ***parviflora***

TAMUS (Dioscoreaceae)

communis	CArn

TANACETUM † (Compositae/Asteraceae)

§ ***argenteum***	IDai MAsh MTho NTow SMad
– ssp. ***canum***	CKni ELan EWes
§ ***balsamita***	CArn CSFH CSev EEls EJud ELan EMar EMon Effi GPoy IEde MBri MHew MSal NHol SHer SSvw WOak WPer WWye
– var. ***tanacetoïdes***	GPoy LHol MSal NSti SIde
– ***tomentosum***	EJud LHol MChe SIde WGwy WWye
♦ ***capitatum***	See SPHAEROMERIA ***capitata***
§ ***cinerariifolium***	CArn GPoy IEde NHol NRar SIde WOak WPer
§ ***coccineum***	GBar GPoy MHew MSal SPer SRms WWin
– 'Alfred'	ELan
– 'Brenda' AGM	CMGP EBre ECED EFou LBre MWat SMrm
– 'Eileen May Robinson' AGM	CMGP EBre ECED ECot LBre MWat NFai SMrm WRus
¶ – 'Evenglow'	EBee SMrm
– 'James Kelway' AGM	ECot LWad MBri MRav NFai SHer SMrm SRms
– 'King Size'	CHol CSam GAul MPit NMir WHil
– 'Queen Mary'	ELan
– 'Red Dwarf'	ELan
– 'Robinson's Pink'	CMGP NOrc NRoo SHer SMrm SRms
– 'Robinson's Red'	CBow NOrc NRoo SMrm
– 'Salmon Beauty'	CMGP EBee
– 'Scarlet Glow'	MWat
– 'Snow Cloud'	EBee EFou MWat SMrm
§ ***corymbosum***	CGle EMon GCal NCat WByw WCot
densum	LHil SHer WWeb
– ssp. ***amani***	ECha EFol EFou ELan EOrc ERav ESis GPlt GTou LBee MCas MPla MRPP MWat NHol NRoo NWCA SIng SSmi WAbe WRus WThu WWin
§ ***haradjanii***	CGle CSam ELan EMNN EPla GCHN LAbb LGro MRPP NKay NNor SAxl SBla SChu SGil SPer WByw WEas WHil WHoo WOld WPer WSHC WWye
herderi	See HIPPOLYTIA ***h.***
¶ ***huronense***	EBee
§ ***macrophyllum***	EMon EPla GCal NHol WCot WPer
niveum	EMon
pallidum	See LEUCANTHEMOPSIS ***pallida***
§ ***parthenium***	CArn CKin ECWi EEls EHer EJud Effi GBar GPoy LHol MChe NFai NMir NPer NRoo SIde WHer WOak WWye
– 'Aureum'	CRow CTom ECha EEls EFou ELan MBri MChe NFai SIng SMad SPer WEas WHal WHer WOak WPer WTyr WWin
– 'Ball's Double White'	SRms
– double white	NPer
– 'Golden Ball'	NTow
– 'Plenum'	MBri SIng WBon WOak
§ – 'Rowallane' (d)	CHan ELan EMon GBuc
– 'Sissinghurst White'	See T. ***p.*** 'Rowallane'
– 'White Bonnet' (d)	CGle CHan ECha ELan EMon NBrk NRar WEas
§ ***praeteritium***	LGre
§ ***ptarmiciflorum***	LBlm
¶ sp. C&Mc 460	GTou
vulgare	CArn CKin CSFH CSev ECWi ECoo ECtt EEls EHer EJud EWFC Effi IEde LHol MBar MChe MHew MSal NLan NMir SHer SIde SPer WByw WCla WHal WOak WWye
– var. ***crispum***	CSFH ELan GBar GCal MBri SIde WGwy
– 'Isla Gold'	EFol EWes MMil WCot
– 'Silver Lace' (v)	CRDP ECha EFol EMar EMon NBrk NSti

TANAKAEA (Saxifragaceae)

radicans	ELan EPot NHol WCru

TANGELO See **CITRUS** x ***tangelo***

TANGERINE See **CITRUS** ***reticulata*** Tangerine Group

TANGOR See **CITRUS** x ***nobilis***

TAPEINOCHILOS (Costaceae)

ananassae	CNew CTro

TARAXACUM (Compositae/Asteraceae)

I ***officinale***	EHer LHol SIde
¶ ***pamiricum***	EPot

TASMANNIA See **DRIMYS**

TAXODIUM (Taxodiaceae)

ascendens	See T. ***distichum imbricatum***
§ ***distichum*** AGM	Widely available
– var. ***imbricatum*** 'Nutans' AGM	EHar IOrc MBlu SHil SMad
– 'Pendens'	EHar
*– 'Pendulum'	EHar
mucronatum	WFro

TAXUS † (Taxaceae)

baccata AGM	Widely available
– f. ***adpressa***	EBre GAri LBre
– 'Adpressa Aurea'	CKen ESis MPla WMou
– 'Adpressa Variegata' AGM	EBre EHul LBre MAsh SLim
– 'Aldenham Gold'	CKen
– 'Amersfoort'	EPla LCon SLim
♦– 'Argentea Minor'	See T. ***b.*** 'Dwarf White'
§ – Aurea Group	SRms
I – 'Aurea Pendula'	EBre ENHC LBre
I – 'Aureomarginata'	CB&S CBra ENHC WStI
– 'Compacta'	EPla
– 'Corley's Coppertip'	CDoC CKen CSam EHul EPot LCon LLin MBar MPla NHol SHer
– 'David'	WMou
– 'Decora'	LCon
– 'Dovastoniana' AGM	CDoC CMac LPan MBar NWea SHil SMad
– 'Dovastonii Aurea' AGM	CDoC CMac EHul EPla LCon LHol MBar MBri SHil SLim SLon SMad SPer WDin
– 'Drinkstone Gold'	EHul EPla
§ – 'Dwarf White'	EPla LCon MAsh NHol
– 'Elegantissima' AGM	EHul MPla NKay NWea
– 'Erecta' (m)	SHBN
§ – 'Fastigiata' AGM	Widely available
– 'Fastigiata Aurea'	CKen EBee EHar EHul ELan IHos IJoh LBuc LLin NBee NEgg NRoo SBla SHer
– 'Fastigiata Aureomarginata' AGM	CDoC CKen CMac CSco EBre EHul GRei IDai IOrc ISea LBre LCon LHol LPan MBal MBar MBri MGos MWat NHol NKay NWea SLim SSta WMou
– 'Fastigiata Robusta'	EBre EPla LBre MBar NHol
– 'Glenroy New Penny'	MBal
¶ – 'Green Diamond'	CKen
– 'Hibernica'	See T. ***b.*** 'Fastigiata'
– 'Nutans'	CKen EHul ESis LCon LLin MBar
– 'Overeynderi'	EHul
– 'Pendula'	MBal MRav
– 'Pumila Aurea'	MAsh
– 'Pygmaea'	CKen IOrc
– 'Repandens' AGM	CDoC EHul ENHC MBar SHBN SPer
– 'Repens Aurea' AGM	CDoC CHig CKen CSco EHul ENHC EPla GCHN LCon LLin MAsh MBar MBri MGos MPla NHol NRoo SHil SPla WEas
– 'Semperaurea' AGM	CB&S CBra CMac EBre EHul ELan ENHC EPla GCHN IJoh LBee LBre LCon LHol MBal MBar MBri MGos NBee NWea SLim SPla WDin WWin
– 'Silver Spire' (v)	CB&S CKen
– 'Standishii' AGM	Widely available
– 'Summergold' (v)	CBra CDoC CSco EBre EHul ELan ENHC ENot EPla GCHN GRei IDai IJoh IOrc LBre LCon MBar MGos NHol NRoo SLim SPer WStI
– 'Variegata'	See T. ***b.*** 'Aurea'
– 'Washingtonii'	SHBN
brevifolia	EPla LCon
cuspidata 'Aurescens'	CKen EPla LCon MAsh SRms
– 'Luteobaccata'	EPla
– f. ***nana***	CDoC EHul GAri LCon LLin MBar NBee NHol
– 'Straight Hedge'	EHul LCon SLim
x ***media*** 'Brownii'	EHul
– 'Hicksii' AGM	CMHG CSco ENHC LNet LPan MBar NRoo SLim
– 'Hillii'	EHul LCon MBar NHol

TAYBERRY See **RUBUS** Tayberry

TECOMA (Bignoniaceae)

capensis AGM	CB&S CHEx CPle CTro EBak ELan EMil ERea SHil SLMG
¶ – 'Apricot'	CTro
– 'Aurea'	ERea LHop SLMG
¶ – 'Lutea'	CTro
– ***nyassae***	ERea
ricasoliana	See PODRANEA ***r.***
stans	CPle CTro

TECOMANTHE (Bignoniaceae)

speciosa	ECou

TECOMARIA See **TECOMA**

TECOPHILAEA (Liliaceae/Tecophilaeaceae)

cyanocrocus AGM	CAvo EPot LAma NRog WChr
– 'Leichtlinii' AGM	CAvo EPot LAma NRog
– 'Violacea'	CAvo EPot
violiflora	EPot LAma NRog

TECTARIA (Dryopteridaceae)

gemmifera	NMar

TELANTHOPHORA (Compositae/Asteraceae)

grandifolia	SArc

TELEKIA (Compositae/Asteraceae)

§ ***speciosa***	CBre CHan CNic CSco CWGN ECro ELan EMon ESma MFir NBro NHol SAxl SDix SFis WByw WDav WOld WPer

TELESONIX See **BOYKINIA**

TELINE See **GENISTA**

TELLIMA (Saxifragaceae)

grandiflora	Widely available
– Alba Group	EGol
– Odorata Group	CBre ECha EFou EPla GCal NBrk NCat NHol NSti WWat WWye

– 'Perky' JLS 86282SCCA EMon
– 'Purpurea' See T. *g.* Rubra Group
– 'Purpurteppich' CGle ECha EPla
§ – Rubra Group Widely available

TELOPEA (Proteaceae)
oreades SArc
speciosissima CHEx
truncata CBrd CHEx ECou ISea

TEPHROSERUS (Compositae/Asteraceae)
See Plant Deletions

TERNSTROEMIA (Theaceae)
gymnanthera See T. ***japonica***

TETRACENTRON (Tetracentraceae)
sinense CAbb CB&S CChu CCla CDoC CGre CMCN CPle CWSG EHar SHil SMad SPer WCoo WWat

TETRACLINIS (Cupressaceae)
¶ ***articulata*** CGre

TETRADIUM (Rutaceae)
§ ***daniellii*** CCla CDoC CMCN EArb EHar SHil WCoo WWat
– Hupehense Group CMCN GCal WCoo

TETRAGONOLOBUS See **LOTUS**

TETRANEURIS (Compositae/Asteraceae)
acaulis var. ***caespitosa***
K 92.258 WDav
grandiflora NHol SIng
– JCA 11422 CPBP SBla
§ ***scaposa*** EPot

TETRAPANAX (Araliaceae)
§ ***papyrifer*** AGM CAbb CBot CHEx CPle CTro SArc

TETRAPATHAEA See **PASSIFLORA**

TETRASTIGMA (Vitaceae)
voinierianum AGM CHEx CTro MBri SArc

TEUCRIUM (Labiatae/Lamiaceae)
ackermannii CLew CShe ESis LHop MBro MCas NHol NVic SBla SChu SCro WHoo WPat
arduinoi CSam WTyn
aroanum EGle LBee MBro MHig MPla MWat NGre NTow SBla WHil
bicolor CDec CGre CPle
botrys MHew MSal
canadense LHop
chamaedrys hort. See T. x ***lucidrys***
chamaedrys Linnaeus GBar MHew NHol SFis
– 'Nanum' CLew CNic WPat WPer WWye
– 'Rose Carpet' CMGP
– 'Variegatum' CHan CLew CNic EFol EWri LLWP MAll NHol NRar WCHb WCot WHer WPer
§ ***cossonii*** NRar
§ ***creticum*** SPer
* ***discolor*** CPle
flavum LBee LGan SIde WHer WOMN WPer
fruticans Widely available
– 'Album' CGle CPle WSHC
– 'Azureum' AGM CB&S CBot CBow ERav LGre LHop SPer WAbe WBod WPat
– 'Compactum' CBow CChu EHic LHop SDry SPla WSHC
hircanicum CElw CPle ELan EMon LHop LRHS MSte WCot
§ x ***lucidrys*** CArn CGle CMea CPle CSco CSev ELan EPot ERea Effi GAbr GPoy IOrc LHol MBal MChe MHig MPla NHar NNor SIde SLon SMad SPer WCla WDin WEas WOak WSHC WWin
lucidum WCla WOak
majoricum See T. ***polium pii-fontii***
marum NHol
massiliense LHop WHer
montanum CLew CMea MHig WDav
musimomum MHig NTow WDav WHil
¶ ***parviflorum*** WCot
polium CShe EBar ESis SFar SIgm WEas
pulverulentum See T. ***cossonii***
pyrenaicum CElw CMea MBro MCas MHig NHol NKay NRed SUsu WOld WPat WThu
rosmarinifolium See T. ***creticum***
scordium CNat ECWi
scorodonia CArn CKin EJud EWFC GPoy LHol MChe MHew MSal NMir NPri SIde WCla WHer WNdy WWye
¶ – 'Cae Rhos Lligwy' (v) WHer
– 'Crispum' CB&S CBos CHan CMer CRDP CRiv ELan EOrc LHil LHol MBri MFir MWat NBro NFai SMrm WBod WCHb WDav WKif WPer
§ – 'Crispum Marginatum' (v) CBot CCla CElw CLew CMea CWGN ECha ECoo ECro EFol EFou EGol EHoe ELan EMar EMon EPla ESis GAbr IBlr LGan LHop NFai NOak NRoo NSti SFis WBon WEas WRus
– 'Winterdown' (v) CNat
subspinosum CMea ITim LBee MHig MPla NHol NMen NTow SLon WPat WThu

THALIA (Marantaceae)
dealbata CHEx MSta

THALICTRUM † (Ranunculaceae)
adiantifolium See T. ***minus a.***
♦ ***angustifolium*** See T. ***lucidum***
aquilegiifolium Widely available
– ***album*** CBot CBre CHad CHol CLew CMil CRDP ECha ECro EFol EFou ELan EPla GAbr GCal LGan MBri NHol NTow SChu SCro SFis SPer WEas WPer WSHC
– dwarf form ECha
*– 'Hybridum' ECro WHil WPer
– 'Purpureum' CSco GAbr GCal SFis

- 'Thundercloud' ('Purple Cloud') AGM — CCla CDoC EBre ECro ECtt EFou LBre MBel MBri MUlv NBar NHol SLga SPer WAbe WMer
§ ***chelidonii*** — GMac MSte NTow
- dwarf form — GDra
coreanum — See T. ***ichangense***
§ ***delavayi*** AGM — Widely available
- CLD 0025 — NHol
- 'Album' — ECha EFou ELan GCra LGre NDea NOak SWas
- 'Hewitt's Double' AGM — Widely available
- 'Sternhimmel' — NHol
diffusiflorum — ECha SBla
dipterocarpum hort. — See T. ***delavayi***
flavum — CGle CHan EBee ECWi EFou ELan GGar NBro NDea NKay NPri SPer
- 'Chollerton' — See T. sp. Afghanistan
§ - ssp. ***glaucum*** AGM — CBot CChu CCla CElw CHad CSco CShe ECha ECro EFol EHoe ELan EOrc EPla GCal GTou LGan MBri MBro MFir NHol NOak NSti SUsu WBon WEas WOld WPer WWin
- 'Illuminator' — MBel
§ ***ichangense*** — CRDP GLil
isopyroïdes — CRDP EBee EBre ECro EMon LBre SBla SUsu WBon
javanicum — ECro NOak
kiusianum — CChu ECha ECro EFol EPla EPot ESis GArf GAri LGre MTho NTow SBla SMrm SPou WAbe WThu
- Kew form — CRDP SWas
koreanum — See T. ***ichangense***
§ ***lucidum*** — CPou EBee EFol ELan NHol
minus — CHan ECro ELan EMon GAbr GCal MBri NOak NRoo NSti SPla WBon WPla
§ - ***adiantifolium*** — CHan CMGP CTom EBee ECro EHic EJud EPla LRHS MFir MUlv NHol NOak SPla WMer WPer WTyr
§ - ssp. ***olympicum*** — WPer
♦- ssp. ***saxatile*** — See T. ***m. olympicum***
occidentale JLS 86255 — EMon
orientale — SBla
¶ ***pauciflorum*** — WCot
polygamum — MHew MSal
rochebrunanum — CBos CChu CGle CHad CHan ESma MUlv NHol SUsu WSHC
speciosissimum — See T. ***flavum glaucum***
§ sp. Afghanistan — CHan CLew EFol ELan ESma GTou LHop NHol WCot
sp. CLD 564 — EMon
sp. EMAK 0444 — NHol
tuberosum — CChu CHan EMon EPot LGre SBla WCot WDav

THAMNOCALAMUS (Gramineae/Poaceae-Bambusoideae)

crassinodus — SDry
- 'Kew Beauty' — EPla SDry WJun
- 'Lang Tang' — WJun
- 'Merlyn' — SDry
falcatus — See DREPANOSTACHYUM ***falcatum***
falconeri — See DREPANOSTACHYUM ***falconeri***
funghomii — See SCHIZOSTACHYUM ***f.***
khasianus — See DREPANOSTACHYUM ***khasianum***
maling — See YUSHANIA ***maling***
spathaceus misapplied — See FARGESIA ***murieliae***
§ ***spathiflorus*** — EFul EPla ISta SBam SDry SHil WJun
§ ***tessellatus*** — EFul EPla ISta LBam SBam SDry SHil WJun

THAPSIA (Umbelliferae/Apiaceae)

¶ ***decipiens*** — WCot
garganica — SIgm

THEA See CAMELLIA

THELYMITRA (Orchidaceae)

¶ ***antennifera*** — WThi

THELYPTERIS (Thelypteridaceae)

♦ ***limbosperma*** — See OREOPTERIS ***l.***
palustris — NMar WRic
phegopteris — See PHEGOPTERIS ***connectilis***

THEMEDA (Gramineae/Poaceae)

triandra japonica — ETPC

THERMOPSIS (Leguminosae/Papilionaceae)

caroliniana — See T. ***villosa***
fabacea — See T. ***lupinoïdes***
lanceolata — CAbb EFou GAbr GAul MNFA MTol NTow SMad WPer
§ ***lupinoïdes*** — CPle ECha ECro EFol NOrc SFis SIgm SOkh SUsu WCru WPer
mollis — EMon EPla GPlt
montana — CCla CElw CHan CMGP CRDP ECro EFol EFou ELan EMon ERav GAbr MNFA NOrc NSti SChu WAbb WByw WHil WPer WRus
§ ***villosa*** — CChu CGle CHan EBee GCal MSte NSti SIgm

THEVETIA (Apocynaceae)

¶ ***peruviana*** 'Alba' — CB&S

THLADIANTHA (Cucurbitaceae)

See Plant Deletions

THLASPI (Cruciferae/Brassicaceae)

¶ ***alpestre*** — WHer
alpinum — CLew CMGP CMHG CShe GTou MCas MPla MWat NKay NMen NNrd NPri NWCA WPer
- ssp. ***brevicaule*** — NKay
¶ ***arvense*** — ECWi
bellidifolium — GDra NBir
* ***biebersteinii*** — GAbr GTou
bulbosum — ESis GTou NWCA WThi
cepaeifolium ssp. ***cenisium*** — WOMN
- ***rotundifolium*** — GTou NGre NWCA WAbe
- - var. ***limosellifolium*** — NKay
densiflorum — NWCA

montanum	ESis WHer WPer
nevadense	NWCA
stylosum	NWCA WHil

THRINAX (Palmae/Arecaceae)

¶ ***radiata***	CTro

THUJA (Cupressaceae)

§ ***koraiensis***	CMHG EHar IBar ISea LCon MBar WThu
occidentalis	WDin
– 'Aurea'	IJoh MBar
– 'Aureospicata'	SHil
*– 'Baurmanii'	NBar
– 'Beaufort' (v)	CKen EHul EPla LBee LCon MBar MPla WGor
– 'Caespitosa'	CMHG CNic EPla ESis LCon LLin NHol
– 'Cristata Argenteovariegata'	EHul EPla
– 'Cristata Aurea'	CKen
– 'Danica' AGM	CMac CSco EBre EHar EHul ENHC ENot GRei IJoh IOrc LBre LCon LLin LPan MAsh MBar MGos MPla MWat NRoo SBod SHer SLim SPer WStI WTyr
– 'Dicksonii'	EHul
– 'Douglasii Aurea'	CKen
– 'Ellwangeriana Aurea'	ENHC LBee MGos
– 'Emerald'	See T. *o.* 'Smaragd'
– 'Ericoides'	CDoC EBee EHul ENHC MAsh MBal MBar SHer SSmi WStI
– 'Europa Gold'	CDoC EBee EHul IOrc LBee MBar MBri MGos SLim
– 'Fastigiata'	MBar
– 'Filiformis'	CKen LCon
– 'Globosa'	CMac LLin MBar MGos SBod WGor
– 'Globosa Variegata'	CKen LCon LLin MBar
– 'Golden Gem'	LPan
– 'Golden Globe'	CSco EHul ENHC ENot LCon LNet MBar MGos MWat SBod SLim WDin
*– 'Golden Minaret'	EHul
– 'Hetz Midget'	CKen EHul EPla ESis LCon LLin MBar MGos NHol SLim SPer SPla
– 'Holmstrup' AGM	CDoC CMac CNic EBre EHul ENHC ENot GWht IOrc LBre LCon MAsh MBal MBar MBri MWat NBee NHol SLim SPla SReu SSmi SSta WAbe WStI
– 'Holmstrup's Yellow'	CDoC CKen EHul LCon MAsh MBri MPla NHol SPla SSmi WWeb
– 'Hoveyi'	EHul ENHC
– 'Little Champion'	EHul GRei NHol WTyr
– 'Little Gem'	EBee EHul ENHC IDai MGos NHol WDin WGor
– 'Lutea Nana' AGM	CMac EHul ENHC LCon MBal MBar SLim
– 'Marrisen's Sulphur'	EHul LBee LCon SLim
– 'Meineckes Zwerg'	CKen EPla MAsh
¶ – 'Miky'	CKen
– 'Milleri'	EPot
– 'Ohlendorffii'	CDoC CKen EHul EPla EPot GWht LCon LLin MBar MWat SSmi
– 'Orientalis Semperaurescens'	See T. ***orientalis*** 'Semperaurea'
– 'Perk Vlaanderen' (v)	MAsh
I – 'Pumila Sudworth'	NHol
– 'Pygmaea'	CKen MBar
– 'Pyramidalis Compacta'	EHul LNet WGor
– 'Recurva Nana'	CMHG EHar EHul LLin MBal MBar NBee NHol SLon
– 'Rheingold' AGM	Widely available
– 'Silver Beauty' (v)	CMHG
§ – 'Smaragd' AGM	CSco EBre EHul ENHC ENot EPla IOrc LBre LBuc LCon LNet MAsh MBar MGos MPla NBee NEgg SBod SPer WStI
*– 'Smaragd Variegated'	EPla
– 'Southport'	CKen EBre LBre LCon MBri
– 'Sphaerica'	MPla
– 'Spiralis'	CMHG EBee EHar MBar
§ – 'Stolwijk'	EHul MBar MGos SLim
– 'Sunkist'	CDoC CKen CMHG CMac EBre EHar EHul ENHC ENot GRei IHos IJoh IOrc LBee LBre LCon LLin LNet MBar MBri MGos MPla MWat NBee NHol NRoo SBod SLim SPer SPla
– 'Suzie'	LLin
– 'Tiny Tim'	CDoC CMac EHul EPot ESis LCon LLin MBar MGos SIng SSta
– 'Trompenburg'	EHul MBri
– 'Wansdyke Silver' (v)	CMac EHar EHul EPla MBar MPla SLim
– 'Wareana'	CDoC CMac
– 'Wareana Aurea'	See T. *o.* 'Wareana Lutescens'
§ – 'Wareana Lutescens'	CMHG CMac EBee EHul ENHC EPla GRei LCon MBal MBar MGos MPla SHil SLim SLon SPer WGor
– 'Woodwardii'	EHul MBar NBee WDin WGor WTyr
– 'Yellow Ribbon'	COtt EBre EHul EPla IJoh LBre NHol SLim SPla SSta
orientalis	NWea
§ – 'Aurea Nana' AGM	Widely available
– 'Beverleyensis'	LLin MBri
– 'Blue Cone'	MBar
– 'Carribean Holiday'	EBre LBre LCon MAsh MBri
– 'Collen's Gold'	EHul LBee MBar NHol SPla
– 'Conspicua'	CKen EHar EHul ENHC LBee LCon MBar MWat SBod
– 'Copper Kettle'	EHul MPla
– 'Elegantissima' AGM	CMHG CMac EHul LBee MBar MBri MGos SBod SGil SHil WStI
– 'Filiformis Erecta'	LCon
– 'Flame'	MGos
*– 'Golden Ball'	MBri
– 'Golden Minaret'	MBri
– 'Golden Pygmy'	CKen MAsh
– 'Golden Wonder'	ENHC
– 'Juniperoides'	EHul EPla IDai LLin MBar
– 'Madurodam'	MAsh
– 'Magnifica'	EHul
– 'Meldensis'	CDoC CLew CMHG EHul ENHC EPla GPen LCon LLin MBal MBar WDin
– 'Miller's Gold'	See T. *o.* 'Aurea Nana'
– 'Minima'	CDoC ESis LCon MAsh MWat
– 'Minima Glauca'	CKen CSco MBar

– 'Purple King'	EPla NHol SLim
I – 'Pyramidalis Aurea'	LPan MBri
– 'Rosedalis'	CKen CMac CNic EBre EHul ENHC EPla IDai LBee LBre LCon LLin MAsh MBal MBar MBri MPla MRPP MWat SBod SLim WThu
– 'Sanderi'	CKen EPla LBee LCon MAsh MBar MBri
§ – 'Semperaurea'	CMac WGor
– 'Sieboldii'	EHul LCon
– 'Southport'	LLin MAsh NHol
¶ – 'Spaethii'	EPla
– 'Summer Cream'	EHul MBar MGos
– 'Westmont'	EPla
plicata	CPer EHar EHul GRei GWht IDai IOrc MBal MBar MGos NEgg NWea SBod SPer WFro WMou WStI WWin
– 'Atrovirens' **AGM**	EBre EHar ENot LBee LBre LBuc LCon LPan MAsh MBri WMou WWeb
– 'Aurea' **AGM**	EHul EPla MAsh SHil SRms WMou WTyr
I – 'Cole's Variety'	CSco MBar
– 'Collyer's Gold'	EHul LCon MBri SPla SRms WTyr
– 'Copper Kettle'	CKen LCon MBar MBri NHol SLim
– 'Cuprea'	CKen CNic EHul LLin MBar
– 'Doone Valley'	CKen CMHG EHul EPla MBar NHol SLim WThu
– 'Dura'	CDoC
– 'Fastigiata' **AGM**	CMac EHar
– 'Gracilis Aurea'	EHul LCon MPla
– 'Hillieri'	EHul EPla MBar NHol
– 'Irish Gold' **AGM**	CMac EPla SHil
– 'Rogersii'	CDoC CKen CMHG CMac EBar EBre EHul EPla EPot ESis GWht IJoh IOrc LBre LCon LLin MAsh MBar MGos MPla NHol SBod SHer SLim SLon SPer SSmi WAbe WThu
– 'Semperaurescens'	EHar LCon WMou
♦– 'Stolwijk's Gold'	See T. ***occidentalis*** 'Stolwijk'
– 'Stoneham Gold' **AGM**	CDoC CMHG CMac CSco EBre EHar EHul ENHC EPla IOrc LBee LBre LCon LLin MAsh MBar MBri MPla SBod SLim SLon SPer SSmi WTyr
*– 'Windsor Gold'	EHar
– 'Winter Pink' (v)	CKen
– 'Zebrina' (v)	CB&S CBra CDoC CMHG CMac CSco EHar EHul ENot IDai LBee LCon MAsh MBal MBar MGos MPla MWat NBee NEgg NWea SBod SGil SLim SLon SPer WWin

THUJOPSIS (Cupressaceae)

dolabrata **AGM**	CB&S CGre CMer CWit EHar EHul ELan ENot GWht IBar IDai IOrc MBar NHed NWea SHBN SHil SMad SPer WBod WWat
– 'Aurea' (v)	CDoC CKen EBre EHar EHul LBre LCon MBar MGos SHBN SLim
♦– 'Laetevirens'	See T. ***d.*** 'Nana'
§ – 'Nana'	CDoC CKen CMac EHar EPot ESis LCon LLin MBar MBri MPla MRPP SGil SLim SLon STre WThu
– 'Variegata'	CDoC CMac CWit EHar EHul ESis IBar LCon LLin MBal MBar NHol SLim WDin WThu WTyr
koraiensis	See THUJA ***k.***

THUNBERGIA (Acanthaceae)

alata	MBri
erecta	CB&S CNew
– 'Alba'	CNew
grandiflora **AGM**	CNew CTro LAbb SLMG
– 'Alba'	CNew CTro SLMG
¶ ***mysorensis***	CNew

THYMUS † (Labiatae/Lamiaceae)

* 'Albus'	CArn GPoy LHol MChe MPla NNor WWin
'Anderson's Gold'	See T. x ***citriodorus*** 'Bertram Anderson'
* 'Aureus'	CKni CSev GPoy WOak WSun
azoricus	See T. ***caespititius***
§ ***caespititius***	CArn CShe EMon EPot GAbr GDra GGar IDai ILis LHol MBar MBro MCas MHig MSte NCat NHol NMen NNrd SSmi WCHb WPer
– 'Aureus'	ECha EFol GAbr LHol SIde
camphoratus	CMea EWes LHop NTow SIde
carnosus	NHol SFis SSmi WDav WHil WSun
¶ ***ciliatus***	WPer
cilicicus	ESis GCHN GPoy IEde MChe NRoo SBla SHer SIng WCHb WPer WTyr WWye
x ***citriodorus***	CArn CBow CDoC CSFH EHer GAbr GCHN GPoy MChe NHol NOak WAbe WHen WOMN WOak WPer WSun WWye
– 'Archer's Gold'	CBow CNic EBre EHoe ELan EPot GAbr LBre LGro LHop MBri MCas MPit MRPP NKay NRoo NSti SHer SSmi WCHb WHil WPer WTyr
– 'Argenteus'	CKni LLWP MBro NHol
– 'Aureus' **AGM**	CSFH CSco CShe CTom EBre EMNN ESis GDra GTou IEde LBre MBal MBar MBri MBro MCas MFos NHol NKay NMen NNrd NRoo NWCA SBla SSvw WHen WHoo
§ – 'Bertram Anderson' **AGM**	CMer CShe EBre ECha EFol EMNN EPot GCHN LBre LHol MBro MHig NGre NHol NKay NMen NNrd NRed NRoo SBla SSmi WAbe WDav WEas WHil WHoo WThu WWin WWye
¶ – 'Carol Ann'	EWes
– 'Fragrantissimus'	CSFH ESis GAbr GPoy IEde LHol LLWP MChe MWil NPri NRoo SIde WPer WWye
– 'Golden King' (v)	EBre ECha ELan EPar LBee LBre MBar MBri MChe NGre NSti SHer WAbe WCHb WDav WHil WHoo WPer WStI
– 'Golden Lemon'	CArn GPoy MChe WSun WWye
– 'Golden Queen' (v)	CLTr CMea CMer EBee EMNN EPot GBar NKay NPri NRoo WWin
– 'Nyewoods'	CSFH GAbr SIde
x ***citriodorus repanda***	SIde

x *citriodorus* 'Silver Posie'	See T. ***vulgaris*** 'Silver Posie'
– 'Silver Queen' AGM	CB&S CBow CLew CRiv CShe ECha ELan EPar GDra GPoy IDai MBal MBar MCas MChe MHig NGre NHol NKay NNrd NRoo SSmi WCla WHoo WStI WWye
§ – 'Variegatus'	CRiv CSFH EOrc ESis LGro LHol MBri MBro MChe MPla NGre NHol NKay NMen WEas WWin
comosus	CNic ESis LHol MChe NHol NTow SIde WAbe WEas WHoo WPat WPer
* ***compactus albus***	CTom EWes GPlt LLWP MBro MPla NMen SIde
'Desboro'	GAbr NHol NNrd
doerfleri	CLew CShe ECha GAbr LHol NKay NMen NNrd SSmi WPer WWye
– 'Bressingham Pink'	CMea CTom EBre ECtt EMNN GAbr LBre LGro LHol MBro MChe MHig MPla NGre NHol NKay NMen NNrd NRoo SBla SSmi WHil WHoo WPat WPer WSun WWye
'Doone Valley' (v)	Widely available
drucei	See T. ***praecox arcticus***
– ***albus***	See T. ***praecox arcticus albus***
– ***minus***	See T. ***praecox arcticus minus***
'E B Anderson'	See T. x ***citriodorus*** 'Bertram Anderson'
* ***epiroticus***	CLew
erectus	See T. ***vulgaris*** 'Erectus'
* ***ericoïdes*** 'Aureus'	EHal EPot
herba-barona	CArn CHad CNic CSFH ECha ESis GAbr GBar GDra GPoy IEde LHol LLWP MBal MCas NHol NNor NRoo NVic SHer SIde SIng SSmi WOak WPer WWye
§ – 'Lemon-scented'	GPoy
'Highland Cream'	CLTr EFol EPot ESis EWes GAri GBar GDra LRHS MChe NRoo SAsh WPat WWin WWye
* ***hirsutus minus***	CNic
hyemalis	GPoy SIde
insertus	MFos
¶ ***integer***	SBla
lanuginosus hort.	See T. ***pseudolanuginosus***
♦ 'Lemon Caraway'	See T. ***herba-barona*** 'Lemon-scented'
leucotrichus	GAbr ILis LHol MHig SSmi WOMN WPat WSun WWye
longicaulis	CArn EBar ECha LGan LHol WWye
marschallianus	See T. ***pannonicus***
mastichina	CArn CDoC EBee ESis LHol LHop MChe SBla SChu SFar WPer WWye
membranaceus	MHig MSto
micans	See T. ***caespititius***
montanus Waldstein & Kitaibel	See T. ***pulegioïdes***
neicefferi	CArn CSev ECha GAbr LHol MHig NTow SIde WPer
odoratissimus	See T. ***pallasianus pallasianus***
'Onyx'	EPot NMen NSti
§ ***pallasianus*** ssp. ***pallasianus***	GCal SIde WOak WSun
pannonicus	LHol WPer
'Pincushion'	NHol SIng
praecox	ECWi GAbr LHol NHol NMir
§ – ssp. ***arcticus***	CKin EEls EPot EWFC GAbr GPoy GTou IEde MFos MHew NLan NSti WPer WTyr WWye
§ – – ***albus*** AGM	ELan LBee NCat SGil
– – ***minus***	WPer
– – silver	WPer
– 'Porlock'	CDoC CTom EBar ESis GPoy LHol LLWP MCas MChe NHol NKay SHer SPla SSvw WDav WHoo WPer
§ ***pseudolanuginosus***	CArn CLew CMea CSFH EBar ECha Effi GTou LBuc LGro LHol MBar MBri MBro MCas MRPP NGre NHol SSmi WAbe WCla WDav WHoo WOak WPer
§ ***pulegioïdes***	CArn CSFH CSev GBar GPoy LHol MBri MHew NPri SHer WOak WPer WWye
richardii ssp. ***nitidus***	CShe IDai LHol NKay WWye
– – ***albus***	LLWP SSmi WPer
– – 'Peter Davis'	CArn CMea CShe EBar ESis LHop MCas MPla NHol NKay NMen NTow SBla SChu SHer WDav
rotundifolius	LLWP SIde
serpyllum	CRiv CSFH EHer ELan Effi GAbr GCHN IEde LAbb LBuc MBri MChe MPla NOak WHil WPer WWye
– ***albus***	CLew CRiv CSFH CShe ECha EMNN EPar ESis GDra GTou MBal MBro MCas NKay NNrd NRed NVic SBla SChu SGil SIng WEas WHil WHoo WOak WThu WWye
– 'Annie Hall'	CDoC CRiv CTom EBre EMNN EPot ESis GAbr LBee LBre LGro LHol MBro MChe MRPP NHol NMen NNor NRoo SBod SHer SIng SSmi WAbe WPer WWye
– ***coccineus*** AGM	Widely available
– – 'Major'	Effi GDra SIde
– – 'Minor'	GAri MChe NRoo
– 'Dartmoor'	GCal
– 'East Lodge'	NHol
– 'Elfin'	EPar EPot GAbr GTou LBee LHol MBri MBro MRPP NGre NMen NNrd NWCA SGil SHer WCla WDav WEas WHil WHoo WThu
– 'Flossy'	NNrd
– 'Goldstream'	CDoC CLew EMNN GAbr LBuc MBar MBri MChe MFir NHol NNrd NRoo NSti WCHb WHal WPer WWye
¶ – 'Hartington Silver'	SIng
– ssp. ***lanuginosus***	See T. ***pseudolanuginosus***
¶ – 'Lavender Sea'	EWes
– 'Lemon Curd'	CDoC GAbr LLWP MChe NSti SHer SIde WCHb WWye
– 'Minimus'	CArn CDoC CLew CMGP CRiv CSFH ECha ESis ESma GAbr LHol MBri MChe MSto NSti NTow SIde WPer WTyr WWye
§ – 'Minor'	CArn CLew ELan EMNN EPot ESis GDra LHol MBro MCas MChe MHig NHol NKay NMen NNrd SIng SSmi WCla WDav WHoo WWin
– 'Minus'	See T. ***s.*** 'Minor'

¶ – ***minus*** 'Petite'	EWes
– 'Pink Chintz' **AGM**	CShe ECha EMNN ESis GAbr GDra GTou LBuc LGro LHol MBar MBri MChe MHig MPit NHol NNrd NRed NRoo SBla SIng SSmi WAbe WHoo WOak WPer WWin WWye
– 'Rainbow Falls' (v)	GAbr GBar MChe NCat NRed NRoo SHer
– 'Ruby Glow'	EWes NHol NRoo
– 'Russetings'	CDoC CLew CTom EMNN EOrc EPot LHol MBar MCas MChe MPit NKay NMen NNrd NRoo SIng WOak WWin WWye
– 'September'	SGil
– 'Snowdrift'	CMea GBar LHol MBar MChe NHol NSti SIde SSmi WAbe WPat WPer
– 'Variegatus'	CMea NHol NTow SGil SIde WHil
– 'Vey'	EFol EGle EMon EOrc ESis GBar MChe NHol SHer SIng
N 'Silver Posie'	See T. ***vulgaris*** 'Silver Posie'
sp. from Turkey	EWes NHol
vulgaris	CChe CMea CSFH CSev ECha EHer GPoy IEde LAbb LLWP MBri MChe MHew NRoo SDix WEas WPer
– ***albus***	SIde WSun
– ***aureus***	LGro MChe NRoo SHer
§ – 'Erectus'	CArn ELan EMon GBar LHol MCas NTow SIde SRms WHer WPer WWye
– 'Lucy'	SIde
¶ – 'Silver Pearl'	EWes
– 'Silver Posie'	CArn CHad CSev EBre EFou EHoe ELan EPot LBre LHol NGre NRoo NSti SBla SChu SDix SSvw WDav WEas WHoo WOak WPer WWye
'Widecombe'	CNic
zygis	CArn LHol WCHb WWye

THYSANOTUS (Liliaceae/Anthericaceae)

patersonii	CMon
tuberosus	CMon

TIARELLA (Saxifragaceae)

collina	See T. ***wherryi***
cordifolia **AGM**	Widely available
¶ 'Glossy'	SWas
polyphylla	CRDP ECro EGol ELan EPar GAbr MNFA MRav NHol NNor NSti SWas WCla WCra WCru
– 'Moorgrün'	GCal
– pink	CBos CGle SWas
'Slick Rock'	CElw SWas
trifoliata	EBee ECro ELan EMon LGan SBla SUsu SWas
– 'Incarnadine'	ECha EMon
unifoliata	MSal NCat
§ ***wherryi*** **AGM**	Widely available
– 'Bronze Beauty'	CBos CMil ECha GBuc SUsu SWas
¶ – 'Pink Foam'	ECha

TIBOUCHINA (Melastomataceae)

* 'Edwardsii'	CBar CNew
¶ ***graveolens***	ERea
organensis	CB&S CPle ERea LBlm
paratropica	CPle CTro
semidecandra	See T. ***urvilleana***
§ ***urvilleana*** **AGM**	CAbb CB&S CCla CDoC CGre CHEx CNew CPle CSPN CSpe CTre CTro CWit EBak ELan ERea IMal IOrc IReg ISea LAbb LHil SArc SHil SLMG SLon SMad
– 'Grandiflora'	ERea IBlr

TIGRIDIA (Iridaceae)

douglasii	WDav
durangense	WDav
– dwarf form	WDav
hybrids	CSut SDeJ
lutea	SDeJ
pavonia	CGre LAma LBow MBri NRog

TILIA † (Tiliaceae)

americana	CLnd CMCN ENot WMou
– 'Dentata'	WMou
– 'Nova'	CDoC CTho WMou
– 'Redmond'	CTho WMou
amurensis	CMCN WMou
begoniifolia	See T. ***dasystyla***
caucasica	WMou
¶ – 'Select'	WMou
¶ – 'Winter Red'	WMou
'Chelsea Sentinel'	SHil
chinensis	WMou
chingiana	WHCr WMou
cordata **AGM**	CKin CLnd CPer EHar ELan ENot GBel GRei IOrc LBuc MBal MBri NBee NWea SHBN SPer WDin WMou WStI WWye
– 'Erecta'	COtt WMou
– 'Greenspire' **AGM**	CDoC CTho ENot GBel IOrc LPan MBri SPer WMou
– 'Len Parvin'	WMou
¶ – 'Lico'	WMou
– 'Morden'	WMou
– 'Plymtree Gold'	CTho
– 'Rancho'	WMou
– 'Roelvo'	WMou
¶ – 'Swedish Upright'	WMou
– 'Umbrella'	WMou
– 'Westonbirt Dainty Leaf'	WMou
– 'Winter Orange'	WMou
dasystyla	WMou
–	WMou
x ***euchlora*** **AGM**	CDoC CLnd EHar ENot GBel IDai LPan MBri MGos MWat SPer WDin WMou WStI
x ***europaea***	CLnd ELan WMou
– 'Pallida'	EHar GBel WMou
– 'Pendula'	WMou
– 'Wratislaviensis' **AGM**	CDoC CTho SHil SMad WMou
– 'Zwarte Linde'	WMou
x ***flavescens*** 'Glenleven'	WMou
'Harold Hillier'	SHil
henryana	CLnd CMCN SHil WMou
– var. ***subglabra***	WMou
heterophylla	WMou
– var. ***michauxii***	WHCr WMou
insularis	CMCN WMou
intonsa	WMou
japonica	WHCr WMou

kiusiana	CMCN GAri WMou
ledebourii	WMou
maximowicziana	SSta WHCr WMou
¶ ***miqueliana***	WMou
'Moltkei'	WMou
mongolica AGM	CLnd CMCN EHar ENot GAri LBuc WMou
monticola	See T. ***heterophylla***
neglecta	WMou
oliveri	CMCN EHar SHil WMou
'Orbicularis'	WMou
paucicostata	WMou
'Petiolaris' AGM	CDoC CLnd CTho EHar ELan ENot IOrc SHBN SMad SPer SSta WDin WMou
platyphyllos	CBra CDoC CKin ENot GBel GRei IJoh LBuc MBri SPer WDin WMou
– 'Aurea'	SHil WMou
– 'Corallina'	See T. ***p.*** 'Rubra'
¶ – 'Delft'	WMou
– ***erecta***	See T. ***p.*** 'Fastigiata'
§ – 'Fastigiata'	CTho ENot WMou
¶ – 'Grandiflora'	WMou
– 'Laciniata'	CTho SMad WMou
– 'Orebro'	WMou
– 'Pannonia'	WMou
– 'Prince's Street'	SHil WMou
§ – 'Rubra' AGM	CDoC CLnd CTho ENot IDai IOrc MBri MGos NBee SPer WDin WMou
– 'Tortuosa'	WMou
– 'Vitifolia'	WMou
tarquetii	WMou
tomentosa	CLnd CTho EHar ENot WDin WMou
– 'Brabant' AGM	CDoC EHar ENot IOrc SPer WMou
– 'Erecta'	WMou
– 'Silver Globe'	WMou
¶ – 'Szeleste'	WMou
– 'Van Koolwijk'	WMou
tuan	WMou

TILLAEA See CRASSULA

TILLANDSIA † (Bromeliaceae)

abdita	MBri NTRF
acostae	MBri
argentea	MBri NTRF
baileyi	MBri NTRF
balbisiana	MBri NTRF
benthamiana	See T. ***erubescens***
brachycaulos	MBri
– var. ***multiflora***	MBri NTRF
bulbosa	MBri NTRF
butzii	MBri NTRF
caput-medusae	MBri NTRF
circinnatoïdes	MBri
cyanea	MBri
x ***erographica***	MBri
* ***fasciculata*** 'Tricolor' (v)	MBri
filifolia	MBri NTRF
flabellata	MBri
¶ ***gardneri***	NTRF
ionantha	MBri
¶ – var. ***ionantha***	NTRF
– ***scaposa***	See T. ***kolbii***
juncea	MBri NTRF
§ ***kolbii***	MBri NTRF
magnusiana	MBri NTRF
§ ***matudae***	MBri
oaxacana	MBri NTRF
polystachia	MBri
pruinosa	NTRF
punctulata	MBri NTRF
seleriana	MBri NTRF
sphaerocephala	MBri
tenuifolia var. ***surinamensis***	See T. ***t. tenuifolia***
tricolor var. ***melanocrater***	MBri NTRF
usneoïdes	NTRF
valenzuelana	See T. ***variabilis***
velickiana	See T. ***matudae***
vicentina	MBri
wagneriana	MBri
xerographica	MBri

TINANTIA (Commelinaceae)

¶ ***undulata***	EBee

TIPUANA (Leguminosae/Papilionaceae)

tipu	CPle

TITHONIA (Compositae/Asteraceae)

rotundifolia 'Torch'	SMrm

TOFIELDIA (Liliaceae/Melanthiaceae)

calyculata	MSto NHol
¶ ***glutinosa*** var. ***brevistyla***	MSto
¶ ***pusilla***	GArf MSto

TOLMIEA (Saxifragaceae)

'Goldsplash'	See T. ***menziesii*** 'Taff's Gold'
menziesii AGM	CGle CHEx CWGN EBar ECha GAri LGro MBri NHol NOrc SHer WByw WCru WFox
– JLS 86284CLOR	EMon
– 'Maculata'	See T. ***m.*** 'Taff's Gold'
§ – 'Taff's Gold' AGM	CCla CElw CGle CMHG CMea CRow CWGN ECha EFol EGol EHoe ELan EPar GCal LHop MBri NHol NMir NNor NRoo NSti SFis WByw WEas
– 'Variegata'	See T. ***m.*** 'Taff's Gold'

TOLPIS (Compositae/Asteraceae)

barbata	MSal

TONESTUS (Compositae/Asteraceae)

§ ***lyallii***	CNic NSla SBod WHil WPer WWin

TOONA (Meliaceae)

sinensis	CChu CGre CMCN CPle EHar EMil ISea MBri WCoo
– 'Flamingo' (v)	CB&S COtt CPMA EFol EHar EMil SMad

TORREYA (Taxaceae)
nucifera LRHS

TORTULA (moss)
ruralis ruraliformis LFle

TOVARA See **PERSICARIA**

TOWNSENDIA (Compositae/Asteraceae)
'Boulder' WEas
¶ *condensata* MFos
exscapa WDav
florifera MFos NWCA WHil
formosa CNic CRiv ELan NMen NNrd NTow SHer SIng WHil WOMN WPer
grandiflora GTou
hookeri MFos NWCA WHil
¶ – K 92.444 WDav
incana WDav
**jonesii tumulosa* CNic NTow
leptotes NWCA WDav
montana NTow
parryi CNic EPad NTow
§ *rothrockii* CNic LGan NGre NHol NMen
spathulata MFos WHil
¶ sp. K 92.512 WDav
wilcoxiana hort. See T. ***rothrockii***

TRACHELIUM (Campanulaceae)
§ *asperuloïdes* CPBP NSla
caeruleum **AGM** CAbb ERea MHlr WCot
jacquinii
ssp. *rumelianum* EPad NTow NWCA WPat WPer

TRACHELOSPERMUM (Apocynaceae)
§ *asiaticum* **AGM** Widely available
– 'Goshiki' CB&S EPla MGos
jasminoïdes **AGM** CB&S CCla CHEx CMCN CMac CNew CPle CSam CTro EMil ERea IHos IOrc LHop LPan MBri MRav SArc SBla SBra SDry SPer SReu SSta WBod WWat
– W 776 CBot CHan CMac EBre EPla ERav IOrc LBre NRar SPer SSta WSHC
§ – 'Japonicum' GCal NSti
– 'Major' CNew
– 'Tricolor' (v) ERav
– 'Variegatum' **AGM** Widely available
– 'Wilsonii' CNew EHic ELan EMil MSta MUlv NRar SArc SReu
majus hort. See T. ***jasminoïdes*** 'Japonicum'
majus Nakai See T. ***asiaticum***
sp. from Nanking CHan EPla

TRACHYCARPUS (Palmae/Arecaceae)
§ *fortunei* **AGM** Widely available
wagnerianus LPal NPal SArc SDry

TRACHYMENE (Umbelliferae/Apiaceae)
See Plant Deletions

TRACHYSTEMON (Boraginaceae)
orientalis CGle CHEx CRDP EBre ECha EFol EFou EGol ELan EPar EPla ERav LBre MFir MUlv SAxl SIng WCru WHal WWat WWin

TRADESCANTIA (Commelinaceae)
albiflora See T. ***fluminensis***
§ x *andersoniana* CRiv EFol MBro MFir MSal NNor SHer SUsu WEas WHil WPer WRus WWin
– 'Bilberry Ice' EFou NTow SFis
– 'Blaby Blue' MUlv
– 'Blue Stone' CNic CSco ECha EPla MNFA NFai SRms WThi
– 'Caerulea Plena' See T. ***virginiana*** 'C.P.'
– 'Croftway Blue' SCro
– 'Innocence' CCla CElw CHad CMil CSco CSpe EBre ECha ECtt EFou EOrc EPla LBre LHop LWad MBel MBri MTho MUlv NFai NOrc SAxl SHer SPer SSte WHoo WMer WRus
– 'Iris Prichard' CBow CHan CMGP CSco EBee ELan EPar EPla MHFP SChu SCro
– 'Isis' **AGM** CB&S CBow CCla CHol CMil CSco ECED ECtt EFou ELan EPar EPla GCHN LHop MBri MUlv NFai NHol NOrc NRoo SAxl SChu SFis SHer SLMG SPer SUsu WAbe WTyr WWin
– 'J C Weguelin' **AGM** CCla CSco EBee MBri NFai SRms WHoo
– 'Karminglut' ('Carmine Glow') CB&S CHol ELan EOrc EPar EPla GCHN NOrc NRoo NVic SHer WHoo WPbr WRus
– 'Leonora' CDoC CSco EBee ENot MBri NBar NFai WThi
¶ – 'Maiden's Blush' CSpe
– 'Osprey' **AGM** Widely available
– 'Pauline' CSco EBre ECtt EFol EFou EPla GCHN LBre MBel MRav MUlv NBir NFai NHol NRoo SChu WHoo WWin
– 'Purewell Giant' CBow CKel EBre ECot EPla LBre NBar NCat NHol SChu SPer WGor WHoo WKif
– 'Purple Dome' CBow CHan CKel CMGP CNic CRDP CSco CTom EBre ECED EPla GCHN LBre MBri MRav NBir NHol NMir SChu SPla WHoo WPbr WRus WTyr
– 'Rubra' CDoC CNic MBel NDea NFai NOrc SChu SCro SFis
– 'Valour' WHil WTyr
– 'Zwanenburg Blue' CMGP CSpe EBre ECha EFou EOrc EPla GCHN LBre MBri MUlv NBar NHol WMer WRus
bracteata NTow
– *alba* WThi
brevicaulis CMon CSco ECha ECro EPla GDra MNFA MTho NOrc SAxl SLMG
canaliculata See T. ***ohiensis***
fluminensis 'Albovittata' SLMG
– 'Aurea' **AGM** MBri
– 'Laekenensis' (v) MBri

– 'Quicksilver' AGM	MBri
multiflora	See TRIPOGANDRA ***m.***
navicularis	See CALLISIA ***n.***
§ ***ohiensis***	EBee LMay SAxl
§ ***pallida***	IBlr
pendula	See TRADESCANTIA ***zebrina***
sillamontana AGM	MBri
virginiana	See also T. x ***andersoniana***
– 'Alba'	CRiv GCal WHil WPer WThi
§ – 'Caerulea Plena'	CMGP ECED EFou ELan EPla LHop MNFA NBee NKay SChu SUsu WRus WThi
– 'Rubra'	CHan CSco WThi
§ ***zebrina*** AGM	SLMG
– ***pendula***	See T. ***z.***

TRAGOPOGON (Compositae/Asteraceae)

porrifolius	GPoy ILis
pratensis	CArn CKin ECWi EWFC MWil NMir
roseus	See T. ***ruber***

TRAPA (Trapaceae)

natans	CHEx CWGN MSta

TREVESIA (Araliaceae)

See Plant Deletions

TRICHOCOLEA (liverwort)

tomentella	LFle

TRICHOPHORUM (Cyperaceae)

cespitosum	ETPC

TRICUSPIDARIA See CRINODENDRON

TRICYRTIS (Liliaceae/Convallariaceae)

'Adbane'	CBro CRDP MBri MUlv WCru WPbr
affinis	WCot
¶ – 'Variegata'	SAxl
bakeri	See T. ***latifolia***
flava	WThi
formosana AGM	CAvo CDoC CGle CHan CRDP CWGN EBre ECha ECro ECtt EGol ELan ELun GCra LBre MBri MTho MUlv NRoo SAxl SBla SCro WCru WEas WMer WPbr WPer WThi WThu WWye
¶ – forms	WPer
§ – Stolonifera Group	CAvo CB&S CBro CChu CCla CHan CLew CRDP CShe ECha EFou EGol ELan ELun EPar LHop MBal MRav MUlv NDea NFai SAxl SCro SPer WPbr WRus WThi WWat WWin
hirta	CB&S CBro CCla CHan CRDP CRiv CSam EBre ECro ECtt EFou EPar GPlt LBre MBri MBro MRav MTho MUlv NBro NFai NHol SCro SIng SPer WCru WHil WHoo WRus WWat
§ – ***alba***	CBro CCla CHan CRDP CRiv CWGN ECro ELan EPot GPlt MBal MBel MBro WCru WHoo WPbr WThi WWat WWin
¶ – 'Makinoi Gold'	ELan
– 'Miyazaki'	CChu CHan CRDP EBee EFou EGle GBuc MUlv SCro SUsu WCru WPbr WThi WWat
– 'Variegata'	CAvo CRDP ECha EFol EGol LGre WCot WCru WHal WPbr
¶ – 'White Flame' (v)	WCot
N Hototogisu	CRDP EBee EGle EMon MTho WCot WCru WPbr
japonica	See T. ***hirta***
§ ***latifolia***	CAvo CBro CChu CGle CRDP EBul ECro ELun EPar EPot GCra LGre MBro MNFA NFai NGar NHol NNrw SAxl SWas WCot WCru WHil WHoo WPer WThi WWat
'Lilac Towers'	EPar
macrantha	MBal SHig SIng WCru
– ssp. ***macranthopsis***	ECha SBla SWas WCot WCru
* ***macrocarpa***	NFai NKay
N ***macropoda***	CChu CCla CGle CHan CHol CMGP CSam ECha ECro ELan EPar GGar NHol WCot WCru WHal WThi
ohsumiensis	CGle CHan CRDP ECha EPar EPot LGre MTho NGar WCot WCru WPbr WThi
perfoliata	LGre SWas WCot WThi
'Shimone'	CBro CRDP LRHS MBri MUlv WPbr
stolonifera	See T. ***formosana*** Stolonifera Group
'Tojen'	CAvo CBro CRDP ECha LRHS MBri MMil WPbr
'White Towers'	CChu CHol CRDP CSpe ECha EMon EPar GCra LGre MNFA NSti SAxl SWas WCru WPbr WThi

TRIENTALIS (Primulaceae)

borealis	CNic
europaea rosea	CNat

TRIFOLIUM (Leguminosae/Papilionaceae)

alpinum	GDra SIng
¶ ***arvense***	ECWi
campestre	CKin
incarnatum	SIde WHer
¶ ***medium***	ECWi
ochroleucum	EWFC MWil NMir
pannonicum	GCal MSte
¶ ***pratense***	ECWi EWFC MWil
♦ – 'Chocolate'	See T. ***p.*** 'Purple Velvet'
– 'Dolly North'	See T. ***p.*** 'Susan Smith'
♦ – 'Ice Cool'	See T. ***p.*** 'Green Ice'
§ – 'Susan Smith' (v)	CElw CGle CHan CMGP CMil CRDP CRow EBre ECha EFol EHal EMar EMon EPla IBlr LBre LHop MBel MTho SFar SUsu WByw WHer
repens	CHEx EWFC NGre
– 'Aureum'	MBal
– 'Gold Net'	See T. ***pratense*** 'Susan Smith'
– 'Good Luck'	CRow
– 'Pentaphyllum'	See T. ***r.*** 'Quinquefolium'

– 'Purpurascens'	CArn CBre CDec CHEx CMer CRiv CRow EFol GCal GDra GMac ILis MBal MCas NRoo NWyt SAxl SDix SUsu WHen WOak
§ – 'Purpurascens Quadrifolium'	CDec CLew CNic ECha ELan EMar EMon EPla LHop MBel NMir SHer SIng SPer WRus WWin
– 'Quadrifolium'	EHoe EPar
§ – 'Quinquefolium'	WPer
– 'Tetraphyllum Purpureum'	See T. *r.* 'Purpurascens Quadrifolium'
– 'Wheatfen' (v)	CNat ECha EMon EPla
¶ ***rubens***	MSte WRus
stellatum	EBee WThi
uniflorum	WThu

TRIGONELLA (Leguminosae/Papilionaceae)

foenum-graecum	CArn EJud GPoy MSal SIde

TRIGONOTIS (Boraginaceae)

¶ ***rotundifolia***	GArf

TRILLIUM † (Liliaceae/Trilliaceae)

¶ ***albidum***	CBro
apetalon	WChr
catesbyi	CBro EPot LAma MSal NRog WChr
cernuum	CBro CWGN EPot LAma NHol NRog WChr
chloropetalum AGM	CBro CChu GCra GDra NHol WDav
– ***rubrum***	SWas
¶ – white	CAvo
cuneatum	CB&S CBro CChu CWGN ELan EOrc EPar EPot LAma MNFA MTho NHol NRog NRoo SDeJ SIng SPer SUsu WChr WCru
– red	CRDP
erectum AGM	CArn CAvo CB&S CBro CChu CCla COtt CRDP CWGN ELan EOrc EPar EPot GDra GPoy LAma LBow MBal MSal MTho NHol NRog SAxl SDeJ SIng SPer WChr
§ – f. ***albiflorum***	CBro EPot LAma MSal NHol WChr WCru
– f. ***luteum***	LAma NHol WChr
grandiflorum AGM	CAvo CB&S CBro CChu CCla CGle CHEx CRDP CWGN EBre ELan EPar EPot GDra LAma LBow LBre NHar NHol NKay NRog SAxl SDeJ SIng SPer SUsu WAbe WChr WHil
– ***flore-pleno*** AGM	EBre LBre SPou SWas WThu
kamtschaticum	CAvo LAma WChr
§ ***luteum*** AGM	CB&S CBro CChu CWGN ELan EOrc EPar EPot LAma LBow NHar NHol NKay NRog NRoo SDeJ SIng SPer SUsu WChr WCru WHil
ovatum	EPot GDra LAma
– var. ***hibbersonii***	CAvo CBro GArf GDra MBal NHar NHol NTow WChr
pusillum var. ***virginianum***	CBro LAma
recurvatum	CB&S CWGN EOrc EPar EPot LAma NHol NRog NRoo SIng SPer WChr WHil
rivale AGM	CBro LAma SBla SWas WChr WOMN WThu
rugelii	LAma NHol WChr
sessile	CCla CDoC CHEx CRDP EBre ELan EPot LAma LBow LBre NBir NHol NKay SPer SUsu WChr
– var. ***luteum***	See T. ***luteum***
smallii	LAma
stylosum	See T. ***catesbyi***
sulcatum	CAvo GDra WChr
tschonoskii	LAma NHol WChr
undulatum	CHEx CRDP CWGN EPot LAma NHol SDeJ SIng WChr WCru
vaseyi	CBro LAma NHol WChr
viride	ELan EPot LAma NHol WChr WCru

TRINIA (Umbelliferae/Apiaceae)

* ***grandiflora***	EMon

TRIOSTEUM (Caprifoliaceae)

See Plant Deletions

TRIPETALEIA (Ericaceae)

See Plant Deletions

TRIPLEUROSPERUM (Compositae/Asteraceae)

See Plant Deletions

TRIPOGANDRA (Commelinaceae)

See Plant Deletions

TRIPTEROSPERMUM (Gentianaceae)

¶ ***lanceolatum***	WCru
¶ ***taiwanense***	WCru

TRIPTERYGIUM (Celastraceae)

See Plant Deletions

TRISETUM (Gramineae/Poaceae)

¶ ***flavescens***	MWil

TRISTAGMA (Liliaceae/Alliaceae)

'Rolf Fiedler'	See IPHEION 'R.F.'
uniflorum	See IPHEION ***u.***

TRISTANIA (Myrtaceae)

conferta	CPle

TRITELEIA (Liliaceae/Alliaceae)

bridgesii	EBul LBow
* ***californica***	ETub WChr
grandiflora	WPer
hyacintha	LAma LBow MFos MHlr WChr
ixioïdes ixioïdes	WChr
– var. ***scabra***	WChr
– 'Splendens'	ETub
§ ***laxa***	CAvo CCla CMea LAma MHlr MWBu NRog WHaw
– PJC 951	WChr

– 'Koningin Fabiola' ('Queen Fabiola') CCla ETub LAma LBow MBri NRog WPer
§ ***peduncularis*** LAma LBow MFos WChr
x ***tubergenii*** LAma LBow WThi
uniflora See IPHEION ***uniflorum***

TRITICUM (Gramineae/Poaceae)
See Plant Deletions

TRITONIA (Iridaceae)
crocata ETub GCal LBow NRog WByw
¶ – ***hyalina*** LBow SPer
§ ***disticha*** ssp. ***rubrolucens*** CBro CChu CElw CHan CPou CRDP ECha GAri GCal IDai MBri MFir NRoo WPbr
¶ ***lineata*** LBow SPer
'Orange Delight' LBlm MHlr WCot
rosea See T. ***distica rubrolucens***
securigera CMon
squalida LBow WCot

TROCHETIOPSIS (Sterculiaceae)
melanoxylon EPad

TROCHOCARPA (Epacridaceae)
thymifolia WThu

TROCHODENDRON (Trochodendraceae)
aralioïdes CB&S CCla CGre EBar EGol EHar ENot MGos MUlv SArc SHil SLon SMad SReu SSta WWat

TROLLIUS † (Ranunculaceae)
acaulis CMea CRDP EGle GDra MTho NGre NHol WAbe WPat
§ ***chinensis*** ECha EPot GAbr NHol
– 'Golden Queen' AGM CBow CHol CSco CWes EBre ECtt EFou ELan EMar LAbb LBre MNFA MUlv MWat NMir NNor NNrw NRoo SChu SFis SPer WCru WEas WGor WHen WHil WHoo WPer
– 'Imperial Orange' CCla CGle CMGP EBee SMrm WCra WTyr WWin
x ***cultorum*** 'Alabaster' CRow ECha
– 'Baudirektor Linne' EBre ECtt GCHN LBre NKay NRoo
– Bressingham hybrids EBre LBre NRoo
– 'Canary Bird' CBow CSco EGol ELan SHer SPer SPla SRms
– 'Commander-in-Chief' COtt
– 'Earliest of All' CCla CDoC CGle CMGP CSco NHol NKay NRoo SChu SHig SMrm SPla SRms WGor
– 'Etna' GCal MBri
– 'Feuertroll' ('Fireglobe') CDoC CWGN ECha NBar
– 'Golden Cup' CCla ECot NHol NRoo SMrm WHal
– 'Golden Monarch' CWGN EPar
¶ – 'Golden Queen' WPer
– 'Goldquelle' AGM EHon MWat NVic SHig
– 'Goliath' CGle CMGP GCal LHop NRoo SPer
– 'Helios' CGle CSam EBee ECha GCal
¶ – 'John Rider' WPer
– 'Lemon Queen' CCla CSco CWGN CWes EPar GCal NNor NRoo SLon SMrm WRus
– 'Maigold' MBri
– 'Orange Crest' GCal
– 'Orange Princess' AGM CSam CWGN EBre GAri LBre LWad MBal MBel NBro NDea NHol SHig SLon SPer SSte
– 'Prichard's Giant' CSco
– 'Salamander' NKay
– 'Superbus' AGM CCla ELan EPar MBri MWat NKay NRoo SHig SPer WRus
*– 'Taleggio' SMrm
europaeus CBot CLew CRow CSam ECha EPad EPot LHop LWad MBal MBro MNFA NDea NMir NNrw NRoo NRya NSti WCla WDav WHoo WPer WSun
ledebourii hort. See T. ***chinensis***
pumilus CBos CGle CNic ECha ELan EMar EPad EPar LBee MHig NHol NMen NNrd NWCA SHer SIng SUsu WHil
– 'Wargrave' NMen NNrd WEas WPer
riederianus EPot
stenopetalus ECha
yunnanensis CGle CRDP ELan EMon ESis GBuc MBal NGre SLon

TROPAEOLUM † (Tropaeolaceae)
¶ ***azureum*** CPla CRDP MSto
¶ ***brachyceras*** CRDP
ciliatum AGM CAvo CHan CMon CRDP ELan EOrc GCal LBlm LBow MSto MTho NCat WChr WCru WHer WMar WNor
¶ ***incisum*** MSto
majus CHEx LHol SIde
– 'Alaska' (v) EMon LBlm SIde
*– 'Clive Innes' ERea
¶ – 'Crimson Beauty' WCot
– 'Crimson Velvet' CRDP
– 'Empress of India' WEas
– 'Hermine Grashoff' AGM CBos CRDP CRow CTbh ERea GCal LBlm LHop NBro SAxl SDix SMad WCru WEas
*– 'Indian Chief' LBlm
– 'Red Wonder' CSpe SMad
– 'Variegatum' EMon ERea
nasturtium EMFW
pentaphyllum CAvo CRDP CRow ECha GCal IBlr LBlm MSto MTho
peregrinum MTho
polyphyllum MSto
¶ ***sessilifolium*** CRDP MSto
speciosum AGM Widely available
sylvestre CMHG LBow WCru
tricolorum AGM CAvo CMon CRDP CRiv ECha EPot MSto MTho SDix WAbe WChr
tuberosum CB&S CChu CGle CMHG CRiv EPot GPoy MBal MFir SLon WAbe WEas
– var. ***lineamaculatum*** 'Ken Aslet' AGM Widely available
– P J Christian's form NRog
– var. ***piliferum*** 'Sidney' CGle CRDP IBlr LBow NCat NTow SAxl WCru WHer

TSUGA (Pinaceae)

canadensis	CGre EHar EHul ENHC GAri IDai LCon MBar SHBN SPer WDin
§ – 'Abbott's Pygmy'	CKen
– 'Abbot's Dwarf'	CKen
– 'Albospica'	ESis LBee
– 'Aurea' (v)	LCon MBar
– 'Baldwin Dwarf Pyramid'	MBar
– 'Bennett'	EHul EPot LCon MBar
– 'Brandley'	CKen
§ – 'Branklyn'	CKen MPla
– 'Cinnamonea'	CKen
– 'Coffin'	CKen
– 'Cole's Prostrate'	CKen EBre EHar EPla LBre LCon MBar MBri NHol SHBN
– 'Compacta'	LCon
– 'Curley'	CKen
– 'Curtis Ideal'	CKen
– 'Dwarf Whitetip'	EPla LCon
– 'Everitt Golden'	CKen
– 'Fantana'	EHul LBee LCon LLin MBar SBod SLim
– 'Gentsch Snowflake'	CKen EPla
– 'Golden Splendor'	EPla
– 'Horsford'	CKen MPla
– 'Hussii'	CKen
– 'Jacqueline Verkade'	CKen
– 'Jeddeloh' AGM	CDoC CMac EBar EBre EHar EHul ENHC ENot EPot ESis IJoh LBre LCon LLin MBal MBar MBri MGos MPla NBee NHar NHol SLim SMad SPer WAbe WStI WThu
– 'Jervis'	CKen
¶ – 'Kingsville Spreader'	CKen
I – 'Lutea'	CKen
– 'Minima'	MBar
– 'Minuta'	CKen EHul ESis LBee LCon NHar
– 'Nana'	CMac EHul IOrc LCon
– 'Palomino'	CKen MBar
– 'Pendula' AGM	CDoC CKen CSco EHar EHul ENot LBee LCon MAsh MBar MBri MWat NHar SHil SLim WThu
♦– 'Prostrata'	See T. *c.* 'Branklyn'
♦– 'Pygmaea'	See T. *c.* 'Abbott's Pygmy'
– 'Rugg's Washington'	CKen MPla
– 'Verkade Petite'	CKen
– 'Verkade Recurved'	CKen MBar
– 'Von Helms'	CKen
*– 'Warnham'	CKen LBee LCon
caroliniana 'La Bar Weeping'	CKen
chinensis	CMCN
diversifolia	EPot
– 'Gotelli'	CKen
heterophylla AGM	CBra CDoC CMCN CPer EHar ENot GAri GRei IOrc LBuc LCon MBar NWea SHBN SMad SPer STre WDin
– 'Iron Springs'	CKen
menziesii	See PSEUDOTSUGA ***menziesii***
¶ ***mertensiana*** 'Elizabeth'	CKen
I – 'Glauca Nana'	CKen

TSUSIOPHYLLUM (Ericaceae)

tanakae	GAri GGGa WAbe WDav

TUBERARIA (Cistaceae)

guttata	WCru
lignosa	CNic ESma NHol WAbe WCla WCru WDav WHil

TULBAGHIA † (Liliaceae/Alliaceae)

¶ ***acutiloba***	CAvo
¶ ***alliacea***	CFee
capensis	CFee LGre
cepacea	EPot GCal WCot
– var. ***maritima***	CMon WThi
coddii	CFee LGre WCot
cominsii	CAvo LGre WCot
natalensis	CAvo LGre
simmleri	CAvo CMon CSam
violacea	CAvo CChu CHan CMon EBul ECha ERav ESma GCal IBlr LAma MTho SHer SIng SMrm SUsu
– ***pallida***	CAvo CChu EBee LGre SAxl WCot
§ – 'Silver Lace' (v)	CAvo CBos CBrk CChu CFee CGle CHan CRDP CRow CSpe ECha ELan EMon EPla ERav ERea LGre LHop MTho SIgm SMrm WCot WThi
– ***tricolor***	CMon
– ***variegata***	See T. *v.* 'Silver Lace'

TULIPA † (Liliaceae/Liliaceae)

'Abu Hassan' (3)	LAma
acuminata	CBro LAma LBow SIng
'Ad Rem' (4)	LAma
'Addis' (14)	LAma
aitchisonii	See T. ***clusiana***
'Aladdin' (6)	LAma MWBu NRog
'Alaska' (6)	LAma
albertii	LAma
'Albino' (3)	LAma
aleppensis	LAma
'Aleppo' (7)	LAma
'Alfred Cortot' AGM	LAma
'Ali Baba' (14)	MBri
'Alice Leclercq' (2)	LAma
'All Bright' (5)	LAma
'Allegretto' (11)	LAma NRog
altaica	EPot LAma
amabilis PF 8955	CMon
'Amulet' (3)	LAma
'Ancilla' AGM	CBro LAma
'Angélique' (11)	ETub LAma MBri MHlr
'Anne Claire' (3)	LAma
'Anneke' (3)	LAma
'Antwerp' (3)	LAma
'Apeldoorn' (4)	ETub LAma MBri NRog
'Apeldoorn's Elite' AGM	LAma MHlr MWBu NRog
'Apricot Beauty' (1)	ETub LAma LBow MBri MWBu NBir NRog
'Apricot Jewel'	See T. ***linifolia*** 'A.J.'
'Apricot Parrot' AGM	LAma MWBu NRog
'Arabian Mystery' (3)	NBir
'Aristocrat' AGM	LAma
'Arlington' (5)	LAma

'Arma' (7)	LAma
'Artist' (8)	CAvo LAma LBow MWBu NBir
'Asta Nielsen' (5)	LAma
'Athleet' (3)	LAma
'Attila' (3)	ETub LAma MWBu NRog
aucheriana **AGM**	CBro CMon EPot ETub LAma LBow WChr WCot
'Aurea'	See T. ***greigii*** 'A.'
'Aureola' (3)	LAma
bakeri	See T. ***saxatilis*** Bakeri Group
'Balalaika' (5)	LAma MWBu
'Bandoeng' (3)	LAma
batalinii	See T. ***linifolia*** Batalinii Group
* 'Beauty' (7)	LAma
'Beauty of Apeldoorn' (4)	LAma NRog
'Belcanto' (3)	LAma
'Bellflower' (7)	LAma
'Bellona' (1)	ETub LAma MWBu
'Berlioz' (12)	LAma
biebersteiniana	LAma WChr
§ ***biflora***	CAvo CBro EPot ETub LAma LBow NRog SIng WChr
bifloriformis	EPot MSto WChr
'Big Chief' **AGM**	LAma MBri
'Bing Crosby' (3)	ETub LAma
'Black Parrot' (10)	LAma LBow
'Bleu Aimable' (5)	ETub LAma
'Blue Heron' (7)	LAma
'Blue Parrot' (10)	LAma MWBu NRog
'Bonanza' (11)	LAma
'Boule de Neige' (2)	LAma
'Bravissimo' (2)	MBri
'Brilliant Star' (1)	LAma MBri MWBu
'Bruno Walter' (3)	LAma
'Burgundy' (7)	ETub LAma
'Burgundy Lace' (7)	LAma
'Burns' (7)	LAma
butkovii	LAma
'Cabaret' (6)	LAma
'Caland' (10)	LAma
'Candela' (13)	LAma
'Cantata' (13)	CBro LAma
'Cantor' (5)	LAma
'Cape Cod' (14)	LAma NRog
'Caprice' (10)	LAma
'Captain Fryatt' (6)	LAma
carinata	LAma
'Carlton' (2)	ETub LAma NRog
'Carnaval de Nice' (11/v)	ETub LAma MBri
'Cashmir' (5)	LAma
'Cassini' (3)	LAma MWBu
§ ***celsiana***	CMon EPot ETub LAma
'César Franck' (12)	LAma
'Charles' (1)	LAma MWBu
'Charles Needham' (5)	LAma
'China Pink' (6)	CAvo ETub LAma LBow NRog
'Chopin' (12)	LAma NRog
'Christmas Marvel' (1)	ETub LAma MWBu
chrysantha	See T. ***clusiana c.***
'Clara Butt' (5)	LAma NRog
§ ***clusiana***	CBro LAma MWBu SIng WChr
§ – var. ***chrysantha*** **AGM**	CAvo LAma LBow NRog SIng
– – 'Tubergen's Gem'	EPar LAma MBri
– ***clusianoïdes***	WChr
– 'Cynthia'	EPar EPot LAma SIng SUsu
§ – var. ***stellata***	LAma
'Compliment' (6)	LAma
'Concerto' (13)	CBro ETub LAma
'Cordell Hull' (5)	CAvo NRog
'Coriolan' (3)	LAma
'Corona' (12)	LAma
'Corrie Kok' (3)	LAma
'Corsage' **AGM**	LAma
'Couleur Cardinal' (1)	ETub LAma LBow NRog
* 'Crispa Pink' (7)	LAma
'Crystal Beauty' (7)	NRog
'Dancing Show' (8)	LAma
dasystemon	EPot LAma MWBu
* 'Delano' (3)	LAma
'Diana' (1)	ETub LAma NRog
'Diantha' (14)	LAma
didieri	CAvo LAma
'Dillenburg' (5)	LAma
'Dix' Favourite' (5)	LAma
'Doctor James Parkinson' (3)	LAma
'Doctor Plesman' (1)	LAma
'Doll's Minuet' (8)	LAma
'Don Quichotte' (3)	LAma
'Donna Bella' **AGM**	LAma
'Douglas Bader' (3)	CAvo LAma NRog
'Dreaming Maid' (3)	LAma
'Duke of Wellington' (5)	LAma
* 'Dutch Gold' (3)	LAma
'Dyanito' (6)	CAvo LAma
'Early Harvest' **AGM**	LAma
'Early Light' (1)	LAma
'Easter Fire' (3)	LAma
'Easter Parade' (13)	EWal LAma
'Easter Surprise' (14)	LAma
§ ***edulis***	CAvo CMon
eichleri	See T. ***undulatifolia***
'El Toreador' (2)	LAma
'Electra' (2)	LAma MBri MWBu
'Elegant Lady' (6)	ETub
'Elizabeth Arden' (4)	ETub LAma
'Elmus' (3)	LAma
'Esperanto' (8/v)	ETub NRog
'Estella Rijnveld' (10)	LAma LBow NBir NRog
'Esther' (5)	ETub LAma
'Etude' (3)	LAma
'Fair Lady' (12)	LAma
'Fantasy' **AGM**	LAma LBow MWBu
'Fashion' (12)	LAma MWBu
ferganica	CMon EPot LAma
'Feu Superbe' (13)	LAma
'Fireside'	See T. 'Vlammenspel'
'First Lady' **AGM**	LAma
'Flair' (1)	LAma MWBu
'Flaming Parrot' (10)	LAma LBow MWBu
'Floradale' (4)	LAma
'Florosa' (8)	LAma
'Flying Dutchman' (5)	LAma
fosteriana	MBri
'Franfurt' (3)	LAma
'Franz Léhar' (12)	LAma
'Frasquita' (5)	LAma
'Fresco' (14)	LAma

'Fringed Apeldoorn' (7) NRog
'Fringed Beauty' (2) ETub MBri
'Fringed Elegance' (7) LAma
'Fritz Kreisler' (12) LAma
fulgens LAma
'G W Leak' (5) LAma
'Gaiety' (12) LAma
'Galata' (13) LAma
galatica LAma
'Garanza' (2) LAma
'Garden Party' (3) LAma
'Generaal de Wet' (1) ETub LAma MBri
'General Eisenhower' (4) LAma
'Georgette' (5) ETub LAma MBri MWBu NRog
'Giuseppe Verdi' (12) EWal LAma LBow MBri MWBu NRog
'Glück' (12) LAma MWBu
'Gold Medal' (11) LAma MBri
'Golden Age' (5) LAma
'Golden Apeldoorn' (4) ETub LAma MBri MWBu NRog
'Golden Artist' (8) LAma MBri MWBu NRog
'Golden Eagle' (13) LAma
'Golden Eddy' (3) LAma
'Golden Emperor' (13) LAma
'Golden Harvest' (5) LAma
'Golden Melody' (3) ETub LAma NRog
'Golden Oxford' (4) LAma
'Golden Parade' (4) LAma
*'Golden Show' (3) LAma
'Golden Springtime' (4) LAma
'Goldenes Deutschland' (4) LAma
'Gordon Cooper' (4) LAma MWBu
'Goudstuk' (12) LAma
'Goya' (2) LAma
'Graceful' (14) LAma
'Grand Prix' (13) LAma
'Green Eyes' (8) LAma
'Green Spot' (8) LAma
greigii CBro CMon
– 'Aurea' CMon LRHS
grengiolensis CAvo EPot LAma
'Greuze' (5) LAma
'Grevel' (3) LAma
'Groenland' (8) LAma MWBu
'Gudoshnik' (4) LAma LBow
'Hadley' (1) LAma
hageri CMon ETub LAma SIng
– 'Splendens' ETub LAma
'Halcro' AGM ETub LAma
'Heart's Delight' (12) CAvo CBro ETub EWal LAma LBow NRog
'Henry Ford' (5) LAma
'Hibernia' (3) LAma
hissarica EPot WChr
'Hit Parade' (13) LAma
'Hoangho' (2) LAma
'Holland's Glorie' AGM LAma
'Hollywood' (8) LAma LBow
hoogiana LAma
§ ***humilis*** CAvo CBro EPar EPot ETub LAma LBow SIng
§ – ***pulchella*** Albocaerulea Oculata Group EPot LAma WChr
– 'Eastern Star' LAma MWBu
– 'Odalisque' EPot LAma
– 'Pallida' LRHS
– 'Persian Pearl' EPot LAma NRog SIng
– Violacea Group CAvo CCla EPar ETub LAma SIng
– yellow centre LAma LBow
§ ***humilis*** Violacea Group black centre CBro LRHS
– – dark yellow centre CBro LRHS SIng
'Humming Bird' (8) LBow
'Humoresque' (13) LAma
'Hytuna' (2) LAma NRog
'Ibis' (1) LAma
'Ile de France' (5) LAma
ingens LAma
'Inglescombe Yellow' (5) LAma
'Inzell' (3) LAma
'Jacqueline' (6) LAma
'James V Forrestal' (10) LAma
'Jan Vermeer' (2) LAma
'Jeantine' AGM LAma
'Jewel of Spring' AGM LAma
'Jimmy ' (3) NRog
'Jockey Cap' (14) LAma
'Joffre' (1) LAma MBri MWBu
'Johann Strauss' (12) CAvo CBro ETub LAma MBri MWBu
'Johanna' (3) LAma
'Juan' (13) LAma MBri
'Kansas' (3) LAma
'Karel Doorman' (10) LAma
'Kareol' (2) LAma
kaufmanniana CAvo CBro ETub LBow NRog SIng SRms
§ 'Kees Nelis' (3) LAma MBri MWBu NRog
'Keizerskroon' AGM LAma MWBu NRog
'Kingsblood' AGM LAma
kolpakowskiana AGM LAma MBri MWBu NRog SIng
kurdica LAma
'La Tulipe Noire' (5) LAma
'Lady Diana' (14) LAma MBri
lanata LAma
'Landseadel's Supreme' AGM LAma
'Large Copper' (14) LAma
'Lefeber's Favourite' (4) LAma
'Libretto' (3) LAma
'Lilac Time' (6) LAma
'Lilac Wonder' See T. ***saxatilis*** 'L.W.'
linifolia AGM CAvo CMea EPar EPot ETub LAma LBow NRog SIng WAbe WChr
§ – Batalinii Group AGM CBro EPot LAma LBow NRog SIng
§ – – 'Apricot Jewel' CAvo CBro
– – 'Bright Gem' (15) CAvo CBro EPot ETub LAma LBow MHlr MWBu NRog SIng WHoo
– – 'Bronze Charm' CAvo CBro LAma
– – 'Red Gem' CBro LAma
*– – 'Yellow Gem' CBro
– – 'Yellow Jewel' LAma
– Maximowiczii Group CBro LAma LBow
'London' (4) LAma
'Longfellow' (14) LAma
'Love Song' (12) LAma
'Lucifer' (7) LAma

'Lucky Strike' (3)	LAma
§ 'Lustige Witwe' ('Merry Widow') (3)	LAma MWBu
§ 'Madame Lefeber' (13)	CBro ETub EWal LAma LBow MBri MWBu
'Madame Spoor' (3)	LAma
'Magier' (5)	LAma
'Maja' (7)	LAma
'Mamasa' (5)	LAma
'March of Time' (14)	MBri
'Maréchal Niel' (2)	LAma
'Mariette' (6)	LAma MWBu
'Marilyn' (6)	ETub
marjoletii	CAvo CBro ETub LAma LBow MWBu NRog SIng
'Marquette' (2)	LAma
'Mary Ann' (14)	LAma
'Maskerade' (5)	LAma
'Maureen' AGM	ETub LAma
mauritiana	LAma
maximowiczii	See T. ***linifolia*** M. Group
'Maytime' (6)	LAma MWBu
'Maywonder' (11)	LAma
'Menton' (5)	ETub
'Merry Widow'	See T. 'Lustige Witwe'
'Mickey Mouse' (1)	NRog
'Minerva' (3)	NRog
'Mirjoran' (3)	LAma
'Miss Holland' (3)	MBri
§ ***montana***	CBro EPot LAma WChr
'Monte Carlo' AGM	ETub LAma
'Most Miles' AGM	LAma
'Mount Tacoma' (11)	ETub LAma MBri NRog
'Mr van der Hoef' (2)	LAma MBri MWBu
'Mrs John T Scheepers' AGM	LAma MWBu
'Murillo' (2)	LAma
'Murillo Maxima' (2)	LAma
'My Lady' AGM	LAma
'Negrita' (3)	LAma
neustreuvae	CBro WChr
'New Design' (3/v)	ETub LAma MBri MWBu NRog
'Orange Bouquet' AGM	LAma NRog
'Orange Cassini' (3)	LAma
'Orange Elite' (14)	LAma MBri
'Orange Emperor' (13)	LAma MBri MWBu NRog
'Orange Favourite' (10)	LAma LBow
'Orange Goblet' (4)	LAma
'Orange Monarch' (3)	ETub LAma
'Orange Sun'	See T. 'Oranjezon'
'Orange Toronto' (14)	MWBu
'Orange Triumph' (11)	MBri
'Orange Wonder' (3)	LAma
'Oranje Nassau' AGM	LAma MBri MWBu NRog
§ 'Oranjezon' (4)	LAma
'Oratorio' (14)	LAma MBri
'Oriental Beauty' (14)	LAma MWBu NRog
'Oriental Splendour' AGM	EWal LAma
'Ornament' (3)	LAma
orphanidea	EPot LAma LBow SIng
– ***flava***	CBro CMon ETub LAma
§ – Whittallii Group	CAvo CBro CMon EPot ETub LAma LBow NRog SIng
ostrowskiana	LAma
'Oxford' AGM	LAma MWBu
'Oxford's Elite' (4)	LAma
'Page Polka' (3)	LAma
'Palestrina' (5)	LAma
* 'Pandit Nehru' (3)	LAma
'Pandour' (14)	LAma MBri MWBu
'Parade' AGM	LAma MBri
'Paris' (3)	LAma
'Paul Crampel' (2)	LAma
'Paul Richter' (3)	LAma
'Pax' (3)	LAma
'Peach Blossom' (2)	ETub LAma LBow MBri NRog
'Peer Gynt'	ETub
'Peerless Pink' (3)	LAma
'Perlina' (14)	LAma
persica	See T. ***celsiana***
'Philippe de Comines' (5)	LAma
'Picture' (5)	LAma
'Pimpernel' (8)	LAma MWBu
'Pink Beauty' (1)	LAma
'Pink Impression' (4)	LAma
'Pink Trophy' (1)	LAma
'Pinkeen' (13)	LAma
'Pinocchio' (14)	EWal NRog
'Plaisir' AGM	ETub LAma MBri
platystigma	CAvo LAma LBow
'Polo' (13)	LAma
polychroma	See T. ***biflora***
praestans	LAma
– 'Fusilier' AGM	CAvo CBro EPot ETub EWal LAma LBow MBri MWBu NRog SIng
– 'Unicum' (v)	ETub LAma MBri NRog SIng
– 'Van Tubergen's Variety'	ETub LAma MWBu NRog
'Preludium' (3)	LAma
'President Kennedy' AGM	LAma
primulina	CMon
'Prince Karl Philip' (3)	NRog
'Prince of Austria' (1)	LAma
'Princeps' (13)	CBro EWal LAma MBri
'Princess Elizabeth' (5)	LAma
'Princess Margaret Rose' (5)	LAma MWBu
'Prins Carnaval' (1)	LAma
'Prinses Irene' AGM	ETub LAma LBow MBri NBir
'Prominence' (3)	LAma
pulchella	See T. ***humilis pulchella***
– ***humilis***	See T. ***humilis***
§ 'Purissima' (13)	CAvo CBro ETub LAma LBow MWBu
'Purple Cupland' (5)	LAma
'Queen' (4)	LAma
'Queen Ingrid' (14)	LAma
'Queen of Bartigons' (5)	LAma NRog
'Queen of Night' (5)	CAvo ETub LAma LBow MBri MHlr MWBu
'Queen of Sheba' (6)	LAma
'Queen Wilhelmina'	See T. 'Koningin Wilhelmina'
'Recreado' (3)	ETub LAma
'Red Champion' (10)	LAma
'Red Emperor'	See T. 'Madame Lefeber'
'Red Georgette' AGM	MBri MWBu
'Red Matador' (4)	LAma
'Red Parrot' (10)	LAma
'Red Present' (3)	LAma

'Red Riding Hood' AGM CAvo CBro EPot ETub EWal LAma LBow MBri MWBu NBir NRog
'Red Sensation' (10) LAma MWBu
'Red Shine' (6) LAma
'Reforma' (3) LAma
Rembrandt MBri
'Renown' (5) LAma MWBu
'Rheingold' (2) LAma
rhodopea See T. ***urumoffii***
'Rijnland' (3) LAma
'Ringo' See T. 'Kees Nelis'
'Rockery Beauty' (13) LAma
'Rockery Master' (14) LAma
'Rockery Wonder' (14) LAma
*'Rose Emperor' (13) LAma
'Rosy Wings' (5) LAma
saxatilis CAvo CBro CCla EPot LAma MBri MWBu NRog SIng
– MS 769 CMon
§ – Bakeri Group EPot LAma WChr
§ – 'Lilac Wonder' CAvo CBro EPot LAma MBri MWBu NRog SIng
'Scarlet Cardinal' (2) LAma
'Scarlett O'Hara' (5) LAma
'Schoonoord' (2) ETub LAma MBri
schrenkii ETub LAma
'Scotch Lassie' (5) LAma
'Shakespeare' (12) CBro LAma LBow MWBu NRog
'Shirley' (5) CAvo ETub LAma MBri MWBu NRog
'Showwinner' AGM CBro ETub LAma MBri MWBu
'Sigrid Undset' (5) LAma
'Silentia' (3) LAma
'Sint Maarten' (1) LAma
'Smiling Queen' (5) LAma
'Snowflake' (3) LAma
'Snowpeak' (5) LAma
sogdiana LAma
'Sorbet' AGM LAma
sosnowskyi LRHS
'Sothis' (7) LAma
'Spalding' (3) LAma
'Sparkling Fire' (14) ETub LAma
'Spectacular Gold' See T. 'Goldenes Deutschland'
sprengeri AGM CAvo CBro CFil CMon CNic ELan EPar LAma
– Trotter's form WCot
'Spring Green' AGM ETub LAma LBow MBri MWBu NRog
'Spring Pearl' (13) LAma
'Spring Song' (4) LAma
stellata See T. ***clusiana s.***
'Stockholm' AGM LAma
'Stresa' AGM CBro LAma MWBu
'Striped Apeldoorn' (4) LAma NRog
subpraestans EPot LAma
'Success' (3) LAma
'Summit' (13) LAma
'Sundew' (7) LAma NRog
'Sunkist' (5) LAma
'Sunray' (3) LAma
'Susan Oliver' (8) LAma
'Swan Wings' (7) LAma
'Sweet Harmony' AGM ETub LAma MBri NRog
'Sweet Lady' (14) LAma NRog
'Sweetheart' (13) CBro LAma MWBu NRog
sylvestris CAvo CBro EPar ETub EWFC LAma LBow MHlr NLan NRog SIng WShi
'Tamara' (3) LAma
'Tango' (14) LAma
tarda AGM CAvo CBro CCla CNic EPar EPot ETub EWal LAma LBow MBri MBro NRog SIng WPat
'Teenager' (14) LAma
'Teheran' (3) LAma
'Tender Beauty' (13) LAma
tetraphylla LAma
'Texas Flame' (10) LAma
'Texas Gold' (10) LAma LBow
'The First' (12) CBro LAma
'Thule' (3) LAma
'Topscore' (3) LAma
'Toronto' AGM ETub LAma MBri MWBu
'Toulon' (13) MBri
'Towa' (14) LAma
'Trance' (3) LAma
'Trinket' (14) LAma
'Triumphator' (2) LAma
tschimganica LAma
tubergeniana LAma
– 'Keukenhof' LAma
turkestanica AGM CAvo CBro CCla CNic EPar EPot ETub LAma LBow MBri MWBu NRog SIng WHil
'Uncle Tom' (11) LAma MBri
§ ***undulatifolia*** CBro LAma LBow SIng
'Union Jack' (5) CAvo LAma
urumiensis AGM CAvo CBro CCla EPot ETub LAma MBri MBro MWBu NRog SIng WAbe WHoo WPat
§ ***urumoffii*** LAma
'Valentine' (3) LAma
'Van der Neer' (1) LAma
'Varinas' (3) LAma
violacea See T. ***humilis*** Violacea Group
viridiflora ETub
'Vivaldi' (12) LAma
'Vivex' (4) LAma
§ 'Vlammenspel' (1) LAma
'Vuurbaak' (2) LAma
vvedenskyi CBro LAma NRog SIng
– 'Blanka' EPot
– 'Hanka' EPot
– 'Lenka' EPot
– 'Tangerine Beauty' SIng
'Wallflower' (5) ETub
'West Point' (6) CAvo ETub LAma LBow MWBu
*'White Alba' (7) LAma
*'White Bouquet' (5) NRog
'White Dream' (3) ETub LAma
'White Emperor' See T. 'Purissima'
'White Parrot' (10) LAma NRog
'White Swallow' (3) NRog
'White Triumphator' (6) CAvo ETub LAma LBow MWBu NRog
'White Virgin' (3) LAma
whittallii See T. ***orphanidea*** Whittallii Group
'Wilhelm Kordes' (2) LAma
'Willem van Oranje' (2) LAma
'Willemsoord' (2) LAma MBri MWBu
wilsoniana See T. ***montana***

'Wim van Est' (5) LAma
'Yellow Dawn' (14) LAma
'Yellow Dover' (4) LAma
'Yellow Emperor' (13) CBro MBri
'Yellow Empress' (13) LAma
'Yellow Present' (3) LAma
'Yellow Purissima' (13) MWBu NRog
'Yokohama' (1) LAma
'Zampa' **AGM** LAma
zenaidae EPot
'Zombie' (13) LAma
'Zomerschoon' (5) ETub
'Zwanenburg' (5) LAma

TUNICA See PETRORHAGIA, DIANTHUS

TURRAEA (Meliaceae)
obtusifolia CTro

TUSSILAGO (Compositae/Asteraceae)
farfara CArn CKin CSFH ECWi GPoy LHol MHew MSal SIde WHer WNdy

TUTCHERIA (Theaceae)
See Plant Deletions

TWEEDIA (Asclepiadaceae)
§ ***caerulea*** **AGM** CGle CNew CPle CTro ELan EMil EOrc ERea ESma GCal IBlr LAbb LBlm LGan LGre LHop SAxl SMad SPer SUsu WEas WPer

TYPHA (Typhaceae)
angustifolia CBen CKin CRDP CRow CWGN EBre ECWi EHon EMFW EWav LBre LMay MSta SHig SWat SWyc WChe WHol WWye
latifolia CBen CHEx CRDP CRow CWGN ECWi EHon EMFW EWav LMay MSta SWat SWyc WChe WHer WWye
– 'Variegata' CBen CRDP CRow ELan EMFW MSta SWyc
§ ***laxmannii*** CBen CRiv EHon EMFW LMay MSta SRms
minima CBen CRDP CRiv CRow CWGN EBre ECWi EHon EMFW EWav LBre LMay MSta NDea SHig SWat SWyc WChe WHol
– var. ***gracilis*** ETPC
shuttleworthii IDai
stenophylla See T. ***laxmannii***

UGLI See CITRUS x *tangelo* 'Ugli'

UGNI (Myrtaceae)
§ ***molinae*** CDec CDoC CMHG CMer CPle CSam ESim GAri ISea MBal WCHb WDin WSHC WWat WWye

ULEX (Leguminosae/Papilionaceae)
europaeus CDoC ECWi ENot GAul GRei LBuc WDin WMou
– 'Aureus' CB&S EBar SPer
§ – 'Flore Pleno' **AGM** CB&S CDoC CSco ENot GAbr IDai IJoh MBal MGos NTow SHBN SPer WStI WWeb
– 'Plenus' See U. ***e.*** 'Flore Pleno'
– 'Prostratus' MBar
– 'Strictus' IJoh
gallii 'Mizzen' ESis GCal LRHS MBri MPla
§ ***minor*** EPla ISea
nanus See U. ***minor***

ULMUS (Ulmaceae)
'Dodoens' LBuc
§ ***glabra*** CKin CPer NWea WDin WMou
– 'Camperdownii' CDoC ELan MBen SPer WMou
– 'Exoniensis' CTho
– 'Gittisham' CTho
– 'Nana' NHol WPat
x ***hollandica*** 'Commelin' CDoC EMil
– 'Groeneveld' CDoC EMil
– 'Jacqueline Hillier' CCla CLew CShe CTre EBre EFol EHar ELan EMil ESis GDra GWht LBre LHop MAsh MBal MBar MPla NBar NHar NHol SIng SSta STre WAbe WDav WHCG WPat
– 'Lobel' CDoC MGos
– 'Wredei' See U. ***minor*** 'Dampieri Aurea'
minor 'Cornubiensis' CDoC CTho
§ – 'Dampieri Aurea' CBot CLnd EBre ELan IJoh LBre LNet LPan MBar MBlu NBee NHol SHBN SMad SPer WDin WPat
– 'Variegata' EPot
montana See U. ***glabra***
parvifolia EHal GAri SMad STre WFro WNor
– 'Frosty' (v) CKni ELan EPla EPot ESma SGil SHer
– 'Geisha' (v) CPMA CWSG EHar ELan ESma IJoh LHop MBar MGos MPla SBla SGil SMad STre WAbe WPat WWeb
§ – 'Hokkaido' EPla LGre SBla SGil SIng WAbe WPat
– ***pygmaea*** See U. ***p.*** 'Hokkaido'
– 'Yatsubusa' EPot NHol SGil SIng STre WPat
'Plantijn' CDoC
procera CKin STre
– 'Argenteovariegata' SMad
pumila GAri WNor
'Regal' EHar
'Sapporo Autumn Gold' EBre EHar LBre

UMBELLULARIA (Lauraceae)
californica CArn CMCN SArc SBor WSHC

UMBILICUS (Crassulaceae)
erectus CChu CRDP EWFC
rupestris CNat ELan EPot NGre NWCA SIde WCla WHer WPer WWye

UNCINIA (Cyperaceae)
clavata EPla ETPC GCal
ferruginea NHar
N ***rubra*** Widely available
– var. ***phallax*** EPla
¶ sp. ex China EPla

uncinata	CFil ECha EHoe EMar EPar EPla ETPC MBal NHar NHol NWCA SUsu WByw

UNGNADIA (Sapindaceae)

See Plant Deletions

UNIOLA (Gramineae/Poaceae)

latifolia	See CHASMANTHIUM ***latifolium***

URCEOLINA (Liliaceae/Amaryllidaceae)

miniata	See STENOMESSON ***miniatum***

URGINEA (Liliaceae/Hyacinthaceae)

fugax SF 62	CMon
maritima	GPoy LAma WHer
– SF 275	CMon
undulata SF 2/279/323	CMon

UROSPERMUM (Compositae/Asteraceae)

delachampii	CChu CGle CSev EBar ECha ECoo EPla LGre SAxl SSvw SUsu

URSINIA (Compositae/Asteraceae)

See Plant Deletions

URTICA (Urticaceae)

¶ ***galeopsifolia***	CNat
pilulifera dodartii	NBro

UTRICULARIA (Lentibulariaceae)

¶ ***alpina***	MHel
dichotoma	EFEx MHel
exoleta	See U. ***gibba***
§ ***gibba***	WHal
intermedia	EFEx
laterifolia	EFEx MHel
livida	EFEx MHel WMEx
longifolia	EFEx
menziesii	EFEx
monanthos	EFEx
nephrophylla	EFEx
praelonga	EFEx
pusilla	EFEx
reniformis	EFEx MHel WHal
sandersonii	EFEx MHel WHal
simplex	EFEx
subulata	EFEx WHal
tricolor	EFEx
vulgaris	EFEx SAWi

UVULARIA (Liliaceae/Convallariaceae)

disporum	LAma
grandiflora AGM	Widely available
– ***pallida***	CChu EFou EPar IBlr LGre SAxl SWas
perfoliata	CChu CHan CMea ECha EPar EPot LAma MSal SBla SPou WBon WCru WThu WWat
pudica	See U. ***carolininana***
§ ***sessilifolia***	EBul EPar EPot LAma MSal SPou

VACCINIUM (Ericaceae)

arctostaphylos	MAsh NHar NHol SSta
bracteatum	CCla
caespitosum	GDra
corymbosum AGM	CB&S ELan GWht MBal MBar MGos NBee SReu SSta WDin
F – 'Berkeley'	CTrh GTwe LBuc
F – 'Bluecrop'	CDoC CMac CTrh GTwe LBuc MBri MGos NBar WHig WStI WWeb
F – 'Bluetta'	CTrh GTwe
F – 'Coville'	CTrh
F – 'Duke'	ELan
F – 'Goldtraube'	CDoC MBlu MBri MGos WHig
F – 'Herbert '	GTwe MGos
F – 'Northland'	CTrh GAri GTwe
F – 'Patriot'	CTrh GAri GTwe
F – 'Pioneer'	MBar
F – 'Spartan'	CTrh GAri GTwe
F – 'Sunrise'	GTwe
F – 'Toro'	GTwe
F – 'Trovor'	ELan
F ***crassifolium*** 'Well's Delight'	CNic MAsh MBri
cylindraceum AGM	CCla SHil WAbe WBod WPat
delavayi	EPot GArf GCHN GWht MBal MBar MBlu MHig SReu SSta WAbe WThu
– 'Drummondii'	NHol
donianum	See V. ***sprengelii***
duclouxii	CB&S
dunalianum	CB&S
* ***eriophyllum***	SSta
erythrinum	SSta
erythrocarpum	NHol
floribundum	CGre CMHG EBre GDra GWht LBre MBal NHar NHol SHil SPer SSta WAbe WPat
glaucoalbum AGM	CAbP CKni GWht IBar MBar MBlu MRav SHil SPer SReu WBod WDin
– B 173	MBal
griffithianum	SSta
§ ***macrocarpon***	CMac ELan ESim GTwe MBal MBar MBri SPer SSta WThu
F – 'CH'	ESim
F – 'Early Black'	CB&S ESim LBuc SSta
F – 'Franklin'	ESim
F – 'Hamilton'	GArf GDra NHol SSta WAbe WPat WThu
F – 'Pilgrim'	ESim SSta
* 'McMinn'	GAri MBal
moupinense	CChu CCla CNic CRiv GWht IBar ITim MBal MBlu MGos NHol SPer SPla SSta WThu
– small-leaved	MBal
– 'Variegatum'	WPat
myrtillus	GPoy MBal WDin
'Nimo Pink'	MBar
nummularia	CCla CNic EPot GDra MBal MHig NHar WAbe WBod WThu
– LS&H 17294	NHar NHol
ovalifolium	NHol
ovatum	CCla CMHG GWht IBar MBal MBar NHar SHil SPer SSta WThu
§ ***oxycoccos***	CArn MGos
padifolium	CGre MBal
palustre	See V. ***oxycoccos***

parvifolium	NHar
praestans	GAri GGGa NHol SIng WThu
retusum	CGre CTrw MBal SSta WAbe WBod
sikkimense	GArf
uliginosum	WPat
virgatum	MBal
vitis-idaea	CNic EPot ESim GPoy GWht IJoh MBal MBar MGos MHig SHer SLon SPer SReu WHig WThu
– 'Compactum'	MBal NHar WAbe WDav
– Koralle Group **AGM**	CCla EBre ESis IBar LBre MBal MBar MBri MGos MRav NBar NHol SIng SPer SReu SSta WAbe WPat WThu
– ssp. ***minus***	ECou ESis GArf GAri MAsh MBal MHig SSta WAbe WDav WThu
– 'Red Pearl'	CDoC MAsh SPer

VALERIANA (Valerianaceae)

'Alba'	See CENTRANTHUS ***ruber albus***
alliariifolia	EMon GCal WCot
arizonica	CLew CNic MSte MTho NCat NKay SIng
'Coccinea'	See CENTRANTHUS ***ruber***
¶ ***dioica***	CRDP
montana	CLew EBur GArf MCas NHol NMen NNrd NRya WHal WHil
officinalis	CArn CKin CRDP CSFH ECWi ECoo Effi GPoy IEde ILis LHol MChe MHew NBro NRoo SIde WHal WHer WNdy WOak WPer WWye
– ssp. ***sambucifolia***	CHan
phu 'Aurea'	Widely available
*– 'Purpurea'	ECoo
pyrenaica	EFol EMon
saxatilis	EFol NRoo NRya SRms
supina	NWCA
¶ ***tatamana***	WEas

VALERIANELLA (Valerianaceae)

eriocarpa	EJud
§ ***locusta***	GPoy
olitoria	See V. ***locusta***

VALLEA (Elaeocarpaceae)

stipularis pyrifolia	CGre CPle

VALLOTA See CYRTANTHUS

VANCOUVERIA (Berberidaceae)

chrysantha	CBos CElw CRDP ECha EMon EPla SAxl SUsu SWas WCru WPla
hexandra	CHEx CNic ECha EMon GCal LHop MBal MBel NCat NHol NKay NRya NSti SGil WCru WDav WWin
planipetala	CRDP WHal

VEITCHIA (Palmae/Arecaceae)

See Plant Deletions

VELTHEIMIA (Liliaceae/Hyacinthaceae)

§ ***bracteata*** **AGM**	CAvo CMon EBak ETub IBlr LBow NRog
§ ***capensis*** **AGM**	SLMG
viridifolia hort.	See V. ***capensis***
viridifolia Jacquin	See V. ***bracteata***

X VENIDIOARCTOTIS See ARCTOTIS

VENIDIUM See ARCTOTIS

VERATRUM † (Liliaceae/Melanthiaceae)

album	CBot ECha GPoy NRar SBla WPer
¶ ***californicum***	CBot ECha
¶ ***caudatum***	CRDP
nigrum **AGM**	CBot CBro CHEx COtt EBre ECha EFou EMon ENot GDra LBre LGre MBri NHol SBla SChu SMad WByw WCot WPer
viride	CBot ECha ELun ERav IBlr WHaw WPer WPla

VERBASCUM † (Scrophulariaceae)

* ***acaule*** 'Album'	WCru
adzharicum	WHoo
¶ Allstree Hybrids	CFee
'Arctic Summer'	See V. ***bombyciferum*** 'Polarsommer'
arcturus	EBee MSte SUsu WPer
* ***bakerianum***	EBar MPit NNrw WEas
'Bill Bishop'	LHop SIng
blattaria	CGle CHan CPou CTom ECWi ELan LGan MHew MNFA NBir WEas WHer WNdy WPer
– f. ***albiflorum***	CMil CNic EMar LGan LGre MBro NNrw NSti SSvw WBon WHer WHoo WNdy WPer WRus WSun
– pink	LWad
¶ – 'Pink Beauty'	WHer
§ ***bombyciferum*** **AGM**	CSam EBee EFol NSti SLga SRms SSvw WByw WEas WOld
§ – 'Polarsommer'	CBow CDoC CHad CHol CSam EMar GAbr GAul LWad MBri NBir SRms WCot WHil
– 'Silver Lining'	ECoo NNor
'Broussa'	See V. ***bombyciferum***
chaixii	CDoC ECha ECro GBuc NBir WHil WHoo WPer
– 'Album'	Widely available
¶ – x ***phoeniceum*** 'Clent Sunrise'	WMar
Cotswold Hybrid Group 'Boadicea'	CSco CShe
– 'Bridal Bouquet'	CSam
– 'C L Adams'	CSco
– 'Cotswold Beauty' **AGM**	CSam EMon
– 'Cotswold Gem'	CSco
¶ – 'Cotswold King'	WCot
– 'Cotswold Queen'	CCla CDoC CGle CHan CSev EBre ECED ECas EFou ELan LBre NKay NRar NWyt SFis SMrm SPer WEas WHil WRus WSun

– 'Gainsborough' AGM	CDoC CGle CHad CRDP CSam CSco EBre ECas ECha ECtt EFou ELan LBre MBri MUlv MWat SMrm SPer WCra WEas WTyr
– 'Mont Blanc'	CBot CCla CGle CHad CMGP CSco EBre ECot EFou LBre NCat SPer
– 'Pink Domino' AGM	CDoC CGle CHad CMGP CRDP CSco EBre ECas EFou ELan LBre MBri NBrk NCat NSti SFis SHer SMrm SPer WCra WRus WTyr
– 'Royal Highland'	CGle CHad CMGP CSco EBee ECas ECot EFou ELan EMar SFis SHer SMrm WRus
creticum	EBee ECoo GCra WCla WPla
§ ***densiflorum***	CArn CSco Effi LHol MSal NPri SFis SIde SPer WCla WHer WPer
dumulosum AGM	EBre EPot GCal LBre NHar NTow NWCA SBla WAbe WDav WPer
elegantissimum	CSco
¶ 'Frosted Gold'	LGre
'Golden Wings' AGM	EPot GArf ITim WPat
'Helen Johnson' AGM	CBot CChu CCla CFee CGle CHad CMGP CRDP EBre ECha ECot EFou EGol EOrc LBre LGre LHop LRHS MUlv NBir NSti SHer SMrm SUsu WCra WRus
'Jackie'	LGre SBla
'Letitia' AGM	CRiv EBre EBur ELan EPad EPot GCal LBee LBre LGre MTho NHol NRar NTow SBla SIng SUsu SWas WAbe WEas WHoo WPer WThu WWin
longifolium	
var. ***pannosum***	See V. ***olympicum***
lychnitis	CArn CLTr ECWi EWoo WHaw WHer
nigrum	CArn CKin CSFH ECro EOrc EWFC MChe MHew MSal WHer WNdy WOak WPer
§ ***olympicum***	CGle CLTr CSam EBar ECha ELan NOak NSti WOld WPer WPla
phlomoïdes	MHew MSal
phoeniceum	CArn CBow CGle EHal ELan MPit NBee NBro NMir NOak NWCA SHer SSvw WCla WCra WEas WHen WPer WPla WSun WWin
*– 'Album'	SFis SSvw
– 'Candy Spires'	WBon
¶ – 'Flush of White'	CBot
– hybrids	CBot LAbb WPer
pulverulentum	CKin EWFC MWil
¶ ***rorippifolium***	CMGP EHic
¶ ***spicatum***	CBot
spinosum	CGle
thapsiforme	See V. ***densiflorum***
thapsus	CKin CRDP CSFH ECWi EJud EWFC GPoy IEde MChe MHew NMir NNor WHaw WNdy WOak WWye
'Turkey'	NKay
undulatum	EWoo
'Vernale'	CBot CSco
virgatum	EMon
wiedemannianum	LGre

VERBENA † (Verbenaceae)

'Apple Blossom'	NRar
'Aveyron'	EOrc SChu SMrm
¶ 'Blue Cascade'	NPri
§ ***bonariensis***	Widely available
'Boughton House'	CSpe MSte
'Bramley'	SChu
canadensis	MSal
'Carousel'	CMer NPri
chamaedrifolia	See V. ***peruviana***
corymbosa	CGre CRDP ECha LHop SChu SMrm SUsu WCot WPer
– 'Gravetye'	CGle EHal EMon GBuc GCal GMac
'Cupido'	CSpe MPit
* 'Foxhunter'	LAbb LHop
hastata	CHan CSFH CSev ECot EFol EMon EOrc GBar GCal LHol MChe MHew MSal NSti SMrm SUsu WCot WHer WPer
– JLS 88010WI	EMon
– 'Alba'	CHol EFol EHal EMon GBuc GCal MBel WCot WPer
– 'Rosea'	CBre EFou EMon GBuc GCal
'Hidcote Purple'	CBrk CGle GCal MRav MSte NFai SAxl WEas
'Huntsman'	CGle GBuc GCal MSte NTow SAxl
N 'Kemerton'	CSev ERom LHop
'Kurpfalz'	IHos
* 'La France'	MRav SChu SMrm SUsu
'Lawrence Johnston' AGM	CBrk CGle EOrc GCal MRav NTow SAxl SLMG WEas WHen
'Loveliness'	CSpe EOrc GCal IBlr LHop MUlv SAxl SMrm WEas
x ***maonettii***	CBar CRiv CSpe ELan EOrc LHop NTow WEas
¶ 'Nero'	NPri
officinalis	CArn CSFH ECWi EJud EWFC Effi GPoy IEde LHol MChe MHew SIde WHer WNdy WOak WPer WWye
'Othello'	CSpe
patagonica	See V. ***bonariensis***
§ ***peruviana***	CBrk CSam EBre ELan EOrc LAbb LBre LHop MPit MRav NRar NTow SAxl SChu SCro SIng WEas WHoo WOMN WPer WWin
– 'Alba'	CBrk CRiv CSpe ELan EOrc GCal LHop MPit MRav NTow SAxl SChu SCro SIde
phlogiflora	CBrk LHop
'Pink Bouquet'	See V. 'Silver Anne'
¶ 'Pink Parfait'	LHop
'Pink Pearl'	ECtt EOrc
pulchella	See V. ***tenera***
'Purple Kleopat'	IHos
¶ 'Red Cascade'	NPri
§ ***rigida*** AGM	CAbb CGre CMea ECha LGre LHil MHlr NCat SIde SMrm SRms SUsu WCot WEas
¶ 'Romance Silver'	CSpe
* 'Rose du Barry'	SAxl SMrm
* 'Royal Purple'	NPri
scabrida glandulosa	WPer
§ 'Silver Anne' AGM	CB&S CBrk CCla CGle CHad CSam ECha ECtt EOrc GCal LAbb LHop MRav MUlv NFai NPri NTow SAxl SChu SCro SDix SMrm SUsu WEas WHen

§ 'Sissinghurst' AGM — CArn CB&S CBot CBrk CCla CGle CHad CHan CMer CSam ECtt EOrc ERom GCal LAbb LHop MPit NFai NPri NRar SAxl SCro SLMG SUsu WEas WHen WHoo WRus WWin
stricta — GBar MSal WCot
– JLS 88008WI — CRDP EMon
§ *tenera* — CSpe LHop
'Tenerife' — See V. 'Sissinghurst'
tenuisecta — CBrk GCal SChu SDix WPer
– var. *alba* — SChu
venosa — See V. *rigida*
'White Cascade' — ECtt EOrc NPri
* 'White Knight' — CBrk CCla WRus

VERNONIA (Compositae/Asteraceae)

¶ *baldwinii* — GCal
crinita — ECha ECro GCal MUlv SFis
¶ *nudiflora* — CGre

VERONICA † (Scrophulariaceae)

amethystina — See V. *spuria*
armena — CShe EWes MBro MSte MWat NRya SHer SIgm SMrm WThi
§ *austriaca* — GCal SFis
– Corfu form — EWes LGre SAxl WPer
– *dubia* — See V. *prostrata*
– 'Ionian Skies' — ESis GBuc MBel SChu SIgm SUsu SWas WKif
§ – ssp. *teucrium* — CArn CHan CHol CPle EHal GAul NNor NRoo NWCA SChu SFis SRms SUsu WPer
¶ – – 'Blue Blazer' — SCro
– – 'Blue Fountain' — MPit
– – 'Crater Lake Blue' AGM — CB&S CHad CKel ECha ECtt EFol EFou ELan ESis ESma LGre MFir MRav NFai NNor SMrm WByw WCot WEas WPer WWin
– – 'Kapitän' — CKel ECha EFol LHop MFir SMrm WPer
– – 'Knallblau' — EFou MBri
– – 'Royal Blue' AGM — CKel CLTr CLew CMGP CSco ECot EFou IDai LAbb LGan MArl NHol NKay NSti SIng WHoo
– – 'Shirley Blue' — See V. 'Shirley Blue'
beccabunga — CBen CKin CRDP CWGN EBre ECWi ECoo EHon ELan EMFW EWFC GPoy LBre LMay MHew MSta NDea NMir SHig SWat WChe WHer WHol
bellidioïdes — GTou NGre
'Blue Spire' — LHil LWad WPer
bombycina — EPot NMen NTow NWCA SIgm SIng WDav WOMN
¶ – ssp. *bolkardaghensis* — SIgm
bonarota — See PAEDEROTA *bonarota*
caespitosa — WDav
– Mac&W 5849 — EPot
¶ – ssp. *caespitosa* — SIgm
candida — See V. *spicata incana*
x *cantiana* 'Kentish Pink' — EMon GBuc SPla
caucasica — EHal ELan EMon LGre NCat
chamaedrys — CKin ECWi IEde NMir
§ – 'Miffy Brute' (v) — ELan
– 'Variegata' — See V. *c.* 'Miffy Brute'
cinerea AGM — CMHG CShe CTom ECha EFol MBro MCas NKay NTow SIgm SSmi WAbe WDav WEas WHil WOld WPat WSun
– JCA 983.400 — CNic
dabneyi — NHol SIng
dichrus — ELan
* *didwelli* 'Vera' — EGle
exaltata — EBee EHal EMon GBuc GMac LGre LRHS MNFA MSte MTol SAsh WCot WPer
filifolia — WHoo
filiformis — ECWi NFai
formosa — See PARAHEBE *f.*
§ *fruticans* — CNic EMNN GTou NCat NKay NMen SIng WCla
fruticulosa — NWCA SIde SSmi
gentianoïdes AGM — Widely available
– 'Alba' — EOrc GCal NSti
– 'Nana' — EBre EOrc GAul LBre MMil
– 'Robusta' — ECha GCra
¶ – 'Tissington White' — CVer
– 'Variegata' — CGle CLew CRDP CRow CSev CShe ECha EFou EGol ELan ELun EOrc LHop MBri MBro MCas NHol NKay NNor NRoo NSti SPer WEas WHil WMer WPbr WWin
x *guthrieana* — CNic MAll WCru WPer
hendersonii — See V. *subsessilis h.*
incana — See V. *spicata incana*
kellereri — See V. *spicata*
kiusiana — CBot EMon MBel
kotschyana — NGre
* 'Lila Karina' — WPer
liwanensis — ELan ESis GCHN MBro NTow WThi
– Mac&W 5936 — EPot GDra MHig WHil
longifolia — CBre CHan CKel EJud ELan GMac LHil MBel MFir NBee NCat SFis WEas WOld
– 'Alba' — CSco ELan EMon MBel SIde
– 'Blaue Sommer' — CMGP EBee EFou NBar NWyt SPer
§ – 'Blauriesin' — CHol CSco ECtt EOrc GCal MBri MUlv NFai NHol NWyt SFis
– 'Foerster's Blue' — See V. *l.* 'Blauriesin'
– 'Incarnata' — EMon
– 'Joseph's Coat' (v) — EMon WCot
¶ – pink shades — NHol
– 'Rose Tone' — SUsu
– 'Rosea' — WByw WPer
– 'Schneeriesin' — ECha ECtt EFol EOrc MBri NHol SFis WRus
lyallii — See PARAHEBE *l.*
montana — CKin
– 'Corinne Tremaine' (v) — CNat WHer
¶ *morrisonicola* B&SWJ 086 — WCru
nipponica — WPer
* *nivalis nivea* — CRDP
nummularia — CTom ESis NTow WOMN WPer
officinalis — CKin ECWi EWFC NHol
oltensis — CMHG ESis GArf WEas WPat
– JCA 984.150 — MBro NTow SIng
orientalis — WHil
ornata — ECha WPer
pectinata — ESis GDra MBel NCat NMen NSti

– 'Rosea'	CMHG CNic ESis GAbr GDra MCas NKay NMen SHer SSmi WPer WThi WWin
peduncularis	CNic CSpe EOrc LBee LRHS SBla SUsu WEas
§ – 'Georgia Blue'	Widely available
♦– 'Oxford Blue'	See V. ***p.*** 'Georgia Blue'
perfoliata	See PARAHEBE ***perfoliata***
petraea 'Madame Mercier'	MMil SIng
'Pink Damask'	EFou EMon LGre
pinnata 'Blue Eyes'	ESis LHop
prenja	See V. ***austriaca***
§ ***prostrata*** AGM	CSam CShe ELan EMNN EPot ESis GDra LHop MBar MBro MCas MHig MPla MWat NGre NHol NKay NNrd NRed NRoo SIng SSmi WDav WEas WHil WHoo WOld WWin
– ***alba***	WHoo
– 'Blauspiegel' ('Blue Mirror')	SBla SIgm SWas WCru
– 'Blue Ice'	SSmi
– 'Blue Sheen'	CTom ECtt EHic ESis GPlt LGre SChu WAbe WPer WWin
– 'Loddon Blue'	IDai MRav NVic SBla WPer
– 'Miss Willmott'	See V. ***p.*** 'Warley Blue'
– 'Mrs Holt'	CMea CNic CSam CShe EBre EFol EMNN ESis GPlt LBre LGan LGre MCas MFir NCat NMen NNor NNrd NNrw NVic SBla SSmi WHal WPer WSun WThi WWin
– 'Nana'	EMNN EPot ESis EWes MCas MHig MPla NKay NMen NNrd
– 'Rosea'	ELan ESis MPla NHol NKay NRed SHer SIgm WDav WHil WPer
– 'Silver Queen'	CTom SRms
– 'Spode Blue'	CLTr CMGP CMea CMer CShe EGle ESis LBee LGre LHop MBro MMil NCat NWCA SBla SHer WDav
– 'Trehane'	CRiv CShe CTom EBre ECha EFol ELan EPar EPla ESis LBre LGro LHop MBro MWat NGre NHar NKay NNrd SFis SIng SUsu WDav WHal WHil WPer WThi WWin
§ – 'Warley Blue'	CMGP
repens	See V. ***reptans***
§ ***reptans***	CNic EHal MCas NCat SFis WPer
* 'Romany'	CB&S
'Rosalinde'	CBot EBre GBuc LBre NBee NCat SFis SPla WPer
rupestris	See V. ***prostrata***
saturejoïdes	CNic GAbr MBro SRms WDav WPer
saxatilis	See V. ***fruticans***
schmidtiana	GTou WPer
¶ – ***bandaiana***	WCot
– ***nana***	CLew MBro WPat
– – ***rosea***	WThi
selleri	See V. ***wormskjoldii***
¶ ***serpyllifolia***	ECWi
§ 'Shirley Blue' AGM	CBow CShe CTom EBar EBre ECro EFou GCHN LBre LWad MBel MFir MWat NBar NMir SFis SPer WHen WPer
§ ***spicata***	CRDP ECWi ELan EWFC GDra LGan MBro MHew MSal NMen NNor NPri SSvw WCla WCot WHal WPer WSun
– 'Alba'	NPri SSvw WPer
– 'Barcarolle'	ELan SFis
– 'Blaufuchs' ('Blue Fox')	CMHG CSam EBre EFou LBre
* – 'Corali'	SFis
§ – 'Erika'	ECha ECtt EOrc GBuc MTol NOak NPri NRoo SIde SUsu WCla
– 'Heidekind'	CGle CHol CLew CMea CSco CShe EBre ECha EFol EFou ELan EOrc ESis GDra LBre LHop MBri MCas MFir MWat NHar NHol NNor NVic SBla SIng SSmi WDav WEas WWin
¶ – hybrids	CNat
– 'Icicle'	EFou NTow SAsh SAxl
§ – ssp. ***incana*** AGM	CBot CGle CHol CShe EGol EHoe ELan ENot ESis GAbr GMac LGan MBri MBro MCas MHew MWat NKay NMir NNor NRar SBla SPer SSvw WHoo WPer WRus
– – 'Mrs Underwood'	ECha
– – 'Nana'	ECha EPla ESis LGre SAxl WHal
– – 'Saraband'	CSco MHlr WCot
– – 'Silver Carpet'	CCla CMGP EBee EBre EFou EGol EOrc EPla LBre MNFA NBar NHol NSti SMrm WHow WSun
– – 'Wendy' AGM	GCal WSun
– 'Minuet'	SFis WByw
– 'Pavane'	SFis
– 'Romiley Purple'	EFou EMon GCal LGre MSte NBar NSti SAxl SChu WCot
– ***rosea***	See V. ***s.*** 'Erika'
– 'Rotfuchs' ('Red Fox')	CCla CGle CMGP CMHG CRDP CSam EBre ECha ECtt EFou ELan EPar ERav GLil LBre MRav NHol NRoo NSti SCro SHer SPer WByw WEas WHoo WPer WRus WWin
¶ – 'Saraband'	WPer
* – 'Sightseeing'	EHal NMir NRoo SHer WHil
– ssp. ***spicata*** 'Nana'	SSmi
– ***variegata***	EFol EMon NBir NRar
§ ***spuria***	EMon WPer
stelleri	See V. ***wormskjoldii***
subsessilis	GCal
– 'Blau Pyramide'	LGre NHol
§ – ***hendersonii***	EHal GCal
sumilensis	EPla
¶ 'Sunny Border Blue'	WCot
surculosa	SBla
¶ ***tauricola***	NTow
¶ – JH 92101536	LGre
– Mac&W 5835	EPot SIgm
telephiifolia	CLew CMea EMNN ESis GPlt MPla NMen NRed NTow NWCA SFis WAbe WPat
teucrium	See V. ***austriaca t.***
thessalica	NTow
thymoïdes	WDav
¶ – ssp. ***pseudocinerea***	NWCA
– ***thymoïdes***	CNic ESis SIgm
virginica	See VERONICASTRUM ***virginicum***
waldsteiniana	EMon

'Waterperry Blue' ELan LGre MRav SBod
wherryi WPer
'White Spire' CBot
whitleyi GAbr NKay NNrd NOrc SFis WHil WWin
§ *wormskjoldii* CHan CMGP CRiv EFol ELan ESis LHop MBro MHig NHol NKay NMen NNrd SBla SHer SIgm WCla WHil WOMN WPer WWin
– 'Alba' WPer

VERONICASTRUM (Scrophulariaceae)

§ *virginicum* CRow ECha EFol EFou GMac MFir MSal MUlv NSti WPer WTyr WWin
– *album* CBot CChu CCla CDoC CHan CLew CRDP CShe EFol ELan GCal LGan MBri MBro MUlv MWat NFai NSti NWyt SCro SFis SPer WEas WHoo WSun
– 'Pink Glow' EFou ELan
– *roseum* CRDP LRHS MBri MUlv SCro SFis SPer WCot WTyr
– var. *sibiricum* EMon

VESTIA (Solanaceae)

§ *foetida* AGM CB&S CBra CGre CMHG CPle CTro ELan ERea ESma EWri GCal GWht IBlr IReg ISea LHil NBir NRar SIgm WHer WOMN WPer WTyr
lycioïdes See V. *foetida*

VIBURNUM † (Caprifoliaceae)

acerifolium WWat
'Allegheny' SHil
alnifolium See V. *lantanoïdes*
atrocyaneum CPle
betulifolium CB&S CBow CChu CPle CTrw MBal WHCG WThu WWat
bitchiuense ELan
x *bodnantense* CBot CChu CPle CTrw ELan ENot GRei IDai IJoh MRav MWat NHol NNor SLon WEas WStI WWat WWin
– 'Charles Lamont' AGM CBot CSam ECtt EHar ESma IBlr MBri MGos MPla NHol SFai SPer WPat WWat WWeb
– 'Dawn' AGM Widely available
– 'Deben' AGM ECtt EGol EHar ENot EPla MBri SPer
bracteatum CPle
buddlejifolium CChu CCla CPle EHal WHCG WWat
x *burkwoodii* Widely available
– 'Anne Russell' AGM CB&S CCla CPMA CSco CShe EBre EHar EPla IOrc LBre NHol SHBN SHil SPer WAbe WRus
– 'Chenaultii' EHal ELan SPer SSta
– 'Fulbrook' AGM CMHG EHar ERav MUlv NHol
– 'Park Farm Hybrid' AGM CBow CChu CCla CPMA CTre EBre EGol ENot IJoh IOrc LBre LHop MBal NHol NKay SHer SPer WBod WPat WWat
x *carlcephalum* AGM CB&S CChu CSco EBre EGol ELan ENot IDai IJoh IOrc LBre MBri MGos MRav MUlv MWat NHol NKay NNor SHer SLon SPer SReu WBod WDin WHCG WPat
carlesii CB&S CBra CPle ECtt ENot GRei IOrc LHol NBee SGil SHer SPer SReu WStI
– 'Aurora' AGM Widely available
– 'Charis' CMHG NBar NHol WAbe WBod
– 'Diana' CMHG CRos EBre ELan LAbb LBre SGil SHil SSta
cassinoïdes WOld WPat WWat
'Chesapeake' CChu CCla CPle CSam EHar NTow SBla SFai
chingii ELan EMon WWat
cinnamomifolium AGM CBow CLan CPle ELan ISea LNet SArc SBor SLon SMad SPer WWat
congestum ELan
cotinifolium CChu
cylindricum CBot CBrd ELan GWht SBor WCru WWat
dasyanthum EPla
davidii AGM CBra CChe CDec CHEx CPle CShe EBre EGol EHar ELan ENot GRei IDai IJoh ISea LBre LHop MBal MBar MBri MGos MWat NHol NNor NRoo SHBN SLon WDin WHCG WWin
– (f) CB&S CBot CDoC CPMA CSco EHar ELan MBal MGos MUlv NBee NKay SHBN SPer SPla SReu SSta WBod WPat WWat WWeb
– (m) CB&S CBot CDoC CSco EHar ELan MBal MGos MUlv NBee SPer SPla SReu SSta WBod WWat WWeb
dentatum CPle
dilatatum EHar ELan
– f. *xanthocarpum* EPla
erosum CFil
erubescens WWat
– var. *gracilipes* WWat
'Eskimo' CDoC EBre EPla LBre LHop SHil WHCG WPat
§ *farreri* AGM CB&S CBra CChu CSco CShe ECtt ELan ENot GRei ISea LBuc LHol MBal MBar MGos MPla NHol NNor NRoo NWea SHBN SPer WAbe WBod WDin WHCG WWat
– 'Album' See V. *f.* 'Candidissimum'
§ – 'Candidissimum' CBot CCla CFil EFol EHar ELan ENot LHop NHol WPat WThu WWat
– 'Farrer's Pink' CCla CPMA NHol WWat
– 'Nanum' CPMA EGol LHop MPla NHol SChu SSta WHCG WPat WWat
fragrans Bunge See V. *farreri*
furcatum AGM CChu SHil WWat
x *globosum* 'Jermyns Globe' CB&S CBow CDoC CMHG CPle CSco EGol EPla IBar MBar MBri NHol SHil SLon WWat
grandiflorum SLon WBod
harryanum CCla CPle ECou EPla IOrc MBal MUlv WCru WWat
henryi CChu CCla CPle EHar EPla MBri NHol SMad SPer SPla WPat WWat
x *hillieri* CAbP CPle EPla SLon WCru WKif

Plant	Suppliers
– 'Winton' AGM	CDoC CMHG ISea MBri MUlv SHBN SHil SPer
japonicum	CChu CDoC CHEx CPle CSam SHBN WWat
x ***juddii*** AGM	CB&S CBot CBow CCla CLan CPle CSco CShe EBre ECtt EHar ELan ENot IOrc LBre MBal MBar MGos NBee NHol SPer SReu SSta WBod WDin WHCG WPat
lantana	CKin CPer EHic ENot IJoh IOrc LBuc MBar NWea SPer WDin WMou
– 'Aureum'	EFol EPla
– 'Mohican'	SFai
– 'Xanthocarpum'	CSco ISea
§ ***lantanoïdes***	SHil
lentago	MRav
macrocephalum	SHil
mariesii	See V. ***plicatum*** 'Mariesii'
'Mohawk'	SMad
nudum	CCla
– 'Pink Beauty'	CChu CCla
odoratissimum	CB&S CChu CGre CHEx CPle EPla SHBN SMad WSHC
opulus	CB&S CBow CBra CChu CKin CPer CSam ECtt ELan ENot GPoy IOrc LBuc LHol MBar MBri MWat NBee NNor NRoo NWea SHBN SPer WDin WMou
– 'Aureum'	CBra CCla CMHG CPMA CSam CSco EBre EFol EGol EHar EHoe ELan IJoh IOrc LBre MBal MBel MBri MGos MPla MUlv NHol NRoo SHBN SPer SPla SSta WHCG WPat WWat
– 'Compactum' AGM	CB&S CCla CHan CSco EBre EFou EGol ELan ENot IJoh IOrc ISea LBre LHop MBar MBri MGos MPla MWat NHol SDix SPer SReu WDin WHCG WRus WWat
– 'Nanum'	CAbP CCla EGol ELan EPla EPot ERav ESis MBal MBar MBel MBri MCas MPla NHol WDin WHCG
– 'Notcutt's Variety' AGM	CSco EBee ENot SHBN
– 'Park Harvest'	CRos EFol EPla MUlv SPla
§ – 'Roseum' AGM	CB&S CBot CBow CCla CPle CSco EBre EGol ELan ENot IDai IOrc ISea LBre MBar MBri MGos MPla MWat NNor NWea SHBN SPer SPla SReu SSta WDin WStI
– 'Sterile'	See V. ***o.*** 'Roseum'
N– 'Xanthocarpum' AGM	CChu CCla CMHG CSam CSco EBre EGol ELan IOrc LBre LHop MBar MRav MUlv MWat NHol SLon SPer SPla WBod WDin WOMN WSHC WWat WWin
N***plicatum***	CB&S CBow CShe EHar ENot MBar SHer WDin
– 'Cascade'	EGol EPla SHBN
– 'Dart's Red Robin'	ECtt EHic MBri SHer SSta
– 'Grandiflorum' AGM	CPle CSco EBee EGol EHar IDai MBar NHol SBla SMad SPla SReu WBod WHCG
– 'Lanarth'	CB&S CBra CCla CPle CSam CSco CShe CTre ECtt EGol EHar ENot IOrc LHop MBri MPla SLon SPer SPla SSta STre WBod WDin WEas WHCG
§ – 'Mariesii' AGM	Widely available
– 'Nanum'	See V. ***p.*** 'Nanum Semperflorens'
§ – 'Nanum Semperflorens'	CB&S CCla CSco EBre ECtt EHar ELan EPla ESis IJoh IOrc LBre LHop MAsh MBal MBel MBri MGos MPla MUlv NHol NTow SHBN SLon SPer WHCG WKif WWat
– 'Pink Beauty' AGM	Widely available
*– 'Prostratum'	EPla ESis
– 'Rotundifolium'	MBri SHBN
– 'Rowallane' AGM	CSco WWat
¶ – 'Saint Keverne'	SHBN
N– 'Sterile'	EHar SHil
– 'Summer Snowflake'	CBow CCla ELan IJoh IOrc MAsh MBal MBri MPla MWat SHBN SHer SPer SPla WDin WHCG WWeb
– f. ***tomentosum***	CBra CDoC CLan EFol ELan EPla ISea NNor WDin WHCG WStI
– 'Watanabe'	See V. ***p.*** 'Nanum Semperflorens'
'Pragense' AGM	CChu CMCN CPle EGol EHar EPla MBar MBri MGos SHil SLon SPer WPat
pubescens	See V. ***dentatum p.***
recognitum	CCla
x ***rhytidophylloïdes***	CPle NNor WWat
– 'Dart's Duke'	MBri SLPl
rhytidophyllum	Widely available
– 'Roseum'	CBot CSco CShe WWat
– 'Variegatum'	CBot ELan EPla EWri SDry
¶ – 'Willowwood'	SMad
sargentii	IOrc
– 'Onondaga' AGM	Widely available
– 'Susquehanna'	SPer
semperflorens	See V. ***plicatum*** 'Nanum Semperflorens'
§ ***setigerum***	CChu CCla CPle EPla SHil
'Shasta'	CCla CDoC COtt CRos EHar EHic EPla MBri NHol NWyt SSta
theiferum	See V. ***setigerum***
tinus	CB&S CBot CBra CLan CPle CSco CShe CTrw ELan ENot IDai IJoh LBuc LNet MBal MBar MBel MBri MGos MWat NNor SArc SLon SReu SSta WDin WHCG WPat WWin
– 'Bewley's Variegated'	CB&S EBee IBar MGos
– 'Eve Price' AGM	Widely available
– 'French White'	CGre EHic EPla IJoh SGil WWat
– 'Gwenllian' AGM	CDoC CSco EBre ECtt EGol EHar ELan ENot EPla IJoh LBre MBal MGos MPla MRav MUlv NHar NTow SHer SLon SPer SPla WAbe WBod WPat WRus WWat WWeb
– ***hirtellum***	CTre
– 'Israel'	CB&S CBow EGol SMad SPer
– 'Lucidum'	CB&S CSam CSco CShe MGos MUlv NNor SHBN SLon SPla WCru
– 'Lucidum Variegatum'	CLan EMon SDry
– 'Pink Prelude'	SSta
– 'Prostratum'	SHBN
– 'Purpureum'	CB&S CBow CDoC EGol EHal EHoe ELan EPla MAsh SHBN SLon SPer SPla SReu SSta WWeb
– 'Pyramidale'	See V. ***t.*** 'Strictum'

§ – 'Strictum' SLon
– 'Variegatum' Widely available
tomentosum See V. ***plicatum***
trilobum CGre
utile CPle EHal WHCG WThu WWat
wrightii NHol WPat
– var. ***hessei*** MBri MUlv

VICIA (Leguminosae/Papilionaceae)

angustifolia See V. ***sativa nigra***
cracca CKin ECWi MWil NLan WNdy
§ ***sativa nigra*** CKin
sepium CKin EWFC WNdy
sylvatica MWil WGwy

VICTORIA (Nymphaeaceae)

regia See V. ***amazonica***

VIGNA (Leguminosae/Papilionaceae)

See Plant Deletions

VILLADIA (Crassulaceae)

hemsleyana See SEDUM ***hemsleyanum***

VILLARESIA See CITRONELLA

VILLARSIA (Menyanthaceae)

bennettii See NYMPHOIDES ***peltata*** 'Bennettii'

VINCA † (Apocynaceae)

difformis CGle CRDP EBre ECha ELan EPla IDai LBre LHop NCat NHol SDix SDry SIng SUsu WHal WHer WWat
– ***alba*** WWat
– ***bicolor*** 'Jenny Pym' EMon LHop
– ssp. ***difformis*** EMon
– Greystone form WRus
– 'Oxford' SLPl
– 'Snowmound' CMil
herbacea EMon WEas
'Hidcote Purple' See V. ***major*** 'Oxyloba'
major CB&S CBow CChe CDoC CSFH CSco CShe ELan ENot EOrc ERav GPoy GRei IJoh ISea LBuc MBri MFir MGos MWat SBod SHBN SIng SPer SReu WDin WOak WStI WTyr WWin
– ***alba*** GBuc IBlr LHop WPer WWat WWeb
– 'Caucasian Blue' LMer
– 'Elegantissima' See V. ***m.*** 'Variegata'
– ssp. ***hirsuta*** CShe CTom EMon EOrc WCot WFox WWye
– 'Jason Hill' ELan EMon MBel WCot
§ – 'Maculata' (v) CBow CElw CGre CRDP EFol ELan EMon ENot EPla GAbr IBar MBri NHol NRoo NSti SDry SFai SPer WAbe WCru WStI
§ – 'Oxyloba' CNic ECtt ELan EMon EPla ESma LHop MRav SLPl SPla WHen
– var. ***pubescens*** See V. ***m. hirsuta***
– 'Reticulata' ELan EMon MBel NSti SDry
– 'Starlight' NSti
– 'Surrey Marble' See V. ***m.*** 'Maculata'
§ – 'Variegata' AGM Widely available
minor CBow CBra CDoC CKin ELan ENot EPar ERav GCHN GPoy GRei IJoh LBuc MBar MBro MFir MWat SReu STre WDin WOak WTyr WWin WWye
– f. ***alba*** Widely available
– 'Alba Aureavariegata' See V. ***m.*** 'Alba Variegata'
§ – 'Alba Variegata' CBow CCla CGle CSFH CTom EBre EGol EHoe EJud EOrc EPla IJoh LBre MBar MFir NHol NKay NRoo SPer STre WAbe WEas WHer WWat
§ – 'Argenteovariegata' AGM CB&S CChe CCla CGle CSco CShe ECha EFou EGol ELan ENot GDra GRei LBuc LGro MBar MBri MGos NHol NRoo SBod SIng SPer WDin WEas WWat WWin
§ – 'Atropurpurea' AGM CB&S CCla CSam CSco CShe EBre ECha EGol ELan EPla IJoh LBre MBar MBri MGos NHol NKay NRoo NSti SBod SChu SHBN SPer WBon WEas WOak WWeb
– 'Aurea' EPla
§ – 'Aureovariegata' CB&S CBot CCla CSco ECha EFol ELan EOrc EPla GPoy IJoh MBal MBar MBri MFir NNor NRoo SReu WAbe WHen
§ – 'Azurea Flore Pleno' AGM Widely available
– 'Blue Cloud' CBow EBee SBod
– 'Blue Drift' SBod
*– 'Blue Moon' ECtt NHol
– 'Bowles' Blue' See V. ***m.*** 'La Grave'
– 'Bowles' Variety' See V. ***m.*** 'La Grave'
– 'Burgundy' CBre CShe EPar GGar MBal SIng SRms WWat
– 'Caerulea Plena' See V. ***m.*** 'Azurea Flore Pleno'
– 'Dartington Star' See V. ***major*** 'Oxyloba'
– 'Dart's Blue' MBri
– 'Double Burgundy' See V. ***m.*** 'Multiplex'
– 'Gertrude Jekyll' AGM CAbb CBow CCla CRiv CSco CTom EGol ELan EPla IBar IDai MBri NHol NRoo NSti SBod SChu SPer WAbe WHer WSun
– 'Grüner Teppich' ('Green Carpet') EMon MBri SPla
§ – 'La Grave' AGM CChe CCla CDoC CLew CRiv CSco CShe ECha ENot EPla GAbr GPlt MBri MBro NHol NNor SBod SChu SPer SSvw STre WBod WDav WWat
– 'Maculata' (v) ELan SHer
*– 'Marion Cran' NHol
§ – 'Multiplex' (d) CCla CGre CMil CNic CTom ECtt EGol ELan EPar EPla ERav ESma MBri NHol NNor NRoo SFai SMrm WBod WBon WCru WWat WWeb
– 'Purpurea' See V. ***m.*** 'Atropurpurea'
– 'Rubra' See V. ***m.*** 'Atropurpurea'
– 'Sabinka' EMon EPla
– 'Silver Service' (v) CElw CMil EMon EPla ESma LRHS MBel NHol WCot
*– 'Spring Morning' CElw

– 'Variegata' See V. ***m.*** 'Argenteovariegata'
– 'Variegata Aurea' See V. ***m.*** 'Aureovariegata'
– 'White Gold' CBow ESma MPla NHol

VINCETOXICUM (Asclepiadaceae)

§ ***hirundinaria*** GPoy MSal
nigrum EMon EPla MSal WThi
officinale See V. ***hirundinaria***

VIOLA † (Violaceae)

'Abigail' (Vtta) SCaw
'Achilles' (Va) SCaw
'Adelina' (Va) SCaw
'Admiral Avallon' See V. 'Amiral Avallon'
'Admiration' (Va) CFul GMac SCaw SHaz WBou
adunca 'Alba' EFol GMac
¶ – ***minor*** GLil
aetolica CPla EBar EFol NKay NWCA
'Agneta' (Va) SCaw
'Alanta' (Va) LGre MTho SCaw
§ ***alba*** CPla CRiv EFou ELan EWes LHop NHol NSti NVic SCro SHer SPla WEas WWin
albanica See V. ***magellensis***
I 'Alcea' SCaw
'Alethia' (Va) SCaw
'Alexander Rayfield' (Va) SCaw
'Alexia' (Va) SCaw
'Alice Woodall' (Va) SCaw
'Alma' (Va) SHaz
altaica SCaw
'Alwyn' (Va) SCaw
'Alys' (Va) SHaz
¶ 'Amandine Pages' CSmi
'Amelia' (Va) GMac SCaw
'Amethyst' (C) CDoC LHop
§ 'Amiral Avellan' (Vt) CCot CCra CGro MRob NBro WRus
'Andrena' (Va) SCaw
'Ann' (ExV) SHaz
'Ann Kean' (Vtta) NRoo SCaw
'Ann Robb' (ExV) SHaz
'Annabelle' (Va) SCaw
'Annaliese' (Va) SCaw
'Anne Mott' (Va) SCaw
'Annette Ross' (Va) SCaw
I 'Annona' (Va) SCaw
'Anthea' (Va) SCaw
'Antique Lace' (Va) GMac SUsu WMar
'Aphrodite' (Va) SCaw
'Apollo' (Va) SCaw
'Arabella' (Va) CMHG SCaw SMrm WBou
arborescens NHol
'Ardross Gem' (Va) CCla CFul CGle CMHG CPla CRDP CSam CShe ERav GArf GCHN GMac LBee LHop NHol NNrd NSti SCaw SHaz SMrm SPer SSvw SUsu WBou WEas WMar WPer WWin
arenaria See V. ***rupestris***
'Arkwright's Ruby' (Va) CLTr EBar NMen
'Artemis' (Va) SCaw
arvensis ECWi
'Aspasia' **AGM** CFul GMac LBee NHol SCaw SHaz WAbe WBou
¶ 'Astrid' SCaw
'Atalanta' (Vtta) SCaw
'Athena' (Va) SCaw
'Aurelia' (Va) SCaw
'Aurora' (Va) SCaw
'Avril Lawson' GMac SHaz
'Baby Lucia' (Va) ELan
'Barbara' (Va) CFul SCaw WBou
'Baronne Alice de Rothschild' (Vt) CCot CRDP CSmi CWes MRob
¶ 'Bates Green Purple' SUsu
'Beatrice' (Vtta) CBos SHaz
§ 'Belmont Blue' (C) CFul CShe EOrc EPla GMac LBee LHop MBel MRav NHol NMen NRoo SCaw SChu SHaz SHer SMrm SPer WBou WMar
'Benjie' (Va) SHaz
'Berna' WHer
§ ***bertolonii*** EBar NHol SCaw WAbe WBou
'Beshlie' **AGM** GMac MArl SCaw WBou WEas
'Bessie Cawthorne' (C) SCaw
'Bessie Knight' (Va) SCaw
betonicifolia GTou WPer WThu
*– ***albescens*** NHar
'Bettina' (Va) SCaw
'Betty' SHaz
'Betty Grace' (Va) SCaw
'Bianca' (Vtta) SCaw
biflora CLew CMHG CPla EPar GDra MRob MTho NGre NRya WBon WEas
'Black Ace' (Va) SCaw
'Black Diamond' (Va) SHaz
*'Black Velvet' NRed
'Blue Carpet' (Va) GMac SHaz
'Blue Cloud' (Va) SCaw
¶ 'Blue Haze' SPer WSun
'Blue Lace' (Va) SHaz
¶ 'Blue Moon' (C) EBee NCat WBou
¶ 'Blue Moonlight' (C) GBuc GMac
'Blue Princess' NMen
'Blue Tit' (Va) WBou
'Bonna Cawthorne' (Va) SCaw
bosniaca See V. ***elegantula b.***
'Boughton Blue' See V. 'Belmont Blue'
'Bournemouth Gem' (Vt) CCra CSmi MRob
§ 'Bowles' Black' (T) CArn CHan CTom ECha ELan EPad GAbr NBro NNrw NRoo NSti SBla WBou WEas
'Boy Blue' (Vtta) EHal SCaw
'Brenda Hall' (Va) SCaw
'Bronwen' (Va) SCaw
bubanii SCaw
'Bullion' (Va) SCaw SHaz WMer
'Buttercup' (Vtta) CFul GMac LBee NRoo SCaw SHaz WBou WMar WWin
'Buxton Blue' (Va) CFul SCaw SChu SHaz
'Byrony' (Vtta) SCaw
calaminaria SCaw
'Calantha' (Vtta) SCaw
calcarata ELan SCaw SHer WThu
§ – ssp. ***zoysii*** EWes GArf GCHN GDra ITim NGre NMen SIng
'California' (Vt) CCot MRob
'Callia' (Va) SCaw
I 'Calypso' (Va) SCaw
canadensis var. ***rugulosa*** CRDP

'Candida' (Vtta) SCaw
canina CKin
'Carberry Seedling' (Va) SCaw
'Carina' (Vtta) SCaw
'Carnival' (Va) GMac NBrk
'Caroline' (Va) SHaz
I 'Cassandra' (Vtta) SCaw
'Cat's Whiskers' GMac NBrk
chaerophylloïdes See V. ***dissecta c.***
'Chantal' (Vtta) SCaw
'Chantreyland' (Va) ECoo MFir SRms WHen WSun
'Charity' (Va) SCaw
'Charlotte Mott' (Va) SCaw
'Chelsea Girl' (Va) SHaz
'Chloe' (Vtta) SCaw
'Christmas' CBre
'Christobel' (Va) SCaw
'Cinderella (Va) CFul
'Cindy' (Va) SHaz
'Citrina' (Va) SCaw
'Clementina' **AGM** CCot EBre GAri GCHN LBre MRav NSti SCro
'Cleo' (Va) CVer GMac SHaz
'Clive Groves' (Vt) CGro
'Clodagh' (Va) CMHG SCaw
'Clover' (Va) SCaw
'Coeur d'Alsace' (Vt) CBre CCot CGro CHol CMea CNic CPla CSmi EFou ELan EPar GMac SHaz SSvw WBon WEas WPer WRus WSun
¶ 'Colette' (V) SCaw
'Colleen' (Vtta) SCaw
'Columbine' (Va) CBos CLew CMHG CRDP GMac SCaw SHaz SMrm
§ 'Comte de Brazza' (dVt) CCot CCra CSmi CVer CWes GMac MRob SHaz
'Comte de Chambord' (dVt) MRob SHaz
'Connie' (Va) CBos SCaw SHaz
'Coralie' (Vtta) SCaw
'Cordelia' (Va) MRob SCaw SHaz
¶ Cornish indigenous mauve CSmi
cornuta **AGM** CFul CGle CHad CMea CPla EOrc LGan LHop MBro MFir MHig NBro NKay NMen NRoo SCaw SDix SIng SMrm SPer WBou WHen WHoo
– Alba Group **AGM** Widely available
§ – 'Alba Minor' CFul CGle CLew CMHG CNic EFol ELan GMac MBro NMen NRoo SCaw SChu WHoo
– blue SCaw WMar WSun WWat
– ***compacta*** CHan GArf
– 'Foliis Aureis' MFir
– Lilacina Group CFul CGle CTom ECha GMac NCat SCaw SChu SHaz SMrm SWas WPer WSun
– 'Minor' **AGM** CFul CNic CPla CSam EPot GMac MBro MFir NNrd SBla SCaw SHaz WBou WDav WRus
– 'Minor Alba' See V. ***c.*** 'Alba Minor'
– Purpurea Group CMea ECha WRus
– 'Rosea' CBos CFul SCaw WMar WSun
– 'Seymour Pink' CFul
– 'Variegata' CRDP SCaw WDav
– 'Violacea' SCaw
'Coronation' CMHG CSam
corsica SCaw
'Cox's Moseley' (ExV) SHaz
¶ ***crassa*** WAbe
'Cream Sensation' (Va) SHaz
'Cressida' (Va) SCaw
cucullata See V. ***obliqua***
cunninghamii CPBP GDra
curtisii See V. ***tricolor c.***
'Cyril Bell' (Va) SCaw
§ 'Czar' (Vt) CPla GAbr ILis MRob NRed NRya SHaz WHen WSun
'Czar Bleu' (Vt) MRob
'Daena' (Vtta) SCaw SMrm
'Daisy Smith' (Va) CFul GMac WBou
'Dartington Hybrid' (Va) SCaw
'Daveron' (C) SCaw
'David Wheldon' (Va) SCaw SHaz
'Davina' (Va) SCaw SChu
'Dawn' (Vtta) CCot CFul GMac LBee MMil SCaw SHaz WBou
'Decima' (Va) SCaw
'Delia' (Va) GMac SCaw SUsu WBou
'Delicia' (Vtta) CMHG NRoo SCaw
'Delmonden' (Va) SAsh SHaz
delphinantha NWCA
'Delphine' (Va) NRoo SCaw SMrm
'Demeter' (Va) SCaw
'Desdemona' (Va) CMHG GMac LGre SHaz WBou
'Desmonda' (Va) SCaw SChu
'Devon Cream' (Va) GMac WBou
'Dimity' (Va) SCaw
'Dione' (Vtta) SCaw
I 'Diosma' (Va) SCaw
§ ***dissecta*** WPer
– var. ***chaerophylloïdes*** f. ***eizanensis*** CCla CHad CRDP EBre ECro ESma LBre MTho WHal WOMN
– var. ***sieboldiana*** EFol MRob
'Dobbie's Bronze' (Va) SCaw SHaz WBou
'Dobbie's Red' (Va) SCaw SHaz WBou
'Doctor Smart' (C) SCaw
doerfleri SCaw
'Dominy' (Vtta) SCaw
'Double White' (dVt) CGle MRob
dubyana GBuc
'Duchesse de Parme' (dVt) CGle CGro CWes GMac MRob SHaz WHer
'Dulcie Rhoda' (Va) SHaz
'Dusk' WBou
'D'Udine' (dVt) GMac MRob
'E A Bowles' See V. 'Bowles' Black'
'Eastgrove Blue Scented (Va) GMac SHaz WAbe WBou WEas
'Ednaston Gem' CSam
eizanensis See V. ***dissecta chaerophylloïdes e.***
§ ***elatior*** CMea CMil CPla CRDP EBar ECha EMon LGan MBel MRob NHol NSti SChu SHaz SIng SWas WBon WDav WMar WPer
§ ***elegantula*** SCaw
– ***bosniaca*** SCaw WEas
'Elisha' (Va) SCaw
'Elizabeth' (Va) CGro CSpe GMac SCaw WBou
'Elizabeth Cawthorne' (C) SCaw
¶ 'Elliot Adam' (Va) SHaz

'Elsie Coombs' (Vt) MRob WPer
'Emily Mott' (Va) SCaw
'Emma' (Va) NHar SCaw
'Emma Cawthorne' (C) SCaw
'Enterea' (Va) SCaw
erecta See V. ***elatior***
'Eris' (Va) SCaw
'Eros' (Va) NRoo SCaw
'Etain' (Va) ECha LGre SCaw
'Ethena' (Va) SCaw
'Etienne' (Va) SCaw
'Evelyn Cawthorne' (C) NRoo SCaw
eximia SCaw
'Fabiola' (Vtta) GMac LBee SCaw WBou
'Felicity' (Va) SCaw
'Finola Galway' (Va) SCaw
'Fiona' (Va) CBos CMHG GMac NBrk NCat NRoo SCaw SUsu WBou WMar WSun
flettii NKay NTow WAbe WHal WOMN
'Florence' (Va) SCaw
'Foxbrook Cream' (C) CBos CFul CVer GAbr GBuc GMac MBel NBrk SHaz SPer WBou WRus WSun
'Francesca' (Va) SCaw
'Freckles' See V. ***sororia*** 'F.'
'Gatina' (Va) SCaw
I 'Gazania' (Va) SCaw WBou
'Gazelle' (Vtta) ECha SCaw
'Gemma' (Va) SHaz
'Genesta Gambier' (Va) CFul CMHG CSam SCaw
'Georgina' (Va) SCaw
'Geraldine' (Vtta) SCaw
'Geraldine Cawthorne' (C) SCaw
'Gina' (Vtta) SCaw
'Giselle' (Va) SCaw
glabella CVer SUsu WOMN
'Gladys Findlay' (Va) GMac SCaw SHaz WBou WHer
'Governor Herrick' (Vt) CShe EFou MRob WPer
'Grace' (Va) EBar NRoo SHaz
§ ***gracilis*** ECha ELan SBla SCaw
– ***lutea*** CNic CSam SBla SMrm SSvw
*– 'Magic' CRDP SMrm
– 'Major' GMac SCaw SHaz
'Grey Owl' (Va) LGre SCaw SChu WKif
grisebachiana CPla NGre NTow
'Griselda' (Vtta) SCaw
'Grovemount Blue' (C) CMea NCat NKay
§ ***grypoceras*** var. ***exilis*** CDec CRDP ESma NWCA WCru WHal WHoo
– 'Variegata' EFol NBir WHal
'Gustav Wermig' (C) GAbr MBel SCaw SHaz WBou
'Gwen Cawthorne' (C) SCaw
'Hadria Cawthorne' (C) SCaw
'Hansa' (C) WMer
'Haslemere' See V. 'Nellie Britton'
¶ 'Hazel Jean' (Va) SHaz
I 'Hebe' (Vtta) SCaw
§ ***hederacea*** CArn CCot CFee CGro CHan CMHG CPla CRDP CSFH CShe ECou EFol ELan ELun EPot ESis GCHN GCal GMac MRob NBro NHar SHaz SUsu WAbe WHer WOMN WWye
– blue CFee CPla CSpe ECou LHil SHaz SHer SIng WHal WOMN WPer
– 'Putty' EBre ECou EWes LBre
– ***sieberi*** See V. ***sieberiana***
'Helen' (Va) SHaz
¶ 'Helen Dillon' EWes
'Helen W Cochrane' (ExV) SHaz
'Helena' (Va) SCaw
'Hera' (Va) SCaw
'Hespera' (Va) SCaw
I 'Hesperis' (Va) SCaw
heterophylla ssp. ***epirota*** See V. ***bertolonii***
'Hextable' (C) SCaw
¶ 'Highland Night' GAbr
hirta CKin ECWi MRob MWil WCla
hispida SCaw
'Honey' (Va) SHaz
'Huntercombe Purple' AGM CBos CCla CFul CGle CSam CVer GMac NNrd SBla SCaw SHaz SPer SUsu WBou WKif WSun
'Hyperion' (Va) SCaw
'Iantha' (Vtta) SCaw
'Iden Gem' (Va) CFul SCaw SHaz
incisa MFos
'Inkie' (Va) CFul
'Inverurie Beauty' AGM EJud MFir NBrk NCat SCaw WBou
'Inverurie Mauve' (Va) SCaw SUsu
'Iona' (Va) SCaw
'Irish Elegance' (Vt) CHad CRDP MRob NRed WHal
'Irish Molly' (Va) CBot CCla CCot CElw CFul CHad CMHG CRDP CSam CShe ECha ELan EPot GCal GMac LBee LHop SBla SCaw SHaz SMrm SUsu WBou WEas WHer WHil WMar WPer WSHC WWin
'Isata' (Va) SCaw
'Isla' (Vtta) LGre SCaw
¶ 'Isobel' EWes
'Ita' (Va) SCaw
'Iver Grove' (Va) SCaw
¶ 'Ivory' CGro
'Ivory Queen' (Va) CCla CFul GMac NBrk SCaw
'Ivory White' (Va) SCaw WOMN
'Jack Frost' (FP) SHaz
'Jackanapes' AGM CBos CBot CCla CCot CElw CFul CGle CMHG CMea CSam CShe ECha ECtt ELan GMac LHop MHig NBrk NRoo NSti SCaw SHaz SMrm WBou WMar WWin
'James Pilling' (Va) CFul GMac SCaw SHaz
'Jamie' (Va) SHaz
'Jane Askew' (Va) SCaw
'Jane Mott' (Va) SCaw
'Janet' (Va) SCaw WBou
'Janine' (Vtta) SCaw
'Janna' (Va) SCaw
¶ ***japonica*** WThi
'Jeannie' (Va) SHaz
'Jeannie Bellew' (Va) GMac NHar SCaw SChu SHaz WBou WKif WMar WSun
'Jemma' (Va) SCaw
'Jenelle' (Vtta) SCaw
'Jenny' (Vtta) SCaw
'Jersey Gem' (Va) GMac SCaw SHaz
'Jessie East' WEas
'Joanna' (Va) SHaz
¶ 'Jodie' (Va) SHaz

'Joella' (Va) SCaw
¶ 'John Fielding' (Va) SHaz
'John Raddenbury' (Vt) CCra CRDP CSmi MRob SHaz
¶ 'John Wallmark' (c) WMer
'John Yelmark' (Va) SCaw
'John Zanini' (Vtta) SCaw
'Johnny Jump Up' (T) MPit
Joker strain (P) NOak
jooi CNic GTou LBee MRob MTho NBir NMen SBla SIng WAbe WDav WPer WThu
¶ 'Jordieland Gem' (c) GMac
'Joyce Gray' (Va) EBar NRoo SHaz
'Julia' (Va) SCaw WBou
'Julian' (Va) CFul CVer EBar GDra GMac NKay NMen NRoo NSti SBla SHaz SIng SUsu WAbe WBou WDav WMar
'Juno' (Va) GMac SCaw
'Jupiter' (Va) SCaw
'Kadischa' (Va) SCaw
'Karen' (Va) SHaz
'Kate' (Va) CFul GMac SHaz
'Katerina' (Va) SCaw
'Kathy' (Vtta) SCaw
'Katinka' (Va) SCaw
keiskii GCHN GTou LGre SHaz WThi
'Kerrie' (Va) SCaw
'Kiki McDonough' SCaw
'Kilruna' (Va) SCaw
'King of the Blues' (Va) SHaz
¶ 'Kinvarna' (V) SCaw
'Kirsty' (Va) SCaw
'Kitty White' (Va) SCaw
'Kizzy' (Va) SHaz
koraiensis MTho
koreana See V. ***grypoceras exilis***
¶ ***kusanoana*** WThi
N***labradorica purpurea*** misapplied See V. ***riviniana*** Purpurea Group
N***labradorica*** hort. See V. ***riviniana*** Purpurea Group
¶ ***lactea*** ECWi
'Lady Finnyoon' (Va) SHaz
'Lady Jane' (Vt) MRob
'Lady Tennyson' (Va) GMac SBla SCaw SHaz WBou
'Lamorna' (Vtta) SCaw
lanceolata CPla GCra
'Larissa' (Va) SCaw
'Latona' (Va) SCaw
'Laura' (C) CFul EFol GMac
'Lavender Lady' CBre CRDP MRob
'Laverna' (Va) SCaw
'Lavinia' (Va) GMac NBrk SCaw SHaz WBou
¶ 'Lawrence' (c) WMer
'Leander' (Va) SCaw
'Leda' (Va) SCaw
'Lee' (Va) SHaz
'Leora' (Vtta) CFul GMac NRoo SCaw
'Leora Hamilton' (C) CMHG SCaw
'Lerosa' (Vtta) SCaw
'Leta' (Vtta) SCaw
'Letitia' (Va) CFul EOrc GAbr GMac NRoo SCaw SHaz WAbe WBou
'Leto' (Va) SCaw
'Lewisa' (Va) SCaw
'Lianne' (Vt) CCra CWes MRob SHaz WPer
'Lilac Rose' (Va) CFul GMac LBee NCat WAbe WBou
'Liliana' (Va) SCaw
'Liriopa' (Va) SCaw
'Lisa Cawthorne' (C) SCaw
'Little David' **AGM** CFul CSam CShe EHal GMac LBee NRoo SCaw SHaz SMrm WAbe WBou WEas WRus
'Little Johnny' (Va) GMac
'Little Liz' (Va) GMac SHaz
'Livia' (Vtta) SCaw WBou
'Lola' (Va) SCaw
'Lord Nelson' (C) WMer
'Lord Plunket' (Va) CFul NCat SCaw SHaz WBou
'Lorna' **AGM** SCaw SUsu
'Lorna Cawthorne' (C) SCaw
'Lorna Moakes' (Va) CRDP SCaw SMrm
'Louisa' (Va) SCaw SUsu
'Louise Gemmell' (Va) SCaw SChu
'Love Duet' NBir
'Luca' (Va) SCaw
'Lucinda' (Va) SCaw
'Lucy' (Va) SCaw
'Ludy May' (Va) SCaw
'Lulu' (Va) SHaz
'Luna' (Vtta) SCaw
lutea CShe SCaw WBou
– ssp. ***elegans*** See V. ***lutea lutea***
'Luxonne' (Vt) CBre CCot MRob SHaz
lyallii ECou
'Lydia' (Va) CShe SCaw SChu SHaz WBou
'Lydia Groves' CGro CRDP GMac MRob
'Lysander' (Va) SCaw
macedonica See V. ***tricolor macedonica***
¶ ***maculata*** WOMN
'Madame Armandine Pages' (Vt) CBre CCra MRob
'Madelaine' (Va) SCaw
'Madge' (Va) SCaw
'Maera' (Vtta) SCaw
§ ***magellensis*** MPit
'Magenta Maid' (Va) CFul GMac LBee MArl
'Maggie' (Va) SCaw
'Maggie Mott' **AGM** CCla CCot CFul CGle CSam CShe ECha ECtt EOrc ERav GArf GMac LHop MBri MHig NBrk NRoo NSti SBla SCaw SHaz SPer SSvw WBou WEas WMar WRus WWin
'Magic' GMac LBee MArl MFir SHaz WBou WCru
'Maid Marion' SRms
'Majella' (Vtta) SCaw
'Malise' (Va) SCaw
'Malvena' (Vtta) SCaw
mandshurica GMac WHal WThu
¶ – 'Bicolor' GMac
– 'Ikedaeana' MFos
'Margaret' (Va) SHaz
'Margaret Cawthorne' (C) SCaw
'Marian' (Va) SCaw
'Marie Louise' (dVt) CCot CCra CGro CPla CRDP CSmi EPar MRob SHaz
'Marika' (Va) SCaw
'Maroon Picotee' ELan SHer
'Mars' (Va) SCaw

'Marsland's Yellow' (Vtta)	SCaw
'Martin' AGM	CBos CCla CFul CMHG CSam CShe CVer ECha GCHN GMac LBee LHop NBrk NKay SCaw SChu SHaz SHer SMrm SPer WBou WMar WSun WWin
'Mary Cawthorne' (C)	SCaw
'Mary Dawson' (Va)	SCaw
'Mary Ellen' (Va)	CFul
'Mattie' (Va)	SHaz
'Mauve Beauty' (Va)	SCaw
'Mauve Haze' (Va)	CCla GMac MTho SHaz SPer WBou WEas WMar
'Mauve Radiance' (Va)	CFul CShe GMac NVic SCaw SHaz SSvw WBou
'May Mott' (Va)	GMac NBrk WAbe
'Mayfly' (Va)	GMac NBrk WBou
'Meena' (Vtta)	SCaw
'Megumi' (Va)	SCaw
'Melinda' (Vtta)	SCaw WBou
I 'Melissa' (Va)	CFul GMac NBrk
'Mercury' (Va)	SCaw
'Midnight Turk' (Va)	SHaz
'Milkmaid' (Va)	CGle EBee ECha ECtt LBee NBir SIng WKif
'Mina Walker' (ExV)	SHaz
'Minerva' (Va)	SCaw
'Miranda' (Vtta)	SCaw
'Miss Brookes' (Va)	CFul GMac SCaw SHaz SMrm WBou
'Mistral' (Va)	SCaw
¶ 'Misty Guy' (Vtta)	SHaz
'Mitzel' (Vtta)	NRoo SCaw
'Molly Sanderson' AGM	Widely available
'Monica' (Va)	SCaw
'Moonlight' AGM	CFul CHad CMea CSam ECha ELan EPla GCHN GMac LBee LHop MCas NKay NRoo NSti SBla SCaw SHaz SPer SUsu WBou WHal WPer
'Moonraker'	CCot NCat NKay NTow
'Morvana' (Va)	SCaw
'Morwenna' (Va)	SCaw
'Moscaria' (Va)	SCaw
'Moseley Ideal' (ExV)	SHaz
'Moseley Perfection' (Va)	SCaw
'Mother's Day'	MRob
'Mrs Chichester' (Va)	GMac LHop NBrk SCaw SHaz WBou
'Mrs David Lloyd George' (dVt)	MRob
'Mrs Lancaster' (Va)	CFul CSam CVer EOrc GMac SCaw SHaz WBou
'Mrs Pinehurst' (Vt)	MRob
'Mrs R Barton' (Vt)	CCot CCra CPla CRDP MRob SHaz WHil
'Myfawnny' (Va)	CSam NRoo SCaw SHaz WBou
'Mylene' (Va)	SCaw
'Myntha' (Vtta)	SCaw
'Mysie' (Va)	CFul
'Nadia' (Va)	SCaw
¶ 'Nancy Jean' (Va)	SHaz
'Natasha' (Va)	SCaw
♦ 'Neapolitan'	See V. 'Pallida Plena'
'Nell' (Va)	CFul
§ 'Nellie Britton' AGM	CCla CFul CGle EOrc GMac LHop NKay NRoo NSti SBla SCaw SChu SHaz WAbe WBou WEas WMar WRus WWin
'Nemesis' (Va)	SCaw
'Neptune' (Va)	SCaw
'Nerena' (Vtta)	SCaw
'Nesta' (Vtta)	SCaw
'Netta Statham' (C)	See V. 'Belmont Blue'
'Nicole' (Va)	SCaw
'Nigra' (Va)	CHol SCaw
'Nimrod' (Va)	SCaw
'Nina' (Va)	SCaw
'Nona' (Va)	SCaw
'Noni' (Vt)	MRob
'Norah Church' (Vt)	CCot CGro CSmi CWes MRob SHaz
'Norah Leigh' (Va)	CCra EBre ESis LBre WBou
§ *obliqua* AGM	CGro NVic SChu SHaz WOMN
– *alba*	See V. *alba*
§ – *rosea*	CBre CSFH EPla EWes
¶ *occulta striata albe*	NBro
'Octavia' (Va)	SCaw
'Odile' (Va)	SCaw
odorata	CArn CB&S CGle CKin CRDP ECWi EPar ERav EWFC GBar GMac GPoy LHol MBri MRob MSal NKay NRoo NSti SIde WCla WOak WWye
§ – *alba*	CKin GAbr WWye
– 'Alba'	CBre CCla CGle CRDP EFou ELan EPad EPar ERav GMac ILis MFir MRob NCat NNrd NRoo NSti SIde WBon WCla WRus WWat
– 'Alba Plena'	CRDP WHer
♦ – apricot	See V. 'Sulphurea'
– *dumetorum*	See V. *alba*
– *flore-pleno*	CRDP EPar
– pink	WCla
– *rosea*	GMac WOMN
– 'Sulphurea'	See V. 'S.'
– 'Wellsiana' AGM	GArf
'Olive Edmonds' (Va)	SCaw
'Opera' (Vt)	CCot CCra CGro GMac MRob
'Orchid Pink' (Vt)	MRob
oreades	SCaw
'Oriana' (Va)	SCaw
orphanidis	SCaw
ossea	SCaw
§ 'Pallida Plena' (dVt)	CSmi
'Palmer's White' (Va)	CFul SCaw SHaz
palustris	CKin CRDP CShe MRob WHer
'Pamela' (Va)	SHaz
'Pamela Zambra' (Vt)	CGro MRob SHaz
'Pam's Fancy' (ExV)	WBou
'Pandora' (Va)	SCaw SHaz WBou
papilionacea	See V. *sororia*
'Parme de Toulouse' (dVt)	MRob
'Pat Creasy' (Va)	GMac SHaz WBou
'Pat Kavanagh'	GMac SCaw
'Patricia Brookes' (Va)	SCaw
pedata	CBro CRDP MRob MSto NHar NHol WAbe WWat
pedatifida	CCla CRiv ECro EFol ELan EMar EPla MRob MTho NNrd NSti SChu SHaz SHer WHal WRus WThu

'Penny Black' (Va)	CNic ECha EMon SCaw
pensylvanica	See V. ***pubescens eriocarpa***
perinensis JCA 992.600	CNic
'Perle Rose' (Vt)	CCot CCra CGro CWes MBel MRob
'Pete'	SChu SUsu
'Petra' (Vtta)	SCaw
'Philippa Cawthorne' (C)	SCaw
'Phoebe' (Va)	SCaw WBou
'Phyllida' (Va)	SCaw
'Pickering Blue' (Va)	CFul GMac SCaw SHaz WBou
¶ 'Piglets' (Vt)	SHaz
'Pilar' (Va)	SCaw
'Piper' (Va)	SHaz
'Pippa' (Vtta)	SCaw SChu
'Pixie' (Va)	SHaz
'Poppy' (Va)	SCaw
'Priam' (Va)	SCaw
'Primrose Cream' (Va)	SCaw
'Primrose Dame' (Va)	CDoC GMac NNrd NRoo SCaw SHaz WBou WMer
'Primrose Pixie' (Va)	WBou
'Prince Henry' (T)	LAbb MPit NKay NMen
'Prince John' (T)	MPit NCat NKay NMen
'Princess Alexandra' (Vt)	MRob
'Princess Mab' (Vtta)	CBos CFul NBrk NNrd NRoo SCaw SHaz WBou
'Princess of Prussia' (Vt)	WWat
'Princess of Wales'	See V. 'Princesse de Galles'
§ 'Princesse de Galles' (Vt)	CB&S CCra CGro CSmi EPar MRob NFai SHaz WRus
§ ***pubescens eriocarpa***	CBro CRDP GMac
'Purity' (Vtta)	SCaw
'Purple Dove' (Va)	SHaz SMrm
'Purple Radiance'	CCla
'Purple Wings' (Va)	GMac SUsu WBou
¶ 'Putty'	WCru
'Quatre Saisons' (Vt)	MRob
'Queen Charlotte' (Vt)	CSmi GCHN ILis MBri MRob NFai NMen WCot
'Queen Disa' (Vtta)	CMHG SCaw
'Quink' (Va)	CFul SHaz
'Ramona' (Va)	SCaw
'Raven (Vtta)	GMac SUsu WBou
'Ravenna' (Va)	SCaw
'Rawson's White' (Vt)	MRob NCat
'Rebecca' (Vtta)	Widely available
'Rebecca Cawthorne' (C)	SCaw
'Red Charm' (Vt)	MBri
'Red Lion'	CGro
'Red Queen' (Vt)	CCot CGro MRob
reichenbachiana	ELan EPar EWFC MWil
'Reliance' (Va)	CFul
'Remora' (Vtta)	SCaw WBou
reniforme	See V. ***hederacea***
'Rhoda' (Va)	SCaw
'Richard Vivian' (Va)	SCaw
'Richard's Yellow' (Va)	SCaw
riviniana	CArn CKin CTom EJud WHer WOak
§ – Purpurea Group	Widely available
¶ – white	NMir
¶ 'Rodney Davey' (Vt)(v)	CPla CRDP
'Romilly' (Va)	SCaw
'Rosine' (Vt)	CBre CCra MRob
'Rowan Hood' (ExV)	SHaz
'Rowena' (Va)	SCaw
'Royal Delft'	GCHN
'Royal Robe' (VT)	CCra MRob
'Rubra' (Vt)	MRob SHaz WPer
rugulosa	See V. ***canadensis r.***
rupestris	CGro
– blue	MRob NCat
§ – ***rosea***	CBre CGro CNic CPla CRDP CTom MBel MRob NCat NGre NRed NRoo NSti NWCA SHaz STre WBon WCla WDav WEas WHal WOMN WSun
'Russian Superb' (Vt)	CCot MRob
'Ruth Blackall' (Va)	SCaw
'Ruth Elkans' (Va)	GMac NBrk SCaw SHaz
'Saint Helena' (Vt)	MRob
'Saint Maur' (Va)	CFul
'Sally' (Vtta)	SCaw
'Samantha' (Vtta)	SCaw
'Sammy Jo' (Va)	SHaz WBou
'Sarah' (Va)	CFul SHaz
saxatilis	See V. ***tricolor subalpina***
schariensis JCA 993.150	CNic
'Scottish Yellow' (Va)	MRob
selkirkii	CNic CPla CRDP CRiv EFol NNrd WCot WHal WThu
– 'Variegata'	NBir
* ***sempervivoïdes***	WOMN
septentrionalis	CCla CCot CCra CMea CMil CRDP ECha EGol ELan MCas MRob NGre NRya SAxl SHaz SSmi WHal WHil WRus
– ***alba***	CMHG CVer MRob WPer WTyr
– 'Rubra'	CMil
'Septima' (Va)	SCaw
'Serena' (Va)	SCaw WBou
'Sheila' (Va)	SHaz WBou
'Sidborough Poppet'	CBre CNic CPBP EFol WPer
§ ***sieberiana***	ECou
'Sigrid' (Va)	SCaw
'Sissinghurst' (Va)	GMac SCaw
'Sky Blue' (Va)	SCaw
'Sophie' (Va)	SCaw SHaz
§ ***sororia***	GCHN LBlm MFir MRob WBon WHal WOMN
– 'Albiflora'	GCal NHar WCot WDav WPer
§ – 'Freckles'	Widely available
– 'Priceana'	CBre CCla CMil CNic EBee NCat NRed SHaz WBon WCot WPer WSun WWat
¶ – 'Red Sister'	WBon
'Soula' (Vtta)	SCaw
'Steyning' (Va)	SCaw
stojanovii	CMea ELan MBro NMen SBla SGil WEas WOMN WPer
striata	WWat
'Sulphurea' (Vt)	CGro CPla CWes EFol ELan ERav GMac MRob NBrk SHaz WOMN WPer
'Susan' (SP)	SHaz
'Susannah' (Va)	CCot ERav GMac SHaz SMrm
'Susie' (Va)	SHaz
'Swanley White'	See V. 'Comte de Brazza'
'Sybil' (ExV)	SHaz

'Sylvia Hart' MTho WBon
*takedana 'Variegata' WThi
'Talitha' (Va) GMac LBee SCaw
*'Tamberti' (Vt) SHaz
'Tamsin' (Va) SCaw
'Tara' (Va) SCaw
'Thalia' (Vtta) CFul SCaw SHaz SUsu WBou
'The Czar' See V. 'Czar'
'Thea' (Va) SCaw
'Thelma' (Va) SCaw
'Thetis' (Va) SCaw
'Tiffany' (Va) SCaw
'Tina' (Va) SHaz WBou
'Tina Whittaker' (Vt) MRob
'Titania' (Vtta) SCaw
'Tom Tit' (Va) SCaw WBou
'Tomose' (Va) CFul
'Tony Venison' (C/v) CBos CCot CRDP EFol EHal EHoe EMon EPla GArf LHop MBel MCas MTho NCat NNrd NSti SHaz WBou WByw WCot WHal WHer WRus
'Translucent Blue' MRob WBon
tricolor CKin CNic ECWi EHer EWFC GBar GPoy IEde LHol MHew MSal NGre NWCA SIde WHer WSun WWye
§ – ssp. ***curtisii*** SCaw
§ – ssp. ***macedonica*** NGre
– 'Sawyer's Blue' WPer
'Tullia' (Vtta) SCaw
'Tuscany' (Vt) MRob
'Una' (Va) SCaw
'Unity' (Va) SCaw
'Velleda' (Vtta) SCaw
velutina See V. ***gracilis***
'Venetia' (Va) SCaw
'Venus' (Va) SCaw
§ ***verecunda***
var. ***yakusimana*** CMHG CNic CRDP CRiv CTom EPot ESis NGre NHol SIng
'Victoria' (Vt) See V. 'Czar Bleu'
'Victoria Cawthorne' (C) GBuc GMac MBel NRoo NSti SCaw SChu SMrm WBou WHoo
'Victoria Regina' (Vt) EMon MRob
'Vignette' (Va) SHaz
'Virginia' (Va) CFul GMac SCaw SHaz SPer WBou
'Virgo' (Va) SCaw
x ***visseriana lutea*** GMac
'Vita' (Va) CFul CMea EBar ERav GCal GMac LGre NRoo SCaw SChu SHaz SUsu WBou WMar
'Wanda' (Va) SCaw
'Wheatley White' SPer
'White Czar' (Vt) MRob
'White Gem' (Va) LBee SHaz
'White Ladies' (Vt) See V. ***obliqua alba***
'White Pearl' (Va) GMac LGre NBrk WBou
'White Superior' CB&S
'White Swan' (Va) GMac LBee SCaw
'William Wallace' (Va) SCaw
'Windward' (Vt) CCot CRDP MRob NBrk NCat
'Winifred Jones' (Va) SHaz
'Winifred Wargent' (Va) SCaw
'Winona' (Vtta) SCaw
'Winona Cawthorne' (C) GMac SCaw SChu
'Woodlands Cream' (Va) GMac SHaz
'Woodlands Lilac' (Va) NRoo SCaw SHaz WBou
'Woodlands White' (Va) SCaw
'Xantha' (Va) SCaw
yakusimana See V. ***verecunda yakusimana***
¶ 'Yellow Snowdon' SUsu
yezoensis CPla GTou SBla
'Yoyo' (Va) SHaz
'Zalea' (Va) SCaw
'Zara' (Va) SHaz SPer WBou
'Zenobia' (Vtta) SCaw
'Zepherine' (Va) SCaw
'Zeta' (Va) SCaw
'Ziglana' (Va) SCaw
'Zoe' (Vtta) GMac NRoo SCaw WBou
'Zona' (Va) SCaw
zoysii See V. ***calcarata zoysii***

VISCARIA (Caryophyllaceae)

vulgaris See LYCHNIS ***viscaria***

VITALIANA (Primulaceae)

§ ***primuliflora*** CRiv GArf GTou MBro NKay WHoo
– ssp. ***praetutiana*** CNic EPot GDra ITim MBro MCas MHig NHar NHol NNrd NTow NWCA WAbe WDav WPat WThu
– – ***chionantha*** EPot
– – ***compacta*** EPot
– ssp. ***tridentata*** WPer

VITEX (Verbenaceae)

agnus-castus CAbb CArn CB&S CCla CDoC CGre CWSG EEls ELan GPoy LHol SHil SMad SPer WHer WOMN WWye
– 'Blue Spire' LRHS
lucens CHEx
negundo CArn
– ***cannabinifolia*** See V. ***incisa***

VITIS † (Vitaceae)

F 'Abouriou' (***vinifera***) (O/B) WStA
F 'Alicante' (***vinifera***) (G/B) CB&S ERea GTwe WStA
amurensis CHEx EWll WCru WWat
F 'Angers Frontignan' (***vinifera***) (G/O/B) ERea
'Apiifolia' (***vinifera***) See V. 'Ciotat'
F 'Appley Towers' (***vinifera***) (G/B) ERea
F 'Ascot Citronelle' (***vinifera***) (G/W) ERea
F 'Auvergne Frontignan' (***vinifera***) (G/O/W) ERea
F 'Auxerrois' (***vinifera***) (O/W) WStA
F 'Bacchus' (***vinifera***) (O/W) WStA
F 'Baco Noir' (O/B) GTwe WStA

'Black Alicante' (*vinifera*)	See V. 'Alicante'
F 'Black Corinth' (*vinifera*) (G/B)	ERea
F 'Black Frontignan' (*vinifera*) (G/O/B)	ERea WStA
'Black Hamburgh'	See V. 'Schiava Grossa'
F 'Black Monukka' (*vinifera*) (G/B)	ERea
F 'Black Prince' (*vinifera*) (G/B)	ERea
F 'Blauburger' (*vinifera*) (O/B)	WCru WStA
'Blue Portuguese' (*vinifera*)	See V. 'Portugieser'
F 'Boskoop Glory' (*vinifera*)	CMac GTwe IJoh SDea WStA
F 'Brant' **AGM**	CB&S CBra CMac CSco EBre ELan ENot ERea EWar GTwe LBre LBuc LHop MBri MGos NElm NRog SDea SHBN SPer SReu SSta WBod WStA WStI
F 'Buckland Sweetwater' (*vinifera*) (G/W)	ERea GTwe MBri
F 'Cabernet Sauvignon' (*vinifera*) (O/B)	WStA
F *californica*	ERea
F 'Canon Hall Muscat' (*vinifera*) (G/W)	ERea
F 'Cardinal' (*vinifera*)	ERea
F 'Cascade' (Seibel 13053) (O/B)	ERea LBuc SDea WStA
F 'Chaouch' (*vinifera*) (G/W)	ERea
F 'Chardonnay' (*vinifera*) (O/W)	SDea WStA
F 'Chasselas' (*vinifera*) (G/O/W)	CB&S CDoC CMac ERea EWar WStA
'Chasselas d'Or' (*vinifera*)	See V. 'Chasselas'
F 'Chasselas Rosé' (*vinifera*) (G/R)	ERea WStA
F 'Chasselas Vibert' (*vinifera*) (G/W)	ERea
F 'Chenin Blanc' (*vinifera*) (O/W)	WStA
F 'Ciotat' (*vinifera*)	EPla ERea SDea WCru WStA
coignetiae **AGM**	Widely available
¶ – Soja 457	EPla
¶ – cut-leaved	SPer
F 'Concord' (*labrusca*) (O/B)	ERea
F 'Cot' (*vinifera*) (O/B)	WStA
F 'Cote House Seedling' (*vinifera*) (O/W)	ERea
* 'Csabyongye' (*vinifera*) (W)	WStA
F 'Dunkelfelder' (*vinifera*) (O/R)	WStA
F 'Early Van der Laan' (*vinifera*)	LHol
F 'Ehrenfelser' (*vinifera*) (O/W)	WStA
F 'Elbling' (*vinifera*) (O/W)	WStA
F 'Espiran' (*vinifera*)	ERea
F 'Excelsior' (*vinifera*) (W)	SDea WStA
F 'Faber' (*vinifera*) (O/W)	WStA
flexuosa	EPla
F 'Forta' (*vinifera*) (O/W)	WStA
F 'Foster's Seedling' (*vinifera*) (G/W)	ERea GTwe SDea SKee WStA
F 'Fragola' (*vinifera*) (O/R)	CMac EBre ECha EPla ERav ERea EWri GTwe LBre SDea WStA WWat
F 'Gagarin Blue' (*vinifera*) (O/B)	ERea SDea WStA
F 'Gamay Hatif' (*vinifera*) (O/B)	ERea
'Gamay Hatif des Voges' (*vinifera*)	WStA
F 'Gamay Noir' (*vinifera*) (O/B)	WStA
F Gamay Teinturier Group (*vinifera*) (O/B)	WStA
F 'Gewürztraminer' (*vinifera*) (O/R)	WStA
'Glory of Boskoop' (*vinifera*)	See V. 'Boskoop Glory'
'Golden Chasselas' (*vinifera*)	See V. 'Chasselas'
F 'Golden Queen' (*vinifera*) (G/W)	ERea
F 'Goldriesling' (*vinifera*) (O/W)	WStA
F 'Grizzley Frontignan' (*vinifera*) (G/R)	ERea
F 'Gros Colmar' (*vinifera*) (G/B)	ERea
F 'Gros Maroc' (*vinifera*) (G/B)	ERea
F 'Gutenborner' (*vinifera*) (O/W)	WStA
henryana	See PARTHENOCISSUS *henryana*
F 'Himrod' (O/W)	ERea GTwe SDea
F 'Incana' (*vinifera*) (O/B)	CSco EPla ERav LGre SHil WCru
inconstans	See PARTHENOCISSUS *tricuspidata*
F 'Interlaken' (*vinifera*)	ERea
F 'King's Ruby' (*vinifera*)	ERea
F 'Kuibishevski' (O/R)	WStA
F 'Lady Downe's Seedling' (*vinifera*) (G/B)	ERea
F 'Lady Hastings' (*vinifera*) (G/B)	ERea
F 'Lady Hutt' (*vinifera*) (G/W)	ERea
F Landot 244 (O/B)	WStA
F 'Léon Millot' (*vinifera*) (O/G/B)	ERea SDea SKee WStA
F 'Lucombe' (*vinifera*)	SDea
F 'Madeira Frontignan' (*vinifera*) (G/R)	ERea
F 'Madeleine Angevine' (*vinifera*) (O/W)	CDoC EBre ERea GTwe LBre SDea WStA
F 'Madeleine Royale' (*vinifera*) (G/W)	ERea WStA

F 'Madeleine Silvaner' *(vinifera)* (O/W)	ERea GTwe LBuc MGos SDea SKee SPer WStA
F 'Madresfield Court' *(vinifera)* (G/B)	ERea GTwe SKee WStA
'Malbec' *(vinifera)*	See V. 'Cot'
F 'Maréchal Joffre' (O/B)	GTwe WStA
F 'Melon de Bourgogne' *(vinifera)* (O/W)	WStA
F 'Mireille' *(vinifera)*	GTwe WStA
F 'Morio Muscat' *(vinifera)* (O/W)	WStA
F 'Mrs Pearson' *(vinifera)* (G/W)	ERea
F 'Mrs Pince's Black Muscat' *(vinifera)* (G/B)	ERea
F 'Müller-Thurgau' (Riesling-Silvaner) *(vinifera)* (O/W)	CB&S ECtt ERea GTwe LBuc MBri MGos NElm SDea SKee SPer WStA
'Muscadet' *(vinifera)*	See V. 'Melon de Bourgogne'
F 'Muscat Blanc à Petits Grains' *(vinifera)* (O/W)	WStA
F 'Muscat Bleu' *(vinifera)* (O/B)	ERea
F 'Muscat Champion' *(vinifera)* (G/R)	ERea
F 'Muscat Hamburg' *(vinifera)* (G/B)	ERea MGos WStA
F 'Muscat of Alexandria' *(vinifera)* (G/W)	CB&S CMac CSam ERea EWar IJoh SPer
F 'Muscat of Hungary' *(vinifera)* (G/W)	ERea
F 'Muscat Ottonel' *(vinifera)* (O/W)	WStA
F 'Muscate de Saumur' *(vinifera)* (W)	WStA
F 'New York Muscat' *(vinifera)* (O/B)	ERea
F 'Noir Hatif de Marseilles' *(vinifera)* (O/B)	ERea
F 'No. 69' *(vinifera)* (W)	WStA
F Oberlin 595 (O/B)	WStA
F 'Oliver Irsay' *(vinifera)* (O/W)	ERea WStA
F 'Optima' *(vinifera)* (O/W)	WStA
F 'Ortega' *(vinifera)* (O/W)	WStA
parsley leaved	See V. 'Ciotat'
F 'Perle' *(vinifera)* (O/W)	WStA
F 'Perle de Czaba' *(vinifera)* (G/O/W)	ERea
F 'Perlette' *(vinifera)* (O/W)	WStA
F 'Pinot Blanc' *(vinifera)* (O/W)	WStA
F 'Pinot Gris' *(vinifera)* (O/B)	WStA
F 'Pinot Noir' *(vinifera)*	WStA
F 'Pirovano 14' (O/B)	CDoC ERea GTwe WStA
F 'Plantet' (O/B)	WStA
F 'Portugieser' *(vinifera)* (O/B)	WStA
F 'Précoce de Bousquet' *(vinifera)* (O/W)	WStA
F 'Précoce de Malingre' *(vinifera)* (O/W)	ERea
F 'Primavis Frontignan' *(vinifera)* (G/W)	ERea WStA
F 'Prince of Wales' *(vinifera)* (G/B)	ERea
'Pulchra'	WCru
F 'Purpurea' *(vinifera)* **AGM**	CB&S CBot CBra CHad CMac CSco EHar EHoe ELan EMil ENot ERav IHos MBri MGos MWat NKay SHBN SMad SPer SReu SSta WBod WDin WHil WPat WSHC WWat
quinquefolia	See PARTHENOCISSUS ***quinquefolia***
F Ravat 51 (O/W)	WStA
F 'Regner' *(vinifera)* (O/W)	WStA
F 'Reichensteiner' *(vinifera)* (O/G/W)	WStA
F 'Reine Olga' *(vinifera)* (O/R)	ERea
F 'Rembrant' *(vinifera)* (R)	WStA
F 'Riesling' *(vinifera)* (O/W)	WStA
riparia	GAri WCru
F 'Royal Muscadine' *(vinifera)*	See V. 'Chasselas'
F 'Saint Laurent' *(vinifera)* (G/O/W)	ERea
F 'Sauvignon Blanc' *(vinifera)* (O/W)	WStA
F 'Scheurebe' *(vinifera)* (O/W)	WStA
F 'Schiava Grossa' *(vinifera)* (G/B)	CB&S CMac CSam ECtt ELan ERea EWar GChr GRei GTwe ISea LBuc LHol MBri NElm NRog SDea SKee SPer WStA
F 'Schönburger' *(vinifera)* (O/W)	WStA
F Seibel	GTwe
Seibel 13053	See V. 'Cascade'
F Seibel 138315 *(vinifera)* (R)	WStA
F Seibel 5409 *(vinifera)* (W)	WStA
Seibel 5455	See V. 'Plantet'
Seibel 7053	WStA
Seibel 9549	WStA
F 'Septimer' *(vinifera)* (O/W)	WStA
F 'Seyval Blanc' (Seyve Villard 5276) (O/W)	ERea GTwe LBuc SDea WStA
Seyve Villard 12.375	See V. 'Villard Blanc'
F Seyve Villard 20.473 *(vinifera)* (W)	WStA
F 'Siegerrebe' *(vinifera)* (O/W)	CDoC ERea GTwe SDea WStA
F 'Silvaner' *(vinifera)* (O/W)	WStA
'Strawberry Grape' *(vinifera)*	See V. 'Fragola'

§ 'Sultana' (*vinifera*) — ERea WStA
F 'Syrian' (*vinifera*) (G/W) — ERea
F Teinturier Group (*vinifera*) (O/B) — ERea
F 'Tereshkova' (O/B) — ERea WStA
'Thompson Seedless' (*vinifera*) — See V. 'Sultana'
F 'Trebbiano' (*vinifera*) (G/W) — ERea
F 'Triomphe d'Alsace' (O/B) — SDea WStA
'Trollinger' — See V. 'Schiava Grossa'
F 'Villard Blanc' (O/W) — WStA
F 'West's St Peter's' (*vinifera*) (G/B) — ERea
F 'Wrotham Pinot' (*vinifera*) (O/B) — WStA
F 'Würzer' (*vinifera*) (O/W) — WStA
F 'Zweigeltrebe' (*vinifera*) (O/B) — WStA

VITTADINIA (Compositae/Asteraceae)

♦ *australis* — See V. *cuneata*
§ *cuneata* — NTow

VRIESEA (Bromeliaceae)

carinata — MBri
hieroglyphica — MBri
x *poelmanii* — MBri
x *polonia* — MBri
saundersii AGM — MBri
splendens AGM — MBri
'Vulkana' — MBri

WACHENDORFIA (Haemodoraceae)

paniculata — NRog
thyrsiflora — CBrd CHEx IBlr NRog SDix WCot
– Trengwainton Form — GCal

WAHLENBERGIA (Campanulaceae)

albomarginata — CNic ECou EPad GArf GCHN GGar GTou LGan NGre NHol NTow NWCA WCru
– 'Blue Mist' — ECou EPad
congesta — EPot GCHN LRHS SHer SIng WThi
gloriosa — CLew CMea CNic EPad EPot GArf NGre NTow WAbe WCru WPat
matthewsii — GTou
pumilio — See EDRAIANTHUS *pumilio*
§ *saxicola* — CLew CNic CRiv CRow CSpe ESma GTou NGre NHol NTow NVic NWCA WCru WDav WPer WThu
♦ *serpyllifolia major* — See EDRAIANTHUS *serpyllifolius* 'M.'
simpsonii — GTou
species — ECou
¶ 'Tasmanian Skies' — LBlm
tasmanica — See W. *saxicola*
trichogyna — LRHS

WALDHEIMIA See ALLARDIA

WALDSTEINIA (Rosaceae)

fragarioïdes — ECro NNrw WPer
¶ *geoïdes* — SPer
ternata — Widely available

WALNUT, Common See JUGLANS *regia*

WASABIA (Cruciferae/Brassicaceae)

japonica — CArn GPoy

WASHINGTONIA (Palmae/Arecaceae)

filifera AGM — CHEx CTbh CTro LPal MBri SArc
¶ *robusta* — CTbh CTro

WATSONIA † (Iridaceae)

aletroïdes — NRog
angusta — CHan GCal
ardernei — See W. *borbonica a.*
beatricis — See W. *pillansii*
§ *borbonica* — CChu IBlr IMal NRog
§ – ssp. *ardernei* — GCal IBlr NRog
brevifolia — See W. *laccata*
bulbillifera — See W. *meriana*
coccinea Baker — See W. *spectabilis*
coccinea dwarf form Herbert ex Baker — NRog
fulgens — CHan
hysterantha — NRog
'Indian Orange' — WThi
§ *laccata* — WThi
marginata — CHan NRog
§ *meriana* — CHan GCra IBlr NRog WCot WThi
§ *pillansii* — CChu CHan CPou CWit EBre GCal IBlr LBre SHer WThi
pyramidata — See W. *borbonica*
socium — CRDP
§ *spectabilis* — GCra NRog
sp. SH 89 — CHan
'Stanford Scarlet' — GCal LGre SCro WEas WSHC
tabularis — CHan
'Tresco Dwarf Pink' — GCal
vanderspuyae — CHan NRog
versfeldii — CHan GCra

WATTAKAKA See DREGEA

WEIGELA † (Caprifoliaceae)

'Abel Carrière' AGM — CBow CSco CShe ECtt ENot EPla MRav SPla WDin WWeb
'Abel Carrière Golden' — EPla
'Avalanche' — ECtt MRav WStI
'Boskoop Glory' — CDoC CSco MBri SPer
Briant Rubidor ® — See W. Olympiade ®
'Bristol Ruby' — CBra CChe CSco CShe ELan ENot GRei IJoh LHop MBar MGos MPla NNor NRoo NWea SHBN SLon SPer SReu SSta WAbe WDin WTyr WWin
'Candida' — ELan EPla MBri NHol SGil SPer SPla WBod
Carnaval ® — CBow CDoC COtt MBri

'Centennial'	MGos
coraeensis 'Alba'	CChu GWht WSHC
decora	CGre CPle
¶ 'Duet'	CMHG
'Espérance'	EPla
'Eva Rathke'	CB&S CBra EPla ISea NWea
'Evita'	CMHG CSco EHic ESis GRei IOrc MBar MGos MPla SPer SPla WPat
'Féerie'	WWeb
florida	CTrw MWat
– ***alba***	CB&S MBar
*– 'Albovariegata'	SMad
§ – 'Aureovariegata'	CDec CMHG CSco IJoh ISea MBal NHol SLon SPer SPla WHCG
– 'Bicolor'	CB&S
– 'Bristol Snowflake'	CBow CCla CDoC CSco LHop SFai SLon SReu
– 'Foliis Purpureis' **AGM**	Widely available
*– 'Langtrees'	EFol
– 'Magee'	CMCN
*– 'Minuet'	CMHG EBre EHic EPla ESis LBre MAsh SEng WPat
– 'Nana Variegata'	CBow EHal ERav MBar MBri MWat NBee NHol
– 'Pink Princess'	CDoC
– 'Rubigold'	See W. Olympiade ®
¶ – 'Rumba'	EHic ESma NRoo
– 'Suzanne'	SCob
– 'Tango'	ECtt MAsh MBri
*– 'Variegata Aurea'	See W. *f.* 'Aureovariegata'
– 'Versicolor'	CChu CMHG LHop MBel
'Florida Variegata'	Widely available
'Gustave Malet'	ISea
hortensis 'Nivea'	CPle
japonica Dart's Colourdream ®	CCla EBre ECtt EHal EPla ERav IOrc LBre MGos MRav NHol SGil SLPl
'Kosteriana Variegata'	NRoo
'Looymansii Aurea'	CBow CChu CCla CMHG CPle CSco EBre EFol EHar ELan EPla LBre LHop MPla NHol SGil SHil SLon SPer SPla WAbe WDin WWat WWin
Lucifer ®	CDoC MHlr WDin WWeb
'Majestueux'	SSta
maximowiczii	CBow CBra CCla CPle NHol SSta WHCG
§ ***middendorffiana***	CB&S CBot CBow CChu CCla CGre CMHG CPle CSco CWit ELan EMil ENot EPla ERav EWri ISea LHop MBal MBar MPla MWat NHol SHil SPer WDin WHCG WSHC WTyr WWin
'Mont Blanc' **AGM**	CBot
'Newport Red'	CBow EBee ENot IDai MRav MWat NBee SPla WStI WTyr
§ Olympiade ® (v)	CB&S CBow CCla EBar ECtt EFol EHoe ELan ERav IOrc MBal MBar MBel MBri MGos NHol NNor SPer SReu WBod WStI
'Praecox Variegata' **AGM**	CChu CMHG EBre EHar EPla LBre LHop MBri NHol SHil SLon SPer SPla SReu SSta WCru WHCG WWeb
'Red Prince'	CBow ELan MBri SCob
'Rubidor'	See W. Olympiade ®
'Snowflake'	CBow CPle EBee EBre ECtt EPla LBre MPla SRms WDin WWeb
'Victoria'	CLTr CMHG COtt EBre ECtt EFol LBre MAsh MBel MBri MWat NBee NHol SCob SHil WDin WGor

WEINMANNIA (Cunoniaceae)

trichosperma	CHEx IBlr SArc

WELDENIA (Commelinaceae)

candida	NHar WChr

WESTRINGIA (Labiatae/Lamiaceae)

angustifolia	ECou
brevifolia	ECou
– Raleighii Group	ECou
§ ***fruticosa*** **AGM**	CB&S CPle CTre CTro LHop MAll SSad
– 'Variegata'	CPle CTre ESma LHop MAll
rosmariniformis	See W. ***fruticosa***

WIDDRINGTONIA (Cupressaceae)

cedarbergensis	GAri
♦ ***cupressoïdes***	See W. ***nodiflora***
§ ***nodiflora***	GAri MBri NHol
♦ ***whytei***	See W. ***nodiflora***

WIGANDIA (Hydrophyllaceae)

urens	CHEx CNew

WINEBERRY See RUBUS *phoenicolasius*

WISTERIA † (Leguminosae/Papilionaceae)

floribunda	CB&S CBow ELan MAsh NKay SHBN SLon WNor
§ – 'Alba' **AGM**	CAlt CB&S CBot CBow CCla CDoC CPMA CSco EBre EHar ELan GAri LBre LNet NEgg NHol SHBN SHil SPer SPla SSta WDin WStI
– 'Burford'	CDoC MAsh MBri MMea MWat NHol
– 'Domino'	CBow CCla CPMA LNet MMea
¶ – 'Fragrantissima'	CCla
– 'Hichirimen'	LNet MMea
*– 'Lavender Lace'	CPMA
*– 'Lipstick'	CB&S CBow CCla LNet
– 'Macrobotrys'	See W. *f.* 'Multijuga'
§ – 'Multijuga' **AGM**	CAlt CB&S CBow CDoC CPMA CWit EBre EHar ELan IOrc LBre LNet MBri MGos MMea MUlv MWat NHol SMad SPer SPla SSta WWat
– 'Murasaki Noda'	MGos
– 'Nana Richin's Purple'	LNet
– 'Peaches and Cream'	CB&S CBow CCla CPMA LNet MMea SPer
– 'Pink Ice'	CB&S CBow CCla CPMA ELan IOrc LNet MBri MMea SHBN WWat
– 'Purple Patches'	CBow CCla CPMA ELan LNet MMea SPer
*– 'Purple Tassle'	LNet
– 'Reindeer'	NHol

– 'Rosea' ('Honko') AGM CBow CCla CMac CPMA EBre EHar ELan ENot IOrc LBre LNet MBar MMea SPer WStI
– 'Royal Purple' ERea MMea WGor
– 'Snow Showers' CBow CCla CPMA IHos LNet MBri MMea SPer SReu WGor
*– 'Variegata' CPMA
– 'Violacea Plena' MBri MMea SHBN SHil
x ***formosa*** CPMA SPla WFro
– 'Issai' CB&S CBow CPMA CSam ELan LNet MBar MGos MMea MUlv NEgg SPer SPla WWat
– 'Kokkuryu' ('Black Dragon') (d) CAlt CB&S CBow CCla CDoC CPMA ELan IOrc LNet MAsh MGos MMea SHer SMad SPer SPla SReu SSta WGor WWat
frutescens WNor
¶ 'Kofuji' LNet
multijuga 'Alba' See W. ***floribunda*** 'Alba'
****russelliana*** SPla
sinensis AGM CB&S CBow CBra CHEx CLan CMac CSco EBre ELan ENot GRei IDai IHos IJoh ISea LBre LNet MBal MBar MGos MMea MPla MWat NNor SHBN SPer SSta WBod WDin WNor
– 'Alba' ('Shiro-capital') AGM CB&S CBow CSco CShe EHar ELan IOrc LNet MBar MBri MMea MWat SPer WDin
– 'Amethyst' CBow CCla CPMA ERea
– 'Caroline' CB&S CBow CDoC CPMA CSam CSco ERea LNet MMea MUlv SPer SReu SSta WStI
– 'Plena' SHil
– 'Prematura' CBow MAsh NHol WSHC
– 'Prematura Alba' WWat
– 'Prolific' CBow CDoC CHad EBee ELan MBri MMea SPer SPla WPat
*– 'Rosea' CBow
venusta CBow CPMA EHar ENot LNet MBri MMea MUlv SHBN SMad SPer WWat
*– 'White Silk' CPMA

WITHANIA (Solanaceae)
somnifera MSal

WITTSTEINIA (Alseuosmiaceae)
vacciniacea WCru

WOODSIA (Dryopteridaceae)
ilvensis NHar
intermedia NBro WRic
obtusa NHar NMar

WOODWARDIA † (Blechnaceae)
fimbriata SArc SMad SPla
martinezii CFil
¶ ***obtusa*** CRDP
****orientalis formosana*** NMar
radicans AGM CGre CHEx CTro NMar SArc WAbe
unigemmata LGre SWas WRic

WORCESTERBERRY See RIBES *divaricatum*

WULFENIA (Scrophulariaceae)
carinthiaca CNic EBar MBel MBro MHig NGre NHol

XANTHOCERAS (Sapindaceae)
sorbifolium AGM CAbb CB&S CBot CChu CCla CFil CMCN CPle ECtt EHar ELan LGre NWyt SHil SIgm SMad WWat

XANTHORHIZA (Ranunculaceae)
simplicissima CChu CCla CFil CRow GCal MUlv SAxl SHil SPer WSHC WWat

XANTHORRHOEA (Xanthorrhoeaceae)
¶ ***australis*** SMad
preisii SIgm
quadrangulata CGre
thorntonii SIgm

XANTHOSOMA (Araceae)
lindenii See CALADIUM ***lindenii***
sagittifolium CHEx SLMG

XERONEMA (Liliaceae/Phormiaceae)
callistemon EBul ECou

XEROPHYLLUM (Liliaceae/Melanthiaceae)
tenax GDra NHol

XYLORHIZA See MACHAERANTHERA

YOUNGBERRY See RUBUS

YUCCA † (Agavaceae)
aloifolia CCan CHEx LBuc MBri MUlv SArc SIgm
– 'Variegata' CCan CHEx LPal SArc
angustifolia See Y. ***glauca***
¶ ***angustissima*** CTbh
¶ ***arizonica*** CTbh
¶ ***baccata*** CTbh
brevifolia CTbh
¶ ***carnerosana*** CTbh
¶ ***elata*** CTbh
§ ***elephantipes*** AGM CCan CHEx MBri SArc
filamentosa AGM CAbb CB&S CBra CCan CHEx CLan CMHG EFou ELan ENot IDai ISea MBal MBlu MGos MWat NBro NHol SHBN SLon SPer SReu WBod WDin WTyr WWin
– 'Bright Edge' AGM CAbb CB&S CBow CCan CDoC CLan CMHG CPMA EBre ECtt EGol ELan EOrc EWri IHos IOrc LBre MBri MGos MUlv NHol SArc SHBN SPer SPla WAbe WPat WStI
– 'Variegata' AGM CB&S CBot CBow CCan CPMA EBre EGol ELan ENot EWri IBar IJoh IOrc LBre LHop MBal MBri MGos SDix SPer SSta WDin WStI

flaccida	CCan MAsh NBee SDix WThu
– 'Golden Sword' AGM	CCan CDoC CLan CMHG CSco EBre EGol EWri IHos IJoh IOrc LBre MBal MBri MHlr MUlv SHer SPer WAbe
– 'Ivory' AGM	CB&S CCan CDoC CPMA CSam CSco CShe ECtt EGol ELan ENot GCal IDai IOrc ISea MBri MRav MUlv NHol NKay NWyt SPer SPla SSta STre WThu
– striated cultivar	CCan
x *floribunda*	SArc
'Garland's Gold' (v)	CDoC CHEx COtt ELan MBri SPla
§ *glauca*	CB&S CCan CHEx CMHG GAri GCal NHol SArc SIgm
gloriosa AGM	CB&S CCan CDoC CHEx CPMA CSco CShe ENot EPla LNet MUlv SArc SHBN SLon SPer WStI
– 'Aureovariegata'	See Y. *g.* 'Variegata'
– 'Nobilis'	SDix
§ – 'Variegata' AGM	CBot CCan CDoC CHEx CSco EBre ELan ENot IBar IJoh LBre MBri MUlv NWyt SArc SCro SDry SHBN SMad SPer
guatemalensis	See Y. *elephantipes*
harrimaniae	EMon SIgm
¶ *kanabensis*	CTbh
¶ *navajoa*	CTbh
neomexicana	CTbh WThu
recurvifolia AGM	CB&S CCan CHEx CLan MBal SArc
– 'Marginata'	CCan
– 'Variegata'	CCan
¶ *rigida*	CTbh
¶ *schidigera*	CTbh
¶ *schottii*	CTbh
¶ *thompsoniana*	CTbh
* *torcelli*	CTbh
¶ *torreyi*	CTbh
treculeana	SArc
* 'Tricolor'	CB&S
¶ *valida*	CTbh
'Vittorio Emanuele II'	MUlv NWyt SArc
'Vomerensis'	CCan
whipplei	CAbb CBot CBow CCan CDoC CGre CHEx CTbh CTro GCra SArc SHil SLMG
– JLS 86188LACA	EMon
– var. *parishii*	CCan

YUSHANIA (Gramineae/Poaceae-Bambusoideae)

§ *anceps* AGM	CDoC CHEx CHad EPla ESiP GAri IOrc ISea ISta LBam MBri MGos MUlv NBee SArc SBam SCob SDry SPer SReu
§ – 'Pitt White'	EPla ISta SBam SDry WJun
maculata	EPla SBam SDry WJun
§ *maling*	EPla SBam SDry WJun

ZALUZIANSKYA (Scrophulariaceae)

ovata	EPot LHop NBir NWCA SAxl SBla SMrm SUsu WMar

ZAMIA (Zamiaceae)

floridana	LPal WNor
furfuracea	LPal

ZAMIOCULCAS (Araceae)

See Plant Deletions

ZANTEDESCHIA † (Araceae)

§ *aethiopica* AGM	CBen CHEx CHol CMHG CRDP CWGN EHon ELun EWav GCal LAma LMay MSta NDea NRog SDix SHer SWat WChe WEas
– 'Apple Court Babe'	CRow SApp
– 'Crowborough'	CAvo CB&S CBro CCla CHEx CHad CHan CKel CRow CSco EBre ECha EFou EGol EHon ELan EMFW LBre MBal MBri MRav MUlv NBar SDeJ SLon SMad SPer WCru
– *gigantea*	SLMG
– 'Green Goddess' AGM	CB&S CHan CMon CRDP CRiv CRow CWGN ECha ELan EWri GCra MHlr SDeJ SRms
– 'Little Gem'	ECha
– 'White Sails'	CRow GCal MUlv
albomaculata	CAvo CMon LAma MWBu NRog
– S&SH 35	CHan
'Best Gold'	LAma LRHS
'Black Magic'	LAma
'Black-eyed Beauty'	CBro LAma LRHS NRog
'Bridal Blush'	LAma LRHS
'Cameo'	LAma LRHS
'Candy'	LRHS
'Christina'	LRHS
'Dominique'	LRHS
elliottiana AGM	CB&S CSut LAma MWBu NRog
'Garnet'	LRHS
'Harvest Moon'	CWit LAma LRHS
'Helen O'Connor'	SLMG
'Jubilee'	LRHS
'Lavender Petite'	LAma NRog
'Mango'	LRHS
'Maroon Dainty'	LAma NRog
'Number 13'	LRHS
'Oriental Sun'	LRHS
'Pacific Pink'	LAma
pentlandii	See Z. *angustiloba*
'Pink Opal'	LRHS
rehmannii AGM	CB&S CMon CRDP LAma LRHS MWBu SRms
*– *superba*	SLMG
'Ruby'	LRHS
'Shell Pink '	LAma NRog
'Solfatare'	LAma
'Yvonne'	LRHS

ZANTHORHIZA See XANTHORHIZA

ZANTHOXYLUM (Rutaceae)

ailanthoïdes	EHar
americanum	CLnd EArb
coreanum	CCla
piperitum	CMCN EArb EHar WWat
simulans	CB&S

ZAUSCHNERIA (Onagraceae)

♦ *arizonica*	See Z. *californica latifolia*

§ ***californica*** ssp. ***cana*** — CHan CLTr CNic CSam ECha ELan EPla GTou IOrc LAbb LGan MCas MPla NKay NWCA NWyt SChu SIgm SUsu WCru WEas WPer WThu
– – 'Albiflora' — CBot CSpe LHop MSte SUsu WCru WOMN WPer
§ – – 'Dublin' AGM — CBot CRDP CRiv CShe ECha EFou ELan EPot ERea ITim LGre LHop MBel MBro MPla SBla SChu SIng SLon WAbe WEas WHil WHoo WOld WPat WPer WSHC WWat WWin
– – 'Sir Cedric Morris' — ELan EMon LHop
¶ – 'Clover Dale' — LGre
¶ – ***etteri*** — LGre
– 'Glasnevin' — See Z. ***califonica*** 'Dublin'
– ssp. ***latifolia*** — CCla CPle EMon GPlt NMen
§ – ssp. ***latifolia*** RMRF 93-0443 — LGre
§ – ssp. ***mexicana*** — SRms WOMN
– 'Olbrich Silver' — LGre LHop SBla WAbe WCru
¶ – 'Sierra Sunshine' — LGre WCru
– 'Solidarity Pink' — CLTr CRDP CSpe ELan LGre LHop MTho SChu SIng SUsu
– 'Western Hills' — CBrk LGre LHop SBla WAbe WCru
cana villosa — See Z. ***californica mexicana***

ZEBRINA See TRADESCANTIA

ZELKOVA † (Ulmaceae)

carpinifolia — CMCN CTho EHar SHil WMou WNor
schneideriana — CMCN
serrata AGM — CB&S CBra CDoC CLnd CMCN CTho CWSG EHar ELan EMil IOrc MBal MBar NHol NPal NWea SEng SPer STre WAbe WDin WFro WMou WNor WWat
– 'Goblin' — NHol SSta WPat
¶ – 'Variegata' — MBlu SSta
¶ – 'Yatsubusa' — STre
– 'Yrban Ruby' — MGos SSta
sinica — STre WNor
x ***verschaffeltii*** — GAri

ZENOBIA (Ericaceae)

pulverulenta — CAbb CB&S CChu CCla CGre CPle CWSG CWit ELan ESis IOrc MBal MBar MBlu MBri MUlv NHol SGil SHBN SHil SPer SReu SSta WDin WPat WWat

ZEPHYRANTHES (Liliaceae/Amaryllidaceae)

¶ ***atamasca*** — WChr
candida — CAvo CBro EPot ERea LAma LBow LHop NHol NRog SDeJ SDix WChr WThu
¶ ***chlorosolen*** — WChr
citrina — LAma NRog WChr
drummondii — WChr
flavissima — CAvo CBro CMon WChr
grandiflora — WAbe WChr
x ***lancasterae*** — CMon WChr
robusta — See HABRANTHUS ***robustus***
rosea — LAma
sulphurea — LAma

ZIERIA (Rutaceae)

See Plant Deletions

ZIGADENUS (Liliaceae/Melanthiaceae)

elegans — CCla EBre EBul ECha ECro ELun EPot LBre LGre MBro MCas NHol NWCA SAsh SBla SMad SPer WHoo WThu
nuttallii — CLew LGre MSte NHol
venenosus — CHan

ZINGIBER (Zingiberaceae)

officinale — NHex

ZINNIA (Compositae/Asteraceae)

See Plant Deletions

ZIZANIA (Gramineae/Poaceae)

aquatica — EMFW

ZIZIA (Umbelliferae/Apiaceae)

aptera — MSal

ZIZIPHORA (Labiatae/Lamiaceae)

See Plant Deletions

Nursery - Code Index

Nurseries that are included in **THE PLANT FINDER** for the first time this year (or have been reintroduced) are marked in **Bold Type**.
Full details of the nurseries with a four letter Code will be found in the **Code-Nursery** Index on page 661.
Nurseries with a number are detailed in the **Additional Nursery** Index on page 734.
Nurseries marked **SEED, SUCC** or **ORCH** are listed in the
Seed Suppliers, Cacti & Succulent or **Orchid Specialist Index**

39 Steps	WThi
Abbey Dore Court Gardens	WAbb
Abbey Plants	CAbP
Abbot's House Garden	LAbb
Abbotsbury Sub-Tropical Gardens	CAbb
Aberconwy Nursery	WAbe
Abriachan Nurseries	GAbr
Acton Beauchamp Roses	WAct
Agar's Nursery	SAga
Paul Allanson	MAll
Misses I Allen & J Huish	CAll
Allwood Bros	SAll
Allwood Bros	SEED
Altoona Nurseries	CAlt
Jacques Amand Ltd.	LAma
Angus Heathers	GAng
Apple Court	SApp
Applegarth Nursery	20
Apuldram Roses	SApu
Arbor Exotica	EArb
Anthony Archer-Wills Ltd.	SAWi
Architectural Plants	SArc
Ardfearn Nursery	GArf
Arivegaig Nursery	GAri
Arley Hall Nursery	MArl
Arne Herbs	CArn
Arne Herbs	SEED
Ashenden Nursery	SAsh
Ashwood Nurseries	MAsh
Ashwood Nurseries	SEED
Askew's Nursery	MAsk
Aultan Nursery	GAul
David Austin Roses Ltd.	MAus
Avon Bulbs	CAvo
Axletree Nursery	SAxl
B & T World Seeds	SEED
Steven Bailey Ltd.	SBai
B & H M Baker	EBak
Ballagan Nursery	03
Ballalheannagh Gardens	MBal
Ballerina Trees Ltd.	EBal
Ballydorn Bulb Farm	IBal
Ballyrogan Nurseries	IBlr
The Bamboo Centre	LBam
Bamboo Nursery Ltd.	SBam
T H Barker & Sons	NBrk
Barkers Primrose Nurseries & Grdn Cntr	NBar
Barncroft Nurseries	MBar
Barnhaven Primroses	SEED
Barnsdale Plants	EBar
Barons Court Nurseries	IBar
Barters Farm Nurseries Ltd.	CBar
Barthelmy & Co	75
Barwinnock Herbs	GBar
Battersby Roses	NBat
Battle & Pears Ltd.	EB&P
John Beach (Nursery) Ltd.	MBea
Beacon's Nurseries	81
Peter Beales Roses	EBls
Beamish Clematis Nursery	NBea
Beechcroft Nursery	LBee
Beechcroft Nurseries	NBee
Beeches Nursery	EBee
R F Beeston	86
Beetham Nurseries	05
Bellhouse Nursery	MBel
Belwood Nurseries Ltd.	GBel
Michael Bennett	MBen
Bennett's Water Lily Farm	CBen
Birchwood Farm Nursery	33
Birkheads Cottage Garden Nursery	NBir
Blackmore & Langdon Ltd	CBla
Blackthorn Nursery	SBla
Blairhoyle Nursery	GBla
Bloomsbury	LBlm
The Bluebell Nursery	MBlu
R J Blythe	EBly
Bodiam Nursery	SBod
Bodnant Garden Nursery Ltd.	WBod
S & E Bond	WBon
Bonhard Nursery	GBon
Borde Hill Garden Ltd.	SBor
Bosvigo Plants	CBos
The Botanic Nursery	CBot
Bouts Cottage Nurseries	WBou
Ann & Roger Bowden	CBdn
Rupert Bowlby	LBow
Bowood Garden Centre	CBow
J W Boyce	SEED
Boyton Nurseries	CBoy
Brackenwood Nurseries	CBra
S & N Brackley	SEED
Bradley Batch Nursery	SUCC
Bradley Gardens Nursery	34

Nursery	Code
Dickson Nurseries Ltd.	IDic
Dingle Nurseries	WDin
Donington Plants	EDon
Jack Drake	GDra
Jack Drake	SEED
John Drake	EDra
John Drake	SEED
Drysdale Garden Exotics	SDry
Duchy of Cornwall	CDoC
Brian Duncan	IDun
East Midlands Cactus Nursery	SUCC
Eastgrove Cottage Garden Nursery	WEas
Eden Plants	IEde
Eggleston Hall	NEgg
Elly Hill Herbs	22
Elm Ridge Gardens Ltd.	NElm
The Garden at the Elms Nursery	WElm
Elsworth Herbs	EEls
Elworthy Cottage Plants	CElw
Emorsgate Seed	SEED
English Water Garden	SEng
Equatorial Plant Co.	ORCH
Equatorial Plants	SEED
Evegate Nursery Floral Workshop	57
Evelix Daffodils	GEve
Exbury Enterprises Ltd.	SExb
Christopher Fairweather Ltd.	SFai
Fairy Lane Nurseries	NFai
Family Trees	SFam
Farmhouse Plants	SFar
Feebers Hardy Plants	CFee
Felspar Cacti	SUCC
The Fern Nursery	EFer
Fernhill Nursery	IFer
Daphne ffiske Herbs	Effi
Fibrex Nurseries Ltd	WFib
Field House Nurseries	MFie
Field House Nurseries	SEED
Fillan's Plants	CFil
The Firs Nursery	MFir
The Margery Fish Plant Nursery	82
Kaytie Fisher	SFis
M V Fletcher	LFle
Flora Exotica	EFEx
The Flower Centre	26
Foliage & Unusual Plants	EFol
Foliage Scented & Herb Plants	01
Fosse Alpines	MFos
Mr Fothergill's Seeds Ltd.	SEED
Four Counties Nursery	WFou
Four Seasons	EFou
Foxbrush Gardens	WFox
Foxgrove Plants	LFox
Fron Nursery	WFro
The Fruit Garden	SFru
Fryer's Nurseries Ltd.	MFry
Fulbrooke Nursery	EFul
Rodney Fuller	CFul
Gandy's (Roses) Ltd.	MGan
Gannock Growers	LGan
Garden Cottage Nursery	GGar
Gardenscape	NGar
Linda Gascoigne Wild Flowers	28
W G Geissler	SUCC
Diana Gilbert	SGil
Glebe Cottage Gardens	29
Glebe Cottage Plants	CGle
Glen Chantry	EGle
Glendoick Gardens Ltd	GGGa
Glenhirst Cactus Nursery	SUCC
Glenhirst Cactus Nursery	SEED
Glenville Nurseries Ltd.	83
Global Orange Groves UK	CGOG
Godly's Roses	LGod
Goldbrook Plants	EGol
Gordon's Nursery	WGor
Goscote Nurseries Ltd	MGos
Goulding's Fuchsias	EGou
Grange Farm Nursery	32
Peter Grayson	SEED
Great Dixter Nurseries	SDix
Green Farm Plants	LGre
Greenacres Nursery	WGre
Greenaway Orchids	ORCH
Greenhead Roses	GGre
Greenslacks Nurseries	NGre
Greenway Gardens	CGre
C W Groves & Son	CGro
Growing Carpets	LGro
Gwydir Plants	WGwy
Hadspen Garden & Nursery	CHad
Halecat Garden Nurseries	NHlc
Hall Farm Nursery	EHal
Hall Farm Nursery	WHal
Halls of Heddon	NHal
Halsway Nursery	CHal
Hanging Gardens Nursery	EHan
The Hannays of Bath	CHan
Hardstoft Herb Garden	NHHG
Hardy Exotics	CHEx
Hardy's Cottage Garden Plants	85
Harrisons Delphiniums	SEED
Harrisons Delphiniums	LHar
Hartshall Nursery Stock	EHar
Hartside Nursery Garden	NHar
Harvest Nurseries	SUCC
Sue Hawthorne Gardens	WHaw
F Haynes & Partners Ltd.	MHay
Hayward's Carnations	SHay
Hazeldene Nursery	SHaz
Hedgerow Nursery	NHed
Heldon Nurseries	MHel
Hellyer's Garden Plants	48
James Henderson & Sons	SEED

Phedar Nursery	**SEED**	Ryal Nursery	**NRya**
A & A Phipps	**SUCC**	Ryans Nurseries	**56**
Pinks & Carnations	**NPin**	S & S Perennials	**MS&S**
Pinks & Carnations	**SEED**	Mrs Jane Sadler	**SSad**
Pitts Farm Nursery	**MPit**	Salley Gardens	**MSal**
The Plant Lovers	**SUCC**	Salley Gardens	**SEED**
Plant World Botanic Gardens	**CPla**	Sampford Shrubs	**CSam**
Plant World Botanic Gardens	**SEED**	John Sanday (Roses) Ltd.	**CSan**
Plantables	**GPlt**	Scotland Farmhouse Herbs	**CSFH**
The Plantation	**WPla**	Robert Scott	**SUCC**
E L F Plants Cramden Nursery Ltd.	**MPla**	Trevor Scott	**ETPC**
Plantworld	**44**	Scotts Nurseries (Merriott) Ltd	**CSco**
Plaxtol Nurseries	**SPla**	Scott's Clematis	**CSCl**
Pleasant View Nursery	**CPle**	Seaforde Gardens	**ISea**
J V Porter	**NPor**	**Martin S Searle**	**CSea**
Porthpean House Gardens	**52**	Seaside Nursery	**14**
Potterton & Martin	**EPot**	The Seed House	**SEED**
Potterton & Martin	**SEED**	Seeds by Size	**SEED**
Roger Poulett	**SPou**	**K R Shanks**	**59**
Roger Poulett	**SEED**	Shaw Rose Trees	**ESha**
Pounsley Plants	**CPou**	Shepton Nursery Garden	**CShe**
Poyntzfield Herb Nursery	**GPoy**	Sherston Parva Nursery	**CSPN**
Primrose Cottage Nursery	**NPri**	John Shipton (Bulbs)	**WShi**
Priorswood Clematis	**LPri**	**John Shipton (Bulbs)**	**SEED**
The Priory	**53**	Clive Simms	**ESim**
R D Plants	**CRDP**	Simply Plants	**ESiP**
R P P Alpines	**MRPP**	Simpsons Nursery	**15**
Rarer Plants	**NRar**	Siskin Plants	**ESis**
Raveningham Gardens	**ERav**	**Slack Top Alpines**	**NSla**
Ravensthorpe Nursery	**MRav**	Smallscape Nursery	**ESma**
Reads Nursery	**ERea**	Alan C Smith	**SSmi**
Redhouse Nurseries	**NRed**	Elizabeth Smith	**CSmi**
Regional Nurseries	**IReg**	John Smith & Son	**MSmi**
Ben Reid and Co	**GRei**	Peter J Smith	**SSmt**
G Reuthe Ltd	**SReu**	Southfield Nurseries	**SUCC**
Rickard's Hardy Fern	**WRic**	Southview Nurseries	**SSvw**
Ridgeway Heather Nursery	**WRid**	Special Plants	**CSpe**
Rileys' Chrysanthemums	**MRil**	Speyside Heather Garden Centre	**GSpe**
Rivendell Alpines	**CRiv**	Rosemary Spreckley	**WSpr**
W Robinson & Sons Ltd.	**SEED**	St Annes Vineyard	**WStA**
Sue Robinson	**47**	St Ishmael's Nurseries	**WStI**
Robinson's of Whaley Bridge	**MRob**	Stam's Nurseries	**ISta**
Rhodes & Rockliffe	**ER&R**	Stapeley Water Gardens Ltd	**MSta**
R V Roger Ltd	**NRog**	Starborough Nursery	**SSta**
R V Roger Ltd	**SEED**	**Stenbury Nursery**	**SSte**
Chris Rodgerson	**SUCC**	Steventon Road Nurseries	**MSte**
The Romantic Garden	**ERom**	Stewart's (Nottingham) Ltd.	**SEED**
Rookhope Nurseries	**NRoo**	Stillingfleet Lodge Nurseries	**NSti**
Roseland House Nursery	**CRHN**	Stockerton Nursery	**67**
Rosewood Nurseries	**SRos**	**Richard Stockwell**	**MSto**
Rougham Hall Nurseries	**ERou**	**Richard Stockwell**	**SEED**
Rowden Gardens	**CRow**	Stone House Cottage Nurseries	**WSHC**
Royal Horticultural Society's Garden	**CRos**	**Stone Cross Nurseries & Garden Cen.**	**68**
Andrew de Ruiter (Rose Specialist)	**MRui**	Stone Lane Gardens	**CSto**
Rumsey Gardens	**SRms**	Henry Street	**LStr**
Rumwood Nurseries	**SRum**	Stydd Nursery	**NSty**
Rushfields of Ledbury	**WRus**	**Brian Sulman**	**EBSP**

Code-Nursery Index

Please note that all these nurseries are listed in alphabetical order of their Codes. All nurseries are listed in alphabetical order of their name in the **Nursery-Code Index** on page 654.

CAbb **Abbotsbury Sub-Tropical Gardens, Abbotsbury, Nr Weymouth, Dorset DT3 4LA**

TEL: (0305) 871344/412 *CONTACT:* David Sutton
OPENING TIMES: 1000-1800 daily mid Mar-1st Nov. 1000-1500 Nov-mid Mar.
MIN MAIL ORDER UK: £10.00 + p&p *MIN VALUE EC:* £20.00 + p&p *EXPORT:* Yes
CAT. COST: A5 Sae + £1.50 *W/SALE or RETAIL:* Both
SPECIALITIES: Less common & tender Shrubs. *MAP PAGE:* **2**

CAbP **Abbey Plants,** Chaffeymoor, Bourton, Gillingham, Dorset SP8 5BY

TEL: (0747) 840841 *CONTACT:* K Potts
OPENING TIMES: 1000-1300 & 1400-1700 Tue-Sat all year
MAIL ORDER: No
CAT. COST: Sae *W/SALE or RETAIL:* Retail
SPECIALITIES: Flowering Trees & Shrubs. Shrub Roses incl. many unusual varieties. *MAP PAGE:* **2**

CAll **Misses I Allen & J Huish,** Quarry Farm, Wraxall, Bristol, Avon BS19 1LE

TEL: (0275) 810435 *CONTACT:*
OPENING TIMES: By appt. only.
MAIL ORDER: No
CAT. COST: 50p + Sae *W/SALE or RETAIL:* Retail
SPECIALITIES: National Reference Collection of Aster. *MAP PAGE:* **2**

CAlt **Altoona Nurseries,** The Windmill, Tigley, Dartington, Totnes Devon TQ9 6DW

TEL: (0803) 868147 *CONTACT:* Paul A Harber
OPENING TIMES: Any time by appt.
MAIL ORDER: No
CAT. COST: Sae *W/SALE or RETAIL:* Both
SPECIALITIES: Japanese Maples. *MAP PAGE:* **1**

CArn **Arne Herbs, Limeburn Nurseries, Limeburn Hill, Chew Magna, Avon BS18 8QW**

TEL: (0275) 333399 *CONTACT:* A Lyman-Dixon & H Lee
OPENING TIMES: Most times - please check first.
MIN MAIL ORDER UK: No minimum charge *MIN VALUE EC:* £75.00 + p&p *EXPORT:* Yes
CAT. COST: £1.00 *W/SALE or RETAIL:* Both
SPECIALITIES: Herbs, Wild Flowers & Cottage Flowers. See also SEED Index. *MAP PAGE:* **2**

CAvo **Avon Bulbs, Burnt House Farm, mid-Lambrook, South Petherton, Somerset TA13 5HE**

TEL: (0460) 242177 *CONTACT:* C Ireland-Jones
OPENING TIMES: Thu, Fri, Sat mid Sep-end Oct & mid Feb-end Mar or by appt.
MIN MAIL ORDER UK: £10.00 + p&p *MIN VALUE EC:* £20.00 + p&p *EXPORT:* Yes
CAT. COST: 4 x 2nd class *W/SALE or RETAIL:* Retail
SPECIALITIES: Smaller & unusual Bulbs. *MAP PAGE:* **1/2**

CBar **Barters Farm Nurseries Ltd.,** Chapmanslade, Westbury, Wiltshire BA13 4AL

TEL: (0373) 832294 *FAX:* (0373) 832677 *CONTACT:* C L Walker
OPENING TIMES: 0900-1700 Mon-Sat & 1000-1700 Sun & Bank Hols.
MAIL ORDER: No
CAT. COST: A4 Sae *W/SALE or RETAIL:* Both
SPECIALITIES: Very wide range of Shrubs. Ground Cover, specimen Patio plants, container & open-ground Trees. Ferns, half-hardy Perennials, Bamboos, Grasses & Herbaceous. *MAP PAGE:* **2**

CBdn **Ann & Roger Bowden, Cleave House, Sticklepath, Okehampton, Devon EX20 2NN**

TEL: (0837) 840481 *FAX:* (0837) 840482 *CONTACT:* Ann & Roger Bowden
◆ *OPENING TIMES:* Appt only.
MIN MAIL ORDER UK: No minimum charge *MIN VALUE EC:* Nmc *EXPORT:* Yes
CAT. COST: 3 x 1st class *W/SALE or RETAIL:* Both
SPECIALITIES: Hosta only. *MAP PAGE:* **1**

CBen **Bennett's Water Lily Farm, Putton Lane, Chickerell, Weymouth, Dorset DT3 4AF**

TEL: (0305) 785150 *FAX:* (0305) 781619 *CONTACT:* J Bennett
OPENING TIMES: Tue-Sun Apr-Aug, Tue-Fri Sep-Mar.
MIN MAIL ORDER UK: No minimum charge *MIN VALUE EC:* £25.00 + p&p
CAT. COST: 2 x 1st class *W/SALE or RETAIL:* Both
SPECIALITIES: Aquatic plants. NCCPG Collection of Water Lilies. *MAP PAGE:* **2**

CBla **Blackmore & Langdon Ltd, Pensford, Bristol Avon BS18 4JL**

TEL: (0275) 332300 *CONTACT:* J S Langdon
OPENING TIMES: 0900-1800 daily.
MIN MAIL ORDER UK: No minimum charge *MIN VALUE EC:* Nmc *EXPORT:* Yes
CAT. COST: Sae *W/SALE or RETAIL:* Retail
SPECIALITIES: Phlox, Delphinium & Begonias. *MAP PAGE:* **2**

CBos **Bosvigo Plants,** Bosvigo House, Bosvigo Lane, Truro, Cornwall TR1 3NH

TEL: (0872) 75774 *CONTACT:* Wendy Perry
OPENING TIMES: 1100-1800 Wed-Sat Mar-end Sep.
MAIL ORDER: No
CAT. COST: 4 x 2nd class *W/SALE or RETAIL:* Retail
SPECIALITIES: Rare & unusual Herbaceous. *MAP PAGE:* **1**

CBot **The Botanic Nursery,** Rookery Nurseries, Cottles Lane, Atworth, Nr Melksham, Wiltshire SN12 8NU

TEL: (0225) 706597/706631 *CONTACT:* T & M Baker
OPENING TIMES: 1000-1700 daily, closed Sun in Winter.
MAIL ORDER: No
CAT. COST: £1.50 *W/SALE or RETAIL:* Both
SPECIALITIES: Rare hardy Shrubs & Perennials for lime soils. Also Conservatory plants. Also at Bath Rd, Atworth, Melksham, Wilts. *MAP PAGE:* **2**

CBow **Bowood Garden Centre,** Bowood Estate, Calne, Wiltshire SN11 0LZ

TEL: (0249) 816828 *FAX:* (0249) 821757 *CONTACT:* Mrs Charlotte Hill-Baldwin
◆ *OPENING TIMES:* 1000-1800 daily Apr-Oct. 1000-1700 daily Nov-Mar. Closed Xmas period.
MIN MAIL ORDER UK: £5.00 + p&p *MIN VALUE EC:* n/a
CAT. COST: A4 Sae *W/SALE or RETAIL:* Retail
SPECIALITIES: Wide range of Old Fashioned Roses, unusual Rhododendrons & Magnolias, plus ever changing selection of Trees, Shrubs & Perennials. Quotations for large schemes. *MAP PAGE:* **2**

CBoy **Boyton Nurseries,** Bragg's Hill, Boyton, Nr Launceston, Cornwall PL15 9LP

TEL: (0566) 776474 *FAX:* (0566) 776474 *CONTACT:* Susan Bean
OPENING TIMES: 0900-1600 Winter, 0830-1800 Summer.
MAIL ORDER: No
CAT. COST: Sae for list *W/SALE or RETAIL:* Both
SPECIALITIES: Cottage Garden plants & old fashioned Roses *MAP PAGE:* **1**

CBra **Brackenwood Nurseries,** 131 Nore Road, Portishead, Nr Bristol, Avon BS20 8DU

TEL: (0275) 843484 *CONTACT:* Mr J Maycock
OPENING TIMES: 0900-1730 daily ex Xmas period.
MAIL ORDER: No
CAT. COST: None issued *W/SALE or RETAIL:* Both
SPECIALITIES: Trees, Shrubs, Conifers & Alpines. Many unusual varieties. *MAP PAGE:* **2/5**

CBrd **Broadleas Gardens Ltd.,** Broadleas, Devizes, Wiltshire SN10 5JQ

TEL: (0380) 722035 *CONTACT:* Lady Anne Cowdray
OPENING TIMES: 1400-1800 Wed, Thu & Sun Apr-Oct.
MAIL ORDER: No
CAT. COST: Sae *W/SALE or RETAIL:* Both
SPECIALITIES: General range. *MAP PAGE:* **2**

CBre Bregover Plants, Hillbrooke, Middlewood, North Hill, Nr Launceston, Cornwall PL15 7NN

TEL: (0566) 782661 *CONTACT:* Jennifer Bousfield
OPENING TIMES: 1100-1700 Wed-Fri Mar-mid Oct and by appt.
MIN MAIL ORDER UK: No minimum charge *MIN VALUE EC:* Nmc
CAT. COST: 2 x 1st class *W/SALE or RETAIL:* Retail
SPECIALITIES: Hardy Perennials inc. Asters, Hardy Geraniums, Primulas. Small supply of Show Auriculas, named Primroses & Violets. (Not all available by Mail Order). *MAP PAGE:* **1**

CBrk Brockings Nursery, Petherwin Gate, North Petherwin, Cornwall PL15 8LW

TEL: (0566) 785533 *CONTACT:* Ian K S Cooke
OPENING TIMES: 1300-1700 Tue-Sat
MIN MAIL ORDER UK: £15.00 + p&p *MIN VALUE EC:* £30.00 + p&p *EXPORT:* Yes
CAT. COST: 3 x 1st class *W/SALE or RETAIL:* Both
SPECIALITIES: Tender Perennials, Cannas, Coleus & Conservatory plants. *MAP PAGE:* **1**

CBro Broadleigh Gardens, Bishops Hull, Taunton, Somerset TA4 1AE

TEL: (0823) 286231 *FAX:* (0823) 323646 *CONTACT:* Lady Skelmersdale
OPENING TIMES: 0900-1600 Mon-Fri for viewing ONLY. Orders collected if prior notice given.
MIN MAIL ORDER UK: No minimum charge *MIN VALUE EC:* Nmc
CAT. COST: 2 x 1st class *W/SALE or RETAIL:* Retail
SPECIALITIES: Two Catalogues. (Jan) - Bulbs in growth, (Galanthus, Cyclamen etc.) & Herbaceous. (June) - Dwarf & unusual Bulbs. *MAP PAGE:* **1**

CB&S Burncoose & South Down Nurseries, Gwennap, Redruth, Cornwall TR16 6BJ

TEL: (0209) 861112 *FAX:* (0209) 860011 *CONTACT:* C H Williams & D Knuckey
OPENING TIMES: 0900-1700 Mon-Sat & 1100-1700 Sun.
MIN MAIL ORDER UK: £10.00 + p&p *MIN VALUE EC:* Nmc* *EXPORT:* Yes
CAT. COST: £1.00 inc p&p *W/SALE or RETAIL:* Both
SPECIALITIES: Extensive range of over 2000 Ornamental Trees & Shrubs and Herbaceous. 30 acre garden. *NOTE: Individual quotations for EC sales. *MAP PAGE:* **1**

CCan Cannington College Plant Centre, Cannington, Bridgwater, Somerset TA5 2LS

TEL: (0278) 652226 *FAX:* (0278) 652479 *CONTACT:* Steve Rudhall
OPENING TIMES: 1400-1700 daily Easter-Sep.
MIN MAIL ORDER UK: No minimum charge *MIN VALUE EC:* Nmc *EXPORT:* Yes
CAT. COST: 50p *W/SALE or RETAIL:* Both
SPECIALITIES: Abutilon, Argyranthemum, Ceanothus, Osteospermum, Salvia, Felicia, Diascia & Euryops. *MAP PAGE:* **1/2**

CChe Cherry Tree Nursery, (Sheltered Work Opportunities) off New Road Roundabout, Northbourne, Dorset BH10 7DA

TEL: (0202) 593537 *CONTACT:* Chris Veale
OPENING TIMES: 0830-1600 Mon-Fri, 0900-1200 most Sats,
MAIL ORDER: No
CAT. COST: Sae *W/SALE or RETAIL:* Both
SPECIALITIES: Hardy Shrubs. *MAP PAGE:* **2**

CChu Churchills Garden Nursery, Exeter Road, Chudleigh, South Devon TQ13 0DD

TEL: (0626) 852585 *FAX:* (0626) 852585 *CONTACT:* Mr M J S Henry
OPENING TIMES: 1400-1700 Mon-Fri, 1000-1700 Sat & Sun, mid Mar-mid Oct. Also by appt.
MAIL ORDER: No
CAT. COST: 3 x 2nd class *W/SALE or RETAIL:* Retail
SPECIALITIES: Extensive & interesting range of garden-worthy Trees, Shrubs, Climbers & Herbaceous - many unusual. *MAP PAGE:* **1**

CCla Clapton Court Gardens, Crewkerne, Somerset TA18 8PT

TEL: (0460) 73220/72200 *FAX:* (0460) 73220 *CONTACT:* Capt. S Loder
◆ *OPENING TIMES:* 1030-1700 Mon-Fri, 1400-1700 Sun Mar-Oct. 1400-1700 Easter Sat only.
MAIL ORDER: No
CAT. COST: £1.35 *W/SALE or RETAIL:* Retail
SPECIALITIES: Rare & unusual Herbaceous, Shrubs, Trees, Clematis & Roses. *MAP PAGE:* **1/2**

CCMG Cranborne Manor Garden Centre, Cranborne, Nr Wimborne, Dorset BH21 5PP

TEL: (0725) 517248 *FAX:* (0725) 517248 *CONTACT:* Miss Sandra Hewitt
OPENING TIMES: 0900-1700 Tue-Sat 1000-1700 Sun.
MIN MAIL ORDER UK: No minimum charge *MIN VALUE EC:* Nmc *EXPORT:* Yes
CAT. COST: £1 (Roses) *W/SALE or RETAIL:* Retail
SPECIALITIES: Roses, Clematis, Herbaceous incl unusual varieties, Topiary, Fan & Espalier Fruit, Shrubs & Trees. *NOTE: Mail Order for Roses only. *MAP PAGE:* **2**

CCor Corsley Mill, Highfield House, High Street, Shrewton, Salisbury, Wiltshire SP3 4BU

TEL: (0980) 621396 *FAX:* (0980) 621321 *CONTACT:* Brigid Quest-Ritson
OPENING TIMES: By appt. for collection.
MIN MAIL ORDER UK: No minimum charge *MIN VALUE EC:* Nmc *EXPORT:* Yes
CAT. COST: 50p *W/SALE or RETAIL:* Both
SPECIALITIES: Roses on own root-stock. NOTE: Mail Order in winter only. *MAP PAGE:* **2**

CCot Cottage Garden Plants Old & New, Cox Cottage, Lower Street, East Morden, Wareham, Dorset BH20 7DL

TEL: (0929) 459496 *CONTACT:* Mrs Alex Brenton
OPENING TIMES: 0900-1500 Mon & Tue Feb-Oct. Please phone to check first at other times.
MIN MAIL ORDER UK: £5.00 + p&p *MIN VALUE EC:* £10.00 + p&p
CAT. COST: 2 x 1st class *W/SALE or RETAIL:* Retail
SPECIALITIES: Primroses, Cheiranthus, Viola & Violets. *MAP PAGE:* **2**

CCra Crankan Nurseries, New Mill, Penzance, Cornwall TR20 8UT

TEL: (0736) 62897 *CONTACT:* Mr J J Jelbert
OPENING TIMES: Daily by appt.
MIN MAIL ORDER UK: No minimum charge *MIN VALUE EC:* Nmc
CAT. COST: Sae *W/SALE or RETAIL:* Both
SPECIALITIES: Violets. *MAP PAGE:* **1**

CDec Decorative Foliage, Higher Badworthy, South Brent, Devon TQ10 9EG

TEL: (03647) 2768 *CONTACT:* Amanda Morris
OPENING TIMES: By appt. only.
MIN MAIL ORDER UK: No minimum charge *MIN VALUE EC:* Nmc
CAT. COST: 2 x 1st class *W/SALE or RETAIL:* Retail
SPECIALITIES: Flower arrangers plants & rarities. *MAP PAGE:* **1**

CDoC Duchy of Cornwall, Penlyne Nursery, Cott Road, Lostwithiel, Cornwall PL22 08W

TEL: (0208) 872668 *CONTACT:* Andrew Carthew
OPENING TIMES: 0900-1700 Mon-Sat, 1000-1700 Sun. Closed Bank Hols.
MAIL ORDER: No
CAT. COST: £1.00 *W/SALE or RETAIL:* Retail
SPECIALITIES: Very wide range of all garden plants incl. Trees, Shrubs, Conifers, Roses, Perennials & Fruit. *MAP PAGE:* **1**

CElw Elworthy Cottage Plants, Elworthy Cottage, Elworthy, Lydeard St Lawrence, Taunton, Somerset TA4 3PX

TEL: (0984) 56427 *CONTACT:* Mrs J M Spiller
OPENING TIMES: 1330-1700 Tue & Thu mid Mar-mid Oct & by appt. Closed Aug except by appt.
MAIL ORDER: No
CAT. COST: 3 x 2nd class *W/SALE or RETAIL:* Retail
SPECIALITIES: Unusual Herbaceous plants esp. Penstemon, Hardy Geranium, Grasses, Campanulas & Erysimum. *MAP PAGE:* **1/2**

CFee Feebers Hardy Plants, 1 Feeber Cottage, Westwood, Broadclyst, nr Exeter, Devon EX5 3DQ

TEL: (0404) 822118 *CONTACT:* Mrs E Squires
◆ *OPENING TIMES:* 1000-1700 Thur & 1400-1800 Sat Mar-Jul & Sep-Oct
MAIL ORDER: No
CAT. COST: Sae + 36p stamp *W/SALE or RETAIL:* Retail
SPECIALITIES: Plants for wet clay soils, Alpines & Hardy Perennials. *MAP PAGE:* **1**

CFil **Fillan's Plants, Pound House Nursery, Buckland Monachorum, Yelverton, Devon PL20 7LJ**

TEL: (0822) 855050 *FAX:* (0822) 855050 *CONTACT:* Mark Fillan
◆ *OPENING TIMES:* By appt. only.
MIN MAIL ORDER UK: No minimum charge* *MIN VALUE EC:* Nmc *EXPORT:* Yes
CAT. COST: 3 x 1st class *W/SALE or RETAIL:* Both
SPECIALITIES: Ferns, Hydrangeas & less usual plants. *NOTE: Mail Order Oct-Mar only.
MAP PAGE: **1**

CFul **Rodney Fuller,** Coachman's Cottage, Higher Bratton Seymour, Wincanton, Somerset BA9 8DA

TEL: *CONTACT:* Rodney Fuller
OPENING TIMES: Not open.
MIN MAIL ORDER UK: £15.00 + p&p *MIN VALUE EC:* n/a
CAT. COST: Sae *W/SALE or RETAIL:* Retail
SPECIALITIES: Violas & Violettas. Please note that stocks are strictly limited.

CGle **Glebe Cottage Plants,** Pixie Lane, Warkleigh, Umberleigh, North Devon EX37 9DH

TEL: (0769) 540554 *CONTACT:* Carol Klein
OPENING TIMES: 1000-1700 Wed-Sun, please check first.
MIN MAIL ORDER UK: £20.00 + p&p *MIN VALUE EC:* n/a
CAT. COST: £1.00 *W/SALE or RETAIL:* Retail
SPECIALITIES: Extensive range of hard-to-find Perennials. *MAP PAGE:* **1**

CGOG **Global Orange Groves UK, PO Box 644, Poole, Dorset BH17 9YB**

TEL: (0202) 691699 *CONTACT:* P K Oliver
◆ *OPENING TIMES:* By appointment only.
MIN MAIL ORDER UK: £30.00 + p&p *MIN VALUE EC:* Nmc
CAT. COST: Sae *W/SALE or RETAIL:* Both
SPECIALITIES: Citrus trees, Citrus fertiliser & book 'Success with Citrus'.

CGre **Greenway Gardens,** Churston Ferrers, Brixham, Devon TQ5 0ES

TEL: (0803) 842382 *CONTACT:* Roger Clark (Manager)
OPENING TIMES: 1400-1700 (Nov-Feb 1630) Mon-Fri, 1000-1200 Sat, ex Bank Hols. Also by appt.
MIN MAIL ORDER UK: No minimum charge *MIN VALUE EC:* n/a
CAT. COST: 3 x 1st class *W/SALE or RETAIL:* Retail
SPECIALITIES: Unusual Trees & Shrubs particularly from temperate South America. *MAP PAGE:* **1**

CGro **C W Groves & Son, West Bay Road, Bridport, Dorset DT6 4BA**

TEL: (0308) 422654 *FAX:* (0308) 420888 *CONTACT:* C W Groves
OPENING TIMES: 0830-1700 Mon-Sat, 1000-1700 Sun.
MIN MAIL ORDER UK: None* *MIN VALUE EC:* £50.00 + p&p *EXPORT:* Yes
CAT. COST: Free *W/SALE or RETAIL:* Retail
SPECIALITIES: Nursery & Garden Centre specialising in Parma & Hardy Viola. * NOTE: Violets Mail Order ONLY. *MAP PAGE:* **1/2**

CHad **Hadspen Garden & Nursery,** Hadspen House, Castle Cary, Somerset BA7 7NG

TEL: (0749) 813707 *CONTACT:* N & S Pope
OPENING TIMES: 0900-1800 Thu-Sun & Bank Hols. 1st Mar-1st Oct. Garden open at the same time.
MAIL ORDER: No
CAT. COST: 3 x 1st class *W/SALE or RETAIL:* Retail
SPECIALITIES: Large leaved Herbaceous. Old fashioned and shrub Roses. *MAP PAGE:* **2**

CHal **Halsway Nursery,** Halsway, Nr Crowcombe, Taunton, Somerset TA4 4BB

TEL: (09848) 243 *CONTACT:* T A & D J Bushen
OPENING TIMES: Most days - please telephone first.
MIN MAIL ORDER UK: £2.00 + p&p *MIN VALUE EC:* n/a
CAT. COST: Sae* *W/SALE or RETAIL:* Retail
SPECIALITIES: Coleus & Begonias (excl. tuberous & winter flowering). Also good range of Greenhouse & garden plants. *NOTE: List for Coleus & Begonias only, no nursery list.
MAP PAGE: **1/2**

CHan **The Hannays of Bath,** Sydney Wharf Nursery, Bathwick, Bath, Avon BA2 4ES
TEL: (0225) 462230 *CONTACT:* Mr V H S & Mrs S H Hannay
OPENING TIMES: 1000-1700 Wed-Mon & by appt.
MAIL ORDER: No *EXPORT:* Yes
CAT. COST: £1.00+40p p&p *W/SALE or RETAIL:* Retail
SPECIALITIES: Unusual Perennials in specimen sizes and uncommon shrubs. *NOTE: For Export items, Certificates arranged but collection only. *MAP PAGE:* **2**

CHEx **Hardy Exotics, Gilly Lane, Whitecross, Penzance, Cornwall TR20 8BZ**
TEL: (0736) 740660 *FAX:* (0736) 741101 *CONTACT:* C Shilton/J Smith/I Lowe
OPENING TIMES: 1000-1700 daily 1st Apr-31st Oct. 1000-1600 Mon-Sat 1st Nov-31st Mar. Please phone first Nov-Mar.
MIN MAIL ORDER UK: £13.50 carriage *MIN VALUE EC:* P.O.A.
CAT. COST: 4 x 1st class *W/SALE or RETAIL:* Retail
SPECIALITIES: Trees, Shrubs & Herbaceous plants to create tropical & desert effects. Hardy & half-Hardy for gardens patios & conservatories. *MAP PAGE:* **1**

CHig **The High Garden, Courtwood, Newton Ferrers, South Devon PL8 1BW**
TEL: (0752) 872528 *CONTACT:* F Bennett
OPENING TIMES: By appt.
MIN MAIL ORDER UK: No minimum charge *MIN VALUE EC:* £20.00 + p&p
CAT. COST: 60p *W/SALE or RETAIL:* Both
SPECIALITIES: Pieris & Rhododendron. *MAP PAGE:* **1**

CHil **Hillside Plants,** Hillside, Gibbet Lane, Whitchurch, Avon BS14 0BQ
TEL: (0275) 837505 *CONTACT:* Josephine Pike
OPENING TIMES: Wed-Sat afternoons & by appt. Please phone first.
MAIL ORDER: No
CAT. COST: 4 x 1st class *W/SALE or RETAIL:* Retail
SPECIALITIES: Hardy Geraniums. *MAP PAGE:* **2**

CHoc **Philip Hocking,** 12 Lambrook Close, Taunton, Somerset TA1 2AQ
TEL: (0823) 278857 *CONTACT:* Philip Hocking
OPENING TIMES: Not open to the public.
MIN MAIL ORDER UK: No minimum charge *MIN VALUE EC:* n/a
CAT. COST: 1x2nd class + Sae *W/SALE or RETAIL:* Retail
SPECIALITIES: Primulas & Auriculas.

CHol **Holme Nurseries,** West Holme Farm, East Holme, Wareham, Dorsetshire BH20 6AG
TEL: (0929) 554716 *CONTACT:* Simon Goldsack
OPENING TIMES: 1000-1700 Mar 1st-Xmas daily.
MAIL ORDER: No
CAT. COST: Sae *W/SALE or RETAIL:* Both
SPECIALITIES: Hardy perennials, incl. many woodland species. Good range of Campanula, Euphorbia, Geranium, Lobelia, Verbena, Digitalis & Schizostylis. *MAP PAGE:* **2**

CJer **Jersey Lavender Ltd.,** rue du Pont Marquet, St Brelade, Jersey, Channel Isles
TEL: (0534) 42933 *FAX:* (0534) 45613 *CONTACT:* David Christie
OPENING TIMES: 1000-1700 Mon-Sat Jun-Sep. Also by appt.
MAIL ORDER: No
CAT. COST: Free *W/SALE or RETAIL:* Retail
SPECIALITIES: National Collection of Lavandula *MAP PAGE:* **1**

CKel **Kelways Nurseries,** Langport, Somerset TA10 9SL
TEL: (0458) 250521 *FAX:* (0458) 253351 *CONTACT:* Mr David Root
OPENING TIMES: 0900-1700 Mon-Fri, 1000-1600 Sat & Sun.
MAIL ORDER: No *EXPORT:* Yes
CAT. COST: Free *W/SALE or RETAIL:* Both
SPECIALITIES: (Spring) Lilium, (Autumn) Peonies, Iris, Herbaceous perennials. *MAP PAGE:* **1/2**

CKen **Kenwith Nursery (Gordon Haddow), The Old Rectory, Littleham, Bideford, North Devon EX39 5HW**
TEL: (0237) 473752 *CONTACT:* G Haddow
◆ *OPENING TIMES:* 1000-1200 & 1400-1630 Wed-Sat & by appt.
MIN MAIL ORDER UK: £10.00 + p&p *MIN VALUE EC:* £30.00 + p&p *EXPORT:* Yes
CAT. COST: 3 x 1st class *W/SALE or RETAIL:* Retail
SPECIALITIES: All Conifer genera. Grafting a speciality. Many new introductions to UK.
MAP PAGE: **1**

CKin **Kingsfield Conservation Nursery, Broadenham Lane, Winsham, Chard, Somerset TA20 4JF**
TEL: (0460) 30070 *FAX:* (0460) 30070 *CONTACT:* Mrs W White
OPENING TIMES: Please phone for details.
MIN MAIL ORDER UK: No minimum charge *MIN VALUE EC:* Nmc *EXPORT:* Yes
CAT. COST: Sae *W/SALE or RETAIL:* Both
SPECIALITIES: Native Trees, Shrubs, Wild flowers & Wild flower Seeds. See also SEED Index under Y.S.J. Seeds. *MAP PAGE:* **1/2**

CKni **Knightshayes Garden Trust,** The Garden Office, Knightshayes, Tiverton, Devon EX16 7RG
TEL: (0884) 259010 (Shop) *FAX:* (0884) 253264 *CONTACT:* M Hickson
OPENING TIMES: 1030-1730 daily 1st Apr-31st Oct.
MAIL ORDER: No
CAT. COST: £2.50 per list *W/SALE or RETAIL:* Retail
SPECIALITIES: Bulbs, Shrubs & Herbaceous. *MAP PAGE:* **1**

CLan **The Lanhydrock Gardens (NT),** Lanhydrock, Bodmin, Cornwall PL30 5AD
TEL: (0208) 72220 *CONTACT:* The National Trust
OPENING TIMES: Daily - Easter (or Apr 1st)-31st Oct.
MAIL ORDER: No
CAT. COST: Free *W/SALE or RETAIL:* Both
SPECIALITIES: Shrubs, especially Camellia, Azalea, Rhododendron, Magnolia, Deutzia. Philadelphus & Ceanothus. *MAP PAGE:* **1**

CLCN **Little Creek Nursery, 39 Moor Road, Banwell, Weston-super-Mare, Avon BS24 6EF**
TEL: (0934) 823739 *CONTACT:* Rhys & Julie Adams
OPENING TIMES: 1000-1630 Thu & Fri. Also most w/ends (but please check first) mid-March to mid-Sept & by appt.
MIN MAIL ORDER UK: No minimum charge *MIN VALUE EC:* Nmc *EXPORT:* Yes
CAT. COST: 3 x 1st class *W/SALE or RETAIL:* Retail
SPECIALITIES: Species Cyclamen (from seed) & Helleborus. *MAP PAGE:* **2**

CLew **Lewdon Farm Alpine Nursery,** Medland Lane, Cheriton Bishop, Nr Exeter, Devon EX6 6HF
TEL: (0647) 24283 *CONTACT:* Betty Frampton
◆ *OPENING TIMES:* Daily - end Mar-end Oct. By appt. in winter.
MAIL ORDER: No
CAT. COST: 2 x 2nd class *W/SALE or RETAIL:* Retail
SPECIALITIES: Alpines, miniature Shrubs, dwarf Conifers & herbaceous. *NOTE: Mail Order by special arrangement only. *MAP PAGE:* **1**

CLit **Littleton Nursery,** GLil Littleton, Somerton, Somerset TA11 6NT
TEL: (0458) 272356 *CONTACT:* G & R Seymour
◆ *OPENING TIMES:* 0900-1700 Mon, Tue, Thu, Fri, Sat. 1000-1600 Sun.
MAIL ORDER: No
CAT. COST: A4 Sae *W/SALE or RETAIL:* Both
SPECIALITIES: Fuchsia, Pelargoniums & half-hardy Perennials *MAP PAGE:* **1/2**

CLnd **Landford Trees,** Landford Lodge, Landford, Salisbury, Wiltshire SP5 2EH
TEL: (0794) 390808 *FAX:* (0794) 390037 *CONTACT:* C D Pilkington
OPENING TIMES: 0800-1700 Mon-Fri.
MAIL ORDER: No *EXPORT:* Yes
CAT. COST: Free *W/SALE or RETAIL:* Both
SPECIALITIES: Deciduous ornamental Trees. *MAP PAGE:* **2**

CLoc C S Lockyer, Lansbury, 70 Henfield Road, Coalpit Heath, Bristol, Avon BS17 2UZ

TEL: (0454) 772219 *CONTACT:* C S Lockyer
◆ *OPENING TIMES:* Appt only. (Many open days & coach parties).
MIN MAIL ORDER UK: 6 plants + p&p *MIN VALUE EC:* n/a
CAT. COST: 3 x 1st class *W/SALE or RETAIL:* Both
SPECIALITIES: Fuchsia. *MAP PAGE:* **5**

CLTr Little Treasures, Wheal Treasure, Horsedowns, Cornwall TR14 0NL

TEL: (0209) 831978 *CONTACT:* Bernadette Jackson
OPENING TIMES: By appt. only.
MIN MAIL ORDER UK: £5.00 + p&p *MIN VALUE EC:* £20.00 + p&p
CAT. COST: 3 x 1st class *W/SALE or RETAIL:* Retail
SPECIALITIES: Wide range of Perennials, Herbs, Shrubs & Climbers. Good selection of Dianthus, Penstemon & scented-leaf Pelargoniums. *MAP PAGE:* **1**

CMac Macpennys Nurseries, 154 Burley Road, Bransgore, Christchurch, Dorset BH23 8DB

TEL: (0425) 672348 *CONTACT:* T & V Lowndes
OPENING TIMES: 0800-1700 Mon-Fri, 0900-1700 Sat 1400-1700 Sun.
MIN MAIL ORDER UK: No minimum charge *MIN VALUE EC:* Nmc
CAT. COST: 50p A5 Sae *W/SALE or RETAIL:* Both
SPECIALITIES: General. *MAP PAGE:* **2**

CMCN Mallet Court Nursery, Curry Mallet, Taunton, Somerset TA3 6SY

TEL: (0823) 480748 *FAX:* (0823) 481009 *CONTACT:* J G S & P M E Harris F.L.S.
OPENING TIMES: 0900-1300 & 1400-1700 Mon-Fri. Sat & Sun by appt.
MIN MAIL ORDER UK: £20.00 + p&p *MIN VALUE EC:* £100.00 + p&p *EXPORT:* Yes
CAT. COST: £1 + 29p Sae *W/SALE or RETAIL:* Both
SPECIALITIES: Maples, Oaks, Magnolias, Hollies & other rare and unusual plants including those from China & South Korea. *MAP PAGE:* **1/2**

CMea The Mead Nursery, Brokerswood, Nr Westbury, Wiltshire BA13 4EG

TEL: (0373) 859990 *CONTACT:* Steve Lewis-Dale
OPENING TIMES: 0900-1700 Wed-Sat, 1200-1700 Sun, 0900-1700 Bank Hols. 2nd Feb-30th Oct.
MAIL ORDER: No
CAT. COST: 4 x 1st class *W/SALE or RETAIL:* Retail
SPECIALITIES: Perennials & Alpines incl. Bulbs. *MAP PAGE:* **2**

CMer Merlin Rooted Cuttings, Little Drym, Praze, Camborne, Cornwall TR14 0NU

TEL: (0209) 831 704 *CONTACT:* Liz & Roger Jackson
◆ *OPENING TIMES:* 1000-1700 Wed-Fri, 0900-1300 Sat Mar-mid Oct & by appt.
MIN MAIL ORDER UK: No minimum charge *MIN VALUE EC:* Nmc
CAT. COST: 4 x 1st class *W/SALE or RETAIL:* Both
SPECIALITIES: Rooted cuttings. *MAP PAGE:* **1**

CMGP Milton Garden Plants, Milton-on-Stour, Gillingham, Dorset SP8 5PX

TEL: (0747) 822484 *FAX:* (0747) 822484 *CONTACT:* Sue & Richard Cumming
OPENING TIMES: Tue-Sun & Bank Hol Mons.
MAIL ORDER: No
CAT. COST: 4 x 1st class *W/SALE or RETAIL:* Retail
SPECIALITIES: Very wide range of Perennials. Ever changing selection of Trees, Shrubs, Conifers, Alpines & Herbs. *MAP PAGE:* **2**

CMHG Marwood Hill Gardens, Barnstaple, North Devon EX31 4EB

TEL: (0271) 42528 *CONTACT:* Dr. Smart
OPENING TIMES: 1100-1300 & 1400-1700 daily.
MAIL ORDER: No
CAT. COST: 70p *W/SALE or RETAIL:* Retail
SPECIALITIES: Large range of unusual Trees & Shrubs. Eucalyptus, Alpines, Camellia, Astilbes & Bog plants. *MAP PAGE:* **1**

CMil Mill Cottage Plants, The Mill, Henley Lane, Wookey, Somerset BA5 1AP

TEL: (0749) 676966 *CONTACT:* Sally Gregson
OPENING TIMES: 1000-1800 Wed Mar-Sep or by appt. Ring for directions.
MIN MAIL ORDER UK: £5.00 + p&p *MIN VALUE EC:* £10.00 + p&p
CAT. COST: 2 x 1st class *W/SALE or RETAIL:* Retail
SPECIALITIES: Unusual & period Cottage plants especially 'old' Pinks, Campanulas, Hardy Geraniums, Euphorbias, Ferns & Pulmonarias. *MAP PAGE:* **1/2**

CMon Monocot Nursery, Jacklands, Jacklands Bridge, Tickenham, Clevedon, Avon BS21 6SG

TEL: *CONTACT:* M R Salmon
OPENING TIMES: 1000-1800 daily.
MIN MAIL ORDER UK: No minimum charge *MIN VALUE EC:* Nmc *EXPORT:* Yes
CAT. COST: Sae *W/SALE or RETAIL:* Retail
SPECIALITIES: Rare & unusual Bulbous plants. Narcissus, Colchicum, Scilla, Crocus, Aroids, S. African & S. American species. See also SEED Index. *MAP PAGE:* **2**

CNat Natural Selection, 1 Station Cottages, Hullavington, Chippenham, Wiltshire SN14 6ET

TEL: (0666) 837369 *CONTACT:* Martin Cragg-Barber
OPENING TIMES: Please telephone first.
MIN MAIL ORDER UK: £6.00 + p&p *MIN VALUE EC:* n/a
CAT. COST: 2 x 1st class *W/SALE or RETAIL:* Retail
SPECIALITIES: Unusual British natives, Pelargoniums & others. See also SEED Index. *MAP PAGE:* **2/5**

CNCN Naked Cross Nurseries, Waterloo Road, Corfe Mullen, Wimborne, Dorset BH21 3SR

TEL: (0202) 693256 *CONTACT:* Mr P J French & Mrs J E Paddon
OPENING TIMES: 0900-1730 daily.
MIN MAIL ORDER UK: No minimum charge *MIN VALUE EC:* n/a
CAT. COST: Free *W/SALE or RETAIL:* Both
SPECIALITIES: Heathers. *MAP PAGE:* **2**

CNew Newington Nurseries, Bathway Farm, Chewton Mendip, Somerset BA3 4LN

TEL: (0761) 241283 *FAX:* (0761) 241283 *CONTACT:* C J & C A Colbourne
OPENING TIMES: 1994 by appt. only or Mail Order. From Jan 1995 1000-1600 Tue-Fri.
MIN MAIL ORDER UK: No minimum charge *MIN VALUE EC:* Nmc *EXPORT:* Yes
CAT. COST: £1.75 *W/SALE or RETAIL:* Retail
SPECIALITIES: Conservatory plants. *MAP PAGE:* **2**

CNic Nicky's Rock Garden Nursery, Broadhayes, Stockland, Honiton, Devon EX14 9EH

TEL: (0404) 881213 *CONTACT:* Diana & Bob Dark
OPENING TIMES: 0900-dusk daily. Please telephone first to check & for directions.
MAIL ORDER: No
CAT. COST: 3 x 1st class *W/SALE or RETAIL:* Retail
SPECIALITIES: Plants for Rock gardens, Alpine house, Scree, Troughs, Banks, Walls & front of border & Dwarf Shrubs. Many unusual. *MAP PAGE:* **1**

COCH Otters' Court Heathers, Otters' Court, West Camel, Yeovil, Somerset BA22 7QF

TEL: (0935) 850285 *CONTACT:* Mrs D H Jones
OPENING TIMES: 0900-1700 Wed-Sun and by appt.
MIN MAIL ORDER UK: £3.00 + p&p *MIN VALUE EC:* Nmc
CAT. COST: 3 x 1st class *W/SALE or RETAIL:* Both
SPECIALITIES: Lime-tolerant Heathers - Erica, Calluna & Daboecia. *MAP PAGE:* **2**

COtt Otter Nurseries Ltd., Gosford Road, Ottery St. Mary, Devon EX11 1LZ

TEL: (0404) 815815 *FAX:* (0404) 815816 *CONTACT:* Mr K Owen
OPENING TIMES: 0800-1700 daily ex Xmas.
MAIL ORDER: No
CAT. COST: Free *W/SALE or RETAIL:* Both
SPECIALITIES: Large Garden Centre & Nursery with extensive range of Trees, Shrubs, Conifers, Climbers, Roses, Fruit & hardy Perennials. *MAP PAGE:* **1/2**

CPas Passiflora (National Collection), Lampley Road, Kingston Seymour, Clevedon, Avon BS21 6XS
TEL: (0934) 833350 *FAX:* (0934) 833320 *CONTACT:* John Vanderplank
OPENING TIMES: 0900-1700 daily
MIN MAIL ORDER UK: No minimum charge *MIN VALUE EC:* £20.00 + p&p *EXPORT:* Yes
CAT. COST: 3 x 1st class *W/SALE or RETAIL:* Both
SPECIALITIES: Passiflora. National Collection of over 150 species & varieties. See also SEED Index.
NOTE: Retail nursery at Smallway Congresbury, Yatton, Avon. *MAP PAGE:* **2**

CPBP Parham Bungalow Plants, Parham Lane, Market Lavington, Devizes, Wiltshire SN10 4QA
TEL: (0380) 812605 *CONTACT:* Mrs D E Sample
OPENING TIMES: Please ring first.
MIN MAIL ORDER UK: No minimum charge *MIN VALUE EC:* Nmc
CAT. COST: Sae *W/SALE or RETAIL:* Retail
SPECIALITIES: Alpines & dwarf Shrubs. *MAP PAGE:* **2**

CPer Perrie Hale Forest Nursery, Northcote Hill, Honiton, Devon EX14 8TH
TEL: (0404) 43344 *FAX:* (0404) 47163 *CONTACT:* N C Davey & Mrs J F Davey
OPENING TIMES: 0800-1630 Mon-Fri, 0800-1300 Sat. Retail sales by appt. please.
MIN MAIL ORDER UK: £5.00 + £12.00 p&p *MIN VALUE EC:* n/a
CAT. COST: Sae *W/SALE or RETAIL:* Both
SPECIALITIES: Forest Trees, native Hedging plants & Shrubs. *MAP PAGE:* **1**

CPev Peveril Clematis Nursery, Christow, Exeter, Devon EX6 7NG
TEL: (0647) 52937 *CONTACT:* Barry Fretwell
OPENING TIMES: 1000-1300 & 1400-1730 Fri-Wed, 1000-1300 Sun. Dec-Mar by appt.
MAIL ORDER: No
CAT. COST: 2 x 1st class *W/SALE or RETAIL:* Retail
SPECIALITIES: Clematis. *MAP PAGE:* **1**

CPla Plant World Botanic Gardens, St Marychurch Road, Newton Abbot, South Devon TQ12 4SE
TEL: (0803) 872939 *CONTACT:* Ray Brown
◆ *OPENING TIMES:* 0900-1700.
MAIL ORDER: No
CAT. COST: 3 x 1st class *W/SALE or RETAIL:* Both
SPECIALITIES: Alpines & unusual Herbaceous plants. Choice seed list available (Meconopsis, Gentians, Primulas, Lewisias). 4 acre world botanic map. NCCPG Primula collections. *MAP PAGE:* **1**

CPle Pleasant View Nursery, Two Mile Oak, Nr Denbury, Newton Abbot, Devon TQ12 6DG
TEL: (0803) 813388 *CONTACT:* Mrs B D Yeo
OPENING TIMES: 1000-1700 Wed-Sat 17th Mar-end Oct. (Closed for lunch 1245-1330)
MIN MAIL ORDER UK: £20.00 + p&p *MIN VALUE EC:* £20.00 + p&p
CAT. COST: 5 x 2nd class *W/SALE or RETAIL:* Retail
SPECIALITIES: Unusual Shrubs, Salvias & Conservatory Plants. National Collection Holders of Abelia & Salvia. *NOTE: Sae for Salvia list. *MAP PAGE:* **1**

CPMA P M A Plant Specialities, Lower Mead, West Hatch, Taunton, Somerset TA3 5RN
TEL: (0823) 480774 *FAX:* (0823) 481046 *CONTACT:* Karan or Nick Junker
OPENING TIMES: STRICTLY by appt. only.
MIN MAIL ORDER UK: No minimum charge *MIN VALUE EC:* Nmc *EXPORT:* Yes
CAT. COST: 5 x 2nd class *W/SALE or RETAIL:* Both
SPECIALITIES: Choice & unusual Shrubs incl. grafted Acer palmatum cvs, Cornus cvs, Magnolia cvs. and a wide range of Daphne. *MAP PAGE:* **1**

CPou Pounsley Plants, Poundsley Combe, Spriddlestone, Brixton, Plymouth, Devon PL9 0DW
TEL: (0752) 402873 *CONTACT:* Mrs Jane Hollow
◆ *OPENING TIMES:* Normally 1000-1700 Mon-Sat but please phone first.
MIN MAIL ORDER UK: £10.00 + p&p* *MIN VALUE EC:* n/a
CAT. COST: 2 x 1st class *W/SALE or RETAIL:* Both
SPECIALITIES: Unusual Herbaceous Perennials & 'Cottage plants'. *Mail Order Nov-Feb only.
MAP PAGE: **1**

CRDP R D Plants, Homelea Farm, Tytherleigh, Axminster, East Devon EX13 7BG

TEL: (0460) 220206 *CONTACT:* Rodney Davey & Lynda Windsor
◆ *OPENING TIMES:* 0900-1300 & 1400-1730 Mon-Fri & most weekends, Mar-end Sep. Please check first.
MAIL ORDER: No
CAT. COST: 3 x 1st class *W/SALE or RETAIL:* Retail
SPECIALITIES: Herbaceous, Woodland, Pond & Moisture loving plants, many rare & unusual. A few choice Alpines. (Over 1,000 varieties). *MAP PAGE:* **1**

CRHN Roseland House Nursery, Chacewater, Truro, Cornwall TR4 8QB

TEL: (0872) 560451 *CONTACT:* C R Pridham
OPENING TIMES: 1000-1600 Tue Mar-Jul.
MAIL ORDER: No
CAT. COST: 2 x 1st class *W/SALE or RETAIL:* Retail
SPECIALITIES: Climbing Plants. *MAP PAGE:* **1**

CRiv Rivendell Alpines, Horton Heath, Wimborne, Dorset BH21 7JN

TEL: (0202) 824013 *CONTACT:* John & Claire Horsey.
OPENING TIMES: 1000-1700 Sat-Thu Mar-Oct. Nov-Feb by appt.
MIN MAIL ORDER UK: £5.00 + p&p *MIN VALUE EC:* n/a
CAT. COST: Sae *W/SALE or RETAIL:* Retail
SPECIALITIES: Alpines & Aquatics. *MAP PAGE:* **2**

CRos Royal Horticultural Society's Garden, Rosemoor, Great Torrington, Devon EX38 8PH

TEL: (0805) 24067 *FAX:* (0805) 24717 *CONTACT:* Plant Sales Manager
OPENING TIMES: 1000-1700 1st Mar-31st Sep, 1000-1600 1st Oct-4th Dec.
MAIL ORDER: No
CAT. COST: None issued *W/SALE or RETAIL:* Retail
SPECIALITIES: National Cornus and part Ilex collections. Many rare & unusual plants. *MAP PAGE:* **1**

CRow Rowden Gardens, Brentor, Nr Tavistock, Devon PL19 0NG

TEL: (0822) 810275 *CONTACT:* John R L Carter
OPENING TIMES: 1000-1700 Sat-Sun & Bank Hols 26th Mar-end Sep. Other times by appt.
MIN MAIL ORDER UK: No minimum charge *MIN VALUE EC:* Nmc *EXPORT:* Yes
CAT. COST: £1.50 *W/SALE or RETAIL:* Both
SPECIALITIES: Aquatics, Bog, unusual & rare specialist plants. NCCPG Polygonum Collection. *MAP PAGE:* **1**

CSam Sampford Shrubs, Sampford Peverell, Tiverton, Devon EX16 7EW

TEL: (0884) 821164 *CONTACT:* M Hughes-Jones & S Proud
OPENING TIMES: 0900-1700 (dusk if earlier) Thu-Sun. Closed 19th Dec-1st Feb.
MIN MAIL ORDER UK: £15.00 + p&p *MIN VALUE EC:* £30.00 + p&p
CAT. COST: Sae *W/SALE or RETAIL:* Retail
SPECIALITIES: Extensive range of good common & uncommon plants including Herbaceous, Shrubs, Trees & Fruit. *MAP PAGE:* **1**

CSan John Sanday (Roses) Ltd., Over Lane, Almondsbury, Bristol, Avon BS12 4DA

TEL: (0454) 612195 *CONTACT:* Thomas Sanday
OPENING TIMES: 0900-1700 Mon-Sat all year. 1000-1700 Sun Mar-Dec.
MIN MAIL ORDER UK: No minimum charge *MIN VALUE EC:* n/a
CAT. COST: Free *W/SALE or RETAIL:* Both
SPECIALITIES: All types of Roses old & new. *MAP PAGE:* **2/5**

CSCl Scott's Clematis, Lee, Nr Ilfracombe, North Devon EX34 8LW

TEL: (0271) 863366 *FAX:* (0271) 863366 *CONTACT:* John Scott
◆ *OPENING TIMES:* 1000-1700 Tue-Fri & Sun & Bank Hols Mon. Sat at Barnstable Market. Closed 31st Oct-31st Jan.
MIN MAIL ORDER UK: See Cat. for details *MIN VALUE EC:* See Cat. *EXPORT:* Yes
CAT. COST: A4 Sae *W/SALE or RETAIL:* Both
SPECIALITIES: Clematis only. *MAP PAGE:* **1/4**

◆ **See also Display Advertisements**

CSco **Scotts Nurseries (Merriott) Ltd,** Merriott, Somerset TA16 5PL
TEL: (0460) 72306 *FAX:* (0460) 77433 *CONTACT:* Mark Wallis
◆ *OPENING TIMES:* 0900-1700 Mon-Sat, 1000-1700 Sun.
MIN MAIL ORDER UK: £5.00 + p&p *MIN VALUE EC:* n/a
CAT. COST: £1.50 *W/SALE or RETAIL:* Both
SPECIALITIES: Wide general range. *MAP PAGE:* **1/2**

CSea **Martin S Searle, Petit Choffin, rue des Choffins, St Saviour, Guernsey, CI. GY7 9FD**
TEL: (0481) 63144 *CONTACT:* Martin S Searle
OPENING TIMES: By appt. only
MIN MAIL ORDER UK: £8.00 + p&p *MIN VALUE EC:* £8.00 + p&p *EXPORT:* Yes
CAT. COST: 4 x 1st class *W/SALE or RETAIL:* Both
SPECIALITIES: NCCPG Collection of Hebes. *MAP PAGE:* **1**

CSev **Lower Severalls Herb Nursery,** Crewkerne, Somerset TA18 7NX
TEL: (0460) 73234 *FAX:* (0460) 76105 *CONTACT:* Mary R Cooper
OPENING TIMES: 1000-1700 Fri-Wed (1400-1700 Sun).
MIN MAIL ORDER UK: £10.00 + p&p *MIN VALUE EC:* n/a
CAT. COST: 4 x 1st class *W/SALE or RETAIL:* Retail
SPECIALITIES: Herbs, Herbaceous & Conservatory plants. *MAP PAGE:* **2**

CSFH **Scotland Farmhouse Herbs,** Virginstow, Beaworthy, North Devon EX21 5EA
TEL: (040921) 585 *CONTACT:* Jean Jewels & Peter Charnley
OPENING TIMES: Any time, but please phone first.
MAIL ORDER: No
CAT. COST: 3 x 1st class *W/SALE or RETAIL:* Both
SPECIALITIES: Herbs, culinary, medicinal & dye plants. Scented foliage plants & plants for the wild garden. *MAP PAGE:* **1**

CShe **Shepton Nursery Garden,** Old Wells Road, Shepton Mallet, Somerset BA4 5XN
TEL: (0749) 343630 *CONTACT:* Mr & Mrs P W Boughton
OPENING TIMES: 0930-1730 Tue-Sat and by appt.
MAIL ORDER: No
CAT. COST: 4 x 2nd class *W/SALE or RETAIL:* Retail
SPECIALITIES: Herbaceous, Alpines & Chaenomeles. *MAP PAGE:* **2**

CSmi **Elizabeth Smith, Downside, Bowling Green, Constantine, Falmouth, Cornwall TR11 5AP**
TEL: (0326) 40787 *CONTACT:* Elizabeth Smith
OPENING TIMES: Mail Order only, but visits can be arranged by prior telephone appt.
MIN MAIL ORDER UK: Negotiable *MIN VALUE EC:* Nmc *EXPORT:* Yes
CAT. COST: Sae *W/SALE or RETAIL:* Retail
SPECIALITIES: Scented Violets. Some seed available for export. NOTE: Telephone or Postal enquiries please.

CSpe **Special Plants, Laurels Farm, Upper Wraxall, Chippenham, Wiltshire SN14 7AG**
TEL: (0225) 891686 *CONTACT:* Derry Watkins
OPENING TIMES: Most days - please ring first to check.
MIN MAIL ORDER UK: £10.00 + p&p *MIN VALUE EC:* £10.00 + p&p
CAT. COST: 4 x 2nd class *W/SALE or RETAIL:* Retail
SPECIALITIES: Tender Perennials, Argyranthemum, Felicia, Diascia, Lotus, Salvia, Osteospermum etc. New introductions of South African plants. * NOTE: Mail Order Oct-Feb only. *MAP PAGE:* **2**

CSPN **Sherston Parva Nursery, *21 Court Street, Sherston, Wiltshire SN16 0LL**
TEL: (0666) 840623 *CONTACT:* Mrs M Morris
◆ *OPENING TIMES:* 1000-1300 & 1400-1700 Tue-Sat. 1200-1700 Sun Easter-Nov. Also Bank Hol Mons (closed Tue).
MIN MAIL ORDER UK: £10.00 + p&p *MIN VALUE EC:* £20.00 + p&p
CAT. COST: £1.00 *W/SALE or RETAIL:* Retail
SPECIALITIES: Clematis, wall Shrubs & Climbers & Conservatory plants. *NOTE: Nursery at Malmesbury Road, Sherston. *MAP PAGE:* **2**

CSto **Stone Lane Gardens, Stone Farm, Chagford, Devon TQ13 8JU**

TEL: (064723) 311 *CONTACT:* Kenneth Ashburner
OPENING TIMES: Appt only.
MIN MAIL ORDER UK: No minimum charge *MIN VALUE EC:* Nmc
CAT. COST: List £1.00* *W/SALE or RETAIL:* Both
SPECIALITIES: Wide range of wild provenance Betula and Alnus. Also interesting varieties of Rubus, Vaccinium, Sorbus etc. *£3.00 for full descriptive & keyed Catalogue. *MAP PAGE:* **1**

CSut **Suttons Seeds Ltd.,** Hele Road, Torquay, South Devon TQ2 7QJ

TEL: (0803) 614455 *FAX:* (0803) 615747 *CONTACT:* Customer Services
OPENING TIMES: (Office) 0830-1700 Mon-Fri Oct-Apr. 0830-1615 Mon-Thu 0830-1200 Fri May-Sep. Answerphone also.
MIN MAIL ORDER UK: No minimum charge *MIN VALUE EC:* n/a
CAT. COST: Free *W/SALE or RETAIL:* Retail
SPECIALITIES: Over 1,300 varieties of flower & vegetable seed, bulbs, plants & sundries. See also SEED Index.

CTbh **Trebah Nursery,** Trebah, Mawnan Smith, Falmouth, Cornwall TR11 5JZ

TEL: (0326) 250448 *FAX:* (0326) 250781 *CONTACT:* Philip McMillan Browse
OPENING TIMES: 1000-1600 Mon-Sat but please phone first.
MAIL ORDER: No
CAT. COST: A4 Sae *W/SALE or RETAIL:* Retail
SPECIALITIES: Agave, Yucca, Palms & Lampranthus. *MAP PAGE:* **1**

CTho **Thornhayes Nursery, St Andrews Wood, Dulford, Cullompton, Devon EX15 2DF**

TEL: (08846) 746 *FAX:* (08846) 739 *CONTACT:* K D Croucher
OPENING TIMES: By appt. only.
MIN MAIL ORDER UK: No minimum charge *MIN VALUE EC:* Nmc *EXPORT:* Yes
CAT. COST: 4 x 1st class *W/SALE or RETAIL:* Both
SPECIALITIES: A broad range of forms of Broadleaved, Ornamental, Amenity & Fruit Trees, including West Country Apple varieties. *MAP PAGE:* **1**

CThr **Three Counties Nurseries, Marshwood, Bridport, Dorset DT6 5QJ**

TEL: (0297) 678257 *CONTACT:* A & D Hitchcock
OPENING TIMES: Not open.
MIN MAIL ORDER UK: No minimum charge *MIN VALUE EC:* £15.00 + p&p
CAT. COST: 2 x 2nd class *W/SALE or RETAIL:* Both
SPECIALITIES: Pinks & Dianthus.

CTom **Tomperrow Farm Nurseries, Tomperrow Farm, Threemilestone, Truro, Cornwall TR3 6BE**

TEL: (0872) 560344 *CONTACT:* Mrs S C Goodswen
OPENING TIMES: 1000-1700 Mon-Sat. Evenings & Suns by appt. Dec, Jan & Aug by appt.
MIN MAIL ORDER UK: No minimum charge *MIN VALUE EC:* Nmc
CAT. COST: 70p in stamps *W/SALE or RETAIL:* Retail
SPECIALITIES: Wide range of hardy Herbaceous plants, some unusual. *MAP PAGE:* **1**

CTor **The Torbay Palm Farm,** St Marychurch Road, Coffinswell, nr Newton Abbot, South Devon TQ12 4SE

TEL: (0803) 872800 *FAX:* (0803) 213843 *CONTACT:* T A Eley
OPENING TIMES: 0900-1730 Mon-Fri, 1030-1700 Sat & Sun.
MIN MAIL ORDER UK: £3.80 + p&p *MIN VALUE EC:* n/a
CAT. COST: Free *W/SALE or RETAIL:* Both
SPECIALITIES: Cordyline australis, Trachycarpus fortuneii & new varieties of Cordyline. *MAP PAGE:* **1**

CTre **Trewidden Estate Nursery, Trewidden Gardens, Penzance, Cornwall TR20 8TT**

TEL: (0736) 62087 *FAX:* (0736) 68142 *CONTACT:* Mr M G Snellgrove.
OPENING TIMES: 0800-1300 & 1400-1700 Mon-Thu & Sat. 0800-1300 & 1400-1600 Fri. Closed some Sats - please phone.
MIN MAIL ORDER UK: No minimum charge *MIN VALUE EC:* Nmc
CAT. COST: 50p *W/SALE or RETAIL:* Both
SPECIALITIES: Camellia & unusual Shrubs. *MAP PAGE:* **1**

CTrh **Trehane Camellia Nursery, J Trehane & Sons Ltd, Stapehill Road, Hampreston, Wimborne, Dorset BH21 7NE**
TEL: (0202) 873490 *FAX:* (0202) 873490 *CONTACT:* Miss J E Trehane
OPENING TIMES: 0900-1630 Mon-Fri & weekends end Feb-Oct.
MIN MAIL ORDER UK: No minimum charge *MIN VALUE EC:* Nmc *EXPORT:* Yes
CAT. COST: Cat/Book £1.50 *W/SALE or RETAIL:* Both
SPECIALITIES: Extensive range of Camellia species, cultivars & hybrids. Many new introductions. Evergreen Azaleas, Pieris, Magnolias, Blueberries & Cranberries. *MAP PAGE:* **2**

CTro **Tropicana Nursery, Westhill Avenue, Torquay, Devon TQ1 4LH**
TEL: (0803) 312618 *CONTACT:* M L Eden
OPENING TIMES: By appt. only.
MIN MAIL ORDER UK: £10.00 + p&p *MIN VALUE EC:* £25.00 + p&p *EXPORT:* Yes
CAT. COST: 4 x 1st class *W/SALE or RETAIL:* Both
SPECIALITIES: Conservatory & sub-tropical plants. *MAP PAGE:* **1**

CTrw **Trewithen Nurseries,** Grampound Road, Truro, Cornwall TR2
TEL: (0726) 882764 *CONTACT:* M Taylor
OPENING TIMES: 0800-1630 Mon-Fri.
MAIL ORDER: No
CAT. COST: £1.00 *W/SALE or RETAIL:* Both
SPECIALITIES: Shrubs, especially Camellia & Rhododendron. *MAP PAGE:* **1**

CVer **Veryans Plants,** Glebe, Coryton, Okehampton, Devon EX20 4PB
TEL: (0822) 86302 day* *CONTACT:* Miss R V Millar
OPENING TIMES: Essential to telephone first for appt. *NOTE: (0566) 83433 evenings.
MIN MAIL ORDER UK: No minimum charge *MIN VALUE EC:* n/a
CAT. COST: 3 x 1st class *W/SALE or RETAIL:* Retail
SPECIALITIES: Range of hardy Perennials inc. Asters, Penstemons & large selection of Primulas, many rare. *MAP PAGE:* **1**

CWal **Wall Cottage Nursery, Lockengate, Bugle, St. Austell, Cornwall PL26 8RU**
TEL: (0208) 831259 *CONTACT:* Mrs J R Clark
OPENING TIMES: 0830-1700 Mon-Sat.
MIN MAIL ORDER UK: £15.00 + p&p *MIN VALUE EC:* £150.00 + p&p *EXPORT:* Yes
CAT. COST: 60p *W/SALE or RETAIL:* Both
SPECIALITIES: Specialist Rhododendron & Azalea plus general range. *MAP PAGE:* **1**

CWes **West Kington Nurseries Ltd.,** Pound Hill, West Kington, Nr Chippenham Wiltshire SN14 7JG
TEL: (0249) 782822 *FAX:* (0249) 782953 *CONTACT:* B H Ellis
◆ *OPENING TIMES:* 1000-1700 Wed-Sun 2nd Mar-27th Nov 1994 & Bank Holiday Mons.
MAIL ORDER: No
CAT. COST: Free *W/SALE or RETAIL:* Both
SPECIALITIES: Herbaceous & Alpines. *MAP PAGE:* **2**

CWGN **The Water Garden Nursery, Highcroft, Moorend, Wembworthy, Chulmleigh, Devon EX18 7SG**
TEL: (0837) 83566 *CONTACT:* J M Smith
OPENING TIMES: 0800-1700 Fri-Tue Apr-Sep & by appt.
MIN MAIL ORDER UK: No minimum charge *MIN VALUE EC:* Nmc
CAT. COST: 3 x 1st class *W/SALE or RETAIL:* Retail
SPECIALITIES: Plants for shade, wetlands, bog & water. *MAP PAGE:* **1**

CWil **H & S Wills, 2 St Brannocks Park Road, Ilfracombe, Devon EX34 8HU**
TEL: (0271) 863949 *CONTACT:* H Wills
OPENING TIMES: Appt only.
MIN MAIL ORDER UK: £3.00 + p&p *MIN VALUE EC:* £5.00 + p&p *EXPORT:* Yes
CAT. COST: 3 x 1st class *W/SALE or RETAIL:* Retail
SPECIALITIES: Sempervivum, Jovibarba & Rosularia.

CWit **Withleigh Nurseries,** Quirkhill, Withleigh, Tiverton, Devon EX16 8JG
TEL: (0884) 253351 *CONTACT:* Chris Britton
OPENING TIMES: 0900-1730 Mon-Sat Mar-Jun, 0900-1730 Tue-Sat Jul-Feb.
MAIL ORDER: No
CAT. COST: None issued *W/SALE or RETAIL:* Retail
SPECIALITIES: Shrubs & Herbaceous. *MAP PAGE:* **1**

CWSG West Somerset Garden Centre, Mart Road, Minehead, Somerset TA24 5BJ
TEL: (0643) 703812 *FAX:* (0643) 706470 *CONTACT:* Mrs J K Shoulders
OPENING TIMES: 0800-1700 Mon-Sat, 1100-1700 Sun (Winter times vary, please phone).
MIN MAIL ORDER UK: No minimum charge *MIN VALUE EC:* Nmc
CAT. COST: Free *W/SALE or RETAIL:* Retail
SPECIALITIES: Wide general range. *MAP PAGE:* **1/4**

EArb Arbor Exotica, The Estate Office, Hall Farm, Weston Colville, Cambridgeshire CB1 5PE
TEL: (0223) 290328/525 *FAX:* (0223) 290650 *CONTACT:* Enid Capewell
◆ *OPENING TIMES:* By appt.
MIN MAIL ORDER UK: No minimum charge *MIN VALUE EC:* Nmc *EXPORT:* Yes
CAT. COST: £1.50 *W/SALE or RETAIL:* Both
SPECIALITIES: Hardy, rare, container grown Ornamental Trees from seed. *MAP PAGE:* **6**

EBak B & H M Baker, Bourne Brook Nurseries, Greenstead Green, Halstead, Essex CO9 1RJ
TEL: (0787) 472900/476369 *CONTACT:* B & H M Baker
OPENING TIMES: 0800-1630 Mon-Fri, 0900-1200 & 1400-1630 Sat & Sun.
MAIL ORDER: No
CAT. COST: 20p+stamp *W/SALE or RETAIL:* Both
SPECIALITIES: Fuchsia & Conservatory Plants. *MAP PAGE:* **6**

EBal Ballerina Trees Ltd., Maris Lane, Trumpington, Cambridgeshire CB2 2LQ
TEL: (0223) 845775 *FAX:* (0223) 842934 *CONTACT:* Julie Murden
OPENING TIMES: 0900-1730 (Office only).
MIN MAIL ORDER UK: £19.95 + p&p *MIN VALUE EC:* n/a
CAT. COST: Free *W/SALE or RETAIL:* Both
SPECIALITIES: Columnar Apple Trees. NOTE: Retail trade only by Mail Order.

EBar Barnsdale Plants, Exton Avenue, Exton, Oakham, Rutland LE15 8AH
TEL: (0572) 813200 *FAX:* (0572) 813346 *CONTACT:* Mr Hamilton
OPENING TIMES: 1000-1700 1st Apr-31st Oct, 1000-1600 1st Nov-31st Mar. Closed Xmas & New Year.
MIN MAIL ORDER UK: No minimum charge *MIN VALUE EC:* n/a
CAT. COST: A4+3x1st class *W/SALE or RETAIL:* Retail
SPECIALITIES: Choice & unusual Garden Plants & Trees. *MAP PAGE:* **8**

EBee Beeches Nursery, Village Centre, Ashdon, Saffron Walden, Essex CB10 2HB
TEL: (0799) 584362 *FAX:* (0799) 584362 *CONTACT:* Alan Bidwell
◆ *OPENING TIMES:* 0830-1700 Mon-Sat, 1000-1700 Sun incl. Bank Hols.
MAIL ORDER: No
CAT. COST: 2 x 2nd class *W/SALE or RETAIL:* Retail
SPECIALITIES: Herbaceous specialists & extensive range of other garden plants. *MAP PAGE:* **6**

EBls Peter Beales Roses, London Road, Attleborough, Norfolk NR17 1AY
TEL: (0953) 454707 *FAX:* (0953) 456845 *CONTACT:* Mr Peter Beales
OPENING TIMES: 0900-1700 Mon-Fri, 0900-1630 Sat, 1000-1600 Sun. Jan closed Sun.
MIN MAIL ORDER UK: No minimum charge *MIN VALUE EC:* Nmc *EXPORT:* Yes
CAT. COST: Free *W/SALE or RETAIL:* Both
SPECIALITIES: Old fashioned Roses. *MAP PAGE:* **8**

EBly R J Blythe, Potash Nursery, Cow Green, Bacton, Stowmarket, Suffolk IP14 4HJ
TEL: (0449) 781671 *CONTACT:* R J Blythe
OPENING TIMES: 1000-1700 Sat, Sun & Mon mid Feb-end June.
MAIL ORDER: No
CAT. COST: 3 x 1st class *W/SALE or RETAIL:* Retail
SPECIALITIES: Fuchsias. *MAP PAGE:* **6**

EBre Bressingham Plant Centre,, Bressingham, Diss, Norfolk IP22 2AB
TEL: (0379 88) 8133 *FAX:* (0379 88) 8289 *CONTACT:* Tony Fry
OPENING TIMES: 1000-1730 daily. (Direct retail Plant Centre).
MAIL ORDER: No
CAT. COST: None issued *W/SALE or RETAIL:* Retail
SPECIALITIES: Very wide general range. Many own varieties. Focus on Hardy Ornamental plants. *MAP PAGE:* **6/8**

◆ See also Display Advertisements

EBro **Brokenbacks Nursery,** Broxhill Road, Havering-atte-Bower, Romford, Essex RM4 1QH

TEL: (0708) 377744 *CONTACT:* A Carter
OPENING TIMES: 0900-1700 Thu-Mon.
MIN MAIL ORDER UK: No minimum charge *MIN VALUE EC:* n/a
CAT. COST: Sae *W/SALE or RETAIL:* Retail
SPECIALITIES: Old fashioned and Hybrid musk Roses. *MAP PAGE:* **6**

EBSP **Brian Sulman, 54 Kingsway, Mildenhall, Bury St Edmunds, Suffolk IP28 7HR**

TEL: (0638) 712297 *CONTACT:* Brian Sulman
OPENING TIMES: Mail Order only.
MAIL ORDER: Only*MIN MAIL ORDER UK:* £9.00 + p&p *MIN VALUE EC:* £9.00 + p&p
CAT. COST: 2 x 1st class *W/SALE or RETAIL:* Retail
SPECIALITIES: Regal, Zonal, Trailing & Coloured-leaf Pelargoniums.

EBul **Bullwood Nursery, 54 Woodlands Road, Hockley, Essex SS5 4PY**

TEL: (0702) 203761 *CONTACT:* D & E Fox
OPENING TIMES: 0930-1730 Wed-Sun.
MIN MAIL ORDER UK: No minimum charge *MIN VALUE EC:* Nmc *EXPORT:* Yes
CAT. COST: Sae *W/SALE or RETAIL:* Retail
SPECIALITIES: Mainly Liliaceae, also a wide range of other Perennials, some uncommon and rare. *MAP PAGE:* **6**

EBur **Jenny Burgess, Alpine Nursery, Sisland, Norwich, Norfolk NR14 6EF**

TEL: (0508) 520724 *CONTACT:* Jenny Burgess
OPENING TIMES: Any time by appt.
MIN MAIL ORDER UK: £5.00 + p&p *MIN VALUE EC:* £10.00 + p&p *EXPORT:* Yes
CAT. COST: 2 x 1st class *W/SALE or RETAIL:* Both
SPECIALITIES: Alpines, Sisyrinchium & Campanula. National Collection of Sisyrinchium. *NOTE: Only Sisyrinchiums by Mail Order. *MAP PAGE:* **8**

EB&P **Battle & Pears Ltd., Glebe Farm, Bracebridge Heath, Lincolnshire LN4 2HZ**

TEL: (0522) 720121 *FAX:* (0522) 723252 *CONTACT:* D J Carmichael or D J Harby
OPENING TIMES: By appt. only.
MIN MAIL ORDER UK: £15.00 + p&p *MIN VALUE EC:* £15.00 + p&p
CAT. COST: 2 x 1st class *W/SALE or RETAIL:* Both
SPECIALITIES: Daphne, hybrid Magnolias & other choice hardy ornamental Shrubs. *MAP PAGE:* **8**

ECas **Castle Rising Plant Centre,** The Hirsel, 38 Church Road, Wimbotsham, Norfolk PE34 3QG

TEL: (0366) 387237 *CONTACT:* Philip C Wing
OPENING TIMES: 1000-1700 Tue-Sun.
MIN MAIL ORDER UK: See Cat. for details *MIN VALUE EC:* n/a
CAT. COST: 2 x 1st class *W/SALE or RETAIL:* Retail
SPECIALITIES: Herbaceous Perennials. Espalier, Cordon & Fanned Fruit Trees & soft Fruit. *MAP PAGE:* **8**

ECED **C E & D M Nurseries, The Walnuts, 36 Main Street, Baston, Peterborough, Lincolnshire PE6 9PB**

TEL: (0778 560) 483 *FAX:* (0778) 347539 *CONTACT:* Mr C E Fletcher
OPENING TIMES: 0900-1700 Fri-Tue Feb-Nov & by appt.
MIN MAIL ORDER UK: See Cat. for details *MIN VALUE EC:* See Cat. *EXPORT:* Yes
CAT. COST: 2 x 1st class *W/SALE or RETAIL:* Both
SPECIALITIES: Hardy Herbaceous Perennials. *MAP PAGE:* **8**

ECha **The Beth Chatto Gardens Ltd., Elmstead Market, Colchester, Essex CO7 7DB**

TEL: (0206) 822007 *FAX:* (0206) 825933 *CONTACT:* Beth Chatto
OPENING TIMES: 0900-1700 Mon-Sat 1st Mar-31st Oct. 0900-1600 Mon-Fri 1st Nov-1st Mar. Closed Sun & Bank Hols.
MIN MAIL ORDER UK: See Cat. for details *MIN VALUE EC:* Ask for details
CAT. COST: £2.50 incl p&p *W/SALE or RETAIL:* Retail
SPECIALITIES: Predominantly Herbaceous. Many unusual for special situations. *MAP PAGE:* **6**

ECoo **Patricia Cooper,** 4 Green Lane, Mundford, Norfolk IP26 5HS

TEL: (0842) 878496 *CONTACT:* Patricia Cooper
OPENING TIMES: 0900-1800 Mon-Fri, 1200-1800 Sat & Sun.
MAIL ORDER: No
CAT. COST: 4 x 1st class *W/SALE or RETAIL:* Retail
SPECIALITIES: Unusual hardy Perennials, Grasses, Wild Flowers, Bog, Aquatic & Foliage plants.
MAP PAGE: **8**

ECop **Copford Bulbs, Dorsetts, Birch Road, Copford, Colchester, Essex CO6 1DR**

TEL: (0206) 330008 *CONTACT:* D J Pearce
OPENING TIMES: By appt.
MIN MAIL ORDER UK: No minimum charge *MIN VALUE EC:* £20.00 + p&p
CAT. COST: 50p credited *W/SALE or RETAIL:* Retail
SPECIALITIES: Daffodil bulbs & Cyclamen tubers. *MAP PAGE:* **6**

ECot **Cottage Gardens,** Langham Road, Boxted, Colchester, Essex CO4 5HU

TEL: (0206) 272269 *CONTACT:* Alison Smith
OPENING TIMES: 0800-1800 daily Spring & Summer. 0800-1800 Thu-Mon Jul-Feb.
MAIL ORDER: No
CAT. COST: Free *W/SALE or RETAIL:* Retail
SPECIALITIES: 400 varieties of Shrubs, 390 varieties of Herbaceous. Huge range of Trees, Alpines, Herbs, Hedging - all home grown. Garden antiques. *MAP PAGE:* **6**

ECou **County Park Nursery,** Essex Gardens, Hornchurch, Essex RM11 3BU

TEL: (0708) 445205 *CONTACT:* G Hutchins
OPENING TIMES: 0900-dusk Mon-Sat ex Wed, 1000-1700 Sun Mar-Oct. Nov-Feb by appt. only.
MAIL ORDER: No
CAT. COST: 3 x 1st class *W/SALE or RETAIL:* Retail
SPECIALITIES: Alpines & rare and unusual plants from New Zealand, Tasmania & Falklands.
MAP PAGE: **6**

ECro **Croftacre Hardy Plants, Croftacre, Ellingham Road, Scoulton, Norfolk NR9 4NT**

TEL: (0953) 850599 *FAX:* (0953) 851399 *CONTACT:* Mrs V J Allen
◆ *OPENING TIMES:* By appt. Please phone first.
MIN MAIL ORDER UK: No minimum charge *MIN VALUE EC:* Nmc
CAT. COST: 3 x 1st class *W/SALE or RETAIL:* Retail
SPECIALITIES: Rare & uncommon Perennials. *MAP PAGE:* **8**

ECtt **Cottage Nurseries, Thoresthorpe, Alford, Lincolnshire LN13 0HX**

TEL: (0507) 466968 *CONTACT:* W H Denbigh
OPENING TIMES: 0900-1700 daily.
MIN MAIL ORDER UK: £5.00 + p&p *MIN VALUE EC:* £15.00 + p&p
CAT. COST: 3 x 1st class *W/SALE or RETAIL:* Both
SPECIALITIES: Wide general range. *MAP PAGE:* **8**

ECWi **Countryside Wildflowers, Somersham, Cambridgeshire PE17 3DN**

TEL: (0487) 841322 *FAX:* (0487) 740206 *CONTACT:* Martin Howell
OPENING TIMES: 1000-1600 daily
MIN MAIL ORDER UK: £12.00 + p&p *MIN VALUE EC:* £12.00 + p&p *EXPORT:* Yes
CAT. COST: Free *W/SALE or RETAIL:* Both
SPECIALITIES: Native British Wildflowers. *MAP PAGE:* **6/8**

EDen **Denbeigh Heather Nurseries, All Saints Road, Creeting St. Mary, Ipswich, Suffolk IP6 8PJ**

TEL: (0449) 711220 *FAX:* (0449) 711220 *CONTACT:* D J & A Small
OPENING TIMES: By appt. only.
MIN MAIL ORDER UK: No minimum charge *MIN VALUE EC:* Nmc *EXPORT:* Yes
CAT. COST: Free *W/SALE or RETAIL:* Both
SPECIALITIES: Rooted Heather cuttings. *MAP PAGE:* **6**

EDon **Donington Plants, Donington House, Main Road, Wrangle, Boston, Lincolnshire PE22 9AT**

TEL: (0205) 870015 *CONTACT:* D W Salt
OPENING TIMES: 10th Apr-17th Apr 1995 or by appt.
MIN MAIL ORDER UK: No minimum charge *MIN VALUE EC:* Nmc
CAT. COST: Sae *W/SALE or RETAIL:* Both
SPECIALITIES: Auricula & Goldlaced Polyanthus. *MAP PAGE:* **8**

EDra **John Drake,** Hardwicke House, Fen Ditton, Cambridgeshire CB5 8TF

TEL: CONTACT: John Drake
OPENING TIMES: 1400-1750 Sunday May 29th 1994 (NGS) & by appt.
MAIL ORDER: No
CAT. COST: W/SALE or RETAIL: Retail
SPECIALITIES: Aquilegia. See also SEED Index.

EEls **Elsworth Herbs, Avenue Farm Cottage, 31, Smith Street, Elsworth, Cambridgeshire CB3 8HY**

TEL: (0954) 267414 *CONTACT:* Drs J D & J M Twibell
OPENING TIMES: Advertised weekends & by appt. only. NCCPG opening Sun 19th June 1994 1000-1730.
MIN MAIL ORDER UK: £10.00 + p&p *MIN VALUE EC:* £10.00 + p&p
CAT. COST: 2 x 1st class *W/SALE or RETAIL:* Retail
SPECIALITIES: Herbs, Artemisia (NCCPG Collection), Cottage garden plants & Nerium oleanders.
MAP PAGE: **6**

EFer **The Fern Nursery, Grimsby Road, Binbrook, Lincolnshire LN3 6DH**

TEL: (0472) 398 092 *CONTACT:* R N Timm
OPENING TIMES: 0900-1700 Sat & Sun Apr-Oct or by appt.
MIN MAIL ORDER UK: £10.00 + p&p *MIN VALUE EC:* £100.00 + p&p
CAT. COST: 2 x 1st class *W/SALE or RETAIL:* Both
SPECIALITIES: Ferns & Hardy Perennials. *MAP PAGE:* **9**

EFEx **Flora Exotica, Pasadena, South-Green, Fingringhoe, Colchester, Essex CO5 7DR**

TEL: (0206) 729414 *CONTACT:* J Beddoes
OPENING TIMES: Not open to public.
MAIL ORDER: Only*MIN MAIL ORDER UK:* Nmc *MIN VALUE EC:* Nmc *EXPORT:* Yes
CAT. COST: £1.50 *W/SALE or RETAIL:* Retail
SPECIALITIES: Insectivorous plants, esp. Pinguicula, Drosera & rare & exotica Flora incl. Orchids.

Effi **Daphne ffiske Herbs,** Rosemary Cottage, Bramerton, Norwich, Norfolk NR14 7DW

TEL: (0508) 538187 *CONTACT:* D ffiske
OPENING TIMES: 1000-1600 Thu-Sun Mar-Sep incl.
MAIL ORDER: No
CAT. COST: Sae *W/SALE or RETAIL:* Retail
SPECIALITIES: Herbs including own cultivars and rarities. *MAP PAGE:* **8**

EFol **Foliage & Unusual Plants,** The Dingle Nursery, Pilsgate, Stamford, Lincolnshire PE9 3HW

TEL: (0780) 740775 *FAX:* (0780) 740838 *CONTACT:* Margaret Handley
◆ *OPENING TIMES:* 1000-1800 (dusk if earlier) daily Mar-14th Nov & Bank Hols.
MIN MAIL ORDER UK: £10.00 + p&p *MIN VALUE EC:* n/a
CAT. COST: 3 x 1st class *W/SALE or RETAIL:* Retail
SPECIALITIES: Variegated, coloured foliage & unusual plants. *MAP PAGE:* **8**

EFou **Four Seasons, Forncett St Mary, Norwich, Norfolk NR16 1JT**

TEL: (0508) 488344 *FAX:* (0508) 488478 *CONTACT:* J P Metcalf & R W Ball
OPENING TIMES: No callers.
MIN MAIL ORDER UK: £15.00 + p&p *MIN VALUE EC:* £15.00 + p&p
CAT. COST: £1.00 *W/SALE or RETAIL:* Retail
SPECIALITIES: Herbaceous Perennials. Aquilegia, Aconitum, Anemone, Aster, Campanula, Dendranthema, Digitalis, Erigeron, Geranium, Helenium, Iris, Kniphofia, Salvia & Grasses.

EFul **Fulbrooke Nursery,** Home Farm, Westley Waterless, Newmarket, Suffolk CB8 0RG
TEL: (0638) 507124 *CONTACT:* Paul Lazard
OPENING TIMES: By appt. most times.
MIN MAIL ORDER UK: £6.00 + p&p *MIN VALUE EC:* n/a
CAT. COST: Sae *W/SALE or RETAIL:* Both
SPECIALITIES: Bamboos *MAP PAGE:* **6**

EGle **Glen Chantry,** Ishams Chase, Wickham Bishop, Essex CM8 3LG
TEL: (0621) 891342 *CONTACT:* Sue Staines
OPENING TIMES: 1000-1600 Fri & Sat 17th Apr-end Oct. Also Sun & Mon on NGS open days.
MAIL ORDER: No
CAT. COST: 3 x 1st class *W/SALE or RETAIL:* Retail
SPECIALITIES: A wide & increasing range of Perennials & Alpines, many unusual. *MAP PAGE:* **6**

EGol **Goldbrook Plants, Hoxne, Eye, Suffolk IP21 5AN**
TEL: (0379) 668770 *CONTACT:* Sandra Bond
OPENING TIMES: 1030-1800 or dusk, if earlier, Thu-Sun ex. Jan, or by appt. Closed 14th May-28th May 1994.
MIN MAIL ORDER UK: £15.00 + p&p *MIN VALUE EC:* £100.00 + p&p *EXPORT:* Yes
CAT. COST: 4 x 1st class *W/SALE or RETAIL:* Retail
SPECIALITIES: Very large range of Hosta (over 500), Hemerocallis & Bog Iris. Interesting Hardy plants esp. for shade & bog. *NOTE: M.O. Perennials and Grasses only. *MAP PAGE:* **6**

EGou **Goulding's Fuchsias, West View, Link Lane, Bentley, Nr Ipswich, Suffolk IP9 2DP**
TEL: (0473) 310058 *CONTACT:* Mr T J Goulding
OPENING TIMES: 1000-1700 daily 1st Jan-3rd Jul 1994, 7th Jan-1st Jul 1995.
MIN MAIL ORDER UK: See Cat. for details *MIN VALUE EC:* See Cat.
CAT. COST: 3 x 1st class *W/SALE or RETAIL:* Retail
SPECIALITIES: Fuchsia - new introductions, Hardy, Encliandra, Terminal flowering (Triphylla), Species, Basket & Bedding. *MAP PAGE:* **6**

EHal **Hall Farm Nursery,** Harpswell, Nr Gainsborough, Lincolnshire DN21 5UU
TEL: (0427) 668412 *FAX:* (0427) 668412 *CONTACT:* Pam & Mark Tatam
OPENING TIMES: 0900-1800 daily. Please telephone in winter to check.
MIN MAIL ORDER UK: No minimum charge* *MIN VALUE EC:* n/a
CAT. COST: Sae *W/SALE or RETAIL:* Retail
SPECIALITIES: Wide range of Shrubs, Trees & Perennials & old Roses. *NOTE: Mail Order for certain plants only. *MAP PAGE:* **8/9**

EHan **Hanging Gardens Nursery,** (Off.) 2 Stable Croft, Springfield, Chelmsford, Essex CM1 5YX
TEL: (0245) 422245 *FAX:* (0245) 422293 *CONTACT:* R D Savill
OPENING TIMES: 0900-1800 daily Summer, 0900-1700 daily Winter.
MIN MAIL ORDER UK: 2 plants + p&p *MIN VALUE EC:* n/a
CAT. COST: 4 x 1st class *W/SALE or RETAIL:* Both
SPECIALITIES: Over 200 varieties of Clematis. NOTE: Nursery at Writtle by-pass, Oxney Green, Writtle. *MAP PAGE:* **3**

EHar **Hartshall Nursery Stock,** Hartshall Farm, Walsham-le-Willows, Nr Bury St Edmunds, Suffolk IP31 3BY
TEL: (0359) 259238 *FAX:* (0359) 259238 *CONTACT:* J D L & M A Wight
OPENING TIMES: 1000-1630 Tue-Sat. Ex all Bank Hols & all July.
MAIL ORDER: No
CAT. COST: 3 x 1st class *W/SALE or RETAIL:* Retail
SPECIALITIES: Hardy Shrubs, Trees & Conifers. Wide general range & rare, esp. Acer, Betula, Fagus, Prunus, Quercus, Salix & Sorbus, Viburnum. Can deliver. *MAP PAGE:* **6**

EHer **The Herbary Prickwillow, Ely, Cambridgeshire CB7 4SJ**
TEL: (0353 88) 456 *FAX:* (0353 88) 451 *CONTACT:* Peter Petts
OPENING TIMES: 0800-1500 Mon-Thu all year by appt. ONLY.
MIN MAIL ORDER UK: £10.00 + p&p *MIN VALUE EC:* £10.00 + p&p *EXPORT:* Yes
CAT. COST: Free *W/SALE or RETAIL:* Both
SPECIALITIES: Culinary Herbs. Will propagate any not on list; minimum of 12 plants. *MAP PAGE:* **6/8**

EHic **Hickling Heath Nursery,** Sutton Road, Hickling, Norwich, Norfolk NR12 0AS
TEL: (0692) 598513 *CONTACT:* Brian & Cindy Cogan
OPENING TIMES: 0930-1700 Tue-Sun & Bank Hol Mons.
MAIL ORDER: No
CAT. COST: A4 Sae *W/SALE or RETAIL:* Retail
SPECIALITIES: Shrubs & Herbaceous, many unusual inc. wide variety of Diascia, Euphorbia, Hydrangea, Lonicera, Penstemon & Viburnum. *MAP PAGE:* **8**

EHMN Home Meadows Nursery Ltd, Martlesham, Woodbridge, Suffolk IP12 4RD
TEL: (0394) 382419 *CONTACT:* S D & M I O'Brien Baker & I D Baker
OPENING TIMES: 0800-1700 Mon-Fri, 0800-1300 Sat.
MIN MAIL ORDER UK: No minimum charge *MIN VALUE EC:* Nmc
CAT. COST: Sae *W/SALE or RETAIL:* Retail
SPECIALITIES: Small general range plus Chrysanthemum esp. Korean. *MAP PAGE:* **6**

EHoe **Hoecroft Plants, Severals Grange, Wood Norton, Dereham, Norfolk NR20 5BL**
TEL: (0362) 844206/860179 *CONTACT:* M Lister
◆ *OPENING TIMES:* 1000-1600 Mon, Wed & Sat 30th Apr-1st Oct.
MIN MAIL ORDER UK: No minimum charge *MIN VALUE EC:* Nmc
CAT. COST: 6x2nd class/£1coin *W/SALE or RETAIL:* Retail
SPECIALITIES: 240 varieties of Variegated and 300 varieties of Coloured-leaved plants in all species. 170 Grasses. *MAP PAGE:* **8**

EHon **Honeysome Aquatic Nursery,** The Row, Sutton, Nr Ely, Cambridgeshire CB6 2PF
TEL: (0353) 778889 *CONTACT:* D B Barker & D B Littlefield
OPENING TIMES: At all times by appt. ONLY.
MIN MAIL ORDER UK: No minimum charge *MIN VALUE EC:* n/a
CAT. COST: 2 x 1st class *W/SALE or RETAIL:* Both
SPECIALITIES: Hardy Aquatic, Bog & Marginal. *MAP PAGE:* **6/8**

EHul **Hull Farm,** Spring Valley Lane, Ardleigh, Colchester, Essex CO7 7SA
TEL: (0206) 230045 *FAX:* (0206) 230820 *CONTACT:* J Fryer & Sons
OPENING TIMES: 1000-1630 daily ex Xmas.
MAIL ORDER: No
CAT. COST: 50p + Sae *W/SALE or RETAIL:* Both
SPECIALITIES: Conifers. *MAP PAGE:* **6**

EJud **Judy's Country Garden,** The Villa, Louth Road, South Somercotes, Louth, Lincolnshire LN11 7BW
TEL: (0507) 358487 *CONTACT:* M J S & J M Harry
OPENING TIMES: 0900-1800 most days Mar-Oct.
MAIL ORDER: No
CAT. COST: 3 x 1st class *W/SALE or RETAIL:* Retail
SPECIALITIES: Herbs, old-fashioned & unusual plants, including scarce & old varieties. *MAP PAGE:* **9**

EKMF Kathleen Muncaster Fuchsias, 18 Field Lane, Morton, Gainsborough, Lincolnshire DN21 3BY
TEL: (0427) 612329 *CONTACT:* Kathleen Muncaster
OPENING TIMES: 1000-Dusk.
MIN MAIL ORDER UK: See Cat. for details *MIN VALUE EC:* See Cat. *EXPORT:* Yes
CAT. COST: 2 x 1st class *W/SALE or RETAIL:* Retail
SPECIALITIES: Fuchsia. *NOTE: Mail Orders to be received before April 1st. *MAP PAGE:* **7/9**

ELan **Langthorns Plantery,** High Cross Lane West, Little Canfield, Dunmow, Essex CM6 1TD
TEL: (0371) 872611 *FAX:* (0371) 872611 *CONTACT:* P & D Cannon
OPENING TIMES: 1000-1700 or dusk (if earlier) daily ex Xmas fortnight.
MAIL ORDER: No
CAT. COST: £1.00 *W/SALE or RETAIL:* Retail
SPECIALITIES: Wide general range with many unusual plants. *MAP PAGE:* **6**

ELun **Ann Lunn, The Fens, Old Mill Road, Langham, Colchester, Essex CO4 5NU**
TEL: (0206) 272259 *CONTACT:* Ann Lunn
OPENING TIMES: Thu & Sat and by appt.
MIN MAIL ORDER UK: No minimum charge *MIN VALUE EC:* Nmc
CAT. COST: 3 x 1st class *W/SALE or RETAIL:* Retail
SPECIALITIES: Primula, Woodland and moisture loving plants. *MAP PAGE:* **6**

EMar Lesley Marshall, Islington Lodge Cottgae, Tilney All Saints, King's Lynn, Norfolk PE34 4SF

TEL: (0553) 765103 *CONTACT:* Lesley & Peter Marshall
OPENING TIMES: Weekends Mar-Oct & by appt.
MIN MAIL ORDER UK: £5.00 + p&p *MIN VALUE EC:* £20.00 + p&p
CAT. COST: £1 refundable *W/SALE or RETAIL:* Retail
SPECIALITIES: Hardy Perennials, Grasses & Foliage plants. *MAP PAGE:* **8**

EMFP Mills' Farm Plants & Gardens, Norwich Road, Mendlesham, Suffolk IP14 5NQ

TEL: (0449) 766425 *CONTACT:* Peter & Susan Russell
OPENING TIMES: 0900-1730 daily except Tue. (Closed Jan).
MIN MAIL ORDER UK: No minimum charge *MIN VALUE EC:* Nmc *EXPORT:* Yes
CAT. COST: 2 x 2nd class *W/SALE or RETAIL:* Retail
SPECIALITIES: Pinks, Old Roses, Wide general range. *NOTE: Mail Order for Pinks& Roses only.
MAP PAGE: **6**

EMFW Mickfield Fish & Watergarden Centre, Debenham Road, Mickfield, Stowmarket, Suffolk IP14 5LP

TEL: (0449) 711336 *FAX:* (0449) 711018 *CONTACT:* Mike & Yvonne Burch
◆ *OPENING TIMES:* 0900-1700 daily.
MIN MAIL ORDER UK: No minimum charge *MIN VALUE EC:* Nmc *EXPORT:* Yes
CAT. COST: 50p *W/SALE or RETAIL:* Both
SPECIALITIES: Hardy Aquatics, Nymphaea & moisture lovers. *MAP PAGE:* **6**

EMic Mickfield Market Garden, The Poplars, Mickfield, Stowmarket, Suffolk IP14 5LH

TEL: (0449) 711576 *CONTACT:* Mr & Mrs R L C Milton
◆ *OPENING TIMES:* By appt. only
MIN MAIL ORDER UK: See Cat. for details *MIN VALUE EC:* See Cat.
CAT. COST: £1 refundable *W/SALE or RETAIL:* Retail
SPECIALITIES: Hostas, over 425 varieties (subject to availability) mostly from USA. *MAP PAGE:* **6**

EMil Mill Race Nursery, New Road Aldham, Colchester, Essex CO6 3QT

TEL: (0206) 242324 *FAX:* (0206) 241616 *CONTACT:* Bill Mathews
OPENING TIMES: 0900-1730 daily.
MAIL ORDER: No
CAT. COST: Sae *W/SALE or RETAIL:* Both
SPECIALITIES: Over 400 varieties of Herbaceous & many unusual Trees, Shrubs & Climbers.
MAP PAGE: **6**

EMNN Martin Nest Nurseries, Grange Cottage, Harpswell Lane, Hemswell, Gainsbor'o, Lincolnshire DN21 5UP

TEL: (0427) 668369 *FAX:* (0427) 668080 *CONTACT:* M & M A Robinson
OPENING TIMES: 1000-1600 daily
MIN MAIL ORDER UK: No minimum charge *MIN VALUE EC:* £30.00 + p&p
CAT. COST: 3 x 2nd class *W/SALE or RETAIL:* Both
SPECIALITIES: Alpines especially Auricula, Primula, Lewisia, & Saxifraga. *MAP PAGE:* **8/9**

EMon Monksilver Nursery, Oakington Road, Cottenham, Cambridgeshire CB4 4TW

TEL: (0954) 251555 *CONTACT:* Joe Sharman & Alan Leslie
OPENING TIMES: 1000-1600 Fri & Sat 1st Apr-30th Jun.
MIN MAIL ORDER UK: £10.00 + p&p *MIN VALUE EC:* £30.00 + p&p
CAT. COST: 6 x 1st class *W/SALE or RETAIL:* Retail
SPECIALITIES: Herbaceous plants, Grasses, Anthemis, Arum, Helianthus, Lamium, Nepeta, Monarda, Salvia, Vinca, Sedges & Variegated plants. Many NCCPG 'Pink Sheet' plants. *MAP PAGE:* **6**

EMor John Morley, North Green Only, Stoven, Beccles, Suffolk NR34 8DG

TEL: *CONTACT:* John Morley
OPENING TIMES: By appt. ONLY.
MIN MAIL ORDER UK: Details in catalogue *MIN VALUE EC:*
CAT. COST: £1.00 + stamp *W/SALE or RETAIL:* Retail
SPECIALITIES: Galanthus, species & hybrids. See also SEED Index.

EMou Frances Mount Perennial Plants, 1 Steps Farm, Polstead, Colchester, Essex CO6 5AE

TEL: (0206) 262811 *CONTACT:* Frances Mount
OPENING TIMES: 1000-1700 Tue Wed Sat Sun & Bank Hols. 1400-1800 Fri. Check weekends & Hols.
MIN MAIL ORDER UK: £5.00 + p&p *MIN VALUE EC:* £5.00 + p&p
CAT. COST: 3 x 1st class *W/SALE or RETAIL:* Retail
SPECIALITIES: Hardy Geraniums. *MAP PAGE:* **6**

ENHC Norwich Heather & Conifer Centre, 54a Yarmouth Road, Thorpe, Norwich, Norfolk NR7 0HE

TEL: (0603) 39434 *CONTACT:* B Hipperson
OPENING TIMES: 0900-1700 Mon Tue Wed Fri Sat, 1400-1700 Sun Mar-Dec. Closed Sun in Jan & Feb.
MIN MAIL ORDER UK: No minimum charge *MIN VALUE EC:* n/a
CAT. COST: 40p *W/SALE or RETAIL:* Retail
SPECIALITIES: Conifers and Heathers. *MAP PAGE:* **8**

ENor Norfolk Lavender, Caley Mill, Heacham, King's Lynn, Norfolk PE31 7JE

TEL: (0485) 570384 *FAX:* (0485) 571176 *CONTACT:* Henry Head
OPENING TIMES: 0930-1700 daily. Closed two weeks after Xmas.
MIN MAIL ORDER UK: No minimum charge *MIN VALUE EC:* Nmc
CAT. COST: Free *W/SALE or RETAIL:* Retail
SPECIALITIES: National collection of Lavandula. *MAP PAGE:* **8**

ENot Notcutts Nurseries, Woodbridge, Suffolk IP12 4AF

TEL: (0394) 383344 *FAX:* (0394) 385460 *CONTACT:* Plant Adviser
◆ *OPENING TIMES:* 0845-1730 Mon-Sat, 1000-1700 Sun.
MIN MAIL ORDER UK: £200.00 + p&p *MIN VALUE EC:* £300.00 + p&p *EXPORT:* Yes
CAT. COST: £3.25 *W/SALE or RETAIL:* Both
SPECIALITIES: Wide general range. Specialist list of Syringa. National Collection of Hibiscus. *MAP PAGE:* **6**

EOrc Orchard Nurseries, Tow Lane, Foston, Grantham, Lincolnshire NG32 2LE

TEL: (0400) 81354 *CONTACT:* R & J Blenkinship
◆ *OPENING TIMES:* 1000-1800 daily 1st Mar-30th Sep.
MAIL ORDER: No
CAT. COST: £1.00 *W/SALE or RETAIL:* Retail
SPECIALITIES: Unusual herbaceous & small flowered Clematis both hardy & for the Conservatory. *MAP PAGE:* **7/8**

EOvi M Oviatt-Ham, (Office) Ely House, 15 Green Street, Willingham, Cambridgeshire CB4 5JA

TEL: (0954) 260481 *CONTACT:* M Oviatt-Ham
OPENING TIMES: Sat & Sun from Easter-end Sept, other times by appt. only.
MIN MAIL ORDER UK: £10.00 + p&p *MIN VALUE EC:* £10.00 + p&p *EXPORT:* Yes
CAT. COST: 50p *W/SALE or RETAIL:* Both
SPECIALITIES: Clematis & climbing plants. Nursery address: Black Pit Drove, Rampton Rd., Willingham. *MAP PAGE:* **6**

EPad Padlock Croft, 19 Padlock Road, West Wratting, Cambridge CB1 5LS

TEL: (0223) 290383 *CONTACT:* Susan & Peter Lewis
OPENING TIMES: 1000-1800 Tue-Sat 1st Apr-31st Oct. Winter by appt.
MAIL ORDER: No
CAT. COST: 4 x 2nd class *W/SALE or RETAIL:* Retail
SPECIALITIES: National Collection of Campanula, Adenophora, Symphyandra & Platycodon. Other Campanulaceae & less common Alpines & Perennials. *MAP PAGE:* **6**

EPar Paradise Centre, Twinstead Road, Lamarsh, Bures, Suffolk CO8 5EX

TEL: (0787 269) 449 *FAX:* (0787 269) 449 *CONTACT:* Cees & Hedy Stapel-Valk
OPENING TIMES: 1000-1700 Sat-Sun & Bank Hols or by appt. Easter-1st Nov.
MIN MAIL ORDER UK: £7.50 + p&p *MIN VALUE EC:* £25.00 + p&p
CAT. COST: 4 x 1st class *W/SALE or RETAIL:* Retail
SPECIALITIES: Unusual bulbous & tuberous plants including shade & bog varieties. *MAP PAGE:* **6**

EPGN Park Green Nurseries, Wetheringsett, Stowmarket, Suffolk IP14 5QH

TEL: (0728) 860139 *FAX:* (0728) 860139 *CONTACT:* Richard & Mary Ford
OPENING TIMES: 1000-1730 Thu-Mon Mar-Oct other times by appt.
MIN MAIL ORDER UK: No minimum charge *MIN VALUE EC:* Nmc
CAT. COST: 3 x 1st class *W/SALE or RETAIL:* Retail
SPECIALITIES: Hosta, Astilbe & Herbaceous. *MAP PAGE:* **6**

EPla P W Plants, Sunnyside, Heath Road, Kenninghall, Norfolk NR16 2DS

TEL: (0953) 888212 *CONTACT:* Paul Whittaker
◆ *OPENING TIMES:* Fridays & some Sats. Please ring first.
MIN MAIL ORDER UK: No minimum charge *MIN VALUE EC:* Nmc
CAT. COST: £1 or 5x1st class *W/SALE or RETAIL:* Retail
SPECIALITIES: Choice Shrubs, Perennials, Grasses, Climbers, Bamboos, Hedera. Wide range of unusual hardy ornamental Shrubs. *MAP PAGE:* **8**

EPot Potterton & Martin, The Cottage Nursery, Moortown Road, Nettleton, Caistor, Lincolnshire LN7 6HX

TEL: (0472) 851792 *FAX:* (0472) 851792 *CONTACT:*
OPENING TIMES: 0900-1700 daily.
MIN MAIL ORDER UK: No minimum charge *MIN VALUE EC:* Nmc *EXPORT:* Yes
CAT. COST: £1 in stamps only *W/SALE or RETAIL:* Both
SPECIALITIES: Alpines, Dwarf Bulbs, Conifers, & Shrubs and Carnivorous. See also SEED Index. *MAP PAGE:* **9**

ERav Raveningham Gardens, Norwich, Norfolk NR14 6NS

TEL: (0508) 548222 *FAX:* (0508) 548958 *CONTACT:* Alison Bowell
◆ *OPENING TIMES:* 0900-1700 Mon-Sat Mar-Oct. 0900-1600 Mon-Fri Nov-Feb. Gardens open - check for details.
MIN MAIL ORDER UK: No minimum charge *MIN VALUE EC:* Nmc
CAT. COST: 3 x 1st class *W/SALE or RETAIL:* Both
SPECIALITIES: Plants noted for Foliage, Berries, Bark & Texture. Variegated & coloured leaf plants & shrubs. *MAP PAGE:* **8**

ERea Reads Nursery, Hales Hall, Loddon, Norfolk NR14 6QW

TEL: (0508) 548395 *FAX:* (0508) 548395 *CONTACT:* Terence & Judy Read
◆ *OPENING TIMES:* 1000-1700 (or dusk if earlier) Tue-Sat & by appt.
MIN MAIL ORDER UK: £10.00 + p&p *MIN VALUE EC:* £10.00 + p&p *EXPORT:* Yes
CAT. COST: 4 x 1st class *W/SALE or RETAIL:* Both
SPECIALITIES: Conservatory plants, Vines, Citrus, Figs & unusual Fruits & Nuts. Wall Shrubs & Climbers. Scented & aromatic Hardy plants. Box & Yew hedging & topiary. UK grown *MAP PAGE:* **8**

ERom The Romantic Garden, Swannington, Norwich, Norfolk NR9 5NW

TEL: (0603) 261488 *FAX:* (0603) 871668 *CONTACT:* John Powles
◆ *OPENING TIMES:* 1000-1700 Wed, Fri & Sat all year.
MIN MAIL ORDER UK: £5.00 + p&p *MIN VALUE EC:* £30.00 + p&p *EXPORT:* Yes
CAT. COST: 4 x 1st class *W/SALE or RETAIL:* Both
SPECIALITIES: Half-hardy & Conservatory. Buxus topiary, Ornamental standards, large specimen & Clematis. *MAP PAGE:* **8**

ERou Rougham Hall Nurseries, Ipswich Road, Rougham, Bury St. Edmunds, Suffolk IP30 9LZ

TEL: (0359) 70577 *FAX:* (0359) 71149 *CONTACT:* A A & K G Harbutt
OPENING TIMES: 1000-1600 Thu-Mon.
MIN MAIL ORDER UK: No minimum charge *MIN VALUE EC:* Nmc
CAT. COST: 4 x 1st class *W/SALE or RETAIL:* Both
SPECIALITIES: Hardy Perennials, esp. Delphiniums, Phlox, Hemerocallis & Iris. *MAP PAGE:* **6**

ER&R Rhodes & Rockliffe, 2 Nursery Road, Nazeing, Essex EN9 2JE

TEL: (0992) 463693 *FAX:* (0992) 440673 *CONTACT:* David Rhodes & John Rockliffe
OPENING TIMES: By appt.
MIN MAIL ORDER UK: £2.50 + p&p *MIN VALUE EC:* £2.50 + p&p *EXPORT:* Yes
CAT. COST: 2 x 1st class *W/SALE or RETAIL:* Both
SPECIALITIES: Begonias *MAP PAGE:* **6**

ESha **Shaw Rose Trees,** 2 Hollowgate Hill, Willoughton, Gainsborough, Lincolnshire DN21 5SF
TEL: (0427) 668230 *CONTACT:* Mr K Shaw
OPENING TIMES: Vary, please check.
MIN MAIL ORDER UK: £3.00 + p&p *MIN VALUE EC:* n/a
CAT. COST: Sae *W/SALE or RETAIL:* Both
SPECIALITIES: Roses. *MAP PAGE:* **9**

ESim **Clive Simms,** Woodhurst, Essendine, Stamford, Lincolnshire PE9 4LQ
TEL: (0780) 55615 *CONTACT:* Clive & Kathryn Simms
OPENING TIMES: By appt. for collection only.
MIN MAIL ORDER UK: No minimum charge *MIN VALUE EC:* n/a
CAT. COST: 3 x 2nd class *W/SALE or RETAIL:* Retail
SPECIALITIES: Uncommon nut Trees & unusual fruiting plants.

ESiP **Simply Plants,** 17 Duloe Brook, Eaton Socon, Cambridgeshire PE19 3DW
TEL: (0480) 475312 *CONTACT:* Christine Dakin
OPENING TIMES: By appt. only
MAIL ORDER: No
CAT. COST: 2 x 1st class *W/SALE or RETAIL:* Both
SPECIALITIES: Ornamental Grasses, Sedges & Bamboos. Also range of Shrubs & Perennials
MAP PAGE: **6**

ESis **Siskin Plants, April House, Davey Lane, Charsfield, Woodbridge, Suffolk IP13 7QG**
TEL: (0473 37) 567 *CONTACT:* Chris & Valerie Wheeler
OPENING TIMES: 1000-1700 Wed-Sat Feb, Jul-Oct. 1000-1700 Tue-Sun Mar-Jun.
MIN MAIL ORDER UK: No minimum charge *MIN VALUE EC:* Nmc
CAT. COST: £1.00 *W/SALE or RETAIL:* Retail
SPECIALITIES: Extensive range of Alpines, miniature Conifers & dwarf Shrubs, esp. dwarf Hebes & plants for Troughs. *NOTE: Young plants also available by Mail Order. *MAP PAGE:* **6**

ESma **Smallscape Nursery, 3 Hundon Close, Stradishall, Nr Newmarket, Suffolk CB8 9YF**
TEL: (0440) 820336 *CONTACT:* Stephen & Leigh Sage
OPENING TIMES: Most times - but please telephone first.
MIN MAIL ORDER UK: No minimum charge *MIN VALUE EC:* Nmc *EXPORT:* Yes
CAT. COST: 4 x 1st class *W/SALE or RETAIL:* Both
SPECIALITIES: Interesting, unusual & rare Alpines, Herbaceous, Shrubs, Trees & tender Perennials sold Mail Order as young plants & rooted cuttings. *MAP PAGE:* **6**

ESul **Pearl Sulman, 54 Kingsway, Mildenhall, Bury St Edmunds, Suffolk IP28 7HR**
TEL: (0638) 712297 *CONTACT:* Pearl Sulman
OPENING TIMES: Not open. Mail Order only.
MAIL ORDER: Only*MIN MAIL ORDER UK:* £9.00 + p&p *MIN VALUE EC:* £9.00 + p&p
CAT. COST: 3 x 1st class *W/SALE or RETAIL:* Retail
SPECIALITIES: Miniature, Dwarf & Scented-leaf Pelargoniums.

ETho **Thorncroft Clematis Nursery,** The Lings, Reymerston, Norwich NR9 4QG
TEL: (0953) 850407 *CONTACT:* Ruth P Gooch
OPENING TIMES: 1000-1700 Thu-Tue 1st March-31st Oct.
MAIL ORDER: No
CAT. COST: 2 x 1st class *W/SALE or RETAIL:* Both
SPECIALITIES: Clematis. *MAP PAGE:* **8**

ETPC **Trevor Scott, Thorpe Park Cottage, Thorpe-le-Soken, Essex CO16 0HN**
TEL: (0255) 861308 *FAX:* (0255) 861308 *CONTACT:* Trevor Scott
◆ *OPENING TIMES:* By appt. only.
MIN MAIL ORDER UK: £10.00 + p&p *MIN VALUE EC:* £25.00 + p&p
CAT. COST: 5 x 1st class *W/SALE or RETAIL:* Retail
SPECIALITIES: Ornamental Grasses. *MAP PAGE:* **6**

ETub **Van Tubergen UK Ltd.,** Bressingham, Diss, Norfolk IP22 2AB
TEL: (0379) 888282 *FAX:* (0379) 88227 *CONTACT:* General Manager
OPENING TIMES: Not open to public.
MAIL ORDER: Only*MIN MAIL ORDER UK:* No minimum charge *MIN VALUE EC:* n/a
CAT. COST: Free *W/SALE or RETAIL:* Both
SPECIALITIES: Bulbs. *NOTE: Retail & Wholesale sales by Mail Order only.

ETWh Trevor White Old Fashioned Roses, Bennetts Brier, The Street, Felthorpe, Norwich, Norfolk NR10 4AB
TEL: (0603) 755135 *FAX:* (0603) 755135 *CONTACT:* Mr T A & Mrs V J White.
OPENING TIMES: 0900-1700 by appt only.
MIN MAIL ORDER UK: Nmc *MIN VALUE EC:* £100 + p&p
CAT. COST: Free *W/SALE or RETAIL:* Both
SPECIALITIES: Old-fashioned, Shrub, Climbing & Rambling Roses *MAP PAGE:* **8**

EVal The Valley Clematis Nursery, Willingham Road, Hainton, Lincolnshire LN3 6LN
TEL: (0507) 313398 *FAX:* (0507) 313705 *CONTACT:* Mr Keith Fair/Mrs Carol Fair
◆ *OPENING TIMES:* 1000-1800 (Dusk in winter) daily. Closed Xmas to New Year.
MIN MAIL ORDER UK: £10.00 + p&p *MIN VALUE EC:* £20.00 + p&p *EXPORT:* Yes
CAT. COST: £1.00 *W/SALE or RETAIL:* Retail
SPECIALITIES: Clematis. *MAP PAGE:* **8**

EWal J Walkers Bulbs, Washway House Farm, Holbeach, Spalding, Lincolnshire PE12 7PP
TEL: (0406) 426216 *FAX:* (0406) 425468 *CONTACT:* J W Walkers
OPENING TIMES: Not open to the public.
MIN MAIL ORDER UK: See Cat. for details *MIN VALUE EC:* See Catalogue
CAT. COST: 50p *W/SALE or RETAIL:* Both
SPECIALITIES: Daffodils & Fritillarias.

EWar Warley Rose Garden Ltd., Warley Street, Great Warley, Brentwood, Essex CM13 3JH
TEL: (0277) 221966/219344 *CONTACT:* J H G Deamer
OPENING TIMES: 0900-1730 Mon-Sat.
MIN MAIL ORDER UK: No minimum charge *MIN VALUE EC:* Nmc
CAT. COST: Free-30p at shop *W/SALE or RETAIL:* Both
SPECIALITIES: Roses & container grown Nursery Stock.. *MAP PAGE:* **6**

EWav Waveney Fish Farm, Park Road, Diss, Norfolk IP22 3AS
TEL: (0379) 642697 *FAX:* (0379) 651315 *CONTACT:* D G Laughlin
OPENING TIMES: 1000-1700 daily.
MAIL ORDER: No
CAT. COST: Free *W/SALE or RETAIL:* Both
SPECIALITIES: Aquatic & Marginals. *MAP PAGE:* **6/8**

EWes West Acre Gardens, West Acre, Kings Lynn, Norfolk PE32 1UJ
TEL: (0760) 755562 *CONTACT:* J J Tuite
OPENING TIMES: 1000-1700 Tue-Sat & Bank Hol. Mons 1st Mar-31st Oct. Other times by appt.
MIN MAIL ORDER UK: No minimum charge *MIN VALUE EC:* n/a
CAT. COST: 2 x 1st class *W/SALE or RETAIL:* Both
SPECIALITIES: Rare & unusual plants esp. Alpines. *MAP PAGE:* **8**

EWFC The Wild Flower Centre, Church Farm, Sisland, Loddon, Norwich, Norfolk NR14 6EF
TEL: (0508) 520235 *CONTACT:* D G Corne
OPENING TIMES: 0900-1700 daily
MIN MAIL ORDER UK: £3.50 + p&p *MIN VALUE EC:* n/a
CAT. COST: 30p or A5 Sae *W/SALE or RETAIL:* Retail
SPECIALITIES: British native and naturalised Wild Flower plants. 250 varieties. *MAP PAGE:* **8**

EWhi Whitehouse Ivies, Brookhill, Halstead Road, Fordham, Colchester, Essex CO6 3LW
TEL: (0206) 240077 *CONTACT:* R Whitehouse
OPENING TIMES: By telephone appt. only.
MIN MAIL ORDER UK: 6 plants + p&p *MIN VALUE EC:* 6 plants + p&p *EXPORT:* Yes
CAT. COST: £1 refundable *W/SALE or RETAIL:* Retail
SPECIALITIES: Hedera only, some 300 varieties. *MAP PAGE:* **6**

EWll The Walled Garden, Park Road, Benhall, Saxmundham, Suffolk IP17 1JB
TEL: (0728) 602510 *FAX:* (0728) 602510 *CONTACT:* J R Mountain
◆ *OPENING TIMES:* 0930-1700 Tue-Sun Feb-Oct, Tue-Sat Nov-Jan.
MAIL ORDER: No
CAT. COST: 2 x 1st class *W/SALE or RETAIL:* Retail
SPECIALITIES: Tender & hardy Perennials & wall Shrubs. *MAP PAGE:* **6**

EWoo **Wootten's Plants,** Wenhaston, Blackheath, Halesworth, Suffolk IP19 9HD

TEL: (050) 270 258 *CONTACT:* M Loftus
OPENING TIMES: 0930-1700 daily.
MAIL ORDER: No
CAT. COST: 2 x 1st class *W/SALE or RETAIL:* Retail
SPECIALITIES: Violas, Pelargoniums, Salvias, Penstemons, Aquilegias, Digitalis, Campanulas & Polemoniums. *MAP PAGE:* **6**

EWri **Kathy Wright,** Frog Hall Cottage, Wildmore Fen, New York, Lincolnshire LN4 4XH

TEL: (0205) 280709 *CONTACT:* Kathy Wright
OPENING TIMES: 1200-1700 Tue, Wed & Sun mid Mar-end Jun. Tue, Wed & 3rd Sun in month Jul-Oct & by appt.
MAIL ORDER: No
CAT. COST: A4 Sae *W/SALE or RETAIL:* Retail
SPECIALITIES: Container grown Shrubs & Climbers, many unusual. *MAP PAGE:* **7**

GAbr **Abriachan Nurseries, Loch Ness Side, Inverness, Invernesshire IV3 6LA**

TEL: (046 386) 232 *CONTACT:* Mr & Mrs D Davidson
OPENING TIMES: 0900-1900 daily, dusk if earlier.
MIN MAIL ORDER UK: No minimum charge *MIN VALUE EC:* Nmc
CAT. COST: 3 x 1st class *W/SALE or RETAIL:* Both
SPECIALITIES: Herbaceous, Primulas, Helianthemum & Hebe. *MAP PAGE:* **10**

GAng **Angus Heathers,** 10 Guthrie Street, Letham, Forfar, Tayside DD8 2PS

TEL: (0307) 818504 *FAX:* (0307) 818055 *CONTACT:* David Sturrock
OPENING TIMES: 1000-1700 daily.
MAIL ORDER: No
CAT. COST: Sae *W/SALE or RETAIL:* Both
SPECIALITIES: Heathers & Gentians. *MAP PAGE:* **10**

GArf **Ardfearn Nursery, Bunchrew, Inverness, Highland IV3 6RH**

TEL: (0463) 243250 *FAX:* (0463) 711713 *CONTACT:* James Sutherland
◆ *OPENING TIMES:* 0900-1700 Mon-Sat, 1300-1700 Sun Mar-Nov & by appt.
MIN MAIL ORDER UK: No minimum charge *MIN VALUE EC:* Nmc
CAT. COST: 4 x 2nd class *W/SALE or RETAIL:* Both
SPECIALITIES: Alpines & Ericaceae, rare & unusual. *NOTE: Mail Order Oct-Mar only. *MAP PAGE:* **10**

GAri **Arivegaig Nursery, Aultbea, Acharacle, Argyll, Scotland PH36 4LE**

TEL: (0967) 431331 *CONTACT:* E Stewart
◆ *OPENING TIMES:* 0900-1700 daily Easter-end Oct.
MIN MAIL ORDER UK: No minimum charge *MIN VALUE EC:* Nmc
CAT. COST: 4 x 1st class *W/SALE or RETAIL:* Both
SPECIALITIES: A wide range of unusual plants, including those suited for the milder parts of the country. *MAP PAGE:* **10**

GAul **Aultan Nursery,** Newton of Cairnhill, Cuminestown, Turriff, Aberdeenshire AB53 7TN

TEL: (0888) 544702 *CONTACT:* Richard King
OPENING TIMES: 1000-1630 Mon & Wed, 1000-1730 Tue, Thu & Fri, 1330-1800 Sat, 1000-1800 Sun.
MIN MAIL ORDER UK: £6.00 + p&p *MIN VALUE EC:* n/a
CAT. COST: Sae *W/SALE or RETAIL:* Both
SPECIALITIES: Herbaceous Perennials & Shrubs, mostly grown in peat-free composts. *MAP PAGE:* **10**

GBar **Barwinnock Herbs, Barrhill, by Girvan, Ayrshire KA26 0RB**

TEL: (046 582) 338 *CONTACT:* Dave & Mon Holtom
◆ *OPENING TIMES:* 0900-1900 Fri-Wed 1st April-31st Oct.
MIN MAIL ORDER UK: No minimum charge *MIN VALUE EC:* Nmc
CAT. COST: 3 x 1st class *W/SALE or RETAIL:* Retail
SPECIALITIES: Culinary, Medicinal & fragrant leaved plants organically grown. *MAP PAGE:* **10**

GBel **Belwood Nurseries Ltd., Mauricewood Mains, Penicuik, Midlothian, Scotland EH26 0NJ**
TEL: (0968) 673621 *FAX:* (0968) 678354 *CONTACT:* Mrs Linda Brock
OPENING TIMES: 0800-1700 Mon-Fri. By appt. only
MIN MAIL ORDER UK: No minimum charge *MIN VALUE EC:* Nmc *EXPORT:* Yes
CAT. COST: Free *W/SALE or RETAIL:* Both
SPECIALITIES: Semi-mature deciduous & coniferous Trees and specimen Shrubs for landscaping.
MAP PAGE: **10**

GBla **Blairhoyle Nursery,** Port of Menteith, Stirling, Central FK8 3LF
TEL: (08775) 669 *CONTACT:* B A & G W Cartwright
OPENING TIMES: 1000-dusk ex Tue & Sat Mar-Nov.
MAIL ORDER: No
CAT. COST: Sae *W/SALE or RETAIL:* Retail
SPECIALITIES: Heathers, Alpines & Dwarf Conifers. *MAP PAGE:* **10**

GBon **Bonhard Nursery,** Murrayshall Road, Scone, Perth, Tayside PH2 7PQ
TEL: (0738) 52791 *CONTACT:* Mr & Mrs Hickman
OPENING TIMES: 1000-1800, or dusk if earlier, daily.
MAIL ORDER: No
CAT. COST: Free *W/SALE or RETAIL:* Retail
SPECIALITIES: Herbaceous, Conifers & Alpines. Fruit & ornamental Trees. Shrub & species Roses.
MAP PAGE: **10**

GBri **Bridge End Nurseries,** Gretna Green, Dumfries & Galloway DG16 5HN
TEL: (0461) 800612 *CONTACT:* R Bird
OPENING TIMES: 0800-1700 daily
MAIL ORDER: No
CAT. COST: None issued *W/SALE or RETAIL:* Retail
SPECIALITIES: Hardy cottage garden Perennials. Many unusual & interesting varieties.
MAP PAGE: **10**

GBuc **Buckland Plants, Whinnieliggate, Kirkcudbright, Scotland DG6 4XP**
TEL: (0557) 331323 *CONTACT:* Rob or Dina Asbridge
◆ *OPENING TIMES:* 1000-1700 Thu-Sun Feb-Nov
MIN MAIL ORDER UK: £15.00 + p&p *MIN VALUE EC:* £50.00 + p&p *EXPORT:* Yes
CAT. COST: 2 x 1st class *W/SALE or RETAIL:* Retail
SPECIALITIES: Very wide range of unusual perennials esp. for flower arrangers. Meconopsis, Lobelia, Cardamine, Euphorbia, etc. *MAP PAGE:* **10**

GBur **Burnside Nursery, by Turnberry, Ayrshire, Scotland KA26 9JH**
TEL: (0465) 4290 *CONTACT:* Mrs C Walker
OPENING TIMES: 1000-dusk Sat & Sun 31st Mar-31st Oct.
MIN MAIL ORDER UK: No minimum charge *MIN VALUE EC:* Nmc
CAT. COST: 3 x 1st class *W/SALE or RETAIL:* Both
SPECIALITIES: Dicentra & Hardy Geraniums. *MAP PAGE:* **10**

GCal **Cally Gardens, Gatehouse of Fleet, Castle Douglas, Scotland DG7 2DJ**
TEL: Not on phone. *CONTACT:* M C Wickenden
◆ *OPENING TIMES:* 1000-1730 Sat & Sun only from 2nd Apr-2nd Oct 1994
MIN MAIL ORDER UK: See Cat. for details *MIN VALUE EC:* £50.00 + p&p *EXPORT:* Yes
CAT. COST: 3 x 1st class *W/SALE or RETAIL:* Both
SPECIALITIES: Unusual perennials. Agapanthus, Crocosmia, Erodium, Eryngium, Euphorbia, Hardy Geraniums & Grasses. Some rare Shrubs, Climbers & Conservatory plants. *MAP PAGE:* **10**

GCHN **Charter House Nursery, 2 Nunwood, Dumfries, Dumfries & Galloway DG2 0HX**
TEL: (0387) 720363 *CONTACT:* John Ross
OPENING TIMES: 1200-1800 Sat & Sun.
MIN MAIL ORDER UK: No minimum charge *MIN VALUE EC:* Nmc *EXPORT:* Yes
CAT. COST: 3 x 1st class *W/SALE or RETAIL:* Retail
SPECIALITIES: Aquileagia, Hypericum, Geranium, Erodium, Pelargonium species and Campanula. Erodium National Collection. *MAP PAGE:* **10**

GChr **T & W Christie (Forres) Ltd,** The Nurseries, Forres, Moray, Grampian IV36 0EA

TEL: (0309) 672633 *FAX:* (0309) 676846 *CONTACT:* Dr S Thompson & D W Williamson
◆ *OPENING TIMES:* 0800-1200 & 1300-1700 Mon-Fri, 0800-1200 Sat.
MIN MAIL ORDER UK: £20.00 + p&p *MIN VALUE EC:* n/a
CAT. COST: Free *W/SALE or RETAIL:* Both
SPECIALITIES: Hedging & screening plants. Woodland & less common Trees, Shrubs & Fruit.
MAP PAGE: **10**

GCLN **Craig Lodge Nurseries, Balmaclellan, Castle Douglas, Kirkcudbrightshire Scotland DG7 3QR**

TEL: (06442) 661 *CONTACT:* Sheila & Michael Northway
OPENING TIMES: 1000-1700 Wed-Mon late Mar-end Oct.
MIN MAIL ORDER UK: No minimum charge *MIN VALUE EC:* Nmc
CAT. COST: A5 Sae + 4x2nd cls *W/SALE or RETAIL:* Retail
SPECIALITIES: Alpines, dwarf Rhododendrons, Bulbs & Conifers. Bulbs & Alpines are mainly grown from wild seed. *MAP PAGE:* **10**

GCoc **James Cocker & Sons,** Whitemyres, Lang Stracht, Aberdeen, Scotland AB9 2XH

TEL: (0224) 313261 *FAX:* (0224) 312531 *CONTACT:* Alec Cocker
OPENING TIMES: 0900-1730 daily.
MIN MAIL ORDER UK: No minimum charge *MIN VALUE EC:* n/a
CAT. COST: Free *W/SALE or RETAIL:* Both
SPECIALITIES: Roses. *MAP PAGE:* **10**

GCra **Craigieburn Classic Plants, Craigieburn House, by Moffat, Dumfriesshire DG10 9LF**

TEL: (0683) 21250 *CONTACT:* Janet Wheatcroft & Bill Chudziak
OPENING TIMES: 1230-1800 Tue-Sun mid Apr-end Oct. Nov-Apr by appt.
MIN MAIL ORDER UK: £10.00 + p&p *MIN VALUE EC:* £25.00 + p&p *EXPORT:* Yes
CAT. COST: 4 x 1st class *W/SALE or RETAIL:* Retail
SPECIALITIES: Codonopsis, Digitalis, Meconopsis & Primula. *MAP PAGE:* **10**

GDra **Jack Drake, Inshriach Alpine Nusery, Aviemore, Invernesshire PH22 1QS**

TEL: (0540 651) 287 *FAX:* (0540 651) 656 *CONTACT:* J C Lawson
◆ *OPENING TIMES:* 0900-1700 Mon-Fri, 0900-1600 Sat.
MIN MAIL ORDER UK: No minimum charge *MIN VALUE EC:* £50.00 + p&p *EXPORT:* Yes
CAT. COST: £1.00 *W/SALE or RETAIL:* Both
SPECIALITIES: Rare and unusual Alpines & Rock plants. Especially Primula, Meconopsis, Gentian, Heathers etc. See also SEED Index. *MAP PAGE:* **10**

GEve **Evelix Daffodils, Aird Asaig, Evelix, Dornoch, Sutherland IV25 3NG**

TEL: (0862) 810715 *CONTACT:* D C MacArthur
OPENING TIMES: By appt. only.
MIN MAIL ORDER UK: No minimum charge *MIN VALUE EC:* Nmc
CAT. COST: 3 x 1st class *W/SALE or RETAIL:* Retail
SPECIALITIES: New Narcissus cultivars for garden display & exhibition. *MAP PAGE:* **10**

GGar **Garden Cottage Nursery,** Tournaig, Poolewe, Achnasheen, Highland IV22 2LH

TEL: (044 586) 339 *CONTACT:* R Rushbrooke
OPENING TIMES: 1200-1900 Mon-Sat (Mar-Oct) or by appt.
MIN MAIL ORDER UK: £10.00 + p&p *MIN VALUE EC:* n/a
CAT. COST: 3 x 1st class *W/SALE or RETAIL:* Retail
SPECIALITIES: Large range of Herbacous & Alpines esp. Primula, Hardy Geraniums & moisture lovers. Range of West Coast Shrubs. *MAP PAGE:* **10**

GGGa **Glendoick Gardens Ltd, Glencarse, Perth, Scotland PH2 7NS**

TEL: (073 886) 205 *FAX:* (073 886) 735 *CONTACT:* P A, E P & K N E Cox
OPENING TIMES: Appt only. Garden Centre open 7 days.
MIN MAIL ORDER UK: £30.00 + p&p *MIN VALUE EC:* £100.00 + p&p *EXPORT:* Yes
CAT. COST: £1.50 *W/SALE or RETAIL:* Retail
SPECIALITIES: Rhododendron, Azalea and Ericaceous, Primula & Meconopsis. National collection of Kalmia & Enkianthus. Many Catalogue plants available at Garden Centre. *MAP PAGE:* **10**

GGre **Greenhead Roses,** Greenhead Nursery, Old Greenock Road, Inchinnan, Renfrew, Strathclyde PA4 9PH
TEL: (041 812) 0121 *FAX:* (041 812) 0121 *CONTACT:* C N Urquhart
OPENING TIMES: 1000-1700 daily.
MAIL ORDER: No
CAT. COST: Sae *W/SALE or RETAIL:* Both
SPECIALITIES: Roses. Wide general range, dwarf Conifers, Azaleas, Rhododendrons, Shrubs, Alpines, Fruit, hardy Herbaceous & Spring & Summer bedding. *MAP PAGE:* **10**

GIsl **Island Plants,, The Old Manse, Knock, Point, Isle of Lewis PA86 0BW**
TEL: (0851) 870281 *CONTACT:* Mr D Ferris
◆ *OPENING TIMES:* Every afternoon ex. Sun.
MIN MAIL ORDER UK: No minimum charge *MIN VALUE EC:* Nmc
CAT. COST: 1 x 1st class *W/SALE or RETAIL:* Retail
SPECIALITIES: Hebes & New Zealand plants esp. for coastal regions. *MAP PAGE:* **10**

GLil **Lilliesleaf Nursery,** Garden Cottage, Linthill, Melrose, Roxburghshire TD6 9HU
TEL: (083 57) 415 *FAX:* (083 57) 415 *CONTACT:* Teyl de Bordes
OPENING TIMES: 0900-1700 Mon-Sat, 1000-1600 Sun. In Dec-Feb please phone first.
MAIL ORDER: No
CAT. COST: *W/SALE or RETAIL:* Both
SPECIALITIES: Epimediums & wide range of common & uncommon plants. *MAP PAGE:* **10**

GMac **Elizabeth MacGregor, Ellenbank, Tongland Road, Kirkcudbright, Dumfries & Galloway DG6 4UU**
TEL: (0557) 330620 *FAX:* Phone first *CONTACT:* Elizabeth MacGregor
OPENING TIMES: Please phone.
MIN MAIL ORDER UK: 6 plants £9.90+p&p *MIN VALUE EC:* £30.00 + p&p *EXPORT:* Yes
CAT. COST: 80p *W/SALE or RETAIL:* Retail
SPECIALITIES: Violets, Violas & Violettas, old and new varieties. Campanula, Geranium, Penstemon & other unusual Herbaceous *MAP PAGE:* **10**

GMon **Monteviot House Gardens,** Doocot Cottage, Monteviot, Jedburgh, Borders TD8 6UQ
TEL: (08353) 380 morn/339 eves *CONTACT:* Andrew Simmons
OPENING TIMES: 1400-1700 Mon-Thu Apr-Aug
MAIL ORDER: No
CAT. COST: Large Sae *W/SALE or RETAIL:* Retail
SPECIALITIES: Hardy Fuchsia. *MAP PAGE:* **10**

GPen **Pennyacre Nurseries, Station Road, Springfield, Fife KY15 5RU**
TEL: (0334) 55852 *CONTACT:* C P Piper
◆ *OPENING TIMES:* 1000-1700 Thu-Sun Mar-Oct.
MIN MAIL ORDER UK: No minimum charge* *MIN VALUE EC:* Nmc*
CAT. COST: 2 x 1st class *W/SALE or RETAIL:* Retail
SPECIALITIES: Heathers, Dwarf Conifers & Fuchsias. *NOTE: Mail Order for Heathers & dwarf Conifers only. *MAP PAGE:* **10**

GPlt **Plantables, Drambuie, St John's Town of Dalry, Castle Douglas, Kirkcudbrightshire DG7 3XR**
TEL: (06443) 349 *CONTACT:* Alan Rumble
OPENING TIMES: By appt. please.
MIN MAIL ORDER UK: No minimum charge *MIN VALUE EC:* Nmc
CAT. COST: 2 x 1st class *W/SALE or RETAIL:* Both
SPECIALITIES: Alpines, Dwarf Shrubs, Dwarf Rhododendron & Hardy plants

GPoy **Poyntzfield Herb Nursery, Nr Balblair, Black Isle, Dingwall, Ross & Cromarty, Highland IV7 8LX**
TEL: (0381) 610352 evs *FAX:* (0381) 610352 24hrs *CONTACT:* Duncan Ross
OPENING TIMES: 1300-1700 Mon-Sat.
MIN MAIL ORDER UK: £5.00 + p&p *MIN VALUE EC:* £10.00 + p&p *EXPORT:* Yes
CAT. COST: Sae&3x1st class *W/SALE or RETAIL:* Retail
SPECIALITIES: Over 350 popular, unusual & rare Herbs, esp. Medicinal. *MAP PAGE:* **10**

GRei **Ben Reid and Co,** Pinewood Park, Countesswells Road, Aberdeen, Grampian AB9 2QL

TEL: (0224) 318744 *FAX:* (0224) 310104 *CONTACT:* John Fraser
OPENING TIMES: 0900-1700 Mon-Sat, 1000-1700 Sun.
MIN MAIL ORDER UK: £10.00 + p&p *MIN VALUE EC:*
CAT. COST: Free *W/SALE or RETAIL:* Both
SPECIALITIES: Trees & Shrubs. *MAP PAGE:* **10**

GSpe **Speyside Heather Garden Centre, Dulnain Bridge, Highland PH26 3PA**

TEL: (047 9851) 359 *FAX:* (047 9851) 396 *CONTACT:* D & B Lambie
OPENING TIMES: 0900-1730 daily in Summer. 0900-1700 Mon-Sat Nov-Mar. Closed Jan.
MIN MAIL ORDER UK: No minimum charge *MIN VALUE EC:* Nmc
CAT. COST: £2.25 inc. p&p *W/SALE or RETAIL:* Retail
SPECIALITIES: Heathers. *MAP PAGE:* **10**

GTou **Tough Alpine Nursery, Westhaybogs, Tough, Alford, Aberdeenshire, Scotland AB33 8DU**

TEL: (09755) 62783 *FAX:* (09755) 62783 *CONTACT:* Fred & Monika Carrie
◆ *OPENING TIMES:* 1st Feb-31st Oct. Please check first.
MIN MAIL ORDER UK: £10.00 + p&p *MIN VALUE EC:* £10.00 + p&p
CAT. COST: 3 x 2nd class *W/SALE or RETAIL:* Both
SPECIALITIES: Alpines *MAP PAGE:* **10**

GTwe **J Tweedie Fruit Trees,** Maryfield Road Nursery, Maryfield, Nr Terregles, Dumfries, Dumfriesshire DG2 9TH

TEL: (0387) 720880 *CONTACT:* John Tweedie
◆ *OPENING TIMES:* 0930-1430 Sat Oct-Mar & by appt.
MIN MAIL ORDER UK: No minimum charge *MIN VALUE EC:* n/a
CAT. COST: Sae *W/SALE or RETAIL:* Retail
SPECIALITIES: Fruit trees & bushes. A wide range of old & new varieties. *MAP PAGE:* **10**

GUzu **Uzumara Orchids, 9 Port Henderson, Gairloch, Rossshire IV21 2AS**

TEL: (0445 83) 228 *CONTACT:* Mrs I F La Croix
OPENING TIMES: Mail Order only
MAIL ORDER: Only*MIN MAIL ORDER UK:* Nmc *MIN VALUE EC:* Nmc *EXPORT:* Yes
CAT. COST: Sae *W/SALE or RETAIL:* Retail
SPECIALITIES: Streptocarpus species. African & Madagascan Orchids. See also SEED & ORCHID Index.

GWht **Whitehills Nurseries, Newton Stewart, Wigtownshire Scotland DG8 6SL**

TEL: (0671) 402049 *FAX:* (0671) 403106 *CONTACT:* Tony Weston
OPENING TIMES: 0830-1630 Mon-Fri or by appt.
MIN MAIL ORDER UK: £30.00 + p&p *MIN VALUE EC:* £50.00 + p&p
CAT. COST: 50p *W/SALE or RETAIL:* Both
SPECIALITIES: Rhododendrons, Azaleas & Shrubs. *MAP PAGE:* **10**

IBal **Ballydorn Bulb Farm, Killinchy, Newtownards, Co. Down, N Ireland BT23 6QB**

TEL: (0238) 541250 *CONTACT:* Sir Frank & Lady Harrison
OPENING TIMES: Not open.
MIN MAIL ORDER UK: £15.00 + p&p *MIN VALUE EC:* £15.00 + p&p *EXPORT:* Yes
CAT. COST: £1.00 *W/SALE or RETAIL:* Retail
SPECIALITIES: New Daffodil varieties for Exhibitors and Hybridisers.

IBar **Barons Court Nurseries, Abercorn Estates, Newtownstewart, Co. Tyrone, N Ireland BT78 4EZ**

TEL: (06626) 61683 *FAX:* (06626) 62059 *CONTACT:* Sales Dept.
OPENING TIMES: 1000-1630 Mon-Sat & 1400-1630 Sun.
MIN MAIL ORDER UK: £50.00 + p&p *MIN VALUE EC:* £50.00 + p&p
CAT. COST: Free *W/SALE or RETAIL:* Both
SPECIALITIES: Meconopsis 'Slieve Donard'. Specimen Trees & container grown Shrubs & Conifers. *MAP PAGE:* **11**

IBlr **Ballyrogan Nurseries, The Grange, Ballyrogan, Newtownards, Co. Down, N Ireland BT23 4SD**
TEL: (0247) 810451 eves *CONTACT:* Gary Dunlop
OPENING TIMES: Not open except for collection.
MIN MAIL ORDER UK: £10.00 + p&p *MIN VALUE EC:* £20.00 + p&p
CAT. COST: 2 x 1st class *W/SALE or RETAIL:* Both
SPECIALITIES: Conservatory & choice Herbaceous & Shrubs. Abutilon, Agapanthus, Crocosmia, Euphorbia, Hardy Geraniums & Grasses. *MAP PAGE:* **11**

ICar **Carncairn Daffodils, Broughshane, Ballymena, Co. Antrim, N Ireland BT43 7HF**
TEL: (0266) 861216 *CONTACT:* Mr & Mrs R H Reade
OPENING TIMES: 1000-1700 Mon-Fri. Please phone in advance.
MIN MAIL ORDER UK: No minimum charge *MIN VALUE EC:* Nmc *EXPORT:* Yes
CAT. COST: Free *W/SALE or RETAIL:* Both
SPECIALITIES: Old and new Narcissus cultivars, mainly for show. *MAP PAGE:* **11**

IDai **Daisy Hill Nurseries Ltd, Hospital Road, Newry, Co. Down, N Ireland BT35 8PN**
TEL: (0693) 62474 *CONTACT:* W A Grills
OPENING TIMES: 0800-1700 Mon-Fri.
MIN MAIL ORDER UK: £5.00 + p&p *MIN VALUE EC:* £10.00 + p&p
CAT. COST: Free *W/SALE or RETAIL:* Retail
SPECIALITIES: Wide variety Trees, Shrubs, Herbaceous, Alpines & Heathers. *MAP PAGE:* **11**

IDic **Dickson Nurseries Ltd., Milecross Road, Newtownards, Co. Down, N Ireland BT23 4SS**
TEL: (0247) 812206 *FAX:* (0247) 813366 *CONTACT:* A P C Dickson OBE.
OPENING TIMES: 0800-1230 & 1300-1700 Mon-Thur. 0800-1330 Fri.
MIN MAIL ORDER UK: One plant *MIN VALUE EC:* £25.00 + p&p *EXPORT:* Yes
CAT. COST: Free *W/SALE or RETAIL:* Both
SPECIALITIES: Roses, especially modern Dickson varieties. *MAP PAGE:* **11**

IDun **Brian Duncan, Novelty & Exhibition Daffodils 15 Ballynahatty Road, Omagh, Co. Tyrone, N Ireland BT78 1PN**
TEL: (0662) 242931 *FAX:* (0662) 242931 *CONTACT:* Brian Duncan
OPENING TIMES: By appointment.
MIN MAIL ORDER UK: £20.00 + p&p *MIN VALUE EC:* £20.00 + p&p *EXPORT:* Yes
CAT. COST: £1.00 inc p&p *W/SALE or RETAIL:* Both
SPECIALITIES: New hybrid & Exhibition Daffodils & Narcissi. *MAP PAGE:* **11**

IEde **Eden Plants, Eden, Rossinver, Co. Leitrim, Rep. of Ireland**
TEL: 010353 (0)7254122 *CONTACT:* Rod Alston
OPENING TIMES: 1400-1800 daily.
MIN MAIL ORDER UK: No minimum charge *MIN VALUE EC:* Nmc
CAT. COST: Sae for list *W/SALE or RETAIL:* Both
SPECIALITIES: Large range of hardy Herbs. NOTE: £1.00 for Catalogue & growing guide. *MAP PAGE:* **11**

IFer **Fernhill Nursery,** Sandyford, Co. Dublin, Rep. of Ireland
TEL: 010353-1-2956158 *CONTACT:* Robert Walker
OPENING TIMES: 1100-1700 Tue-Sat all year & 1400-1700 Sun Mar-Nov.
MAIL ORDER: No
CAT. COST: None issued *W/SALE or RETAIL:* Both
SPECIALITIES: Wide general range. *MAP PAGE:* **11**

IHos **Hosford's Geraniums & Garden Centr, Cappa, Enniskeane, Co. Cork, Rep. of Ireland**
TEL: 010353 (0)2339159 *FAX:* 010353 (0)2339300 *CONTACT:* John Hosford
◆ *OPENING TIMES:* 0900-1800 Mon-Sat (all year inc. Bank Hols). 1430-1830 Sun Feb-mid Sep. 1430-1730 mid-Sep-Xmas.
MIN MAIL ORDER UK: £10.00 + p&p *MIN VALUE EC:* £10.00 + p&p *EXPORT:* Yes
CAT. COST: IR£1.50 *W/SALE or RETAIL:* Retail
SPECIALITIES: Hardy Geraniums, Pelargoniums, Basket & Window box plants, Bedding & Roses. NOTE: Express Courier service available within Ireland. *MAP PAGE:* **11**

IJoh **Johnstown Garden Centre, Johnstown, Naas, Co. Kildare, Rep. of Ireland**

TEL: 010353 (0)4579138 *FAX:* 010353 (0)4579073 *CONTACT:* Jim Clarke
OPENING TIMES: 0930-1800 Mon-Sat & 1400-1800 Sun.
MIN MAIL ORDER UK: £50.00 + p&p *MIN VALUE EC:* £50.00 + p&p
CAT. COST: Free *W/SALE or RETAIL:* Retail
SPECIALITIES: Very wide range of Shrubs, Conifers, Alpines, Herbs & Aquatics. Newest introductions.
MAP PAGE: **11**

ILis **Lisdoonan Herbs,** 98 Belfast Road, Saintfield, Co. Down N Ireland BT24 7HF

TEL: (0232) 813624 *CONTACT:* Barbara Pilcher
OPENING TIMES: Most days - please phone to check.
MAIL ORDER: No
CAT. COST: Sae *W/SALE or RETAIL:* Both
SPECIALITIES: Herbs. Plants and freshly cut herbs & salads. *MAP PAGE:* **11**

IMal **Malahide Nurseries Ltd., Mabestown, Malahide, Co. Dublin, Rep. of Ireland**

TEL: 010353 (0)8450110 *FAX:* 010353 (0)8450872 *CONTACT:* Ann Nutty
OPENING TIMES: 0930-1300 & 1400-1730 Mon-Fri, 0900-1730 Sat & 1400-1730 Sun & Bank Hols.
MIN MAIL ORDER UK: IR£15.00 + p&p *MIN VALUE EC:* IR£15.00 + p&p
CAT. COST: Free *W/SALE or RETAIL:* Retail
SPECIALITIES: Large range of Shrubs, Trees & Aquatics. *MAP PAGE:* **11**

IOrc **Orchardstown Nurseries, 4 miles out, Cork Road, Waterford, Rep. of Ireland**

TEL: 010353 (0)5184273 *FAX:* 010353 (0)5184422 *CONTACT:* Ron Dool
OPENING TIMES: 0900-1800 Mon-Sat, 1400-1800 Sun.
MIN MAIL ORDER UK: No minimum charge *MIN VALUE EC:* Nmc *EXPORT:* Yes
CAT. COST: List IR£1.50 *W/SALE or RETAIL:* Retail
SPECIALITIES: Unusual hardy plants incl. Shrubs, Shrub Roses, Trees, Climbers, Rhododendron species & Water plants. *NOTE: Only SOME plants Mail Order. *MAP PAGE:* **11**

IReg **Regional Nurseries,** Rockfield House, Sandyford Road, Dundrum, Dublin 16, Rep. of Ireland

TEL: 010353-1-2982667 *FAX:* 010353-1-2982667 *CONTACT:* Neil Murray
OPENING TIMES: 0900-1200 Sat.
MAIL ORDER: No
CAT. COST: Sae *W/SALE or RETAIL:* Both
SPECIALITIES: Trees & Shrubs esp. Ilex. NOTE: This is a Wholesale nursery that is only open for Retail sales on Saturday morning, or by appt. *MAP PAGE:* **11**

ISea **Seaforde Gardens, Seaforde, Co. Down, N Ireland BT30 8PG**

TEL: (0396) 811225 *FAX:* (0396) 881370 *CONTACT:* P Forde
OPENING TIMES: 1000-1700 Mon-Fri all year. 1000-1700 Sat & 1400-1800 Sun mid Feb-end Oct.
MIN MAIL ORDER UK: No minimum charge *MIN VALUE EC:* Nmc *EXPORT:* Yes
CAT. COST: Free *W/SALE or RETAIL:* Both
SPECIALITIES: Over 700 varieties of self-propagated Trees & Shrubs. National Collection of Eucryphia.
MAP PAGE: **11**

ISta **Stam's Nurseries,** The Garden House, Cappoquin, Co. Waterford Rep. of Ireland

TEL: 010353 (0)58 54787 *FAX:* 010353 (0)58 54472 *CONTACT:* Peter Stam
OPENING TIMES: By appointment only.
MAIL ORDER: No *EXPORT:* Yes
CAT. COST: Sae *W/SALE or RETAIL:* Both
SPECIALITIES: Bamboos *MAP PAGE:* **11**

ITim **Timpany Nurseries, 77 Magheratimpany Road, Ballynahinch, Co. Down, N Ireland BT24 8PA**

TEL: (0238) 562812 *CONTACT:* Susan Tindall
OPENING TIMES: 1100-1800 Tue-Fri, 1000-1800 Sat & Bank Hols.
MIN MAIL ORDER UK: No minimum charge *MIN VALUE EC:* £30.00 + p&p *EXPORT:* Yes
CAT. COST: 75p in stamps *W/SALE or RETAIL:* Retail
SPECIALITIES: Celmisia, Androsace, Primula, Saxifraga, Helichrysum & Dianthus. *MAP PAGE:* **11**

LAbb **Abbot's House Garden,** 10 High Street, Abbots Langley, Hertfordshire WD5 0AR

TEL: (0923) 264946/262167 *CONTACT:* Dr Peter Tomson & Mrs Joan Gentry
OPENING TIMES: 0900-1300 & 1400-1600 Sat Mar-Oct, 0900-1300 Nov-Dec & by appt. Please check before visiting.
MIN MAIL ORDER UK: No minimum charge *MIN VALUE EC:* n/a
CAT. COST: 3 x 2nd class *W/SALE or RETAIL:* Retail
SPECIALITIES: Conservatory, Tender and Patio plants. Flower arranger's plants. Small nursery. *NOTE: Only SOME plants by Mail Order. *MAP PAGE:* **6**

LAma **Jacques Amand Ltd., The Nurseries, 145 Clamp Hill, Stanmore, Middlesex HA7 3JS**

TEL: (081) 954 8138 *FAX:* (081) 954 6784 *CONTACT:*
OPENING TIMES: 0900-1700 Mon-Fri, 0900-1300 Sat-Sun. Limited Sun opening in Dec & Jan.
MIN MAIL ORDER UK: No minimum charge *MIN VALUE EC:* Nmc
CAT. COST: Free *W/SALE or RETAIL:* Both
SPECIALITIES: Rare and unusual species Bulbs. *MAP PAGE:* **6**

LBam **The Bamboo Centre,** 563 Upper Richmond Road West, London SW14 7ED

TEL: 081-876 3223 *FAX:* 081-876 6888 *CONTACT:* Martin Gibbons
OPENING TIMES: 1000-1800 daily.
MIN MAIL ORDER UK: £10.00 + p&p *MIN VALUE EC:* n/a
CAT. COST: £1.95 *W/SALE or RETAIL:* Both
SPECIALITIES: Hardy Bamboos *MAP PAGE:* **3/6**

LBee **Beechcroft Nursery,** 127 Reigate Road, Ewell, Surrey KT17 3DE

TEL: 081-393 4265 *CONTACT:* C Kimber
◆ *OPENING TIMES:* 1000-1700 May-Sep. 1000-1600 Oct-Apr, Bank Hols & Suns. Closed Xmas-New Year & August
MAIL ORDER: No
CAT. COST: None *W/SALE or RETAIL:* Both
SPECIALITIES: Conifers & Alpines. *MAP PAGE:* **3**

LBlm **Bloomsbury,** Upper Lodge Farm, Padworth Common, Reading, Berkshire RG7 4JD

TEL: (0734) 700239 *CONTACT:* Susan Oakley
OPENING TIMES: 1100-1700 Thu-Sun & Bank Hols, mid Mar-mid Oct. Please check first.
MIN MAIL ORDER UK: £15.00 + p&p *MIN VALUE EC:* n/a
CAT. COST: £1 coin or 4x1st *W/SALE or RETAIL:* Retail
SPECIALITIES: Unusual & essential hardy & Conservatory plants, many rarities. Tender plants, hardy Geraniums & white flowers. Garden open see NGS Yellow Book for details. *MAP PAGE:* **2**

LBow **Rupert Bowlby,** Gatton, Reigate, Surrey RH2 0TA

TEL: (0737) 642221 *FAX:* (0737) 642221 *CONTACT:* Rupert Bowlby
OPENING TIMES: Sat & Sun pm in Mar & Sep-Oct.
MIN MAIL ORDER UK: No minimum charge *MIN VALUE EC:* n/a
CAT. COST: 2 x 2nd class *W/SALE or RETAIL:* Retail
SPECIALITIES: Unusual Bulbs & Corms. *MAP PAGE:* **3**

LBre **Bressingham Plant Centre,** Dorney Court, Dorney, Windsor, Bucks SL4 6QP

TEL: (0628) 669999 *FAX:* (0628) 669693 *CONTACT:* Tim Baylis
OPENING TIMES: 1000-1730 daily. (Direct retail Plant Centre).
MAIL ORDER: No
CAT. COST: *W/SALE or RETAIL:* Retail
SPECIALITIES: Very wide general range. Many own varieties. Focus on Hardy Ornamental plants. *MAP PAGE:* **3/6**

LBro **Mrs P J Brown, V H Humphrey-Iris Specialist, Westlees Farm, Logmore Lane, Westcott, Dorking, Surrey RH4 3JN**

TEL: (0306) 889827 *FAX:* (0306) 889371 *CONTACT:* Mrs P J Brown
◆ *OPENING TIMES:* Open days 1100-1500 Sat 14th & Sun 15th May 1994. Otherwise by appt.
MIN MAIL ORDER UK: No minimum charge *MIN VALUE EC:* Nmc *EXPORT:* Yes
CAT. COST: Large Sae 9x6 *W/SALE or RETAIL:* Both
SPECIALITIES: Dwarf Bearded, Median, Border, Intermediate, Tall Bearded, Spuria, Siberian, Pacific Coast & species Iris. *MAP PAGE:* **3**

LBuc **Buckingham Nurseries, 14 Tingewick Road, Buckingham, Buckinghamshire MK18 4AE**
TEL: (0280) 813556 *FAX:* (0280) 815491 *CONTACT:* R J & P L Brown
◆ *OPENING TIMES:* 0830-1730 (1800 in summer) Mon-Fri, 0930-1730 (1800 in summer) Sun.
MIN MAIL ORDER UK: No minimum charge *MIN VALUE EC:* Nmc
CAT. COST: Free *W/SALE or RETAIL:* Retail
SPECIALITIES: Bare rooted and container grown hedging. Trees & Shrubs. *MAP PAGE:* **5**

LCla **Clay Lane Nursery,** 3 Clay Lane, South Nutfield, Nr Redhill, Surrey RH1 4EG
TEL: (0737) 823307 *CONTACT:* K W Belton
OPENING TIMES: 0900-1800 Tue-Sun 28th Jan-31st Jul. Also Bank Hol. Mons & by appt.
MAIL ORDER: No
CAT. COST: 2 x 1st class *W/SALE or RETAIL:* Retail
SPECIALITIES: Fuchsias. *MAP PAGE:* **3**

LCon **The Conifer Garden,** Hare Lane Nursery, Little Kingshill, Great Missenden, Buckinghamshire HP16 0EF
TEL: (0494) 890624 (11-4)* *CONTACT:* Mr & Mrs M P S Powell
◆ *OPENING TIMES:* 1100-1600 Tue-Fri, 0930-1600 Sat & Bank Hol Mons.
MAIL ORDER: No
CAT. COST: 2 x 1st class *W/SALE or RETAIL:* Retail
SPECIALITIES: Conifers only. *Tel No (0494) 862086 evemimgs. *MAP PAGE:* **5/6**

LCot **Cottage Garden Plants,** 9 Buckingham Road, Newbury, Berkshire RG14 6DH
TEL: (0635) 31941 *CONTACT:* Mrs Hannah Billcliffe
OPENING TIMES: 1000-1700 Mon-Sat Mar-Oct, 1100-1700 Sun & Bank Hols Jun-Aug.
MAIL ORDER: No
CAT. COST: Sae+1 x 1st class *W/SALE or RETAIL:* Retail
SPECIALITIES: Wide range of unusual Perennials incl. Polemoniums. *MAP PAGE:* **2**

LCTD **CTDA, 174 Cambridge Street, London SW1V 4QE**
TEL: 071-821 1801 *CONTACT:* Basil Smith
OPENING TIMES: Not open.
MAIL ORDER: Only*MIN MAIL ORDER UK:* £10+p&p *MIN VALUE EC:* £10+p&p *EXPORT:* SO
CAT. COST: Free *W/SALE or RETAIL:* Both
SPECIALITIES: Hardy Cyclamen for the garden. See also SEED Index.

LDea **Derek Lloyd Dean, 8 Lynwood Close, South Harrow, Middlesex HA2 9PR**
TEL: 081-864 0899 *CONTACT:* Derek Lloyd Dean
OPENING TIMES: Mail Order only.
MAIL ORDER: Only*MIN MAIL ORDER UK:* £2.50+p&p *MIN VALUE EC:* £2.50+p&p*EXPORT:* Yes
CAT. COST: 2 x 1st class *W/SALE or RETAIL:* Retail
SPECIALITIES: Regal, Angel & Ivy Pelargoniums.

LFle **M V Fletcher,** 70 South Street, Reading, Berkshire RG1 4RA
TEL: (0734) 571814 *CONTACT:* M V Fletcher
OPENING TIMES: By appt. only.
MIN MAIL ORDER UK: No minimum charge *MIN VALUE EC:* n/a
CAT. COST: 2 x 1st class *W/SALE or RETAIL:* Retail
SPECIALITIES: Specialist collection of Mosses & Hepaticas (Liverworts), mostly British, also about 100 ssp. from Southern Hemisphere.

LFox **Foxgrove Plants, Foxgrove, Enborne, Nr Newbury, Berkshire RG14 6RE**
TEL: (0635) 40554 *CONTACT:* Miss Louise Vockins
OPENING TIMES: 1000-1700 Wed-Sun & Bank Hols.
MIN MAIL ORDER UK: No minimum charge *MIN VALUE EC:* Nmc
CAT. COST: 65p *W/SALE or RETAIL:* Retail
SPECIALITIES: Alpines, Foliage plants, Galanthus, Auriculas & Saxifraga. *MAP PAGE:* **2**

LGan **Gannock Growers, Gannock Green, Sandon, Buntingford, Hertfordshire SG9 0RH**
TEL: (0763) 287386 *CONTACT:* Penny Pyle
OPENING TIMES: 1000-1600 Tue-Sat Mar-Oct & Bank Hol Mons.
MIN MAIL ORDER UK: No minimum charge *MIN VALUE EC:* £25.00 + p&p
CAT. COST: 3 x 1st class *W/SALE or RETAIL:* Retail
SPECIALITIES: Unusual & some rare herbaceous plants. *MAP PAGE:* **6**

LGod **Godly's Roses, Redbourn, St Albans, Hertfordshire AL3 7PS**

TEL: (0582) 792255 *FAX:* (0582) 794267 *CONTACT:* Colin Godly
OPENING TIMES: 0900-1900 Summer, 0900-dusk Winter Mon-Fri. 0900-1800 Sat & Sun.
MIN MAIL ORDER UK: £2.50 + p&p *MIN VALUE EC:* £50.00 + p&p
CAT. COST: Free *W/SALE or RETAIL:* Retail
SPECIALITIES: Roses. *MAP PAGE:* **6**

LGre **Green Farm Plants,** Bentley, Farnham, Surrey GU10 5JX

TEL: (0420) 23202 *CONTACT:* J Coke & M Christopher
OPENING TIMES: 1000-1800 Wed-Sat, end Mar-early Oct.
MAIL ORDER: No
CAT. COST: 3 x 1st class *W/SALE or RETAIL:* Retail
SPECIALITIES: Small Shrubs, Alpines, Sub-shrubs and Perennials. Many uncommon. *MAP PAGE:* **2/3**

LGro **Growing Carpets,** Christmas Tree House, High Street, Guilden Morden, Nr Royston, Hertfordshire SG8 0jP

TEL: (0763) 852705 *CONTACT:* Mrs E E Moore
◆ *OPENING TIMES:* 1100-1300 & 1400-1600 Mon-Sat, 1400-1600 Sun. Other times by appt.
MAIL ORDER: No
CAT. COST: 4 x 1st class *W/SALE or RETAIL:* Retail
SPECIALITIES: Wide range of Ground-covering plants. *MAP PAGE:* **6**

LHar **Harrisons Delphiniums,** Newbury Cottage, Play Hatch, Reading, Berkshire RG4 9QN

TEL: (0734) 470810 *CONTACT:* Len Harrison
OPENING TIMES: 0900-1630 Sat & Sun Apr-Sep.
MAIL ORDER: No
CAT. COST: 1x1st class *W/SALE or RETAIL:* Both
SPECIALITIES: Delphiniums. See also SEED Index. *MAP PAGE:* **2/3/5**

LHil **Brian Hiley,** 25 Little Woodcote Estate, Wallington, Surrey SM5 4AU

TEL: (081) 647 9679 *CONTACT:* Brian & Heather Hiley
OPENING TIMES: 0900-1700 Wed-Sat (ex Bank Hols). Please check beforehand.
MIN MAIL ORDER UK: £15.00 + p&p *MIN VALUE EC:* n/a
CAT. COST: 3 x 1st class *W/SALE or RETAIL:* Retail
SPECIALITIES: Penstemon, Salvia, Canna, Herbaceous, tender & unusual plants. *MAP PAGE:* **3**

LHol **Hollington Nurseries,** Woolton Hill, Newbury, Berkshire RG15 9XT

TEL: (0635) 253908 *FAX:* (0635) 254990 *CONTACT:* S & J Hopkinson
OPENING TIMES: 1000-1700 Mon-Sat, 1100-1700 Sun & Bank Hols Apr-Sep. 1000-dusk Mon-Fri Oct-Mar.
MAIL ORDER: No
CAT. COST: Sae *W/SALE or RETAIL:* Both
SPECIALITIES: Herbs, Thymes, Old fashioned Roses & Salvia. Cool conservatory plants.
MAP PAGE: **2**

LHop **Hopleys Plants Ltd,** High Street, Much Hadham, Hertfordshire SG10 6BU

TEL: (0279 84) 2509 *FAX:* (0279 84) 3784 *CONTACT:* Aubrey Barker
OPENING TIMES: 0900-1700 Mon & Wed-Sat, 1400-1700 Sun. Closed Jan.
MIN MAIL ORDER UK: No minimum charge* *MIN VALUE EC:* n/a
CAT. COST: £1.00 *W/SALE or RETAIL:* Both
SPECIALITIES: Wide range of Hardy & Half-hardy Shrubs & Perennials. *NOTE:- Mail Order in Autumn only. *MAP PAGE:* **6**

LHyd **Hydon Nurseries Ltd., Clock Barn Lane, Hydon Heath, Godalming, Surrey GU8 4AZ**

TEL: (0483) 860252 *FAX:* (0483) 419937 *CONTACT:* A F George
◆ *OPENING TIMES:* 0800-1700 Mon-Sat. (Closed 1245-1400). Sun by appt. only.
MIN MAIL ORDER UK: No minimum charge *MIN VALUE EC:* £25.00 + p&p *EXPORT:* Yes
CAT. COST: £1.50 *W/SALE or RETAIL:* Both
SPECIALITIES: Large and dwarf Rhododendron, Yakushimanum hybrids & evergreen Azaleas.
MAP PAGE: **3**

LKna **Knap Hill & Slocock Nurseries, Barrs Lane, Knaphill, Woking, Surrey GU21 2JW**

TEL: (0483) 481212/5 *FAX:* (0483) 797261 *CONTACT:* Mrs Joy West
OPENING TIMES: 0900-1700 Mon-Sat & 1000-1700 Sun.
MIN MAIL ORDER UK: No minimum charge *MIN VALUE EC:* Nmc *EXPORT:* Yes
CAT. COST: 50p *W/SALE or RETAIL:* Both
SPECIALITIES: Wide variety Trees & Shrubs especially Rhododendron, Azalea & Ericaceous.
MAP PAGE: **3**

LLin **Lincluden Nursery, Bisley Green, Bisley, Woking, Surrey GU24 9EN**

TEL: (0483) 797005 *FAX:* (0483) 474015 *CONTACT:* Mr & Mrs J A Tilbury
◆ *OPENING TIMES:* 0930-1630 Mon-Sat 2nd Mar-22nd Dec. 1000-1600 Mon-Fri Jan-Feb. Other times by appt. only.
MIN MAIL ORDER UK: No minimum charge *MIN VALUE EC:* Nmc *EXPORT:* Yes
CAT. COST: 3 x 1st class *W/SALE or RETAIL:* Both
SPECIALITIES: Dwarf, slow-growing & unusual Conifers. *MAP PAGE:* **3**

LLWP **L W Plants,** 23 Wroxham Way, Harpenden, Hertfordshire AL5 4PP

TEL: (0582) 768467 *CONTACT:* Mrs M Easter
OPENING TIMES: 1000-1700 most days, but please phone first.
MAIL ORDER: No
CAT. COST: Sae *W/SALE or RETAIL:* Retail
SPECIALITIES: Unusual Hardy Perennials & Herbs. Especially Diascia, Penstemon & Thymus.
MAP PAGE: **6**

LMay **Maydencroft Aquatic Nurseries, Maydencroft Lane, Gosmore, Hitchin, Hertfordshire SG4 7QD**

TEL: (0462) 456020 *FAX:* (0462) 422652 *CONTACT:* P Bromfield
OPENING TIMES: 0900-1300 & 1400-1730 daily Feb-Oct. 1000-1300 Sat-Sun Nov-Jan.
MIN MAIL ORDER UK: £5.00 + p&p *MIN VALUE EC:* £20.00 + p&p
CAT. COST: 50p *W/SALE or RETAIL:* Both
SPECIALITIES: Water Lilies, Marginals, Bog, Alpines, dwarf Conifer. *MAP PAGE:* **6**

LMer **Merrist Wood Plant Shop,** Merrist Wood College, Worplesdon, Guildford Surrey GU3 3PE

TEL: (0483) 232424 *FAX:* (0483) 236518 *CONTACT:* Danny O'Shaughnessy
OPENING TIMES: 0900-1700 Mon-Fri.
MIN MAIL ORDER UK: £5.00 + p&p *MIN VALUE EC:* n/a
CAT. COST: *W/SALE or RETAIL:* Retail
SPECIALITIES: *MAP PAGE:* **3**

LMil **Millais Nurseries, Crosswater Lane, Churt, Farnham, Surrey GU10 2JN**

TEL: (0252) 792698 *FAX:* (0252) 792526 *CONTACT:* David Millais
◆ *OPENING TIMES:* 1000-1300 & 1400-1700 Tue-Sat. Also daily in May & June.
MIN MAIL ORDER UK: £25.00 + p&p *MIN VALUE EC:* £50.00 + p&p *EXPORT:* Yes
CAT. COST: 5 x 2nd class *W/SALE or RETAIL:* Both
SPECIALITIES: Rhododendron & Azalea. *MAP PAGE:* **2/3**

LMor **Morehavens,** 28 Denham Lane, Gerrards Cross, Buckinghamshire SL9 0EX

TEL: (0494) 873601 *CONTACT:* B Farmer
OPENING TIMES: Only for collection.
MIN MAIL ORDER UK: £8.50 incl. p&p *MIN VALUE EC:* n/a
CAT. COST: Free *W/SALE or RETAIL:* Both
SPECIALITIES: Camomile 'Treneague'. *MAP PAGE:* **6**

LNet **Nettletons Nursery, Ivy Mill Lane, Godstone, Surrey RH9 8NF**

TEL: (0883) 742426 *FAX:* (0883) 742426 *CONTACT:* Jonathan Nettleton
◆ *OPENING TIMES:* 0830-1300 & 1400-1730 Mon Tue Thu-Sat, 1000-1300 Sun Mar-Jun. Bank Hols by appt.
MIN MAIL ORDER UK: £100.00 *MIN VALUE EC:* £100.00 + p&p
CAT. COST: 2 x 1st class *W/SALE or RETAIL:* Both
SPECIALITIES: Trees & Shrubs. Especially Conifers, Azalea, Camellia, Rhododendron, Climbers. 100 Japanese Acers. 17 Wisteria. *MAP PAGE:* **3**

LPal **The Palm Centre, 563 Upper Richmond Rd West, London SW14 7ED**

TEL: (081) 876 3223 *FAX:* (081) 876 6888 *CONTACT:* Martin Gibbons
OPENING TIMES: 1000-1800 daily.
MIN MAIL ORDER UK: £10.00 + p&p *MIN VALUE EC:* £10.00 + p$p *EXPORT:* Yes
CAT. COST: £1.95 *W/SALE or RETAIL:* Both
SPECIALITIES: Palms & Cycads, exotic & sub-tropical, hardy, half-hardy & tropical. Seedlings to mature trees. Catalogue for Palms & Cycads. *MAP PAGE:* **3/6**

LPan **Pantiles Nurseries Ltd.,** Almners Road, Lyne, Chertsey, Surrey KT16 0BJ

TEL: (0932) 872195 *FAX:* (0932) 874030 *CONTACT:* Brendan Gallagher
◆ *OPENING TIMES:* 0900-1730 Mon-Sat, 0900-1700 Sun.
MAIL ORDER: No *EXPORT:* Yes
CAT. COST: Sae *W/SALE or RETAIL:* Both
SPECIALITIES: Large Trees, Shrubs & climbers in containers. *MAP PAGE:* **3**

LPlm **A J Palmer & Son, Denham Court Nursery, Denham Court Drive, Denham, Uxbridge, Middlesex UB9 5PG**

TEL: (0895) 832035 *CONTACT:* Sheila Palmer
OPENING TIMES: 0900-dusk daily Jul-Oct, Rose field viewing. 0900-1700 Mon-Sat, 1000-1300 Sun Nov. Dec-Jun phone.
MIN MAIL ORDER UK: No minimum charge *MIN VALUE EC:* Nmc
CAT. COST: Free *W/SALE or RETAIL:* Both
SPECIALITIES: Roses. *MAP PAGE:* **6**

LPri **Priorswood Clematis, Priorswood, Widbury Hill, Ware, Hertfordshire SG12 7QH**

TEL: (0920) 461543 *CONTACT:* G S Greenway
OPENING TIMES: 0800-1700 Tue-Sun & Bank Hol Mondays..
MIN MAIL ORDER UK: £8.75 + p&p *MIN VALUE EC:* £10.00 + p&p *EXPORT:* Yes
CAT. COST: 65p + Sae *W/SALE or RETAIL:* Both
SPECIALITIES: Clematis & other climbing plants. Lonicera, Parthenocissus, Solanum, Passiflora, Vitis etc. *MAP PAGE:* **6**

LRHS **Wisley Plant Centre,** RHS Garden, Nr Ripley, Woking, Surrey GU23 6QB

TEL: (0483) 211113 *FAX:* (0483) 211932 *CONTACT:*
OPENING TIMES: 1000-1830 daily Summer, 1000-1730 Winter.
MAIL ORDER: No
CAT. COST: None issued *W/SALE or RETAIL:* Retail
SPECIALITIES: Very wide range, many rare & unusual. *MAP PAGE:* **3**

LStr **Henry Street, Swallowfield Road Nursery, Arborfield, Reading, Berkshire RG2 9JY**

TEL: (0734) 761223 *FAX:* (0734) 761417 *CONTACT:* Mr M C Goold
OPENING TIMES: 0900-1730 daily.
MIN MAIL ORDER UK: No minimum charge *MIN VALUE EC:* Nmc
CAT. COST: Free *W/SALE or RETAIL:* Both
SPECIALITIES: Roses. *MAP PAGE:* **2/3**

LSur **Surrey Primroses,,** Merriewood, Sandy Lane, Milford, Godalming, Surrey GU8 5BJ

TEL: (0483) 416747 *CONTACT:* Val & Geoff Yates
OPENING TIMES: Not open to the public.
MIN MAIL ORDER UK: No minimum charge *MIN VALUE EC:*
CAT. COST: Sae *W/SALE or RETAIL:* Retail
SPECIALITIES: Primroses, old named varieties. *MAP PAGE:* **3**

LVer **The Vernon Geranium Nursery, Cuddington Way, Cheam, Sutton, Surrey SM2 7JB**

TEL: 081-393 7616 *FAX:* 081 786 7437 *CONTACT:* Janet, Derek & Philip James
OPENING TIMES: 0930-1730 Mon-Sat, 1000-1600 Sun, 1st Feb-31st Aug.
MIN MAIL ORDER UK: No minimum charge *MIN VALUE EC:* Nmc
CAT. COST: £1.50 UK* *W/SALE or RETAIL:* Both
SPECIALITIES: Pelargoniums. *NOTE: Illustrated colour Catalogue. £2.50 for overseas.
MAP PAGE: **3**

LWad **Waddesdon Gardens Nursery,** Queen Street, Waddesdon, Buckinghamshire HP18 0JW

TEL: (0296) 658586 *FAX:* (0296) 658852 *CONTACT:*
OPENING TIMES: 0830-1730 daily Apr-Sep, 0930-1700 Oct-Mar (ex. Xmas).
MAIL ORDER: No
CAT. COST: *W/SALE or RETAIL:* Both
SPECIALITIES: Increasing range of choice & unusual herbaceous Perennials, Shrubs, Bedding, Conservatory & Houseplants. *MAP PAGE:* **5**

MAll **Paul Allanson,** Rhendhoo, Jurby, Isle of Man IM7 3HB

TEL: (0624) 880766 *FAX:* (0624) 880649 *CONTACT:* Paul Allanson
OPENING TIMES: By appt. only. Closed Dec & Jan.
MIN MAIL ORDER UK: £10.00 + p&p *MIN VALUE EC:* n/a
CAT. COST: £1.50 cheque/PO* *W/SALE or RETAIL:* Both
SPECIALITIES: Shrubs for seaside locations, west coast & southern England. Particularly Australian, Tasmanian & New Zealand. *NOTE: English stamps not accepted in IoM. *MAP PAGE:* **4**

MArl **Arley Hall Nursery,** Northwich, Cheshire CW9 6NA

TEL: (0565) 777479/777231 *FAX:* (0565) 777465 *CONTACT:* Jane Foster
OPENING TIMES: 1200-1730 Tue-Sun
MAIL ORDER: No
CAT. COST: 4 x 1st class *W/SALE or RETAIL:* Retail
SPECIALITIES: Herbaceous esp. Geraniums. *MAP PAGE:* **7**

MAsh **Ashwood Nurseries,** Greensforge, Kingswinford, West Midlands DY6 0AE

TEL: (0384) 401996 *FAX:* (0384) 401108 *CONTACT:* John Massey & Philip Baulk
◆ *OPENING TIMES:* 0900-1800 Mon-Sat & 0930-1800 Sun. ex Xmas & Boxing day.
MAIL ORDER: No
CAT. COST: A5 Sae *W/SALE or RETAIL:* Both
SPECIALITIES: Lewisias (Holder of NCCPG Collection). Also large range of hardy plants. Extensive range of dwarf Conifers. See also SEED Index. Mail Order for SEEDS only. *MAP PAGE:* **7**

MAsk **Askew's Nursery,** South Croxton Road, Queniborough, Leicestershire LE7 8RU

TEL: (0664) 840557 *CONTACT:* Mrs Longland
OPENING TIMES: 0900-1900 Wed-Mon Feb-end Sep. Oct-Jan please telephone first.
MIN MAIL ORDER UK: No minimum charge *MIN VALUE EC:* n/a
CAT. COST: 3 x 1st class *W/SALE or RETAIL:* Retail
SPECIALITIES: Fuchsias. *MAP PAGE:* **7**

MAus **David Austin Roses Ltd., Bowling Green Lane, Albrighton, Wolverhampton, West Midlands WV7 3HB**

TEL: (0902) 373931 *FAX:* (0902) 372142 *CONTACT:* D Austin
OPENING TIMES: 0900-1700 Mon-Fri, 1000-1800 Sat, Sun & Bank Hols. Until dusk Nov-Mar.
MIN MAIL ORDER UK: No minimum charge *MIN VALUE EC:* £25.00 + p&p *EXPORT:* Yes
CAT. COST: Free *W/SALE or RETAIL:* Both
SPECIALITIES: Roses, Paeonia, Iris & Hemerocallis& hardy plants. Also Herbaceous perennials at Nursery. *MAP PAGE:* **7**

MBal **Ballalheannagh Gardens, Glen Roy, Lonan, Isle of Man**

TEL: (0624) 861875 *CONTACT:* Clif & Maureen Dadd
OPENING TIMES: 1000-1300 & 1400-1700 or dusk if earlier in Winter. Closed w/ends Nov-Mar. Please telephone first.
MIN MAIL ORDER UK: £10.00 + p&p *MIN VALUE EC:* £20.00 + p&p
CAT. COST: £1.50 *W/SALE or RETAIL:* Retail
SPECIALITIES: Rhododendrons & Ericaceous Shrubs. Small number of rare trees and shrubs for callers not in catalogue. *NOTE: Mail Order on some items only. *MAP PAGE:* **4**

MBar **Barncroft Nurseries,** Dunwood Lane, Longsdon, Nr Leek, Stoke-on-Trent, Staffordshire ST9 9QW

TEL: (0538) 384310 *CONTACT:* R & S Warner
OPENING TIMES: 0900-1900 or dusk if earlier Fri-Sun.
MAIL ORDER: No
CAT. COST: None issued *W/SALE or RETAIL:* Both
SPECIALITIES: Very large range of Heathers, Conifers & Shrubs. *MAP PAGE:* **7**

MBea **John Beach (Nursery) Ltd.,** (Office) 9 Grange Road, Wellesbourne, Warwickshire CV35 9RL
TEL: (0926) 484506 *FAX:* (0926) 484506 *CONTACT:* John Beach
◆ *OPENING TIMES:* 1000-1700 Mon, Wed, Fri, Sat & Sun Mar-Oct. By appt. Nov-Feb.
MIN MAIL ORDER UK: 2 plants + p&p *MIN VALUE EC:* n/a
CAT. COST: 6x1st or £1.50* *W/SALE or RETAIL:* Retail
SPECIALITIES: Clematis, Trees & Shrubs inc. Fruiting plants. *NOTE: Clematis list free. Nursery address:- Fiveways Nursery, Case Lane, Shrewley, Warwick, CV35 7JD. *MAP PAGE:* **5**

MBel **Bellhouse Nursery,** Bellhouse Lane, Moore, Nr Warrington, Cheshire WA4 6TR
TEL: (0925) 740307* *FAX:* (0925) 740672 *CONTACT:* Elaine Soens & Doreen Scott
OPENING TIMES: 1000-1700 Wed-Mon Mar-Oct. 1000-1600 Wed-Mon Nov & Feb. Closed all Dec & Jan.
MAIL ORDER: No
CAT. COST: £1.00 *W/SALE or RETAIL:* Retail
SPECIALITIES: Wide range of Herbaceous plants & Shrubs. Good selection of unusual varieties. *NOTE: Ask for nursery. *MAP PAGE:* **7**

MBen **Michael Bennett, Long Compton, Shipston-on-Stour, Warwickshire CV36 5JN**
TEL: (060 884) 676 *CONTACT:* Michael Bennett
OPENING TIMES:
MIN MAIL ORDER UK: £5.00 + p&p *MIN VALUE EC:* £5.00 + p&p
CAT. COST: Sae *W/SALE or RETAIL:* Both
SPECIALITIES: Asparagus & Globe Artichoke. Ulmus glabra 'Camperdownii'

MBlu **The Bluebell Nursery, Blackfordby, Swadlincote, Derbyshire DE11 8AJ**
TEL: (0283) 222091 *FAX:* (0283) 218282 *CONTACT:* Robert & Suzette Vernon
OPENING TIMES: 0900-1700 (or dusk if earlier) daily. Closed 25th Dec-2nd Jan.
MIN MAIL ORDER UK: No minimum charge *MIN VALUE EC:* Nmc *EXPORT:* Yes
CAT. COST: 50p+2x1st class *W/SALE or RETAIL:* Retail
SPECIALITIES: Uncommon Trees, Shrubs & Climbers. *MAP PAGE:* **7**

MBri **Bridgemere Nurseries,** Bridgemere, Nr Nantwich, Cheshire CW5 7QB
TEL: (09365) 381/239 x 157 *FAX:* (09365) 215 *CONTACT:* Keith Atkey
OPENING TIMES: 0900-2000 Mon-Sat, 1000-2000 Sun summer, until 1700 in winter.
MAIL ORDER: No
CAT. COST: None issued *W/SALE or RETAIL:* Both
SPECIALITIES: Largest variety of Plants, Bulbs & Seeds on one site in UK. Especially dwarf Rhododendrons, herbaceous Perennials, Conifers, Heathers, Alpines, Trees & Shrubs. *MAP PAGE:* **7**

MBrk **Brinkley Nurseries,** Fiskerton Road, Southwell, Nottinghamshire NG25 0TP
TEL: (0636) 814501 *CONTACT:* Mrs C Steven
◆ *OPENING TIMES:* 1000-1600 Mon-Fri winter, 1000-1700 Mon-Fri summer. 1000-1300 Sat & Sun. Closed 24th Dec-1st Feb
MIN MAIL ORDER UK: £10.00 + p&p *MIN VALUE EC:* n/a
CAT. COST: £1.95 *W/SALE or RETAIL:* Both
SPECIALITIES: Shrubs, Conifers, small Trees. Unusual & rare varieties also available. *MAP PAGE:* **7**

MBro **Broadstone Alpines,** 13 The Nursery, High Street, Sutton Courtenay, Abingdon, Oxfordshire OX14 4UA
TEL: (0235) 847557 *CONTACT:* J Shackleton
OPENING TIMES: 1600-1900 Fri, 1500-1900 Sat (except Show days). By appt on other days.
MAIL ORDER: No
CAT. COST: 3 x 1st class *W/SALE or RETAIL:* Retail
SPECIALITIES: Plants for rock garden, scree, troughs & borders. Lime tolerant hardy Alpines, Perennials & unusual plants. *MAP PAGE:* **5**

MBur **Burrows Roses, Meadow Croft, Spondon Road, Dale Abbey, Derby, Derbyshire DE7 4PQ**
TEL: (0332) 668289 *CONTACT:* Stuart & Diane Burrows
OPENING TIMES: 0900-1700
MIN MAIL ORDER UK: £2.70 + p&p *MIN VALUE EC:* 1 plant + p&p
CAT. COST: 20p+1st class *W/SALE or RETAIL:* Retail
SPECIALITIES: Roses *MAP PAGE:* **7**

MCad **Caddick's Clematis Nurseries, Lymm Road, Thelwall, Warrington, Cheshire WA13 0UF**
TEL: (0925) 757196 *CONTACT:* H Caddick
◆ *OPENING TIMES:* 1000-1700 Tue-Sun 1st Feb-30th Nov. 1000-1700 Bank Hols.
MIN MAIL ORDER UK: £5.50 + p&p *MIN VALUE EC:* £5.50 + p&p
CAT. COST: £1.00 cheque/PO *W/SALE or RETAIL:* Both
SPECIALITIES: Clematis. *MAP PAGE:* **7/9**

MCas **Castle Alpines,** Castle Road, Wootton, Woodstock, Oxfordshire OX20 1EG
TEL: (0993) 812162 *CONTACT:* M S & F E Castle
OPENING TIMES: 1000-1700 Mon-Sat Mar 1-Sep 30. Appt only Oct 1-Feb 28.
MAIL ORDER: No
CAT. COST: 3 x 2nd class *W/SALE or RETAIL:* Retail
SPECIALITIES: Alpines & Auriculas. *MAP PAGE:* **5**

MCed **Cedarwood Lily Farm,** 5 Meadowstyle Caravan Park, Newpool Road, Brownlees, Biddulph, Staffordhsire ST8 6AA
TEL: (0782) 519154 *CONTACT:* J & G Ambridge.
OPENING TIMES: Not open.
MAIL ORDER: Only*MIN MAIL ORDER UK:* See Cat. for details *MIN VALUE EC:* n/a
CAT. COST: 2 x 1st class *W/SALE or RETAIL:* Retail
SPECIALITIES: Lilies. Only dry bulbs.

MChe **Cheshire Herbs,** Fourfields, Forest Road, Nr Tarporley, Cheshire CW6 9ES
TEL: (0829) 760578 *FAX:* (0829) 760354 *CONTACT:* Mr & Mrs Ted Riddell
◆ *OPENING TIMES:* 1000-1700 daily 3rd Jan-24th Dec.
MAIL ORDER: No
CAT. COST: 20p *W/SALE or RETAIL:* Both
SPECIALITIES: Display Herb garden & Elizabethan knot garden. See also SEED Index. *MAP PAGE:* **7**

MCol **Collinwood Nurseries,** Mottram St. Andrew, Macclesfield, Cheshire SK10 4QR
TEL: (0625) 582272 *CONTACT:* A Wright
OPENING TIMES: 0830-1800 Mon-Sat 1300-1800 Sun.
MIN MAIL ORDER UK: No minimum charge *MIN VALUE EC:* n/a
CAT. COST: Free *W/SALE or RETAIL:* Retail
SPECIALITIES: Chrysanthemums (Dendranthema). *MAP PAGE:* **7**

MDHE **DHE Plants,** Rose Lea, Darley House Estate, Darley Dale, Matlock, Derbyshire DE4 2QH
TEL: (0629) 732512 *CONTACT:* Peter M Smith
OPENING TIMES: By appt. only, essential to phone first.
MIN MAIL ORDER UK: No minimum charge *MIN VALUE EC:* n/a
CAT. COST: 2 x 1st class *W/SALE or RETAIL:* Retail
SPECIALITIES: Alpines; esp. Helianthemum, Saxifraga & Sisyrinchium. NOTE: Nursery will be moving, please check first by phone. *MAP PAGE:* **7**

MFie **Field House Nurseries, Leake Road, Gotham, Nottingham NG11 0JN**
TEL: (0602) 830278 *CONTACT:* Doug Lochhead & Valerie A Woolley
OPENING TIMES: 0900-1700 Fri-Wed or by appt.
MIN MAIL ORDER UK: No minimum charge *MIN VALUE EC:* Nmc *EXPORT:* Yes
CAT. COST: 4 x 1st class *W/SALE or RETAIL:* Retail
SPECIALITIES: Auriculas, Primulas, Alpines & Rock plants. *NOTE: Mail Order for Auriculas, Primulas & Seeds ONLY. *MAP PAGE:* **7**

MFir **The Firs Nursery,** Chelford Road, Henbury, Macclesfield, Cheshire SK10 3LH
TEL: (0625) 426422 *CONTACT:* Fay J Bowling
OPENING TIMES: 1000-1700 Mon, Tue, Thu, Fri, Sat Mar-Oct.
MAIL ORDER: No
CAT. COST: 2 x 1st class *W/SALE or RETAIL:* Retail
SPECIALITIES: Herbaceous Perennials, Alpines, Hebe, some unusual. *MAP PAGE:* **7**

MFos **Fosse Alpines, 33 Leicester Road, Countesthorpe, Leicestershire LE8 5QU**
TEL: (0533) 778237 *CONTACT:* T K West
OPENING TIMES: By appt. only
MIN MAIL ORDER UK: £8.00 + p&p *MIN VALUE EC:* £8.00 + p&p
CAT. COST: 2 x 1st class *W/SALE or RETAIL:* Retail
SPECIALITIES: Alpines including specialist species in small quantities. *MAP PAGE:* **5**

MFry **Fryer's Nurseries Ltd., Manchester Road, Knutsford, Cheshire WA16 0SX**

TEL: (0565) 755455 *FAX:* (0565) 653755 *CONTACT:* Gareth Fryer
OPENING TIMES: 0900-1730 Mon-Sat & 1000-1730 Sun & Bank Hols.
MIN MAIL ORDER UK: No minimum charge *MIN VALUE EC:* Nmc *EXPORT:* Yes
CAT. COST: Free *W/SALE or RETAIL:* Both
SPECIALITIES: Extensive Rose Nursery & Garden Centre producing over half a million bushes annually. Rose fields in bloom Jun-Oct. *MAP PAGE:* **7**

MGan **Gandy's (Roses) Ltd., North Kilworth, Nr Lutterworth, Leicestershire LE17 6HZ**

TEL: (0858) 880398 *CONTACT:* Miss R D Gandy
OPENING TIMES: 0900-1700 Mon-Sat & 1400-1700 Sun.
MIN MAIL ORDER UK: No minimum charge *MIN VALUE EC:* £25.00 + p&p
CAT. COST: Free *W/SALE or RETAIL:* Both
SPECIALITIES: 580 Rose varieties. *MAP PAGE:* **5/7**

MGos **Goscote Nurseries Ltd, Syston Road, Cossington, Leicestershire LE7 4UZ**

TEL: (0509) 812121 *CONTACT:* D C & R C Cox
◆ *OPENING TIMES:* 0800-1630 Mon-Fri, 0900-1630 Sat, 1000-1630 Sun.
MIN MAIL ORDER UK: £10.00 + p&p *MIN VALUE EC:* £50.00 + p&p
CAT. COST: 4 x 2nd class *W/SALE or RETAIL:* Retail
SPECIALITIES: Rhododendrons, Azaleas, Trees, Shrubs, Heathers, Conifers, Alpines, Herbaceous. Especially Ericaceae. *MAP PAGE:* **7**

MHay **F Haynes & Partners Ltd.,** (Off.) 56 Gordon Street, Kettering, Northamptonshire NN16 0RX

TEL: (0536) 519836 *CONTACT:* Mr Maple
OPENING TIMES: 0800-1530 daily.
MIN MAIL ORDER UK: No minimum charge *MIN VALUE EC:* n/a
CAT. COST: Free *W/SALE or RETAIL:* Both
SPECIALITIES: Roses, especially exhibition & miniature. NOTE: Nursery at Drayton Road, Lowick, Nr Thrapston. *MAP PAGE:* **6/8**

MHel **Heldon Nurseries, Ashbourne Road, Spath, Uttoxeter, Staffordshire ST14 5AD**

TEL: (0889) 563377 *CONTACT:* Mrs J H Tate
OPENING TIMES: 1000-sunset daily.
MIN MAIL ORDER UK: £2.00 + p&p *MIN VALUE EC:* £50.00 + p&p *EXPORT:* Yes
CAT. COST: Free *W/SALE or RETAIL:* Retail
SPECIALITIES: Carnivorous plants, Cactus & Succulents. *MAP PAGE:* **7**

MHew **Hewthorn Herbs & Wild Flowers,, Simkins Farm, Adbolton Lane, West Bridgford, Nottingham NG2 5AS**

TEL: (0602) 812861 *CONTACT:* Julie Scott
OPENING TIMES: Most weekdays during school term & some weekends. Please phone first.
MIN MAIL ORDER UK: No minimum charge *MIN VALUE EC:* £10.00 + p&p
CAT. COST: 3 x 1st class *W/SALE or RETAIL:* Retail
SPECIALITIES: Native Wild flowers for Butterfly gardens, Bees & Wildlife ponds. Culinary & Aromatic Herbs, Dye plants, native Medicinals. All organically grown. *MAP PAGE:* **5**

MHFP **Hill Farmhouse Plants,** Hill Farmhouse, Cottingham, Market Harborough, Leicestershire LE16 8XS

TEL: (0536) 770994 *CONTACT:* R Cain
OPENING TIMES: 0930-1800 Sats only from 1st Mar-31st Jul & 1st Sep-30th Sep. Other times by appt.
MAIL ORDER: No
CAT. COST: 2 x 1st class *W/SALE or RETAIL:* Retail
SPECIALITIES: Geraniums & Cottage Garden plants. *MAP PAGE:* **7/8**

MHig **Highgates Nursery,** 166a Crich Lane, Belper, Derbyshire DE56 1EP

TEL: (0773) 822153 *CONTACT:* R E & D I Straughan
OPENING TIMES: 1030-1630 Mon-Sat mid Mar-mid Oct. Closed Sun.
MAIL ORDER: No
CAT. COST: 2 x 1st class *W/SALE or RETAIL:* Retail
SPECIALITIES: Alpines. *MAP PAGE:* **7**

MHlr **The Hiller Garden,** Dunnington, Nr Alcester, Warwickshire B49 5PD

TEL: (0789) 772771 *FAX:* (0789) 490439 *CONTACT:* Gardener-in-charge
OPENING TIMES: 1000-1730 daily.
MAIL ORDER: No
CAT. COST: 2 x 1st class *W/SALE or RETAIL:* Retail
SPECIALITIES: One acre display garden devoted to Herbaceous Perennials. All plants available for sale during the season. *MAP PAGE:* **5**

MHul **Diana Hull, Fog Cottages, 178 Lower Street, Hillmorton, Rugby, Warwickshire CV21 4NX**

TEL: (0788) 536574 after 1600 *CONTACT:* Diana Hull
OPENING TIMES: By appt. only.
MIN MAIL ORDER UK: No minimum charge *MIN VALUE EC:* Nmc
CAT. COST: Sae for list *W/SALE or RETAIL:* Retail
SPECIALITIES: Pelargonium species. See also SEED Index. *MAP PAGE:* **5**

MJac **Jackson's Nurseries,** Clifton Campville, Nr Tamworth, Staffordshire B79 0AP

TEL: (0827) 373307 *CONTACT:* N Jackson
OPENING TIMES: 0900-1800 Mon Wed-Sat, 1000-1700 Sun.
MAIL ORDER: No
CAT. COST: 2 x 1st class *W/SALE or RETAIL:* Both
SPECIALITIES: Fuchsia. *MAP PAGE:* **7**

MJon **C & K Jones, Golden Fields Nurseries, Barrow Lane, Tarvin, Cheshire CH3 8JF**

TEL: (0829) 740663 *FAX:* (0829) 741877 *CONTACT:* Keith Jones/P Woolley
OPENING TIMES: 0800-1700 daily Mar-Sep, 0900-1600 daily Oct-Feb.
MIN MAIL ORDER UK: 1 plant + p&p *MIN VALUE EC:* 1 plant + p&p *EXPORT:* Yes
CAT. COST: £1.00 *W/SALE or RETAIL:* Both
SPECIALITIES: Roses. *MAP PAGE:* **7**

MLab **Laburnum Nurseries, (Off.) 6 Manor House Gardens, Main Street, Humberstone Village, Leicestershire LE5 1AE**

TEL: (0533) 766522 *CONTACT:* Mr W Johnson
OPENING TIMES: 0900-1600 Mon-Sat 0900-1200 Sat & Sun.
MIN MAIL ORDER UK: No minimum charge *MIN VALUE EC:* Nmc *EXPORT:* Yes
CAT. COST: 1 x 2nd class *W/SALE or RETAIL:* Both
SPECIALITIES: Fuchsia. NOTE: Nursery at Humberstone, Leicester. *MAP PAGE:* **7**

MLea **Lea Rhododendron Gardens Ltd., Lea, Matlock, Derbyshire DE4 5GH**

TEL: (0629 534) 380/260 *FAX:* (0629 534) 260 *CONTACT:* Jon Tye
OPENING TIMES: 1000-1900 daily.
MIN MAIL ORDER UK: £15.00 + p&p *MIN VALUE EC:* £15.00 + p&p *EXPORT:* Yes
CAT. COST: 30p + Sae *W/SALE or RETAIL:* Retail
SPECIALITIES: Rhododendron, Azalea & Kalmia. *MAP PAGE:* **7**

MMat **Mattock's Roses, The Rose Nurseries, Nuneham Courtenay, Oxford, Oxfordshire OX44 9PY**

TEL: (0865) 343265 *FAX:* (0865) 343267 *CONTACT:* Mr Mark W Mattock
OPENING TIMES: 0900-1730 Mon-Sat, 1030-1730 Sun. Closes 1700 Nov-Feb.
MIN MAIL ORDER UK: No minimum charge *MIN VALUE EC:* £100.00 + p&p *EXPORT:* Yes
CAT. COST: Free *W/SALE or RETAIL:* Both
SPECIALITIES: Roses. *MAP PAGE:* **5**

MMea **Mears Ashby Nurseries Ltd.,** Glebe House, Glebe Road, Mears Ashby, Northamptonshire NN6 0DL

TEL: (0604) 812371/811811 *FAX:* (0604) 812353 *CONTACT:* John B & J E Gaggini
◆ *OPENING TIMES:* 0800-1700 Mon-Fri (Wholesale & Retail). 0930-1730 Sat & Sun (Retail only).
MAIL ORDER: No *EXPORT:* Yes
CAT. COST: £1.50 + 24p* *W/SALE or RETAIL:* Both
SPECIALITIES: Specialist growers of container Trees, Shrubs, Conifers & Fruit, esp. Wisteria. *NOTE: Please state Retail or W/sale Catalogue. *MAP PAGE:* **5/6**

MMil **Mill Hill Plants,** Mill Hill House, Elston Lane, East Stoke, Newark, Nottinghamshire NG23 5QJ
TEL: (0636) 525460 *CONTACT:* G M Gregory
◆ *OPENING TIMES:* 1000-1800 Wed-Sun & Bank Hols Mar-Oct & by appt.
MAIL ORDER: No
CAT. COST: 3 x 1st class *W/SALE or RETAIL:* Retail
SPECIALITIES: General range. *MAP PAGE:* **7**

MMor **F Morrey & Sons,** Forest Nursery, Kelsall, Tarporley, Cheshire CW6 0SW
TEL: (0829) 751342 *FAX:* (0829) 752449 *CONTACT:* D F Morrey
OPENING TIMES: 0830-1730 Mon-Sat.
MAIL ORDER: No
CAT. COST: 20p *W/SALE or RETAIL:* Both
SPECIALITIES: Azaleas, Rhododendrons & ornamental Trees. *MAP PAGE:* **7**

MNes **Ness Gardens,** Univ. of Liverpool Bot. Gdns. Ness, Neston, South Wirral, Cheshire L64 4AY
TEL: 051-336 7769 *FAX:* 051-353 1004 *CONTACT:* D Maher
OPENING TIMES: 0930-1700 Mar-Oct, 1000-1600 Nov-Feb daily.
MAIL ORDER: No
CAT. COST: None issued *W/SALE or RETAIL:* Retail
SPECIALITIES: Rhododendrons, Primula, Meconopsis & Penstemons. *MAP PAGE:* **7**

MNFA **The Nursery Further Afield,** Evenley Road, Mixbury, Nr Brackley, Northamptonshire NN13 5YR
TEL: (0280) 848539 eves. *CONTACT:* Gerald Sinclair
OPENING TIMES: 1000-1800 Wed-Sat & Bank Hol Mons 20th Mar-15th Oct. 1400-1800 1st Sun of Apr-Oct.
MAIL ORDER: No
CAT. COST: Sae *W/SALE or RETAIL:* Retail
SPECIALITIES: Hardy Perennials. *MAP PAGE:* **2**

MOke **Okell's Nurseries, Duddon Heath, Nr Tarporley, Cheshire CW6 0EP**
TEL: (0829) 741512 *FAX:* (0829) 741587 *CONTACT:* Gary & Donna Okell
OPENING TIMES: 0900-1730.
MIN MAIL ORDER UK: No minimum charge *MIN VALUE EC:* Nmc
CAT. COST: Free *W/SALE or RETAIL:* Both
SPECIALITIES: Heathers. NOTE: Rooted cuttings only by Mail Order. *MAP PAGE:* **7**

MPhe **Phedar Nursery, Bunkers Hill, Romiley, Stockport, Cheshire SK6 3DS**
TEL: (061 430) 3772 *FAX:* (061 430) 3772 *CONTACT:* Will McLewin
OPENING TIMES: Frequent, esp. in Spring but irregular. Please telephone to arrange appt.
MIN MAIL ORDER UK: No minimum charge *MIN VALUE EC:* Nmc
CAT. COST: A5 Sae. *W/SALE or RETAIL:* Both
SPECIALITIES: Helleborus, Paeonia, Erythronium. See also SEED Index. *MAP PAGE:* **7/9**

MPit **Pitts Farm Nursery,** Shrewley, Warwick, Warwickshire CV35 7BB
TEL: (0926 84) 2737 *CONTACT:* Mrs J Farmer
OPENING TIMES: 1000-1800 daily.
MAIL ORDER: No
CAT. COST: Sae *W/SALE or RETAIL:* Retail
SPECIALITIES: Perennials & Bedding. *MAP PAGE:* **5**

MPla **E L F Plants Cramden Nursery Ltd.,** Harborough Road North, Northampton, Northamptonshire NN2 8LU
TEL: (0604) 846246 Eve. *CONTACT:* E L Fincham-Nichols
◆ *OPENING TIMES:* 1000-1700 Thu-Sat ex Dec & Jan.
MAIL ORDER: No
CAT. COST: 3 x 1st class *W/SALE or RETAIL:* Retail
SPECIALITIES: Dwarf and slow growing Shrubs & Conifers, many unusual. Some Alpines & Heathers. *MAP PAGE:* **5**

MRav Ravensthorpe Nursery, 6 East Haddon Road, Ravensthorpe, Northamptonshire NN6 8ES
TEL: (0604) 770548 *CONTACT:* Jean & Richard Wiseman
OPENING TIMES: 1000-1800 (dusk if earlier) Tue-Sun. Also Bank Hol Mons.
MIN MAIL ORDER UK: No minimum charge *MIN VALUE EC:* Nmc
CAT. COST: 4 x 1st class *W/SALE or RETAIL:* Retail
SPECIALITIES: Over 1,600 different Trees, Shrubs, & Perennials with many unusual varieties. Search & delivery service for large orders - winter months only. *MAP PAGE:* **5**

MRil Rileys' Chrysanthemums, Alfreton Nurseries, Woolley Moor, Alfreton, Derbyshire DE55 6FF
TEL: (0246) 590320 *CONTACT:* C A & G K Riley
OPENING TIMES: 0900-1700 Mon-Fri, Mail Order only. 0900-1700 Sun Feb-May, collection only. 0900-1600 Sun in Sep.
MIN MAIL ORDER UK: No minimum charge *MIN VALUE EC:* Nmc
CAT. COST: 25p *W/SALE or RETAIL:* Both
SPECIALITIES: Chrysanthemum. *MAP PAGE:* **7**

MRob Robinson's of Whaley Bridge, 20 Vaughan Road, Whaley Bridge, Stockport Cheshire SK12 7JT
TEL: (0663) 732991 *CONTACT:* J & D Robinson
OPENING TIMES: By appt. only.
MIN MAIL ORDER UK: No minimum charge *MIN VALUE EC:* Nmc *EXPORT:* Yes
CAT. COST: 3 x 1st class *W/SALE or RETAIL:* Retail
SPECIALITIES: Violets, Iris & Auriculas.

MRPP R P P Alpines, 6 Bentley Road, Bushbury, Wolverhampton West Midlands WV10 8DZ
TEL: (0902) 784508 *CONTACT:* R Smallwood
◆ *OPENING TIMES:* 1000-1700 Tue-Sat, 1200-1700 Sun.
MIN MAIL ORDER UK: £10.00 + p&p *MIN VALUE EC:* n/a
CAT. COST: 30p + 1x2nd class *W/SALE or RETAIL:* Retail
SPECIALITIES: Choice plants from the mountains of Europe, Himalaya, Greece, New Zealand & America. Dwarf Conifers. *MAP PAGE:* **7**

MRui Andrew de Ruiter (Rose Specialist), 9 Ingersley Road, Bollington, Cheshire SK10 5RE
TEL: (0625) 574389* *CONTACT:* Andrew de Ruiter
OPENING TIMES: By appt.
MIN MAIL ORDER UK: No minimum charge *MIN VALUE EC:* Nmc
CAT. COST: 2 x 2nd class *W/SALE or RETAIL:* Both
SPECIALITIES: Roses, esp. Miniature, also good range of English Roses. *NOTE: Only available before 1000 or after 1700.

MSal Salley Gardens, Flat 3, 3 Millicent Road, West Bridgford, Nottingham NG2 7LD
TEL: (0602) 821366 evngs *CONTACT:* Richard Lewin
OPENING TIMES: Mail Order only.
MAIL ORDER: Only*MIN MAIL ORDER UK:* Nmc *MIN VALUE EC:* Nmc *EXPORT:* Yes
CAT. COST: Sae *W/SALE or RETAIL:* Retail
SPECIALITIES: Medicinal plants, esp. from North America & China. Dye plants. See also SEED Index.

MSmi John Smith & Son, Hilltop Nurseries, Thornton, Leicestershire LE67 1AN
TEL: (0530) 230331 *FAX:* (0530) 230331 *CONTACT:* J Smith
OPENING TIMES: 0800-1730 Mon-Sat.
MIN MAIL ORDER UK: No minimum charge *MIN VALUE EC:* n/a
CAT. COST: Sae *W/SALE or RETAIL:* Both
SPECIALITIES: Hardy & Half-hardy Fuchsia, dwarf Conifers, Heathers, Hardy Plants, Shrubs & Trees. *MAP PAGE:* **7**

MSta Stapeley Water Gardens Ltd, London Road, Stapeley, Nantwich, Cheshire CW5 7LH
TEL: (0270) 623868 *FAX:* (0270) 624919 *CONTACT:* Mr R G A Davies (Chairman)
◆ *OPENING TIMES:* 0900-1800 Mon-Fri, 1000-1800 Sat, 1000-1900 Sun & Bank Hols summer. 1000-1700 daily winter.
MIN MAIL ORDER UK: £15.00 + p&p *MIN VALUE EC:* Nmc *EXPORT:* Yes
CAT. COST: £1.00 *W/SALE or RETAIL:* Both
SPECIALITIES: World's largest Water Garden Centre. Full range of Hardy & Tropical Water Lilies, Aquatic, Bog & Poolside plants. Also large general stock. *MAP PAGE:* **7**

MSte **Steventon Road Nurseries,** Steventon Road, East Hanney, Wantage, Oxfordshire OX12 0HS
TEL: *CONTACT:* John Graham
OPENING TIMES: 1000-1600 Wed-Fri, 1000-1630 (dusk) Sat & Sun, 5th Mar-30th Oct 1994.
MAIL ORDER: No
CAT. COST: £1 refunded *W/SALE or RETAIL:* Both
SPECIALITIES: Insectivorous plants. Tender & hardy Perennials. *MAP PAGE:* **5**

MSto **Richard Stockwell, 64 Weardale Road, off Hucknall Road, Sherwood, Nottingham NG5 1DD**
TEL: (0602) 691063* *CONTACT:* Richard Stockwell
◆ *OPENING TIMES:* Any time, by appt., for collection of postal or telephone orders only.
MIN MAIL ORDER UK: No minimum charge *MIN VALUE EC:* Nmc *EXPORT:* SO
CAT. COST: Free *W/SALE or RETAIL:* Retail
SPECIALITIES: Very rare climbing species, also dwarf species. Available in small numbers. See also SEED Index. *NOTE 0115-969 1063 after April 16th 1995. *MAP PAGE:* **7**

MS&S **S & S Perennials,** 24 Main Street, Normanton Le Heath, Leicestershire LE6 1TB
TEL: (0530) 262250 *CONTACT:* Shirley Pierce
OPENING TIMES: 0900-1730 daily.
MAIL ORDER: No
CAT. COST: Sae *W/SALE or RETAIL:* Retail
SPECIALITIES: Erythronium, Fritillaria, hardy Cyclamen, Lilies, Iris, dwarf Narcissus & Hepatica. *MAP PAGE:* **7**

MTho **A & A Thorp,** Bungalow No 5, Main Street, Theddingworth, Leicestershire LE17 6QZ
TEL: (0858) 880496 *CONTACT:* Anita & Andrew Thorp
OPENING TIMES: Dawn to Dusk all year.
MAIL ORDER: No
CAT. COST: 50p + Sae *W/SALE or RETAIL:* Retail
SPECIALITIES: Unusual plants or those in short supply. *MAP PAGE:* **5/7**

MTol **Tollgate Cottage Nursery, Ladbroke, Leamington Spa, Warwickshire CV33 0BY**
TEL: (0926) 814020 *CONTACT:* Brenda Timms
OPENING TIMES: 1100-1700 Fri, Sat & Sun Mar-mid Oct & Bank Hol Mons. Closed 22nd Aug-11th Sep.
MIN MAIL ORDER UK: No minimum charge *MIN VALUE EC:* Nmc
CAT. COST: 2 x 1st class *W/SALE or RETAIL:* Retail
SPECIALITIES: Hardy Herbaceous, some unusual. *MAP PAGE:* **5**

MUlv **Ulverscroft Grange Nursery,** Priory Lane, Ulverscroft, Markfield, Leicestershire LE67 9PB
TEL: (0530) 243635 *CONTACT:* Ted Brown
OPENING TIMES: From 1000 Wed-Sun Mar-Nov. Other times by appt.
MAIL ORDER: No
CAT. COST: None issued *W/SALE or RETAIL:* Both
SPECIALITIES: Herbaceous & Shrubs, many unusual *MAP PAGE:* **7**

MWar **Ward Fuchsias,** 5 Pollen Close, Sale, Cheshire M33 3LP
TEL: (061973) 6467 *CONTACT:* K Ward
OPENING TIMES: 0930-1800 Tue-Sun Feb-Jun incl Bank Hols.
MIN MAIL ORDER UK: No minimum charge *MIN VALUE EC:* n/a
CAT. COST: Free* *W/SALE or RETAIL:* Retail
SPECIALITIES: Fuchsia. *Includes cultural leaflet. *MAP PAGE:* **7/9**

MWat **Waterperry Gardens Ltd.,** Waterperry, Nr Wheatley, Oxfordshire OX33 1JZ
TEL: (0844) 339226/254 *FAX:* (0844) 339883 *CONTACT:* Miss S Elliott
OPENING TIMES: 1000-1730 Mon-Fri, 1000-1800 Sat & Sun Summer. 1000-1700 Winter.
MAIL ORDER: No
CAT. COST: 35p *W/SALE or RETAIL:* Retail
SPECIALITIES: General plus National Reference Collection of Saxifraga Porophyllum. *MAP PAGE:* **5**

MWBu Wilford Bulb Co. Ltd., 69 Main Street, East Leake, Leicestershire LE12 6PF

TEL: (0509) 852905 *FAX:* (0509) 852905 *CONTACT:* Tony Cross
OPENING TIMES: 0900-1700 Mon-Sat.
MIN MAIL ORDER UK: £10.00 + p&p *MIN VALUE EC:* £10.00 + p&p *EXPORT:* Yes
CAT. COST: 2 x 1st class *W/SALE or RETAIL:* Retail
SPECIALITIES: Lilies & wide range of speciality Bulbs. See also SEED Index. *MAP PAGE:* **7**

MWhe A D & N Wheeler, Pye Court, Willoughby, Rugby, Warwickshire CV23 8BZ

TEL: (0788) 890341 *CONTACT:* Mrs N Wheeler
OPENING TIMES: 1000-1630 1st Oct-1st Jun. 1st Jun-1st Oct please phone first for appt.
MIN MAIL ORDER UK: £4.50 + p&p *MIN VALUE EC:* n/a
CAT. COST: 2 x 1st class *W/SALE or RETAIL:* Retail
SPECIALITIES: Fuchsia & Pelargonium. *MAP PAGE:* **5**

MWil The Wildlife Gardening Centre, Witney Road, Kingston Bagpuize, Abingdon, Oxfordshire OX13 5AN

TEL: (0865) 821660 *CONTACT:* Jenny Steel & Alan Pottinger
◆ *OPENING TIMES:* Please ring for opening times.
MIN MAIL ORDER UK: No minimum charge *MIN VALUE EC:* n/a
CAT. COST: 3 x 1st class *W/SALE or RETAIL:* Both
SPECIALITIES: Native Wild Flowers & Shrubs, Cottage garden plants, Herbs & native Trees.
MAP PAGE: **5**

MWol H Woolman Ltd, Grange Road, Dorridge, Solihull, West Midlands B93 8QB

TEL: (0564) 776283 *FAX:* (0564) 770830 *CONTACT:* John Woolman
OPENING TIMES: 0730-1615 Mon-Fri.
MIN MAIL ORDER UK: No minimum charge *MIN VALUE EC:* Nmc *EXPORT:* Yes
CAT. COST: Free *W/SALE or RETAIL:* Both
SPECIALITIES: Chrysanthemum. *MAP PAGE:* **5**

MWoo Woodfield Bros, Wood End, Clifford Chambers, Stratford-on-Avon, Warwickshire CV37 8HR

TEL: (0789) 205618 *CONTACT:* B Woodfield
OPENING TIMES: 1000-1630 Mon-Fri, 1000-1600 Sat & 0900-1200 Sun for plant collection ONLY.
MIN MAIL ORDER UK: See list for details *MIN VALUE EC:* n/a
CAT. COST: Sae *W/SALE or RETAIL:* Both
SPECIALITIES: Carnations, Lupins & Delphiniums. UK Mail Order for Carnations only.
MAP PAGE: **5**

MYat R J Yates, The Gardens, Roecliffe Manor, Woodhouse Eaves, Leicestershire LE12 8TN

TEL: (0533) 303422 *CONTACT:* R J Yates
OPENING TIMES: 0930-1630 Sat & Sun only.
MIN MAIL ORDER UK: £10.00 + p&p *MIN VALUE EC:* £20.00 + p&p
CAT. COST: Large Sae *W/SALE or RETAIL:* Retail
SPECIALITIES: Primulas & Kabschia Saxifrages. *MAP PAGE:* **7**

NBar Barkers Primrose Nurseries & Grdn Cntr, Whalley Road, Clitheroe, Lancashire BB7 1HT

TEL: (0200) 23521 *FAX:* (0200) 28160 *CONTACT:* W or N Barker
◆ *OPENING TIMES:* 0830-1730 Mon-Sat, 1000-1700 Sun.
MAIL ORDER: No
CAT. COST: 3 x 2nd class *W/SALE or RETAIL:* Retail
SPECIALITIES: Uncommon Trees & Shrubs, Roses, Perennials etc. *MAP PAGE:* **9**

NBat Battersby Roses, Peartree Cottage, Old Battersby, Great Ayton, Cleveland TS9 6LU

TEL: (0642) 723402 *CONTACT:* Eric & Avril Stainthorpe
OPENING TIMES: 1000-dusk most days.
MAIL ORDER: No
CAT. COST: Sae *W/SALE or RETAIL:* Both
SPECIALITIES: Exhibition Roses. *MAP PAGE:* **9**

NBea **Beamish Clematis Nursery,,** Burntwood Cottage, Stoney Lane, Beamish, Co Durham DH9 0SJ
TEL: (091) 3700202 *CONTACT:* C F Brown
OPENING TIMES: 0900-1700 Mon-Sat Feb-Oct.
MAIL ORDER: No
CAT. COST: None issued *W/SALE or RETAIL:* Both
SPECIALITIES: 180 varieties of Clematis. *MAP PAGE:* **9/10**

NBee **Beechcroft Nurseries, Bongate, Appleby-in-Westmorland, Cumbria CA16 6UE**
TEL: (07683) 51201 *FAX:* (07683) 52546 *CONTACT:* Roger Brown
OPENING TIMES: 0800-1800 Mon-Sat, 1100-1800 Sun.
MIN MAIL ORDER UK: No minimum charge *MIN VALUE EC:* n/n
CAT. COST: £2. Tree list Sae *W/SALE or RETAIL:* Retail
SPECIALITIES: Hardy field-grown Trees & Shrubs. Mail Order Trees Nov-Mar only. *MAP PAGE:* **9**

NBir **Birkheads Cottage Garden Nursery,** Birkheads Lane, Nr Sunniside, Newcastle upon Tyne, Tyne & Wear NE16 5EL
TEL: (0207) 232262 *FAX:* (0207) 232262 *CONTACT:* Mrs Christine Liddle
OPENING TIMES: 1000-1800 Sat & Sun & Bank Hols Apr-mid Oct & by appt.
MAIL ORDER: No
CAT. COST: None issued *W/SALE or RETAIL:* Retail
SPECIALITIES: Allium, Campanula, Digitalis, Euphorbia, Hardy Geraniums, Meconopsis, Primula & Herbs. *MAP PAGE:* **10**

NBra **Brambling House Alpines,** 119 Sheffield Road, Warmsworth, Doncaster, South Yorkshire DN4 9QX
TEL: (0302) 850730 *CONTACT:* Tony & Jane McDonagh
OPENING TIMES: 0900-dusk Tue-Sun.
MIN MAIL ORDER UK: £3.20 + p&p *MIN VALUE EC:* n/a
CAT. COST: Large Sae *W/SALE or RETAIL:* Retail
SPECIALITIES: Auriculas, Diascia, Saxifraga, Lewisia, Sempervivum (over 150 varieties). Unusual Alpine House plants. *MAP PAGE:* **9**

NBrk **T H Barker & Sons,** Baines Paddock Nursery, Haverthwaite, Ulverston, Cumbria LA12 8PF
TEL: (05395) 58236 *CONTACT:* W E Thornley
◆ *OPENING TIMES:* 0930-1730 Wed-Mon Mar-Oct & by appt.
MIN MAIL ORDER UK: 2 plants + p&p *MIN VALUE EC:* n/a
CAT. COST: 3 x 1st class *W/SALE or RETAIL:* Retail
SPECIALITIES: Clematis & Cottage garden plants. *MAP PAGE:* **9**

NBro **Brownthwaite Hardy Plants,** Fell Yeat, Casterton, Kirkby Lonsdale, Lancashire LA6 2JW
TEL: (05242) 71340 *CONTACT:* Chris Benson
OPENING TIMES: Tue-Sun 1st Apr-31st Oct.
MIN MAIL ORDER UK: No minimum charge *MIN VALUE EC:* n/a
CAT. COST: 2 x 1st class *W/SALE or RETAIL:* Retail
SPECIALITIES: Herbaceous Perennials & Grasses. *MAP PAGE:* **9**

NCat **Catforth Gardens,** Roots Lane, Catforth, Preston, Lancashire PR4 0JB
TEL: (0772) 690561/690269 *CONTACT:* Judith Bradshaw & Chris Moore
OPENING TIMES: 1030-1700 19th Mar-Sep 1994.
MAIL ORDER: No
CAT. COST: 4 x 1st class *W/SALE or RETAIL:* Retail
SPECIALITIES: National Collection of Hardy Geraniums. Also many other unusual herbaceous incl. Campanula, Euphorbia, Pulmonaria & Viola. *MAP PAGE:* **9**

NCra **Craven's Nursery, 1 Foulds Terrace, Bingley, West Yorkshire BD16 4LZ**
TEL: (0274) 561412 *CONTACT:* S R Craven & M Craven
OPENING TIMES: Mail Order only
MAIL ORDER: Only*MIN MAIL ORDER UK:* £10.00 + p&p *MIN VALUE EC:* £50.00 + p&p
CAT. COST: £1.00 *W/SALE or RETAIL:* Both
SPECIALITIES: Show Auricula, Primula, Pinks, Alpines and specialist Seeds.

NDea **Deanswood Plants,** Pottteries Lane, Littlethorpe, Ripon, North Yorkshire HG4 3LF

TEL: (0765) 603441 *CONTACT:* Jacky Barber
OPENING TIMES: 1000-1700 Tue-Sun 1st Apr-30th Sep.
MAIL ORDER: No
CAT. COST: £1.30 *W/SALE or RETAIL:* Retail
SPECIALITIES: Pond, Marginals & Bog plants. *MAP PAGE:* **9**

NEgg **Eggleston Hall,** Barnard Castle, Co Durham DL12 0AG

TEL: (0833) 650403/378 *CONTACT:* Mrs R H Gray
OPENING TIMES: 1000-1700 daily
MAIL ORDER: No
CAT. COST: £1.50 + Sae *W/SALE or RETAIL:* Retail
SPECIALITIES: Rare & Unusual plants with particular emphasis to Flower Arrangers. *MAP PAGE:* **9**

NElm **Elm Ridge Gardens Ltd.,** Coniscliffe Road, Darlington, Co Durham DL3 8DJ

TEL: (0325) 462710 *CONTACT:* Mr C Blake & M Blake
OPENING TIMES: 0800-1830 Mon-Sat Apr-Jul, 0800-1730 Aug-Mar.
MAIL ORDER: No
CAT. COST: Free *W/SALE or RETAIL:* Both
SPECIALITIES: Very large selection of Pot Plants for home & industry, bedding plants, cut flowers & floristry. *MAP PAGE:* **9**

NFai **Fairy Lane Nurseries,** Fairy Lane, Sale, Greater Manchester M33 2JT

TEL: 061-905 1137 *CONTACT:* John B Coxon
OPENING TIMES: 1000-1730 daily Summer, 1000-1630 daily Winter. Closed 19th Dec-2nd Jan 1995.
MAIL ORDER: No
CAT. COST: None issued *W/SALE or RETAIL:* Retail
SPECIALITIES: Hardy & tender Perennials, Herbs, Hebes & less usual Shrubs. *MAP PAGE:* **7/9**

NGar **Gardenscape, Fairview, Summerbridge, Nr Harrogate, North Yorkshire HG3 4DH**

TEL: (0423) 780291 *CONTACT:* Michael D Myers
OPENING TIMES: By appt only. Mail Order predominantly.
MIN MAIL ORDER UK: No minimum charge *MIN VALUE EC:* £10.00 + p&p
CAT. COST: 3 x 2nd class *W/SALE or RETAIL:* Both
SPECIALITIES: National Collections of Wood Anemones, Hepaticas & Primula marginata. Also Galanthus, hardy Orchids, Ferns. dwarf Bulbs, Grasses &uncommon plants. *MAP PAGE:* **9**

NGre **Greenslacks Nurseries, Ocot Lane, Scammonden, Huddersfield, Yorkshire HD3 3FR**

TEL: (0484) 842584 *CONTACT:* Mrs V K Tuton
OPENING TIMES: 1000-1600 Wed-Sun 1st Mar-31st Oct.
MIN MAIL ORDER UK: No minimum charge *MIN VALUE EC:* £20.00 + p&p *EXPORT:* Yes
CAT. COST: £1.00 or 2IRCs *W/SALE or RETAIL:* Both
SPECIALITIES: Unusual & Hardy plants esp. Succulents *MAP PAGE:* **9**

NHal **Halls of Heddon, (Off.) West Heddon Nurseries, Heddon-on-the-Wall, Newcastle-upon-Tyne, Northumberland NE15 0JS**

TEL: (0661) 852445 *CONTACT:* Judith Lockey
OPENING TIMES: 0900-1700 Mon-Sat 1000-1700 Sun.
MIN MAIL ORDER UK: No minimum charge *MIN VALUE EC:* £25.00 + p&p* *EXPORT:* Yes
CAT. COST: 2 x 2nd class *W/SALE or RETAIL:* Retail
SPECIALITIES: Chrysanthemum & Dahlia. Wide range of Herbaceous. *NOTE: Mail Order Dahlia & Chrysanthemum only, EC & Export Dahlia tubers ONLY. *MAP PAGE:* **10**

NHar **Hartside Nursery Garden, Nr Alston, Cumbria CA9 3BL**

TEL: (0434) 381372 *CONTACT:* S L & N Huntley
OPENING TIMES: 0900-1700 Mon-Fri, 1000-1600 Sat & B/hols, 1230-1600 Sun 1st Mar-31st Oct. 1st Nov-28th Feb by appt.
MIN MAIL ORDER UK: No minimum charge *MIN VALUE EC:* Nmc
CAT. COST: 4 x 2nd class *W/SALE or RETAIL:* Retail
SPECIALITIES: Alpines grown at altitude of 1100 feet in Pennines. *MAP PAGE:* **9/10**

NHed Hedgerow Nursery, 24 Braithwaite Edge Road, Keighley, West Yorkshire BD22 6RA
TEL: (0535) 606531 *CONTACT:* Nigel Hutchinson
OPENING TIMES: 0900-dusk Wed-Sun & Bank Hols.
MIN MAIL ORDER UK: No minimum charge *MIN VALUE EC:* Nmc
CAT. COST: 3 x 2nd class *W/SALE or RETAIL:* Retail
SPECIALITIES: NCCPG Collection of dwarf Hebe. Saxifraga, Primula, Rhododendrons, & Conifers.
MAP PAGE: **9**

NHex Hexham Herbs, Chesters Walled Garden, Chollerford, Hexham Northumberland NE46
TEL: (0434) 681 483 *CONTACT:* Susie & Kevin White
◆ *OPENING TIMES:* 1000-1700 Easter-Oct daily. Please phone for Winter opening times.
MAIL ORDER: No
CAT. COST: £1.50 inc. p&p *W/SALE or RETAIL:* Retail
SPECIALITIES: Extensive range of Herbs & National Collection of Thymus & Origanum. Unusual Perennials & Wild Flowers. *MAP PAGE:* **10**

NHHG Hardstoft Herb Garden,, Hall View Cottage, Hardstoft, Pilsley, Nr Chesterfield, Derbyshire S45 8AH
TEL: (0246) 854268 *CONTACT:* Lynne & Steve Raynor
OPENING TIMES: 1000-1800 daily, 1st Mar-30th Sep.
MAIL ORDER: No
CAT. COST: Free *W/SALE or RETAIL:* Retail
SPECIALITIES: Very wide range of Herb Plants. Over 40 Lavenders & 12 Rosemary. Scented Pelargoniums. *MAP PAGE:* **7**

NHip Hippopottering Nursery, Orchard House, Brackenhill Road, Haxey, Nr Doncaster, South Yorkshire DN9 2LR
TEL: (0427) 752185 *CONTACT:* John Gibbons
OPENING TIMES: By appt. only.
MIN MAIL ORDER UK: £15.00 + p&p *MIN VALUE EC:* £15.00 + p&p
CAT. COST: 2 x 1st class *W/SALE or RETAIL:* Retail
SPECIALITIES: Uncommon grafted Acer palmatum & japonicum cultivars. Selected Acer seedlings. Bonsai starters, mature trees, mixed seed with cultural instructions. *MAP PAGE:* **7**

NHlc Halecat Garden Nurseries, Witherslack, Grange over Sands, Cumbria LA11 6RU
TEL: (044 852) 229 *CONTACT:* Mrs M Stanley
◆ *OPENING TIMES:* 0900-1630 Mon-Fri, 1400-1600 Sun & parties by appointment.
MAIL ORDER: No
CAT. COST: 40p *W/SALE or RETAIL:* Retail
SPECIALITIES: Hosta, Hydrangea, Euphorbia, grey foliage and perenial border plants. *MAP PAGE:* **9**

NHol Holden Clough Nursery, Holden, Bolton-by-Bowland, Clitheroe, Lancashire BB7 4PF
TEL: (0200) 447 615* *CONTACT:* P J Foley
◆ *OPENING TIMES:* 1300-1630 Mon-Thu, 0900-1630 Sat all year. 1400-1630 Sun (Apr & May only incl Easter Sun)*.
MIN MAIL ORDER UK: No minimum charge *MIN VALUE EC:* Nmc *EXPORT:* Yes
CAT. COST: £1.20 *W/SALE or RETAIL:* Both
SPECIALITIES: Large general list incl. Primula, Saxifrage, Pulmonaria, Androsace, Astilbe, Gentiana & Hosta. See also SEED Index. *NOTE: Closed 24th Dec-2nd Jan 1995. *MAP PAGE:* **9**

NH&H Herb & Heather Centre, West Haddlesey, Nr Selby, North Yorkshire YO8 8QA
TEL: (0757) 228279 *CONTACT:* Carole Atkinson
OPENING TIMES: 0930-1730 daily Mar-Oct. 0930-dusk daily Nov-Feb.
MIN MAIL ORDER UK: £20.00 + p&p *MIN VALUE EC:* Nmc
CAT. COST: 3 x 1st class* *W/SALE or RETAIL:* Both
SPECIALITIES: 450 Herbs, 200 Heathers & 100 Conifers. *NOTE: Herb Catalogue & Heather Catalogue each 3 x 1st class stamps. National Collection of Santolina *MAP PAGE:* **9**

NJap The Japanese Garden Co., Spout House, Lupton, via Carnforth, Lancashire LA6 1PQ
TEL: (05395) 67802 *CONTACT:* Susan Gott
OPENING TIMES: Mail Order only.
MAIL ORDER: Only*MIN MAIL ORDER UK:* No minimum charge *MIN VALUE EC:* Nmc
CAT. COST: Sae for list *W/SALE or RETAIL:* Retail
SPECIALITIES: Primula, Acer, Bamboo, Herbaceous. Japanese garden design service. Booklet on design £3.75.

NKay **Reginald Kaye Ltd,** Waithman Nurseries, Silverdale, Carnforth, Lancashire LA5 0TY
TEL: (0524) 701252 *CONTACT:* Mrs L M Kaye
OPENING TIMES: 0800-1230 & 1400-1700 Mon-Fri all year. 1000-1230 & 1400-1700 Sat & 1430-1700 Sun Mar-Nov only.
MAIL ORDER: No
CAT. COST: 60p *W/SALE or RETAIL:* Both
SPECIALITIES: Hardy ferns, Alpines, Herbaceous, some Shrubs. *MAP PAGE:* **9**

NKin **Kingswood Pelargoniums, 113 Kingsway North, Clifton, Yorkshire YO3 6JH**
TEL: (0904) 636785 *CONTACT:* Ben & Jane Wood
◆ *OPENING TIMES:* All year incl. Bank Hols by appt. Please telephone between 0900-1700.
MIN MAIL ORDER UK: No minimum charge *MIN VALUE EC:* £10.00 + p&p
CAT. COST: 2 x 1st class *W/SALE or RETAIL:* Retail
SPECIALITIES: Miniature & Dwarf Zonal Pelargoniums. *MAP PAGE:* **9**

NLan **Landlife Wildflowers Ltd., The Old Police Station, Lark Lane, Liverpool, Lancashire L17 8UU**
TEL: (051) 728 7011 *FAX:* (051) 728 8413 *CONTACT:* Gillian Watson
OPENING TIMES: By appt for collection only.
MIN MAIL ORDER UK: No minimum charge *MIN VALUE EC:* Nmc
CAT. COST: Free *W/SALE or RETAIL:* Both
SPECIALITIES: Wild herbaceous plants. See also SEED Index. *MAP PAGE:* **7/9**

NLin **Lingholm Gardens,** Lingholm, Keswick, Cumbria CA12 5UA
TEL: (07687) 72003 Ext 17 *FAX:* (07687) 75213 *CONTACT:* Mr M J Swift
OPENING TIMES: 1000-1700 daily Apr-Oct. Nov-Mar by appt. only.
MAIL ORDER: No
CAT. COST: No retail cat. *W/SALE or RETAIL:* Both
SPECIALITIES: Meconopsis & Primula. Other unusual plants from the garden. *MAP PAGE:* **9**

NMar **J & D Marston,** Culag, Green Lane, Nafferton, Driffield, East Yorkshire YO25 0LF
TEL: (0377) 254487 *CONTACT:* J & D Marston
◆ *OPENING TIMES:* 1350-1700 Easter-mid Sep, Sat, Sun & other times by appt.
MIN MAIL ORDER UK: £15.00 + p&p *MIN VALUE EC:* n/a
CAT. COST: £1.00 *W/SALE or RETAIL:* Retail
SPECIALITIES: Hardy & Greenhouse Ferns only. *MAP PAGE:* **9**

NMen **Mendle Nursery, Holme, Scunthorpe, DN16 3RF**
TEL: (0724) 850864 *CONTACT:* Mrs A Earnshaw
OPENING TIMES: 1000-1800 daily
MIN MAIL ORDER UK: No minimum charge *MIN VALUE EC:* Nmc
CAT. COST: 2 x 1st class *W/SALE or RETAIL:* Retail
SPECIALITIES: Alpines esp. Saxifraga. *MAP PAGE:* **9**

NMGN **Markham Grange Nurseries,** Long Lands Lane, Brodsworth, Nr Doncaster, South Yorkshire DN5 7XB
TEL: (0302) 330430 *FAX:* (0302) 727571 *CONTACT:* Wayne Gollick
OPENING TIMES: 0900-1630 daily, later in summer.
MAIL ORDER: No
CAT. COST: *W/SALE or RETAIL:* Both
SPECIALITIES: Fuchsia. *MAP PAGE:* **9**

NMir **Mires Beck Nusery, Low Mill Lane, North Cave, Brough, North Humberside HU15 2NR**
TEL: (0430) 421543 *CONTACT:* Dr I G & R Tinklin
OPENING TIMES: 1000-1600 Wed-Sat, 1st Mar-31st Oct & by appt.
MIN MAIL ORDER UK: £15.00 + p&p *MIN VALUE EC:* £15.00 + p&p
CAT. COST: 3 x 1st class *W/SALE or RETAIL:* Both
SPECIALITIES: British native wild flower plants. Yorkshire-hardy border Perennials. *MAP PAGE:* **9**

NMos **Stanley Mossop, Boonwood Garden Centre, Gosforth, Seascale, Cumbria CA20 1BP**
TEL: (0946) 821817 *CONTACT:* Stanley & Gary Mossop.
OPENING TIMES: 1000-1700 daily.
MIN MAIL ORDER UK: No minimum charge *MIN VALUE EC:* £50.00 + p&p *EXPORT:* Yes
CAT. COST: Free *W/SALE or RETAIL:* Both
SPECIALITIES: Achimenes, Achimenantha, Eucodonia, Gloxinia (incl. species) & Smithiantha. *MAP PAGE:* **9**

NMun Muncaster Castle, Ravenglass, Cumbria CA18 1RQ

TEL: (0229) 717357 *FAX:* (0229) 717010 *CONTACT:* Susan Clark
OPENING TIMES: 1000-1700 daily 1st Mar-31st Oct. All other times by appt.
MIN MAIL ORDER UK: £20.00 + p&p *MIN VALUE EC:* £50.00 + p&p *EXPORT:* Yes
CAT. COST: 3 x 1st class *W/SALE or RETAIL:* Retail
SPECIALITIES: Rhododendrons & Azaleas *MAP PAGE:* **9**

NNor Northumbria Nurseries, Castle Gardens, Ford, Berwick-upon-Tweed, Northumberland TD15 2PZ

TEL: (0890) 820379 *FAX:* (0890) 820594 *CONTACT:* Hazel M Huddleston
◆ *OPENING TIMES:* 0900-1800 Mon-Fri all year, & 1000-1800 Sat-Sun & Bank Hols Mar-Oct & by appt. (Or till dusk).
MIN MAIL ORDER UK: No minimum charge *MIN VALUE EC:* Nmc
CAT. COST: £2.30 PO/Chq. *W/SALE or RETAIL:* Both
SPECIALITIES: Over 1300 different species of container grown hardy ornamental Shrubs, Perennials & Alpines. *MAP PAGE:* **10**

NNrd Norden Alpines, Hirst Road, Carlton, Nr Goole, Humberside DN14 9PX

TEL: (0405) 861348 *CONTACT:* Norma & Denis Walton
OPENING TIMES: 1000-1700 Sat-Sun & Bank Hols Mar-Sep, or by appt.
MIN MAIL ORDER UK: £10.00 + p&p *MIN VALUE EC:* n/a
CAT. COST: 50p in stamps *W/SALE or RETAIL:* Retail
SPECIALITIES: Many unusual Alpines esp. Campanula, Primula & Saxifraga. *MAP PAGE:* **9**

NNrw Norwell Nurseries, Woodhouse Road, Norwell, Newark, Nottinghamshire NG23 6JX

TEL: (0636) 636337 *CONTACT:* Dr Andrew Ward
◆ *OPENING TIMES:* 1000-1700 Sun-Thu Mar-20th Oct, Sat-Thu May-Jun, Thu & Fri Nov-Feb & by appt. Except Aug 12-28th.
MIN MAIL ORDER UK: £10.00 + p&p *MIN VALUE EC:* n/a
CAT. COST: 2 x 1st class *W/SALE or RETAIL:* Both
SPECIALITIES: New nursery with increasing range of unusual & choice herbaceous Perennials & Alpines. Esp. Penstemon, hardy Geraniums & Dianthus. *MAP PAGE:* **7**

NOak Oak Tree Nursery, Mill Lane, Barlow, Selby, North Yorkshire YO8 8EY

TEL: (0757) 618409 *CONTACT:* Gill Plowes
OPENING TIMES: 1000-1630 Tue-Sun mid Feb-end Oct.
MAIL ORDER: No
CAT. COST: 2 x 1st class *W/SALE or RETAIL:* Retail
SPECIALITIES: Herbaceous & unusual Perennials. *MAP PAGE:* **9**

NOrc Orchard House Nursery, Orchard House, Wormald Green, Nr Harrogate, North Yorks HG3 3PX

TEL: (0765) 677541 *CONTACT:* Mr B M Corner
OPENING TIMES: 0800-1700 Mon-Sat, 1400-1700 Sun.
MAIL ORDER: No
CAT. COST: £1.00 *W/SALE or RETAIL:* Both
SPECIALITIES: Herbaceous, Herbs, Alpines, Ferns & unusual cottage garden plants. *MAP PAGE:* **9**

NPal The Palm Farm, Thornton Hall Gardens, Station Road, Thornton Curtis, Nr Ulceby, Humberside DN39 6XF

TEL: (0469) 531232 *CONTACT:* W W Spink
◆ *OPENING TIMES:* 1400-1700 daily ex Winter when advised to check by phone first.
MIN MAIL ORDER UK: £11.00 + p&p *MIN VALUE EC:* £25.00 + p&p *EXPORT:* Yes
CAT. COST: 1 x 2nd class *W/SALE or RETAIL:* Both
SPECIALITIES: Hardy & half-Hardy Palms, Meconopsis & unusual Trees, Shrubs & Conservatory plants. *MAP PAGE:* **9**

NPer Perry's Plants, The River Garden, Sleights, Whitby, North Yorkshire YO21 1RR

TEL: (0947) 810329 *CONTACT:* Pat & Richard Perry
◆ *OPENING TIMES:* 1000-1700 Easter to October.
MAIL ORDER: No
CAT. COST: Large Sae *W/SALE or RETAIL:* Retail
SPECIALITIES: Lavatera, Malva, Erysimum, Euphorbia, Anthemis, Osteospermum & Hebe. *MAP PAGE:* **9**

NPin **Pinks & Carnations,** 22 Chetwyn Avenue, Bromley Cross, Bolton, Lancashire BL7 9BN
TEL: (0204) 306273 *CONTACT:* R & T Gillies
◆ *OPENING TIMES:* Appt only.
MIN MAIL ORDER UK: No minimum charge *MIN VALUE EC:* n/a
CAT. COST: Sae *W/SALE or RETAIL:* Both
SPECIALITIES: Pinks, Perpetual Flowering Carnations and Malmaison Carnations. See also SEED Index. *MAP PAGE:* **9**

NPor **J V Porter, 12 Hazel Grove, Southport, Merseyside PR8 6AX**
TEL: (0704) 533902 *FAX:* (0704) 832196 *CONTACT:* John Porter
OPENING TIMES: 1030-1600 Thu-Sun Jan-May & by appt. (Wholesale open all year 0800-1615)
MIN MAIL ORDER UK: £4.40 + p&p *MIN VALUE EC:* £4.40 + p&p *EXPORT:* Yes
CAT. COST: 2 x 1st class *W/SALE or RETAIL:* Both
SPECIALITIES: Fuchsia. *MAP PAGE:* **9**

NPri **Primrose Cottage Nursery,** Ringway Road, Moss Nook, Wythenshawe, Manchester M22 5WF
TEL: 061-437 1557 *FAX:* 061-499 9932 *CONTACT:* Caroline Dumville
◆ *OPENING TIMES:* 0815-1800 Mon-Sat, 0900-1730 Sun.
MAIL ORDER: No
CAT. COST: 2 x 1st class *W/SALE or RETAIL:* Retail
SPECIALITIES: Hardy Herbaceous Perennials, Alpines & Herbs. *MAP PAGE:* **7**

NRar **Rarer Plants,** Ashfield House, Austfield Lane, Monk Fryston, Leeds, North Yorkshire LS25 5EH
TEL: (0977) 682263 *CONTACT:* Anne Watson
OPENING TIMES: 1000-1600 Sun Feb-Easter for Hellebores. 0930-1530 Mon & Fri, 0930-1700 Sat & Sun Easter-15th Sep.
MAIL ORDER: No
CAT. COST: 3 x 1st class *W/SALE or RETAIL:* Retail
SPECIALITIES: Unusual plants, variegated plants and Penstemons & Hellebors. *MAP PAGE:* **9**

NRed **Redhouse Nurseries, c/o 46 Salisbury Terrace, South Bank, Middlesbrough, Cleveland TS6 6EX**
TEL: *CONTACT:* C Elliott
OPENING TIMES: No callers.
MAIL ORDER: Only*MIN MAIL ORDER UK:* No minimum charge *MIN VALUE EC:* £25.00 + p&p
CAT. COST: 2 x 1st class *W/SALE or RETAIL:* Both
SPECIALITIES: Show Auriculas, Alpines (beginners & collectors) & dwarf Shrubs.

NRog **R V Roger Ltd, The Nurseries, Pickering, North Yorkshire YO18 7HG**
TEL: (0751) 472226 *FAX:* (0751) 476749 *CONTACT:* J R Roger, S Peirson & A G & I M Roger
OPENING TIMES: 0900-1700 Mon-Sat, 1300-1700 Sun. Closed Dec 25th-Jan 2nd each year.
MIN MAIL ORDER UK: No minimum charge *MIN VALUE EC:* Nmc *EXPORT:* Yes
CAT. COST: £1.00 *W/SALE or RETAIL:* Both
SPECIALITIES: General list, hardy in North of England. Co-holders of National Erodium & Erythronium Collection. See also SEED Index. *MAP PAGE:* **9**

NRoo **Rookhope Nurseries,** Rookhope, Upper Weardale, Co Durham DL13 2DD
TEL: (0388) 517272 *CONTACT:* Karen Blackburn
OPENING TIMES: 0830-1700 daily mid Mar-Sep, 1000-1600 most days Oct-mid Mar, please phone to check.
MAIL ORDER: No
CAT. COST: 3 x 1st class *W/SALE or RETAIL:* Retail
SPECIALITIES: Wide range of Hardy plants grown at 1,100 feet in the northern Pennines. *MAP PAGE:* **9/10**

NRya **Ryal Nursery, East Farm Cottage, Ryal, Northumberland NE20 0SA**
TEL: (0661) 886562 *CONTACT:* R F Hadden
OPENING TIMES: 1300-1700 Tue, 1000-1700 Sun Mar-Jul & by appt.
MIN MAIL ORDER UK: £5.00 + p&p *MIN VALUE EC:* £5.00 + p&p
CAT. COST: Sae *W/SALE or RETAIL:* Both
SPECIALITIES: Alpines & Primula. *MAP PAGE:* **10**

NSla **Slack Top Alpines,** Hebden Bridge, West Yorkshire HX7 7HA
TEL: (0422) 845348 *CONTACT:* M R or R Mitchell
◆ *OPENING TIMES:* 1000-1800 Wed-Sun & Bank Hol Mons 1st Mar-31st Oct.
MAIL ORDER: No
CAT. COST: Sae *W/SALE or RETAIL:* Retail
SPECIALITIES: Alpine & Rockery plants. *MAP PAGE:* **9**

NSti **Stillingfleet Lodge Nurseries,** Stillingfleet, Yorkshire YO4 6HW
TEL: (0904) 728506 *FAX:* (0904) 728506 *CONTACT:* Vanessa Cook
OPENING TIMES: 1000-1600 Tue Wed Fri & Sat 1st Apr-18th Oct.
MIN MAIL ORDER UK: No minimum charge *MIN VALUE EC:* n/a
CAT. COST: 5 x 1st class *W/SALE or RETAIL:* Retail
SPECIALITIES: Foliage & unusual perennials. Hardy Geraniums, Pulmonaria, variegated plants & Grasses. Holder of National Pulmonaria Collection. *MAP PAGE:* **9**

NSty **Stydd Nursery, Stoneygate Lane, Ribchester, Nr Preston, Lancashire PR3 3YN**
TEL: (0254) 878797 *FAX:* (0254) 878254 *CONTACT:* Mr & Mrs J A Walker
OPENING TIMES: 1330-1700 Tue-Fri, 0900-1700 Sat all year, 1400-1700 Sun 1st Apr-23rd Dec.
MIN MAIL ORDER UK: No minimum charge *MIN VALUE EC:* £50.00 + p&p
CAT. COST: 50p *W/SALE or RETAIL:* Both
SPECIALITIES: Old Roses & ornamental foliage. Half-hardy Perennials. *MAP PAGE:* **9**

NTow **Town Farm Nursery,** Whitton, Stillington, Stockton on Tees, Cleveland TS21 1LQ
TEL: (0740) 631079 *CONTACT:* F D Baker
◆ *OPENING TIMES:* 1000-1800 Fri-Mon Mar-Oct.
MIN MAIL ORDER UK: £5.00 + p&p *MIN VALUE EC:* n/a
CAT. COST: Sae *W/SALE or RETAIL:* Retail
SPECIALITIES: Unusual Alpines, Border Perennials & Shrubs. *MAP PAGE:* **9**

NTRF **The Tropical Rain Forest, 66 Castle Grove Avenue, Leeds, West Yorkshire LS6 4BS**
TEL: (0532) 789810 *CONTACT:* Mike Harridge
OPENING TIMES: Not open to the public.
MAIL ORDER: Only*MIN MAIL ORDER UK:* £10+p&p *MIN VALUE EC:* £20+p&p *EXPORT:* Yes
CAT. COST: £1.00 *W/SALE or RETAIL:* Both
SPECIALITIES: Nursery grown Bromeliads. Specialise in Tillandsia.

NVic **The Vicarage Garden, Carrington, Urmston, Manchester, M31 4AG**
TEL: (061 775) 2750 *CONTACT:* Miss M Zugor
OPENING TIMES: 1000-1800 Fri-Wed Apr-Sept. 1030-1700 Fri-Wed Oct-Mar.
MIN MAIL ORDER UK: £5.00 + p&p *MIN VALUE EC:* £10.00 + p&p
CAT. COST: £1.00 *W/SALE or RETAIL:* Both
SPECIALITIES: Herbaceous & Alpines. *MAP PAGE:* **9**

NWCA **White Cottage Alpines, Eastgate, Rudston, Driffield, East Yorkshire YO25 0UX**
TEL: (0262) 420668 *CONTACT:* Sally E Cummins
OPENING TIMES: 1000-1700 (or dusk) Thu-Sun & Bank Hol Mons. Closed Dec & Jan.
MIN MAIL ORDER UK: No minimum charge *MIN VALUE EC:* Nmc
CAT. COST: 2 x 1st class *W/SALE or RETAIL:* Both
SPECIALITIES: Alpines. Nursery expects to move during 1994/95. *MAP PAGE:* **9**

NWea **Weasdale Nurseries, Newbiggin-on-Lune, Kirkby Stephen, Cumbria CA17 4LX**
TEL: (05396) 23246 *FAX:* (05396) 23277 *CONTACT:* Andrew Forsyth
OPENING TIMES: 0900-1700 Mon-Fri.
MIN MAIL ORDER UK: No minimum charge *MIN VALUE EC:* Nmc
CAT. COST: £2.30 *W/SALE or RETAIL:* Retail
SPECIALITIES: Hardy forest trees, hedging & ornamental Shrubs grown at 850 feet. Mail Order a speciality. *MAP PAGE:* **9**

NWin **Wingates,** 62A Chorley Road, Westhoughton, Bolton, Lancashire BL5 3PL
TEL: (0942) 813357 *CONTACT:* G Lambert
OPENING TIMES: 1400-dusk daily. Check during winter months.
MAIL ORDER: No
CAT. COST: 30p *W/SALE or RETAIL:* Retail
SPECIALITIES: Mainly Heathers, also Dwarf Conifers & Shrubs, Ericaceous plants, Alpines & dwarf Rhododendrons. *MAP PAGE:* **5/4**

NWyt **Wytherstone Nurseries,** The Estate Office, Pockley, Yorkshire YO6 5TE

TEL: (0439) 71239/70012 Office *FAX:* (0439) 70468 *CONTACT:* Ian Powell
OPENING TIMES: 1000-1700 Wed-Sun 1st Apr-20th Oct & Bank Hols Mon. Also by appt.
MIN MAIL ORDER UK: £10.00 + p&p* *MIN VALUE EC:* n/a
CAT. COST: 2 x 1st class *W/SALE or RETAIL:* Retail
SPECIALITIES: Rare & hard to find Perennials, Shrubs & Conservatory plants. *NOTE: Mail Order for Pelargoniums only. *MAP PAGE:* **9**

NZep **Zephyrwude Irises, 48 Blacker Lane, Crigglestone, Wakefield, West Yorkshire WF4 3EW**

TEL: (0924) 252101 *CONTACT:* Richard L Brook
◆ *OPENING TIMES:* Viewing only 0900-dusk daily, variable May-June periods. Phone first, dark-2300.
MIN MAIL ORDER UK: £2.50 + p&p *MIN VALUE EC:* £2.50 + p&p
CAT. COST: 1 x 1st class *W/SALE or RETAIL:* Retail
SPECIALITIES: Bearded Iris, dwarf, intermediate & tall, mainly modern American varieties. 700 variety trial/display garden. Delivery Aug-Sep only. Cat. available Apr-Sep. *MAP PAGE:* **9**

SAga **Agar's Nursery,** Agars Lane, Hordle, Lymington, Hampshire SO41 0FL

TEL: (0590) 683703 *CONTACT:* George & Diana Tombs
OPENING TIMES: 1000-1700 Fri-Wed Mar-Oct, 1000-1600 Fri-Wed Feb & Nov-20th Dec. Closed 20th Dec-31st Jan.
MIN MAIL ORDER UK: £15.00 + p&p *MIN VALUE EC:* n/a
CAT. COST: 3 x 1st class *W/SALE or RETAIL:* Retail
SPECIALITIES: Penstemon, Salvia & Iris. Also wide range of Hardy plants inc. Shrubs & Climbers. *MAP PAGE:* **2**

SAll **Allwood Bros, Mill Nursery, Hassocks, West Sussex BN6 9NB**

TEL: (0273 84) 4229 *CONTACT:* W Rickaby
OPENING TIMES: 0900-1700 Mon-Fri.
MIN MAIL ORDER UK: No minimum charge *MIN VALUE EC:* Nmc *EXPORT:* SO
CAT. COST: 2 x 1st class *W/SALE or RETAIL:* Both
SPECIALITIES: Dianthus, incl Hardy Border Carnations, Pinks, Perpetual & Allwoodii. Gypsophila, most available as Seed. See also SEED Index. *MAP PAGE:* **3**

SApp **Apple Court, Hordle Lane, Hordle, Lymington, Hampshire S041 0HU**

TEL: (0590) 642130 *FAX:* (o590) 642130 *CONTACT:* Diana Grenfell & Roger Grounds
◆ *OPENING TIMES:* Thu-Mon Feb-Nov. Closed Dec & Jan & one week end-Aug.
MIN MAIL ORDER UK: £10.00 + p&p *MIN VALUE EC:* £50.00 + p&p *EXPORT:* Yes
CAT. COST: 3 x 1st class *W/SALE or RETAIL:* Retail
SPECIALITIES: Hosta, Grasses, Ferns, Hemerocallis. National Collection Woodwardia, Rohdea, Camassia & Hosta. *MAP PAGE:* **2**

SApu **Apuldram Roses, Apuldram Lane, Dell Quay, Chichester, Sussex PO20 7EF**

TEL: (0243) 785769 *FAX:* (0243) 536973 *CONTACT:* Mrs Sawday
OPENING TIMES: 0900-1700 Mon-Sat, 1030-1630 Sun & Bank Hols. ex. Dec 23rd-Jan 10th.
MIN MAIL ORDER UK: £2.95 + p&p *MIN VALUE EC:* £2.95 + p&p *EXPORT:* Yes
CAT. COST: 25p *W/SALE or RETAIL:* Both
SPECIALITIES: Roses. *MAP PAGE:* **2/3**

SArc **Architectural Plants, Cooks Farm, Nuthurst, Horsham, West Sussex RH13 6LH**

TEL: (0403) 891772 *FAX:* (0403) 891056 *CONTACT:* Angus White
◆ *OPENING TIMES:* 0900-1700 Mon-Sat.
MIN MAIL ORDER UK: None. £13 min p&p *MIN VALUE EC:* £150.00 + p&p *EXPORT:* Yes
CAT. COST: Free *W/SALE or RETAIL:* Both
SPECIALITIES: Architectural plants & hardy Exotics. *MAP PAGE:* **3**

SAsh **Ashenden Nursery,** Cranbrook Road, Benenden, Cranbrook, Kent TN17 4ET

TEL: (0580) 241792 *CONTACT:* Kevin McGarry
OPENING TIMES: 1000-1300 & 1400-1700 Mon-Sat.
MAIL ORDER: No
CAT. COST: Sae *W/SALE or RETAIL:* Retail
SPECIALITIES: Rock garden & perennials *MAP PAGE:* **3**

SAWi **Anthony Archer-Wills Ltd.,** Broadford Bridge Road, West Chiltington, West Sussex RH20 2LF
TEL: (0798) 813204 *FAX:* (0798) 815080 *CONTACT:* Anthony Archer-Wills
OPENING TIMES: By appt. only - please telephone.
MIN MAIL ORDER UK: £15.00 + p&p *MIN VALUE EC:* n/a
CAT. COST: *W/SALE or RETAIL:* Both
SPECIALITIES: Ponds, Lakes & Water garden plants. *MAP PAGE:* **3**

SAxl **Axletree Nursery,** Starvecrow Lane, Peasmarsh, Rye, East Sussex TN31 6XL
TEL: (0797) 230470 *CONTACT:* D J Hibberd
OPENING TIMES: 1000-1700 Wed-Sat mid Mar-Sep.
MAIL ORDER: No
CAT. COST: 4 x 1st class *W/SALE or RETAIL:* Retail
SPECIALITIES: Herbaceous plants, esp. Hardy Geraniums & Euphorbia. *MAP PAGE:* **3**

SBai **Steven Bailey Ltd., Silver Street, Sway, Lymington, Hampshire SO41 6ZA**
TEL: (0590) 682227 *FAX:* (0590) 683765 *CONTACT:* Fiona Whittles
OPENING TIMES: 1000-1300 & 1400-1630 Mon-Fri all year. 1000-1300 & 1400-1600 Sat Mar-Jun ex Bank Hols.
MIN MAIL ORDER UK: Quotation *MIN VALUE EC:* Quotation *EXPORT:* Yes
CAT. COST: 2 x 2nd class *W/SALE or RETAIL:* Both
SPECIALITIES: Carnations, Pinks & Alstroemeria. *MAP PAGE:* **2**

SBam **Bamboo Nursery Ltd., Kingsgate Cottage, Wittersham, Tenterden, Kent TN30 7NS**
TEL: (0797) 270607 *FAX:* (0797) 270825 *CONTACT:* A Sutcliffe
OPENING TIMES: Appt only.
MIN MAIL ORDER UK: No minimum charge *MIN VALUE EC:* £50.00 + p&p *EXPORT:* Yes
CAT. COST: Sae *W/SALE or RETAIL:* Both
SPECIALITIES: Bamboo. *MAP PAGE:* **3**

SBla **Blackthorn Nursery,** Kilmeston, Alresford, Hampshire SO24 0NL
TEL: (0962) 771796 *CONTACT:* A R & S B White
OPENING TIMES: 0900-1700 Fri & Sat Mar-15th Oct 1994.
MAIL ORDER: No
CAT. COST: 3 x 1st class *W/SALE or RETAIL:* Retail
SPECIALITIES: Choice perennials, Shrubs & Alpines esp. Daphne & Helleborus. *MAP PAGE:* **2**

SBod **Bodiam Nursery,** Ockham House, Bodiam, Robertsbridge, East Sussex TN32 5RA
TEL: (0580) 830811/830649 *FAX:* (0580) 830071 *CONTACT:* Richard Biggs
OPENING TIMES: 0900-1800 or dusk.
MIN MAIL ORDER UK: £30.00 + p&p *MIN VALUE EC:* n/a
CAT. COST: 3 x 1st class *W/SALE or RETAIL:* Both
SPECIALITIES: Heathers, herbaceous Perennials, Conifers, Azaleas, Camellias & Clematis. *MAP PAGE:* **3**

SBor **Borde Hill Garden Ltd.,** Haywards Heath, West Sussex RH16 1XP
TEL: (0444) 450326 *FAX:* (0444) 440427 *CONTACT:* Emma Jackson
OPENING TIMES: 1000-1800 daily 1st Apr-16th Oct & Sun in March in good weather. - same as garden.
MAIL ORDER: No
CAT. COST: None issued *W/SALE or RETAIL:* Retail
SPECIALITIES: Herbaceous & tender Perennials, unusual Shrubs. *MAP PAGE:* **3**

SBra **J Bradshaw & Son,** Busheyfield Nursery, Herne, Herne Bay, Kent CT6 7LJ
TEL: (0227) 375415 *FAX:* (0227) 375415 *CONTACT:* D J Bradshaw
OPENING TIMES: Not open to public except to collect phone or letter orders.
MAIL ORDER: No *EXPORT:* No*
CAT. COST: Sae *W/SALE or RETAIL:* Both
SPECIALITIES: Clematis & Climbers. Mainly wholesale. NCCPG collection of climbing Lonicera.
*NOTE:- Trade export ONLY.

SBro **Jarvis Brook Geranium Nurseries, Tubwell Lane, Jarvis Brook, Crowborough, Sussex TN6 3RH**
TEL: (0892) 662329 *CONTACT:* Mrs W M Mitchell
OPENING TIMES: 1030-1730 Thu-Sun Apr-Aug.
MIN MAIL ORDER UK: No minimum charge *MIN VALUE EC:* Nmc*
CAT. COST: 2 x 1st class *W/SALE or RETAIL:* Both
SPECIALITIES: Miniature & Dwarf Pelargonium. *NOTE: Unrooted cuttings only to EC.
MAP PAGE: **3**

SCaw **R G M Cawthorne, Lower Daltons Nursery, Swanley Village, Swanley, Kent BR8 7NU**
TEL: Ex-Directory *CONTACT:* R G M Cawthorne
OPENING TIMES: Written appt. only. Plants may be collected ex nursery during April only.
MIN MAIL ORDER UK: 12 plants + p&p *MIN VALUE EC:* 24 plants + p&p
CAT. COST: 70p *W/SALE or RETAIL:* Retail
SPECIALITIES: 450 named Violas & Violettas. (Largest collection in the world). Holder of NCCPG Viola collection. Assorted Viola Seed sent to US, Japan, China & Australasia.

SChu **Church Hill Cottage Gardens,** Charing Heath, Ashford, Kent TN27 0BU
TEL: (023 371) 2522* *CONTACT:* Mr & Mrs Michael Metianu.
OPENING TIMES: 1000-1700 1st Feb-30th Nov Tue-Sun & Bank Hols Mon. Other times by appt.
MAIL ORDER: No
CAT. COST: 3 x 1st class *W/SALE or RETAIL:* Retail
SPECIALITIES: Unusual hardy plants, Dianthus, Alpines & Shrubs. *MAP PAGE:* **3**

SCob **Coblands Nursery,** (Off.) Trench Road, Tonbridge, Kent TN10 3HQ
TEL: (0732) 770999 *FAX:* (0732) 770271 *CONTACT:* Ken Turner
OPENING TIMES: 0830-1600 Mon-Fri.
MAIL ORDER: No
CAT. COST: *W/SALE or RETAIL:* Both
SPECIALITIES: General range, esp. Bamboos, Grasses & Ferns. NOTE:- Nursery at Back Lane, Ightham, Sevenoaks. *MAP PAGE:* **3**

SCog **Coghurst Nursery, Ivy House Lane, Near Three Oaks, Hastings, East Sussex TN35 4NP**
TEL: (0424) 756228 *CONTACT:* J Farnfield, L A & D Edgar
OPENING TIMES: 1200-1630 Mon-Fri, 1000-1630 Sun.
MIN MAIL ORDER UK: No minimum charge *MIN VALUE EC:* Nmc
CAT. COST: 2 x 2nd class *W/SALE or RETAIL:* Both
SPECIALITIES: Camellias, Rhododendrons, Azaleas & Eucryphia. *MAP PAGE:* **3**

SCou **Coombland Gardens, Coombland, Coneyhurst, Billingshurst, West Sussex RH14 9DG**
TEL: (0403) 741549 *FAX:* (0403) 741549 *CONTACT:* Mrs Rosemary Lee
◆ *OPENING TIMES:* 1400-1600 Mon-Fri. Bank Hols & other times by appt. only.
MIN MAIL ORDER UK: £10.00 + p&p *MIN VALUE EC:* 8 plants + p&p*
CAT. COST: 4 x 1st class *W/SALE or RETAIL:* Retail
SPECIALITIES: Hardy Geranium, Erodium and choice Herbaceous. *NOTE: Hardy Geraniums only to EC. *MAP PAGE:* **3**

SCro **Croftway Nursery, Yapton Road, Barnham, Bognor Regis, West Sussex PO22 0BH**
TEL: (0243) 552121 *CONTACT:* Graham Spencer
OPENING TIMES: 0900-1730 daily. Closed Wed from 1st Nov-28th Feb.
MIN MAIL ORDER UK: No minimum charge* *MIN VALUE EC:* Nmc*
CAT. COST: £1.00 *W/SALE or RETAIL:* Both
SPECIALITIES: Wide general range, emphasis on Perennials. Specialists in Irises & Hardy Geraniums. *NOTE: Mail Order for Iris & Geraniums only. *MAP PAGE:* **3**

SDea **Deacon's Nursery, Moor View, Godshill, Isle of Wight PO38 3HW**
TEL: (0983) 840750/522243 *CONTACT:* G D & B H W Deacon
◆ *OPENING TIMES:* 0800-1600 Mon-Sat.
MIN MAIL ORDER UK: No minimum charge *MIN VALUE EC:* Nmc *EXPORT:* Yes
CAT. COST: 29p stamp *W/SALE or RETAIL:* Both
SPECIALITIES: Over 250 varieties of Apple, old & new. Pears, Plums, Gages, Damsons, Cherries etc. Fruit & Nut trees, triple Peaches, Ballerinas. Modern Soft Fruit. *MAP PAGE:* **2**

SDeJ **De Jager & Sons, The Nurseries, Marden, Kent TN12 9BP**

TEL: (0622) 831235 *FAX:* (0622) 832416 *CONTACT:* Mrs M Guiney
OPENING TIMES: 0900-1700 Mon-Fri.
MIN MAIL ORDER UK: No minimum charge *MIN VALUE EC:* Nmc *EXPORT:* Yes
CAT. COST: Free *W/SALE or RETAIL:* Both
SPECIALITIES: Wide general range, esp. Bulbs. Lillium, Tulipa, Narcissus species & miscellaneous. Large range of Perennials. *MAP PAGE:* **3**

SDen **Denmead Geranium Nurseries, Hambledon Road, Denmead, Waterlooville, Hampshire PO7 6PS**

TEL: (0705) 240081 *CONTACT:* I H Chance
OPENING TIMES: 0800-1300 & 1400-1700 Mon-Fri, 0800-1230 Sat (ex Aug), 1400-1700 Sat May-Jun & 0930-1230 Sun Apr-May
MIN MAIL ORDER UK: 6 plants + p&p *MIN VALUE EC:* 6 plants + p&p
CAT. COST: 3 x 2nd class *W/SALE or RETAIL:* Both
SPECIALITIES: Pelargoniums - Zonals, Ivy-leaved, Scented, Unique, Rosebud, Stellars, Miniature, Dwarf, Swiss Balcony, Mini Cascade, Ornamental & Regals. *MAP PAGE:* **2**

SDix **Great Dixter Nurseries, Northiam, Rye, East Sussex TN31 6PH**

TEL: (0797) 253107 *CONTACT:* C Lloyd
OPENING TIMES: 0900-1230 & 1330-1700 Sat. 1400-1700 Sun & Bank Hols.
MIN MAIL ORDER UK: £10.00 + p&p *MIN VALUE EC:* £10.00 + p&p
CAT. COST: 75p *W/SALE or RETAIL:* Retail
SPECIALITIES: Clematis, Shrubs and Plants. (Gardens open). *MAP PAGE:* **3**

SDry **Drysdale Garden Exotics, Bowerwood Road, Fordingbridge, Hampshire SP6 1BN**

TEL: (0425) 653010 *CONTACT:* David Crampton
OPENING TIMES: 0930-1730 Wed-Fri, 1000-1730 Sun. Closed 24th Dec-2nd Jan incl.
MIN MAIL ORDER UK: £10.00 + p&p *MIN VALUE EC:* £15.00 + p&p
CAT. COST: 3 x 1st class *W/SALE or RETAIL:* Retail
SPECIALITIES: Plants for exotic & foliage effect. Plants for Mediterranean gardens. National Reference Collection of Bamboos. *MAP PAGE:* **2**

SEng **English Water Garden,** Rock Lane, Washington, West Sussex RH20 3BL

TEL: (0903) 892006/892408 *FAX:* (0903) 892006 *CONTACT:* J M Quick
OPENING TIMES: 0900-1730 daily.
MIN MAIL ORDER UK: No minimum charge *MIN VALUE EC:* n/a
CAT. COST: None issued *W/SALE or RETAIL:* Both
SPECIALITIES: Specimen Trees, Shrubs, Waterplants & unusual species. Some Trees & Shrubs available in very large sizes. *MAP PAGE:* **3**

SExb **Exbury Enterprises Ltd.,** Exbury, Nr. Southampton, Hampshire SO4 1AZ

TEL: (0703) 898625/891203 *FAX:* (0703) 243380 *CONTACT:*
OPENING TIMES: 1000-1730 Plant Centre. 0900-1700 Office.
MIN MAIL ORDER UK: £15.00 + p&p *MIN VALUE EC:* n/a
CAT. COST: Sae *W/SALE or RETAIL:* Both
SPECIALITIES: Rhododendron, Azalea, Camellia & Pieris *MAP PAGE:* **2**

SFai **Christopher Fairweather Ltd.,** High Street, Beaulieu, Hampshire SO42 7YB

TEL: (0590) 612307 *FAX:* (0590) 612615 *CONTACT:* C Fairweather
OPENING TIMES: 0900-1700 daily.
MAIL ORDER: No
CAT. COST: No retail Cat. *W/SALE or RETAIL:* Both
SPECIALITIES: Shrubs & Trees. *MAP PAGE:* **2**

SFam **Family Trees, PO Box 3, Botley, Hampshire SO3 2EA**

TEL: (0329) 834812 *CONTACT:* Philip House
◆ *OPENING TIMES:* 0900-1200 Wed & Sat mid Oct-mid Apr,
MIN MAIL ORDER UK: £30.00 + p&p *MIN VALUE EC:* £100.00 + p&p
CAT. COST: Free *W/SALE or RETAIL:* Retail
SPECIALITIES: Fruit & Ornamental trees. Old Roses & trained Fruit trees. Also hedgerow & woodland Trees. *MAP PAGE:* **2**

SFar **Farmhouse Plants,** Royal Farm House, Elstead, Godalming, Surrey GU8 6LA

TEL: (0252) 702460 *CONTACT:* Mrs S Cole
OPENING TIMES: By appointment.
MAIL ORDER: No
CAT. COST: 3 x 2nd class *W/SALE or RETAIL:* Retail
SPECIALITIES: General range, esp. Grasses & Euphorbia. *MAP PAGE:* **3**

SFis **Kaytie Fisher,** The Nursery, South End Cottage, Long Reach, Ockham, Surrey GU23 6PF

TEL: (0483) 282304 *FAX:* (0483) 284858 *CONTACT:* Kaytie Fisher
OPENING TIMES: 1000-1700 daily May-Jul, Wed-Fri Mar & Oct, Wed-Sun Apr, Aug & Sep. Oct-Feb by appt. only.
MIN MAIL ORDER UK: £10.00 + p&p *MIN VALUE EC:* n/a
CAT. COST: 3 x 1st class *W/SALE or RETAIL:* Retail
SPECIALITIES: Mainly hardy Herbaceous, Alpines some Shrubs. Old Shrub Roses & Climbing Roses. *MAP PAGE:* **3**

SFru **The Fruit Garden, Mulberry Farm, Woodnesborough, Sandwich, Kent CT13 0PT**

TEL: (0304) 813454 *FAX:* (0304) 813454 *CONTACT:* Patricia & Peter Dodd
OPENING TIMES: By appt. for collection of orders.
MIN MAIL ORDER UK: No minimum charge *MIN VALUE EC:* £50.00 + p&p
CAT. COST: Free *W/SALE or RETAIL:* Retail
SPECIALITIES: Old & unusual quality Fruit Trees. Comprehensive backup service for customers. *MAP PAGE:* **3**

SGil **Diana Gilbert,** 25 Virginia Road, South Tankerton, Whitstable, Kent CT5 3HY

TEL: (0227) 273128 *CONTACT:* Diana Gilbert
◆ *OPENING TIMES:* 1000-1800 Thu-Sat Mar-Jun & Sep-Oct. Please see Display advert. Also welcome by appt.
MAIL ORDER: No
CAT. COST: 2 x 1st class *W/SALE or RETAIL:* Retail
SPECIALITIES: Uncommon & interesting Shrubs, Perennials & Alpines. Foliage & Flower arrangers plants. *MAP PAGE:* **3**

SHay **Hayward's Carnations, The Chace Gardens, Stakes Road, Purbrook, Waterlooville, Hampshire PO7 5PL**

TEL: (0705) 263047 *CONTACT:* A N Hayward
OPENING TIMES: 0930-1700 Mon-Fri.
MIN MAIL ORDER UK: £10.00 + p&p *MIN VALUE EC:* £50.00 + p&p *EXPORT:* Yes
CAT. COST: 1 x 1st class *W/SALE or RETAIL:* Both
SPECIALITIES: Hardy Pinks & Border Carnations. Greenhouse perpetual Carnations. *MAP PAGE:* **2**

SHaz **Hazeldene Nursery,** Dean Street, East Farleigh, Maidstone, Kent ME15 0PS

TEL: (0622) 726248 *CONTACT:* Mr W W Adams
OPENING TIMES: 1000-1500. Please ring prior to visit. Oct-Feb by appt. only.
MIN MAIL ORDER UK: No minimum charge *MIN VALUE EC:* n/a
CAT. COST: Sae *W/SALE or RETAIL:* Retail
SPECIALITIES: Pansies, Viola & Violets. *MAP PAGE:* **3**

SHBN **High Banks Nurseries,** Slip Mill Road, Hawkhurst, Kent TN18 5AD

TEL: (0580) 753031 *CONTACT:* Jeremy Homewood
OPENING TIMES: 0800-1700 daily
MAIL ORDER: No
CAT. COST: £1+Large Sae *W/SALE or RETAIL:* Both
SPECIALITIES: Wide general range with many unusual plants. *MAP PAGE:* **3**

SHer **The Herbary Plant Centre,** 89 Station Road, Herne Bay, Kent CT6 5QQ

TEL: (0227) 362409 *CONTACT:* Mrs J R Giles
◆ *OPENING TIMES:* 1000-1700 Tue, Wed, Fri, Sat & Sun Mar-Oct.
MAIL ORDER: No
CAT. COST: 50p *W/SALE or RETAIL:* Retail
SPECIALITIES: Plants suitable for Tufa growing. Aromatic Herbs, interesting Shrubs & Herbaceous. Shrubs for Winter Colour. *MAP PAGE:* **3**

SHHo **Highfield Hollies,** Highfield Farm, Hatch Lane, Liss Hampshire GU33 7NH
TEL: (0730) 892372 *CONTACT:* Mrs Louise Bendall
◆ *OPENING TIMES:* By appt.
MAIL ORDER: No
CAT. COST: 1 x 1st class *W/SALE or RETAIL:* Both
SPECIALITIES: Ilex. Over 50 species & cultivars including many specimen trees. *MAP PAGE:* **2/3**

SHig **Higher End Nursery,** Hale, Fordingbridge, Hampshire SP6 2RA
TEL: (0725) 22243 *CONTACT:* D J Case
OPENING TIMES: 1000-1700 Wed-Sat 1400-1700 Sun Apr-Aug.
MIN MAIL ORDER UK: £12.00 + p&p *MIN VALUE EC:* n/a
CAT. COST: 2 x 1st class *W/SALE or RETAIL:* Retail
SPECIALITIES: Water Lilies, Bog & Marginal, Hellebore, Rodgersia, Trollius, Bergenia.
MAP PAGE: **2**

SHil **Hillier Nurseries (Winchester) Ltd, Ampfield House, Ampfield, Nr. Romsey, Hampshire SO51 9PA**
TEL: (0794) 368733 *FAX:* (0794) 368813 *CONTACT:* Mrs Sheila Pack
OPENING TIMES: Office 0830-1700 Mon-Fri. Garden Centres 0900-1730 Mon-Sat, 1000-1730 Sun.
MIN MAIL ORDER UK: n/a *MIN VALUE EC:* £250.00* *EXPORT:* Yes
CAT. COST: Free* *W/SALE or RETAIL:* Both
SPECIALITIES: Very large range of Trees, Shrubs, Conifers, Climbers, Roses. Catalogue from Premier Plant Stockist - phone for list. *French orders via Delbard SA, Paris. *MAP PAGE:* **2**

SHya **Brenda Hyatt, 1 Toddington Crescent, Bluebell Hill, Chatham, Kent ME5 9QT**
TEL: (0634) 863251 *CONTACT:* Mrs Brenda Hyatt
OPENING TIMES: Appt only.
MIN MAIL ORDER UK: No minimum charge *MIN VALUE EC:* Nmc
CAT. COST: 70p *W/SALE or RETAIL:* Retail
SPECIALITIES: Show Auricula. *MAP PAGE:* **3**

SIde **Iden Croft Herbs, Frittenden Road, Staplehurst, Kent TN12 0DH**
TEL: (0580) 891432 *FAX:* (0580) 892416 *CONTACT:* Rosemary & D Titterington
OPENING TIMES: 0900-1700 Mon-Sat all year & 1100-1700 Sun & Bank Hols. 1st Mar- 30th Sep.
MIN MAIL ORDER UK: No minimum charge *MIN VALUE EC:* £20.00 + p&p
CAT. COST: £2.50* *W/SALE or RETAIL:* Retail
SPECIALITIES: Herbs & Aromatic plants. National Mentha & Origanum collection. Export orders undertaken for dispatch during Spring months. * Sae for plant list. *MAP PAGE:* **3**

SIgm **Tim Ingram,** Copton Ash, 105 Ashford Road, Faversham, Kent ME13 8XW
TEL: (0795) 535919 *CONTACT:* Dr T J Ingram
◆ *OPENING TIMES:* 1400-1800 Tue-Thur & Sat-Sun Mar-Oct. Nov-Feb by appt.
MIN MAIL ORDER UK: £8.00 + p&p* *MIN VALUE EC:* n/a
CAT. COST: 3 x 1st class *W/SALE or RETAIL:* Retail
SPECIALITIES: Unusual Perennials, Alpines & Australasian plants. Fruit & ornamental Trees. *NOTE: Only Fruit Trees by Mail Order (Nov-Mar). *MAP PAGE:* **3**

SIng **W E Th. Ingwersen Ltd, Birch Farm Nursery, Gravetye, E. Grinstead, West Sussex RH19 4LE**
TEL: (0342) 810236 *CONTACT:* M P & M R Ingwersen
OPENING TIMES: 0900-1300 & 1330-1600 daily 1st Mar-30th Sep. 0900-1300 & 1330-1600 Mon-Fri Oct-Feb.
MIN MAIL ORDER UK: No minimum charge *MIN VALUE EC:* £50.00 + p&p *EXPORT:* Yes
CAT. COST: £1.00 stamps* *W/SALE or RETAIL:* Retail
SPECIALITIES: Very wide range of hardy plants mostly alpines. *NOTE: Mail Order only during Mar-May & Sep-Nov. *NOTE: Catalogue £1.50 if cheque or P.O. *MAP PAGE:* **3**

SJus **Just Roses, Beales Lane, Northiam, Nr Rye, East Sussex TN31 6QY**
TEL: (0797) 252355 *CONTACT:* Mr J Banham
OPENING TIMES: 0900-1200 & 1300-1700 Tue-Fri & 0900-1200 & 1300-1600 Sat & Sun.
MIN MAIL ORDER UK: 1 plant + p&p *MIN VALUE EC:* Nmc
CAT. COST: Free *W/SALE or RETAIL:* Retail
SPECIALITIES: Roses *MAP PAGE:* **3**

SKee **Keepers Nursery,** 446 Wateringbury Road, East Malling, Kent ME19 6JJ
TEL: (0622) 813008 *CONTACT:* Anne & Mike Cook
OPENING TIMES: All reasonable hours by appt.
MIN MAIL ORDER UK: £10.00 + p&p *MIN VALUE EC:* n/a
CAT. COST: Sae *W/SALE or RETAIL:* Retail
SPECIALITIES: Old & unusual Top Fruit varieties. Wide range of Soft Fruit. Top Fruit, ornamental varieties and Fruit seedlings propagated to order. Fruit tree rootstock. *MAP PAGE:* **3**

SKen **Kent Street Nurseries,** Sedlescombe, Battle, East Sussex TN33 0SF
TEL: (0424) 751134 *CONTACT:* Mrs D Downey
OPENING TIMES: 0900-1800 daily all year.
MIN MAIL ORDER UK: 10 plants + p&p *MIN VALUE EC:* n/a
CAT. COST: A5 Sae* *W/SALE or RETAIL:* Both
SPECIALITIES: Fuchsia, Pelargonium, Bedding & Perennials. *NOTE: Separate Fuchsia & Pelargonium lists. Please specify which required. *MAP PAGE:* **3**

SLan **Langley Boxwood Nursery, Rake, Nr Liss, Hampshire GU33 7JL**
TEL: (0730) 894467 *FAX:* (0730) 894703 *CONTACT:* Elizabeth Braimbridge
◆ *OPENING TIMES:* By appt. only.
MIN MAIL ORDER UK: £20.00 + p&p *MIN VALUE EC:* £100.00 + p&p *EXPORT:* Yes
CAT. COST: 4 x 1st class *W/SALE or RETAIL:* Both
SPECIALITIES: Buxus species, cultivars & hedging. Good range of topiary. *MAP PAGE:* **2/3**

SLBF **Little Brook Fuchsias,** Ash Green Lane West, Ash Green, Nr Aldershot, Hampshire GU12 6HL
TEL: (0252) 29731 *CONTACT:* Carol Gubler
OPENING TIMES: 0900-1700 Wed-Sun 1st Jan-3rd Jul.
MAIL ORDER: No
CAT. COST: 30p + Sae *W/SALE or RETAIL:* Both
SPECIALITIES: Fuchsia old & new. *MAP PAGE:* **3**

SLeo **Leonardslee Gardens,** 1 Mill Lane, Lower Beeding, West Sussex RH13 6PX
TEL: (0403) 891 412 *CONTACT:* A J Clark
OPENING TIMES: 1000-1800 Tue Thu & Sun BY APPOINTMENT ONLY.
MIN MAIL ORDER UK: £50.00 + p&p *MIN VALUE EC:*
CAT. COST: £2.00 *W/SALE or RETAIL:* Retail
SPECIALITIES: Rhododendron & Azalea in all sizes. *MAP PAGE:* **3**

SLga **Longacre Nursery,** Perry Wood, Selling, Nr Faversham, Kent ME13 9SE
TEL: (0227) 752254 *CONTACT:* Dr & Mrs G G Thomas
◆ *OPENING TIMES:* 1400-1700 daily, 1st Apr-31st Oct.
MAIL ORDER: No
CAT. COST: 2 x 1st class *W/SALE or RETAIL:* Retail
SPECIALITIES: Hardy Herbaceous only. *MAP PAGE:* **3**

SLim **Lime Cross Nursery,** Herstmonceux, Hailsham, East Sussex BN27 4RS
TEL: (0323) 833229 *FAX:* (0323) 833944 *CONTACT:* J A Tate
◆ *OPENING TIMES:* 0830-1700 Mon-Sat & 0930-1700 Sun.
MAIL ORDER: No
CAT. COST: Free *W/SALE or RETAIL:* Both
SPECIALITIES: Conifers. *MAP PAGE:* **3**

SLMG **Long Man Gardens, Lewes Road, Wilmington, Polegate, East Sussex BN26 5RS**
TEL: (0323) 870816 *CONTACT:* O Menzel
OPENING TIMES: 0900-1800 Tue-Sun. Please check day before visit.
MIN MAIL ORDER UK: See list for details *MIN VALUE EC:* See list *EXPORT:* Yes
CAT. COST: Free list *W/SALE or RETAIL:* Both
SPECIALITIES: Mainly conservatory plants. *MAP PAGE:* **3**

SLon **Longstock Park Nursery,** Stockbridge, Hampshire SO20 6EH
TEL: (0264) 810894 *FAX:* (0264) 810439 *CONTACT:* General Manager
OPENING TIMES: 0830-1630 Mon-Sat.
MAIL ORDER: No
CAT. COST: £1.50 inc p&p *W/SALE or RETAIL:* Both
SPECIALITIES: Shrubs & Conifers. Herbaceous and moisture loving and Aquatics. *MAP PAGE:* **2**

SLPl **Landscape Plants, Cattamount, Grafty Green, Maidstone, Kent ME17 2AP**
TEL: (0622) 850245 *FAX:* (0622) 858063 *CONTACT:* Tom La Dell
OPENING TIMES: By appointment only.
MIN MAIL ORDER UK: £50.00 + p&p *MIN VALUE EC:* £100.00 + p&p *EXPORT:* Yes
CAT. COST: 2 x 1st class *W/SALE or RETAIL:* Both
SPECIALITIES: Low maintenance Shrubs. *MAP PAGE:* **3**

SMad **Madrona Nursery, Harden Road, Lydd, Kent TN29 9LT**
TEL: (0679) 20868 *CONTACT:* Liam MacKenzie
OPENING TIMES: 1400-2000 Tue-Thu 22nd Mar-31st Oct.
MIN MAIL ORDER UK: No minimum charge *MIN VALUE EC:* Nmc
CAT. COST: £1.00 *W/SALE or RETAIL:* Retail
SPECIALITIES: Unusual Shrubs, Conifers & Perennials. *MAP PAGE:* **3**

SMit **Mary & Peter Mitchell, 11 Wingle Tye Road, Burgess Hill, West Sussex RH15 9HR**
TEL: (0444) 236848 *CONTACT:* Mary & Peter Mitchell
OPENING TIMES: Appt only.
MIN MAIL ORDER UK: No minimum charge *MIN VALUE EC:* Nmc
CAT. COST: Stamp *W/SALE or RETAIL:* Retail
SPECIALITIES: Sempervivum, Jovibarba, Rosularia. *MAP PAGE:* **3**

SMrm **Merriments Nursery & Gardens,** Hawkhurst Road, Hurst Green, East Sussex TN19 7RA
TEL: (0580) 860666 *FAX:* (0580) 860324 *CONTACT:* Mark & Amanda Buchele
◆ *OPENING TIMES:* 0900-1730.
MAIL ORDER: No
CAT. COST: 75p *W/SALE or RETAIL:* Retail
SPECIALITIES: Tender & Hardy Perennials. *MAP PAGE:* **3**

SOgg **Stuart Ogg, Hopton, Fletching Street, Mayfield, East Sussex TN20 6TL**
TEL: (0435) 873322 *CONTACT:* Stuart Ogg
OPENING TIMES: Appt. only, unless advertised in local press.
MIN MAIL ORDER UK: No minimum charge *MIN VALUE EC:* Nmc
CAT. COST: Sae *W/SALE or RETAIL:* Retail
SPECIALITIES: Delphiniums. See also SEED Index

SOkh **Oakhurst Nursery,** Mardens Hill, Crowborough, East Sussex TN6 1XL
TEL: (0892) 653273 *CONTACT:* Stephanie Colton
OPENING TIMES: Most afternoons Apr-Oct. Please phone first.
MAIL ORDER: No
CAT. COST: 2 x 1st class *W/SALE or RETAIL:* Retail
SPECIALITIES: Common & uncommon Herbaceous Perennials. *MAP PAGE:* **3**

SOld **Oldbury Nurseries,** Brissenden Green, Bethersden, Kent TN26 3BJ
TEL: (0233) 820416 *CONTACT:* Peter & Wendy Dresman
OPENING TIMES: 0930-1700 daily 1st Feb-27th Jul.
MIN MAIL ORDER UK: £10.50 + p&p *MIN VALUE EC:* n/a
CAT. COST: 36p *W/SALE or RETAIL:* Retail
SPECIALITIES: Fuchsia. *MAP PAGE:* **3**

SPer **Perryhill Nurseries,** Hartfield, East Sussex TN7 4JP
TEL: (0892) 770377 *FAX:* (0892) 770929 *CONTACT:* P J Chapman (Manager)
OPENING TIMES: 0900-1700 daily March 1-Oct 31. 0900-1630 Nov 1-Feb 28.
MAIL ORDER: No *EXPORT:* Yes
CAT. COST: £1.65 *W/SALE or RETAIL:* Retail
SPECIALITIES: Wide range of Trees, Shrubs, Conifers, Rhododendron etc. Over 1000 Herbaceous varieties, 300 shrub & climbing Roses. *MAP PAGE:* **3**

SPla **Plaxtol Nurseries, The Spoute, Plaxtol, Sevenoaks, Kent TN15 0QR**
TEL: (0732) 810550 *CONTACT:* Tessa N & Donald M Forbes.
OPENING TIMES: 1000-1700 daily. Closed two weeks from Xmas eve.
MIN MAIL ORDER UK: £10.00 + p&p* *MIN VALUE EC:* £30.00 + p&p
CAT. COST: 2 x 1st class *W/SALE or RETAIL:* Retail
SPECIALITIES: Hardy Shrubs & Herbaceous esp. for Flower Arranger. Old-fashioned Roses, Ferns & Climbers. *NOTE: Mail Order Nov-Mar ONLY. *MAP PAGE:* **3**

SPou **Roger Poulett,** Nurse's Cottage, North Mundham, Chichester, Sussex PO20 6JY

TEL: Not available *CONTACT:* Roger Poulett
OPENING TIMES: By arrangement only.
MIN MAIL ORDER UK: £10.00 + p&p *MIN VALUE EC:* n/a
CAT. COST: 3 x 1st class *W/SALE or RETAIL:* Retail
SPECIALITIES: Hepaticas, Corydalis, Crocus, Cyclamen and many unusual plants. List in June. See also SEED Index. *MAP PAGE:* **2/3**

SReu **G Reuthe Ltd, Crown Point Nursery, Sevenoaks Road, Ightham, Nr Sevenoaks, Kent TN15 0HB**

TEL: (0732) 810694 *FAX:* (0732) 862166 *CONTACT:* C Tomlin & P Kindley
◆ *OPENING TIMES:* 0900-1630 Mon-Sat. 1000-1630 Sun & Bank Hols during Apr & May ONLY. Occasionally in June; check.
MIN MAIL ORDER UK: £25.00 + p&p *MIN VALUE EC:* £500.00* *EXPORT:* Yes
CAT. COST: £1.50 *W/SALE or RETAIL:* Retail
SPECIALITIES: Rhododendrons, Azaleas, Trees, Shrubs & Conifers. *NOTE: Certain plants only to EC & Export. *MAP PAGE:* **3**

SRms **Rumsey Gardens, 117 Drift Road, Clanfield, Hampshire**

TEL: (0705) 593367 *CONTACT:* Mr N R Giles
OPENING TIMES: 0900-1700 Mon-Sat & 1000-1700 Sun & Bank Hols.
MIN MAIL ORDER UK: No minimum charge *MIN VALUE EC:* Nmc
CAT. COST: W/SALE or RETAIL: Both
SPECIALITIES: Wide general range. National Collection of Cotoneaster. *MAP PAGE:* **2**

SRos **Rosewood Nurseries,** 70 Deansway Avenue, Sturry, Nr Canterbury, Kent CT2 0NN

TEL: (0227) 711071 *FAX:* (0227) 711071 *CONTACT:* Chris Searle
OPENING TIMES: 1000-1700 Thu-Sat Mar-Oct but please ring first. Other times by appt.
MAIL ORDER: No
CAT. COST: 2 x 1st class *W/SALE or RETAIL:* Retail
SPECIALITIES: Hemerocallis, mainly newer American varieties & Penstemon. *MAP PAGE:* **3**

SRum **Rumwood Nurseries, Langley, Maidstone, Kent ME17 3ND**

TEL: (0622) 861477 *FAX:* (0622) 863123 *CONTACT:* Mr R Fermor
OPENING TIMES: 0800-1700 Mon-Sat 1000-1700 Sun.
MIN MAIL ORDER UK: No minimum charge *MIN VALUE EC:* Nmc *EXPORT:* Yes
CAT. COST: Sae *W/SALE or RETAIL:* Both
SPECIALITIES: Roses & Trees. *MAP PAGE:* **3**

SSad **Mrs Jane Sadler,** Ingrams Cottage, Wisborough Green, Billingshurst, West Sussex RH14 0ER

TEL: (0403) 700234 *CONTACT:* Mrs Jane Sadler
OPENING TIMES: Irregular. Please phone first.
MAIL ORDER: No
CAT. COST: Sae *W/SALE or RETAIL:* Retail
SPECIALITIES: Small nursery specialising in less common varieties, esp. Auriculas, Lathyrus, Lavenders & Pelargoniums. *MAP PAGE:* **3**

SSmi **Alan C Smith,** 127 Leaves Green Road, Keston, Kent BR2 6DG

TEL: (0959) 572531 *CONTACT:* Alan C Smith
OPENING TIMES: Appt only.
MIN MAIL ORDER UK: No minimum charge *MIN VALUE EC:* n/a
CAT. COST: 50p *W/SALE or RETAIL:* Retail
SPECIALITIES: Over 1000 kinds of Sempervivum & Jovibarba. *MAP PAGE:* **3**

SSmt **Peter J Smith, Chanctonbury Nurseries, Rectory Lane, Ashington, Pulborough, Sussex RH20 3AS**

TEL: (0903) 892870 *FAX:* (0903) 893036 *CONTACT:* Peter J Smith
◆ *OPENING TIMES:* By appt. only
MIN MAIL ORDER UK: £6.00 + p&p *MIN VALUE EC:* £30.00 + p&p
CAT. COST: 50p *W/SALE or RETAIL:* Both
SPECIALITIES: The Princess® & Little Princess® range of hybrid Alstroemeria for conservatory & garden.

SSta **Starborough Nursery, Starborough Road, Marsh Green, Edenbridge, Kent TN8 5RB**

TEL: (0732) 865614 *FAX:* (0732) 862166 *CONTACT:* C Tomlin & P Kindley
◆ *OPENING TIMES:* 1000-1600 Thu-Mon. Closed Jan & Jul.
MIN MAIL ORDER UK: £25.00 + p&p *MIN VALUE EC:* £500.00* *EXPORT:* Yes
CAT. COST: £1.50 *W/SALE or RETAIL:* Retail
SPECIALITIES: Rare and unusual Shrubs especially Daphne, Acer, Rhododendron, Azalea, Magnolia & Hamamelis. *NOTE: Certain plants only to EC & Export. *MAP PAGE:* **3**

SSte **Stenbury Nursery, Smarts Cross, Southford, Nr Whitwell Isle of Wight PO38 2AG**

TEL: (0983) 840115 *CONTACT:* Claire Ewington/Jan Wyers
OPENING TIMES: 1000-1700 daily.
MIN MAIL ORDER UK: £10.00 + p&p* *MIN VALUE EC:* £10.00 + p&p
CAT. COST: 3 x 1st class *W/SALE or RETAIL:* Retail
SPECIALITIES: Hemerocallis, Penstemon & Osteospermum. *NOTE: Mail Order for Hemerocallis only. *MAP PAGE:* **2**

SSvw **Southview Nurseries, Chequers Lane, Eversley Cross, Basingstoke, Hampshire RG27 0NT**

TEL: (0734) 732206 *CONTACT:* Mark Trenear
◆ *OPENING TIMES:* 0900-1300 & 1400-1630 Thu-Sat 1st Feb-31st Oct. Nov-Jan by appt. only.
MIN MAIL ORDER UK: No minimum charge *MIN VALUE EC:* Nmc
CAT. COST: Free *W/SALE or RETAIL:* Retail
SPECIALITIES: Unusual Hardy plants, specialising in Old Fashioned Pinks & period plants. *MAP PAGE:* **2/3**

STil **Tile Barn Nursery, Standen Street, Iden Green, Benenden, Kent TN17 4LB**

TEL: (0580) 240221 *CONTACT:* Peter Moore
OPENING TIMES: 0900-1700 Wed-Sat.
MIN MAIL ORDER UK: £10.00 + p&p *MIN VALUE EC:* £25.00 + p&p *EXPORT:* Yes
CAT. COST: Sae *W/SALE or RETAIL:* Both
SPECIALITIES: Cyclamen species. *MAP PAGE:* **3**

STre **Peter Trenear, Chantreyland, Chequers Lane, Eversley Cross, Hampshire RG27 0NX**

TEL: (0734) 732300 *CONTACT:* Peter Trenear
◆ *OPENING TIMES:* 0900-1630 Mon-Sat.
MIN MAIL ORDER UK: £5.00 + p&p *MIN VALUE EC:* £10.00 + p&p
CAT. COST: 1 x 1st class *W/SALE or RETAIL:* Retail
SPECIALITIES: Trees, Shrubs, Conifers & Pinus. *MAP PAGE:* **2/3**

SUsu **Usual & Unusual Plants,** Onslow House, Magham Down, Hailsham, East Sussex BN27 1PL

TEL: (0323) 840967 *CONTACT:* Jennie Maillard
OPENING TIMES: 0900-1630 Mon-Fri 0930-1700 Sat & Sun 14th Feb-31st Oct. Tue & Wed only in Aug. Ring before visiting
MAIL ORDER: No
CAT. COST: 1x1st + Sae *W/SALE or RETAIL:* Retail
SPECIALITIES: Small quantities of a wide variety of unusual perennials, esp. Erysimum, Euphorbia, Hardy Geraniums & Penstemon. *MAP PAGE:* **3**

SWas **Washfield Nursery,** Horn's Road (A229), Hawkhurst, Kent TN18 4QU

TEL: (0580) 752522 *CONTACT:* Elizabeth Strangman & G Gough
OPENING TIMES: 1000-1700 Wed-Sat.
MAIL ORDER: No
CAT. COST: 4 x 1st class *W/SALE or RETAIL:* Retail
SPECIALITIES: Alpine, Herbaceous & Woodland, many unusual & rare. Helleborus, Epimedium, Hardy Geranium. *MAP PAGE:* **3**

SWat **Water Meadow Nursery, Cheriton, Nr Alresford, Hampshire SO24 0JT**

TEL: (0962) 771895 *FAX:* (0962) 771895 *CONTACT:* Mrs Sandy Worth
◆ *OPENING TIMES:* 0900-1700 Fri & Sat, 1400-1700 Sun, Mar-Nov.
MIN MAIL ORDER UK: £10.00 + p&p *MIN VALUE EC:* £50.00 + p&p *EXPORT:* Yes
CAT. COST: 3 x 1st class *W/SALE or RETAIL:* Both
SPECIALITIES: Water Lilies, extensive Water Garden plants, unusual Herbaceous Perennials, aromatic & hardy Shrubs & Climbers. *MAP PAGE:* **2**

SWes **Westwood Nursery, 65 Yorkland Avenue, Welling, Kent DA16 2LE**

TEL: 081 301-0886 *CONTACT:* Mr S Edwards
OPENING TIMES: Not open.
MIN MAIL ORDER UK: No minimum charge *MIN VALUE EC:* £50.00 + p&p
CAT. COST: Sae *W/SALE or RETAIL:* Retail
SPECIALITIES: Pleiones & Hardy Orchids.

SWyc **Wychwood Carp Farm, Farnham Road, Odiham, Basingstoke, Hampshire RG25 1HS**

TEL: (0256) 702800 *CONTACT:* Reg, Ann & Clair Henley
OPENING TIMES: 1000-1800 Fri-Wed & Bank Hols.
MIN MAIL ORDER UK: £1.00 + p&p *MIN VALUE EC:* £1.00 + p&p *EXPORT:* Yes
CAT. COST: 1 x 1st class *W/SALE or RETAIL:* Retail
SPECIALITIES: Aquatics. Nymphaea, Moisture loving, Marginals & Oxygenating plants. Moist & Water Iris inc. American ensata. *MAP PAGE:* **2/3**

WAbb **Abbey Dore Court Gardens,** Abbeydore, nr Hereford, Herefordshire HR2 0AD

TEL: (0981) 240419 *CONTACT:* Mrs C Ward
OPENING TIMES: 1100-1800 Thu-Tue from Mar-3rd Sun Oct.
MAIL ORDER: No
CAT. COST: None issued *W/SALE or RETAIL:* Retail
SPECIALITIES: Shrubs & hardy Perennials, many unusual, which may be seen growing in the garden. National Collection of Euphorbia. Some Seeds available from garden. *MAP PAGE:* **5**

WAbe **Aberconwy Nursery,** Graig, Glan Conwy, Colwyn Bay, Clwyd LL28 5TL

TEL: (0492) 580875 *CONTACT:* Dr & Mrs K G Lever
OPENING TIMES: 0900-1700 Tue-Sun.
MAIL ORDER: No
CAT. COST: 1 x 2nd class *W/SALE or RETAIL:* Retail
SPECIALITIES: Alpines, including specialist varieties, esp. Autumn Gentians. Trees, Shrubs, Conifers & Herbaceous plants. *MAP PAGE:* **4**

WAce **International Acers,** Acer Place, Coalash Lane, Hanbury, Bromsgrove, Worcestershire B60 4EY

TEL: (0527) 821774 *CONTACT:* D L Horton
◆ *OPENING TIMES:* 0900-1730 Sat, Sun & Bank Hols and by appt.
MAIL ORDER: No
CAT. COST: Sae *W/SALE or RETAIL:* Both
SPECIALITIES: Acers. (Some cultivars in very short supply at present). *MAP PAGE:* **5**

WAct **Acton Beauchamp Roses, Acton Beauchamp, Worcester Hereford & Worcester WR6 5AE**

TEL: (0531) 640433 *FAX:* (0531) 640802 *CONTACT:* Lindsay Bousfield
OPENING TIMES: 1000-1700 Tue-Fri & 1400-1700 Sun Mar-Jul & Oct-Dec. 1000-1700 Sat-Mon Bank Hols. Also by appt.
MIN MAIL ORDER UK: No minimum charge *MIN VALUE EC:* Nmc *EXPORT:* Yes
CAT. COST: 3 x 1st class *W/SALE or RETAIL:* Both
SPECIALITIES: Species Roses, Old Roses, modern shrub, English, climbers, ramblers & ground-cover Roses. *MAP PAGE:* **5**

WBod **Bodnant Garden Nursery Ltd., Tal-y-Cafn, Colwyn Bay, Clwyd LL28 5RE**

TEL: (0492) 650460 *FAX:* (0492) 650448 *CONTACT:* Martin Puddle (Gen. Man.)
◆ *OPENING TIMES:* All year.
MIN MAIL ORDER UK: £10.00 + p&p *MIN VALUE EC:* £100.00 + p&p
CAT. COST: 3 x 1st class *W/SALE or RETAIL:* Retail
SPECIALITIES: Rhododendron, Camellia & Magnolia. Wide range of unusual Trees and Shrubs. *MAP PAGE:* **4**

WBon **S & E Bond,** Gardeners Cottage, Letton, Herefordshire HR3 6DH

TEL: (0544) 328422 after 6 *CONTACT:* Miss S Bond
OPENING TIMES: 1000-1800 Wed-Sat, 1300-1700 Sun, 1st Mar-24th Dec.
MIN MAIL ORDER UK: No minimum charge *MIN VALUE EC:* n/a
CAT. COST: A5 Sae *W/SALE or RETAIL:* Retail
SPECIALITIES: Shade plants. *MAP PAGE:* **5**

WBou Bouts Cottage Nurseries, Bouts Lane, Inkberrow, Worcestershire WR7 4HP

TEL: (0386) 792923 *CONTACT:* M & S Roberts
OPENING TIMES: Not open to the public.
MIN MAIL ORDER UK: No minimum charge *MIN VALUE EC:* Nmc
CAT. COST: Sae *W/SALE or RETAIL:* Retail
SPECIALITIES: Viola.

WByw Byways, Daisy Lane, Whittington, Oswestry, Shropshire

TEL: (0691) 659539 *CONTACT:* Barbara Molesworth
OPENING TIMES: 0900-1700 Mon Mar-Nov. Please phone first.*
MAIL ORDER: No
CAT. COST: Sae+1x2nd class *W/SALE or RETAIL:* Retail
SPECIALITIES: Asters, Campanulas, Hardy Geraniums, Pulmonarias & Salvias. *NOTE: Also at Newtown Market on Tue & Oswestry on Wed. *MAP PAGE:* **7**

WCel Celyn Vale Nurseries, Carrog, Corwen, Clwyd LL21 9LD

TEL: (0490) 83671 *FAX:* (0490) 83671 *CONTACT:* Andrew McConnell
◆ *OPENING TIMES:* Please telephone first. March to end-Oct.
MIN MAIL ORDER UK: 3 Plants + p&p *MIN VALUE EC:* 3 plants + p&p *EXPORT:* Yes
CAT. COST: 1 x 1st class *W/SALE or RETAIL:* Both
SPECIALITIES: Hardy Eucalyptus & Acacia. *MAP PAGE:* **4**

WCHb The Cottage Herbery, Mill House, Boraston, Nr Tenbury Wells, Worcestershire WR15 8LZ

TEL: (058 479) 575 *CONTACT:* K & R Hurst
OPENING TIMES: 1000-1800 Sun and by appt.
MAIL ORDER: No
CAT. COST: 4 x 2nd class *W/SALE or RETAIL:* Retail
SPECIALITIES: Over 400 varieties of Herbs. Aromatic & scented foliage plants, esp. Symphytum, Pulmonaria, Lamium, Monarda, Ajuga & Salvia. Also scented Pelargoniums. *MAP PAGE:* **2**

WChe Checkley Waterplants, The Knoll House, Checkley, Herefordshire HR1 4ND

TEL: (0432) 860672 *CONTACT:* Mrs M P Bennett
OPENING TIMES: By appt. only.
MIN MAIL ORDER UK: No minimum charge *MIN VALUE EC:* n/a
CAT. COST: Sae *W/SALE or RETAIL:* Both
SPECIALITIES: Pond, Bog and moisture loving plants. *MAP PAGE:* **5**

WChr Paul Christian - Rare Plants, PO Box 468, Wrexham, Clwyd LL13 9XR

TEL: (0978) 366399 *FAX:* (0978) 366399 *CONTACT:* Dr. P Christian
OPENING TIMES: Not open.
MIN MAIL ORDER UK: No minimum charge *MIN VALUE EC:* Nmc *EXPORT:* Yes
CAT. COST: 3x1st or $3 *W/SALE or RETAIL:* Both
SPECIALITIES: Bulbs, Corms, Tubers, especially Colchicum, Crocus, Erythronium, Fritillaria, Iris, Rhodohypoxis & Trillium. Also Greenhouse bulbs.

WCla John Clayfield, Llanbrook Alpine Nursery, Hopton Castle, Clunton, Shropshire SY7 0QG

TEL: (05474) 298 *CONTACT:* John Clayfield
OPENING TIMES: Daily - but please check first.
MAIL ORDER: No
CAT. COST: None issued *W/SALE or RETAIL:* Both
SPECIALITIES: Alpines & Wildflowers. *MAP PAGE:* **5/7**

WCoo Mrs Susan Cooper, Firlands Cottage, Bishop Frome, Worcestershire WR6 5BA

TEL: (0885) 490358* *CONTACT:* Mrs Susan Cooper
OPENING TIMES: Appt only.
MIN MAIL ORDER UK: £20.00 + p&p *MIN VALUE EC:* £20.00 + p&p
CAT. COST: Small Sae *W/SALE or RETAIL:* Retail
SPECIALITIES: Rare & unusual Trees & Shrubs. Provenances on request. *NOTE Cheney Court, Bishops Frome, Worcs. WR6 5AS until June 6th 1994. (No phone). *MAP PAGE:* **5**

WCot Cotswold Garden Flowers, 1 Waterside, Evesham, Worcestershire WR11 6BS

TEL: (0386) 47337 *CONTACT:* Bob Brown
OPENING TIMES: 0800-1630 Mon-Fri all year. 1000-1800 Sat & Sun Mar-Sep, Oct-Feb by appt.
MIN MAIL ORDER UK: No minimum charge* *MIN VALUE EC:* Nmc *EXPORT:* Yes
CAT. COST: Free *W/SALE or RETAIL:* Retail
SPECIALITIES: Easy & unusual Perennials for the Flower Garden. NOTE: Nursery at Sands Lane, Badsey. *NOTE: NO Mail Order to UK, only to Scotland & Overseas. *MAP PAGE:* **5**

WCra Cranesbill Nursery, White Cottage, Stock Green, Nr. Redditch, Worcestershire B96 6SZ

TEL: (0386) 792414 *CONTACT:* Mrs S M Bates
OPENING TIMES: 1000-1700 Fri-Wed 15th March-mid Oct. August by appt. only.
MIN MAIL ORDER UK: No minimum charge *MIN VALUE EC:* Nmc
CAT. COST: 4 x 1st class *W/SALE or RETAIL:* Retail
SPECIALITIES: Hardy Geraniums. NOTE:- Mail Order Autumn only. *MAP PAGE:* **5**

WCru Crûg Farm Plants, Griffith's Crossing, Nr Caernarfon, Gwynedd LL55 1TU

TEL: (0248) 670232 *FAX:* (0248) 670232 *CONTACT:* Mr B Wynn-Jones
◆ *OPENING TIMES:* 1000-1800 Thu-Sun 26th Feb-25th Sep & Bank Hols.
MAIL ORDER: No
CAT. COST: Sae+1x2nd class *W/SALE or RETAIL:* Both
SPECIALITIES: Shade plants, climbers, Hardy Geraniums, Pulmonarias, rare Shrubs, Tropaeolums, Herbaceous & bulbous incl. self-collected new introductions from the far East. *MAP PAGE:* **4**

WDav Kim W Davis, Lingen Alpine Nursery, Lingen, Nr Bucknell, Shropshire SY7 0DY

TEL: (0544) 267720 *CONTACT:* Kim W Davis
◆ *OPENING TIMES:* 1000-1800 daily Feb-Oct. Fri-Sun Nov-Jan by appt.
MIN MAIL ORDER UK: No minimum charge *MIN VALUE EC:* Nmc
CAT. COST: Sae *W/SALE or RETAIL:* Both
SPECIALITIES: Alpines & Rock Plants, esp. Androsace, Aquilegia, Campanula, Primula & Penstemon. *MAP PAGE:* **5**

WDib Dibley's Nurseries, Llanelidan, Ruthin, Clwyd LL15 2LG

TEL: (0978) 790677 *CONTACT:* R Dibley
◆ *OPENING TIMES:* 0900-1700 daily Apr-Sept.
MIN MAIL ORDER UK: No minimum charge *MIN VALUE EC:* £20.00 + p&p
CAT. COST: Sae *W/SALE or RETAIL:* Both
SPECIALITIES: Streptocarpus, Columneas, other Gesneriads & Begonias. *MAP PAGE:* **4**

WDin Dingle Nurseries, Welshpool, Powys SY21 9JD

TEL: (0938) 555145 *FAX:* (0938) 554734* *CONTACT:* Ceri Hamer
OPENING TIMES: 0900-1700 Wed-Mon. (Wholesale Mon-Sat only).
MAIL ORDER: No
CAT. COST: None issued *W/SALE or RETAIL:* Both
SPECIALITIES: Trees, Shrubs & Conifers. Herbaceous, Forestry & Hedging Tress. *Wholesale FAX number. *MAP PAGE:* **4/7**

WEas Eastgrove Cottage Garden Nursery, Sankyns Green, Nr Shrawley, Little Witley, Worcestershire WR6 6LQ

TEL: (0299) 896389 *CONTACT:* Malcolm & Carol Skinner
OPENING TIMES: 1400-1700 Thu-Mon 1st Apr-31st July. Closed Aug. 1400-1700 Thu, Fri & Sat 1st Sep-15th Oct.
MAIL ORDER: No
CAT. COST: 5 x 2nd class *W/SALE or RETAIL:* Retail
SPECIALITIES: Outstanding country flower garden from which exceedingly wide range of well grown hardy & half-hardy plants are produced. *MAP PAGE:* **5**

WElm The Garden at the Elms Nursery, Frenchlands Lane, Lower Broadheath, Worcestershire WR2 6QU

TEL: (0905) 640841 *FAX:* (0905) 640675 *CONTACT:* Mrs E Stewart
OPENING TIMES: 1000-1600 Tue & Wed 1st Apr-30th Sep.
MAIL ORDER: No
CAT. COST: 3 x 1st class *W/SALE or RETAIL:* Retail
SPECIALITIES: Unusual hardy plants & cottage garden favourites, esp. Geraniums, all grown on the nursery from stock in an old farmhouse garden. *MAP PAGE:* **5**

WFib **Fibrex Nurseries Ltd, Honeybourne Road, Pebworth, Stratford-on-Avon, Warwickshire CV37 8XT**
TEL: (0789) 720788 *FAX:* (0789) 721162 *CONTACT:* H M D Key & R L Godard-Key
OPENING TIMES: 1200-1700. Hellebores only available for collection mid Jan-end Mar.
MIN MAIL ORDER UK: No minimum charge *MIN VALUE EC:* £10.00 + p&p *EXPORT:* Yes
CAT. COST: 2 x 2nd class *W/SALE or RETAIL:* Both
SPECIALITIES: Ivys, Ferns & Pelargoniums. *MAP PAGE:* **5**

WFou **Four Counties Nursery,** Todenham, Moreton-in-Marsh, Gloucestershire GL56 9PN
TEL: (0608) 650522/650591 *FAX:* (0608) 650591 *CONTACT:* Sandra Taylor
OPENING TIMES: 0900-1800 daily Summer, 0900-1700 Mon-Sat, 1000-1700 Sun in Winter.
MIN MAIL ORDER UK: £30.00 + p&p *MIN VALUE EC:* n/a
CAT. COST: £1.00 *W/SALE or RETAIL:* Both
SPECIALITIES: Citrus & Conservatory plants, plus rare & unusual Trees & Shrubs *MAP PAGE:* **5**

WFox **Foxbrush Gardens,** Portdinorwic, Gwynedd LL56 4JZ
TEL: (0248) 670463 *CONTACT:* Mrs J Osborne
OPENING TIMES: Apr-end Sep by prior arrangement only.
MAIL ORDER: No
CAT. COST: Sae *W/SALE or RETAIL:* Retail
SPECIALITIES: Acers & Camellias. Conifers & hardy Perennials. *MAP PAGE:* **4**

WFro **Fron Nursery, Fron Issa, Rhiwlas, Oswestry, Shropshire SY10 7JH**
TEL: (069176) 605 *CONTACT:* Thoby Miller
OPENING TIMES: By appt. only. Please phone first.
MIN MAIL ORDER UK: £20.00 + p&p *MIN VALUE EC:* £50.00 + p&p *EXPORT:* Yes
CAT. COST: Sae *W/SALE or RETAIL:* Both
SPECIALITIES: Rare and unusual Trees, Shrubs & Perennials. *MAP PAGE:* **4/7**

WGor **Gordon's Nursery,** 1 Cefnpennar Cottages, Cefnpenner, Mountain Ash mid Glamorganshire CF45 4EE
TEL: (0443) 474593 *FAX:* (0443) 475835 *CONTACT:* D A Gordon
OPENING TIMES: 1000-1800 1st Mar-31st Oct daily. 1100-1600 1st Nov-28th Feb Sat & Sun only.
MAIL ORDER: No
CAT. COST: 2 x 1st class *W/SALE or RETAIL:* Retail
SPECIALITIES: Conifers, Shrubs & Alpines. *MAP PAGE:* **4**

WGre **Greenacres Nursery,** Bringsty, Worcestershire WR6 5TA
TEL: (0885) 482206 *CONTACT:* D & M Everett
OPENING TIMES: Appt only.
MAIL ORDER: No
CAT. COST: Free *W/SALE or RETAIL:* Both
SPECIALITIES: Heathers. *MAP PAGE:* **5**

WGwy **Gwydir Plants,** Plas Muriau, Betws-y-coed, Gwynedd LL24 0HD
TEL: (0690) 710201 *FAX:* (06906) 379 *CONTACT:* Mrs D Southgate & Mrs L Schärer
OPENING TIMES: 1100-1800 Tue-Sun & Bank Hols Mar-Oct.
MAIL ORDER: No
CAT. COST: 2 x 1st class *W/SALE or RETAIL:* Retail
SPECIALITIES: Herbs, Wild flowers & Cottage garden plants including many unusual ones.
MAP PAGE: **4**

WHal **Hall Farm Nursery,** Kinnerley, Nr Oswestry, Shropshire SY10 8DH
TEL: (0691) 682219 *CONTACT:* Mrs C Ffoulkes-Jones
OPENING TIMES: 1000-1700 Tue-Sun 1st Mar-30th Oct 1994. Closed Mon ex. Bank Hols.
MAIL ORDER: No
CAT. COST: 4 x 1st class *W/SALE or RETAIL:* Retail
SPECIALITIES: Unusual Herbaceous plants. Also Alpines & Carnivorous plants. *MAP PAGE:* **7**

WHaw **Sue Hawthorne Gardens,,** The Yews, Clunbury, Craven Arms, Shropshire SY7 0HG
TEL: (05887) 428 *CONTACT:* Sue Hawthorne
OPENING TIMES: Daily by appt.
MIN MAIL ORDER UK: No minimum charge *MIN VALUE EC:* n/a
CAT. COST: 3 x 2nd class *W/SALE or RETAIL:* Both
SPECIALITIES: Pre-Victorian Cottage Garden plants. Garden design. *MAP PAGE:* **5**

WHCG Hunts Court Garden & Nursery, North Nibley, Dursley, Gloucestershire GL11 6DZ

TEL: (0453) 547440 *CONTACT:* T K & M M Marshall
◆ *OPENING TIMES:* Nursery 0900-1700 Tue-Sat ex Aug. Garden 1400-1800 ex Aug. Also by appt.
MAIL ORDER: No
CAT. COST: 3 x 2nd class *W/SALE or RETAIL:* Retail
SPECIALITIES: Old Rose species & climbers. Hardy Geraniums. Shrubby Potentilla, Penstemon & unusual shrubs. *MAP PAGE:* **5**

WHCr Hergest Croft Gardens, Kington, Herefordshire HR5 3EG

TEL: (0544) 230160 *CONTACT:* Stephen Lloyd
OPENING TIMES: 1330-1830 daily Apr-Oct.
MAIL ORDER: No
CAT. COST: None issued *W/SALE or RETAIL:* Retail
SPECIALITIES: Acer, Betula & unusual woody plants. *MAP PAGE:* **5**

WHen Henllys Lodge Plants, Henllys Lodge, Beaumaris, Anglesey, Gwynedd LL58 8HU

TEL: (0248) 810106 *CONTACT:* Mrs E Lane
OPENING TIMES: 1100-1700 Tue, Wed, Fri, Sat, Sun & by appt. Apr-Oct.
MAIL ORDER: No
CAT. COST: 2 x 1st class *W/SALE or RETAIL:* Retail
SPECIALITIES: Hardy Geranium, Ground cover & cottage style Perennials. See also SEED Index. *MAP PAGE:* **4**

WHer The Herb Garden, Plant Hunter's Nursery, Capel Ulo, Pentre Berw, Gaerwen, Anglesey, Gwynedd LL60 6LF

TEL: (0248) 421064 *CONTACT:* Corinne & David Tremaine-Stevenson
OPENING TIMES: 0900-1700 Wed-Sun all year & Bank Hols. (Please ring first out of season).
MIN MAIL ORDER UK: £15.00 + p&p *MIN VALUE EC:* n/a
CAT. COST: List £1 in stamps *W/SALE or RETAIL:* Retail
SPECIALITIES: Wide range of Herbs, Wild flowers, unusual Perennials. Scented Pelargoniums, Salvia, old Roses & Hardy Geraniums. *MAP PAGE:* **4**

WHig Highfield Plant & Garden Centre, Bristol Road, Whitminster, Gloucestershire GL2 7PB

TEL: (0452) 741444 *FAX:* (0452) 740750 *CONTACT:* Mr P Evans (Garden Centre Manager)
OPENING TIMES: 0900-1800 Mon-Sat, 1000-1800 Sun.
MIN MAIL ORDER UK: No minimum charge *MIN VALUE EC:* n/a
CAT. COST: Free *W/SALE or RETAIL:* Retail
SPECIALITIES: Wide general range including Fruit. *NOTE:- Mail Order address, Highfield Nurseries, School Lane, Whitminster, Glos. GL2 7PL. *MAP PAGE:* **5**

WHil Hillview Hardy Plants, Worfield, Nr Bridgnorth, Shropshire WV15 5NT

TEL: (074 64) 454 *CONTACT:* Ingrid Millington
OPENING TIMES: 1000-1700 Mon-Sat Mar-mid Oct. By appt. mid Oct-Feb.
MIN MAIL ORDER UK: £10.00 + p&p *MIN VALUE EC:* £10.00 + p&p *EXPORT:* Yes
CAT. COST: 4 x 2nd class *W/SALE or RETAIL:* Both
SPECIALITIES: Hardy Perennials & Alpines. Contract growing for Wholesale. *MAP PAGE:* **7**

WHol Holberrow Aquatics, Holberrow Green, Astwood Bank, Redditch West Midlands B96 6SB

TEL: (0386) 792521 *CONTACT:* B L Fowler
OPENING TIMES: 0830-1800
MIN MAIL ORDER UK: No minimum charge *MIN VALUE EC:* n/a
CAT. COST: 50p *W/SALE or RETAIL:* Both
SPECIALITIES: Aquatic plants, Bog plants. Plants for pools and surrounds. *MAP PAGE:* **5**

WHoo Hoo House Nursery, Hoo House, Gloucester Road, Tewkesbury, Gloucestershire GL20 7DA

TEL: (0684) 293389 *CONTACT:* Robin & Julie Ritchie
◆ *OPENING TIMES:* 1400-1700 Mon-Sat.
MIN MAIL ORDER UK: £5.00 + p&p* *MIN VALUE EC:* n/a
CAT. COST: 3 x 1st class *W/SALE or RETAIL:* Both
SPECIALITIES: Wide range of Herbaceous & Alpines - some unusual. *NOTE: Mail Order only available Oct-Mar. *MAP PAGE:* **5**

WHow How Caple Court Gardens, How Caple Court, How Caple, Herefordshire HR1 4SX
TEL: (0989) 86626 *FAX:* (0989) 86611 *CONTACT:* P L Lee
OPENING TIMES: 0900-1700 Mon-Sat all year also Sun 1st May-31st Oct.
MAIL ORDER: No
CAT. COST: Sae *W/SALE or RETAIL:* Retail
SPECIALITIES: English & old Rose varieties. Old Apples varieties. Herbaceous Perennials.
MAP PAGE: **5**

WJas Paul Jasper (Trees & Roses), The Lighthouse, Bridge Street, Leominster, Herefordshire HR6 8DU
TEL: FAX only for orders. *FAX:* (0568) 616499 *CONTACT:* Paul Jasper
OPENING TIMES: Not open for Retail sales.
MIN MAIL ORDER UK: £15.00 + p&p *MIN VALUE EC:* £50.00 + p&p
CAT. COST: 2 x 1st class *W/SALE or RETAIL:* Both
SPECIALITIES: Full range of Fruit & Ornamental Trees. Worthy old & modern Apple varieties grown on MM 111 (Standards), MM 106 (General) & M 27 (Dwarfing) root stock.

WJun Jungle Giants, Plough Farm, Wigmore, Herefordshire HR6 9UW
TEL: (0568) 86708 *FAX:* (0568) 86383 *CONTACT:* Michael Brisbane
OPENING TIMES: Daily - by appt. only please.
MIN MAIL ORDER UK: £10.00 + p&p *MIN VALUE EC:* £25.00 + p&p *EXPORT:* Yes
CAT. COST: £5.75 info.pack *W/SALE or RETAIL:* Both
SPECIALITIES: Bamboo and hardy plants for tropical effect gardens. *MAP PAGE:* **5**

WKif Kiftsgate Court Gardens, Kiftsgate Court, Chipping Camden, Gloucestershire GL55 6LW
TEL: (0386) 438777 *CONTACT:* Mrs J Chambers
OPENING TIMES: 1400-1800 Wed, Thu & Sun Apr 1st-Sep 30th & Bank Hol Mons.
MAIL ORDER: No
CAT. COST: None issued *W/SALE or RETAIL:* Retail
SPECIALITIES: Small range of unusual plants. *MAP PAGE:* **5**

WMal Marshall's Malmaison, 4 The Damsells, Tetbury, Gloucestershire GL8 8JA
TEL: (0666) 502589 *CONTACT:* J M & M I Marshall
◆ *OPENING TIMES:* By appt. only.
MIN MAIL ORDER UK: £14.50 incl. p&p *MIN VALUE EC:* £14.50 incl p&p *EXPORT:* Yes
CAT. COST: Sae *W/SALE or RETAIL:* Both
SPECIALITIES: Malmaison Carnations.

WMAq Merebrook Aquatics, Merebrook Farm, Hanley Swan, Worcester, Worcestershire WR8 0DX
TEL: (0684) 310950 *CONTACT:* Roger Kings
OPENING TIMES: 1000-1700 Tue-Sat Easter-Sep. Sun by appt. only.
MIN MAIL ORDER UK: No minimum charge *MIN VALUE EC:* n/a
CAT. COST: Sae *W/SALE or RETAIL:* Retail
SPECIALITIES: Nymphaea (Water Lilies) & other Aquatic plants. *MAP PAGE:* **5**

WMar Marley Bank Nursery, Bottom Lane, Whitbourne, Worcester WR6 5RU
TEL: (0886) 821576 *CONTACT:* Roger & Sue Norman
OPENING TIMES: By appt. and as for National Garden Scheme.
MAIL ORDER: No
CAT. COST: Sae *W/SALE or RETAIL:* Retail
SPECIALITIES: Alpines, Cyclamen, tender Perennials, Penstemon & Violas. *MAP PAGE:* **5**

WMer Merton Nurseries, Holyhead Road, Bicton, Shrewsbury, Shropshire SY3 8EF
TEL: (0743) 850773 *FAX:* (0743) 850773 *CONTACT:* Jessica Pannett
◆ *OPENING TIMES:* 0900-1730 daily ex. Christmas & New Year
MAIL ORDER: No
CAT. COST: 2 x 1st class *W/SALE or RETAIL:* Retail
SPECIALITIES: Hardy Perennials & Clematis *MAP PAGE:* **7**

WMEx Marston Exotics, Brampton Lane, Madley, Herefordshire HR2 9LX
TEL: (0981) 251140 *FAX:* (0981) 251649 *CONTACT:* Paul Gardner
OPENING TIMES: 0800-1630 Mon-Fri all year, 1300-1700 Sat & Sun Mar-Oct.
MIN MAIL ORDER UK: See Cat. for details *MIN VALUE EC:* £100.00 + p&p *EXPORT:* Yes
CAT. COST: £1.00 *W/SALE or RETAIL:* Both
SPECIALITIES: Carnivorous plants. *MAP PAGE:* **5**

WMou Mount Pleasant Trees, Rockhampton, Berkeley, Gloucestershire GL13 9DU

TEL: (0454) 260348 *CONTACT:* G Locke
◆ *OPENING TIMES:* Appt only.
MIN MAIL ORDER UK: £20.00 + p&p* *MIN VALUE EC:* £100.00 + p&p*
CAT. COST: 3 x 2nd class *W/SALE or RETAIL:* Both
SPECIALITIES: Wide range of Trees for forestry, hedging, woodlands & gardens esp. Tilia & Sequoiadendron. *NOTE: Only some items available by Mail Order. *MAP PAGE:* **5**

WNdy Nordybank Nurseries, Clee St Margaret, Craven Arms, Shropshire SY7 9EF

TEL: (0584 75) 322 *CONTACT:* P J Bolton
OPENING TIMES: 1000-1800 Mon, Wed & Sun Easter-mid Oct.
MAIL ORDER: No
CAT. COST: 50p in stamps *W/SALE or RETAIL:* Retail
SPECIALITIES: Native & Hardy Herbaceous plants esp. Geraniums & Campanulas. *MAP PAGE:* **5/7**

WNor Andrew Norfield Trees & Seeds, Lower Meend, St Briavels, Gloucestershire GL15 6RW

TEL: (0594) 530134 *FAX:* (0594) 530113 *CONTACT:* Andrew Norfield
OPENING TIMES: Not open.
MIN MAIL ORDER UK: £3.00 + p&p *MIN VALUE EC:* £3.00 + p&p *EXPORT:* Yes
CAT. COST: 1 x 1st class *W/SALE or RETAIL:* Retail
SPECIALITIES: Wide range of Tree seedlings for growing on. Acer, Betula, Stewartia & pregerminated seed. See also SEED Index.

WOak Oak Cottage Herb Garden, Nesscliffe, nr Shrewsbury, Shropshire SY4 1DB

TEL: (074381) 262 *FAX:* (074381) 262 *CONTACT:* Jane & Edward Bygott.
◆ *OPENING TIMES:* Usually 1100-1800 weekdays & weekends.
MIN MAIL ORDER UK: £3.50 + p&p *MIN VALUE EC:* £10.00 + p&p
CAT. COST: 3 x 1st class *W/SALE or RETAIL:* Retail
SPECIALITIES: Herbs, Wild flowers & Cottage plants. Design of Herb Gardens. *MAP PAGE:* **7**

WOld Old Court Nurseries, Colwall, Nr Malvern, Worcestershire WR13 6QE

TEL: (0684) 40416 *CONTACT:* Paul & Meriel Picton
OPENING TIMES: 1000-1300 & 1415-1730 Wed-Sun Apr-Oct. 1415-1700 Wed-Fri (by appt.) Nov-Mar.
MIN MAIL ORDER UK: £15.00 + p&p *MIN VALUE EC:* £15.00 + p&p
CAT. COST: 2 x 1st class *W/SALE or RETAIL:* Retail
SPECIALITIES: National collection of Michaelmas Daisies. Herbaceous Perennials & Alpines. (Mail order for Asters only). *MAP PAGE:* **5**

WOMNThe Old Manor Nursery, Twyning, Gloucestershire GL20 6DB

TEL: (0684) 293516 *CONTACT:* Mrs Joan Wilder
OPENING TIMES: 1400-1700, or dusk if earlier, Mons 1st Mar-31st Oct. Winter visits by appt.
MAIL ORDER: No
CAT. COST: 30p+A5 Sae *W/SALE or RETAIL:* Retail
SPECIALITIES: Predominately Alpines, small supply of unusual and rare varieties of other Perennial plants. *MAP PAGE:* **5**

WPat Chris Pattison, Brookend, Pendock, Gloucestershire GL19 3PL

TEL: (0531) 650480 *CONTACT:* Chris Pattison
◆ *OPENING TIMES:* 0900-1700 Mon-Fri. Weekends by appt. only.
MAIL ORDER: No
CAT. COST: 3 x 1st class *W/SALE or RETAIL:* Both
SPECIALITIES: Choice & rare Shrubs and Alpines. Grafted Stock - esp. Japanese Maples, Liquidambars & Daphne. *MAP PAGE:* **5**

WPbr Perrybrook Nursery, Brook Cottage, Wykey, Ruyton XI Towns, Shropshire SY4 1JA

TEL: (0939) 261120 *CONTACT:* Gayle Williams
OPENING TIMES: By appointment. Mar-Oct open most days.
MAIL ORDER: No
CAT. COST: 3 x 1st class *W/SALE or RETAIL:* Both
SPECIALITIES: Herbaceous Perennials. Many unusual varieties available in small numbers, esp. Tricyrtis. *MAP PAGE:* **7**

WPer **Perhill Nurseries,** Worcester Road, Great Witley, Worcestershire WR6 6JT
TEL: (0299) 896329 *FAX:* (0299) 896990 *CONTACT:* Jon Baker & Duncan Straw
OPENING TIMES: 0900-1800 Mon-Sat 0900-1700 Sun.
MAIL ORDER: No
CAT. COST: 6 x 2nd class *W/SALE or RETAIL:* Both
SPECIALITIES: Over 2050 varieties of rare & unusual Alpines & Herbaceous Perennials. Old fashioned Dianthus, Penstemon, Campanulas, Salvia, Thymes, Herbs & Pelargoniums. *MAP PAGE:* **5**

WPhl **Just Phlomis, Sunningdale, Grange Court, Westbury-on-Severn, Gloucestershire GL14 1PL**
TEL: (0452) 760268 *FAX:* (0452) 760268 *CONTACT:* J Mann Taylor
OPENING TIMES: Appt only.
MIN MAIL ORDER UK: £7.50 + p&p *MIN VALUE EC:* £7.50 + p&p
CAT. COST: 2 x 2nd class *W/SALE or RETAIL:* Retail
SPECIALITIES: Phlomis from the National Collection. *MAP PAGE:* **5**

WPla **The Plantation,** Garden Cottage, Delbury Hall, Craven Arms, Shropshire SY7 9DH
TEL: (058 476) 603 *CONTACT:* Nicky Fraser
OPENING TIMES: 1000-1730 Tue-Sun & Bank Hols, Mar-Nov.
MAIL ORDER: No
CAT. COST: Sae *W/SALE or RETAIL:* Retail
SPECIALITIES: Classic & hard to find Border Perennials. *MAP PAGE:* **5/7**

WRic **Rickard's Hardy Fern, Kyre Park, Tenbury Wells, Worcestershire WR15 8RP**
TEL: (0885) 410282 *FAX:* (0885) 410398 *CONTACT:* Hazel & Martin Rickard
OPENING TIMES: Most times but please make appt. first.
MIN MAIL ORDER UK: £6.00 + p&p *MIN VALUE EC:* £20.00 + p&p
CAT. COST: Sae *W/SALE or RETAIL:* Retail
SPECIALITIES: Ferns, hardy & half-hardy. National Reference Collection of Polypodium, Cystopteris & Thelypteroid ferns. *MAP PAGE:* **5**

WRid **Ridgeway Heather Nursery,** Park House, Plaish, Church Stretton, Shropshire SY6 7HY
TEL: (0694) 771574 *CONTACT:* Mrs N Cordingley
OPENING TIMES: 1000-1800 Tue-Sun, ex. Bank Holiday Monday.
MIN MAIL ORDER UK: No minimum charge *MIN VALUE EC:* n/a
CAT. COST: Free *W/SALE or RETAIL:* Both
SPECIALITIES: Heathers *MAP PAGE:* **7**

WRus **Rushfields of Ledbury, Ross Road, Ledbury, Herefordshire HR8 2LP**
TEL: (0531) 632004 *CONTACT:* B & J Homewood
OPENING TIMES: 1100-1700 Wed-Sat. Other times by appt.
MIN MAIL ORDER UK: £15.00 + p&p* *MIN VALUE EC:* £15.00 + p&p*
CAT. COST: A5 Sae 29p + £1.00 *W/SALE or RETAIL:* Both
SPECIALITIES: Unusual Herbaceous, incl. Euphorbias, Hardy Geraniums, Helleborus, Hostas, Osteospermum, Penstemon, Primroses & Grasses. *NOTE: Mail Order for Hellebores only.
MAP PAGE: **5**

WSHC **Stone House Cottage Nurseries,** Stone, Nr Kidderminster, Worcestershire DY10 4BG
TEL: (0562) 69902 *CONTACT:* J F & L N Arbuthnott
◆ *OPENING TIMES:* 1000-1800 Wed-Sat, & Sun in May & June. Appt. only in Nov. Closed Dec-Feb.
MAIL ORDER: No
CAT. COST: Sae *W/SALE or RETAIL:* Retail
SPECIALITIES: Small general range, especially wall Shrubs, Climbers and unusual plants.
MAP PAGE: **5**

WShi **John Shipton (Bulbs), Y Felin, Henllan Amgoed, Whitland, Dyfed SA34 0SL**
TEL: (0994) 240125 *CONTACT:* John Shipton
OPENING TIMES: By appt. only.
MIN MAIL ORDER UK: No minimum charge *MIN VALUE EC:* Nmc *EXPORT:* Yes
CAT. COST: Sae *W/SALE or RETAIL:* Both
SPECIALITIES: Native British Bulbs & Daffodils. See also SEED Index. *MAP PAGE:* **4**

WSpr **Rosemary Spreckley, Hailey House, Great Comberton, Pershore, Worcestershire WR10 3DS**
TEL: (0386) 710733 *CONTACT:* Rosemary Spreckley
OPENING TIMES: By appt. only.
MIN MAIL ORDER UK: No minimum charge *MIN VALUE EC:* Nmc *EXPORT:* Yes
CAT. COST: Large Sae *W/SALE or RETAIL:* Both
SPECIALITIES: Penstemons. *MAP PAGE:* **5**

WStA **St Annes Vineyard, Wain House, Oxenhall, Newent, Gloucestershire GL18 1RW**
TEL: (098 982) 313 *CONTACT:* B R Edwards
OPENING TIMES: 1400-1900 Wed-Fri, 1000-1900 Weekends & Bank Hols.
MIN MAIL ORDER UK: £5.00 + p&p *MIN VALUE EC:* * *EXPORT:* Yes
CAT. COST: Sae *W/SALE or RETAIL:* Both
SPECIALITIES: Vines. * EC sales by arrangement. *MAP PAGE:* **5**

WStI **St Ishmael's Nurseries,** Haverfordwest, Pembrokeshire SA62 3SX
TEL: (0646) 636343 *FAX:* (0646) 636343 *CONTACT:* Mr D & Mrs H Phippen
OPENING TIMES: 0900-1730 daily Summer. 0900-1700 daily Winter.
MAIL ORDER: No
CAT. COST: Sae *W/SALE or RETAIL:* Retail
SPECIALITIES: Wide general range. *MAP PAGE:* **4**

WSun **Sunnybank House Nursery, Little Birch, Hereford, Herefordshire HR2 8BB**
TEL: (0981) 540684 *FAX:* (0981) 540932 *CONTACT:* Mrs Pat Jones
OPENING TIMES: Visitors welcome Apr-Oct but please phone first.
MIN MAIL ORDER UK: £6.00 + p&p *MIN VALUE EC:* £20.00 + p&p
CAT. COST: 2 x 1st class *W/SALE or RETAIL:* Retail
SPECIALITIES: Cottage garden & Herb plants incl. Aquilegia, Pulmonaria, Primroses, Viola & hardy Geraniums. *MAP PAGE:* **5**

WThi **39 Steps,** Grove Cottage, Forge Hill, Lydbrook, Gloucestershire GL17 9QS
TEL: (0594) 860544 *CONTACT:* Graham Birkin
OPENING TIMES: 1000-1600 Mon-Fri 1st Mar-30th Sep. Weekends by appt. Please phone first.
MAIL ORDER: No
CAT. COST: 3 x 1st class *W/SALE or RETAIL:* Retail
SPECIALITIES: Alpines, shade lovers & Irises. *MAP PAGE:* **5**

WThu **Thuya Alpine Nursery, Glebelands, Hartpury, Gloucestershire GL19 3BW**
TEL: (0452) 700548 *CONTACT:* S W Bond
OPENING TIMES: 1000-dusk Sat & Bank hol. 1100-dusk Sun, Weekdays appt. advised.
MIN MAIL ORDER UK: £4.00 + p&p *MIN VALUE EC:* £4.00 + p&p
CAT. COST: 4 x 2nd class *W/SALE or RETAIL:* Retail
SPECIALITIES: Wide and changing range including rarities. See also SEED Index. *MAP PAGE:* **5**

WToa **Toad Hall Produce, Frogmore, Weston-under-Penyard, Herefordshire HR9 5TQ**
TEL: (0989) 750214 *CONTACT:* S V North
◆ *OPENING TIMES:* 1000-1800 Mon Apr-Sep.
MIN MAIL ORDER UK: No minimum charge *MIN VALUE EC:* Nmc
CAT. COST: Sae *W/SALE or RETAIL:* Retail
SPECIALITIES: Hardy Geranium & Ground cover plants. *MAP PAGE:* **5**

WTre **Treasures of Tenbury Ltd,** Burford House Gardens, Tenbury Wells, Worcestershire WR15 8HQ
TEL: (0584) 810777 *FAX:* (0584) 810673 *CONTACT:* Mrs P A Cox
◆ *OPENING TIMES:* 1000-1800 daily. Until dusk in Winter
MAIL ORDER: No
CAT. COST: 95p *W/SALE or RETAIL:* Retail
SPECIALITIES: Clematis and Herbaceous, many unusual. *MAP PAGE:* **5**

WTyn **Ty'n Garreg Nurseries, Rhyd-y-Clafdy, Pwllheli, Gwynedd LL53 8PL**
TEL: (0758) 720868 *FAX:* (0758) 720868 *CONTACT:* Nigel Pittard
◆ *OPENING TIMES:* 1000-1700 daily 15th Mar-15th Sep.
MIN MAIL ORDER UK: £15.00 + p&p *MIN VALUE EC:* £20.00 + p&p
CAT. COST: 2 x 1st class *W/SALE or RETAIL:* Retail
SPECIALITIES: Aquilegia, Agapanthus, Campanula, hardy herbaceous Perennials & unusual Annuals. *MAP PAGE:* **4**

WTyr Ty'r Orsaf Nursery, Maentwrog Road (A470), Ty Nant, Nr Gellilydan, Gwynedd LL41 4RB

TEL: (076 685) 233 *CONTACT:* A G & M Faulkner
OPENING TIMES: 1000-1800 daily Summer, 1000-dusk daily Winter.
MAIL ORDER: No
CAT. COST: None issued *W/SALE or RETAIL:* Retail
SPECIALITIES: Hardy herbaceous, Shrubs & Alpines incl. Astilbes, Campanulas, Geraniums, Sidalcea, Potentilla etc. *MAP PAGE:* **4**

WWar Warners Roses, Greenfields, Brockton, Newport, Shropshire TF10 9EP

TEL: (0952) 604217 *FAX:* (0952) 604217 *CONTACT:* Mr C H Warner
OPENING TIMES: 1000-1930 Mon-Sat, 1430-1830 Sun from 2nd week in July to 2nd week in April.
MIN MAIL ORDER UK: £10.00 + p&p *MIN VALUE EC:* £20.00 + p&p *EXPORT:* Yes
CAT. COST: Free *W/SALE or RETAIL:* Both
SPECIALITIES: New and climbing Rose varieties. *MAP PAGE:* **7**

WWat Waterwheel Nursery, Bully Hole Bottom, Usk Road, Shirenewton, Chepstow, Gwent NP6 6SA

TEL: (0291) 641577 *CONTACT:* Desmond & Charlotte Evans
◆ *OPENING TIMES:* Almost always, but best to phone to check & for directions. Closed on Sundays.
MIN MAIL ORDER UK: No minimum charge* *MIN VALUE EC:* £50.00 + p&p
CAT. COST: 2 x 1st class *W/SALE or RETAIL:* Retail
SPECIALITIES: Wide range of Trees, Shrubs & Perennials - many unusual. *NOTE: Mail Order Oct-Mar only. *MAP PAGE:* **5**

WWeb Webbs Garden Centres Ltd, Wychbold, Droitwich, Worcestershire WR9 0DG

TEL: (0527) 861777 *FAX:* (0527) 861284 *CONTACT:* Mr John Grunsell
◆ *OPENING TIMES:* 0900-1700 Mon-Sat 1000-1700 Sun Winter. 0900-1745 Mon-Sat 1000-1700 Sun Summer
MAIL ORDER: No
CAT. COST: *W/SALE or RETAIL:* Both
SPECIALITIES: Hardy Trees & Shrubs, Climbers, Conifers, Alpines, Heathers, Herbaceous, Herbs, Roses & Fruit. *MAP PAGE:* **5**

WWes Westonbirt Arboretum, (Forest Enterprise), Tetbury, Gloucestershire GL8 8QS

TEL: (0666) 880544 *FAX:* (0666) 880559 *CONTACT:* Glyn R Toplis
OPENING TIMES: 1000-1800 daily Summer, 1000-1700 Winter.
MAIL ORDER: No
CAT. COST: Free *W/SALE or RETAIL:* Retail
SPECIALITIES: Trees & Shrubs, many choice & rare. *MAP PAGE:* **5**

WWin Wintergreen Nurseries, Bringsty Common, Worcestershire WR6 5UJ

TEL: (0886) 821858 eves. *CONTACT:* S Dodd
OPENING TIMES: 1000-1730 Wed-Sun 1st Mar-29th Oct & by appt.
MIN MAIL ORDER UK: £5.00 + p&p *MIN VALUE EC:* £10.00 + p&p
CAT. COST: 2 x 2nd class *W/SALE or RETAIL:* Both
SPECIALITIES: General, especially Alpines & Herbaceous. *MAP PAGE:* **5**

WWye Wye Valley Herbs, The Nurtons, Tintern, Chepstow, Gwent NP6 7NX

TEL: (0291) 689253 *CONTACT:* Adrian & Elsa Wood
◆ *OPENING TIMES:* 1030-1700 daily 1st Mar-mid Oct. Other times by appt.
MAIL ORDER: No
CAT. COST: 3 x 1st class *W/SALE or RETAIL:* Retail
SPECIALITIES: Aromatic, Culinary, Medicinal & Dye Herbs. Unusual Perennials. *MAP PAGE:* **5**

Additional Nursery Index

Please note that all these nurseries are listed in ascending order of their numeric Codes.
All nurseries are listed in alphabetical order of their name in the **Nursery-Code** Index on page 654.

01 Foliage Scented & Herb Plants, Walton Poor Cottage, Crocknorth Rd, Ranmore Common, Dorking, Surrey RH5 6SX
TEL: (0483) 282273 *CONTACT:* Mrs Prudence Calvert
◆ *OPENING TIMES:* 1000-1700 Wed-Sun & Bank Hols.
MAIL ORDER: No
CAT. COST: Free *W/SALE or RETAIL:* Retail
SPECIALITIES: Herbs, aromatic & scented plants. *MAP PAGE:* **3**

02 Jasmine Cottage Gardens, 26 Channel Road, Walton St. Mary, Clevedon, Avon BS21 7BY
TEL: (0275) 871850 *CONTACT:* Mr & Mrs M Redgrave
OPENING TIMES: Thurs. afternoon & by appt.
MAIL ORDER: No
CAT. COST: None issued *W/SALE or RETAIL:* Retail
SPECIALITIES: Rhodochiton, Asarina, Isotoma. Seed also available. *MAP PAGE:* **2**

03 Ballagan Nursery, Gartocharn Road, Nr Balloch, Alexandria, Strathclyde G83 8NB
TEL: (0389) 52947 *FAX:* (0389) 52947 *CONTACT:* Mr G Stephenson
OPENING TIMES: 0900-1800 daily.
MAIL ORDER: No
CAT. COST: None issued *W/SALE or RETAIL:* Retail
SPECIALITIES: Home grown bedding and general nursery stock. *MAP PAGE:* **10**

04 Clonmel Garden Centre, Glenconnor House, Clonmel, Co. Tipperary Rep. of Ireland
TEL: 010353 (0)52 23294 *CONTACT:* C E Hanna
OPENING TIMES: 1000-1800 Mon-Sat, 1400-1800 Sun.
MAIL ORDER: No
CAT. COST: *W/SALE or RETAIL:* Both
SPECIALITIES: Wide range of plants incl. many less common varieties. *MAP PAGE:* **11**

05 Beetham Nurseries, Pool Darkin Lane, Beetham, Nr Milnthorpe, Cumbria LA7 7AP
TEL: (05395) 63630 *FAX:* (05395) 64487 *CONTACT:* S J Abbit
OPENING TIMES: 0900-1800 Summer, 0900-dusk Winter.
MAIL ORDER: No
CAT. COST: None issued *W/SALE or RETAIL:* Retail
SPECIALITIES: Comprehensive range of Trees, Shrubs & Herbaceous Plants. Many unusual varieties. *MAP PAGE:* **9**

07 Liscahane Nursery, Ardfert, Tralee, Co. Kerry, Rep. of Ireland
TEL: 010353 (0)6634222 *FAX:* 010353 (0)6634600 *CONTACT:* Dan Nolan/Bill Cooley
◆ *OPENING TIMES:* 0900-1800 Tue-Sat & 1400-1800 Sun. Closed Mon.
MAIL ORDER: No
CAT. COST: *W/SALE or RETAIL:* Retail
SPECIALITIES: Coastal shelter plants, Eucalyptus & Pines. *MAP PAGE:* **11**

08 Deelish Garden Centre, Skibbereen, Co. Cork Rep. of Ireland
TEL: 010353 (0)2821374 *FAX:* 010353 (0)02763187 *CONTACT:* Bill & Rain Chase
OPENING TIMES: 1000-1300 & 1400-1800 Mon-Sat, 1400-1800 Sun.
MIN MAIL ORDER UK: IR£50.00 + p&p *MIN VALUE EC:* IR£100.00 + p&p
CAT. COST: None *W/SALE or RETAIL:* Both
SPECIALITIES: Unusual plants for the mild coastal climate of Ireland. Conservatory plants. Sole Irish agents for Chase Organic Seeds. *MAP PAGE:* **11**

09 Bretby Nurseries, Bretby Lane, Burton-on-Trent, Staffordshire DE15 0QR
TEL: (0283) 703355 *FAX:* (0283) 704035 *CONTACT:* Mr David Cartwright
OPENING TIMES: 0900-1700 daily.
MAIL ORDER: No
CAT. COST: 3 x 1st class *W/SALE or RETAIL:* Both
SPECIALITIES: Wide range of shrubs. *MAP PAGE:* **7**

See note on Mail Order, EC sales & Export on page 7

10 Kingfisher Nurseries, Catshill, Bromsgrove, Worcestershire B61 0BW

TEL: (0527) 835084 *CONTACT:* Gary Booker
OPENING TIMES: 0900-1730 Mon-Sat, (0900-2000 Wed), 1000-1700 Sun all year.
MAIL ORDER: No
CAT. COST: None issued *W/SALE or RETAIL:* Retail
SPECIALITIES: Half-hardy Perennials for Patio gardening. Annual flowering plants. *MAP PAGE:* **5**

11 Northern Ireland Young Plants, 6 Old Ballyclare Road, Templepatrick, Ballyclare, Co Antrim, N Ireland BT39 0BJ

TEL: (08494) 32513 *FAX:* (08494) 32151 *CONTACT:* Mr Alan Coleman
OPENING TIMES: 0900-1730 Mon-Fri, 0900-1700 Sat.
MIN MAIL ORDER UK: £150.00 + p&p *MIN VALUE EC:* £200.00 + p&p *EXPORT:* Yes
CAT. COST: Free *W/SALE or RETAIL:* Both
SPECIALITIES: Over 2000 varieties of plants. Specialist propagation of Hardy Nursery Stock.
MAP PAGE: **11**

12 Woodlands Cottage Nursery, Summerbridge, Harrogate, North Yorkshire HG3 4BT

TEL: (0423) 780765 *CONTACT:* Mrs Ann Stark
OPENING TIMES: 1000-1800 Fri-Mon end Mar-end Sep.
MAIL ORDER: No
CAT. COST: 3 x 1st class *W/SALE or RETAIL:* Retail
SPECIALITIES: Herbs, plants for Shade & Hardy Perennials. *MAP PAGE:* **9**

14 Seaside Nursery, Claddaghduff, Co. Galway, Rep. of Ireland

TEL: 010353 (0)9544687 *FAX:* 010353 (0)9544687 *CONTACT:* Charles Dyck
OPENING TIMES: 0900-1300 & 1400-1800 Mon-Sat, 1400-1800 Sun.
MAIL ORDER: No
CAT. COST: £1.00 *W/SALE or RETAIL:* Both
SPECIALITIES: Plants & Hedging suitable for seaside locations. Rare plants originating from Australia & NewZealand. *MAP PAGE:* **11**

15 Simpsons Nursery, The High Street, Marsham, Norwich, Norfolk NR10 5QA

TEL: (0263) 733432 *CONTACT:* Gillian Simpson
OPENING TIMES: 1000-1730 Wed-Sun & Bank Hols Easter-Christmas
MAIL ORDER: No
CAT. COST: None issued *W/SALE or RETAIL:* Both
SPECIALITIES: Conifers, Shrubs & Bedding plants. *MAP PAGE:* **8**

16 Daleside Nurseries, Ripon Road, Killinghall, Harrogate, North Yorks HG3 2AY

TEL: (0423) 506450 *FAX:* (0423) 527872 *CONTACT:* Messrs Darley & Townsend.
OPENING TIMES: 0900-1700 Mon-Sat, 1000-1200 & 1330-1630 Sun.
MAIL ORDER: No
CAT. COST: *W/SALE or RETAIL:* Retail
SPECIALITIES: Many plants & trees not generally available. Container grown Fruit, Apples, Pears & Soft Fruit. *MAP PAGE:* **9**

17 Old Manor Nurseries, South Leverton, Retford, Nottinghamshire DN22 0BX

TEL: (0427) 880428 *FAX:* (0427) 881101 *CONTACT:* Rebecca Vickers
OPENING TIMES: 1000-1700 Fri & Mon Mar-Oct.
MIN MAIL ORDER UK: No minimum charge *MIN VALUE EC:* n/a
CAT. COST: 3 x 1st class *W/SALE or RETAIL:* Retail
SPECIALITIES: Hardy Perennials. *MAP PAGE:* **7**

19 Denmans Ltd. (Denmans Garden), Clock House, Denmans, Fontwell, Nr Arundel, West Sussex BN18 0SU

TEL: (0243) 542808 *FAX:* (0243) 544064 *CONTACT:* John Brookes
OPENING TIMES: 0900-1700 daily 4th Mar-15th Dec.
MAIL ORDER: No
CAT. COST: £2.50 *W/SALE or RETAIL:* Retail
SPECIALITIES: Rare and unusual plants. *MAP PAGE:* **3**

20 **Applegarth Nursery,** The Elms, Maesbrook, Oswestry, Shropshire SY10 8QF

TEL: (0691) 831577 *CONTACT:* Cathy Preston
OPENING TIMES: 1400-1800 Thu, Fri & Sat. Advisable to phone before visiting.
MAIL ORDER: No
CAT. COST: 1 x 1st class *W/SALE or RETAIL:* Both
SPECIALITIES: Herbs & Wild Flowers with particular speciality in plants with a wildlife value.
MAP PAGE: **7**

21 **Mugswell Nursery,** Bisley, Stroud, Gloucestershire GL6 7AN

TEL: (0452) 770105 *CONTACT:* Peter Dinning
OPENING TIMES: 1000-1700 (dusk if earlier) Wed-Sun. Please check.
MAIL ORDER: No
CAT. COST: 5 x 1st class* *W/SALE or RETAIL:* Both
SPECIALITIES: Mainly Alpines and Herbaceous Perennials. *Price List only 2 x 1st class stamps.
MAP PAGE: **5**

22 **Elly Hill Herbs,** Elly Hill House, Barmpton, Darlington, Co. Durham DL1 3JF

TEL: (0325) 464682 *CONTACT:* Mrs Nina Pagan
OPENING TIMES: By appt. only
MAIL ORDER: No
CAT. COST: 50p+large Sae *W/SALE or RETAIL:* Retail
SPECIALITIES: Herbs. *MAP PAGE:* **9**

24 **Woodborough Garden Centre,,** Nursery Farm, Woodborough, Nr Pewsey, Wiltshire SN9 5PF

TEL: (0672) 851249 *CONTACT:* Els M Brewin
OPENING TIMES: 0900-1700 daily
MAIL ORDER: No
CAT. COST: None issued *W/SALE or RETAIL:* Retail
SPECIALITIES: Wide range of Shrubs, Trees, Herbaceous, Alpines & Herbs. Large selection of Climbers, esp. Clematis, & spring Bulbs. *MAP PAGE:* **2**

26 **The Flower Centre,** 754 Howth Road, Raheny, Dublin 5, Rep. of Ireland

TEL: 010353-1-8327047 *FAX:* 010353-1-8327251 *CONTACT:* Eugene Higgins
OPENING TIMES: 1000-1300 & 1430-1800 Summer, 1000-1300 & 1430-1700 Winter daily. Mon-Sat only Jan & Feb.
MAIL ORDER: No
CAT. COST: None issued *W/SALE or RETAIL:* Both
SPECIALITIES: Impatiens, Universal pansies, Fuchsia & hanging baskets. *MAP PAGE:* **11**

27 **Chennels Gate Gardens & Nursery,** Eardisley, Herefordshire HR3 6LJ

TEL: (05446) 288 *CONTACT:* Una Dawson
OPENING TIMES: 0900-1800 Mon, Fri & Sat Apr-Sep.
MAIL ORDER: No
CAT. COST: None issued *W/SALE or RETAIL:* Retail
SPECIALITIES: Interesting Herbaceous. Micropropagated Roses, Clematis & Azaleas. *MAP PAGE:* **5**

28 **Linda Gascoigne Wild Flowers, 17 Imperial Road, Kibworth Beauchamp, Leicestershire LE8 0HR**

TEL: (0533) 793959 *CONTACT:* Linda Gascoigne
OPENING TIMES: By appt. only
MIN MAIL ORDER UK: £5.00 + p&p *MIN VALUE EC:* £10.00 + p&p
CAT. COST: 3 x 1st class *W/SALE or RETAIL:* Retail
SPECIALITIES: Wide range of attractive Wild Flowers & Wildlife plants. No peat used. *MAP PAGE:* **7**

29 **Glebe Cottage Gardens,** Church Lane, Stockerston, Oakham, Leicestershire LE15 9JD

TEL: (0572) 821253 *CONTACT:* A V Burwood
OPENING TIMES: 1000-1700 Sat, Sun Mar-May or by appt. Closed Aug 1st-14th. Please telephon at other times.
MAIL ORDER: No
CAT. COST: 3 x 1st class *W/SALE or RETAIL:* Retail
SPECIALITIES: Alpines & Cottage garden plants. Only small quantities of each, please check availability.
MAP PAGE: **7/8**

 See note on Mail Order, EC sales & Export on page 7

30 Nanney's Bridge Nursery, Church Minshull, Nantwich, Cheshire CW5 6DY
TEL: (0270) 522239 *CONTACT:* C M Dickinson
OPENING TIMES: By appt. only.
MAIL ORDER: No
CAT. COST: 3 x 1st class *W/SALE or RETAIL:*
SPECIALITIES: Erysimums, Geranium, Penstemon, Salvias & Ornamental Grasses. *MAP PAGE:* **7**

31 Cold Harbour Nursery, (Off.) 19 Hilary Road, Poole, Dorset BH17 7LZ
TEL: *CONTACT:* Steve Saunders
OPENING TIMES: 1400-1800 Sat, 1000-1800 Sun & Bank Hols (dusk if earlier) Mar-Oct.
MAIL ORDER: No
CAT. COST: Sae *W/SALE or RETAIL:* Retail
SPECIALITIES: Herbaceous Perennials, incl. hardy Geraniums, Wild Flowers & Grasses. NOTE:- Nursery at Bere Road, (opp. Silent Woman Inn), Wareham, Dorset. *MAP PAGE:* **2**

32 Grange Farm Nursery, Guarlford, Malvern, Worcestershire WR13 6NY
TEL: (0684) 562544 *CONTACT:* Mrs C Nicholls
◆ *OPENING TIMES:* 0900-1730 daily Summer. 0900-1700 daily Winter. ex Xmas & 2 weeks in Jan.
MAIL ORDER: No
CAT. COST: Free pamphlet *W/SALE or RETAIL:* Retail
SPECIALITIES: Wide general range of container grown hardy Shrubs, Trees, Conifers, Heathers, Alpines & Herbaceous. Shrub, climbing & bush Roses. *MAP PAGE:* **5**

33 Birchwood Farm Nursery, Portway, Coxbench, Derbyshire DE21 5BE
TEL: (0332) 880685 *CONTACT:* Mr & Mrs S Crooks
OPENING TIMES: 0900-1730 Wed-Sat Mar-Oct or by appt.
MAIL ORDER: No
CAT. COST: None issued *W/SALE or RETAIL:* Retail
SPECIALITIES: Unusual Hardy Perennials & Shrubs. *MAP PAGE:* **7**

34 Bradley Gardens Nursery, Sled Lane, Wylam, Northumberland NE41 8JL
TEL: (0661) 852176 *FAX:* (0434) 606221 *CONTACT:* Sue & Jim Hick
OPENING TIMES: 0900-1630 Tue-Sun 21st Mar-21st Oct 1994
MAIL ORDER: No
CAT. COST: 1 x 1st class *W/SALE or RETAIL:*
SPECIALITIES: Herbs & Cottage Garden plants. *MAP PAGE:* **10**

35 Christie's Nursery, Downfield, Westmuir, Kirriemuir, Angus DD8 5LP
TEL: (0575) 572977 *FAX:* (0575) 572977 *CONTACT:* Ian & Ann Christie
◆ *OPENING TIMES:* 1000-1700 daily 1st Mar-31st Oct.
MIN MAIL ORDER UK: 5 plants + p&p *MIN VALUE EC:* On request
CAT. COST: Sae *W/SALE or RETAIL:* Both
SPECIALITIES: Alpines, esp. Gentians, Cassiope. Primula, Lewisia & Ericaceous. *MAP PAGE:* **10**

36 Herterton House Garden Nursery, Hartington, Cambo, Morpeth, Northumberland NE61 4BN
TEL: (067074) 278 *CONTACT:* Mrs M Lawley & Mr Frank Lawley
OPENING TIMES: 1330-1730 Mon Wed Fri-Sun 1st April-end Sep. (Earlier or later in the year weather permitting).
MAIL ORDER: No
CAT. COST: None issued *W/SALE or RETAIL:* Retail
SPECIALITIES: Achillea, Aquilegia, Geum, Geranium, Polemonium. *MAP PAGE:* **10**

38 The Laurels Nursery, Benenden, Cranbrook, Kent TN17 4JU
TEL: (0580) 240463 *CONTACT:* Mr P H Kellett
OPENING TIMES: 0800-1700 Mon-Thu, 0800-1600 Fri, 0900-1200 Sat, Sun by appt. only.
MAIL ORDER: No
CAT. COST: Free *W/SALE or RETAIL:* Both
SPECIALITIES: Flowering Cherries, open ground ornamental Trees & Shrubs *MAP PAGE:* **3**

39 Willowholme Herb Farm, Upton, Retford, Nottinghamshire DN22 0RA
TEL: (0777) 248053 *CONTACT:* Margaret Farr
OPENING TIMES: Please phone first.
MIN MAIL ORDER UK: £10.00 + p&p *MIN VALUE EC:* n/a
CAT. COST: 4 x 2nd class *W/SALE or RETAIL:*
SPECIALITIES: Culinary, Aromatic & Medicinal Herbs. *MAP PAGE:* **7**

◆ **See also Display Advertisements**

40 Layham Garden Centre, Lower Road, Staple, Canterbury, Kent CT3 1LH

TEL: (0304) 813267 *FAX:* (0304) 615349 *CONTACT:* L W Wessel
OPENING TIMES: 0900-1700 Mon-Sat 1000-1700 Sun.
MAIL ORDER: No
CAT. COST: Free *W/SALE or RETAIL:* Both
SPECIALITIES: Roses, Herbaceous, Shrubs, Trees, Conifers, Liners & Whips. Aquatic plants. *MAP PAGE:* **3**

41 Westwinds Perennial Plants, Filpoke Lane, High Hesleden, Hartlepool, Cleveland TS27 4BT

TEL: (091) 5180225 *CONTACT:* Harry Blackwood
◆ *OPENING TIMES:* Dawn until Dusk Sun & Mon and by appt.
MAIL ORDER: No
CAT. COST: £1.00 *W/SALE or RETAIL:* Retail
SPECIALITIES: Penstemon, Diascia, Erysimum, Hosta, Geranium, Phygelius plus a range of specimen size Shrubs & Climbers. *MAP PAGE:* **10**

42 Manningford Nurseries, Manningford Abbots, Nr Pewsey, Wiltshire SN9 5PB

TEL: (0672) 62232 *CONTACT:* Peter Jones
OPENING TIMES: 0830-1700 Mon, Tue, Thu, Fri & Sat, 1030-1300 & 1400-1700 Sun.
MIN MAIL ORDER UK: £10.00 + p&p *MIN VALUE EC:* n/a
CAT. COST: None issued *W/SALE or RETAIL:* Both
SPECIALITIES: Plants of the 18th & 19th century. Digitalis, Penstemon, Hemerocallis, Nepeta, Aconitum volubile, Maurandya. *MAP PAGE:* **2**

43 Marle Place Plants & Gardens, Marle Place, Brenchley, Nr Tonbridge, Kent TN12 7HS

TEL: (0892 72) 2304 *FAX:* (0732) 464466 *CONTACT:* Mrs L M Williams
OPENING TIMES: Easter-end Oct. Gardens open 1000-1730.
MIN MAIL ORDER UK: No minimum charge *MIN VALUE EC:* £300.00 + p&p *EXPORT:* Yes
CAT. COST: 1 x 1st class *W/SALE or RETAIL:* Both
SPECIALITIES: Herbs & Wild Flowers. *MAP PAGE:* **3**

44 Plantworld, Burnham Road, South Woodham Ferrers, Chelmsford, Essex CM3 5QP

TEL: (0245) 320482 *FAX:* (0245) 320482 *CONTACT:* F Waterworth
OPENING TIMES: 1000-1700 daily. Please phone first if travelling.
MIN MAIL ORDER UK: No minimum charge *MIN VALUE EC:* Nmc *EXPORT:* Yes
CAT. COST: £2.00 *W/SALE or RETAIL:* Both
SPECIALITIES: Tropaeolum speciosum & wide range of hardy plants. *MAP PAGE:* **6**

46 Cilwern Plants, Cilwern, Talley, Llandeilo, Dyfed SA19 7YH

TEL: (0558) 685526 *CONTACT:* Anne Knatchbull-Hugessen
◆ *OPENING TIMES:* 1100-1800 Sat-Thu. Closed Fri.
MIN MAIL ORDER UK: £10.00 + p&p *MIN VALUE EC:* £30.00 + p&p
CAT. COST: 50p *W/SALE or RETAIL:* Retail
SPECIALITIES: Hardy Perennials, esp. Geraniums & Penstemon. *MAP PAGE:* **4**

47 Sue Robinson, 21 Bederic Close, Bury St Edmunds, Suffolk IP32 7DN

TEL: (0284) 764310 *CONTACT:* Sue Robinson
OPENING TIMES: By appt. only.
MAIL ORDER: No
CAT. COST: None issued *W/SALE or RETAIL:* Retail
SPECIALITIES: Variegated & Foliage plants. Garden open. Lectures at Clubs & Societies, group bookings welcome.

48 Hellyer's Garden Plants, Orchards, Rowfant, Nr Crawley Sussex RH10 4NJ

TEL: (0342) 718280 *CONTACT:* Penelope Hellyer
OPENING TIMES: 1000-1600 (dusk if earlier) Fri, Sat & Sun Mar-Nov & by appt.
MAIL ORDER: No
CAT. COST: List 1x1st + Sae *W/SALE or RETAIL:* Retail
SPECIALITIES: Hardy & tender Herbaceous Perennials incl. Geraniums, Penstemons, Salvias & small selection of Shrubs, Climbers & Alpines. *MAP PAGE:* **3**

See note on Mail Order, EC sales & Export on page 7

49 Elizabeth Burnett, Munlochy, Rosshire IV8 8PF

TEL: (046 381) 246* *FAX:* (046 381) 525* *CONTACT:* Elizabeth Burnett
OPENING TIMES: 1400-1700 Tue, Wed & Fri May-Oct.
MIN MAIL ORDER UK: No minimum charge *MIN VALUE EC:* n/a
CAT. COST: 2 x 1st class *W/SALE or RETAIL:* Retail
SPECIALITIES: Hardy Perennials & Grasses. *NOTE: Phone number due to change during summer '94 to (0463)811246/525 *MAP PAGE:* **10**

51 N & J Wake, 27 Clifton Road, Henlow, Bedfordshire SG16 6BL

TEL: (0462) 815223 *CONTACT:* N K Wake
OPENING TIMES: By appt.
MIN MAIL ORDER UK: No minimum charge *MIN VALUE EC:* Nmc
CAT. COST: 3 x 1st class *W/SALE or RETAIL:* Retail
SPECIALITIES: Herbaceous Perennials. *MAP PAGE:* **6**

52 Porthpean House Gardens, Porthpean, St. Austell, Cornwall PL26 6AX

TEL: (0726) 72888 *CONTACT:* Mrs Petherick
OPENING TIMES: 0900-1700 Mon-Fri. Sat & Sun by appt.
MAIL ORDER: No
CAT. COST: None issued *W/SALE or RETAIL:* Both
SPECIALITIES: Camellia & Shrubs for acid soils. *MAP PAGE:* **1**

53 The Priory, Kemerton, Tewkesbury, Gloucestershire GL20 7JN

TEL: (0386) 725258 *CONTACT:* Mrs P Healing
OPENING TIMES: 1400-1900 Thurs afternoons.
MAIL ORDER: No
CAT. COST: None issued *W/SALE or RETAIL:* Retail
SPECIALITIES: Rare and unusual plants. *MAP PAGE:* **5**

54 Bucknell Nurseries, Bucknell, Shropshire SY7 0EL

TEL: (05474) 606 *FAX:* (05474) 699 *CONTACT:* A N Coull
OPENING TIMES: 0800-1700 Mon-Fri & 1000-1300 Sat.
MAIL ORDER: No
CAT. COST: Free *W/SALE or RETAIL:* Both
SPECIALITIES: Bare rooted hedging Conifers & forest Trees. *MAP PAGE:* **5**

55 Manorbier Garden Centre, Manorbier, nr Tenby, Dyfed SA70 7SN

TEL: (0834) 871206 *FAX:* (0834) 871678 *CONTACT:* Mrs E I Thompson
OPENING TIMES: 0900-1700 daily
MAIL ORDER: No
CAT. COST: None issued *W/SALE or RETAIL:* Retail
SPECIALITIES: Wide general range. *MAP PAGE:* **4**

56 Ryans Nurseries, Lissivigeen, Killarney, Co. Kerry, Rep. of Ireland

TEL: 010353 (0)64 33507 *FAX:* 010353 (0)64 33507 *CONTACT:* Mr T Ryan
OPENING TIMES: 0900-1800 Mon-Sat 1400-1800 Sun.
MAIL ORDER: No
CAT. COST: *W/SALE or RETAIL:* Retail
SPECIALITIES: Camellias, Pieris, Azaleas, Acacia, Eucalyptus, Dicksonia & many tender & rare plants. *MAP PAGE:* **11**

57 Evegate Nursery Floral Workshop, Evegate Farm Complex, Station Road, Smeeth, Nr Ashford, Kent TN25 6SX

TEL: (0303) 813775 *CONTACT:* M C Dickerson
OPENING TIMES: 0930-1700 Tue-Sat, 1000-1700 Sun.
MAIL ORDER: No
CAT. COST: 1 x 1st class *W/SALE or RETAIL:* Retail
SPECIALITIES: Plants for Foliage & Floral effect, many of interest to the flower arranger. *MAP PAGE:* **3**

58 Longhall Nursery, Stockton, Nr Warminster, Wiltshire BA12 0SE

TEL: (0985) 50914 *CONTACT:* H V & J E Dooley
OPENING TIMES: 0930-1800 Wed-Sun 23rd Mar-2nd Oct.
MIN MAIL ORDER UK: £5.00 + p&p *MIN VALUE EC:* £5.00 + p&p
CAT. COST: 3 x 1st class *W/SALE or RETAIL:* Both
SPECIALITIES: Uncommon herbaceous. *MAP PAGE:* **2**

◆ See also Display Advertisements

59 K R Shanks, Old Orchard Nursery, Burwash Common, Etchingham, Sussex TN19 7NE

TEL: (0435) 882060 *FAX:* (0435) 882728 *CONTACT:* K R Shanks
◆ *OPENING TIMES:* 0900-1700 Tue-Sun
MAIL ORDER: No
CAT. COST: 1 x 1st class *W/SALE or RETAIL:* Retail
SPECIALITIES: Herbaceous plants, Shrubs, Climbers, Ornamental & Fruit Trees. *MAP PAGE:* **3**

60 Muckross Garden Centre, Muckross. Killarney, Co. Kerry, Rep. of Ireland

TEL: 010353 (0)6434044 *FAX:* 010353 (0)6431114 *CONTACT:* John R Fuller B.Ag.Sc.(Hort.)
OPENING TIMES: 1000-1800 Tue-Sat & 1415-1800 Sun. Jan & Feb please check first.
MAIL ORDER: No
CAT. COST: None issued *W/SALE or RETAIL:* Retail
SPECIALITIES: Many rare & unusual plants. *MAP PAGE:* **6**

61 Wards Nurseries, Dawes Lane, Sarratt, Nr Rickmansworth, Hertfordshire WD3 6BQ

TEL: (0923) 263237 *FAX:* (0923) 270930 *CONTACT:* M F Rawlins
OPENING TIMES: 0800-1700 Mon-Sat, 0900-1700 Sun & Bank Hols.
MAIL ORDER: No
CAT. COST: Sae* *W/SALE or RETAIL:* Both
SPECIALITIES: Shrubs & Climbers, fragrant & aromatic plants. *State interest when asking for lists.
MAP PAGE: **6**

63 Kayes Garden Nursery, 1700 Melton Road, Rearsby, Leicestershire LE7 4YR

TEL: (0664) 424578 *CONTACT:* J E & Hazel Kaye
OPENING TIMES: 1000-1730 Wed-Sat & Bank Hols 1000-1200 Sun Mar-Oct. 1000-1600 Fri & Sat Nov, Dec & Feb. ClosedJan.
MAIL ORDER: No
CAT. COST: 2 x 1st class *W/SALE or RETAIL:* Retail
SPECIALITIES: Herbaceous inc. Campanula, Nepeta, Potentilla, Pulmonaria, Sedum, Digitalis, Euphorbia. Geranium, Lathyrus, Viola etc. *MAP PAGE:* **7**

64 Totties Nursery, Greenhill Bank Road, New Mill, Holmfirth, West Yorkshire HD7 1UN

TEL: (0484) 683363 *FAX:* (0484) 688129 *CONTACT:* David A Shires
OPENING TIMES: 0900-1915 Mon-Fri & 0900-1800 Sat & Sun Summer. 0900-1700 daily Winter.
MAIL ORDER: No
CAT. COST: None issued *W/SALE or RETAIL:* Both
SPECIALITIES: Large selection of ornamental Trees, field and container grown Conifers. Rhododendron & Azalea.Huge range of herbaceous Perennials. *MAP PAGE:* **9**

66 Triscombe Nurseries, West Bagborough, Nr Taunton, Somerset TA4 3HG

TEL: (098 48) 267 *CONTACT:* S Parkman
◆ *OPENING TIMES:* 0900-1300 & 1400-1730 Mon-Sat. 1400-1730 Sun & Bank Hols.
MAIL ORDER: No
CAT. COST: None issued *W/SALE or RETAIL:* Retail
SPECIALITIES: Rock plants & Alpines, Herbaceous, Conifers and unusual Shrubs. *MAP PAGE:* **1/2**

67 Stockerton Nursery,, Kirkcudbright, Galloway, Scotland DG6 4XS

TEL: (0557) 331266 *CONTACT:* Martin Gould
OPENING TIMES: Mail Order only. Visits by arrangement.
MAIL ORDER: Only*MIN MAIL ORDER UK:* £3.00 + p&p *MIN VALUE EC:* n/a
CAT. COST: 3 x 1st class *W/SALE or RETAIL:* Both
SPECIALITIES: Native British species.

68 Stone Cross Nurseries & Garden Cen., Rattle Road, Pevensey, Sussex BN24 5EB

TEL: (0323) 763250 *FAX:* (0323) 460406 *CONTACT:* Mr & Mrs G F Winwood
◆ *OPENING TIMES:* 0830-1730 Mon-Sat & 0930-1730 Sun & Bank Hols.
MAIL ORDER: No
CAT. COST: 50p refundable *W/SALE or RETAIL:* Both
SPECIALITIES: Hebe & Clematis, Evergreen Shrubs. Lime tolerant & coastal Shrubs & Plants.
MAP PAGE: **3**

 See note on Mail Order, EC sales & Export on page 7

70 Palmers' Nurseries, Ferry Road, Clenchwarton, Kings Lynn, Norfolk PE34 4BU

TEL: (0553) 761035 *CONTACT:* B E Palmer
OPENING TIMES: 0900-1200 & 1300-1630 Mon-Sat, 0900-1200 Sun.
MAIL ORDER: No
CAT. COST: Free *W/SALE or RETAIL:* Both
SPECIALITIES: Shrubs & Conifers. *MAP PAGE:* **8**

71 Cley Nurseries Ltd., Holt Road, Cley-Next-the-Sea, Holt, Norfolk NR25 7TX

TEL: (0263) 740892 *FAX:* (0263) 741138 *CONTACT:* Alec or Gill Mellor
OPENING TIMES: 1000-1600 daily.
MIN MAIL ORDER UK: £10.00 + p&p *MIN VALUE EC:* n/a
CAT. COST: List 2 x 1st class *W/SALE or RETAIL:* Retail
SPECIALITIES: Roses *MAP PAGE:* **8**

72 Intakes Farm, Sandy Lane, Longsdon, Stoke-on-Trent, Staffordshire ST9 9QQ

TEL: (0538) 398452 *CONTACT:* Mrs Kathleen Inman
OPENING TIMES: By appt. only.
MAIL ORDER: No
CAT. COST: Sae *W/SALE or RETAIL:* Retail
SPECIALITIES: Double, Variegated & unusual forms of British natives & Cottage Garden plants.
MAP PAGE: **7**

73 Newton Hill Alpines, 335, Leeds Road, Newton Hill, Wakefield, Yorkshire WF1 2JH

TEL: (0924) 377056 *CONTACT:* Sheena Vigors
OPENING TIMES: 0900-1700 Fri-Wed all year. Closed Thur. Please phone first.
MAIL ORDER: No
CAT. COST: 50p *W/SALE or RETAIL:* Both
SPECIALITIES: Alpines, esp. Saxifrages, also Heathers, Conifers & dwarf Shrubs. *MAP PAGE:* **9**

75 Barthelmy & Co, The Nurseries 262 Wimborne Road West, Stapehill, Wimborne, Dorset BH21 2DZ

TEL: (0202) 874283 *FAX:* (0202) 897482 *CONTACT:* John K Skinner
OPENING TIMES: 0900-1300 & 1400-1700 Mon-Sat 2nd Apr-31st Dec
MIN MAIL ORDER UK: No minimum charge *MIN VALUE EC:* Nmc *EXPORT:* Yes
CAT. COST: Sae *W/SALE or RETAIL:*
SPECIALITIES: Japanese Maples, grafted plants & seedlings. *MAP PAGE:* **2**

76 Woodlands Nurseries, Woodlands View, Blakemere, Herefordshire HR2 9PY

TEL: (0981) 500306 *CONTACT:* Larry & Mal Lowther
OPENING TIMES: By appt. only.
MIN MAIL ORDER UK: £10.00 + p&p *MIN VALUE EC:* n/a
CAT. COST: 2 x 1st class *W/SALE or RETAIL:* Both
SPECIALITIES: Common & unusual herbaceous Perennials & Wild Flowers. *MAP PAGE:* **5**

77 The Old Mill Herbary, Helland Bridge, Bodmin, Cornwall PL30 4QR

TEL: (020 884) 206* *FAX:* (020 884) 206* *CONTACT:* Mrs B Whurr
OPENING TIMES: 1000-1700 Apr-Oct
MAIL ORDER: No
CAT. COST: £1.50 *W/SALE or RETAIL:* Retail
SPECIALITIES: Culinary, Medicinal & Aromatic Herbs, Shrubs, Climbing & Herbaceous plants. NOTE: Tel/Fax No. from June 1994 (0208) 841206. *MAP PAGE:* **1**

78 Bressingham Gardens Mail Order, Bressingham, Diss, Norfolk IP22 2AB

TEL: (0379 88) 464 *FAX:* (0379 88) 8289 *CONTACT:* Sarah O'Hara
◆ *OPENING TIMES:* 0830-1630 daily. (24-hour answering machine)
MIN MAIL ORDER UK: £15.00 + p&p *MIN VALUE EC:* P.O.A *EXPORT:* Yes
CAT. COST: £2.00 *W/SALE or RETAIL:* Retail
SPECIALITIES: Very wide general range. Many own varieties. Focus on Hardy Ornamental plants.
MAP PAGE: **6**

80 Kinlochlaich House, Garden Plant Centre, Appin, Argyll PA38 4BD

TEL: (063 173) 342 *FAX:* (063 173) 482 *CONTACT:* D E Hutchison M.I.Hort.
OPENING TIMES: 0930-1730 Mon-Sat 1030-1730 Sun Apr-Oct, 0930-1700 Mon-Sat Nov-Mar.
MAIL ORDER: No
CAT. COST: None issued *W/SALE or RETAIL:* Retail
SPECIALITIES: Wide general range of Shrubs & Perennials (over 2000 plants varieties). Particularly suitable for West coast locations i.e. damp and acid. *MAP PAGE:* **10**

81 Beacon's Nurseries, Tewkesbury Road, Eckington, Nr Pershore Worcestershire WR10 3DE

TEL: (0386) 750359 *CONTACT:* Jonathan Beacon
OPENING TIMES: 0900-1300 & 1400-1700 daily
MAIL ORDER: No
CAT. COST: None issued *W/SALE or RETAIL:* Retail
SPECIALITIES: Wide range of Shrubs, Herbaceous, Aquatics, Conifers, Heathers, climbing plants & Roses. *MAP PAGE:* **5**

82 The Margery Fish Plant Nursery, East Lambrook Manor, East Lambrook, South Petherton, Somerset TA13 5HL

TEL: (0460) 240328 *FAX:* (0460) 242344 *CONTACT:* Mr M Stainer
OPENING TIMES: 1000-1700 Mon-Sat.
MIN MAIL ORDER UK: £10.00 + p&p *MIN VALUE EC:* n/a
CAT. COST: 4 x 1st class *W/SALE or RETAIL:* Retail
SPECIALITIES: Hardy Geranium, Euphorbia, Helleborus, Primula vulgaris, Penstemon, Salvia & Herbaceous.

83 Glenville Nurseries Ltd., King John Bank, Walpole, Wisbech, Cambridgeshire PE14 7LD

TEL: (0945) 61660/780020 *FAX:* (0945) 476590 *CONTACT:* B R Towler
OPENING TIMES: Normal business hours.
MIN MAIL ORDER UK: £6.00 + p&p *MIN VALUE EC:* n/a
CAT. COST: 2 x 2nd class *W/SALE or RETAIL:* Both
SPECIALITIES: Shrubs, Conifers & Alpines. *MAP PAGE:* **8**

84 Crocknafeola Nursery, KIllybegs, Co. Donegal, Rep. of Ireland

TEL: 010353 (0)7351018 *CONTACT:* Andy McKenna
OPENING TIMES: 0900-2100 Mon-Sat & 1200-1800 Sun in Summer. Until dusk in winter.
MAIL ORDER: No
CAT. COST: *W/SALE or RETAIL:* Retail
SPECIALITIES: Hardy Shrubs, Trees & Hedging suitable for exposed areas. *MAP PAGE:* **11**

85 Hardy's Cottage Garden Plants, The Walled Garden, Laverstoke Park, Laverstoke, Whitchurch, Hampshire RG28 7NT

TEL: (0256) 896533 *CONTACT:* Rosy Hardy
OPENING TIMES: 0900-1730 daily 1st Mar-31st Oct.
MAIL ORDER: No
CAT. COST: 3 x 1st class *W/SALE or RETAIL:* Both
SPECIALITIES: Lavatera & Penstemon. *MAP PAGE:* **2**

86 R F Beeston, (Office) 294 Ombersley Rd., Worcestershire WR3 7HD

TEL: (0905) 453245 *CONTACT:* R F Beeston
OPENING TIMES: 1000-1300 & 1400-1700 Wed-Fri Mar 1-Oct 31 & by appt.
MIN MAIL ORDER UK: No minimum charge *MIN VALUE EC:* £50.00 + p&p
CAT. COST: Sae *W/SALE or RETAIL:* Retail
SPECIALITIES: Rare Alpines, esp. Androsace, Dionysia, Primula, Saxifraga, Gentiana. NOTE: Nursery at Bevere Nursery, Bevere, Worcester. *MAP PAGE:* **5**

98 Mackey's Garden Centre, Castlepark Road, Sandycove, Co. Dublin, Rep. of Ireland

TEL: 010353-1-2807385 *FAX:* 010353-1-2841922 *CONTACT:* Breda Roseingrave
OPENING TIMES: 0900-1730 Mon-Sat. 1400-1730 Sun & Public Hols.
MAIL ORDER: No
CAT. COST: Free *W/SALE or RETAIL:* Retail
SPECIALITIES: Roses, Trees, Houseplants, Alpines, Shrubs & Aquatics. *MAP PAGE:* **11**

 See note on Mail Order, EC sales & Export on page 7

Seed Suppliers

Allwood Bros, Hassocks, West Sussex BN6 9NB
TEL: (0273) 844229 *CONTACT:* W Rickaby *CAT. COST:* 2 x 1st class *MIN. ORDER:* No minimum charge
SPECIALITIES: Carnations, Pinks & Dianthus. See also in Nursery Index under Code 'SAll'.

Arne Herbs, Limeburn Nurseries, Limeburn Hill, Chew Magna, Avon BS18 8QW
TEL: (0275) 333399 *CONTACT:* A Lyman-Dixon & H Lee *CAT. COST:* £1.00 *MIN. ORDER:* None
SPECIALITIES: Seeds available in retail packs for most ANNUAL Culinary Herbs & Wild Flowers by Mail Order only. See also in Nursery Index under Code 'CArn'.

Ashwood Nurseries, Greensforge, Kingswinford, West Midlands DY6 0AE
TEL: (0384) 401996 *FAX:* (0384) 401108 *CONTACT:* John Massey & Philip Baulk *CAT. COST:* 2 x 1st class *MIN. ORDER:* None
◆*SPECIALITIES:* Lewisias, Cyclamen, Hellebores & Auriculas. See also in Nursery Index under Code 'MAsh'

B & T World Seeds, Whitnell House, Fiddington, Bridgwater, Somerset TA5 1JE
TEL: (0278) 733209 *FAX:* (0278) 733209 *CONTACT:* David Sleigh *CAT. COST:* £10 (Europe)*
MIN. ORDER: £5.00
SPECIALITIES: Master list contains some 30,000 items. *£14 to non-European destinations. Sub-lists available.

Barnhaven Primroses, 25 Warstones Crescent, Penn, Wolverhampton, West Midlands WV4 4LQ
TEL: (0902) 334350 *CONTACT:* Mrs Janet Bradford *CAT. COST:* £1.00 *MIN. ORDER:* No minimum charge
SPECIALITIES: Primula - Barnhaven strains. Seed available worldwide. Plants available only in France from their French nursery.

J W Boyce, 40 Fordham, Ely, Cambridgeshire CB7 5JU
TEL: (0638) 721158 *CONTACT:* Mr Roger Morley *CAT. COST:* Free *MIN. ORDER:* 75p under £7.50
SPECIALITIES: Pansy & Vegetables seed and plants, Onion 'Oakey'. Wide range of separate colours for cut flowers, bedding & drying.

S & N Brackley, 117 Winslow Road, Wingrove, Aylesbury, Buckinghamshire HP22 4QB
TEL: (0296) 681384 *CONTACT:* S Brackley & K Earwicker *CAT. COST:* Sae *MIN. ORDER:* No minimum charge
◆*SPECIALITIES:* Gold Medal Sweet Peas & Exhibition Vegetables

Carters Seeds Ltd., Hele Road, Torquay, Devon TQ2 7QJ
TEL: (0803) 616156 *FAX:* (0803) 615747 *CONTACT:* D G Arnold *CAT. COST:* Free *MIN. ORDER:*
SPECIALITIES: General range.

Chadwell Seeds, Himalayan Plant Association, 81 Parlaunt Road, Slough, Berkshire SL3 8BE
TEL: (0753) 542823 *CONTACT:* Chris Chadwell *CAT. COST:* 3 x 2nd class *MIN. ORDER:* No minimum charge
SPECIALITIES: Seed collecting expedition to the Himalaya. Seed available to subscribers only. Separate general Seed list of Japanese, N. America & Himalayan plants.

Chase Organics (GB) Ltd., Coombelands House, Addlestone, Weybridge, Surrey KT15 1HY
TEL: (0932) 820958 *FAX:* (0932) 821258 *CONTACT:* Mrs P Hughes *CAT. COST:* Free
MIN. ORDER: 65p p&p under £10.00
SPECIALITIES: 'The Organic Gardening Catalogue' offers Vegetable, Herb & Flower seeds & garden sundries especially for Organic gardeners.

Cheshire Herbs, Fourfields, Forest Road, Little Budworth, Cheshire CW6 9ES
TEL: (0829) 760578 *FAX:* (0829) 760354 *CONTACT:* Mr & Mrs Ted Riddell *CAT. COST:* 20p
MIN. ORDER: No minimum charge
◆*SPECIALITIES:* Herbs. See also in Nursery Index under Code 'MChe'.

Chiltern Seeds, Bortree Stile, Ulverston, Cumbria LA12 7PB
TEL: (0229) 581137 *FAX:* (0229) 584549 *CONTACT:* *CAT. COST:* 3 x 2nd class *MIN. ORDER:* No minimum charge
◆*SPECIALITIES:* Over 4,000 items of all kind - Wild Flowers, Trees, Shrubs, Cacti, Annuals, Houseplants, Vegetables & Herbs.

◆ **See also Display Advertisements**

Craven's Nursery, 1 Foulds Terrace, Bingley, West Yorkshire BD16 4LZ

TEL: (0274) 561412 *CONTACT:* S R Craven & M Craven *CAT. COST:* £1.00 *MIN. ORDER:* £5.00
SPECIALITIES: Seeds of Show Auriculas, Primulas, Pinks & Alpines. See also in Nursery Index under Code 'NCra'.

CTDA, 174 Cambridge Street London SW1V 4QE

TEL: 071-821 1801 *CONTACT:* Basil Smith *CAT. COST:* Free *MIN. ORDER:*
SPECIALITIES: Hardy Cyclamen. See also in Nursery Index under Code 'LCTD'.

B & D Davies, 2 Wirral View, Connah's Quay, Deeside, Clwyd CH5 4TE

TEL: *CONTACT:* Mr B Davies *CAT. COST:* 3 x 2nd class *MIN. ORDER:* £6.00
SPECIALITIES: Trees & Shrubs especially Conifers.

Jack Drake, Inshriach Alpine Nursery, Aviemore, Invernesshire PH22 1QS

TEL: (0540 651) 287 *FAX:* (0540 651) 656 *CONTACT:* J C Lawson *CAT. COST:* *MIN. ORDER:* No minimum charge
◆*SPECIALITIES:* Rare & unusual Alpines & Rock Plants especially Primulas, Gentians & many others. See also in Nursery Index under Code 'GDra'.

John Drake, Hardwicke House, Fen Ditton, Cambridgeshire CB5 8TF

TEL: *CONTACT:* John Drake *CAT. COST:* 50p + stamp* *MIN. ORDER:*
SPECIALITIES: Aquilegia. See also in Nursery Index under Code 'EDra'. *NOTE Seed Catalogue available Aug/Sep.

Emorsgate Seed, Terrington Court, Terrington St Clement, Kings Lynn Norfolk PE34 4NT

TEL: (0553) 829028 *FAX:* (0553) 829028 *CONTACT:* Donald MacIntyre *CAT. COST:* Free
MIN. ORDER: No minimum charge
SPECIALITIES: Wild British Flowers & Grasses.

Equatorial Plants, 7 Gray Lane, Barnard Castle, Co. Durham DL12 8PD

TEL: (0833) 690519 *FAX:* (0833) 690519 *CONTACT:* Richard Warren PhD. *CAT. COST:* Free
MIN. ORDER: £5.00
SPECIALITIES: Orchid seed.

Field House Nurseries, Leake Road, Gotham, Nottingham NG11 0JN

TEL: (0602) 830278 *CONTACT:* Doug Lochhead & Valerie A Woolley *CAT. COST:* 4 x 1st class
MIN. ORDER: No minimum charge
SPECIALITIES: Primulas & Alpines. See also in Nursery Index under Code 'MFie'.

Mr Fothergill's Seeds Ltd., Gazeley Road, Kentford, Newmarket, Suffolk CB8 7QB

TEL: (0638) 751161 *FAX:* (0638) 751624 *CONTACT:* Customer services *CAT. COST:* Free
MIN. ORDER: No minimum charge
SPECIALITIES: Annuals, Biennials, Perennials, Herbs, Vegetables, plus Plants, soft Fruit and Garden Sundries.

Glenhirst Cactus Nursery, Station Road, Swineshead, Nr Boston, Lincolnshire PE20 3NX

TEL: (0205) 820314 *CONTACT:* N C & S A Bell *CAT. COST:* 2 x 1st class *MIN. ORDER:* No minimu charge
SPECIALITIES: Extensive range of Cacti & Succulent seeds. See also under Cacti & Succulent Specialists Index.

Peter Grayson, Sweet Pea Seedsman, 34 Glenthorne Close, Brampton, Chesterfield Derbyshire S40 3AR

TEL: (0246) 278503 *CONTACT:* Peter Grayson *CAT. COST:* Sae *MIN. ORDER:* No minimum charge
SPECIALITIES: Lathyrus species & cultivars. (Sweet Peas).

Harrisons Delphiniums, Newbury Cottage, Play Hatch, Reading, Berkshire RG4 9QN

TEL: (0734) 470810 *CONTACT:* Len Harrison *CAT. COST:* 1 x 1st class *MIN. ORDER:* No minimum charge
SPECIALITIES: Delphiniums. See also in Nursery Index under Code 'LHar'.

James Henderson & Sons, Kingholm Quay, Dumfries DG1 4SU

TEL: (0387) 52234 *FAX:* (0387) 62302 *CONTACT:* J H & R J Henderson *CAT. COST:* Sae *MIN. ORDER:*
◆*SPECIALITIES:* Over 30 varieties of Scottish Seed Potatoes

Henllys Lodge Plants, Henllys Lodge, Beaumaris, Anglesey, Gwynedd LL58 8HU
TEL: (0248) 810106 *CONTACT:* Mrs E Lane *CAT. COST:* 2 x 2nd class *MIN. ORDER:* No minimum charge
SPECIALITIES: Small range of hardy Perennials, esp. hardy Geraniums. See also in Nursery Index under Code 'WHen'.

Holden Clough Nursery, Holden, Bolton-by-Bowland Clitheroe Lancashire BB7 4PF
TEL: (0200) 447615 *CONTACT:* Peter Foley *CAT. COST:* Sae *MIN. ORDER:* No minimum charge
◆*SPECIALITIES:* Alpines & hardy Perennials. See also in Nursery Index under Code 'NHol'.

Holly Gate Cactus Nursery, Billingshurst Road, Ashington, West Sussex RH20 3BA
TEL: (0903) 892 930 *CONTACT:* Mr T M Hewitt *CAT. COST:* 2 x 2nd class *MIN. ORDER:* £2.00 + p&p
SPECIALITIES: Cacti & Succulents.

Diana Hull, Fog Cottages, 178 Lower Street, Hillmorton, Rugby, Warwickshire CV21 4NX
TEL: (0788) 536574 after 1600 *CONTACT:* Diana Hull *CAT. COST:* Sae for list *MIN. ORDER:* No minimum charge
SPECIALITIES: Pelargonium species. See also in Nursery Index under Code 'MHul'.

Iden Croft Herbs, Frittenden Road, Staplehurst, Kent TH12 0DN
TEL: (0580) 891432 *FAX:* (0580) 892416 *CONTACT:* Rosemary & D Titterington *CAT. COST:* Sae
MIN. ORDER: No minimum charge
SPECIALITIES: Herbs

W E Th. Ingwersen Ltd., Birch Farm Nursery, Gravetye, E. Grinstead, West Sussex RH19 4LE
TEL: (0342) 810236 *CONTACT:* M P & M R Ingwersen *CAT. COST:* Sae *MIN. ORDER:* No minimum charge
SPECIALITIES: Alpines & rock garden plants.

Landlife Wildflowers Ltd., The Old Police Station, Lark Lane, Liverpool, Merseyside L17 8UU
TEL: (051 728) 7011 *FAX:* (051 728) 8413 *CONTACT:* Gillian Watson *CAT. COST:* Free
MIN. ORDER: No minimum charge
SPECIALITIES: Native Herbaceous plants. See also in Nursery Index under Code 'NLan'.

Mackay's Garden Centre, Castlepark Road, Sandycove, Co. Dublin, Rep. of Ireland
TEL: 010353-1-2807385 *FAX:* 010353-1-2841922 *CONTACT:* Breda Roseingrave *CAT. COST:* Free
MIN. ORDER: No minimum charge
SPECIALITIES: See also in Nursery Index under Code '98'.

S M McArd (Seeds), 39 West Road, Pointon, Sleaford, Lincolnshire NG34 0NA
TEL: (0529) 240765 *FAX:* (0529) 240765 *CONTACT:* Susan McArd *CAT. COST:* 2 x 2nd class
MIN. ORDER: No minimum charge
SPECIALITIES: Unusual & giant Vegetables. Seeds & Plants.

Monocot Nursery, Jacklands, Jacklands Bridge, Tickenham, Clevedon Avon BS21 6SG
TEL: *CONTACT:* M R Salmon *CAT. COST:* Sae *MIN. ORDER:* No minimum charge
SPECIALITIES: Rare & unusual Bulbous & Tuberous plants. See also in Nursery Index under Code 'CMon'.

John Morley, North Green Only, Stoven, Beccles, Suffolk NR34 8DG
TEL: *CONTACT:* John Morley *CAT. COST:* 50p + stamp *MIN. ORDER:* No minimum charge
SPECIALITIES: Small specialist range of Galanthus, Allium & Fritillaria Seed. See also in Nursery Index under Code 'EMor'.

Natural Selection, 1 Station Cottages, Hullavington, Chipenham, Wiltshire SN14 6ET
TEL: (0666) 837369 *CONTACT:* Martin Cragg-Barber *CAT. COST:* A5 Sae *MIN. ORDER:* No minimum charge
SPECIALITIES: Unusual British natives. See also in Nursery Index under Code 'CNat'.

Andrew Norfield Trees & Seeds, Lower Meend, St Briavels, Gloucestershire GL15 6RW
TEL: (0594) 530134 *FAX:* (0594) 530113 *CONTACT:* Andrew Norfield *CAT. COST:* 1 x 1st class
MIN. ORDER: No minimum charge
SPECIALITIES: Germinated & pretreated Seed of hardy Trees, Shrubs, Herbaceous & House plants. See also in Nursery Index under Code 'WNor'.

Stuart Ogg, Hopton, Fletching Street, Mayfield, East Sussex TN20 6TL

TEL: (0435) 873322 *CONTACT:* Stuart Ogg *CAT. COST:* Sae *MIN. ORDER:* No minimum charge
SPECIALITIES: Delphiniums. See also in Nursery Index under Code 'SOgg'.

Passiflora (National Collection), Lampley Road, Kingston Seymour, Clevedon, Avon BS21 6XS

TEL: (0934) 833350 *FAX:* (0934) 833320 *CONTACT:* John Vanderplank *CAT. COST:* 3 x 1st class
MIN. ORDER: £4.00
SPECIALITIES: Over 150 Passiflora. See also in Nursery Index under Code 'WGre'.

Phedar Nursery, Bunkers Hill, Romiley, Stockport, Cheshire SK6 3DS

TEL: (061 430) 3772 *FAX:* (061 430) 3772 *CONTACT:* Will McLewin *CAT. COST:* Sae
MIN. ORDER: No minimum charge
SPECIALITIES: Helleborus. Species seed wild collected. Hybrid seed in colour & spotting categories. All supplied fresh July onwards. See also in Nursery Index under 'MPhe'

Pinks & Carnations, 22 Chetwyn Avenue, Bromley Cross, Nr Bolton, Lancashire BL7 9BN

TEL: (0204) 306273 *CONTACT:* Ruth & Tom Gillies *CAT. COST:* Sae *MIN. ORDER:* No minimum charge
◆*SPECIALITIES:* Perpetual Flowing Carnations, Border Carnations, Allwoodii Alpinus & Knappii - (The Yellow Pink). See also in Nursery Index under Code 'NPin'.

Plant World Botanic Gardens, Seed Dept. (PF) St Marychurch Road, Newton Abbot, Devon TQ12 4SE

TEL: (0803) 872939 *CONTACT:* Ray Brown *CAT. COST:* 3 x 1st class *MIN. ORDER:* £8.00
◆*SPECIALITIES:* Meconopsis, Gentiana, Primula, Aquilegia, Campanula, Viola, Lewisia, Salvia, Eryngium. See also in Nursery Index under Code 'CPla'. No plants by Mail Order.

Potterton & Martin, The Cottage Nursery, Moortown Road, Nettleton, Caister, Lincolnshire LN7 6HX

TEL: (0472) 851792 *FAX:* (0472) 851792 *CONTACT:* *CAT. COST:* 50p in stamps only *MIN. ORDER:* No minimum charge
SPECIALITIES: Alpines & dwarf Bulbs. Seed list sent out in November. See also in Nursery Index under Code 'EPot'.

Roger Poulett, Nurse's Cottage, North Mundham, Chichester, Sussex PO20 6JY

TEL: Not available *CONTACT:* Roger Poulett *CAT. COST:* 3 x 1st class* *MIN. ORDER:* No minimum charge
SPECIALITIES: Cyclamen, Corydalis, Helleborus, Hepatica etc. for summer sowing, June to Sept only. *Seed list included in plant Catalogue. See also Nursery Index under 'SPou'

W Robinson & Sons Ltd., Sunny Bank, Forton, Nr Preston, Lancashire PR3 0BN

TEL: (0524) 791210 *FAX:* (0524) 791933 *CONTACT:* Miss Robinson *CAT. COST:* Free
MIN. ORDER: No minimum charge
SPECIALITIES: Mammoth Vegetable seed.

R V Roger Ltd, The Nurseries, Pickering, North Yorkshire YO18 7HG

TEL: (0751) 472226 *FAX:* (0751) 476749 *CONTACT:* J R Roger, S Peirson & A G & I M Roger
CAT. COST: Sae *MIN. ORDER:* No minimum charge
SPECIALITIES: Bulbs & Seed Potatoes. See also in Nursery Index under Code 'NRog'.

Salley Gardens, Flat 3, 3 Millicent Road, West Bridgford, Nottingham NG2 7LD

TEL: (0602) 821366 evngs *CONTACT:* Richard Lewin *CAT. COST:* Sae *MIN. ORDER:* No minimum charge
SPECIALITIES: Wildflower & Medicinal Herbs. See also in Nursery Index under Code 'MSal'.

The Seed House, 9a Widley Road, Cosham, Portsmouth, PO6 2DS

TEL: (0705) 325639 *CONTACT:* Mr R L Spearing *CAT. COST:* 4 x 1st class *MIN. ORDER:* £5.00
◆*SPECIALITIES:* Australian seeds suitable for the European climate.

Seeds by Size, 45 Crouchfield, Boxmoor, Hemel Hempstead, Hertfordshire HP1 1PA

TEL: (0442) 251458 *CONTACT:* Mr John Robert Size *CAT. COST:* Sae *MIN. ORDER:* 60p if under £5.00
SPECIALITIES: Flowers & Vegetables. 1,100 varieties of Vegetable, (155 Cabbage, 93 Cauliflower, 65 Onion) & 3000 flowers such as 230 varieties of Sweet Pea.

John Shipton (Bulbs), Y Felin, Henllan Amgoed, Whitland, Dyfed SA34 0SL

TEL: (0994) 240125 *CONTACT:* John Shipton *CAT. COST:* Sae *MIN. ORDER:* No minimum charge
SPECIALITIES: Species native to the British Isles. See also in Nursery Index under Code 'WShi'.

Stewart's (Nottingham) Ltd., 3 George Street, Nottingham NG1 3BH

TEL: (0602) 476338 *CONTACT:* Brenda Lochhead *CAT. COST:* Sae *MIN. ORDER:* No minimum charge
SPECIALITIES: Large general range esp. Vegetables.

Richard Stockwell, 64 Weardale Road, Sherwood, Nottingham NG5 1DD

TEL: (0602) 691063* *CONTACT:* Richard Stockwell *CAT. COST:* Free *MIN. ORDER:* No minimum charge
◆*SPECIALITIES:* Very rare climbing species, also dwarf species. See also in Nursery Index under Code 'MSto'. * 0115-969 1063 from 15/04/95.

Suttons Seeds Ltd., Hele Road, Torquay, Devon TQ2 7QJ

TEL: (0803) 614455 *FAX:* (0803) 615747 *CONTACT:* Customer Services *CAT. COST:* Free
MIN. ORDER: No minimum charge
SPECIALITIES: Wide general range of Flower & Vegetable Seed. Also summer flowering bulbs etc. in 'Suttons Plus' Catalogue. See also in Nursery Index under Code 'CSut'.

Thompson & Morgan, London Road, Ipswich, Suffolk IP2 0BA

TEL: (0473) 688821 *FAX:* (0473) 680199 *CONTACT:* Martin Thrower *CAT. COST:* Free
MIN. ORDER: No minimum charge
SPECIALITIES: Largest illustrated Seed catalogue in the world.

Thuya Alpine Nursery, Glebelands, Hartpury, Gloucestershire GL19 3BW

TEL: (0452) 700548 *CONTACT:* S W Bond *CAT. COST:* Sae *MIN. ORDER:* No minimum charge
SPECIALITIES: General range. See also in Nursery Index under Code 'WThu'.

Edwin Tucker & Sons, Brewery Meadow, Stonepark, Ashburton, Newton Abbot, Devon TQ13 7DG

TEL: (0364) 652403 *FAX:* (0364) 654300 *CONTACT:* Geoff Penton *CAT. COST:* Free *MIN. ORDER:* No minimum charge
SPECIALITIES: Over 40 varieties of Seed Potatoes. Wide range of Vegetables, Green Manures & sprouting seeds in packets. All not dressed or treated.

Unwins Seeds Ltd., Mail Order Dept. Histon, Cambridge, Cambridgeshire CB4 4ZZ

TEL: (0945) 588522 *FAX:* (0945) 475255 *CONTACT:* Customer Services Dept. *CAT. COST:* Free
MIN. ORDER: No minimum charge
SPECIALITIES: Wide general range. Over 50 varieties of Sweet Peas.

Uzumara Orchids, 9 Port Henderson, Gairloch Rosshire IV21 2AS

TEL: (0445 83) 228 *CONTACT:* Mrs I F La Croix *CAT. COST:* Sae *MIN. ORDER:* No minimum charge
SPECIALITIES: Streptocarpus species. See also in Nursery Index under Code 'GUzu'.

Wilford Bulb Co. Ltd., 69 Main Street, East Leake, Leicestershire LE12 6PF

TEL: (0509) 852905 *FAX:* (0509) 852905 *CONTACT:* Tony Cross *CAT. COST:* 2 x 1st class
MIN. ORDER: £10.00 + p&p
SPECIALITIES: Wide range of Vegetables, Trees & Shrubs. See also in Nursery Index under Code 'MWBu'.

Y.S.J Seeds, Kingsfield Conservation, Broadenham Lane, Winsham, Chard, Somerset TA20 4JF

TEL: (0460) 30070 *FAX:* (0460) 30070 *CONTACT:* Mrs M White *CAT. COST:* Sae *MIN. ORDER:* No minimum charge
SPECIALITIES: British Wild Flowers seeds from native stock plants. See also in Nursery Index under Code 'CKin'

Roy Young Seeds, 23 Westland Chase, West Winch, King's Lynn, Norfolk PE33 0QH

TEL: (0553) 840867 *FAX:* (0553) 768372 *CONTACT:* Mr Roy Young *CAT. COST:* 2nd cls/3xIRC
MIN. ORDER: No minimum charge*
SPECIALITIES: Cactus & Succulent seeds only. 24 pg Cat. listing approx. 1,500 species, varieties & forms (Retail). 6 pg A4 listing (Wholesale). *£25 min Wholesale charge.

Seed Suppliers

Cacti & Succulent Suppliers

Bradley Batch Nursery, 64 Bath Road, Bridgwater, Somersetshire TA7 9QJ
TEL: (0458) 210256 *CONTACT:* J E White
OPENING TIMES: 1000-1800 Tue-Sun. *W/SALE or RETAIL:* Both
MAIL ORDER: No *CAT. COST:* None issued
SPECIALITIES: Echeveria, Haworthia, Lithops & Cacti.

Bridgemere Nurseries, Bridgemere, Cheshire CW5 7QB
TEL: (09365) 381/239 x 138 *FAX:* (09365) 215 *CONTACT:* Jim Speed
OPENING TIMES: 0900-2000 Mon-Sat, 1000-2000 Sun, in summer, until 1700 winter. *W/SALE or RETAIL:* Retail
MAIL ORDER: No *CAT. COST:*
SPECIALITIES: General range of Cacti & other Succulents incl. specimen plants. See also in ORCHID Index andNursery Index under Code 'MBri'

Connoisseurs' Cacti, (Off.) 51 Chelsfield Lane, Kent BR5 4HG
TEL: (0689) 837781 *CONTACT:* John Pilbeam
OPENING TIMES: 1030-1430 but please phone first. *W/SALE or RETAIL:* Both *MIN VALUE:* No minimum charge
CAT. COST: Sae or IRC
SPECIALITIES: Mammillaria, Sulcorebutia, Gymnocalycium, Rebutia, Haworthia, Conophytum, Asclepiads etc. NOTE:Nursery at, Woodlands Farm, Shire Lane, Nr Farnborough, Kent.

Croston Cactus, 43 Southport Road, Chorley, Lancashire PR7 6ET
TEL: (0257) 452555 *CONTACT:* John Henshaw
OPENING TIMES: Evenings & Weekends. Please phone before visit. (New opening times planned for 1994)
W/SALE or RETAIL: Retail *MIN VALUE:* No minimum charge *CAT. COST:* 2x1st or 2 IRCs
SPECIALITIES: Mexican Cacti, Echeveria hybrids & some Bromeliads.

Cruck Cottage Cacti, Cruck Cottage, Pickering, North Yorkshire YO18 8PJ
TEL: (0751) 472042 *CONTACT:* R J A Wood
OPENING TIMES: 0900-sunset. Closed Sat a.m. & Mon. Please ring first. *W/SALE or RETAIL:* Both
MAIL ORDER: No *CAT. COST:*
SPECIALITIES: Large range of Cacti & Succulents. Exhibition area of mature plants - entrance FREE. Nursery ina garden setting.

East Midlands Cactus Nursery, Manor Close, Milton Keynes, Buckinghamshire MK10 9AA
TEL: (0908) 665584 *CONTACT:* Mike & Eileen Watson
OPENING TIMES: 0900-1800 Wed-Mon *W/SALE or RETAIL:* Retail *MIN VALUE:* No minimum charge *CAT. COST:* Large Sae*
SPECIALITIES: Cacti, Succulents & Carnivorous plants. *NOTE: Please add 3 IRCs if outside EC.

Felspar Cacti, 20 Reawla Lane, Hayle, Cornwall TR27 5HQ
TEL: (0736) 850321 *CONTACT:* Mrs M Negus
OPENING TIMES: 1000-1700 Mon, Tue & Thu 1230-1700 Fri. *W/SALE or RETAIL:* Retail *MIN VALUE:* £2.80 + p&p *CAT. COST:* Sae
SPECIALITIES: Cacti, Succulents & Fuchsias. Amateur hybridist. Collection of 6 hybrid Fuchsias inc. 2 newvarieties for 1994 £6.80 incl p&p.

W G Geissler, Winsford, Slimbridge, Gloucestershire GL2 7BW
TEL: (0453) 890340 *CONTACT:* W G Geissler
OPENING TIMES: 0900-1700 (2000 in summer) Mar-Nov. *W/SALE or RETAIL:* Retail
MAIL ORDER: No *CAT. COST:* Sae
SPECIALITIES: Hardy Cacti & Succulents & related books.

Glenhirst Cactus Nursery, Station Road, Nr Boston, Lincolnshire PE20 3NX
TEL: (0205) 820314 *CONTACT:* N C & S A Bell
OPENING TIMES: 1000-1700 Thu, Fri & Sun 1st Mar-31st Oct. Other times by appt. *W/SALE or RETAIL:* Retail
MIN VALUE: No minimum charge *CAT. COST:* 2 x 1st class
SPECIALITIES: Extensive range of Cacti & Succulent plants & seeds. All stock fully described on lists.

Harvest Nurseries, Harvest Cottage, Iden, Nr Rye Sussex TH31 7QA
TEL: (0797) 280 493 *CONTACT:* D A Smith
OPENING TIMES: *W/SALE or RETAIL:* Retail
MAIL ORDER: Only *MIN VALUE:* No minimum charge *CAT. COST:* 2 x 1st class
SPECIALITIES: Cacti & Succulents.

See note on Mail Order, EC sales & Export on page 7

Holly Gate Cactus Nursery, Billingshurst Road, West Sussex RH20 3BA
TEL: (0903) 892 930 *CONTACT:* Mr T M Hewitt
OPENING TIMES: 0900-1700 daily. *W/SALE or RETAIL:* Both *MIN VALUE:* £5.00 + p&p *CAT. COST:* 50p + 29p&p
SPECIALITIES: Cactus, Succulents & Pelargoniums.

K & C Cacti, Fern Cottage, Barnstaple, Devon EX32 0SF
TEL: (0598) 760393 *CONTACT:* Keith & Jane Comer
OPENING TIMES: Phone first please. *W/SALE or RETAIL:* Retail *MIN VALUE:* £5 + p&p *CAT. COST:* Sae or IRC
SPECIALITIES: Echeveria, Euphorbia, Haworthia, Conophytum, Adromischus, Crassula, Gasteria, Sulcorebutia &dwarf Opuntia.

Kent Cacti, (Off.) 35 Rutland Way, Kent BR5 4DY
TEL: (0689) 836249 *CONTACT:* Mr D Sizmur
OPENING TIMES: 1000-1700 most days. Please phone first. *W/SALE or RETAIL:* Retail *MIN VALUE:* See Cat. for details *CAT. COST:* A5 Sae
SPECIALITIES: Agave, Astrophytum, Conophytum, Crassula, Echeveria, Echinocereus, Mammillaria etc. NOTE:Nursery at Woodlands Farm, Shire Lane, Farnborough, Kent.

Long Man Gardens, Lewes Road, Polgate, East Sussex BN26 5RS
TEL: (0323) 870816 *CONTACT:* O Menzel
OPENING TIMES: 0900-1800 Tue-Sun. Please check before visiting. *W/SALE or RETAIL:* Both *MIN VALUE:* 1 plant + p&p *CAT. COST:* Free list
SPECIALITIES: Agave, Echeveria, Euphorbia etc.

Pete & Ken Cactus Nursery, Saunders Lane, Nr Canterbury, Kent CT3 2BX
TEL: (0304) 812170 *CONTACT:* Ken Burke
OPENING TIMES: 0900-1800 daily. *W/SALE or RETAIL:* Retail *MIN VALUE:* £3.00 + p&p *CAT. COST:* Sae for list
SPECIALITIES: Cactus, Succulents, Lithops (Living stones).

A & A Phipps, 62 Samuel White Road, Bristol, Avon BS15 3LX
TEL: (0272) 607591 *CONTACT:* A Phipps
OPENING TIMES: All times, but prior phone call ESSENTIAL. *W/SALE or RETAIL:* Both *MIN VALUE:* £5.00 + p&p *CAT. COST:* Sae or 2 IRC
SPECIALITIES: Rebutia, Mammillaria & Astrophytum.

The Plant Lovers, Candesby House, Spilsby, Lincolnshire PE23 5RU
TEL: (0754) 85256 *CONTACT:* Tim Wilson
OPENING TIMES: Daily, but please phone first. *W/SALE or RETAIL:* Both
MAIL ORDER: No *CAT. COST:* None issued
SPECIALITIES: Sempervivum (Houseleeks) & wide range of Cacti and other Succulents. Brochure in course ofpreparation.

Chris Rodgerson, 35 Lydgate Hall Crescent, Sheffield South Yorkshire S10 5NE
TEL: (0742) 685533 *CONTACT:* Chris Rodgerson
OPENING TIMES: Mail Order only. *W/SALE or RETAIL:* Retail *MIN VALUE:* £10.00 + p&p *CAT. COST:* Sae or IRC
SPECIALITIES: Conophytum & Adromischus propagated from original wild material with locality data.

Robert Scott, 78 Bousley Rise, Surrey KT16 0LB
TEL: (0932) 872667 *FAX:* (0932) 872667 *CONTACT:* Robert Scott
OPENING TIMES: By appt. only. *W/SALE or RETAIL:* Both
MAIL ORDER: No *CAT. COST:*
SPECIALITIES: Cactaceae & Mesembryanthemaceae. Seed raised plants from many families & large specimen plants.

Southfield Nurseries, Bourne Road, Nr Bourne Lincolnshire PE10 0RH
TEL: (0778) 570168 *CONTACT:* Mr & Mrs B Goodey
OPENING TIMES: 1000-1230 & 1330-1600 daily (ex Xmas & New Year). *W/SALE or RETAIL:* Both *MIN VALUE:* No minimum charge *CAT. COST:* 1 x 1st class
SPECIALITIES: A wide range of Cacti & Succulents including some of the rarer varieties all grown on our ownnursery.

Toobees Nursery, 20 Inglewood, Woking, Surrey GU21 3HX
TEL: (0483) 722600 *FAX:* (0483) 751995 *CONTACT:* Bob Potter
OPENING TIMES: By appt. only, *W/SALE or RETAIL:* Retail *MIN VALUE:* No minimum charge *CAT. COST:* Sae
SPECIALITIES: South African & Madagascan Succulents. Many rare & unusual species.

Westfield Cacti, Kennford, Devon EX6 7XD
TEL: (0392) 832921 *CONTACT:* Ralph & Marina Northcott
OPENING TIMES: 1000-dusk daily. *W/SALE or RETAIL:* Both *MIN VALUE:* £5 + p&p *CAT. COST:* 4x1st or £1.00
SPECIALITIES: Epiphytes & Sempervivum.

Whitestone Gardens Ltd., The Cactus Houses, Thirsk, Yorkshire YO7 2PZ
TEL: (0845) 597467 *FAX:* (0845) 597467 *CONTACT:* Roy Mottram
OPENING TIMES: Daylight hours Sat-Thu. *W/SALE or RETAIL:* Retail *MIN VALUE:* No minimum charge *CAT. COST:* 4 x 2nd class
SPECIALITIES: Cacti & other Succulents, Books & Sundries.

H & S Wills, 2 St Brannocks Park Road, Devon EX34 8HU
TEL: (0271) 863949 *CONTACT:* H Wills
OPENING TIMES: Appt. only *W/SALE or RETAIL:* Retail
MAIL ORDER: Tes *MIN VALUE:* £3.00 + p&p *CAT. COST:* 3 x 1st class
SPECIALITIES: Sempervivum, Jovibarba & Rosularia.

Roy Young Seeds, 23 Westland Chase, King's Lynn, Norfolk PE33 0QH
TEL: (0553) 840867 *CONTACT:* Mr Roy Young
OPENING TIMES: Not open. *W/SALE or RETAIL:* Both
MAIL ORDER: Only *MIN VALUE:* No minimum charge *CAT. COST:* 2nd cls/3xIRC
SPECIALITIES: Cactus & Succulent SEEDS only.

See note on Mail Order, EC sales & Export on page 7

Orchid Suppliers

Bridgemere Nurseries, Bridgemere, Nr Nantwich, Cheshire CW5 7QB

TEL: (09365) 381/239 x 138 *FAX:* (09365) 215 *CONTACT:* Jim Speed
OPENING TIMES: 0900-2000 Mon-Sat, 1000-2000 Sun in summer, until 1700 in winter. *W/SALE or RETAIL:* Bridge
MAIL ORDER: No *CAT. COST:*
SPECIALITIES: Cymbidium, Paphiopedilum, Phalaenopsis, Miltonia, Odontoglossum.

Burnham Nurseries, Forches Cross, Newton Abbot, Devon TQ12 6PZ

TEL: (0626) 52233 *FAX:* (0626) 62167 *CONTACT:* Brian Rittershausen
OPENING TIMES: 0900-1700 Mon-Fri & 1000-1600 Sat & Sun. *W/SALE or RETAIL:* Burnha
MAIL ORDER: Yes *MIN VALUE:* £10.00 + p&p *CAT. COST:* Large Sae
SPECIALITIES: All types of Orchid.

Equatorial Plant Co., 7 Gray Lane, Barnard Castle, Co. Durham DL12 8PD

TEL: (0833) 690519 *FAX:* (0833) 690519 *CONTACT:* Richard Warren PhD
OPENING TIMES: By appt. only. *W/SALE or RETAIL:* Equato
MAIL ORDER: Yes *MIN VALUE:* No minimum charge *CAT. COST:* Free
SPECIALITIES: Laboratory raised Orchids only.

Greenaway Orchids, Rookery Farm, Puxton, Nr Weston-super-Mare, Avon BS24 6TL

TEL: (0934) 820448 *FAX:* (0934) 820209 *CONTACT:* Robert Dadd
OPENING TIMES: 0800-1800 Tue-Sun *W/SALE or RETAIL:* Greena
MAIL ORDER: No *CAT. COST:* None issued
SPECIALITIES: Large selection of tropical Orchid species & hybrids. Flask seed raising, seedling to floweringsize including endangered species.

Mansell & Hatcher Ltd., Cragg Wood Nurseries, Woodlands Drive, Rawdon, Leeds LS19 6LQ

TEL: (0532) 502016 *CONTACT:* Mr Allan Long
OPENING TIMES: 0900-1700 Mon-Fri. *W/SALE or RETAIL:* Mansel
MAIL ORDER: Yes *MIN VALUE:* No minimum charge *CAT. COST:* 3 x 1st class
SPECIALITIES: Odontoglossum, Masdevallia, Miltonia & Cattleya & species Orchids.

McBeans Orchids, Cooksbridge, Lewes, Sussex BN8 4PR

TEL: (0273) 400228 *FAX:* (0273) 401181 *CONTACT:* Mr Raymond Bilton
OPENING TIMES: 0930-1630 daily ex. Xmas & Boxing day, New Year & Good Friday. *W/SALE or RETAIL:* McBean
MAIL ORDER: Yes *MIN VALUE:* £50.00 + p&p *CAT. COST:* Sae
SPECIALITIES: Orchids - Cymbidium, Odontoglossum, Phalaenopsis, Paphiopedilum, Miltonia, Cattleya & othergenera.

Orchid Sundries & Hardy Orchids Ltd., New Gate Farm, Scotchey Lane, Stour Provost, Gillingham, Dorset SP8 5LT

TEL: (0747) 838368 *FAX:* (0747) 838308 *CONTACT:* N J Heywood
OPENING TIMES: 0800-1300 & 1400-1700 Mon-Fri, Sat by appt. only. *W/SALE or RETAIL:* Orchid
MAIL ORDER: Yes *MIN VALUE:* £10.00 + p&p *CAT. COST:* 4 x 1st class
SPECIALITIES: Hardy Orchids & Disa.

Uzumara Orchids, 9 Port Henderson, Gairloch, Rosshire IV21 2AS

TEL: (0445 83) 228 *CONTACT:* Mrs I F La Croix
OPENING TIMES: *W/SALE or RETAIL:* Uzumar
MAIL ORDER: Only *MIN VALUE:* No minimum charge *CAT. COST:* Sae
SPECIALITIES: Streptocarpus species. African & Madagascan Orchids. See also in Nursery Index under Code'GUzu'

Westwood Nursery, 65 Yorkland Avenue, Welling, Kent DA16 2LE

TEL: 081 301-0886 *CONTACT:* Mr S Edwards
OPENING TIMES: Not open *W/SALE or RETAIL:* Westwo
MAIL ORDER: Yes *MIN VALUE:* No minimum charge *CAT. COST:* Sae
SPECIALITIES: Pleione & Hardy Orchids.

Woodstock Orchids, Woodstock House, 50 Pound Hill, Great Brickhill, Buckinghamshire MK17 9AS

TEL: (0525 261) 352 *FAX:* (0525 261) 724 *CONTACT:* Joan & Bill Gaskell
OPENING TIMES: Strictly by appt only. *W/SALE or RETAIL:* Woodst
MAIL ORDER: Yes *MIN VALUE:* See Cat. for details *CAT. COST:* Free
SPECIALITIES: Orchids, Carnivorous plants & Exotic House plants.

Reverse Synonyms

In order to assist users to establish from which Genera an unfamiliar plant name may have been transferred, the following list of reverse synonyms may help.

Acacia - Racosperma
Acanthocalyx - Morina
Acca - Feijoa
x Achicodonia - Eucodonia
Achillea - Anthemis
Acinos - Calamintha
Acinos - Micromeria
Actinidia - Kiwi Fruit
Aethionema - Eunomia
Agapetes - Pentapterygium
Agarista - Leucotho
Agastache - Cedronella
Aichryson - Aeonium
Albizia - Acacia
Alcea - Althaea
Allardia - Waldheimia
Allocasuarina - Casuarina
Aloysia - Lippia
Alyogyne - Hibiscus
Alyssum - Ptilotrichum
x Amarygia - Amaryllis
Amaryllis - Brunsvigia
Amomyrtus - Myrtus
Amsonia - Rhazya
Anaphalis - Gnaphalium
Anchusa - Lycopsis
Androsace - Douglasia
Anisodontea - Malvastrum
Anomatheca - Lapeirousia
Anredera - Boussingaultia
Antirrhinum - Asarina
Aphanes - Alchemilla
Arctanthemum - Chrysanthemum
Arctostaphylos - Arbutus
Arctotis - x Venidioarctotis
Arctotis - Venidium
Arenga - Didymosperma
Argyranthemum - Anthemis
Argyranthemum - Chrysanthemum
Armoracia - Cochlearia
Arundinaria - Pseudosasa
Asarina - Antirrhinum
Asclepias - Gomphocarpus
Asparagus - Smilax
Asperula - Galium
Asphodeline - Asphodelus
Asplenium - Camptosorus
Asplenium - Ceterach
Asplenium - Phyllitis
Asplenium - Scolopendrium
Aster - Crinitaria
Aster - Microglossa
Asteriscus - Pallensis
Astilboides - Rodgersia
Atropanthe - Scopolia
Aurinia - Alyssum
Austrocedrus - Libocedrus
Azorina - Campanula
Bambusa - Arundinaria
Bellevalia - Muscari
Bellis - Erigeron
Blechnum - Lomaria
Bolax - Azorella
Borago - Anchusa
Boykinia - Telesonix
Brachyglottis - Senecio
Bracteantha - Helichrysum
Brimeura - Hyacinthus
Brugmansia - Datura
Brunnera - Anchusa
Buglossoides - Lithospermum
Bulbine - Bulbinopsis
Buphthalmum - Inula
Caiophora - Loasa
Caladium - Xanthosoma
Calamintha - Clinopodium
Calliergon - Acrocladium
Callisia - Phyodina
Callisia - Tradescantia
Calocedrus - Libocedrus
Calomeria - Humea
Caloscordum - Nothoscordum
Calytrix - Lhotzkya
Camellia - Thea
Cardamine - Dentaria
Carica - Paw Paw
Carpobrotus - Lampranthus
Carya - Pecan
Cassiope - Harrimanella
Castanea - Chestnut, Sweet
Catapodium - Desmazeria
Cayratia - Parthenocissus
Centaurium - Erythraea
Centella - Hydrocotyle
Centranthus - Kentranthus
Centranthus - Valeriana
Cephalaria - Scabiosa
Ceratostigma - Plumbago
Cercestis - Rhektophyllum
Chaenomeles - Cydonia
Chaenorhinum - Linaria
Chamaecyparis - Cupressus
Chamaecytisus - Cytisus
Chamaedaphne - Cassandra
Chamaemelum - Anthemis
Chasmanthium - Uniola
Chiastophyllum - Cotyledon
Chimonobambusa - Arundinaria
Chimonobambusa - Quiongzhuea
Chionohebe - Pygmaea
x Chionoscilla - Scilla
Chlorophytum - Diuranthera
Chondrosum - Bouteloua
Cicerbita - Lactuca
Cionura - Marsdenia
Cissus - Ampelopsis
Cissus - Parthenocissus
x Citrofortunella - Calamondin
x Citrofortunella - Citrus
Citronella - Villaresia
Citrus - Citron
Citrus - Grapefruit
Citrus - Lemon
Citrus - Lime
Citrus - Mandarin
Citrus - Pummelo
Citrus - Satsuma
Citrus - Orange, Sour Or Seville
Citrus - Shaddock
Citrus - Orange, Sweet
Citrus - Tangelo
Citrus - Tangerine
Citrus - Tangor
Citrus - Ugli
Clarkia - Godetia
Clavinodum - Arundinaria
Claytonia - Calandrinia
Claytonia - Montia
Clematis - Atragene
Cleyera - Eurya
Clinopodium - Acinos
Clinopodium - Calamintha
Clytostoma - Bignonia
Clytostoma - Pandorea
Cnicus - Carduus
Cocos - Coconut
Coffea - Coffee
Cordyline - Dracaena
Cornus - Chamaepericlymenum
Cornus - Dendrobenthamia
Coronilla - Securigera
Cortaderia - Gynerium
Corylus - Nut, Cob
Corylus - Cobnut
Corylus - Filbert
Corylus - Nut, Filbert
Cosmos - Bidens
Cotinus - Rhus
Cotula - Leptinella
Crambe - Seakale
Crassula - Rochea
Crassula - Sedum
Crassula - Tillaea
Cremanthodium - Ligularia
Crinodendron - Tricuspidaria
Crocosmia - Antholyza
Crocosmia - Curtonus
Crocosmia - Montbretia
Cruciata - Galium
Ctenanthe - Calathea
Ctenanthe - Stromanthe
x Cupressocyparis - Chamaecyparis
Cyathodes - Leucopogon
Cyathodes - Styphelia
Cyclosorus - Pneumatopteris
Cydonia - Quince
Cymbalaria - Linaria

Cynara - Artichoke, Globe
Cynara - Scolymus
Cyperus - Mariscus
Cyrtanthus - Anoiganthus
Cyrtanthus - Vallota
Cyrtomium - Polystichum
Cytisus - Argyrocytisus
Cytisus - Genista
Cytisus - Lembotropis
Cytisus - Spartocytisus
Daboecia - Menziesia
Dacrycarpus - Podocarpus
Dactylorhiza - Orchis
Dana - Ruscus
Darmera - Peltiphyllum
Dasypyrum - Haynaldia
Datura - Brugmansia
Datura - Datura
Davallia - Humata
Delairea - Senecio
Delosperma - Lampranthus
Delosperma - Mesembryanthemum
Dendranthema - Chrysanthemum
Derwentia - Hebe
Desmodium - Lespedeza
Dichelostemma - Brodiaea
Dicliptera - Justicia
Dietes - Moraea
Disporopsis - Polygonatum
Distictis - Phaedranthus
Distylium - Sycopsis
Dolicothrix - Helichrysum
Dracaena - Pleomele
Dracunculus - Arum
Dregea - Wattakaka
Drepanostachyum - Arundinaria
Drepanostachyum - Thamnocalamus
Drepanostachyum - Chimonobambusa
Drimys - Tasmannia
Duchesnea - Fragaria
Dunalia - Acnistus
Echinacea - Rudbeckia
Edraianthus - Wahlenbergia
Egeria - Elodea
Elatostema - Pellionia
Eleutherococcus - Acanthopanax
Elliottia - Botryostege
Elliottia - Cladothamnus
Elymus - Agropyron
Elymus - Leymus
Ensete - Musa
Epilobium - Chamaenerion
Epipremnum - Philodendron
Epipremnum - Scindapsus
Episcia - Alsobia
Eranthis - Aconitum
Erigeron - Aster
Erigeron - Haplopappus
Eriobotrya - Loquat
Erysimum - Cheiranthus
Eucodonia - Achimenes
Eupatorium - Ageratina
Eupatorium - Ayapana
Eupatorium - Bartlettina
Euphorbia - Poinsettia
Euryops - Senecio
Fallopia - Bilderdykia
Fallopia - Polygonum
Fallopia - Reynoutria
Farfugium - Ligularia
Fargesia - Arundinaria
Fargesia - Sinarundinaria
Fargesia - Thamnocalamus
Fatsia - Aralia
Felicia - Agathaea
Felicia - Aster
Fibigia - Farsetia
Ficus - Fig
Filipendula - Spiraea
Foeniculum - Ferula
Fortunella - Citrus
Fragaria - Strawberry
Furcraea - Agave
Galium - Asperula
Gaultheria - Chiogenes
Gaultheria - x Gaulnettya
Gaultheria - Pernettya
Gelasine - Sisyrinchium
Genista - Chamaespartium
Genista - Cytisus
Genista - Echinospartum
Genista - Teline
Gentianopsis - Gentiana
Gladiolus - Acidanthera
Gladiolus - Homoglossum
Gladiolus - Petamenes
Glechoma - Nepeta
Gloxinia - Seemannia
Goniolimon - Limonium
Graptopetalum - Sedum
Graptopetalum - Tacitus
Greenovia - Sempervivum
Gymnospermium - Leontice
Habranthus - Zephyranthes
Hacquetia - Dondia
x Halimiocistus - Cistus
x Halimiocistus - Halimium
Halimium - Cistus
Halimium - x Halimiocistus
Halimium - Helianthemum
Halocarpus - Dacrydium
Hedychium - Brachychilum
Hedyscepe - Kentia
Helianthella - Helianthus
Helianthemum - Cistus
Helianthus - Artichoke, Jerusalem
Helichrysum - Gnaphalium
Helictotrichon - Avena
Helictotrichon - Avenula
Hepatica - Anemone
Herbertia - Alophia
Hermodactylus - Iris
Heterocentron - Schizocentron
Heterotheca - Chrysopsis
Hibbertia - Candollea
Hieracium - Andryala
Himalayacalamus - Arundinaria
Himalayacalamus - Drepanostachyum
Hippocrepis - Coronilla
Hippolytia - Achillea
Hippolytia - Tanacetum
Hoheria - Plagianthus
Homalocladium - Muehlenbeckia
Howea - Kentia
Hyacinthoides - Endymion
Hyacinthoides - Scilla
Hymenocallis - Elisena
Hymenocallis - Ismene
Hyophorbe - Mascarena
Hypochaeris - Hieracium
Incarvillea - Amphicome
Indocalamus - Sasa
Ipheion - Tristagma
Ipheion - Triteleia
Ipomoea - Mina
Ipomoea - Pharbitis
Ipomopsis - Gilia
Ischyrolepis - Restio
Isolepis - Scirpus
Jovibarba - Sempervivum
Juglans - Walnut, Common
Juncus - Scirpus
Jurinea - Jurinella
Justicia - Beloperone
Justicia - Jacobinia
Justicia - Libonia
Kalancho - Brylophyllum
Kalancho - Kitchingia
Kalimeris - Aster
Kalimeris - Boltonia
Kalopanax - Eleutherococcus
Keckiella - Penstemon
Knautia - Scabiosa
Kohleria - Isoloma
Kunzea - Leptospermum
Lablab - Dolichos
Lagarosiphon - Elodea
Lagarostrobos - Dacrydium
Lamium - Galeobdolon
Lamium - Lamiastrum
Lampranthus - Mesembryanthemum
Lampranthus - Oscularia
Laurentia - Hippobroma
Lavatera - Malva
Ledebouria - Scilla
x Ledodendron - Rhododendron
Lepechinia - Sphacele
Lepidothamnus - Dacrydium
Leptinella - Cotula
Leucanthemella - Chrysanthemum
Leucanthemella - Leucanthemum
Leucanthemopsis - Chrysanthemum
Leucanthemopsis - Tanacetum
Leucanthemum - Chrysanthemum
Leucopogon - Cyathodes
x Leucoraoulia - Raoulia
Leuzea - Centaurea
Leymus - Elymus
Ligularia - Senecio
Ligustrum - Parasyringa
Lilium - Nomocharis
Limonium - Statice

Linanthus - Linanthastrum
Lindelofia - Adelocaryum
Lindera - Parabenzoin
Liriope - Ophiopogon
Lithocarpus - Quercus
Lithodora - Lithospermum
Lophomyrtus - Myrtus
Lophomyrtus - Myrtus
Lophospermum - Asarina
Lophospermum - Maurandya
Lotus - Dorycnium
Lotus - Tetragonolobus
Ludwigia - Jussiaea
Luma - Myrtus
x Lycene - Lychnis
Lychnis - Agrostemma
Lychnis - Silene
Lychnis - Viscaria
Lycianthes - Solanum
Lytocaryum - Cocos
Lytocaryum - Microcoelum
Macfadyena - Bignonia
Macfadyena - Doxantha
Machaeranthera - Xylorhiza
Mackaya - Asystasia
Macleaya - Bocconia
Mahonia - Berberis
Malus - Apple
Malus - Apple, Crab
Mandevilla - Dipladenia
Mandragora - Atropa
Mangifera - Mango
Matricaria - Chamomilla
Matricaria - Tripleurospermum
Maurandella - Asarina
Maurandya - Asarina
Melicytus - Hymenanthera
Melinis - Rhynchelytrum
Mentha - Preslia
Merremia - Ipomoea
Mespilus - Medlar
Mimulus - Diplacus
Minuartia - Arenaria
Modiolastrum - Malvastrum
Moltkia - Lithodora
Moltkia - Lithospermum
Morina - Acanthocalyx
Morus - Mulberry
Mukdenia - Aceriphyllum
Musa - Banana
Muscari - Hyacinthus
Muscari - Leopoldia
Muscari - Leopoldia
Muscari - Muscarimia
Muscari - Pseudomuscari
Myricaria - Tamarix
Myrteola - Myrtus
Naiocrene - Claytonia
Naiocrene - Montia
Nectaroscordum - Allium
Nematanthus - Hypocyrta
Nemesia - Diascia
Neopaxia - Claytonia
Neopaxia - Montia
Neoregelia - Guzmania
Neoregelia - Nidularium
Nepeta - Dracocephalum
Nepeta - Origanum
Nipponanthemum - Chrysanthemum
Nipponanthemum - Leucanthemum
Nymphoides - Villarsia
Oemleria - Osmaronia
Olearia - Pachystegia
Olsynium - Phaiophleps
Olsynium - Sisyrinchium
Onixotis - Dipidax
Ophiopogon - Convallaria
Orchis - Dactylorhiza
Orostachys - Sedum
Osmanthus - x Osmarea
Osmanthus - Phillyrea
Othonna - Hertia
Othonna - Othonnopsis
Ozothamnus - Helichrysum
Pachyphragma - Cardamine
Packera - Senecio
Paederota - Veronica
Papaver - Meconopsis
Parahebe - Derwentia
Parahebe - Hebe
Parahebe - Veronica
Paraserianthes - Albizia
Paris - Daiswa
Parthenocissus - Ampelopsis
Parthenocissus - Vitis
Passiflora - Granadilla
Passiflora - Tetrapathaea
Passiflora - Passion Fruit, Yellow
Paxistima - Pachystema
Pecteilis - Habenaria
Pelargonium - Geranium
Peltoboykinia - Boykinia
Penstemon - Chelone
Pentaglottis - Anchusa
Pericallis - Senecio
Persea - Avocado
Persea - Machilus
Persicaria - Aconogonon
Persicaria - Bistorta
Persicaria - Polygonum
Persicaria - Tovara
Petrocoptis - Lychnis
Petrophytum - Spiraea
Petrorhagia - Tunica
Petroselinum - Carum
Phegopteris - Thelypteris
Phoenicaulis - Parrya
Phoenix - Date
Photinia - Heteromeles
Photinia - Stransvaesia
Photinia - x Stravinia
Phuopsis - Crucianella
Phyla - Lippia
Phymosia - Sphaeralcea
Physalis - Gooseberry, Cape
Physoplexis - Phyteuma
Physostegia - Dracocephalum
Pieris - Arcterica
Pilosella - Hieracium
Piper - Macropiper
Pisonia - Heimerliodendron
Plagiomnium - Mnium
Plecostachys - Helichrysum
Plectranthus - Solenostemon
Pleioblastus - Arundinaria
Pleioblastus - Sasa
Podranea - Tecoma
Polianthes - Bravoa
Polygonum - Persicaria
Polypodium - Phlebodium
Polystichum - Phanerophlebia
Poncirus - Aegle
Potentilla - Comarum
Pratia - Lobelia
Prumnopitys - Podocarpus
Prunus - Almond
Prunus - Amygdalus
Prunus - Apricot
Prunus - Bullace
Prunus - Damson
Prunus - Cherry, Duke
Prunus - Cherry, Sour Or Morello
Prunus - Nectarine
Prunus - Peach
Prunus - Plum
Prunus - Cherry, Sweet
Pseudocydonia - Chaenomeles
Pseudofumaria - Corydalis
Pseudofumaria - Fumaria
Pseudopanax - Metapanax
Pseudopanax - Neopanax
Pseudopanax - Nothopanax
Pseudosasa - Arundinaria
Pseudotsuga - Tsuga
Pseudowintera - Drimys
Psidium - Guava
Pterocephalus - Scabiosa
Ptilostemon - Cirsium
Pulsatilla - Anemone
Punica - Pomegranate
Pyrethropsis - Argyranthemum
Pyrethropsis - Chrysanthemum
Pyrethropsis - Leucanthemopsis
Pyrethropsis - Leucanthemum
Pyrus - Pear, Asian
Pyrus - Pear
Reineckea - Liriope
Retama - Genista
Rhapis - Chamaerops
Rheum - Rhubarb
Rhodanthemum - Chrysanthemopsis
Rhodanthemum - Chrysanthemum
Rhodanthemum - Pyrethropsis
Rhodiola - Rosularia
Rhodiola - Sedum
Rhododendron - Azalea
Rhododendron - Azaleodendron
Rhododendron - Rhodora
Rhodophiala - Hippeastrum
Ribes - Currant, Black
Ribes - Blackcurrant
Ribes - Gooseberry

Ribes - Currant, Pink
Ribes - Currant, Red
Ribes - Currant, White
Ribes - Worcesterberry
Rosularia - Cotyledon
Rosularia - Sempervivella
Rothmannia - Gardenia
Rubus - Blackberry
Rubus - Boysenberry
Rubus - Hildaberry
Rubus - Loganberry
Rubus - Nectarberry
Rubus - Raspberry
Rubus - Sunberry
Rubus - Tayberry
Rubus - Wineberry
Rubus - Youngberry
Ruellia - Dipteracanthus
Ruschia - Mesembryanthemum
Saccharum - Erianthus
Sagina - Minuartia
Salvia - Salvia
Sambucus - Elderberry
Sanguisorba - Dendriopoterium
Sanguisorba - Poterium
Sasa - Arundinaria
Sasa - Pleioblastus
Sasaella - Arundinaria
Sasaella - Pleioblastus
Sasaella - Sasa
Sasamorpha - Sasa
Sauromatum - Arum
Saussurea - Jurinea
Scadoxus - Haemanthus
Schefflera - Brassaia
Schefflera - Dizygotheca
Schefflera - Heptapleurum
Schizachyrium - Andropogon
Schizostachyum - Arundinaria
Schizostachyum - Thamnocalamus
Schoenoplectus - Scirpus
Scirpodes - Scirpus
Scirpus - Eriophorum
Sedum - Hylotelephium
Sedum - Rhodiola
Sedum - Sedastrum
Sedum - Villadia
Semiaquilegia - Aquilegia
Semiaquilegia - Paraquilegia
Semiarundinaria - Arundinaria
Senecio - Cineraria
Senecio - Ligularia
Sequoia - Abies
Seriphidium - Artemisia
Shortia - Schizocodon
Sibbaldiopsis - Potentilla
Sieversia - Geum
Silene - Lychnis
Silene - Melandrium
Silene - Saponaria
Sinacalia - Ligularia
Sinacalia - Senecio
Sinarundinaria - Semiarundinaria
Sinningia - Gesneria
Sinningia - Rechsteineria
Sisymbrium - Hesperis
Sisyrinchium - Phaiophleps
x Smithicodonia - x Achimenantha
Soleirolia - Helxine
Solenopsis, - Isotoma
Solenostemon, - Coleus
x Solidaster - Aster
x Solidaster - Solidago
Sorbaria - Spiraea
Sparaxis - Synnotia
Sphaeralcea - Iliamna
Spirodela - Lemna
Spraguea - Calyptridium
Stachys - Betonica
Steirodiscus - Gamolepis
Stenomesson - Urceolina
Stenotus - Haplopappus
Steptocarpus - Streptocarpella
Stewartia - Stuartia
Stipa - Achnatherum
Stipa - Lasiagrostis
Strobilanthes - Pteracanthus
Succisa - Scabiosa
Syagrus - Arecastrum
Syagrus - Cocos
Tanacetum - Achillea
Tanacetum - Balsamita
Tanacetum - Chrysanthemum
Tanacetum - Matricaria
Tanacetum - Pyrethrum
Tecoma - Tecomaria
Telekia - Buphthalmum
Tephroserus - Senecio
Tetradium - Euodia
Tetraneuris - Actinella
Tetrapanax - Fatsia
Thamnocalamus - Arundinaria
Thamnocalamus - Sinarundinaria
Thlaspi - Hutchinsia
Thlaspi - Noccaea
Thuja - Platycladus
Thuja - Thujopsis
Tonestus - Haplopappus
Toona - Cedrela
Trachelium - Diosphaera
Trachycarpus - Chamaerops
Tradescantia - Rhoeo
Tradescantia - Setcreasea
Tradescantia - Tradescantia
Tradescantia - Zebrina
Tripetaleia - Elliottia
Tripogandra - Tradescantia
Tristagma - Beauverdia
Triteleia - Brodiaea
Tritonia - Crocosmia
Tropaeolum - Nasturtium hort.
Tuberaria - Helianthemum
Tulipa - Amana
Tweedia - Oxypetalum
Ugni - Myrtus
Ursinia - Euryops
Uvularia - Oakesiella
Vaccinium - Blueberry
Vaccinium - Cranberry
Vaccinium - Oxycoccus
Verbascum - Celsia
Verbascum - x Celsioverbascum
Verbena - Glandularia
Verbena - Lippia
Veronicastrum - Veronica
Vigna - Phaseolus
Villadia - Sedum
Viola - Erpetion
Vitaliana - Androsace
Vitis - Grape
Weigela - Diervilla
Weigela - Macrodiervilla
Xanthorhiza - Zanthorhiza
Yushania - Arundinaria
Yushania - Sinarundinaria
Yushania - Thamnocalamus
Zantedeschia - Calla
Zauschneria - Epilobium
Zephyranthes - x Cooperanthes
Zephyranthes - Cooperia

Plant Deletions

Plants marked with a '7', '8', '9', '0', '1' ,'2' or '3' were listed in the 1987, '88, '89, '90/91, '91/92, '92/93 or '93/94 editions respectively. Back editions of **THE PLANT FINDER** may be obtained from Lakeside, Whitbourne, Worcester, WR6 5RD. Price £6.00 each inclusive of p&p.

ABELMOSCHUS
0 ***esculentus***
2 ***moschatus*** 'Mischief'

ABIES
2 ***amabilis*** 'Spreading Star'
1 x ***arnoldiana***
7 ***chensiensis chensiensis***
0 ***cilicica***
9 ***concolor*** 'Aurea'
2 – ***lowiana***
7 ***durangensis coahuilensis***
2 ***fargesii***
2 – ***faxoniana***
2 ***forrestii***
7 x ***insignis*** 'Beissneriana'
9 ***koreana*** 'Prostrate Beauty'
2 ***magnifica*** 'Glauca'
0 ***nebrodensis***
8 ***procera*** 'Noble's Dwarf'
7 ***recurvata***
3 ***sachalinensis***
7 x ***shastensis***
3 ***sibirica***

ABROTANELLA
0 ***emarginata***
0 ***forsterioïdes***

ABUTILON
2 'Cynthia Pike' (v)
3 ***indicum***
9 'Lopen Red'
3 ***megapotamicum*** 'Compactum'
3 – 'Joy Bells'
2 ***ochsenii***
1 x ***suntense*** 'Gorer's White'
2 – 'White Charm'
7 'White Swan'

ACACIA
0 ***adunca***
1 ***decurrens***
1 ***farnesiana***
3 ***genistifolia***
7 ***implexa***
9 ***jonesii***
9 ***myrtifolia***
0 ***neriifolia***

ACAENA
9 'Greencourt Hybrid'
3 ***saccaticupula***

ACALYPHA
0 ***godseffiana***
3 ***wilkesiana***
3 – 'Can-Can'
3 – 'Gold Cant'
3 – ***pudsiana***

ACANTHOLIMON
2 ***acerosum***
3 ***armenum***
8 ***confertiflorum***
0 ***hohenackeri***
3 ***litvinovii***

ACANTHUS
2 ***caroli-alexandri***

ACER
3 ***griseum*** 'Tilgates'
2 ***japonicum*** 'Filicifolium'
3 ***maximowiczianum morifolium***
9 ***morifolium***
7 ***palmatum*** 'Akaji-nishiki'
1 – 'Atropurpureum'
7 – ***dissectum*** 'Dissectum Rubrifolium'
3 – 'Filigree Lace'
3 – 'Flamingo'
3 – 'Green Trompenburg'
0 – 'Hamaotome'
3 – 'Heptalobum Lutescens'
3 – 'Jirô-shidare'
8 – 'Junihitoye'
3 – 'Kasen-nishiki'
9 – 'Koshimino'
2 – 'Maimori'
3 – 'Red Filigree Lace'
9 – 'Sango-nishiki'
3 – 'Yasmine'
1 ***platanoïdes*** 'Summershade'
1 ***rubrum*** 'Columnare'
1 ***saccharum grandidentatum***
3 ***sieboldianum*** 'Miyami-nishiki'
3 ***tataricum***
9 – ***ginnala*** 'Durand Dwarf'

ACHILLEA
3 ***distans tanacetifolia***
2 'Forncett Tapestry'
8 x ***hausmanniana***
0 'Heidi'
3 ***millefolium*** 'Fire King'
3 – 'Kelwayi'
9 – 'Purpurea'
1 – 'Rougham Beauty'
0 ***oxyloba***
7 x ***prichardii***
3 ***ptarmica*** The Pearl Group 'Boule de Neige'(clonal) (d)
3 – 'The Pearl'(clonal) (d)
1 'Rougham Salmon'

ACHIMENES
2 ***antirrhina***
2 – 'Redcap'
2 'Ballerina'
2 'Blue John'
2 'Bright Jewel'
1 'Cameo Lilac'
2 'Camille Pink'
2 'Carmencita'
2 'Carnelian'
2 ***cettoana***
2 – 'Tiny Blue'
2 'Coral Cameo'
2 'Crystal'
2 'Diadem'
2 ***erecta*** 'Mexican Dwarf'
2 – ***rosea***
2 'Erlkönig'
2 'Fascination'
2 'Flamboyant'
2 'Garnet'
2 'Glacier'
1 ***grandiflora***
2 'India Hybrid'
2 'Jewel Glow'
2 'Lady Lyttelton'
2 'Lavender Jade'
2 'Leonora'
2 'Madame Gehune'
2 'Mair's White'
2 'Margarita'
2 'Mauve Delight'
2 ***mexicana***
2 'Miniata'
2 'National Velvet'
2 'Opal'
2 'Painted Lady'
1 'Pearly Grey'
2 ***pedunculata***
2 'Purple Queen'
2 'Purple Triumph'
2 'Red Riding Hood'
2 'Schneewittchen' ('Snow White')
2 ***skinneri***
2 'Sunburst'
9 'Tetra Altrote Charm'
2 'Tetra Blauer Planet'
9 'Tetra Dark Violet Charm'
2 'Tetra Orange Star'
2 'Tetra Purpur Elfe'
9 'Tetra Rokoko Elfe'
2 'Tetra Rosa Queen'
2 'Tetra Verschaffelt'
2 'Tetra Weinrote Elfe'
2 'The Monarch'
2 'Tiger Eye'
2 'Topaz'
2 'Tresco'
2 ***warscewicziana***
2 'White Giant'
2 'White Knight'
2 'White Marvel'
2 'Yellow Beauty'

ACHLYS
3 ***triphylla***

ACIPHYLLA
0 ***congesta***
2 ***crenulata***
0 ***ferox***
3 ***glacialis***
8 ***lecomtei***
0 ***montana***
8 – ***montana***
2 ***similis***
9 ***spedenii***

ACONITUM
1 ***carmichaelii*** Wilsonii Group 'Kelmscott Variegated'
9 ***chasmanthum***
2 ***falconeri***
8 ***heterophyllum***
9 ***hookeri***
2 ***kirinense***
9 ***spicatum***

ACTINIDIA
1 ***arguta*** 'Meader No 2'(f)
9 ***callosa***
8 ***deliciosa*** 'Abbott'(f)
3 – 'Bruno'(f)
3 – hermaphrodite
8 – 'Matua'(m)
2 ***giraldii***
3 ***polygama***
8 ***purpurea***

ACTINOTUS
3 ***helianthi***

ADENOPHORA
3 ***khasiana***
2 ***kurilensis***
3 sp. AGSJ 227
3 ***triphylla hakusanensis***

ADIANTUM
0 ***raddianum*** 'Goldelse'
2 – 'Lady Geneva'
2 ***tenerum*** 'Scutum Roseum'
1 ***trapeziforme***

ADONIS
3 ***brevistyla***
2 ***chrysocyathus***

AECHMEA
0 ***blumenavii***
0 ***cylindrata***
0 ***fulgens discolor*** AGM
0 ***gamosepala***
0 ***lueddemanniana***
9 ***recurvata recurvata***
2 ***servitensis***

AEONIUM
3 ***arboreum*** 'Albovariegatum'
3 ***lindleyi***

AESCHYNANTHUS
0 Black Pagoda Group
3 'Greensleeves'

AESCULUS
3 ***chinensis***
3 ***glabra*** 'October Red'
1 ***hippocastanum*** 'Hampton Court Gold'
7 x ***hybrida***
3 ***sylvatica***
9 ***wilsonii***

AETHIONEMA
9 ***armenum*** 'Mavis Holmes'
3 ***diastrophis***
3 ***saxatile***
8 ***stylosum***
3 ***thomasianum***

AGAPANTHUS
3 'Buckingham Palace'
9 ***campanulatus*** 'Slieve Donard Variety'
3 – 'Ultramarine'
7 ***inapertus pendulus***
3 'Marjorie'
3 'Moonstar'
3 'Windsor Castle'

AGAPETES
2 ***serpens*** 'Scarlet Elf'

AGASTACHE
3 ***barberi***
2 – 'Tutti-Frutti'

AGAVE
1 ***colorata***
3 ***ellemeetiana***
1 ***funkiana***
1 ***mitriformis***
9 ***parviflora***
0 ***shawii***
1 ***sobria sobria***
1 ***toumeyana***
1 – ***bella***
2 ***utahensis nevadensis***

AGLAONEMA
0 ***commutatum maculatum***
0 – 'Pseudobracteatum'
0 ***nitidum*** 'Curtisii'
1 'Silver King'

AGROSTIS
2 ***nebulosa***

AGROSTOCRINUM
1 ***scabrum***

AJUGA
3 'Brockbankii'
1 ***chamaepitys***

ALANGIUM
1 ***platanifolium macrophyllum***

ALBUCA
1 ***setosa***
0 ***spiralis***

ALCEA
0 ***rosea*** 'Sutton's Single Brilliant'

ALCHEMILLA
1 ***bulgarica***
9 ***hoppeana***
2 ***mollis*** 'Variegata'
3 ***scalaris***

ALKANNA
9 ***aucheriana***

ALLAMANDA
2 ***schottii*** AGM

ALLIUM
3 ***amphibolum***
0 ***auctum***
1 ***barszczewskii***
9 ***campanulatum***
3 ***cyaneum*** 'Cobalt Blue'
3 ***denudatum***
8 ***douglasii***
3 ***drummondii***
3 ***heldreichii***
3 ***humile***
2 'Laxton Sunset'
0 ***nutans***
3 ***roseum bulbiferum***
9 ***rubellum***
3 ***scorzonerifolium xericense***
2 ***splendens***
1 ***victorialis***
2 ***virgunculae***

ALNUS
9 ***acuminata arguta***
7 ***hirsuta sibirica***
0 ***lanata***

ALOCASIA
0 x ***argyraea***
0 x ***chantrieri***
0 ***cuprea***
0 'Green Velvet'
0 ***korthalsii***
0 ***longiloba***
0 ***macrorrhiza***
0 ***watsoniana***
0 ***wentii***

ALOE
3 ***ferox***

ALONSOA
2 ***incisifolia***
2 ***meridionalis*** 'Shell Pink'

ALOPECURUS
3 ***geniculatus***

ALSTROEMERIA
9 Annabel ® / 'Stalan'
9 Appelbloesem ® / 'Stakaros'
0 Atlas ® / 'Stalrama'
1 Butterfly hybrids
0 Canaria ® / 'Stagelb'
1 'Furie'
2 ***haemantha***
0 Isabella ® / 'Stalis'
1 'Joli Coeur'
0 Jubilee ® / 'Stalilas'
0 Libelle ® / 'Stalbel'
0 Mandarin ® / 'Stalrin'
0 Mona Lisa ® / 'Stablaco'
0 Monika ® / 'Stalmon'
0 Pink Triumph ® / 'Stapink'
0 Ramona ® / 'Stapiram'
0 Red Sunset ® / 'Stamarko'
0 Rita ® / 'Zelido'
1 Rosello ® / 'Stalrobu'
0 Rosita ® / 'Starosello'
0 Samora ® / 'Stalsam'
3 sp. ex Patagonia
1 'Sweetheart'
0 Tango ® / 'Staltang'
1 Walter Fleming ®
0 Zebra ® / 'Stazeb'

ALYSSUM
0 ***markgrafii***
1 ***scardicum***
3 ***stribrnyi***
9 ***troodii***

AMARYLLIS
1 ***bella-donna*** 'Bloemfontein'
1 – 'Hathor'
1 – 'Purpurea'
1 – 'Windhoek'

AMELANCHIER
2 ***alnifolia semi-integrifolia***
9 ***asiatica sinica***

AMORPHA
3 ***nana***

AMORPHOPHALLUS
3 ***rivierei***

AMPELOPSIS
8 ***bodinieri***
8 ***chaffanjonii***
2 ***glandulosa brevipedunculata citrulloïdes***

AMSONIA
1 ***illustris***

ANAGALLIS
3 ***arvensis latifolia***
1 ***monelli*** 'Caerulea'

ANANAS
0 ***comosus***

ANAPHALIS
9 ***keriensis***
3 sp. CLD 1322

ANCHUSA
3 ***azurea*** 'Italian Pride'

ANDROMEDA
3 ***glaucophylla*** 'Latifolia'
8 ***polifolia angustifolia***
2 – 'Compacta Alba' AGM
3 – 'Iwasugo'

ANDROSACE
9 ***alpina***
1 ***carnea brigantiaca*** 'Myer's form'
3 ***chaixii***
2 ***chamaejasme***
8 – ***lehmanniana***
3 ***foliosa***
3 ***globifera*** x ***muscoidea***
0 x ***heeri*** pink
3 ***kochii tauricola***
8 ***rotundifolia*** 'Elegans'
2 ***sempervivoïdes*** dark form
3 ***spinulifera***
0 ***tapete***
1 ***uliginosa***
3 ***villosa taurica*** 'Palandoken'
8 ***wulfeniana***

ANEMONE
2 ***apennina*** 'Petrovac'
0 ***biflora***
0 ***blanda*** 'Blue Pearl'
8 – ***scythinica***
2 ***bucharica***
1 ***coronaria*** De Caen Group 'Excelsior'
8 ***elongata***
2 ***eranthoïdes***
9 'French Hill'
3 x ***hybrida*** 'King George V'
0 ***lithophila***
3 ***multifida*** pink
1 ***nemorosa*** 'Currie's Pink'
3 – 'Lady Doneraile'
3 – 'Parlez Vous'
3 – 'Purity'
0 ***nikoensis***
7 ***obtusiloba patula***
2 ***petiolulosa***
9 ***raddeana***
3 ***reflexa***
2 ***sylvestris*** 'Macrantha'

ANETHUM
9 ***sowa***

ANGELICA
3 ***ursina***

ANIGOZANTHOS
1 ***bicolor***
1 ***flavidus*** green
1 – grey
1 – orange
1 ***gabrielae***
1 ***viridis***

ANISOTOME
2 ***aromatica***
2 ***flexuosa***
3 ***haastii***

ANOMATHECA
1 ***laxa alba-maculata***

ANTENNARIA
3 ***alpina***
9 ***plantaginifolia***

ANTHEMIS
3 ***carpatica*** 'Karpatenschnee'

ANTHOCERCIS
1 ***littorea***

ANTHURIUM
0 ***andreanum album***
0 'Aztec'
0 'Brazilian Surprise'
3 ***clarinervium***
0 ***crystallinum***
0 x ***ferrierense***
3 – 'Roseum'

0 *leuconeurum*
0 *magnificum*
0 'Nova'
0 *scherzianum album*
0 – *minimum*
0 – 'Rothschildianum'
0 – 'Wardii'
0 *veitchii*
9 *warocqueanum*

ANTHYLLIS
9 *barba-jovis*

ANTIRRHINUM
3 *majus*

APHELANDRA
0 'Snow Queen'

APONOGETON
0 *desertorum*

AQUILEGIA
9 *bernardii*
3 *bertolonii australis*
3 'Betty Barton'
2 *brevicalcarata*
1 *brevistyla*
8 *caerulea daileyae*
3 *canadensis* 'Corbett'
1 *chrysantha hinckleyana*
3 'Coronato'
7 'Edelweiss'
2 *formosa* Nana Group
1 Harbutt's hybrids
8 Langdon's Rainbow hybrids
0 *longissima* 'Flore Pleno'
9 *viscosa hirsutissima*
2 *vulgaris* 'Crystal Star '
2 – *flore-pleno* purple
3 – – 'Warwick'
9 – 'Millicent Bowden'

ARABIS
3 *alpina caucasica* 'Corfe Castle'
7 – – 'Snowflake'
2 *blepharophylla* 'Alba'
9 *breweri*
1 *bryoïdes olympica*
1 *collina*
1 *ferdinandi-coburgi* 'Reversed'
2 *koehleri*
3 'Pink Snow'
1 *procurrens*
9 *pumila*
1 *scopoliana*
1 *serrata japonica*
1 *turrita*

ARACHNIODES
3 *aristata*
3 *standishii*

ARALIA
2 *spinosa*

ARBUTUS
3 *unedo* 'Elfin King'
1 – 'Merriott'
7 *xalapensis*

ARCHONTOPHOENIX
2 *alexandrae*

ARCTOSTAPHYLOS
8 *auriculata*
0 *densiflora* 'Emerald Carpet'
2 *manzanita*
3 *pumila*
3 *stanfordiana*
3 *uva-ursi* 'Clyde Robin'

ARCTOTIS
3 x *hybrida* cream and green

ARECA
2 *aliceae*
2 *triandra*

ARENARIA
3 *aggregata*
3 *canescens*
2 *fendleri*
3 *ludoviciana* 'Valerie Finnis'
3 *scariosa*

ARENGA
9 *caudata*

ARGEMONE
0 *platyceras*

ARGYRANTHEMUM
1 *adauctum*
1 – *gracile*
1 'Brontes'
1 *sundingii*

ARISAEMA
8 *kiushianum*
1 *robustum*
8 *thunbergii*

ARISTEA
2 *major*

ARISTOLOCHIA
3 *baetica*
3 *contorta*
2 *heterophylla*
2 *sempervirens*
3 *trilobata*

ARMERIA
9 *alliacea* 'Grandiflora'
7 *arctica*
9 'Bloodgood'
Carlux hybrids
3 *filicaulis*
0 *maritima* 'Birch Pink'
3 – 'La Pampa'
7 – *sibirica*
3 – 'Splendens Alba'

ARNICA
3 *angustifolia*
2 – *alpina*
0 *cordifolia*
3 *longifolia*
2 *unalaschkensis*

ARRHENATHERUM
2 *elatius*

ARTEMISIA
7 *absinthium* 'Poland's Variety'
2 *genipi*
2 *judaica*
7 *lactiflora* 'Variegata'

ARTHROPODIUM
9 *cirrhatum* bronze
2 – pink

ARUM
0 *byzantinum*
3 *italicum neglectum*
0 *maculatum* 'Pleddel'

ARUNCUS
0 *dioicus* 'Aphrodite'

ARUNDO
3 *pliniana*

ASARUM
2 *hartwegii* 'Silver Heart'

ASCLEPIAS
3 *albicans*
3 *subulata*
3 *viridiflora*

ASPARAGUS
3 *asparagoïdes* 'Myrtifolius'
1 *scandens*

ASPLENIUM
2 *aethiopicum*
0 *dalhousieae*
3 *oblongifolium*
0 *scolopendrium* 'Apple Court'
3 – Crispum Fimbriatum Group
3 – 'Crispum Robinson'
0 *squamulatum*

ASTELIA
7 *nivicola*

ASTER
0 *alpinus dolomiticus*
2 *amellus* 'Danzig'
7 – 'Mrs Ralph Woods'
8 – 'Rotfeuer'
2 *asteroïdes*
1 *bellidiastrum*
0 *cordifolius*
3 – 'Aldebaran'
2 *ericoïdes* 'Schneetanne'
0 *falconeri*
3 *farreri*
2 *laevis* 'Blauschleier'
0 *novi-belgii* 'Amethyst'
3 – 'Antwerpse Parel' ('Antwerp Pearl')
1 – 'Ashwick'
9 – 'Autumn Princess
2 – 'Barker's Double'
2 – 'Beechwood Lady'
0 – 'Blue Jacket'
0 – 'Blue Orb'
1 – 'Camerton'
0 – 'Candelabra'
0 – 'Catherine Chiswell'
0 – 'Charmwood'
1 – 'Coombe Delight'
0 – 'Desert Song'
0 – 'Dunkerton'
3 – 'Dymbro'
1 – 'Emma'
0 – 'Fair Trial'
3 – 'Festival'
8 – 'Gayborder Rapture'
8 – 'Gayborder Rose'
1 – 'Gayborder Supreme'
9 – 'Glorious'
0 – 'Goblin Coombe'
0 – 'Grey Lady'
1 – 'Happiness'
2 – 'Jezebel'
2 – 'Jugendstil'
2 – 'Kassel'
1 – 'Kilmersdon'
1 – 'Leona'
3 – 'Lilakönigin'
1 – 'Lucille'
1 – 'Maid of Athens'
1 – 'Malvern Castle'
0 – 'Minster'
1 – 'Mittelmeer'
0 – 'Moderator
0 – 'Monkton Coombe'
2 – 'Nesthäkchen'
0 – 'Newton's Pink'
2 – 'Norma Chiswell'
1 – 'Owen Tudor'
1 – 'Owen Wells'
1 – 'Peaceful'
1 – 'Penelope'
2 – 'Petunia'
0 – 'Pink Bonnet'
1 – 'Pink Cascade'
3 – 'Pink Perfection'
3 – 'Pink Profusion'
1 – 'Pitcott'
0 – 'Powder Puff'
0 – 'Princess Marie Louise'
3 – 'Priory Maid'
9 – 'Queen of Sheba'
1 – 'Real Pleasure'
3 – 'Rebecca'
0 – 'Red King'
0 – 'Rosy Dreams'
0 – 'Ruby Glow'
3 – 'Silberblaukissen'
1 – 'Taplow Spire'
1 – 'The Urchin'
1 – 'Vice Regal'
0 – 'Walkden's Pink'
1 – 'Winsome Winnie'
3 *oblongifolius*
3 *stracheyi*
1 *tongolensis* 'Leuchtenburg'
3 – 'Sommergrüss' ('Summer Greeting')
9 *trinervius ageratoïdes*
2 *yunnanensis*

ASTERISCUS
3 *intermedius*

ASTILBE
3 'Catherine Deneuve'
1 *chinensis davidii*
0 x *crispa rosea*
3 'Ellie'
2 'Intermezzo' (*chinensis*)
1 *koreana*
3 'Lilliput' (x *crispa*)
2 'Mainz' (*japonica x*)
1 'Peter Pan' (x *crispa*)
9 'Purple Splendour' (x *arendsii*)

2 'Queen of Holland' (x *arendsii*)
0 'Robinson's Pink'

ASTRAGALUS
1 *alopecuroïdes*
0 *arnottii*
9 *crassicarpus paysonii*
2 *falcatus*
1 *kentrophyta implexus*
1 *purpureus*
2 *purshii purshii*
3 *thompsoniae*
1 *vexilliflexus nobilis*
3 *whitneyi sonneanus*

ASYNEUMA
0 *linifolium*
9 – *eximium*

ATHAMANTA
0 *turbith*

ATHYRIUM
0 *distentifolium*
3 *filix-femina* 'Clarissimum'

ATRAPHAXIS
0 *billardierei tournefortii*

AUBRIETA
2 'Aurea'
2 'Barker's Double'
7 'Bridesmaid'
1 'Bright Eyes'
3 'Claret Cascade'
8 'Crimson Bedder'
7 'Crimson Queen'
7 'Eileen Longster'
9 Eversley hybrids
2 *gracilis*
8 'Graeca Superba'
3 'Leichtlinii'
3 *mastichina*
3 *pinardii*
7 'Purple Splendour'
9 'Rose Cascade'
2 'Vindictive'
2 'Violet Queen'

AUCUBA
9 *japonica* 'Dentata'

AURINIA
3 *saxatilis* 'Argentea'
1 – 'Nelly Reuben'(v)

AZARA
2 *uruguayensis*

BACCHARIS
1 *patagonica* prostrate form

BAECKEA
2 *virgata*

BALLOTA
9 *frutescens*

BAMBUSA
1 *multiplex riviereorum*

BANKSIA
3 *benthamiana*
1 *caleyi*
3 *canei*
3 *hookeriana*
2 *occidentalis*
3 *ornata*
3 *petiolaris*
3 *praemorsa*
3 *repens*
3 *serrata*
1 *serratifolia*
3 *violacea*

BAPTISIA
3 *sphaerocarpa*

BARBAREA
3 *vulgaris*

BARTSIA
2 *alpina*

BAUERA
0 *rubioïdes*

BEGONIA
0 *acutifolia*
1 'Amoena' (T)
3 *annulata*
0 'Aruba'
1 'Bali Hi' (T)
1 'Bertinii Compacta'
0 'Black Velvet'
0 *bowerae nigramarga*
0 'Bow-Mag'
0 *burle-marxii*
0 'Camouflage'
3 x *cheimantha* 'Gloire de Lorraine'
0 'Chimbig'
0 'Chumash'
1 'City of Ballarat' (T)
0 'Clifton'
1 'Corona' (T)
0 *dichroa (C)*
1 'Dorothy White' (T)
1 'Elaine Tarttelin' (T)
0 'Enchantment'
1 'Falstaff' (T)
1 'First Love' (T)
0 'Fuscomaculata'
3 *grandis* dark form
0 – *evansiana* 'Claret Jug'
1 'Guardsman' (T)
2 x *hiemalis* 'Aida'
2 – 'Aphrodite Pink'
2 – 'Arosa'
2 – 'Barbara'
2 – 'Christel'
2 – 'Elatior'
2 – 'Elfe'
2 – 'Heidi'
2 – 'Ilona'
2 – 'Korona'
2 – 'Lara'
2 – 'Lorina'
2 – 'Mandela'
2 – 'Mark Rosa'
2 – 'Nelly'
2 – 'Nelson'
2 – 'Nixe'
2 – 'Nymphe'
2 – 'Pia Elise'
2 – 'Radiant'
2 – 'Rosalea'
2 – 'Schwabenland'
2 – 'Schwabenland Mini'
2 – 'Schwabenland Red'
2 – 'Schwabenland Rose'
2 – 'Schwabenland White'
2 – 'Schwabenland Yellow'
2 – 'Sirène'
2 – 'Sylvia'
2 – 'Toran
0 *hispida cucullifera*
0 'Holmes Chapel'
3 hybrids
0 'Ingramii'
1 'Joy Towers' (T)
0 'Lexington'
0 'Linda Harley'
0 'Linda Myatt'
0 'Mac MacIntyre'
3 'Madame Richard Gallé' (T)
2 'Margaritae'
1 'Mrs T White' (T)
0 'Panther'
0 'Paul Harley'
1 'Peach Melba' (T)
0 *plagioneura*
1 'Rose Princess' (T)
0 'Royal Lustre'
0 'Silbreen'
1 'Snow Bird' (T)
1 'Sunburst' (T)
0 Superba Group (C)
2 'Tigerlash'
0 'Universe'
1 'Zoe Colledge' (T)

BELLIS
2 *perennis* 'Bunter Teppich'
2 – 'Chevreuse'
2 – 'Dawn Raider'
2 – 'Double Bells'
2 – 'Lilliput Rose'
2 – 'Pink Buttons'
9 – 'Red Alice'
2 – 'Roggli'
2 – 'Shrewley Gold'(v)
2 – 'String of Pearls'
2 – 'Tuberosa Monstrosa'
9 *sylvestris*

BERBERIS
0 *amurensis* 'Flamboyant'
1 – *latifolia*
7 *atrocarpa*
1 *brachypoda*
1 *brevipaniculata*
2 x *carminea* 'Bountiful'
1 *concinna*
2 *dictyophylla approximata*
9 *dumicola*
9 *francisci-ferdinandii*
2 x *frikartii* 'Mrs Kennedy'
2 'Haalboom'
2 *hakeoïdes*
9 *hookeri viridis*
0 *ilicifolia*
2 x *interposita*
1 *koreana* 'Harvest Fire'
2 *linearifolia* 'Jewel'
2 x *mentorensis*
2 *montana*
2 *morrisonensis*
9 *orthobotrys canescens*
7 *poiretii*
3 *sargentiana* 'Nana'
8 x *stenophylla* 'Cornish Cream'
1 – 'Etna'
9 – 'Pendula'
2 – 'Prostrata'
7 – 'Semperflorens'
2 *thunbergii* 'Coronita'
7 – 'Dart's Red Devil'
3 – 'Green Marble'
3 – 'Green Ring'
0 – 'Pearly Queen'
9 *valdiviana* x *darwinii*
2 *wilsoniae stapfiana*
3 – *subcaulialata*
2 *yunnanensis*

BERGENIA
7 'Perfect'
3 'Pugsley's Purple'
3 *purpurascens* hybrid
3 x *spathulata*
7 'White Dwarf'

BERLANDIERA
3 *lyrata*

BESSERA
3 *elegans*

BESSEYA
3 *ritteriana*
0 *wyomingensis*

BETULA
3 *calcicola*
1 *ermanii genuina saitoana*
0 *fontinalis* 'Inopina'
9 *nana* 'Walter Ingwersen'
3 *ovalifolia*
3 *utilis* 'Kyelang'

BIDENS
3 *ferulifolia* 'Golden Goddess'

BILLBERGIA
0 *bucholtzii*
0 *chlorosticta*
0 *distachya*
0 *leptopoda*
0 'Santa Barbara' (v)

BLACKSTONIA
3 *perfoliata*

BLECHNUM
0 *moorei*

BOEHMERIA
3 *nivea*

BOLUSANTHUS
3 *speciosus*

BOMAREA
3 *multiflora*
3 *volubilis*

BOTHRIOCHLOA
3 *saccharoïdes*

BOUGAINVILLEA
1 'Alabama Sunset'
2 'Alison Davey'
2 *floribunda*
1 'Jamaica Red'
2 'Jawhuri'

1 'Lateritia' (Spectoglabra Group)
2 Manila Red ®
1 'Maureen Hatten'
1 'Roy Walker'
1 'Speciosa Floribunda' (*spectabilis*)
2 'Sunfire Jennifer'
1 'Tropical Bouquet'

BOUVARDIA
3 ***bouvardioïdes***
1 'Jourhite'
1 'Lichtrose'
1 'Roxane'
1 'Torosa'
1 'Zywerden'

BOWIEA
3 ***volubilis***

BRACHYGLOTTIS
0 ***kirkii*** 'Variegatus'

BRACHYSCOME
0 ***diversifolia***
1 ***stolonifera***

BRACTEANTHA
3 ***subundulata***

BREYNIA
2 ***nivosa***

BRIMEURA
0 ***fastigiata***

BRIZA
7 ***subaristata***

BROCCHINIA
3 ***reducta***

BROUSSONETIA
8 ***papyrifera*** 'Laciniata'

BRUGMANSIA
3 x ***candida*** 'Plena'
3 – 'Variegata'
3 hybrids

BUDDLEJA
8 ***caryopteridifolia*** 'Variegata'
2 ***crispa*** 'Variegata'
1 ***davidii*** 'Bluegown'
7 – 'Opéra'
9 – 'Pink Pearl'
2 – 'Salicifolia'
7 – 'Southcombe Splendour'
7 – 'Widecombe'
7 – 'Windtor'
8 ***latiflora***
9 'Town Foot'
7 x ***weyeriana*** 'Golden Tassels'
3 'White Butterfly'

BULBINELLA
3 ***caudata***
2 ***setosa***

BUPLEURUM
9 ***triradiatum***

BUXUS
3 ***natalensis***
1 ***sempervirens*** 'Bullata'
9 – 'Elegans'
3 – 'Lawson's Golden'

CAESALPINIA
2 ***decapetala japonica***
3 ***sappan***

CAIOPHORA
3 ***lateritia***

CALADIUM
0 ***bicolor*** 'John Peel'
0 – 'June Bride'
0 – 'Mrs Arno Nehrling'
0 – 'Pink Beauty'
0 – 'Postman Joyner'
0 – 'Rosebud'
0 'Candidum'

CALAMINTHA
3 ***cretica variegata***

CALANDRINIA
2 ***discolor***
3 sp. JCA 12570

CALATHEA
0 ***elliptica*** 'Vittata'
0 ***eximia***
0 ***fasciata***
0 ***lancifolia***
0 ***leopardina***
0 ***louisae***
0 ***majestica*** 'Sanderiana'
0 ***micans***
0 ***musaica***
3 ***pendula***
0 ***rufibarba***

CALCEOLARIA
3 'Brownii'
9 ***corymbosa***

CALLIANDRA
1 ***eriophylla***

CALLIANTHEMUM
9 ***angustifolium***
1 ***kernerianum***

CALLICARPA
0 ***mollis***

CALLISIA
3 ***elegans*** AGM
3 ***navicularis***

CALLISTEMON
0 ***citrinus*** purple
2 'King's Park Special'
9 ***macropunctatus***
9 ***montanus***
2 ***pachyphyllus***
0 ***pallidus*** lilac
2 ***shiressii***

CALLUNA
8 ***vulgaris alba***
2 – 'Baby Wicklow'
8 – 'Beoley Crimson Variegated'
8 – 'Diana'
8 – 'Gnome'
9 – 'Goldsworth Purple'
8 – 'Gynodioica'
8 – 'Lime Gold'
8 – 'Mallard'
2 – 'Melanie'
8 – 'Monstrosa'
9 – 'Orange Beauty'
8 – 'Procumbens'
2 – 'Rotfuchs'
8 – 'Spicata Nana'
8 – 'Tomentosa'

CALOCHORTUS
3 ***catalinae***
3 ***clavatus***
2 ***kennedyi***
2 ***weedii***

CALOTHAMNUS
1 ***quadrifidus***
1 ***sanguineus***

CALTHA
3 ***palustris*** 'Multiplex'
0 ***sagittata***

CALYCANTHUS
2 ***fertilis laevigatus***
2 – 'Purpureus'

CALYSTEGIA
3 ***hederacea***

CALYTRIX
3 ***alpestris***
9 ***glutinosa***
1 ***tetragona***

CAMASSIA
2 ***cusickii*** 'Zwanenburg'
2 ***leichtlinii*** Atroviolacea Group
1 – ***suksdorfii***

CAMELLIA
9 'Alba Superba' (***japonica***)
9 'Alta Gavin' (***japonica***)
3 'Angela Cocchi' (***japonica***)
9 'Anna Bruneau' (***japonica***)
9 'Anna M Page' (***japonica***)
9 'Anne Smith' (***japonica***)
2 'Apollo 14' (***japonica***)
1 'August Delfosse' (***japonica***)
0 'Australis' (***japonica***)
3 'Azumakagami' (***japonica***)
1 'Baronne Leguay' (***japonica***)
3 'Betty Sheffield Blush' (***japonica***)
9 'Billie McCaskill' (***japonica***)
0 'Bride's Bouquet' (***japonica***)
7 'Candy Stripe' (***japonica***)
9 'Captain Folk' (***japonica***)
7 'Cardinal Variegated' (***japonica***)
9 'Centenary' (***japonica***)
7 'Charlean Variegated' (x ***williamsii***)
9 'Charlotte Bradford' (***japonica***)
3 'Christmas Beauty' (***japonica***)
7 'Clarissa' (***japonica***)
9 'Clark Hubbs' (***japonica***)
9 'Coccinea' (***japonica***)
3 'Conspicua' (***japonica***)
3 'Contessa Samailoff' (***japonica***)
7 'Coral Pink Lotus' (***japonica***)
7 'Coral Queen' (***japonica***)
8 'Cornish Cream' (***saluenensis*** x ***cuspidata***)
9 ***crapnelliana***
3 'Daviesii' (***japonica***)
2 'De Notaris' (***japonica***)
2 'Diddy Mealing' (***japonica***)
3 'Doris Ellis' (***japonica***)
7 'Dorothy James' (hybrid)
9 'Drama Girl Variegated' (***japonica***)
9 'Dream Castle' (***reticulata*** x ***japonica***)
1 'Edith Linton' (***japonica***)
1 'Eleanor Hagood' (***japonica***)
7 'Elena Nobili' (***japonica***)
3 'Elizabeth Le Bey' (***japonica***)
3 'Ellen Sampson' (***japonica***)
9 'Emmett Barnes' (***japonica***)
1 'Etherington White' (***japonica***)
1 'Etoile Polaire' (***japonica***)
3 'Evalina' (***japonica***)
7 'Evelyn' (***japonica***)
3 'Eximia' (***japonica***)
1 'Ezo-nishiki' (***japonica***)
9 'Fanny Bolis' (***japonica***)
3 'Fimbriata' (***japonica***)
0 'Fortune Teller' (***japonica***)
3 'Gay Chieftain' (***japonica***)
9 'Gay Marmee' (***japonica***)
9 'Geisha Girl' (***japonica***)
2 'Général Leclerc' (***japonica***)
3 'Ginryû' (x ***vernalis***)
9 'Goshoguruma' (***japonica***)
7 'Grand Prix Variegated' (***japonica***)
9 'Grand Sultan' (***japonica***)
7 'Gus Menard' (***japonica***)
9 'Hassaku-shibori' (***japonica***)
7 'Helen Bower' (***japonica***)
9 'High, Wide 'n' Handsome' (***japonica***)
3 'Hikarugenji' ('Herme') (***japonica***)
9 'Hishikaraito' (***japonica***)
9 'Hody Wilson' (***reticulata***)

3 'Ice Queen' (*japonica*)
3 'Ichisetsu' (*japonica*)
2 'Iwane-shibori' (*japonica*)
9 'Jennifer Turnbull' (*japonica*)
9 'Judge Solomon' (*japonica*)
7 'Julia Drayton' (*japonica*)
3 'Kate Thrash' (*japonica*)
7 'Katherine Nuccio' (*japonica*)
2 'King Size' (*japonica*)
1 'Koyoden' (*japonica*)
9 'La Belle France' (*japonica*)
2 'La Pace' (*japonica*)
3 'Lady Campbell' (*japonica*)
2 'Lady Gowrie' (x *williamsii*)
9 'Lady Kay' (*japonica*)
3 'Lady Mackinnon' (*japonica*)
3 'Lady McCulloch Pink' (*japonica*)
2 'Latifolia Variegated' (*japonica*)
2 'Leonora Novick' (*japonica*)
9 'Lillian Rickets' (*japonica*)
9 'Lisa Gael' (*reticulata*)
9 'Lois Shinault' (*reticulata* x *granthamiana*)
9 'Louise Wilson' (*japonica*)
9 'Lucinda' (*sasanqua*)
7 'Mabel Blackwell' (*japonica*)
3 'Madame Charles Blard' (*japonica*)
3 'Magic Moments' (*japonica*)
1 'Marchioness of Exeter' (*japonica*)
7 'Margaret Rose' (*japonica*)
7 'Marian Mitchell' (*japonica*)
8 'Mary Agnes Patin' (*japonica*)
3 'Mary Charlotte' (*japonica*)
0 'Mary Williams' (*reticulata*)
7 'Masterpiece' (*japonica*)
9 'Mildred Pitkin' (*reticulata*)
9 'Miss Anaheim' (*japonica*)
9 'Miss Betty' (*japonica*)
3 'Miya' (*japonica*)
2 'Miyakodori' (*japonica*)
1 'Monsieur Faucillon' (*japonica*)
1 'Moonlight' (*japonica*)
2 'Moshe Dayan' (*japonica*)
3 'Moshio' (*japonica*)
9 'Mrs Baldwin Wood' (*japonica*)
9 'Mrs George Bell' (*japonica*)
9 'Mrs Swan' (*japonica*)
7 'Mrs Tingley' (*japonica*)
1 'Mrs William Thompson' (*japonica*)
9 'Nancy Bird' (*japonica*)
9 'Paulette Goddard' (*japonica*)
1 'Pearl Harbor' (*japonica*)
3 'Pearl Maxwell' (*japonica*)
9 'Phyl Doak' (*saluenensis* x *reticulata*)
1 'Pink Ball' (*japonica*)
1 'Pink Cherub' (x *williamsii*)
3 'Pink Diddy' (*japonica*)
9 'Pink Sparkle' (*reticulata* x *japonica*)
0 'Premier' (*japonica*)
8 'Prince Murat' (*japonica*)
3 'Prince of Orange' (*japonica*)
9 'Princess Lear' (*japonica*)
9 'Purple Swirl' (*japonica*)
0 'Queen's Escort' (*japonica*)
3 'Rebel Yell' (*japonica*)
9 'Red Elephant' (*japonica*)
9 'Richard Nixon' (*japonica*)
0 'Richfield' (*japonica*)
9 'Rosemary Elsom' (*japonica*)
3 'Rosie Anderson' (x *williamsii*)
0 'Rosina Sobeck' (*japonica*)
1 'Sacco Vera' (*japonica*)
7 'Sawada's Dream' (*japonica*)
9 'Sheridan' (*japonica*)
3 'Shimna' (x *williamsii*)
1 'Shin-azuma-nishiki' (*sasanqua*)
3 'Shiragiku' (*japonica*)
9 'Shiro Chan' (*japonica*)
9 'Simeon' (*japonica*)
8 'Snow Chan' (*japonica*)
7 'Spring Fever' (*japonica*)
1 'Suibijin' (*japonica*)
2 'Sunset Oaks' (*japonica*)
9 'Terrell Weaver' (*reticulata* x *japonica*)
3 'Tick Tock' (*japonica*)
3 'Tongzimian' (*reticulata*)
9 'Touchdown' (*japonica*)
0 x *vernalis*
9 'Ville de Nantes' (*japonica*)
7 'Waltz Time' (x *williamsii*)
9 'Waverley' (*japonica*)
0 'White Giant' (*japonica*)
9 'Wild Silk' (*reticulata*)
9 'Wildwood' (*japonica*)
1 'William Bull' (*japonica*)

CAMPANULA
7 'Abundance'
0 *alliariifolia* x *makaschvilii*
1 *argaea*
0 *cochleariifolia*
0 *barbata* deep blue
9 *carpatica* 'Albescens'
9 – 'Jingle Bells'
7 – 'Loddon Bell'
7 – *turbinata* 'Grandiflora'
2 *cenisia*
7 *cochleariifolia* 'Patience Bell'
3 – x *arvatica*
3 *crispa*
9 *davisii*
1 *garganica* 'Major'
9 *glomerata* 'Wisley Supreme'
2 *hierosolymitana*
2 *hypopolia*
7 'Iceberg'
8 *lactiflora* 'Superba' AGM
1 *latifolia* 'Lavender'
3 *lusitanica*
2 *morettiana*
2 – 'Alba'
0 *persicifolia* 'Curiosa'
3 *petrophila*
2 *poscharskyana* 'Blue Gown'
0 *pyramidalis* 'Aureovariegata'
3 *rigidipila*
2 *scouleri*
2 *stevenii*
7 'Warley Gem'
3 *witasekiana*

CAMPYLOTROPIS
8 *macrocarpa*

CANNA
3 'City of Portland'

CAPPARIS
2 *spinosa*

CARAGANA
2 *aurantiaca*
1 *pygmaea*

CARDIOSPERMUM
1 *halicacabum*

CARDUNCELLUS
1 *mitissimus*

CAREX
3 *berggrenii* narrow-leaved
0 *buxbaumii*
3 'Everbright' (v)
1 *fraseri*
3 *pendula* 'Variegata'
3 *saxatilis* 'Variegata'
2 *solandri*
3 sp. ex Chile

CARICA
3 *pubescens*

CARPINUS
8 *caroliniana virginiana*
1 *cordata*
2 *henryana*
2 *laxiflora macrostachya*
2 *tschonoskii*

CARYA
2 *aquatica*

CARYOPTERIS
3 *divaricata*

CASSINIA
9 *quinquefaria*
1 *sturtii*

CASSIOPE
1 *hypnoïdes*
3 *lycopodioïdes crista pilosa*
3 – 'Major'
2 *mertensiana ciliolata*
9 *wardii*
1 – x *fastigiata* Askival Strain

CASUARINA
3 *torulosa*

CATALPA
9 *speciosa* 'Pulverulenta'

CAYRATIA
2 *thomsonii*

CEANOTHUS
1 'Blue Boy'
0 *burfordiensis*
3 'Gentian Plume'
1 *griseus*
9 x *pallidus* 'Plenus'

CEDRUS
1 *deodara* 'Golden Jubilee'
2 – 'Inversa Pendula'
0 – Paktia Group
0 – 'Polar Winter'
2 – 'Prostrata'
1 *libani brevifolia* 'Horizon'

CELASTRUS
2 *hypoleucus*

CELMISIA
0 *armstrongii*
0 *asteliifolia*
2 *glandulosa*
0 *haastii*
0 *holosericea*
2 *hookeri*
9 *ramulosa tuberculata*
0 *spectabilis argentea*

CELTIS
7 *caucasica*
9 *tournefortii*

CENTAUREA
1 *babylonica*
1 *chilensis*
9 *cineraria* 'Colchester White'
3 *nigra rivularis*
3 sp. DS&T 89061T
3 sp. DS&T 89073T

3 sp. DS&T 89075T
7 ***triumfettii stricta alba***

CENTRADENIA
3 ***inaequilateralis*** 'Mini Cascade'

CEPHALOTAXUS
2 ***harringtonia***
3 – 'Gnome'

CERASTIUM
8 ***biebersteinii***
0 ***candidissimum***

CERATONIA
8 ***siliqua***

CERATOSTIGMA
0 ***minus***

CERATOTHECA
3 ***triloba alba***

CERCIS
7 ***chingii***
2 ***occidentalis***
3 ***siliquastrum*** 'Bodnant'
9 – 'Rubra'

CERCOCARPUS
3 ***montanus paucidentatus***

CEROPEGIA
3 ***barklyi***

CHAENACTIS
9 ***alpina***

CHAENOMELES
2 ***japonica*** 'Orange Beauty'
1 ***speciosa*** 'Atrococcinea Plena'
2 – 'Brilliant'
1 x ***superba***
0 – 'Alba'
2 – 'Ernst Finken'
1 – 'Vesuvius'

CHAETACANTHUS
3 ***setiger*** 'White Lady'

CHAMAECYPARIS
9 ***lawsoniana*** 'Annesleyana'
1 – 'Barry's Bright'
9 – 'Booth'
7 – 'Boy Blue'
9 – 'Darleyensis'
0 – 'Ellwoodii Glauca'
8 – 'Ellwood's Prize'
0 – 'Gold Lace'
2 – 'Gold Pyramid'
1 – 'Grayswood Bronze'
8 – 'Green Monarch'
8 – 'Holden Gold'
0 – 'Juvenalis Stricta'
0 – 'Lemon Pillar'
2 – 'Merrist Wood'
0 – 'Moerheimii'
3 – 'Rock Gold'
0 – 'Shawii'
8 – 'Suffolk Belle'
7 – 'Tilgate'
7 – 'Trentham Gold'
9 – 'Van Eck'
8 – 'Watereri'
3 – 'Wissel's Saguaro'
2 ***nootkatensis*** 'Aurea'
9 – 'Tatra'
1 ***obtusa*** 'Bronze Elegance'
9 – 'Goldspire'
0 – 'Heinrich'
2 – 'Nana Pyramidalis'
2 – 'Repens'
8 ***pisifera*** 'Floral Arts'
2 – 'Nana Variegata'
2 – 'Teddy Bear'
2 – 'Tsukumo'
8 ***thyoïdes*** 'Marwood'
2 – 'Purple Heather'

CHAMAEDOREA
0 ***elegans*** 'Bella'

CHARA
3 ***vulgaris***

CHASMANTHIUM
0 ***latifolium*** 'Variegatum'

CHEILANTHES
2 ***alabamensis***
0 ***distans***
2 ***guanchica***

CHELONE
8 ***obliqua*** 'Praecox Nana'

CHENOPODIUM
8 ***ambrosioïdes***
9 ***bonus-henricus*** 'Variegatum'
2 ***foliosum***

CHEVREULIA
0 ***lycopodioïdes***

CHIMAPHILA
3 ***maculata***
1 ***umbellata***

CHIMONANTHUS
7 ***nitens***
1 ***praecox*** 'Mangetsu'
3 – 'Trenython'
3 ***yunnanensis***

CHIONOCHLOA
3 ***beddiei***

CHIONODOXA
1 ***albescens***
2 ***forbesii*** 'Tmoli'

CHIONOHEBE
1 ***ciliolata***

CHLOROPHYTUM
3 ***comosum*** 'Mandaianum'(v)
2 ***majus***

CHORISIA
1 ***speciosa***

CHRYSOCOMA
1 ***coma-aurea***

CHRYSOLEPIS
2 ***chrysophylla***

CHRYSOTHAMNUS
0 ***nauseosus***

CHRYSOTHEMIS
3 ***pulchella*** **AGM**

CICERBITA
2 ***alpina***

CICUTA
9 ***virosa***

CIMICIFUGA
3 ***heracleifolia***
3 ***japonica compacta***

CIONURA
2 ***erecta***

CISSUS
3 ***discolor***

CISTUS
0 'Elma Colicte'
0 x ***glaucus***
0 ***heterophyllus***
0 ***ladanifer*** 'Albiflorus'
3 x ***laxus***
0 x ***nigricans***
2 ***ochreatus***
1 x ***platysepalus***
1 ***salviifolius*** 'Sienna'
0 ***varius***

X CITROFORTUNELLA
0 ***floridana***

X CITRONCIRUS
9 ***webberi***
3 'Zehnder' (***paradisi x***)

CITRUS
3 ***aurantium***
1 x ***tangelo*** 'Ugli'

CLADRASTIS
2 ***sinensis***

CLARKIA
3 ***amoena***

CLAYTONIA
2 ***megarhiza***

CLEMATIS
2 ***armandii*** Trengwainton form
1 'Betina' (A)
9 'Blue Diamond'
3 ***campaniflora*** hybrid
0 'Elizabeth Foster'
2 ***fremontii***
0 ***grata argentilucida***
9 ***lanuginosa***
9 ***macropetala*** 'White Lady'
2 'Mercurius' (J)
2 ***ochotensis (A)***
9 ***parviflora depauperata***
3 'Patricia Ann Fretwell'
0 'Perryhill Pearl'
3 ***pierotii***
8 'Prairie River' (A)
1 'Pruinina' (A)
3 ***tangutica obtusiuscula***

CLEOME
3 ***spinosa***

CLERODENDRUM
1 ***cyrtophyllum***

CLETHRA
3 ***acuminata***
0 ***alnifolia*** 'Nana'
3 ***tomentosa***

CLINTONIA
0 ***uniflora***

CLUSIA
9 ***major***

COCCULUS
7 ***occulatus***

CODIAEUM
0 ***variegatum pictum (v)***
0 – – 'Excellent'(v)
0 – – 'Gold Star(v)
3 – – 'Nervia'(v)
0 – – 'Norma'(v)

X CODONATANTHUS
3 'Aurora'
1 'Fiesta'
2 'Vista'

CODONOPSIS
3 ***rotundifolia***
3 ***thalictrifolia***

COIX
3 ***lacryma-jobi***

COLCHICUM
3 ***autumnale*** pink
3 'Beaconsfield'
3 'Darwin'
3 'Huxley'
9 'Lilac Bedder'
3 'Little Woods'
3 'Nancy Lindsay'
1 ***szovitsii***

COLEONEMA
3 ***virgatum***

COLLOMIA
2 ***grandiflora***

COLOBANTHUS
3 ***apetalus***
0 ***strictus***
0 ***subulatus***

COLUMNEA
1 ***fendleri***
3 'Flamingo'
3 ***hosta***
3 'Mary Ann'
0 ***microphylla***
3 Yellow Dragon Group

COLUTEA
0 ***arborescens*** 'Variegata'

COLUTEOCARPUS
3 ***vesicaria***

CONIUM
2 ***maculatum***

CONVALLARIA
3 ***majalis*** 'Berlin Giant'
9 – 'Flore Pleno'
1 ***transcaucasica***

COPROSMA
9 ***ciliata***
3 'Green Globe'
3 ***rigida (f)***

0 *serrulata*
0 *spathulata (m)*
0 *viridis (f)*

COPTIS
2 *laciniata*
1 *quinquefolia*

CORDYLINE
0 *banksii* 'Purpurea'
1 *baueri*
0 *fruticosa*
0 – 'Negri'
9 *pumilio*

COREOPSIS
3 *grandiflora* 'Domino'

CORIARIA
0 *angustissima*

CORIS
1 *monspeliensis*

CORNUS
2 *bretschneideri*
0 *drummondii*
0 *florida* 'Barton's White'
3 *glabrata*
2 *kousa* 'Robert'
3 – 'Tilgates'
0 – 'Variegata'
3 *mas* 'Golden Glory'
9 x *unalaschkensis*

COROKIA
1 x *virgata* 'Bronze Knight'
1 – 'Pink Delight'

CORREA
8 'Kane's Hybrid'

CORYDALIS
2 *afghanica*
1 *aitchisonii*
3 *alexeenkoana*
2 *ambigua*
9 *cava blanda*
9 – – *alba*
9 *conorhiza*
2 *darwasica*
3 *diphylla*
3 *fargesii*
2 *lineariloba*
3 *nudicaulis*
1 *scouleri*
3 *solida tauricola*
3 – *transsylvanica* pink
3 *unifolia*
9 *vittae*

CORYLOPSIS
7 *coreana*
9 *himalayana griffithii*

CORYLUS
2 *maxima* 'Garibaldi'
2 – 'Neue Riesennuss' ('New Giant')
2 – 'Waterloo'

COTINUS
9 *coggygria* 'Drinkstone Form'

COTONEASTER
2 *affinis*
2 *apiculatus*
2 *buxifolius* blue-leaved
0 *frigidus* 'Saint Monica'
2 *glabratus*
1 *henryanus* 'Anne Cornwallis'
2 *microphyllus* 'Inermis'
1 *nitens*
2 *prostratus*
2 *racemiflorus*
0 'Saldam'
2 *salicifolius* 'Avonbank'
1 – 'Klampen'
9 – 'Perkeo'
0 *schlechtendalii* 'Eastleigh'
3 *sikangensis*
2 *sikkimensis* Lowndes
9 x *suecicus* 'Greensleeves'
8 – 'Jürgl'
7 *tomentosus*
2 'Valkenburg'
7 x *watereri* 'Inchmery'

COTULA
2 *coronopifolia* 'Cream Buttons'

COWANIA
2 *mexicana*

CRAMBE
3 *filiformis*

CRASPEDIA
2 *incana*

CRASSULA
0 *lactea*
3 *pellucida marginalis*
3 *perforata* 'Variegata'

CRATAEGUS
9 *laevigata* 'Cheal's Crimson'
9 – 'Masekii'(d)
9 – 'Punicea'
9 – 'Rosea'
2 *mollis*
3 *opaca*
3 'Red Italian'
1 *stipulacea*

CREMANTHODIUM
9 *oblongatum*
2 *reniforme*

CRINUM
0 *campanulatum*

CROCOSMIA
3 *masoniorum* 'Rowallane'
2 'Météore' (x *crocosmiiflora*)
9 'Orange Flame'
1 'Saracen'
2 'Vesuvius' (x *crocosmiiflora*)

CROCUS
1 *biflorus* 'Bowles' Blue'
2 – *melantherus*
8 – *weldenii*
1 *candidus*
3 *chrysanthus* 'Snowwhite'
1 *corsicus albus*
3 *hadriaticus lilacinus*
3 – 'Tom Blanchard'
3 *imperati imperati*
9 *korolkowii* 'Unicoloratus'
3 *kotschyanus cappadocicus*
1 – *hakkariensis*
3 – *suworowianus*
0 *niveus* 'Cape Mataplan'
3 *pallasii pallasii*
9 *reticulatus*
1 – *hittiticus*
3 *serotinus* forms
2 *sieberi sublimis*
9 *speciosus* 'Globosus'
3 – x *pulchellus* 'Big Boy'
3 – *xantholaimos*
9 *vernus* 'Early Perfection'
3 – 'Glory of Limmen'
3 – 'Kathleen Parlow'
9 – 'King of the Striped'
2 *versicolor*

CROTALARIA
2 *grevei*

CROWEA
1 *angustifolia*
8 *exalata* x *saligna*

CRYPTANTHUS
0 *acaulis*
2 – *ruber*
2 – – 'New Coster's Favorite'(v)
2 *beuckeri*
3 *bivittatus* AGM
0 – 'Minor'
3 – 'Roseus Pictus'
2 Black Mystic
0 *bromelioides tricolor (v)* AGM
2 Carnival
2 Feuerzauber
2 *fosterianus* AGM
2 'It' (v) AGM
2 Italy
0 'Luddemannii'
2 'Red Star'
2 Silber Lila
0 'Zebrinus'
2 *zonatus*
3 – *argyraeus*

X CRYPTBERGIA
0 'Rubra'

CRYPTOMERIA
1 *japonica* 'Dacrydioides'
9 – 'Elegantissima'
2 – 'Fasciata'
0 – 'Knaptonensis'
0 – 'Mankichi-sugi'
0 – 'Spiraliter Falcata'
1 – 'Tansu'
9 – 'Viridis'

CTENANTHE
0 *kummeriana*
0 *oppenheimiana* 'Tricolor' AGM

CUNILA
1 *origanoïdes*

CUNNINGHAMIA
8 *lanceolata* 'Glauca'

CUPHEA
0 'Mickey Mouse'
1 x *purpurea* 'Firefly'
1 *viscosissima*

X CUPRESSOCYPARIS
2 *leylandii* 'Haggerston Grey' AGM
0 – 'Leighton Green'
3 *notabilis* AGM
3 – 'Brookhill'

CUPRESSUS
1 *arizonica glabra* 'Silver Smoke'
1 – 'Variegata'
1 *chengiana*
2 *guadalupensis forbesii*
1 *macrocarpa* 'Coneybearii Aurea'
1 – 'Golden Flame'
1 – 'John Keown'
9 – 'Pendula'
1 *sempervirens* 'Stricta Aurea'
8 *torulosa*
8 – 'Vladivostock'

CYANANTHUS
8 *lobatus* 'Inshriach Blue'
3 sp. CLD 1492

CYANOTIS
3 *somaliensis* AGM

CYATHEA
0 *cuninghamii*
0 *kermadecensis*

CYCLAMEN
0 *cilicium* patterned leaf
3 *coum* 'Boothman's'
9 – *caucasicum album*
1 – 'Dazzle'
2 – TK form
0 *hederifolium* Corfu form
3 – red
9 – x *africanum*

CYDONIA
1 *oblonga* 'Broadview'

CYMBIDIUM
9 *goeringii*

CYMBOPOGON
0 *flexuosus*

CYMOPHYLLUS
1 *fraseri*

CYNARA
1 *cardunculus* Scolymus Group 'Brittany Belle'
0 – 'Glauca'

CYNOGLOSSUM
2 *amabile* 'Album'
3 *germanicum*
2 *wallichii*

CYPELLA
2 *coelestis* 'Platensis'

CYPERUS
9 *ustulatus*

CYPRIPEDIUM
1 *calceolus pubescens*
1 *guttatum*

CYRTOSPERMA
0 *johnstonii*

CYSTOPTERIS
8 *fragilis* 'Cristata'

CYTISUS
9 'Baronscourt Amber'
9 'Boskoop Ruby' AGM
2 'C E Pearson'
7 'Charmaine'
7 'Donard Seedling'
7 'Eastern Queen'
3 'Garden Magic'
2 'Johnson's Crimson'
9 'Lady Moore'
7 'Orange Arch'
7 x *praecox* 'Buttercup'
7 'Southcombe Apricot'
9 *subspinescens*
2 *supranubius*

DABOECIA
8 *azorica*
8 *cantabrica blumii*
8 – 'Heraut'

DACTYLORHIZA
0 *sambucina*
1 'Tinney's Spotted'

DAHLIA
2 'Abridge Ben' (MinD)
2 'Abridge Fox' (MinD)
2 'Abridge Taffy' (MinD)
1 'Ace of Hearts' (Col)
3 'Adelaide Fontane' (LD)
0 'Aladdin' (SD)
8 'Alfred C' (GSC)
2 'Alltami Alpine' (MD)
9 'Alltami Coral' (MSC)
9 'Alltami Ruby' (MSC)
3 'Almand's Climax' (GD)
2 'Alva's Doris' (SC) AGM
0 'Amanda' (SC)
9 'Amaran Guard' (LD)
2 'Amaran Pico' (MD)
2 'Amaran Relish' (GD)
8 'Amelisweerd' (MSC)
7 'Anchorite' (SD)
3 'Andrew Lockwood' (Pom)
8 'Andries' Orange' (MinSC)
8 'Ann Hilary' (SD)
8 'Anniversary Doc'
3 'Appenzell' (MSC)
2 'Appetizer' (SSC)
9 'Apple Blossom' (MC)
8 'Armgard Coronet' (MD)
9 'Arthur Lashlie' (MC)
3 'Autumn Fairy' (D)
2 'Bacchus' (MSC)
9 'Bach' (MC)
7 'Barbara Schell' (GD)
2 'Barbarry Flush' (MinD)
0 'Baseball' (MinBa)
1 'Bassingbourne Beauty' (SD)
2 'Bella Rose' (SSC)
2 'Belle Epoque' (MC)
9 'Belle of Barmera' (GD)
0 'Bettina' (SSC)
8 'Betty Ann' (Pom)
7 'Birchwood' (Pom)
7 'Bitsa' (MinBa)
3 'Black Jack' (SD)
0 'Blaisdon Red' (SD)
7 'Bob Fitzjohn' (GSC)
9 'Bonne Esperance' (Sin)(Lil)
2 'Bright'
9 'Brookfield Dierdre (MinBa)
9 'Brownie' (Sin)(Lil)
2 'Brunton' (MinD)
9 'Bulls Pride' (GD)
9 'Bushfire' (Pom)
1 'Café au Lait' (LD)
2 'Cameo' (WL)
8 'Cantab Symbol' (MSC)
8 'Carol Channing' (GSC)
9 'Caroussel' (MC)
8 'Cefn Glow' (SSC)
8 'Centenary Symbol' (MSC)
3 'Cheerio' (SSC)
8 'Cherida' (MinBa)
3 'Cherry Fire' (SC)
0 'Cherry Wine' (SD)
8 'Chiltern Amber' (SD)
7 'Chinese Lantern' (SD)
0 'Chorus Girl' (MinD)
1 'Christine' (SWL)
2 'Clair de Lune' (Col)
8 'Claire' (Misc)
0 'Cocktail' (SC)
9 'Color Spectacle' (LSD)
2 'Conway' (SSC) AGM
1 'Coral Puff'
7 'Corfu'
8 'Corrine'
7 'Cortez Silver' (MD)
3 'Cream Alvas' (GD)
2 'Cream Kerkrade' (SC)
2 'Cream Linda' (SD)
0 'Cream Pontiac' (SC)
1 'Crichton Cherry' (MinD)
0 'Crossfield Sceptre' (MSC)
3 'Croydon Supreme' (LD)
9 'Cryfield Jane' (MinBa)
9 'Cryfield Max' (SC)
7 'Cryfield Rosie' (SBa)
9 'Curiosity' (Col)
8 'Dad's Delight' (MinD)
7 'Daleko Adonis' (GSC)
3 'Daleko Gold' (MD)
3 'Daleko Olympic' (LD)
0 'Daleko Tangerine' (MD)
9 'Daleko Venus' (MSC)
8 'Dana Audrey' (MinC)
8 'Dana Judy' (SSC)
3 'Dana Louise' (MD)
9 'Dana Peerless' (SSC)
8 'Dancing Queen'
8 'Dandy' (Sin)(Lil)
3 'Danum Cream' (MSC)
7 'Danum Cupid' (MinBa)
3 'Danum Pinky' (MSC)
2 'Dauntless' (GSC)
9 'Davenport Lesley' (MinD)
8 'Dedham' (SD)
2 'Defile' (MD)
9 'Delectus' (SD)
3 'Denise Willow' (Pom)
9 'De-la-Haye' (MSC)
1 'Diamant' (MD)
2 'Diana Gregory' (Pom)
3 'Doctor Caroline Rabbitt' (SD)
0 'Doctor John Grainger' (MinD)
0 'Donald van de Mark' (GD)
8 'Doris Knight' (SC)
0 'Dorothy Whitney Wood' (SSC)
7 'Downham Royal' (MinBa)
8 'Duncan'
3 'Dutch Baby' (Pom)
1 'Earl Marc' (SC)
0 'Early Bird' (SD)
0 'Eastwood Pinky' (MSC)
7 'Eastwood Star' (MSC)
8 'Eden Marc' (SC)
3 'Edith Arthur' (SSC)
2 'Eileen Denny' (MSC)
8 'Elizabeth Hammett' (MinD)
0 'Elizabethan' (SD)
0 'Elmbrook Rebel' (GSC)
2 'Emmerdale' (SC)
9 'Exotic Dwarf' (Sin)(Lil)
3 'Extase' (MD)
2 'Fernhill Champion' (MD)
3 'Fille du Diable' (LSC)
3 'Fiona Stewart' (SB)
9 'Flying Picket' (SD)
9 'Formby Perfection' (MD)
3 'Frank Hornsey' (SD)
0 'Fred Sheard' (MinD)
0 'Free Lance' (MSC)
3 'Frits' (MinBa)
9 'Gale Lane' (Pom)
2 'Garden News' (SD)
3 'Gay Mini' (MinD)
0 'Gerald Grace' (LSC)
3 'Gilt Edge' (MD)
0 'Ginger Nut' (Pom)
8 'Ginger Willo'
3 'Giraffe' (Misc)
8 'Glenafton' (Pom)
8 'Glenbank Honeycomb' (Pom)
3 'Gloria Romaine' (SD)
3 'Glorie van Naardwijk' (SD)
2 'Golden Festival'
0 'Golden Fizz' (MinBa)
0 'Golden Hope' (MinD)
3 'Golden Willo' (Pom)
3 'Good Hope' (MinD)
3 'Gypsy Boy' (LD)
2 'Hallmark' (Pom)
3 'Hamari Bride' (MSC) AGM
0 'Hamari Saffron' (MSC)
0 'Hamari Sunset' (MSC)
2 'Hamilton Lilian' (SD) AGM
0 'Haseley Cameo' (SD)
0 'Haseley Pearl' (DBa)
0 'Haseley Triumph' (SD)
8 'Hazel' (Pom)
0 'Hazel's Surprise' (SD)
1 'Heljo's Flame' (SC)
8 'Higherfield Crown' (SC)
0 'Highgate Lustre' (MSC)
8 'Highgate Torch' (MSC)
8 'Hilda Clare' (Col)
0 'Holland Herald' (LSC)
7 'Horn of Plenty' (MinD)
0 'Hot Spot' (MinD)
8 'Ice Queen' (SWL)
9 'Imp' (Sin)(Lil)
3 'Inca Matchless' (MD)
7 'Inca Metropolitan' (LD) AGM
9 'Inflammation' (Sin)(Lil)
9 'Invader' (SC)
3 'Jacqueline Tivey' (SD)
2 'Jaldec Jerry' (GSC)
9 'Jancis' (MinSC)
8 'Jane Horton' (Col)
8 'Janet Clarke' (Pom)
3 'Janet Goddard' (SD)
2 'Jean Bailiss' (MSC)
2 'Jean Fairs' (MinWL)
8 'Jescot Jess' (MinD)
0 'Jescot Jim' (SD)
3 'Jescot Julie' (O)
8 'Jescot Nubia' (SSC)
8 'Jill Day' (SC)
9 'Jill Doc' (MD)
1 'John Street' (SWL)
9 'Joy Bennett' (MD)
9 'Joyce Green' (GSC)
8 'Jo's Choice' (MinD)
3 'Just Julia' (MSC)
3 'Just Mary' (SD)
3 'Katisha' (MinD)
8 'Kenora Carousel' (MSC)
8 'Kenora Sunburst' (LSC)
2 'Kenora Valentine' (GD)
2 'Kenora Wildfire' (GD)
8 'Kimi' (O)
0 'Kim's Marc' (SC)
9 'Kiwi Nephew' (SSC)
3 'Kung Fu' (SD)
9 'La Cierva' (Col)
9 'La Corbiere' (DwBa)
0 'Lady Orpah' (SD)
8 'Lady Sunshine' (SSC)
0 'Laurence Fisher' (MSC)
0 'Lavendale' (MinD)
7 'Lavender Leycett'
2 'Lavender Nunton Harvest' (SD)
0 'Lavender Pontiac' (SC)
2 'Le Vonne Splinter' (GSC)
8 'Lemon Hornsey' (SD)
0 'Leverton Chippy' (SD)
2 'Leycett' (GD)
3 'Liberator' (GD)
3 'Life Force'
2 'Lilac Athalie' (SC)

7 'Limited Edition'
3 'Linda Lusardi' (SSC)
2 'Lipoma' (MinBa)
8 'Little Conn' (Pom)
9 'Little Dorrit' (Sin)(Lil)
0 'Little Sally' (Pom)
9 'Lloyd Huston' (GSC)
7 'Louise Bailey' (MinD)
9 'Love's Dream' (SWL)
9 'Lula Pattie' (GD)
8 'Madame Vera' (SD)
7 'Madelaine Ann' (GD)
2 'Magic Moment' (MSC)
2 'Magnificat' (MinD)
2 'Majestic Athalie' (SC)
2 'Majestic Kerkrade' (SC)
2 'Majjas Symbol' (MSC)
3 'Margaret Ann' (MinD)
7 'Margaret Duross' (GD)
7 'Margaret Jean' (GD)
8 'Mariposa' (Col)
3 'Mark Lockwood' (Pom)
2 'Mark Willo' (Pom)
8 'Masons' (SWL)
3 'Match' (SSC)
3 'Matterhorn' (SWL)
8 'Mauvine' (Pom)
8 'Meiktila' (SWL)
3 'Meiro' (SD)
0 'Melanie Jane' (MSC)
9 'Melton' (MinD)
9 'Merriwell Topic' (MD)
3 'Mies' (Sin)
0 'Millbank Inferno' (SD)
3 'Minder' (GD)
8 'Minley Iris' (Pom)
2 'Miramar' (SD)
0 'Miranda' (MSC)
3 'Miss Blanc' (SD)
1 'Miss Swiss' (SD)
2 'Mistill Beauty' (SC)
3 'Monk Marc' (SC)
9 'Morley Lady' (SD)
0 'Morley Lass' (SSC)
7 'Mrs Silverston' (SD)
3 'Mummies Favourite' (SD)
3 'Nationwide' (SD)
3 'Nellie Birch' (MinBa)
9 'Nescio' (Pom)
0 'Nettie' (MinBa)
8 'Neveric' (LSC)
0 'Newby' (MinD)
2 'Night Editor' (GD)
3 'Nijinsky' (SBa)
8 'Norm Williams'
9 'Omo' (Sin)(Lil)
7 'Onslow Linda Ann' (MD)
8 'Ornamental Rays' (SC)
8 'Pamela' (SD)
0 'Pastel Pontiac' (SC)
0 'Pat Seed' (MD)
0 'Patti-Pink' (SSC)
2 'Paul's Delight' (SD)
9 'Peace Pact' (SWL)
0 'Peach Pontiac' (SC)
9 'Peachette' (Misc)(Lil)
0 'Pearl Hornsey' (SD)
9 'Pearl Sharowean' (MSC)
2 'Pensford Willo' (Pom)
9 'Peters Glorie' (MD)
3 'Pied Piper' (MinBa)
3 'Pink Frank Hornsey' (SD)
3 'Pink Giraffe' (O)
3 'Pink Katisha' (MinD)
9 'Pink Leycett' (GD)
3 'Pink Risca Miner' (SBa)
3 'Pink Shirley Alliance' (SC)
2 'Pink Vaguely Noble' (SBa)
0 'Pink Worton Ann' (MinD)
3 'Pioneer' (MSC)
3 'Piper's Pink' (SSC)(DwB) AGM
8 'Pippa' (SC)
3 'Playboy' (GD)
2 'Polar Sight' (GC)
2 'Polyand' (LD)
3 'Pontiac' (SC)
7 'Pop Stretton' (GSC)
7 'Poppa Jim' (SD)
8 'Porcelain' (SWL)
9 'Pot Black' (MinBa)
3 'Prefect' (MSC)
8 'Primrose Bryn' (SSC)
0 'Promise' (MSC)(Fim)
2 'Purbeck Lydia' (LSC)
0 'Purple Doris Day' (SC)
7 'Purple Joy' (MD)
3 'Quel Diable' (LSC)
8 'Rachel's Place' (Pom)
7 'Raffles' (SD)
2 'Raisa' (LD)
8 'Rani' (Pom)
0 'Readley' (SWL)
8 'Red Admiral' (MinBa)
3 'Red Alert' (LBa)
3 'Red and White' (SD)
8 'Red Delight' (Col)
9 'Red Dwarf' (Sin)(Lil)
9 'Red Lotus'
8 'Red Schweitzer' (MinD)
8 'Regal Kerkrade' (SC)
3 'Richard Marc' (SC)
7 'Richard Nash' (SD)
3 'Risca Miner' (SBa)
0 'Robbie Huston' (LSC)
8 'Roberta' (LD)
3 'Robin Hood' (SBa)
8 'Rokesley Mini' (MinC)
9 'Rosalie' (Pom)
1 'Rosalinde'
2 'Rose Cupid' (MinBa)
9 'Rose Newby' (MinD)
7 'Rose Symbol' (MSC)
8 'Rose Willo' (Pom)
8 'Rosewood' (SSC)
3 'Rothesay Reveller' (MD)
8 'Rotonde' (SC)
2 'Ruskin Belle' (MSC)
9 'Ruskin Emil' (SC)
8 'Ruskin Melody'
3 'Ruskin Petite' (MinBa)
3 'Rusty Hope' (MinD)
9 'Saint Croix' (GSC)
3 'Saiva'
7 'Salmon Athalie'
7 'Salmon Kokarde'
2 'Salmon Symbol' (MSC)
9 'Samantha' (DwB)
0 'Sandra Chapman' (MSC)
0 'Sango' (MinBa)
8 'Scarborough'
9 'Scaur Princess' (SD)
9 'Scott's United' (MinD)
7 'Senzoe Jenny'
9 'Sharowean Pride' (MSC)
3 'Sherwood Monarch' (GSC)
9 'Sherwood Sunrise' (SD)
3 'Sherwood Titan' (GSC)
3 'Shirley Alliance' (SC)
3 'Shooting Star'
1 'Shoreline' (D)
2 'Shy Lass' (SC)
9 'Shy Princess' (MC)
3 'Silver Slipper' (SSC)
3 'Sky High' (SD)
2 'So Dainty' (MinSC) AGM
1 'Spencer' (SD)
9 'Stoke Festival '86' (SSC)
9 'Stoneleigh Cherry' (Pom)
8 'Stoneleigh Joyce' (Pom)
8 'Strawberry Gem' (Pom)
7 'Stump Cross'
3 'Stylemaster' (MC)
8 'Sue Willo' (Pom)
0 'Sugar Candy' (MSC)
1 'Sultan'
8 'Sunburst' (Col)
2 'Sunray Symbol' (MSC)
0 'Supermarket' (MSC)
9 'Sure Thing' (MC)
7 'Swallow Falls' (SD)
2 'Sweet Symbol' (MSC)
9 'Sweetheart' (SD)
7 'Symbol Jim'
3 'Syston Sophia' (LBa)
3 'Syston Zone' (LSC)
3 'Tahiti Sunrise' (MSC)
1 'Tango' (SD)
8 'Teatime' (MSC)
3 'Thais' (Col)
0 'The Bride' (SC)
3 'Thelma Clements' (LD)
3 'Tiger Tiv' (MD)
0 'Tinker's White' (SD)
9 'Tiny Tot' (Misc)(Lil)
9 'Topaz Puff'
0 'Tourbillon' (LC)
0 'Trelawny' (GD)
7 'Twiggy' (SWL)
2 'Twilight Time' (MD)
3 'Union Jack' (Sin)
0 'Val Saint Lambert' (MC)
2 'Vazon Bay' (MinB)
3 'Venlo' (D)
8 'Vicky Crutchfield' (SWL)
7 'Vicky Jackson' (SWL)
9 'Vidal Rhapsody' (MSC)
8 'Vidal Tracy' (SSC)
0 'Vigor' (SWL)
3 'Violet'
3 'Violet Davies' (MSC)
8 'Walter Hardesty' AGM
3 'Wanda's Sunshine' (GD)
8 'Weston Aramac'
9 'Weston Forge' (SC)
2 'Whale's Rhonda' (Pom)
2 'White Aster' (Pom)
2 'White Klankstad' (SC)
8 'White Lady Linda' (SD)
7 'White Marc' (SC)
8 'William Gregory'
2 'William 'B'' (GD)
8 'Willo's Fairy'
8 'Willo's Flame'
8 'Winston Churchill' (MinD)
8 'Winter Dawn' (SWL)
2 'Wittem' (MD)
9 'Wood Plumpton' (MC)
8 'Wootton Amber'
3 'Wootton Carol' (SD)
2 'Worton Ann' (MinD)
8 'Worton Bluestreak' (SSC)
7 'Worton Ruth' (SD)
7 'Wyndal Horizon' (MSC)
8 'Yellow Jubilee'
8 'Yellow Symbol' (MSC)
8 'Yelno Harmony' (SWL)
3 'Yes Sir' (MD)

DAPHNE

2 ***aurantiaca***
2 x ***burkwoodii*** 'Lavenirii'
9 ***cneorum*** 'Major'
2 – 'Ruby Glow'
1 – ***verlotii***
2 ***euboica***
3 ***gnidioïdes***
2 ***gnidium***
2 ***kamtschatica***
0 ***kiusiana***
3 ***longilobata***
0 'Louis Mountbatten'
0 ***mezereum*** 'Variegata'
1 ***petraea*** 'Flore Pleno'
9 'Rossetii'
2 'Silver Y'
1 ***tangutica*** 'Aureomarginata'

DASYLIRION

2 ***texanum***

DASYPYRUM

3 ***villosum***

DELONIX

3 ***regia***

DELOSPERMA

3 ***lehmannii***
9 ***ornatulum***
3 ***pallidum***

DELPHINIUM

8 'Antares'
8 'Aphrodite'
1 'Apollo'
1 'Baby Doll'
2 ***barbeyi***
3 'Basil Clitheroe'
1 x ***belladonna*** 'Blue Bees'
9 – 'Capri'
1 – 'Lamartine'

1 – 'Orion'
1 ***bellamania***
3 'Blue Mirror'
8 Blue Springs Group
1 'Blue Triumph'
8 'Ceylon'
8 ***cheilanthum***
0 'Cinderella'
8 'Claire'
1 'Cream Cracker'
1 'Dairymaid'
9 ***denudatum***
3 'Dreaming Spires'
3 ***elatum elatum***
7 ***glareosum***
1 ***grandiflorum*** 'Azure Fairy'
8 Great Expectations Group
1 'Hilda Lucas'
0 'Horizon'
1 'Icecap'
0 'Jennifer Langdon'
0 'Jo-Jo'
2 'Julia Medcalf'
0 'Jumbo'
0 'Lady Eleanor'
3 'Layla'
8 'Loch Lomond'
0 'Loch Maree'
0 'Loch Morar'
0 'Magic Moment'
8 Moody Blues Group
2 'Mount Everest'
0 'Patricia'
1 'Patricia, Lady Hambleden'
0 'Peacock'
0 'Peter Pan'
3 'Radiance'
3 ***requienii*** variegated
0 'Rev E Lascelles'
1 'Rosina'
8 Rosy Future Group
0 'Round Table'
3 'Royal Copenhagen'
1 'Royal Wedding'
1 'Sarabande'
8 'Sarah Edwards'
0 'Savrola'
1 'South Seas'
3 sp. CLD 1476
3 sp. CLD 349
3 ***stachydeum***
1 'Stardust'
1 'Summer Wine'
2 'Summerfield Viking'
2 'Taj Mahal'
3 ***tatsienense*** 'Blue Ice'
1 'Thelma Rowe' **AGM**
2 'Tiny Tim'
1 'Turiddu'
8 'Wheatear'
1 'William Richards'
3 ***xantholeucum***
1 'Xenia Field'
8 'Zeus'

DENDRANTHEMA

9 'Alf Price' (25b)
7 'Alice Fitton' (7b)
9 'Alison McNamara' (3b)
1 'Allison '88' (Rub)
1 'Allswell' (24b)
7 'Amanda' (11)
8 'Amber Chessington' (25a)
7 'Amber Leading Lady' (25b)
7 'Amy Fitton' (4a)
8 'Ann Dickson' (25a)
7 'Apricot Harry Gee' (1)
1 'Apricot New Stylist' (24b)
0 'Arcadian' (24b)
9 'Ark Royal' (24b)
9 'Arkle' (25a)
7 'Arnold Fitton' (1)
0 'Arthur' (25a)
1 'Bambi' (24b)
9 'Bambino' (29c)
7 'Barbara Hall' (23a)
3 'Barbara Ward' (7b)
7 'Barker's Wine' (24c)
7 'Barnsley' (5a)
8 'Batley Centenary' (25b)
7 'Beaujolais' (24b)
7 'Bergerac' (24b)
9 'Betty Saxton' (24a)
2 'Bill Florentine' (3b)
2 'Birchwood' (24b)
7 'Birmingham' (2)
7 'Blanche Poitevine' (5b)
8 'Bonus' (24a)
7 'Bowers Jim'
7 'Breakaway'
2 'Brideshead' (13b)
3 'Brierton Lad' (7b)
8 'Brighton' (25b)
7 'Broadway Flare' (29c)
7 'Broadway Magic' (19e)
7 'Broadway Peach' (29c)
7 'Broadway Royal' (29c)
3 'Broadway Sovereign' (29c)
7 'Bronze Eda Fitton' (23a)
8 'Bronze Emilia' (29c)
9 'Bronze Juweeltje'
7 'Bronze Miss World' (24a)
9 'Bronze Nathalie' (29c)
7 'Bronze Shoesmith Salmon (4a)
0 'Bronze Venice' (24b)
1 'Bronze Wessex Charms' (29d)
2 'Bronze World of Sport' (25a)
1 'Buckland' (25c)
2 'Buff Courtier' (24a)
1 'Buff Margaret' (24b)
7 'Candy' (7a)
9 'Capulet' (3b)
8 'Carmine Margaret' (24b)
9 'Carol Moonlight' (29b)
7 'Carrie' (25a)
2 'Chamoirose'
7 'Chanelle' (25a)
0 'Chatsworth' (29c)
7 'Cheltenham Show' (25a)
1 'Chempak Crimson' (24b)
9 'Cherry Chintz' (24a)
7 'Chesswood Beauty' (7b)
8 'Chintz' (24b)
8 'Chippendale' (24a)
9 'Christina' (25b)
8 'Clarette'
2 'Cloth of Gold' (24b)
7 'Conderton' (15a)
1 'Contour' (24a)
3 'Copper Hedgerow' (7b)
0 'Copper Rylands Gem' (24b)
8 'Copper Spoon'
9 'Countdown' (5a)
7 'Countryman' (24b)
7 'Cranforth' (24b)
1 'Cream Pennine Pink' (29c)
9 'Crimson Daily Mirror' (5a)
0 'Crimson Purple Glow' (5a)
9 'Crimson Venice' (24b)
7 'Crimson Woolman's Glory' (7a)
0 'Crown Derby' (15a)
9 'Daily Mirror' (5a)
7 'Dark Eve Gray' (24b)
8 'Dark Pennine Pink' (29c)
1 'Darlington Jubilee' (25a)
2 'David Higgins' (3b)
1 'Dee Prince' (29c)
2 'Denise Oatridge' (5a)
2 'Distinction' (3b)
2 'Dolly' (9c)
0 'Doreen Bircumshaw' (24a)
3 'Dorridge Dream' (23b)
8 'Dorridge Jewel' (15a)
1 'Dorridge Lady' (24b)
1 'Dorridge Snowball' (3b)
1 'Dorridge Sun' (3b)
0 'Dragoon' (9c)
0 'Early Bird' (24b)
9 'Early Red Cloak' (24b)
7 'Eda Fitton' (23a)
7 'Edith Goodall' (24a)
9 'Elsie Prosser' (1)
8 'Emilia' (29c)
1 'Enbee Sunray' (29d)
7 'Enid Whiston' (4b)
1 'Eugene' (25b)
9 'Eve Gray' (24b)
1 'Evelyn' (25a)
3 'Fair Lady' (5a)
9 'Fairisle' (24b)
0 'Fairway' (15a)
7 'Far North' (5a)
0 'Fiona Lynn' (24a)
9 'Flambard' (24b)
3 'Flash Point'
9 'Flo Cooper' (25a)
3 'Folk Song' (4b)
7 'Forest Flare' (24b)
1 'Frank Taylor' (15a)
7 'Fred Raynor'
9 'Gemma Jones' (5b)
7 'Gerrie Hoek' (29c)
2 'Gerry Milner' (23b)
2 'Gillette' (23b)
7 'Gillian Gore' (23b)
0 'Ginger' (30)
2 'Gladys Sharpe' (25a)
9 'Glorie'
2 'Glorietta' (4b)
1 'Gold Coin' (7b)
9 'Goldcrest' (25b)
9 'Golden Echo' (4a)
9 'Golden Oyster' (25b)
9 'Golden Percy Salter' (24b)
3 'Golden Queen' (3b)
7 'Golden Shoesmith Salmon (4a) **AGM**
0 'Golden Stardust' (24b)
7 'Golden Woolman's Glory' (7a)
7 'Goldway' (25b)
3 ***grandiflorum***
9 'Granny Gow' (29d)
9 'Graphic' (23b)
9 'Green Goddess' (1)
9 'Greensleeves' (11)
0 'Hamburg' (25a)
8 'Harford'
7 'Harry Whiston' (1)
2 'Havelsonne'
9 'Hayley Boon' (25b)
2 'Hazel Macintosh' (5a)
1 'Helen' (29K)
3 'Helmsman' (24a)
9 'Highland Skirmish' (29d)
9 'Honey Margaret' (29e)
0 'Horace Martin'
2 'International' (3a)
1 'Isabel' (15b)
2 'Isabellrosa' (29K)
2 'Jack Wood' (25a)
0 'James Hall' (5a)
1 'Jessica' (29c)
7 'Jessie Gilmour' (23a)
9 'Jessie Habgood' (1)
2 'Jessie Raynor'
1 'Jill Collins' (24b)
7 'Jinx' (7b)
2 'John Statham' (23b)
7 'John Wood' (5a)
1 'Joy Hughes' (4b)
1 'Joyce Stevenson' (24b)
1 'Jubilee' (9c)
7 'Julie Ann' (25b)
1 'Juliet' (24b)
7 'Just Tom' (24b)
2 'Kampfhahn'
3 'Kento-homari' (9f)
7 'Kissy'
3 'Kokinran' (9f)
3 'Komaki-zukura' (9f)
8 'Lady Anna' (25a)
7 'Lapley Blush' (29b)
7 'Lapley Bracken' (29d)
7 'Lapley Hallmark' (29c)
7 'Lapley Princess' (29c)
7 'Lapley Rose' (29b)
7 'Lapley Snow' (29d)
7 'Lapley Sunset'
1 'Legend'
0 'Lemon Drop' (23a)
2 'Lemon Rynoon' (9d)
1 'Lemon Tench' (29K)
3 'Len Futerill' (25b)
2 'Liberty' (15a)
7 'Linda Young' (5b)
7 'Lipstick' (28)
7 'Littleton'

9 'Lovely Charmer' (7b)
7 'Lydia' (25a)
9 'Madge Welby' (25b)
0 'Manito'
7 'Margaret Fitton' (23b)
0 'Marian Gosling' (24b)
9 'Marie Taylor' (29c)
1 'Mark Slater' (2)
0 'Martina' (24b)
2 'Mary Blomfield' (4a)
0 'Mary Dyer' (24a)
7 'Mason's Golden'
3 'Mauve Mist' (30K)
2 'Medallion' (9c)
8 'Michael Fish' (25b)
7 'Michael Pullom' (25a)
3 'Milltown' (24b)
7 'Mosquito' (28b)
8 'Mrs Farley'
8 'Munsel'
9 'Muriel Foster' (29d)
7 'My Jeanie' (25a)
3 'Myako-no-suki' (9f)
7 'Naden Pound'
9 'Ned Holdaway' (25b)
7 'Nora Brook'
3 'Noshi-no-nuki' (9f)
8 'Olga Williams' (25b)
7 'Olwyn' (4b)
0 'Orchid Helen'
8 'Orlando' (25a)
9 'Oyster' (25b)
1 'Oyster Fairweather' (3b)
2 'Pacific' (15a)
8 'Paint Box' (24b)
7 'Pandora' (5a/ 12a)
7 'Pat Amos' (23a)
9 'Peach Chessington' (25a)
9 'Peach Juweeltje'
7 'Pelsall Lady' (25a)
3 'Pennine Ace' (29f)
0 'Pennine Air' (29d)
9 'Pennine Alfie' (29f)
1 'Pennine Angel' (29a)
9 'Pennine Ann' (29a)
9 'Pennine Belle' (29d)
9 'Pennine Brandy' (29c)
8 'Pennine Brighteye' (29c)
8 'Pennine Bronze' (29c)
9 'Pennine Cadet' (29a)
3 'Pennine Calypso' (29b) **AGM**
2 'Pennine Cameo' (29a)
8 'Pennine Champ' (29c)
9 'Pennine Chorus' (29c)
9 'Pennine Chum' (29d)
3 'Pennine Copper' (29c)
2 'Pennine Dancer' (29d)
0 'Pennine Dandy' (29c)
9 'Pennine Darkeye' (29c)
9 'Pennine Dew' (29c)
9 'Pennine Dixie' (29d)
9 'Pennine Dream' (29d)
8 'Pennine Echo' (29d)
9 'Pennine Elf' (29c)
1 'Pennine Ember' (29d)
8 'Pennine Fairy' (29c)
9 'Pennine Flirt' (29b)
2 'Pennine Flute' (29f) **AGM**
3 'Pennine Gambol' (29a) **AGM**
9 'Pennine Gem' (29c)
9 'Pennine Globe' (29a)
8 'Pennine Gloss' (29d)
7 'Pennine Gold' (29c)
2 'Pennine Ivory' (29d)
0 'Pennine Jewel' (29f)
3 'Pennine Jude' (29a)
2 'Pennine Lemon' (29c)
3 'Pennine Light' (29d)
2 'Pennine Lotus' (29c)
3 'Pennine Magic' (29c)
9 'Pennine Marvel' (29c)
2 'Pennine Mary' (29d)
2 'Pennine Mist' (29c)
8 'Pennine Model' (29c)
1 'Pennine Orchid' (29d)
8 'Pennine Penny' (29d)
1 'Pennine Pet' (29f)
2 'Pennine Phyllis' (29b) **AGM**
9 'Pennine Plume' (29d)
8 'Pennine Polka' (29c)
1 'Pennine Poppet' (29a)
9 'Pennine Prince' (29c)
9 'Pennine Prize' (29a)
9 'Pennine Quiver' (29d)
3 'Pennine Rascal' (29c)
9 'Pennine Rave' (29a)
7 'Pennine Red' (29c)
9 'Pennine Rose' (29c)
0 'Pennine Salute' (29d)
8 'Pennine Sand' (29c)
7 'Pennine Shell' (29c)
9 'Pennine Shield' (29c)
3 'Pennine Signal' (29d) **AGM**
3 'Pennine Silk' (29c)
2 'Pennine Silver' (29c)
8 'Pennine Smile' (29c)
3 'Pennine Smoke' (29d)
8 'Pennine Solo' (29d)
2 'Pennine Spice' (29c)
0 'Pennine Sweetheart' (29c)
9 'Pennine Tan' (29c)
9 'Pennine Torch' (29d)
2 'Pennine Trinket' (29c)
8 'Pennine Tune' (29a)
1 'Pennine Vista' (29c)
3 'Pennine Wine' (29c)
7 'Penny Lane' (25b)
9 'Peter Pan' (24b)
0 'Phil Oultram' (5b)
7 'Pilsley Queen' (29c)
2 'Pink Chessington' (25a)
9 'Pink Gambit' (24a)
7 'Pink Mason' (7b)
7 'Plushred' (4b)
1 'Polar Queen' (3b)
7 'Poppet' (28a) **AGM**
0 'Port Stanley' (5b)
2 'Primrose Doreen Bircumshaw' (24a)
2 'Primrose Fairweather' (3b)
1 'Primrose Heide' (29c)
7 'Primrose Olwyn' (4b)
3 'Primrose World of Sport' (25a)
1 'Pure Silk' (14b)
2 'Purple Pennine Wine' (29c) **AGM**
3 'Purple-Pink'
1 'Ralph Lambert' (1)
0 'Rebecca Walker' (25a)
2 'Red Cassandra' (5b)
9 'Red Claire Louise' (24b)
8 'Red Cropthorne'
0 'Red Early Bird' (24b)
7 'Red Fair Lady' (5a)
7 'Red Glory' (7a)
1 'Red Lilian Hoek' (29c)
2 'Red Pennine Jade' (29d)
1 'Red Resilient' (4b)
9 'Redwing' (4b)
2 'Reg Pearce' (15a)
1 'Resilient' (4b)
1 'Rheingold' (29c)
2 'Robert Earnshaw' (3b)
7 'Romany' (2)
7 'Ronald Rowe' (24b)
8 'Rose Madeleine' (29c)
7 'Rosedew' (25a) **AGM**
1 'Rosette' (29c)
0 'Rutland' (24a)
1 'Rybronze' (9d)
7 'Rychart' (9d)
7 'Rychoice' (9d)
0 'Ryfire' (9d)
1 'Rystar' (9d) **AGM**
9 'Sally Ball' (29a)
0 'Sally Duchess' (25a)
0 'Salmon Allouise' (25b)
7 'Salmon Chessington' (25a)
2 'Salmon Margaret Riley' (25a)
0 'Salmon Orpheus' (1)
2 'Salmon Pennine Gambol' (29a) **AGM**
1 'Salmon Pennine Pink' (29c)
2 'Salmon Pennine Wine' (29c) **AGM**
7 'Salmon Primrose'
8 'Salmon Rutland' (24a)
3 'Salmon Shirley McMinn' (15a)
3 'Samuri Bronze' (Rub)
0 'Sassen'
0 'Scarlet Pennine Crimson' (29c)
2 'Schaffhausen'
1 'Sentry' (24b)
7 'Seychelle' (2)
0 'Sheffield Anniversary' (24a)
1 'Sheffield Centenary' (3b)
1 'Sheila Morgan' (5b)
9 'Sherwood Forester' (24a)
9 'Shirley Imp' (3b)
1 'Shirley Sunburst' (3a)
1 'Shirley Victoria' (25a)
3 'Sid Griffiths' (29c)
7 'Sierra' (25b)
1 'Skater's Waltz' (5a)
9 'Skylark'
2 'Snooker' (23b)
7 'Snow Elf' (28)
9 'Snowcap' (14a)
7 'Snowdon' (5b/ 9c)
0 'Soccer' (25a)
2 'Solitaire' (24a)
0 'Southway Seville' (29c)
8 'Spartan Bronze' (29c)
3 'Spartan Pink' (29c)
3 'Spartan Wendy' (29c)
2 'Spartan Yellow' (29c)
9 'Standby' (24b)
0 'Stardust' (24b)
1 'Stuart Shoesmith' (4b)
9 'Sun Blaze' (29a)
0 'Suncharm Orange' (22a)
7 'Sunflash' (5b/ 12a)
8 'Sunset Rylands Gem' (24b)
0 'Susan Freestone' (24b)
9 'Susan Pullom' (25a)
3 'Swallow'
9 'Sydenham Girl' (24b)
2 'Talbot Classic' (29c)
3 'Tanaga'
7 'Terry Morris' (7b)
7 'Tiara' (28a)
3 'Tolima'
9 'Tom Stillwell'
2 'Tone Dragon' (29a)
1 'Tone Girl' (29a)
9 'Tone Glow' (29a)
9 'Tone Sail' (29a)
2 'Tone Tints' (29a)
2 'Tone Yellow' (29a)
2 'Trudie Bye' (3b)
2 'Twinkle' (28)
2 'Vanessa Lynn' (24b)
0 'Vanity Apricot'
0 'Vanity Yellow'
3 'Vesuvius'
1 'Violet Lawson' (15a)
1 'Vitax Victor' (25a)
9 'Wagtail' (22a)
1 'Wessex Charms' (29d)
2 'Wessex Opal' (29d)
1 'Wessex Pearl' (29d)
2 'Wessex Prince' (29d)
2 'Wessex Royal' (29d)
0 'Wessex Sentry' (29d)
0 'Wessex Shell' (29d) **AGM**
2 'Wessex Tune' (29d)
8 'White Len Futerill' (25a)
3 'White Pamela' (29c)
0 'White Sally Duchess' (25a)
7 'Winter Queen' (5b)
9 'Woody's Choice' (5b)
2 'Woolman's Celebration' (23b)
9 'Worcester' (14b)
1 'Xenia Noelle' (4b)
2 'Yellow Allouise' (25b)
0 'Yellow Broadway Sovereign' (29c)
1 'Yellow Cassandra' (15b)
9 'Yellow Chessington' (25a)
2 'Yellow Cornish' (25b)
7 'Yellow Cricket' (25b)
3 'Yellow Dorridge Crown' (25b)
8 'Yellow Emilia' (29c)
2 'Yellow Fair Lady' (5a)

2 'Yellow Jack Wood' (25a)
9 'Yellow Jemma Wilson' (23b)
8 'Yellow Juweeltje'
0 'Yellow Pamela' (29c)
1 'Yellow Pennine Pink' (29c)
1 'Yellow Resilient' (5b)
7 'Yellow Sam Vinter' (5a)
2 'Yellow Shirley Imp' (3b)
2 'Yellow Vitax Victor' (25a)
9 'Yorkshire Television' (5a)

DERMATOBOTRYS
3 ***saundersii***

DESCHAMPSIA
9 ***cespitosa*** 'Tardiflora'
9 – 'Tauträger'

DEUTZIA
1 x ***hybrida*** 'Reuthe's Pink'
3 x ***magnifica*** 'Staphyleoïdes'
1 x ***maliflora***
0 – 'Avalanche'
8 ***purpurascens***
2 x ***rosea*** 'Rosea'
1 ***scabra*** 'Watereri'
8 ***vilmoriniae***

DIANTHUS
2 'Achievement' (p)
3 'Ada Wood' (pf)
9 'Alfriston' (b)
2 'Allspice Sport' (p)
9 ***alpinus*** 'Ascreavie Form'
1 – 'Cherry Beauty'
9 – 'Ruby Venus'
0 – x ***callizonus***
2 'Alyson' (p)
0 ***angulatus***
1 'Anna' (pf)
9 'Anne Jones' (b)
9 'Anthony' (p)
9 'Apollo' (b)
3 'Arbel' (pf)
3 x ***arvernensis*** 'Albus'
2 'Autumn Glory' (b)
2 'Autumn Tints' (b)
8 'Avoca Purple' (p)
9 'Barbara Norton' (p)
9 'Barton's Pink' (p)
9 'Belle of Bookham' (b)
7 'Beryl Giles' (pf)
1 ***biflorus***
2 Black and White Minstrel's Group (p,a)
2 'Bookham Beau' (b)
3 'Bookham Heroine' (b)
2 'Bookham Prince' (b)
9 'Bressingham Pink' (p)
2 ***brevicaulis***
9 'Brilliance' (p)
1 'Buckfast Abbey' (p)
2 'Candy' (p)
0 ***carthusianorum*** Atrorubens Group
1 – 'Nanus'
1 'Castleroyal Princess' (p)
2 'Celestial' (b)
9 'Charles Edward' (p)
7 'Cherry Heldenbrau' (pf)
9 'Cherry Pie' (p)
1 'Clarabelle' (b)
1 'Coleton Fishacre'
2 'Countess of Lonsdale' (b)
9 'Cranborne Seedling' (p)
9 'Crimson Clove' (p)
9 'Crimson Treasure' (p)
3 ***cruentus***
0 'Crusader' (b)
2 'Dainty' (b)
2 'Daphne' (p)
2 'Delicata'
1 ***deltoïdes*** 'Hilltop Star'
3 – ***splendens***
9 – 'Steriker'(p)
2 – 'Vampir'
2 'Desert Song' (b)
7 'Diane Marie' (pf)
9 'Dianne' (pf)
3 'Dianne Hewins' (pf)
9 'Dicker Clove' (b)
2 'Diplomat' (b)
0 'Doctor Danger'
8 'Donizetti' (p)
1 'Dot Clark' (b)
3 double dark red
0 'Double Devon' (p)
2 double mauve
1 'Douglas Fancy' (b)
3 'Downs Glory' (b)
9 'Downs Souvenir' (b)
9 'Downs Unique' (b)
0 'Duchess of Fife' (p)
2 'Dusty Sim' (pf)
9 'Edenside Glory' (b)
9 'Eileen Neal' (b)
9 'Elizabeth Jane' (p)
2 'Eve' (p)
1 'Fancy Monarch' (b)
9 'Fay' (p)
0 'Firefly' (b)
9 'Flanders' (b)
1 'Forest Violet' (b)
1 'Fragrans' (pf)
2 'Fred Sutton' (pf)
9 'Gaiety' (p)
1 'Gaydena' (b)
8 'George Vernon' (pf)
3 'Gertrude' (p)
9 'Glenda' (p)
9 'Glory'
2 'Glory Lyonnaise' (p)
9 'Goblin' (p)
9 'Grace How' (b)
0 'Grace Mather' (p)
1 ***gracilis***
7 'Grandad' (p)
1 ***graniticus***
0 ***gratianopolitanus*** 'Compactus Eydangeri'(p)
3 – 'Corinne Tremaine'
0 – x ***subacaulis***
1 'Green Lane' (p)
9 'Grey Dove' (b)
2 'Greystone' (b)
9 'Grome' (p)
2 'Hambledon' (p)
7 'Hardwicke's Pink' (p)
3 'Harvest Moon' (pf)
9 'Heldenbrau' (pf)
9 'Helen Keates' (b)
9 'Helga' (p)
2 'Herbert's Pink' (p)
9 'Highland Gem' (p)
2 'Hollycroft Rose' (p)
3 'Horton'
1 'Hound Tor'
8 'Houstan House' (p)
8 'Ipswich Crimson' (p)
0 'Irish Pink' (p)
2 'Isobel Templeton' (b)
8 'Jack Wood' (pf)
9 'Jack's Lass' (pf)
0 'Jacqueline's Delight' (p)
9 'Jane Bowen' (p)
1 'Janet' (p)
1 'Janet Walker' (p)
2 'Jester' (p)
3 'Joanne Taylor' (pf)
9 'John Malcolm' (p)
2 'Judy' (p)
3 'Julian' (p)
9 'Kathleen Hitchcock' (b)
9 'Katy' (b)
1 'Kesteven Kirkstead' **AGM**
2 'King of the Blacks' (p,a)
1 'Kitty Jay'
2 'Kobusa' (pf)
2 'Laddie Sim' (pf)
2 'Lancing Lass' (p)
3 ***langeanus***
3 'Le Rêve' (pf)
2 'Lena' (pf)
3 'Lilian' (p)
9 'Lily Lesurf' (b)
9 'Little Beauty' (pf)
3 'Little Gem' (pf)
2 'Lord Grey' (b)
9 'Lord Nuffield' (b)
3 'Louise's Choice' (p)
9 'Maggie' (p)
9 'Maisie Neal' (b)
9 'Margaret Curtis' (p)
2 'Mark' (p)
2 'Mary Livingstone' (b)
2 'Mary Murray' (b)
2 'Maurice Prichard' (p)
2 'Melody' (pf)
9 'Messines White' (p)
3 'Molly Blake'
8 'Monarch' (pf)
9 'Mrs Blarney's Old Pink' (p)
8 'Mrs Dunlop's Old Pink'
1 'Mrs Holt' (p)
2 'Mrs Perkins' (b)
2 'Murray's Laced Pink' (p)
1 'Murton' (p)
1 'Nora Urling Clark' (pf)
2 'Oakwood Bill Ballinger' (p)
7 'Oakwood Dainty' (p)
9 'Oakwood Dorothy' (p)
2 'Oakwood Sparkler' (p)
0 'Old Crimson Clove' (b)
3 'Old Fringed Pink' (p)
9 'Orchid Lace' (p,a)
2 'Pallas' (b)
1 ***pavonius albus***
9 – 'Roaschia'
9 'Peter Adamson' (b)
9 'Peter Wood' (b) **AGM**
9 'Petula' (p)
3 'Phyllis Marshall' (b)
1 'Pink Baby' (p)
9 'Pink Bouquet' (p)
0 'Pink Delight' (p)
3 'Pink Monica Wyatt' (p)
0 'Plum Diadem' (p)
9 'Pluto' (p)
3 ***pontederae***
9 'Portrait Sim' (pf)
2 'Portsdown Sunset' (b)
2 'Prichard's Variety' (p)
8 'Pride of Ayrshire' (p)
8 'Raeden Pink' (p)
1 'Ralph Gould' (p)
9 'Raspberry Ripple' (p)
3 'Red Denim' (p)
2 ***repens***
3 'Rhian's Choice' (p)
9 'Richard Pollak' (b)
9 'Robert Douglas' (b)
9 'Robert Smith' (b)
2 'Rose Bradwardine' (b)
3 'Ruffles' (p)
3 'Rupert Lambert'
9 'Sacha' (pf)
2 'Sally's Mauve'
9 'Salmon Fragrant Ann' (p)
9 'Salmon Queen' (b)
3 'Samantha Holtom' (pf)
2 'Sandra' (p)
2 ***serotinus***
1 'Sevilla' (pf)
2 'Shaston Delight' (b)
9 'Shaston Supreme' (b)
9 'Sheila Short' (pf)
0 'Sheila Weir' (b)
3 'Sheila's Choice' (p)
9 'Show Ideal' (p)
9 'Shrimp' (b)
2 ***simulans***
3 'Sir David Scott' (p)
3 'Spark' (p)
2 ***spiculifolius***
2 'Spindrift' (b)
3 'Spotty' (p)
2 'Sprite' (b)
3 sp. NS 643
3 ***subacaulis brachyanthus***
3 'Sullom Voe'
2 'Surrey Clove' (b)
2 'Sway Breeze' (p)
9 'Syston Beauty' (p)
3 ***tianschanicus***
1 'Timothy' (p)
1 'Tom Bradshaw' (pf)
9 'Tom Welborn' (p)
9 'Tony Cutler' (b)
2 'Trevor' (p)
3 'Trisha's Choice' (p)
1 'Truly Yours' (pf)
3 'Valerie' (p)
2 'Vanda' (p)
3 'Victoria' (p)
2 'Water Nymph' (b)
1 'Welland' (p)
8 'Welwyn' (p)

3 'Whatfield Rose' (p)
1 'White Bouquet' (p)
9 'Whitesmith' (b) AGM
2 'William Newell' (b)
9 'William of Essex' (p)
9 'Wisp' (p)
0 *xylorrizus*
3 *zederbaueri*
9 'Zephyr' (b)

DIAPENSIA
9 *lapponica obovata*

DIASCIA
1 *capensis*
2 *rigescens* 'Variegata'
2 *stricta*

DICENTRA
2 *formosa* 'Sweetheart'
1 *pauciflora*
8 *peregrina alba*

DICOMA
2 *zeyheri*

DICRANOSTIGMA
3 *lactucoïdes*

DIEFFENBACHIA
0 x *bausei (v)*
0 'Janet Weidner' (v)
0 *seguine* 'Exotica'(v)
0 – 'Jenmanii'(v)
0 'Wilson's Delight' (v)

DIGITALIS
3 *grandiflora* 'Dropmore Yellow'
9 *lutea* 'Sarah'
3 *purpurea mariana*

DIONYSIA
9 *archibaldii*
9 *aretioïdes* 'Paul Furse'
0 *bryoïdes*
0 *curviflora*
0 *denticulata*
0 *janthina*
0 *michauxii*
0 *revoluta canescens*
0 – *revoluta*

DIOSCOREA
3 *japonica*

DIOSPYROS
7 *glaucifolia*

DIPELTA
3 *ventricosa*
2 *yunnanensis*

DIPLARRHENA
3 *moraea minor*

DIPLAZIUM
3 *japonicum*

DIPSACUS
1 *laciniatus*

DISCARIA
0 *toumatou*

DISPORUM
8 *sessile yakushimense*
2 *smilacinum*

DISTYLIUM
9 *myricoïdes*

DODECATHEON
1 *alpinum purpureum*
2 *integrifolium*
3 *meadia* 'Queen Victoria'
1 *redolens*
2 'Sooke's Variety'

DORYANTHES
1 *excelsa*

DRABA
3 Alaskan species
8 *alpina*
3 *arabisans canadensis*
2 *asprella*
3 *athoa*
1 *borealis*
3 *bruniifolia olympica*
3 *cappadocica*
1 *carinthiaca*
2 *cinerea*
3 *cretica*
8 *fladnizensis*
3 *glabella*
3 *hispanica segurensis*
2 *mollissima* x *longisiliqua*
3 *oreades*
0 *oreibata*
1 *paysonii paysonii*
0 *setosa*
1 *sibirica*
3 sp. AGS/ J 214
3 sp. JJH 171
1 *stellata*

DRACAENA
0 *fragrans* 'Lindenii'
0 *fragrans* Compacta Group 'Compacta'
0 *reflexa*

DRACOCEPHALUM
0 *heterophyllum*
2 *imberbe*
9 *integrifolium*
2 *nutans*

DRACOPHYLLUM
1 *fiordense*
2 *pronum*

DRIMYS
2 *winteri winteri*

DROSERA
3 *heloïdes*
3 *paleacea*
3 *subhirtella subhirtella*
3 *whittakeri*

DRYANDRA
3 *formosa*
3 *obtusa*

DRYAS
9 *octopetala lanata*

DRYOPTERIS
3 *affinis borreri*
3 – 'Crispa Cristata'
1 *filix-mas* 'Crispatissima'
3 – 'Decomposita'
3 – Grandiceps Group

3 *lepidopoda*
3 *sublacera*

DUDLEYA
1 *brittonii*
3 *cymosa*

ECHEVERIA
3 'Paul Bunyon'
3 *pulvinata* AGM

ECHINACEA
1 *purpurea* 'The King'

ECHINOPS
0 *chantavicus*
1 *tournefortii albus*

ECHIUM
3 *pininana* x *wildpretii*
3 x *scilloniense*

EICHHORNIA
7 *crassipes* 'Major'

ELAEAGNUS
0 *angustifolia orientalis*
8 x *ebbingei* 'Tricolor'(v)

ELAEOCARPUS
9 *decipiens*
1 *hookerianus*
0 *pusillus*

ELATOSTEMA
3 *repens* AGM

ELEUTHEROCOCCUS
9 *henryi*
3 *sieboldianus*

ELLIOTTIA
3 *pyroliflora*
9 *racemosa*

ELODEA
3 *callitrichoïdes*

ELYMUS
1 *interruptus*

EMILIA
3 *coccinea*

EMINIUM
1 *stipitatum*

EMPETRUM
8 *hermaphroditum*
8 *nigrum* 'Bernstein'
8 – 'Compactum'
8 – 'Smaragd'

ENGELMANNIA
0 *pinnatifida*

ENKIANTHUS
3 *campanulatus* Nymans form
0 *cernuus*
3 *deflexus*
9 *serrulatus*
3 *tectus*

EPACRIS
3 *impressa*
0 *pauciflora*

EPHEDRA
1 *affinis intermedia*
0 *intermedia*

EPILOBIUM
0 *glabellum* 'Roseum'
9 *gunnianum*

EPIMEDIUM
0 *grandiflorum* 'Rose Glow'
3 – 'Shikinomai'
1 – 'White Beauty'

EPIPREMNUM
3 *aureum* 'Marble Queen'(v)

EQUISETUM
9 *telmateia*

ERANTHIS
3 *hyemalis* Tubergenii Group
3 *longistipitata*

EREMAEA
1 *purpurea*

EREMURUS
2 Himrob Group

ERICA
8 *andevalensis*
2 *baccans*
2 *bauera*
8 *carnea* 'Amy Backhouse'
8 – 'Mayfair White'
8 – 'Mr Reeves'
8 – 'Urville'
8 – 'Winter Red'
3 *cerinthoïdes*
3 *ciliaris*
8 – 'Jennifer Anne'
8 – 'Rock Pool'
3 *cinerea*
2 – 'A E Mitchell'
9 – 'Creel'
0 – 'Electra'
9 – 'Hutton Pentreath'
7 – 'Lankidden'
0 – 'Lilian Martin'
1 – 'Pink Lace'
8 – 'Rose Gem'
3 *colorans*
3 *conspicua*
0 x *darleyensis*
3 *glandulosa*
3 *gracilis* red
3 x *hiemalis* 'Limelight'
2 'January Sun'
3 *mackayana*
8 *maderensis*
3 *mauritanica*
3 *mollis*
1 *multiflora*
2 'Netherfield Orange'
8 *oatesii*
3 *pageana*
8 *perlata*
3 *persoluta*
3 *perspicua*
0 *scoparia*
3 – *platycodon* 'Lionel Woolner'
3 *sessiliflora*
2 'Sneznick'
8 *taxifolia*
3 *transparens*

9 *vagans* 'Alba Nana'
8 – 'Bianca'
8 – 'Elegant Spike'
9 *verticillata*
8 *vestita*
1 x *watsonii*
2 x *williamsii*

ERIGERON
1 *allocatus*
3 *annuus*
2 *caespitosus*
1 *chrysopsidis brevifolius*
2 *delicatus*
0 *glabellus*
1 *glaucus* 'Sennen'
3 'Goliath'
3 'H E Beale'
1 *humilis*
3 *linearis*
9 *myosotis*
3 'Nachthimmel'
3 'Pamela'
3 *radicatus*
8 *roylei*
3 *rydbergii*
9 *speciosus* 'Roseus'
2 'Viridis'

ERINUS
2 *alpinus* pink

ERIOCEPHALUS
8 *africanus*

ERIOGONUM
1 *flavum xanthum*
9 *giganteum*
3 *kennedyi*
0 – *gracilipes*
3 *lobbii robustum*
3 *multiceps*
3 *ovalifolium depressum*
2 – *nivale*
3 *thymoïdes*

ERIOPHORUM
0 *brachyantherum*
1 *scheuchzeri*

ERIOPHYLLUM
3 *lanatum integrifolium*

ERITRICHIUM
1 *howardii*
3 *nanum*

ERODIUM
2 'Crimson Glow'
3 *petraeum* 'Burgundy'
2 – *petraeum*
9 *romanum*
2 *sibthorpianum*

ERYNGIUM
3 *alpinum* 'Violet Lace'
2 'Calypso' (v)
1 *nivale*
7 x *zabelii* 'Spring Hills'

ERYSIMUM
1 'Bicolor'
1 *cheiri* double yellow
0 *linifolium glaucum*
3 'Newark Park'
2 *nivale*
9 *odoratum*
1 *sempervirens*

ERYTHRINA
2 *princeps*

ERYTHRONIUM
3 *dens-canis* 'Pajares Giant'
2 *grandiflorum chrysandrum*
2 – *pallidum*
2 *mesochoreum*
2 'Miss Jessopp'
3 *montanum*

ESCALLONIA
2 'Bantry Bay'
3 'Donard Gem'
2 'Donard Glory'
2 'Greenway'
0 'Lord Headfort's Seedling'
0 'Red Guard'
0 *rubra macrantha* 'Sanguinea'
3 *viscosa*
0 'William Watson'
0 'Wintonensis'

EUCALYPTUS
2 *alpina*
2 *amygdalina*
2 *bridgesiana*
8 *lehmannii*
8 *maculata*
2 *moorei*
9 *populnea*
8 *preissiana*
1 *radiata*
8 *rodwayi*
9 *rossii*

EUCODONIA
2 *ehrenbergii*
2 *verticillata*

EUCOMIS
2 *autumnalis autumnalis*
3 *bicolor* 'Alba'

EUCRYPHIA
1 x *hillieri*

EUGENIA
3 *uniflora*

EUONYMUS
2 *americanus*
3 *bungeanus semipersistens*
8 x *buxifolius* 'Nanus'
2 *europaeus* 'Brilliant'
0 – 'Chrysophyllus'
1 *fortunei*
2 – 'Carrierei'
0 – 'Dart's Covergirl'
2 – 'Emerald Charm'
9 – *radicans*
1 – 'Sarcoxie'
3 *grandiflorus*
9 *hamiltonianus maackii*
3 *wilsonii*

EUPHORBIA
8 *dendroïdes*
1 x *gayeri* 'Betten'
0 'Goldburst'
1 *marginata*
9 *millotii*
2 *regis-jubae*
1 *tenuissimus*

EUPTELEA
2 *pleiosperma*

EURYA
2 *japonica*

EURYOPS
2 *linearis*

EVOLVULUS
1 *passerinoïdes*

EXOCHORDA
7 *giraldii*
3 x *macrantha* 'Irish Pearl'

FAGUS
0 *moesiaca*
2 *orientalis*
3 *sylvatica* 'Horizontalis'
2 – *latifolia*
3 – 'Miltonensis'
3 – 'Trompenburg'
2 – *variegata*

FALLOPIA
0 *elliptica*

FALLUGIA
9 *paradoxa*

FARGESIA
9 *nitida* 'Chenevieres'

FELICIA
1 *filifolia*

FERULA
1 *purpurea*

FESTUCA
3 *glauca* 'Blausilber'
3 *vivipara glauca*

FICUS
0 *elastica*
3 – 'Belgica'
1 – 'Schrijveriana'(v) AGM
0 *natalensis leprieurii*
0 *religiosa*
3 *rubiginosa* 'Variegata'

FITTONIA
3 *albivenis* Verschaffeltii Group AGM

FOENICULUM
3 *vulgare* black

FORSYTHIA
9 x *intermedia* 'Phyllis'

FORTUNEARIA
1 *sinensis*

FRAGARIA
2 x *ananassa* 'Cantata'
2 – 'Domanil'
2 – 'Gento'
1 – 'Grandee'
1 – 'Hedley'
2 – 'Maxim'
2 – 'Rabunda'
2 – 'Serenata'
1 – 'Sweetheart'
1 – 'Tantallon'
2 – 'Vigour'
2 *vesca* 'Delicious'
8 – 'Reine des Vallées'

FRASERA
2 *speciosa*

FRAXINUS
9 *bungeana*
7 *cuspidata*
2 *dipetala*
9 *excelsior* 'Argenteovariegata'
0 *paxiana*
9 *pennsylvanica subintegerrima*
2 – 'Summit'
7 *quadrangulata*
7 *rotundifolia* 'Flame'
0 'Veltheimii'

FREMONTODENDRON
3 'San Gabriel'

FRITILLARIA
3 *affinis* 'Sunray'
1 – 'Wayne Roderick'
3 *agrestis*
8 *alfredae platyptera*
9 *ariana*
3 *camschatcensis* yellow
0 *caucasica caucasica*
3 *cirrhosa*
1 *eduardii*
2 *forbesii*
1 *gibbosa*
3 *imperialis* 'Blom's Orange Perfection'
8 – 'Sulphurino'
1 *japonica*
9 *meleagris* 'Jupiter'
9 – 'Poseidon'
9 – 'Purple King'
9 – 'Saturnus'
3 *montana*
2 *olgae*
2 *orientalis*
3 *persica* 'Senkoy'
1 *pluriflora*
2 *roylei*
3 *tuntasia*

FUCHSIA
3 'A 1'
0 'Aad Franck'
9 'Aber Falls'
9 'Abt. Koloman Holzinger'
3 'Abundance'
3 'Achilles'
3 'Admiration'
9 'Airball'
2 'Al Stettler'
0 'Aladna's Marina'
1 'Alan's Joy'
0 'Albert H'
0 'Albertina'
1 'Alexandra Dyos'
3 'Alice Topliss'
3 'Allegra'
3 'Alsa Garnett'
1 'Althea Green'

3 'Altmark'
3 'American Flaming Glory'
0 'American Prelude'
9 ***americana elegans***
3 'Andrew Ryle'
9 'Angela'
1 'Ann Margaret'
0 'Ann Pacey'
0 'Anne Howard Tripp'
3 'Anne Smith'
0 'Anniek Geerlings'
3 'Ann's Beauty'
0 'Anthea Bond'
0 'Anthonetta'
1 'Antonella Merrills'
3 'Antonia'
3 'Arabella'
0 'Arc en Ciel'
9 'Architect Ludwig Mercher'
0 'Arels Fleur'
3 'Ark Royal'
3 'Arlendon'
3 'Arthur Cope'
3 'Ashley and Isobel'
2 'Aubrey Harris'
3 'Auntie Maggie'
2 'Avril Lunn'
0 'Axel of Denmark'
2 'Baby Face'
2 'Baby Lilac'
0 'Baby Love'
0 'Baby Veerman'
3 'Balcony Queen'
3 'Ballerina'
1 'Barbara Anne'
1 'Barbara Edwards'
0 'Barry Sheppard'
1 'Beacon Kon'
3 'Beauty Queen'
3 'Bedford's Park'
0 'Belinda Allen'
2 'Bella Madina'
3 'Bella Mia'
3 'Bellbottoms'
3 'Belvoir Elf'
3 'Belvoir Lakes'
1 'Benjamin Pacey'
0 'Berbanella'
1 'Berba's Delight'
0 'Berba's Fleur'
0 'Berba's Francis Fenke'
0 'Berba's Impossible'
0 'Berba's Ingrid'
0 'Berba's Love'
0 'Berba's Trio'
0 'Bernard Rawdin'
2 'Bernisser Stein'
9 'Beryl's Jewel'
0 'Betma Whitison'
2 'Betty Wass'
3 'Beverley Baby'
3 'Biddy Lester'
3 'Bill Kennedy'
3 'Bits'
3 'Black Beauty'
3 'Blaze'
3 'Blue Anchor'
3 'Blue Bonnet'
3 'Blue Boy'
3 'Blue Halo'
0 'Blue Ranger'
3 'Bob Armbruster'
3 'Bonanza'
3 'Bonnie Doan'
3 'Born Free'
9 'Bosun's Superb'
1 'Boy Blue'
3 'Bravo'
9 'Bridal Pink'
3 'British Sterling'
0 'Brunette'
3 'Bubble Hanger'
3 'Buenos Aires'
3 'Cable Car'
3 'Caetar'
3 'Cameron Ryle'
3 'Carefree'
9 'Carmen'
0 'Caroline Imp'
0 'Catherine Claire'
0 'Cecil Glass'
0 'Cees van Braunschott'
9 'Chance Encounter'
2 'Charles Edward'
3 'Charleston'
0 'Chartwell'
0 'Chatsworth'
0 'Checkmate'
1 'Cherry Pie'
3 'Cheviot Princess'
0 'Chris'
0 'Chris van der Linden'
0 'Christine Clements'
2 'Christine Pugh'
3 'Christine Windsor'
3 'Christmas Holly'
3 'Cicely Ann'
0 'Cindy Robijn'
0 'Cinnamon'
0 'Cissbury Gem'
3 'City of Derby'
3 'Cliff's Own'
2 'Cliff's Supreme'
9 'Clipper'
9 'Coconut Ice'
2 'Concord'
2 'Contamine'
3 'Contramine'
3 'Cookie'
3 'Copycat'
1 'Coral Rose'
3 'Corsage'
9 'Country Girl'
3 'Cracker'
3 'Creampuff'
3 'Cropwell Butler'
0 'Crown Derby'
3 'Cyndy Robyn'
3 'Cyril Holmes'
3 'Danish Pastry'
3 'Daphne Arlene'
0 'Dark Spider'
0 'Dark Treasure'
3 'De Bono's Pride'
9 'Deben Petite'
1 'Deborah Louise'
2 'Deborah Young'
2 'Debra Imp'
3 'Dedham Vale'
2 'Dee Star'
3 'Delicia'
3 'Deltaschön'
0 'Delta's Fellow'
2 'Delta's Glorie'
2 'Delta's Rien'
0 'Delta's Robijn'
3 'Delta's Wonder'
0 'Derby Belle'
0 'Derby Countess'
0 'Derby Star'
2 'Diabolo'
9 'Diana Wright'
9 'Diana's Calypso'
1 'Diane Christiansen'
0 'Didi'
0 'Diny Hetterscheid'
3 'Dirk van Delen'
3 'Doctor Manson'
9 'Donauweibchen'
3 'Doreen Stroud'
9 'Dorothy Woakes'
2 'Dove Cottage'
3 'Drama Girl'
2 'Drooping Lady'
1 'Duchess of Cornwall'
9 'Duchess of Petitport'
0 'Dutch Firebird'
0 'Dutch Flamingo'
3 'Dutch Pearl'
3 'Dutch Shoes'
3 'Duyfken'
3 'E J Goulding'
1 'Eden Dawn'
3 'Edith Emery'
3 'Edna'
1 'Edwin Miles'
3 'Eelco Brinkman'
0 'El Matador'
3 'Elanor Grace'
9 'Elisabeth Nutzinger'
2 'Elizabeth Brown'
3 'Elizabeth Burton'
3 'Elsie Johnson'
0 'Elsine'
3 'Elsstar'
2 'Emile Zola'
9 'Enstone'
2 'Erica Memlis'
3 'Eric's Hardy'
9 'Erika Köth'
0 'Eroica'
3 'Eschott Elf'
3 'Esther'
3 'Ethel'
0 'Ethel Weeks'
9 'Ethel Wilson'
0 'Eva Watkins'
2 'Fair Play'
3 'Fancy Flute'
3 'Fancy Sockeye'
0 'Fatima'
3 'Felixstowe Display'
3 'Feltham's Pride'
2 'Fenrother Fairy'
3 'Fire Lady'
3 'Firebird'
0 'Firenzi'
2 'First Kiss'
3 'Fizzy Lizzy'
9 'Flamingo'
9 'Flarepath'
9 'Flim Flam'
0 'Flirt'
3 'Florence Taylor'
3 'Florrie Bambridge'
3 'Fluffy Ruffles'
2 'Fly-by-Night'
3 'Foxtrot'
0 'Francois Villon'
0 'Frank Veerman'
3 'Franz Veernan'
0 'Frauke'
0 'Fred Standen'
9 'Fred's First'
0 'Freestyle'
2 'Frosted Amethyst'
0 'Frosty Bell'
1 'Gabriel Rose'
0 'Garden Beauty'
0 'Gazette'
0 'Geertien'
0 'Geertje'
0 'Général Negrier'
0 'Geoff Barnett'
9 'Georg Bornemann'
2 'George Bunstead'
0 'George Johnson'
2 'George Robinson'
0 'George Roe'
3 'George 'n' Jo'
0 'Gerharda's Kiebeboe'
0 'Gidding'
3 'Gillian Althea'
0 'Gillian Shepherd'
2 'Glendale'
9 'Gleneagles'
1 'Golden Lustre'
0 'Golden Lye's Favourite'
0 'Golden Spade'
0 'Gondolier'
1 'Goose Girl'
0 'Grace'
9 'Grace Groom'
3 'Grady'
1 'Granada'
9 'Grand Duke'
3 'Grange Farm'
3 'Gray Dawn'
9 'Grayrigg'
0 'Guurtje'
9 'H M S Victorious'
3 'Hampshire Leonora'
3 'Hampshire Prince'
3 'Hampshire Treasure'
0 'Harbour Bridge'
9 'Harlequin'
0 'Harriet Lye'
3 'Harvest Glow'
3 'Hay Wain'
1 'Haylettes Gold'
0 'Heather'
2 'Helen McDermott'
0 'Helene Houwen Claessen'
8 'Henriette Ernst'
3 'Heydon'
0 'Hiawatha'
1 'High Peak'
3 'Highland Beauty'
2 'Hilda Fitzsimmons'
3 'Hilda May Salmon'
1 'Hill Top'
0 'HMS Victorious'
9 'Hobson'
3 'Honnepon'
1 'Humpty Dumpty'
3 'Ice Festival'
3 'Improved Hanna'
0 'Ina Buxton'
3 'Indian Princess'

3 'Iolanthe'
0 'Irene van Zoeren'
2 'Irish Wedding'
0 'Ivan Gadsby'
1 'Ivor Moore'
1 'Jack Horner'
0 'Jack King'
1 'Jack Sprat'
9 'James Shurvell'
0 'Jan Bremer'
0 'Jan Houtsma'
2 'Jane Elizabeth'
1 'Janet Williams'
3 'Janie'
3 'Janneke'
2 'Jason Slaney-Welch'
0 'Jaspers Donderslag'
0 'Je Maintiendrai'
9 'Jean Burton'
1 'Jean Ewart'
2 'Jewel'
3 'Jim Dowers'
3 'Joan Barnes'
3 'Joan Gilbert'
0 'Joanne'
0 'Joan's Delight'
0 'Johannes Novinski'
3 'John Baker'
1 'John Waugh'
0 'Joker'
0 'Jolanda Weeda'
2 'Jolly Jorden'
1 'Joseph Holmes'
3 'Jubie-Lin'
3 'Julia Ditrich'
2 'Julie Adams'
0 'Julie Horton'
0 'Karen'
0 'Kathleen'
0 'Kathy Louise'
3 'Kay Louise'
3 'Kegworth Clown'
9 'Kentish Belle'
0 'Kentish Maid'
1 'Kim Hampson'
0 'King George V'
2 'King of Siam'
0 'Klein Beekestein'
9 'Kocarde'
0 'Kolibrie'
9 'Komeet'
2 'Kursal'
2 'La Bergère'
3 'Lady Beth'
0 'Lady Bower'
9 'Lady Dorothy'
0 'Larissa'
3 'Larksfield Skylark'
3 'Lavender Lady'
0 'Lavender Thumb'
3 'Lechlade Debutante'
9 'Lechlade Fairy'
0 'Lechlade Maiden'
3 'Lemacto'
0 'Leo Goetelen'
9 'Liemers Lantaern'
0 'Lila Sunsa'
1 'Lilac Sceptre'
0 'Lilian Windsor'
2 'Lilo Vogt'
3 'Linda Copley'
9 'Linda Pratt'
3 'Lindy'

0 'L'Ingenue'
9 'Little One'
0 'Liver Bird'
3 'Loni Jane'
0 'Lonneke'
0 'Look East'
2 'Lord Leverhulme'
1 'Lorna Doone'
2 'Loulabel'
0 'Love in Bloom'
9 'Love It'
0 'Loverdale'
3 'Lucerowe'
1 'Lucie Harris'
3 'Lucinda'
2 'Lucy Harris'
3 'Lunter's Glorie'
1 'Lunter's Klokje'
3 'Lunter's Roehm'
3 'Lunter's Trots'
3 'Luscious'
9 'Lustre Improved'
1 'Lycioides'
0 'Lye's Elegance'
0 'Lye's Perfection'
0 'Lynhurst'
2 'Mabel Grey'
0 'Madame Danjoux'
0 'Madame Lanteime'
1 'Madame Theobald'
3 'Madame van der Strasse'
0 'Madurodam'
0 ***magdalenae***
1 ***magellanica conica***
9 – 'Ghostly Pink'
8 – ***myrtifolia***
3 'Maggie Little'
3 'Margaret Swales'
0 'Margaret Thatcher'
3 'Margharitte'
9 'Margie'
1 'Marie Julie'
0 'Marja'
3 'Marlies'
1 'Marta Frädrich'
0 'Martha Franck'
0 'Martyn Smedley'
2 'Mary Ellen'
3 'Mary Fairclo'
3 'Mary Kipling'
3 'Maryn'
2 'Matthew Welch'
2 'Maudena'
1 'Mazarine'
2 'Mediterranean'
9 'Medusa'
0 'Melissa Heavens'
0 'Mendocino Rose'
7 'Mephisto'
9 'Mercurius'
0 'Mia van der Zee'
0 'Millie Butler'
3 'Mini Skirt'
3 'Minx'
2 'Miranda Morris'
3 'Miss Leucadia'
1 'Miss Muffett'
0 'Mistique'
2 'Misty Haze'
0 'Mon Ami'
9 'Monsieur Joule'
3 'Monument'

3 'Mordred'
3 'Morning Glow'
0 'Mosedale Hall'
3 'Mounbatten'
9 'Mrs John D Fredericks'
9 'My Love'
0 'Nanne'
9 'Naomi Adams'
0 'Nemerlaer'
2 'New Constellation'
2 'Nicola White'
0 'Nicolina'
0 'Night and Day'
3 'Noblesse'
3 'Norfolk Belle'
3 'Nunthorpe Gem'
0 'Oddfellow'
3 'Oetnang'
3 'Old Rose'
0 'Olympia'
2 'Omar Giant'
1 'Orange Cocktail'
3 'Orange Pip'
3 'Orangy'
3 'Oriental Lace'
3 'Ortenburger Festival'
1 'Pale Beauty'
0 'Pamela Hutchinson'
0 'Panylla Prince'
2 'Paramour'
0 'Patricia Bardgett'
0 'Patricia Ewart'
1 'Paula Baylis'
1 'Pauline Flint'
3 'Pearl Farmer'
9 'Pèredrup'
9 'Petit Point'
1 'Phyllis Stevens'
0 'Piet G Vergeer'
9 'Pink Cornet'
2 'Pink Domino'
1 'Pink Haze'
3 'Pink Ruffles'
9 'Pink Trumpet'
2 'Pink Veil'
3 'Pinto'
0 'Piquant'
0 'Playboy'
1 'Pole Star'
1 'Polly Flinders'
9 'Präsident Walter Morio'
3 'Pretty Belinda'
3 'Pretty Grandpa'
3 'Priest Land'
9 'Prince Syray'
2 'Princess Saranntoe'
0 'Pukkie'
3 'Purple Showers'
9 'Puttenden Manor'
3 'Queen of Hearts'
0 'R L Lockerbie'
0 'Rachel Catherine'
9 'Rading's Michelle'
2 'Raintree Legend'
0 'Rambo'
2 'Ratae Beauty'
9 'Ravensbarrow'
1 'Rebecca Louise'
0 'Recy Holmes'
3 'Red Petticoat'
0 'Red Rain'
0 'Red Rover'
9 'Red Rum'

0 'Reflexa'
3 'Regal Robe'
2 ***regia***
0 'Regina van Zoeren'
0 'Revival'
0 'Rhanee'
3 'Richard Livesy'
2 'Rigoletto'
3 'Rika'
0 'Robert Hall'
0 'Robert Lutters'
3 'Robin'
2 'Robin Pacey'
2 'Rolts'
1 'Ron's Pet'
0 'Rosabell'
0 'Rosedale'
1 'Rosetta'
2 'Roslyn Lowe'
9 'Royal Ruby'
9 'Royal Sovereign'
2 'Royal Splendour'
1 'Ruby Glow'
3 'Ruthie'
3 'Sacramento Bells'
3 'San Pasqual'
1 'Santa Claus'
3 'Sarina'
0 'Saxondale Sue'
3 'Schnabel'
3 'Sensation'
3 'Serendipity'
9 'Severn Queen'
0 'Shady Blue'
3 'Shady Lady'
2 'Shanley'
9 'Sheila Hobson'
2 'Sheila Joy'
0 'Sherwood'
2 'Shining Knight'
0 'Shower of Stars'
0 'Showtime'
3 'Shuna'
3 'Shuna Lindsay'
0 'Shy Look'
2 'Silver Jubilee'
1 'Simple Simon'
0 'Skyway'
0 'Slender Lady'
9 'Snowcap Variegated'
1 'Snowfall'
0 'Snowflake'
2 'Soldier of Fortune'
8 'Spangles'
3 'Sparks'
3 'Spellbound'
3 'Sportsknight'
9 'Spotlight'
2 'Spring Bells'
3 'Square Peg'
3 'St Andrews'
3 'Stathern Surprise'
3 'Stephanie'
9 'Steve Wright'
3 'Stevie Doidge'
1 'Storm'
0 'Storm Petrel'
3 'Sugar Plum'
0 'Summer Mist'
0 'Summer Night'
2 'Summer Snow'
0 'Sundance'
2 'Sunny Jim'

0 'Susan Allen'
3 'Susan Jill'
2 'Susan Young'
0 'Sweet Revenge'
3 'Sweetie Dear'
3 'Swiss Miss'
2 'Tahiti'
3 'Tahoe'
3 'Tam O'Shanter'
3 'Tamar Isobel'
3 'Ted Heath'
9 'Ted's'
8 'Telegraph'
1 'Temple Bells'
0 ***tetradactylla***
2 'The Observer'
3 'The Patriot'
3 'The Phoenix'
3 'The Speedbird'
3 'This England'
3 'Thistle Hill'
0 'Thomos'
0 'Tina Head'
2 'Tolemac'
3 'Tom Hobson'
2 'Tom Silcock'
1 'Tommy Tucker'
0 'Topsin'
2 'Torotino'
3 'Tortorina'
9 'Tourtonne'
0 'Toven'
0 'Traviata'
9 'Tresco'
3 'Trisha'
3 'Trixie Coleman'
2 'Troutbeck'
0 'Trubell'
3 'Twiggy'
3 'U F O'
0 'Ultralight'
1 'Uncle Jinks'
3 'Unique'
1 'Valamay'
0 'Vale of Belvoir'
3 'Valerie'
0 'Valerie Cotterell'
2 'Vera Stuart'
3 'Vespa'
1 'Vi Whitehouse'
3 'Victoria Louise'
3 'Victorian'
1 'Violet Lace'
2 'Violet Mist'
1 'Vivien Harris'
3 'Vulcan'
0 'W F C Kampionen'
0 'Waltraud Strumper'
0 'Walz Blaukous'
0 'Walz Bugel'
0 'Walz Doedelzak'
0 'Walz Gitaar'
0 'Walz Gong'
0 'Walz Hobo'
0 'Walz Kalebas'
0 'Walz Kattesnoor'
0 'Walz Knipperbol'
0 'Walz Meermin'
0 'Walz Piano'
0 'Walz Ratel'
0 'Walz Tam Tam'
0 'Walz Toeter'
0 'Walz Viool'
0 'Wassernymph'
9 'Waveney Unique'
3 'Waxen Beauty'
0 'Wee Lass'
2 'Wee One'
2 'Wendy Blythe'
0 'Wentelwieck'
2 'Westergeest'
0 'Whistling Rufus'
3 'White Bride'
8 'White Clove'
3 'White Fairy'
8 'White Gem'
1 'White Haven'
3 'White Loeky'
3 'White Marshmallow'
1 'White Swan'
3 'White Water'
3 'Whitehaven'
0 'Whiteknights Glister'
8 'Wicked Lady'
9 'Wild Glove'
0 'Wilf Tolley'
3 'Willie Lott'
1 'Willy Winky'
0 'Wilma Versloot'
3 'Wilson's Joy'
3 'Wingfield Sheppard'
9 'Winifred'
0 'Wise Choice'
3 'Woodside Gem'
0 'Yankee Clipper'
1 'Yolanda Franck'
0 'Zaanlander'

GAHNIA

0 ***grandis***

GAILLARDIA

9 'Aurea'
9 'Chloe'
9 'Croftway Yellow'
9 'Fackelschein' ('Torchlight')
1 'Golden Queen'
2 x ***grandiflora*** 'Nana Nieske'
8 'Ipswich Beauty'
3 'Kahome'
1 'Tokajer'

GALANTHUS

2 ***caucasicus*** late form
3 ***elwesii*** from Alanya Yayla
0 – 'Whitallii'
3 green-tipped Greatorex
2 'Lavinia' (d)
9 'Maidwell C'
2 'Melvillei'
3 'Mrs Backhouse Number Twelve'
3 'Mrs Backhouse's Spectacles'
2 ***plicatus*** 'Beth Chatto'
3 – 'Silverwells'

GALEGA

1 'Her Majesty'

GALIUM

2 ***firmum***

GALPHIMIA

3 ***glauca***

GALTONIA

9 ***princeps praecox***

GARDENIA

0 ***augusta*** 'Belmont'
3 ***spatulifolia***

GARRYA

3 x ***issaquahensis***
0 ***laurifolia macrophylla***
2 x ***thuretii***

GAULTHERIA

9 ***cordifolia***
2 ***coriacea***
2 ***cumingiana***
2 ***depressa novae-zelandiae***
9 ***erecta***
3 ***eriophylla***
2 ***mucronata angustifolia***
3 – Davis's hybrids
9 – 'Goldsworth Pink'
9 – 'Goldsworth Red'
3 ***parvula*** 'Ohau'
3 – 'Rough Creek'
0 ***procumbens*** 'Darthuizer'
2 ***semi-infera***
3 sp. Gillanders 110
3 ***tetramera***
3 ***trichophylla*** red
0 ***wardii***

GAZANIA

3 'Garden Sun'
3 'New Magic'
8 ***rigens*** 'Torquay Silver'
3 'Silverbrite'
1 'Vinner's Variegated'

GENISTA

8 ***berberidea***
0 ***falcata***
3 ***florida***
3 ***horrida***
3 ***januensis***
9 ***maderensis magnifoliosa***
3 ***radiata***
2 ***sericea***
2 ***tinctoria*** 'Golden Plate'

GENTIANA

2 ***acaulis*** 'A G Week's Form'
9 – 'Leith Vale'
8 – 'Nora Bradshaw'
0 ***algida igarishii***
9 ***alpina*** Trotter's form
2 ***altaica***
2 ***angustifolia*** from Priin Mountains
2 – from Scoulor Pass
8 'Bucksburn Azure'
9 ***burseri***
3 x ***caroli*** 'Coronation'
2 ***clusii alba***
3 – ***clusii***
2 – ***corbariensis***
8 – 'Mount Rax'
8 ***cruciata phlogifolia***
2 ***dinarica*** 'Harlin'
2 ***divisa***
2 'Drumcairn White'
8 'Elizabeth Brand'
1 ***frigida***
0 'Inverdevon'
9 'Mount Everest'
9 ***occidentalis***
1 ***olivieri***
3 ***ornata***
2 ***prolata*** Beer form
2 – McBeath form
9 ***pyrenaica***
7 'Queen of the Blues'
0 ***sceptrum***
1 ***straminea***
7 'The Souter'
0 ***tianschanica***
3 ***triptosperma japonica***
1 'Tweeddale Strain'
9 'Utterby Seedling'
1 ***verna tergestina***
3 – x ***pumila***
1 ***villosa***
1 'Wendy Jean'
9 ***wilsonii***

GENTIANOPSIS

0 ***crinita***

GEOGENANTHUS

0 ***undatus***

GERANIUM

2 ***caeruleatum***
8 x ***cantabrigiense*** 'Ingwersen'
3 ***dalmaticum*** Coombeland form
9 ***divaricatum***
1 ***drakensbergense***
9 ***himalayense*** 'Frances Perry'
1 x ***lindavicum***
0 – 'Lissadel'
2 ***lingreum***
9 ***mascatense***
1 'Maxwelton'
1 ***peloponnesiacum***
3 ***phaeum phaeum***
9 ***sanguineum*** 'Hadspen'
3 'Southcombe Beauty'
3 ***wallichianum*** pink

GEUM

1 ***calthifolium***
2 – ***nipponicum***
1 ***elatum***
1 ***japonicum***
3 ***rivale*** apricot
9 – cream
1 ***rossii***
7 ***triflorum campanulatum***

GIBASIS

9 ***linearis***

GLADIOLUS

7 'Ali Baba' (B)
2 'Andorra' (B)
2 'Anglia' (B)
9 'Blue Conqueror' (L)
3 'Blushing Bride' (N)
2 'Campanella' (B)
2 'Carmen' (L)
9 'Chanson'
9 'City Lights'
2 'Confetti' (B)

2 'Deciso' (L)
3 'Desirée' (B)
2 Dream Party ® (L)
1 'Dutch Parade' (L)
2 'Erin' (Min)
2 'Greenland' (L)
1 'Gypsy Baron' (G)
3 'Herman van der Mark'
9 ***imbricatus***
2 'Introspection' (L)
9 'Invitation'
3 'Joyeuse Entrée'
2 'Little Darling' (P)
2 ***longicollis***
2 'Lorena' (B)
1 Love Letter ® (M)
9 'Lovely Day' (G)
2 'Madonna' (L)
2 'Madrilene' (B)
3 Maestro ® (L)
3 'Mandy'
9 'Merry'
2 'Misty Eye' (L)
2 'Pandion' (G)
3 'Peach Blossom' (N)
2 'Piccolo' (B)
2 'Pink Lady' (L)
9 'Pink Pearl' (S)
1 Pink Perfection ® (L)
9 'Plum Tart' (L)
9 'Prince Carnival' (L)
3 Promise ® (M)
9 'Prosperity'
2 'Queen of Night' (L)
2 'Royal Beauty' (G)
2 'Royal Violet' (G)
2 Sancerre ® (B)
9 'Scout'
2 'Shamrock' (L)
9 'Shell Pink'
9 'Shocking Pink'
3 'Spitfire' (N)
9 'Spring Gem'
2 'Storiette' (B)
2 Sundance ®
3 'Tangerine' (P)
2 'Treasure' (P)
3 Up to Date ®
3 'Vidi Napoli'
2 'Yellow Special' (P)

GLEDITSIA
3 ***japonica***
9 ***sinensis***
2 ***triacanthos*** 'Bujotii'
2 – 'Shademaster'

GLOBULARIA
2 ***aphyllanthes***

GLOXINIA
3 'Tessa'

GLYCERIA
3 ***fluitans***
3 ***notata***

GLYCYRRHIZA
3 ***missouriensis***

GMELINA
3 ***arborea***

GNAPHALIUM
0 ***andicolum***
3 ***mackayi***

GOODENIA
9 ***lunata***
2 ***repens***

GOSSYPIUM
1 ***sturtianum***

GRAPTOPETALUM
1 ***paraguayense bernalense***

GRATIOLA
2 ***nana***

GREVILLEA
9 ***aspleniifolia*** 'Robin Hood'
9 – 'Robyn Gordon'
1 ***banksii forsteri***
1 ***bipinnatifida***
7 'Claret'
1 ***fasciculata***
7 ***jephcottii***
1 ***juniperina*** prostrate yellow
8 ***lanigera***
1 ***pilulifera***
2 'Red Cloud'

GRINDELIA
3 ***integrifolia***
3 ***lanceolata***
3 ***oregana***

GRISELINIA
2 ***littoralis*** 'Gold Edge'(v)
3 – 'Milkmaid'
9 ***lucida*** 'Variegata'

GUICHENOTIA
2 ***ledifolia***
2 ***macrantha***

GUZMANIA
2 'Atilla'
2 Carine
2 'Claudine'
2 ***conifera***
2 ***donnellsmithii***
2 Gisela
2 'Golden King'
2 ***lingulata cardinalis***
2 – ***minor*** 'Red'
2 – – 'Vella'
2 Muriel
2 ***musaica*** **AGM**
2 'Nellie'
2 Rana
2 'Remembrance'
2 'Ruby'
2 ***scherzeriana***
2 ***wittmackii***

GYMNOCARPIUM
3 ***jessoense***

GYPSOPHILA
3 ***libanotica***
3 'Pacific Rose'
2 ***repens*** 'Monstrosa'

HAASTIA
7 ***sinclairii***

HAEMANTHUS
0 ***carneus***

HAKEA
0 ***epiglottis***
2 ***francisiana***
8 ***macraeana***
8 ***nitida***
8 ***platysperma***
1 ***stenocarpa***
3 ***teretifolia***
8 ***victoriae***

HALESIA
1 ***parviflora***

HAMAMELIS
3 x ***intermedia*** 'Nina'
3 – 'Perfume'
2 ***vernalis***

HAPLOPAPPUS
9 ***clementis***
1 ***hirsutus***

HAWORTHIA
3 ***reinwardtii***

HEBE
2 x ***andersonii***
3 'Anne Pimm' (v)
1 ***armstrongii*** x ***selaginoïdes***
8 'Barnettii'
2 'Boscawenii'
7 'Brian Kessell'
0 ***buchananii*** 'Major'
7 'Cilsouth'
1 'Croftway Emberglow'
2 ***cupressoïdes*** 'Glauca'
3 – 'Neil's Choice'
9 ***diosmifolia*** 'Variegated'
8 'Ettrick Shepherd'
8 'Gillanders'
9 ***giselli***
8 'Greenway Purple'
7 'Harlequin'
8 'Lycing'
2 'Marlene'
3 'Mauvena'
3 'Moppets Hardy'
7 'Obora Gold'
3 ***parviflora*** 'Christine Eggins'
2 –
7 ***plano-petiolaris***
1 ***propinqua*** 'major'
2 ***rupicola***
7 'Southcombe Pink'
0 ***subsimilis***
8 ***tetragona*** 'Southcombe Dwarf'
8 ***treadwellii***
7 'Wakehurst'
0 'Wendy'
7 'Widecombe'

HEBENSTRETIA
3 ***dentata***

HECTORELLA
8 ***caespitosa***

HEDEOMA
3 ***pulegioïdes***

HEDERA
3 ***azorica*** 'Variegata'
0 ***colchica*** 'Dendroides'
3 ***helix caucasigena*** 'Telavi'
0 – ***helix*** 'Arrowhead'
3 – – 'Blarney'
3 – – 'Bulgaria'
0 – – 'Cavendishii Latina'
3 – – 'Christian'
3 – – 'Compacta'
3 – – 'Corrugata'
3 – – 'Dark Knight'
3 – – 'Digitata-Hesse'
3 – – 'Dorado'(v)
3 – – 'Emerald Jewel'
3 – – 'Erin'
3 – – 'F C Coates'
3 – – 'Feenfinger'
2 – – 'Finger Point'
3 – – 'Galaxy'
3 – – 'Geranium'
3 – – 'Glacier Improved'(v)
3 – – 'Gladiator'(v)
3 – – 'Gold Dust'
3 – – 'Golden Arrow'
3 – – 'Golden Emblem'
3 – – 'Golden Envoy'
3 – – 'Golden Fleece'
3 – – 'Goldtobler'(v)
3 – – 'Goldwolke'(v)
3 – – 'Good's'
3 – – 'Green Heart'
3 – – 'Green Survival'
3 – – 'Guinevere'
3 – – 'Hahn Variegated'
3 – – 'Hebron'
3 – – 'Holly'
3 – – 'Ideal'
3 – – 'Imp'
3 – – 'Irish Lace'
3 – – 'Itsy Bitsy'
3 – – 'Jersey Doris'(v)
3 – – 'Knobby Eight'
3 – – 'Kobold'
3 – – 'Konsforth'
3 – – 'Laubfrosch'
3 – – 'Lee's Silver'(v)
3 – – 'Lise'(v)
1 – – 'Little Eve'
3 – – 'Lucida Aurea'
3 – – 'Manda's Star'
3 – – 'Milford'
2 – – 'Minature Needlepoint'
3 – – 'Minigreen'
3 – – 'Modern Times'
3 – – 'Mount Vernon'
3 – – 'Nebulosa'
3 – – 'Obscura'
3 – – 'Old English'
3 – – 'Old Lace'
3 – – 'Peppermint'
3 – – 'Perfection'
3 – – 'Permanent Wave'
3 – – 'Plattensee'
3 – – 'Plimpton'
3 – – 'Rochester'
3 – – 'Rubaiyat'
3 – – 'Rumania'
3 – – 'Schafer Four'(v)
0 – – 'Schimmer'
3 – – 'Silver Emblem'(v)
3 – – 'Silver Kolibri'(v)
0 – – 'Sinclair Silverleaf'

3 – – 'Star'
3 – – 'Star Dust'(v)
3 – – 'Sterntaler'
3 – – 'Stiftpark'
3 – – 'Student Prince'(v)
0 – – 'Teena'
3 – – 'Thorndale'
3 – – 'Tomboy'
3 – – 'Transit Road'
3 – – 'Tribairn'
3 – – 'Triloba'
2 – – 'Victoria'
3 – – 'Welsomii'
3 – – 'Wilson'
3 – – 'Wingertsberg'
3 – – 'Yalta'

HEDYSARUM
0 ***hedysaroïdes exaltatum***

HELENIUM
3 'Blütentisch'
3 'Bressingham Gold'
1 'Gartensonne'
3 'Helena'
3 'July Sun'
3 'Königstiger'
3 'Mahogany'
2 'Rubinkuppel'
2 'Septemberfuchs'
8 'Tawny Dwarf'

HELIANTHEMUM
3 'Brilliant'
7 'Cherry Pink'
0 'Cupreum
3 'Etna'
3 'Firefly'
0 'Harlequin'
8 'Low Yellow'
0 'Loxbeare Gold'
8 ***nummularium grandiflorum***
0 – ***obscurum***
3 ***oblongatum***
3 'Orange Surprise'
8 'Peach'
3 'Pink Beauty'
8 'Prima Donna'
8 Trenear's hybrids
8 'Wisley Yellow'

HELIANTHUS
0 ***angustifolius***

HELICHRYSUM
3 ***amorginum***
1 – 'Pink Bud'
1 – 'White Bud'
1 – 'Yellow Bud'
9 ***bellidioïdes gracile***
7 – large form
3 ***chionophyllum***
9 ***cooperi***
7 'Darwin Gold'
9 ***dealbatum***
1 ***diosmifolium***
8 ***frigidum*** 'Miffy Beauty'
8 ***purpurascens***
9 ***retortum***
0 ***selaginoïdes***
3 'Silver Princess'
3 'Silver Streams'

HELIOPHILA
3 ***longifolia***

HELIOPSIS
8 ***helianthoïdes*** 'Mid West Dream'
3 – ***scabra*** 'Desert King
3 – – 'Goldgefieder' ('Golden Plume') AGM
3 – – 'Incomparabilis'
1 – – 'Patula'
9 – – 'Sunburst'
2 – 'Sonnenschild'
2 – 'Spitzentänzerin'
1 – 'The Monarch'

HELIOTROPIUM
3 ***europaeum***
0 x ***hybridum***

HELIPTERUM
9 ***albicans***
1 ***roseum***

HELLEBORUS
2 ***argutifolius*** large flowered
9 ***foetidus*** compact form
1 ***orientalis antiquorum***
2 – 'Apple Blossom'
0 – 'Blowsy'
1 – 'Blue Showers'
0 – 'Blue Spray'
7 – 'Blue Wisp'
1 – 'Button'
3 – 'Christmas Lantern'
1 – 'Citron'
9 – 'Cosmos'
2 – 'Darley Mill'
1 – 'Dawn'
9 – 'Dick Crandon'
7 – 'Dotty'
0 – 'Dusk'
9 – 'Ernest Raithby'
2 – 'Freckleface'
9 – 'Garnet'
3 – 'Greencups'
1 – 'Hazel Key'
1 – 'Helen Ballard'
9 – 'John Cross'
0 – 'Laura'
9 – 'Lynne'
8 – 'Mercury'
1 – 'Mystery'
1 – 'Nancy Ballard'
9 – 'Nocturne'
9 – 'Parrot'
0 – 'Patchwork'
9 – 'Peggy Ballard'
1 – 'Rembrandt'
1 – 'Richard Key'
9 – 'Rosa'
9 – 'Rossini'
0 – 'Rubens'
1 – 'Sarah Ballard'
1 – 'Saturn'
3 – 'Sunny'
0 – 'Sylvia'
1 – 'Tom Wilson'
2 – 'Tommie'
0 – 'Upstart'
3 – 'Ushba'
2 – 'Vulcan'
9 – 'Yellow Button'
0 ***torquatus*** ex Nero
1 – 'Pluto'

HEMEROCALLIS
8 'A la Mode'
8 'After Glow'
2 'Amazon Amethyst'
8 'Angel Face'
2 'Ann Kelley'
7 'Apollo'
8 'Applause'
1 'Apple Court Damson'
1 'Apple Tart'
9 'Ariadne'
2 'Arkansas Post'
9 'Atlas'
9 'Atomic Age'
8 'August Pink'
3 ***aurantiaca***
1 'Ava Michelle'
2 'Avanti'
2 'Azor'
1 'Bald Eagle'
0 'Bees Rose'
8 'Belinda'
8 'Bellringer'
1 'Bitsy'
3 'Black Falcon'
2 'Blaze of Fire'
8 'Bold Ruler'
8 'Bonnie Rose'
8 'Bourbon Prince'
8 'Bright Charm'
8 'Brilliant Red'
9 'Broad Ripples'
1 'Buffy's Doll'
8 'Buried Treasure'
1 'By Myself'
2 'Cadence'
9 'Candle Glow'
8 'Candy Fluff'
8 'Capri'
8 'Carriage Trade'
7 'Chantilly Lace'
8 'Charlotte Holman'
3 'Cherry Smoke'
1 'Chestnut Lane'
8 'Chetco'
1 'Chicago Cameo'
1 'Chicago Sugar Plum'
8 'Childscraft'
9 'Christmas Isle'
9 'Claret Cup'
8 'Coquinna'
2 'Corsican Bandit'
3 'Cosmic Flash'
2 'Cosmic Hummingbird'
2 'Crimson Icon'
7 'Cuddlesome'
1 'Curls'
8 'Dauntless'
8 'Dawn Supreme'
9 'Delft Rose'
2 'Delicate Splendor'
8 'Demure'
0 'Deva'
1 'Double Coffee'
0 'Double Firecracker'
2 'Double Grapette'
1 'Dutch Beauty'
8 'Dynamo'
2 'Edelweiss'
8 'Eden'
9 'Esther Murray'
1 'Fairy Delight'
8 'Far Afield'
2 'Far East'
8 'Finlandia'
8 'First Romance'
7 'Flair'
3 'Flaming Sword'
8 'Fond Caress'
8 'Fortyniner'
9 'Fox Grape'
8 'Gay Music'
8 'Georgia Peach'
2 'Gold Dust'
9 'Golden Dewdrop'
9 'Golden Glory'
8 'Goldensong'
3 'Graceful Eye'
8 'Grecian Gift'
2 'Green Puff'
1 'Hemlock'
8 'High Glory'
8 'Hippity Hop'
1 'Holiday Harvest'
3 'Home Run'
0 'How About That'
8 'Illinois'
2 'Indian Serenade'
8 'Inlaid Gold'
8 'Irene Felix'
8 'Jack Frost'
9 'Jake Russell'
8 'Janet'
8 'Joan Durelle'
8 'July Gold'
8 'June Royalty'
1 'Kathleen Ormerod'
0 'Kathleen Woodbury'
2 'Kecia'
2 'Kinfolk'
9 'King Haiglar'
3 'Lady Limelight'
3 'Ladykin'
1 'Late Advancement'
8 'Late Date'
8 'Laurel Anne'
8 'Lester Pastel'
7 'Lilac Chiffon'
7 'Lilly Dache'
3 'Little Greenie'
2 'Littlest Angel'
3 'Lively Set'
3 'Magic Dawn'
9 'Mantra'
1 'Marcus Perry'
0 'Margaret Perry'
8 'Mary Anne'
9 'Mascot'
8 'Melotone'
1 'Michele Coe'
3 ***middendorffii esculenta***
8 'Momento'
1 'Mormon Spider'
9 'Mrs B F Bonner'
9 'Multinomah'
8 'Nehoiden'
3 'New Swirls'
1 'Night Hawk'
2 'North Star'
8 'Northfield'
7 'Old Vintage'
1 'Ophir'
1 'Oriontio'
3 'Patricia Fay'
2 'Peach Supreme'
8 'Pecheron'

7 'Pink Perfection'
8 'Polar Bear'
8 'Powder Puff'
3 'Prairie Sunset'
9 'Precious'
3 'Precious Treasure'
0 'President'
0 'Purple Water'
7 'Radiant'
1 'Raspberry Pixie'
3 'Right On'
9 'Rose Motif'
8 'Rosetta'
8 'Roseway'
0 'Royal Robe'
8 'Satin Glass'
7 'Sawanne Belle'
7 'Sea Gypsy'
8 'Shell Cameo'
8 'Sherwood'
3 'Siloam Pocket Size'
8 'Sleeping Beauty'
8 'Snappy Rhythm'
1 'Soft Whisper'
2 'Soledad'
9 'Star Ruby'
2 'Stoke Poges' AGM
2 'Stolen Hours'
3 'Sun Pixie'
3 'Sure Thing'
8 'Sweetheart Supreme'
9 'Taj Mahal'
8 'Temple Bells'
3 'Thelma Perry'
8 'Theresa Hall'
1 'Tinker Bell'
7 'Tiny Tex'
8 'Torpoint'
3 'Turkish Turban'
3 'Walt Disney'
8 'War Clouds'
8 'Whirl of Lace'
8 'Yellow Beacon'
2 'Zampa'

HEMIPHRAGMA
9 ***heterophyllum***

HEPATICA
3 ***nobilis*** 'Little Abington'
3 – red
1 – 'Tabby'
2 ***transsilvanica*** 'Ada Scott'

HERACLEUM
3 ***antasiaticum***

HERPOLIRION
3 ***novae-zealandiae***

HESPERIS
0 ***matronalis*** double pink

HEUCHERA
3 'Baby's Breath'
3 'Charles Bloom'
7 'Damask'
8 'Edge Hill'
7 'Freedom'
9 ***glabra***
1 'Gloriana'
3 'Ibis'
7 'Lady Romney'
8 'Pruhoniciana'
3 'Rosemary Bloom'
1 ***sanguinea*** dwarf form
0 – 'Superba'
8 – 'Variegata'
1 'Shere Variety'

HIBISCUS
1 ***diversifolius***
3 ***militaris***
8 ***moscheutos palustris***
3 ***purpureus*** 'Variegatus'
0 ***rosa-sinensis*** 'Colombo'
0 – 'Nairobi'
0 – 'Paramaibo'
0 – rose
9 ***sabdariffa***
9 ***syriacus*** 'Caeruleus Plenus'
2 – 'Hinomaru'(d)
0 – 'Violet Clair'

HIERACIUM
3 ***candidum***
1 ***mixtum***
8 x ***rubrum***

HIPPEASTRUM
1 'Amadeus'
1 'Bright Red'
1 'Cantate'
1 'Christmas Gift'
1 'Dark Red'
1 'Minerva'
1 'Orange Souvereign' AGM
1 'Orange Star'
1 'Salmon Beauty'
1 'Star of Holland' AGM
1 'Valentine'
1 'Wonderful'

HOHERIA
2 ***populnea*** 'Alba Variegata'
7 – ***sinclairii***

HOLODISCUS
3 ***dumosus***

HOMALOCLADIUM
3 ***platycladum***

HOSTA
2 'Anne Arett' (v)
1 'Baby Blue' (Tardiana)
1 'Besançon' (***ventricosa***)
3 'Big John' (***sieboldiana***)
1 'Blue Fan Dancer'
1 'Blue Piecrust'
1 'Claudia'
2 'Dark Victory'
1 'Eric Smith Gold'
1 'Fond Hope' (***sieboldiana***)
3 ***fortunei albopicta viridis***
1 'Freising'
2 'Gold Streak' (***tardiflora***)
1 'Green Formal'
2 'Green Ripples'
1 'Grenfell's Greatest' (***sieboldiana***)
1 'Hadspen Dolphin' (Tardiana)
2 'Hadspen Nymphaea'
3 'Harvest Moon'
2 'Helen Field Fischer' (***fortunei***)
1 'June Beauty' (***sieboldiana***)
2 'Leviathan'
1 'Little Fatty'
3 'Maple Leaf'
2 ***minor alba***
1 'Neat Splash' (v)
3 'On Stage' (***montana***)(v)
8 'Pixie Power'
2 'Primrose' (***kikutii***)
2 ***rohdeifolia aureomarginata***
1 'Royal Lady' (***sieboldii***)
1 'Royal Tiara' (***nakaiana***)(v)
2 'Sea Sprite' (v)
1 'Sentinels'
1 ***sieboldiana mira***
2 ***sieboldii spathulata***
2 – ***subcrocea***
1 'Sprengeri'
1 'Susy'
2 ***tardiva***
9 ***tsushimensis***
2 'Variegata' (***longissima***)
1 'Verte' (***sieboldii***)
1 'Viette's Yellow Edge' (***fortunei***)(v)
1 'Willy Nilly'
2 'Yakushima-mizu' (***gracillima***)
2 'Zager White Edge' (v)

HOUSTONIA
7 ***serpyllifolia***

HOYA
3 ***carnosa*** 'Nana'

HUGUENINIA
9 ***tanacetifolia***

HUMULUS
1 ***lupulus*** variegated

HYACINTHELLA
0 ***leucophaea***

HYACINTHOÏDES
3 ***hispanica*** 'Azalea'
3 – 'Mount Everest'
3 – 'Myosotis'
0 – 'Rose'
2 ***italica vicentina***
3 ***non-scripta*** pink bell
3 – white bell

HYACINTHUS
3 ***orientalis*** 'Apollo'
1 – 'Blue Ice'
3 – 'Blushing Dolly'
3 – 'Cherry Blossom'
9 – 'Cote d'Azur'
3 – 'Debutante'
9 – 'Eros'
3 – 'Fireball'
1 – 'General Köhler'(d)
3 – 'Grace Darling'
3 – 'Indian Prince'
2 – 'Madame Sophie'(d)
3 – 'Maryon'
3 – 'Morning Star'
3 – 'Orange Queen'
3 – 'Paul Hermann'
3 – 'Princess Victoria'
3 – 'Sky Jacket'
2 – 'Tubergen's Scarlet'
9 – 'Yellow Hammer'

HYDRANGEA
9 ***arborescens discolor***
0 – ***radiata*** 'Robusta'
3 ***aspera*** 'Rocklon'
9 – 'Rosthornii'
2 ***heteromalla*** 'Morrey's Form'
2 – ***wilsonii***
2 'Impératrice Eugénie'
9 ***longipes***
1 ***macrophylla*** 'Adria'
3 – 'Aduarda'
3 – 'Amethyst'(H/ d)
9 – 'Draps Pink'(H)
9 – 'Fargesii'
1 – 'Fischers Silberblou'(H)
3 – 'Joseph Banks'(H)
3 – 'Mariesii Variegata'(L)
8 – 'Max Löbner'
8 – 'Mousseline'(H)
8 – 'Oamacha'
0 – 'Queen Elizabeth'
1 – 'Red Emperor'(H)
3 – 'Rheinland'(H)
3 – 'Rotdressel'
3 – 'Rotsawana'
7 – 'Ursula'
7 – 'Val de Loire'
9 – 'Yodogawa'
1 ***paniculata*** 'Everest'
1 – 'Greenspire'
3 ***quercifolia*** 'Harmony'
2 – 'Sike's Dwarf'
0 – sterile
2 – 'Tennessee Clone'
3 ***serrata*** 'Amagyana'
2 – ***koreana***
2 'Thomas Hogg'

HYDROCLEYS
1 ***nymphoïdes***

HYMENOCALLIS
3 x ***festalis*** 'Zwanenburg'

HYPERICUM
3 ***acmosepalum***
3 ***armenum***
3 ***calycinum aureum***
8 ***canariense***
2 ***cerastioïdes meuselianum***
3 ***delphicum***
2 'Eastleigh Gold'
3 ***ericoïdes***
8 ***hircinum albimontanum***
3 ***hyssopifolium***
9 x ***inodorum*** 'Hysan'
9 – 'Summer's End'
1 ***nanum***
0 ***oblongifolium***
9 ***pallens***
1 ***patulum***
8 ***pulchrum procumbens***
3 ***reptans***
9 'Summer Sunshine'
9 ***xylosteifolium***

HYPOLEPIS
2 ***rugulosa***
HYPOXIS
2 ***hirsuta***
HYPSELA
9 ***rivalis***
HYSSOPUS
0 ***officinalis officinalis***
IBERIS
0 ***sempervirens*** 'Correifolia'
7 – 'Garrexiana'
8 – 'Gracilis'
3 – pink
3 – 'Variegata'
7 – 'Zwergschneefloke' ('Snowdrift')
ILEX
7 x ***altaclerensis*** 'Balearica'
1 – 'Howick'(f)
9 – 'Maderensis'
1 – 'Moria'(f/ v)
2 – 'Mundyi'(m)
2 – 'Purple Shaft'(f)
1 – 'W J Bean'(f)
1 ***aquifolium*** 'Angustimarginata Aurea'(m)
1 – 'Apricot'(f)
1 – 'Cookii'(f)
3 – 'Donningtonensis'(m)
1 – 'Grandis'
1 – 'Green Sentinel'(f)
3 – 'Harpune'(f)
1 – 'Heterophylla Aurea Marginata'(m)
3 – 'Monstrosa'(m)
7 – 'Ovata'(m)
3 – 'Scotica'(f)
1 – 'Weeping Golden Milkmaid'(f/ v)
3 x ***attenuata*** x ***opaca***
2 ***buergeri***
3 ***cassine angustifolia (f)***
0 ***chinensis***
0 ***corallina***
3 ***crenata*** 'Congesta'
3 – 'David Ellis'
8 – 'Dwarf Pagoda'(f)
1 – 'Firefly'(m)
3 – 'Green Lustre'(f)
3 – 'Ivory Tower'(f)
1 – ***paludosa***
3 – 'Piccolo'(f)
3 – ***watanabeana (f)***
2 ***dipyrena***
3 ***fargesii***
3 ***georgei***
3 ***glabra***
1 – ***leucocarpa***
1 – 'Nana'
1 ***integra***
0 – ***leucoclada***
2 x ***meserveae***
1 – 'Blue Stallion'(m)
1 ***opaca*** 'Natalie Webster'(f)
3 – 'Villanova'(f)
2 ***pernyi*** 'Jermyns Dwarf'(f)
3 'Shin Nien' (m)
2 ***vomitoria***
ILLICIUM
3 ***anisatum laurifolium***
IMPATIENS
2 'Ballerina'
3 ***capensis***
2 'Cardinal Red'
3 ***congolensis***
3 'Dan White'
3 'Danbee'
3 'Dandin'
3 'Danova'
3 'Danrose'
3 'Danshir'
3 'Dansky'
2 'Evening Blush'
9 ***glandulifera*** white
3 'Lambada'
2 'Salmon Princess'
3 'Samba'
2 ***scabrida***
2 'Strawberry Ripple'
INCARVILLEA
3 ***emodi***
INDIGOFERA
2 ***australis***
9 ***decora alba***
INULA
2 ***candida***
9 ***obtusifolia***
2 ***rhizocephala rhizocephaloïdes***
3 ***viscosa***
IOCHROMA
3 ***coccinea***
1 ***coelestis***
1 ***purpurea***
IPHEION
1 ***sellowianum***
IPOMOEA
0 ***coccinea***
3 ***lobata***
IPOMOPSIS
2 ***aggregata***
2 – ***macrosiphon***
IRESINE
3 ***herbstii*** 'Aureoreticulata'
IRIS
9 'Ablaze' (DB)
1 ***acutiloba lineolata***
9 'Airy Fancy' (Spuria)
1 ***albomarginata***
9 'Already' (MDB)
3 'Alsterquelle' (SDB)
7 'Amber' (TB)
3 'Amigo' (TB)
3 'Angel Eyes' (MDB)
3 'April Sweetheart' (SDB)
2 'Astralite' (SDB)
3 'Auburn Valley' (SDB)
3 'Aunt Martha' (BB)
0 'Autumn Primrose' (TB)
1 ***babadagica***
1 'Ballerina'
2 'Barnett Anley'
9 ***barnumae urmiensis***
9 'Belief' (Spuria)
9 'Bellboy' (MTB)
0 'Belvi Queen' (TB)
8 'Benton Yellow' (TB)
8 'Bibelot' (BB)
1 'Black Forest' (TB)
3 'Black Ink' (TB)
2 'Black Magic' (***sibirica***)
2 'Black Onyx' (TB)
3 'Black Star' (SDB)
3 'Blockley' (SDB)
3 'Blood Dance' (SDB)
3 'Blue Admiral' (TB)
0 'Blue Beret' (MDB)
1 'Blue Brilliant' (***sibirica***)
2 'Blue Frost' (DB)
2 'Blue Petticoat' (TB)
8 'Blue Valley' (TB)
3 'Born Graceful'
1 'Bright Spring' (DB)
8 'Britomas' (TB)
3 'Brown Chocolate'
3 'Buckeye Blue' (SDB)
8 'Buster Brown' (DB)
0 'Butter Cookie' (IB)
3 'Buttertubs' (TB)
9 'Calypso Clown' (AB)
1 'Camberley' (***sibirica***)
3 'Cambridge Blue' (Spuria)
2 'Candy Apple' (SDB)
8 'Candy Cane' (BB)
2 'Cape Town' (TB)
2 'Cappucino' (CH)
3 'Captain Gallant' (TB)
0 'Catani' (SDB)
0 'Chain White' (SDB)
3 'Chickee' (MTB)
1 'Chione' (Aril)
3 'Chippendale' (TB)
1 'Christmas Rubies' (TB)
3 ***chrysographes*** 'Rob'
3 – 'Rubens'
1 – yellow
3 'Chubby Cheeks' (SDB)
1 'Chubby Cherub' (MDB)
9 'Cinnamon Roll' (Spuria)
9 'Cinnamon Stick' (Spuria)
9 'Circlette' (SDB)
9 'City of Lincoln' (TB)
8 'Clotho' (Aril)
3 'Cloud Fluff' (IB)
0 'Clouded Moon' (***sibirica***)
9 'Confetti' (TB)
8 'Constance Meyer' (TB)
3 'Copper Pot' (TB)
3 'Coquette Doll' (SDB)
3 'Coral Strand' (TB)
8 'Craithie' (TB)
3 ***crenata*** 'Lady Gem'
3 'Crimson Velvet' (SDB)
2 'Crispette' (TB)
2 'Crystal Bright' (SDB)
3 ***cycloglossa***
1 'Dainty Belle' (MDB)
2 'Daisy Powell' (TB)
2 'Dark Fairy' (SDB)
2 'Dark Fury' (TB)
3 'Dash Away' (SDB)
2 'Debra Jean' (TB)
3 ***delavayi*** 'Didcot'
2 'Doll Dress' (TB)
2 'Dotted Swiss'
9 ***douglasiana*** 'Apple Court White'
3 – pale pink
2 'Driftwood' (Spuria)
3 'Dumpling' (MDB)
3 'Dusky Dancer' (TB)
3 'Early Snowbird' (TB)
3 'Echo Pond' (MTB)
2 'Ecstatic Night' (TB)
2 'Egret Snow' (MDB)
2 'Ellen Manor' (TB)
2 'Elusive Quest' (IB)
2 'Emerald Fountain' (TB)
9 ***ensata*** 'Balathea'
9 – 'Buri-cho'
9 – 'Chidori'
9 – 'Chigesyo'
2 – 'Koko-no-iro'
2 – ruby
3 – 'Springtime Showers'
2 'Esther Fay' (TB)
3 'Etched Apricot' (TB)
0 'Ethel Hope' (Spuria)
1 'Fairy Footsteps' (SDB)
2 'Fantasy Faire' (TB)
2 'Fashion Show' (TB)
3 'Fiji Dancer' (TB)
3 'First Step' (SDB)
3 'Flareup' (TB)
2 'Foggy Dew' (TB)
3 'Forte' (SDB)
3 'Fracas' (SDB)
9 'Frenchii' (BB)
3 'From the Heart' (IB)
3 'Fun Time' (SDB)
2 'Galillee' (TB)
3 'Garden Gnome' (MDB)
2 'Gemini' (BB)
9 'Gentle Grace' (SDB)
2 'Gilston Guitar' (TB)
2 'Gingerbread Castle' (TB)
9 'Golden Chocolate' (Spuria)
2 'Golden Chord' (TB)
3 'Golden Emperor' (Dutch)
3 'Golden Forest' (TB)
9 'Golden Glow' (TB)
2 'Golden Hind' (TB)
2 'Gosau' (TB)
3 'Gossamer Steel' (TB)
8 'Grace Sturtevant' (TB)
3 'Graclac'
1 'Gudrun' (TB)
1 'Gypsy Eyes' (SDB)
2 'Gypsy Jewels' (TB)
8 'Gypsy Smoke' (IB)
8 ***haynei***
3 'Heather Hawk' (TB)
2 'Helen Traubel' (TB)
8 ***hermona***
8 'Hipermestra' (Aril)
1 ***histrioïdes*** 'Lady Beatrix Stanley'
3 – ***sophenensis***
9 ***hoogiana*** 'Noblesse'

2 ***hookeriana***
3 'Hugh Miller' (TB)
2 'Immortal Hour'
1 'Impelling' (BB)
0 'In the Buff' (IB)
1 'Instructor'
2 'Invisible Ink' (MDB)
1 'Iris King' (TB)
2 'Irish Lullaby' (TB)
0 'I'm Yellow' (SDB)
2 ***japonica*** 'Martyn Rix'
3 – 'Rudolph Spring'
1 'Jill Welch' (MTB)
3 'Jillian Mason' (IB)
7 'Jirovette' (***sibirica***)
8 'Joanna' (TB)
2 'Just So' (SDB)
1 ***kochii***
3 ***korolkowii***
9 – 'Concolor'
2 'La Senda' (Spuria)
3 'Lady River' (TB)
9 ***laevigata*** 'Murakumo'
3 'Langport Carnival' (IB)
9 'Lavender Light' (***sibirica***)
1 'Lavender Ribbon'
1 'Lemon Charm' (SDB)
2 'Lemon Duet'
1 'Lemon Flame'
3 'Lemon Lark' (SDB)
3 'Lemon Queen' (Dutch)
1 'Lighten Up' (SDB)
2 'Lilac Festival' (TB)
3 'Lilac Mist' (TB)
2 'Lima Colada' (SDB)
2 'Lime Ripples' (IB)
2 'Little Sheba' (AB)
9 'Little Swinger' (BB)
2 'Little Wonder' (IB)
8 'L'lita' (TB)
3 'Logo' (IB)
1 ***lortetii***
2 'Los Angeles'
2 'Lovely Letty' (TB)
3 'Love's Allure' (TB)
3 'Lucinda' (TB)
3 'Lunar Fire' (TB)
1 ***lutescens*** 'Nancy Lindsey'
0 – white
3 'Lynn Hall' (TB)
1 'Mabel Cody' (***sibirica***)
2 'Mademoiselle Yvonne Pelletier' (TB)
2 ***magnifica alba***
9 'Mariposa Tarde' (Spuria)
3 'Maritima' (Spuria)
0 'Mary B' (MDB)
9 'Masked Ball' (TB)
2 'May Thirty-First' (SDB)
3 'Memphis Delight' (TB)
2 'Mill Pond' (MDB)
0 'Mini Plic' (MDB)
3 'Miss Banbury' (TB)
8 'Miss Underwood' (***sibirica***)
3 'Mockingbird' (MTB)
2 'Morning Sunlight' (TB)
7 'Mountain Lake' (***sibirica***)
1 'Mrs Perry' (***sibirica***)
3 'Mulberry Rose' (TB)
2 'Murmuring Morn' (TB)
3 'Music Maker' (TB)
0 'Nancy's Khaki' (TB)
3 'Narnia' (SDB)
3 'Nightfall'
9 'Of Course' (IB)
8 'Oracle' (BB)
1 'Orangerie'
3 'Owlet' (SDB)
3 ***pallida*** x ***tectorum***
1 ***pamphylica***
1 'Panda' (MTB)
1 ***paradoxa choschab***
1 ***parvula***
3 'Patacake' (SDB)
3 'Peach Float' (TB)
1 'Pearl Queen' (***sibirica***)
9 'Pepper Mill' (SDB)
3 'Perry Hill' (TB)
3 'Persian Fancy' (TB)
3 'Persian Romance' (TB)
8 'Pink Charm' (TB)
3 'Pink Pussycat'
3 'Pinnacle' (TB)
2 'Playgirl' (TB)
3 'Poet' (TB)
3 'Powder Pink' (TB)
3 'Powder Rock' (TB)
3 'Prairie Sunset' (TB)
2 'Primrose Drift' (TB)
2 'Princely' (TB)
0 'Princess of Love' (SDB)
3 'Privileged Character' (SDB)
3 'Proud Land' (TB)
1 ***pseudacorus*** 'Mandshurica'
2 'Pussycat' (MDB)
1 'Rainbow Rock'
3 'Rainbow Sherbet' (SDB)
2 'Raspberry Ripples' (TB)
8 'Real Gold' (AB)
2 'Red Atlast' (MDB)
3 'Red Oak' (Spuria)
2 'Redwood Falls' (Spuria)
2 'Regal Splendour'
3 'Reluctant Dragon' (SDB)
9 'Reuthe's Bronze' (CH)
2 'Revved Up' (IB)
3 'Reward'
3 'Rio Tulare'
9 'Ripe Wheat' (Spuria)
2 'Risque' (TB)
2 'Roanoke's Choice' (***sibirica***)
3 'Royal Sparks' (SDB)
2 'Rumbling Thunder' (TB)
2 'Runaway' (IB)
3 'Rushing Stream' (TB)
3 'Saffron Charm' (AB)
9 'Sahara Sands' (Spuria)
2 'Saint Teresa' (IB)
2 'Saintbury' (SDB)
8 ***samariae***
1 x ***sambucina***
2 'San Leandro' (TB)
3 'Sand Princess' (MTB)
3 'Satin Gown' (TB)
3 'Seawolf' (TB)
3 'Serena' (TB)
1 ***setosa canadensis***
1 'Shawsii'
3 'Shepherd's Delight' (TB)
2 'Sherborne' (SDB)
3 'Sigh' (SDB)
8 'Silver Shower' (TB)
3 'Sindpers' (Juno)
3 ***sintenisii brandzae***
3 'Sky Bolt' (SDB)
3 'Snappie' (IB)
8 'Snow Princess' (***sibirica***)
3 'Somerset Girl' (TB)
3 'Something Special' (BB)
0 'Southcombe Velvet'
0 'Sparkling Water' (TB)
0 'Spartan'
3 'Speckled Bird' (AB)
2 'Spring Fern' (SDB)
9 'Spring Reverie (Spuria)
3 'Stardate' (SDB)
3 'Starlight Waltz' (SDB)
2 'Sterling Silver' (TB)
9 'Steve' (***sibirica***)
2 'Strawberry Sundae' (TB)
3 'Striking Gold' (MTB)
3 'Strum' (IB)
8 'Sugar Pie' (BB)
3 'Summer Pearl' (TB)
3 'Sun King' (TB)
3 'Sun Miracle' (TB)
2 'Sunrise Point' (TB)
2 'Tea Rose' (TB)
2 'Techny Chimes' (TB)
1 'Tender Tears' (SDB)
3 'Tequila Sunrise' (TB)
0 'Tetra-white Rose' (***sibirica***)
3 'The Desert' (TB)
1 'The Gower'
8 'Three Oaks' (TB)
3 'Tic Tac' (MDB)
3 'Tillamook' (TB)
1 ***timowejewii***
3 ***tingitana fontanesii***
2 'Ting-a-Ling' (MTB)
0 Tol-Long
3 'Tricks' (SDB)
1 'Triple Crown'
3 'Trout River'
1 'Tulare' (BB)
9 'Turquoise Cup' (***sibirica***)
3 'Twist of Lemon' (MDB)
2 'Two Bits' (MTB)
2 'Ultrapoise' (TB)
3 'Valimar' (TB)
1 'Velvet Toy' (MDB)
1 ***versicolor alba***
1 ***vicaria***
2 'Violet Bouquet' (MTB)
0 ***virginica***
3 'Virtue' (IB)
3 'Whisky' (MDB)
3 'White Sails' (***sibirica***)
2 'Wigit' (IB)
2 'Wild Ginger' (TB)
9 'Wine Wings' (***sibirica***)
2 'Winged Melody' (TB)
2 'Winkieland' (IB)
0 'Witch Doctor' (TB)
3 'Worlds Beyond' (TB)
2 'Wyckhill' (SDB)
3 'Xamagito' (CH)
2 ***xiphium lusitanica***
2 'Yellow and White'
9 'Yellow Queen' (Dutch)

ISOPOGON
2 ***anethifolius***

ISOPYRUM
3 ***affine-stoloniferum***

IXIA
3 ***conferta***
3 'Hubert'
3 ***rapunculoïdes***
3 'Uranus'

JASIONE
3 ***crispa crispa***
8 ***laevis orbiculata***
9 ***tuberosa***

JASMINUM
1 ***dispermum***

JEFFERSONIA
2 ***dubia alba***

JOVIBARBA
2 ***heuffelii*** 'Blaze'
2 – 'Bolero'
0 – 'Cameo'
2 – 'Capricorn'
2 – 'Cinnabar'
9 – ***glabra*** from Sapka
2 – 'Iobates'
2 – ***patens***
2 – 'Purple Light'
2 – 'Starlight'
2 – 'Sylvan Memory'
9 – 'Wotan'
0 – 'Xanthoheuff'
2 x ***kwediana*** 'Pickwick'
2 x ***nixonii*** 'Stefan'
2 x ***smithii*** 'Ritz'

JUANIA
0 ***australis***

JUANULLOA
1 ***mexicana***

JUGLANS
3 ***regia*** 'Fords Farm'
3 – 'Northdown Clawnut'

JUNCUS
1 ***concinnus***
3 ***effusus*** 'Aureostriatus'
0 ***pusillus***

JUNIPERUS
0 ***chinensis*** 'Belvedere'
0 – 'Kuriwao Mist'
0 ***communis*** 'Edgbaston'
8 – 'Effusa'
7 – 'Gimborn'
2 – 'Hibernica Variegata'
7 – 'Inverleith'
9 – 'Nana Aurea'
3 – 'Nana Prostrata'
0 – ***oblonga***
1 – 'Oblonga Pendula'
2 – 'Prostrata'

2 – 'Prostrata Nana'
2 – 'Repanda' Waddon clone
3 – 'Silver Lining'
3 – 'Suecica Aurea'
0 – 'Windsor Gem'
2 ***drupacea***
8 ***flaccida***
2 ***horizontalis*** 'Coast of Maine'
1 – 'Jade Spreader'
1 – 'Petraea'
1 – 'Prostrata'
0 – 'Schoodic Point'
9 x ***media*** 'Arctic'
1 – 'Gold Star'
1 – 'Mathot'
1 ***pinchotii***
9 ***sabina*** 'Knap Hill'
1 – 'Von Ehren'
0 ***salturaria***
1 ***scopulorum*** 'Blue Pyramid'
0 – 'Hillborn's Silver Globe'
8 – 'Lakewood Globe'
2 – 'Tolleson's Weeping'
0 ***silicicola***
8 ***squamata*** 'Blue Spreader'
7 – 'Forrestii'
3 ***virginiana*** 'Compressa'
3 ***wallichiana***

JUSTICIA
1 ***plumbaginifolia***

KALANCHOË
3 ***blossfeldiana***
2 – 'Annetta'
2 – 'Attraction'
2 – 'Bali'
2 – 'Beta'
2 – 'Calypso'
2 – 'Caprice'
2 – 'Charm'
2 – 'Cinnabar'
2 – 'Flores'
2 – 'Fortyniner'
2 – 'Inspiration'
2 – 'Lucky Island'
2 – 'Pollux'
2 – 'Regulus'
2 – 'Sensation'
2 – 'Sentosa'
2 – 'Seraya'
2 – 'Siam'
2 – 'Singapore'
2 – 'Yellow Nugget'
3 ***fedtschenkoi***
3 – 'Variegata'
3 ***manginii***
8 ***uniflora***

KALMIA
3 ***latifolia*** 'Brilliant'
3 – 'Candy'
3 – 'Carol'
3 – 'Hearts Desire'
3 – ***myrtifolia***
3 – 'Nancy'
3 – 'Olympic Wedding'
3 – 'Raspberry Glow'
3 – 'Willowcrest'
3 – 'Yankee Doodle'

KECKIELLA
2 ***antirrhinoïdes***
1 – 'Microphylla'
3 ***corymbosa***

KELSEYA
3 ***uniflora***

KENNEDIA
0 ***beckxiana***
0 ***eximia***
2 ***prostrata***
0 – West Australian form
0 – West Coast form
0 ***rubicunda***

KERNERA
9 ***saxatilis***

KNIPHOFIA
3 'Bressingham Sunbeam'
1 'Comet'
7 'David' AGM
7 'Earliest of All'
1 ***ensifolia***
9 'Firefly'
2 ***foliosa***
9 'Lye End'
9 'Ross Sunshine'
1 'Rougham Beauty'
8 'Saturn'
3 'Strawberry Split'
8 'Sunset'
8 'Timothy'
0 'Tubergeniana'
0 'Underway'
3 'Vesta'

KOBRESIA
9 ***simpliciuscula***

KOELERIA
2 ***alpina***

KOHLERIA
2 'Linda'
1 'Longwood'

KUMMEROWIA
8 ***stipulacea***

KUNZEA
3 ***baxteri***
8 ***capitata***
1 ***ericifolia***
1 ***muelleri***

LABICHEA
1 ***punctata***

LABURNUM
2 ***anagyroïdes*** 'Aureum'

LACCOSPADIX
2 ***australasica***

LACHENALIA
0 ***arbuthnotiae***
0 ***bachmanii***
1 ***liliiflora***
2 ***orchioïdes glaucina***
9 ***unifolia***
9 'Violet Queen'

LACTUCA
0 ***macrantha***
1 ***sibirica***
8 ***tenerrima***

LAGENOPHORA
9 ***pumila***
3 ***stipitata***

LAGERSTROEMIA
7 ***fauriei***
0 ***indica*** 'Berlingot Menthe'
1 – 'Little Chief'
1 – Petite Orchid ®
3 – 'Petite Pinkie'
1 – Petite Red ®
1 – 'Watermelon'

LALLEMANTIA
2 ***canescens***

LAMARCKIA
2 ***aurea***

LAMIUM
2 'Alan Leslie'
2 ***garganicum*** 'Golden Carpet'(v)

LANTANA
2 ***camara*** 'Arlequin'
1 – 'Drap d'Or' ('Cloth of Gold')
0 – 'Miss Tibbs'
2 – 'Naide'
2 'Sunkiss'

LAPAGERIA
3 ***rosea*** 'Picotee'

LARIX
0 ***griffithiana***
2 ***kaempferi*** 'Blue Haze'
9 ***occidentalis***
2 ***principis-rupprechtii***
3 ***sieboldii***

LASERPITIUM
3 ***halier***

LATHYRUS
0 ***sativus caeruleus***

LAURENTIA
3 ***longiflora***

LAVANDULA
1 ***angustifolia*** 'Jackman's Dwarf'
7 – 'Nana Rosea'
3 ***stoechas luisieri***
3 ***viridis*** white-bracted

LAVATERA
9 ***cretica***

LAWSONIA
1 ***inermis***

LEDUM
3 ***palustre decumbens***
3 – ***diversipilosum***

LEEA
0 ***rubra***

LEIOPHYLLUM
3 ***buxifolium*** 'Nanum'

LEONOTIS
3 ***ocymifolia albiflora***
2 'Staircase'

LEONTICE
2 ***leontopetalum***
1 – ***ewersmannii***

LEONTOPODIUM
1 ***discolor***
3 ***hayachinense***
3 ***himalayanum***
2 ***leontopodioïdes***

LEPECHINIA
1 ***chamaedryoïdes***

LEPTINELLA
2 ***albida***
2 ***goyenii***

LEPTODACTYLON
1 ***pungens***

LEPTOSPERMUM
1 ***arachnoïdes***
2 ***glaucescens***
2 ***liversidgei*** x ***scoparium***
8 ***micromyrtus***
1 ***minutifolium***
3 ***scoparium*** 'Album'
7 – 'Big Red'
8 – 'Flore Pleno'
9 – 'Gaiety'
0 – Jervis Bay form
1 – 'Karekare'
7 – ***nanum*** 'Elizabeth Jane'
9 – – 'Ruru'
9 – 'Pink Pearl'
2 – 'Roland Bryce'
2 – 'Rosy Morn'
1 ***squarrosum***

LESPEDEZA
3 ***davurica***
2 ***juncea***

LESQUERELLA
9 ***kingii sherwoodii***
1 ***multiceps***

LEUCADENDRON
3 ***discolor***
3 ***sessile***

LEUCANTHEMOPSIS
7 ***pallida spathulifolia***

LEUCANTHEMUM
0 x ***superbum*** 'Juno'
1 – 'Marion Collyer'
1 – 'Mayfield Giant'
9 – 'Moonlight'
3 – 'Wirral Pride'
3 ***vulgare*** 'Hullavington'(v)

LEUCOJUM
3 ***autumnale aportense***

LEUCOPOGON
9 ***collinus***

LEUCOSPERMUM
2 ***cordifolium*** yellow

LEUCOTHOË
0 ***keiskei*** 'Minor'

LEWISIA
8 'Chastity'
2 ***cotyledon cotyledon***

2 'Joyce Halley'
2 'Karen'
3 ***longipetala arizonica***
2 ***oppositifolia*** 'Richeyi'
2 ***rediviva*** pink
1 ***stebbinsii***
2 'Susan'
2 ***tweedyi*** Mount Wenatchee form

LIATRIS
1 'Snow Queen'

LICUALA
0 ***spinosa***

LIGUSTRUM
2 ***japonicum*** 'Macrophyllum'
0 ***lucidum*** 'Macrophyllum'

LILIUM
1 'Achilles' (Ia)
3 ***amabile*** (IX)
2 'Amber Gold' (Ic)
1 ***amoenum*** (IX)
9 'Anne Boleyn' (Ia)
9 'Apricot' (Ia)
9 'Apricot Beauty' (Ib)
3 ***auratum*** 'Cinnabar'(IX)
2 – 'Red Band'
9 Aurelian hybrids (VIIa)
3 'Ballade' (Ia)
2 'Beckwith Tiger' (Ic)
2 Bellmaid hybrids (IV)
2 'Bright Beauty' (Ia)
3 ***bulbiferum croceum*** (IX) AGM
1 'Bull's Eye' (Ib)
1 Burgundy (Ic)
2 'Cambridge' (Ic)
3 'Canasta' (Ia)
3 'Carla Luppi' (Ia)
8 ***concolor*** (IX)
2 'Connecticut Yankee' (Ic)
1 'Crimson Sun' (VIb)
9 'Damson' (VIa)
3 'Discovery' (Ic)
2 'Electric' (Ia)
9 'Escapade' (Ia)
2 'Esther' (Ia)
2 'Eurovision' (Ia)
3 'Feuerzauber' (Ia)
3 ***formosanum*** 'Snow Queen'(IX)
3 'Fuga' (Ic)
2 'Genève' (Ia)
2 'Gold Medal' (Ia)
0 Golden Clarion (VIa)
2 'Hallmark' (Ic)
2 Imperial Crimson (VIIc)
0 x ***imperiale*** (VIa)
2 'Joanna' (Ia)
9 'John Dix' (Ib)
0 'Langtry' (Ic)
1 ***lankongense*** (IX)
2 Mabel Violet (VIa)
9 'Magic Fire' (VId)
1 'Manuella' (Ia)
2 'Marilyn Monroe' (Ia)
3 ***martagon pilosiusculum*** (IX)
1 – x ***hansonii***(II)
3 'Massa'
2 'Maxwill' (Ic)
9 ***michiganense*** (IX)
0 Mid-Century Hybrids (Ia)
1 'Monte Negro' (Ia)
2 'Nell Gwyn'
3 'Orange Sensation'
1 'Orestes' (Ib)
3 Oriental Superb
1 'Pan' (Ic)
3 'Paprika' (Ib)
2 'Passat' (Ia)
2 ***philadelphicum*** (IX)
2 'Phoebus' (Ia)
3 'Pink Panther'
2 Pink Pearl Trumpets (VIa)
2 'Pink Tiger' (Ib)
1 ***polyphyllum*** (IX)
2 'Prins Constantijn' (Ib)
1 'Purple Sensation' (Ia)
3 ***pyrenaicum pyrenaicum*** (IX)
1 'Red Fox' (Ic)
3 'Red Marvel'
3 'Redstart' (Ib)
0 ***regale*** yellow (IX)
2 'Rosepoint Lace' (Ic)
2 'Roter Cardinal' ('Red Knight') (Ia)
8 ***rubellum*** (IX)
2 'Sirocco' (Ia)
3 ***speciosum*** 'Ida Uchida'(IX)
3 – 'Rosemede'(IX)
1 – 'Twinkle'(IX)
9 'Staccato' (Ia)
2 'Sunset' (Ia)
3 'Tabasco' (Ia)
3 'Tiger White' (Ic)
2 'Tropicana' (Ia)
3 'Troubadour' (VIIc)
1 'Unique' (Ia)
9 'Vermilion Brilliant' (Ia)
3 'White Lady' (VIa)
2 'White Prince' (Ia)
3 'Yellowhammer'

LIMONIUM
7 ***chilwellii***
3 ***platyphyllum*** 'Grandiflorum'

LINARIA
2 x ***dominii***
7 ***lilacina***
1 ***maroccana*** 'Fairy Bouquet'
8 ***nobilis***
3 'Parham Variety'
2 ***triornithophora*** cream
1 ***tristis***
0 – ***lurida***
8 ***vulgaris*** 'Flore Pleno'

LINDELOFIA
1 ***spectabilis*** 'Hartington White'

LINDERA
8 ***praecox***
0 ***triloba***

LINUM
3 ***mucronatum armenum***
9 ***narbonense album***
0 ***perenne*** dwarf form
1 ***usitatissimum***
3 ***viscosum***

LIRIOPE
0 ***koreana***
3 ***minor***
3 ***muscari*** 'Curley Twist'
2 – 'Paul Aden'

LITHOCARPUS
2 ***henryi***

LITHODORA
2 ***oleifolia*** 'Barker's Form'

LITHOSPERMUM
3 ***arvense***

LIVISTONA
0 ***rotundifolia***

LOASA
9 ***nana***

LOBELIA
2 ***alata***
9 ***begonifolia***
2 x ***gerardii*** 'Alba'
2 'Huntsman'
9 ***linnaeoïdes*** 'Dobson'
3 ***minorescens***
1 ***nicotinifolia***
0 ***physaloïdes***
8 ***puberula***
1 ***tenuior***
0 ***villosa***

LOMATIA
1 ***myricoïdes*** glaucous form

LONICERA
2 ***acuminata***
7 ***alpigena***
0 ***discolor***
3 ***hispida***
3 ***japonica***
9 ***morrowii***
9 ***myrtillus***
1 ***obovata***
7 ***trichosantha***
2 – ***deflexicalyx***
9 ***utahensis***
3 ***webbiana***
3 ***xylosteum***

LOPHOMYRTUS
1 'Pinkalina'
3 x ***ralphii*** 'Lilliput'
3 – 'Pixie'

LOPHOSPERMUM
1 ***erubescens*** white

LUCULIA
1 ***gratissima rosea***

LUDWIGIA
1 ***longifolia***
1 ***octovalvis***
3 ***palustris***

LUMA
3 ***apiculata*** 'Penwith'(v)
7 – purple

LUNARIA
0 ***annua*** purple stem

LUPINUS
2 ***albifrons collinus***
3 – ***emineus***
3 ***argenteus***
3 'Boningale Lass'
3 'Catherine of York'
9 'Cherry Pie'
9 'Comet'
9 'Daydream'
3 'Fred Yule'
0 'Freedom'
3 'Gold Dust'
9 'Guardsman'
1 'Halina'
9 'Harlequin'
9 'Harvester'
0 ***hirsutissimus***
9 'Joy'
3 'Lady Fayre'
3 ***lepidus utahensis***
9 'Lilac Time'
9 'Limelight'
0 ***longifolius***
3 'Loveliness'
9 'Mystic Charm'
3 'Nellie B Allen'
1 'Orangeade'
9 'Pat Baird'
2 ***rivularis***
8 'Rougham Beuaty'
3 'Royal Parade' AGM
9 'Serenade'
3 sp. F&W 7366
0 ***succulentus***
7 ***texensis***

LUZULA
0 ***banksiana***
1 ***canariensis***
1 ***celata*** NZ Ohau
1 'Mount Dobson'
2 ***sylvatica*** 'Select'

LYCHNIS
3 ***coronata sieboldii***
3 sp. Andes

LYCIUM
8 ***pallidum***

LYCORIS
8 ***radiata***
8 ***squamigera***

LYGODIUM
3 ***japonicum***

LYONIA
9 ***lucida***
1 ***mariana***

LYSIMACHIA
3 ***ciliata*** 'Purpurea'

LYTHRUM
1 ***salicaria*** 'Red Gem'

MACHAERANTHERA
9 ***bigelovii***

MAGNOLIA
3 ***acuminata*** 'Kobandori'
3 'Albatross'
3 'Anne Rosse'

3 ***biondii***
3 x ***brooklynensis*** 'Evamaria'
3 – 'Hattie Cartham'
3 'Butterflies'
1 'Caerhays Surprise'
2 ***campbellii*** 'Darjeeling'
2 – 'Ethel Hillier'
7 – 'Visa'
2 ***campbellii*** Raffillii Group 'Princess Margaret'
2 – 'Wakehurst'
3 'Cecil Nice'
2 'Coral'
9 ***dawsoniana*** 'Caerhays'
3 – 'Clarke'
3 – 'Ruby Rose'
3 ***denudata*** late form
2 – 'Purple Eye'
3 'Emma Cook'
3 'Fourteen Carat'
3 'Frank Gladney'
1 'Freeman'
2 'Glow'
3 ***grandiflora*** 'Charles Dickens'
0 – 'Edith Bogue'
0 – 'Rosemoor'
3 – 'Saint George'
2 x ***highdownensis***
3 'Jon Jon'
3 'Koban Dori'
3 'Ko-1'
3 ***liliiflora*** 'Doris'
3 – 'Mini Mouse'
7 x ***loebneri*** 'Spring Snow'
3 'Mag's Pirouette'
2 'Michael Rosse'
3 'Mossman's Giant'
7 ***nitida***
3 ***officinalis***
3 – ***biloba*** AGM
2 'Orchid'
1 'Pickard's Maime'
2 'Pickard's Opal'
1 'Pickard's Pearl'
1 'Pickard's Ruby'
3 'Pickard's Stardust'
1 x ***proctoriana*** 'Slavin's Snowy'
3 'Randy' AGM
3 'Rouged Alabaster'
3 ***sargentiana*** 'Nymans'
3 'Seyu'
3 x ***soulangeana*** 'Coimbra'
3 – 'Just Jean'
7 – 'Purple Dream'
1 – 'Rose Superb'
9 – 'Triumphans'
3 ***sprengeri diva*** 'Claret Cup'
3 – 'Lanhydrock'
3 ***stellata*** 'Centennial'
3 'Tina Durio'
3 ***tripetala*** 'Woodlawn'
3 'Ursula Grau'
3 'Wada's Snow White'
3 ***zenii***

MAGNOLIA X MICHELIA
3 'Yuchelia No 1'

X MAHOBERBERIS
2 ***neubertii***

MAHONIA
2 ***aquifolium*** 'Donewell'
0 – dwarf form
3 – 'Orange Flame'
3 – 'Scallywag'
2 'Cantab'
3 ***haematocarpa***
2 ***higginsiae***
2 x ***media*** 'Arthur Menzies'
1 – 'Hope'
2 ***napaulensis*** 'Maharajah'
3 ***trifoliolata***
0 x ***wagneri***
2 – 'Hastings Elegant'
0 – 'Vicaryi'

MAIANTHEMUM
1 ***bifolium*** Yakushima form

MALPIGHIA
3 ***coccigera***
9 ***glabra*** 'Fairchild'

MALUS
3 ***brevipes***
1 'Coralburst'
2 ***domestica*** 'Bolingbroke Beauty'(D)
3 – 'Calville Rouge d'Hiver'(C)
2 – 'Compact Mac'
2 – 'Compact Sue'
3 – 'Foxwhelp'(Cider)
3 – 'Invicta'(D)
3 – 'Lady Lambourne'(C/D)
2 – 'Red Bramley'(C)
2 – 'Red Jonagold'
3 – 'Tenroy'(D)
9 'Elise Rathke'
0 ***hupehensis rosea***
3 'Makamik'
3 'Pom-Zai'
1 'Red Flash'
9 ***sikkimensis***
9 ***tschonoskii*** 'Bonfire'
1 'Weeping Red Jade'
2 ***yunnanensis veitchii***

MALVA
3 ***pyramidalis***
1 ***sylvestris*** 'Alba'
0 – 'Mest'

MANDRAGORA
3 ***arborescens***

MANGLIETIA
3 ***insignis***

MARANTA
0 ***leuconeura massangeana***

MARRUBIUM
3 ***vulgare*** variegated

MATTHIOLA
8 East Lothian

MAYTENUS
2 ***magellanica***

MAZUS
9 ***miquelii***

MECONOPSIS
3 ***betonicifolia*** 'Glacier Blue'
2 ***horridula alba***
2 ***latifolia***
2 ***sherriffii***
0 'White Swan'

MEDICAGO
1 ***falcata*** 'Cambot'
9 ***intertexta***

MELALEUCA
1 ***biconvexa***
3 ***capitata***
9 ***citrina***
1 ***coccinea***
1 ***diosmatifolia***
1 ***ericifolia nana***
1 ***glaberrima***
9 ***halmaturorum***
1 ***lateritia***
1 ***scabra***
1 ***spathulata***
1 ***striata***

MELIANTHUS
8 ***comosus***

MELIOSMA
7 ***cuneifolia***
2 ***parviflora***
1 ***pinnata oldhamii***

MELITTIS
3 ***melissophyllum albida***

MENISPERMUM
7 ***davuricum***

MENTHA
1 ***angustifolia*** 'Variegata'
2 x ***piperita officinalis***
3 x ***villosa alopecuroïdes*** 'Cae Rhos Lligwy'(v)

MERENDERA
1 ***robusta***

MERTENSIA
8 ***alpina***
2 ***viridis***

MERYTA
3 ***sinclairii*** 'Moonlight'(v)

MESPILUS
3 ***germanica*** 'Westerveld'

METASEQUOIA
2 ***glyptostroboïdes*** 'Emerald Feathers'

METROSIDEROS
3 'Mistral'

MIBORA
3 ***mimima***

MICHELIA
0 ***champaca***
3 ***crassipes***
7 ***maudiae***
3 'Touch of Pink'

MICROMERIA
0 ***cristata***

MICROSERIS
1 ***lanceolatus alpinus***

MICROSTROBOS
3 ***niphophilus***

MILLIGANIA
8 ***densiflora***

MIMOSA
2 ***pudica***

MIMULUS
2 'Caribbean Cream'
3 'Doreen's Delight'
9 'Fire King'
8 'Firedragon'
9 ***minimus***
2 'Royal Velvet'
1 'Shep'
3 sp. JCA 64
1 'Tigrinus Queen's Prize'
7 'Wildwood's'
8 'Yellow Velvet'

MINUARTIA
2 ***imbricata***
2 ***juniperina***
2 ***kashmirica***
3 ***obtusiloba***
2 ***recurva***
1 ***verna caespitosa***

MISCANTHUS
1 ***litoralis*** 'Zuneigung'

MITELLA
9 ***pentandra***

MODIOLASTRUM
7 ***peruvianum***

MONARDA
8 'Cerise Pink'
1 ***russeliana***

MONARDELLA
3 ***villosa*** 'Sheltonii'

MONSTERA
0 ***obliqua***
0 – ***expilata***

MONTIA
1 ***chamissoi***

MORINA
9 ***coulteriana***
1 ***ramallyi***

MORUS
2 ***alba*** 'Nana'
1 ***australis***

MUNDULEA
3 ***sericea***

MUSCARI
3 ***armeniacum*** 'Blue Pearl'
1 – 'Cantab'
1 ***bourgaei***
3 'Dark Eyes'

8 ***parviflorum***

MUSSCHIA

3 ***aurea***

MUTISIA

2 ***brachyantha***

MYOSOTIS

9 ***alpestris***
8 – 'Nana'
8 ***azorica***
0 ***forsteri***
2 ***macrantha***
9 ***petiolata***
1 ***pygmaea***
2 ***saxosa***
2 ***sylvatica***
9 ***symphytifolia***
2 ***uniflora***

MYOSURUS

9 ***minimus***

MYRCEUGENIA

2 ***exsucca***

MYRICA

2 ***cerifera***

MYRICARIA

2 ***germanica***

MYRIOPHYLLUM

2 ***elatinoïdes***

NANDINA

0 ***domestica*** 'Little Princess'
9 – 'Umpqua Chief'

NARCISSUS

3 'Advocat' (3)
3 'Akala' (1)
3 'Alba Pax' (2)
9 'Albacrest' (3)
9 'Aldringham' (2)
3 'Alice's Pink' (2)
9 'Alray' (1)
9 'Andrew Marvell' (9)
9 'Ann Cameron' (2)
9 'April Message' (1)
9 'Arctic Flame' (2)
3 'Arie Hoek' (2)
3 'Armagh' (1)
2 'Arragon' (2)
3 'Aurum' (1)
9 'Backchat' (6)
3 'Badanloch' (3)
9 'Balalaika' (2)
3 'Ballintoy' (2)
9 'Ballyroan' (2)
3 'Balvraid Lass' (2)
9 'Bandolier' (2)
9 'Bar None' (1)
3 'Barley Cove' (2)
1 'Barnby Moor' (3)
3 'Barnwell Alice' (2)
3 'Beauticol' (11)
9 'Ben Hee' (2)
3 'Ben Loyal' (2)
9 'Ben Rinnes' (3)
3 'Benvarden' (3)
3 'Bergerac' (11)
2 'Big Cycla' (6)
9 'Birdalone' (2)
3 'Birdsong' (3)
3 'Birkdale' (2)
3 'Bit o'Gold' (2)
3 'Bovagh' (2)
9 'Brave Adventure' (2)
9 'Bright Spark' (3)
0 'Brindisi' (2)
3 'Broadway Rose' (2)
3 'Brookfield' (2)
3 'Broughshane' (1)
3 ***bulbocodium bulbocodium nivalis***
3 'Burning Torch' (2)
2 'Canasta' (11)
3 'Canby' (2)
1 'Canford' (3)
3 'Cantatrice' (1)
9 'Capstan' (2)
9 'Caracas' (2)
9 'Carrara' (3)
3 'Carrickbeg' (1)
9 'Carrickmannon' (2)
3 'Carrigeen' (2)
9 'Celtic Gold' (2)
3 'Chagall' (2)
3 'Chapeau' (2)
3 'Charade' (2)
2 'Charity Fair' (6)
3 'Cha-Cha' (6)
3 'Checkmate' (2)
3 'Chelsea Derby' (2)
2 'Chiloquin' (1)
3 'Chungking' (3)
3 'Church Bay' (2)
9 'Citronita' (3)
9 'City Lights' (2)
3 'Clare Park' (2)
3 'Cloudcap' (2)
3 'Cloud's Hill' (4)
3 'Cloyfin' (2)
9 'Cold Overton' (2)
3 'Colorama' (11)
3 'Comal' (1)
3 'Cool Autumn' (2)
9 'Coral Ribbon' (2)
3 'Coralline' (6)
9 'Coylum' (3)
3 'Craigtara' (2)
3 'Cranborne' (2)
9 'Crater' (2)
2 'Curly' (2)
1 'Cushendun' (3)
1 'Cyclope' (1)
9 'Dalinda' (1)
9 'Dawncrest' (2)
9 'Debbie Rose' (2)
3 'Debrett' (2)
3 'Debutante' (2)
3 'Delamont' (2)
9 'Delightful' (3)
3 'Derg Valley' (1)
9 'Deseado' (1)
3 'Diane' (6)
3 'Dilemma' (3)
9 'Dorada Dawn' (2)
3 'Double Event' (4) AGM
3 'Downhill' (3)
3 'Dramatis' (9)
9 'Dress Circle' (3)
3 'Drumadoon' (2)
3 'Drumnasole' (3)
3 'Drumragh' (1)
3 'Drumtullagh' (2)
3 'Duke of Windsor' (2)
1 'Dulcie Joan' (2)
9 'Dumbleton' (1)
3 'Dundarave' (2)
1 'Dunlambert' (2)
3 'Dunskey' (3)
3 'Durango' (6)
9 'Earlicheer' (4)
9 'Earthlight' (3)
9 'El Camino' (6)
9 'Elmley Castle' (1)
3 'Ernevale' (3)
3 'Euphony' (2)
3 'Exception' (1)
1 'Fairmaid' (3)
9 'Fiery Flame' (2)
3 'Fly Half' (2)
0 'Fontmell' (1)
1 'Fortissimo' (2)
1 'Fourways' (3)
9 'Galahad' (1)
9 'Gambler's Gift' (2)
3 'Gay Challenger' (4)
9 'Gay Record' (4)
9 'Gay Symphony' (4)
3 'Glacier' (1)
9 'Glandore' (2)
3 'Glen Clova' (2)
9 'Glenside' (2)
3 'Gold Quest' (1)
3 'Golden Rapture' (1) AGM
1 'Golden Rupee' (1)
1 'Golden Sand' (1)
3 'Green Ice' (2)
1 'Green Peace' (3)
3 'Greenholm' (2)
9 'Gunsynd' (2)
1 'Hartington' (2)
3 'Heart Throb' (2)
2 'High Church' (2)
9 'High Tower' (3)
3 'Hoodsport' (11)
1 'Hot Sun' (3)
1 'Ida May' (2)
1 'Irish Charm' (2)
9 'Irish Minstrel' (2) AGM
9 'Irish Rover' (2)
9 'Ivory Crown' (2)
3 Jonquil Single
1 'Karelia' (1)
9 'Kelpie' (6)
9 'Kentucky Cardinal' (2)
1 'Ken's Favourite' (2)
9 'King's Ransom' (1)
9 'Kipling' (3)
9 'Knowehead' (2)
3 'Ladybank' (1)
9 'Lancelot' (1)
9 'Leader' (2)
3 'Lemon Drops' (5)
9 'Leonora' (3)
3 'Limegrove' (3)
3 'Limehurst' (2)
9 'L'Innocence' (8)
1 'Lisbane' (3)
3 'Loch Loyal' (2)
2 'Louise de Coligny' (2)
9 'Lucky Star' (3)
3 'Lyles' (2)
3 'Lyric' (9)
9 'Maid of Ulster' (2)
9 'Mandolin' (2)
3 'Mantle' (2)
9 'Matapan' (3)
9 'May Queen' (2)
3 'Melancholy' (1)
9 'Milestone' (2)
9 'Mill Grove' (2)
0 'Mint Julep' (3)
9 'Modest Maiden' (2)
3 'Monterrico' (4)
9 'Moonlight Sonata' (1)
3 'Morag MacDonald' (2)
9 'Mrs Ernst H Krelage' (1)
9 'Music Hall' (1)
9 'My Love' (2)
9 'Navarone' (1)
3 ***nevadensis***
3 'Nevta' (2)
3 'New Generation' (1)
9 'Norval' (2)
3 'Nymphette' (6)
3 'Obelisk' (11)
9 'Ocean Spray' (7)
9 'Ohio' (2)
3 'Orange Lodge' (2)
3 'Orange Queen' (3)
9 'Owston Wood' (1)
9 'Papua' (4) AGM
9 'Park Royal' (2)
9 'Parkdene' (2)
9 'Parkridge' (2)
3 'Pearl Wedding' (4)
1 'Pearly King' (1)
9 'Perky' (6)
9 'Pimm' (2)
3 'Pink Silhouette' (2)
9 'Polonaise' (2)
9 'Privateer' (3)
2 ***pseudonarcissus pallidiflorus***
3 'Pzaz' (3)
9 'Queen of Spain' (10)
9 'Queensland' (2)
3 'Rame Head' (1)
9 'Raspberry Ring' (2)
1 'Rathowen Flame' (2)
9 'Rathowen Gold' (1)
9 'Red Curtain' (1)
3 'Red Devon' (2)
9 'Red Hot' (2)
9 'Red Mars' (2)
3 'Red Rascal' (2)
9 'Red Rum' (2)
1 'Revelry' (2)
9 'Revenge' (1)
9 'Rich Reward' (1)
1 'Richhill' (2)
9 'Right Royal' (2)
9 'Rimster' (2)
1 'Ringway' (3)
1 'Rose Noble' (2)
3 'Rosedew' (2)
3 'Rotarian' (3)
3 'Roulette' (2)
3 'Rousillon' (11)
1 'Royal Oak' (1)
9 'Rubythroat' (2)
9 'Rutland Water' (2)
2 'Sabik' (2)
3 'Salmon Spray' (2)
2 'Samba' (5)
3 'Sammy Boy' (2)
9 'Santa Rosa' (2)
9 'Scarlet Thread' (3)

1 'Sea Princess' (3)
9 'Sealed Orders' (3)
9 'Sedate' (2)
3 'Shandon' (2)
9 'Shell Bay' (2)
3 'Shuttlecock' (6)
9 'Silent Cheer' (3)
9 'Silent Morn' (3)
3 'Silver Shell' (11)
9 'Sir Ivor' (1)
3 'Slowcoach' (3)
3 'Snow Gleam' (1)
9 'Snow Magic' (3)
1 'Southgrove' (2)
3 'Sovereign' (11)
3 'Spey Bay' (3)
9 'Spring Fashion' (2)
3 'Springwood' (2)
3 'Sputnik' (6)
9 'Standfast' (1)
9 'Star War' (2)
3 'Starship' (2)
3 'Strangford' (3)
9 'Suave' (3)
3 'Sun Chariot' (2)
3 'Sun Salver' (2)
9 'Sunapee' (3)
2 'Sunlover' (2)
3 'Svenska Bojan' (2)
2 'Sweet Harmony' (2)
9 'Tara Rose' (2)
9 'The Prince' (2)
9 'Timandaw' (3)
1 'Tingford' (3)
1 'Tollymore' (2)
9 'Tomphubil' (2)
9 'Torch Bearer' (2)
9 'Touch of Silver' (2)
9 'Trelay' (3)
3 'Trillick' (3)
3 'Trilune' (11)
0 'Troon' (2)
2 'Troutbeck' (3)
3 'Tudor Rose' (2)
3 'Tullybeg' (3)
2 'Tweedsmouth' (9)
3 'Undertone' (2)
9 'Verve' (2)
9 'Viennese Rose' (4)
2 'Vincent van Gogh' (1)
3 'Vital' (2)
3 'Vocation' (2)
3 'Waxwing' (5)
9 'White Prince' (1)
9 'Woodland Splendour' (3)
3 'Woodland Star' (3)
1 'Woodvale' (2)
3 'Xanthin Gold' (1)

NEMATANTHUS
1 'Bijou'
3 'Black Gold'
3 'Jungle Lights'

NEMOPANTHUS
8 ***mucronatus***

NEOLITSEA
0 ***caerulea***

NEOPAXIA
2 ***australasica*** 'Arthur'
2 – 'Lomond'

NEOREGELIA
2 ***carolinae tricolor*** 'Perfecta'(v)
2 ***carolinae*** Meyendorffii Group
0 ***concentrica*** 'Plutonis'
9 ***cyanea***
2 Picta
0 ***spectabilis*** AGM
0 ***tristis***

NEPENTHES
1 ***alata*** x ***merrilliana***
1 – x ***ventricosa***
1 ***albomarginata***
1 ***ampullaria***
1 ***bicalcarata***
1 ***hirsuta***
1 ***leptochilia***
1 ***maxima***
1 ***merrilliana***
1 ***mirabilis***
1 ***rafflesiana***
1 – ***gigantea***
1 – x ***ampullaria***
1 ***reinwardtiana***
0 ***stenophylla***
1 – – ***reinwardtiana***
1 ***ventricosa***

NEPETA
1 ***floccosa***
3 x ***gigantea***
3 ***longiflora***
3 sp. DS&T 09054T
0 'Valerie Finnis'

NEPHROLEPIS
2 ***cordifolia*** 'Plumosa'
2 ***exaltata***
2 – 'Whitmanii'

NERINE
1 'Joan'
0 'Lady de Walden'
2 'Lady Llewellyn'
0 'Mrs Cooper'

NERIUM
3 ***oleander*** 'Cardinal'
3 – double apricot
3 – 'Madame Allen'
3 – 'Marie Gambetta'
3 – 'Mont Blanc'
3 – 'Papa Gambetta'
3 – 'Souvenir des Iles Canaries'
3 – 'Souvenir d'Emma Schneider'

NICANDRA
9 ***physalodes violacea***

NICOTIANA
1 'Hopley's'
0 'Sissinghurst Green'

NIDULARIUM
0 ***billbergioïdes*** 'Flavum'
0 ***burchellii***
0 ***fulgens***
0 ***regelioïdes***

NOMOCHARIS
1 x ***finlayorum***

NOTHOFAGUS
1 ***antarctica*** 'Benmore'

NOTHOSCORDUM
3 ***bonariense***
3 ***gracile***

NYMPHAEA
2 'Chateau la Rouge'
2 'Emily Grant Hutchings' (T/N)
3 'Maxima' (H)
3 'Pumila Rubis'
2 'Radiant Red' (T/D)
3 'Souvenir de Fridolfing' (H)
3 ***tuberosa*** 'Alba'(H)

NYSSA
9 ***sylvatica*** 'Sheffield Park'
3 – 'Windsor'

OENOTHERA
1 ***fruticosa*** 'Hoheslicht' ('Highlight')
9 – 'Sundrops'

OLEARIA
2 ***bidwellii***
1 ***erubescens***
9 ***megalophylla***
9 ***minor***
9 ***phlogopappa*** 'Comber's Mauve'

OMPHALODES
1 ***cappadocica*** 'Bridget Bloom'
2 ***luciliae alba***

OMPHALOGRAMMA
9 ***elegans***
7 ***minus***

ONIXOTIS
3 ***triquetra***

ONONIS
7 ***crispa balearica***
2 ***fruticosa***

ONOPORDUM
1 ***acaule***

ONOSMA
2 ***albopilosa***
0 ***aucheriana***
3 ***helvetica***

OPHIOPOGON
2 ***planiscapus*** green

OPITHANDRA
1 ***primuloïdes***

OPLISMENUS
3 ***africanus*** 'Variegatus' AGM

OREOBOLUS
8 ***pauciflorus***

ORIGANUM
2 x ***applei***
3 'Emma Stanley'
0 'French'
0 'Gold Splash'
3 ***laevigatum*** 'Dingle'
9 'Roding'
0 ***vulgare*** 'Curly Gold'
3 – 'Tracy's Yellow'

OROSTACHYS
2 ***furusei***

ORYZOPSIS
2 ***hymenoïdes***
3 ***lessoniana***

OSMANTHUS
1 ***delavayi*** 'Latifolius'
3 ***heterophyllus*** 'Dodd and Zinger's Variegated'
1 ***suavis***

OSMUNDA
1 ***regalis*** 'Gracilis'

OSTEOSPERMUM
1 'Cannington Sally'
3 'Cannington Vernon'
3 'Croftway Blush'
3 'Croftway Eveningstar'
3 'Croftway Goldback'
3 'Croftway Hall'
3 'Croftway Halo'
3 'Croftway Humbug'
3 'Croftway Silverspoons'
3 'Croftway Tufty'
3 'Croftway Velvetspoons'
0 'Croftway Whirlydots'
3 'Croftway Wonderwhirls'
0 ***ecklonii*** x ***jucundum***
3 'Falmouth'
1 'Goulds'
8 'Lilac Beauty'
0 'Pink Whirls' low form
2 'Trailing Whirl'
1 'Valerie Finnis'

OSTROWSKIA
2 ***magnifica***

OTANTHUS
2 ***maritimus***

OTHONNA
3 ***capensis***
7 ***coronopifolia***

OURISIA
9 ***breviflora***
8 ***macrocarpa***
9 ***racemosa***

OXALIS
2 ***enneaphylla*** 'Ruth Tweedie'
3 ***flava***
0 ***laciniata*** blue
2 ***latifolia***
1 ***pes-caprae***
0 ***rubra***
0 ***tetraphylla alba***

OXYLOBIUM
0 ***parviflorum***

OXYTROPIS
2 ***adamsiana***
3 ***campestris gracilis***
3 ***jacquinii***
2 ***lagopus***
2 ***lambertii***
2 ***splendens***

2 ***todomoshiriensis***
1 ***uralensis***

OZOTHAMNUS

3 ***purpurascens***
2 ***selago*** 'Major'
2 – ***tumidus***

PAEONIA

9 ***anomala intermedia***
2 ***californica***
9 ***chamaeleon***
3 'Claire de Lune'
2 'Defender' **AGM**
1 'Empress of India'
3 'Friendship'
2 'Jenny'
0 ***lactiflora*** 'Amo-no-sode'
3 – 'Aureolin'
2 – 'Auten's Pride'
0 – 'Break o' Day'
0 – 'Carolina Moon'
0 – 'Charles' White'
0 – 'Cheddar Cheese'
3 – 'Couronne d'Or'
2 – 'Dandy Dan'
0 – 'Do Tell'
3 – 'Duchess of Kent'
0 – 'Emma Klehm'
3 – 'Fairy's Petticoat'
3 – 'Fedora'
1 – 'François Ortegat'
0 – 'Fuji-no-mine'
3 – 'Gay Ladye'
0 – 'Gloriana'
0 – 'Glory Hallelujah'
0 – 'Honey Gold'
3 – 'Kelway's Gorgeous'
3 – 'Kelway's Perfection'
3 – 'King George VI'
0 – 'King Midas'
0 – 'La France'
3 – 'La Lorraine'
0 – 'Lake of Silver'
0 – 'Largo'
1 – 'Le Cygne'
2 – 'Louis Barthelot'
3 – 'Lowell Thomas'
2 – 'Madame Jules Dessert'
2 – 'Madame Lemoine'
0 – 'Marguérite Gerard'
0 – 'Marietta Sisson'
2 – 'Matilda Lewis'
1 – 'Minnie Shaylor'
1 – 'Monsieur Martin Cahuzac'
9 – 'Moon River'
0 – 'Moonglow'
0 – 'Mr Thim'
2 – 'Mrs F J Hemerik'
0 – 'Mrs J V Edlund'
0 – 'My Pal Rudy'
1 – 'Nancy Nicholls'
0 – 'Nice Gal'
0 – 'Philippe Rivoire'
1 – 'Pink Lemonade'
3 – 'Sante Fe'
1 – 'Snow Mountain'
0 – 'Souvenir d'A Millet'
0 – 'The Moor'
0 – 'Toro-no-maki'
0 – 'Victoria'
0 – 'Wilbur Wright'
1 – 'Zuzu'
2 'Laddie'
2 x ***lemoinei*** 'Alice Harding'(S)
3 ***mascula arietina*** 'Purple Emperor'
3 'Rose Gem'
3 sp. ex Stern
1 ***suffruticosa*** 'Gosho-zakura' ('Cherries of Imperial Palace')(S)
1 – 'Kaoh'(S)
3 – 'Montrose'(S)
1 – 'No-kagura' ('Knight's Dance')(S)
1 – 'Yatsu-kazishi'(S)
3 'Tango'
0 ***tenuifolia*** 'Plena'
2 ***wittmanniana wittmanniana***

PALIURUS

0 ***ramosissimus***

PANDANUS

0 ***veitchii***

PAPAVER

7 ***aprokinomenton***
2 ***corona-sancti-stephani***
2 ***fauriei***
3 'French Grey'
7 ***kwanense***
7 ***nudicaule*** Meadhome Strain
1 ***orientale*** 'Constance Finnis'
0 – 'Lavender Girl'
9 – 'Lighthouse'
2 – 'Mrs George Stobart'
7 – 'Salome'
7 – 'Snowflame'
7 – 'Stormtorch' ('Sturmfackel')
0 ***pyrenaicum degenii***
0 ***rhoeas*** 'Whispering Fairies Group'
9 ***thianschanicum***

PARAHEBE

2 x ***bidwillii*** 'Rose Hybrid'
1 ***birleyi***
2 ***catarractae*** dwarf form
1 – 'Tiny Tot'
0 ***hookeriana compacta***

PARONYCHIA

3 ***argyroloba***
8 ***cephalotes***

PARROTIA

1 ***persica*** 'Prostrata'

PARTHENOCISSUS

8 ***inserta***
3 ***semicordata***

PASSIFLORA

2 ***bryonioïdes***
2 ***caerulea rosea***
2 x ***caponii*** 'John Innes'
2 ***cirrhiflora***
2 x ***decaisneana*** 'Innesii'
2 ***edulis*** 'Alice'
2 'Hartwiesiana'
2 ***rubra*** forms
3 ***seemannii***
8 x ***tresederi*** 'Lilac Lady'
2 ***trifoliata***
2 ***truxillensis***
1 'Wilcrowl'

PELARGONIUM

1 'Ada Sutcliffe' (Min)
2 'Aida' (R)
2 Alba ® (Z/ d)
2 'Alison Jill' (Z/ d)
3 'Aloe' (Z)
1 'Amour' (R)
2 'Andenken an Emil Eschbach' (I/ d)
9 'Annette Kellerman' (Z)
2 'Aquarell' (R)
3 ***australe*** from Tasmania
2 'Avenida' (Z)
2 'Baby Snooks' (A)
2 'Barbara Rice' (Z/ d)
2 'Belvedere' (R)
3 'Biedermeier' (R)
2 'Blossomtime' (Z/ d)
1 'Bodey's Picotee' (R)
3 'Bold Appleblossom' (Z)
9 'Bold Sunrise' (Z)
0 'Bovey Beauty'
2 'Brick Giant'
1 'Burge' (R)
3 'C Z' (Ca)
0 'Cardinal Pink' (Z/ d)
1 'Carol Ann' (Z)
1 'Carol Cooper' (Fr/ d)
2 'Carol's Treasure' (Z/ C)
1 Champagne ® (Z)
1 'Chang' (Z)
3 'Cherie Salmon'
3 'Christine Read' (Dw)
9 'Clown' (R)
0 'Copper Flair' (Z/ C)
0 'Corot' (I/ d)
2 'County Girl' (Z)
3 'Crimson Nosegay'
1 ***crispum*** 'Minor'
2 'Danielle' (Z)
2 'Dark Lady' (Sc)
0 'David Gamble' (Z)
3 'Dawn Bonanza' (R)
2 'Delilah' (Z)
0 'Desert Dawn' (Z/ C)
0 'Double Skies of Italy' (Z/ C/ d)
1 'Edgar Chisnall' (Z)
2 'Elizabeth Iris' (Dw)
0 'Emily De Sylva' (I/ d)
0 'Fabel' (Z)
1 'Faircop' (Sc)
1 'Fandango' (Z/ St/ d)
2 'Flamboyant' (I/ d)
2 Flirtpel ® (Z/ d)
3 'Flynn' (Min)
2 'Fortuna' (Z)
1 Fortuna ® (Z)
9 'Fraulein Gruss' (R)
2 'Freckles' (Z/ d)
1 'Friesian Beauty' (Z)
2 'Gallant' (Z/ d)
9 'Gaudy' (Z)
3 'Gemma Pride' (R)
3 'Gemma Rose' (R)
2 'Gilda' (Z)
2 'Gladys Washbrooke' (Z/ d)
2 'Glen' (Z/ d)
2 'Glenys Carey' (Z/ d)
2 'Gloria' (Z/ d)
1 'Golden Magaluf' (I/ d/ C/ v)
3 'Golden Oriole' (Dw/ C)
1 'Gottweig' (Z)
1 'Grasmere Beauty' (Z)
2 'Grollie's Cream'
1 'Guernsey'
2 'Hans Rigler' (Z/ d)
0 'Harvest Moon' (Z)
1 'Hayley Clover'
1 'Hazel Candy' (R)
1 'Hazel Dream' (R)
1 'Hazel Fire' (R)
1 'Hazel Orchid' (R)
1 'Hazel Perfection' (R)
0 'Hazel White' (R)
3 'Henley' (Min/ d)
3 'Henry Jacoby' (Z)
2 'Henry's Rose' (Z/ C)
1 'High Glow' (R)
0 'Highfields Fiesta' (Z)
9 'Highfields Glory' (Z)
2 'Highfields Harmony' (Z)
2 'Highfields Jazz' (Z/ d)
2 'Highfields Peerless' (Z)
2 'Highfields Perfecta' (Z)
2 'Highfields Progress' (Z)
2 'Highfields Romance' (Z)
2 'Highfields Sensation' (Z)
3 'Hi-Jinks' (Z/ v)
1 'Honeywood Margaret' (R)
3 ***hystrix***
2 'Improved Goertz'
2 'Jean Viaud' (Z/ d)
1 'Jennifer Strange' (R)
1 'Jim Small' (Z/ C)
1 'Joy Thorp' (I)
9 'Joyrider' (Z/ d)
2 'Juniper' (Sc)
2 'Karen Gamble Improved' (Z)
2 'Kathleen Gamble Improved' (Z)
0 'Katina' (Z)
9 'Kelly's Eye' (Z/ C)
9 'Kelvendon Wonder' (Min)
1 'Lady Mavis Pilkington' (Z/ d)
1 'Legende' (R)
0 'Lesley Kefford' (Z)
1 'Lilac Gemma' (R)
2 'Lilian Woodberry' (Z)
1 'Little Dandy'
3 ***longifolium***
1 'Loveliness' (Z)
3 'Luscious' (Min)
0 'Lyrik' (Z/ d)
2 'Madame Irene' (Z/ d)
1 'Madeline Crozy'
9 'Mary Screen' (Min)
1 'Meill Jamison' (Min)
1 'Mere Seville' (Z)
2 'Mickey' (R)

2 'Mikado' (R)
0 'Milka' (R)
1 'Mill Wine' (I/ d)
3 'Monkwood Beacon' (R)
3 'Monkwood Bonanza' (R)
3 'Monkwood Jester' (Z/ d)
3 'More Mischief' (Dw/ Ca/ d)
3 'Mrs Brock' (Z)
1 'Mrs Margaret Thorp' (R)
1 'Mrs Mayne'
0 'Müttertag' (R)
2 'Mystery' (U)
2 'Orange' (Z/ St)
1 'Ostergruss' (R)
0 'Otley Slam' (R)
0 'Our Jim' (Z)
9 'Pam Screen'
1 'Partisan' (R)
1 Pearl Necklace ® (Z)
1 'Phyllis Brooks' (R)
3 'Pico'
2 'Pink Cloud' (Z/ d)
1 'Pink Delight' (Z/ d)
2 'Pink Lady' (Z)
1 'Pink Lady Harold' (Z)
3 'Pink Moon'
1 'Pink Pandora' (T)
3 'Pink Snowdrift' (I/ d)
0 'Poetic' (Z)
2 Polka ® (Z/ d)
2 'Portsmouth' (R)
2 Prelude ® (Z)
3 'Purple Rogue' (R)
1 'Radio' (Z/ d)
2 'Raola Lemon'
3 'Red Beauty' (Z/ d)
2 'Red Capri' (Sc)
9 'Red Doll'
0 'Red Grande' (I)
0 'Red Patricia Andrea' (T)
3 ***ribifolium***
1 'Ric-Rac'
2 Rio ® (Z)
0 'Robin Hood' (Dw/ d)
1 'Roi des Balcons Rouge' (I)
0 'Ron' (R)
0 'Ron's Delight' (R)
1 'Rose Lady Lexington' (I/ v)
0 'Rose Star' (Z/ d)
3 'Rosebud' (Z/ d)
1 'Rouge' (R)
9 'Royal Pageant'
3 'Ruben' (Z/ d)
1 'Rubin' (Z/ d)
2 'Sabrina' (Z/ d)
0 'Salmon Kovalevski' (Z)
3 'Salmon Nosegay'
2 'Salmon Satifaction' (Z)
3 ***scabroïde***
2 'Scarlet Galilee' (I/ d)
3 'Scarlet Nosegay'
2 'Schwarzwalderin' (I)
0 'Sea Mist' (Min)
2 'Serenade' (Z/ d)
2 'Shrubland Rose' (Sc)
0 'Silver Monarch'
2 'Silvia' (R)
2 'Simon Portas' (I/ d)
9 'Spray Paint' (Min)
0 'Stellar Pixie Rose' (St)
0 'Stellar Red Devil' (Z/ St/ d)
9 'Stellar Snowflake' (Z/ St)
2 'Stuart Gamble' (Z/ d)
9 'Sugar Plum Fairy' (I)
1 'Summer Idyll'
1 'Sunday's Child'
1 'Sundridge Surprise' (Z)
2 'Sunset' (Z)
2 'Susan Jane' (Z/ d)
2 'Susie' (Z/ C)
1 'Swan Song' (Z)
1 'Sweet Miriam' (Sc)
1 'The Mary Rose' (R)
3 'Tutti Frutti' (Z)
2 Twist ® (Z/ I)
1 'Variegated Oak' (Sc/ v)
0 'Velley Court' (I/ v)
1 Velvet ® (I)
1 'Victoria' (Z/ d)
2 'Volcano' (Z)
1 'Wallace's Pink' (Fr)
1 Waltz ® (Z)
1 'Wembley Gem' (Z)
0 'Whistling Dancer' (Z/ C)
3 'White Queen' (Z/ d)
0 'White Startel' (Z)
1 'Wirral Cascade' (Fr/ d)
0 'Zoe Washbrooke' (Z/ d)

PENNISETUM
2 ***alopecuroïdes*** 'Weserbergland'
3 ***americanum***
3 ***flaccidum***

PENSTEMON
1 ***acaulis***
3 ***ambiguus***
3 ***aridus***
3 ***australis***
2 ***caryi***
8 'Claret'
1 ***compactus***
0 ***crandallii***
0 ***digitalis nanus***
1 ***dissectus***
3 ***ellipticus***
8 'Eva'
2 'Fairy Bouquet'
1 ***frederici-augusti***
8 ***fruticosus scouleri*** 'Boulder'
3 ***gairdneri oreganus***
0 ***gormanii***
8 'Greencourt Purple'
9 ***grinnellii***
2 ***harvardii***
9 ***hirsutus*** 'Darnley Violet'
3 ***humilis***
2 – 'Albus'
1 ***impressus***
2 ***labrosus***
2 ***lanceolatus***
2 ***laricifolius exilifolius***
1 ***leonardii***
0 'Lilactime'
3 ***mensarum***
8 ***mexicanus***
2 ***mucronatus***
2 ***newberryi berryi***
3 – ***sonomensis***
8 'Newbury Gem'
2 ***nitidus***
2 ***pachyphyllus***
2 ***parryi***
2 ***paysoniorum***
2 ***procerus procerus***
3 ***procurrens***
2 ***pseudospectabilis***
3 'Purpurglocken'
3 ***sanguineus***
2 ***speciosus***
1 – ***kennedyi***
2 ***stenophyllus***
2 ***subulatus***
2 ***thurberi***
2 ***traceyi***
2 ***virens*** pale blue
1 ***virgatus asa-grayi***
8 'Waterloo'
2 ***whippleanus*** dark form

PENTAS
0 ***lanceolata*** 'Kermesina'
0 – 'Quartiniana'

PENTASCHISTIS
3 sp. SH 44

PEPEROMIA
3 ***arifolia***
3 ***caperata*** 'Little Fantasy' **AGM**
2 – 'Luna'
3 – 'Variegata'
3 ***clusiifolia*** 'Variegata' **AGM**
2 ***columbiana***
2 – 'Carnival'
2 ***deppeana***
0 ***fraseri***
3 ***glabella***
2 'Green Valley'
3 ***griseoargentea***
2 ***maculosa***
2 ***miqueliana***
0 ***obtusifolia*** 'Variegata'
2 ***obtusifolia*** Magnoliifolia Group
2 'Pauline'
2 ***pereskiifolia***
2 ***puteolata***
2 ***rubella***
2 'Teresa'
2 'Tine'
2 ***tristachya***
3 ***verticillata***

PERESKIA
3 ***aculeata*** 'Variegata'

PERIPLOCA
8 ***sepium***

PERSEA
0 ***thunbergii***

PERSICARIA
9 ***affinis*** 'George Taylor'
0 ***amplexicaulis oxyphylla***
3 – 'Taurus'
1 ***emodi*** 'George Taylor'

PETASITES
1 ***japonicus***

PETROCOSMEA
2 ***kerrii***

PETROMARULA
0 ***pinnata***

PHACELIA
8 ***sericea***

PHAGNALON
3 ***helichrysoïdes***

PHELLODENDRON
3 ***chinense***

PHILADELPHUS
3 'Albâtre'
1 ***argyrocalyx***
2 'Atlas'
7 'Burkwoodii'
0 ***coronarius*** Threave form
3 ***delavayi***
9 'Etoile Rose'
2 'Falconeri'
2 x ***lemoinei*** 'Lemoinei'
3 ***mexicanus***
0 ***microphyllus*** 'Superbus'
0 'Mrs Reid'
7 'Norma'
1 'Pentagon'
9 ***pubescens***
0 ***purpurascens***
1 x ***purpureomaculatus***
3 'Rosace'
1 ***satsumi***
9 ***schrenkii***
0 ***sericanthus***
3 'Silver Slipper'
2 'Snowbelle'
2 ***tenuifolius***

PHILLYREA
2 ***angustifolia rosmarinifolia***

PHILODENDRON
3 ***bipennifolium*** **AGM**
0 – 'Variegatum'
0 ***ilsemannii***
0 ***imbe*** 'Variegatum'
0 'Painted Lady'
3 ***scandens*** **AGM**

PHLEUM
9 ***alpinum***

PHLOMIS
3 ***crinita***
1 ***orientalis***

PHLOX
8 'Boris'
3 ***caerulea*** x ***aleutica***
3 ***caespitosa pulvinata***
0 'Chequers'
0 ***diffusa*** 'Octopus'
0 ***douglasii*** 'Petra'
1 – 'Star Dust'
3 ***drummondii***
1 'Geddington Cross'
2 ***hoodii glabra***
9 'Lee Raden'
8 'Moonlight'
3 ***nana*** 'Chameleon'

3 – 'Denver Sunset'
1 – 'Lilacina'
3 – *lutea*
3 – 'Tangelo'
7 ***paniculata*** 'Ann'
2 – 'Blue Mist'
0 – 'Blue Moon'
1 – 'Buccaneer'
1 – 'Cherry Pink'
9 – 'Denny'
0 – 'Eclaireur'
2 – 'Frau Antonin Buchner'
7 – 'Glow'
1 – 'Inspiration'
0 – 'Jules Sandeau'
3 – 'Kelway's Cherub'
0 – 'Little Lovely'
3 – 'Marlborough'
3 – 'Pax'
1 – 'Pink Gown'
3 – 'Purpurkuppel'
7 – 'Scheerausch'
9 – 'Silver Salmon'
1 – 'Snowball'
1 – 'The King'
3 'Pleu de Pervanche'
3 x ***procumbens***
8 'Snowflake'
0 ***subulata*** 'Brilliant'
7 – 'Jill Alexander'
7 – 'Pink Delight'
0 – pink seedling
3 – 'Sarah'
0 – 'White Drift'
3 – 'Woodside'
3 x ***weseli***

PHOENIX
9 ***rupicola***

PHORMIUM
1 'Burgundy'
3 'Guardsman' (v)
3 'Sunset' (v)
1 ***tenax*** 'Veitchianum'(v)

PHOTINIA
0 ***lasiogyna*** Hangzhou 11818
3 ***lindleyana***
0 ***villosa longipes***

PHRAGMITES
2 ***australis altissimus***

PHYGELIUS
3 ***aequalis*** 'Apricot Trumpet'
3 ***capensis albus***

PHYLLOSTACHYS
8 ***bambusoïdes*** 'Kronberg'
8 ***edulis subconvexa***
7 ***elegans***

PHYSARIA
0 ***alpina***
1 ***bellii***
2 ***chambersii***
1 ***didymocarpa***
1 ***vitulifera***

PHYTEUMA
2 ***globulariifolium***
9 ***ovatum***

PICEA
7 ***abies*** 'Gregoryana Parsonsii'
2 – 'Humilis'
3 – 'Kámon'
0 – 'Mariae Orffiae'
0 – 'Pseudoprostrata'
2 – 'Rubrospicata'
0 ***glauca*** 'Densata'
2 – 'Elf'
2 ***glehnii***
3 ***koraiensis***
0 ***mariana*** 'Beissneri'
1 ***morrisonicola***
1 ***omorika*** 'Glauca'
1 – 'Gnom'
3 ***orientalis*** 'Aureospicata'
2 – 'Skylands Prostrate'
9 ***pungens*** 'Compacta'
3 – 'Fat Albert'
3 – 'Glauca Pendula'
3 – 'Mrs Cesarini'
2 – 'Pendula'
2 – 'Rovellis Monument'
1 – 'Schovenhorst'
2 – 'Spek'
1 ***schrenkiana tianschanica***
2 ***spinulosa***
2 ***wilsonii***

PIERIS
3 'Brouwer's Beauty'
2 ***floribunda*** 'Elongata'
2 ***formosa forrestii*** 'Ball of Fire'
2 ***japonica*** 'Crystal'
3 – 'Green Pillar'
3 – 'Kakashima'
0 – 'Stockman'
9 – 'Valley Fire'
3 – 'Weeping Bride'
3 – 'Weeping Groom'
9 – 'Whitecaps'

PILEA
3 ***depressa***
2 ***involucrata***
2 – 'Bronze'
2 – 'Moon Valley' AGM
3 – 'Norfolk' AGM
3 ***microphylla***
3 'Silver Tree'

PIMELEA
2 ***ferruginea*** 'Magenta Mist'

PIMPINELLA
3 ***minima rosea***

PINGUICULA
2 ***oaxaca***
3 ***primulifolia***
3 ***rotundifolia***

PINUS
3 ***ayacahuite veitchii***
7 ***balfouriana***
7 ***banksiana*** 'Schoodic'
2 – 'Uncle Fogy'
8 ***bhutanica***
3 ***cembra sibirica***
7 ***densata***
7 ***flexilis*** 'Van der Woolf's Pyramid'
7 ***gordoniana***
9 ***greggii***
2 ***halepensis***
2 x ***holfordiana***
2 x ***hunnewellii***
0 ***koraiensis*** 'Silver Mop'
2 ***kwangtungensis***
1 ***luchuensis***
7 ***mugo*** 'Hesse'
7 – 'Spingarn's Form'
2 – 'Trompenburg'
1 – 'Yellow Point'
0 ***nigra caramanica*** 'Pyramidata'
3 – 'Géant de Suisse'
7 – 'Globosa'
3 – ***laricio*** 'Aurea'
7 – 'Strypemonde'
2 ***parviflora*** 'Blue Giant'
7 – 'Fukusumi'
0 – 'Shikoku'
7 ***peuce*** 'Nana'
1 ***ponderosa scopulorum***
0 ***resinosa***
9 ***rudis***
7 ***strobus*** 'Compacta'
2 – 'Macopin'
2 – 'Pendula'
2 – 'Prostrata'
7 – 'Pumila'
3 – 'Radiata Aurea'
7 – 'Umbraculifera'
7 ***sylvestris*** 'Corley'
0 – 'Iceni'
2 – 'Mongolia'
7 – 'Nana Compacta'
2 – ***prostrata***
2 – 'Pyramidalis Compacta'
7 – 'Scott's Dwarf'
3 – 'Sei'
7 – 'Umbraculifera'
2 – 'Vera Hayward'
2 – 'Viridis Compacta'
7 ***tabuliformis mukdensis***
2 ***thunbergii*** 'Oculus Draconis'
7 ***wincesteriana***

PIPER
2 ***ornatum***

PITTOSPORUM
9 ***chathamicum***
2 ***cuneatum***
1 'Green Flame'
0 ***heterophyllum aculeatum***
3 ***moluccanum***
3 ***omeiense***
3 ***patulum***
3 ***phillyreoïdes***
2 ***tenuifolium*** 'All Gold'
0 – 'Silver Sheen'
9 – 'Snowflake'

PITYROGRAMMA
2 ***chrysophylla***

PLAGIANTHUS
7 ***divaricatus***

PLANERA
2 ***aquatica***

PLANTAGO
1 ***arborescens maderensis***
2 ***argentea***
1 ***barbata***

PLATANUS
1 x ***hispanica*** 'Pyramidalis'
3 ***wrightii***

PLATYCERIUM
2 ***superbum***

PLATYCODON
3 ***grandiflorus*** double blue
3 – 'Flore Pleno'

PLECTRANTHUS
0 ***coleoïdes***
3 ***thyrsoideus***

PLEIOBLASTUS
8 'Chigogasa'

PLEIONE
0 ***formosana*** 'Blush of Dawn'
3 – 'Lilac Jubilee'
3 – 'Polar Star'
3 – 'Serenity'
3 – 'Snow White'
2 ***scopulorum***
0 Shantung 'Ducat'

POA
3 ***alpina***
3 ***buchananii***
9 ***flabellata***

PODOCARPUS
0 ***latifolius***
7 ***macrophyllus*** 'Aureus'
9 ***nivalis*** dwarf form
2 ***nubigenus***

PODOPHYLLUM
9 ***pleianthum***

POGOSTEMON
2 ***heyneanus***

POLEMONIUM
2 ***caeruleum grandiflorum***
3 – ***nipponicum album***
0 ***californicum***
8 ***lanatum***
0 x ***richardsonii*** 'Album'

POLYGALA
2 ***vayredae***

POLYGONATUM
9 x ***hybridum*** 'Nanum'
9 ***involucratum***
3 ***odoratum pluriflorum***
9 ***oppositifolium***
9 ***orientale***
3 ***stewartianum***

POLYMNIA
0 ***sonchifolia***

POLYPODIUM
3 'Addison'
0 ***aureum*** 'Glaucum'
0 – 'Undulatum'

POLYPOGON
2 *monspeliensis*
POLYSCIAS
0 *filicifolia*
POLYSTICHUM
9 *lonchitoïdes*
3 *setiferum bulbosum*
2 – 'Gracile'
9 – 'Thompsoniae'
8 *setiferum* Divisilobum Group 'Oakfield'
9 *setiferum* Perserratum Group 'Schroeder'
3 *setiferum* Revolvens Group
POMADERRIS
3 *kumeraho*
POPULUS
0 x *canescens* 'Macrophylla'
9 *ciliata*
3 *deltoïdes* 'Cordata'(f)
2 x *generosa*
9 *grandidentata*
9 *koreana*
9 *szechuanica*
8 *tomentosa*
POTENTILLA
2 *bifurca*
1 *brauniana*
9 *crantzii ternata*
9 'Cyril'
9 'Daphne'
9 *fruticosa* 'Daisy Hill Variety'
3 – *davurica* 'Farrer's White'
3 – 'Golden Spreader'
3 – 'Honey'
1 – 'Macpenny's Cream'
2 – 'Pink Queen'
0 – 'Yellow Dome'
8 *lignosa*
9 *multifida*
3 *nepalensis* 'Flammenspiel'
2 – 'Salmon Seedling'
1 *neumanniana aurea*
2 *nitida* 'Alannah'
3 *nivalis*
8 'Orange Glow'
0 *pamirica*
8 *pensylvanica*
9 'Roulette'
8 'Southcombe White'
PRATIA
9 *angulata* 'Tennyson'
9 *pedunculata* 'Tunnack'
PRIMULA
1 *allionii* 'Clarkes'(2)
2 – 'Jane'(2)
3 – Lismore P45/ 16 (2)
1 American Pink Hose-in-Hose (Prim)
1 'Amethyst' (Poly)
2 *apennina (2)*
2 'April Snowflake' (Prim)
9 *atrodentata (9)*
2 *aurantiaca* hybrids (4)
1 *aureata fimbriata (21)*
3 – 'R B Cooke'(21)
1 *auricula* 'A Delbridge'(A)
2 – A74 (A)
3 – 'Admiral'
1 – *albocincta (2)*
9 – 'Alpine Violet'(A)
3 – 'Amethyst'(S)
3 – 'Ann Hill'(S)
2 – 'Archer'(D)
9 – 'Aubergine'(B)
1 – 'Balihai'(S)
9 – 'Barnhill'(D)
3 – 'Bartle's Cross'(S)
3 – 'Beauty of Bath'(S)
3 – 'Ben Lawers'(S)
3 – 'Ben Wyves'(S)
3 – 'Betty Sheriff'(B)
3 – 'Big Ben'(S)
1 – 'Black Ice'(S)
9 – 'Blackcock'(S)
3 – 'Blakeney'(D)
1 – 'Blue Bonnet'(A)
0 – 'Blue Lagoon'(S)
3 – 'Bluebird'(S)
3 – 'Bookham Star'(S)
2 – 'Brass Dog'(S)
2 – 'Carcerot'(A)
9 – 'Carolina Duck'(S)
1 – 'Cherie'(S)
3 – 'Chirichua'(S)
3 – 'Chloris'(S)
2 – 'Citron'(S)
3 – 'Clare'(S)
3 – 'County Park'(B)
3 – 'County Park Cream'(B)
9 – 'Crackley Seashell'(D)
3 – 'Crackley Tagetes'(D)
2 – 'Cream Blush'(D)
3 – 'Daftie Green'(S)
9 – 'Desert Dawn'(A)
9 – 'Desert Magic'(A)
9 – 'Desert Peach'(A)
9 – 'Desert Queen'(A)
9 – 'Desert Rose'(A)
9 – 'Desert Sands'(A)
9 – 'Desert Star'(A)
3 – 'Douglas Blue'(S)
2 – 'Downlands'(S)
2 – 'Dunlin'(S)
3 – 'Durness'(S)
1 – 'Ed Spivey'(A)
9 – 'Elizabeth Saunders'(D)
3 – 'Esso Blue'(S)
3 – 'Eve Guest'(A)
9 – 'Firecrest'(S)
3 – 'Forsinard'(S)
2 – 'Frank Faulkner'(A)
3 – 'George Edge'(B)
3 – 'George Harrison'(B)
2 – 'Girlguide'(S)
2 – 'Gnome'(B)
3 – 'Golden Lilliput'(S)
2 – 'Graisley'(S)
1 – 'Green Edge Pin Eye'
3 – 'Green Jacket'(S)
3 – 'Green Mansions'(S)
2 – 'Green Woodpecker'(S)
2 – 'Greenfinch'(S)
1 – 'Grey Edge'
3 – 'Grey Friar'(S)
9 – 'Grey Lady'(S)
3 – 'Grey Shrike'(S)
3 – 'Grey Yellow'(S)
3 – 'Hardley'(S)
3 – 'Hew Dalrymple'(S)
9 – 'Holne'(A)
1 – 'Ida'(A)
2 – 'Janie Hill'(A)
9 – 'King Cole'(S)
3 – 'Lee'(A)
2 – 'Light Sussex'(S)
3 – 'Margot'(S)
3 – 'Martin's Red'
1 – 'McWatt's Blue'
0 – 'Milk Chocolate'(S)
2 – 'Monoglow'(S)
0 – 'Moonlight'(S)
2 – 'Mrs C Warne'
1 – 'Old Mustard'
3 – 'Ower'(A)
2 – 'Parchment'(S)
3 – 'Party Time'(S)
2 – 'Pat Berwick'(A)
0 – 'Pathan'(A)
0 – 'Peach Blossom'
9 – 'Pennant's Parakeet'(S)
2 – 'Philip Green'(S)
3 – 'Pixie'(A)
3 – 'Proctor's Yellow'(B)
3 – 'Prospero'(A)
9 – 'Purple Heron'(S)
9 – 'Purple Lake'(S)
7 – 'Queen Alexandar'(B)
3 – 'Queen of Sheba'(S)
2 – 'Radiance'(A)
3 – 'Roxburgh'(A)
2 – 'Ruffles'(S)
0 – 'Sam Gordon'
9 – 'Scarlet Ibis'(S)
9 – 'Scarlet Lancer'(S)
2 – 'Senorita'(A)
9 – 'Shaheen'(S)
2 – 'Shako'(A)
2 – 'Shogun'(A)
8 – 'Show Red'(S)
3 – 'Spinney Lane'(A)
2 – 'Spitfire'(S)
9 – 'Sunburst'(S)
9 – 'Sungold'(S)
2 – 'Sunny Boy'(S)
3 – 'Tally-ho'(A)
0 – 'Tiphareth'(A)
1 – 'Tony Murloch'
2 – 'Turnbull'(A)
9 – 'Velvet Knight'(B)
9 – 'Violetta'(S)
3 – 'Vivien'(S)
2 – 'Wexland'(S)
9 – 'Woodpigeon'(S)
3 – 'Woodstock'(S)
2 – 'Yellow Hammer'(S)
1 'Barrowby Gem' (Poly)
1 'Beamish Foam' (Poly)
2 x *berninae (2)*
0 'Blue Diamond'
3 'Blue Rhapsody'
2 'Blue Triumph'
1 'Bon Accord Cerise' (D.Poly)
1 'Bon Accord Lavender' (D.Poly)
1 'Bon Accord Lilac' (D.Poly)
3 Bootheosa Group (21)
1 *boothii alba (21)*
1 Bressingham (4)
9 'Butter-pat' (Prim)
3 'Caerhays Ruby' (Prim)
9 *calderiana strumosa (21)*
2 *capitellata (11)*
9 *carniolica (2)*
2 x *caruelii (2)*
2 *cawdoriana (8)*
2 'Charlotte' (Prim)
9 'Charmian' (D.Prim)
9 'Cheerleader'
9 'Cherry Pie' (Prim)
3 *clusiana* 'Murray-Lyon'(2)
9 'Coerulea' (Prim)
3 Cowichan Red Group (Poly)
2 'Crimson Beauty' (D.Prim)
1 'Crispii' (Prim)
2 *cuneifolia (8)*
1 dark scarlet (Prim)
3 'David Valentine'
8 *denticulata* 'Prichard's Ruby'(9)
2 *deorum (2)*
7 *deuteronana (21)*
1 'Doctor Mary' (Prim)
1 'Doctor Molly' (Prim)
1 'Double Red' (D.Poly)
8 *duthieana (18)*
1 'Eastgrove's Gipsy' (Poly)
2 *edgeworthii alba (21)*
1 *elatior ruprechtii (30)*
1 'Elizabeth Dickey' (D.Poly)
0 *ellisiae alba (21)*
1 'Enchantress' (Poly)
0 *erythrocarpa (9)*
1 'Evonne' (D.Poly)
2 'Exhilaration'
9 x *facchinii (2)*
0 *fedtschenkoi (11)*
1 'Fife Yellow' (D.Poly)
1 'Finesse' (Prim)
1 x *floerkeana biflora (2)*
1 – *alba(2)*
1 'Gloria' (Prim)
2 *griffithii* 'Fantail'(21)
3 'Hall Barn Blue'
3 'Hall Barn White'
2 'Helge' (Prim)
9 *hidakana (24)*
0 'Highland Jewel' (D.Prim)
1 'Hipperholme'
3 *hirsuta* 'Dyke's Variety'
2 *integrifolia (2)*
9 'Jubilee' (D.Prim)
3 'Julian'
2 'Ladybird' (Prim)
9 'Lambrook Peach' (Poly)
1 'Lambrook Pink' (Poly)
0 *latifolia cynoglossifolia (2)*
7 *latisecta (7)*
2 'Lemon Soufflé' (Prim)

1 lilac purple (D.Poly)
3 'Lopen Red' (Poly)
3 'Madame Pompadour' (D.Poly)
3 ***marginata*** 'Alpbach'
3 – 'Gold Plate'(2)
1 – 'Longifolia'(2)
2 – maritime form (2)
1 – 'Sharp's Variety'(2)
2 'Matthew Pixton'
2 'Mauve Queen' (Prim)
0 ***megaseifolia (6)***
9 ***minutissima (16)***
9 ***modesta*** 'Flore Pleno'(11)
3 ***mollis (7)***
9 x ***muretiana dinyana (2)***
2 ***nipponica (8)***
2 ***pedemontana*** 'Alba'(2)
1 'Penlan Cream' (D.Poly)
1 'Pink Lady'
1 'Pink Profusion' (Prim)
9 'Pink Ruffles' (Prim)
3 x ***pubescens*** 'Nivea'(2)
2 – 'Old Rose'(2)
3 – 'Paul'(2)
7 – 'The Fawn'(2)
3 – yellow (2)
0 ***pulverulenta*** Pyramid Pinks Group (4)
2 'Pyramid Pink' (4)
9 'Quarry Wood' (4)
1 'Queen of the Whites' (Prim)
1 'Red Warbler' (Prim)
2 ***reidii*** hybrids (28)
3 ***reptans (16)***
2 'Rhapsody' (D.Prim)
3 ***rosea elegans (11)***
9 'Royal Purple' (Prim)
9 'Ruby Button' (Prim)
0 'Schneekissen Improved' (Prim)
1 'Shocking Pink'
1 ***sieboldii*** 'Cherokee'(7)
0 – 'Chinese Mountain'(7)
7 – 'Deechin'(7)
7 – 'Hakutsuri'(7)
7 – 'Harunuyuki'(7)
9 – 'Shironyi'(7)
7 – 'Sunrokumare'(7)
9 – 'Tsu-no-motana'(7)
9 – 'Ykiguruma'(7)
1 ***sikkimensis hopeana (26)***
1 Silver Dollar Group (Poly)
1 'Silverwells' (4)
1 single green (Prim)
3 'Sir Bedivere' (Prim)
2 'Sir Galahad' (Prim)
3 ***soldanelloïdes (28)***
1 ***sonchifolia*** Tibetan form
9 'Stardust' (Prim)
3 'Sunrise'
1 ***tanneri tsariensis alba***
2 Tartan Reds Group (Prim)
9 'The Bride' (Poly)
0 'Tina' (Prim)
9 'Tinney's Apple Blossom' (21)
7 'Tinney's Dairymaid'
3 'Tyrian Purple' (D.Poly)
0 ***tyrolensis (2)***
2 x ***venusta*** Askival hybrids (2)
3 ***veris macrocalyx (30)***
2 ***villosa commutata (2)***
3 ***vulgaris*** 'Lutea'(30)
2 'Wanda Cherry Red' (Prim)
2 Wanda Group
1 'Wanda Improved' (Prim)
1 'Wedgwood'
1 'Westmorland Blue' (Prim)
2 'Whipped Cream'
3 'White Lady'
3 'White Linda Pope' (2)
1 ***whitei*** 'Arduaine'(21)

PRINSEPIA
7 ***utilis***

PRITCHARDIA
2 ***pacifica***

PROSOPIS
2 ***glandulosa***

PROSTANTHERA
7 ***caerulea***
9 ***chlorantha***
2 ***eurybioïdes***
8 ***stricta***

PROTEA
2 ***burchellii***
3 ***eximia***

PRUNUS
8 ***americana***
2 x ***amygdalopersica***
0 ***armeniaca ansu*** 'Flore Pleno'
1 ***avium*** 'Grandiflora'
0 ***cerasifera*** 'Mirage'
8 – 'Woodii'
7 ***davidiana*** 'Alba'
7 – 'Rubra'
1 ***domestica*** 'Pixy'
2 ***dulcis*** 'Roseoplena'
2 'Edo-zakura'
2 'Fugenzô'
9 'Gyoiko'
7 'Hilling's Weeping'
3 ***hirtipes***
3 'Hokusai'
3 ***incisa*** 'Beniomi'
0 – 'Rubra'
3 ***institia*** 'Black Bullace'
2 x ***juddii***
1 ***laurocerasus*** 'Barmstedt'
1 – 'Goldglanz'
2 – 'Greenmantle'
1 – 'Holstein'
3 ***mandshurica***
3 x ***nigrella*** 'Muckle'
2 'Ojôchin'
1 ***persica*** 'Alboplena'
1 – 'Cardinal'(d)
7 – 'Crimson Cascade'
2 – 'Eros'
9 – 'Foliis Rubris'
0 – 'New Award'
0 – 'Pink Peachy'
3 – 'Saturne'
0 – 'Weeping Flame'
3 – 'Windle Weeping'(d)
3 ***pumila***
2 ***salicifolia***
2 ***serrulata hupehensis***
2 'Uzu-zakura'
7 ***virginiana***
1 x ***yedoensis*** 'Erecta'
7 – 'Moerheimii'

PSEUDOMERTENSIA
9 ***moltkioïdes***
3 sp. SEP 234

PSEUDOPANAX
2 ***davidii***
2 ***laetivirens***
3 ***lessonii*** 'Purpureus' AGM

PSEUDOTSUGA
7 ***guinieri***
2 ***macrocarpa***
2 ***menziesii flahaultii***
9 – 'Knap Hill Seedling'
8 – 'Oudemansii'
7 ***rehderi***

PSIDIUM
3 ***littorale littorale***

PSILOSTROPHE
1 ***tagentinae***

PTELEA
1 ***nitens***

PTERIS
2 ***cretica*** 'Major'
0 – 'Wilsonii'
0 ***longifolia*** 'Mariesii'
2 ***vittata***
3 ***wallichiana***

PTEROCELTIS
9 ***tatarinowii***

PTEROCEPHALUS
1 ***pinardii***

PTILOSTEMON
2 ***afer***
2 ***diacantha***

PUERARIA
3 ***lobata***

PULMONARIA
3 'Chintz'
3 'Fiona'
1 ***rubra alba***
0 ***saccharata*** 'White Barn'
9 – 'Wisley White'
3 'Skylight'

PULSATILLA
0 ***albana armena***
2 ***campanella***
3 ***caucasica***
9 ***halleri*** 'Budapest'
3 – ***rhodopaea***
9 ***montana australis***
3 ***pratensis hungarica***
3 ***sibirica***
1 ***vulgaris*** Balkan form
8 – 'Barton's Pink'
2 – Heiler hybrids
2 – 'Mrs Van der Elst'

PUSCHKINIA
2 ***scilloïdes***

PUYA
2 ***lanata***

PYCNOSTACHYS
0 ***urticifolia***

PYRACANTHA
0 ***augustifolia variegata***
3 'Dart's Red'
2 'Fiery Cascade'
2 'Knap Hill Lemon'
2 ***koidzumii*** 'Victory'
2 'Lavinia Rutgers'
3 'Orange Sun'
3 'Steadman's Seedling'

X PYRACOMELES
8 ***vilmorinii***

PYRUS
3 ***caucasica***
2 ***communis*** 'Gros Blanquet'(D)
3 – 'Jeanne d'Arc'
1 – 'Marquise'(D)
2 – 'Merton Star'(D)
2 – 'Messire Jean'(D)
1 – 'Pierre Corneille'
2 – 'Swan's Egg'(D)
2 – 'Windsor'(D)
3 ***pashia***
3 ***pyrifolia*** 'Hosui'
3 – 'Yakumo'

QUERCUS
3 x ***hickelii*** 'Gieszelhorst'
2 ***hypoleucoïdes***
2 x ***lucombeana*** 'Ambrozyana'
0 Macon
3 ***petraea*** 'Columna'
3 'Pondaim'
2 ***pontica***
3 ***pungens***
3 ***robur*** 'Albomarmorata'
3 – 'Argenteomarginata'
3 – 'Fastigiata Kassel'
3 – 'Salicifolia Fastigiata'
2 – –
2 ***teucotrichophora***

QUESNELIA
0 ***liboniana***

RAMONDA
0 ***myconi alba***

RANUNCULUS
2 ***adoneus***
9 ***amplexicaulis*** 'Grandiflorus'
2 ***anemoneus***
3 ***bilobus***
1 ***cadmicus***
3 ***creticus***
7 ***eschscholtzii***
1 ***ficaria*** 'Hoskins Miniature'
1 – 'Hoskins Spider'
2 – 'Wyatt's White'
0 ***hirtellus***
9 ***lappaceus***
9 ***macrophyllus***
3 ***nivicola***

1 ***pygmaeus***
3 ***sceleratus***
3 ***seguieri***
0 ***traunfellneri***

RAOULIA
3 ***parkii***

REEVESIA
9 ***pubescens***

REGELIA
1 ***cymbifolia***
1 ***inops***
1 ***megacephala***
1 ***velutina***

REINECKEA
2 ***carnea*** 'Variegata'

RESEDA
1 ***odorata***

RETAMA
3 ***sphaerocarpa***

RHAMNUS
2 ***alaternus***
2 ***citrifolius***
2 ***procumbens***

RHEUM
1 'Green Knight'
2 x ***hybridum*** 'Early Albert'
3 ***nobile***
3 ***palmatum*** 'Saville'
3 sp. CLD 1408
2 ***webbianum***

RHINANTHUS
3 ***minor***

RHODIOLA
1 ***hirsuta***
1 – Baetica Group
0 ***komarovii***
1 ***wallichiana stephanii***

RHODODENDRON
0 ***alabamense***
1 ***ambiguum*** best form
1 ***arboreum delavayi peramoenum***
9 – 'Patterson'
9 Azalea 'Agamujin'(E)
9 – 'Alice de Stuers'(M)
9 – 'Ambush'
3 – 'Angelus'(E)
8 – 'Anne van Hoeke'
1 – 'Anthony Koster'(M)
9 – 'Apollo'(E)
3 – 'Arctic Regent'(K)
2 – 'Ardeur'
3 – 'Atalanta'(E)
3 – 'Aurora'(K)
9 – 'B Y Morrison'(E)
3 – 'Babeuff'(M)
3 – 'Beaulieu Manor'
3 – 'Ben Morrison'(E)
3 – 'Betty Kelly'(K)
3 – 'Bob White'(E)
0 – 'Bulstrode'(E)
3 – 'Buttercup'(K)
2 – 'Carmel'(E)
2 – 'Cavalier'(E)
0 – 'Challenger'(E)
3 – 'Charlemagne'(G)
3 – 'Charlotte de Rothschild'
3 – 'Chelsea Manor'
2 – 'Cherokee'
0 – 'Chichibu'(E)
2 – 'Chinsai'(E)
1 – 'Citroen'
1 – 'Colleen'(E)
9 – 'Comte de Gomer'(M)
9 – 'Comte de Papadopoli'(M)
1 – 'Con Amore'(E)
1 – 'Conversation Piece'(E)
0 – 'Coquille'
3 – 'Coral Beauty'
3 – 'Corot'
9 – 'Crepello'
1 – 'Crown Supreme'
0 – 'Crystal Violet'
3 – 'Cytherea'(E)
2 – 'Dandy'(E)
1 – 'Daphne'(E)
7 – 'Dart'(K)
0 – 'Dawn's Chorus'(K)
3 – 'Dawn's Glory'
0 – 'Dayspring'(E)
9 – 'Devon'(K)
9 – Diamant Group (salmon pink) (E)
1 – 'Directeur Moerlands'(M) AGM
2 – 'Doctor Reichenbach'(M)
3 – 'Dorothy Gish'(E/ d)
1 – 'Dorothy Rees'(E)
9 – 'Drury Lane'
2 – 'Easter Parade'(E)
2 – 'Edward M Boehm'(E)
2 – 'Eisenhower'(K)
9 – 'Embley Crimson'(K)
1 – 'Eucharis'(E)
3 – 'Evening Glow'
2 – 'Explorer'(E)
1 – 'Favor Major'(K)
1 – 'Fawley'(K)
1 – 'Ferndown Beauty'(E)
2 – 'Feuerwerk'(K)
3 – 'Fiesta'(E/ d)
0 – 'Flaire'(K)
1 – 'Freya'(R/ d)
3 – 'Frieda'(E)
3 – 'Gabriele'(E)
7 – 'Garden Beauty'(E)
2 – 'Gardenia'(E)
3 – 'Gauche'
2 – 'Gaugin'
0 – 'Geisha'(E)
0 – 'Glacier'(E)
3 – 'Glamora'(E)
3 – 'Glon Komachi'(EA)
2 – 'Gnome'(E)
2 – 'Gold Dust'(K)
2 – 'Golden Hind'
1 – 'Gosho-zakura'(E)
2 – 'Greenwood Yukon'(E)
2 – 'Greeting'(E)
0 – 'Gretchen'(E)
9 – 'Gwynidd Lloyd'(E)
3 – 'Gypsy'(E)
1 – 'Hachika-tsugi'(E)
3 – 'Hanah-fubuki'(E)
9 – 'Hanio-no-shion'(E)
2 – 'Harkwood Orange'
2 – 'Haru-no-yuki'
9 – 'Harwell'(K)
1 – 'Helena'(E)
9 – 'Hershey's Bright Red'
3 – 'Hiawatha'(K)
9 – 'Hikkasen'(E)
1 – 'Hinode-no-taka'(E)
3 – 'Hino-Red'(E)
9 – 'Hollandia'(G)
2 – 'Hopeful'(E)
8 – 'Hotspur Orange'(K)
2 – 'Hugh Wormald'(K)
3 – 'Hyde and Seek'
9 – 'Igneum Novum'(G)
0 – 'Imazuma'(E)
9 – 'Imperator'(M)
9 – 'Jan Steen'(M)
1 – 'Janet Baker'
1 – 'Jeff Hill'(E)
0 – 'Joho-ngodor-akako'
3 – 'Kasane-kagaribi'(E)
2 – 'Kasumi-gaseki'
3 – 'Kentucky Minstrel'(K)
3 – 'Kilauea'(K)
3 – 'King's Red'(K)
3 – 'Kojo-no-hikari'(E)
2 – 'Kormesing'
1 – 'Krishna'
9 – 'Kumoidori'(E)
1 – 'Kurai-no-himo'(E)
9 – 'La France'(E)
1 – 'Lady Louise'(E)
1 – 'Lady Robin'(E)
2 – 'Litany'(E)
1 – 'Little Beauty'(E)
7 – 'Louisa Hill'
2 – 'Louise Gable'(E)
3 – 'Madrigal'(E)
1 – 'Mahler'(E)
1 – 'Marina'(K)
0 – 'Matsukasa Pink'
3 – 'Matsuyo'(E)
9 – 'Medway'(K)
3 – 'Midori'(E)
9 – 'Midsummer Beauty'(E)
9 – 'Miyagino'(E)
2 – 'Modesty'(E)
1 – 'Moira'(E)
2 – 'Multatuli'(M)
1 – 'Naniwagata'(E)
1 – 'Natalie Coe Vitetti'(E)
1 – 'Niphetos'(E)
1 – 'Noordtianum'(E)
3 – 'Nuccio's Allegro'(E/ d)
3 – 'Nuccio's Carnival'(E)
3 – 'Nuccio's Carnival Blaze'(E)
3 – 'Nuccio's Carnival Candy'(E)
3 – 'Nuccio's Carnival Clown'(E)
3 – 'Nuccio's Carnival Jackpot'(E)
3 – 'Nuccio's Carnival Magic'(E)
3 – 'Nuccio's Dew Drop'(E)
3 – 'Nuccio's Dream Clouds'(E/ d)
3 – 'Nuccio's Feathery Touch'(E)
3 – 'Nuccio's Garden Party'(E/ d)
3 – 'Nuccio's Happy Days'(E/ d)
3 – 'Nuccio's Harvest Moon'(E)
3 – 'Nuccio's High Society'(E)
3 – 'Nuccio's Magnificence'(E/ d)
3 – 'Nuccio's Mama Mia'(E)
3 – 'Nuccio's Masterpiece'(E/ d)
3 – 'Nuccio's Melody Lane'(E)
3 – 'Nuccio's Mexicali Rose'(E)
3 – 'Nuccio's Misty Moon'(E)
3 – 'Nuccio's Pink Bubbles'(E/ d)
3 – 'Nuccio's Pink Champagne'(E/ d)
3 – 'Nuccio's Pink Snow'(E)
3 – 'Nuccio's Pink Tiger'(E)
3 – 'Nuccio's Polka'(E)
3 – 'Nuccio's Primavera'(E)
3 – 'Nuccio's Rain Drops'(E)
3 – 'Nuccio's Snow Storm'(E)
3 – 'Nuccio's Spring Triumph'(E)
3 – 'Nuccio's Sunburst'(E/ d)
3 – 'Nuccio's Wild Cherry'(E)
2 – 'Opal'(E)
9 – 'Orchid Lights'
1 – 'Oregon Trail'
3 – 'Orient'(K)
1 – 'Otome'(E)
3 – 'Otome Zakura'(E)
1 – 'Panaché'
2 – 'Papineau'(E)
3 – 'Peach Blow'(E)
3 – 'Peach Glow'(K)
8 – 'Perfection'(E)
8 – 'Peter Koster'(M)
1 – 'Pickard's Gold'
0 – 'Picotee'(E)
3 – 'Pink Beauty'
2 – 'Pink Mimosa'(Vs)
9 – 'Pink Treasure'(E)
3 – 'Polonaise'(E)
3 – 'Princess Margaret of Windsor'(K)
2 – 'Psyche'(E)
8 – 'Pure Gold'(K)
1 – 'Purple Velvet'
2 – 'Quaker Maid'(K)
3 – 'Queen Louise'(K)
3 – red selected (K)
2 – 'Rhapsody'(E)
0 – 'River Belle'
1 – 'Robin Hill Congo'(E)

7 – 'Rogue River Belle'(O)
2 – 'Rosalie'(E)
3 – 'Rose Queen'
9 – 'Rosella'(K)
2 – 'Rubinstern'(E)
3 – 'Sakuragata'(E)
3 – 'Salmon King'(E)
9 – 'Salmon Queen'(M)
9 – 'Satrap'(E)
2 – 'Seikai'(E)
1 – 'Sherbrook'(E)
3 – 'Shiko-no-kagami'(E)
7 – 'Shinto'(E)
3 – 'Shinyomo-no-haru'(E)
1 – 'Shin-utena'(E)
3 – 'Shira-fuji'(E/ v)
2 – 'Spek's Brilliant'(M)
9 – 'Spinoza'(M)
0 – 'Splendens'(E)
0 – 'Sui-yohi'(E)
8 – 'Sunset Boulevard'(K)
0 – 'Superbum'(O)
9 – 'Tamarind'
1 – 'Tama-no-utena'(E)
1 – 'Tay'(K)
1 – 'Tebotan'(E/ d)
3 – 'Toucan'(K)
9 – 'Tyrian Rose'(E)
3 – 'Uta-maru'
0 – 'Viscosepalum'(G)
9 – 'Wadai-akasuba'(E)
9 – 'Wada's Pink Delight'
1 – 'Wee Willie'(E)
1 – 'Werrington'
1 – 'White Moon'(E)
3 – 'White Prince'(E/ d)
0 – 'Wye'(K)
1 – 'Yaye-giri'(E)
2 – 'Yaye-hiryu'(E)
0 – 'Yellow'
9 – 'Yokohama'(E)
0 – 'Yokora'
1 – 'Yorozuyo'(E)
3 – nakaharae x 'Kin-no-zai'
3 Azaleodendron 'Broughtonii Aureum'
3 – 'Galloper Light'
3 – 'Glory of Littleworth'
0 – 'Tottenham'
9 ***brachycarpum brachycarpum*** Tigerstedii Group
2 ***bureaui*** 'Berg'
2 ***campanulatum campanulatum*** 'Roland Cooper'
0 ***campylogynum*** Brodick form
0 – 'Crushed Strawberry'
1 – 'Hillier's Pink'
3 – yellow
1 ***camtschaticum*** Murray-Lyon form
9 ***caucasicum*** 'Cunningham's Sulphur'
7 ***cinnabarinum*** 'Caerhays Yellow'
1 – 'Magnificum'
1 – ***xanthocodon*** Exbury AM form
8 ***cuneatum*** Ravum Group
3 ***dauricum*** x ***formosum***
9 ***degronianum heptamerum*** 'Oki Island'
0 – – 'Wada'
9 – Kyomaruense Group
1 x ***detonsum*** Edinburgh select form
8 ***ferrugineum*** 'Plenum'
0 ***fittianum***
9 ***forrestii*** 'Branklyn'
0 ***fortunei*** 'Lu-Shan'
0 ***fulgens*** Leonardslee form
0 ***glaucophyllum*** 'Prostratum'
1 ***hanceanum*** x ***lutescens***
2 ***hippophaëoïdes hippophaëoïdes*** 'Sunningdale'
2 – 'Inshriach'
2 Hybrid 'Abe Arnott'
3 – 'Akbar'(g.&cl.)
0 – Aladdin (g.&cl.)
2 – 'Albatross Townhill White'
1 – 'Album'
9 – 'Alice Martineau'
1 – Alix (g.&cl.)
3 – 'Anilin'
1 – 'Ann Aberconway'
2 – 'Anne Dring'
1 – 'Annette'
3 – 'Apricot Lady Chamberlain'
2 – 'Arctic Snow'
9 – 'Arlie'
1 – Ayesha
3 – 'Ayton'
3 – 'B de Bruin'
1 – 'Babylon'
2 – 'Bach Choir'
3 – 'Bali'
9 – 'Balta'
3 – Baron Phillipe de Rothschild (g.&cl.)
3 – Bauble
0 – 'Beefeater'
3 – Bellerophon
1 – 'Bishopsgate'
9 – 'Black Beauty'
3 – 'Blurettia'
0 – 'Bray'
1 – 'Brightwell'
3 – 'Brinny'
3 – 'Brown Eyes'
3 – 'Cadis'
1 – Calrose
1 – Campirr
0 – 'Candi'
1 – 'Caperci Special'
0 – 'Carex White'
2 – 'Carita Charm'
3 – 'Caroline'
1 – Chanticleer
0 – 'Chelsea'
3 – 'Cherry Pink'
3 – 'Chinmar'
1 – 'Chippewa'
1 – 'Concerto'
3 – 'Concessum'
2 – 'Cool Haven'
3 – Cremorne (g.&cl.)
0 – 'Cunningham's Album Compactum'
3 – 'Dame Edith Evans'
0 – 'Director Dorsman'
1 – 'Dollar Princess'
9 – 'Duchess of Teck' AGM
9 – Duke of Cornwall (g.&cl.)
9 – Dusky Maid
3 – 'Edmond Amateis'
3 – Edmondii
0 – Elena
3 – 'Elsa Crisp'
0 – Emerald Isle
3 – 'Ems'
1 – 'Endsleigh Pink'
0 – 'Esveld Select'
3 – 'Everything Nice'
1 – Exburiense
0 – 'Exbury Matador'
1 – 'Fabia Roman Pottery'
2 – 'Fabia Waterer'
3 – 'Falkner Alison'
3 – Fancy Free (g.&cl.)
9 – 'Feespite'
3 – 'Fittra'
9 – 'Flip'
3 – Gaul (g.&cl.)
3 – 'Gemstone'
3 – Gibraltar
1 – 'Gill's Crimson'
0 – 'Gladys Rose'
3 – Glamour (g.&cl.)
1 – Goblin (g.&cl.)
0 – 'Goldbukett'
1 – 'Golden Spur'
1 – Goldfinch
9 – 'Good News'
1 – Grenadine (g.&cl.) AGM
1 – Gretia (g.&cl.)
1 – 'Grilse'
3 – 'Gwen Bell'
7 – 'Halopeanum'
0 – 'Hansel'
3 – 'Happy Occasion'
0 – Hawk (g.&cl.)
8 – Hawk 'Buzzard'
3 – Hawk 'Merlin'
3 – 'Hazel'
9 – 'Helen Johnson'
0 – hemsleyanum x 'Polar Bear
8 – 'Hillcrest'
9 – Huntsman
1 – 'Hydon Harrier'
0 – 'Ightham White'
3 – Inamorata
1 – Indiana
0 – 'Inshriach Blue'
1 – Intrepid
2 – 'Irene'
3 – Isabella (g.&cl.)
3 – Ispahan
3 – 'Ivan D Wood'
2 – 'J H Agnew'
1 – 'J H van Nes'
3 – Jan Steen (g.&cl.)
2 – Janet
2 – 'Janet Blair'
1 – 'Jasper Pimento'
3 – 'Jerez'
9 – Joanita
3 – Josephine
3 – 'Joyful'
0 – 'July Fragrance'
2 – Jutland
1 – Karkov (g.&cl.)
2 – 'Kathleen'
3 Hybrid keiskei x Carolinianum Group
9 Hybrid Kiev (g.&cl.)
3 – 'Lady Malmesbury'
3 – 'Laurie'
0 – 'Lemon Grass'
8 – 'Leonard Messel'
0 – 'Limbatum'
0 – Linswegeanum
2 – Lodauric
3 – 'Lodestar'
1 – 'Lucy Lockhart'
8 – 'Madame Carvalho'
2 – 'Madame Fr V Chauvin'
3 – 'Madison Snow'
3 – 'Mah Jong'
2 – Major
3 – 'Malemute'
3 – 'Manderley'
1 – 'March Sun'
1 – 'Margaret Falmouth'
0 – Margaret Findlay (g.&cl.)
2 – 'Mariner'
0 – 'Mayfair'
0 – 'Melpomene'
9 – 'Melville'
9 – 'Midsummer Snow'
1 – 'Molly Miller'
1 – 'Montreal'
1 – 'Mortimer'
2 – 'Mrs A M Williams'
2 – 'Mrs Alfred Taubman'
9 – 'Mrs Mary Ashley'
9 – 'Mrs Tom Agnew'
1 – 'Multiflorum'
8 – 'Multimaculatum'
9 – 'Mum'
0 – 'Nancy Fortescue'
3 – 'Naomi Early Dawn'
3 – Nehru
2 – 'Nero'
3 – 'Nicholas'
9 – 'Nimrod Scheherezade'
3 – 'Normandy'
3 – Oklahoma
3 – 'Ooh Gina'
9 – 'Oporto'
9 – Orestes
3 – 'Organdie'
0 – 'Ostbo's Low Yellow'
0 – 'Overstreet'
2 – 'Parsons' Gloriosum'
1 – 'Patricia's Day'
3 – 'Paul Vossberg'
3 – 'Pelopidas'
0 – 'Pink Beauty'
3 – 'Pink Cameo'
1 – 'Pink Lady Rosebery'
9 – 'Platinum Pearl'
9 – 'Polly Clarke'
1 – Portia (g.&cl.)

3 – 'Primula'
1 – 'Princess Elizabeth'
1 – 'Princess Juliana'
8 – 'Prinses Marijke'
0 – 'Prosti'
2 – 'Purple Lace'
9 – 'Purpureum Grandiflorum'
9 – Quaker Girl
1 – 'R W Rye' AGM
3 – 'Radmosum'
9 – 'Raoul Millais'
9 – 'Red Bells'
3 – 'Red Jack'
1 – 'Rijneveld'
3 – 'Rimini'
3 – 'Robert Korn'
3 – 'Robert Louis Stevenson'
1 – 'Rosa Regen'
1 – Rosalind (g.&cl.)
9 – Rouge (g.&cl.)
1 – 'Royal Purple'
0 – 'Royal Windsor'
3 – 'Salute'
3 – 'Sammetglut'
1 – 'Scandinavia'
0 – 'Schneebukett'
3 – 'Schneewolke'
3 – 'Seattle Gold'
0 – 'Serena'
2 – Snow White
2 – Solent Queen
1 – Soulking
0 – 'Souvenir de D A Koster'
3 – 'Spring Dawn'
3 – 'Spring Glory'
3 – 'Spring Rose'
7 – Stonehurst hybrids
3 – 'Sumer Snow'
9 – 'Susan Everett'
3 – 'Swen'
1 – 'Tensing'
1 – Tessa pink
3 – 'The Lizzard'
1 – 'Tiger'
3 – 'Tow Head'
2 – 'Van'
2 – 'Van Weerden Poelman'
1 – 'Veesprite'
1 – Vega
3 – 'Vellum'
1 – 'Venapens'
3 – 'Victoria de Rothschild'
3 – 'Vienna'
7 – 'Violette'
0 – 'Virgo'
0 – 'Viscount Powerscourt'
3 – 'Vivacious'
1 – 'Wantage'
0 – 'Wavertree'
0 – 'William Fortescue'
9 – 'Windle Brook'
1 – 'Windsor Hawk'
3 – 'Yellow Pippin'
3 – 'Yvonne Opaline'
3 – 'Yvonne Pride'
1 ***imberbe***
2 ***impeditum*** 'Drake's Hybrid'
1 – Litangense Group
9 ***kaempferi*** 'Hall's Red'
9 – 'Troll'
1 ***keiskei*** Windsor Great Park form
0 ***kiusianum*** 'Chidori'
1 – 'Tenshi'
3 – 'Troll'
3 ***lapponicum***
0 ***lepidotum*** Obovatum Group
3 ***lysolepis***
2 – 'Woodland Purple'
1 ***minus chapmanii***
9 – ***minus*** Carolinianum Group 'Album'
1 ***moupinense*** white
0 ***mucronulatum*** best form (EA)
1 – Reuthe's form
0 ***nakaharae*** 'Benenden'
2 ***nivale boreale*** Nigropunctatum Group
2 ***niveum*** 'Clyne Castle'
1 ***oblongifolium (A)***
1 ***parryae***
1 ***polycladum*** Compactum Group
1 ***ponticum*** 'Gilt Edge'
0 ***pseudochrysanthum*** dwarf form
3 ***racemosum*** 'Forrest'
1 ***russatum album***
9 – 'Hill of Tarvit'
9 – 'Keillour'
2 – tall form
1 ***sargentianum*** Leonardslee form
1 ***seinghkuense***
1 ***serrulatum (A)***
1 ***simsii*** double form
0 ***sinogrande*** Trewithen form
1 ***tanastylum pennivenium***
0 ***telmateium*** Drumonium Group
8 ***temenium***
1 ***thomsonii lopsangianum***
2 ***trichostomum*** deep form
1 ***virgatum album***
8 – ***oleifolium*** 'Penheale Pink'
1 ***williamsianum*** 'Exbury White'
2 – x ***martinianum***
3 ***yakushimanum*** 'Mist Maiden'
0 ***yedoense poukhanense***
0 – – ***album***
2 ***yungningense*** Glomerulatum Group

RHODOPHIALA
2 ***rosea***

RHOICISSUS
0 ***capensis*** AGM

RHOPALOBLASTE
1 ***ceramica***

RIBES
0 ***alpinum*** 'Pumilum'
2 ***burejense***
3 ***glandulosum***
1 ***glutinosum***
2 ***henryi***
9 ***leptanthum***
1 ***menziesii***
1 ***nigrum*** 'Tsema'
1 ***roezlii cruentum***
9 ***sanguineum*** 'Atrorubens'
9 – 'Carneum'
1 ***uva-crispa reclinatum*** 'Admiral Beattie'
1 – – 'Angler'
1 – – 'Antagonist'
1 – – 'Beauty'
1 – – 'Beauty Red'(D)
1 – – 'Belle de Meaux'
1 – – 'Berry's Early Giant'(C)
1 – – 'Black Seedling'
1 – – 'Bobby'
1 – – 'British Oak'(D)
1 – – 'Brown's Red'(D)
1 – – 'Champion'
1 – – 'Coiner'
1 – – 'Colossal'
1 – – 'Conquering Hero'
1 – – 'Early Green Hairy'(D)
1 – – 'Echo'(D)
1 – – 'Emerald'(D)
1 – – 'Faithful'(C)
1 – – 'Fascination'
1 – – 'Forever Amber'(D)
1 – – 'Gautrey's Earliest'
1 – – 'Gem'(D)
1 – – 'Glencarse Muscat'(D)
1 – – 'Globe Yellow'
1 – – 'Golden Lion'
1 – – 'Green Overall'(C)
1 – – 'Green Walnut'
1 – – 'Grüne Flashen Beere'
1 – – 'Grüne Kugel'(C)
1 – – 'Grüne Reisen'(C)
1 – – 'Guy's Seedling'(D)
1 – – 'Helgrüne Samtbeere'(C)
1 – – 'Highlander'(D)
1 – – 'Höning Früheste'(D)
1 – – 'Hot Gossip'
1 – – 'Hough's Supreme'
1 – – 'Hue and Cry'(C)
1 – – 'Improved Mistake'
1 – – 'Independence'
1 – – 'Ingal's Prolific Red'(C)
1 – – 'Jenny Lind'
1 – – 'Jolly Angler'
1 – – 'Jolly Potter'
1 – – 'Katherina Ohlenburg'(C)
1 – – 'Kathryn Hartley'(C)
1 – – 'Lady Delamere'(C)
1 – – 'Lady Haughton'(D)
1 – – 'Lady Leicester'(D)
1 – – 'Langley Green'(C)
1 – – 'Lauffener Gelbe'
1 – – 'Leader'(C)
1 – – 'Lily of the Valley'
1 – – 'Lloyd George'
1 – – 'Lord Audley'(D)
1 – – 'Lord Elcho'
1 – – 'Lord George'
1 – – 'Marmorierte Goldkugel'(D)
1 – – 'Maurer's Seedling'(D)
1 – – 'Mertensis'
1 – – 'Mischief'
1 – – 'Monarch'(D)
1 – – 'Montgomery'
1 – – 'Mrs Westlon'
1 – – 'Muttons'(D)
1 – – 'Nailer'
1 – – 'Napoléon le Grand'(D)
1 – – 'Norden Hero'(D)
1 – – 'Ostrich'(C)
1 – – 'Pixwell'
1 – – 'Plain Long Green'
1 – – 'Postman'
1 – – 'Pottage'
1 – – 'Preston's Seedling'(D)
1 – – 'Profit'
1 – – 'Railway'
1 – – 'Ries von Kothen'(C)
1 – – 'Roaring Lion'
1 – – 'Robustenda'
1 – – 'Rushwick Seedling'(C)
1 – – 'Sensation'(C)
1 – – 'Shiner'
1 – – 'Slap Bang'(C)
1 – – 'Smaragdbeere'(C)
1 – – 'Smiling Beauty'(C)
1 – – 'Snow'
1 – – 'Souter Johnny'
1 – – 'Stockwell'
1 – – 'Sulphur'(D)
1 – – 'Talfourd'(D)
1 – – 'Thatcher'
1 – – 'Viper'(C)
1 – – 'Weisse Riesen'
1 – – 'Weisse Volltriesen'(C)
1 – – 'Werdersche Frühemarkt'(D)
1 – – 'White Fig'(C)
1 – – 'White Swan'(C)

RICINUS
2 ***communis***
3 – 'Impala'

RIGIDELLA
0 ***orthantha***

ROBINIA
2 x ***ambigua*** 'Decaisneana'
9 ***boyntonii***
2 x ***margaretta***
0 ***pseudoacacia*** 'Sandraudiga'
3 – 'Semperflorens'

RODGERSIA
2 ***podophylla*** 'Pagode'

ROHDEA
3 ***japonica*** 'Tuneshige Rokujo'

ROMANZOFFIA
2 ***suksdorfii***

ROMULEA

1 ***bulbocodium leichtliniana***

ROSA

3 'Aberdonian' (F)
1 'Abundance' (F)
0 'Aglaia' (Ra)
9 'Alamein' (F)
3 'Alison Wheatcroft' (F)
2 Allotria ® (F)
0 'Amarillo' (HT)
2 'Améthyste' (Ra)
0 'Amorette' (Patio)
1 'Andrea, Climbing' (MinCl)
0 'Andrew's Rose' (F)
2 Anna Zinkeisen ® (S)
2 Anneka ® (F)
0 'Appreciation' (HT)
2 Apricot Spice ® (HT)
0 'Apricot Wine' (F)
2 'Arabesque' (F)
0 'Artistic' (F)
9 'Ascot' (F)
1 Baccará ® (HT)
2 'Bambino' (Min)
2 Baron Meillandina ®
3 x ***beanii (Ra)***
2 Beauty Queen ® (F)
2 'Beauty Secret' (Min)
1 'Bel Ange' (HT)
2 Benevolence ® (HT)
9 'Berlin' (S)
2 Beryl Bach ® (HT)
2 Bill Slim ® (F)
2 Bischofsstadt Paderborn ® (S)
2 'Blaze Away' (F)
9 Blue Peter, Climbing ® (Min/ Cl)
3 'Bold Bells' (S)
0 'Bountiful' (F)
0 'Brandy Butter' (HT)
2 'Bridgwater Pride' (F)
2 Bright Eyes ® (F)
2 'Buccaneer' (HT)
1 'Burning Love' (F)
0 'Capistrano' (HT)
1 Carol Ann ® (F)
3 'Centurion' (F)
3 'Chaplin's Pink Companion' (Cl)
2 Charles de Gaulle ® (HT)
2 'Charm of Paris' (HT)
2 'Chatterbox' (F)
2 Christingle ® (F)
1 'Chuckles' (F)
2 City of Bradford ® (F)
3 'Coalite Flame' (HT)
9 'Cologne Carnival' (HT)
1 'Comtesse d'Oxford' (HP)
2 'Comtesse O'Gorman' (HP)
2 Conqueror's Gold ® (F)
1 'Coral Star' (HT)
3 'Coronet' (F)
2 Corsair ® (F)
3 Country Heritage ® (HT)
2 'Countryman' (S)
2 'Crarae' (HT)
1 Crimson Wave ® (F)
0 'Culverbrae' (Ru)
2 'Dale Farm' (F/ Patio)
2 'Dame de Coeur' (HT)
2 Dame Vera Lynn ® (F)
9 'Dekorat' (HT)
1 Diamant ® (F)
3 'Dian' (Min)
9 'Doctor F L Skinner'
1 'Dornröschen' (Cl)
2 Dwarf Favourite ® (Patio)
1 'Eiffel Tower' (HT)
0 'Eleanor' (Min)
2 Elegant Pearl ® (Min/ Patio)
2 'Ellen Mary' (HT)
2 'Ellinor LeGrice' (HT)
1 'Ellinor LeGrice, Climbing' (HT/ Cl)
9 'Else Poulsen' (Poly)
2 'Embassy Regal' (HT)
2 'Emily Carter'
2 Emily Louise ® (Patio)
1 Eminence ® (HT)
2 Esperanto Jubileo ®
9 'Eve Allen' (HT)
3 'Evening Sentinel' (F)
1 'Eyecatcher' (F)
2 'Fairlight' (F)
2 'Fairy Prince' (GC)
1 'Fashion' (F)
9 ***fedtschenkoana*** 'Flore Pleno'
1 ***filipes*** 'Toby Tristram'(Ra)
1 'Fillette' (F)
0 'Firecrest' (F)
0 'Firecrest, Climbing' (F/ Cl)
2 Flanders Field ® (F)
9 'Flashlight' (F)
1 'Florida von Scharbeutz' (F)
3 'Fosse Way' (HT)
2 Friction Lights ® (F)
9 'Frost Fire' (Min)
1 'Garden Princess'
1 'Garnette Golden' (Gn)
2 'Garnette Rose' (Gn)
1 'Garnette Salmon' (Gn)
2 'Garnette Yellow' (Gn)
2 'Gay Gordons' (HT)
3 'Gay Vista' (S)
2 Gentle Maid ® (F/ Patio)
1 Glowing Embers ® (F)
2 'Gold Coin' (Min)
2 'Gold Marie' (F)
1 Gold Topaz ® (F)
3 'Golden Angel' (Min)
0 'Golden Autumn' (HT)
9 'Grace Kimmins' (F)
1 'Granadina'
2 'Grandpa's Delight' (F)
2 'Grey Dawn' (F)
0 'Hadspen Arthur'
0 'Hadspen Eleanor'
2 'Halley's Comet' (F)
3 'Hamburg Love' (F)
0 x ***hardyi***
2 'Harriny' (HT)
2 'Harry Edland' (F)
3 'Harvester' (HT)
1 'Hazel Le Rougetel' (Ru)
3 'Heather' (Min)
2 Heather Honey ® (HT)
2 Heidelberg ® (S)
2 Heidi ® (Min/ Mo)
2 Helga ® (HT/ F)
1 'Help the Aged' (HT)
0 ***hemsleyana***
3 'Highlight' (F)
2 Hiroshima's Children ® (F)
2 Ice Fairy ® (GC)
2 'Ice White' (F)
1 IGA '83 München ® (GC)
2 ***iliensis***
9 'Incense' (HT)
0 Indian Song ® (HT)
2 Iris Webb ® (F)
2 'Isabel de Ortiz' (HT)
2 'Isobel Harkness' (HT)
2 'Janice Tellian' (Min)
2 'Jean Thomson Harris' (F)
2 Jimmy Savile ® (F)
2 'John Abrams' (F)
2 'Jules Margottin' (HP)
2 Juliet Anne ® (Min)
1 'June Bride' (F)
1 'June Park' (HT)
9 'Junior Miss' (F)
0 'K of K' (HT)
1 'Korona, Climbing' (F/ Cl)
2 'Korp' (F)
9 'Kumbaya' (F)
3 'La Jolla' (HT)
0 'Lady Hamilton' (pimpinellifolia)
2 Lady Meillandina ® (Min)
2 Lady Mitchell ® (HT)
0 Lakeland Princess ® (HT)
1 'Laure Davoust'
2 'Lemon Delight' (Min/ Mo)
1 'Lemon Yellow' (F)
3 Letchworth Garden City ® (F)
1 'Liberty Bell' (HT)
2 Lilac Airs ® (HT)
2 Little One ®
2 'Lively Lady' (F)
2 Lolita ® (HT)
2 Lordly Oberon ® (S)
2 'Love Affair' (Min)
9 'Madame Caroline Testout' (HT)
2 'Madame Jules Bouché, Climbing' (HT/ Cl)
1 'Mainzer Wappen' (HT)
3 'Mala Rubinstein' (HT)
2 'Malmesbury' (HT)
2 Mandy ® (HT)
3 Mannheim ® (S)
2 'Marchioness of Salisbury' (HT)
3 'Marianne Powell' (HT)
2 Marion Harkness ® (HT)
2 Maritime Bristol ® (HT)
2 Marty ® (F)
2 'Mary Barnard' (F)
2 Mary Jean ® (HT)
2 Mary Sumner ® (F)
2 Midas ® (HT)
9 'Midget' (Min)
2 'Mission Supreme' (HT)
1 'Montezuma' (HT)
2 'Mood Music' (Min)
0 ***moyesii*** 'Nassau'
0 'Mrs Reynolds Hole' (T)
0 'Mrs Wakefield Christie-Miller' (HT)
0 'Mrs Wemyss Quin' (HT)
3 'Munster' (S)
2 Muriel ® (F/ Patio)
3 'My Guy' (HT)
2 'Naomi' (HT)
3 Neville Gibson ® (HT)
2 Nigel Hawthorne ® (S)
1 'Nikki' (F)
2 Nimbus ® (F)
2 ***nitida*** 'Kebu'
2 Nona ® (F)
9 'Nymph'
1 x ***odorata*** 'Miss Willmott's Crimson China'
0 'Ohio' (S)
2 Olive ® (F)
2 Olympic Spirit ® (F)
2 'Only You' (HT)
2 'Opera' (HT)
1 'Orange Goliath' (HT)
0 Orange Minimo ® (Min)
0 'Orange Mother's Day' (F)
3 'Orangeade, Climbing' (F/ Cl)
2 Pacemaker ® (HT)
2 Paint Box ® (F/ Min)
2 Pallas ® (Min)
2 Pat James ® (F)
3 'Peaches 'n' Cream' (Min)
2 'Penny' (F)
3 'Percy Thrower' (HT)
9 'Petula Clarke' (HT)
2 Phoebe ® (R)
2 Phoenix ® (Min)
3 'Pineapple Poll' (F)
9 'Pink Cloud' (HT/ Cl)
2 'Pink Fountain' (F)
3 'Pink Heather' (Min)
1 'Pink Meteor' (F)
3 'Pink Showers' (HT/ Cl)
2 Playboy ® (F)
2 Potton Heritage ® (HT)
0 'Poulbright' (F)
3 'President Herbert Hoover' (HT)
2 Pride of Maldon ® (F)
2 'Prince Charming' (Min)
1 Prins Claus ® (HT)
2 Proud Titania ® (S)
1 'Purple Elf'
2 'Queen Esther' (HT)
0 'Queenie' (F)
2 'Ralph Tizzard' (F)
2 'Red Maid' (F)
0 'Red Planet' (HT)
3 'Red Queen' (HT)
1 'Red Sprite' (F)

2 'Redcliffe' (F)
1 Rediffusion Gold ® (F)
2 'Redland Court' (F)
3 x ***reversa*** white
2 'Ripples' (F)
2 'Robin' (Min)
2 Rochester Cathedral ® (S)
2 Roddy McMillan ® (HT)
1 'Rosamini Gold' (Patio)
1 'Rosamini Orange' (Patio)
1 'Rosamini Pink' (Patio)
1 'Rosamini Red' (Patio)
1 'Rosamini White' (Patio)
2 'Rose of Clifton' (F)
1 'Rose of Tralee' (F)
3 'Rosmarin' (Min)
2 'Royal Bath and West' (F)
0 'Royal Conquest' (F)
2 'Royal Lavender' (HT/ Cl)
3 'Ruth Woodward' (Fl)
1 'Saga' (F)
3 Saint Hugh's ® (HT)
2 'Salmon Sprite' (F)
0 'Sandra Marie' (HT)
0 'Santa Catalina' (FCl)
1 'Saul' (HT)
2 Save the Children ® (F/ Patio)
2 Seafarer ® (F)
2 ***serafinii***
1 'Serenade' (HT)
2 ***sericea omeiensis pteracantha*** 'Atrosanguinea'
0 Shalom ® (F)
2 Sheila Macqueen ® (F)
1 'Shepherdess' (F)
2 Shire County ® (HT)
2 Showman ® (HT)
2 'Silver Charity' (F)
1 'Snowgoose' (Min)
2 'Sonatina' (F)
1 'Souvenir di Castagneto'
1 'Spartan' (F)
9 'Spica Red'
2 Spirit of Pentax ® (F)
1 'Stanley Duncan' (Min)
2 'Stephen Langdon' (F)
2 'Stirling Castle' (F)
1 'Stromboli' (F)
2 'Sugar Sweet' (F)
1 'Summer Song' (F)
3 'Sun Blush' (HT)
3 'Sunbeam' (Min)
1 'Sunday Times' (F)
9 'Sunny Queen'
1 'Sunny South' (HT)
2 Suspense ® (HT)
2 'Swinger' (Min)
9 'Sylvian Dot'
1 Tender Night ® (F)
2 The Fisherman's Cot ® (F)
3 'The Friar' (S)
2 'The Queen Alexandra' (Ra)
2 'The Yeoman' (S)
1 'Tinker Bell' (Min)
9 'Toddler' (F)
3 'Tom Brown' (F)
2 Tonight ® (HT)
2 'Tricia's Joy' (Cl)
2 'Twinkles' (Min)
2 'Typhoo Tea' (HT)
1 'Tyrius' (HT)
9 'Tzigane' (HT)
9 'Una' (Ra)
2 'Uncle Joe' (HT)
1 'Vanda Beauty'
2 'Velvet Hour' (HT)
2 Velvia ® (F)
2 'Vesper' (F)
2 Volunteer ® (F)
1 Wagbi ® (F)
1 ***webbiana microphylla***
3 'Wendy Cussons, Climbing' (HT/ Cl)
3 'Whippet' (HT)
9 'White Dick Koster'
3 'White Flight' (Ra)
1 'White Sunblaze' (Min)
1 'Winefred Clarke' (HT)
9 'Wisbech Gold' (HT)
1 'Woburn Gold' (F)
3 'Yellow Pixie' (Patio)
3 'Yellow Queen Elizabeth' (F)
1 Young Venturer ® (F)
1 'Zorina' (F)

ROSMARINUS
9 ***creticus***
7 ***officinalis angustissimus***
7 – 'Pat Vlasto'
9 – 'Suffolk Blue'

ROSULARIA
0 ***libanotica*** from Kaypak
0 ***radiciflora glabra*** from Beyas Dag
0 – ***radiciflora*** from Bitlis
2 ***serpentinica*** from Sandras Dag
0 ***stylaris***

RUBUS
3 ***coreanus*** 'Dart's Mahogany'
2 'King's Acre Berry'
9 ***lasiostylus***
0 ***ulmifolius***

RUDBECKIA
1 ***hirta*** 'Irish Eyes'

RUMEX
3 ***acetosa*** 'Hortensis'
9 ***alpestris*** 'Ruber'

RUSCHIA
3 ***schollii*** pale pink

RUSCUS
3 ***aculeatus*** andromonoecious

RUTTYA
2 ***fruticosa***

SAGINA
3 ***subulata***

SAINTPAULIA
2 'Alexander'
1 'Alma'
2 'Barnados'
1 'Bella'
1 'Bertini'
1 'Blue Nymph'
2 'Bright Eyes' AGM
2 'Celebration'
2 'Centenary'
2 'Colorado' AGM
2 'Delft' AGM
2 'Emma Louise'
2 'Fred'
1 'Fusspot'
2 'Garden News' AGM
2 'Gisela'
2 'Gredi' AGM
2 'Ice Maiden' AGM
2 'Iona'
2 'Jupiter'
2 'Kim'
1 'Lotte'
2 'Lupus'
1 'Ma Cherie'
2 'Maria' AGM
2 'Meteor Trail'
2 'Midnight Trail'
1 'Miki'
2 'Orion'
2 'Phoenix' AGM
2 'Porcelain'
2 'Rococo Pink' AGM
1 'Sarah'
1 'Silver Milestone Star'
2 'Starry Trail' AGM
2 'Susi'
1 'Wonderland'

SALIX
3 'Aegma Brno' (f)
2 ***babylonica pekinensis***
3 x ***bebbii*** x ***hastata***
3 ***burjatica*** 'Germany'
3 – 'Korso'
3 x ***calodendron (f)***
1 ***caprea*** 'Weeping Sally'(f)
9 ***cordata***
2 ***daphnoïdes*** 'Oxford Violet'
3 x ***dasyclados***
0 x ***ehrhartiana***
0 x ***erdingeri***
0 ***eriocephala*** 'American Mackay'
0 x ***gillotii***
0 ***glabra***
0 ***gooddingii***
7 'Harlequin'
2 ***humilis***
0 ***kitaibeliana***
1 ***lucida***
0 ***mackenzieana***
9 x ***meyeriana***
2 'Micrugosa' (m)
3 ***myrsinites***
1 ***myrtilloïdes***
9 ***pendulina elegantissima***
3 ***purpurea lambertiana***
3 – 'Richartii'(f)
0 ***repens*** 'Pygmaea'
3 – Saint Kilda form
3 ***retusa pygmaea***
0 ***retusoïdes***
0 ***schwerinii***
3 x ***sericans***
0 x ***sirakawensis***
3 'The Hague'
7 ***thibetica***
3 ***triandra*** 'Black Maul'
3 – 'Champion'
1 ***waldsteiniana***

SALVIA
3 ***angustifolia***
2 ***farinacea*** 'Porcelain'
0 ***huberi***
1 ***nelsonii***
3 ***ningpo***
1 ***officinalis*** 'Cedric'
2 – 'Grete Stolze'
1 ***prostrata***
3 'Rosentraum'
2 ***rosifolia***
3 ***scabra***
2 ***sessei***
8 x ***sylvestris***

SALVINIA
9 ***auriculata***

SAMBUCUS
2 ***alba*** 'Variegata'
1 ***canadensis*** 'Hidden Springs'
1 – 'John's'
3 – 'Rubra'
1 ***mexicana***
2 ***nigra*** 'Albovariegata'
2 – 'Fructu Luteo'

SANCHEZIA
3 ***nobilis***

SANGUISORBA
3 ***dodecandra***

SANSEVIERIA
3 ***trifasciata*** 'Moonshine' AGM

SAPIUM
3 ***japonicum***

SAPONARIA
2 x ***boissieri***
7 ***ocymoïdes*** 'Splendens'

SARCOCOCCA
3 ***hookeriana hookeriana***

SARCOPOTERIUM
9 ***spinosum***

SARRACENIA
3 ***alata*** pubescent form
9 ***alata*** x ***minor***
3 ***flava*** copperlid form
3 – heavy veined form
9 – x ***alata***
9 x ***gilpinii***
3 ***minor*** x ***oreophila***
9 ***psittacina*** x ***alata***
3 ***rubra alabamensis***
3 – ***wherryi***
8 x ***wrigleyana*** AGM

SASSAFRAS
3 ***tzumu***

SATUREJA
3 ***spinosa***
1 ***thymbra***

SATYRIUM
3 ***nepalense***

Plant Deletions

SAUSSUREA
2 ***ceratocarpa***

SAXIFRAGA
2 'Aladdin' (x ***borisii***)(8)
2 'Alan Hayhurst'
8 'Albida' (***callosa***)(7)
2 'Aphrodite' (***sempervivum***)(8)
3 ***aquatica***
2 'Arabella' (x ***edithiae***)(8)
0 'Armida' (x ***boeckeleri***)(8)
2 'Avoca Gem'
2 'Balkan' (***marginata rocheliana***)(8)
2 'Beauty of Letchworth'
0 'Bellisant' (x ***hornibrookii***)(8)
1 'Ben Lawers' (***oppositifolia***)(9)
8 'Big MD' (***andersonii***)(8)
3 'Blanik' (x ***borisii***)(8)
2 ***bronchialis (5)***
1 'Buchholzii' (x ***fleischeri***)(8)
0 'Buster' (x ***hardingii***)(8)
3 ***canaliculata (12)***
3 'Carnival' (12)
2 'Cervinia' (***oppositifolia***)(9)
0 'Chelsea Pink' (x ***urbium***)(3)
2 ***cinerea (8)***
1 'Clare' (x ***anglica***)(8)
3 'Coningsby Queen' (x ***hornibrookii***)(8)
2 'Crinkle' (3)
2 ***crustata vochinensis (7)***
9 'Dawn' (8)
3 ***decumbens***
2 'Diana' (x ***lincoln-fosteri***)(8)
7 ***diversifolia (2)***
0 'Dulcimer' (x ***petraschii***)(8)
3 ***erioblasta (12)***
3 'Ernst Heinrich' (x ***heinrichii***)(8)
0 'Felicity' (x ***anglica***)(8)
1 ***flagellaris flagellaris (2)***
7 'Forsteriana' (***petraea***)
3 'Foster's Gold' (8)
3 'Gaertneri' (***mariae-theresiae***)(8)
2 'Grace'
2 'Grandiflora' (***burseriana***)(8)
0 ***grisebachii montenegrina (8)***
2 'Harry Marshall' (x ***irvingii***)(8)
8 ***hirsuta paucicrenata***
0 ***hypostoma (8)***
0 'Intermedia' (***marginata***)(8)
2 'Josef Mánes' (x ***borisii***)(8)
0 'Jubilee' (x ***edithiae***)(8)
3 'Kathleen'
3 'Kelso' (x ***boydii***)(8)
2 'Kew Green'
2 'Knapton Red' (12)
3 'Knebworth' (***longifolia***)(7)
1 ***latepetiolata (11)***
2 'Loeflingii' (x ***grata***)(8)
3 'Lohmuelleri' (x ***biasolettoi***)(8)
0 ***lolaensis***
0 'London Cerise' (x ***urbium***)(3)
3 'Louise' (***marginata***)(8)
2 ***lyallii (1)***
3 'Magdalena' (x ***thomasiana***)(8)
3 'Major' (***paniculata cartilaginea***)(7)
2 'Mangart' (***burseriana***)(8)
2 x ***mariae-theresiae (8)***
8 ***michauxii (1)***
2 'Midas' (x ***elisabethae***)(8)
1 'Minor' (***marginata coriophylla***)(8)
2 'Monika' (***webrii***)(8)
7 ***mucronulata (2)***
2 'Muffet' (***burseriana***)(8)
1 'Multipunctata' (***paniculata***)(7)
9 'Nana' (***bronchialis***)(5)
7 ***nipponica (4)***
3 ***nivalis (1)***
3 'Oberon' (8)
3 'Old Britain' (x ***boydii***)(8)
7 ***oppositifolia grandiflora (9)***
0 – Iceland form (9)
2 – ***rudolphiana (9)***
3 'Orientalis' (***paniculata***)(7)
2 ***paniculata punctata (7)***
1 x ***patens (6x7)***
0 ***pedemontana cervicornis (12)***
3 ***pentadactylis (12)***
7 'Pike's Primrose' (12)
7 'Pike's White' (12)
2 'Pollux' (x ***boydii***)(8)
3 ***portosanctana (12)***
1 'Priestwood White' (12)
2 x ***pseudoforsteri (3)***
2 'Pseudofranzii' (x ***paulinae***)(8)
1 'Pseudokellereri' (8)
2 'Pseudopaulinae' (x ***paulinae***)(8)
2 'Pseudopungens' (x ***apiculata***)(8)
2 'Pseudoscardica' (x ***wehrhahnii***)(8)
0 ***pulvinaria (8)***
3 'Quarry Wood' (x ***anglica***)(8)
2 'Romeo' (x ***hornibrookii***)(8)
3 'Ronald Young'
3 ***rosacea (12)***
2 'Russell Vincent Prichard' (x ***irvingii***)(8)
2 ***scardica erythrantha (8)***
2 'Seissera' (***burseriana***)(8)
2 ***squarrosa (7)***
8 'Subluteiviridis' (x ***gusmusii***)(8)
2 'Suendermannii Major' (x ***kellereri***)(8)
7 'Theresia' (x ***mariae-theresiae***)
9 'Valerie Keevil' (x ***anglica***)(8)
8 ***vandellii (8)***
1 'Variegata' (***exarata moschata***)(12)
7 'Wargrave Rose' (12)
8 'Waterperry' (***sempervivum***)(8)
2 'White Imp' (8)
3 'Wilhelm Tell' (x ***malbyana***)(8)
3 'Winton'
3 'Witham's Compact'
9 'Zita' (8)

SCABIOSA
2 ***atropurpurea*** dark form
9 ***caucasica*** 'Backhouse'
2 ***japonica*** 'Alba'
9 ***pseudograminifolia***
2 ***speciosa***

SCADOXUS
2 ***multiflorus multiflorus***

SCAEVOLA
1 'Blue Jade'
3 ***calendulacea***

SCHEFFLERA
3 ***arboricola*** 'Beauty'
3 – 'Diane'
3 – 'Henriette'
3 – 'Milena'
3 – 'Worthy'
1 ***elegantissima*** AGM
1 – 'Castor'
1 – 'Castor Variegata'
0 'Starshine'

SCHIMA
9 ***yunnanensis***

SCHINUS
0 ***molle***
0 ***patagonicus***

SCHISANDRA
2 ***sphaerandra***

SCHIZOSTYLIS
3 ***coccinea*** 'Madonna'
8 – 'Rosalie'
8 – 'Rose Glow'

SCHOTIA
3 ***brachypetala***

SCILLA
0 ***bifolia danubialis***
2 ***litardierei hoogiana***
2 ***monanthos***
8 ***nivalis***
3 ***reverchonii***
2 ***siberica*** 'Taurica'
1 ***vvedenskyi***

SCINDAPSUS
0 ***pictus argyraeus*** AGM

SCLERANTHUS
2 ***brockiei***

SCOLIOPUS
3 ***hallii***

SCOPOLIA
3 ***stramoniifolia***

SCROPHULARIA
2 ***grandiflora***
3 ***scorodonia***

SCUTELLARIA
0 ***albida***
2 ***alpina*** 'Alba'
3 ***hyssopus***
1 ***ovata***
3 ***tournefortii***
2 ***ventenatii***

SEDUM
3 ***acre neglectum***
3 ***adolphi***
1 ***album album balticum***
1 – ***ibizicum***
1 – ***teretifolium turgidum***
1 ***alfredii nagasakianum***
1 ***allantoïdes***
1 ***alsinifolium fragrans***
1 ***amecamecanum***
1 ***anglicum anglicum hibernicum***
1 – ***microphyllum***
1 – ***pyrenaicum***
1 ***apoleipon***
2 x ***battandieri***
1 ***borissovae***
1 ***borschii***
1 ***brevifolium induratum***
1 – ***novum***
1 ***brissemoretii***
1 ***burrito***
1 ***caducum***
0 ***cauticola*** 'Robustum'
1 ***cepaea gracilescens***
1 ***chontalense***
1 ***clavatum***
1 ***commixtum***
1 ***compactum***
1 ***compressum***
3 ***confusum***
1 ***craigii***
1 ***dasyphyllum oblongifolium***
3 – – ***riffense***
1 – ***suendermannii***
1 ***decumbens***
1 ***dendroïdeum***
1 ***diffusum***
1 ***ewersii cyclophyllum***
2 – ***hayesii***
1 ***forsterianum purpureum***
1 ***frutescens***
1 ***furfuraceum***
1 ***fusiforme***
1 ***greggii***
3 ***gypsicola glanduliferum***
1 'Harvest Moon'
1 ***hemsleyanum***
1 ***hispanicum*** 'Pewter'
1 ***indicum densirosulatum***
1 – ***yunnanense***
1 ***japonicum***

1 – *senanense*
1 *kostovii*
1 *laconicum*
1 *lancerottense*
1 *laxum*
1 *liebmannianum*
9 *lineare* 'Major'
1 'Little Gem'
1 *longipes*
1 *lucidum*
1 – 'Obesum'
1 x *luteolum*
1 x *luteoviride*
1 *magellense*
3 *middendorfianum* 'Striatum'
1 *moranii*
1 *multiflorum*
1 *nanifolium*
1 *nussbaumerianum*
1 *nutans*
1 *oaxacanum*
1 *obcordatum*
1 *ochroleucum montanum*
2 *oreades*
9 *oreganum boreale*
3 – 'Variegatum'
1 *oryzifolium*
1 *oxycoccoïdes*
1 *oxypetalum*
3 *pachyphyllum*
3 – x *treleasei*
2 *parvum*
9 *pluricaule* 'Rosenteppich' ('Rose Carpet')
1 *potosinum*
9 *reflexum albescens*
8 – 'Major'
1 – 'Viride'
1 *reptans*
1 – *carinatifolium*
1 *rosulatobulbosum*
1 *rubens*
1 – *praegeri*
1 x *rubrotinctum* 'Aurora'
1 *rupifragum*
1 *ruwenzoriense*
9 *sediforme* 'Gran Canaria'
1 *serpentinii*
1 *sexangulare elatum*
1 *sieboldii ettyuense*
1 *spectabile* 'Carmen'
2 – 'Green Ice'
1 – 'Humile'
1 *spurium* 'Bronze Carpet'
1 – *carneum*
1 – *salmoneum*
3 *stahlii*
1 *stefco*
1 *stelliforme*
1 *stenopetalum*
1 *subtile*
1 *treleasei*
9 *tschernokolevii*
1 *tuberiferum*
1 *urvillei*
1 – Hillebrandtii Group
1 – Sartorianum Group
1 – Stribrnyi Group
1 *versadense*
1 – *villadioïdes*
0 *yabeanum*
1 *yesoense*
1 *zentaro-tashiroi*

SELAGINELLA
2 *lepidophylla*
2 *sanguinolenta*

SELAGO
2 *thunbergii*

SELINUM
3 *carvifolia*

SEMPERVIVUM
1 'Alaric'
9 'Big Red'
1 'Blue Moon'
0 *calcareum* 'Benz'
0 'Caliph's Hat'
8 *ciliosum* x *leucanthum*
8 'Clipper'
0 *davisii*
1 'Disco Dancer'
1 *dolomiticum*
0 'Dunstan'
1 *erythraeum* 'Red Velvet'
2 'Ford's Shadows'
2 'Georgette'
2 *glabrifolium*
0 *globiferum*
1 'Haullauer's Seedling'
9 'Jubilation'
9 'Jungle Shadows'
8 'Kolagas Mayfair'
9 'Kristina'
1 'Kubi'
1 Le Clair's Hybrid No 4
0 *leucanthum*
0 'Madame Arsac'
8 *marmoreum* x *dinaricum* from Karawanken
0 *minus*
0 *montanum carpaticum* 'Cmiral's Yellow'
9 'Mors'
8 'Mount Usher'
0 'Mrs Elliott'
7 *pumilum* x *arachnoïdeum*
0 'Purdy's 90-1'
9 'Red Planet'
0 'Red Rum'
9 'Roosemaryn'
1 x *roseum*
1 'Rotund'
2 'Rubrum Ash'
8 'Ruby'
8 'Samba'
9 'Sponnier'
9 'Syston Flame'
8 *tectorum cantalicum*
9 'Wega'
9 'Witchery'
0 *zeleborii* x *kosaninii* from Koprivnik

SENECIO
0 *adonidifolius*
1 *canus*
1 *confusus*
8 *doronicum*
3 *gillesii*
3 *gnaphaloïdes*
0 *hypochionaeus argaeus*
1 *incanus carniolicus*
1 *jacquemontianus*
3 *leucophyllus*
9 *littoralis*
2 *natalensis*
2 *pectinatus*
3 *tamoïdes*

SENNA
8 *acutifolia*
1 *retusa*

SERENOA
0 *repens*

SESBANIA
2 *punicea*

SHORTIA
0 *galacifolia*
0 – *brevistyla*
9 x *interdexta* 'Wimborne'
3 *soldanelloïdes*
3 – dwarf form
3 – *ilicifolia* 'Askival'
0 – *magna*
0 – *minima*
1 *uniflora*
9 – *kantoensis*

SIBBALDIOPSIS
2 *tridentata*

SIDA
3 *napaea*

SIDALCEA
3 'Monarch'
3 'Rosanna'
0 'Rose Bouquet'

SIDERITIS
3 *scardica*

SILENE
0 *acaulis variegata*
1 *altaica*
1 'Bill Mackenzie'
0 *burchellii*
3 *californica alba*
1 *caryophylloïdes*
1 – *echinus*
3 *ciliata*
3 *dioica* 'Perkin'(v)
0 – 'Tresevern Gold'
3 *flavescens*
9 *hookeri bolanderi*
8 'Pink Bells'
1 *rupestris*
9 *saxifraga*
8 *schafta* 'Robusta'
1 *scouleri*
3 *undulata*
1 *vulgaris prostrata*

SINNINGIA
2 'Brilliant Scarlet'
3 *canescens* AGM
3 'Foxy Blue'
3 *leucotricha*
2 'Royal Purple'

SINOJACKIA
2 *xylocarpa*

SINOWILSONIA
2 *henryi*

SISYMBRIUM
9 *officinale*

SISYRINCHIUM
2 *californicum* British Columbia form
2 *convolutum*
3 'Wisley Blue'

SKIMMIA
0 *multinervia*

SMILAX
3 *china*

SMYRNIUM
9 *perfoliatum rotundifolium*

SOLANUM
1 *aculeatissimum*
0 *capsicastrum* 'Variegatum'
0 *elaeagnifolium*
1 *muricatum* 'Ryburn'
3 *nigrum*
3 *pseudocapsicum* 'Mandarin'
0 *valdiviense*
1 – 'Variegatum'

SOLDANELLA
2 x *ganderi*

SOLENOPSIS
1 *erianthum*

SOLENOSTEMON
3 'Brightness' (v)
3 'Charles Rudd'
3 'Midnight'

SOLIDAGO
9 'Goldenplume'
2 'Goldwedel'
8 'Leraft'
2 'Septembergold'
0 *ulmifolia*

SOPHORA
9 *japonica* 'Violacea'
1 *tetraptera* 'Goughensis'
2 – 'Grandiflora'

SORBUS
3 *aucuparia* gold
8 – 'Pendula'
2 'Ethel's Gold'
1 *graeca*
1 *hupehensis obtusa* 'Rufus'
0 *mougeotii*
3 *pygmaea*
2 'Red Marbles'
2 'Signalman'
2 'Tundra'
3 *vexans*

SPARTINA
1 *pectinata* 'Variegata'

SPATHICARPA
0 *sagittifolia*

SPATHIPHYLLUM
0 *cannifolium*
0 *cochlearispathum*
0 *cuspidatum*
0 *floribundum*

0 'Mauna Loa' AGM
0 'McCoy'
0 *patinii*

SPHAERALCEA
3 Dixfield hybrids

SPHENOTOMA
1 *gracilis*

SPIGELIA
2 *marilandica*

SPIRAEA
3 *nipponica* 'Rotundifolia'

SPIRANTHES
3 *spiralis*

SPIRODELA
9 *polyrhiza*

STACHYS
3 *alpina*
3 *byzantina* 'Margery Fish'
7 *corsica*
3 *niveum*

STACHYTARPHETA
1 *jamaicensis*

STACHYURUS
1 *leucotrichus*
9 *spinosus*

STAEHELINA
3 *uniflosculosa*

STANLEYA
0 *pinnata*
8 *pinnatifida*

STENANTHIUM
9 *robustum*

STENOTUS
8 *andersonii*

STICTOCARDIA
2 *beraviensis*

STIPA
1 *atropurpurea*
3 *calensis*
3 *pulcherrima*

STREPTOCARPUS
3 'Anna'
3 'Blue Nymph'
3 'Diana' AGM
2 'Eira'
3 *holstii*
3 hybrids
3 'Lesley'
3 'Marie'
3 'New Buckenham'
3 'Olga'

STREPTOPUS
0 *axillaris*
1 *simplex*

STROBILANTHES
2 *urticifolius*

STROMANTHE
0 *porteana*

STROPHANTHUS
3 *divaricatus*

STYLIDIUM
1 *graminifolium*

STYLOMECON
3 *heterophylla*

STYRAX
2 *dasyanthus*
0 *officinalis*
2 *wilsonii*

SUCCISA
3 Orkney dwarf form
9 *pratensis rosea*

SUTERA
2 *pristisepala*

SWAINSONA
1 *procumbens*

SWERTIA
0 *longifolia*
1 *petiolata*

SYMPHORICARPOS
2 x *doorenbosii* 'Erect'

SYMPHYANDRA
2 *ossettica* hybrids

SYMPHYTUM
1 *officinale* 'Bohemicum'

SYNEILESIS
1 *palmata*

SYNGONIUM
0 *podophyllum* AGM
3 – 'Emerald Gem'

SYRINGA
9 x *chinensis*
2 x *henryi*
7 x *hyacinthiflora* 'Alice Eastwood'
2 – 'Blue Hyacinth'
8 – 'Buffon'
2 – 'Clarke's Giant'
2 *julianae*
0 'Minuet'
0 'Miss Canada'
9 *oblata*
9 x *persica* 'Gigantea'
1 x *prestoniae* 'Coral'
9 – 'Hiawatha'
1 – 'James Macfarlane'
3 – 'Kim'
1 – 'Nocturne'
1 – 'Redwine'
1 *reticulata* 'Ivory Silk'
3 *tomentella*
1 *villosa*
9 *vulgaris* 'Alphonse Lavallée'(d)
9 – 'Ambassadeur'
9 – 'Charles X'
2 – 'Ellen Willmott'(d)
9 – 'Etna'
9 – 'General John Pershing'(d)
7 – 'Lavaliensis'
9 – 'Maréchal de Bassompierre'(d)
9 – 'Maréchal Foch'(d)
0 – 'Marie Legraye'
7 – 'Monique Lemoine'(d)
7 – 'Night'
2 – 'Paul Thirion'(d)
7 – 'Réaumur'
9 – 'Ruhm von Horstenstein'
9 – 'Souvenir d'Alice Harding'(d)
0 – 'William Robinson'(d)
0 *wolfii*

TAIWANIA
2 *cryptomerioïdes*

TALINUM
1 *okanoganense* pink-stemmed
2 *parviflorum*
3 *rugospermum*

TANACETUM
9 *bipinnatum*
9 *coccineum* 'Bees' Pink Delight'
3 – 'J N Twerdy'
2 – 'Jubilee Gem'
0 – 'Kelway's Glorious'
9 – 'Langport Scarlet'
3 – 'Laurin'
0 – 'Marjorie Robinson'
3 – 'Peter Pan'
3 – 'Phillipa'
8 – 'Red King'
1 – 'Sam Robinson'
7 – 'Silver Challenger'
7 *corymbosum clusii*
9 *dolichophyllum*
3 *parthenium* 'Golden Moss'
3 – 'Selma Tetra'
2 – 'Snowball'(d)
2 – 'Spirit'
2 – 'Sundew'
3 sp. JJH 463

TARAXACUM
1 *albidum*

TAXODIUM
3 *distichum imbricatum*

TAXUS
0 *baccata* 'Cavendishii'
1 – 'Cheshuntensis'
1 – 'Glauca'
3 – 'Gracilis Pendula'
2 – 'Grayswood Hill'
2 – 'Lutea'
7 – 'Nana'
9 – 'Prostrata'
0 – 'Pyramidalis'
3 – 'Rushmore'
9 *cuspidata*
7 – 'Densa'
3 – 'Golden Jubilee'
1 – 'Minima'
3 – 'Robusta'
0 x *hunnewelliana* 'Richard Horsey'
0 x *media* 'Halloran'
1 – 'Kelseyi'
1 – 'Skalborg'

TECOMA
1 *garrocha*

TELLIMA
1 *grandiflora* 'Perky'
0 – 'Pinky'

TEPHROSERUS
2 *takedanus*

TERNSTROEMIA
1 *japonica*

TETRADIUM
7 *velutinum*

TETRANEURIS
0 *acaulis glabra*
2 – *ivesiana*

TEUCRIUM
9 *polium pii-fontii*
3 *scoridifolia*
8 *subspinosum roseum*
2 *webbianum*

THALICTRUM
8 *delavayi* 'Amethystine'
8 *petaloïdes*
2 *reniforme*

THAMNOCALAMUS
3 *aristatus*

THELYPTERIS
9 *dentata*
3 sp. from Nepal

THEVETIA
3 *peruviana*

THLASPI
9 *alpinum auerswalde*

THRINAX
0 *parviflora*

THUJA
7 *occidentalis* 'Cloth of Gold'
8 – 'Columbia'
3 – 'Cuprea'
2 – 'Globosa Compacta Nana'
2 – 'Indomitable'
1 – 'Madurodam'
2 – 'Malonyana'
0 – 'Mastersii'
0 – 'Robusta'
8 – 'Semperaurea'
2 – 'Vervaeneana'
1 *orientalis* 'Berckman'
3 – 'Golden Sceptre'
1 – 'Green Cone'
9 – 'Hillieri'
3 – 'Minima Aurea'
3 – 'Shirley Chilcott'
2 *plicata* 'Extra Gold'
8 – 'Savill Gardens'
2 *standishii*

THYMUS
3 'Belle Orchard'
2 *carnosus* 'Argenteus'
3 *cephalotos*
0 *corsicus*
1 *hirsutus*
1 *hyemalis* 'Albus'
3 *pseudolanuginosus* 'Hall's Variety'
2 *serpyllum* 'Carol Ann'(v)
7 – 'Little Heath'

1 – 'Pink Ripple'
2 – 'Silver Dew'
8 – 'Winter Beauty'
7 'Southcombe Spreader'
9 *striatus*
8 'Wintergold'

TIGRIDIA
2 *van-houttei*

TILIA
3 *cordata* 'Dainty Leaf'
1 x *flavescens*
3 *koreana*

TILLANDSIA
2 *achyrostachys*
3 *acostae concolor*
2 *aëranthos*
2 *albertiana*
2 *albida*
2 *anceps*
2 *andreana*
2 *andrieuxii*
2 *araujei*
2 *arhiza*
2 *atroviridipetala*
2 *bartramii*
2 *bergeri*
2 *cacticola*
2 *capitata* 'Peach'
2 – 'Rubra'
2 *carlsoniae*
2 *chiapensis*
2 *complanata*
2 *compressa*
2 *concolor*
2 *crocata*
2 *disticha*
2 *duratii*
2 *ehlersiana*
2 *elizabethiae*
2 *erubescens*
2 *exserta*
2 *fasciculata*
2 *festucoïdes*
3 *flabellata rubra*
2 *flexuosa*
2 *floribunda*
2 *funckiana*
2 *gymnobotrya*
2 *hammeri*
2 *harrisii*
3 *himmorum*
2 *incarnata*
3 *ionantha* 'Blushing Bride'
3 – 'Fireball'
3 – 'Fuego'
2 – *stricta*
2 – *vanhyningii*
2 *ixioïdes*
2 *jaliscomonticola*
2 *kautskyi*
2 *kirchhoffiana*
3 *lampropoda*
2 *latifolia divaricata*
2 *leiboldiana*
2 *loliacea*
2 *lucida*
2 *macdougallii*
2 *makoyana*
2 *mallemontii*
2 *massiliense vivipara*
2 *mauryana*
2 *meridionalis*
2 *mima*
2 *mitlaensis*
2 *monadelpha*
2 *multicaulis*
2 *multiflora*
2 *myosura*
2 *neglecta*
2 *paleacea*
2 *paucifolia*
2 – *prolifera*
2 *plagiotropica*
2 *plumosa*
3 x *polita*
3 *prodigiosa*
2 *pseudobaileyi*
2 *pueblensis*
2 *purpurea*
2 *recurvata*
2 *roland-gosselinii*
2 *schatzlii*
2 *schiedeana glabrior*
2 – *major*
2 *setacea*
2 *straminea*
2 *streptocarpa*
2 *streptophylla*
2 *stricta*
2 *tectorum*
2 *tenuifolia*
2 – *saxicola*
2 – *tenuifolia*
2 *tricholepis*
2 *tricolor*
3 *utriculata*
2 *variabllis*
2 *vernicosa*
3 *vicentina glabra*
2 *viridiflora*

TITHONIA
2 *rotundifolia*

TONESTUS
1 *pygmaeus*

TORREYA
3 *californica*
0 *grandis*
0 *nucifera* 'Spreadeagle'

TOWNSENDIA
1 *eximia*
0 *hirsuta*

TRACHELIUM
3 *jacquinii*

TRACHYMENE
0 *humilis*

TRADESCANTIA
0 x *andersoniana* 'Lilacina Plena'
8 – 'Purple Glow'
9 – 'Taplow Crimson'
7 *brevicaulis caerulea*
3 *chilensis*
0 *spathacea*
2 *tabulaemontana*
3 *zebrina discolor*
3 – 'Purpusii' AGM
3 – 'Quadricolor'(v) AGM

TRAGOPOGON
0 *ruber*

TREVESIA
9 *palmata* 'Micholitzii'

TRICYRTIS
3 *formosana* 'Shelley's'
9 – 'Variegata'
0 *hirta* dwarf form
1 *japonica* 'Kinkazan'
3 *lambertii*
3 *puberula*

TRIFOLIUM
3 *pratense* 'Green Ice'
3 – 'Harlequin'(v)
3 – 'Purple Velvet'
3 *repens* 'Variegatum'

TRILLIUM
2 *decumbens*
2 *discolor*
2 *erectum roseum*
9 *flexipes*
3 *lancifolium*
2 *nervosum*
3 *nivale*
2 *pusillum*
2 *rugelii* pink

TRIOSTEUM
1 *erythrocarpum*

TRIPETALEIA
2 *bracteata*

TRIPLEUROSPERUM
3 *maritimum*

TRIPOGANDRA
3 *multiflora*

TRITICUM
2 *spelta*

TROCHOCARPA
2 *gunnii*

TROLLIUS
8 x *cultorum* 'Byrne's Giant'
0 – 'Empire Day'
0 – 'Glory of Leiden'
0 – 'Meteor'
0 – 'Orange Glow'
0 – 'Orangekönig'
0 – 'Oranje Nassau'
0 – 'T Smith'
0 – 'Yellow Beauty'

TSUGA
3 *canadensis* 'Ammerland'
7 – 'Dawsonia'
7 – 'Essex'
7 – 'Gentsch Variegated'
7 – 'Greenwood Lake'
2 – 'Nana Gracilis'
2 *caroliniana*
7 *chinensis tchekiangensis*
7 *dumosa*
2 *heterophylla* 'Greenmantle'
2 – 'Laursen's Column'
3 *mertensiana*
2 – 'Glauca'
0 *sieboldii*
9 *yunnanensis*

TUBERARIA
9 *globulariifolia*

TULBAGHIA
1 *capensis* 'Variegatus'
3 *fragrans*

TULIPA
3 'African Queen' (3)
9 'Aga Khan'
1 'Akela' (3)
9 'Annie Salomons' (14)
3 'Arie Alkemade's Memory (2)
1 'Astarte' (3)
2 *aximensis*
1 'Baby Doll' (2)
3 'Ballade' (6) AGM
1 'Ballerina' (6)
1 'Baronesse' (3)
1 Beauty Queen ® (1)
1 *biflora* forms
1 'Bird of Paradise' (10)
1 'Black Diamond' (5)
3 'Black Swan' (5)
3 'Blizzard' (1)
9 'Blushing Beauty' (S)
9 'Blushing Bride' (5)
1 *buhseana*
9 'Chatham' (5)
1 'China Lady' (14) AGM
1 'Christmas Dream' (1)
1 *clusiana chrysantha* 'Diplomate' (4)
9 'Compostella' (14)
9 'Dante' (2)
3 'Daydream' (4)
9 'Demeter' (5) AGM
9 'Dreamboat' (14)
1 'Dreamland' (5)
9 'Dutch Princess' (3)
1 Early Glory ® (3)
9 'Ellen Willmott' (6)
3 'Fancy Frills' (7)
3 'Fidelio' (3) AGM
1 Fire Queen ® (1)
1 'Françoise' (5)
1 'Gerbrand Kieft' (11)
9 'Gold Coin'
8 *goulimyi*
1 'Hamilton' (7)
2 'Happy Family' (3)
3 'Hermione' (11)
3 'High Society' (3)
9 'Hocus Pocus' (5)
3 *humilis* 'Violet Queen'
1 'Ivory Floradale' (4)
1 'Jenny' (1)
3 'Johann Gutenberg' (7)
1 *julia*
1 'Juri Gagarin' (14)
3 *karabaghensis*
3 'Koningin Wilhelmina' (4) AGM
3 'Kryptos' (5)
1 'Lady Montgomery' (11)
1 'Laverock' (7)
1 'Leen van der Mark' (3)
3 'Lighting Sun' (5)
3 'Lilac Perfection' (11)
9 'Lutea Major' (10)
1 'Majestic' (14)

3 'Marjolein' (6) AGM
3 'Meissner Porzellan' (3)
3 'Mirella' (5) AGM
1 'Modern Style' (5)
9 'Musical' (3)
9 'Niphetos' (5)
1 'Noranda' (7)
3 'Olympic Flame' (4)
3 'Olympic Gold' (4)
8 'Orange Boy' (12)
1 'Orange King' (5)
0 ***orphanidea*** 'Splendens'
1 'Oscar' (3)
9 Peacock strain (***greigii*** x ***kaufmanniana***)
3 'Perfecta' (10)
9 'Pink Emperor' (13)
0 ***planifolia***
9 'Primrose' (12)
9 'Prince Charles' (3)
2 'Princesse Charmante' (14)
3 'Prinses Margriet' (1)
1 'Red Reflection' (14)
3 'Redwing' (7)
2 'Rhodos' (5)
3 'Robinea' (3)
1 'Rococo' (10)
1 'Rosanna' (14)
1 'Rosella' (5)
1 'Rosy Queen' (2)
1 'Salmon Parrot' (10)
3 'San Marino' (5)
9 'Show Girl' (5)
1 'Smyrna' (14)
3 'Snow Queen' (2)
1 'Sun Dance' (14)
3 'Sussex' (5)
2 'Sylvia Warder' (14)
9 'Tambour Maître' (3)
9 'Tarakan' (5)
1 'Temple of Beauty' (5) AGM
9 'Timay'
1 'Treasure' (14)
1 Trendsetter ® (3)
8 ***vvedenskyi*** 'Josef Marks'
0 – 'Orange Sunset'
9 'Water Lily'
1 'Wienerwald' (3)
1 'Wirosa' (11)
1 'Yellow Parrot' (10)
9 'Yellow River'

TUTCHERIA
9 ***spectabilis***

UGNI
0 ***molinae*** 'Variegata'

ULEX
2 ***europaeus*** 'Dubloon'
3 ***gallii***

ULMUS
9 ***glabra*** 'Lutescens'
2 – 'Pendula'
2 'Louis van Houtte'
0 ***minor*** 'Sarniensis'

UNCINIA
3 ***egmontiana***

UNGNADIA
7 ***speciosa***

URSINIA
2 ***chrysanthemoïdes***
1 ***sericea***

UTRICULARIA
3 ***aurea***
3 ***australis***
3 ***caerulea***
3 ***capensis***
3 ***fibrosa***

UVULARIA
2 ***caroliniana***

VACCINIUM
2 ***angustifolium***
3 – Newfoundland form
0 ***consanguineum***
3 ***constablei***
2 ***corymbosum*** 'Blue Ray'
2 – 'Earliblue'
9 – 'Tifblue'
9 – 'Woodward'
3 ***deliciosum***
2 ***membranaceum***
2 ***myrsinites***
1 ***nubigenus***
2 ***sprengelii***

VALLEA
3 ***stipularis***

VEITCHIA
2 ***merrillii***

VERBASCUM
3 ***acaule***
2 Cotswold Hybrid Group 'Hartleyi'
9 'Golden Bush'
9 ***pestalozzae***

VERBENA
2 ***bipinnatifida***
3 ***canadensis*** 'Perfecta'
2 'Cardinal'
1 'Hecktor'
1 ***peruviana*** Japanese form
3 ***rigida*** 'Lilacina'

VERNONIA
3 ***mespilifolia***

VERONICA
7 ***armena rosea***
8 ***cusickii***
7 x ***cynarium***
0 'Green Mound'
3 ***prostrata*** 'Pavlava Hills'
3 ***spicata*** 'Mori's Form'
3 – 'Nana Blauteppich'
0 ***tauricola*** Ala Dag
3 ***teucrioïdes***
3 ***virense***
8 ***virgata***

VIBURNUM
7 'Aldenhamensis'
1 ***burejaeticum***
1 ***calvum***
1 ***dentatum pubescens*** 'Longifolium'
9 ***dilatatum*** 'Erie'
3 ***foetidum***
2 ***grandiflorum*** Foetens Group
2 ***hupehense***
1 ***ichangense***
1 ***kansuense***
3 ***koreanum***
2 ***lobophyllum***
1 ***mullaha***
1 ***opulus*** 'Andrews'
1 – 'Apricot'
2 – 'Flore Pleno'
3 – 'Fructu Luteo'
1 – 'Hans'
2 – 'Harvest Gold'
9 – 'Wentworth'
1 ***parvifolium***
2 ***plicatum*** 'Rosace'
2 – 'Roseum'
2 ***propinquum***
2 ***prunifolium***
2 ***rigidum***
3 ***sempervirens***
2 ***setigerum sulcatum***
3 ***sieboldii***
3 – 'Seneca'
2 ***tinus*** 'Little Bognor'
1 ***veitchii***

VICIA
9 ***bithynica***
0 ***orobus***

VICTORIA
0 ***amazonica***
0 ***cruziana***

VIGNA
3 ***caracalla***

VILLADIA
1 ***ramossisima***

VINCA
2 ***difformis argentea***
3 ***minor acutiloba***

VIOLA
0 'Adam's Gold' (Va)
1 ***adunca***
2 'Agnes Susannah'
3 'Anita' (Va)
1 'Anna' (Va)
9 'Arlington' (C)
2 'Avalanche' (Va)
2 'Baby Blue'
2 'Baby Franjo'
2 'Bambini' (Va)
0 'Barbara Swan' (ExV)
0 'Beth'
3 ***betonicifolia oblonga sagittata***
0 – white
3 'Bishop's Belle' (FP)
9 ***blanda***
3 'Blue Emperor'
2 'Blue Heaven' (Va)
2 'Blue Perfection' (Va)
1 'Blue Ripple'
2 'Blue Skies' (C)
0 'Blue Waves'
7 'Bob's Bedder'
1 'Bonnie Heather' (Va)
9 ***camschatalorum***
9 ***canina montana***
9 'Captivation'
2 'Cendrillon' (Vt)
9 ***cenisia***
9 'Chandler's Glory'
0 'Cheekie Chappie'
2 'Colwall' (C)
2 'Constellation'
0 ***cornuta*** pale blue
1 – ***rotundiflora***
9 ***crassiuscula***
2 'Cuty' (Va)
2 CW 5021
3 'Dirty Molly'
2 'Double Blue' (dVt)
2 'Double Russian' (dVt)
3 'Elizabeth Robb' (FP)
1 'Evelyn Jackson' (Va)
0 'Fairy Tales' (Va)
3 'George Rowley' (FP)
3 'Glenroyd Fancy' (ExV)
3 'Gloriole'
9 ***gracilis*** x ***cornuta***
0 'Haze' (Va)
1 'Horrie' (Va)
3 'Hudsons Blue'
3 'Hugh Campbell' (ExV)
3 'Hyacintha' (C)
3 'Irene Missen'
1 'Irina' (Va)
3 'James Christie' (FP)
8 'Jane' (Va)
0 'Jenny Wren' (Va)
3 'Jimmie's Dark' (ExV)
3 'Joan Christie' (FP)
3 'Joe Millet' (FP)
1 'John Rodger' (SP)
1 'Josie'
3 'Kathleen Hoyle' (ExV)
0 'Kathleen Williams' (ExV)
8 'Lady May'
0 'Lady Saville'
2 'Lindy'
1 'Lizzie's Favourite' (Va)
2 ***lutea lutea***
9 'Magic Lantern'
7 'Major'
0 ***mandshurica triangularis bicolor***
0 'Mandy Miller' (Va)
3 'Mark Talbot' (Va)
2 'Marquis de Brazais' (Vt)
3 'Mavis Tuck'
3 'May Roberts' (ExV)
2 'Melita'
3 'Midnight' (Va)
9 'Moonshadow'
2 'Moonshine'
1 'Moseley Bedder'
0 'Mrs Alex Forrest' (ExV)
3 'Mrs Reid's French'
7 'Nickie's Blue' (C)
3 'Nora May' (Va)
3 ***nuttallii vallicola***
3 ***odorata*** 'Aurea'
0 – blue double
0 – 'Caerulea Plena'
9 'Old Blue'
8 'Old Jordans'
2 'Oxbrook Cream'
0 'Peggy Brookes' (FP)
3 ***riviniana*** 'Autumn White'
0 'Roem van Aalsmeer'
2 'Royal Picotee'
3 ***scariensis***
1 ***sempervirens***

3 ***sheltonii***
1 'Spey' (C)
3 'Spode Blue'
3 'Stewart William' (FP)
2 'Sulphur Queen'
3 'Sunshine' (Va)
2 'Sybil Cornfield'
1 'The Clevedon Violet' (Vt)
9 ***tricolor subalpina***
9 'Triumph' (Vt)
1 'Tropical Waves'
2 x ***visseriana***
0 'Wendy' (SP)
1 'White Waves'
3 'William Fife' (ExV)
3 'Woodlands Gold' (Va)

VITALIANA
2 ***primuliflora cinerea***
2 – silver-leaved

VITEX
7 ***agnus-castus*** 'Albus'
3 – 'Silver Spire'
2 ***incisa***
1 ***negundo heterophylla***

VITIS
3 'Alden' (O/ W)
3 'Alzey Red' (***vinifera***)(O/ R)
3 'Aris' (O/ W)
2 ***betulifolia***
3 'Canadice'
2 ***davidii***
1 – ***cyanocarpa***
3 'Emerald Riesling' (***vinifera***)(O/ W)
3 'Glenora'
8 'Isabella' (***vinifera***)
1 'Madame Mathias Muscat' (***vinifera***)
3 'Maréchal Foch' (O/ B)
3 'Nobling' (***vinifera***)(O/ W)
3 'Phoenix' (***vinifera***)(O/ W)
8 ***piasezkii***
3 'Pinot Meunier' (***vinifera***)(O/ B)
3 'Ramdas' (O/ W)
3 'Rotberger' (***vinifera***)(O/ G/ B)
3 'Schuyler' (O/ B)
3 'Traminer' (***vinifera***)(O/ W)
3 'Vanessa'
3 'Venus'
1 'Wabetta' (***vinifera***)
3 ***wilsoniae***

VRIESEA
2 ***barclayana barclayana***
2 – ***minor***
2 ***cereicola***
2 ***espinosae***
2 'Favorite'
0 ***fenestralis***
0 ***fosteriana*** AGM
0 – 'Red Chestnut'
0 ***gigantea***
2 Hitchcockiana
2 'Margot'
0 ***platynema***
0 – 'Variegata'
2 ***rauhii***
1 ***splendens*** 'Fire'
2 ***tequendamae***
2 Tiffany
2 ***zamorensis***

WAHLENBERGIA
7 ***cartilaginea***
3 ***ceracea***
1 ***gloriosa*** white
2 ***lobelioïdes***
2 ***undulata***

WALDSTEINIA
2 ***rosaceae***

WASHINGTONIA
0 ***lindenii***

WATSONIA
0 ***fourcadei***
1 ***marginata alba***
7 'Starspike'
2 Tresco hybrids

WEIGELA
9 'Conquête'
2 ***florida venusta***
8 ***japonica***
1 ***lonicera***
2 ***praecox***
0 'Stelzneri'
9 ***subsessilis***
9 'Van Houttei'

WIGANDIA
3 ***caracasana***

WISTERIA
9 ***floribunda*** 'Kuchi-beni'

WOODSIA
3 ***mollis***

WOODWARDIA
0 ***orientalis***
3 ***virginica***

WULFENIA
2 ***amherstiana***
2 ***baldaccii***
2 x ***suendermanii***

XANTHOSOMA
0 ***violaceum***

YUCCA
0 ***aloifolia*** 'Purpurea'
2 ***filamentosa*** 'Schneefichte'
9 ***gloriosa*** 'Albovariegata'

ZAMIOCULCAS
0 ***zamiifolia***

ZANTEDESCHIA
3 ***aethiopica*** 'Childsiana'
1 ***angustiloba***
2 'Aztec Gold'
3 'Carmine Red'
2 'Dusky Pink'
1 'Galaxy'
2 'Golden Affair'
1 'Golden Sun'
1 'Lady Luck'
2 'Majestic Red'
3 'Monique'
1 'Treasure'

ZANTHOXYLUM
2 ***schinifolium***

ZAUSCHNERIA
9 ***californica cana*** 'Splendens Plena'
3 – ***garrettii***

ZENOBIA
7 ***pulverulenta nitida***

ZIERIA
8 ***arborescens***

ZIGADENUS
3 ***fremontii***
9 ***glaberrimus***
3 ***leimanthoïdes***
1 ***muscitoxicus***

ZINNIA
1 ***grandiflora***

ZIZIPHORA
3 ***pamiroalaica***

Hardy Plant Society Search List

The following plants, for which no source is known in the British Isles, are being sought by the Hardy Plant Society. If any one knows the whereabouts of any items, seed or plant, on this list, in the British Isles or overseas, would they please contact:-
Mrs Jean Sambrook, Garden Cottage, 214 Ruxley Lane, West Ewell, Surrey KT19 9EZ

ABRONIA
umbellata
ACAENA
caesiiglauca 'Frikart'
ACONITUM
delavayi
fletcherianum
pulchellum
ADONIS
dahurica 'Pleniflora'
AGAPANTHUS
'Dorothy Palmer'
nutans
praecox
'Aureovariegatus'
'Rosemary'
'Victoria'
AGERATUM
orientale 'Leichtlinii'
– 'Pallidum'
AJUGA
reptans 'Silver Beauty'
ALLIUM
protensum
ALSTROEMERIA
'Afterglow'
'Ballerina'
caryophyllea 'Alba'
haemantha 'Parigo Charm'
'Sonata'
AMARYLLIS
bella-donna 'Barberton'
– 'Cape Town'
– 'Elata' ('Pallida')
– 'Jagersfontein'
– 'Maxima'
– 'Rosea'
– 'Rosea Perfecta'
– 'Spectabilis' ('S. Tricolor')
ANEMONE
glauciifolia
hupehensis 'Crispa'
x *hybrida* 'Beauté Parfait'
– 'Brilliant'
– 'Collerette'
– 'Herbstrose'
– 'Herzblut'
– 'Lady Ardilaun'
– 'Lord Ardilaun'
– 'Magdalena Uhink'
– 'Magenta'
– 'Mignon'
– 'Stuttgard'
– 'Treasure'
– 'Turban'
– 'Vase d'Argent'
nemorosa 'Rubra Plena'
tenuifolia
ANTHEMIS
tinctoria 'Moonlight'
– 'Perry's Variety'
ARISAEMA
angustina
ARISTOLOCHIA
moupinensis
ARMERIA
maritima white foliage
ARTEMISIA
ifranensis
ARUM
besserianum
longispathum
orientale danicum
ASARUM
shuttleworthii 'Callaway'
ASCLEPIAS
tuberosa 'Gerbe d'Or'
ASPARAGUS
tenuifolius
ASPHODELINE
amurensis 'Flore Pleno'
lutea 'Flore Pleno'
ASTER
amellus 'Bessie Chapman'
paternus
thomsonii 'Winchmore Hill'
ASTILBE
'Aureoreticulata' (*japonica*)
'Mars' (x *arendsii*)
ASYNEUMA
campanuloïdes
ATHYRIUM
vidalii
AUBRIETA
'Aileen'
'King of the Purples'
'Purple Splendour'
BAPTISIA
alba
perfoliata
BEGONIA
grandis 'Maria'
– 'Simsii'
BELLIS
perennis 'Eliza'
– 'Helichrysiflora'
– 'Lutea'
– 'Madame Crousse'
– 'Mavourneen'
– 'Mount Etna'
– 'Rubriflora'
– 'Victoria'
BERGENIA
crassifolia 'Variegata'
'Walter Kienli'
BERKHEYA
macrophylla
BETA
vulgaris 'Variegata'
BOMAREA
andimarcana
carderi
BRASSICA
Four Seasons Cabbage
BRUNNERA
macrophylla 'Blaukuppel'
BULBINELLA
modesta
BUPLEURUM
ranunculoïdes 'Canalease'
CACCINIA
macrantha
CALCEOLARIA
integrifolia white
CALTHA
laeta alpestris
leptosepala 'Grandiflora'
– *leptosepala* blue flowered
novae-zelandiae
palustris Elata Group
– 'Pallida Plena'
– 'Pleurisepala'
– 'Purpurascens'
– 'Semiplena'
– Silvestris Group
CALYSTEGIA
gigantea
CAMASSIA
leichtlinii 'Orion'
CAMPANULA
'Fergusonii'
'Gremlin'
'Pamela'
persicifolia 'Blue Bell'
– 'Spetchley'
'Profusion'
rapunculoïdes 'Plena'
trachelium 'Versicolor'
'Woodstock'
zoysii alba
CANNA
'Feuerzauber'
x *generalis* 'America'
'Liebesglut'
CARDAMINE
nemorosa 'Plena'
CATANANCHE
caerulea 'Perry's White'
CENTAUREA
atropurpurea 'Alba'
CENTRANTHUS
ruber 'Bragg's Variety'
CHAEROPHYLLUM
hirsutum 'Rubriflorum'
CHASMANTHE
intermedia
CHELONE
obliqua 'Praecox Nana'
CIMICIFUGA
simplex 'Braunlaub'
variegated form
CLEMATIS
recta 'Plena'
COCHLEARIA
officinalis 'Variegata'
COLCHICUM
callicymbium 'Danton'
guadarramense
'Mr Kerbert'
'President Coolidge'
triphyllum
CONVALLARIA
majalis 'Gigantea'
– 'Robusta'
– 'Rosea Plena'
COREOPSIS
grandiflora 'Perry's Variety'
CORTADERIA
selloana 'Bertini'
COSMOS
scabiosoïdes
CRAMBE
pinnatifida
CRINUM
x *powellii* 'Krelagei'
– 'Variegatum'
CROCOSMIA
'Mephistopheles'
CROCUS
'Albidus'
chrysanthus 'Al Jolson'
– 'Andromeda'
– 'Atom'
– 'Aubade'
– 'Belle Jaune'
– 'Bloemfontein'
– 'Blue Beauty'
– 'Blue Bonnet'

– 'Blue Butterfly'
– 'Blue Jacket'
– 'Blue Jay'
– 'Blue Princess'
– 'Blue Rock'
– 'Blue Throat'
– 'Bullfinch'
– 'Bumble-bee'
– 'Buttercup'
– 'Constellation'
– 'Crescendo'
– 'Cum Laude'
– 'Cupido'
– 'Curlew'
– 'Dandy'
– 'Distinction'
– 'Golden Pheasant'
– 'Golden Plover'
– 'Goldene Sonne'
– 'Grand Gala'
– 'Grey Lady'
– 'Harlequin'
– 'Ivory Glory'
– 'Ivory Glow'
– 'Jester'
– 'Johan Cruyff'
– 'Khaki'
– 'Koh-i-Nor'
– 'Lemon Queen'
– 'Lentejuweel'
– 'Lilette'
– 'Lilliputaner'
– 'Magic'
– 'Mannequin'
– 'Mariette'
– 'Marion'
– 'Marlene'
– 'Morning Star'
– 'Mrs Moon'
– 'Mystic'
– 'Nanette'
– 'Olympiade'
– 'Opal'
– 'Palette'
– 'Parade'
– 'Paradiso'
– 'Plaisir'
– 'Reverence'
– 'Rising Sun'
– 'Ruby Gown'
– 'Shot'
– 'Siskin'
– 'Solfatare'
– 'Solo'
– 'Sorrento'
– 'Spotlight'
– 'Spring Song'
– 'Sulphur Glory'
– 'Sunset'
– 'Sunshine'
– 'Susie'
– 'Symphonia'
– 'Topolino'
– 'Trance'
– 'Uschak Orange'
– 'White Egret'
– 'White Splendour'
– 'Winter Gold'
– 'Yellow Gem'
– 'Yellow Hammer'
– 'Yellow Queen'
vernus 'Blue Ribbon'

CYPRIPEDIUM
arietinum
candidum
montanum
tibeticum
x ***ventricosum***

DACTYLIS
glomerata aurea

DACTYLORHIZA
elata white
majalis 'Glasnevin'

DAHLIA
'Emperor Franz-Joseph'

DEINANTHE
caerulea alba

DELPHINIUM
brachycentrum

DENDRANTHEMA
'Anna Hay' (30)
'Ceres'
'Jean Harlowe'
'Tiny'
'Venus' (30k)

DIANTHUS
'Beverley Pink' (p)
'Black Prince' (p)
'Evelyn'
'Granado' (b)
'Lambrook Beauty' (p)
'Lincolnshire Lass' (p) **AGM**
'Lucy Glendill' (b)
'Old Man's Head' (p)
'Ruth Fischer' (p)

DICENTRA
'Appleblossom'
'Queen of Hearts'
'Silver Smith'

DISPORUM
menziesii

DORONICUM
pardalianches 'Goldstrauss'

DRACOCEPHALUM
isabellae
rupestre
tanguticum

ECHINACEA
purpurea 'Abendsonne'

ECHINOPS
exaltatus albus

EPILOBIUM
angustifolium variegatum

EPIMEDIUM
x ***youngianum*** Yenomoto form

EREMURUS
afghanicus
aitchisonii 'Dawn'
x ***isabellinus*** 'Highdown Dwarf'
– 'Highdown Gold'
kaufmannii
'Lady Falmouth'
'Primrose'
robustus tardiflorus
'Sunset'

ERIGERON
'Double Beauty'
glaucus 'B Ladhams'
pulchellus 'Meadow Muffin'

ERYNGIUM
floribundum
lassauxii
x ***zabelii*** 'James Ivory'

ERYSIMUM
'Miss Massey' (d)

EUPATORIUM
fistulosum 'Gateway'
purpureum 'Album'

FRAGARIA
vesca 'Alpina Scarletta'

FRANCOA
rupestris

FRITILLARIA
imperialis 'Flore Pleno'

GAILLARDIA
x ***grandiflora*** 'Ipswich Beauty'

GALANTHUS
'Allen's Perfection'
'Cupid'
'Jenny Wren'
'Rebecca'
'Romeo'
'Tomtit'
'Valentine'
'White Swan'

GALEGA
officinalis compacta

GENTIANA
asclepiadea 'Caelestina'
– 'Phaeina'
x ***japonica***

GERANIUM
sanguineum double

GEUM
x ***ewenii***
pentapetalum 'Plenum'

GLADIOLUS
x ***brenchleyensis***

GLYCERIA
maxima 'Pallida'

GUNNERA
tinctoria 'Nana'

HEDYCHIUM
'F W Moore'

HELENIUM
autumnale 'Aurantiacum'
'Baronin Linden'
'Chanctonbury'
'Flammenrad'
'Goldreif'
'July Sun'
'Spätrot'
'Wonadonga'

HELIANTHUS
tomentosus

HELLEBORUS
niger 'Mr Poë's Variety'

HEMEROCALLIS
'Aurantiaca Major'
'E A Bowles'
fulva rosea
'Gay Music'

HEUCHERA
'Crimson Cascade'
'Gaiety'
'Honeybells'
'June Bride'
'Lady Warwick'
'Montrose'
'Mount St Helens'
'Orphei'
'Oxfordii'
'Rose Cavalier'
'Rufus'
'Scarlet Beauty'
'Tattletale'

HIDALGOA
wercklei

HYPERICUM
olympicum minus 'Schwefelperle'

IBERIS
sempervirens 'Plena'

IMPERATA
cylindrica 'Major'

IRIS
'Barcarole' (Regeliocyclus)
'Big Blue' (***sibirica***)
'Blue Reverie' (***sibirica***)
'Camilla' (Regeliocyclus)
'Clara' (Regeliocyclus)
cristata 'Abbey's Violet'
'Dorothea'
'Dress Circle' (Spuria)
'Emily Grey'
ensata 'Benibotan'
– 'Kegoromo'
– 'Kumazumi'
– 'Lady in Waiting'
– 'Pin Stripe'
– 'Reign of Glory'
– 'Sky Mist'
– 'Tinted Cloud'
– 'Warei Hotei'
'Highline Halo' (Spuria)
'Ice Blue'
'Lutetas' (Regeliocyclus)
'Marshmallow Frosting' (***sibirica***)
'Medea' (Regeliocyclus)
'Mercurius' (Regeliocyclus)
'Myddelton Blue'
orientalis 'Snowflake'
pseudacorus 'Gigantea'
tectorum 'Lilacina'
Tollong Group
Toltec Group
unguicularis 'Bowles' White'
– 'Ellis's Variety'
'Zwanenburg Beauty'

JEFFERSONIA
dubia 'Flore Pleno'
KNIPHOFIA
'Adam'
'Amberlight'
'Bees' Flame'
'Bees' Orange'
'Bees' Yellow'
'Bressingham Gleam'
'Bressingham Glow'
'Bressingham Torch'
'Burnt Orange'
'Buttercrunch'
'C M Prichard'
'Canary Bird'
'Chartreuse'
'Cleopatra'
'Cool Lemon'
'Enchantress'
'Florella'
'Green Lemon'
'Honeycomb'
'Hortulanus Laren'
'Indian'
leichtlinii 'Aurea'
'Lemon Queen'
'Maxima'
parviflora
'Primulina'
rogersii
'Russell's Gold'
'Slim Coral Red'
'Slim Orange'
'Snow Maiden'
'Spanish Gold'
'The Rocket'
KNOWLTONIA
capensis
LATHYRUS
latifolius violet
ornatus
LAVANDULA
'Backhouse Purple'
'Glasnevin Variety'
LEONTOPODIUM
haplophylloïdes
LEUCANTHEMUM
x ***superbum*** 'Beauté Anversoise'
LIATRIS
pycnostachya 'Alba'
scariosa 'White Spire'
spicata 'Picador'
– 'Silvertips'
– 'Snow Queen'
LIGULARIA
altaica
dentata 'Golden Queen'
– 'Moorblut'
persica
sibirica racemosa
LIGUSTICUM
mutellina
LILIUM
arboricola
brownii australe
candidum 'Peregrinum'
– purple-spotted flowers
x ***maculatum*** 'E A Bowles'
x ***princeps*** 'Myddelton House'
sherriffiae
LIMONIUM
platyphyllum 'Blue Cloud'
– ***roseum***
LINARIA
aeruginea 'Aureopurpurea'
LINUM
narbonense 'June Perfield'
– 'Six Hiils'
LOBELIA
fulgens 'Elmfeuer'
'Mrs Humbert'
x ***speciosa*** 'Anne'
'Twilight Time'
'Wildwood Splendour'
LUPINUS
'Betty Astell'
'Billy Wright'
'Blue Jacket'
'City of York'
'George Russell'
ornatus
'Pink Pearls'
polyphyllus 'Downer's Delight'
'Tom Reeves'
LYCHNIS
chalcedonica 'Alba Plena'
coronaria 'Flore Pleno'
coronata 'Speciosa'
flos-cuculi 'Adolph Muss'
LYSIMACHIA
leschenaultii
MATELEA
carolinensis
MECONOPSIS
x ***cookei***
grandis 'Keillour Crimson'
– 'Miss Dickson'
x ***sheldonii*** 'Archie Campbell'
– 'Springhill'
torquata
MELITTIS
melissophyllum 'Variegata'
MIMULUS
lewisii 'Albus'
– 'Sunset'
MONARDA
'Gardenway Red'
'Magnifica'
'Violet Queen'
MULGEDIUM
giganteum
MYOSOTIS
dissitiflora 'Elegantissima'(v)
NARCISSUS
'Alpha of Donard' (1)
'Astron' (2)
'Gog'
'Golden Miller' (1)
'Golden Thought'
'Green Mantle' (3)
'Lucinda'
'Magistrate' (1)
'Precentor' (1)
'Red Light' (2)
'Saint Dorothea' (1)
'Slieve Bernagh' (1)
'Slieve Donard' (1)
'Solid Gold' (1)
NEPETA
racemosa 'Blue Wonder'
– 'White Wonder'
OENOTHERA
fruticosa 'Best Red'
ORIGANUM
vulgare 'Bury Hill'
PAEONIA
lactiflora 'Coral Charm'
– 'Doris Cooper'
– 'Jean Bockstoce'
– 'Sea Shell'
– 'Sword Dance'
mascula arietina 'Hilda Milne'
officinalis 'Phyllis Prichard'
– 'Red Ensign'
– 'Splendens'
Saunders hybrid 'Archangel'
– 'Argosy'
– 'Black Douglas'
– 'Black Pirate'
– 'Chalice'
– 'Constance Spry'
– 'Cytherea'
– 'Daystar'
– 'Early Bird'
– 'Early Windflower'
– 'Good Cheer'
– 'Legion of Honour'
– 'Little Dorrit'
– 'Moonrise'
– 'Roman Gold'
– 'Rose Garland'
– 'Victoria Lincoln'
– 'White Innocence'
suffruticosa 'Bijou de Chusan'
– 'Elizabeth'
'Sybil Stern'
'Windchimes'
wittmanniana nudicarpa
PANICUM
'Squaw'
'Warrior'
PAPAVER
orientale 'Atrosanguineum Maximum'
– 'Australia's Orange'
– 'Barr's White'
– 'Blush Queen'
– 'Bobs'
– 'Border Beauty'
– 'Brightness'
– 'Burgundy'
– 'Cavalier'
– 'Cerise Bedder'
– 'Colonel Bowles'
– 'Countess of Stair'
– 'Crimped Beauty'
– 'Crimson Pompon'
– 'Curtis's Strain'
– 'Dégas'
– 'Delicatum'
– 'Duke of Teck'
– 'E A Bowles'
– 'Edna Perry'
– 'Enchantress'
– 'Enfield Beauty'
– 'Ethel Swete'
– 'Fire King'
– 'Fringed Beauty'
– 'Gibson's Salmon'
– 'Goldschmidt'
– 'Grenadier'
– 'Henri Cayeux Improved'
– 'Hewiit's Old Rose'
– 'Humphrey Bennett'
– 'Ida Brailsford'
– 'Immaculatum'
– 'Iris Perry'
– 'Ivy Perry'
– 'Jeannie Mawson'
– 'Joyce'
– 'Lady Haig'
– 'Lady Haskett'
– 'Lady Roscoe'
– 'Lavender Glory'
– 'Little Prince'
– 'Lovely'
– 'Magnificence'
– 'Mahony'
– 'Margherite'
– 'Marie Studholme'
– 'Masterpiece'
– 'Max Leichtlin'
– 'May Curtis'
– 'Medusa'
– 'Menelik'
– 'Minimum'
– 'Miss Julia'
– 'Mogul'
– 'Mrs Carl Skinner'
– 'Mrs John Harkness'
– 'Mrs Lockett Agnew'
– 'Mrs M Bevan'
– 'Mrs Marsh'
– 'Orange King'
– 'Orange Queen'
– 'Oriental King'
– 'Oriental Queen'
– 'Oriflamme'
– 'Pale Face'
– 'Parkmanii'
– 'Perry's Blush'
– 'Perry's Favorite'
– 'Perry's Pigmy'
– 'Perry's Unique'
– 'Persepolis'
– 'Peter Pan'
– 'Prince of Orange'

– 'Princess Ena'
– 'Princess Mary'
– 'Purity'
– 'Queen Alexander'
– 'Rose Queen'
– 'Royal Prince'
– 'Royal Scarlet'
– 'Ruby Perry'
– 'Salmon Beauty'
– 'Salmon Perfection'
– 'Salmon Queen'
– 'Sass Pink'
– 'Semiplenum'
– 'Silberblick'
– 'Silver Queen'
– 'Silverblotch'
– 'Snoflame'
– 'Sonata'
– 'Souvenir'
– 'Splendens'
– 'Suleika'
– 'Sungold'
– 'Surprise'
– 'The King'
– 'The Queen'
– 'Thora Perry'
– 'Tom Tit'
– 'Toreador'
– 'Van der Glotch'
– 'Vuurkogel'
– 'Winnie'
– 'Wurtemburgia'

PENNISETUM
'Cassian's Choice'

PENSTEMON
'Prairie Dawn'
'Prairie Dusk'

PHLEUM
pratense 'Aureum'

PHLOX
amoena 'Pinstripe'
– 'Snowdrift'
– 'Vein Mountain'
buckleyi
carolina forms
caryophylla
dolichantha
floridana
– ***bella***
glaberrima
idahoensis
maculata 'Schneelawine'
paniculata 'Antoine Mercier'
– 'Hochgesang'
stansburyi

PHORMIUM
'Aurora'
tenax 'Goliath'
– 'Purple Giant'
– 'Yellow Queen'

PHYSALIS
alkekengi franchetii monstrous forms

PHYTOLACCA
variegated forms

PIMPINELLA
saxifraga 'Rosea'

PODOPHYLLUM
pleianthum

POLEMONIUM
carneum 'Rose Queen'
laxiflorum

POLYGONUM
coriaceum

POTENTILLA
alba 'Snow White'
'Arc-en-Ciel'
'Congo'
'Hamlet'
ovalis

PRIMULA
'Donard Gem'

PULMONARIA
officinalis immaculata

RANUNCULUS
aconitifolius 'Luteus Plenus'
alpestris 'Flore Pleno'
parnassiifolius 'Semiplenus'

RESEDA
odorata 'Parson's White'

RHEUM
'Dr Baillon'
palmatum 'Atropurpureum Dissectum'

RHEXIA
mariana
– ***purpurea***

RIGIDELLA
flammea
orthantha

ROMNEYA
coulteri 'Butterfly'

ROSCOEA
cautleoïdes 'Bees' Dwarf'

RUDBECKIA
laciniata 'Foliis Variegatis'

RUTA
graveolens 'Blue Beauty'

SACCHARUM
strictum

SALVIA
beckeri
ceratophylla
cryptantha
dichroa
doyamae
eichleriana
fercanensis
formosa
'Glory of Stuttgart'
guaranitica 'Costa Rica'
– 'Indigo Blue'
– 'Purple Splendor'
ianthina
indica
napifolia
pinnata
teddii
valentina
yunnanensis

SANGUISORBA
officinalis 'Shiro-fukurin'

SAXIFRAGA
virginiensis 'Flore Pleno'

SCABIOSA
caucasica 'Blue Mountain'
– 'Challenger'
– 'Constancy'
– 'Diamond'
– 'Loddon White'
– 'Mrs Isaac House'
– 'Penhill Blue'
– 'Rhinsburg Glory'
fischeri

SENECIO
cineraria 'Hoar Frost'

SIDALCEA
'Donard Queen'
'H Blanchard'
malviflora 'Pompadour'
'Rosy Gem'
'Scarlet Beauty'

SILENE
dioica 'Alba Plena'

SILPHIUM
'Carpenter's Cup'

TANACETUM
coccineum 'A M Kelway'
– 'Allurement'
– 'Avalanche'
– 'Beau Geste'
– 'Bishop of Salisbury'
– 'Bridal Pink'
– 'Bright Boy'
– 'Charming'
– 'China Rose'
– 'Comet'
– 'Countess Poulett'
– 'Duke of York'
– 'Kelway's Lovely'
– 'Kelway's Magnificent'
– 'Langport Scarlet'
– 'Lorna'
– 'Mrs Bateman Brown'
– 'Progression'
– 'Radiant'
– 'Somerset'
– 'White Madeleine'

TEUCRIUM
polium 'Album'

THLADIANTHA
oliveri (f)

TIARELLA
cordifolia 'Montrose'

TRILLIUM
catesbyi album
erectum blandum
– ***cahnae***
– ***polymerum***
– ***sulcatum***
gracile
'Hokkaido'
japonicum
kamtschaticum 'Tsuzuki'
kurabayashii
ovatum 'Edith'
– 'Kenmore'
– ***roseum***
– 'Tillicum'
persistens
petiolatum
reliquum
rivale 'Del Norte'
– 'Verne Ahiers'
texanum
tschonoskii violaceum
vaseyi album

TROLLIUS
asiaticus aurantiacus
'Miss Mary Russell'

VERATRUM
stenophyllum
wilsonii
yunnanense

VERNONIA
angustifolia

VERONICA
spicata 'Gina's Pale Blue'

VIOLA
'Red Giant'

XEROPHYLLUM
asphodeloïdes

ZANTEDESCHIA
aethiopica 'Compacta'

The National Council For The Conservation Of Plants & Gardens (NCCPG) Collections

All or part of the following Genera are represented by a National Collection.

Full details of these collections are contained in the *National Plant Collection Directory 1994* available from: NCCPG, The Pines, c/o Wisley Gardens, Woking, Surrey GU23 6QB. Price £3.50 including post & packing.

Abelia
Abies
Abutilon
Acacia
Acanthus
Acer
Achillea
Actinidia
Adenophora
Adiantum
Aechmea
Aesculus
Agapanthus
Alchemilla
Allium
Alnus
Alstoemeria
Amelanchier
Ampelopsis
Anemone
Anthericum
Aquilegia
Arabis
Araceae
Aralia
Arbutus
Argyranthemum
Artemisia
Arundinaria
Asplenium
Aster
Astilbe
Athyrium
Aubrieta
Azara
Bambusa
Begonia
Berberis
Bergenia
Betula
Borago
Borzicactinae
Brachyglottis
Buddleja
Buxus
Calamintha
Calathea
Calceolaria
Calluna
Caltha
Camassia
Camellia
Campanula
Canna
Carpinus
Carya
Caryopteris
Cassiope
Castanea
Catalpa
Ceanothus
Celmisia
Ceratostigma
Cercidiphyllum
Chamaecyparis
Chionodoxa
Chusquea
Cimicifuga
Cistus
Citrus
Clematis
Codiaeum
Colchicum
Coleus
Conifers
Convallaria
Coprosma
Cordyline
Coreopsis
Cornus
Cortaderia
Corylopsis
Corylus
Cotinus
Cotoneaster
Crocosmia
Crocus
Cyclamen
Cystopteris
Cytisus
Daboecia
Dahlia
Daphne
Delphinium
Dendranthema
Dendrobium
Deutzia
Dianella
Dianthus
Diascia
Dicentra
Dicksoniaceae
Diervilla
Digitalis
Dodecatheon
Doronicum
Dracaena
Dryopteris
Echeveria
Echinocerus
Elaeagnus
Embothrium
Enkianthus
Epimedium
Erica
Erigeron
Erodium
Eryngium
Erysimum
Erythronium
Escallonia
Eucalyptus
Eucryphia
Euonymus
Euphorbia
Fagus
Fallopia
Ferns
Ficus
Fragaria
Fraxinus
Fritillaria
Fuchsia
Galanthus
Garrya
Gaultheria
Gentiana
Geranium
Geum
Gladiolus
Grevillea
Griselinia
Halimium
Hamamelis
Hebe
Hedera
Hedychium
Helenium
Helianthemum
Helianthus
Helichrysum
Heliopsis
Helleborus
Hemerocallis
Hepatica
Hesperis
Heuchera
Hibiscus
Hosta
Hoya
Hyacinthus
Hydrangea
Hypericum
Ilex
Inula
Iris
Jasminum
Juglans
Juniperus
Kalmia
Kniphofia
Laburnum
Lamium
Lathyrus
Lavandula
Leptospermum
Leucanthemum
Leucojum
Lewisia
Libertia
Ligustrum
Linum
Liriodendron
Liriope
Lithocarpus
Lonicera
Lupinus
Lycaste
Lychnis
Lysimachia
Magnolia
Mahonia
Malus
Meconopsis
Mentha
Monarda
Monsonia
Muscari
Narcissus
Nepeta
Nerine
Nothofagus
Nymphaea
Oenothera
Olearia
Ophiopogon
Origanum
Osmunda
Osteospermum
Ourisia
Oxalis
Paeonia

Papaver
Paphiopedilum
Paradisea
Parahebe
Parthenocissus
Passiflora
Pelargonium
Penstemon
Pernettya
Persicaria
Philadelphus
Phlomis
Phlox
Phormium
Photinia
Phyllodoce
Phyllostachys
Picea
Pieris
Pinguicula
Pinus
Pittosporum
Pleiblastus
Platanus
Platycodon
Pleione
Polemonium
Polygonum
Polypodium
Polystichum
Populus
Potentilla
Primula
Prunus
Pseudopanax
Pulmonaria
Pyracantha
Pyrus
Quercus
Ranunculus
Rheum
Rhododendron
Rhus
Ribes
Robinia
Rodgersia
Rohdea
Rosa
Roscoea
Rosmarinus
Rubus
Ruscus
Salix
Salvia
Sambucus
Santolina
Sarcocaulon
Sarcococca
Sarracenia
Sasa
Saxifraga
Scabiosa
Schizostylis
Sedum
Semiaquilegia
Semiarundinaria
Sempervivum
Shibataea
Sidalcea
Sinarundinaria
Sisyrinchium
Skimmia
Slieve Donard
Sorbaria
Sorbus
Spiraea
Sir F Stern
Stewartia
Styracaceae
Symphyanda
Symphytum
Syringa
Tanacetum
Taxus
Thalictrum
Thelyptaceae
Thymus
Tilia
Tillandsia
Trillium
Trollius
Tropaeolum
Tulbaghia
Tulipa
Variegated
Veratrum
Verbascum
Verbena
Veronica
Viburnum
Vinca
Viola
Vitis
Watsonia
Weigela
Wisteria
Woodwardia
Yucca
Zantedeschia
Zelkova
Zingiberaceae

Bibliography

International Plant Finders

Canada

The Canadian Plant Source Book (1992). Anne & Peter Ashley, 93 Fentiman Avenue, Ottawa, ON, CANADA K1S OT7. $17 (Canadian or US) inc. p&p. Add $5 for airmail. 14,000 hardy plants available at retail and wholesale nurseries across Canada, including those who ship to US. English names & English & French cross-indexes.

France and Belgium

25,000 Plantes, où et comment les acheter. (1993). Société National d'Horticulture de France, 84 rue de Grenelle, Paris 75007. ISBN 2-7066-1731-4. Contains details of about 25,000 plants and 350 nurseries in France.

Germany

Pflanzen-Einkaufsführer. (1990) Anne & Walter Erhardt. Verlag Eugen Ulmer, PO Box 70 05 61, D-70574 Stuttgart. ISBN 3-8001-6393-4. Some 14,000 plants from German nurseries.

Netherlands

Plantenvinder Voor de Lage Landen. ed. Sarah Hart. Terra, Uitgeverij TERRA, Posbus 188, 7200AD Zutphen, Netherlands.ISBN 90-6255-584-5. Approx. 30,000 plants and 100 nurseries.

Switzerland

Der Stauden Finder. Balz Schneider, Glaernischstrasse 82, 8618 Oetwil a/s, Switzerland. Lists about 5,000 herbaceous perennials from over 40 nurseries in Switzerland.

United Kingdom

Find That Rose! British Rose Growers' Association, Editor, 303 Mile End Road, Colchester, Essex CO4 5EA. Over 2,500 Roses, approx. 70 growers. (Sae for further information).

The Vegetable Finder. HDRA, Ryton-on-Dunmore, Coventry CV8 3LG. ISBN 0-905343-19-0. Nearly 3,000 different Vegetable seeds from 43 suppliers.

USA

The Andersen's Horticultural Library's Source List of Plants and Seeds . Andersen Horticultural Library, Minnesota Landscape Arboretum, 3675 Arboretum Drive, Box 39, Chanhassen, MN 55317 USA. Compiled by Richard Isaacson. (1993). Approx. 47,000 plants and seeds from 400 retail & wholesale outlets in the US & Canada. All are prepared to ship interstate. Does not include Orchids, Cacti or Succulents.

Combined Rose List. (1994) Beverly R Dobson & Peter Schneider, PO Box 677, Mantua, Ohio 44255. Lists over 8,500 roses from 208 nurseries In US, Canada & Overseas.

Cornucopia - A Source Book of Edible Plants. (1990). Stephen Facciola, Kampong Publications, 1870 Sunrise Drive, Vista, California 92084. ISBN 0-9628087-0-9. A very substantial and comprehensive volume, (678 pages), which documents 3,000 species of edible plants & 7,000 cultivars available in the US and abroad. An Electronic version will be available mid-1994.

Fruit, Berry and Nut Inventory. (1993). Ed. Kent Whealy. Seed Saver Publications, 3076 North Winn Road, Decorah, Iowa 52101. An inventory of all fruit, berry and nut varieties available from over 250 mail-order nurseries in the US.

Garden Seed Inventory. (1992). Ed. Kent Whealy. Seed Saver Publications, 3076 North Winn Road, Decorah, Iowa 52101. List every non-hybrid vegetable variety available from 223 mail-order seed companies in the USA and Canada with description and sources for each.

Gardening by Mail (1994). 4th ed. Barbara J Barton. Tusker Press, PO Box 1338, Sebastopol, California 95473. A directory of mail order resources for gardeners in the USA and Canada, including seed companies, nurseries, suppliers of all garden necessaries and ornaments, horticultural and plant societies, magazines, libraries and books.

Hortus Source List. (1992). Bailey Hortorium, 462 Mann Library, Cornell University, Ithaca, 14853 NY, USA. Over 22,000 plant entries from 63 nurseries, most in New York State.

Northwest Native Plant Directory. (Issue 4 - 1993). ed. Dale Shank. Hortus Northwest, PO Box 955, Canby, OR 97013. 126 native plant nurseries in Oregon, Washington, British Columbia and northern California.

Northwind Farm's Herb Resource Directory. (1994-95 edition). ed. Paula Oliver. Northwind Farm Publications, Route 2, Box 246, Shevlin, MN 56676-9535. Over 1,100 sources & resources for herb growers & enthusiasts. Bi-monthly journal also available.

Nursery Sources, Native Plants and Wild Flowers. New England Wild Flower Society, Garden in the Woods, 180 Hemenway Road, Framingham, MA 01701-2699. Over 200 native North American wild flowers, ferns, grasses and shrubs. Details of 45 nurseries

Perennials: A Nursery Source Manual (1989). ed. Barbara Pesch. Brooklyn Botanic Garden, 1000 Washington Avenue, Brooklyn, NY 11225-1099. ISBN 0 945352 48 4. List 320 nurseries and some 4000 perennials.

Taylor's Guide to Speciality Nurseries (1993). Houghton Miffin Co., 222 Berkeley Street, Boston, MA 02114, USA. Over 300 nursereis in the US selliung ornamental garden plants, all of which will ship.

General

The following list of bibliographic sources and references is by no means exhaustive, but lists some of the more useful and available works used in the preparation of **THE PLANT FINDER.**

The Plantsman is published regularly by The Royal Horticultural Society, Vincent Square, London SW1P 2PE

Armitage, A M. 1989. *Herbaceous Perennial Plants*. Varsity Press, Athens, Georgia.

Bailey, L H Bailey, E Z et al. 1976. *Hortus Third*. Macmillan, New York.

Bean, W J. 1970-1988. *Trees and Shrubs Hardy in the British Isles* (8th ed. edited Sir George Taylor & D L Clarke & Supp. ed. D L Clarke). John Murray, London.

Beckett, K A. 1987. *The RHS Encyclopaedia of House Plants*. Century Hutchinson, London.

Blundell, M. 1992. *Wild Flowers of East Africa*. Collins, London.

Bond, P & Goldblatt, P. 1984. *Plants of the Cape Flora*. Journal of South African Botany. (Sup. Vol. No 13). Kirstenbosch.

Bramwell, D & Z. 1974. *Wild Flowers of the Canary Islands*. Stanley Thomas, London, 1974.

Brickell, C D (ed.) et al. 1980. *International Code of Nomenclature for Cultivated Plants*. Utrecht.

Brickell, C D (ed.) 1989. *Gardeners' Encyclopaedia of Plants and Flowers*. Dorling Kindersley, London.

Brummitt, R K & Powell, C E. 1992. *Authors of Plant Names*. Royal Botanic Gardens, Kew.

Brummitt, R K. 1992. *Vascular Plant Families and Genera*. Royal Botanic gardens, Kew.

Bryan, J E 1989. *Bulbs* (Vols I & II). Christopher Helm, Bromley, Kent.

Chittenden, F J (ed.). 1965. *The Royal Horticultural Society Dictionary of Gardening* (2nd ed.). Oxford University Press.

Clausen, R R & Ekstrom, N H. *Perennials for American Gardens*. Random House, New York.

Clayton, W D & Renvoize, S A. 1986. *Genera Graminum*. HMSO, London

Cribb, P & Bailes, C. 1989. *Hardy Orchids*. Christopher Helm, Bromley, Kent.

Davis, P H et al. (ed.). 1965-1988. *Flora of Turkey* (Vols 1-10). University Press, Edinburgh.

Flora of New Zealand. (Vols. I-III). 1961-80. Wellington, New Zealand.

Du Plessis, N and Duncan, G. 1989. *Bulbous Plants of Southern Africa*. Tafelberg, Cape Town, South Africa.

Forrest, M. (ed. Nelson, E C.) 1985. *Trees and Shrubs Cultivated in Ireland*. Boethius Press for An Taisce, Dublin.

Galbraith, J. 1977. *Field Guide to the Wild Flowers of South-East Australia*. Collins, London.

Graf, A B. 1981. *Tropica* (2nd ed.). Roehrs, New Jersey.

Grierson, A J C & Long D G. 1983-91. (Vols. 1 Pt I-III & Vol. 2 Pt. I) *Flora of Bhutan*. Royal Botanic Garden Edinburgh.

Harkness, M G & D'Angelo, D. 1986. *The Bernard E Harkness Seedlist Handbook*. Timber Press, Portland, Oregon.

Heath, R E. 1981. *Collectors Alpines*. Collinridge, Twickenham, UK.

Hillier Manual of Trees and Shrubs. (6th ed.). 1991. David & Charles, Newton Abbot.

Hogg, R. 1884. *The Fruit Manual.* (5th ed.). Journal of Horticulture Office, London.

Huxley, A (ed). 1992. *The New Royal Horticultural Society Dictionary of Gardening.* Macmillan, London.

Index Kewensis (Vols. I-IV & Supps. I-XIX). 1893-1991. Clarendon Press, Oxford.

Innes, C F. 1985. *The World of Iridaceae.* Holy Gate International Ashington, Sussex.

Jacobsen, H. 1973. *Lexicon of Succulent Plants.* Blandford, London.

Jellitto, L & Schacht, W. *Hardy Herbaceous Perennials.* (3rd ed. edited by W. Schacht & A Fessler). Timber Press, Portland, Oregon, USA.

Johns, R J. 1991. *Pteridophytes of Tropical East Africa.* Royal Botanic Gardens, Kew.

Jones, D L. 1987. *Encyclopaedia of Ferns.* Lothian, Melbourne, Australia.

Krussmann, G. (English ed. trans. M E Epp). 1984-1986. *Manual of Cultivated Broadleaved Trees & Shrubs* (Vol I-III). Batsford, London.

Laar, H J van de. 1989. *Naamlijst van Houtige Gewassen.* Proefstation voor de Boomteelt en het Stedelijk Groen, Boskoop, Holland.

Laar, H J van de & Fortgens, Ing. G. 1988. *Naamlijst van Vaste Planten.* Proefstation voor de Boomkwekerij, Boskoop, Holland.

Leslie, A C, 1993. *New Cultivars of Herbaceous Perennial Plants 1985-1990.* Hardy Plant Society.

Lewis, J. ed. Leslie, A C. 1987 & 1989. *The International Conifer Register.* Pt.I (*Abies* to *Austrotaxus*), Pt.II (*Belis* to *Pherosphaera* (excluding Cypresses and Junipers). Pt.III: *Cypresses.* Royal Horticultural Society, London.

Mabberley, D J. 1987. *The Plant-Book.* Cambridge University Press.

McGregor, R L, Barkley, T M et al. 1986. *Flora of the Great Plains.* University Press of Kansas, USA.

Metcalf, L J. 1987. *The Cultivation of New Zealand Trees and Shrubs.* Reed Methuen, Auckland, New Zealand.

Ohwi, J. (ed F G Meyer & E H Walker). 1965. *Flora of Japan.* Smithsonian Institute, Washington.

Phillips, R. & Rix, E M. *Shrubs.* 1989. Pan Books, London.

Phillips, R. & Rix, E M. 1991/2. *Perennials.* Pan Books, London.

Phillips, R & Rix, E M. 1993 *Vegetables.* Pan Books Ltd, London.

The Plantsman. The Royal Horticultural Society, Vincent Square, London SW1P 2PE.

Polunin, O & Stainton, A. 1984. *Flowers of the Himalaya.* Oxford University Press.

Rehder, R. 1940. *Manual of Cultivated Trees & Shrubs Hardy in North America.* (2nd ed.) Macmillan, New York.

Stafleu, F A et al. 1978. *International Code of Botanical Nomenclature.* Bohn, Scheltema & Holkema, Utrecht.

Stace, C A. 1992. *New Flora of the British Isles.* St Edmundsbury Press, Bury St Edmunds, Suffolk.

Stainton, A. 1988. *Flowers of the Himalaya: A Supplement.* Oxford University Press.

Stearn, Prof. W T. *Botanical Latin.* David & Charles. Newton Abbot, England.

Stearn, Prof. W T. 1992. *Stearn's Dictionary of Plant Names for Gardeners.* Cassell, London.

Thomas, G S. 1990. *Perennial Garden Plants.* (3rd ed.) J M Dent & Sons, London.

Trehane, R P. 1989. *Index Hortensis.* Quarterjack Publishing, Wimborne, Dorset.

Tutin, T G. 1964-1980. *Flora Europaea* (Vols I-V). Cambridge University Press.

Tutin, T G et al. 1993. *Flora Europaea* (2nd ed. Vol I). Cambridge University Press.

Uhl, N J. & Dransfield, J. 1987. *Genera Palmarum.* Alan Press, Lawrence, Kansas, USA.

Walters, S M (ed.) et al. 1984, 1986 & 1989. *The European Garden Flora.* (Vols I-III). Cambridge University Press, UK.

Willis, J C. 1973. *A Dictionary of the Flowering Plants and Ferns* (8th ed.) revised H K Airy Shaw. Cambridge University Press.

Wilson, H D. 1978. *Wild Plants of Mount Cook National Park.* Christchurch, New Zealand.

Van Scheepen, J. 1991. *International Checklist for Hyacinths and Miscellaneous Bulbs.* KAVB, Hillegom, Netherlands.

Genera

Acacia

Beckett, K A. 1993. *The Plantsman* (Vol 15 Pt III).

Simmons, MH. 1987. *Acacias of Australia* (2nd ed). Nelson, Melbourne, Australia.

Acaena

Yeo, P F. 1972. 'The species of Acaena with Spherical Heads Cultivated and Naturalized in the British Isles' in *Plants wild and Cultivated.* (ed. Green, P S). Botanical Society of the British Isles, Milddlesex.

Acer

De Jong, P C et al. *International Dendrology Society Year Book 1991.* London.

Harris, J G S. 1983. *The Plantsman.* (Vol 5 Pt I).

Vertrees, J D. 1978. *Japanese Maples.* Timber Press, Oregon.

Adiantum

Goudry, C J. 1985. *Maidenhair Ferns in Cultivation.* Lothian, Melbourne, Australia.

Aeschynanthus

Dates, J D. *The Gesneriad Register 1990: Check List of Aeschynanthus.* American Gloxinia and Gesneriad Society, Galesburg, Illinois.

Aesculus

Wright, D. 1985. *The Plantsman.* (Vol 7 Pt IV).

Agapetes

Argent, G C G & Woods, P J B. 1988. *The Plantsman.* (Vol 8 Pt II).

Ajuga

Adam, C G. *Alpine Garden Society Bulletin.* (Vol 50 Pt I).

Allium

Davies, D. 1992. *Alliums.* Batsford, London.

Alnus

Ashburner, K. *The Plantsman.* (Vol 8 Pt III).

Androsace

Smith, G F & Lowe, D B. 1977. *Androsaces.* Alpine Garden Society.

Anemone, Japanese

McKendrick, M. 1990. *The Plantsman.* (Vol 12 Pt III).

Anemone nemorosa

Toubol, U. 1981. *The Plantsman.* (Vol 3 Pt III).

Aquilegia

Munz, P A. 1946. *Aquilegia: The Cultivated and Wild Columbines. Gentes Herbarum* (Vol VII Fasc I). Bailey Hortorium, New York.

Araceae

Bown, D. 1988. *Aroids.* Century Hutchinson, London.

Argyranthemum

Cheek, R. 1993. *The Garden.* (Vol 118 Pt 8). Royal Horticultural Society, London.

Humphries, C J. 1976. *A Revision of the Macaronesian Genus Argyranthemum.* The Bulletin of the British Museum (Natural History) Botany Vol. 5 No. 4, London.

Arisaema

Mayo, J J. 1982. *The Plantsman.* (Vol 3 Pt IV).

Pradhan, UC. 1990. *Himalayan Cobra-lilies (Arisaema): Their Botany and Culture.* Primulaceae Books, Kalimpong, West Bengal, India.

Arum

Boyce, P. 1993. *The Genus Arum.* HMSO, London.

Aster

Ranson, E R. 1947. *Michaelmas Daisies.* Garden Book Club.

Aubrieta

International Registration Authority Checklist. Weihenstephan.

Bamboos

Chao, C S. 1989. *A Guide to Bamboos Grown in Britain.* Royal Botanic Gardens, Kew.

McClintock, D. 1992. *The Plantsman.* (Vol 14 Pt III).

Wang Dajun & Shen Shao-Jin. 1987. *Bamboos of China.* Timber Press, Oregon.

Begonia

Ingles, J. 1990. *American Begonia Society Listing of Begonia Cultivars* (Revised Edition Buxton Checklist).

Wall, B. 1989. *The Plantsman.* (Vol 11 Pt I).

Thompson, M L. & Thompson, E J. 1981. *Begonias: The Complete Reference Guide.* Times Books, New York.

Betula

Ashburner, K. 1980. *The Plantsman.* (Vol 2 Pt I).

Ashburner, K & Schilling, A D. 1985. *The Plantsman.* (Vol 7 Pt II).

Hunt, D (ed). 1993. *Betula: Proceedings of the IDS Betula Symposium* Richmond, Surrey.

Bougainvillea

Bor, N L. & Raizada, M B. 1982. *Some Beautiful Indian Climbers and Shrubs.* (2nd ed.) pp 291-304. Bombay Natural History Society.

Gillis, W T. 1976 *Bougainvilleas of Cultivation. Baileya.* Vol 20(1) pp34-41. New York.

Iredell, J. 1990. *The Bougainvillea Grower's Handbook.* Simon & Schuster, Brookvale, Australia.

MacDaniels, L H. 1981. *A Study of Cultivars in Bougainvillea. Baileya.* Vol 21(2) pp77-100. New York.

Bromeliaceae

Beadle, D A. 1991. *A Preliminary Listing of all the known Cultivar and Grex Names for the Bromeliaceae.* Bromeliad Society, Corpus Christi, Texas, USA.

Luther, H E & Sieff, E. 1991. *An Alphabetical List of Bromeliad Binomials.* Bromeliad Society, Orlando, Florida, USA.

Rauh, W. 1979. *Bromeliads.* Blandford Press, Dorset.

Buddleja

Maunder, M. 1987. *The Plantsman.* (Vol 9 Pt II).

Bulbs

Grey-Wilson, C & Matthew, B. 1981. *Bulbs.* Collins, London.

Innes, C. 1985. *The World of Iridaceae.* Hollygate International, Sussex.

Rix, M & Phillips, R. 1981. *The Bulb Book.* Pan Books, London.

Buxus

Batdorf, L R. 1989. *Checklist of Buxus.* American Boxwood Society.

Braimbridge, E. 1994. *The Plantsman.* (Vol 13 Pt IV).

Callistemon

Mitchem, C M. 1993. *The Plantsman.* (Vol 13 Pt I).

Camellia

Savige, T J. 1993. (Corrected 1994). *The International Camellia Register.* The International Camellia Society, Wirlinga, Australia.

Campanula

Lewis, P & Lynch, M. 1989. *Campanulas.* Christopher Helm, Bromley, Kent.

Carnivorous Plants

Pietropaulo, J & Pietropaulo, P. 1986 *Carnivorous Plants of the World.* Timber Press, Oregon.

Slack, A. 1988. *Carnivorous Plants.* (rev. ed.). Alphabooks, Sherbourne, Dorset.

Carpinus

Rushforth, K. 1986. *The Plantsman* (Vol 7 Pts III & IV).

Caryopteris

Pattison, G. 1989. *The Plantsman* (Vol 11 Pt I).

Cassiope

Blake, F S. *Alpine Garden Society Bulletin.* (Vol 53 Pt I).

Starling, B. 1989. *The Plantsman.* (Vol 11 Pt II).

Cestrum

Beckett, K A. 1987. *The Plantsman.* (Vol 9 Pt III).

Chrysanthemum (Dendranthema)
British National Register of Chrysanthemums. National Chrysanthemum Society. 1964-1992.

Chaenomeles
Weber, C. 1963. *Cultivars in the Genus Chaenomeles*. Arnoldia. (Vol 23 No 3) Arnold Arboretum, Harvard, Massachusetts.

Cimicifuga
Compton, J. 1992. *The Plantsman*. (Vol 14 Pt II).

Cistus
Page, R G. 1991. *The Plantsman*. (Vol 13 Pt III).

Citrus
Saunt, J. 1990. *Citrus Varieties of the World*. Sinclair International Ltd., Norwich, England.

Clematis
Fisk, J. 1989. *Clematis, the Queen of Climbers*. Cassell, London.
Fretwell, B. 1989. *Clematis*. Collins, London.
Grey-Wilson, C. 1986. *The Plantsman*. (Vol 7 Pt IV).
Hutchins, G. 1990. *The Plantsman*. (Vol 11 Pt IV).
Lloyd, C & Bennett, T H. 1989. *Clematis*. Viking, London.
Snoeijer, W. 1991. *Clematis Index*. Fopma, Boskoop, Netherlands.

Codonopsis
Alpine Garden Society Bulletin. (Vol 48 Pt 2).
Grey-Wilson, C. 1990. *The Plantsman*. (Vol 12 Pt II).

Conifers
Krussmann, G. (English trans. M E Epp). 1985. *Manual of Cultivated Conifers*. Batsford, London.
Ouden, P. den & Boom, B K. 1965. *Manual of Cultivated Conifers*. Martinus Nijhorff, The Haque, Netherlands.
Welch, H J. 1979. *Manual of Dwarf Conifers*. Theophrastus, New York.
Welch, H J. 1990. *The Conifer Manual*. Vol I. Kluwer Academic Publishers, Dordrecht, Holland.
Welch, H J. 1993. *The World Checklist of Conifers*. Landsman's Bookshops Ltd., Bromyard, Herefordshire.

Cornus
Howard, R A. 1961. Registration Lists of Cultivar Names in *Cornus* L., Arnoldia. (Vol 21 No 2). Arnold Arboretum, Harvard, Massachusetts.

Corokia
Hutchins, G. 1994. *The Plantsman*. (Vol 15 Pt IV).

Corydalis
Lidn, M and Zetterlund, H. 1988. A.G.S. Bulletin. (Vol 56 No 2).
Rix, E M. 1993. *The Plantsman*. (Vol 15 Pt III).

Corylopsis
Wright, D. 1982. *The Plantsman*. (Vol 4 Pt I).

Crocosmia
Kostelijk, P J. 1984. *The Plantsman*. (Vol 5 Pt IIII).

Cyclamen
Grey-Wilson, C. 1988. *The Genus Cyclamen*. Christopher Helm, Bromley, Kent.
Grey-Wilson, C. 1991. *The Plantsman*. (Vol 13 Pt I).

Cynara
Wiklund, A. 1992. *The Genus Cynara*. Botanical Journal of the Linnean Society. (Vol 109 No 1).

Cyrtanthus
Holford, F. 1989. *The Plantsman*. (Vol 11 Pt III).

Daphne
Brickell, C D & Mathew, B. 1976. *Daphne*. Alpine Garden Society.

Deutzia

Taylor, J. 1990. *The Plantsman.* (Vol 11 Pt IV).

Dianthus

Leslie, A C. 1983-93. *The International Dianthus Register.* (2nd ed. & supps. 1-10). Royal Horticultural Society, London.

Diascia

Benham, S. 1987. *The Plantsman.* (Vol 9 Pt I).

Dierama

Hilliard, O M. & Burtt, B L. 1990. *The Plantsman.* (Vol 12 Pt II).

Hilliard, O M and Burtt, B L. 1991. *Dierama.* Acorn Books CC. Johannesburg, South Africa.

Dionysia

Grey-Wilson, C. 1989. *The Genus Dionysia.* Alpine Garden Society, Woking, Surrey.

Dodecatheon

Mitchem, C M. 1991. *The Plantsman.* (Vol 13 Pt III).

Dracaena

Bos, J J, Graven, P, Hetterscheid, W L A & van de Wege, J Jj. 1992. *Edinburgh Journal of Botany* (Vol 10 Pt 3). Edinburgh.

Drosera

Cheek, M. 1993. *Kew Magazine* (Vol 10 Pt 3). Blackwell, Oxford.

Episcia

Arnold, P. *The Gesneriad Register 1977: Episcia.* American Gloxinia and Gesneriad Society, Binghamton, New York.

Eriogonum

Elliott, J. 1993. *A.G.S. Bulletin.* (Vol 61 No 2).Erodium

Bacon, L. 1990. *A.G.S. Bulletin.* (Vol 58 No 1).

Leslie, A C. 1980. *The Plantsman.* (Vol 2 Pt III).

Erythronium

Mathew, B. 1992. *A Taxonomic and Horticultural Review of Erythronium.* Botanical Journal of the Linnean Society. (Vol 109 No 4)

Eucomis

Compton, J. 1990. *The Plantsman.* (Vol 12 Pt III).

Eucryphia

Wright, D. 1983. *The Plantsman.* (Vol 5 Pt III).

Euonymus

Lancaster, R. 1981. *The Plantsman.* (Vol 3 Pt III).

Euphorbia

Turner, R & Radcliffe-Smith, A. 1983. *The Plantsman.* (Vol 5 Pt III).

Fagus

Wyman, D. 1964. Registration List of Cultivar Names of *Fagus* L., Arnoldia. (Vol 24 No 1). Arnold Arboretum, Harvard, Massachusetts.

Ferns

Kaye, R. 1968. *Hardy Ferns.* Faber & Faber, London.

Rush, R. 1984. *A Guide to Hardy Ferns.* The British Pteridological Society, London.

Festuca

Wilkinson, M J. & Stace, C A. 1991. *A new taxonomic treatment of the Festuca ovina aggregate in the British Isles.* Botanical Journal of the Linnean Society. (Vol 106 No 4). London.

Fremontodendron

McMillan Browse, P. 1992. *The Plantsman.* (Vol 14 Pt 1).

Fritillaria

Turrill, W B & Seely, J R. 1980. *Studies in the Genus Fritillaria.* Hooker's Icones Plantarum, (Vol XXXIX Pts I & II), Royal Botanic Gardens, Kew.

Fuchsia

Boullemier, L B. 1991. *The Checklist of Species, Hybrids & Cultivars of the Genus Fuchsia.* (2nd ed.). Blandford Press, Dorset, UK.

Gaultheria (inc. Pernettya)

Middleton, D J. 1990/91 *The Plantsman.* (Vol 12 Pt III & Vol 13 Pt III).

Middleton, D J. 1991. *Infrageneric Classification of the Genus Gaultheria.* Botanical Journal of the Linnean Society. (Vol106 No 3).

Gentiana

Bartlett, M. 1975. *Gentians.* Blandford Press, Dorset.

Wilkie, D. 1950. *Gentians.* (2nd ed.) Country Life, London.

Geranium

Bath, T, & Jones, J. 1994. *The Gardener's Guide to Growing Hardy Geraniums.* David & Charles, Newton Abbot, Devon.

Clifton, R T F. 1992. *Geranium Family Species Checklist* ed IV pt 2: Geranium. The Geraniaceae Group of the British Pelargonium and Geranium Society, Kent.

Yeo, P F. 1985. *Hardy Geraniums.* Croom Helm, London.

Gesneriaceae

Dates, J D. *The Gesneriad Register 1986: Check List of Intergeneric Hybrids in the tribe Gloxinieae.* American Gloxinia and Gesneriad Society, Sugar Grove, Illinois.

Dates, J D. *The Gesneriad Register 1987: Check List of Bucinellina, Columnea, Dalbergaria, Pentadenia, Trichantha and Intergeneric Hybrids.* American Gloxinia and Gesneriad Society, Galesburg, Illinois.

Dates, J D. *The Gesneriad Register 1990: Appendix C: Registered Gesneriads 1957-90.* American Gloxinia and Gesneriad Society, Galesburg, Illinois.

Gladiolus

Lewis, G J & Obermeyer, A A & Barnard, T T. 1972. *A Revision of the South African Species of Gladiolus.* (Sup. Vol. 10). Journal of South African Botany, Purnell, Cape Town.

List of Gladiolus Cultivars. The British Gladiolus Society.

Gleditsia *triacanthos*

Santamour, F S Jr & McArdle, A J. 198?. *Checklist of Cultivars of Honeylocust.* USA.

Gramineae (Bambuseae)

Wang Dajun & Shen Shap-Jin. 1987. *Bamboos of China.* Timber Press, Portland, Oregon.

Grasses

Grounds, R. 1979. *Ornamental Grasses.* Pelham Books, London.

Haemanthus

Snijman, D. 1984. *A Revision of the Genus Haemanthus. Journal of South African Botany.* Supplementary Vol 12. National Botanic Gardens, Kirstenbosch.

Hamamelidaceae

Wright, D. 1982. *The Plantsman.* (Vol 4 Pt I).

Heathers

Small, D. and Small, A. 1992. *Handy Guide to Heathers.* Debeigh Heather Nurseries, Suffolk, England.

Hebe

Hayter, T (ed.) 1986-92. *Hebe News.* Macclesfield, Cheshire, UK.

Hutchins, G. 1979. *Hebe and Parahebe Species in Cultivation.* County Park Nursery, Essex.

Chalk, D. 1988. *Hebes and Parahebes.* Christopher Helm, London.

Hedera

McAllister, H. 1988. *The Plantsman.* (Vol 10 Pt I).

McAllister, H A. & Rutherford, A. 1990. *Hedera helix & H. hibernica in the British Isles.* Watsonia Vol 18.

Rose, P Q. 1980. *Ivies.* Blandford Press, Dorset, UK.

Rutherford, A, McAllister, H A & Rill, R R 1993. *The Plantsman* (Vol 15 Pt II).

Hedychium

Schilling, A D. 1982. *The Plantsman.* (Vol 4 Pt III).

Helichrysum

Hilliard, O M & Burtt, B L. 1987. *The Garden.* (Vol 112 Pt VI). Royal Horticultural Society, London.

Heliconia

Berry, F & Kress, WJ. 1991. *Heliconia: An Identification Guide.* Smithsonian Institution Press, Washington.

Helleborus

Mathew, B. 1981. *The Plantsman.* (Vol 3 Pt I).

Hemerocallis

Erhardt, W. 1988. *Hemerocallis Daylilies.* Batsford, London.

Kitchingman, R M. 1985. *The Plantsman.* (Vol 7 Pt II).

Munson, R W. 1989. *Hemerocallis, The Daylily.* Timber Press, Oregon.

Webber, S. (ed.) 1988. *Daylily Encyclopaedia.* Webber Gardens, Damascus, Maryland, USA.

Hibiscus

Beers, L. & Howie, J. 1990. *Growing Hibiscus.* (2nd ed.). Kangaroo Press, Kenthurst, Australia.

Hippeastrum

Alfabetische Lisjt van de in Nederland in cultuur zijnde Amaryllis (Hippeastrum) Cultivars. 1980. Koninklijke Algemeene Veereniging voor Bloembollencultur, Hillegom, Netherlands.

Hosta

Grenfell, D. 1985. *The Plantsman.* (Vol 7 Pt IV).

Grenfell, D. 1990. *Hosta.* Batsford, London.

Grenfell, D. 1993. *The Plantsman.* (Vol 15 Pt I).

Hensen, K J W. 1985. *The Plantsman.* (Vol 7 Pt I).

Schmid, W G. 1991. *The Genus Hosta.* Timber Press, Oregon.

Hoya

Innes, C. 1988. *The Plantsman.* (Vol 10 Pt III).

Hydrangea

Haworth-Booth, M. 1975. *The Hydrangeas.* Garden Book Club, London.

Mallet, C. 1992. *Hydrangeas.* Centre d'Art Floral, Varengeville-sur-Mer, France

Hypericum

Robson, N K B. 1980. *The Plantsman.* (Vol 1 Pt IIII).

Ilex

Andrews, S. 1983. *The Plantsman.* (Vol 5 Pt II).

Andrews, S. 1984. *The Plantsman.* (Vol 6 Pt III).

Andrews, S. *The Garden.* (Vol 110 p11). Royal Horticultural Society, London.

Dudley, T R & Eisenbeiss, G K. 1973 & 1992. *International Checklist of Cultivated Ilex* Pt1: *Ilex opaca*; Pt 2: *Ilex crenata.* US Department of Agriculture, US National Arboretum, Washington.

Impatiens

Grey-Wilson, C. 1983. *The Plantsman.* (Vol 5 Pt II).

Iris

Hoog, M H. 1980. *The Plantsman.* (Vol 2 Pt III).

Mathew, B. 1981. *The Iris.* Batsford, London.

Mathew, B. 1993. *The Plantsman.* (Vol 15 Pt I).

Iris (Series Unguculares)

Service, N. 1990. *The Plantsman.* (Vol 12 Pt I).

Kniphofia

Taylor, J. 1985. *The Plantsman.* (Vol 7 Pt III).

Kohleria

Dates, J D (ed.). *The Gesneriad Register 1985: Check List of Kohleria.* American Gloxinia and Gesneriad Society, Lincoln Acres, California.

Lachenalia
Duncan, G D. 1988. *The Lachenalia Handbook. Annals of Kirstenbosch Botanic Gardens.* Vol 17. Republic of South Africa.

Lantana
Howard, R A. 1969. A Check List of Cultivar Names used in the Genus *Lantana Arnoldia.* (Vol 29 No 11). Arnold Arboretum, Harvard, Massachusetts.

Larix
Horsman, J. 1988 *The Plantsman.* (Vol 10 Pt I).

Lavandula
Tucker, A O. & Hensen, K J W. 1985. *The Cultivars of Lavender and Lavandin.* Baileya. Vol 22(4) pp168-177. New York.

Leptospermum
Nomenclature Committee of the Royal New Zealand Institute of Horticulture. 1963. *Check List of Leptospermum Cultivars.* Journal of the Royal New Zealand Institute of Horticulture. (Vol V No V).

Leucojum
Elliott, J. 1992. *The Plantsman.* (Vol 14 Pt 2).

Lewisia
Elliott, R. 1978. *Lewisias.* Alpine Garden Society, Woking.
Mathew, B. 1989. *The Genus Lewisia.* Christopher Helm, Bromley, Kent.

Liliaceae
Mathew, B. 1989. *The Plantsman.* (Vol 11 Pt II).

Lilium
Leslie, A C. 1982-94. *The International Lily Register.* (3rd ed. & supps. 1-11). Royal Horticultural Society, London.

Liriodendron
Andrews, S. 1993. *IDS Yearbook 1992. London.*

Lonicera
Bradshaw, D. 1991. *The Plantsman.* (Vol 13 Pt II).
Wright, D. 1983. *The Plantsman.* (Vol 4 Pt IV).

Magnolia
Calaway, D J. 1994. *Magnolias.* Batsford, London.
Holman, N. 1979. *The Plantsman.* (Vol 7 Pt I).
Treseder, N G. 1978. *Magnolias.* Faber & Faber, London.

Malus
Parfitt, B. 1965. *Index of the Apple Collection at the National Fruit Trials.* Ministry of Agriculture, Fisheries and Food, Faversham, Kent.
Taylor, H V. 1948. *The Apples of England.* Crosby Lockwood, London.

Meconopsis
Cobb, J L S. 1989. *Meconopsis.* Christopher Helm, Bromley, Kent.
Grey-Wilson, C. 1992. *The Plantsman.* (Vol 14 Pt 1).

Moraea
Goldblatt, P. 1986. *The Moraeas of Southern Africa.* National Botanic Gardens of South Africa.

Narcissus
Blanchard, J W. 1990. *Narcissus.* Alpine Garden Society, Woking, Surrey.
Kington, S. 1989-94 (2nd ed.) *The International Daffodil Checklist.* (2nd ed. & supps. 14-19). Royal Horticultural Society, London.
Throckmorton, T D (ed.). 1985. *Daffodils to Show & Grow and Abridged Classified List of Daffodil Names.* Royal Horticultural Society and American Daffodil Society, Hernando, Mississippi.

Nematanthus
Arnold, P. *The Gesneriad Register 1978: Check List of Nematanthus.* American Gloxinia and Gesneriad Society,

Nerium
Pagen, F J J. 1987. *Oleanders.* Agricultural University, Wageningen, Holland.

Nothofagus

Hill, R S. & Read, J. 1991. *Botanical Journal of the Linnean Society.* (Vol 105 No 1).

Nymphaea

1994. *Identification of Hardy Nymphaea.* Stapley Water Gardens Ltd. for the International Water Lily Society.

Swindells, P. 1983. *Waterlilies.* Croom Helm, London.

Ostrya

Rushforth, K. 1986. *The Plantsman.* (Vol 7 Pts III & IV).

Paeonia

Harding, A, & Klehm, R G. 1993. *The Peony.* Batsford, London.

Haw, S G. 1991. *The Plantsman.* (Vol 13 Pt II).

Haworth-Booth, M. 1963. *The Moutan or Tree Peony.* Garden Book Club, London.

Kessenich, G M. 1976. *Peonies.* (Variety Check List, Pts 1-3). American Peony Society.

Papaveraceae

Grey-Wilson, C. 1993. *Poppies.* Batsford, London.

Passiflora

Vanderplank, J. 1991. *Passion Flowers.* Cassell, London.

Pelargonium

Baggust, H. 1988. *Miniature and Dwarf Geraniums.* Christopher Helm, Bromley, Kent.

A Checklist and Register of Pelargonium Cultivar Names. Part 1 (1978) and Part 2 (unpublished). Australian Geranium Society, Sydney.

Clifford, D. 1958. *Pelargoniums.* Blandford Press, London.

Complete Copy of the Spalding Pelargonium Checklist. Unpublished. USA.

Van der Walt, J J A et al. 1977-88. *Pelargoniums of South Africa.* (Vols I-III). National Botanic Gardens, Kirstenbosch, Republic of South Africa.

Philadelphus

Taylor, J. 1990. *The Plantsman.* (Vol 11 Pt IV).

Wright, D. 1980. *The Plantsman.* (Vol 2 Pt II).

Phlox

Wherry, E T. 1955. *The Genus Phlox.* Morris Arboretum Monographs III, Philadelphia, Penn.

Phormium

Heenan, P B. 1991. *Checklist of Phormium Cultivars.* Royal New Zealand Institute of Horticulture, Canterbury, New Zealand.

Phygelius

Coombes, A J. 1988. *The Plantsman.* (Vol 9 Pt IV).

Pieris

Bond, J. 1982. *The Plantsman.* (Vol 4 Pt II).

Wagenknecht, B L. 1961. Registration List of Names in the Genus *Pieris.* D. Don, Arnoldia Vol 21 No 8. Arnold Arboretum, Harvard, Massachusetts.

Pinus

Muir, N. 1992. *The Plantsman.* (Vol 14 Pt II).

Podocarpus

Hutchins, G. 1991. *The Plantsman.* (Vol 13 Pt II).

Polypodium

Leslie, A C. 1993. *The Garden.* (Vol 118 Pt 10). Royal Horticultural Society, London.

Potentilla

Brearley, C. 1991. *The Plantsman.* (Vol 13 Pt I).

Brearley, C. 1992. *A.G.S. Bulletin.* (Vol 60 Nos 3 & 4).

Davidson, C G. & Lenz, L M. 1989. *Experimental Taxonony of Potentilla fruticosa. Canadian Journal of Botany.* (Vol 67 No 12) pp3520-3528.

Potentilla (Shrubby)

Brearley, C. 1987. *The Plantsman.* (Vol 9 Pt II)

Primula

Fenderson, G K. 1986. *A Synoptic Guide to the Genus Primula.* Allen Press, Lawrence, Kansas.

Green, R. 1976. *Asiatic Primulas.* The Alpine Garden Society,Woking.

Halda, J J. 1992. *The Genus Primula.* Tethys Books, Colorado.

Hecker, W R. 1971. *Auriculas & Primroses.* Batsford, London.

Richards, J. 1993. *Primula.* Batsford, London.

Smith, G F, Burrow, B & Lowe, D B. 1984. *Primulas of Europe and America.* The Alpine Garden Society, Woking.

Wemyss-Cooke, T J. 1986. *Primulas Old and New.* David & Charles, Newton Abbot.

Primula allionii

Marcham, A J. 1992. *A.G.S. Bulletin.* (Vol 60 No 3).

Prunus

Bultitude, J. *Index of the Plum Collection at the National Fruit Trials.* Ministry of Agriculture, Fisheries & Food, Faversham, Kent.

Grubb, N H. 1949. *Cherries.* Crosby Lockwood, London.

Index of the Cherry Collection at the National Fruit Trials. 1986. Ministry of Agriculture, Fisheries & Food, Faversham, Kent.

Jefferson, R M & Wain, K K. 1984. *The Nomenclature of Cultivated Flowering Cherries (Prunus): The Sato-zakura Group.* U S D A.

Smith, M W G. 1978. *Catalogue of the Plums at the National Fruit Trials.* Ministry of Agriculture, Fisheries & Food, Faversham, Kent.

Taylor, H V. 1949. *The Plums of England.* Crosby Lockwood, London.

Pulmonaria

Mathew, B. 1982. *The Plantsman.* (Vol 4 Pt II).

Pyrus

Parfitt, B. 1981. *Index of the Pear Collection at the National Fruit Trials.* Ministry of Agriculture, Fisheries & Food, Faversham, Kent.

Smith, M W G. 1976. *Catalogue of the British Pears.* Ministry of Agriculture, Fisheries & Food, Faversham, Kent

Quercus

Miller, H A & Lamb, S H. 1985. *Oaks of North America.* Naturegraph Publishers, Happy Camp, California, USA.

Mitchell, A. 1994. *The Plantsman.* (Vol 15 Pr IV).

Raoulia

Hutchins, G. 1980. *The Plantsman.* (Vol 2 Pt II).

Rhododendron

Chamberlain, D F. 1982. *Notes from the Royal Botanic Garden Edinburgh.* (Vol 39 No 2). H M S O, Edinburgh.

Chamberlain, D F. & Rae, S J. 1990. *A Revision of Rhododendron IV Subgenus Tsutsusi* (in Edinburgh Journal of Botany Vol 47 No 2). HMSO, Edinburgh.

Cox, P A & Cox, K N E. 1988 *Encyclopaedia of Rhododendron Hybrids.* Batsford, London.

Cullen, J. 1980. *Notes from the Royal Botanic Garden Edinburgh.* (Vol 39 No 1). H M S O, Edinburgh.

Davidian, H H. 1982, 1989 & 1992. *The Rhododendron Species.* (Vol I-III). Batsford, London.

Galle, F C. 1987. *Azaleas.* Timber Press, Portland, Oregon.

Lee, F P. 1958. *The Azalea Book.* D Van Nostrand, New York.

Leslie, A C. (compiler). 1980. *The Rhododendron Handbook.* Royal Horticultural Society, London.

Leslie, A C. 1989 *The International Rhododendron Register: Checklist of Rhododendron Names registered 1989-1994 & supps 28-33. Royal Horticultural Society, London.*

Salley, H E & Greer, H E. 1986. *Rhododendron Hybrids.* Batsford, London.

Ribes

Index of the Bush Fruit Collection at the National Fruit Trials. 1987. Ministry of Agriculture, Fisheries & Food, Faversham, Kent.

Romneya

McMillan Browse, P. 1989. *The Plantsman.* (Vol 11 Pt II)

Rosa

Austin, D. 1988. *The Heritage of the Rose.* Antique Collectors' Club, Woodbridge, Suffolk.

Beales, P. 1992. *Roses.* Harvill, London.

Bean, W J. 1900-1988 (rev. D L Clarke & G S Thomas) *Rosa* in *Trees and Shrubs Hardy in the British Isles* 8th ed. (Vol IV & Supp.)

McCann, S. 1985. *Miniature Roses.* David & Charles, Newton Abbot, Devon.

Pawson, A. 1992. *Find That Rose (10th ed).* Rosegrowers' Association, Colchester, Essex.

Phillips, R & Rix, M. 1988. *Roses.* Macmillan, London.

Thomas, G S. 1955 (rev. 1983). *The Old Shrub Roses.* Dent, London.

Thomas, G S. 1962. *Shrub Roses of Today.* Dent, London.

Thomas, G S. (rev. ed 1978). *Climbing Roses Old and New.* Dent, London.

Rosularia

Eggli, U. 1988. *A monograph study of the genus Rosularia.* (*Bradleya*, Vol 6 Suppl.). British Cactus & Succulent Society, Bury, Lancashire, UK.

Salix

Newsholme, C. 1992. *Willows.* Batsford, London.

Salvia

Compton, J. 1994. *The Plantsman.* (Vol 15 Pt IV).

Saxifraga

Horn, R. Webr, K M & Byam-Grounds, J. 1986. *Porophyllum Saxifrages.* Byam-Grounds Publications, Stamford, Lincolshire, UK.

Kohlein, F. 1984. *Saxifrages and Related Genera.* Batsford, London.

Webb, D A & Cornell, R J. 1989. *Saxifrages of Europe.* Christopher Helm, Bromley, Kent.

Sedum

Evans, R L. 1983. *Handbook of Cultivated Sedums.* Ivory Head Press Motcombe, Dorset.

Hensen, K J W & Groendijk-Wilders, N. 1986. *The Plantsman.* (Vol 8 Pt I).

Sempervivum

Mitchell, P J. 1985. *International Cultivar Register for Jovibarba, Rosularia, Sempervivum.* The Sempervivum Society, W Sussex.

Shortia

Barnes, P G. 1990 *The Plantsman.* (Vol 12 Pt I).

Sinningia

Dates, J D. *The Gesneriad Register 1988: Check List of Sinningia.* American Gloxinia and Gesneriad Society, Galesburg, Illinois.

Skimmia

Brown, P D. 1980. *The Plantsman.* (Vol 1 Pt IV).

Solenostemon

Pedley, W K. & Pedley, R. 1974. *Coleus - A Guide to Cultivation and Identification.* Bartholemew, Edinburgh.

Sophora

Hutchins, G. 1993. *The Plantsman.* (Vol 15 Pt I).

Sorbus

McAllister, H. 1985. *The Plantsman.* (Vol 6 Pt IV).

Rushforth, K. 1991. *The Plantsman.* (Vol 13 Pt II).

Rushforth, K. 1992. *The Plantsman.* (Vols 13 Pt IV & 14 Pt I).

Wright, D. 1981. *The Plantsman.* (Vol 3 Pt II).

Streptocalyx

Innes, C. 1993. *The Plantsman.* (Vol 15 Pt II).

Streptocarpus

Arnold, P. *The Gesneriad Register 1979: Check List of Streptocarpus.* American Gloxinia and Gesneriad Society, Binghamton, New York.

Sutherlandia

Schrire, BD & Andrews, S. 1992. *The Plantsman.* (Vol 14 Pt II).

Syringa

Fiala, Fr J L. 1988. *Lilacs*. Christopher Helm, Bromley, Kent.

Rogers, O M. 1976. *Tentative International Register of Cultivar Names in the Genus Syringa*. University of New Hampshire.

Taylor, J. 1990. *The Plantsman*. (Vol 11 Pt IV).

Vrugtman, F. 1976-83. *Bulletin of the American Association of Botanical Gardens and Arboreta*.

Tilia

Muir, N. 1984. *The Plantsman*. (Vol 5 Pt IV).

Muir, N. 1988. *The Plantsman*. (Vol 10 Pt II).

Tillandsia

Kiff, LF. 1991. *A Distributional Checklist of the Genus Tillandsia*. Botanical Diversions, Encino, California.

Tricyrtis

Matthew, B. 1985. *The Plantsman*. (Vol 6 Pt IV).

Trillium

Mitchell, R J. 1989-92. *The Plantsman*. (Vol 10 Pt IV, 11 Pts II & III, 12 Pt I, 13 Pt IV).

Tulbaghia

Benham, S. 1993. *The Plantsman*. (Vol 15 Pt II).

Tulipa

Classified List and International Register of Tulip Names. 1987. Royal General Bulbgrowers' Association, Hillegom, Holland.

Ulmus

Green, P S. 1964. Registration of the Cultivar Names in *Ulmus*. Arnoldia, Vol 24 Nos 608, Arnold Arboretum, Harvard, Massachusetts.

Veratrum

Mathew, B. 1989. *The Plantsman*. (Vol 11 Pt I).

Viola

Coombs, R E. 1981 *Violets*. Croom Helm, London.

Farrar, E. 1989. *Pansies, Violas & Sweet Violets*. Hurst Village Publishing, Reading.

Fuller, R. 1990. *Pansies, Violas & Violettas* Crowood Press, Marlborough, Wiltshire.

Vitis

Pearkes, G. 1989. *Vine Growing in Britain*. Dent, London.

Robinson, J. 1986. *Vines, Grapes and Wines* Mitchell Beazley, London.

Watsonia

Goldblatt, P. 1989. *The Genus Watsonia*. National Botanic Gardens, Republic of South Africa.

Weigela

Howard, R A. 1965. A Check-list of Cultivar Names in *Weigela*. Arnoldia, Vol 25 Nos 9-11. Arnold Arboretum, Harvard, Massachusetts.

Taylor, J. 1990. *The Plantsman*. (Vol 12 Pt IV).

Wisteria

McMillan-Browse, P. 1984. *The Plantsman* (Vol 6 Pt II).

Zauschneria (Epilobium)

Raven, P H. 1976. *Annals of the Missouri Botanic Garden*. (Vol 63 pp326-340).

Zelkova

Ainsworth, P. 1989. *The Plantsman*. (Vol 11 Pt II).

Muir, N. 1991. *The Plantsman*. (Vol 13 Pt II).

INDEX MAP

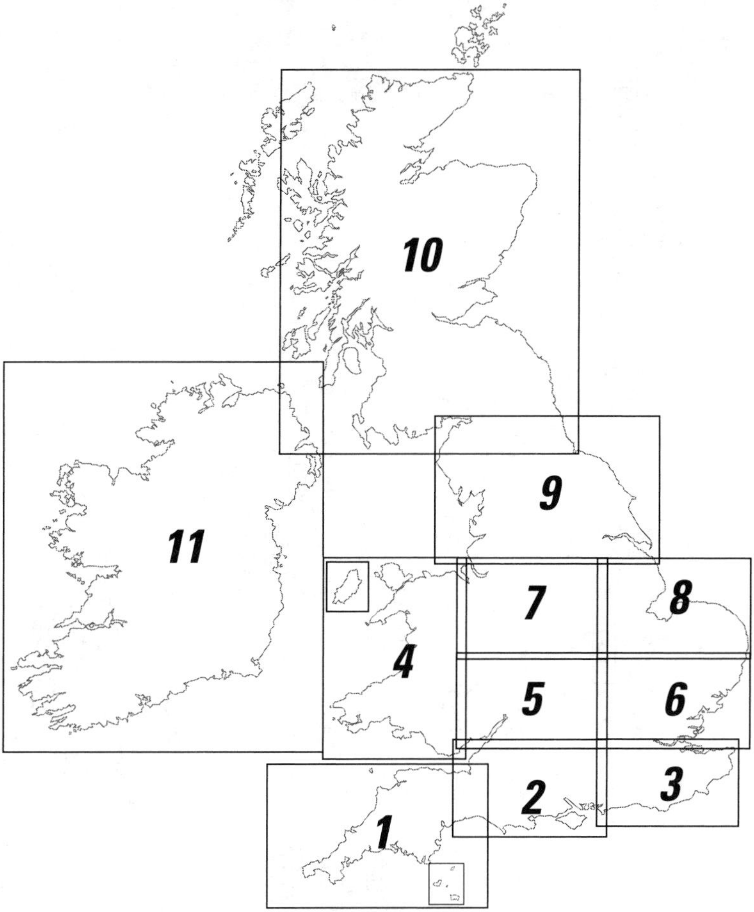

10

9

11

7

8

4

5

6

2

3

1

Motorways

Primary routes

Other 'A' roads

The maps on the following pages show the approximate location of the nurseries whose details are listed in this directory.

Details of nurseries with letter Codes in boxes are given in the CODE-NURSERY Index. **CRow**

Details of nurseries with number Codes in circles are given in the ADDITIONAL NURSERY Index. 

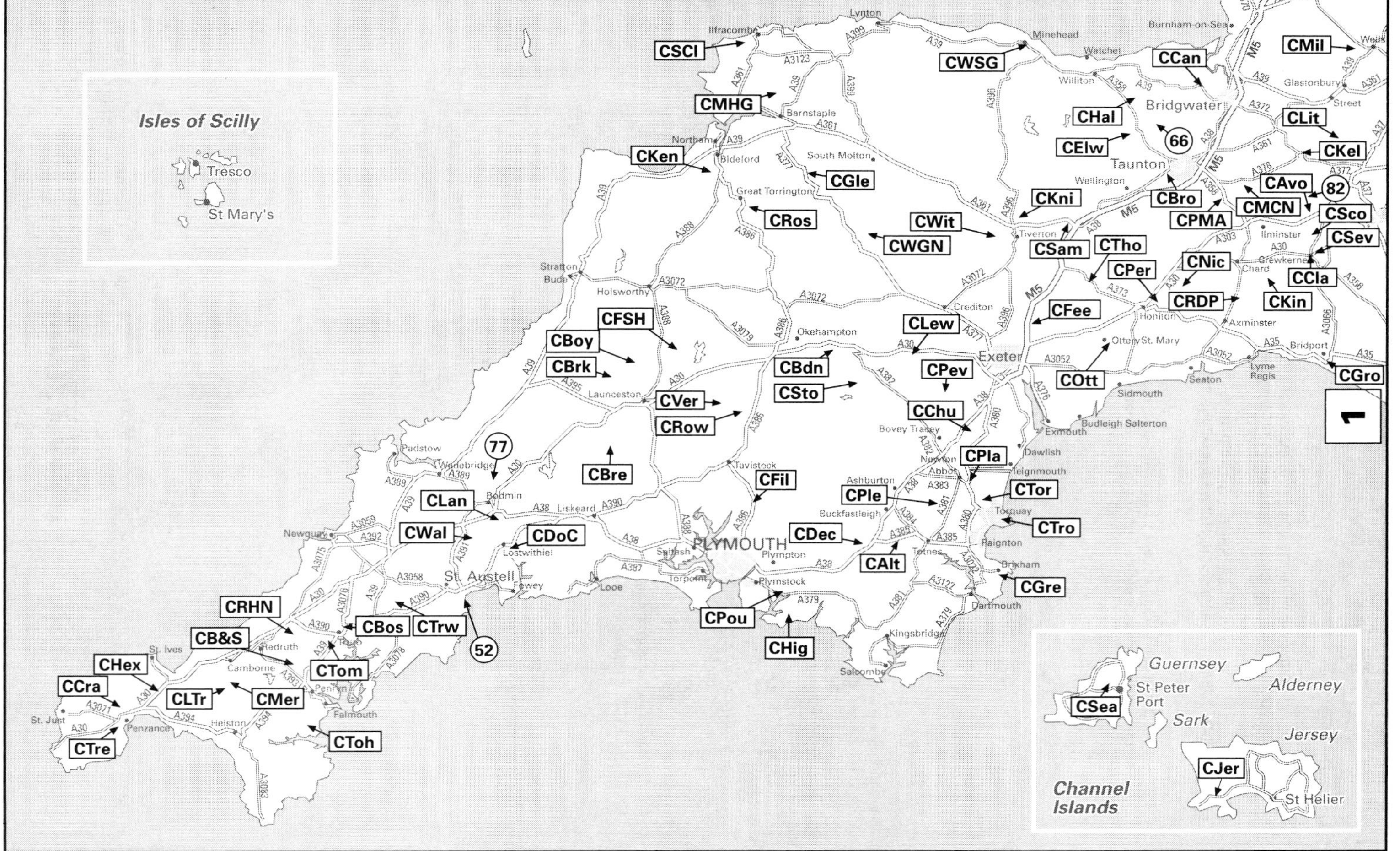
Isles of Scilly
Tresco
St Mary's
Channel Islands
Guernsey
St Peter Port
Alderney
Sark
Jersey
St Helier
1
CSea
CJer
CSCI
CWSG
CCan
CMil
CMHG
CHal
CElw
CLit
CKel
CKen
CGle
CRos
CWit
CWGN
CKni
CBro
CAvo
CMCN
CPMA
CSco
CSev
CSam
CTho
CNic
CPer
CCla
CRDP
CKin
CFee
CLew
CFSH
CBoy
CBrk
CBdn
CSto
CPev
COtt
CGro
CVer
CRow
CChu
CBre
CPla
CTor
CTro
CFil
CPle
CLan
CWal
CDoC
CDec
CAlt
CGre
CPou
CHig
CRHN
CB&S
CBos
CTrw
CHex
CCra
CLTr
CMer
CTom
CToh
CTre
52
66
77
82
Lynton
Ilfracombe
Minehead
Watchet
Williton
Burnham-on-Sea
Wells
Glastonbury
Street
Bridgwater
Taunton
Wellington
Barnstaple
Northam
Bideford
South Molton
Great Torrington
Tiverton
Ilminster
Crewkerne
Chard
Axminster
Bridport
Lyme Regis
Seaton
Honiton
Ottery St. Mary
Sidmouth
Budleigh Salterton
Exmouth
Exeter
Crediton
Dawlish
Teignmouth
Newton Abbot
Torquay
Paignton
Brixham
Dartmouth
Totnes
Kingsbridge
Salcombe
Ashburton
Buckfastleigh
Bovey Tracey
Okehampton
Tavistock
PLYMOUTH
Plympton
Plymstock
Saltash
Torpoint
Looe
Liskeard
Launceston
Holsworthy
Stratton
Bude
Padstow
Wadebridge
Bodmin
Lostwithiel
Fowey
St. Austell
Newquay
Truro
Redruth
Camborne
St. Ives
Penryn
Falmouth
Helston
Penzance
St. Just
M5
A30
A38
A39

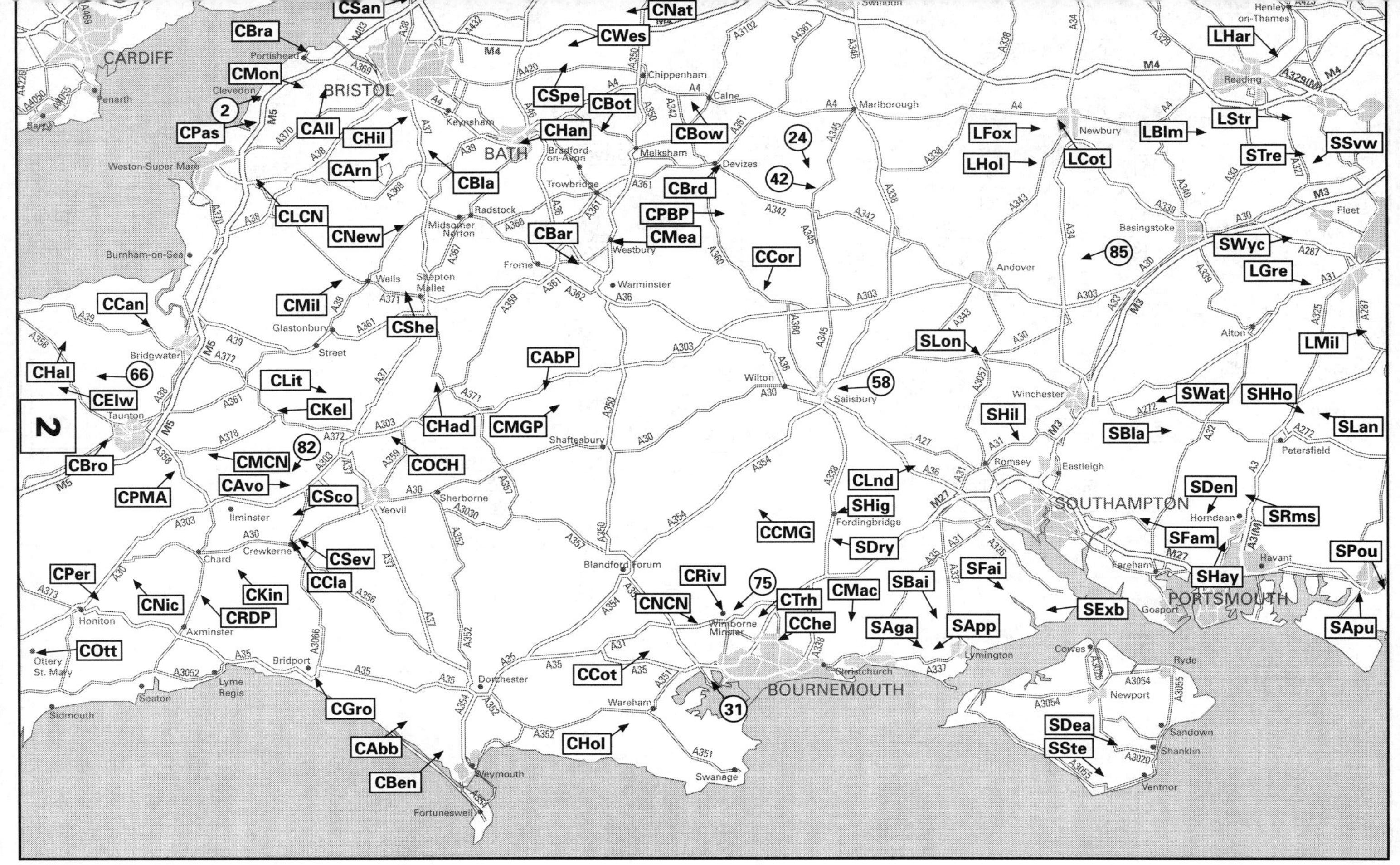
2
CSan
CNat
CBra
CWes
CMon
CPas
2
CAll
CHil
CSpe
CBot
CHan
CBow
CArn
CBla
CLCN
CNew
CBrd
CPBP
CMea
CBar
CCor
24
42
LFox
LHol
LCot
LBlm
LStr
STre
SSvw
LHar
SWyc
85
LGre
LMil
SLan
SHHo
SWat
SBla
SHil
SLon
58
CCan
CMil
CShe
CAbP
CMGP
CHad
COCH
CHal
66
CElw
CLit
CKel
CBro
CMCN
82
CAvo
CPMA
CSco
CSev
CCla
CKin
CRDP
CNic
CPer
COtt
CGro
CAbb
CBen
CHol
CCot
31
CNCN
CRiv
75
CTrh
CChe
CMac
CCMG
SDry
SHig
CLnd
SBai
SAga
SApp
SFai
SExb
SDea
SSte
SDen
SRms
SFam
SHay
SPou
SApu
CARDIFF
Penarth
Barry
Portishead
Clevedon
BRISTOL
Keynsham
BATH
Weston-Super Mare
Burnham-on-Sea
Chippenham
Calne
Melksham
Bradford-on-Avon
Trowbridge
Devizes
Marlborough
Swindon
Radstock
Midsomer Norton
Frome
Westbury
Warminster
Wells
Shepton Mallet
Glastonbury
Street
Bridgwater
Taunton
Ilminster
Yeovil
Sherborne
Shaftesbury
Wilton
Salisbury
Andover
Newbury
Reading
Henley-on-Thames
Basingstoke
Fleet
Alton
Winchester
Romsey
Eastleigh
SOUTHAMPTON
Petersfield
Horndean
Havant
Fareham
Gosport
PORTSMOUTH
Fordingbridge
Chard
Crewkerne
Honiton
Axminster
Ottery St. Mary
Sidmouth
Seaton
Lyme Regis
Bridport
Dorchester
Weymouth
Fortuneswell
Blandford Forum
Wimborne Minster
Wareham
Swanage
BOURNEMOUTH
Christchurch
Lymington
Cowes
Ryde
Newport
Sandown
Shanklin
Ventnor

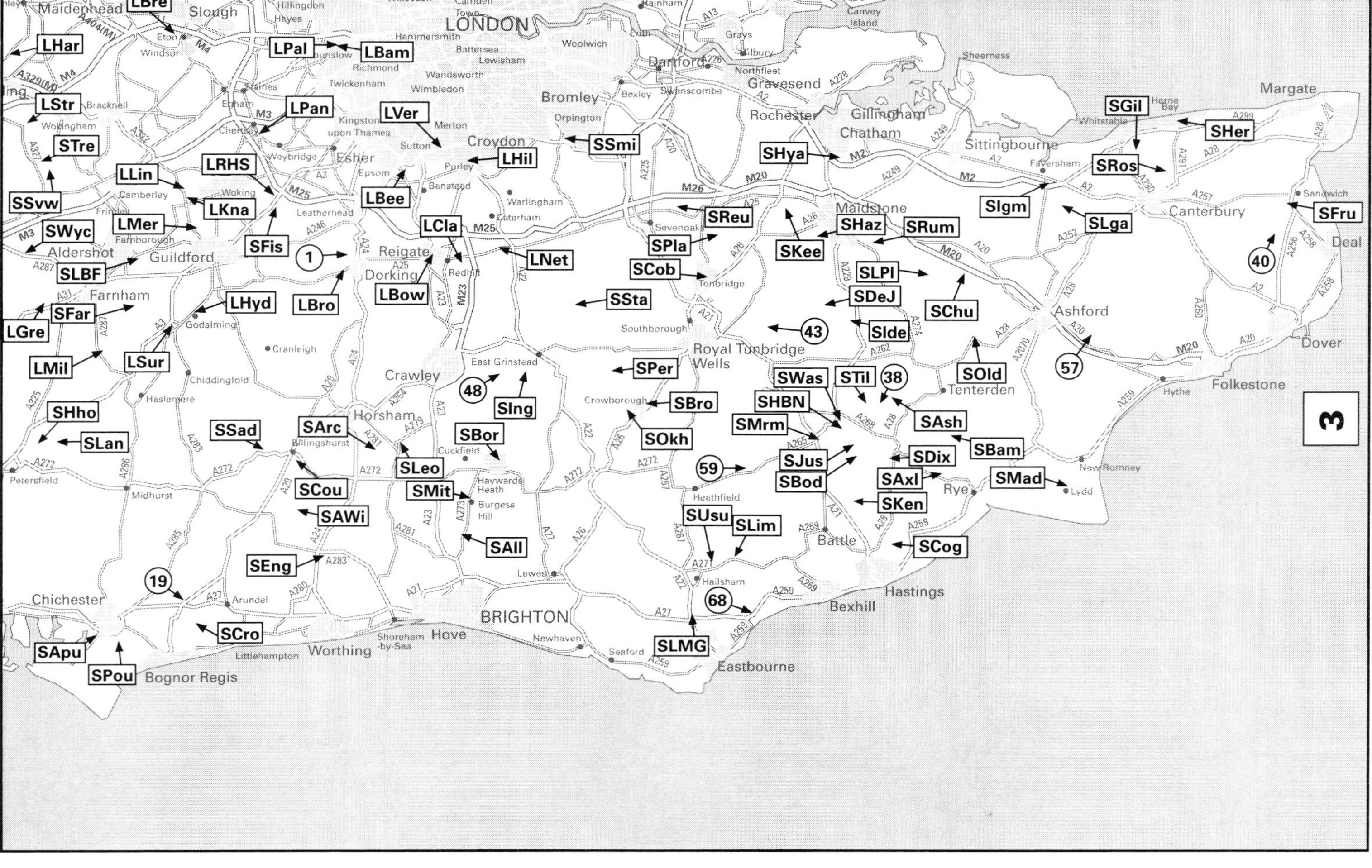

LONDON
Maidenhead
Slough
Eton
Windsor
Hillingdon
Hayes
Hounslow
Hammersmith
Battersea
Lewisham
Richmond
Wandsworth
Twickenham
Wimbledon
Kingston upon Thames
Merton
Sutton
Croydon
Bromley
Orpington
Woolwich
Dartford
Bexley
Swanscombe
Gravesend
Northfleet
Grays
Tilbury
Canvey Island
Rainham
Rochester
Gillingham
Chatham
Sheerness
Sittingbourne
Faversham
Whitstable
Herne Bay
Margate
Sandwich
Deal
Canterbury
Dover
Folkestone
Hythe
Ashford
New Romney
Lydd
Rye
Tenterden
Maidstone
Sevenoaks
Tonbridge
Southborough
Royal Tunbridge Wells
Crowborough
East Grinstead
Heathfield
Hailsham
Battle
Hastings
Bexhill
Eastbourne
Seaford
Newhaven
Lewes
BRIGHTON
Hove
Shoreham -by-Sea
Worthing
Littlehampton
Arundel
Bognor Regis
Chichester
Petersfield
Midhurst
Haslemere
Chiddingfold
Cranleigh
Godalming
Farnham
Aldershot
Farnborough
Frimley
Camberley
Bracknell
Wokingham
Staines
Egham
Chertsey
Weybridge
Woking
Esher
Epsom
Leatherhead
Guildford
Dorking
Reigate
Redhill
Banstead
Purley
Caterham
Warlingham
Crawley
Horsham
Billingshurst
Cuckfield
Haywards Heath
Burgess Hill
LBre
LHar
LPal
LBam
LStr
LPan
LVer
STre
SSmi
LHil
SHya
SGil
SHer
SRos
LLin
LRHS
SSvw
LKna
LBee
LMer
SWyc
SFis
LCla
SReu
SHaz
SRum
SIgm
SLga
SFru
1
LNet
SPla
SKee
SLBF
LBow
SCob
SLPl
40
LBro
SSta
SDeJ
SChu
SFar
LHyd
LGre
SIde
43
LSur
LMil
SPer
SOld
57
48
SWas
STil
38
SHBN
SBro
SIng
SHho
SAsh
SArc
SMrm
SSad
SBor
SOkh
SLan
SBam
SLeo
SJus
SDix
59
SBod
SAxl
SMad
SCou
SMit
SKen
SAWi
SUsu
SLim
SAll
SCog
SEng
19
68
SCro
SLMG
SApu
SPou
3

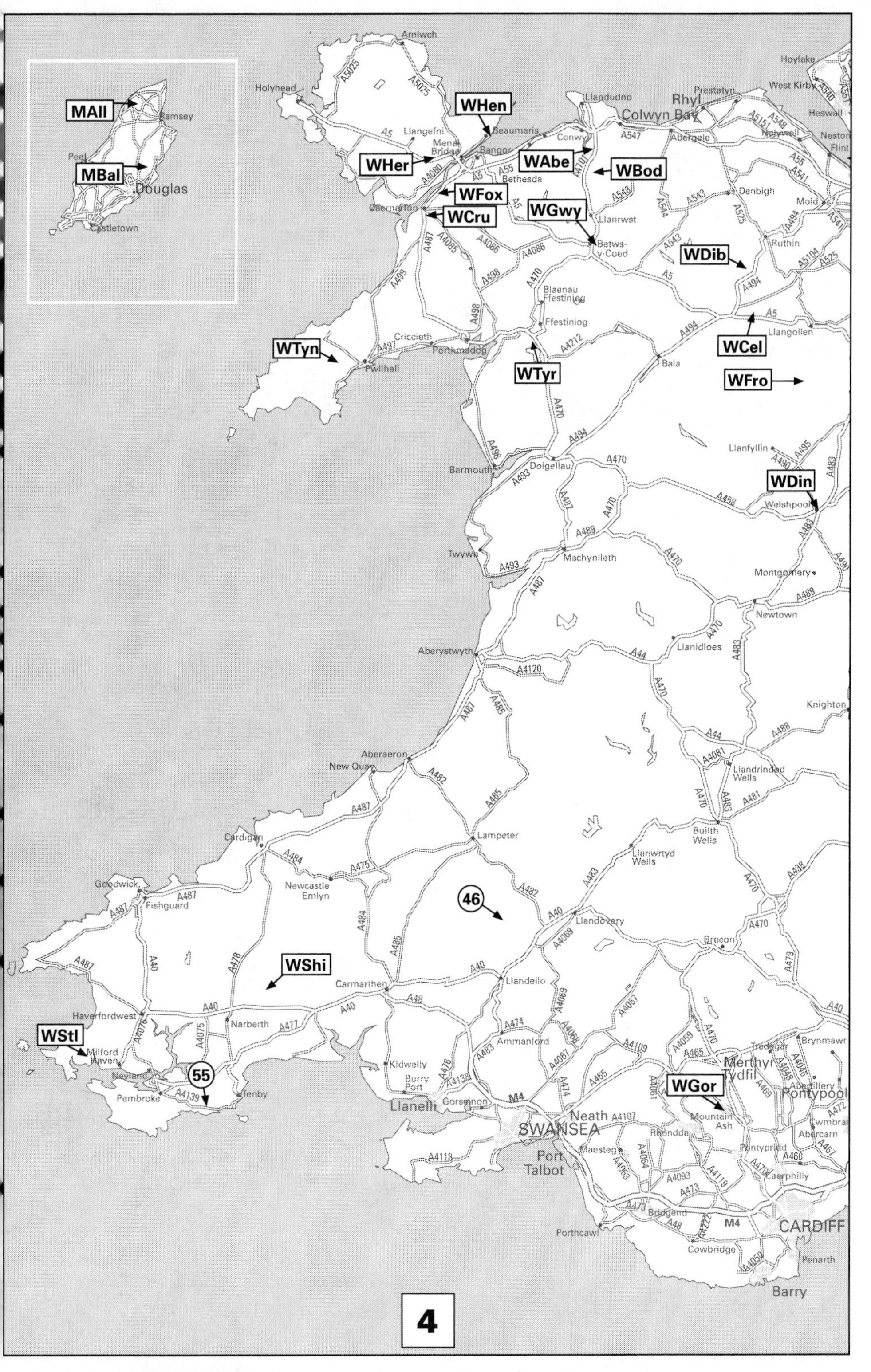
MAll
Ramsey
Peel
MBal
Douglas
Castletown
Amlwch
Holyhead
Llangefni
WHen
Beaumaris
Menai Bridge
Bangor
WHer
Llandudno
Rhyl
Prestatyn
Colwyn Bay
Conwy
Abergele
WAbe
WBod
Bethesda
Hoylake
West Kirby
Heswall
Holywell
Neston
Flint
Mold
Denbigh
Ruthin
WFox
Caernarfon
WCru
WGwy
Llanrwst
Betws-y-Coed
WDib
Blaenau Ffestiniog
Ffestiniog
Criccieth
Porthmadog
Pwllheli
WTyn
WTyr
Bala
WCel
Llangollen
WFro
Llanfyllin
WDin
Welshpool
Barmouth
Dolgellau
Machynlleth
Tywyn
Montgomery
Newtown
Aberystwyth
Llanidloes
Knighton
Aberaeron
New Quay
Llandrindod Wells
Builth Wells
Cardigan
Lampeter
Llanwrtyd Wells
Goodwick
Fishguard
Newcastle Emlyn
46
Llandovery
Brecon
WShi
Carmarthen
Llandeilo
Haverfordwest
Narberth
Ammanford
WStI
Milford Haven
Neyland
Pembroke
55
Tenby
Kidwelly
Burry Port
Llanelli
Gorseinon
Merthyr Tydfil
Tredegar
Brynmawr
Abertillery
Pontypool
WGor
Mountain Ash
Neath
SWANSEA
Port Talbot
Maesteg
Rhondda
Pontypridd
Abercarn
Caerphilly
Bridgend
Porthcawl
Cowbridge
CARDIFF
Penarth
Barry
4

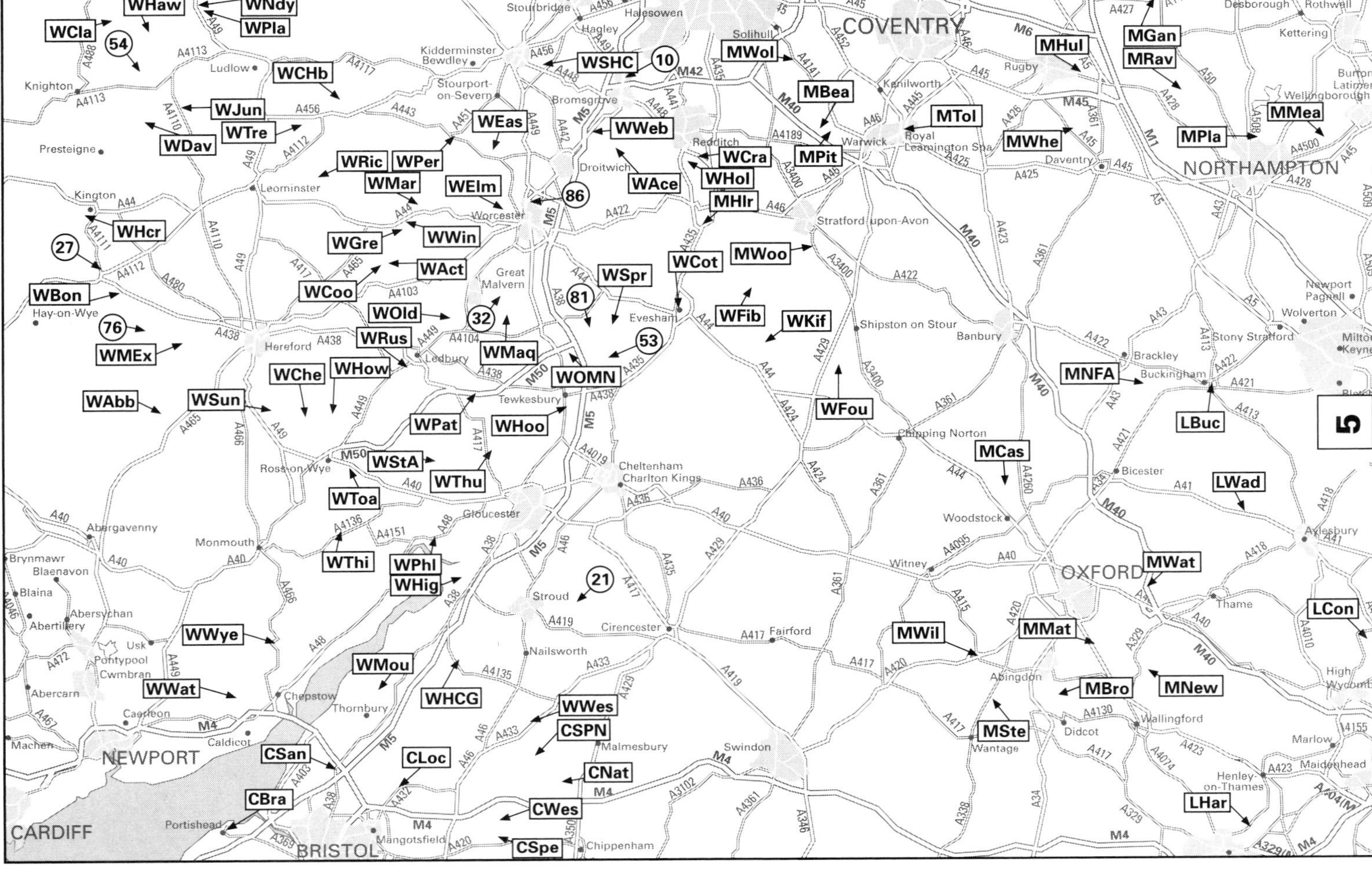

5
WHaw
WNdy
WPla
WCla
54
WCHb
WJun
WTre
WDav
WEas
WSHC
10
MWol
MHul
MGan
MRav
MBea
MTol
MWeb
MMea
MPla
WWeb
WRic
WPer
WMar
WElm
86
WAce
WCra
WHol
MHlr
MPit
MWhe
WHcr
27
WWin
WGre
WAct
WCoo
WBon
WOld
32
WSpr
81
WCot
MWoo
WFib
WKif
76
WMEx
WRus
WMaq
53
WOMN
WChe
WHow
WAbb
WSun
WPat
WHoo
WFou
MNFA
LBuc
WStA
WThu
MCas
WToa
LWad
WThi
WPhl
WHig
21
MWat
LCon
WWye
MWil
MMat
WMou
WHCG
MBro
MNew
WWat
WWes
CSPN
MSte
CSan
CLoc
CNat
LHar
CBra
CWes
CSpe
COVENTRY
NORTHAMPTON
OXFORD
NEWPORT
CARDIFF
BRISTOL
Stourbridge
Halesowen
Hagley
Solihull
Desborough
Rothwell
Kettering
Kidderminster
Bewdley
Ludlow
Knighton
Stourport-on-Severn
Bromsgrove
Kenilworth
Rugby
Burton Latimer
Wellingborough
Presteigne
Leominster
Droitwich
Redditch
Warwick
Royal Leamington Spa
Daventry
Kington
Worcester
Stratford-upon-Avon
Great Malvern
Hay-on-Wye
Evesham
Shipston on Stour
Banbury
Newport Pagnell
Wolverton
Stony Stratford
Milton Keynes
Hereford
Ledbury
Brackley
Buckingham
Tewkesbury
Chipping Norton
Ross-on-Wye
Cheltenham
Charlton Kings
Bicester
Gloucester
Woodstock
Abergavenny
Monmouth
Aylesbury
Brynmawr
Blaenavon
Witney
Blaina
Stroud
Thame
Abersychan
Abertillery
Cirencester
Fairford
Usk
Pontypool
Cwmbran
Nailsworth
Abingdon
High Wycombe
Abercarn
Chepstow
Thornbury
Wallingford
Caerleon
Didcot
Caldicot
Malmesbury
Swindon
Wantage
Marlow
Machen
Maidenhead
Henley-on-Thames
Portishead
Mangotsfield
Chippenham

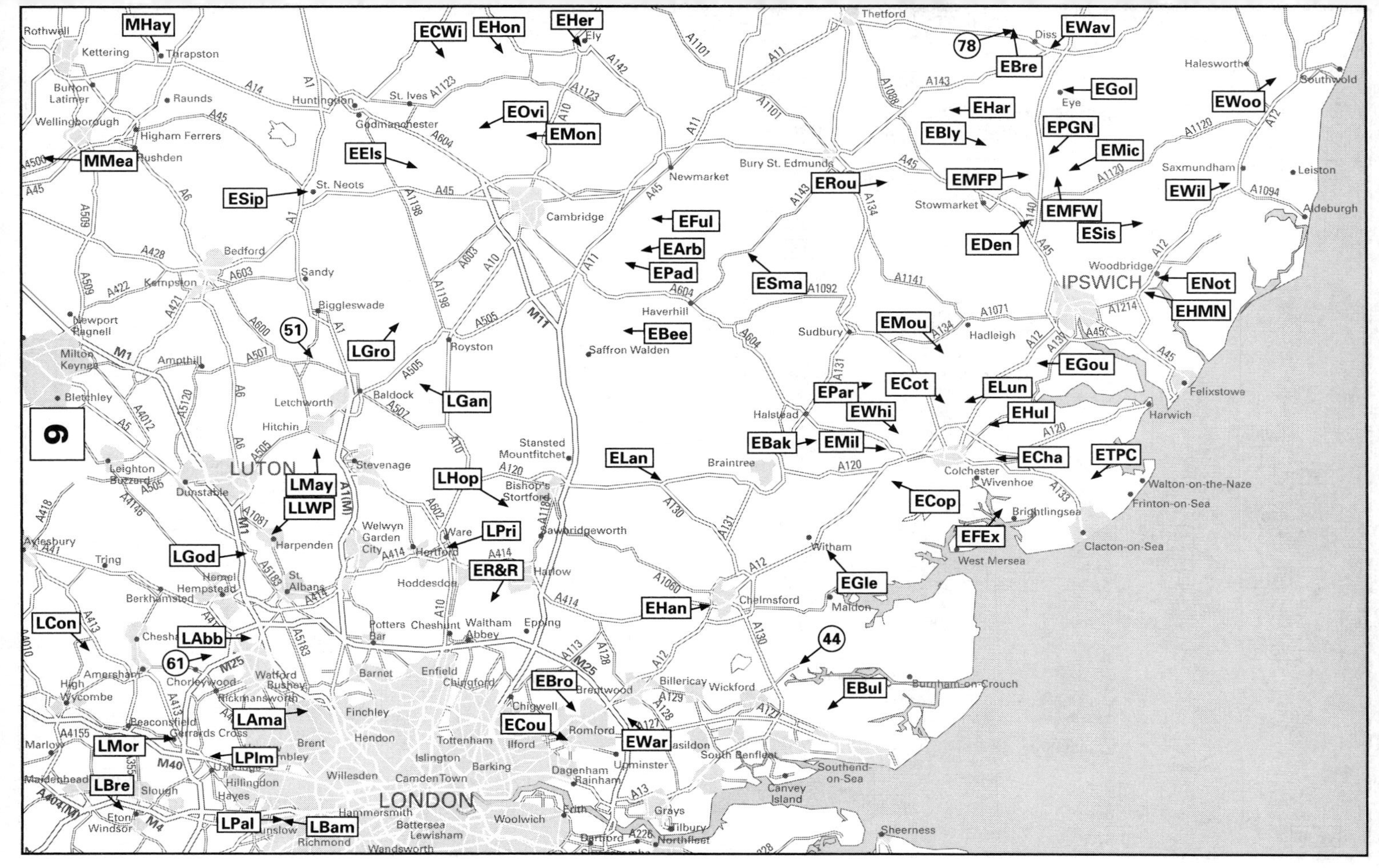

6
MHay
ECWi
EHon
EHer
EWav
EBre
78
EGol
EHar
EWoo
EOvi
EMon
EBly
EPGN
EMic
MMea
EEls
ERou
EMFP
EWil
ESip
EFul
EMFW
ESis
EDen
EArb
EPad
ESma
ENot
EHMN
51
LGro
EBee
EMou
EGou
LGan
EPar
ECot
ELun
EWhi
EHul
EBak
EMil
ELan
ECha
ETPC
LMay
LHop
LLWP
ECop
LPri
EFEx
LGod
ER&R
EGle
LCon
EHan
LAbb
61
44
EBro
EBul
LAma
ECou
EWar
LMor
LPlm
LBre
LPal
LBam
Rothwell
Kettering
Thrapston
Burton Latimer
Raunds
Wellingborough
Higham Ferrers
Rushden
Huntingdon
St. Ives
Godmanchester
Ely
Thetford
Diss
Eye
Halesworth
Southwold
Saxmundham
Leiston
Aldeburgh
Bury St. Edmunds
Newmarket
Stowmarket
St. Neots
Cambridge
Bedford
Sandy
Kempston
Biggleswade
Newport Pagnell
Milton Keynes
Bletchley
Ampthill
Letchworth
Baldock
Royston
Hitchin
Haverhill
Saffron Walden
Sudbury
Hadleigh
IPSWICH
Woodbridge
Felixstowe
Harwich
Halstead
Stansted Mountfitchet
Braintree
Colchester
Wivenhoe
Walton-on-the-Naze
Frinton-on-Sea
Brightlingsea
Clacton-on-Sea
West Mersea
LUTON
Stevenage
Bishop's Stortford
Leighton Buzzard
Dunstable
Welwyn Garden City
Ware
Hertford
Sawbridgeworth
Witham
Harpenden
Aylesbury
Tring
Hemel Hempstead
St. Albans
Hoddesdon
Harlow
Chelmsford
Maldon
Berkhamsted
Potters Bar
Cheshunt
Waltham Abbey
Epping
Amersham
Chorleywood
Watford
Bushey
Rickmansworth
Barnet
Enfield
Chingford
Chigwell
Brentwood
Billericay
Wickford
Burnham-on-Crouch
High Wycombe
Beaconsfield
Gerrards Cross
Finchley
Hendon
Brent
Tottenham
Ilford
Romford
Basildon
South Benfleet
Southend-on-Sea
Marlow
Uxbridge
Islington
Willesden
Barking
Dagenham
Upminster
Rainham
Canvey Island
Maidenhead
Slough
Hillingdon
Hayes
CamdenTown
LONDON
Hammersmith
Woolwich
Erith
Grays
Tilbury
Windsor
Eton
Hounslow
Battersea
Lewisham
Richmond
Wandsworth
Dartford
Northfleet
Sheerness
M1
M11
M25
M40
M4
A1(M)

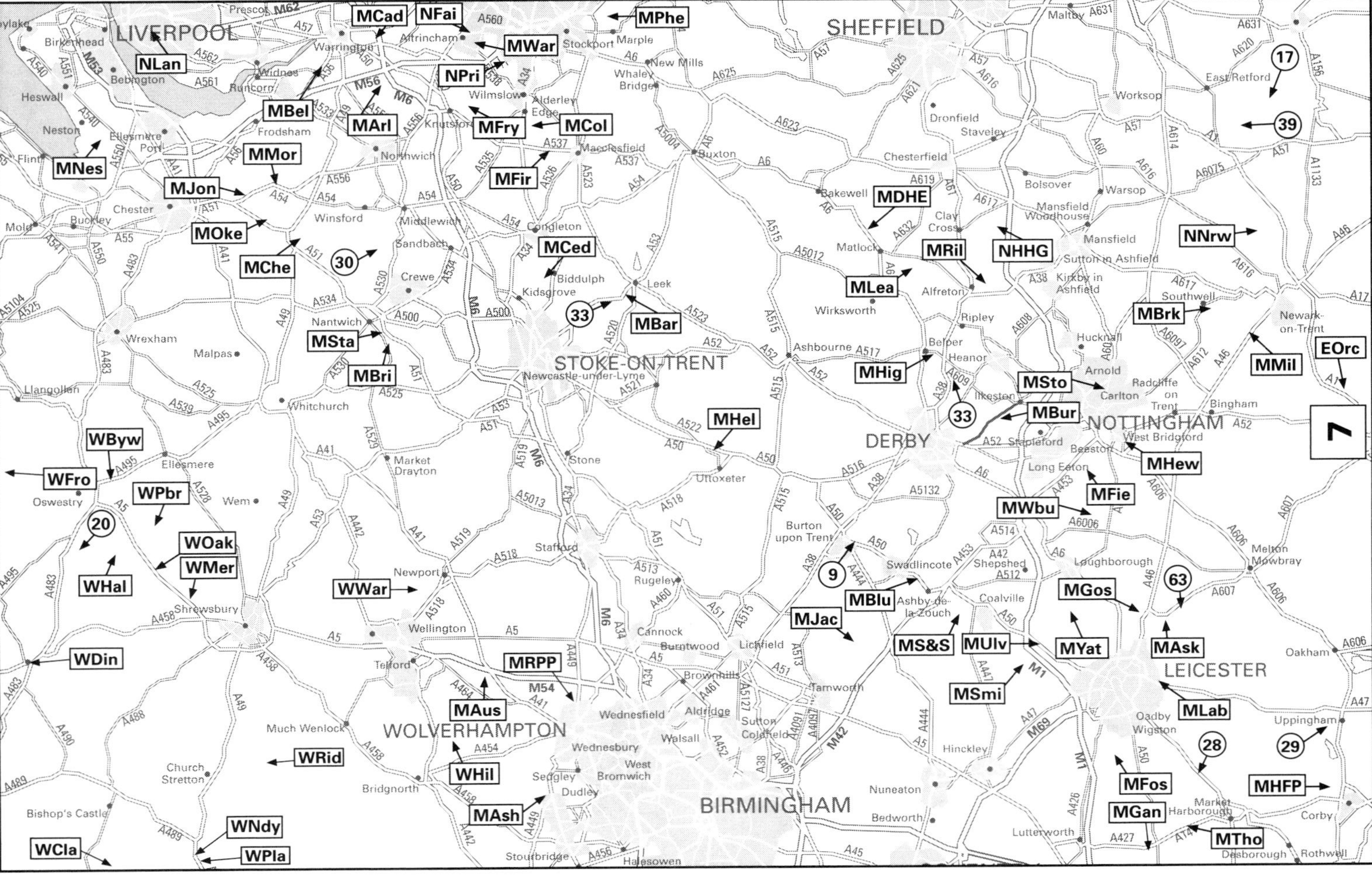

LIVERPOOL
SHEFFIELD
STOKE-ON-TRENT
DERBY
NOTTINGHAM
LEICESTER
WOLVERHAMPTON
BIRMINGHAM
7
NLan
MBel
MArl
MCad
NFai
MWar
NPri
MFry
MCol
MPhe
MNes
MJon
MMor
MFir
MOke
MChe
MCed
MDHE
MRil
NHHG
MLea
NNrw
MSta
MBri
MBar
MBrk
MMil
EOrc
MHig
MSto
MBur
MHel
MHew
MFie
MWbu
WByw
WFro
WPbr
WOak
WMer
WHal
WWar
MBlu
MJac
MS&S
MUlv
MYat
MGos
MAsk
MSmi
WDin
MRPP
MAus
MLab
WRid
WHil
MFos
MHFP
MAsh
MGan
MTho
WNdy
WCla
WPla
17
39
30
33
20
9
63
28
29
Birkenhead
Bebington
Heswall
Neston
Ellesmere Port
Flint
Mold
Buckley
Chester
Runcorn
Widnes
Frodsham
Warrington
Altrincham
Wilmslow
Alderley Edge
Knutsford
Northwich
Macclesfield
Stockport
Marple
New Mills
Whaley Bridge
Buxton
Winsford
Middlewich
Sandbach
Congleton
Crewe
Biddulph
Kidsgrove
Leek
Nantwich
Wrexham
Malpas
Newcastle-under-Lyme
Llangollen
Whitchurch
Market Drayton
Stone
Ellesmere
Oswestry
Wem
Shrewsbury
Stafford
Newport
Uttoxeter
Wellington
Telford
Cannock
Burntwood
Rugeley
Lichfield
Brownhills
Aldridge
Walsall
Wednesfield
Wednesbury
West Bromwich
Sutton Coldfield
Tamworth
Much Wenlock
Bridgnorth
Church Stretton
Bishop's Castle
Sedgley
Dudley
Stourbridge
Halesowen
Nuneaton
Bedworth
Hinckley
Lutterworth
Burton upon Trent
Swadlincote
Ashby-de-la-Zouch
Coalville
Shepshed
Loughborough
Melton Mowbray
Oakham
Uppingham
Oadby
Wigston
Market Harborough
Desborough
Rothwell
Corby
Ashbourne
Wirksworth
Matlock
Bakewell
Chesterfield
Dronfield
Staveley
Bolsover
Clay Cross
Alfreton
Ripley
Belper
Heanor
Ilkeston
Stapleford
Beeston
Long Eaton
West Bridgford
Hucknall
Arnold
Carlton
Radcliffe on Trent
Bingham
Kirkby in Ashfield
Sutton in Ashfield
Mansfield
Mansfield Woodhouse
Warsop
Southwell
Newark-on-Trent
Worksop
East Retford
Maltby
Prescot
M62
M53
M56
M6
M54
M42
M69
M1
A57
A560
A631
A562
A561
A540
A551
A550
A41
A56
A5117
A49
A533
A50
A556
A556
A538
A34
A535
A536
A537
A523
A6
A625
A621
A623
A5004
A616
A619
A632
A61
A617
A60
A614
A6075
A1133
A156
A620
A1
A46
A17
A54
A51
A55
A483
A541
A530
A534
A500
A53
A5104
A525
A539
A495
A528
A5
A458
A488
A490
A489
A529
A442
A518
A519
A5013
A520
A521
A522
A515
A5012
A517
A52
A609
A38
A608
A6097
A612
A516
A5132
A6006
A453
A514
A42
A512
A444
A447
A5127
A4091
A4097
A452
A461
A513
A460
A464
A454
A449
A456
A426
A427
A4304
A14
A607
A606
A47
A45

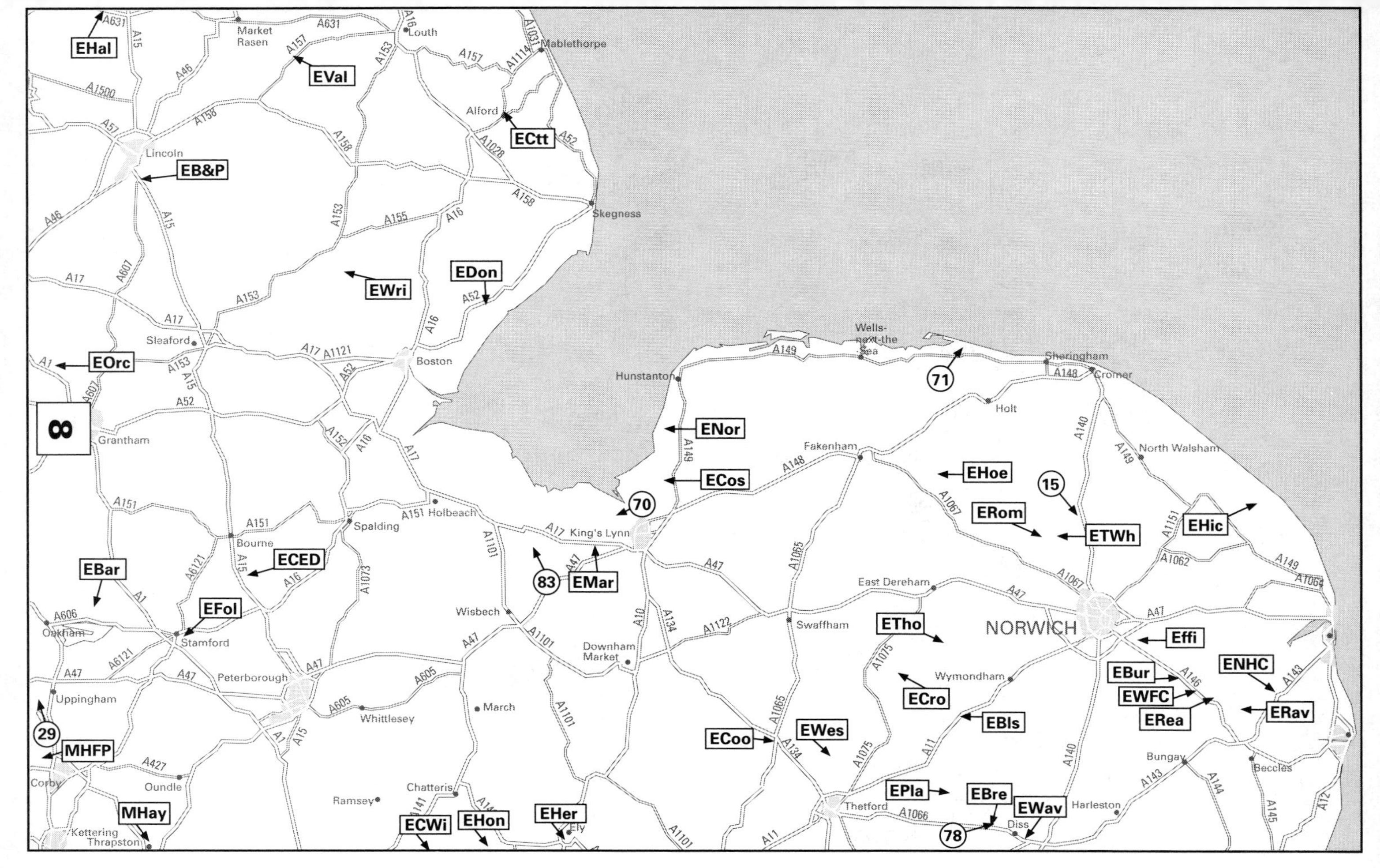
8
EHal
EVal
ECtt
EB&P
EDon
EWri
EOrc
ENor
ECos
EHoe
ERom
ETWh
EHic
EMar
ECED
EBar
EFol
ETho
ECro
EBls
ECoo
EWes
EPla
EBre
EWav
Effi
EBur
EWFC
ERea
ENHC
ERav
MHFP
MHay
ECWi
EHon
EHer
15
29
70
71
78
83
Market Rasen
Louth
Mablethorpe
Alford
Lincoln
Skegness
Sleaford
Boston
Grantham
Spalding
Holbeach
Bourne
Stamford
Oakham
Uppingham
Peterborough
Whittlesey
March
Ramsey
Chatteris
Wisbech
Downham Market
King's Lynn
Hunstanton
Wells-next-the Sea
Sheringham
Cromer
Holt
Fakenham
North Walsham
East Dereham
Swaffham
NORWICH
Wymondham
Thetford
Diss
Harleston
Bungay
Beccles
Ely
Oundle
Corby
Kettering
Thrapston

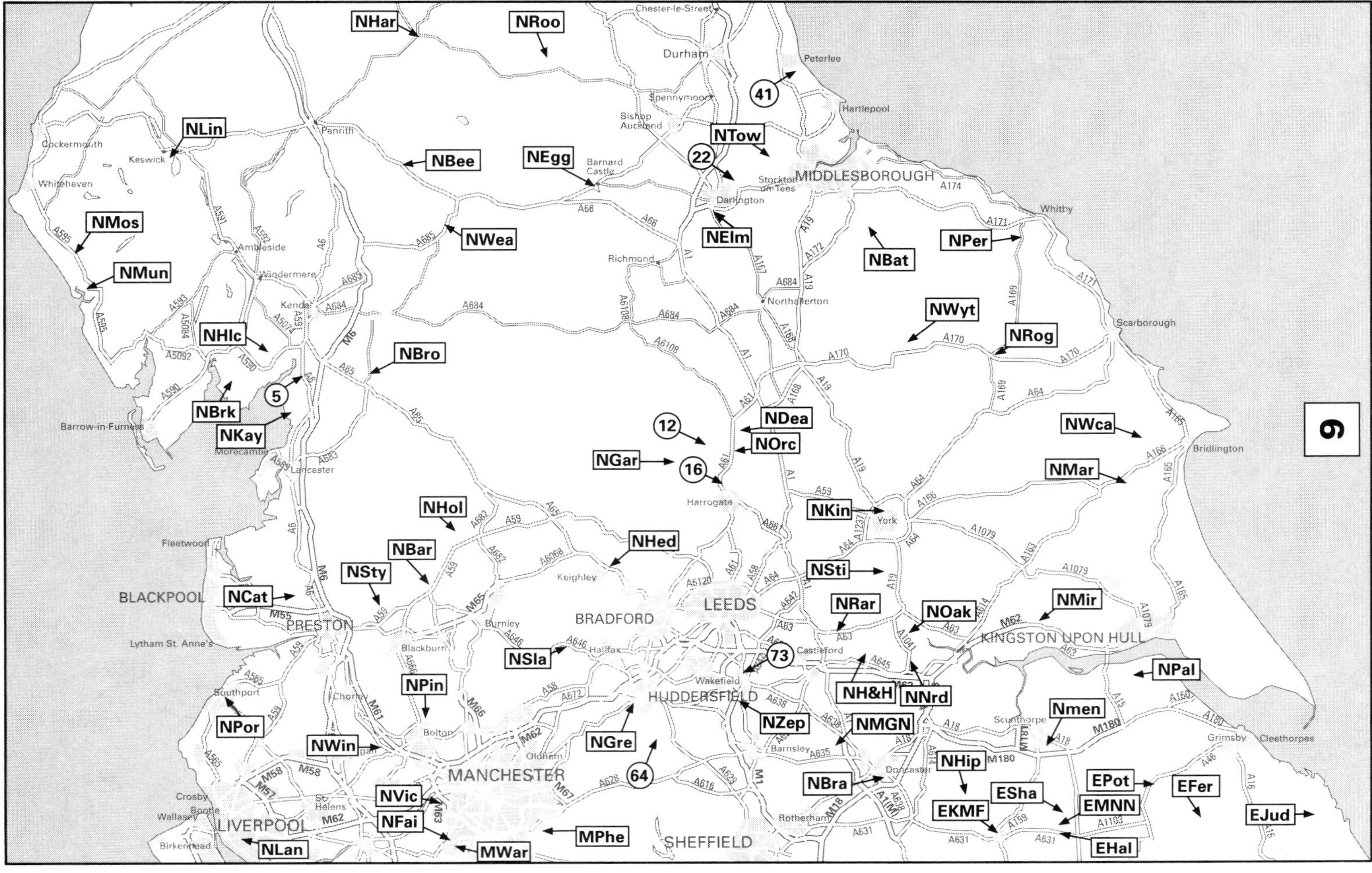

9
NHar
NRoo
NLin
NBee
NEgg
NTow
NMos
NMun
NWea
NElm
NBat
NPer
NHlc
NBro
NWyt
NRog
NBrk
NKay
NDea
NOrc
NWca
NGar
NMar
NHol
NHed
NKin
NBar
NSty
NSti
NCat
NRar
NOak
NMir
NSla
NPal
NPin
NH&H
NNrd
NPor
NZep
NMGN
Nmen
NWin
NGre
NHip
NBra
EPot
EFer
NVic
ESha
EMNN
EKMF
EJud
NFai
MPhe
EHal
NLan
MWar
5
12
16
22
41
64
73
Chester-le-Street
Durham
Peterlee
Spennymoor
Hartlepool
Bishop Auckland
Cockermouth
Penrith
Keswick
Barnard Castle
Stockton on-Tees
MIDDLESBOROUGH
Whitehaven
Darlington
Whitby
Ambleside
Richmond
Windermere
Kendal
Northallerton
Scarborough
Barrow-in-Furness
Morecambe
Bridlington
Lancaster
Harrogate
York
Fleetwood
Keighley
BLACKPOOL
PRESTON
BRADFORD
LEEDS
KINGSTON UPON HULL
Burnley
Lytham St. Anne's
Blackburn
Halifax
Castleford
Wakefield
Southport
Chorley
HUDDERSFIELD
Bolton
Scunthorpe
Barnsley
Grimsby
Cleethorpes
Oldham
MANCHESTER
Doncaster
Crosby
Bootle
St. Helens
Wallasey
LIVERPOOL
Rotherham
Birkenhead
SHEFFIELD

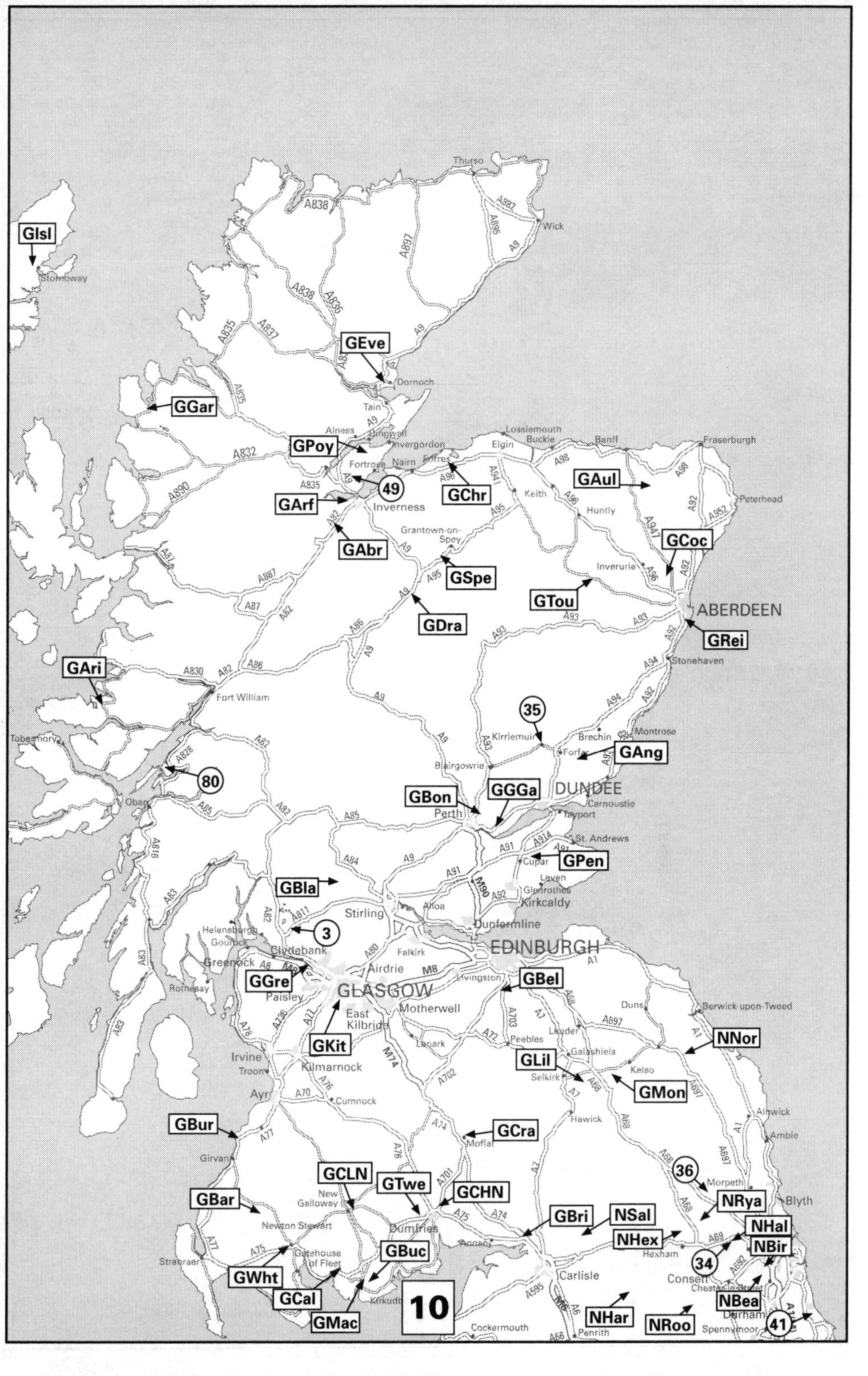

Thurso
A838
A882
A895
Wick
A897
A9
GIsl
Stornoway
A838
A836
A835
A837
A9
GEve
Dornoch
GGar
A835
Tain
A9
Ainess
Dingwall
GPoy
Invergordon
A832
Lossiemouth
Buckie
Banff
Fraserburgh
Elgin
Fortrose
Nairn
Forres
A98
A98
GAul
A835
A9
49
A96
GChr
A941
A890
GArf
Inverness
Keith
A96
Huntly
A92
A952
Peterhead
A95
A947
GCoc
A82
Grantown-on-Spey
A9
GAbr
A87
A887
A95
GSpe
Inverurie
A96
A92
A9
GTou
A87
A82
A86
GDra
A93
A93
ABERDEEN
A93
A92
GRei
A9
A94
Stonehaven
GAri
A830
A82
A86
Fort William
A9
A94
A92
35
Montrose
Brechin
Tobermory
A82
A9
Kirriemuir
A93
Forfar
GAng
A828
80
Blairgowrie
GBon
GGGa
DUNDEE
Oban
A85
A82
A85
Perth
Carnoustie
Tayport
A816
A914
A91
St. Andrews
A84
A9
Cupar
GPen
A91
M90
Leven
A83
GBla
A92
Glenrothes
Kirkcaldy
A82
A811
Alloa
Stirling
Helensburgh
3
Dunfermline
Gourock
A83
Greenock
Clydebank
A80
Falkirk
EDINBURGH
A1
A8
M8
Airdrie
M8
GGre
Livingston
GBel
Rothesay
GLASGOW
Paisley
A68
Duns
Berwick-upon-Tweed
A737
A77
Motherwell
A703
A1
East Kilbride
Lauder
A697
A78
GKit
A72
Peebles
A1
NNor
Irvine
Lanark
M74
Galashiels
Troon
Kilmarnock
GLil
Kelso
A76
A702
Selkirk
A68
GMon
A697
Ayr
A70
Cumnock
A7
Hawick
Alnwick
GBur
A77
A74
GCra
A1
Amble
Moffat
A76
A68
A697
Girvan
A7
36
GCLN
A701
GTwe
Morpeth
GCHN
A68
Blyth
New Galloway
NRya
GBar
A75
A74
GBri
NSal
Newton Stewart
Dumfries
NHal
Annan
NHex
A69
A77
A75
Hexham
Gatehouse of Fleet
GBuc
34
NBir
A692
Stranraer
Carlisle
GWht
Consett
A595
Chester-le-Street
GCal
M6
NBea
Kirkcudbright
10
A6
NHar
Durham
GMac
NRoo
Cockermouth
41
A66
Penrith
Spennymoor

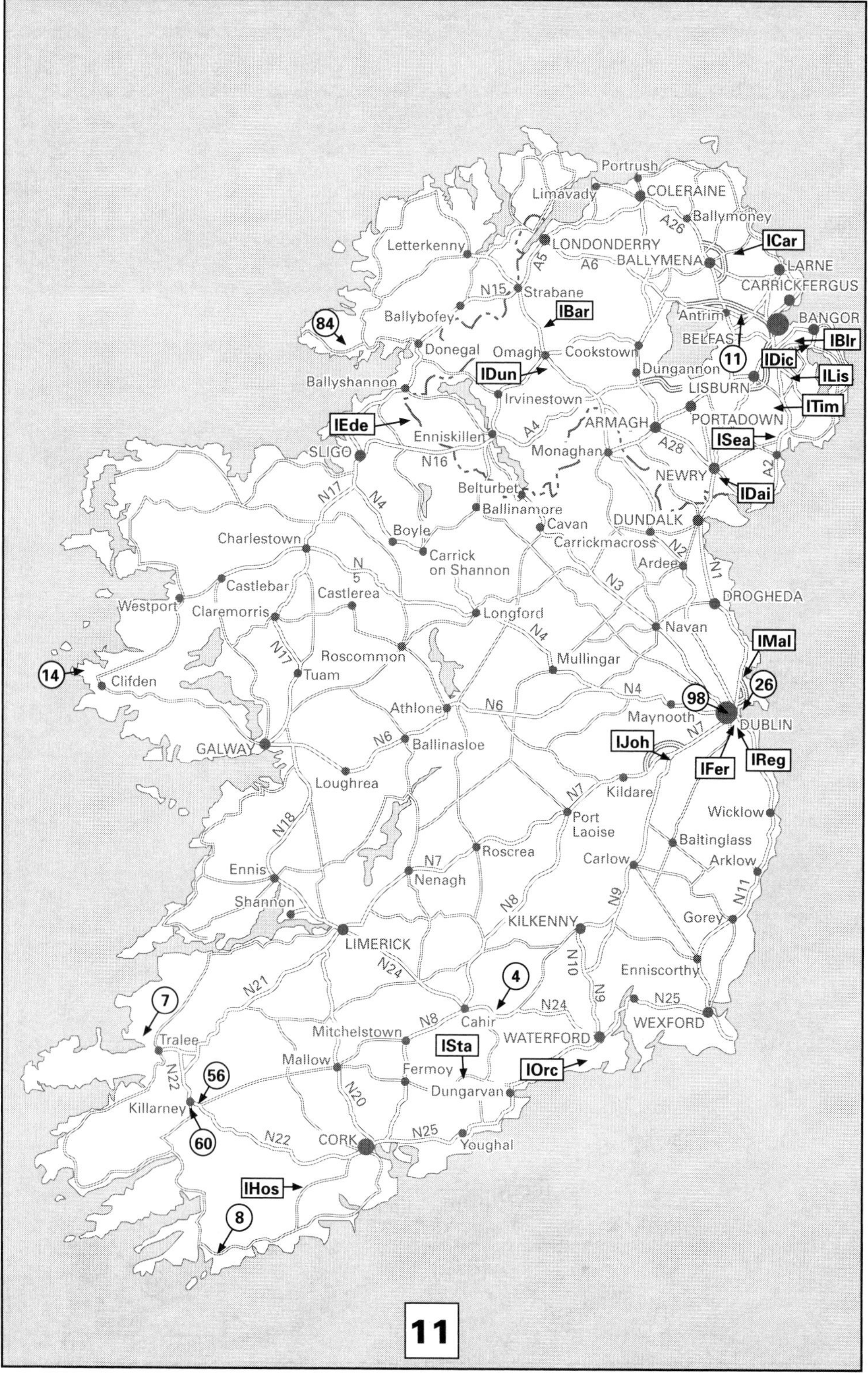

Portrush
Limavady
COLERAINE
Ballymoney
A26
ICar
Letterkenny
LONDONDERRY
A5
A6
BALLYMENA
LARNE
CARRICKFERGUS
N15
Strabane
Antrim
BANGOR
84
Ballybofey
IBar
BELFAST
IBlr
Donegal
Omagh
Cookstown
11
IDic
Dungannon
ILis
IDun
Ballyshannon
LISBURN
Irvinestown
ITim
PORTADOWN
IEde
A4
ARMAGH
Enniskillen
A28
ISea
SLIGO
Monaghan
N16
A2
NEWRY
Belturbet
IDai
N17
N4
Ballinamore
DUNDALK
Cavan
Boyle
Charlestown
Carrickmacross
N2
Carrick on Shannon
Ardee
N
5
N3
N1
Castlebar
Castlerea
DROGHEDA
Westport
Claremorris
Longford
N4
Navan
IMal
N17
Roscommon
Mullingar
14
Clifden
Tuam
26
N4
98
Athlone
N6
Maynooth
DUBLIN
N7
IJoh
GALWAY
N6
Ballinasloe
IFer
IReg
Loughrea
Kildare
N7
Wicklow
N18
Port Laoise
Baltinglass
Roscrea
Carlow
Arklow
Ennis
N7
Nenagh
N9
N8
N11
Shannon
KILKENNY
Gorey
LIMERICK
N10
N24
Enniscorthy
N21
4
N9
N25
7
N24
N8
Cahir
WEXFORD
Mitchelstown
ISta
WATERFORD
Tralee
Mallow
Fermoy
IOrc
N22
56
N20
Dungarvan
Killarney
60
N22
N25
CORK
Youghal
IHos
8
11

Foliage Scented & Herb Plants

Walton Poor, Crocknorth Rd.,
Ranmore Common, Dorking, Surrey
Tel: 0483 282273.

Wide variety of unusual Herbs, Shrubs and Scented plants available.

(Scented and Herb Gardens Designed.)

Herb Gardens open Wed. to Sun. from April to October

READS of LODDON

HALES HALL, NORFOLK NR14 6QW
Telephone: 0508 548 395

NATIONAL COLLECTIONS of CITRUS, FIGS, GREENHOUSE GRAPES

Conservatory Plant Specialists.
Unusual Garden Fruit & Nuts.
Climbing & wall Shrubs. Box & Yew for Hedging & Topiary.
Descriptive catalogue 4 x 1st class stamps.

NURSERYMEN SINCE 1890

THE PLANT CENTRE

AT WEST KINGTON NURSERIES

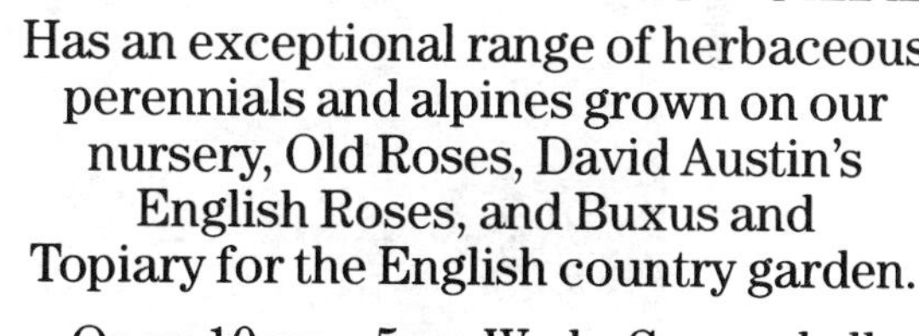

Has an exceptional range of herbaceous perennials and alpines grown on our nursery, Old Roses, David Austin's English Roses, and Buxus and Topiary for the English country garden.

Open 10am – 5pm Wed – Sun and all Bank Holiday Mondays from 2nd March – 27th November

The private 2 acre garden is open on the same days from 2pm – 5pm

WEST KINGTON NURSERIES
West Kington,
Nr Chippenham, Wilts.
Tel. (0249) 782822

WEST KINGTON NURSERIES

HOSTAS

ANN & ROGER BOWDEN

have a Garden display of 300 HOSTA PLANTS

Send 3 x 1st class stamps for list of 110 varieties. Visitors by arrangement only

Telephone: 083 784 0481
Sticklepath, Okehampton, Devon
Collecting box

ARIVEGAIG NURSERY

Acharacle, Argyll PH36 4LE
Tel. 0967 431331

For an interesting range of **Alpines, Bamboos, Climbing Plants, Ferns, Grasses, Heathers, Trees & Shrubs**, all grown on the wild and beautiful Ardnamurchan Peninsula.

Why not pay us a visit if you are holidaying in the area or, send 4 First Class stamps for our Mail Order Catalogue of young plants.

SUSSEX BY THE SEA

Situated in the lovely village of Rottingdean, just 3 miles from the centre of Brighton you will find Cliffway Cottage, a small family run Guest House offering Bed and Breakfast accommodation. Rooms with sea views and en suite facilities are available. A choice of eating places are within minutes walking distance. Newhaven Port 5 miles.

For further details please write or telephone:

Cliffway Cottage, 30 Marine Drive, Rottingdean, Brighton BN2 7HQ

Tel: Brighton (0273) 301269

HOLDEN CLOUGH NURSERY

(Established 1927)

offer the widest range of ALPINE and PERENNIAL PLANTS in the North of England. Grown under hardy Pennine conditions.

Also CHOICE SHRUBS, DWARF RHODODENDRONS & CONIFERS, FERNS, HEATHERS, GRASSES, CLIMBING PLANTS.

Visitors welcome all year at the Nursery situated in the picturesque Forest of Bowland near to A59/A65.

WORLDWIDE MAIL ORDER SERVICE

Seed list available – SAE please

Please send £1.20 for Descriptive 1994 Catalogue and Collectors Corner Supplement

Dept PF, Bolton-by-Bowland, Clitheroe, Lancashire BB7 4PF

Tel: 020 0447 615

KIM W DAVIS

NURSERYMAN

OFFERS A WIDE RANGE OF ALPINE AND ROCK GARDEN PLANTS WITH SOME CHOICE HERBACEOUS

VISITORS TO THE NURSERY AND GARDEN ARE WELCOME
OPEN FEB-OCT EVERY DAY
10am-6pm
Nov - Jan by Appointment
EXPORT ENQUIRIES WELCOME

Send SAE for 1994 catalogue of over 900 plants for the alpine house, troughs, scree or open garden, for the novice and more experienced alpine gardener

LINGEN ALPINE NURSERY
LINGEN, Nr BUCKNELL,
SHROPSHIRE SY7 0DY

Telephone Presteigne
(0544) 267720

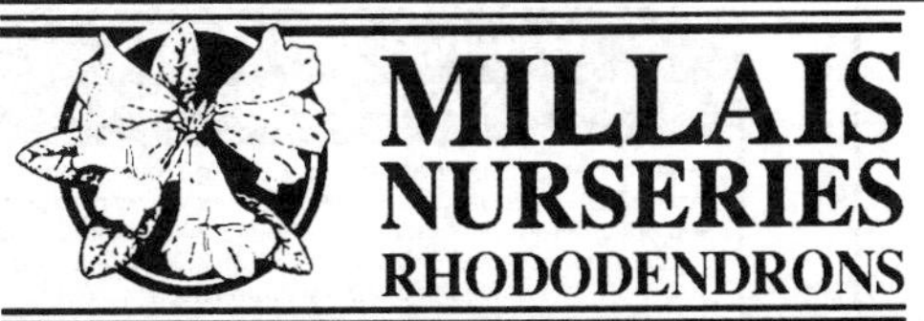

Crosswater Farm,
Churt, Farnham,
Surrey, GU10 2JN
Tel: Frensham (0252) 792698
Fax: (0252) 792526

Specialist growers of 600 varieties of Choice Hybrids and Rare Species.

ONE OF THE WIDEST SELECTIONS IN THE WORLD!

Mail Order Catalogue, 5x2nd class stamps.

TUESDAY – SATURDAY 10.00am – 1.00pm, 2.00pm – 5.00pm

GARDEN OPEN DAILY MAY AND EARLY JUNE

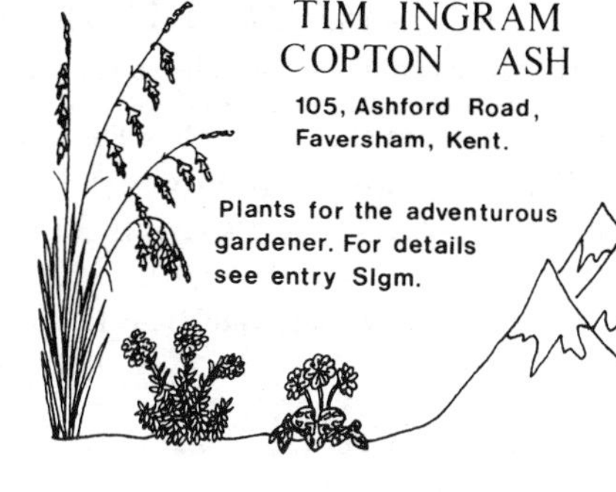

TIM INGRAM
COPTON ASH
105, Ashford Road,
Faversham, Kent.
Plants for the adventurous gardener. For details see entry SIgm.

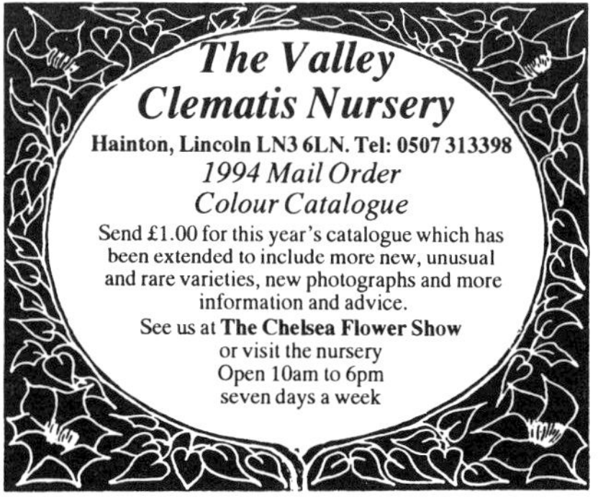

The Valley
Clematis Nursery
Hainton, Lincoln LN3 6LN. Tel: 0507 313398
1994 Mail Order
Colour Catalogue
Send £1.00 for this year's catalogue which has been extended to include more new, unusual and rare varieties, new photographs and more information and advice.
See us at The Chelsea Flower Show
or visit the nursery
Open 10am to 6pm
seven days a week

FUCHSIA'S
LITTLETON NURSERY
GERANIUMS
LITTLETON
SOMERTON SOMERSET
TA11 6NT
(on the B3151)
TELEPHONE
0458 272356
ARGYRANTHEMUMS
Wholesale & Retail
Half Hardy Perennials & Shrubs

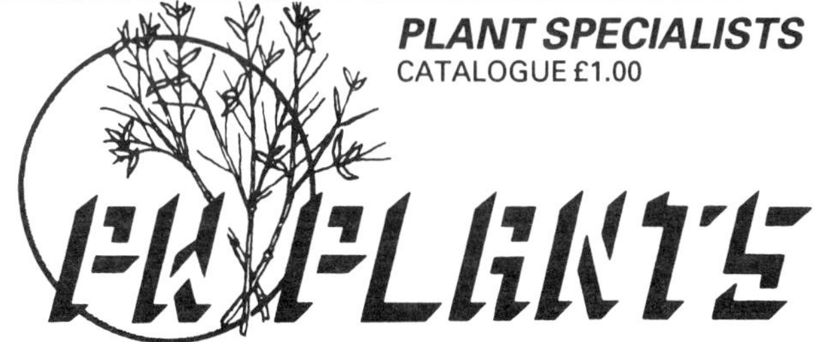

PLANT SPECIALISTS
CATALOGUE £1.00
see code E Pla
BAMBOOS
GRASSES
SHRUBS
CLIMBERS
PERENNIALS
CONIFERS

OLD PINKS AND HARDY PLANTS
Our free catalogue lists over 200 choice perennials including old fashioned Pinks, Digitalis and Penstemon.
Mail order our speciality.
Tel. 0734 732206
SOUTHVIEW NURSERIES
Dept PF, Chequers Lane, Eversley Cross, Basingstoke, Hants. RG27 0NT

NETTLETON'S NURSERY
Ivy Mill Lane, Godstone, Surrey
Tel: 0883 742426
Specialist Growers of Acers, Wisterias and unusual trees and shrubs.

SOIL ANALYSIS
Electronic estimation of pH, lime requirement, major element levels, with organic/inorganic remedial recommendations.
Sutherland Soil Services
Dornoch, Scotland IV25 3NG
S.A.E. for further details/sampling instructions.

HUNTS COURT
Garden and Nursery
Open Tues-Sat all year except August
Nursery 9-5pm. Garden 2-6pm. Also for charities
Suns. June 12th, 19th & 26th, July 3rd & 10th, and by appt.
Old Roses and uncommon shrubs and perennials.
Hunts Court, North Nibley, Dursley, Glos. Tel. (0453) 547440

Longacre Nursery
UNUSUAL HARDY HERBACEOUS PLANTS
PERRY WOOD, SELLING, NEAR FAVERSHAM, KENT
Tel: (0227) 752254
OPEN DAILY – 2.00pm-5.00pm APRIL to OCTOBER

NEW SEED LIST
Botanical Garden offers wide range:
Lilies, Perennials, Herbs, Shrubs, Trees.
Send 2 International reply coupons to:
Roman Plaskota
PL-95-200 Pabianice, Box 6, Poland

LEWDON FARM ALPINE NURSERY
Cheriton Bishop, Nr Exeter. 0647 24283
Alpines, herbaceous, miniature shrubs, dwarf conifers. Open daily.
From village, take Yeoford road and after 1½ miles fork right.

DEVON, SOMERSET
First property in Devon on A358 midway Chard to Axminster. Many choice, unusual & rare herbaceous perennials, including, woodland, bog, ferns & pond plants. Over 1,000 varieties. See CRDP. List 3x1st class stamps.
R.D. PLANTS
Homelea Farm, Tytherleigh, Axminster, E. Devon EX13 7BG

PETER TRENEAR
TREES, SHRUBS, CONIFERS
For Garden or Bonsai. List free. Mail order or callers welcome 9 – 4.30. Closed Sundays
Tel. 0734 732300
Chequers Lane, Eversley Cross, Hants

R.P.P. ALPINES
for both the enthusiasts and beginners
Choice Alpines and Dwarf Conifers.
List 30p + 2nd class stamp
6 Bentley Rd, Bushbury, Wolverhampton WV10 8DZ
Tel: 0902 784508

International Acers
Acer Place, Coalash Lane, Hanbury, Bromsgrove, Worcestershire B60 4EY. Tel: Hanbury (0527) 821774
OPENING HOURS:
Saturday – Sunday, Bank Holidays
9.00am – 5.30pm and at all other times by appointment (please telephone)
FOR SALE: JAPANESE MAPLES, BAMBOOS, etc
N.B: Nursery within vicinity of: The Gate Hangs Well P.H.

LISCAHANE NURSERY
A general nursery offering a selection of coastal shelter plants including trees and shrubs.
Open Tues-Sat 9-6pm. Sun 2-6pm. CLOSED EACH MONDAY
LISCAHANE NURSERY, ARDFERT, TRALEE, CO. KERRY. TEL: 066 34222

MINIATURE AND DWARF ZONALS
Rooted cuttings supplied by post all year round
Please send 2 x 1st class stamps for catalogue listing over 200 varieties.
KINGSWOOD PELARGONIUMS
113, KINGSWAY NORTH, CLIFTON, YORK YO3 6JH
TEL: (0904) 636785
Visitors by appointment only

PERRY'S PLANTS
The River Gardens, Sleights, Whitby, North Yorkshire.
Visiting the North York Moors or the Yorkshire coast? Come and see all the hardy plants we sell growing in our beautiful riverside gardens. Open daily, Easter to October.

CHRISTIES OF FORRES
One of the oldest established Scottish Nurseries, trading continuously since 1826.
We offer an extremely wide range of plants for gardeners, landscapers and foresters.
T. & W. CHRISTIE (FORRES) LTD
The Nurseries, Forres, Grampian. Tel. (0309) 672633.
Fax. (0309) 676846. *Do send for our catalogue*

'PRINCESS®' ALSTROEMERIA HYBRIDS

from Europe's foremost specialist breeders of hardy garden Alstroemerias.

Magnificent new varieties in the widest range of colours.

LITTLE PRINCESSES® the first miniature Alstroemerias for patio or tubs.

LIMONIUM – Blue Dream® and White Dream®

Exclusive new garden perennials from Japan. Ideal as cut flowers and drying.

Awarded Gold Medals at Chelsea Flower Show and Hampton Court International Flower Show.

Colour brochure and cultural details – send 40p.

Peter J. Smith M. Hort., M.Inst.Hort.
Chanctonbury Nurseries, Rectory Lane, Ashington, West Sussex RH20 3AS

Tel: 0903 892870
Fax: 0903 893036

Visitors by appointment only

CALLY GARDENS

GATEHOUSE OF FLEET, CASTLE DOUGLAS, SCOTLAND DG7 2DJ

Specialist growers of the scarcer perennials, grasses, shrubs and climbers. Unique collection of 3,000 varieties planted out in a 2.7 acre 18thc. walled garden with sales area – open Sat & Sun Easter to mid October. Please send 3 x 1st class stamps for the new mail order catalogue.

Order your **BEARDED IRISES** from ***Zephyrwude*** before Sept 15th from £2.50 each

Delivery August-September ONLY NZep

Finest range of modern American SDB IB MTB TB
Trialled for garden impact before listing

New lines for larger growers to bulk up

BUCKLAND PLANTS

Grow an extensive range of perennials, grasses and larger alpines.
Many unique and rare varieties, together with the best of the new.

See GBuc for details

GARDEN CENTRES

Notcutts have for 90 years been leading nurserymen. We invite you to draw on that wealth of experience at each of our 11 Garden Centres. Open 7 days.

Over 2,000 different varieties in stock

NOTCUTTS BOOK OF PLANTS
is a wealth of information.

The **Plants for a Purpose** pages are especially helpful in choosing plants suitable for difficult sites.

COPIES OF THIS BOOK MAY BE PURCHASED IN OUR BOOK SALES AREA or £3.25 inc p&p.

Notcutts Garden Centres at:

Woodbridge, Ipswich Road, Woodbridge. Tel (0394) 383344

Ardleigh, Station Road, Ardleigh, Colchester. Tel: (0206) 230271

St Albans, Hatfield Road, St. Albans. Tel: (0727) 853224

Birmingham, Stratford Road, Shirley, Solihull. Tel: (021) 744 4501.

Norwich, Daniels Road, Norwich. Tel: (0603) 53155.

Peterborough, Oundle Road, Peterborough. Tel: (0733) 234600.

Bagshot, Waterers Nurseries, Bagshot. Tel: (0276) 472288.

Maidstone, Bearsted Road, Maidstone. Tel: (0622) 39944.

Oxford, Mattocks Rose Nurseries, Nuneham Courtenay, Oxford. Tel: (086738) 454.

Cranleigh, Guildford Road, Cranleigh. Tel: (0483) 274222.

Tunbridge Wells, Tonbridge Road, Pembury, Tunbridge Wells, Kent, TN2 4QN. Tel: (089282) 2636/4848.

INDEX OF ADVERTISERS

For further information concerning Display Advertisements in future editions, please write to:– Leslie Morris, c/o The Plant Finder, Lakeside, Whitbourne, Worcester WR6 5RD. Tel. 0273 301269.

THE HARDY PLANT SOCIETY

The Hardy Plant Society was formed to foster interest in hardy herbaceous plants on the widest possible scale. It aims to give its members information about the wealth of both well known and little known hardy plants, how to grow them to the best advantage and where they may be obtained. It also aims to ensure that all worthy hardy plants remain in cultivation and have the widest possible distribution.

Regional and Local Groups

Members may join any of the growing number of local groups organising many events in their own area including plant sales, garden visits, demonstrations and lectures. Most groups issue their own newsletter. The Groups form a basis for friendly exchange of information and plants and are an invaluable way of meeting other keen plantsmen locally. There is also a Correspondents Group for those not able to get out and about.

Genus and special Groups

Members may also join any of the specialised groups within the Society which will put them in touch with other members having similar interests. At present there are seven such groups covering 'Variegated Plants', 'Geraniums', 'Grasses', 'Paeony', 'Half-Hardy', 'Bellflowers' & 'Pulmonarias'

Publications and Slide Library

The Society's Journal 'The Hardy Plant' is currently issued twice a year containing major illustrated articles on a wide variety of plants and gardens. Regular newsletters keep members informed of current events. A central collection of slides is available for loan to members wishing to compile illustrated lectures.

Seed Distribution

Each year members are encouraged to collect seed from plants in their gardens for the Seed Distribution which produces a printed list of all available seed, much of which comes from overseas. This currently lists over 2,000 varieties of seed, the majority of which is not available from commercial sources and, for a nominal sum members may select a number of packets from this.

Plant Sales and Shows

At organised meetings, both national and local, members bring interesting and unusual plants which are sold to aid the Society's funds. The Society puts on displays at the Royal Horticultural Society and other shows around the country and members can be involved by helping with the stands or by supplying plants to be shown.

Propagation and Wants scheme

This is run by the Southern Counties Group which propagates material from rarer or more difficult plants to ensure that the plants have the widest possible distribution. Some groups regularly issue lists of plants that members want but have been unable to locate. Word of mouth often helps locate wanted plants.

Conservation

The Society is most concerned about the conservation of garden plants. Countless fine plants have totally disappeared from cultivation and remain but a memory. In close cooperation with the National Council for the Conservation of Plants and Gardens, the Society is making efforts to ensure that all worthy plants are kept in cultivation.

For further information or Membership Application Form please write to:

The Administrator
Mrs Pam Adams
Little Orchard
Great Comberton
Pershore
Worcs. WR10 3DP
Tel No. (0386) 710317